Tennessee

Prentice Hall

Geometry

Randall I. Charles
Basia Hall
Dan Kennedy
Laurie E. Bass
Art Johnson
Stuart J. Murphy
Grant Wiggins

PEARSON

Boston, Massachusetts • Chandler, Arizona • Glenview, Illinois • Upper Saddle River, New Jersey

Acknowledgments appear on page T492, which constitute an extension of this copyright page.

ISBN-13: 978-0-13-253162-7
ISBN-10: 0-13-253162-3
1 2 3 4 5 6 7 8 9 10 V057 14 13 12 11 10

VOLUME 1

Geometry *Teacher's Edition Contents*

Teacher Handbook

Series *Authors*

Randall I. Charles, Ph.D., is Professor Emeritus in the Department of Mathematics and Computer Science at San Jose State University, San Jose, California. He began his career as a high school mathematics teacher, and he was a mathematics supervisor for five years. Dr. Charles has been a member of several NCTM committees and is the former Vice President of the National Council of Supervisors of Mathematics. Much of his writing and research has been in the area of problem solving. He has authored more than 75 mathematics textbooks for kindergarten through college.

Dan Kennedy, Ph.D., is a classroom teacher and the Lupton Distinguished Professor of Mathematics at the Baylor School in Chattanooga, Tennessee. A frequent speaker at professional meetings on the subject of mathematics education reform, Dr. Kennedy has conducted more than 50 workshops and institutes for high school teachers. He is coauthor of textbooks in calculus and precalculus, and from 1990 to 1994 he chaired the College Board's AP Calculus Development Committee. He is a 1992 Tandy Technology Scholar and a 1995 Presidential Award winner.

Basia Hall currently serves as Manager of Instructional Programs for the Houston Independent School District. With 33 years of teaching experience, Ms. Hall has served as a department chair, instructional supervisor, school improvement facilitator, and professional development trainer. She has developed curricula for Algebra 1, Geometry, and Algebra 2 and co-developed the Texas state mathematics standards. A 1992 Presidential Awardee, Ms. Hall is past president of the Texas Association of Supervisors of Mathematics and is a state representative for the National Council of Supervisors of Mathematics (NCSM).

Consulting *Authors*

Stuart J. Murphy is a visual learning author and consultant. He is a champion of developing visual learning skills and using related strategies to help children become more successful students. He is the author of MathStart, a series of children's books that presents mathematical concepts in the context of stories. A graduate of the Rhode Island School of Design, he has worked extensively in educational publishing and has been on the authorship teams of a number of elementary and high school mathematics programs. He is a frequent presenter at meetings of the National Council of Teachers of Mathematics, the International Reading Association, and other professional organizations.

Grant Wiggins, Ed.D., is the President of Authentic Education in Hopewell, New Jersey. He earned his Ed.D. from Harvard University and his B.A. from St. John's College in Annapolis. Dr. Wiggins consults with schools, districts, and state education departments on a variety of reform matters; organizes conferences and workshops; and develops print materials and Web resources on curricular change. He is perhaps best known for being the coauthor, with Jay McTighe, of *Understanding by Design* and *The Understanding by Design Handbook*, the award-winning and highly successful materials on curriculum published by ASCD. His work has been supported by the Pew Charitable Trusts, the Geraldine R. Dodge Foundation, and the National Science Foundation.

Program *Authors*

Geometry

Laurie E. Bass is a classroom teacher at the 9–12 division of the Ethical Culture Fieldston School in Riverdale, New York. A classroom teacher for more than 30 years, Ms. Bass has a wide base of teaching experience, ranging from Grade 6 through Advanced Placement Calculus. She was the recipient of a 2000 Honorable Mention for the Radio Shack National Teacher Awards. She has been a contributing writer for a number of publications, including software-based activities for the Algebra 1 classroom. Among her areas of special interest are cooperative learning for high school students and geometry exploration on the computer. Ms. Bass is a frequent presenter at local, regional, and national conferences.

Art Johnson, Ed.D., is a professor of mathematics education at Boston University. He is a mathematics educator with 32 years of public school teaching experience, a frequent speaker and workshop leader, and the recipient of a number of awards: the Tandy Prize for Teaching Excellence, the Presidential Award for Excellence in Mathematics Teaching, and New Hampshire Teacher of the Year. He was also profiled by the Disney Corporation in the American Teacher of the Year Program. Dr. Johnson has contributed 18 articles to NCTM journals and has authored over 50 books on various aspects of mathematics.

Algebra 1 and Algebra 2

Allan E. Bellman, Ph.D., is a Lecturer/Supervisor in the School of Education at the University of California, Davis. Before coming to Davis, he was a mathematics teacher for 31 years in Montgomery County, Maryland. He has been an instructor for both the Woodrow Wilson National Fellowship Foundation and the T^3 program. He has been involved in the development of many products from Texas Instruments. Dr. Bellman has a particular expertise in the use of technology in education and speaks frequently on this topic. He was a 1992 Tandy Technology Scholar and has twice been listed in Who's Who Among America's Teachers.

Sadie Chavis Bragg, Ed.D., is Senior Vice President of Academic Affairs at the Borough of Manhattan Community College of the City University of New York. A former professor of mathematics, she is a past president of the American Mathematical Association of Two-Year Colleges (AMATYC), co-director of the AMATYC project to revise the standards for introductory college mathematics before calculus, and an active member of the Benjamin Banneker Association. Dr. Bragg has coauthored more than 50 mathematics textbooks for kindergarten through college.

William G. Handlin, Sr., is a classroom teacher and Department Chairman of Technology Applications at Spring Woods High School in Houston, Texas. Awarded Life Membership in the Texas Congress of Parents and Teachers for his contributions to the well-being of children, Mr. Handlin is also a frequent workshop and seminar leader in professional meetings throughout the world.

Reviewers *Tennessee*

Camilla Horton
Secondary Instruction Support
Memphis School District
Memphis, Tennessee

Marcia White
Mathematics Specialist
Academic Operations,
Technology and Innovations
Memphis City Schools
Memphis, Tennessee

Reviewers *National*

Steven Sachs
Mathematics Department Chair
Lawrence North High School
Indianapolis, Indiana

Tammy Baumann
K-12 Mathematics Coordinator
School District of the City of Erie
Erie, Pennsylvania

Sandy Cowgill
Mathematics Department Chair
Muncie Central High School
Muncie, Indiana

Kari Egnot
Mathematics Teacher
Newport News High School
Newport News, Virginia

Sheryl Ezze
Mathematics Chairperson
DeWitt High School
Lansing, Michigan

Dennis Griebel
Mathematics Coordinator
Cherry Creek School District
Aurora, Colorado

Bill Harrington
Secondary Mathematics Coordinator
State College School District
State College, Pennsylvania

Michael Herzog
Mathematics Teacher
Tucson Small School Project
Tucson, Arizona

Gary Kubina
Mathematics Consultant
Mobile County School System
Mobile, Alabama

Sharon Liston
Mathematics Department Chair
Moore Public Schools
Oklahoma City, Oklahoma

Ann Marie Palmeri Monahan
Mathematics Supervisor
Bayonne Public Schools
Bayonne, New Jersey

Indika Morris
Mathematics Department Chair
Queen Creek School District
Queen Creek, Arizona

Jennifer Petersen
K-12 Mathematics Curriculum Facilitator
Springfield Public Schools
Springfield, Missouri

Tammy Popp
Mathematics Teacher
Mehlville School District
St. Louis, Missouri

Mickey Porter
Mathematics Teacher
Dayton Public Schools
Dayton, Ohio

John Staley
Secondary Mathematics Coordinator
Office of Mathematics, PK-12
Baltimore County, Maryland

Robert Thomas, Ph.D.
Mathematics Teacher
Yuma Union High School District #70
Yuma, Arizona

Linda Ussery
Mathematics Consultant
Alabama Department of Education
Tuscumbia, Alabama

Denise Vizzini
Mathematics Teacher
Clarksburg High School
Montgomery County, Maryland

Merrie Wolfe
Mathematics Department Chair
Tulsa Public Schools
Tulsa, Oklahoma

Contents *in Brief*

Welcome to Pearson's ***Prentice Hall Geometry*** student book. Throughout this textbook, you will find content that has been developed to cover all of the Geometry concepts and skills of the Tennessee Math Curriculum Framework. The **TN Chapter** offers timely review and practice to help you prepare for the Geometry End-of-Course Test. The End-of-Course Assessment can provide additional practice.

TEACH ME
PREPARE ME
INSPIRE ME

ENGAGE ME

HELP ME

Change

the way students see math.

Prentice Hall Geometry helps students see math like never before. This blended print and digital curriculum provides an environment where you can engage students, teach for understanding, and promote mastery—for success today and through life. It's a whole new way to look at math. See for yourself.

PowerGeometry.com

Using the latest in digital instructional technology, PowerGeometry.com provides a pedagogically relevant interface to support your math classroom. PowerGeometry.com can be used as a stand-alone digital course or integrated with print materials to provide a balanced classroom environment for you and your students to engage in the study of math. This online learning environment is designed to enable you to easily access resources, plan lessons, incorporate presentation tools, assign student work and support student understanding.

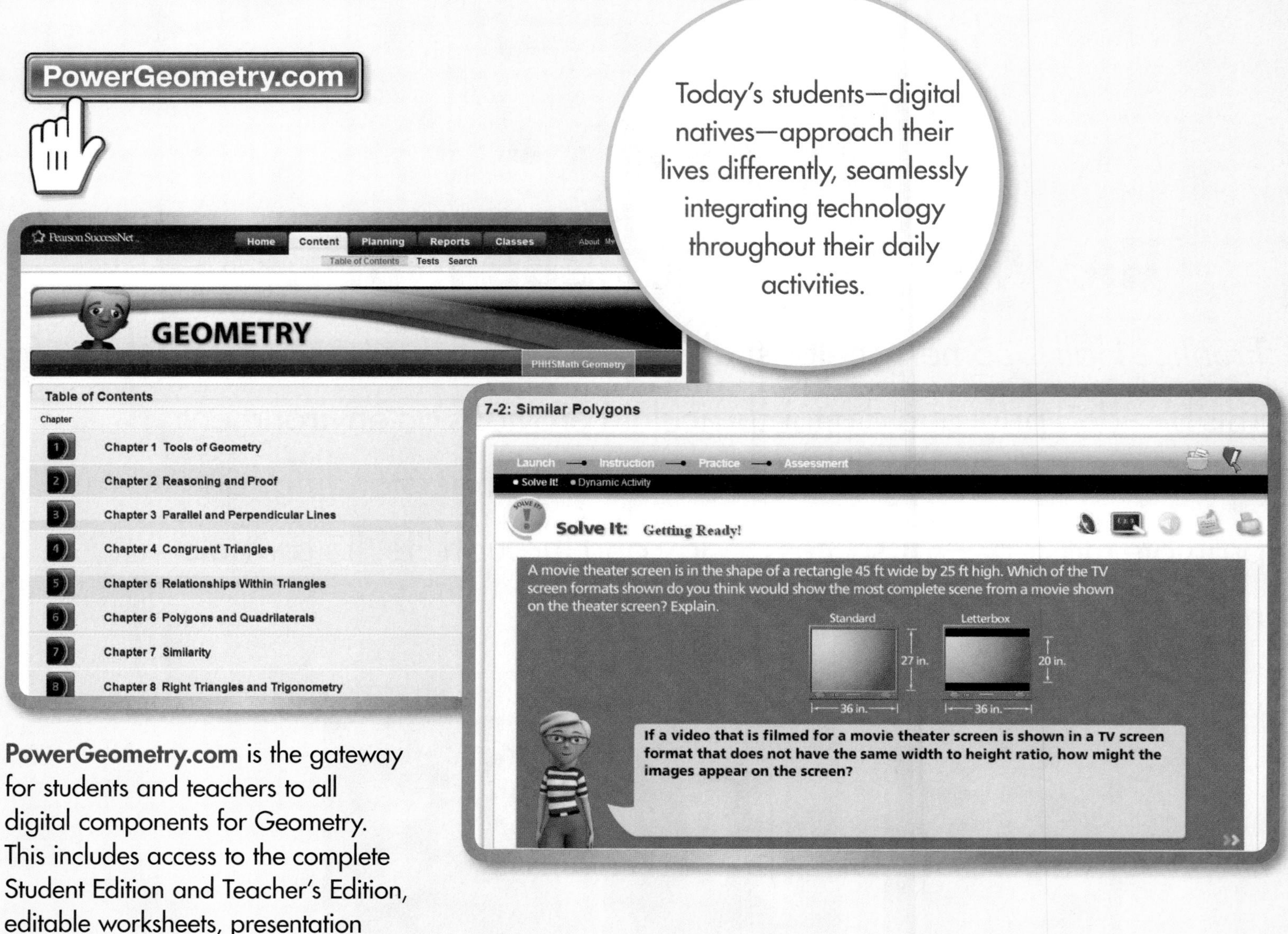

Today's students—digital natives—approach their lives differently, seamlessly integrating technology throughout their daily activities.

PowerGeometry.com is the gateway for students and teachers to all digital components for Geometry. This includes access to the complete Student Edition and Teacher's Edition, editable worksheets, presentation tools and a sophisticated classroom management system.

"Today's students are digital natives. These students are not merely technology-savvy; they are approaching their lives differently as they integrate digital technologies seamlessly throughout their daily activities. Let's not have them power-down when they get to math class."

—*Laurie Bass*

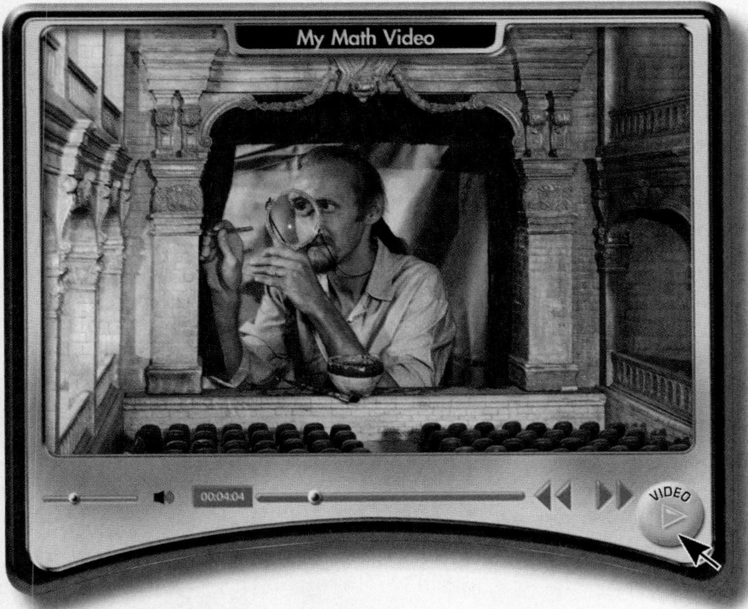

PEARSON

video challenge

My Math Videos are student-produced videos that engage students in math concepts and are relevant to their lives. Through the Pearson Video Challenge, students can generate and submit their own videos to be included on PowerGeometry.com.

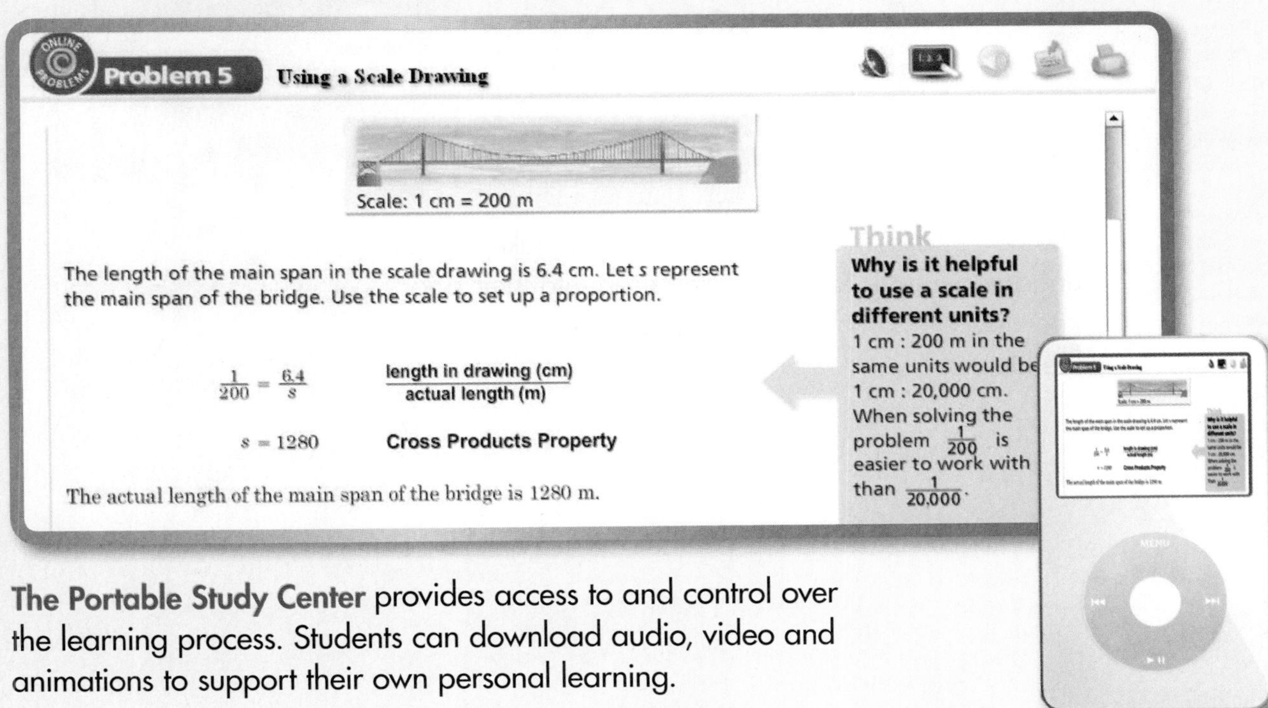

ONLINE PROBLEMS
Problem 5
Using a Scale Drawing
Scale: 1 cm = 200 m
The length of the main span in the scale drawing is 6.4 cm. Let s represent the main span of the bridge. Use the scale to set up a proportion.
$\frac{1}{200} = \frac{6.4}{s}$
length in drawing (cm) / actual length (m)
$s = 1280$
Cross Products Property
The actual length of the main span of the bridge is 1280 m.
Think
Why is it helpful to use a scale in different units?
1 cm : 200 m in the same units would be 1 cm : 20,000 cm. When solving the problem $\frac{1}{200}$ is easier to work with than $\frac{1}{20,000}$.

The Portable Study Center provides access to and control over the learning process. Students can download audio, video and animations to support their own personal learning.

Visual *Learning*

Visual learning is about acquiring and communicating information. By presenting concepts visually, and through different media, students can understand the importance of a mathematical idea and the context in which it is useful.

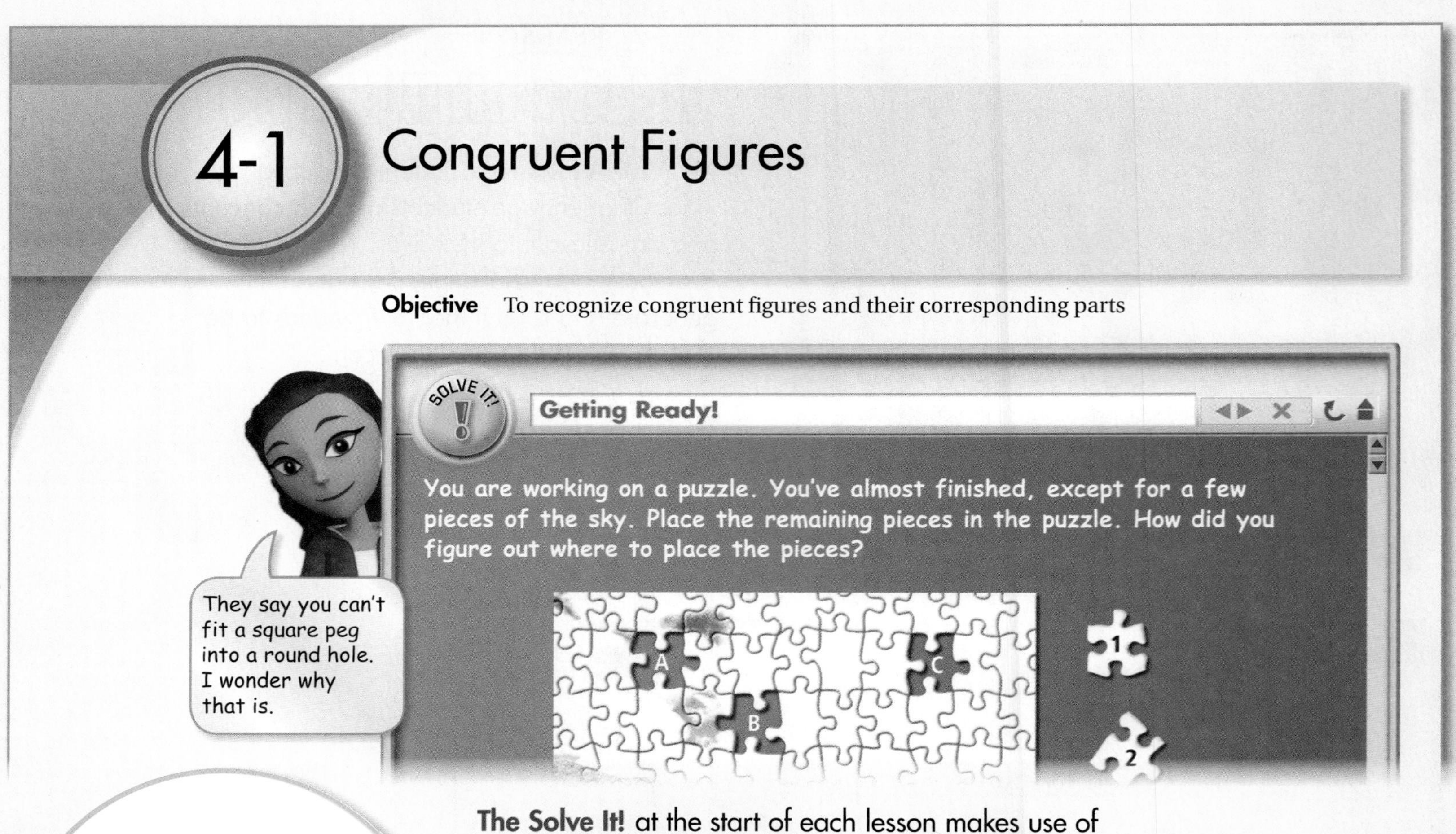

The Solve It! at the start of each lesson makes use of engaging visuals to help students tap into their prior knowledge and connect it to important concepts in the lesson.

Visual learning strategies increase the learning potential of all students.

"Through visual models, students interact with mathematical concepts, process information, observe change, reflect on their experiences, modify their thinking, and draw conclusions. They learn."

—Stuart J. Murphy

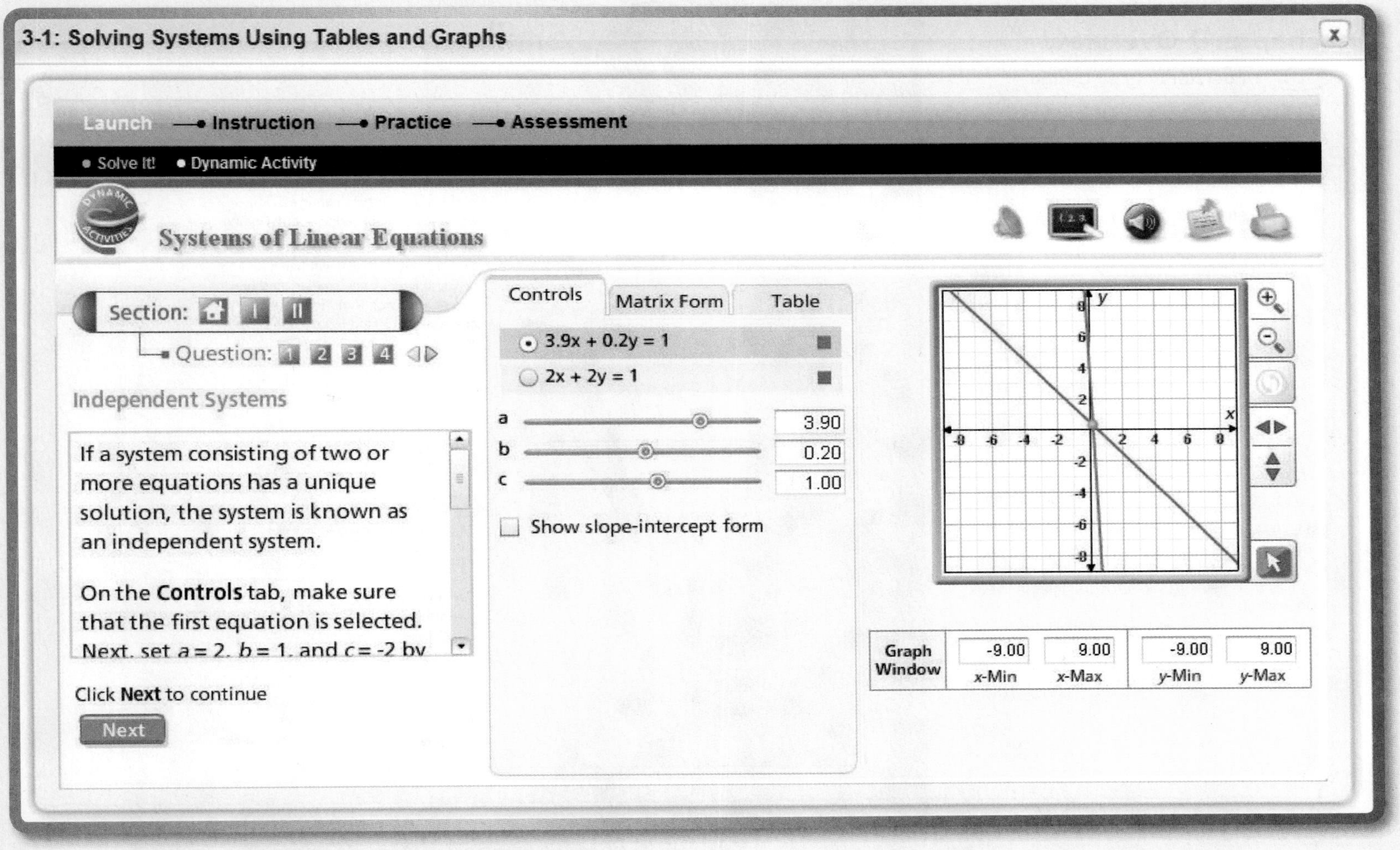

3-1: Solving Systems Using Tables and Graphs

Launch —• Instruction —• Practice —• Assessment

• Solve It! • Dynamic Activity

Systems of Linear Equations

Section: I II

Question: 1 2 3 4

Independent Systems

If a system consisting of two or more equations has a unique solution, the system is known as an independent system.

On the **Controls** tab, make sure that the first equation is selected. Next, set $a = 2$, $b = 1$, and $c = -2$ by

Click **Next** to continue

Next

Controls | Matrix Form | Table

$3.9x + 0.2y = 1$

$2x + 2y = 1$

a	3.90
b	0.20
c	1.00

Show slope-intercept form

Graph Window	-9.00	9.00	-9.00	9.00
	x-Min	x-Max	y-Min	y-Max

Dynamic Activities at PowerGeometry.com provide an interactive way for students to explore lesson concepts. Additionally, Math Tools enable students and teachers to utilize the functionality of tools such as a graphing calculator, algebra tiles, and geometry software.

TENNESSEE TENNESSEE TENNESSEE

Big *Ideas*

Big Ideas are the organizing ideas for all of the lessons in the program. They appear in every lesson and throughout the chapters and courses. These Big Ideas help students focus on the key mathematical concepts they will be studying.

BIG ideas focus student learning.

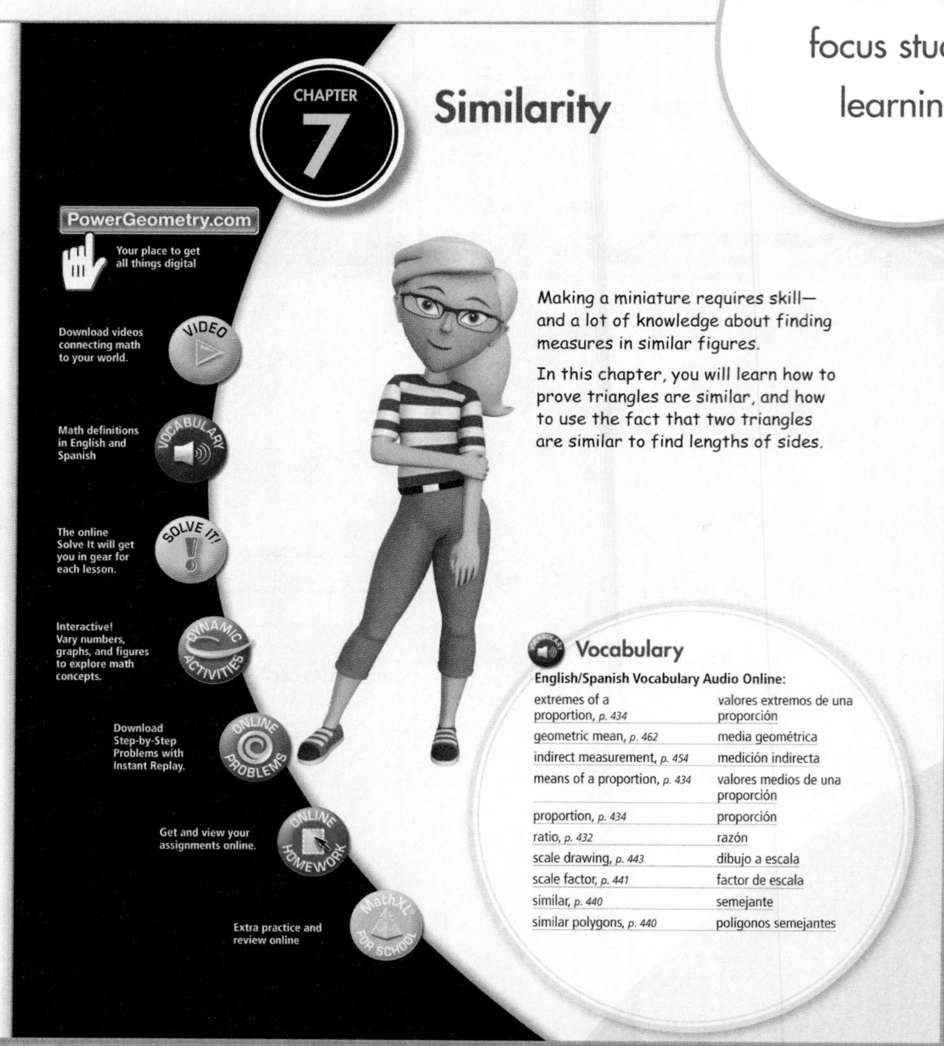

Chapter 7 Overview
UbD Understanding by Design
Chapter 7 expands on students' understandings and skills related to similarity. In this chapter, students will develop the answers to the Essential Questions posed on the opposite page as they learn the concepts and skills bulleted below.
BIG idea Similarity
ESSENTIAL QUESTION How do you use proportions to find side lengths in similar polygons?
• Students will form proportions based on known lengths of corresponding sides.
BIG ideas Reasoning and Proof
ESSENTIAL QUESTION How do you show two triangles are similar?
• Students will use the Angle-Angle Similarity Postulate.
• Students will use the Side-Angle-Side Similarity Theorem.
• Students will use the Side-Side-Side Similarity Theorem.
BIG idea Visualization
ESSENTIAL QUESTION How do you identify corresponding parts of similar triangles?
• A key to understanding corresponding parts of similar triangles is to show the triangles in like orientations.
CHAPTER 7
Similarity
PowerGeometry.com
Your place to get all things digital
Download videos connecting math to your world.
VIDEO
Math definitions in English and Spanish
VOCABULARY
The online Solve It will get you in gear for each lesson.
SOLVE IT!
Interactive! Vary numbers, graphs, and figures to explore math concepts.
DYNAMIC ACTIVITIES
Download Step-by-Step Problems with Instant Replay.
ONLINE PROBLEMS
Get and view your assignments online.
ONLINE HOMEWORK
Extra practice and review online
MathXL FOR SCHOOL
Making a miniature requires skill—and a lot of knowledge about finding measures in similar figures.
In this chapter, you will learn how to prove triangles are similar, and how to use the fact that two triangles are similar to find lengths of sides.
Vocabulary
English/Spanish Vocabulary Audio Online:
extremes of a proportion, p. 434 | valores extremos de una proporción
geometric mean, p. 462 | media geométrica
indirect measurement, p. 454 | medición indirecta
means of a proportion, p. 434 | valores medios de una proporción
proportion, p. 434 | proporción
ratio, p. 432 | razón
scale drawing, p. 443 | dibujo a escala
scale factor, p. 441 | factor de escala
similar, p. 440 | semejante
similar polygons, p. 440 | polígonos semejantes

Understanding by Design uses backward design to create a comprehensive curriculum. By starting with the end results in mind, instruction can be planned more effectively.

Essential Questions help students think about the Big Ideas presented in the lesson.

"A Big Idea is a way of seeing better and working smarter, not just another piece of knowledge."

—*Grant Wiggins*

7 Chapter Review

Connecting BIG ideas and Answering the Essential Questions

1 Similarity
You can set up and solve proportions using corresponding sides of similar polygons.

2 Reasoning and Proof
Two triangles are similar if certain relationships exist between two or three pairs of corresponding parts.

3 Visualization
Sketch and label triangles separately in the same orientation to see how the vertices correspond.

Ratios and Proportions (Lesson 7-1)
The Cross Products Property states that if $\frac{a}{b} = \frac{c}{d}$, then $ad = bc$.

Similar Polygons (Lesson 7-2)
Corresponding angles of similar polygons are congruent, and corresponding sides of similar polygons are proportional.

Proving Triangles Similar (Lesson 7-3)
Angle-Angle Similarity (AA ~) Postulate
Side-Angle-Side Similarity (SAS ~) Theorem
Side-Side-Side Similarity (SSS ~) Theorem

Seeing Similar Triangles (Lessons 7-3 and 7-4)

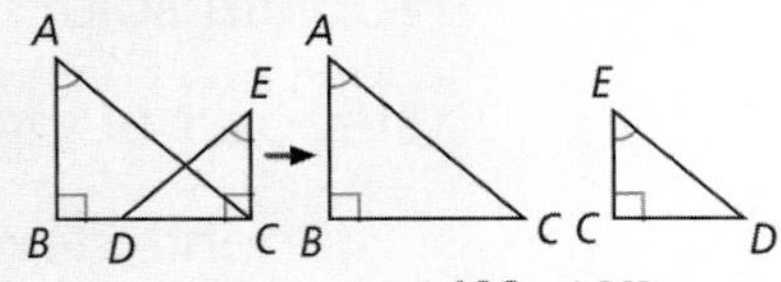

$\triangle ABC \sim \triangle ECD$

Proportions in Triangles (Lessons 7-4 and 7-5)

Geometric Means in Right Triangles

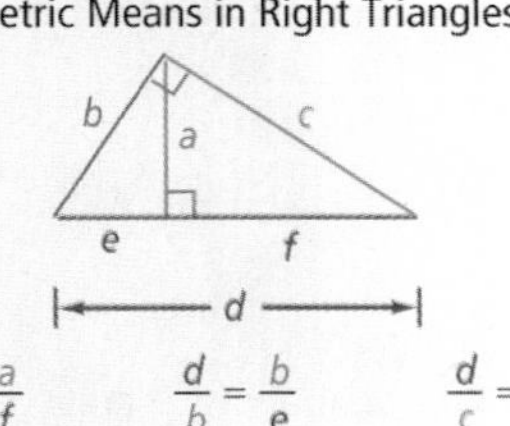

$\frac{e}{a} = \frac{a}{f}$ $\frac{d}{b} = \frac{b}{e}$ $\frac{d}{c} = \frac{c}{f}$

Side-Splitter Theorem

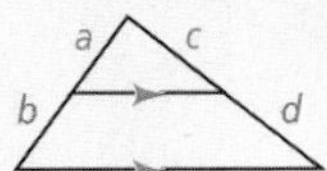

$\frac{a}{b} = \frac{c}{d}$

Triangle-Angle-Bisector Theorem

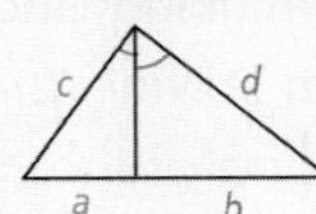

$\frac{a}{b} = \frac{c}{d}$

In the Chapter Review, students will find answers to the Essential Questions for the Big Ideas. The Chapter Review also provides a comprehensive set of notes for student reference.

Problem *Solving*

Problem solving strategies are an integral part of the program and are embedded throughout each lesson. The worked-out problems model effective thinking and reasoning strategies and can help foster students' mathematical reasoning. These important skills can help students score well on the Geometry End-of-Course exam.

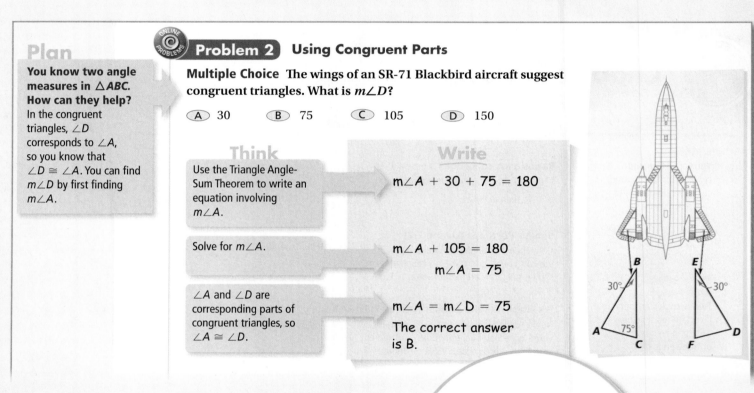

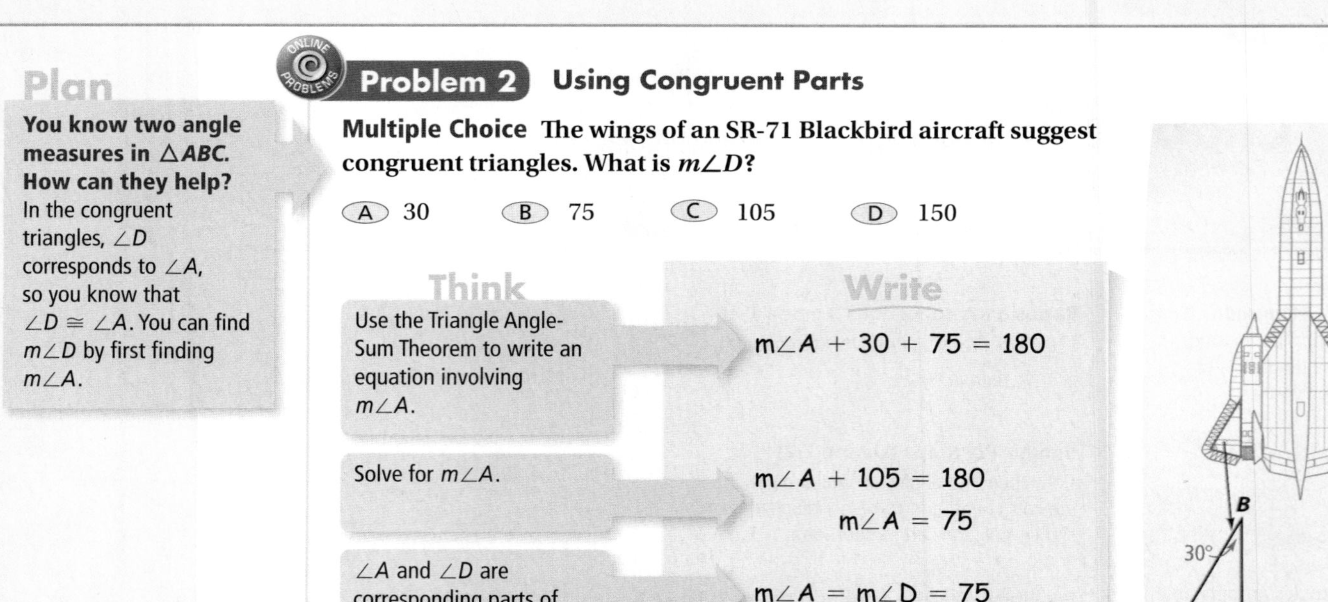

Plan
You know two angle measures in $\triangle ABC$. How can they help?
In the congruent triangles, $\angle D$ corresponds to $\angle A$, so you know that $\angle D \cong \angle A$. You can find $m\angle D$ by first finding $m\angle A$.
ONLINE PROBLEMS
Problem 2 Using Congruent Parts
Multiple Choice The wings of an SR-71 Blackbird aircraft suggest congruent triangles. What is $m\angle D$?
(A) 30 (B) 75 (C) 105 (D) 150
Think
Write
Use the Triangle Angle-Sum Theorem to write an equation involving $m\angle A$.
$m\angle A + 30 + 75 = 180$
Solve for $m\angle A$.
$m\angle A + 105 = 180$
$m\angle A = 75$
$\angle A$ and $\angle D$ are corresponding parts of congruent triangles, so $\angle A \cong \angle D$.
$m\angle A = m\angle D = 75$
The correct answer is B.
B
E
30°
30°
A
75°
C
F
D

Think-Write Boxes guide students' thinking and reasoning by modeling the problem solving process. Students gain a deeper understanding of the problem and learn how to arrive at the solution.

Problem solutions are stepped out to help students develop mathematical thinking and reasoning skills.

"Research shows that understanding develops during the process of solving problems in which important math concepts and skills are embedded."

—*Randy Charles*

Online Problems at PowerGeometry.com provide students with step-by-step instruction at their own pace—and include guided support from an avatar. These problems can be used for in-class presentation or assigned to students on their own.

TENNESSEE TENNESSEE TENNESSEE

Differentiated *Instruction*

Differentiating instruction helps all students develop conceptual understanding, fosters mathematical reasoning, and refines problem solving strategies. The program offers options for differentiating instruction at the start of each chapter and throughout the lessons.

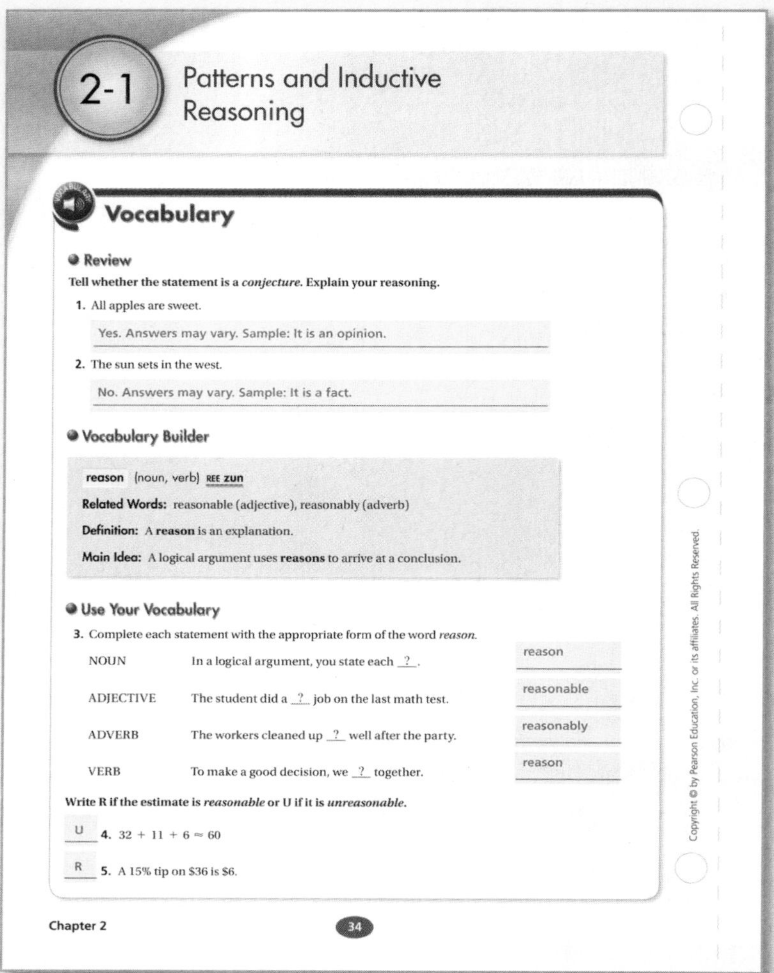

2-1 Patterns and Inductive Reasoning

Vocabulary

Review

Tell whether the statement is a *conjecture*. Explain your reasoning.

1. All apples are sweet.

   Yes. Answers may vary. Sample: It is an opinion.

2. The sun sets in the west.

   No. Answers may vary. Sample: It is a fact.

Vocabulary Builder

reason (noun, verb) REE zun

Related Words: reasonable (adjective), reasonably (adverb)

Definition: A **reason** is an explanation.

Main Idea: A logical argument uses **reasons** to arrive at a conclusion.

Use Your Vocabulary

3. Complete each statement with the appropriate form of the word *reason*.

NOUN	In a logical argument, you state each _?_.	reason
ADJECTIVE	The student did a _?_ job on the last math test.	reasonable
ADVERB	The workers cleaned up _?_ well after the party.	reasonably
VERB	To make a good decision, we _?_ together.	reason

Write R if the estimate is *reasonable* or U if it is *unreasonable*.

U 4. $32 + 11 + 6 \approx 60$

R 5. A 15% tip on \$36 is \$6.

Chapter 2 34

The Student Companion, a student worktext, has graphic organizers and other tools, such as Vocabulary Builder and Think-Write Boxes, that allow for differentiated instruction.

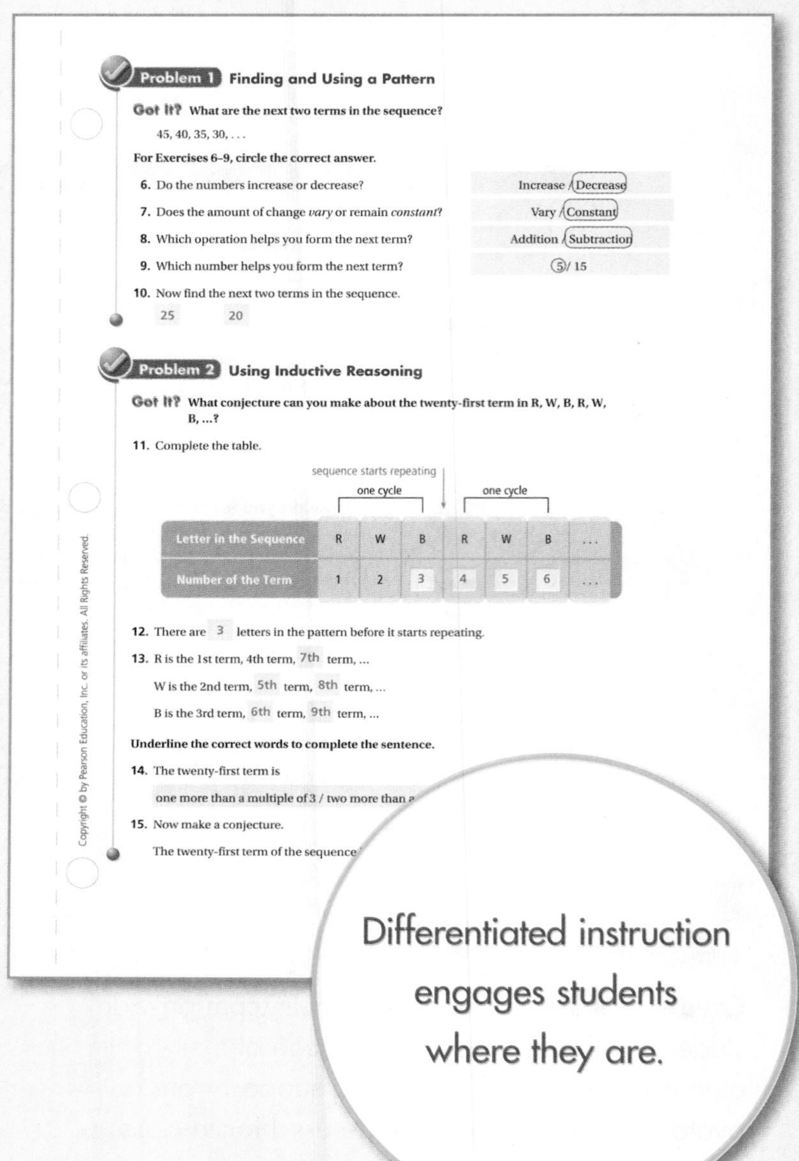

Problem 1 **Finding and Using a Pattern**

Got It? **What are the next two terms in the sequence?**

45, 40, 35, 30, . . .

For Exercises 6–9, circle the correct answer.

6. Do the numbers increase or decrease? Increase / Decrease
7. Does the amount of change *vary* or remain *constant*? Vary / Constant
8. Which operation helps you form the next term? Addition / Subtraction
9. Which number helps you form the next term? 5 / 15
10. Now find the next two terms in the sequence. 25 20

Problem 2 **Using Inductive Reasoning**

Got It? **What conjecture can you make about the twenty-first term in R, W, B, R, W, B, ...?**

11. Complete the table.

sequence starts repeating; one cycle; one cycle

Letter in the Sequence	R	W	B	R	W	B	...
Number of the Term	1	2	3	4	5	6	...

12. There are 3 letters in the pattern before it starts repeating.
13. R is the 1st term, 4th term, 7th term, ...

    W is the 2nd term, 5th term, 8th term, ...

    B is the 3rd term, 6th term, 9th term, ...

Underline the correct words to complete the sentence.

14. The twenty-first term is

    one more than a multiple of 3 / two more than a

15. Now make a conjecture.

    The twenty-first term of the sequence

Differentiated instruction engages students where they are.

"Differentiated instruction does not change what is taught; it changes how it is taught."

—*Basia Hall*

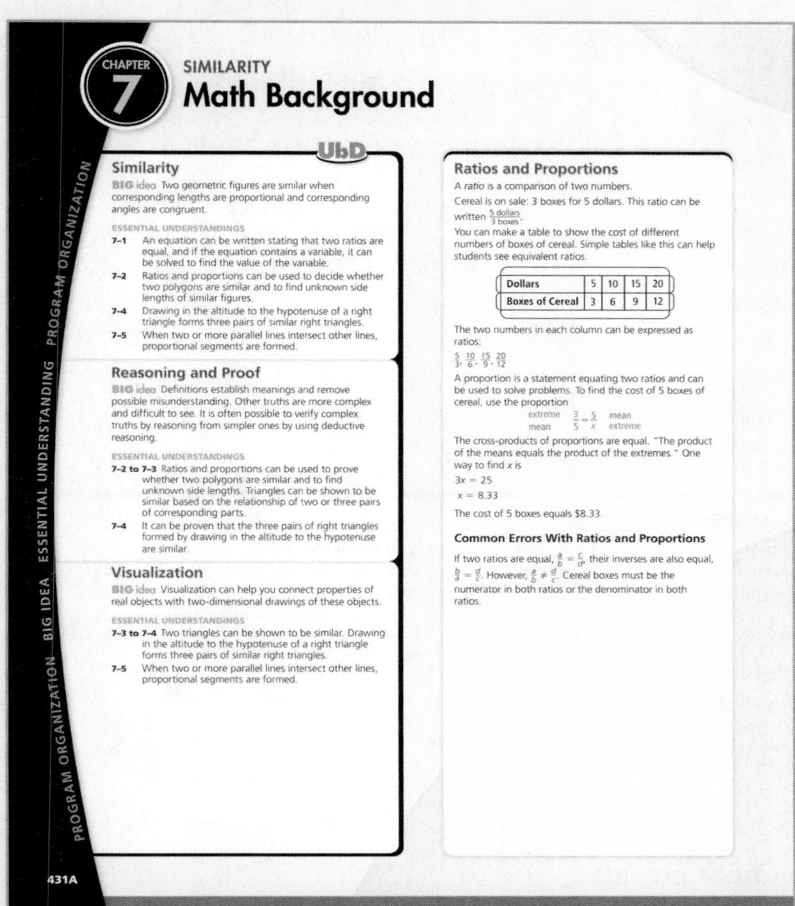

CHAPTER 7

SIMILARITY

Math Background

UbD

Similarity

BIG idea Two geometric figures are similar when corresponding lengths are proportional and corresponding angles are congruent.

ESSENTIAL UNDERSTANDINGS

7-1 An equation can be written stating that two ratios are equal, and if the equation contains a variable, it can be solved to find the value of the variable.

7-2 Ratios and proportions can be used to decide whether two polygons are similar and to find unknown side lengths of similar figures.

7-4 Drawing in the altitude to the hypotenuse of a right triangle forms three pairs of similar right triangles.

7-5 When two or more parallel lines intersect other lines, proportional segments are formed.

Reasoning and Proof

BIG idea Definitions establish meanings and remove possible misunderstanding. Other truths are more complex and difficult to see. It is often possible to verify complex truths by reasoning from simpler ones by using deductive reasoning.

ESSENTIAL UNDERSTANDINGS

7-2 to 7-3 Ratios and proportions can be used to prove whether two polygons are similar and to find unknown side lengths. Triangles can be shown to be similar based on the relationship of two or three pairs of corresponding parts.

7-4 It can be proven that the three pairs of right triangles formed by drawing in the altitude to the hypotenuse are similar.

Visualization

BIG idea Visualization can help you connect properties of real objects with two-dimensional drawings of these objects.

ESSENTIAL UNDERSTANDINGS

7-3 to 7-4 Two triangles can be shown to be similar. Drawing in the altitude to the hypotenuse of a right triangle forms three pairs of similar right triangles.

7-5 When two or more parallel lines intersect other lines, proportional segments are formed.

Ratios and Proportions

A *ratio* is a comparison of two numbers.

Cereal is on sale: 3 boxes for 5 dollars. This ratio can be written $\frac{5 \text{ dollars}}{3 \text{ boxes}}$.

You can make a table to show the cost of different numbers of boxes of cereal. Simple tables like this can help students see equivalent ratios.

Dollars	5	10	15	20
Boxes of Cereal	3	6	9	12

The two numbers in each column can be expressed as ratios:

$\frac{5}{3}, \frac{10}{6}, \frac{15}{9}, \frac{20}{12}$

A proportion is a statement equating two ratios and can be used to solve problems. To find the cost of 5 boxes of cereal, use the proportion

extreme, mean $\frac{3}{5} = \frac{5}{x}$ mean, extreme

The cross-products of proportions are equal. "The product of the means equals the product of the extremes." One way to find x is

$3x = 25$

$x = 8.33$

The cost of 5 boxes equals $8.33.

Common Errors With Ratios and Proportions

If two ratios are equal, $\frac{a}{b} = \frac{c}{d}$, their inverses are also equal, $\frac{b}{a} = \frac{d}{c}$. However, $\frac{a}{b} \neq \frac{d}{c}$. Cereal boxes must be the numerator in both ratios or the denominator in both ratios.

Math Background provides ongoing professional development in key content for each chapter and lesson, enabling teachers to adapt and respond to the needs of each individual learner.

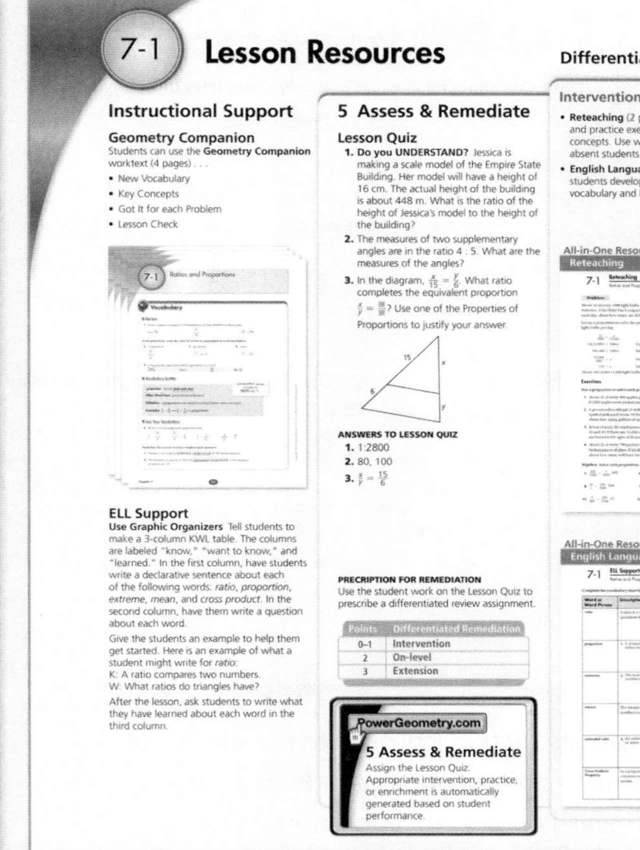

7-1 Lesson Resources

Instructional Support

Geometry Companion

Students can use the **Geometry Companion** worktext (4 pages) . . .

- New Vocabulary
- Key Concepts
- Got It for each Problem
- Lesson Check

ELL Support

Use Graphic Organizers Tell students to make a 3-column KWL table. The columns are labeled "know," "want to know," and "learned." In the first column, have students write a declarative sentence about each of the following words: *ratio, proportion, extreme, mean,* and *cross product*. In the second column, have them write a question about each word.

Give the students an example to help them get started. Here is an example of what a student might write for *ratio*:

K: A ratio compares two numbers.

W: What ratios do triangles have?

After the lesson, ask students to write what they have learned about each word in the third column.

5 Assess & Remediate

Lesson Quiz

1. **Do you UNDERSTAND?** Jessica is making a scale model of the Empire State Building. Her model will have a height of 16 cm. The actual height of the building is about 448 m. What is the ratio of the height of Jessica's model to the height of the building?
2. The measures of two supplementary angles are in the ratio 4 : 5. What are the measures of the angles?
3. In the diagram, $\frac{x}{15} = \frac{y}{6}$. What ratio completes the equivalent proportion $\frac{x}{y} = \frac{■}{■}$? Use one of the Properties of Proportions to justify your answer.

ANSWERS TO LESSON QUIZ

1. 1:2800
2. 80, 100
3. $\frac{x}{y} = \frac{15}{6}$

PRECRIPTION FOR REMEDIATION

Use the student work on the Lesson Quiz to prescribe a differentiated review assignment.

Points	Differentiated Remediation
0–1	Intervention
2	On-level
3	Extension

PowerGeometry.com

5 Assess & Remediate

Assign the Lesson Quiz. Appropriate intervention, practice, or enrichment is automatically generated based on student performance.

Differentiated Remediation

Intervention

- **Reteaching** (2 pages) Provides reteaching and practice exercises for the key lesson concepts. Use with struggling students or absent students.
- **English Language Learner Support** Helps students develop and reinforce mathematical vocabulary and key concepts.

All-in-One Resources/Online

Reteaching

All-in-One Resources/Online

English Language Learner Support

Lesson Resources 438A

Lesson Resources provide a detailed blueprint for instruction, assessment, and remediation that includes prescriptions for all levels of students from intervention to extension.

Assessment

Effective and useful assessments are frequent and varied. The program includes formative assessment, such as Got It?, that allows teachers to evaluate students' understanding of concepts and informs instruction. The summative assessments at the end of each lesson and chapter are more structured and give students valuable practice for the Geometry End-of-Course exam.

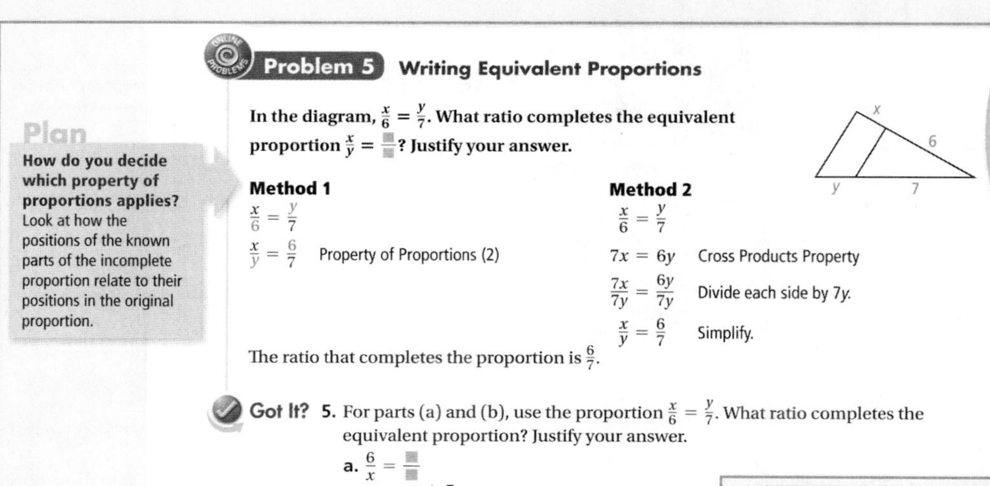

Problem 5 Writing Equivalent Proportions

Plan

How do you decide which property of proportions applies? Look at how the positions of the known parts of the incomplete proportion relate to their positions in the original proportion.

In the diagram, $\frac{x}{6} = \frac{y}{7}$. What ratio completes the equivalent proportion $\frac{x}{y} = \frac{■}{■}$? Justify your answer.

Method 1

$\frac{x}{6} = \frac{y}{7}$

$\frac{x}{y} = \frac{6}{7}$ Property of Proportions (2)

Method 2

$\frac{x}{6} = \frac{y}{7}$

$7x = 6y$ Cross Products Property

$\frac{7x}{7y} = \frac{6y}{7y}$ Divide each side by 7y.

$\frac{x}{y} = \frac{6}{7}$ Simplify.

The ratio that completes the proportion is $\frac{6}{7}$.

Got It? 5. For parts (a) and (b), use the proportion $\frac{x}{6} = \frac{y}{7}$. What ratio completes the equivalent proportion? Justify your answer.

a. $\frac{6}{x} = \frac{■}{■}$

b. $\frac{■}{■} = \frac{y + 7}{7}$

c. **Reasoning** Explain why $\frac{6}{x - 6} = \frac{7}{y - 7}$ is an to $\frac{x}{6} = \frac{y}{7}$.

Frequent, varied assessments allow accurate measurement of student learning from start to finish.

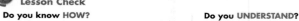

Lesson Check

Do you know HOW?

1. To the nearest millimeter, a cell phone is 84 mm long and 46 mm wide. What is the ratio of the width to the length?
2. Two angle measures are in the ratio 5 : 9. Write expressions for the two angle measures in terms of the variable x.
3. What is the solution of the proportion $\frac{20}{z} = \frac{5}{3}$?
4. For $\frac{a}{7} = \frac{13}{b}$ complete each equivalent proportion.
   a. $\frac{a}{■} = \frac{7}{■}$ b. $\frac{a - 7}{7} = \frac{■}{■}$ c. $\frac{7}{a} = \frac{■}{■}$

Do you UNDERSTAND?

5. **Vocabulary** What is the difference between a ratio and a proportion?
6. **Open-Ended** The lengths of the sides of a triangle are in the extended ratio 3 : 6 : 7. What are two possible sets of side lengths, in inches, for the triangle?
7. **Error Analysis** What is the error in the solution of the proportion shown at the right?
8. What is a proportion that has means 6 and 18 and extremes 9 and 12?

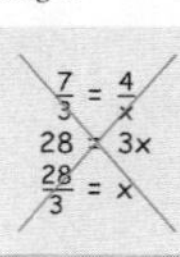

Got It? checkpoints after each problem in the lesson constantly monitor student understanding. These quick assessments keep instruction on track for all students and allow teachers to make informed instructional decisions.

Lesson Check provides opportunities for students to show what they know and offers valuable feedback on student understanding.

"The key to education is to be fair and consistent. The same is true for assessment. Fair, consistent, quality assessment is the only way to ensure that students are learning what you are teaching."

—Bill Handlin

	8OH P8 Select appropriate operations to solve problems...	8OH P9 Use appropriate operations to solve problems...	8OH P10 Evaluate a solution for reasonableness.	8OH P11 Use multiplication by a constant factor...
# of students who have mastered standards	12	29	25	24
Total Students	30	30	30	30
Andrew Lauer	✗	✓	✓	✓
Belinda Cortez	✗	✓	✓	✓
Christopher Hale	✗	✗	✗	✗
Dora diConti	✓	✓	✓	✓
Edward Robertson	✗	✓	✓	✓
Emily Whitham	✗	✓	✓	✓
Felicity Withers	✗	✓	✓	✓
George Slate	✗	✗	✓	✗
Kevin Jackson	✓	✓	✓	✓
Marcus Cooper	✗	✓	✓	✓
Mark Jacobs	✗	✓	✓	✓
Susan Kim	✗	✓	✓	✓
Theresa Valdez				

Success Tracker™

The Success Tracker online assessment system provides instant analysis of student performance. Success Tracker includes built-in diagnostic and benchmark tests, diagnoses student mastery, prescribes automatically assigned remediation for every standard not mastered, and reports on student and class progress.

MathXL® for School

MathXL® for School is a powerful online homework, tutorial, and assessment system for *Prentice Hall Geometry.* It provides students with a personalized, interactive learning environment where they can learn at their own pace. MathXL for School assigns students homework problems, automatically grades their work, and then provides immediate feedback and tutorial assistance to ensure mastery before high-stakes tests.

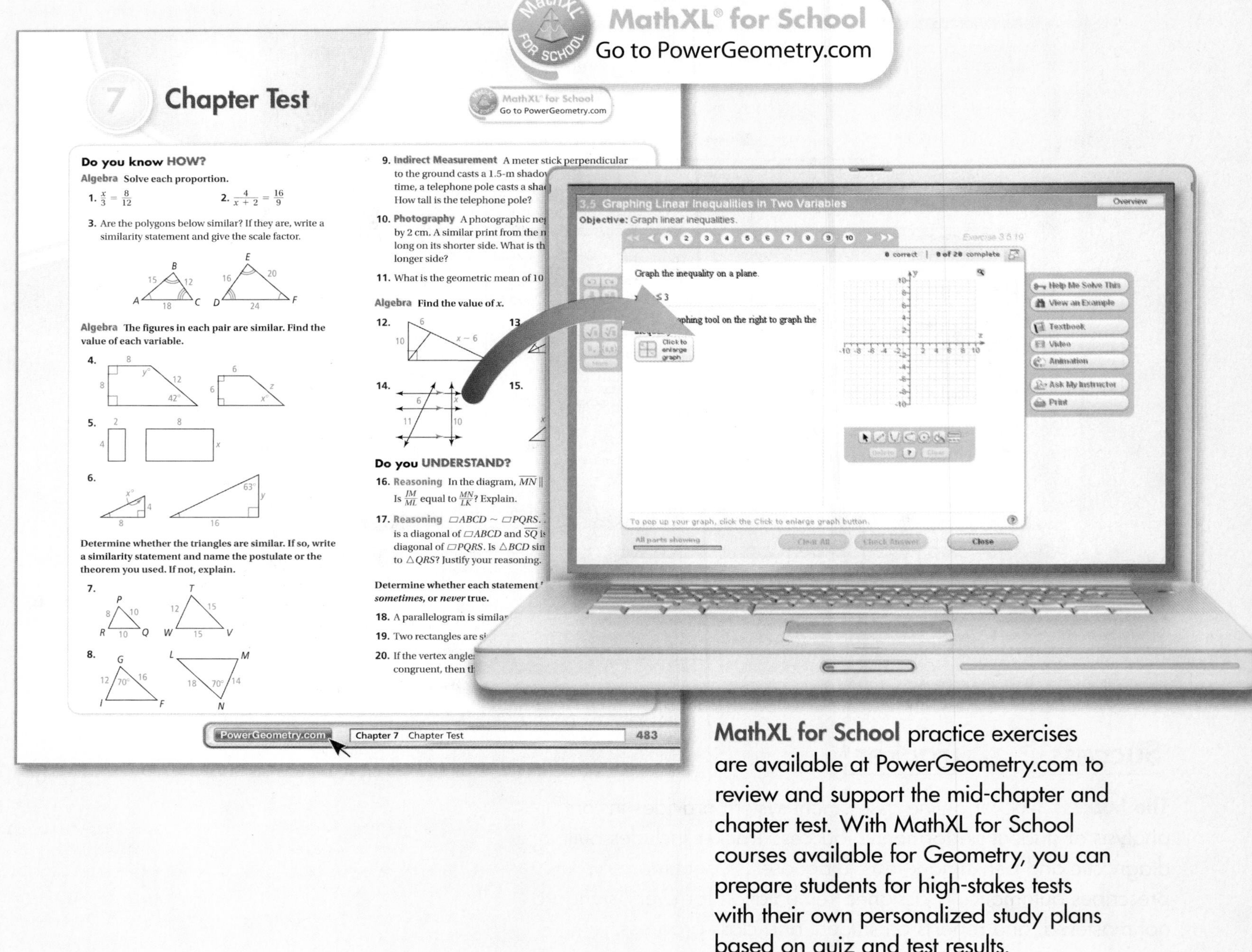

MathXL for School practice exercises are available at PowerGeometry.com to review and support the mid-chapter and chapter test. With MathXL for School courses available for Geometry, you can prepare students for high-stakes tests with their own personalized study plans based on quiz and test results.

Success for All Students

Success in mathematics is essential for students facing rigorous coursework in college, career challenges, and global competitiveness. But success can no longer be determined solely by a student's performance on a math assessment. Students need to develop the thinking and reasoning habits that will empower them to reach full potential in their lives at school and in their career paths. While only some students will pursue further math education or careers in math and science, all students will benefit from learning to analyze problems independently and solve them in different applications. They will need those abilities to lead successful lives as citizens and leaders of the 21st century.

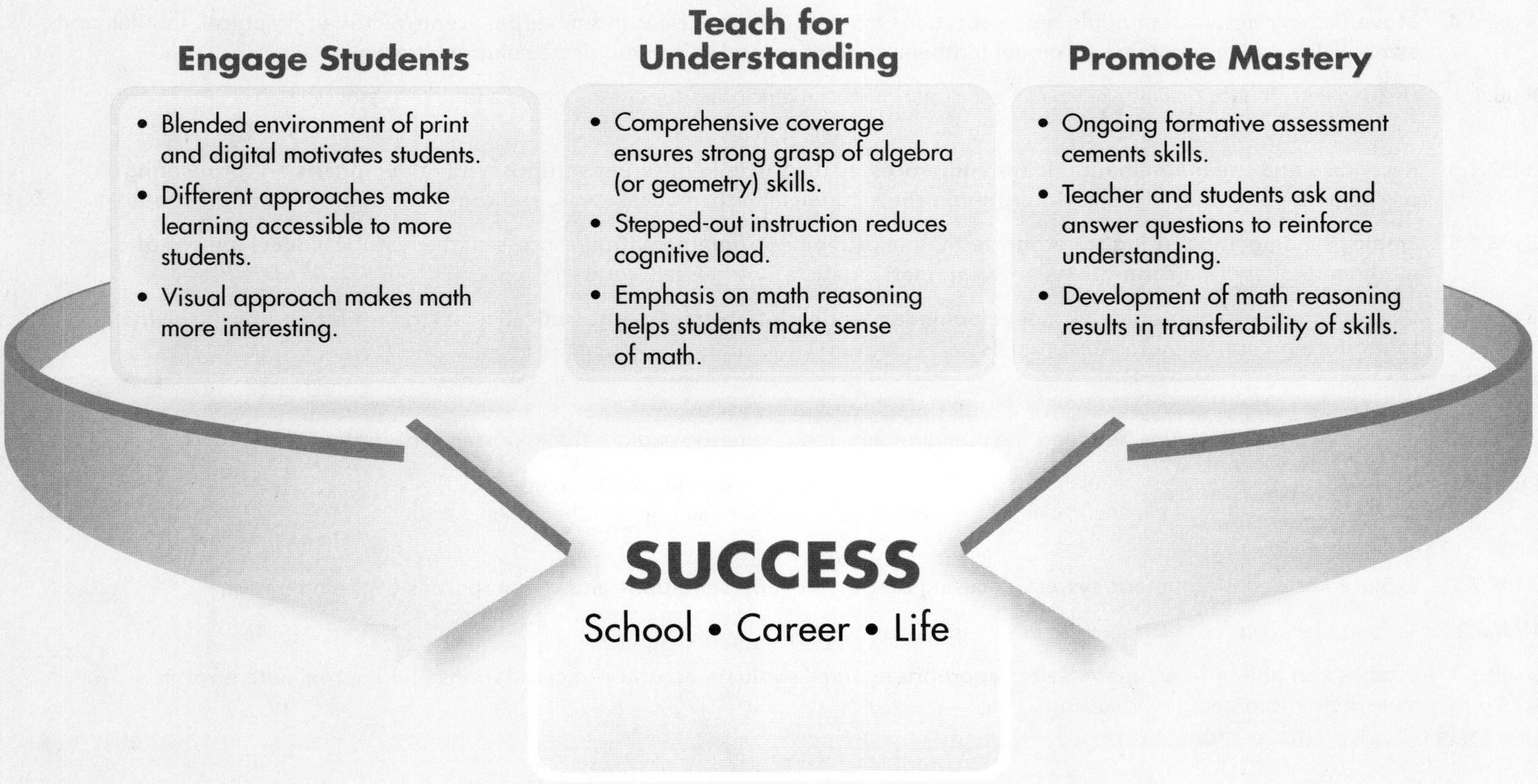

Engage Students

- Blended environment of print and digital motivates students.
- Different approaches make learning accessible to more students.
- Visual approach makes math more interesting.

Teach for Understanding

- Comprehensive coverage ensures strong grasp of algebra (or geometry) skills.
- Stepped-out instruction reduces cognitive load.
- Emphasis on math reasoning helps students make sense of math.

Promote Mastery

- Ongoing formative assessment cements skills.
- Teacher and students ask and answer questions to reinforce understanding.
- Development of math reasoning results in transferability of skills.

SUCCESS

School • Career • Life

State Performance Indicators for Geometry

The following chart shows where each State Performance Indicator for Geometry is presented in Pearson's *Prentice Hall Geometry* text.

	State Performance Indicators	Where to Find
Standard 1 – Mathematical Processes		
CLE 3108.1.1	**Use mathematical language, symbols, definitions, proofs and counterexamples correctly and precisely in mathematical reasoning.**	
SPI 3108.1.1	Give precise mathematical descriptions or definitions of geometric shapes in the plane and space.	Lessons: 4-5, 6-1, 6-2, 6-4, 6-6, 10-3, 10-6, 11-2, 11-3, 11-6
CLE 3108.1.2	**Apply and adapt a variety of appropriate strategies to problem solving, including testing cases, estimation, and then checking induced errors and the reasonableness of the solution.**	
SPI 3108.1.4	Use definitions, basic postulates, and theorems about points, lines, angles, and planes to write/complete proofs and/or to solve problems.	Lessons: 1-2, 2-5, 2-6, 3-1, 3-2, 3-3, 3-4, 3-5
SPI 3108.1.2	Determine areas of planar figures by decomposing them into simpler figures without a grid.	Lessons: 1-8, 10-1 Concept Byte: pp. 614–615
CLE 3108.1.3	**Develop inductive and deductive reasoning to independently make and evaluate mathematical arguments and construct appropriate proofs; include various types of reasoning, logic, and intuition.**	
SPI 3108.1.4	Use definitions, basic postulates, and theorems about points, lines, angles, and planes to write/complete proofs and/or to solve problems.	Lessons: 1-2, 2-5, 2-6, 3-1, 3-2, 3-3, 3-4, 3-5
CLE 3108.1.4	**Move flexibly between multiple representations (contextual, physical written, verbal, iconic/pictorial, graphical, tabular, and symbolic), to solve problems, to model mathematical ideas, and to communicate solution strategies.**	
SPI 3108.1.3	Use geometric understanding and spatial visualization of geometric solids to solve problems and/or create drawings.	Lessons: 1-1, 1-2 Concept Byte: pp. 696–697
CLE 3108.1.5	**Recognize and use mathematical ideas and processes that arise in different settings, with an emphasis on formulating a problem in mathematical terms, interpreting the solutions, mathematical ideas, and communication of solution strategies.**	
CLE 3108.1.6	**Employ reading and writing to recognize the major themes of mathematical processes, the historical development of mathematics, and the connections between mathematics and the real world.**	
CLE 3108.1.7	**Use technologies appropriately to develop understanding of abstract mathematical ideas, to facilitate problem solving, and to produce accurate and reliable models.**	
Standard 2 – Number & Operations		
CLE 3108.2.1	**Establish the relationships between the real numbers and geometry; explore the importance of irrational numbers to geometry.**	
SPI 3108.2.1	Analyze, apply, or interpret the relationships between basic number concepts and geometry (e.g. rounding and pattern identification in measurement, the relationship of pi to other rational and irrational numbers)	Lesson: TN-1
CLE 3108.2.2	**Explore vectors as a numeric system, focusing on graphic representations and the properties of the operation.**	
SPI 3108.2.2	Perform operations on vectors in various representations.	Lessons: 8-5, TN-3
CLE 3108.2.3	**Establish an ability to estimate, select appropriate units, evaluate accuracy of calculations and approximate error in measurement in geometric settings.**	

State Performance Indicators		Where to Find
Standard 3 – Algebra		
CLE 3108.3.1	**Use analytic geometry tools to explore geometric problems involving parallel and perpendicular lines, circles, and special points of polygons.**	
SPI 3108.3.1	Use algebra and coordinate geometry to analyze and solve problems about geometric figures (including circles).	Lessons: 6-7, 6-8, 6-9, 12-5
SPI 3108.3.2	Use coordinate geometry to prove characteristics of polygonal figures.	Lessons: 6-7, 6-8, 6-9, 12-5
CLE 3108.3.2	**Explore the effect of transformations on geometric figures and shapes in the coordinate plane.**	
SPI 3108.3.3	Describe algebraically the effect of a single transformation (reflections in the x- or y-axis, rotations, translations, and dilations) on two-dimensional geometric shapes in the coordinate plane.	Lessons: 9-1, 9-2, 9-5 Concept Bytes: pp. 566–567, 582–583
Standard 4 – Geometry & Measurement		
CLE 3108.4.1	**Develop the structures of geometry, such as lines, angles, planes, and planar figures, and explore their properties and relationships.**	
SPI 3108.4.1	Differentiate between Euclidean and non-Euclidean geometries.	Concept Byte: pp. 179–180
SPI 3108.4.2	Define, identify, describe, and/or model plane figures using appropriate mathematical symbols (including collinear and non-collinear points, lines, segments, rays, angles, triangles, quadrilaterals, and other polygons).	Lessons: 1-2, 1-4, 1-5, 4-5, 6-1, 6-2, 6-4, 6-5, 6-6 Review: p. 57
CLE 3108.4.2	**Describe the properties of regular polygons, including comparative classification of them and special points and segments.**	
SPI 3108.4.3	Identify, describe and/or apply the relationships and theorems involving different types of triangles, quadrilaterals and other polygons.	Lessons: 4-5, 6-2, 6-3, 6-4, 6-5, 6-6 Review: p. 57 Skills Handbook: p. 825
CLE 3108.4.3	**Develop an understanding of the tools of logic and proof, including aspects of formal logic as well as construction of proofs.**	
SPI 3108.4.4	Analyze different types and formats of proofs.	Lessons: 2-5, 2-6, 3-3, 5-5, 5-6, 5-7
CLE 3108.4.4	**Develop geometric intuition and visualization through performing geometric constructions with straightedge/compass and with technology.**	
CLE 3108.4.5	**Extend the study of planar figures to three-dimensions, including the classical solid figures, and develop analysis through cross-sections.**	
SPI 3108.4.5	Describe solids and/or surfaces in three-dimensional space when given two-dimensional representations for the surfaces of three-dimensional objects.	Lessons: 11-2, 11-3, 11-4, 11-5, 11-6
CLE 3108.4.6	**Generate formulas for perimeter, area, and volume, including their use, dimensional analysis, and applications.**	
SPI 3108.4.6	Use various area of triangle formulas to solve contextual problems (e.g., Heron's formula, the area formula for an equilateral triangle and $A = \frac{1}{2}ab \sin C$).	Lesson: 10-5
SPI 3108.4.7	Compute the area and/or perimeter of triangles, quadrilaterals and other polygons when one or more additional steps are required (e.g. find missing dimensions given area or perimeter of the figure, using trigonometry).	Lessons: 1-8, 10-1, 10-2, 10-3, 10-4, 10-5
SPI 3108.4.8	Solve problems involving area, circumference, area of a sector, and/or arc length of a circle.	Lessons: 10-6, 10-7

State Performance Indicators		Where to Find
Standard 4 – Geometry & Measurement (continued)		
CLE 3108.4.7	**Apply the major concepts of transformation geometry to analyzing geometric objects and symmetry.**	
SPI 3108.4.10	Identify, describe, and/or apply transformations on two and three dimensional geometric shapes	Lessons: 9-1, 9-2, 9-3, 9-4, 9-5, 9-6
CLE 3108.4.8	**Establish processes for determining congruence and similarity of figures, especially as related to scale factor, contextual applications, and transformations.**	
SPI 3108.4.11	Use basic theorems about similar and congruent triangles to solve problems.	Lessons: 4-2, 4-3, 4-6, 7-3, 7-4
SPI 3108.4.12	Solve problems involving congruence, similarity, proportional reasoning and/or scale factor of two similar figures or solids.	Lessons: 4-2, 4-3, 4-4, 4-5, 4-6, 4-7, 5-1, 5-2, 5-3, 5-4, 5-5, 7-1, 7-2, 7-3, 7-4, 7-5
CLE 3108.4.9	**Develop the role of circles in geometry, including angle measurement, properties as a geometric figure, and aspects relating to the coordinate plane.**	
SPI 3108.4.13	Identify, analyze and/or use basic properties and theorems of circles to solve problems (including those relating right triangles and circles).	Lessons: 12-1, 12-2, 12-3, 12-4
CLE 3108.4.10	**Develop the tools of right triangle trigonometry in the contextual applications, including the Pythagorean Theorem, Law of Sines and Law of Cosines**	
SPI 3108.4.9	Use right triangle trigonometry and cross-sections to solve problems involving surface areas and/or volumes of solids. volume of prisms, cylinders, cones, pyramids, spheres, and hemispheres.	Lesson: TN-4
SPI 3108.4.14	Use properties of right triangles to solve problems (such as involving the relationship formed when the altitude to the hypotenuse of a right triangle is drawn).	Lesson: 7-4
SPI 3108.4.15	Determine and use the appropriate trigonometric ratio for a right triangle to solve a **contextual problem**.	Lessons: 8-2, 8-3, 8-4
Standard 5 – Data Analysis, Statistics, & Probability		
CLE 3108.5.1	**Analyze, interpret, employ and construct accurate statistical graphs.**	
SPI 3108.5.1	Use area to solve problems involving geometric probability (e.g. dartboard problem, shaded sector of a circle, shaded region of a geometric figure).	Lesson: 10-8
CLE 3108.5.2	**Develop the basic principles of geometric probability.**	

Tennessee Leveled Pacing Chart

This Leveled Pacing Chart is provided as a guide to help you customize your course and to provide for differentiated instruction.

The suggested number of days for each chapter is based on a traditional 45-minute class period and on a 90-minute block period. The total of 160 days of instruction leaves time for assessments, projects, assemblies, preparing for your state test, or other special days that vary from school to school.

KEY

✓ = Geometry Content

❍ = Reviews the Previous Year

❑ = Content for Enrichment

	Performance Indicator	Basic	Average	Advanced
Chapter 1 Tools of Geometry		**Traditional 10**		**Block 5**
1-1 Nets and Drawings for Visualizing Geometry	SPI 3108.1.3	✓	✓	✓
1-2 Points, Lines, and Planes	SPI 3108.1.3, SPI 3108.1.4, SPI 3108.4.2	✓	✓	✓
1-3 Measuring Segments		❍	❍	❍
1-4 Measuring Angles	SPI 3108.4.2	✓	✓	✓
1-5 Exploring Angle Pairs	SPI 3108.4.2	✓	✓	✓
Concept Byte: Compass Designs		❑	❑	❑
1-6 Basic Constructions		❑	❑	❑
Concept Byte: Exploring Constructions		❑	❑	❑
1-7 Midpoint and Distance in the Coordinate Plane		✓	✓	✓
Review: Classifying Polygons	SPI 3108.4.2, SPI 3108.4.3	✓	✓	✓
1-8 Perimeter, Circumference, and Area	SPI 3108.1.2, SPI 3108.4.7	✓	✓	✓
Concept Byte: Comparing Perimeters and Areas			❑	❑
Chapter 2 Reasoning and Proof		**Traditional 12**		**Block 6**
2-1 Patterns and Inductive Reasoning		✓	✓	✓
2-2 Conditional Statements		✓	✓	✓
Concept Byte: Logic and Truth Tables			❑	❑
2-3 Biconditionals and Definitions		✓	✓	✓
2-4 Deductive Reasoning		✓	✓	✓
2-5 Reasoning in Algebra and Geometry	SPI 3108.1.4, SPI 3108.4.4	✓	✓	✓
2-6 Proving Angles Congruent	SPI 3108.1.4, SPI 3108.4.4	✓	✓	✓

	Performance Indicator	Basic	Average	Advanced
Chapter 3 Parallel and Perpendicular Lines			**Traditional 12**	**Block 6**
3-1 Lines and Angles	SPI 3108.1.4	✓	✓	✓
Concept Byte: Parallel Lines and Related Angles		✓	✓	✓
3-2 Properties of Parallel Lines	SPI 3108.1.4	✓	✓	✓
3-3 Proving Parallel Lines	SPI 3108.1.4, SPI 3108.4.4	✓	✓	✓
3-4 Parallel and Perpendicular Lines	SPI 3108.1.4	✓	✓	✓
Concept Byte: Perpendicular Lines and Planes		✓	✓	✓
3-5 Parallel Lines and Triangles	SPI 3108.1.4	✓	✓	✓
Concept Byte: Exploring Spherical Geometry	SPI 3108.4.1	✓	✓	✓
3-6 Constructing Parallel and Perpendicular Lines			❑	❑
3-7 Equations of Lines in the Coordinate Plane			❑	❑
3-8 Slopes of Parallel and Perpendicular Lines			❑	❑
Chapter 4 Congruent Triangles			**Traditional 16**	**Block 8**
4-1 Congruent Figures		✓	✓	✓
Concept Byte: Building Congruent Triangles		✓	✓	✓
4-2 Triangle Congruence by SSS and SAS	SPI 3108.4.11, SPI 3108.4.12	✓	✓	✓
4-3 Triangle Congruence by ASA and AAS	SPI 3108.4.11, SPI 3108.4.12	✓	✓	✓
Concept Byte: Exploring AAA and SSA		✓	✓	✓
4-4 Using Corresponding Parts of Congruent Triangles	SPI 3108.4.12	✓	✓	✓
Concept Byte: Paper-Folding Conjectures		✓	✓	✓
4-5 Isosceles and Equilateral Triangles	SPI 3108.1.1, SPI 3108.4.2, SPI 3108.4.3, SPI 3108.4.12	✓	✓	✓
4-6 Congruence in Right Triangles	SPI 3108.4.11, SPI 3108.4.12	✓	✓	✓
4-7 Congruence in Overlapping Triangles	SPI 3108.4.12	✓	✓	✓
Chapter 5 Relationships Within Triangles			**Traditional 16**	**Block 8**
Concept Byte: Investigating Midsegments		✓	✓	✓
5-1 Midsegments of Triangles	SPI 3108.4.12	✓	✓	✓
5-2 Perpendicular and Angle Bisectors	SPI 3108.4.12	✓	✓	✓
Concept Byte: Paper Folding Bisectors		✓	✓	
5-3 Bisectors in Triangles	SPI 3108.4.12	✓	✓	✓
Concept Byte: Special Segments in Triangles		✓	✓	✓
5-4 Medians and Altitudes	SPI 3108.4.12	✓	✓	✓
5-5 Indirect Proof	SPI 3108.4.4, SPI 3108.4.12	✓	✓	✓
5-6 Inequalities in One Triangle	SPI 3108.4.4	✓	✓	✓
5-7 Inequalities in Two Triangles	SPI 3108.4.4	✓	✓	✓

	Performance Indicator	Basic	Average	Advanced
Chapter 6 Polygons and Quadrilaterals		**Traditional 18**		**Block 9**
Concept Byte: Exterior Angles of Polygons		✓	✓	✓
6-1 The Polygon-Angle Sum Theorems	SPI 3108.1.1, SPI 3108.4.2	✓	✓	✓
6-2 Properties of Parallelograms	SPI 3108.1.1, SPI 3108.4.2, SPI 3108.4.3	✓	✓	✓
6-3 Proving That a Quadrilateral Is a Parallelogram	SPI 3108.4.3	✓	✓	✓
6-4 Properties of Rhombuses, Rectangles, and Squares	SPI 3108.1.1, SPI 3108.4.2, SPI 3108.4.3	✓	✓	✓
6-5 Conditions for Rhombuses, Rectangles, and Squares	SPI 3108.4.2, SPI 3108.4.3	✓	✓	✓
6-6 Trapezoids and Kites	SPI 3108.1.1, SPI 3108.4.2, SPI 3108.4.3	✓	✓	✓
6-7 Polygons in the Coordinate Plane	SPI 3108.3.1, SPI 3108.3.2	✓	✓	✓
6-8 Applying Coordinate Geometry	SPI 3108.3.1, SPI 3108.3.2	✓	✓	✓
Concept Byte: Quadrilaterals in Quadrilaterals			❑	❑
6-9 Proofs Using Coordinate Geometry	SPI 3108.3.1, SPI 3108.3.2	✓	✓	✓
Chapter 7 Similarity		**Traditional 10**		**Block 5**
7-1 Ratios and Proportions	SPI 3108.4.11, SPI 3108.4.12	✓	✓	✓
7-2 Similar Polygons	SPI 3108.4.12	✓	✓	✓
7-3 Proving Triangles Similar	SPI 3108.4.11, SPI 3108.4.12	✓	✓	✓
7-4 Similarity in Right Triangles	SPI 3108.4.11, SPI 3108.4.12, SPI 3108.4.14	✓	✓	✓
Concept Byte: The Golden Ratio			❑	❑
Concept Byte: Exploring Proportions in Triangles	SPI 3108.4.12	✓	✓	✓
7-5 Proportions in Triangles				❑
Chapter 8 Right Triangles and Trigonometry		**Traditional 10**		**Block 6**
Concept Byte: The Pythagorean Theorem		❍	❍	❍
8-1 The Pythagorean Theorem and Its Converse		❍	❍	❍
8-2 Special Right Triangles	SPI 3108.4.15	✓	✓	✓
Concept Byte: Exploring Trigonometric Ratios		✓	✓	✓
8-3 Trigonometry	SPI 3108.4.15	✓	✓	✓
Concept Byte: Measuring From Afar		✓	✓	✓
8-4 Angles of Elevation and Depression	SPI 3108.4.15	✓	✓	✓
Concept Byte: Laws of Sines and Laws of Cosines				❑
8-5 Vectors	SPI 3108.2.2	✓	✓	✓

	Performance Indicator	Basic	Average	Advanced
Chapter 9 Transformations		Traditional 10		Block 5
9-1 Translations	SPI 3108.3.3, SPI 3108.4.10	✓	✓	✓
Concept Byte: Paper Folding and Reflections		✓	✓	✓
9-2 Reflections	SPI 3108.3.3, SPI 3108.4.10	✓	✓	✓
9-3 Rotations	SPI 3108.4.10	✓	✓	✓
Concept Byte: Tracing Paper Transformations	SPI 3108. 3.3	✓	✓	✓
9-4 Symmetry	SPI 3108.4.10	✓	✓	✓
9-5 Dilations	SPI 3108.3.3, SPI 3108.4.10	✓	✓	✓
Concept Byte: Transformations Using Vectors and Matrices	SPI 3108.3.3	✓	✓	✓
9-6 Compositions of Reflections	SPI 3108.4.10	✓	✓	✓
Concept Byte: Frieze Patterns			❑	❑
Concept Byte: Creating Tessellations			❑	❑
9-7 Tessellations				❑
Chapter 10 Area		Traditional 12		Block 6
Concept Byte: Transforming to Find Area	SPI 3108.1.2	✓	✓	✓
10-1 Areas of Parallelograms and Triangles	SPI 3108.1.2	✓	✓	✓
10-2 Areas of Trapezoids, Rhombuses, and Kites	SPI 3108.4.7	✓	✓	✓
10-3 Areas of Regular Polygons	SPI 3108.1.1, SPI 3108.4.7	✓	✓	✓
10-4 Perimeters and Areas of Similar Figures	SPI 3108.4.7	✓	✓	✓
10-5 Trigonometry and Area	SPI 3108.4.6, SPI 3108.4.7	✓	✓	✓
10-6 Circles and Arcs	SPI 3108.1.1, SPI 3108.4.8	✓	✓	✓
Concept Byte: Circle Graphs			❑	❑
10-7 Areas of Circles and Sectors	SPI 3108.4.8	✓	✓	✓
Concept Byte: Exploring Area and Circumference				❑
10-8 Geometric Probability	SPI 3108.5.1, SPI 3108.5.2	✓	✓	✓
Tennessee Chapter		Traditional 8		Block 4
TN-1 Estimation and Precision	Checks for Understanding: 3108.1.1, 3108.2.6	✓	✓	✓
TN-2 Understanding Pi	Check for Understanding: 3108.2.1	✓	✓	✓
TN-3 Operations with Vectors	SPI 3108.2.2	✓	✓	✓
TN-4 Using Right Triangle Trigonometry	SPI 3108.4.9	✓	✓	✓
TN-5 Conic Sections	Check for Understanding: 3108.4.26	✓	✓	✓
TN-6 Translating Among Data Representations	Check for Understanding: 3108.5.2	✓	✓	✓

	Performance Indicator	Basic	Average	Advanced
Chapter 11 Surface Area and Volume		Traditional 16	Block 8	
11-1 Space Figures and Cross Sections		✓	✓	✓
Concept Byte: Perspective Drawing	SPI 3108.1.3			
11-2 Surface Areas of Prisms and Cylinders	SPI 3108.1.1, SPI 3108.4.5	✓	✓	✓
11-3 Surface Areas of Pyramids and Cones	SPI 3108.1.1, SPI 3108.4.5	✓	✓	✓
11-4 Volumes of Prisms and Cylinders	SPI 3108.4.5	✓	✓	✓
Concept Byte: Finding Volume		✓	✓	✓
11-5 Volumes of Pyramids and Cones	SPI 3108.4.5	✓	✓	✓
11-6 Surface Areas and Volumes of Spheres	SPI 3108.1.1, SPI 3108.4.5	✓	✓	✓
Concept Byte: Exploring Similar Solids			❑	❑
11-7 Areas and Volumes of Similar Solids			❑	❑
Chapter 12 Circles		Traditional 10	Block 5	
12-1 Tangent Lines	SPI 3108.4.13	✓	✓	✓
Concept Byte: Paper Folding With Circles		✓	✓	✓
12-2 Chords and Arcs	SPI 3108.4.13	✓	✓	✓
12-3 Inscribed Angles	SPI 3108.4.13	✓	✓	✓
Concept Byte: Exploring Chords and Secants		✓	✓	✓
12-4 Angle Measures and Segment Lengths	SPI 3108.4.13	✓	✓	✓
12-5 Circles in the Coordinate Plane	SPI 3108.3.1	✓	✓	✓
12-6 Locus: A Set of Points				❑

1 Tools of Geometry

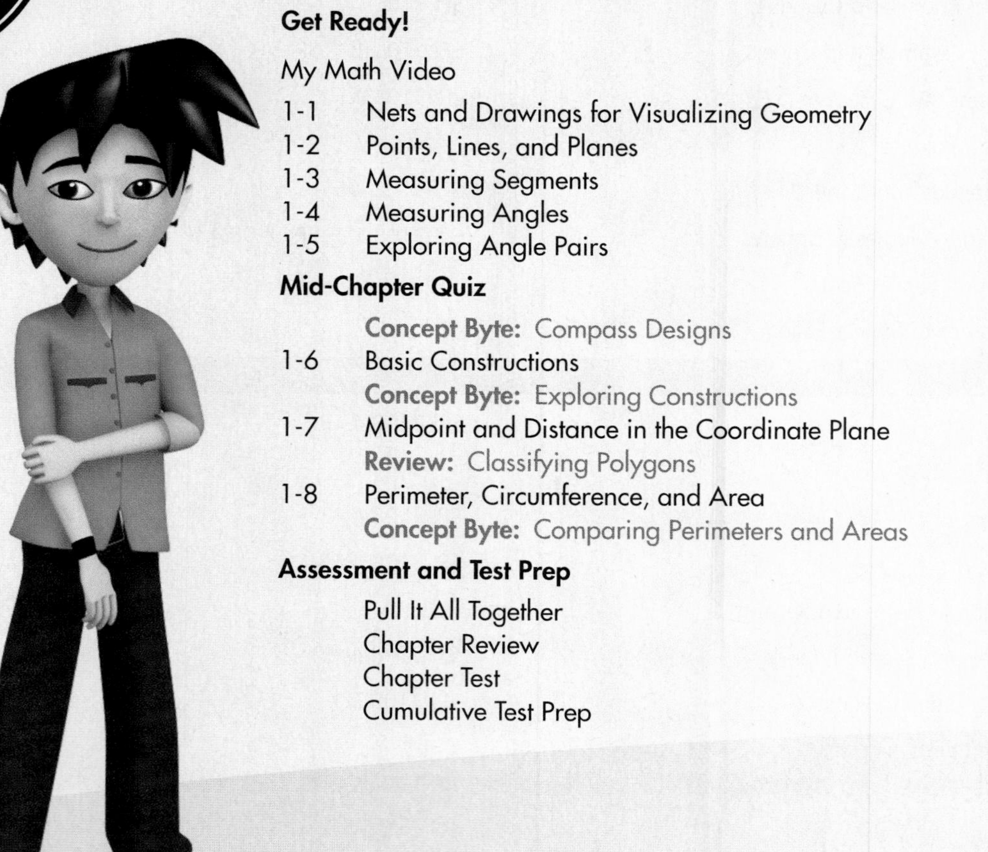

TN State Performance Indicators

Chapter 1

SPI 3108.1.2 Determine areas of planar figures by decomposing them into simpler figures without a grid.

SPI 3108.1.3 Use geometric understanding and spatial visualization of geometric solids to solve problems and/or create drawings.

SPI 3108.4.3 Identify, describe and/or apply the relationships and theorems involving different types of triangles, quadrilaterals and other polygons.

SPI 3108.4.7 Compute the area and/or perimeter of triangles, quadrilaterals and other polygons when one or more additional steps are required (e.g. find missing dimensions given area or perimeter of the figure, using trigonometry).

Chapter 2

SPI 3108.1.4 Use definitions, basic postulates, and theorems about points, lines, angles, and planes to write/complete proofs and/or to solve problems.

SPI 3108.4.4 Analyze different types and formats of proofs.

Reasoning and Proof

Visual See It!

Reasoning Try It!

Practice Do It!

3

Parallel and Perpendicular Lines

TN State Performance Indicators

Chapter 3

SPI 3108.1.3 Use geometric understanding and spatial visualization of geometric solids to solve problems and/or create drawings.

SPI 3108.1.4 Use definitions, basic postulates, and theorems about points, lines, angles, and planes to write/complete proofs and/or to solve problems.

SPI 3108.4.1 Differentiate between Euclidean and non-Euclidean geometries.

SPI 3108.4.4 Analyze different types and formats of proofs.

Chapter 4

SPI 3108.1.1 Give precise mathematical descriptions or definitions of geometric shapes in the plane and space.

SPI 3108.4.2 Define, identify, describe, and/or model plane figures using appropriate mathematical symbols (including collinear and non-collinear points, lines, segments, rays, angles, triangles, quadrilaterals, and other polygons).

SPI 3108.4.11 Use basic theorems about similar and congruent triangles to solve problems.

SPI 3108.4.12 Solve problems involving congruence, similarity, proportional reasoning and/or scale factor of two similar figures or solids.

Congruent Triangles

Visual See It!

Reasoning Try It!

Practice Do It!

Relationships Within Triangles

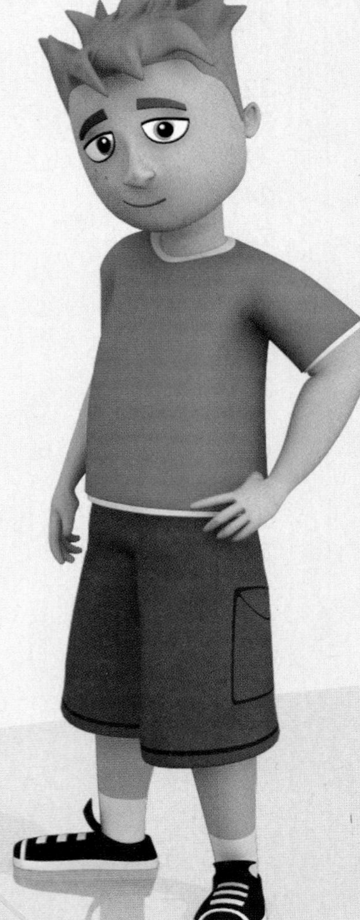

TN State Performance Indicators

Chapter 5

SPI 3108.4.4 Analyze different types and formats of proofs.

Chapter 6

SPI 3108.3.1 Use algebra and coordinate geometry to analyze and solve problems about geometric figures (including circles).

SPI 3108.3.2 Use coordinate geometry to prove characteristics of polygonal figures.

SPI 3108.4.2 Define, identify, describe, and/or model plane figures using appropriate mathematical symbols (including collinear and non-collinear points, lines, segments, rays, angles, triangles, quadrilaterals, and other polygons).

SPI 3108.4.3 Identify, describe and/or apply the relationships and theorems involving different types of triangles, quadrilaterals and other polygons.

Polygons and Quadrilaterals

Visual See It!

Reasoning Try It!

Practice Do It!

7 Similarity

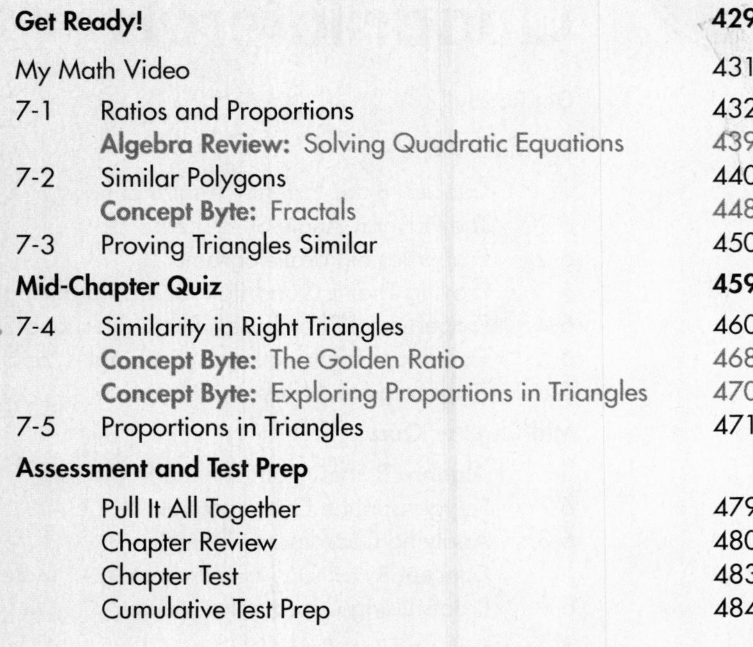

TN State Performance Indicators

Chapter 7

SPI 3108.4.11 Use basic theorems about similar and congruent triangles to solve problems.

SPI 3108.4.12 Solve problems involving congruence, similarity, proportional reasoning and/or scale factor of two similar figures or solids.

SPI 3108.4.14 Use properties of right triangles to solve problems (such as involving the relationship formed when the altitude to the hypotenuse of a right triangle is drawn).

Chapter 8

SPI 3108.2.2 Perform operations on vectors in various representations.

SPI 3108.4.15 Determine and use the appropriate trigonometric ratio for a right triangle to solve a contextual problem.

Right Triangles and Trigonometry

Visual See It!

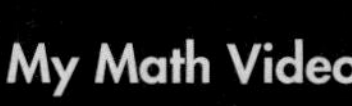

Reasoning Try It!

Practice Do It!

9 Transformations

TN State Performance Indicators

Chapter 9

SPI 3108.3.3 Describe algebraically the effect of a single transformation (reflections in the *x*- or *y*-axis, rotations, translations, and dilations) on two-dimensional geometric shapes in the coordinate plane.

SPI 3108.4.10 Identify, describe, and/or apply transformations on two and three dimensional geometric shapes

Chapter 10

SPI 3108.4.6 Use various area of triangle formulas to solve contextual problems.

SPI 3108.4.7 Compute the area and/or perimeter of triangles, quadrilaterals and other polygons when one or more additional steps are required.

SPI 3108.4.8 Solve problems involving area, circumference, area of a sector, and/or arc length of a circle.

SPI 3108.5.1 Use area to solve problems involving geometric probability.

SPI 3108.5.2 Develop the basic principles of geometric probability.

Area

Use this Tennessee chapter to review and practice for the Geometry End-of-Course Test.

TN TENNESSEE *Lessons and Standards Review*

TENNESSEE TENNESSEE TENNESSEE TENN

11 Surface Area and Volume

Indicators

Chapter 11

SPI 3108.1.1 Give precise mathematical descriptions or definitions of geometric shapes in the plane and space.

SPI 3108.1.3 Use geometric understanding and spatial visualization of geometric solids to solve problems and/or create drawings.

SPI 3108.4.5 Describe solids and/or surfaces in three-dimensional space when given two-dimensional representations for the surfaces of three-dimensional objects.

SPI 3108.4.9 Use right triangle trigonometry and cross-sections to solve problems involving surface areas and/or volumes of solids.

Chapter 12

SPI 3108.3.1 Use algebra and coordinate geometry to analyze and solve problems about geometric figures (including circles).

SPI 3108.4.13 Identify, analyze and/or use basic properties and theorems of circles to solve problems (including those relating right triangles and circles).

Circles

Visual See It!

Reasoning Try It!

Practice Do It!

Answers

1. B
2. I
3. A
4. H
5. C
6. H
7. A
8. I
9. A
10. I
11. D
12. F

Entry-Level Assessment

Multiple Choice

Read each question. Then write the letter of the correct answer on your paper.

1. What is the solution to $5a - 15 + 9a = 3a + 29$?
   (A) $a = \frac{14}{11}$ (B) $a = 4$ (C) $a = 7$ (D) $a = 44$

2. What is the simplified form of $4x - (2 - 3x) + 5$?
   (F) $x + 3$ (G) $x + 7$ (H) $7x - 7$ (I) $7x + 3$

3. What is the simplified form of $\sqrt{45a^5}$?
   (A) $3a^2\sqrt{5a}$ (B) $a^2\sqrt{45a}$ (C) $5a\sqrt{3a^2}$ (D) $9a^2\sqrt{5a}$

4. In the diagram below, the perimeter of the triangle is equal to the perimeter of the square. What is the length of a side of the square?

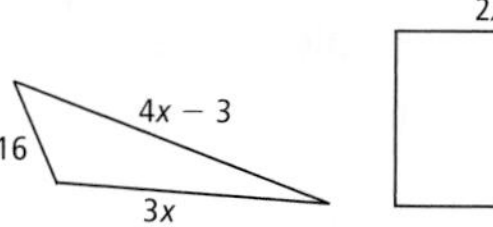

   (F) 7 (G) 13 (H) 26 (I) 52

5. What is $5\frac{3}{4}$ written as a decimal?
   (A) 3.75 (B) 5.25 (C) 5.75 (D) 20.3

6. Maria gave one half of her jelly beans to Carole. Carole gave one third of those to Austin. Austin gave one fourth of those to Tony. If Tony received two jelly beans, how many did Maria start with?
   (F) 8 (G) 24 (H) 48 (I) 96

7. What is the ratio 0.6 : 2.4 written in simplest form?
   (A) 1 : 4 (B) 3 : 4 (C) 4 : 1 (D) 6 : 24

8. What is the solution to $|x| - 7 = 6$?
   (F) $x = \pm 1$ (G) $x = 1$ (H) $x = -13$ (I) $x = \pm 13$

9. What is the solution to the system of equations?
   $$y = x - 2$$
   $$2x + 2y = 4$$
   (A) (2, 0) (B) (0, −2) (C) (−2, 0) (D) (0, 2)

10. What is the next figure in the sequence?

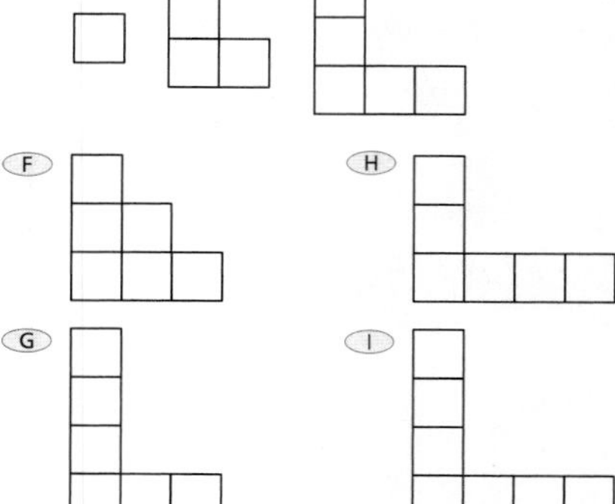

11. Which of the following is equivalent to $(-21)^2$?
    (A) −441 (B) −42 (C) 42 (D) 441

12. How many feet are in 180 in.?
    (F) 15 ft (G) 30 ft (H) 1080 ft (I) 2160 ft

13. What is the next term in the pattern?

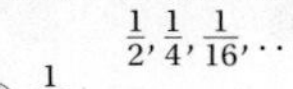

$\frac{1}{2}, \frac{1}{4}, \frac{1}{16}, \ldots$

(A) $\frac{1}{20}$ (C) $\frac{1}{64}$

(B) $\frac{1}{32}$ (D) $\frac{1}{256}$

14. What is the area of $\triangle ABC$, to the nearest tenth?

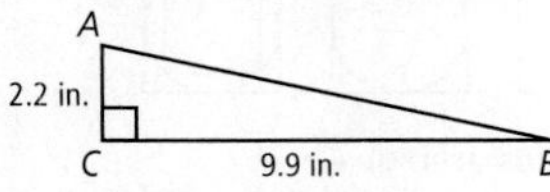

(F) 10.1 in.^{2} (H) 21.8 in.^{2}

(G) 10.9 in.^{2} (I) 217.8 in.^{2}

15. What is the value of the expression $-x(y - 8)^2$ for $x = -2$ and $y = 5$?

(A) -18 (C) 6

(B) -6 (D) 18

16. You and some friends go out for dinner. The bill is \$68.50. You want to tip the waiter 18%. What is the total amount you and your friends should pay?

(F) \$3.79 (H) \$80.83

(G) \$12.33 (I) \$122.40

17. What is the solution to $y - 7 > 3 + 2y$?

(A) $y < -10$ (C) $y > -\frac{10}{3}$

(B) $y > 4$ (D) $y < -4$

18. Through which quadrants does the graph pass?

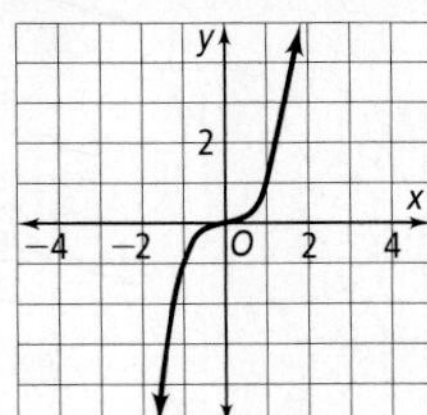

(F) I and II (H) II and III

(G) I and III (I) II and IV

19. What is the ratio $18b^2$ to $45b$ written in simplest form?

(A) 18 to 45 (C) b to 2.5

(B) $2b^2$ to $5b$ (D) $2b$ to 5

20. A farmer leans a 12-ft ladder against a barn. The base of the ladder is 3 ft from the barn. To the nearest tenth, how high on the barn does the ladder reach?

(F) 9.2 ft (H) 11.6 ft

(G) 10.8 ft (I) 13.4 ft

21. A map has a scale of 1 in. : 25 mi. Two cities are 175 mi apart. How far apart are they on the map?

(A) 3 in. (C) 6 in.

(B) 5 in. (D) 7 in.

22. What is the equation of the line that is parallel to the line $y = 5x + 2$ and passes through the point $(1, -3)$?

(F) $y = -5x + 2$ (H) $y = \frac{1}{5}x - 8$

(G) $y = 5x + 8$ (I) $y = 5x - 8$

23. The graph below shows the distance and time of your car trip. What does the slope of the line mean?

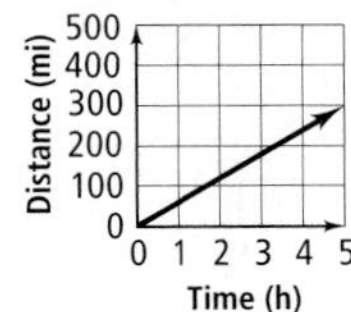

(A) You traveled 0.017 mi/h.

(B) You traveled for 5 h.

(C) You traveled 60 mi/h.

(D) You traveled 300 mi.

24. You are building a rectangular dog pen with an area of 90 ft^2. You want the length of the pen to be 3 ft longer than twice its width. Which equation can you use to find the width w of the pen?

(F) $90 = w(w + 3)$ (H) $90 = 2w(w + 3)$

(G) $90 = w(2w + 3)$ (I) $90 = (2 + w)(w + 3)$

25. The formula for the surface area of a sphere is $A = 4\pi r^2$. What is the formula solved for r?

(A) $r = \frac{A}{2\sqrt{\pi}}$ (C) $r = \frac{1}{2}\sqrt{\frac{A}{\pi}}$

(B) $r = \frac{A}{2\pi}$ (D) $r = 2\sqrt{\frac{A}{\pi}}$

13. D
14. G
15. D
16. H
17. A
18. G
19. D
20. H
21. D
22. I
23. C
24. G
25. C

Answers

26. H
27. A
28. I
29. C
30. I
31. D
32. G
33. C
34. H
35. A
36. I

26. A square has an area of 25 cm^2. If its perimeter increases by 4 cm, what is its area?

(F) 26 cm^2 (H) 36 cm^2

(G) 29 cm^2 (I) 41 cm^2

27. A bag contains 4 blue marbles, 6 green marbles, and 2 red marbles. You select one ball at random from the bag. What is *P*(red)?

(A) $\frac{1}{6}$ (C) $\frac{1}{2}$

(B) $\frac{1}{5}$ (D) $\frac{5}{6}$

28. You select one green marble from the full bag in Exercise 27. What is the probability that the next marble you select will be blue?

(F) $\frac{1}{3}$ (H) $\frac{4}{7}$

(G) $\frac{1}{5}$ (I) $\frac{4}{11}$

29. What are the coordinates of points *A*, *B*, and *C* in the coordinate plane below?

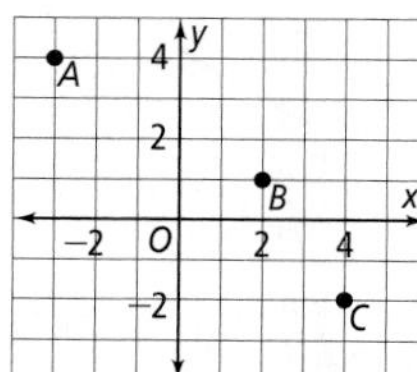

(A) $A(3, -4), B(-2, -1), C(-4, 2)$

(B) $A(4, -3), B(1, 2), C(-2, 4)$

(C) $A(-3, 4), B(2, 1), C(4, -2)$

(D) $A(-4, 3), B(-1, -2), C(2, -4)$

30. What is $3\sqrt{20} + 2\sqrt{5}$ in simplest form?

(F) $5\sqrt{5}$ (H) $14\sqrt{5}$

(G) $5\sqrt{25}$ (I) $8\sqrt{5}$

31. An athletic club has 248 members. Of these, 164 lift weights and 208 perform cardiovascular exercises regularly. All members do at least one of these activities. How many members do both?

(A) 40 (C) 84

(B) 44 (D) 124

32. What is the slope of the line through $(-4, 2)$ and $(5, 8)$?

(F) $\frac{1}{6}$ (H) $\frac{3}{2}$

(G) $\frac{2}{3}$ (I) 6

33. What is the next figure in the sequence below?

(A) a circle inside a square

(B) a square inside a circle inside a square

(C) a circle inside a square inside a circle inside a square

(D) a square inside a circle inside a square inside a circle

34. What is an equation of the line that passes through the point (1, 3) with slope −2?

(F) $y = 2x - 5$ (H) $y = -2x + 5$

(G) $y = -2x + 2$ (I) $y = 2x + 1$

35. Which is the graph of a line with a slope of 3 and a *y*-intercept of −2?

(A)

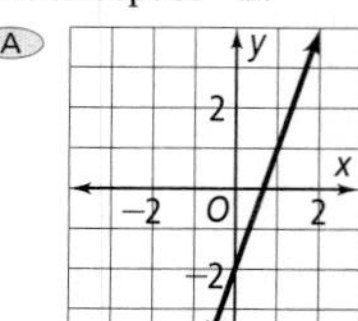

(C)

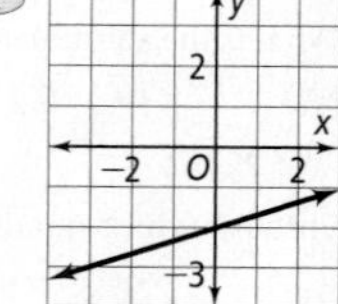

(B)

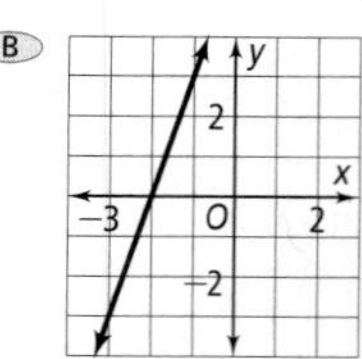

(D)

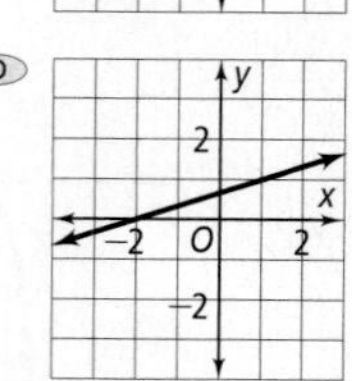

36. A circular pond has a radius of $2x - 3$. Which expression describes the area of the pond?

(F) $(4x - 6)\pi$ (H) $(4x^2 + 12x - 9)\pi$

(G) $(4x + 9)\pi$ (I) $(4x^2 - 12x + 9)\pi$

Get Ready!

Skills Handbook, p. 829

Squaring Numbers

Simplify.

1. 3^2 2. 4^2 3. 11^2

Skills Handbook, p. 830

Simplifying Expressions

Simplify each expression. Use 3.14 for π.

4. $2 \cdot 7.5 + 2 \cdot 11$ 5. $\pi(5)^2$ 6. $\sqrt{5^2 + 12^2}$

Skills Handbook, p. 830

Evaluating Expressions

Evaluate the following expressions for $a = 4$ and $b = -2$.

7. $\frac{a+b}{2}$ 8. $\frac{a-7}{3-b}$ 9. $\sqrt{(7-a)^2 + (2-b)^2}$

Skills Handbook, p. 832

Finding Absolute Value

Simplify each absolute value expression.

10. $|-8|$ 11. $|2 - 6|$ 12. $|-5 - (-8)|$

Skills Handbook, p. 834

Solving Equations

Algebra Solve each equation.

13. $2x + 7 = 13$ 14. $5x - 12 = 2x + 6$ 15. $2(x + 3) - 1 = 7x$

Looking Ahead Vocabulary

16. A child can *construct* models of buildings by stacking and arranging colored blocks. What might the term *construction* mean in geometry?
17. The *Mid*-Autumn Festival, celebrated in China, falls exactly in the middle of autumn, according to the Chinese lunar calendar. What would you expect a *midpoint* to be in geometry?
18. Artists often use long streaks to show *rays* of light coming from the sun. A ray is also a geometric figure. What do you think the properties of a *ray* are?
19. You and your friend work with each other. In other words, you and your friend are *co*-workers. What might the term *collinear* mean in geometry?

Answers

Get Ready!

1. 9
2. 16
3. 121
4. 37
5. 78.5
6. 13
7. 1
8. $-\frac{3}{5}$
9. 5
10. 8
11. 4
12. 3
13. 3
14. 6
15. 1
16. Answers may vary. Sample: building or making a geometric object, possibly involving several steps
17. Answers may vary. Sample: a point that falls exactly in the middle of a geometric object
18. Answers may vary. Sample: a type of line that has a source and no ending point
19. Answers may vary. Sample: part of the same line

Get Ready!

Assign this diagnostic assessment to determine if students have the prerequisite skills for Chapter 1.

Lesson	Skill
Skills Handbook, p. 829	Squaring Numbers
Skills Handbook, p. 830	Simplifying Expressions
Skills Handbook, p. 830	Evaluating Expressions
Skills Handbook, p. 832	Finding Absolute Value
Skills Handbook, p. 834	Solving Equations

To remediate students, select from these resources (available for every lesson).

- Online Problems (PowerGeometry.com)
- Reteaching (All-in-One Teaching Resources)
- Practice (All-in-One Teaching Resources)

Why Students Need These Skills

SQUARING NUMBERS Squaring numbers is necessary when calculating areas of certain figures.

SIMPLIFYING EXPRESSIONS Throughout geometry, students will need to evaluate expressions that represent length, volume, angle measure, and other geometric quantities.

EVALUATING EXPRESSIONS Students will be given formulas and will substitute known values.

FINDING ABSOLUTE VALUE Students will examine distances of segments on a number line and on a coordinate plane.

SOLVING EQUATIONS Students will be given information for which they will write equations and solve for an unknown.

Looking Ahead Vocabulary

CONSTRUCTION Ask students to name various objects that are constructed.

MIDPOINT Have students name other words that use *mid-* as a prefix.

RAY Show example drawings of sun rays.

COLLINEAR Have students name other words that use *co-* as a prefix

Chapter 1 Overview

UbD Understanding by Design

Chapter 1 introduces various topics in the study of geometry. In this chapter, students will develop the answers to the Essential Questions posed on the opposite page as they learn the concepts and skills bulleted below.

BIG idea Visualization

ESSENTIAL QUESTION How can you represent a three-dimensional figure with a two-dimensional drawing?

- Students will make nets for solid figures.
- Isometric drawings and orthographic drawings will be used to show attributes of figures.

BIG idea Reasoning

ESSENTIAL QUESTION What are the building blocks of geometry?

- Students will define basic geometric figures.
- Undefined terms such as point, line, and plane will be shown with visual representations.
- Postulates, which will lead to proofs later in the text, will be presented.

BIG idea Measurement

ESSENTIAL QUESTION How can you describe the attributes of a segment or angle?

- Segments will be measured with and without a coordinate grid.
- Students will use the Midpoint and Distance Formulas.
- Protractors will be used to measure angles.

TN Checks for Understanding

3108.1.2 Determine position using spatial sense with two and three-dimensional coordinate systems.
3108.1.3 Comprehend the concept of length on the number line.
3108.1.4 Recognize that a definition depends on undefined terms and on previous definitions.
3108.1.5 Use technology, hands-on activities, and manipulatives to develop the language and the concepts of geometry. including specialized vocabulary.
3108.1.10 Use visualization, spatial reasoning, and geometric modeling to solve problems.
3108.1.14 Identify and explain the necessity of postulates, theorems, and corollaries in a mathematical system.
3108.3.4 Apply the midpoint and distance formulas to points and segments to find midpoints, distances, and missing information in two and three dimensions.
3108.4.3 Solve problems involving betweeness of points and distance between points (including segment addition).
3108.4.5 Use vertical, adjacent, complementary, and supplementary angle pairs to solve problems and write proofs.
Also 3108.1.10, 3108.4.6, 3108.4.9, 3108.4.22, and 3108.4.23

CHAPTER
1
PowerGeometry.com
Your place to get all things digital
Download videos connecting math to your world.
VIDEO
Math definitions in English and Spanish
VOCABULARY
The online Solve It will get you in gear for each lesson.
SOLVE IT!
Interactive! Vary numbers, graphs, and figures to explore math concepts.
DYNAMIC ACTIVITIES
Download Step-by-Step Problems with Instant Replay.
ONLINE PROBLEMS
Get and view your assignments online.
ONLINE HOMEWORK
Extra practice and review online
MathXL FOR SCHOOL

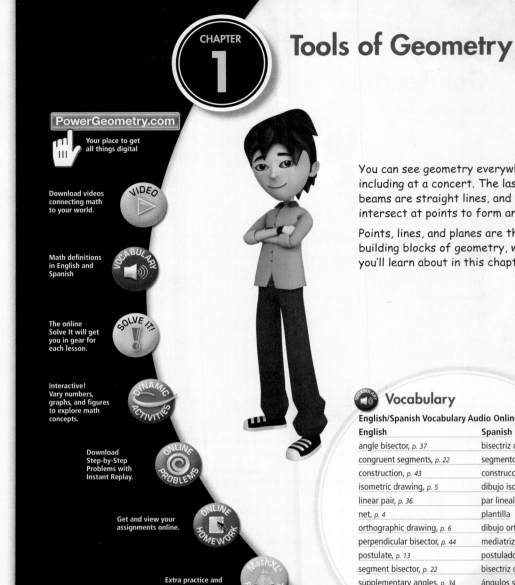

Tools of Geometry

You can see geometry everywhere, including at a concert. The laser beams are straight lines, and they intersect at points to form angles.

Points, lines, and planes are the building blocks of geometry, which you'll learn about in this chapter.

Vocabulary

English/Spanish Vocabulary Audio Online:

English	Spanish
angle bisector, *p. 37*	bisectriz de un ángulo
congruent segments, *p. 22*	segmentos congruentes
construction, *p. 43*	construcción
isometric drawing, *p. 5*	dibujo isométrico
linear pair, *p. 36*	par lineal
net, *p. 4*	plantilla
orthographic drawing, *p. 6*	dibujo ortográfico
perpendicular bisector, *p. 44*	mediatriz
postulate, *p. 13*	postulado
segment bisector, *p. 22*	bisectriz de un segmento
supplementary angles, *p. 34*	ángulos suplementarios
vertical angles, *p. 34*	ángulos verticales

PowerGeometry.com

Chapter 1 Overview

Use these online assets to engage your students. These include support for the Solve It and step-by-step solutions for Problems.

Show the student-produced video demonstrating relevant and engaging applications of the new concepts in the chapter.

Find online definitions for new terms in English and Spanish.

Start each lesson with an attention-getting problem. View the Problem online with helpful hints.

BIG ideas

1 **Visualization**
Essential Question How can you represent a three-dimensional figure with a two-dimensional drawing?

2 **Reasoning**
Essential Question What are the building blocks of geometry?

3 **Measurement**
Essential Question How can you describe the attributes of a segment or angle?

Chapter Preview

Increase students' depth of knowledge with interactive online activities.

Show Problems from each lesson solved step by step. Instant replay allows students to go at their own pace when studying online.

Assign homework to individual students or to an entire class.

Prepare students for the Mid-Chapter Quiz and Chapter Test with online practice and review.

My Math Video

FACILITATE Use this photo to discuss geometry in the real world. In this chapter students will learn about the basic elements of geometry, such as points, lines, and planes. Examples of these elements are visible in the photo.

Q How would you describe the appearance of the lasers in the photo? **[The lasers are lines extending into the concert space.]**

Q How would you describe the level of the audience compared to the level of the light show? **[The audience is on a level below and parallel to the level of the light show.]**

Q The basic figures in geometry are points, lines, and planes. Can you identify a model of each of these in the photo? **[Yes. Answers may vary. Samples: point: origin of the lasers; line: each laser beam; plane: the heads of the audience]**

EXTENSION

Have students identify items that model each of the basic elements of geometry in the classroom or in another picture that you supply. Students should recognize that points can be any location in the room or photo. Be sure that students understand that lines must be straight. A desktop, the floor, or ceiling is a good representation of a plane.

CHAPTER 1

TOOLS OF GEOMETRY

Math Background

UbD

Visualization

BIG idea Visualization can help you connect properties of real objects with two-dimensional drawings of these objects.

ESSENTIAL UNDERSTANDING

1-1 Three-dimensional objects can be represented with a two-dimensional figure using special drawing techniques.

Reasoning and Proof

BIG idea Definitions establish meanings and remove possible misunderstanding. Other truths are more complex and difficult to see. It is often possible to verify complex truths by reasoning from simpler ones by using deductive reasoning.

ESSENTIAL UNDERSTANDINGS

1-2 Geometry is a mathematical system built on accepted facts, basic terms, and definitions.

1-5 Special angle pairs can be used to identify geometric relationships and to find angle measures.

Measurement

BIG idea Some attributes of geometric figures, such as length, area, volume, and angle measure, are measurable. Units are used to describe these attributes.

ESSENTIAL UNDERSTANDINGS

1-3 to 1-4 Number operations can be used to find and compare the lengths of segments and the measures of angles.

1-7 Formulas can be used to find the midpoint and length of any segment in the coordinate plane.

1-8 Perimeter and area are two different ways of measuring the size of geometric figures.

Representations of Geometric Figures

There are multiple techniques for representing three-dimensional objects with two-dimensional figures.

Two-dimensional representations include *net drawings* and *orthogonal drawings*. A *net* represents the figure as if it were unfolded into a flat shape. An *orthogonal drawing* shows the view of the figure from each side.

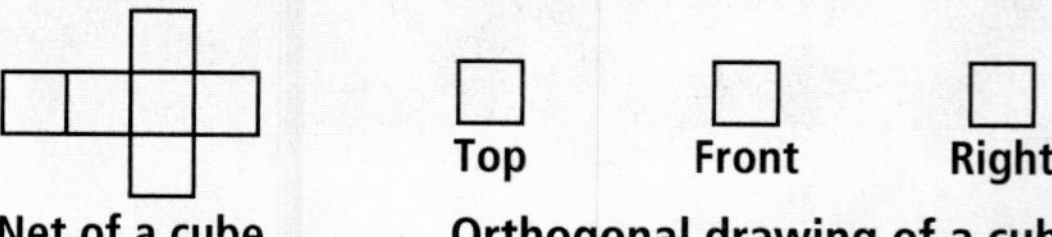

Net of a cube **Orthogonal drawing of a cube**

Three-dimensional representations include *isometric drawings* and *perspective drawings*.

An *isometric drawing* can be drawn using isometric dot paper. In an isometric drawing, the parallel edges of a cube are represented by parallel lines. The lengths of the segments have equal measure. The term *isometric* means "equal measure."

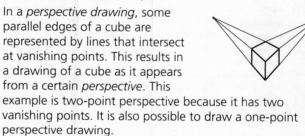

In a *perspective drawing*, some parallel edges of a cube are represented by lines that intersect at vanishing points. This results in a drawing of a cube as it appears from a certain *perspective*. This example is two-point perspective because it has two vanishing points. It is also possible to draw a one-point perspective drawing.

Common Errors With Isometric Drawings

Isometric drawings are drawn such that a person is looking straight toward an edge. Students might start off by making a drawing in which they are looking straight toward a face, as shown at the right. This is not an isometric drawing.

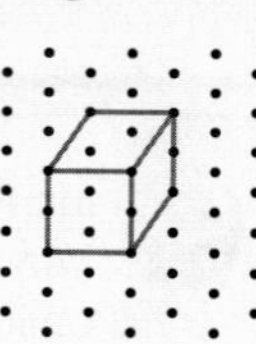

PROGRAM ORGANIZATION BIG IDEA ESSENTIAL UNDERSTANDING PROGRAM ORGANIZATION

Measuring Segments

The length of a segment is the distance between its endpoints.

The distance between two points on a number line is given by the formula $|a - b|$, where a and b are the two endpoints.

−5 −4 −3 −2 −1 0 1 2 3 4 5

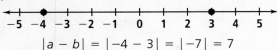

$$|a - b| = |-4 - 3| = |-7| = 7$$

The distance between two points on the coordinate plane is given by the Distance Formula,

$d = \sqrt{(x_2 - x_1)^2 + (y_2 - y_1)^2}$, where (x_1, y_1) and (x_2, y_2) are the endpoints.

For the segment shown:

$$\begin{aligned} d &= \sqrt{(x_2 - x_1)^2 + (y_2 - y_1)^2} \\ &= \sqrt{(5 - (-4))^2 + (2 - (-3))^2} \\ &= \sqrt{(9)^2 + (5)^2} \\ &= \sqrt{81 + 25} = \sqrt{106} \approx 10.3 \end{aligned}$$

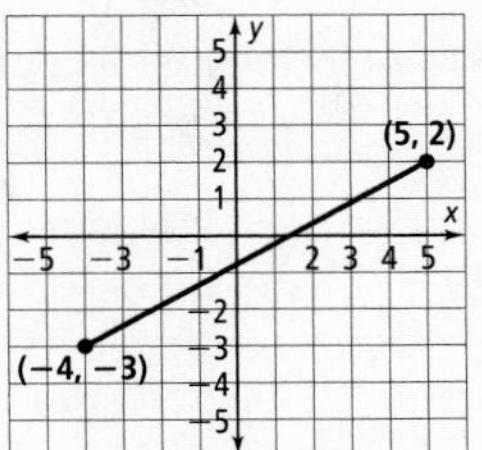

Common Errors Measuring Segments

When measuring the length of a segment on a number line, students might forget how to subtract a negative number.

For example:

−16 −15 −14 −13 −12 −11 −10 −9 −8 −7 −6 −5 −4

$$|-14 - (-5)| \neq |-19|$$

When using the Distance Formula, students are often confused about which point is the first and which point is the second. It does not matter which point is considered the first point or the second point as long as the elements from an ordered pair are used consistently. Have students label their ordered pairs as (x_1, y_1) and (x_2, y_2) as shown.

(x_1, y_1)	(x_2, y_2)
(2, 6)	(−3, 0)
(2, 6)	(−3, 0)

Angle Pairs

Below are several pairs of angles used in geometry.

Adjacent angles have a common vertex and one common side. $\angle A$ and $\angle B$ are adjacent angles.

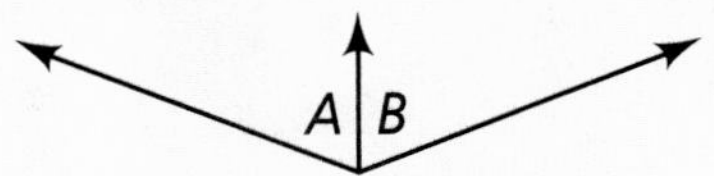

Vertical angles have a common vertex and their sides are opposite rays. $\angle C$ and $\angle E$ are vertical angles, and $\angle D$ and $\angle F$ are vertical angles.

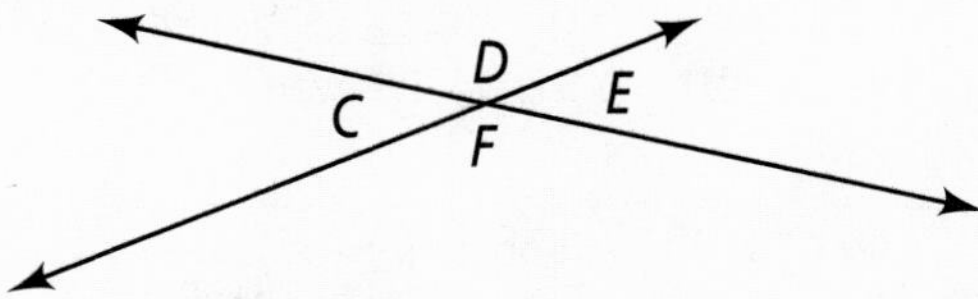

Complementary angles are angles whose measures have a sum of 90°. The angles below are complementary.

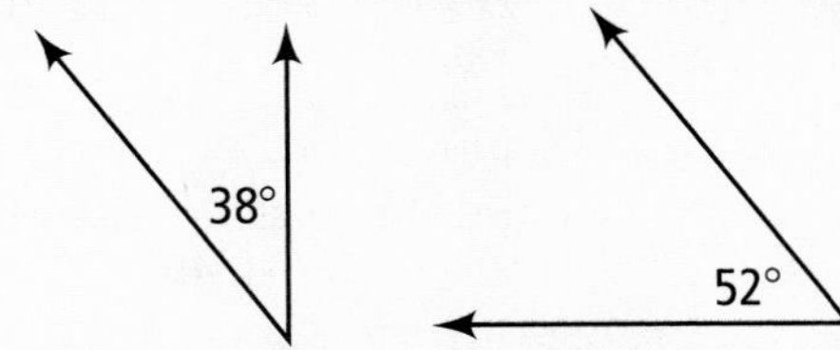

Supplementary angles are angles whose measures have a sum of 180°. The two angles below are supplementary.

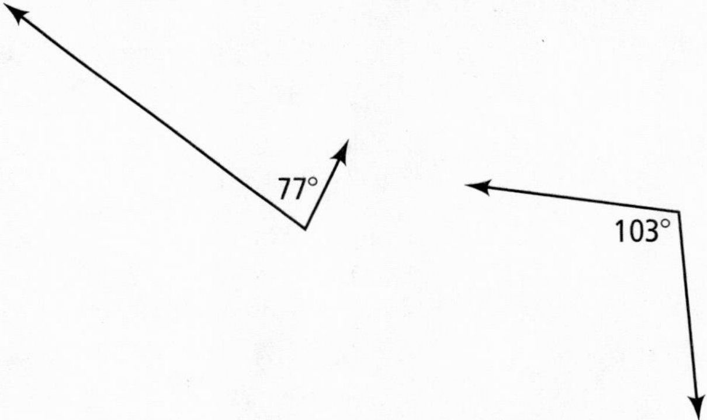

Common Errors With Complementary and Supplementary Angles

Students will often confuse complementary and supplementary angles, thinking that angle pairs that sum to 180° are complementary and angle pairs that sum to 90° are supplementary. One way of remembering this is to think that 90 comes before 180 and C comes before S in the alphabet.

TOOLS OF GEOMETRY

Pacing and Assignment Guide

		TRADITIONAL			BLOCK
Lesson	**Teaching Day(s)**	**Basic**	**Average**	**Advanced**	**Block**
1-1	**1**	Problems 1–4 Exs. 6–19 all, 20–26 even, 27, 28–36 even, 43–51	Problems 1–4 Exs. 7–19 odd, 20–38, 43–51	Problems 1–4 Exs. 7–19 odd, 20–51	**Day 1** Problems 1–4 Exs. 7–19 odd, 20–38, 43–51
1-2	**1**	Problems 1–2 Exs. 8–14 all, 65–80	Problems 1–2 Exs. 9–13 odd, 65–80	Problems 1–2 Exs. 9–13 odd, 65–80	Problems 1–2 Exs. 9–13 odd, 65–80
	2	Problems 3–4 Exs. 15–26 all, 28–46 even, 51, 54–58 even	Problems 3–4 Exs. 15–25 odd, 27–58	Problems 3–4 Exs. 15–25 odd, 27–64	**Day 2** Problems 3–4 Exs. 15–25 odd, 27–58
1-3	**1**	Problems 1–4 Exs. 8–22 all, 24–34 even, 35, 37–39, 44–56	Problems 1–4 Exs. 9–21 odd, 23–41, 44–56	Problems 1–4 Exs. 9–21 odd, 23–56	Problems 1–4 Exs. 9–21 odd, 23–41, 44–56
1-4	**1**	Problems 1–2 Exs. 6–17 all, 41–49	Problems 1–2 Exs. 7–17 odd, 41–49	Problems 1–4 Exs. 7–23 odd, 24–49	**Day 3** Problems 1–4 Exs. 7–23 odd, 24–32, 41–49
	2	Problems 3–4 Exs. 18–23 all, 24–28 even, 29, 31–32, 41–49	Problems 3–4 Exs. 19–23 odd, 24–32, 41–49		
1-5	**1**	Problems 1–2 Exs. 7–23 all, 48–59	Problems 1–2 Exs. 7–23 odd, 48–59	Problems 1–4 Exs. 7–25 odd, 27–59	**Day 4** Problems 1–4 Exs. 7–25 odd, 27–41, 48–59
	2	Problems 3–4 Exs. 7–26 all, 28–30 even, 31, 34–38 even, 39–40	Problems 3–4 Exs. 25, 27–41		
1-6	**1**	Problems 1–2 Exs. 7–12 all, 20, 39–47	Problems 1–2 Exs. 7–11 odd, 20, 39–47	Problems 1–2 Exs. 7–11 odd, 20, 39–47	**Day 5** Problems 1–2 Exs. 7–11 odd, 20, 39–47
	2	Problems 3–4 Exs. 13–16 all, 18, 19, 22, 24, 25, 26–30 even, 36–38	Problems 3–4 Exs. 13, 15, 17–19, 21–32, 36–38	Problems 3–4 Exs. 13, 15, 17–19, 21–38	
1-7	**1**	Problems 1–2 Exs. 6–21 all, 62–72	Problems 1–2 Exs. 7–21 odd, 62–72	Problems 1–2 Exs. 7–21 odd, 62–72	**Day 6** Problems 1–4 Exs. 7–35 odd, 36–57, 62–72
	2	Problems 3–4 Exs. 22–35 all, 36–44 even, 45–47 all, 48–56 even	Problems 3–4 Exs. 23–35 odd, 36–57	Problems 3–4 Exs. 23–35 odd, 36–61	
1-8	**1**	Problems 1–3 Exs. 7–17 all, 60–69	Problems 1–3 Exs. 7–17 odd, 60–69	Problems 1–3 Exs. 7–17 odd, 60–69	**Day 7** Problems 1–6 Exs. 7–33 odd, 34–56, 60–69
	2	Problems 4–6 Exs. 18–33 all, 34–46 even, 47–48, 52, 55	Problems 4–6 Exs. 19–33 odd, 34–56	Problems 4–6 Exs. 19–33 odd, 34–59	
Review	**1**	Chapter 1 Review	Chapter 1 Review	Chapter 1 Review	**Day 8** Chapter 1 Review Chapter 1 Test
Assess	**1**	Chapter 1 Test	Chapter 1 Test	Chapter 1 Test	
Total		**16 Days**	**16 Days**	**14 Days**	**8 Days**

Note: Pacing does not include Concept Bytes and other feature pages.

Resources

KEY

I = Interactive asset at PowerGeometry.com
E = Editable master at PowerGeometry.com
P = Available in Print
T = Available as a Transparency
M = Master at PowerGeometry.com
✓= CD-ROM

	For the Chapter	1-1	1-2	1-3	1-4	1-5	1-6	1-7	1-8
Planning									
Teacher Center Online Planner & Grade Book	I	I	I	I	I	I	I	I	I
Interactive Learning & Guided Instruction									
My Math Video	I								
Solve It!		I TM	I TM	I TM	I TM	I TM	I TM	I TM	I TM
Student Companion (SP)*		P M	P M	P M	P M	P M	P M	P M	P M
Vocabulary Support		I P M	I P M	I P M	I P M	I P M	I P M	I P M	I P M
Got It? Support		I P	I P	I P	I P	I P	I P	I P	I P
Dynamic Activity							I	I	I
Online Problems		I	I	I	I	I	I	I	I
Additional Problems		M	M	M	M	M	M	M	M
English Language Learner Support (TR)		E P M	E P M	E P M	E P M	E P M	E P M	E P M	E P M
Activities, Games, and Puzzles		E M	E M	E M	E M	E M	E M	E M	E M
Teaching With TI Technology With CD-ROM							✓ P		
TI-Nspire™ Support CD-ROM		✓	✓	✓	✓	✓	✓	✓	✓
Lesson Check & Practice									
Student Companion (SP)*		P M	P M	P M	P M	P M	P M	P M	P M
Lesson Check Support		I P	I P	I P	I P	I P	I P	I P	I P
Practice and Problem Solving Workbook (SP)		P	P	P	P	P	P	P	P
Think About a Plan (TR)*		E P M	E P M	E P M	E P M	E P M	E P M	E P M	E P M
Practice Form G (TR)*		E P M	E P M	E P M	E P M	E P M	E P M	E P M	E P M
Standardized Test Prep (TR)*		P M	P M	P M	P M	P M	P M	P M	P M
Practice *Form K* (TR)*		E P M	E P M	E P M	E P M	E P M	E P M	E P M	E P M
Extra Practice	E M								
Find the Errors!	M								
Enrichment (TR)		E P M	E P M	E P M	E P M	E P M	E P M	E P M	E P M
Answers and Solutions CD-ROM	✓	✓	✓	✓	✓	✓	✓	✓	✓
Assess & Remediate									
ExamView CD-ROM	✓	✓	✓	✓	✓	✓	✓	✓	✓
Lesson Quiz		I TM	I TM	I TM	I TM	I TM	I TM	I TM	I TM
Quizzes and Tests *Form G* (TR)*	E P M					E P M			E P M
Quizzes and Tests *Form K* (TR)*	E P M					E P M			E P M
Reteaching (TR)*		E P M	E P M	E P M	E P M	E P M	E P M	E P M	E P M
Performance Tasks (TR)*	P M								
Cumulative Review (TR)*	P M								
Progress Monitoring Assessments	I P M								

(TR) Available in All-In-One Teaching Resources * Spanish available

1 Interactive Learning

Solve It!

PURPOSE To visualize the surfaces of a three-dimensional object that are not visible in a two-dimensional drawing

PROCESS Students may use visual judgment or prior knowledge of how shadows are cast.

FACILITATE

Q How many surfaces does the object shown in the picture have? **[5]**

Q What are the shapes of the surfaces? **[3 rectangles and 2 triangles]**

Q What is the shape of the surface that is facing the wall on the left? **[rectangle]**

Q What is the shape of the surface that is facing the wall on the right? **[triangle]**

ANSWER See Solve It in Answers on next page.

CONNECT THE MATH In the Solve It, students described the surfaces of the three-dimensional object and its shadow. In this lesson, students investigate different ways to view and identify three-dimensional figures.

2 Guided Instruction

Problem 1 VISUAL LEARNERS

Q How can you determine by looking at the net that surface E and surface F will be opposite one another in the cube? **[They both share an edge with surface C, but are on opposite sides of C.]**

Q If the cube were turned one quarter-turn counterclockwise without lifting the bottom surface, which surface would be at the front of the drawing of the cube? **[surface B]**

1-1 Nets and Drawings for Visualizing Geometry

TN State Performance Indicator
SPI 3108.1.3 Use geometric understanding and spatial visualization of geometric solids to solve problems and/or create drawings.

Objective To make nets and drawings of three-dimensional figures

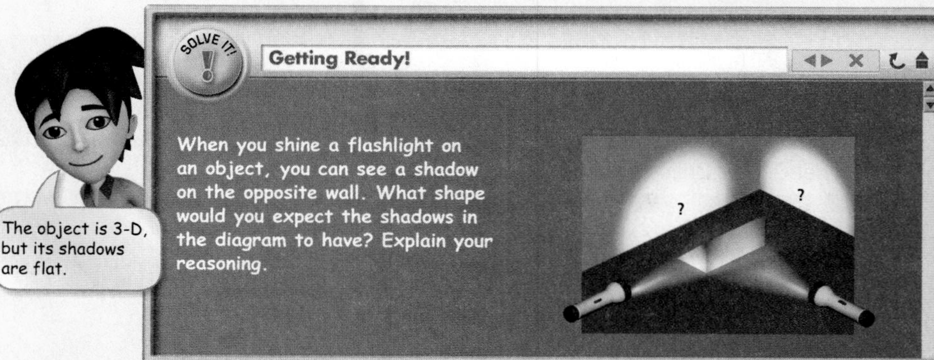

Getting Ready!
The object is 3-D, but its shadows are flat.
When you shine a flashlight on an object, you can see a shadow on the opposite wall. What shape would you expect the shadows in the diagram to have? Explain your reasoning.
?
?

Lesson Vocabulary
- net
- isometric drawing
- orthographic drawing

In the Solve It, you had to "see" the projection of one side of an object onto a flat surface. Visualizing figures is a key skill that you will develop in geometry.

Essential Understanding You can represent a three-dimensional object with a two-dimensional figure using special drawing techniques.

A **net** is a two-dimensional diagram that you can fold to form a three-dimensional figure. A net shows all of the surfaces of a figure in one view.

Think
How can you see the 3-D figure?
Visualize folding the net at the seams so that the edges join together. Track the letter positions by seeing one surface move in relation to another.

Problem 1 Identifying a Solid From a Net

The net at the right folds into the cube shown beside it. Which letters will be on the top and front of the cube?

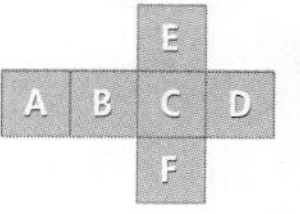

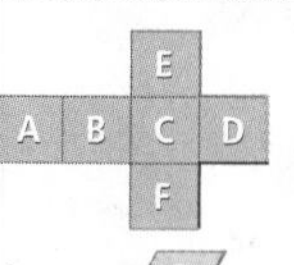

A, C, E, and F all share an edge with D when you fold the net, but only two of those sides are visible in the cube shown.

A wraps around and joins with D to become the back of the cube. B becomes the left side. F folds back to become the bottom.

E folds down to become the top of the cube. C becomes the front.

1-1 Preparing to Teach

BIG idea Visualization UbD

ESSENTIAL UNDERSTANDING

- A three-dimensional object can be represented with a two-dimensional figure using special drawing techniques such as nets, isometric drawings, and orthographic drawings.

Math Background

This lesson focuses on developing the spatial visualization skills that students will use throughout their study of geometry.

Many students may already be familiar with isometric and orthographic drawings, while others will need special attention because their visualization skills have not been sufficiently developed.

The representation of three-dimensional objects using two-dimensional figures provides an opportunity to stress the connection that exists between artistry and mathematics. During the Renaissance, artists sought out methods of painting and drawing that allowed them to depict nature in ways that more closely resembled what is seen by the human eye. Leonardo da Vinci studied geometry extensively and used geometric techniques in his paintings.

Support Student Learning

Use the **Geometry Companion** to engage and support students during instructions. See Lesson Resources at the end of this lesson for details.

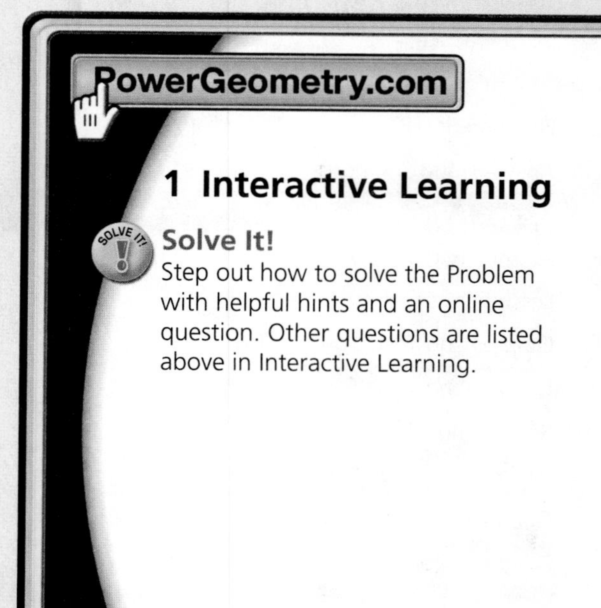

 **Got It?** 1. The net in Problem 1 folds into the cube shown at the right. Which letters will be on the top and right side of the cube?

Packaging designers use nets to design boxes and other containers like the box in Problem 2.

Think
How can you see the net?
Visualize opening the top and bottom flaps of the box. Separate one of the side seams. Then unfold and flatten the box completely.

 **Problem 2** **Drawing a Net From a Solid**

Package Design **What is a net for the graham cracker box to the right? Label the net with its dimensions.**

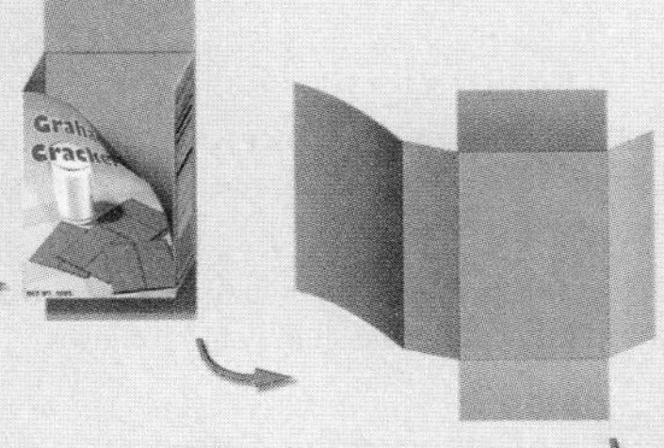

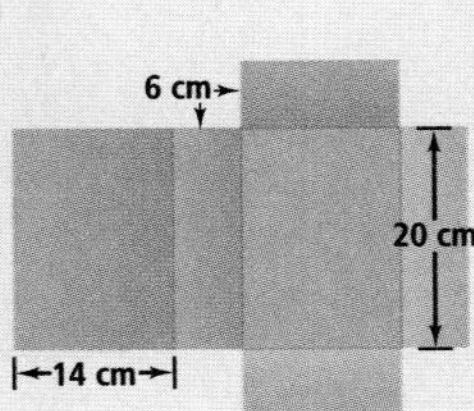

Got It? 2. a. What is a net for the figure at the right? Label the net with its dimensions.
b. **Reasoning** Is there another possible net for the figure in part (a)? If so, draw it.

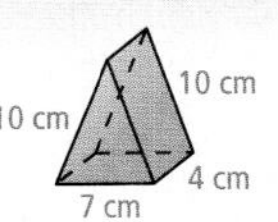

An **isometric drawing** shows a corner view of a three-dimensional figure. It allows you to see the top, front, and side of the figure. You can draw an isometric drawing on isometric dot paper. The simple drawing of a file cabinet at the right is an isometric drawing.

A net shows a three-dimensional figure as a folded-out flat surface. An isometric drawing shows a three-dimensional figure using slanted lines to represent depth.

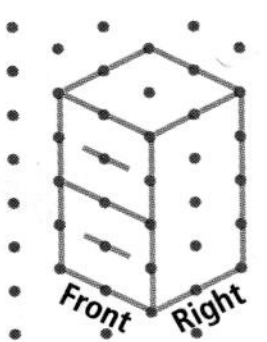

Got It?

Students can reorient the cube in Problem 1 so that surface B is the front surface or students can visually reconstruct the cube with the knowledge that surface B is the front surface.

Problem 2

Q How many pairs of matching surfaces does the graham cracker box contain? Explain. **[3 pairs: top and bottom; front and back; left side and right side]**

Q How would the net for the graham cracker box differ if you were to separate a different side seam than the one shown in the solution? How would the nets be the same? **[The top and bottom rectangle would remain the same; The three rectangles not connected to the top and bottom rectangle would be rearranged.]**

Got It?

Q How many surfaces does the figure contain? Explain. **[5; 3 rectangles and 2 triangles]**

Q Do all of the rectangles have the same dimensions? Explain. **[No, the rectangles that are standing have a side length of 10 cm, while the rectangle on the bottom has a side length of 7 cm.]**

2 Guided Instruction

 Each Problem is worked out and supported online.

Problem 1
Identifying a Solid From a Net

Problem 2
Drawing a Net From a Solid
Animated

Problem 3
Isometric Drawing
Animated

Problem 4
Orthographic Drawing
Animated

Support in Geometry Companion
- Vocabulary
- Key Concepts
- Got It?

Answers

Solve It!

The shadow on the wall opposite the triangular face of the prism is a triangle. The shadow on the wall opposite the rectangular side is a rectangle. Explanations may vary. Sample: The flashlights are shining directly at each side of the object, so the shadows will be the shape that you would see if you looked at each side straight on.

Got It?

1. E, C
2. See back of book.

Problem 3

Q What surfaces are visible from the corner view? **[top surface(s), right surface(s), and front surface(s)]**

Q What surfaces are not visible from the corner view? **[bottom surface(s), left surface(s), and back surface(s)]**

Got It? SYNTHESIZING

Ask students to compare and contrast the isometric drawings for Problem 3 and the Solve It. Elicit that while the front edge shape is the same, the left and back edges differ.

Problem 4

Q Which of the drawings cannot be used to determine the height of the object? **[top view]**

Q Would a bottom view of the figure be different than the top view? Explain. **[Yes; it would not show a visible edge between the tall column and the rest of the figure.]**

Got It? TACTILE LEARNERS

Provide students with cubes to use as models for completing the three orthographic drawings.

Plan

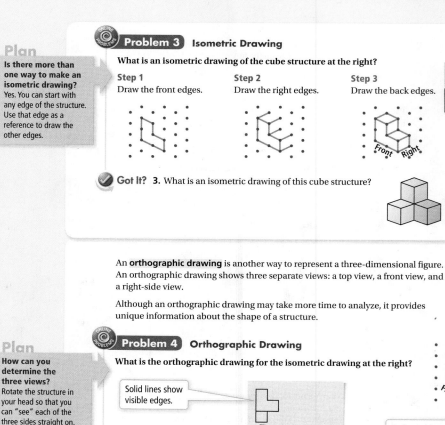

Is there more than one way to make an isometric drawing?
Yes. You can start with any edge of the structure. Use that edge as a reference to draw the other edges.

Problem 3 Isometric Drawing

What is an isometric drawing of the cube structure at the right?

Step 1 Draw the front edges.

Step 2 Draw the right edges.

Step 3 Draw the back edges.

Got It? 3. What is an isometric drawing of this cube structure?

An **orthographic drawing** is another way to represent a three-dimensional figure. An orthographic drawing shows three separate views: a top view, a front view, and a right-side view.

Although an orthographic drawing may take more time to analyze, it provides unique information about the shape of a structure.

Plan

How can you determine the three views?
Rotate the structure in your head so that you can "see" each of the three sides straight on.

Problem 4 Orthographic Drawing

What is the orthographic drawing for the isometric drawing at the right?

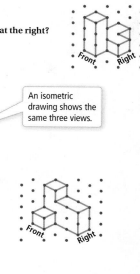

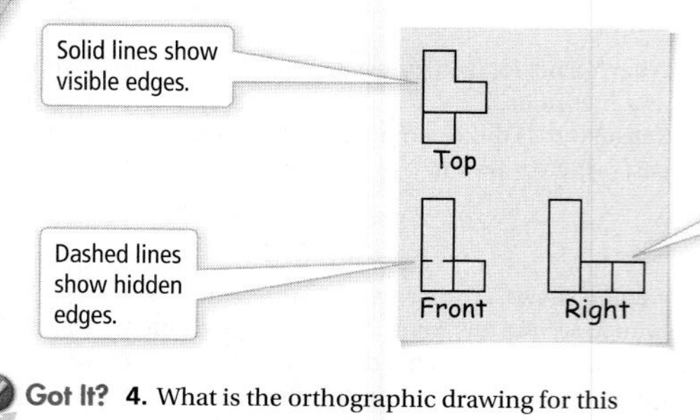

An isometric drawing shows the same three views.

Got It? 4. What is the orthographic drawing for this isometric drawing?

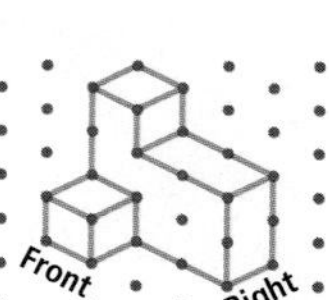

Additional Problems

1. The net below folds into a cube. Which letters will be on the top and front of the cube?

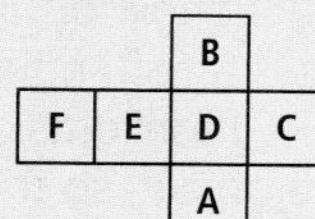

ANSWER B becomes the top, D becomes the front.

2. What is a net for the cereal box below? Label the net with its dimensions.

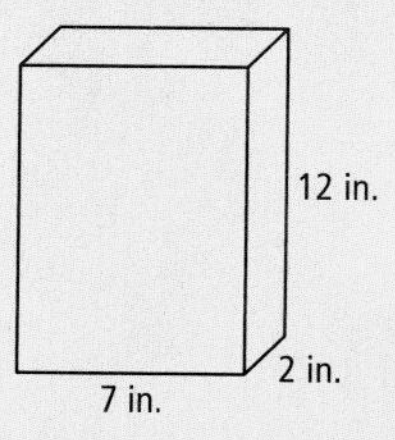

ANSWER

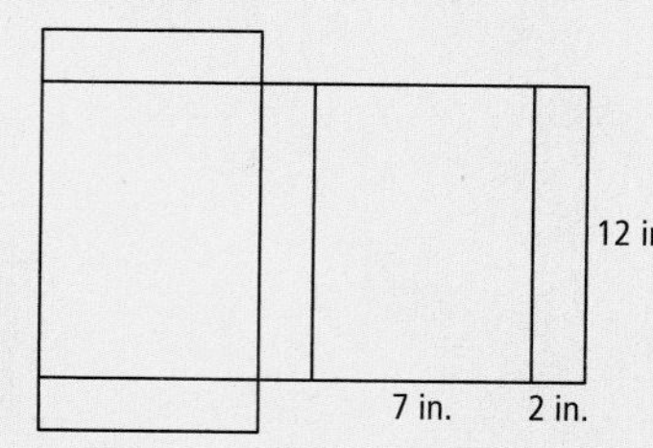

(Other solutions are possible.)

3. What is the isometric drawing of the cube structure below?

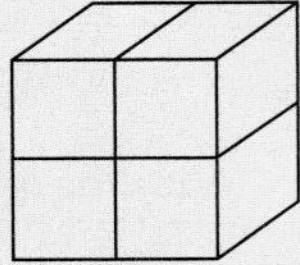

ANSWER

4. What is the front orthographic drawing for the isometric drawing below?

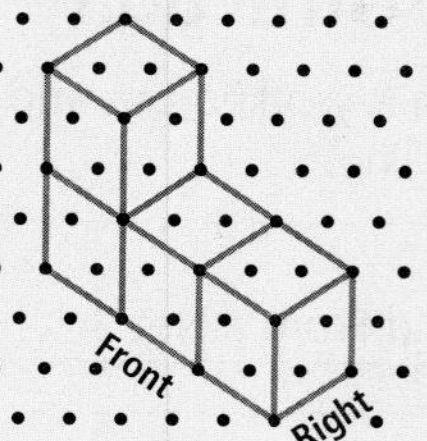

ANSWER

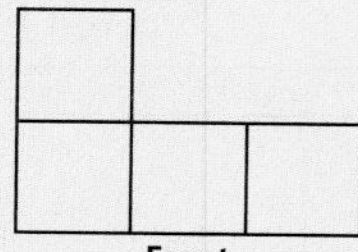

Lesson Check

Do you know HOW?

1. What is a net for the figure below? Label the net with its dimensions.

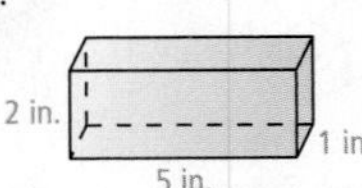

2. What is an isometric drawing of the cube structure?

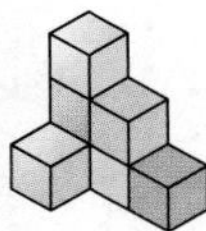

3. What is the orthographic drawing of the isometric drawing at the right? Assume there are no hidden cubes.

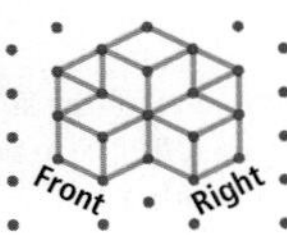

Do you UNDERSTAND?

4. **Vocabulary** Tell whether each drawing is *isometric*, *orthographic*, a *net*, or *none*.

a. 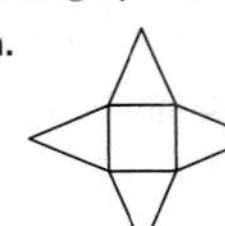

b. 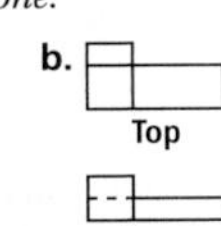

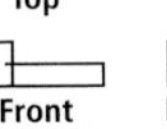

c. 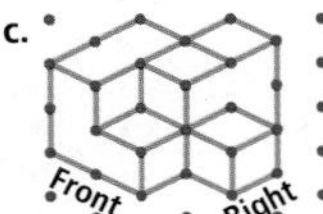

d. 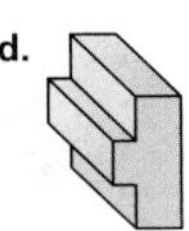

5. **Compare and Contrast** What are the differences and similarities between an isometric drawing and an orthographic drawing? Explain.

Practice and Problem-Solving Exercises

A Practice Match each three-dimensional figure with its net.

See Problem 1.

6. 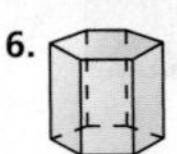

7. 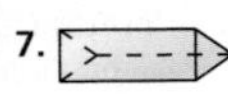

8. 
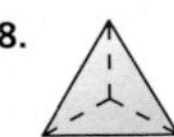

A. 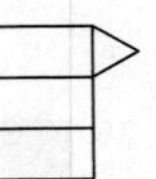

B. 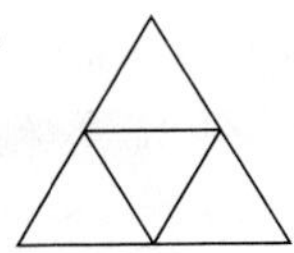

C. 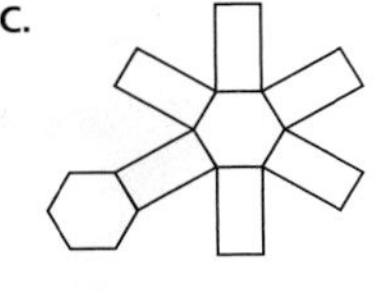

Draw a net for each figure. Label the net with its dimensions.

See Problem 2.

9. 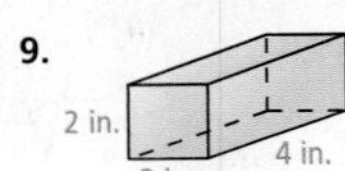

10. 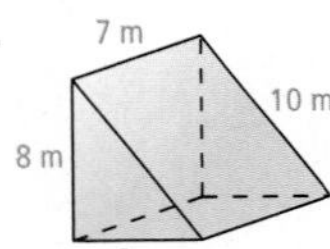

11. 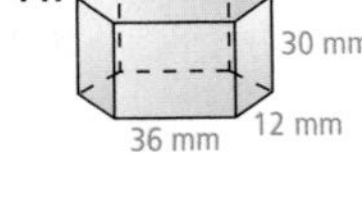

3 Lesson Check

Do you know HOW?

- If students have difficulty with Exercise 1, then have them make and cut out the faces on separate pieces of paper. Then they can tape the pieces together to model the figure and cut them apart again to lay the faces out flat.

Do you UNDERSTAND?

- If students have difficulty with Exercise 4, then have them review vocabulary and terminology from the lesson.

Close

Q What are methods for representing three-dimensional objects using two-dimensional figures? **[nets, isometric drawings, and orthographic drawings]**

Answers

Got It? (continued)

3. 4.

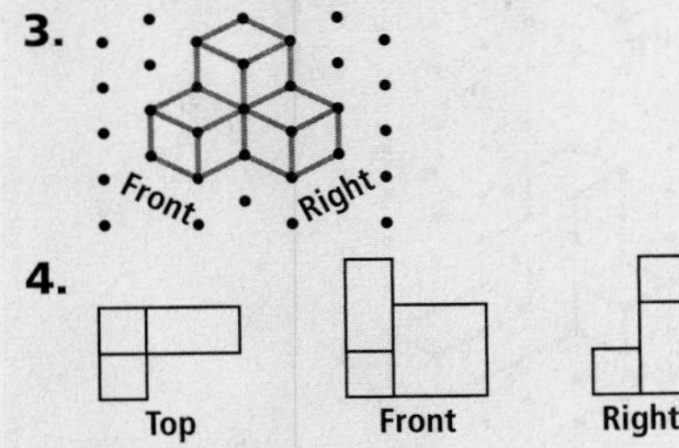

Lesson Check

1. Answers may vary. Sample:

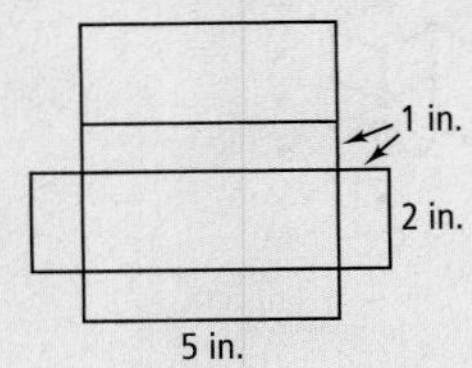

2. 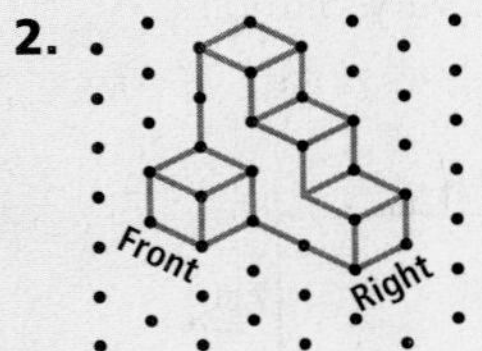

3. 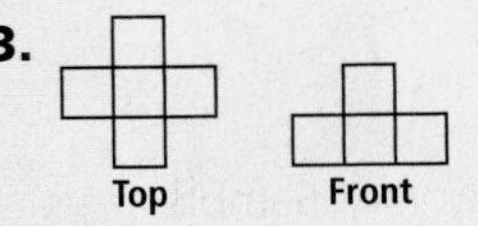

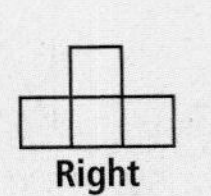

4a. net
b. orthographic
c. isometric
d. none
5. See next page.

Practice and Problem-Solving Exercises

6–11. See next page.

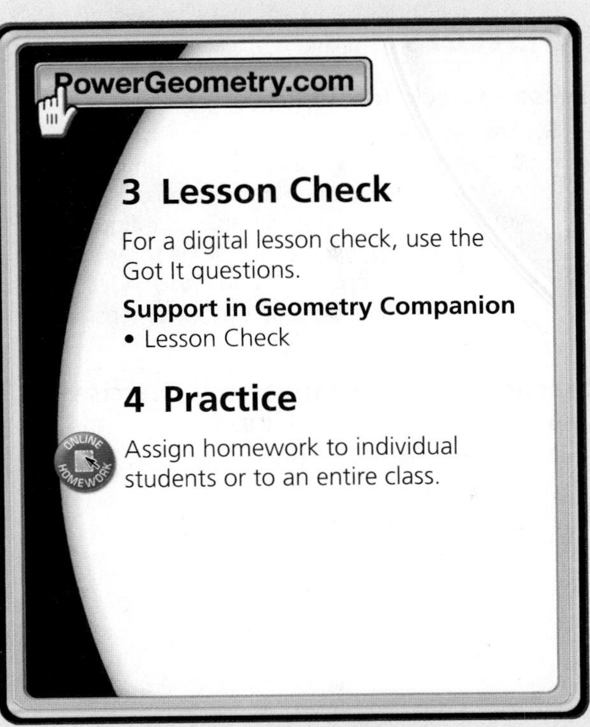

4 Practice

ASSIGNMENT GUIDE

Basic: 6–19 all, 20–26 even, 27, 28–36 even
Average: 7–19 odd, 20–38
Advanced: 7–19 odd, 20–42
Standardized Test Prep: 43–45
Mixed Review: 46–51
Reasoning exercises have blue headings.
Applications exercises have red headings.
EXERCISE 20: Use the Think About a Plan worksheet in the **Practice and Problem Solving Workbook** (also available in the Teaching Resources in print and online) to further support students' development in becoming independent learners.

HOMEWORK QUICK CHECK

To check students' understanding of key skills and concepts, go over Exercises 11, 13, 20, 22, and 27.

Make an isometric drawing of each cube structure on isometric dot paper. See Problem 3.

12. 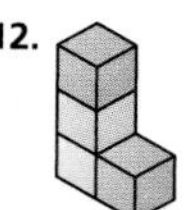

13. 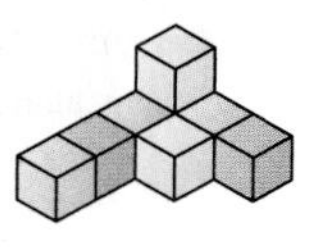

14. 

15. 

For each isometric drawing, make an orthographic drawing. Assume there are no hidden cubes. See Problem 4.

16. 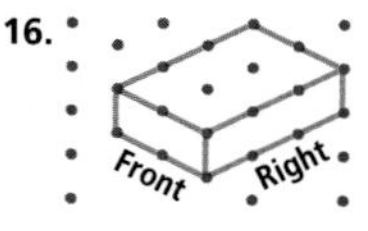

17. 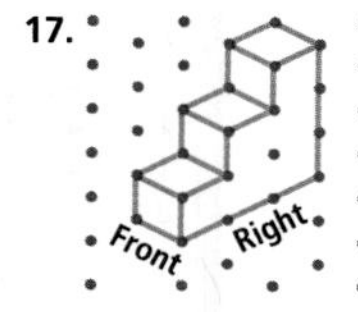

18. 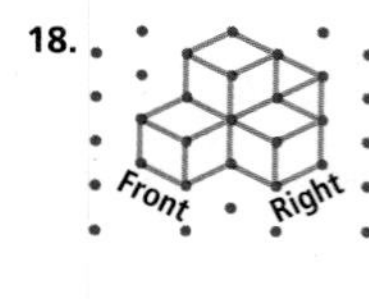

19. 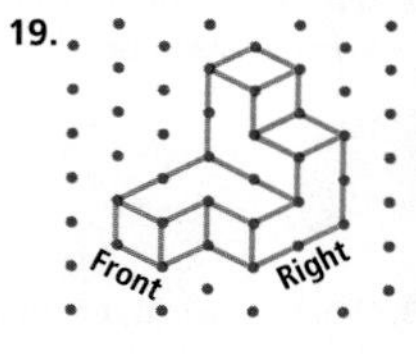

B Apply

20. **Multiple Representations** There are eight different nets for the solid shown at the right. Draw as many of them as you can. (*Hint*: Two nets are the same if you can rotate or flip one to match the other.)

21. a. **Open-Ended** Make an isometric drawing of a structure that you can build using 8 cubes.
b. Make an orthographic drawing of this structure.

22. **Think About a Plan** Draw a net of the can at the right.
- What shape are the top and bottom of the can?
- If you uncurl the body of the can, what shape do you get?

23. **History** In 1525, German printmaker Albrecht Dürer first used the word *net* to describe a printed pattern that folds up into a three-dimensional shape. Why do you think he chose to use the word *net*?

Manufacturing **Match the package with its net.**

24.

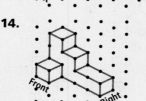

25. 

26. 

A. 

B. 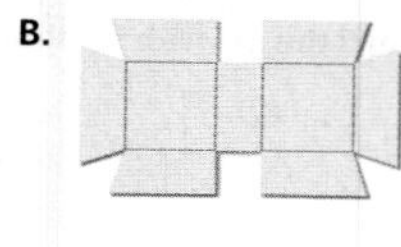

C. 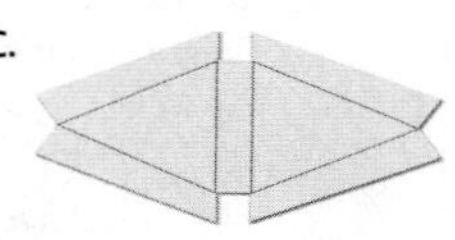

Answers

Lesson Check (continued)

5. Answers may vary. Sample: In an isometric drawing, you see three sides of a figure from one corner view. In an orthographic drawing, you see three separate views of the figure. In both drawings, you see the same three sides of the figure (top, front, and right). Also, both drawings represent a three-dimensional object in two-dimensions.

Practice and Problem-Solving Exercises

6. C **7.** A **8.** B

9. Answers may vary. Sample:

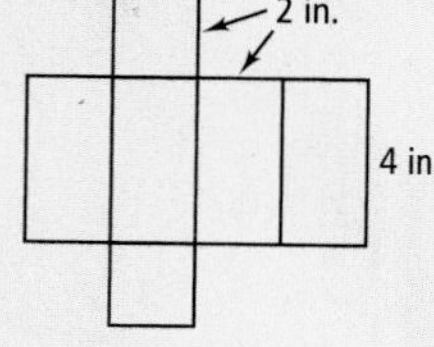

10. Answers may vary. Sample:

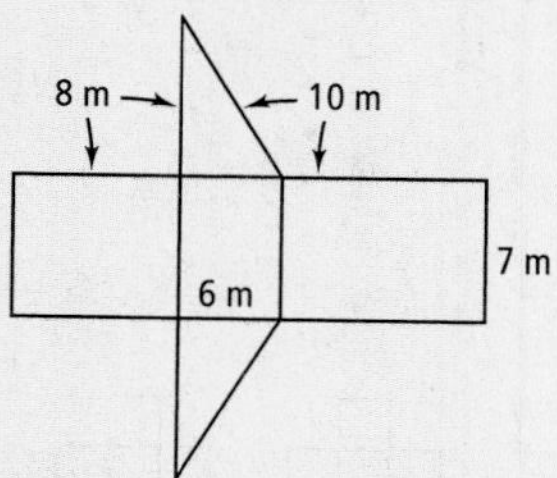

11. Answers may vary. Sample:

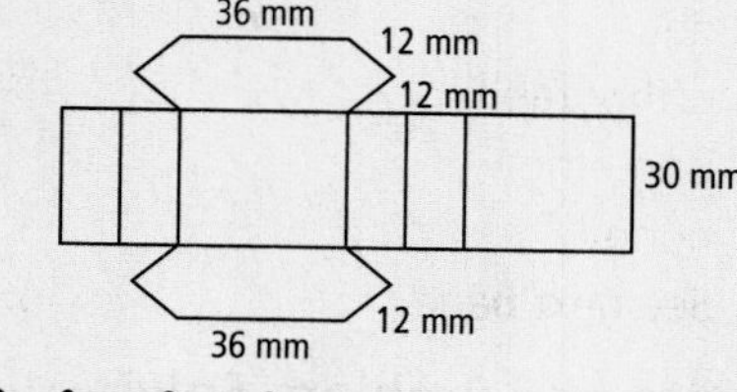

12.

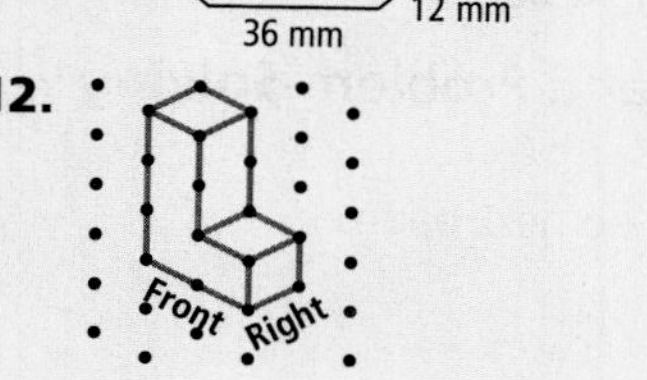

13.

14.

15.

16.

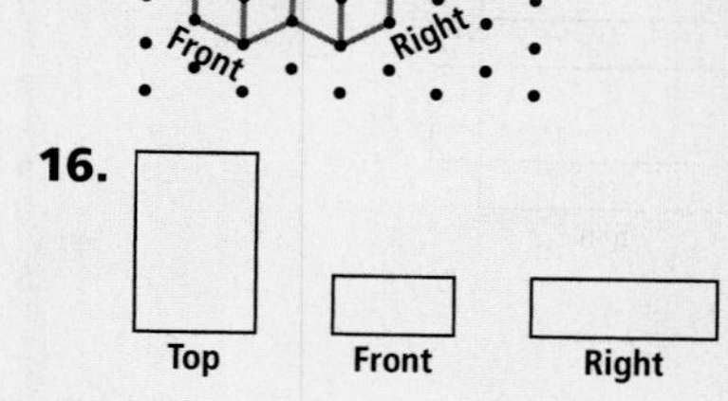

27. **Error Analysis** Miquela and Gina drew orthographic drawings for the cube structure at the right. Who is correct?

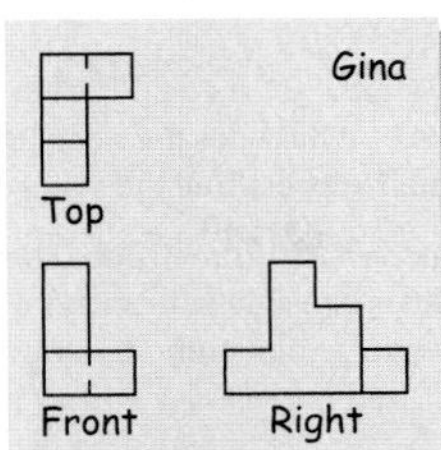

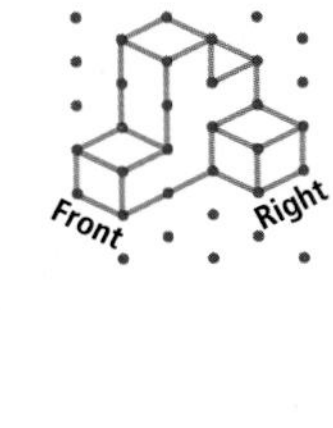

Make an orthographic drawing for each isometric drawing.

28. 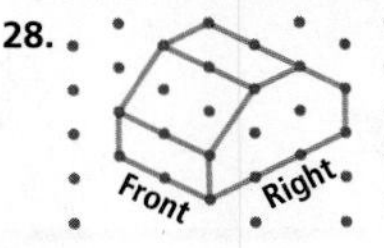

29. 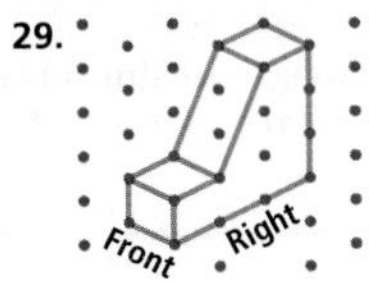

30. 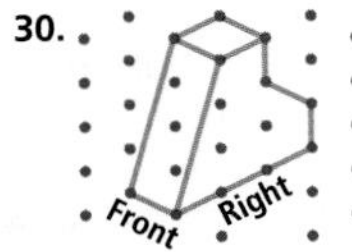

31. **Fort** Use the diagram of the fort at the right.
   a. Make an isometric drawing of the fort.
   b. Make an orthographic drawing of the fort.

32. **Aerial Photography** Another perspective in aerial photography is the "bird's-eye view," which shows an object from directly overhead. What type of drawing that you have studied in this lesson is a bird's-eye view?

33. **Writing** Photographs of buildings are typically not taken from a bird's-eye view. Describe a situation in which you would want a photo showing a bird's-eye view.

Visualization **Think about how each net can be folded to form a cube. What is the color of the face that will be opposite the red face?**

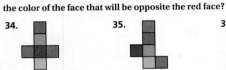

34. 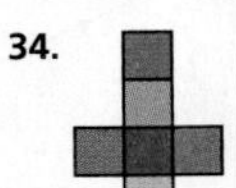
35. 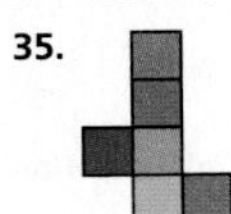
36. 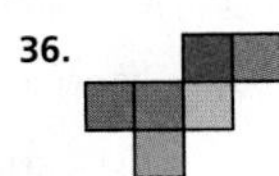
37. 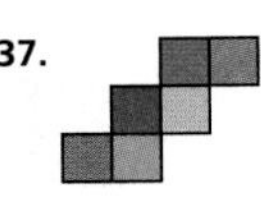

38. **Multiple Representations** There are 11 different nets for a cube. Four of them are shown above.
   a. Draw the other seven nets.
   b. **Writing** Suppose you want to make 100 cubes for an art project. Which of the 11 nets would you use? Explain why.

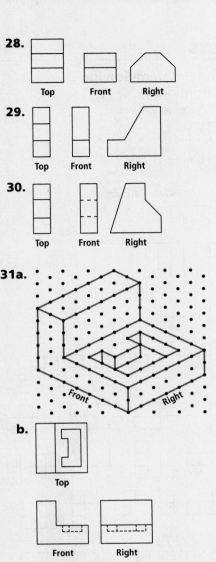

17. 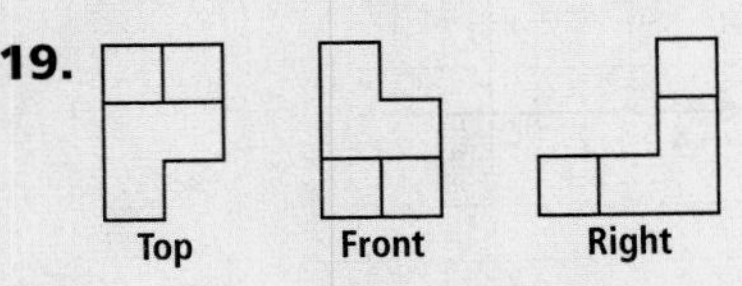

18. 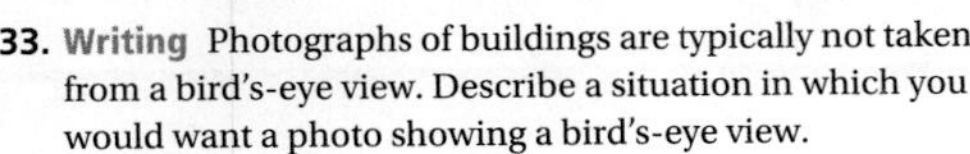

19.

20. 

21a. Answers may vary. Sample:

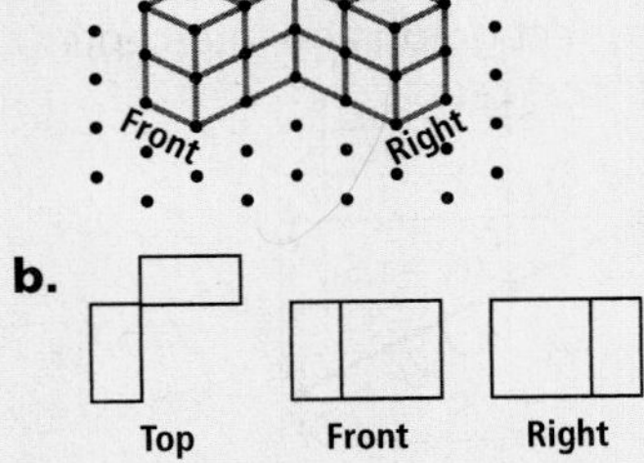

b.

22. Answers may vary. Sample:

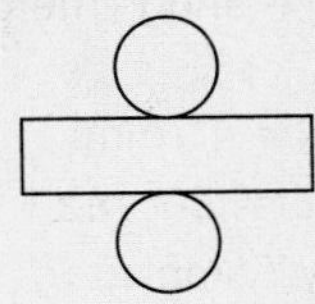

23. Answers may vary. Sample: Dürer may have thought that the printed pattern resembled a fishing net.

24. B **25.** C **26.** A

27. Miquela

28.

29.

30.

31a. 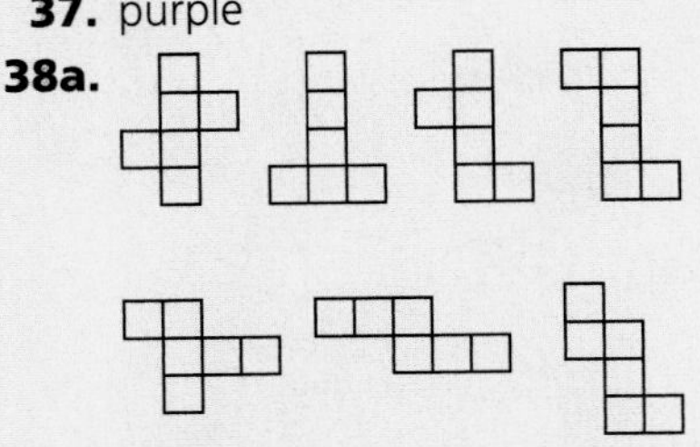

b.

32. top view of an orthographic drawing

33. Answers may vary. Sample: for a tourist map showing locations of attractions

34. blue

35. green

36. orange

37. purple

38a. 

b. Answers may vary. Sample: The net in Exercise 34; it is easy to cut and fold.

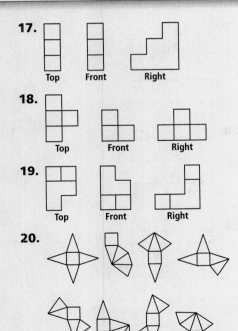

Answers

Practice and Problem-Solving Exercises (continued)

39. Answers may vary. Sample:

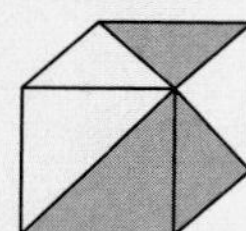

40. Answers may vary. Sample:

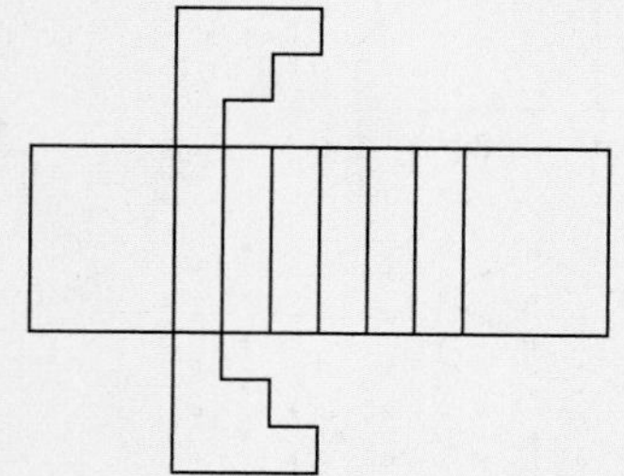

41.

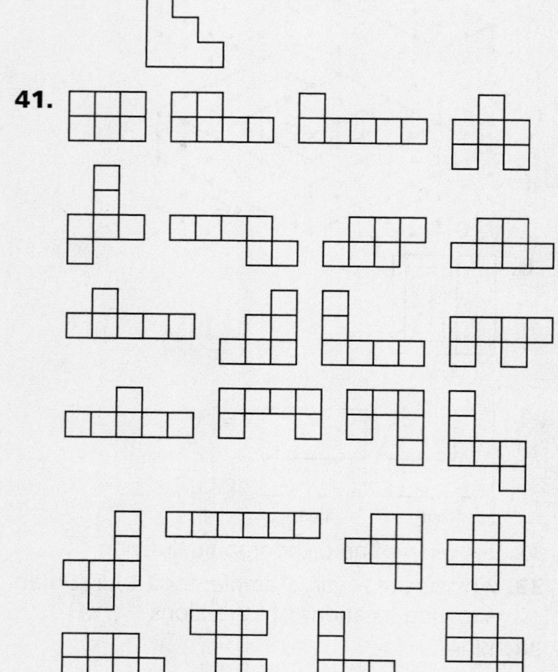

42a.

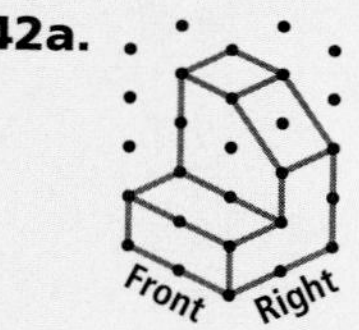

b.

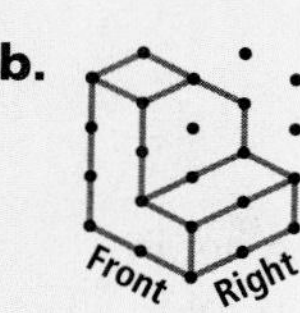

c.

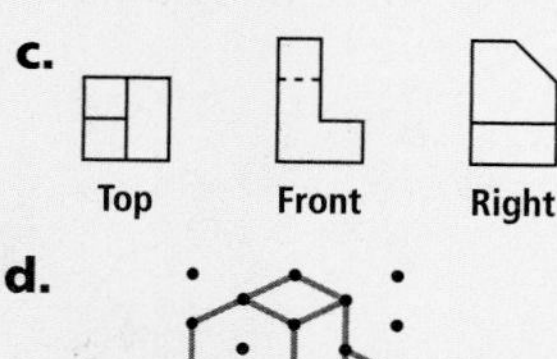

d.

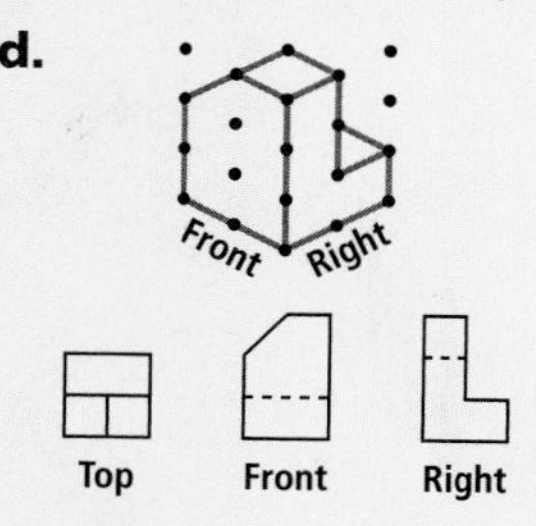

39. The net at the right folds into a cube. Sketch the cube so that its front face is shaded as shown below.

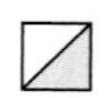

40. Architecture What does the net of the staircase shown look like? Draw the net. (*Hint:* Visualize stretching the stairs out flat.)

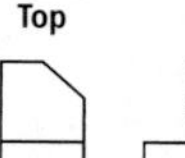

41. A hexomino is a two-dimensional figure formed with six squares. Each square shares at least one side with another square. The 11 nets of a cube that you found in Exercise 38 are hexominoes. Draw as many of the remaining 24 hexominoes as you can.

42. Visualization Use the orthographic drawing at the right.
- **a.** Make an isometric drawing of the structure.
- **b.** Make an isometric drawing of the structure from part (a) after it has been turned on its base 90° counterclockwise.
- **c.** Make an orthographic drawing of the structure from part (b).
- **d.** Turn the structure from part (a) 180°. Repeat parts (b) and (c).

Top Front Right

Standardized Test Prep

SAT/ACT

43. How many possible nets does the solid at the right have?

 (A) 1 (B) 2  (C) 3  (D) 4

44. Solve $10a - 5b = 25$ for b.

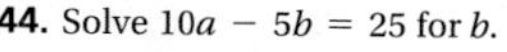 (F) $b = 10a + 25$ (G) $b = 10a - 25$ (H) $b = 2a + 5$ (I) $b = 2a - 5$

Short Response

45. Graph the equation $x + 2y = -3$. Label the x- and y-intercepts.

Mixed Review

For Exercises 46 and 47, use the diagram at the right. See p. 824.

46. Measure DE and EF to the nearest millimeter.

47. Measure each angle to the nearest degree.

48. Draw a triangle that has sides of length 6 cm and 5 cm with a 90° angle between those two sides.

Get Ready! **To prepare for Lesson 1-2, do Exercises 49–51.**

Coordinate Geometry Graph the points on the coordinate plane. See p. 833.

49. (0, 0), (2, 2), (0, 3) **50.** (1, 2), (−4, 3), (−5, 0) **51.** (−4, −5), (0, −1), (3, −2)

43. C

44. I

45. [2] correct graph and intercepts

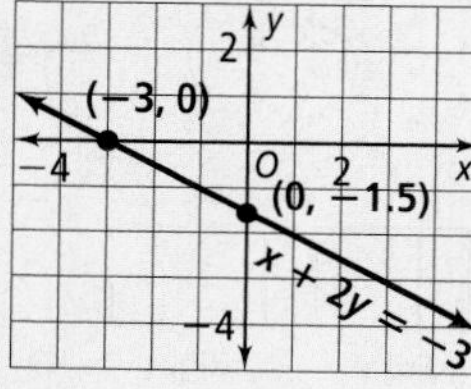

[1] incorrect graph OR missing intercepts OR x- and y-intercepts interchanged

46. $DE = 31$ mm, $EF = 41$ mm

47. $m\angle D = 60$, $m\angle E = 80$, $m\angle F = 40$

48. Answers may vary. Sample:

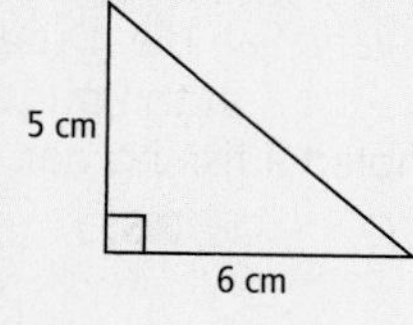

49.

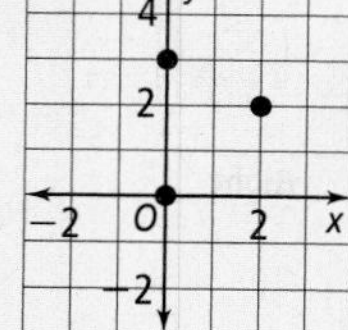

50.

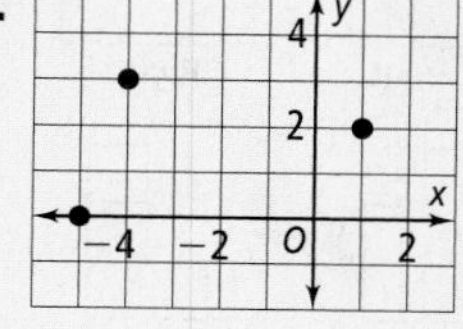

51.

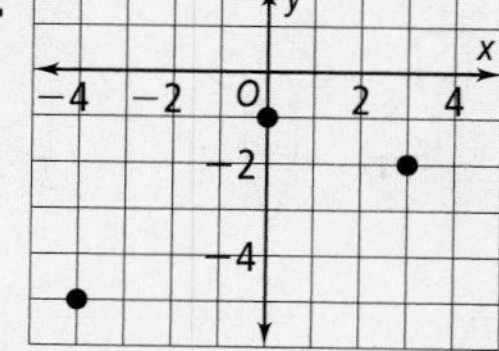

1-1 Lesson Resources

Differentiated Remediation

Instructional Support

Geometry Companion

Students can use the **Geometry Companion** worktext (4 pages) . . .

- New Vocabulary
- Key Concepts
- Got It for each Problem
- Lesson Check

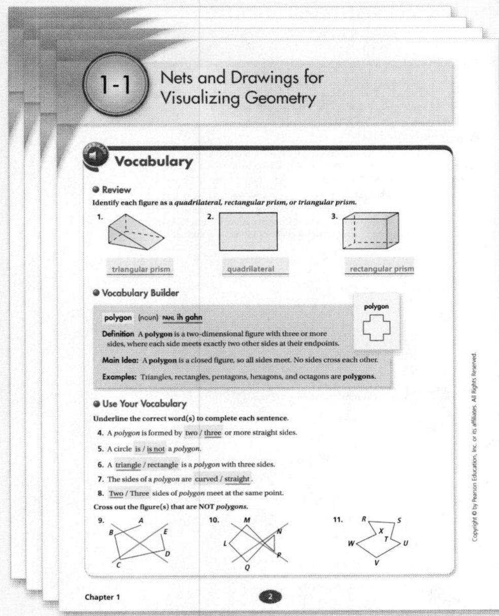
1-1 Nets and Drawings for Visualizing Geometry

Vocabulary

Review

Identify each figure as a *quadrilateral, rectangular prism, or triangular prism.*

1. triangular prism
2. quadrilateral
3. rectangular prism

Vocabulary Builder

polygon (noun) PAHL ih gahn

Definition A **polygon** is a two-dimensional figure with three or more sides, where each side meets exactly two other sides at their endpoints.

Main Idea: A **polygon** is a closed figure, so all sides meet. No sides cross each other.

Examples: Triangles, rectangles, pentagons, hexagons, and octagons are **polygons**.

Use Your Vocabulary

Underline the correct word(s) to complete each sentence.

4. A *polygon* is formed by two / three or more straight sides.
5. A circle is / is not a *polygon*.
6. A triangle / rectangle is a *polygon* with three sides.
7. The sides of a *polygon* are curved / straight.
8. Two / Three sides of *polygon* meet at the same point.

Cross out the figure(s) that are NOT *polygons*.

9.
10.
11.

Chapter 1 2

ELL Support

Use Graphic Organizers Have students fold a piece of paper into thirds lengthways. Tell them to label each section with one of the three vocabulary words. Discuss examples of each, then draw or project a net, an isometric drawing, and an orthographic drawing on the board. Ask volunteers to classify each type of two-dimensional drawing and to identify the three-dimensional figure it represents. Have students suggest other figures and their two-dimensional drawings. These can be drawn into the correct place on their papers.

5 Assess & Remediate

Lesson Quiz

1. What is a net for the box below? Label the net with its dimensions.

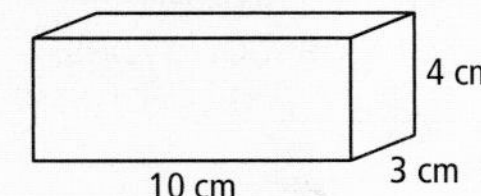

2. **Do you UNDERSTAND?** What is the isometric drawing of the cube structure below?

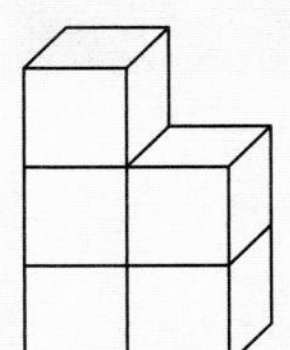

ANSWERS TO LESSON QUIZ

1. Answers may vary. Sample:

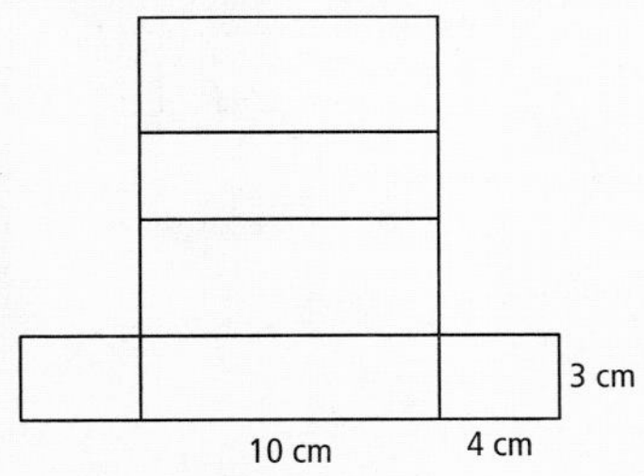

2.

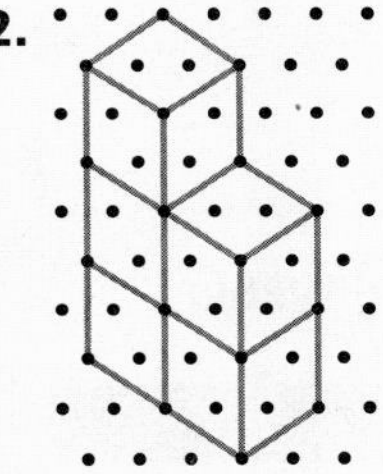

PRESCRIPTION FOR REMEDIATION

Use the student work on the Lesson Quiz to prescribe a differentiated review assignment.

Points	Differentiated Remediation
0	Intervention
1	On-level
2	Extension

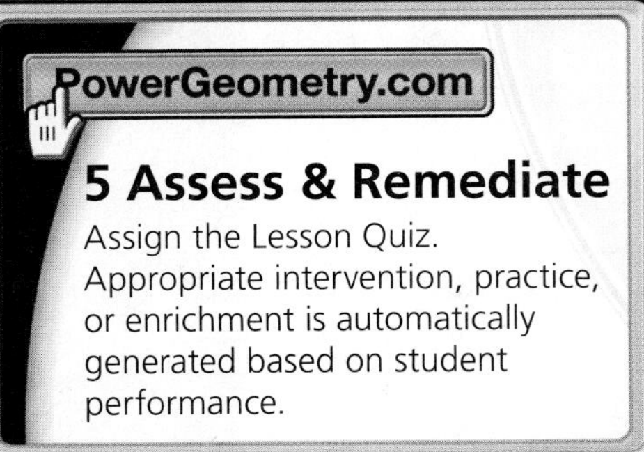

5 Assess & Remediate

Assign the Lesson Quiz. Appropriate intervention, practice, or enrichment is automatically generated based on student performance.

Intervention

- **Reteaching** (2 pages) Provides reteaching and practice exercises for the key lesson concepts. Use with struggling students or absent students.
- **English Language Learner Support** Helps students develop and reinforce mathematical vocabulary and key concepts.

All-in-One Resources/Online

Reteaching

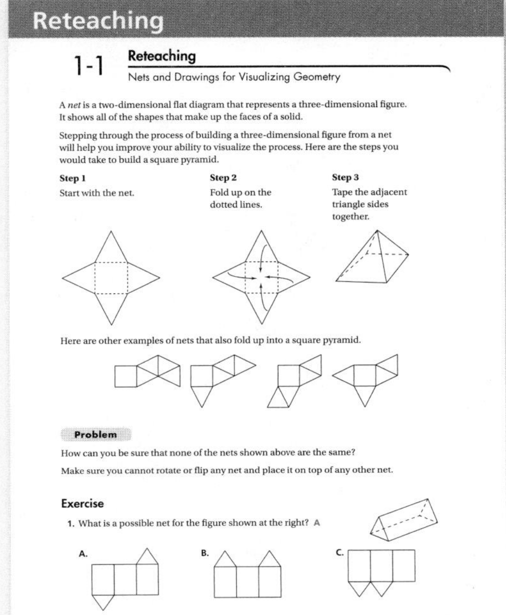
1-1 **Reteaching**

Nets and Drawings for Visualizing Geometry

A *net* is a two-dimensional flat diagram that represents a three-dimensional figure. It shows all of the shapes that make up the faces of a solid.

Stepping through the process of building a three-dimensional figure from a net will help you improve your ability to visualize the process. Here are the steps you would take to build a square pyramid.

Step 1 Start with the net.

Step 2 Fold up on the dotted lines.

Step 3 Tape the adjacent triangle sides together.

Here are other examples of nets that also fold up into a square pyramid.

Problem

How can you be sure that none of the nets shown above are the same?

Make sure you cannot rotate or flip any net and place it on top of any other net.

Exercise

1. What is a possible net for the figure shown at the right? A

A. B. C.

All-in-One Resources/Online

English Language Learner Support

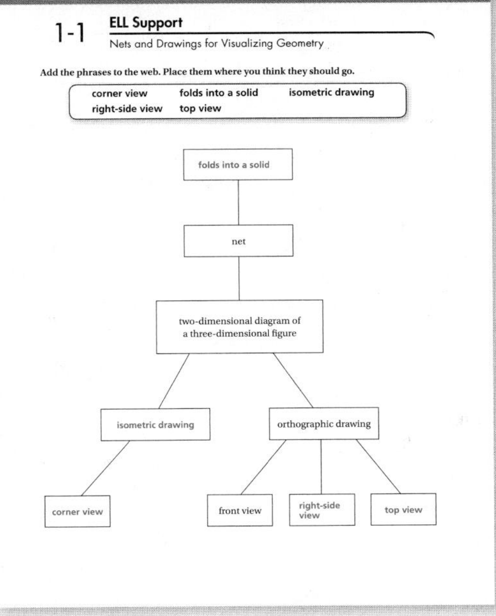
1-1 **ELL Support**

Nets and Drawings for Visualizing Geometry

Add the phrases to the web. Place them where you think they should go.

corner view folds into a solid isometric drawing right-side view top view

Differentiated Remediation *continued*

On-Level

- **Practice** (2 pages) Provides extra practice for each lesson. For simpler practice exercises, use the Form K Practice pages found in the All-in-One Teaching Resources and online.
- **Think About a Plan** Helps students develop specific problem-solving skills and strategies by providing scaffolded guiding questions.
- **Standardized Test Prep** Focuses on all major exercises, all major question types, and helps students prepare for the high-stakes assessments.

Practice and Problem Solving Wkbk/ All-in-One Resources/Online

Practice page 1

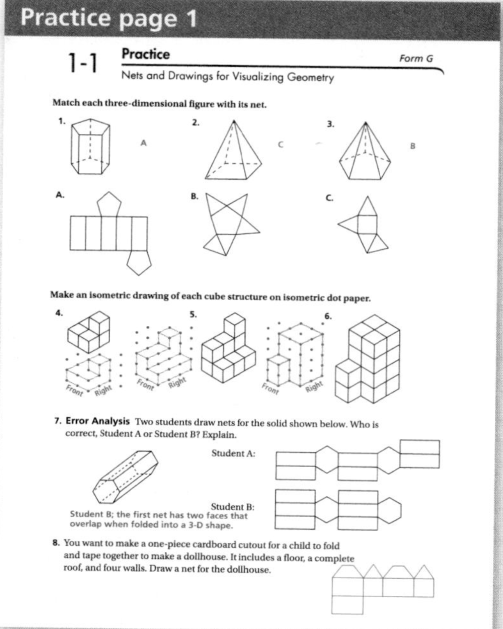

1-1 **Practice** *Form G*

Nets and Drawings for Visualizing Geometry

Match each three-dimensional figure with its net.

1. A
2. C
3. B

Make an isometric drawing of each cube structure on isometric dot paper.

4.
5.
6.

7. **Error Analysis** Two students draw nets for the solid shown below. Who is correct, Student A or Student B? Explain.
Student A:
Student B:
Student B; the first net has two faces that overlap when folded into a 3-D shape.

8. You want to make a one-piece cardboard cutout for a child to fold and tape together to make a dollhouse. It includes a floor, a complete roof, and four walls. Draw a net for the dollhouse.

Practice and Problem Solving Wkbk/ All-in-One Resources/Online

Practice page 2

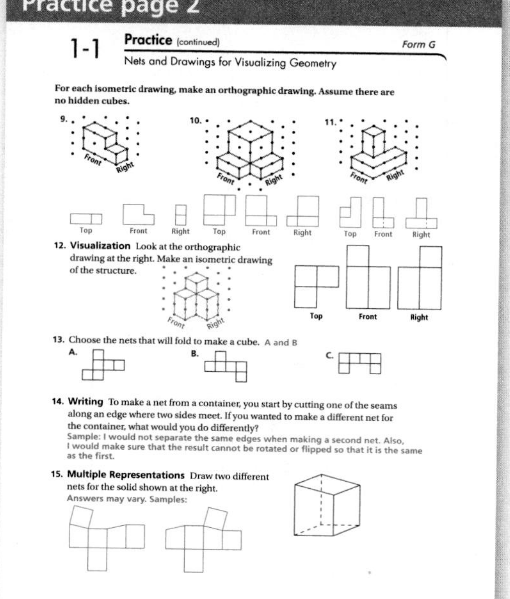

1-1 **Practice** (continued) *Form G*

Nets and Drawings for Visualizing Geometry

For each isometric drawing, make an orthographic drawing. Assume there are no hidden cubes.

9. Top Front Right
10. Top Front Right
11. Top Front Right

12. **Visualization** Look at the orthographic drawing at the right. Make an isometric drawing of the structure.
Top Front Right

13. Choose the nets that will fold to make a cube. A and B

14. **Writing** To make a net from a container, you start by cutting one of the seams along an edge where two sides meet. If you wanted to make a different net for the container, what would you do differently?
Sample: I would not separate the same edges when making a second net. Also, I would make sure that the result cannot be rotated or flipped so that it is the same as the first.

15. **Multiple Representations** Draw two different nets for the solid shown at the right.
Answers may vary. Samples:

Practice and Problem Solving Wkbk/ All-in-One Resources/Online

Think About a Plan

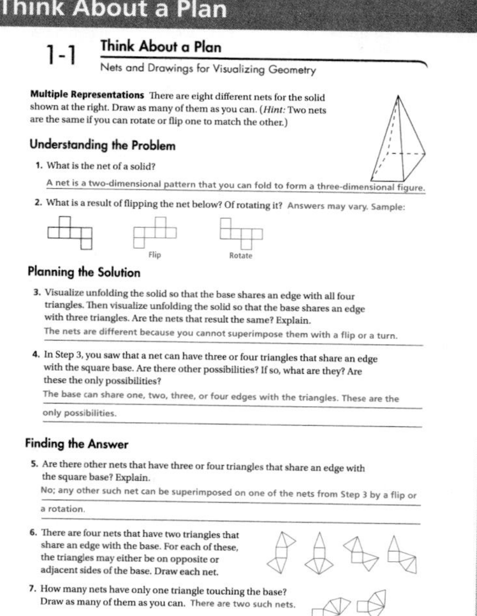

1-1 **Think About a Plan**

Nets and Drawings for Visualizing Geometry

Multiple Representations There are eight different nets for the solid shown at the right. Draw as many of them as you can. (*Hint:* Two nets are the same if you can rotate or flip one to match the other.)

Understanding the Problem

1. What is the net of a solid?
A net is a two-dimensional pattern that you can fold to form a three-dimensional figure.
2. What is a result of flipping the net below? Of rotating it? Answers may vary. Sample:
Flip Rotate

Planning the Solution

3. Visualize unfolding the solid so that the base shares an edge with all four triangles. Then visualize unfolding the solid so that the base shares an edge with three triangles. Are the nets that result the same? Explain.
The nets are different because you cannot superimpose them with a flip or a turn.
4. In Step 3, you saw that a net can have three or four triangles that share an edge with the square base. Are there other possibilities? If so, what are they? Are these the only possibilities?
The base can share one, two, three, or four edges with the triangles. These are the only possibilities.

Finding the Answer

5. Are there other nets that have three or four triangles that share an edge with the square base? Explain.
No; any other such net can be superimposed on one of the nets from Step 3 by a flip or a rotation.
6. There are four nets that have two triangles that share an edge with the base. For each of these, the triangles may either be on opposite or adjacent sides of the base. Draw each net.
7. How many nets have only one triangle touching the base? Draw as many of them as you can. There are two such nets.

Practice and Problem Solving Wkbk/ All-in-One Resources/Online

Standardized Test Prep

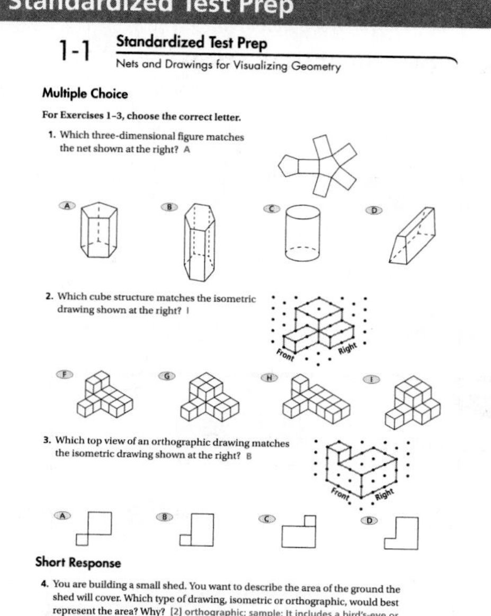

1-1 **Standardized Test Prep**

Nets and Drawings for Visualizing Geometry

Multiple Choice

For Exercises 1–3, choose the correct letter.

1. Which three-dimensional figure matches the net shown at the right? A
(A) (B) (C) (D)
2. Which cube structure matches the isometric drawing shown at the right? I
(F) (G) (H) (I)
3. Which top view of an orthographic drawing matches the isometric drawing shown at the right? B
(A) (B) (C) (D)

Short Response

4. You are building a small shed. You want to describe the area of the ground the shed will cover. Which type of drawing, isometric or orthographic, would best represent the area? Why? [2] orthographic; sample: It includes a bird's-eye or top-down view, which gives the building's footprint on the ground. [1] correct answer with incomplete explanation [0] incorrect answer with no explanation given

Extension

- **Enrichment** Provides students with interesting problems and activities that extend the concepts of the lesson.
- **Activities, Games, and Puzzles** Worksheets that can be used for concepts development, enrichment, and for fun!

All-in-One Resources/Online

Enrichment

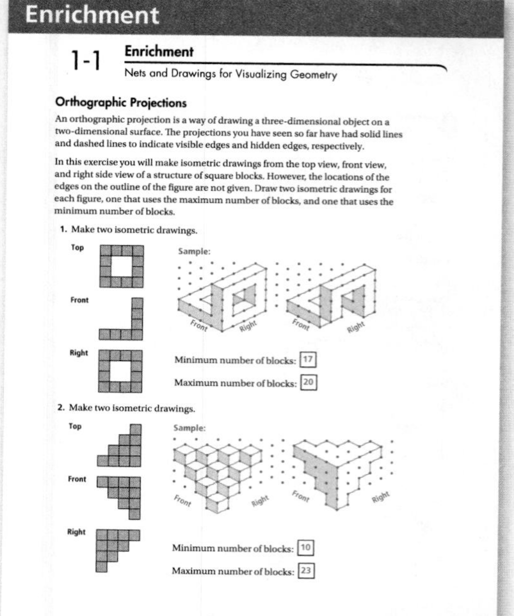

1-1 **Enrichment**

Nets and Drawings for Visualizing Geometry

Orthographic Projections

An orthographic projection is a way of drawing a three-dimensional object on a two-dimensional surface. The projections you have seen so far have had solid lines and dashed lines to indicate visible edges and hidden edges, respectively.

In this exercise you will make isometric drawings from the top view, front view, and right side view of a structure of square blocks. However, the locations of the edges on the outline of the figure are not given. Draw two isometric drawings for each figure, one that uses the maximum number of blocks, and one that uses the minimum number of blocks.

1. Make two isometric drawings.
Top Front Right Sample:
Minimum number of blocks: 17
Maximum number of blocks: 20
2. Make two isometric drawings.
Top Front Right Sample:
Minimum number of blocks: 10
Maximum number of blocks: 23

Online Teacher Resource Center

Activities, Games, and Puzzles

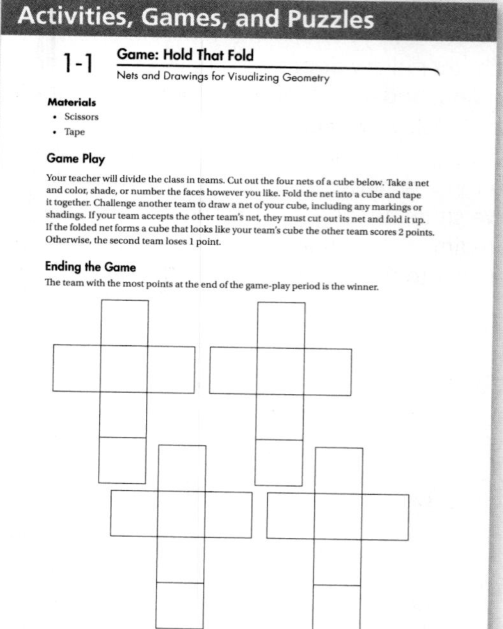

1-1 **Game: Hold That Fold**

Nets and Drawings for Visualizing Geometry

Materials

- Scissors
- Tape

Game Play

Your teacher will divide the class in teams. Cut out the four nets of a cube below. Take a net and color, shade, or number the faces however you like. Fold the net into a cube and tape it together. Challenge another team to draw a net of your cube, including any markings or shadings. If your team accepts the other team's net, they must cut out its net and fold it up. If the folded net forms a cube that looks like your team's cube the other team scores 2 points. Otherwise, the second team loses 1 point.

Ending the Game

The team with the most points at the end of the game-play period is the winner.

1-2 Points, Lines, and Planes

TN State Performance Indicators
SPI 3108.1.4 Use definitions, basic postulates, and theorems about points, lines, angles, and planes to write/complete proofs and/or to solve problems.
Also SPI 3108.1.3 and SPI 3108.4.2

Objective To understand basic terms and postulates of geometry

Getting Ready!
Make the figure at the right with a pencil and a piece of paper. Is the figure possible with a straight arrow and a solid board? Explain.
Look at where the arrow goes through the board.

In this lesson, you will learn basic geometric facts to help you justify your answer to the Solve It.

Lesson Vocabulary
- point
- line
- plane
- collinear points
- coplanar
- space
- segment
- ray
- opposite rays
- postulate
- axiom
- intersection

Essential Understanding Geometry is a mathematical system built on accepted facts, basic terms, and definitions.

In geometry, some words such as *point*, *line*, and *plane* are undefined. Undefined terms are the basic ideas that you can use to build the definitions of all other figures in geometry. Although you cannot define undefined terms, it is important to have a general description of their meanings.

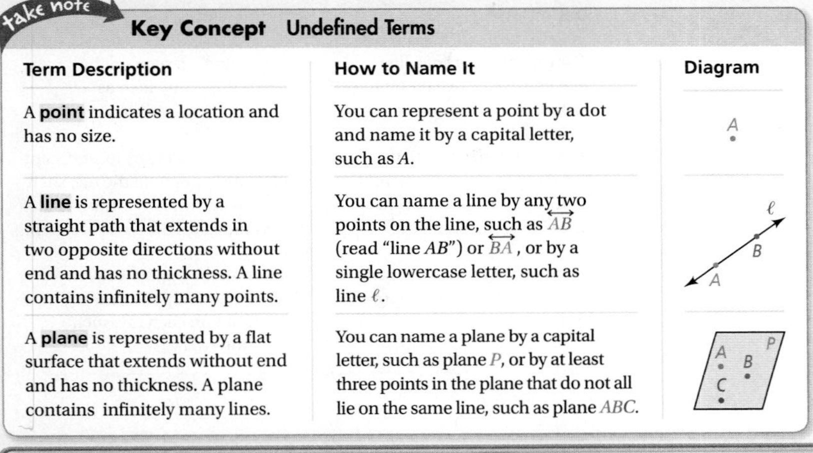

take note **Key Concept** Undefined Terms

Term Description	How to Name It	Diagram
A **point** indicates a location and has no size.	You can represent a point by a dot and name it by a capital letter, such as *A*.	A
A **line** is represented by a straight path that extends in two opposite directions without end and has no thickness. A line contains infinitely many points.	You can name a line by any two points on the line, such as $\overleftrightarrow{AB}$ (read "line *AB*") or $\overleftrightarrow{BA}$, or by a single lowercase letter, such as line ℓ.	ℓ, B, A
A **plane** is represented by a flat surface that extends without end and has no thickness. A plane contains infinitely many lines.	You can name a plane by a capital letter, such as plane *P*, or by at least three points in the plane that do not all lie on the same line, such as plane *ABC*.	P, A, B, C

1 Interactive Learning

Solve It!

PURPOSE To visualize the possible intersections of a plane and a line

PROCESS Students may
- use a physical model to test conjectures.
- use visual judgment.

FACILITATE

Q Is the pencil a good model for the arrow? Explain. **[Yes, the pencil is straight and unbendable like an arrow.]**

Q Is the paper a good model for the board? Explain. **[No, the paper is bendable, while a board is not.]**

ANSWER See Solve It in Answers on next page.

CONNECT THE MATH The Solve It investigates three possible arrangements of the board and the arrow. Clarify that the arrow can lie on the board, can intersect the board in only one place, or can lie above or below the board so that they do not intersect. In this lesson students will examine ways to represent geometric figures.

2 Guided Instruction

Take Note

VISUAL LEARNERS

Point out to students the building-block nature of geometric knowledge with these first three undefined terms. The word *point* is used in the description of a line, and the word *line* is used in the description of a plane.

1-2 Preparing to Teach

BIG idea **Reasoning and Proof** UbD

ESSENTIAL UNDERSTANDINGS
- Geometry is a mathematical system built on accepted facts, basic terms, and definitions.
- A postulate or axiom is an accepted statement of fact.

Math Background

It may be difficult for students to understand that the terms *point*, *line*, and *plane* are undefined. They may assume that the description provided must be a definition.

The notion of being undefined in mathematics is based on the principles of logic. Any term that cannot be defined using only previously defined terms is considered undefined.

Explain that undefined terms are needed to avoid circular definitions and that they are the foundation for the definition of other terms.

It is important to emphasize the description of a point as having no length, width, or area. Guide students to realize that although lines are named by two points, they are composed of an infinite number of points that extend infinitely in both directions. Emphasize that planes are unbounded flat surfaces with no edges or corners.

Support Student Learning

Use the **Geometry Companion** to engage and support students during instructions. See Lesson Resources at the end of this lesson for details.

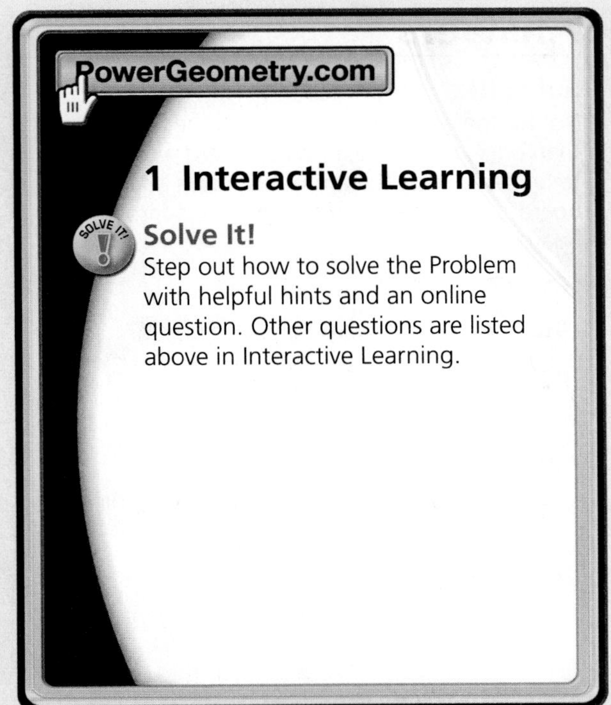

Problem 1

Q How can you tell that the label P is naming a plane instead of a point? **[P is the name for a plane because it does not have a point associated with it.]**

Q Why is plane RQS not a valid name for the plane? **[because R, Q, and S are collinear]**

Q What point(s) do lines ℓ and m have in common? **[point Q]**

Got It? ERROR PREVENTION

Make sure that students understand the difference between the limited number of points labeled on a line or plane and the infinite number of points that actually lie on a line or plane.

Take Note VISUAL LEARNERS

Emphasize to students that the terms *segment*, *ray*, and *opposite rays* are defined as opposed to the terms *point*, *line*, and *plane* that remain undefined but understood.

Q How is a segment different from a line? **[A line extends infinitely in both directions; a segment has two endpoints.]**

Q Why is $\overrightarrow{AB}$ not an acceptable name for the opposite ray shown in the diagram? **[The name must include the shared endpoint.]**

Points that lie on the same line are **collinear points.** Points and lines that lie in the same plane are **coplanar.** All the points of a line are coplanar.

Think

Why can figures have more than one name? Lines and planes are made up of many points. You can choose any two points on a line and any three or more noncollinear points in a plane for the name.

Problem 1 Naming Points, Lines and Planes

A **What are two other ways to name $\overleftrightarrow{QT}$?**

Two other ways to name $\overleftrightarrow{QT}$ are $\overleftrightarrow{TQ}$ and line m.

B **What are two other ways to name plane P?**

Two other ways to name plane P are plane RQV and plane RSV.

C **What are the names of three collinear points? What are the names of four coplanar points?**

Points R, Q, and S are collinear. Points R, Q, S, and V are coplanar.

Got It? **1. a.** What are two other ways to name $\overleftrightarrow{RS}$?
b. What are two more ways to name plane P?
c. What are the names of three other collinear points?
d. What are two points that are *not* coplanar with points R, S, and V?

The terms *point*, *line*, and *plane* are not defined because their definitions would require terms that also need defining. You can, however, use undefined terms to define other terms. A geometric figure is a set of points. **Space** is the set of all points in three dimensions. Similarly, the definitions for *segment* and *ray* are based on the definitions of points and lines.

Take note **Key Concept** Defined Terms

Definition	How to Name It	Diagram
A **segment** is part of a line that consists of two endpoints and all points between them.	You can name a segment by its two endpoints, such as $\overline{AB}$ (read "segment AB") or $\overline{BA}$.	A B
A **ray** is part of a line that consists of one endpoint and all the points of the line on one side of the endpoint.	You can name a ray by its endpoint and another point on the ray, such as $\overrightarrow{AB}$ (read "ray AB"). The order of points indicates the ray's direction.	A B
Opposite rays are two rays that share the same endpoint and form a line.	You can name opposite rays by their shared endpoint and any other point on each ray, such as $\overrightarrow{CA}$ and $\overrightarrow{CB}$.	A C B

Answers

Solve It!

No; for the arrow to pass through the board more than once, either the arrow or board would need to be bent. Since the arrow is straight and the board is stiff, the arrow can only pass through the board once.

Got It?

1a. Answers may vary. Sample: $\overleftrightarrow{RQ}$, $\overleftrightarrow{QS}$
b. Answers may vary. Sample: plane RVS, plane VQS
c. N, Q, T
d. N, T
2. No; they do not have the same endpoint.

PowerGeometry.com

2 Guided Instruction

Each Problem is worked out and supported online.

Problem 1
Naming Points, Lines, and Planes
Animated

Problem 2
Naming Segments and Rays
Animated

Problem 3
Finding the Intersection of Two Planes
Animated

Problem 4
Using Postulate 1-4

Support in Geometry Companion
- Vocabulary
- Key Concepts
- Got It?

Plan

How do you make sure you name all the rays?
Each point on the line is an endpoint for a ray. At each point, follow the line both left and right to see if you can find a second point to name the ray.

Problem 2 Naming Segments and Rays

A What are the names of the segments in the figure at the right?

The three segments are $\overline{DE}$ or $\overline{ED}$, $\overline{EF}$ or $\overline{FE}$, and $\overline{DF}$ or $\overline{FD}$.

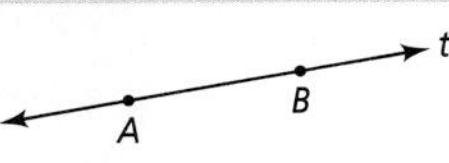

B What are the names of the rays in the figure?

The four rays are $\overrightarrow{DE}$ or $\overrightarrow{DF}$, $\overrightarrow{ED}$, $\overrightarrow{EF}$, and $\overrightarrow{FD}$ or $\overrightarrow{FE}$.

C Which of the rays in part (B) are opposite rays?

The opposite rays are $\overrightarrow{ED}$ and $\overrightarrow{EF}$.

Got It? 2. **Reasoning** $\overrightarrow{EF}$ and $\overrightarrow{FE}$ form a line. Are they opposite rays? Explain.

A **postulate** or **axiom** is an accepted statement of fact. Postulates, like undefined terms, are basic building blocks of the logical system in geometry. You will use logical reasoning to prove general concepts in this book.

You have used some of the following geometry postulates in algebra. For example, you used Postulate 1-1 when you graphed equations such as $y = 2x + 8$. You graphed two points and drew the line through the points.

take note Postulate 1-1

Through any two points there is exactly one line.

Line t passes through points A and B. Line t is the only line that passes through both points.

When you have two or more geometric figures, their **intersection** is the set of points the figures have in common.

In algebra, one way to solve a system of two equations is to graph them. The graphs of the two lines $y = -2x + 8$ and $y = 3x - 7$ intersect in a single point (3, 2). So the solution is (3, 2). This illustrates Postulate 1-2.

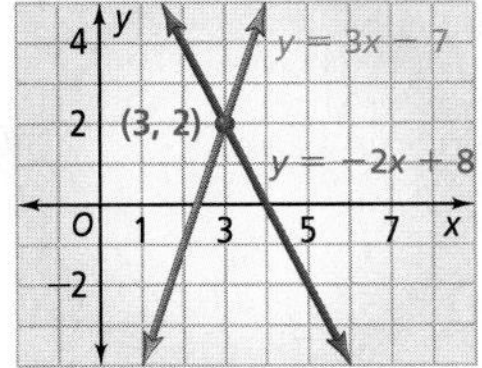

take note Postulate 1-2

If two distinct lines intersect, then they intersect in exactly one point.

$\overleftrightarrow{AE}$ and $\overleftrightarrow{DB}$ intersect in point C.

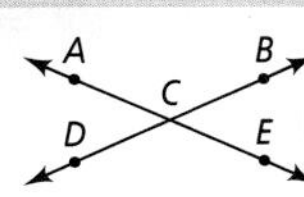

Problem 2

Q Do the names $\overline{DE}$ and $\overline{ED}$ represent different segments? Explain. **[No, they are two ways to name the set of points between point *D* and point *E*.]**

Q Can the three points shown on the line be used to name a plane? Explain. **[No, the points used to name a plane cannot be collinear.]**

Q How are segments $\overline{DE}$, $\overline{EF}$, and $\overline{DF}$ related to each other? **[$\overline{DF}$ is a combination of segments $\overline{DE}$ and $\overline{EF}$.]**

Got It?

Q What are two opposite rays? **[$\overrightarrow{EF}$ and $\overrightarrow{ED}$]**

Take Note ERROR PREVENTION

Make certain that students realize that the statement "any one line contains exactly two points" is not a logical conclusion of this postulate.

Take Note TACTILE LEARNERS

Allow students to use strands of uncooked spaghetti as models for lines to experiment and comprehend the assumption made by this postulate. It may be necessary to help students make a distinction between two lines that intersect in one point, and two lines which intersect in all points and are thus the same line.

Additional Problems

1.

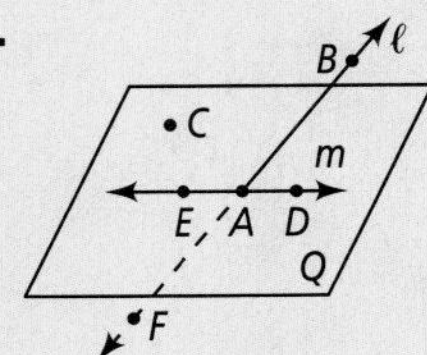

a. What are two other ways to name $\overleftrightarrow{AB}$?

b. What are two ways to name plane Q?

c. What are the names of three collinear points?

d. What are the names of four coplanar points?

ANSWER a. line ℓ and $\overleftrightarrow{BA}$ **b.** plane *AEC*, plane *ADC* **c.** points *E*, *A*, and *D* **d.** points *C*, *E*, *A*, and *D*

2. a. What are the names of the segments in the figure below?

b. What are the names of the rays in the figure?

c. Which of the rays in part (b) are opposite rays?

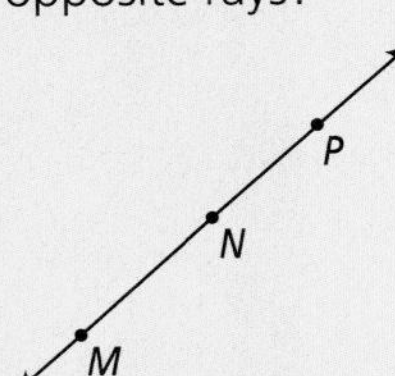

ANSWER a. $\overline{MN}$ or $\overline{NM}$, $\overline{NP}$ or $\overline{PN}$, $\overline{MP}$ or $\overline{PM}$ **b.** $\overrightarrow{MP}$, $\overrightarrow{NP}$, $\overrightarrow{MN}$, $\overrightarrow{PN}$, $\overrightarrow{NM}$, and $\overrightarrow{PM}$ **c.** $\overrightarrow{NP}$ and $\overrightarrow{NM}$

3. What is the intersection of plane *AEH* and plane *EGH*?

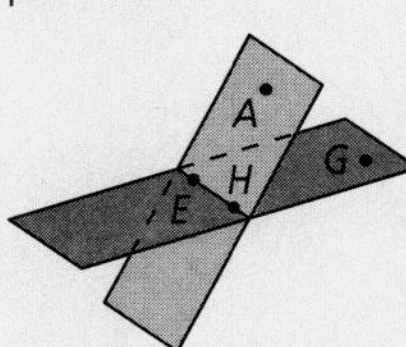

ANSWER line *EH*

4. Each surface of the box represents part of a plane.

a. Which plane contains points *J*, *M*, and *L*?

b. Which plane contains points *L*, *P*, and *Q*?

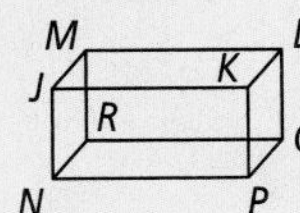

ANSWER a. plane *JML* on the top of the figure **b.** plane *LPQ* on the right of the figure

Take Note

ERROR PREVENTION

Some students may contend that two planes can intersect in a single point if one plane is arranged such that it touches a "corner" of the other plane. Remind students that the boundaries drawn for a plane are arbitrary and that planes extend infinitely in all directions.

Problem 3

Q What is another name for plane *ADC*? plane *BFG*? **[plane *ABC*; plane *BCG*]**

Q Why is $\overline{BC}$ not a correct way to represent the intersection of the two planes? **[Since the two planes extend without end, the intersection of the planes also extends without end.]**

Q Is it possible for a third plane to intersect in $\overleftrightarrow{BC}$? Explain. **[Yes, a plane defined by the points *E*, *B*, and *C* would also intersect in $\overleftrightarrow{BC}$.]**

Got It?

TACTILE LEARNERS

Q What are two planes that do not share any points in common? **[Answers may vary. Sample: plane *ADC* and plane *EHG*]**

There is a similar postulate about the intersection of planes.

Postulate 1-3

If two distinct planes intersect, then they intersect in exactly one line.

Plane *RST* and plane *WST* intersect in $\overleftrightarrow{ST}$.

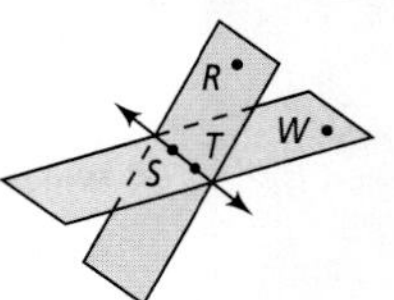

When you know two points that two planes have in common, Postulates 1-1 and 1-3 tell you that the line through those points is the intersection of the planes.

Problem 3 Finding the Intersection of Two Planes

Each surface of the box at the right represents part of a plane. What is the intersection of plane *ADC* and plane *BFG*?

Know
Plane *ADC* and plane *BFG*

Need
The intersection of the two planes

Plan
Find the points that the planes have in common.

Think
Is the intersection a segment?
No. The intersection of the sides of the box is a segment, but planes continue without end. The intersection is a line.

Focus on plane *ADC* and plane *BFG* to see where they intersect.

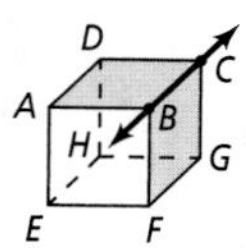

You can see that both planes contain point *B* and point *C*.

The planes intersect in $\overleftrightarrow{BC}$.

Got It? **3. a.** What are the names of two planes that intersect in $\overleftrightarrow{BF}$?

b. Reasoning Why do you only need to find two common points to name the intersection of two distinct planes?

When you name a plane from a figure like the box in Problem 3, list the corner points in consecutive order. For example, plane *ADCB* and plane *ABCD* are also names for the plane on the top of the box. Plane *ACBD* is not.

Photographers use three-legged tripods to make sure that a camera is steady. The feet of the tripod all touch the floor at the same time. You can think of the feet as points and the floor as a plane. As long as the feet do not all lie in one line, they will lie in exactly one plane.

This illustrates Postulate 1-4.

take note **Postulate 1-4**

Through any three noncollinear points there is exactly one plane.

Points *Q*, *R*, and *S* are noncollinear. Plane *P* is the only plane that contains them.

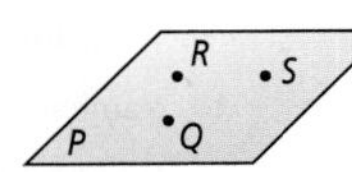

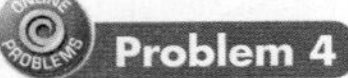

Problem 4 Using Postulate 1-4

Use the figure at the right.

Plan

How can you find the plane?
Try to draw all the lines that contain two of the three given points. You will begin to see a plane form.

A What plane contains points *N*, *P*, and *Q*? Shade the plane.

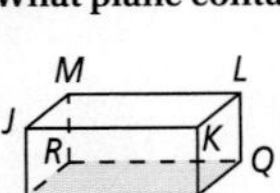

The plane on the bottom of the figure contains points *N*, *P*, and *Q*.

B What plane contains points *J*, *M*, and *Q*? Shade the plane.

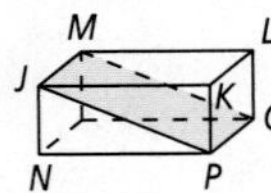

The plane that passes at a slant through the figure contains points *J*, *M*, and *Q*.

Got It? 4. a. What plane contains points *L*, *M*, and *N*? Copy the figure in Problem 4 and shade the plane.

b. Reasoning What is the name of a line that is coplanar with $\overleftrightarrow{JK}$ and $\overleftrightarrow{KL}$?

Take Note

Although students can readily see that three noncollinear points drawn on a two-dimensional surface are contained in exactly one plane, students may struggle to visualize that three noncollinear points in space are also contained in exactly one plane.

Problem 4

Q What other point is in the same plane as points *N*, *P*, and *Q*? **[R]**

Q What other point is in the same plane as points *J*, *M*, and *Q*? **[P]**

Q What lines contain two of the four points: *J*, *K*, *L*, and *M*? **[$\overleftrightarrow{JM}$, $\overleftrightarrow{JK}$, $\overleftrightarrow{ML}$, $\overleftrightarrow{LK}$, $\overleftrightarrow{MK}$, $\overleftrightarrow{JL}$]**

Q What is the intersection of plane *JMQP* and plane *JKLM*? **[$\overleftrightarrow{JM}$]**

Got It? TACTILE LEARNERS

Provide students with a clear rectangular prism model. Students can use a sheet of paper to model a plane.

Answers

Got It? (continued)

3a. Answers may vary. Sample: plane *BFE*, plane *BFG*

b. Postulate 1-3 says that two distinct planes intersect in exactly one line, so you only need two points to name the line of intersection, by Postulate 1-1.

4a.

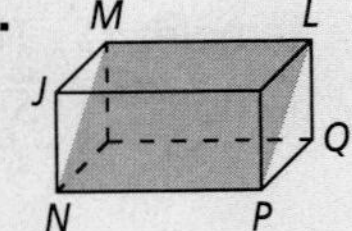

b. Answers may vary. Sample: $\overleftrightarrow{JM}$

3 Lesson Check

Do you know HOW?

- If students have difficulty with Exercise 3, then remind students that planes continue without end, and the boundaries for a plane shown in a diagram are artificial boundaries.

Do you UNDERSTAND?

- If students have difficulty with Exercise 5, then have them make a sketch of both rays and direct them to the Key Concept Box on the bottom of page 12 for clarification on the naming convention for rays.

Close

Q Is the following statement true? "Through any line and noncollinear point, there is exactly one plane." Explain. **[Yes, since any two points on the line and the third point would provide the three noncollinear points necessary for Postulate 1-4.]**

Lesson Check

Do you know HOW?

Use the figure at the right.

1. What are two other names for $\overleftrightarrow{XY}$?

2. What are the opposite rays?

3. What is the intersection of the two planes?

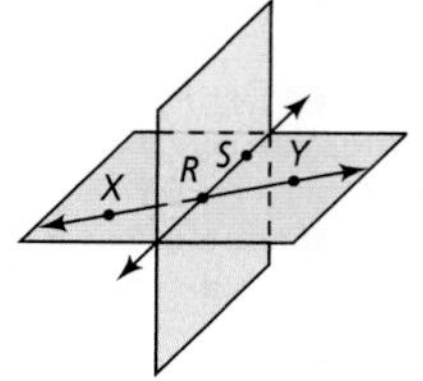

X
R
S
Y

Do you UNDERSTAND?

4. Vocabulary A segment has endpoints R and S. What are two names for the segment?

5. Are $\overrightarrow{AB}$ and $\overrightarrow{BA}$ the same ray? Explain.

6. Reasoning Why do you use two arrowheads when drawing or naming a line such as $\overleftrightarrow{EF}$?

7. Compare and Contrast How is naming a ray similar to naming a line? How is it different?

Practice and Problem-Solving Exercises

A Practice

Use the figure at the right for Exercises 8–11.

See Problem 1.

8. What are two other ways to name $\overleftrightarrow{EF}$?

9. What are two other ways to name plane C?

10. Name three collinear points.

11. Name four coplanar points.

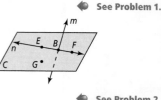

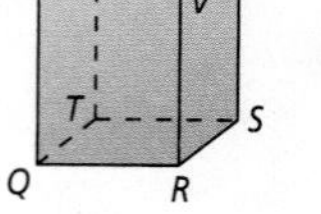

m
E
B
F
n
C
G

Use the figure at the right for Exercises 12–14.

See Problem 2.

12. Name the segments in the figure.

13. Name the rays in the figure.

14. a. Name the pair of opposite rays with endpoint T.
b. Name another pair of opposite rays.

Use the figure at the right for Exercises 15–26.

Name the intersection of each pair of planes.

See Problem 3.

15. planes QRS and RSW **16.** planes UXV and WVS

17. planes XWV and UVR **18.** planes TXW and TQU

Name two planes that intersect in the given line.

19. $\overleftrightarrow{QU}$ **20.** $\overleftrightarrow{TS}$ **21.** $\overleftrightarrow{XT}$ **22.** $\overleftrightarrow{VW}$

Copy the figure. Shade the plane that contains the given points.

See Problem 4.

23. R, V, W **24.** U, V, W **25.** U, X, S **26.** T, U, V

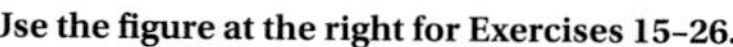

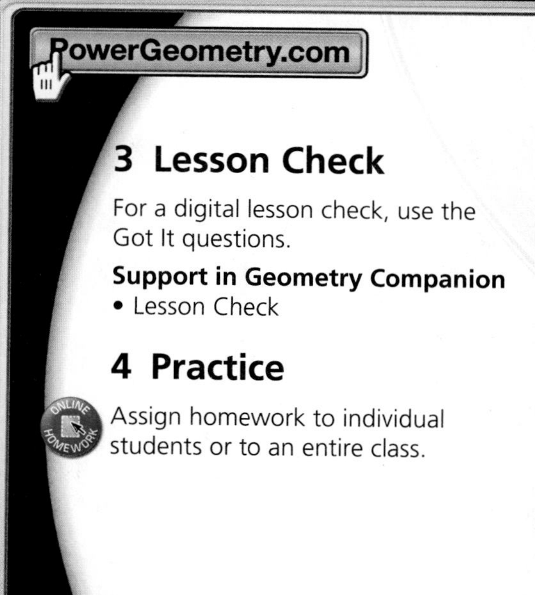

PowerGeometry.com
3 Lesson Check
For a digital lesson check, use the Got It questions.
Support in Geometry Companion
• Lesson Check
4 Practice
Assign homework to individual students or to an entire class.

Answers

Lesson Check

1. Answers may vary. Sample: $\overleftrightarrow{XR}$, $\overleftrightarrow{RY}$

2. $\overrightarrow{RX}$, $\overrightarrow{RY}$

3. $\overleftrightarrow{RS}$

4. $\overline{RS}$, $\overline{SR}$

5. No; they have different endpoints and extend in opposite directions.

6. to show that the line extends in both directions

7. To name both, you need to identify two points on the ray or line. For a ray, you use a single-sided arrow that must point away from the endpoint. For a line, the two letters can be written in either order, and a double-sided arrow appears above the letters. A line can also be named with a single lowercase letter, but a ray cannot.

Practice and Problem-Solving Exercises

8. Answers may vary. Sample: $\overleftrightarrow{EB}$, $\overleftrightarrow{FB}$

9. Answers may vary. Sample: plane EBG, plane BFG

10. E, B, F

11. E, B, F, G

12. $\overline{RS}$ or $\overline{SR}$, $\overline{ST}$ or $\overline{TS}$, $\overline{TW}$ or $\overline{WT}$, $\overline{RT}$ or $\overline{TR}$, $\overline{SW}$ or $\overline{WS}$, $\overline{RW}$ or $\overline{WR}$

13. $\overrightarrow{RS}$, $\overrightarrow{SR}$, $\overrightarrow{ST}$, $\overrightarrow{TS}$, $\overrightarrow{TW}$, $\overrightarrow{WT}$, $\overrightarrow{TR}$, $\overrightarrow{RT}$, $\overrightarrow{WR}$, $\overrightarrow{RW}$, $\overrightarrow{WS}$, $\overrightarrow{SW}$

14a. Answers may vary. Sample: $\overrightarrow{TS}$, $\overrightarrow{TW}$

b. Answers may vary. Sample: $\overrightarrow{ST}$, $\overrightarrow{SR}$

15. $\overleftrightarrow{RS}$

16. $\overleftrightarrow{VW}$

17. $\overleftrightarrow{UV}$

18. $\overleftrightarrow{XT}$

19. plane QUX, plane QUV

20. plane TSR, plane TSW

21. plane XTQ, plane XTS

22. plane VWX, plane VWS

23–26. See next page.

 Apply

Postulate 1-4 states that any three noncollinear points lie in exactly one plane. Find the plane that contains the first three points listed. Then determine whether the fourth point is in that plane. Write *coplanar* or *noncoplanar* to describe the points.

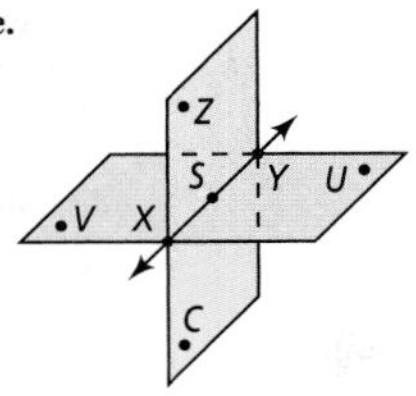

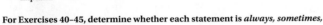

27. Z, S, Y, C
28. S, U, V, Y
29. X, Y, Z, U
30. X, S, V, U
31. X, Z, S, V
32. S, V, C, Y

If possible, draw a figure to fit each description. Otherwise, write *not possible*.

33. four points that are collinear
34. two points that are noncollinear
35. three points that are noncollinear
36. three points that are noncoplanar

37. Open-Ended Draw a figure with points B, C, D, E, F, and G that shows $\overleftrightarrow{CD}$, $\overleftrightarrow{BG}$, and $\overleftrightarrow{EF}$, with one of the points on all three lines.

38. Think About a Plan Your friend drew the diagram at the right to prove to you that two planes can intersect in exactly one point. Describe your friend's error.
- How do you describe a plane?
- What does it mean for two planes to intersect each other?
- Can you define an endpoint of a plane?

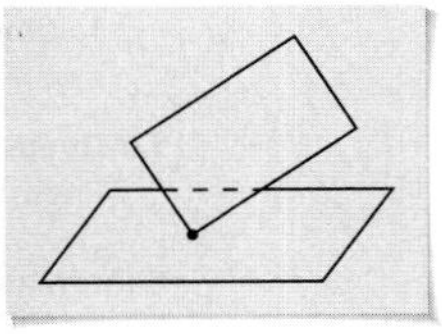

39. Reasoning If one ray contains another ray, are they the same ray? Explain.

For Exercises 40–45, determine whether each statement is *always, sometimes,* or *never* true.

40. $\overleftrightarrow{TQ}$ and $\overleftrightarrow{QT}$ are the same line.
41. $\overrightarrow{JK}$ and $\overrightarrow{JL}$ are the same ray.
42. Intersecting lines are coplanar.
43. Four points are coplanar.
44. A plane containing two points of a line contains the entire line.
45. Two distinct lines intersect in more than one point.

46. Use the diagram at the right. How many planes contain each line and point?
a. $\overleftrightarrow{EF}$ and point G
b. $\overleftrightarrow{PH}$ and point E
c. $\overleftrightarrow{FG}$ and point P
d. $\overleftrightarrow{EP}$ and point G
e. Reasoning What do you think is true of a line and a point not on the line? Explain. (*Hint*: Use two of the postulates you learned in this lesson.)

4 Practice

ASSIGNMENT GUIDE
Basic: 8–26 all, 28–46 even, 51, 54–58 even
Average: 9–25 odd, 27–58
Advanced: 9–25 odd, 27–64
Standardized Test Prep: 65–68
Mixed Review: 69–80
Reasoning exercises have blue headings.
Applications exercises have red headings.
EXERCISE 51: Use the Think About a Plan worksheet in the **Practice and Problem Solving Workbook** (also available in the Teaching Resources in print and online) to further support students' development in becoming independent learners.

HOMEWORK QUICK CHECK
To check students' understanding of key skills and concepts, go over Exercises 11, 19, 38, 46, and 51.

23. 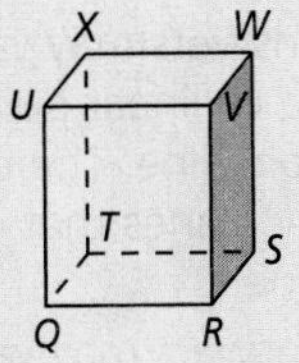
24. 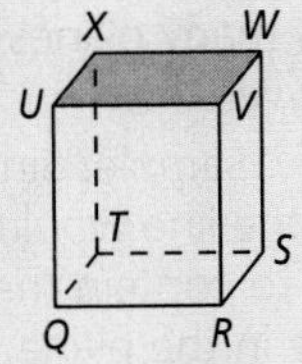
25. 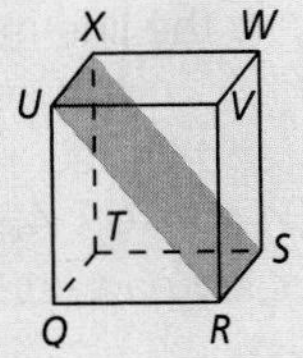
26.

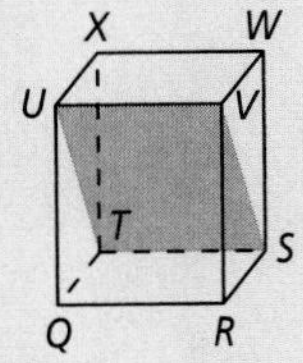

27. coplanar **28.** coplanar
29. noncoplanar **30.** coplanar
31. noncoplanar **32.** noncoplanar
33.

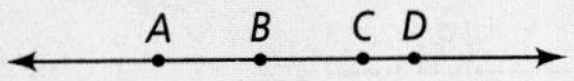

34. not possible
35.

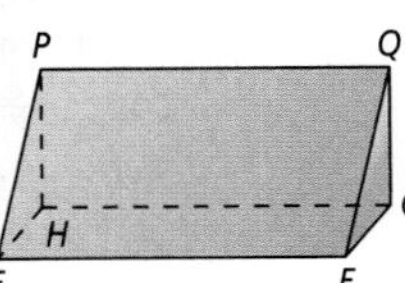

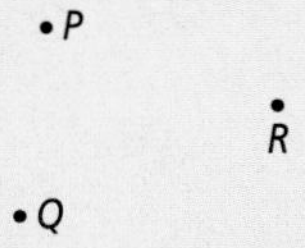

36. not possible
37.

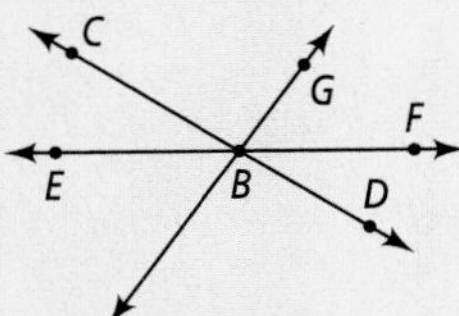

38. Answers may vary. Sample: You can represent a plane by drawing a four-sided shape. However, planes do not have boundaries, so they extend past the drawn edges without end. Since a plane does not have an endpoint, the intersection of the two planes your friend drew cannot be a point.
39. Not always; $\overrightarrow{AC}$ contains $\overrightarrow{BC}$, but they are not the same ray.

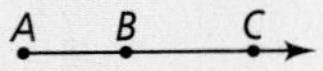

40. always
41. sometimes
42. always
43. sometimes
44. always
45. never
46a. one **b.** one
c. one **d.** one
e. A line and a point not on that line are always coplanar; Postulate 1-4 says that through any three noncollinear points there is exactly one plane. Postulate 1-1 says that there is exactly one line that contains two of those three coplanar points. So, through any line and a point not on that line, there is exactly one plane, so they are coplanar.

Answers

Practice and Problem-Solving Exercises (continued)

47.

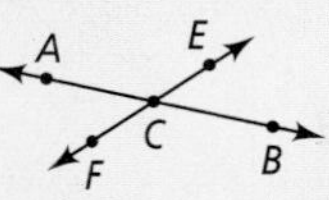

Postulate 1-2

48.

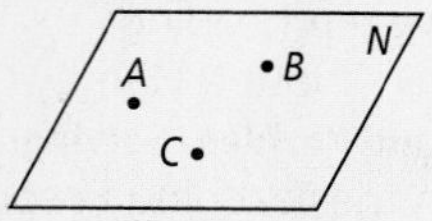

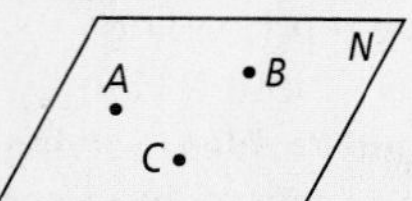

Postulate 1-4

49.

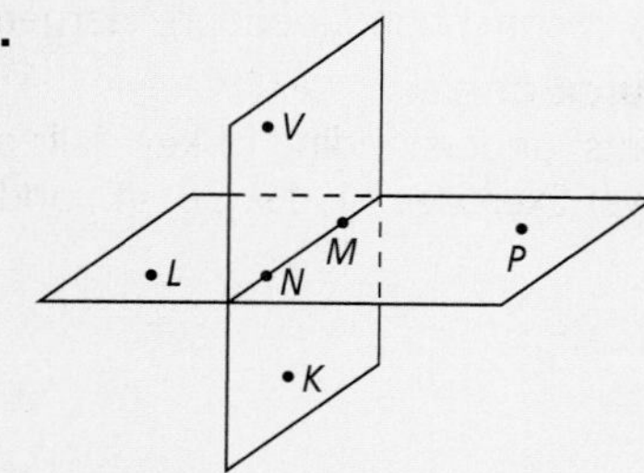

Postulate 1-3

50.

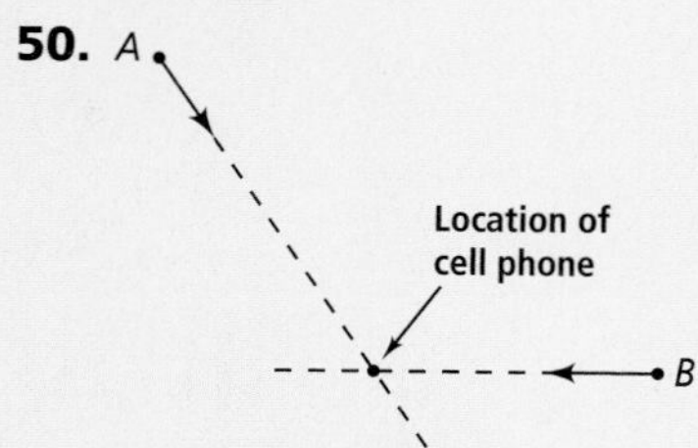

By Postulate 1-1, the location of the cell phone and point *A* determine a line, and the location of the cell phone and point *B* determine a line. By Postulate 1-2, the two lines intersect at, or share, only one point. Since the cell phone signal is on both lines, its location must be at the intersection of the lines.

51. Answers may vary. Sample: 6:00 is the only "exact" time. Other times are about 1:38, 2:43, 3:49, 4:54, 5:59, 7:05, 8:11, 9:16, 10:22, 11:27, and 12:33.

52. Answers may vary. Sample: now, think, exist

53.

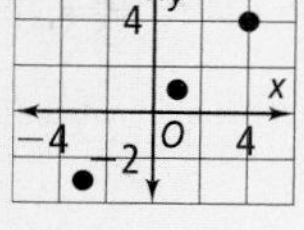

yes

54.

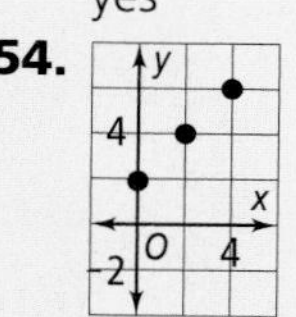

yes

55.

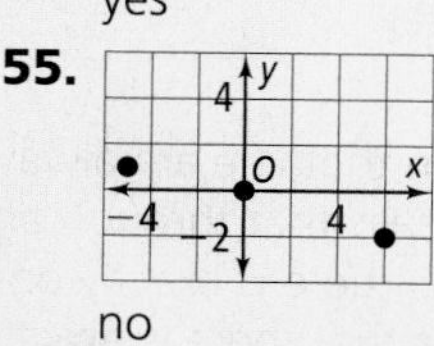

no

In Exercises 47–49, sketch a figure for the given information. Then state the postulate that your figure illustrates.

47. $\overleftrightarrow{AB}$ and $\overleftrightarrow{EF}$ intersect in point *C*.

48. The noncollinear points *A*, *B*, and *C* are all contained in plane *N*.

49. Planes *LNP* and *MVK* intersect in $\overleftrightarrow{NM}$.

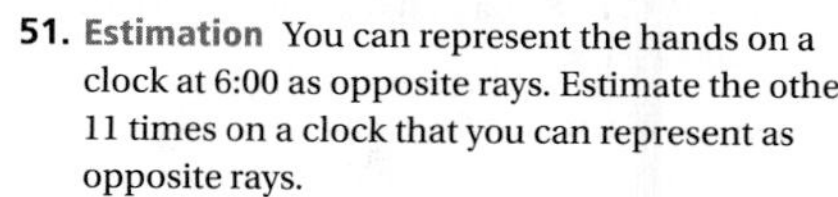

50. Telecommunications A cell phone tower at point *A* receives a cell phone signal from the southeast. A cell phone tower at point *B* receives a signal from the same cell phone from due west. Trace the diagram at the right and find the location of the cell phone. Describe how Postulates 1-1 and 1-2 help you locate the phone.

51. Estimation You can represent the hands on a clock at 6:00 as opposite rays. Estimate the other 11 times on a clock that you can represent as opposite rays.

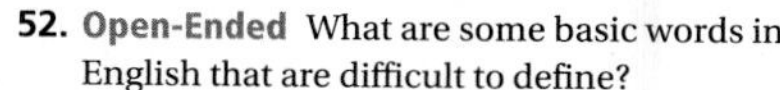

52. Open-Ended What are some basic words in English that are difficult to define?

Coordinate Geometry Graph the points and state whether they are collinear.

53. (1, 1), (4, 4), (−3, −3)
54. (2, 4), (4, 6), (0, 2)
55. (0, 0), (−5, 1), (6, −2)
56. (0, 0), (8, 10), (4, 6)
57. (0, 0), (0, 3), (0, −10)
58. (−2, −6), (1, −2), (4, 1)

59. How many planes contain the same three collinear points? Explain.

60. How many planes contain a given line? Explain.

61. a. Writing Suppose two points are in plane *P*. Explain why the line containing the points is also in plane *P*.

b. Reasoning Suppose two lines intersect. How many planes do you think contain both lines? Use the diagram at the right and your answer to part (a) to explain your answer.

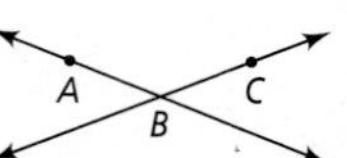

Probability Suppose you pick points at random from *A*, *B*, *C*, and *D* shown below. Find the probability that the number of points given meets the condition stated.

62. 2 points, collinear
63. 3 points, collinear
64. 3 points, coplanar

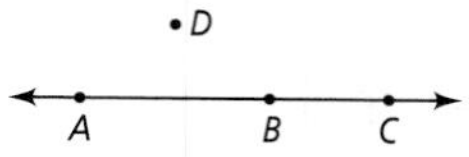

D
A B C

56. 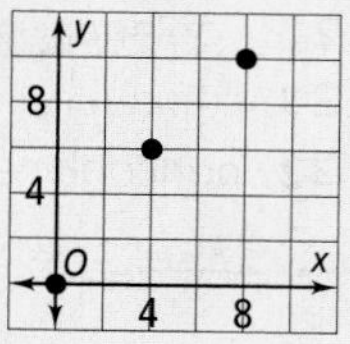 no

57. yes

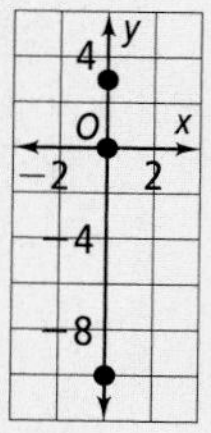

58. no

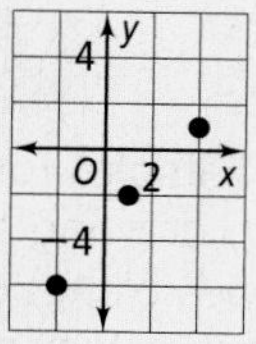

59. Infinitely many; answers may vary. Sample: The three collinear points are contained in one line. There are infinitely many planes that can intersect in that line.

60. Infinitely many; answers may vary. Sample: Infinitely many planes can intersect at the given line.

61a. Answers may vary. Sample: Since the plane is flat, the line would have to curve in order to contain the two points and not lie in the plane, but lines are straight, so the line must also be in plane *P*.

b. One; points *A*, *B*, and *C* are noncollinear. By Postulate 1-4, they are coplanar. Thus, by part (a), $\overleftrightarrow{AB}$ and $\overleftrightarrow{BC}$ are coplanar.

62. 1

63. $\frac{1}{4}$

64. 1

Standardized Test Prep

SAT/ACT

65. Which geometric term is undefined?

Ⓐ segment
Ⓑ collinear
Ⓒ ray
Ⓓ plane

66. Which diagram is a net of the figure shown at the right?

Ⓕ 

Ⓗ

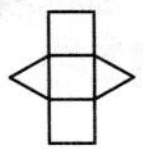

Ⓖ

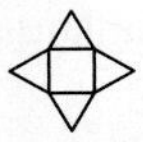

Ⓘ

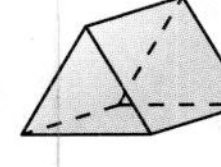

67. You want to cut a block of cheese into four pieces. What is the least number of cuts you need to make?

Ⓐ 2
Ⓑ 3
Ⓒ 4
Ⓓ 5

Short Response

68. The figure at the right is called a tetrahedron.
a. Name all the planes that form the surfaces of the tetrahedron.
b. Name all the lines that intersect at D.

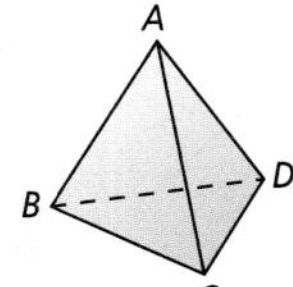

Mixed Review

Make an orthographic drawing for each figure. Assume there are no hidden cubes.

See Lesson 1-1.

69. 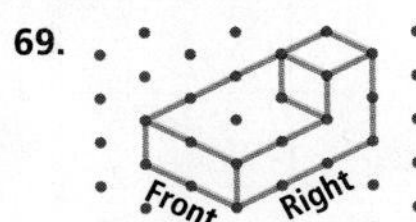

70. 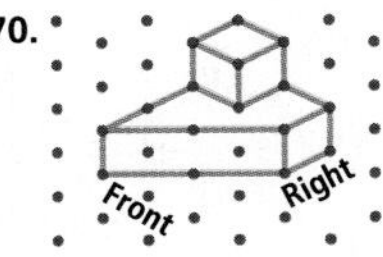

71. 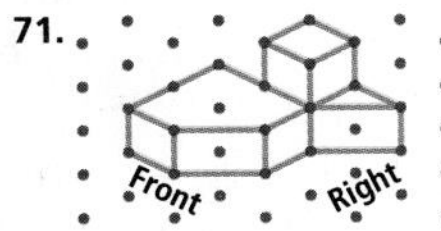

Simplify each ratio. See p. 831.

72. 30 to 12

73. $\frac{15x}{35x}$

74. $\frac{n^2 + n}{4n}$

Get Ready! To prepare for Lesson 1-3, do Exercises 75–80.

Simplify each absolute value expression. See p. 832.

75. $|-6|$

76. $|3.5|$

77. $|7 - 10|$

Algebra **Solve each equation.** See p. 834.

78. $x + 2x - 6 = 6$

79. $3x + 9 + 5x = 81$

80. $w - 2 = -4 + 7w$

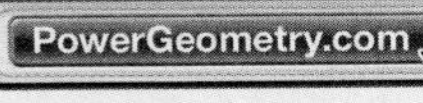

65. D
66. H
67. A19
68. [2] **a.** planes ABC, ACD, ABD, BCD
b. $\overleftrightarrow{BD}$, $\overleftrightarrow{CD}$, $\overleftrightarrow{AD}$
[1] incomplete list for part (a) or part (b)

69.

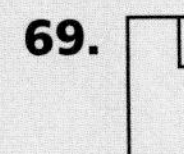

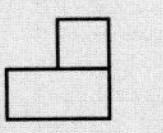
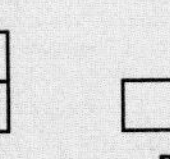

70.

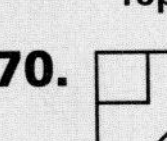
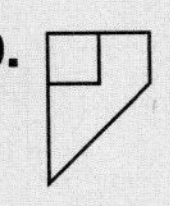
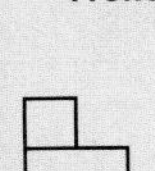
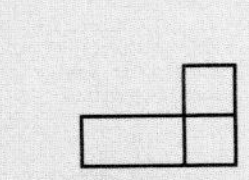

71.

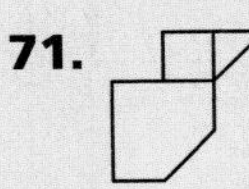

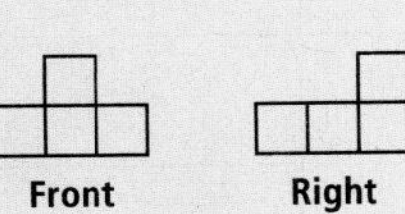

72. 5 to 2
73. $\frac{3}{7}$
74. $\frac{n + 1}{4}$
75. 6
76. 3.5
77. 3
78. 4
79. 9
80. $\frac{1}{3}$

1-2 Lesson Resources

Differentiated Remediation

Instructional Support

Geometry Companion

Students can use the **Geometry Companion** worktext (4 pages) . . .

- New Vocabulary
- Key Concepts
- Got It for each Problem
- Lesson Check

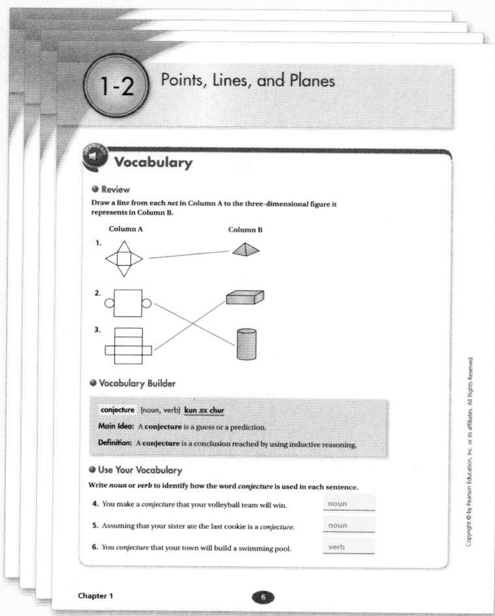

1-2 Points, Lines, and Planes

Vocabulary

Review

Draw a line from each *net* in Column A to the three-dimensional figure it represents in Column B.

Column A | Column B

1.

2.

3.

Vocabulary Builder

conjecture (noun, verb) **kun JEK chur**

Main Idea: A **conjecture** is a guess or a prediction.

Definition: A **conjecture** is a conclusion reached by using inductive reasoning.

Use Your Vocabulary

Write *noun* or *verb* to identify how the word *conjecture* is used in each sentence.

4. You make a *conjecture* that your volleyball team will win. noun
5. Assuming that your sister ate the last cookie is a *conjecture*. noun
6. You *conjecture* that your town will build a swimming pool. verb

Chapter 1 6

ELL Support

Assess Understanding Divide students into small groups of mixed abilities. Discuss the meanings of each of the vocabulary terms. Then have students find objects in the classroom that represent each word (except postulate and axiom). Groups can present their findings and explain how their objects represent the term. Include a discussion on the shortcomings of their objects and why they do not represent the term accurately.

Assess Understanding Have students work in pairs. Tell them to write the vocabulary word on one side of an index card and the meaning on the other. Tell them to include a sketch if possible. Students can use the flashcards to quiz each other and also for later review.

5 Assess & Remediate

Lesson Quiz

Use the figure below to answer Questions 1–3.

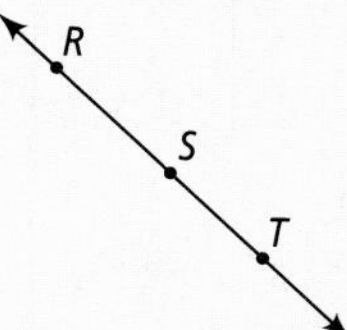

1. What are the names of the segments in the figure?
2. What are the names of the rays in the figure?
3. Which ray is opposite $\overrightarrow{ST}$?
4. **Do you UNDERSTAND?** What is the intersection of planes *ABG* and *BCD* in the figure below?

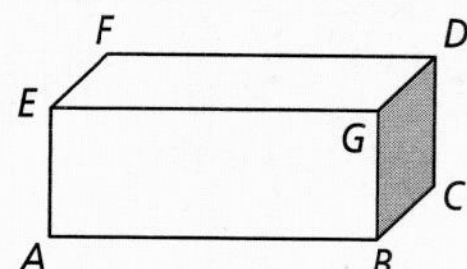

ANSWERS TO LESSON QUIZ

1. segments $\overline{RS}$ or $\overline{SR}$, $\overline{ST}$ or $\overline{TS}$, $\overline{RT}$ or $\overline{TR}$
2. rays $\overrightarrow{RS}$, $\overrightarrow{ST}$, $\overrightarrow{RT}$, $\overrightarrow{TS}$, $\overrightarrow{SR}$, $\overrightarrow{TR}$
3. ray $\overrightarrow{SR}$
4. line $\overleftrightarrow{BG}$ or $\overleftrightarrow{GB}$

PRESCRIPTION FOR REMEDIATION

Use the student work on the Lesson Quiz to prescribe a differentiated review assignment.

Points	Differentiated Remediation
0–2	Intervention
3	On-level
4	Extension

PowerGeometry.com

5 Assess & Remediate

Assign the Lesson Quiz. Appropriate intervention, practice, or enrichment is automatically generated based on student performance.

Intervention

- **Reteaching** (2 pages) Provides reteaching and practice exercises for the key lesson concepts. Use with struggling students or absent students.
- **English Language Learner Support** Helps students develop and reinforce mathematical vocabulary and key concepts.

All-in-One Resources/Online

Reteaching

1-2 **Reteaching**

Points, Lines, and Planes

Review these important geometric terms.

Term	Examples of Labels	Diagram
Point	Italicized capital letter: *D*	*D*
Line	Two capital letters with a line drawn over them: $\overleftrightarrow{AB}$ or $\overleftrightarrow{BA}$ One italicized lowercase letter: *m*	*A* *B* *m*
Line Segment	Two capital letters (called endpoints) with a segment drawn over them: $\overline{AB}$ or $\overline{BA}$	*A* *B*
Ray	Two capital letters with a ray symbol drawn over them: $\overrightarrow{AB}$	*B* *A*
Plane	Three capital letters: *ABF, AFB, BAF, BFA, FAB,* or *FBA* One italicized capital letter: *W*	*A* *B* *F* *W*

Remember:

1. When you name a ray, an arrowhead is not drawn over the beginning point.
2. When you name a plane with three points, choose no more than two collinear points.
3. An arrow indicates the direction of a path that extends without end.
4. A plane is represented by a parallelogram. However, the plane actually has no edges. It is flat and extends forever in all directions.

Exercises

Identify each figure as a *point, segment, ray, line,* or *plane,* and name each.

1. *L* point; point *L*
2. *L* *N* *M* plane; Answers may vary. Sample: plane *LMN*
3. *C* *D* line; $\overleftrightarrow{CD}$
4. *P* *O* segment; $\overline{PO}$
5. *E* *F* *G* line; answers may vary. Sample: $\overleftrightarrow{EG}$
6. *T* *S* ray; $\overrightarrow{ST}$

All-in-One Resources/Online

English Language Learner Support

1-2 **ELL Support**

Points, Lines, and Planes

Complete the vocabulary chart by filling in the missing information.

Word or Word Phrase	Definition	Picture or Example
intersection	An *intersection* is the set of points two or more figures have in common.	Point *E* is the intersection of the lines.
ray	A *ray* is part of a line that consists of one endpoint and all the points of the line on one side of the endpoint.	1.
opposite rays	2. *Opposite rays* are two rays that share the same endpoint and form a line.	Point *Q* is the endpoint shared by these two rays.
segment	A *segment* is part of a line that consists of two endpoints and all points between them.	3. *A* *B*
collinear	Points that lie on the same line are *collinear.*	4. *X* *Y*
postulate	5. A *postulate* is an accepted statement of fact.	Example: Through any two points there is exactly one line.
coplanar	6. Points that lie on the same plane are *coplanar.*	Points *G, H,* and *Z* are coplanar.

Differentiated Remediation *continued*

On-Level

- **Practice** (2 pages) Provides extra practice for each lesson. For simpler practice exercises, use the Form K Practice pages found in the All-in-One Teaching Resources and online.
- **Think About a Plan** Helps students develop specific problem-solving skills and strategies by providing scaffolded guiding questions.
- **Standardized Test Prep** Focuses on all major exercises, all major question types, and helps students prepare for the high-stakes assessments.

Practice and Problem Solving Wkbk/ All-in-One Resources/Online

Practice page 1

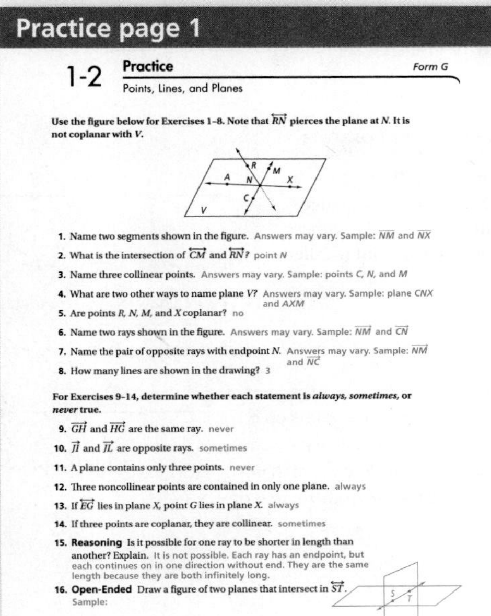

1-2 **Practice** — Points, Lines, and Planes — *Form G*

Use the figure below for Exercises 1–8. Note that $\overleftrightarrow{RN}$ pierces the plane at N. It is not coplanar with V.

1. Name two segments shown in the figure. Answers may vary. Sample: $\overline{NM}$ and $\overline{NX}$
2. What is the intersection of $\overleftrightarrow{CM}$ and $\overleftrightarrow{RN}$? point N
3. Name three collinear points. Answers may vary. Sample: points C, N, and M
4. What are two other ways to name plane V? Answers may vary. Sample: plane CNX and AXM
5. Are points R, N, M, and X coplanar? no
6. Name two rays shown in the figure. Answers may vary. Sample: $\overrightarrow{NM}$ and $\overrightarrow{CN}$
7. Name the pair of opposite rays with endpoint N. Answers may vary. Sample: $\overrightarrow{NM}$ and $\overrightarrow{NC}$
8. How many lines are shown in the drawing? 3

For Exercises 9–14, determine whether each statement is *always, sometimes*, or *never* true.

9. $\overrightarrow{GH}$ and $\overrightarrow{HG}$ are the same ray. never
10. $\overrightarrow{JI}$ and $\overrightarrow{JL}$ are opposite rays. sometimes
11. A plane contains only three points. never
12. Three noncollinear points are contained in only one plane. always
13. If $\overline{EG}$ lies in plane X, point G lies in plane X. always
14. If three points are coplanar, they are collinear. sometimes
15. **Reasoning** Is it possible for one ray to be shorter in length than another? Explain. It is not possible. Each ray has an endpoint, but each continues on in one direction without end. They are the same length because they are both infinitely long.
16. **Open-Ended** Draw a figure of two planes that intersect in $\overleftrightarrow{ST}$. Sample:

Practice and Problem Solving Wkbk/ All-in-One Resources/Online

Practice page 2

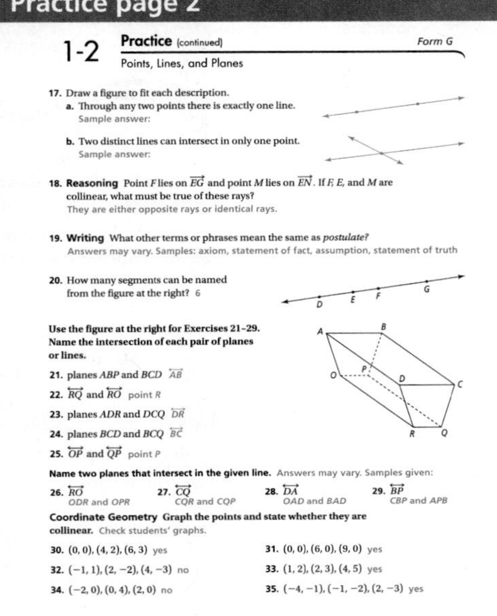

1-2 **Practice** (continued) — Points, Lines, and Planes — *Form G*

17. Draw a figure to fit each description.
    a. Through any two points there is exactly one line. Sample answer:
    b. Two distinct lines can intersect in only one point. Sample answer:
18. **Reasoning** Point F lies on $\overrightarrow{EG}$ and point M lies on $\overrightarrow{EN}$. If F, E, and M are collinear, what must be true of these rays? They are either opposite rays or identical rays.
19. **Writing** What other terms or phrases mean the same as *postulate*? Answers may vary. Samples: axiom, statement of fact, assumption, statement of truth
20. How many segments can be named from the figure at the right? 6

Use the figure at the right for Exercises 21–29. Name the intersection of each pair of planes or lines.

21. planes ABP and BCD $\overleftrightarrow{AB}$
22. $\overleftrightarrow{RQ}$ and $\overleftrightarrow{RO}$ point R
23. planes ADR and DCQ $\overleftrightarrow{DR}$
24. planes BCD and BCQ $\overleftrightarrow{BC}$
25. $\overleftrightarrow{OP}$ and $\overleftrightarrow{QP}$ point P

Name two planes that intersect in the given line. Answers may vary. Samples given:

26. $\overleftrightarrow{RO}$ ODR and OPR
27. $\overleftrightarrow{CQ}$ CQR and CQP
28. $\overleftrightarrow{DA}$ OAD and BAD
29. $\overleftrightarrow{BP}$ CBP and APB

Coordinate Geometry Graph the points and state whether they are collinear. Check students' graphs.

30. (0, 0), (4, 2), (6, 3) yes
31. (0, 0), (6, 0), (9, 0) yes
32. (−1, 1), (2, −2), (4, −3) no
33. (1, 2), (2, 3), (4, 5) yes
34. (−2, 0), (0, 4), (2, 0) no
35. (−4, −1), (−1, −2), (2, −3) yes

Practice and Problem Solving Wkbk/ All-in-One Resources/Online

Think About a Plan

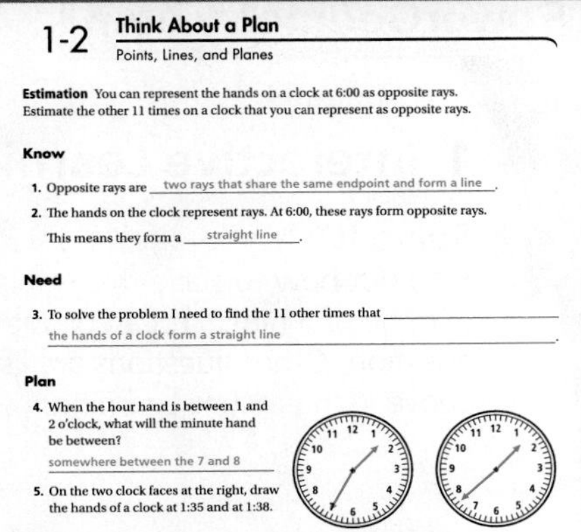

1-2 **Think About a Plan** — Points, Lines, and Planes

Estimation You can represent the hands on a clock at 6:00 as opposite rays. Estimate the other 11 times on a clock that you can represent as opposite rays.

Know

1. Opposite rays are two rays that share the same endpoint and form a line.
2. The hands on the clock represent rays. At 6:00, these rays form opposite rays. This means they form a straight line.

Need

3. To solve the problem I need to find the 11 other times that the hands of a clock form a straight line.

Plan

4. When the hour hand is between 1 and 2 o'clock, what will the minute hand be between? somewhere between the 7 and 8
5. On the two clock faces at the right, draw the hands of a clock at 1:35 and at 1:38.
6. At which time, 1:35 or 1:38, do you think opposite rays form? Explain. Answers may vary. Sample: Opposite rays form at 1:38. Even though 1 and 7 are opposite each other on the clock face, the minute hand is not at 7 when the hour hand is at 1, so the hands are not opposite rays at 1:35.
7. Complete the table to show all of the times when the hands on a clock represent opposite rays. Answers may vary. Note that 6:00 is the only "exact" time. Reasonable estimates might be within 2 min of these times.

Hour	6	7	8	9	10	11	12	1	2	3	4
Time when opposite rays form	6:00	7:05	8:11	9:16	10:22	11:27	12:33	1:38	2:43	3:49	4:54

Practice and Problem Solving Wkbk/ All-in-One Resources/Online

Standardized Test Prep

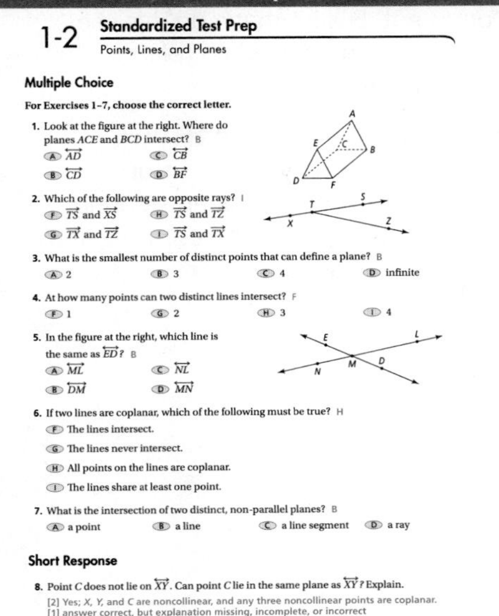

1-2 **Standardized Test Prep** — Points, Lines, and Planes

Multiple Choice

For Exercises 1–7, choose the correct letter.

1. Look at the figure at the right. Where do planes ACE and BCD intersect? B
   A. $\overleftrightarrow{AD}$ B. $\overleftrightarrow{CD}$ C. $\overleftrightarrow{CB}$ D. $\overleftrightarrow{BF}$
2. Which of the following are opposite rays? I
   F. $\overrightarrow{TS}$ and $\overrightarrow{XS}$ G. $\overrightarrow{TX}$ and $\overrightarrow{TZ}$ H. $\overrightarrow{TS}$ and $\overrightarrow{TZ}$ I. $\overrightarrow{TS}$ and $\overrightarrow{TX}$
3. What is the smallest number of distinct points that can define a plane? B
   A. 2 B. 3 C. 4 D. infinite
4. At how many points can two distinct lines intersect? F
   F. 1 G. 2 H. 3 I. 4
5. In the figure at the right, which line is the same as $\overleftrightarrow{ED}$? B
   A. $\overleftrightarrow{ML}$ B. $\overleftrightarrow{DM}$ C. $\overleftrightarrow{NL}$ D. $\overleftrightarrow{MN}$
6. If two lines are coplanar, which of the following must be true? H
   F. The lines intersect.
   G. The lines never intersect.
   H. All points on the lines are coplanar.
   I. The lines share at least one point.
7. What is the intersection of two distinct, non-parallel planes? B
   A. a point B. a line C. a line segment D. a ray

Short Response

8. Point C does not lie on $\overleftrightarrow{XY}$. Can point C lie in the same plane as $\overleftrightarrow{XY}$? Explain.
   [2] Yes; X, Y, and C are noncollinear, and any three noncollinear points are coplanar.
   [1] answer correct, but explanation missing, incomplete, or incorrect
   [0] no explanation given

Extension

- **Enrichment** Provides students with interesting problems and activities that extend the concepts of the lesson.
- **Activities, Games, and Puzzles** Worksheets that can be used for concepts development, enrichment, and for fun!

All-in-One Resources/Online

Enrichment

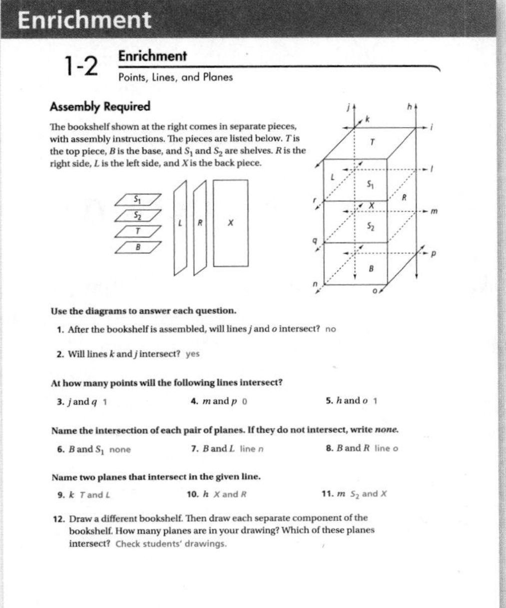

1-2 **Enrichment** — Points, Lines, and Planes

Assembly Required

The bookshelf shown at the right comes in separate pieces, with assembly instructions. The pieces are listed below. T is the top piece, B is the base, and S_1 and S_2 are shelves. R is the right side, L is the left side, and X is the back piece.

Use the diagrams to answer each question.

1. After the bookshelf is assembled, will lines j and o intersect? no
2. Will lines k and j intersect? yes

At how many points will the following lines intersect?

3. j and q 1
4. m and p 0
5. h and o 1

Name the intersection of each pair of planes. If they do not intersect, write *none*.

6. B and S_1 none
7. B and L line n
8. B and R line o

Name two planes that intersect in the given line.

9. k T and L
10. h X and R
11. m S_2 and X
12. Draw a different bookshelf. Then draw each separate component of the bookshelf. How many planes are in your drawing? Which of these planes intersect? Check students' drawings.

Online Teacher Resource Center

Activities, Games, and Puzzles

1-2 **Game: Points Around the Room** — Points, Lines, and Planes

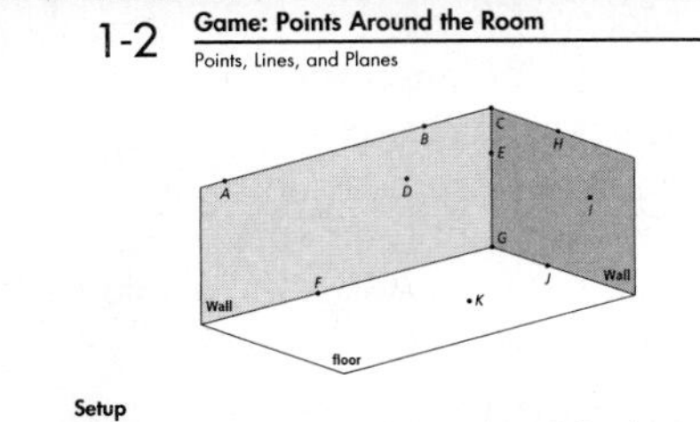

Setup

Your teacher will position points around the room, as shown in the figure above.

Game Play

Work in your team to answer the following questions about the points, lines, and planes your teacher has labeled. If there is more than one answer or more than one way to write the same answer, record each possibility.

1. What is another name for plane FGK? Samples: plane GJK, FJK, or FGJ or floor
2. What is the intersection of plane ABF and plane HIG? $\overleftrightarrow{CG}$, $\overleftrightarrow{GC}$, $\overleftrightarrow{CE}$, $\overleftrightarrow{EC}$, $\overleftrightarrow{EG}$, $\overleftrightarrow{GE}$
3. What point is collinear with points E and C? G
4. What point is coplanar with points H, E, and C? I, J, G
5. What is another way to name $\overrightarrow{GE}$? $\overrightarrow{GC}$
6. What two rays are opposite rays? $\overrightarrow{BA}$ and $\overrightarrow{BC}$, $\overrightarrow{EC}$ and $\overrightarrow{EG}$
7. What is the intersection of $\overleftrightarrow{GE}$ and $\overleftrightarrow{AB}$? C
8. What line is coplanar with $\overleftrightarrow{FG}$ and $\overleftrightarrow{GJ}$? Samples: $\overleftrightarrow{KG}$, $\overleftrightarrow{FK}$, $\overleftrightarrow{JK}$, or $\overleftrightarrow{FJ}$
9. What is the intersection of $\overleftrightarrow{GE}$ and $\overleftrightarrow{CE}$? $\overleftrightarrow{GC}$
10. What point is collinear with A? Any two points are collinear. B, C, D, E, F, G, H, I, J, or K.

Ending the Game

As a class, compile a list of correct answers on the board. For each correct answer, your team scores a point. This means many points may be possible for some questions. For each incorrect answer, deduct a point from your score. The team with the most points wins!

1 Interactive Learning

Solve It!

PURPOSE To measure the length of a line segment
PROCESS Students may physically count units or may use subtraction to determine the number of units on the ruler from the tip to the tail of the fish.

FACILITATE

Q How far above zero is the tip of the fish? the tail of the fish? **[4 inches; 16 inches]**

Q What are the possible measurements for fish that you can keep? **[less than 15 inches or greater than 19 inches]**

Q How can you determine the number of units on the ruler between the 4-inch mark and the 16-inch mark? **[Answers may vary. Sample: You can count them.]**

ANSWER See Solve It in Answers on next page.
CONNECT THE MATH In the Solve It students measure length in a real-world situation. In this lesson, students will determine the length of geometric objects.

2 Guided Instruction

Take Note

Make sure that students understand that every point can be paired with a real number and every real number can be paired with a point. Also, stress that the reason for numbering the points on a line is to measure lengths.

1-3 Measuring Segments

Objective To find and compare lengths of segments

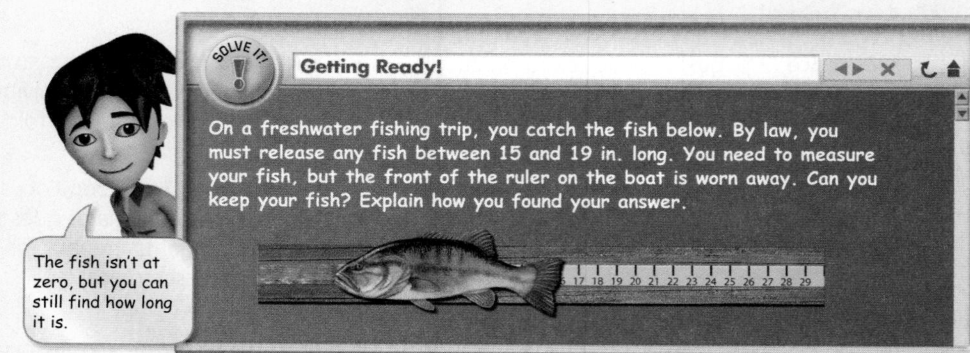

Solve It!
Getting Ready!
On a freshwater fishing trip, you catch the fish below. By law, you must release any fish between 15 and 19 in. long. You need to measure your fish, but the front of the ruler on the boat is worn away. Can you keep your fish? Explain how you found your answer.
17 18 19 20 21 22 23 24 25 26 27 28 29
The fish isn't at zero, but you can still find how long it is.

Lesson Vocabulary
- coordinate
- distance
- congruent segments
- midpoint
- segment bisector

In the Solve It, you measured the length of an object indirectly.

Essential Understanding You can use number operations to find and compare the lengths of segments.

Take note

Postulate 1-5 Ruler Postulate

Every point on a line can be paired with a real number. This makes a one-to-one correspondence between the points on the line and the real numbers. The real number that corresponds to a point is called the **coordinate** of the point.

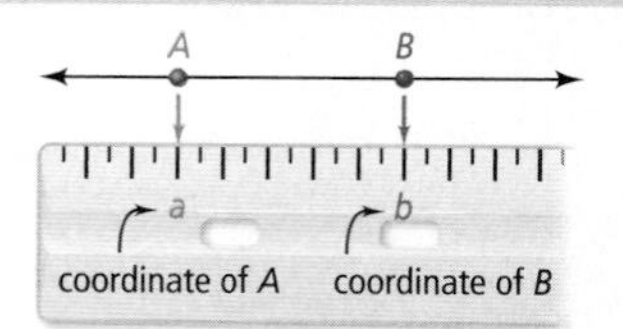

A
B
a
b
coordinate of A
coordinate of B

The Ruler Postulate allows you to measure lengths of segments using a given unit and to find distances between points on a number line. Consider $\overleftrightarrow{AB}$ at the right. The **distance** between points A and B is the absolute value of the difference of their coordinates, or $|a - b|$. This value is also AB, or the length of $\overline{AB}$.

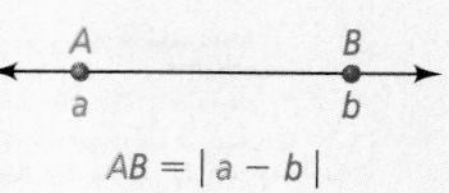

A
B
a
b
AB = |a − b|

1-3 Preparing to Teach

BIG ideas **Measurement**
Reasoning and Proof

UbD

ESSENTIAL UNDERSTANDINGS
- Number operations can be used to find and compare the lengths of segments.
- The Ruler and Segment Addition Postulates can be used in reasoning about lengths.

Math Background

The notion that there is a one-to-one correspondence between the points on the line and the real numbers was not formally stated as a postulate by Euclid. However, it is evident by his proofs that he implicitly incorporated this notion in his logical reasoning. The Ruler Postulate has been incorporated in modern geometry with the clear understanding that it is an assumption and cannot be proven.

This lesson provides an opportunity to discuss further the notion of congruence versus equality. Two segments that are equal in length are said to be congruent. Two segments cannot be equal and two lengths cannot be congruent. Ensure that students use proper terminology when referring to geometric figures.

Support Student Learning

Use the **Geometry Companion** to engage and support students during instructions. See Lesson Resources at the end of this lesson for details.

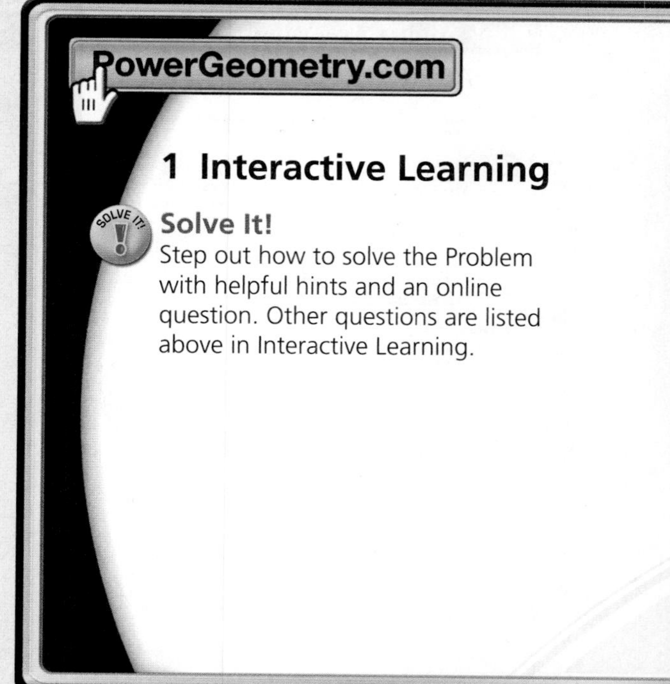

PowerGeometry.com
1 Interactive Learning
Solve It!
Step out how to solve the Problem with helpful hints and an online question. Other questions are listed above in Interactive Learning.

Problem 1 Measuring Segment Lengths

Think
What are you trying to find?
ST represents the length of $\overline{ST}$, so you are trying to find the distance between points *S* and *T*.

What is *ST*?

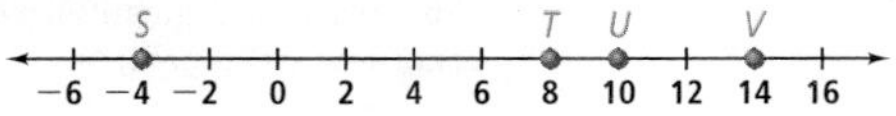

The coordinate of *S* is −4.
The coordinate of *T* is 8. — Ruler Postulate

$ST = |-4 - 8|$ Definition of distance

$= |-12|$ Subtract.

$= 12$ Find the absolute value.

Got It? 1. What are *UV* and *SV* on the number line above?

take note

Postulate 1-6 Segment Addition Postulate

If three points *A*, *B*, and *C* are collinear and *B* is between *A* and *C*, then $AB + BC = AC$.

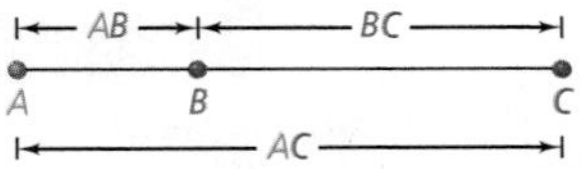

Problem 2 Using the Segment Addition Postulate

Algebra **If $EG = 59$, what are *EF* and *FG*?**

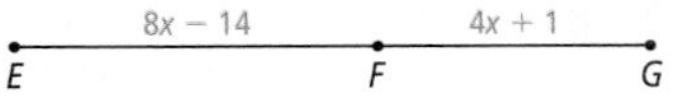

Know	Need	Plan
$EG = 59$ $EF = 8x - 14$ $FG = 4x + 1$	*EF* and *FG*	Use the Segment Addition Postulate to write an equation.

$EF + FG = EG$ Segment Addition Postulate

$(8x - 14) + (4x + 1) = 59$ Substitute.

$12x - 13 = 59$ Combine like terms.

$12x = 72$ Add 13 to each side.

$x = 6$ Divide each side by 12.

Use the value of *x* to find *EF* and *FG*.

$EF = 8x - 14 = 8(6) - 14 = 48 - 14 = 34$

$FG = 4x + 1 = 4(6) + 1 = 24 + 1 = 25$ — Substitute 6 for *x*.

Got It? 2. In the diagram, $JL = 120$. What are *JK* and *KL*?

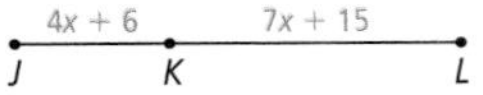

Problem 1

Q How could you use counting to find *ST*? **[There are 6 marked points from point *S* to point *T*, and the distance between each point is 2, so 6 · 2 = 12.]**

Q Would the answer change if you subtracted the coordinates in the reverse order? Explain. **[No, 8 − (−4) = 12, and the absolute value of 12 is 12.]**

Got It? ERROR PREVENTION

Q If a point *W* is added to the number line and *WV* equals *UV*, what coordinate should be labeled as point *W*? **[18]**

Take Note

Emphasize the important components of this postulate by showing counterexamples that demonstrate that segment addition does not apply to three noncollinear points, nor does it apply if *B* is not between *A* and *C* on a line.

Problem 2

Q What algebraic expression represents *EG*? **[12*x* − 13]**

Q What is the numeric value given for *EG*? **[59]**

Q How should you check to make sure that the segment lengths are correct? **[You should check that 34 + 25 = 59.]**

Got It? ERROR PREVENTION

If students give an answer of 9, remind them that the solution to the equation is not the same as the answer to the question.

2 Guided Instruction

Each Problem is worked out and supported online.

Problem 1
Measuring Segment Lengths

Alternative Problem 1
Measuring Segment Lengths
Animated

Problem 2
Using the Segment Addition Postulate
Animated

Problem 3
Comparing Segment Lengths
Animated

Problem 4
Using the Midpoint

Support in Geometry Companion

- Vocabulary
- Key Concepts
- Got It?

Answers

Solve It!

Yes; explanations may vary. Sample: You can measure the fish with a ruler and transfer the length to a different part of the ruler. The length of the fish can be found by counting the tick marks, or by subtracting the smaller mark from the larger mark. The length of the fish is 12 in., so you can keep the fish.

Got It?

1. $UV = 4$, $SV = 18$
2. $JK = 42$, $KL = 78$

Explain that when an overbar is shown with the name of a segment, then the congruence symbol must be used. When the overbar is not shown with the name of the segment, then the reference is to the length of the segment, and the equals symbol is used. In short, one segment is congruent to another segment, while the length of one segment is equal to the length of another segment.

Problem 3

Q How can you determine if two segments are congruent? **[You must compare segment lengths to determine congruence.]**

Q How do you find the length of a segment shown on a number line? **[Find the absolute value of the difference of the coordinates of the endpoints.]**

Got It? ERROR PREVENTION

Q Why is a statement such as: $AB \cong DE$ incorrect? **[AC and BD represent numeric values, so an equal sign should be used in place of the congruence symbol.]**

Students may be familiar with the term "dissect" from Biology class. To dissect means to cut in pieces. Students are also likely to know that the prefix "bi" means two. Students can use this knowledge to remember that bisect means to cut into two equal pieces.

When numerical expressions have the same value, you say that they are equal (=). Similarly, if two segments have the same length, then the segments are **congruent (≅) segments.**

This means that if $AB = CD$, then $\overline{AB} \cong \overline{CD}$. You can also say that if $\overline{AB} \cong \overline{CD}$, then $AB = CD$.

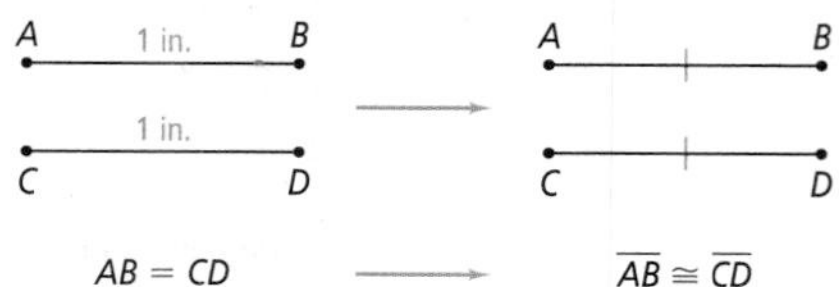

As illustrated above, you can mark segments alike to show that they are congruent. If there is more than one set of congruent segments, you can indicate each set with the same number of marks.

Plan

How do you know if segments are congruent?
Congruent segments have the same length. So find and compare the lengths of $\overline{AC}$ and $\overline{BD}$.

Problem 3 Comparing Segment Lengths

Are $\overline{AC}$ and $\overline{BD}$ congruent?

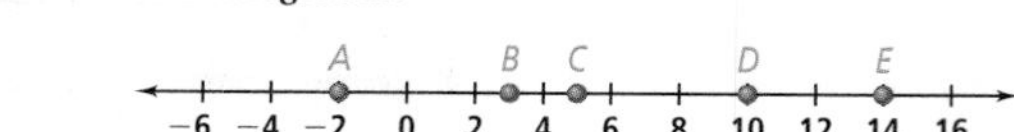

$AC = |-2 - 5| = |-7| = 7$

$BD = |3 - 10| = |-7| = 7$ Definition of distance

Yes. $AC = BD$, so $\overline{AC} \cong \overline{BD}$.

Got It? 3. a. Use the diagram above. Is $\overline{AB}$ congruent to $\overline{DE}$?

b. **Reasoning** To find AC in Problem 3, suppose you subtract −2 from 5. Do you get the same result? Why?

The **midpoint** of a segment is a point that divides the segment into two congruent segments. A point, line, ray, or other segment that intersects a segment at its midpoint is said to *bisect* the segment. That point, line, ray, or segment is called a **segment bisector.**

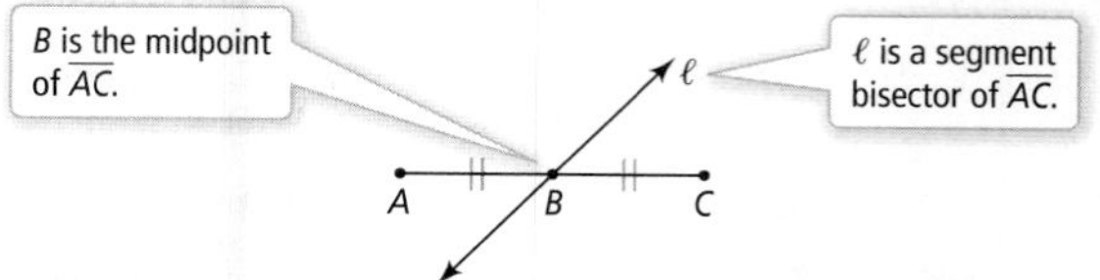

Additional Problems

1. What is CD?

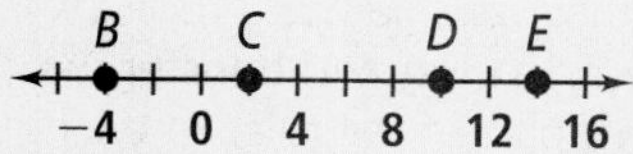

ANSWER 8

2. If $LN = 32$, what are LM and MN?

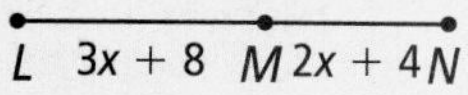

L 3x + 8 M 2x + 4 N

ANSWER $LM = 20$, $MN = 12$

3. Are $\overline{AD}$ and $\overline{BE}$ congruent?

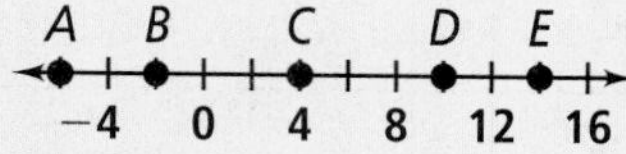

ANSWER Yes, $AD = BE$.

4. S is the midpoint of $\overline{RT}$. What are RS, ST, and RT?

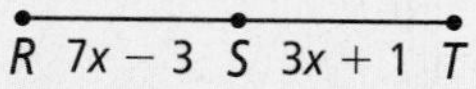

R 7x − 3 S 3x + 1 T

ANSWER $RS = 4$, $ST = 4$, $RT = 8$

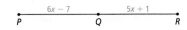

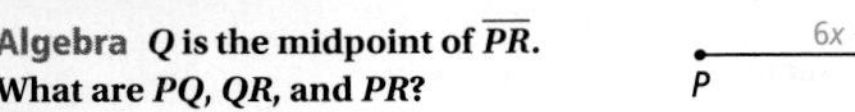

Problem 4 Using the Midpoint

Plan

How can you use algebra to solve the problem?
The lengths of the congruent segments are given as algebraic expressions. You can set the expressions equal to each other.

Algebra Q is the midpoint of $\overline{PR}$. What are PQ, QR, and PR?

Step 1 Find x.

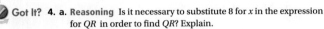

$PQ = QR$	Definition of midpoint
$6x - 7 = 5x + 1$	Substitute.
$x - 7 = 1$	Subtract 5x from each side.
$x = 8$	Add 7 to each side.

Step 2 Find PQ and QR.

$PQ = 6x - 7$		$QR = 5x + 1$
$= 6(8) - 7$	Substitute 8 for x.	$= 5(8) + 1$
$= 41$	Simplify.	$= 41$

Step 3 Find PR.

$PR = PQ + QR$	Segment Addition Postulate
$= 41 + 41$	Substitute.
$= 82$	Simplify.

PQ and QR are both 41. PR is 82.

Got It? 4. a. **Reasoning** Is it necessary to substitute 8 for x in the expression for QR in order to find QR? Explain.

b. U is the midpoint of $\overline{TV}$. What are TU, UV, and TV?

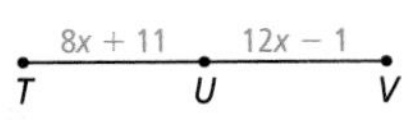

Lesson Check

Do you know HOW?

Name each of the following.

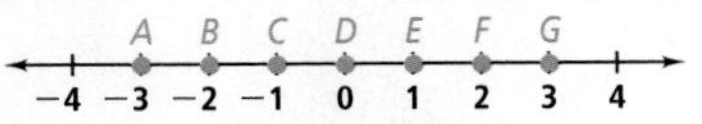

1. The point on $\overrightarrow{DA}$ that is 2 units from D
2. Two points that are 3 units from D
3. The coordinate of the midpoint of $\overline{AG}$
4. A segment congruent to $\overline{AC}$

Do you UNDERSTAND?

5. **Vocabulary** Name two segment bisectors of $\overline{PR}$.

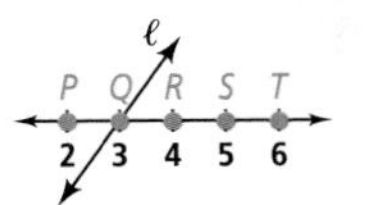

6. **Compare and Contrast** Describe the difference between saying that two segments are *congruent* and saying that two segments have *equal length*. When would you use each phrase?
7. **Error Analysis** You and your friend live 5 mi apart. He says that it is 5 mi from his house to your house and −5 mi from your house to his house. What is the error in his argument?

Problem 4

Q Which point on the segment is a segment bisector? **[Q]**

Q What symbol would you use to show the relationship between $\overline{PQ}$ and $\overline{QR}$? **[$\overline{PQ} \cong \overline{QR}$]**

Q What is the relationship between PQ and PR? **[PR is twice PQ, or $PR = 2PQ$.]**

Got It?

In 4b, remind students that $TU = UV$ because U is the midpoint of $\overline{TV}$.

3 Lesson Check

Do you know HOW?

- If students have difficulty with Exercise 1, then tell them to identify $\overrightarrow{DA}$ before completing the problem.

Do you UNDERSTAND?

- If students have difficulty with Exercise 7, then encourage them to use the term *absolute value* in their answers.

Close

Q A segment has endpoints at coordinate A and coordinate B on a number line. How can you determine the length of the segment connecting point A with the midpoint of $\overline{AB}$? **[Answers may vary. Sample: Determine the length of the segment, and then divide that length by 2.]**

Answers

Got It? (continued)

3a. no

b. yes; $|5 - (-2)| = |7| = 7$

4a. No; since $PQ = QR$, when you solve and get PQ, you know QR.

b. $TU = 35$, $UV = 35$, $TV = 70$

Lesson Check

1. B
2. A, G
3. 0
4. Answers may vary. Sample: $\overline{BD}$
5. line ℓ, point Q
6. Answers may vary. Sample: You would use "congruent" when you are referring to a segment, for example, when describing the trusses of a bridge. You would use "equal length" when you are referring to the measurement of a segment, for example, when describing the distance between two buildings.
7. Answers may vary. Sample: Distance is always a nonnegative measure because it is the absolute value of the difference of two values.

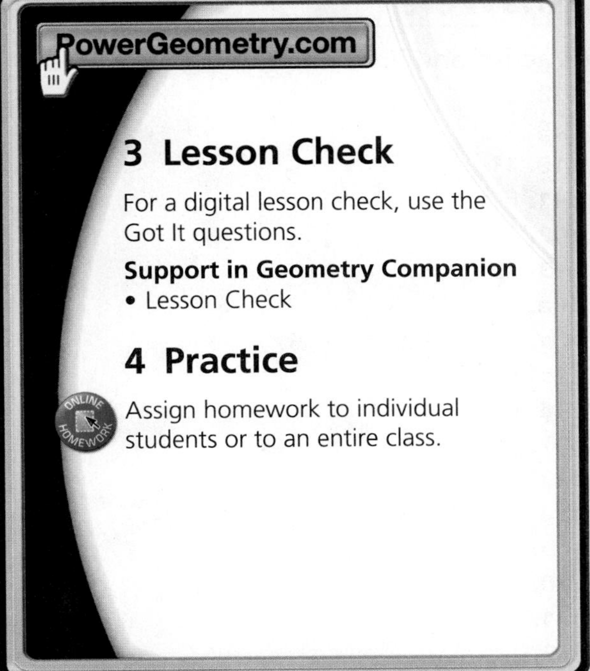

4 Practice

ASSIGNMENT GUIDE
Basic: 8–22 all, 24–34 even, 35, 37–39
Average: 9–21 odd, 23–41
Advanced: 9–21 odd, 23–43
Standardized Test Prep: 44–47
Mixed Review: 48–56
Reasoning exercises have blue headings.
Applications exercises have red headings.
EXERCISE 39: Use the Think About a Plan worksheet in the **Practice and Problem Solving Workbook** (also available in the Teaching Resources in print and online) to further support students' development in becoming independent learners.

HOMEWORK QUICK CHECK
To check students' understanding of key skills and concepts, go over Exercises 13, 19, 35, 37, and 39.

Practice and Problem-Solving Exercises

A Practice

Find the length of each segment. See Problem 1.

8. $\overline{AB}$ **9.** $\overline{BD}$
10. $\overline{AD}$ **11.** $\overline{CE}$

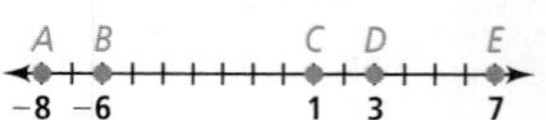

Use the number line at the right for Exercises 12–14. See Problem 2.

R S T

12. If $RS = 15$ and $ST = 9$, then $RT = \blacksquare$.
13. If $ST = 15$ and $RT = 40$, then $RS = \blacksquare$.
14. Algebra $RS = 8y + 4$, $ST = 4y + 8$, and $RT = 15y - 9$.
a. What is the value of y?
b. Find RS, ST, and RT.

Use the number line below for Exercises 15–18. Tell whether the segments are congruent. See Problem 3.

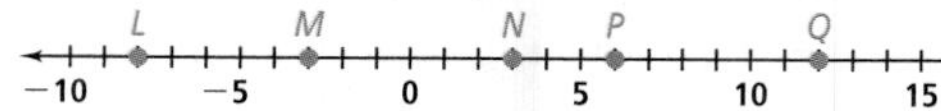

15. $\overline{LN}$ and $\overline{MQ}$ **16.** $\overline{MP}$ and $\overline{NQ}$ **17.** $\overline{MN}$ and $\overline{PQ}$ **18.** $\overline{LP}$ and $\overline{MQ}$

19. Algebra A is the midpoint of $\overline{XY}$. See Problem 4.
a. Find XA.
b. Find AY and XY.

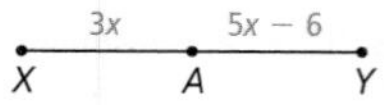

$3x$ $5x - 6$
X A Y

Algebra For Exercises 20–22, use the figure below. Find the value of PT.

20. $PT = 5x + 3$ and $TQ = 7x - 9$
21. $PT = 4x - 6$ and $TQ = 3x + 4$
22. $PT = 7x - 24$ and $TQ = 6x - 2$

P T Q

Apply

On a number line, the coordinates of X, Y, Z, and W are -7, -3, 1, and 5, respectively. Find the lengths of the two segments. Then tell whether they are congruent.

23. $\overline{XY}$ and $\overline{ZW}$ **24.** $\overline{ZX}$ and $\overline{WY}$ **25.** $\overline{YZ}$ and $\overline{XW}$

Suppose the coordinate of A is 0, $AR = 5$, and $AT = 7$. What are the possible coordinates of the midpoint of the given segment?

26. $\overline{AR}$ **27.** $\overline{AT}$ **28.** $\overline{RT}$

29. Suppose point E has a coordinate of 3 and $EG = 5$. What are the possible coordinates of point G?

Answers

Practice and Problem-Solving Exercises

8. 2
9. 9
10. 11
11. 6
12. 24
13. 25
14a. 7
b. $RS = 60$, $ST = 36$, $RT = 96$
15. no
16. yes
17. yes
18. no
19a. 9
b. $AY = 9$, $XY = 18$
20. 33
21. 34
22. 130
23. $XY = 4$, $ZW = 4$; congruent
24. $ZX = 8$, $WY = 8$; congruent
25. $YZ = 4$, $XW = 12$; not congruent
26. -2.5 or 2.5
27. -3.5 or 3.5
28. -6, -1, 1, or 6
29. -2 or 8

Visualization **Without using your ruler, sketch a segment with the given length. Use your ruler to see how well your sketch approximates the length provided.**

30. 3 cm **31.** 3 in. **32.** 6 in. **33.** 10 cm **34.** 65 mm

35. Think About a Plan The numbers labeled on the map of Florida are mile markers. Assume that Route 10 between Quincy and Jacksonville is straight.

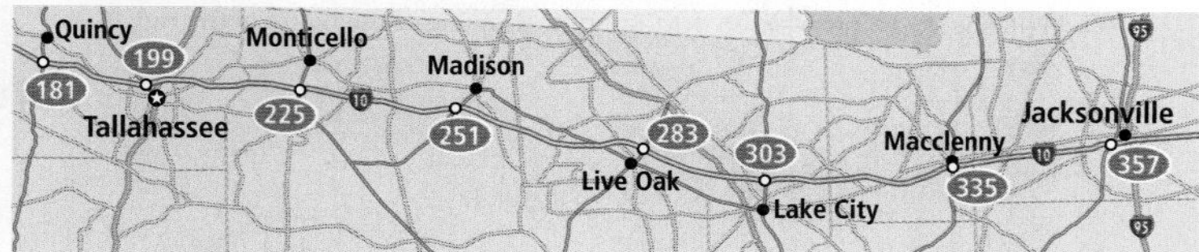

Suppose you drive at an average speed of 55 mi/h. How long will it take to get from Live Oak to Jacksonville?

- How can you use mile markers to find distances between points?
- How do average speed, distance, and time all relate to each other?

36. Travel Use the map above. Suppose you drive at an average speed of 58 mi/h. How long will it take to get from Macclenny to Tallahassee?

Error Analysis **Use the highway sign for Exercises 37 and 38.**

37. A driver reads the highway sign and says, "It's 145 miles from Mitchell to Watertown." What error did the driver make? Explain.

38. Your friend reads the highway sign and says, "It's 71 miles to Watertown." Is your friend correct? Explain.

Algebra **Use the diagram at the right for Exercises 39 and 40.**

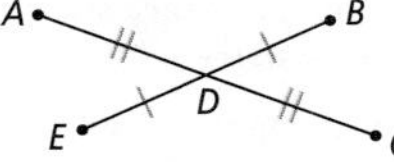

39. If $AD = 12$ and $AC = 4y - 36$, find the value of y. Then find AC and DC.

40. If $ED = x + 4$ and $DB = 3x - 8$, find ED, DB, and EB.

41. Writing Suppose you know PQ and QR. Can you use the Segment Addition Postulate to find PR? Explain.

42. C is the midpoint of $\overline{AB}$, D is the midpoint of $\overline{AC}$, E is the midpoint of $\overline{AD}$, F is the midpoint of $\overline{ED}$, G is the midpoint of $\overline{EF}$, and H is the midpoint of $\overline{DB}$. If $DC = 16$, what is GH?

43. a. Algebra Use the diagram at the right. What algebraic expression represents GK?

b. If $GK = 30$, what are GH and JK?

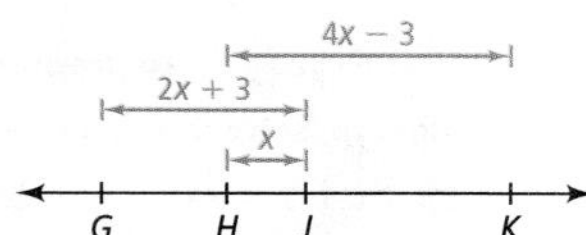

30–34. Check students' work.

35. about 1 h, 21 min

36. about 2 h, 21 min

37. The distance is $|65 - 80|$, or 15 mi. The driver added the values instead of subtracting them.

38. No; your friend calculated the distance as if you were in Hudson. From the sign, the distance to Watertown is 80 mi.

39. $y = 15$; $AC = 24$, $DC = 12$

40. $ED = 10$, $DB = 10$, $EB = 20$

41. Not always; the Segment Addition Postulate can be used only if P, Q, and R are collinear points.

42. 30

43a. $(2x + 3) - x + (4x - 3)$, or $5x$

b. $GH = 9$, $JK = 15$

Answers

Practice and Problem-Solving Exercises (continued)

44. B

45. G

46. D

47. [4]

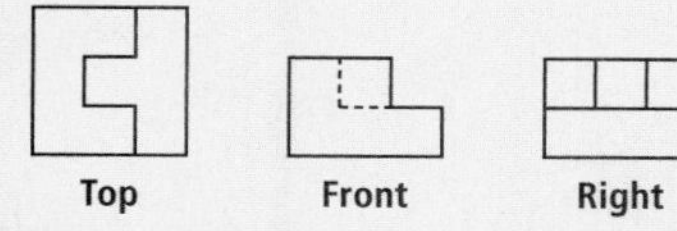

[3] one error in one of the views OR views without labels

[2] two errors in the views OR only two views

[1] more than two errors OR only one view

48. always

49. always

50. never

51. always

52a. yes

b. no

c. no

d. yes

53. 14

54. 6.5

55. −3

56. 12.8

Standardized Test Prep

SAT/ACT

44. Points X, Y, and Z are collinear and Y is between X and Z. Which statement must be true?

(A) $XY = YZ$ (C) $XY + XZ = YZ$

(B) $XZ - XY = YZ$ (D) $XZ = XY - YZ$

45. Which is the top view of an orthographic drawing of the figure at the right?

(F) 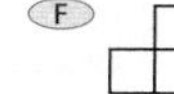 (H) 

(G) 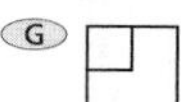 (I)

46. Which statement is true based on the diagram?

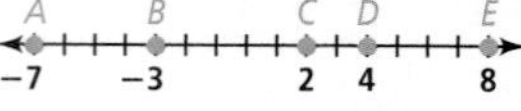

(A) $\overline{BC} \cong \overline{CE}$ (C) $AC + BD = AD$ 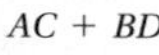

(B) $BD < CD$ (D) $AC + CD = AD$ 

Extended Response

47. Make an orthographic drawing of the structure at the right.

Mixed Review

Complete each statement with *always*, *sometimes*, or *never* to make a true statement.

See Lesson 1-2.

48. Opposite rays __?__ form a line.

49. Three distinct points are __?__ coplanar.

50. If two distinct planes intersect, then their intersection is __?__ a plane.

51. The intersection of two distinct planes is __?__ a line.

52. Can you conclude the information stated from the given diagram?

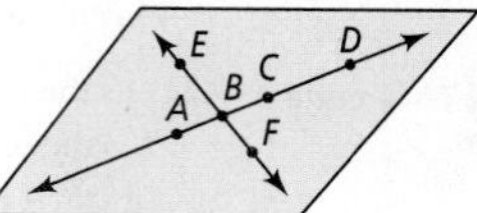

a. A, B, and D are collinear. **b.** $\overline{AB} \cong \overline{BC}$

c. $\overrightarrow{BC}$ contains A. **d.** E, F, and B are coplanar.

Get Ready! **To prepare for Lesson 1-4, do Exercises 53–56.**

Algebra **Solve the equation.** See p. 834.

53. $2x + 7 = 35$ **54.** $3y = 19.5$ **55.** $4z + 21 = 9$ **56.** $5t - 16 = 48$

1-3 Lesson Resources

Differentiated Remediation

Instructional Support

Geometry Companion

Students can use the **Geometry Companion** worktext (4 pages) . . .

- New Vocabulary
- Key Concepts
- Got It for each Problem
- Lesson Check

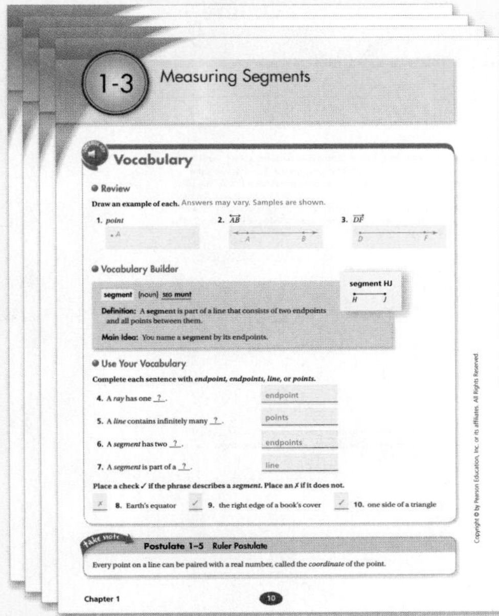

1-3 Measuring Segments

Vocabulary

Review

Draw an example of each. Answers may vary. Samples are shown.

1. point
2. $\overleftrightarrow{AB}$
3. $\overrightarrow{DF}$

Vocabulary Builder

segment (noun) SEG munt

Definition: A segment is part of a line that consists of two endpoints and all points between them.

Main Idea: You name a segment by its endpoints.

segment HJ

Use Your Vocabulary

Complete each sentence with *endpoint, endpoints, line,* or *points.*

4. A *ray* has one ? . endpoint
5. A *line* contains infinitely many ? . points
6. A *segment* has two ? . endpoints
7. A *segment* is part of a ? . line

Place a check ✓ if the phrase describes a *segment*. Place an ✗ if it does not.

✗ 8. Earth's equator ✓ 9. the right edge of a book's cover ✓ 10. one side of a triangle

Take note: Postulate 1-5 Ruler Postulate

Every point on a line can be paired with a real number, called the *coordinate* of the point.

Chapter 1 10

ELL Support

Use Manipulatives Draw a number line from −10 to 10 on the board. Label points *A* and *B* at −4 and 3, respectively. While thinking aloud, use absolute value to measure the segment. Show another example while repeating the same statements so students will see a pattern. For example: To find the distance between the points, find the absolute value of their differences. Verify the length by counting. Have students draw a number line on paper and follow along as you do another example on the board. Allow students to work independently as you monitor their progress. Do this activity again, labeling and then adding three line segments.

5 Assess & Remediate

Lesson Quiz

1. What is *LN*?

L M N; −4 0 4 8 12 16

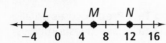

2. If $PR = 40$, what are *PQ* and *QR*?

P $5x - 2$ Q $x + 12$ R

3. Are $\overline{BD}$ and $\overline{CE}$ congruent?

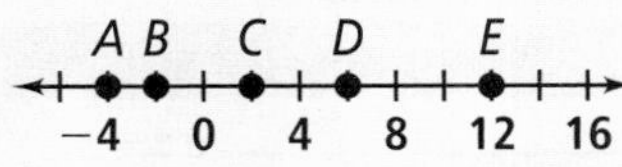

4. Do you UNDERSTAND? *J* is the midpoint of $\overline{HK}$. What are *HJ*, *JK*, and *HK*?

H $9x - 2$ J $4x + 13$ K

ANSWERS TO LESSON QUIZ

1. 14

2. $PQ = 23$, $QR = 17$

3. No

4. $HJ = 25$, $JK = 25$, $HK = 50$

PRECRIPTION FOR REMEDIATION

Use the student work on the Lesson Quiz to prescribe a differentiated review assignment.

Points	Differentiated Remediation
0–2	Intervention
3	On-level
4	Extension

PowerGeometry.com

5 Assess & Remediate

Assign the Lesson Quiz. Appropriate intervention, practice, or enrichment is automatically generated based on student performance.

Intervention

- **Reteaching** (2 pages) Provides reteaching and practice exercises for the key lesson concepts. Use with struggling students or absent students.
- **English Language Learner Support** Helps students develop and reinforce mathematical vocabulary and key concepts.

All-in-One Resources/Online

Reteaching

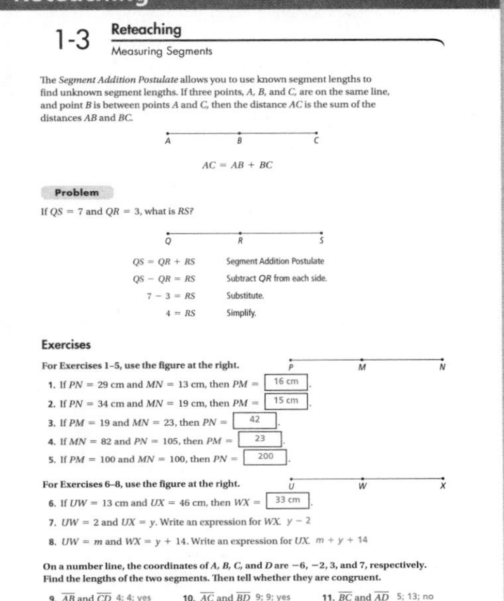

1-3 Reteaching

Measuring Segments

The *Segment Addition Postulate* allows you to use known segment lengths to find unknown segment lengths. If three points, *A*, *B*, and *C*, are on the same line, and point *B* is between points *A* and *C*, then the distance *AC* is the sum of the distances *AB* and *BC*.

A B C

$AC = AB + BC$

Problem

If $QS = 7$ and $QR = 3$, what is *RS*?

Q R S

$QS = QR + RS$	Segment Addition Postulate
$QS - QR = RS$	Subtract *QR* from each side.
$7 - 3 = RS$	Substitute.
$4 = RS$	Simplify.

Exercises

For Exercises 1–5, use the figure at the right. (P M N)

1. If $PN = 29$ cm and $MN = 13$ cm, then $PM =$ 16 cm.
2. If $PN = 34$ cm and $MN = 19$ cm, then $PM =$ 15 cm.
3. If $PM = 19$ and $MN = 23$, then $PN =$ 42.
4. If $MN = 82$ and $PN = 105$, then $PM =$ 23.
5. If $PM = 100$ and $MN = 100$, then $PN =$ 200.

For Exercises 6–8, use the figure at the right. (U W X)

6. If $UW = 13$ cm and $UX = 46$ cm, then $WX =$ 33 cm.
7. $UW = 2$ and $UX = y$. Write an expression for *WX*. $y - 2$
8. $UW = m$ and $WX = y + 14$. Write an expression for *UX*. $m + y + 14$

On a number line, the coordinates of *A*, *B*, *C*, and *D* are −6, −2, 3, and 7, respectively. Find the lengths of the two segments. Then tell whether they are congruent.

9. $\overline{AB}$ and $\overline{CD}$ 4; 4; yes
10. $\overline{AC}$ and $\overline{BD}$ 9; 9; yes
11. $\overline{BC}$ and $\overline{AD}$ 5; 13; no

All-in-One Resources/Online

English Language Learner Support

1-3 ELL Support

Measuring Segments

The column on the left shows the steps used to find the lengths of line segments. Use the column on the left to answer each question in the column on the right.

Problem Using the Midpoint *T* is the midpoint of $\overline{SU}$. What are *ST*, *TU*, and *SU*? S $5x - 2$ T $3x + 4$ U	1. What is the midpoint of a line segment? a point that divides the line segment into two congruent segments
Write an equation to relate *ST* to *TU*. $\overline{ST} \cong \overline{TU}$, so $ST = TU$.	2. What does $\overline{ST} \cong \overline{TU}$ mean? Why is this true? It means the segments are congruent. The midpoint divides $\overline{SU}$ into two congruent segments.
Write an equation to find *x* by substituting. $5x - 2 = 3x + 4$	3. What does it mean to substitute here? It means to replace *ST* and *TU* with the given algebraic expressions.
Subtract 3*x* from each side. Add 2 to each side. $2x - 2 = 4$ $2x = 6$	4. Why do you add 2 to each side? To get the term with *x* alone on one side of the equation.
Divide each side by 2. $x = 3$ Use *x* to find *ST* and *TU*. Substitute 3 for *x*. $ST = 5(3) - 2 = 13$ $TU = 3(3) + 4 = 13$	5. What does it mean to substitute 3 for *x*? It means to replace *x* in the algebraic expression with the number 3.
Check that $ST = TU$. $ST = 13, TU = 13, ST = TU$	6. What would you do if *ST* were not equal to *TU* when you checked the problem? Solve for *x* again.
Find *SU* by adding *ST* and *TU*. $ST + TU = 13 + 13 = 26$	7. What is another way to find *SU*? Multiply *ST* or *TU* by 2.

Differentiated Remediation *continued*

On-Level

- **Practice** (2 pages) Provides extra practice for each lesson. For simpler practice exercises, use the Form K Practice pages found in the All-in-One Teaching Resources and online.
- **Think About a Plan** Helps students develop specific problem-solving skills and strategies by providing scaffolded guiding questions.
- **Standardized Test Prep** Focuses on all major exercises, all major question types, and helps students prepare for the high-stakes assessments.

Extension

- **Enrichment** Provides students with interesting problems and activities that extend the concepts of the lesson.
- **Activities, Games, and Puzzles** Worksheets that can be used for concepts development, enrichment, and for fun!

Practice and Problem Solving Wkbk/ All-in-One Resources/Online

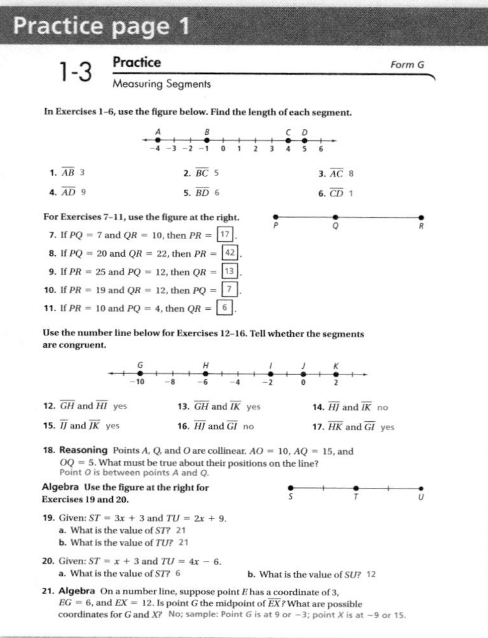

Practice page 1

1-3 Practice — Form G

Measuring Segments

In Exercises 1–6, use the figure below. Find the length of each segment.

1. $\overline{AB}$ 3
2. $\overline{BC}$ 5
3. $\overline{AC}$ 8
4. $\overline{AD}$ 9
5. $\overline{BD}$ 6
6. $\overline{CD}$ 1

For Exercises 7–11, use the figure at the right.

7. If $PQ = 7$ and $QR = 10$, then $PR =$ 17.
8. If $PQ = 20$ and $QR = 22$, then $PR =$ 42.
9. If $PR = 25$ and $PQ = 12$, then $QR =$ 13.
10. If $PR = 19$ and $QR = 12$, then $PQ =$ 7.
11. If $PR = 10$ and $PQ = 4$, then $QR =$ 6.

Use the number line below for Exercises 12–16. Tell whether the segments are congruent.

12. $\overline{GH}$ and $\overline{HI}$ yes
13. $\overline{GH}$ and $\overline{IK}$ yes
14. $\overline{HJ}$ and $\overline{IK}$ no
15. $\overline{IJ}$ and $\overline{JK}$ yes
16. $\overline{HJ}$ and $\overline{GI}$ no
17. $\overline{HK}$ and $\overline{GI}$ yes
18. **Reasoning** Points A, Q, and O are collinear. $AO = 10$, $AQ = 15$, and $OQ = 5$. What must be true about their positions on the line? Point O is between points A and Q.

Algebra Use the figure at the right for Exercises 19 and 20.

19. Given: $ST = 3x + 3$ and $TU = 2x + 9$.
    a. What is the value of ST? 21
    b. What is the value of TU? 21
20. Given: $ST = x + 3$ and $TU = 4x - 6$.
    a. What is the value of ST? 6
    b. What is the value of SU? 12
21. **Algebra** On a number line, suppose point E has a coordinate of 3, $EG = 6$, and $EX = 12$. Is point G the midpoint of $\overline{EX}$? What are possible coordinates for G and X? No; sample: Point G is at 9 or -3; point X is at -9 or 15.

Practice and Problem Solving Wkbk/ All-in-One Resources/Online

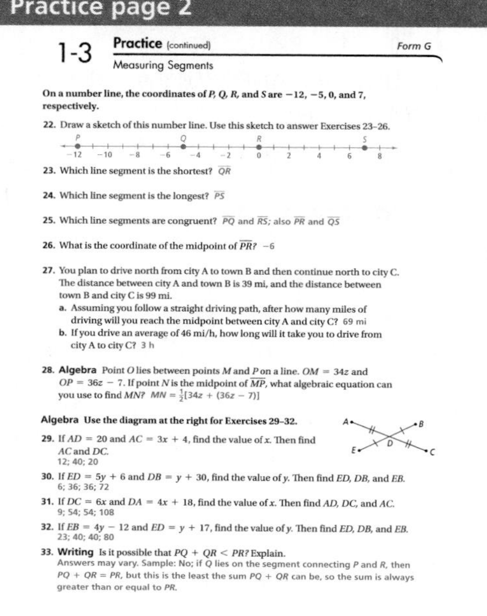

Practice page 2

1-3 Practice (continued) — Form G

Measuring Segments

On a number line, the coordinates of P, Q, R, and S are -12, -5, 0, and 7, respectively.

22. Draw a sketch of this number line. Use this sketch to answer Exercises 23–26.
23. Which line segment is the shortest? $\overline{QR}$
24. Which line segment is the longest? $\overline{PS}$
25. Which line segments are congruent? $\overline{PQ}$ and $\overline{RS}$; also $\overline{PR}$ and $\overline{QS}$
26. What is the coordinate of the midpoint of $\overline{PR}$? -6
27. You plan to drive north from city A to town B and then continue north to city C. The distance between city A and town B is 39 mi, and the distance between town B and city C is 99 mi.
    a. Assuming you follow a straight driving path, after how many miles of driving will you reach the midpoint between city A and city C? 69 mi
    b. If you drive an average of 46 mi/h, how long will it take you to drive from city A to city C? 3 h
28. **Algebra** Point O lies between points M and P on a line. $OM = 34z$ and $OP = 36z - 7$. If point N is the midpoint of $\overline{MP}$, what algebraic equation can you use to find MN? $MN = \frac{1}{2}[34z + (36z - 7)]$

Algebra Use the diagram at the right for Exercises 29–32.

29. If $AD = 20$ and $AC = 3x + 4$, find the value of x. Then find AC and DC. 12; 40; 20
30. If $ED = 5y + 6$ and $DB = y + 30$, find the value of y. Then find ED, DB, and EB. 6; 36; 36; 72
31. If $DC = 6x$ and $DA = 4x + 18$, find the value of x. Then find AD, DC, and AC. 9; 54; 54; 108
32. If $EB = 4y - 12$ and $ED = y + 17$, find the value of y. Then find ED, DB, and EB. 23; 40; 40; 80
33. **Writing** Is it possible that $PQ + QR < PR$? Explain. Answers may vary. Sample: No; if Q lies on the segment connecting P and R, then $PQ + QR = PR$, but this is the least the sum $PQ + QR$ can be, so the sum is always greater than or equal to PR.

All-in-One Resources/Online

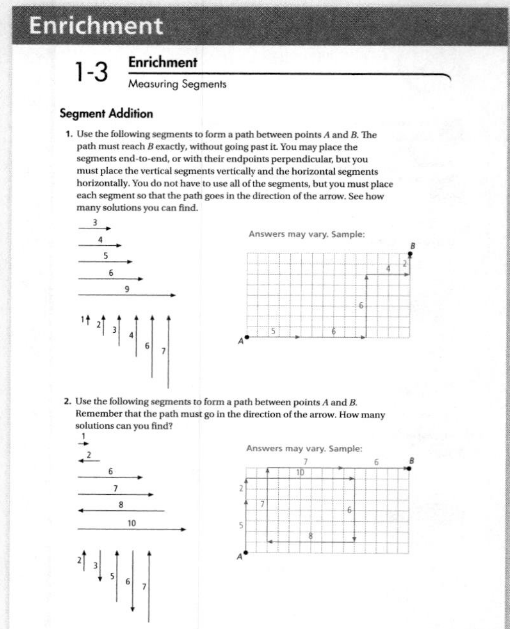

Enrichment

1-3 Enrichment

Measuring Segments

Segment Addition

1. Use the following segments to form a path between points A and B. The path must reach B exactly, without going past it. You may place the segments end-to-end, or with their endpoints perpendicular, but you must place the vertical segments vertically and the horizontal segments horizontally. You do not have to use all of the segments, but you must place each segment so that the path goes in the direction of the arrow. See how many solutions you can find.

   Answers may vary. Sample:

2. Use the following segments to form a path between points A and B. Remember that the path must go in the direction of the arrow. How many solutions can you find?

   Answers may vary. Sample:

Practice and Problem Solving Wkbk/ All-in-One Resources/Online

Think About a Plan

1-3 Think About a Plan

Measuring Segments

If $AD = 12$ and $AC = 4y - 36$, find the value of y. Then find AC and DC.

Understanding the Problem

1. What are the two congruence relationships that the diagram shows? $AD = DC$, $BD = DE$
2. What is the value of DC? 12
3. Write an equation that describes the relationship between AC, DC, and AD. $AC = AD + DC$

Planning the Solution

4. How can you use the equation in Exercise 3 above to find the value of y? Substitute the given values for AC and AD, and the value of DC, into the equation above.

Getting an Answer

5. Write an equation for y using the method described in Exercise 4 above. $4y - 36 = 12 + 12$ or $4y - 36 = 24$
6. Solve for y. $y = 15$
7. $AC = 4y - 36$. Substitute the value of y to find AC. 24
8. Check your answer. Does it make the equation that you wrote in Step 5 true? yes

Practice and Problem Solving Wkbk/ All-in-One Resources/Online

Standardized Test Prep

1-3 Standardized Test Prep

Measuring Segments

Gridded Response

Solve each exercise and enter your answer on the grid provided.

1. What is the length of $\overline{BD}$?
2. Points G, H, and I are collinear and H is between G and I. If $GH = 12$ and $GI = 23$, what is HI?
3. Look at the diagram below. If $XY = 7$ and $XZ = 30$, what is the value of t?

For Exercises 4 and 5, use the figure at the right.

4. M is the midpoint of $\overline{LN}$. What is LM?
5. What is LN?

Answers

1. 7 2. 11 3. 12 4. 6 5. 12

Online Teacher Resource Center

Activities, Games, and Puzzles

1-3 Puzzle: What Is a Line's Favorite Kind of Fruit?

Measuring Segments

Solve the problems below to answer the riddle:

What is a line's favorite kind of fruit?

Look for your answer in the key at the right and put the corresponding letter in the answer blank at the bottom of the page.

1. Points A, B, and C are collinear and A is between B and C. $AB = 4x - 3$, $BC = 7x + 5$, and $AC = 5x - 16$. Find each value.
   a. BC
   b. AB
   c. AC
2. On a number line, $G = 8$ and $H = -3$. If H is the midpoint of $\overline{GI}$, find the coordinate of I.
3. J is the midpoint of $\overline{KL}$. Find KJ if $KL = 38$.

For 4–6, refer to the number line below.

4. Suppose O is the midpoint of $\overline{MQ}$ and N is the midpoint of $\overline{MO}$. If $NO = 8$, find MQ.
5. Suppose P is the midpoint of $\overline{NQ}$, $OP = 11$, and $OQ = 35$. Find NO.
6. If $NO = 2y + 11$, $OP = 3y - 2$, $NP = 6y + 3$, and $MP = 64$, find each value.
   a. NO
   b. MN

a	−14
b	20
c	−18
d	−13
e	32
f	3
g	23
h	39
i	16
j	41
k	−11
l	12
m	13
n	89
o	44
p	−26
q	6
r	19
s	45
t	25
u	42
v	10
w	−7
x	16
y	27
z	50

An o (1c) r (3) a (2) n (1a) g (6a) e (4) because it is made of s (1b) e (4) g (6a) m (5) e (4) n (1a) t (6b) s (1b).

1-4 Measuring Angles

TN State Performance Indicator

SPI 3108.4.2 Define, identify, describe, and/or model plane figures using appropriate mathematical symbols (including collinear and non-collinear points, lines, segments, rays, angles, triangles, quadrilaterals, and other polygons).

Objective To find and compare the measures of angles

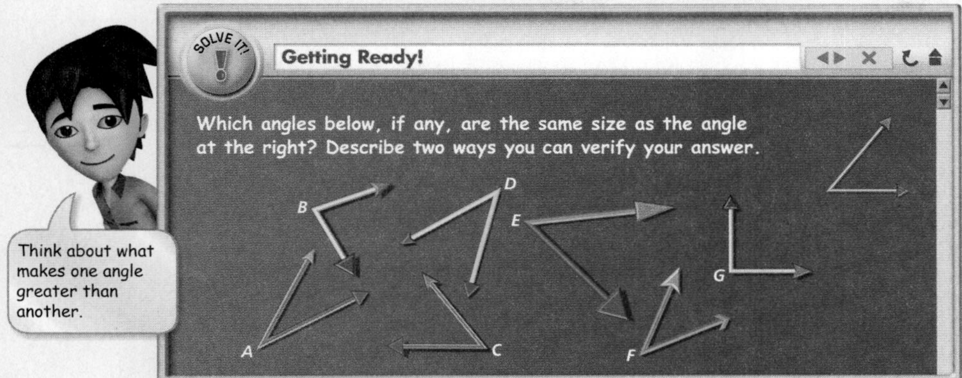

Getting Ready!
Which angles below, if any, are the same size as the angle at the right? Describe two ways you can verify your answer.
Think about what makes one angle greater than another.
A
B
C
D
E
F
G

Lesson Vocabulary
- angle
- sides of an angle
- vertex of an angle
- measure of an angle
- acute angle
- right angle
- obtuse angle
- straight angle
- congruent angles

In this lesson, you will learn to describe and measure angles like the ones in the Solve It.

Essential Understanding You can use number operations to find and compare the measures of angles.

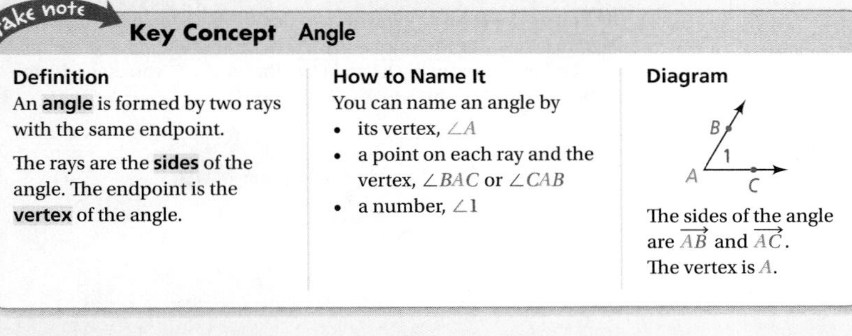

Take note

Key Concept Angle

Definition	How to Name It	Diagram
An **angle** is formed by two rays with the same endpoint. The rays are the **sides** of the angle. The endpoint is the **vertex** of the angle.	You can name an angle by • its vertex, $\angle A$ • a point on each ray and the vertex, $\angle BAC$ or $\angle CAB$ • a number, $\angle 1$	The sides of the angle are $\overrightarrow{AB}$ and $\overrightarrow{AC}$. The vertex is A.

When you name angles using three points, the vertex must go in the middle.

The *interior* of an angle is the region containing all of the points between the two sides of the angle. The *exterior* of an angle is the region containing all of the points outside of the angle.

exterior
interior

1 Interactive Learning

Solve It!

PURPOSE To consider how an angle's size is measured and to compare the sizes of angles

PROCESS Students may
- use visual judgment.
- use a measuring tool such as a protractor.

FACILITATE

Q How can you describe an angle using words defined in Lesson 1-2? **[An angle is two rays that share a common endpoint.]**

Q Is the size of an angle determined by the length of its rays? Explain. **[No, the rays continue indefinitely, so they do not have a length.]**

ANSWER See Solve It in Answers on next page.

CONNECT THE MATH Students may already be familiar with the use of a protractor. In this lesson, students will measure angles, but will use concepts of angle classification to verify that their measures are in the range of a given class.

2 Guided Instruction

Take Note

Ask students to recall the other figure introduced in the chapter that is formed by two rays. After eliciting the term *opposite rays*, ask students if opposite rays meet the definition of an angle.

1-4 Preparing to Teach

BIG ideas **Measurement**
Reasoning and Proof

UbD

ESSENTIAL UNDERSTANDINGS
- Number operations can be used to find and compare the measures of angles.
- The Protractor and Angle Addition Postulates can be used in reasoning about angle measures.

Math Background

Many students erroneously think that the measure of an angle is related to the lengths of its rays. Students need to understand that the measure of an angle is related to the portion of the circle an angle takes up when the angle vertex is placed at the circle's center. A right angle takes up one fourth of a circle and a 60° angle takes up one sixth of a circle.

Because our measurement of angles is based on the definition that there are 360 degrees in a circle, students may wonder why a circle is divided into 360 degrees. The ancient Babylonians, who used a base-60 number system instead of a base-10 number system, are responsible for defining 360 as the number of degrees in a circle. Similarly, the Babylonians are responsible for dividing an hour into 60 minutes and a minute into 60 seconds.

Support Student Learning

Use the **Geometry Companion** to engage and support students during instructions. See Lesson Resources at the end of this lesson for details.

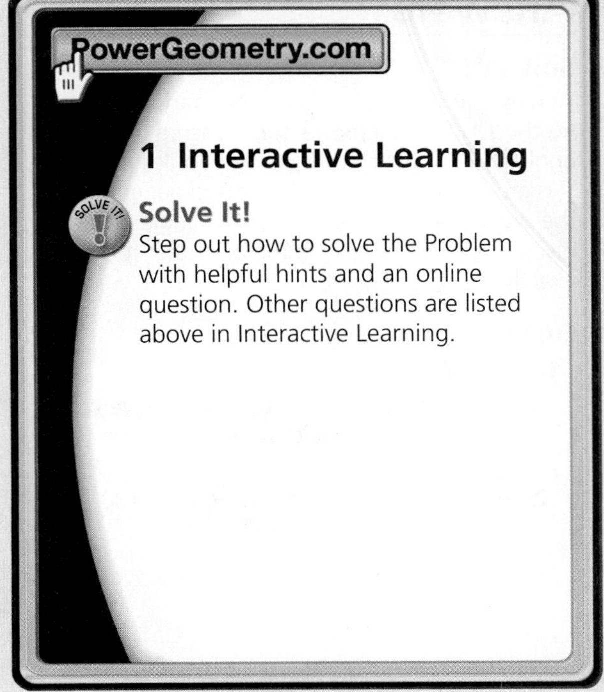

Problem 1

Q Why is $\angle JKM$ not a correct way to name $\angle 1$? **[Because the vertex of the angle must be the middle letter.]**

Q Which point is in the exterior of $\angle 1$? **[L]**

Got It? — VISUAL LEARNERS

Q What are the names of the three angles which share vertex M? **[$\angle JMK$, $\angle KML$, $\angle JML$]**

Have students explore degree measurement through a teacher-led activity such as:

1) Draw a right angle in standard position.
2) Using a compass, draw a circle that intersects the angle using the vertex as the center.
3) Tell students that a full circle is defined to have 360 degrees, and elicit that the right angle is one-fourth of the circle and must therefore measure 90.

Take Note — ERROR PREVENTION

One common mistake that students make is not reading from the correct scale on the protractor. Two ways to guide students to use a protractor correctly are:

- Instruct students to direct their eye to the ray along the straight edge of the protractor and note if the 0° mark is in the top or bottom row of numbers. The angle's measure is read from the same row on the scale as that 0°.
- Ask students to identify the angle by visual inspection as acute or obtuse. Then tell them to read the measurement of the corresponding type from the scale on the protractor.

Think

What rays form $\angle 1$?

$\overrightarrow{MJ}$ and $\overrightarrow{MK}$ form $\angle 1$.

Problem 1 Naming Angles

What are two other names for $\angle 1$?

$\angle JMK$ and $\angle KMJ$ are also names for $\angle 1$.

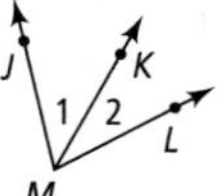

Got It? **1. a.** What are two other names for $\angle KML$?
b. Reasoning Would it be correct to name any of the angles $\angle M$? Explain.

One way to measure the size of an angle is in degrees. To indicate the measure of an angle, write a lowercase m in front of the angle symbol. In the diagram, the measure of $\angle A$ is 62. You write this as $m\angle A = 62$. In this book, you will work only with degree measures.

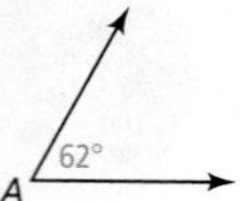

A circle has 360°, so 1 degree is $\frac{1}{360}$ of a circle. A protractor forms half a circle and measures angles from 0° to 180°.

take note

Postulate 1-7 Protractor Postulate

Consider $\overrightarrow{OB}$ and a point A on one side of $\overrightarrow{OB}$. Every ray of the form $\overrightarrow{OA}$ can be paired one to one with a real number from 0 to 180.

The Protractor Postulate allows you to find the measure of an angle. Consider the diagram below. The **measure** of $\angle COD$ is the absolute value of the difference of the real numbers paired with $\overrightarrow{OC}$ and $\overrightarrow{OD}$. That is, if $\overrightarrow{OC}$ corresponds with c, and $\overrightarrow{OD}$ corresponds with d, then $m\angle COD = |c - d|$.

Notice that the Protractor Postulate and the calculation of an angle measure are very similar to the Ruler Postulate and the calculation of a segment length.

Answers

Solve It!

Angles C and E; explanations may vary. Sample: Method 1: Using a protractor, measure the given angle and see which of the given angles matches this measure. Method 2: On tracing paper, trace the original angle. Then, place the angle on all the given angles to determine the ones that it overlaps exactly.

Got It?

1a. $\angle LMK$, $\angle 2$

b. No; since there are three ∠s that have vertex M, it would not be clear which one you intended.

2. $m\angle LKH = 35$, acute; $m\angle HKN = 180$, straight; $m\angle MKH = 145$, obtuse

PowerGeometry.com

2 Guided Instruction

Each Problem is worked out and supported online.

Problem 1
Naming Angles
Animated

Problem 2
Measuring and Classifying Angles
Animated

Problem 3
Using Congruent Angles

Problem 4
Using the Angle Addition Postulate
Animated

Support in Geometry Companion
- Vocabulary
- Key Concepts
- Got It?

You can classify angles according to their measures.

Key Concept Types of Angles

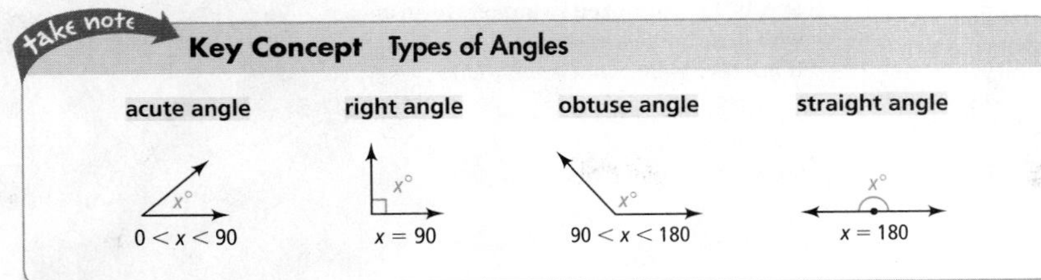

take note
acute angle
right angle
obtuse angle
straight angle
0 < x < 90
x = 90
90 < x < 180
x = 180

The symbol ⌐ in the diagram above indicates a right angle.

Problem 2 **Measuring and Classifying Angles**

What are the measures of $\angle LKN$, $\angle JKL$, and $\angle JKN$? Classify each angle as *acute, right, obtuse,* or *straight*.

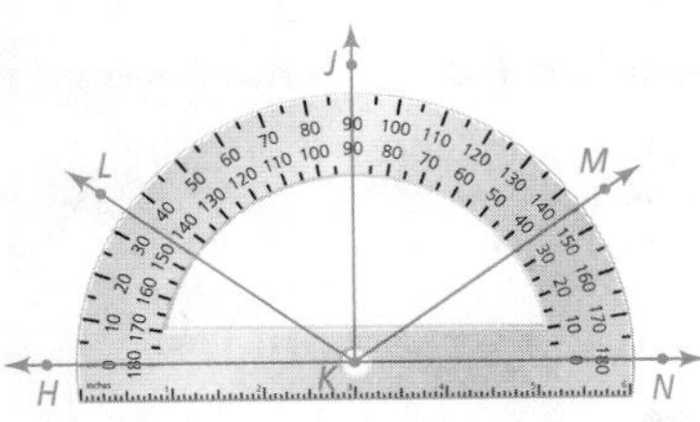

Think

Do the classifications make sense?
Yes. In each case, the classification agrees with what you see in the diagram.

Use the definition of the measure of an angle to calculate each measure.

$m\angle LKN = |145 - 0| = 145$; $\angle LKN$ is obtuse.

$m\angle JKL = |90 - 145| = |-55| = 55$; $\angle JKL$ is acute.

$m\angle JKN = |90 - 0| = 90$; $\angle JKN$ is right.

Got It? **2.** What are the measures of $\angle LKH$, $\angle HKN$, and $\angle MKH$? Classify each angle as *acute, right, obtuse,* or *straight*.

Angles with the same measure are **congruent angles.** This means that if $m\angle A = m\angle B$, then $\angle A \cong \angle B$. You can also say that if $\angle A \cong \angle B$, then $m\angle A = m\angle B$.

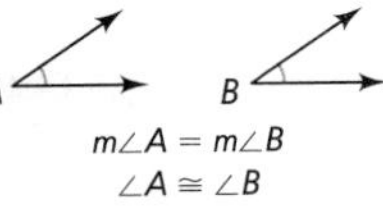

$m\angle A = m\angle B$
$\angle A \cong \angle B$

You can mark angles with arcs to show that they are congruent. If there is more than one set of congruent angles, each set is marked with the same number of arcs.

Take Note — VISUAL LEARNERS

Ask students to locate and identify an example of each type of angle in the classroom. Remind students to clearly identify the object(s) which represent the rays, the vertex, and the plane in which the rays lie. If they cannot find appropriate examples from observation, ask them to hold two pencils together to form angles of the various types.

Problem 2

Q When you calculate $m\angle JKL$, is it correct to use the expression $|145 - 90|$ or $|90 - 145|$? Explain. **[Both are correct; the value of each expression is 55.]**

Q How could you measure an angle if the rays were not long enough to intersect with the scale on the protractor? **[Answers may vary. Sample: You could use a straightedge to extend the rays so that they do intersect.]**

Got It? — ERROR PREVENTION

If students claim to be able to identify right angles by visual inspection alone, stress that an angle which appears to be a right angle might actually have a measure of 89 or a measure of 91, which would make the angle acute and obtuse, respectively.

Demonstrate how to mark two different pairs of angles in the same drawings so that it is clear which angles are congruent to each other, and which angles are not congruent.

Discuss that using single, double, and triple arcs may not be feasible in a small diagram. An alternate way to show congruent angles is a single arc with a single tick mark, double tick mark, or even a triple tick mark.

Additional Problems

1. What are two other names for $\angle 1$?

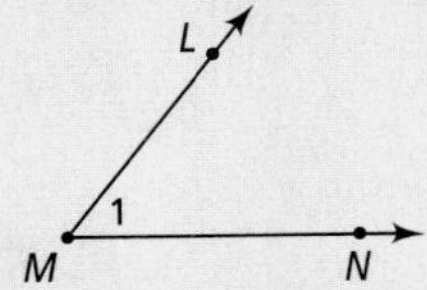

ANSWER $\angle LMN$ and $\angle NML$

2. What are the measures of $\angle LKN$, $\angle NKM$, and $\angle JKN$? Classify each angle as acute, right, obtuse, or straight.

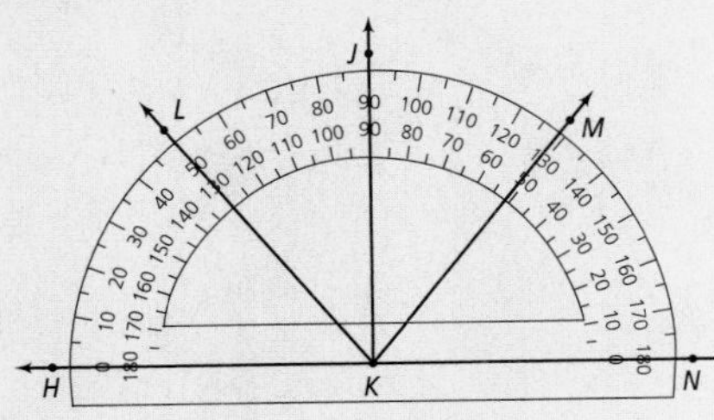

ANSWER $m\angle LKN = 130$, obtuse; $m\angle NKM = 50$, acute; $m\angle JKN = 90$, right

3. Use the diagram below. Which angle is congruent to $\angle WBM$?

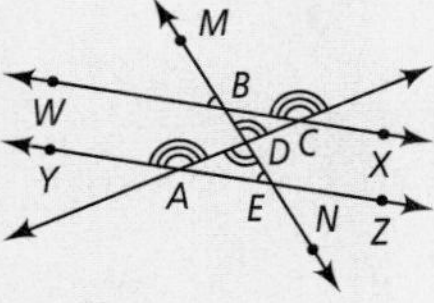

ANSWER $\angle AED$

4. If $m\angle ABC = 175$, what are $m\angle ABD$ and $m\angle CBD$?

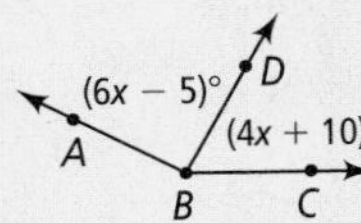

ANSWER $m\angle ABD = 97$ and $m\angle CBD = 78$

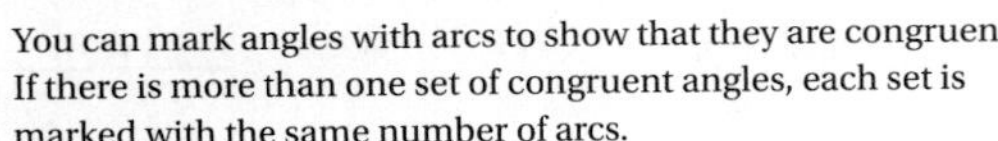

Problem 3

Q Can you rely on visual inspection or a protractor to determine if two angles in a diagram are congruent? Explain. **[No, neither visual inspection nor measurement is completely reliable. You can only assume that angles are congruent if they are marked congruent or labeled with equal degree measures.]**

Got It? ERROR PREVENTION

Remind students that an equals sign is used to show that numbers are equivalent while a congruence symbol is used to show that two geometric figures are equivalent.

Take Note TACTILE LEARNERS

Have students use a protractor to measure the angles in the given figure to verify the Angle Addition Postulate. Remind students that this one example does not prove the postulate.

Problem 4

Q What algebraic expression represents $m\angle RQT$? **[$7x - 6$]**

Q What kinds of angles are $\angle RQS$ and $\angle TQS$? **[Both are acute angles.]**

Got It?

Q Is it possible for both $\angle DEC$ and $\angle CEF$ to be acute angles? Explain. **[No, both angle measures cannot be less than 90 degrees, because the sum would be less than 180 degrees.]**

Problem 3 Using Congruent Angles

Think

Look at the diagram. What do the angle marks tell you?
The angle marks tell you which angles are congruent.

Sports **Synchronized swimmers form angles with their bodies, as shown in the photo. If $m\angle GHJ = 90$, what is $m\angle KLM$?**

$\angle GHJ \cong \angle KLM$ because they both have two arcs.
So, $m\angle GHJ = m\angle KLM = 90$.

Got It? 3. Use the photo in Problem 3. If $m\angle ABC = 49$, what is $m\angle DEF$?

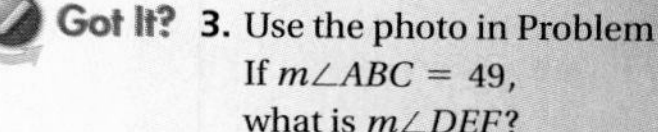

The Angle Addition Postulate is similar to the Segment Addition Postulate.

Postulate 1-8 Angle Addition Postulate

If point B is in the interior of $\angle AOC$, then $m\angle AOB + m\angle BOC = m\angle AOC$.

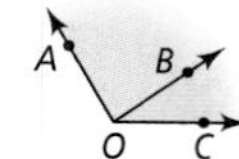

Problem 4 Using the Angle Addition Postulate

Plan

How can you use the expressions in the diagram?
The algebraic expressions represent the measures of the smaller angles, so they add up to the measure of the larger angle.

Algebra **If $m\angle RQT = 155$, what are $m\angle RQS$ and $m\angle TQS$?**

$m\angle RQS + m\angle TQS = m\angle RQT$	Angle Addition Postulate
$(4x - 20) + (3x + 14) = 155$	Substitute.
$7x - 6 = 155$	Combine like terms.
$7x = 161$	Add 6 to each side.
$x = 23$	Divide each side by 7.

$m\angle RQS = 4x - 20 = 4(23) - 20 = 92 - 20 = 72$
$m\angle TQS = 3x + 14 = 3(23) + 14 = 69 + 14 = 83$

Substitute 23 for x.

Got It? 4. $\angle DEF$ is a straight angle. What are $m\angle DEC$ and $m\angle CEF$?

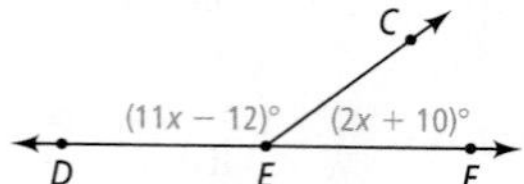

Answers

Got It? (continued)

3. 49

4. $m\angle DEC = 142$, $m\angle CEF = 38$

Lesson Check

Do you know HOW?

Use the diagram for Exercises 1–3.

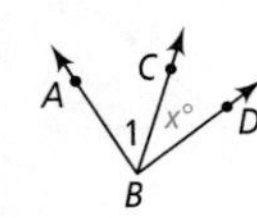

1. What are two other names for ∠1?
2. **Algebra** If $m\angle ABD = 85$, what is an expression to represent $m\angle ABC$?
3. Classify ∠ABC.

Do you UNDERSTAND?

4. **Vocabulary** How many sides can two congruent angles share? Explain.
5. **Error Analysis** Your classmate concludes from the diagram below that ∠JKL ≅ ∠LKM. Is your classmate correct? Explain.

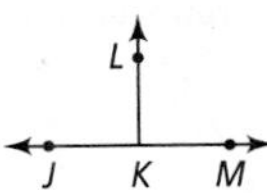

Practice and Problem-Solving Exercises

A Practice Name each shaded angle in three different ways. See Problem 1.

6. 7. 8.

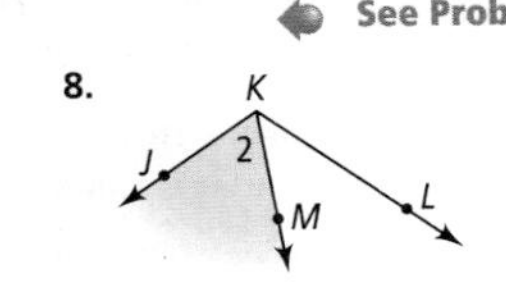

Use the diagram below. Find the measure of each angle. Then classify the angle as *acute*, *right*, *obtuse*, or *straight*. See Problem 2.

9. ∠EAF
10. ∠DAF
11. ∠BAE
12. ∠BAC
13. ∠CAE
14. ∠DAE

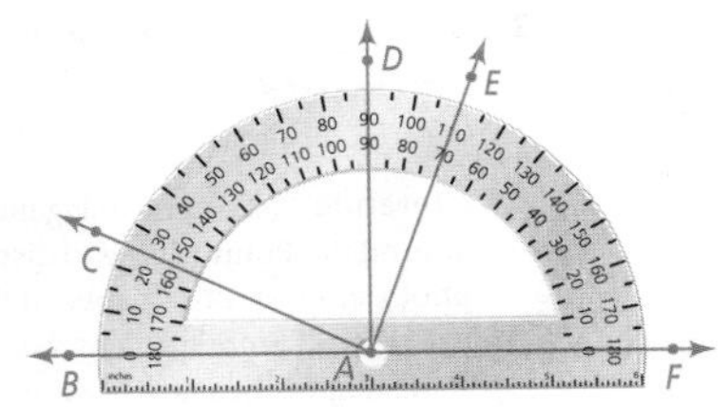

Draw a figure that fits each description.

15. an obtuse angle, ∠RST
16. an acute angle, ∠GHJ
17. a straight angle, ∠KLM

Use the diagram below. Complete each statement. See Problem 3.

18. ∠CBJ ≅ ■
19. ∠FJH ≅ ■
20. If $m\angle EFD = 75$, then $m\angle JAB =$ ■.
21. If $m\angle GHF = 130$, then $m\angle JBC =$ ■.

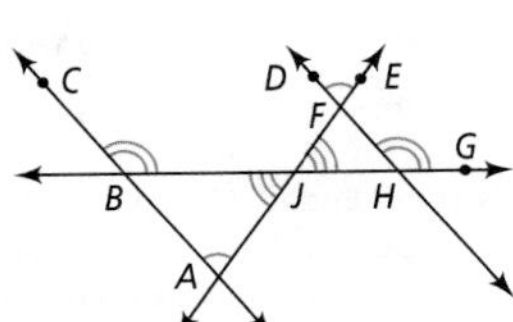

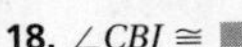

3 Lesson Check

Do you know HOW?

- If students have difficulty with Exercise 2, then remind them that the Angle Addition Postulate states that $m\angle ABC + m\angle CBD = m\angle ABD$, thus $m\angle ABC + x = 85$. Students can transform this equation to write an expression to represent $m\angle ABC$.

Do you UNDERSTAND?

- If students have difficulty with Exercise 5, then have them look for a way to show that they are not congruent.

Close

Q How are degrees used to measure and classify angles? **[Degrees are used to measure angles based on the definition that a full circle has 360°. The measurement of an angle in degrees is used to classify angles as acute, right, obtuse, or straight.]**

Lesson Check

1. ∠ABC, ∠CBA
2. 85 − x
3. acute
4. 0 or 1; congruent ∠s may be two separate angles, or they may have the same vertex and share one side.
5. No; the diagram is not marked with ≅ ∠s or with ⊥ lines.

Practice and Problem-Solving Exercises

6. ∠XYZ, ∠ZYX, ∠Y
7. ∠ABC, ∠CBA, ∠B or ∠1
8. ∠JKM, ∠MKJ, or ∠2
9. 70, acute
10. 90, right
11. 110, obtuse
12. 25, acute
13. 85, acute
14. 20, acute

15–16. Answers may vary. Samples are given.

15.–17.

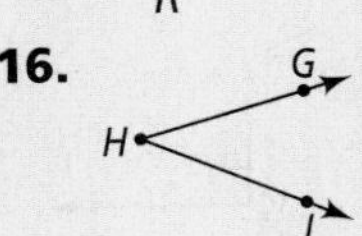

18. ∠FHG
19. ∠BJA
20. 75
21. 130

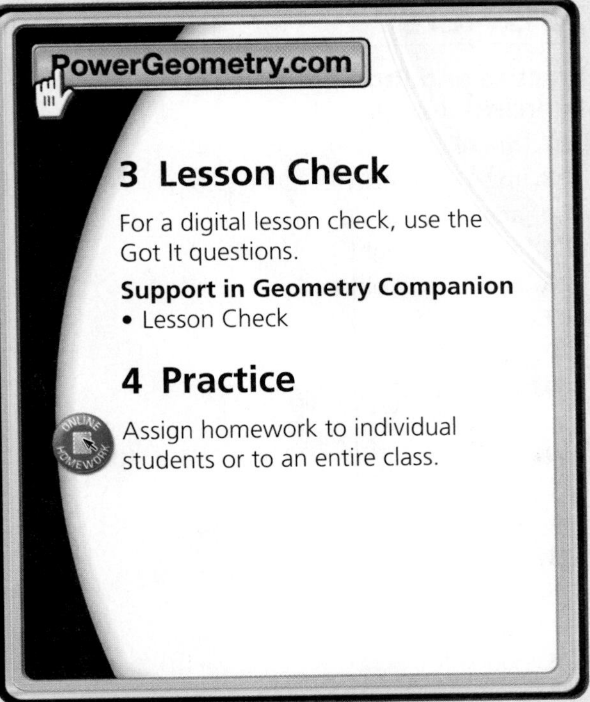

4 Practice

ASSIGNMENT GUIDE

Basic: 6–23 all, 24–28 even, 29, 31–32
Average: 7–23 odd, 24–32
Advanced: 7–23 odd, 24–40
Standardized Test Prep: 41–43
Mixed Review: 44–49
Reasoning exercises have blue headings.
Applications exercises have red headings.
EXERCISE 29: Use the Think About a Plan worksheet in the **Practice and Problem Solving Workbook** (also available in the Teaching Resources in print and online) to further support students' development in becoming independent learners.

HOMEWORK QUICK CHECK

To check students' understanding of key skills and concepts, go over Exercises 7, 19, 28, 29, and 32.

See Problem 4.

22. If $m\angle ABD = 79$, what are $m\angle ABC$ and $m\angle DBC$?

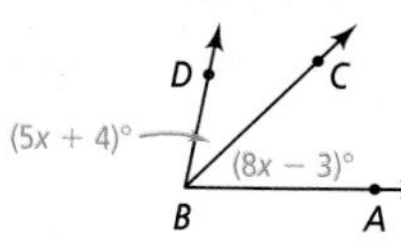

23. $\angle RQT$ is a straight angle. What are $m\angle RQS$ and $m\angle TQS$?

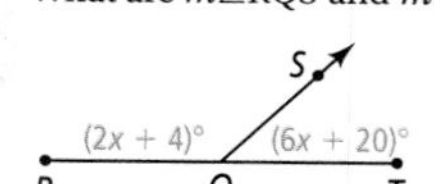
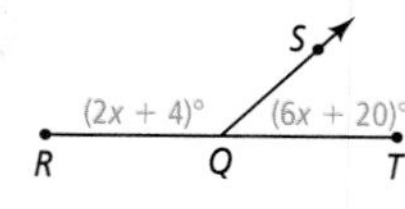

B Apply

Use a protractor. Measure and classify each angle.

24. 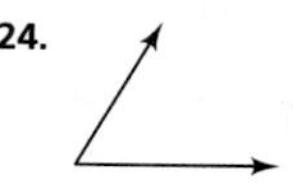

25. 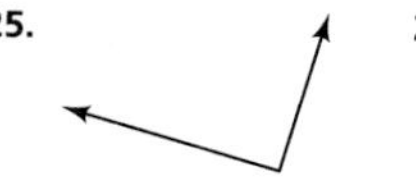

26. 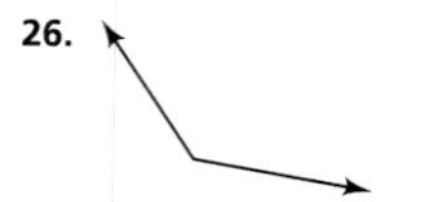

27. 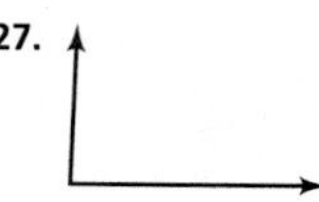

28. Think About a Plan A pair of earrings has blue wedges that are all the same size. One earring has a 25° yellow wedge. The other has a 14° yellow wedge. Find the angle measure of a blue wedge.

- How do the angle measures of the earrings relate?
- How can you use algebra to solve the problem?

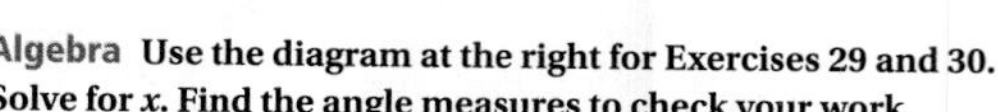

Algebra **Use the diagram at the right for Exercises 29 and 30. Solve for x. Find the angle measures to check your work.**

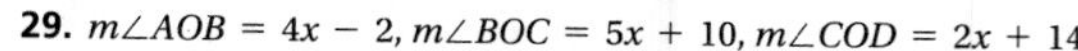

29. $m\angle AOB = 4x - 2$, $m\angle BOC = 5x + 10$, $m\angle COD = 2x + 14$

30. $m\angle AOB = 28$, $m\angle BOC = 3x - 2$, $m\angle AOD = 6x$

31. If $m\angle MQV = 90$, which expression can you use to find $m\angle VQP$?

Ⓐ $m\angle MQP - 90$
Ⓑ $90 - m\angle MQV$
Ⓒ $m\angle MQP + 90$
Ⓓ $90 + m\angle VQP$

32. Literature According to legend, King Arthur and his knights sat around the Round Table to discuss matters of the kingdom. The photo shows a round table on display at Winchester Castle, in England. From the center of the table, each section has the same degree measure. If King Arthur occupied two of these sections, what is the total degree measure of his section?

C Challenge

Time **Find the angle measure of the hands of a clock at each time.**

33. 6:00 **34.** 7:00 **35.** 11:00

36. 4:40 **37.** 5:20 **38.** 2:15

39. Open-Ended Sketch a right angle with vertex V. Name it $\angle 1$. Then sketch a 135° angle that shares a side with $\angle 1$. Name it $\angle PVB$. Is there more than one way to sketch $\angle PVB$? If so, sketch all the different possibilities. (*Hint:* Two angles are the same if you can rotate or flip one to match the other.)

Answers

Practice and Problem-Solving Exercises (continued)

22. $m\angle ABC = 45$, $m\angle DBC = 34$
23. $m\angle RQS = 43$, $m\angle TQS = 137$
24. about 60°; acute
25. about 90°; right
26. about 135°; obtuse
27. about 88°; acute
28. 5.5
29. $x = 8$; $m\angle AOB = 30$, $m\angle BOC = 50$, $m\angle COD = 30$
30. $x = 18$; $m\angle BOC = 52$, $m\angle AOD = 108$
31. A
32. 27.7
33. 180
34. 150
35. 30
36. 100
37. 40
38. 22.5
39a. yes;

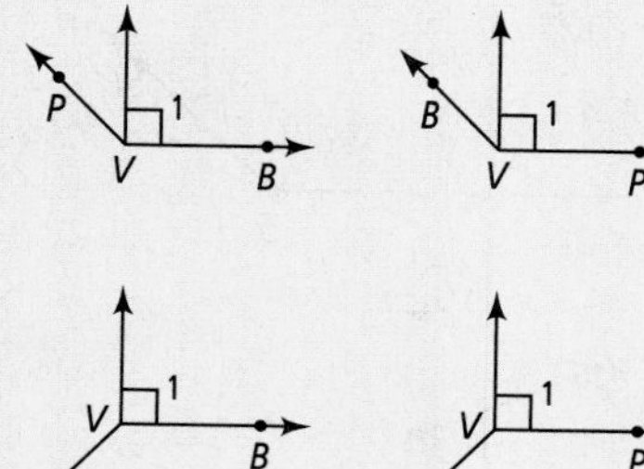

40. Technology Your classmate constructs an angle. Then he constructs a ray from the vertex of the angle to a point in the interior of the angle. He measures all the angles formed. Then he moves the interior ray as shown below. What postulate do the two pictures support?

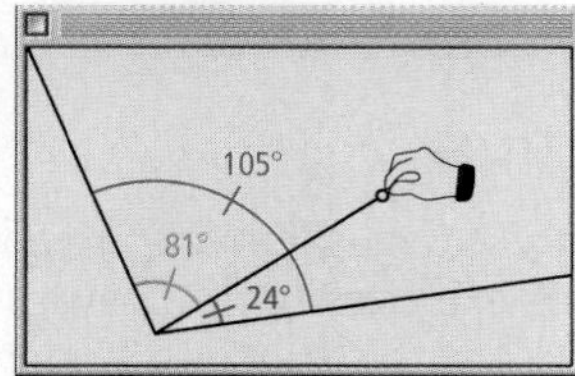

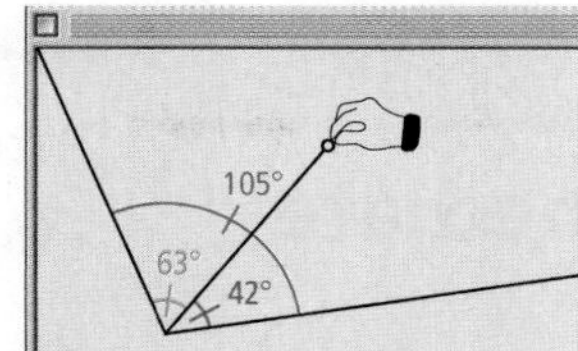

Standardized Test Prep

SAT/ACT

41. Which diagram shows the figure you can fold from the net at the right?

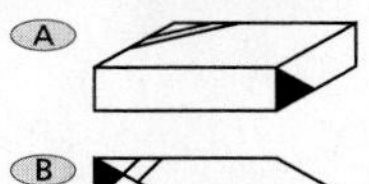

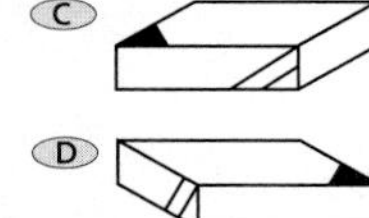

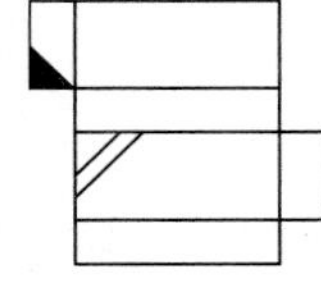

Ⓐ Ⓑ Ⓒ Ⓓ

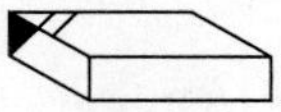

42. $\overline{XY}$ has coordinates $x = -72$ and $y = 43$. What is XY?

Ⓕ -115 Ⓖ -29 Ⓗ 29 Ⓘ 115

Short Response

43. Use the figure at the right.

a. What is the value of x?

b. What is AC?

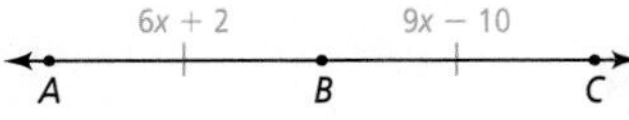

Mixed Review

Use the figure at the right.

E F G

See Lesson 1-3.

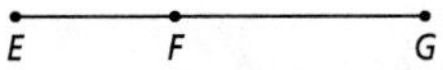

44. If $EG = 75$ and $EF = 28$, what is FG?

45. If $EG = 49$, $EF = 2x + 3$, and $FG = 4x - 2$, find x. Then find EF and FG.

Get Ready! **To prepare for Lesson 1-5, do Exercises 46–49.**

Algebra **Write and solve an equation to find the number(s).**

See p. 834.

46. Twice a number added to 4 is 28.

47. A number subtracted from 90 is three times that number.

48. The sum of two numbers is 180. One number is 5 times the other.

49. If $m\angle WXZ = 180$ and $m\angle ZXY = 115$, what is the measure of $\angle WXY$?

See Lesson 1-4.

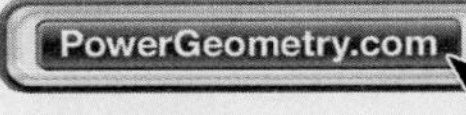

40. Angle Addition Postulate
41. B
42. I
43. [2] **a.** 4
b. 52
[1] one error
44. 47
45. $x = 8$, $EF = 19$, $FG = 30$
46. $2x + 4 = 28$; 12
47. $90 - x = 3x$; 22.5
48. $x + 5x = 180$; 30, 150
49. 65

1-4 Lesson Resources

Differentiated Remediation

Instructional Support

Geometry Companion

Students can use the **Geometry Companion** worktext (4 pages) . . .

- New Vocabulary
- Key Concepts
- Got It for each Problem
- Lesson Check

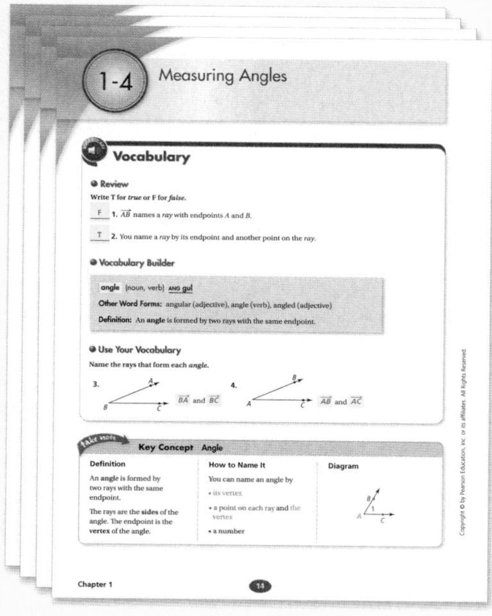

1-4 Measuring Angles

Vocabulary

Review

Write T for *true* or F for *false*.

F 1. $\overrightarrow{AB}$ names a *ray* with endpoints *A* and *B*.

T 2. You name a *ray* by its endpoint and another point on the *ray*.

Vocabulary Builder

angle (noun, verb) ANG gul

Other Word Forms: angular (adjective), angle (verb), angled (adjective)

Definition: An **angle** is formed by two rays with the same endpoint.

Use Your Vocabulary

Name the rays that form each *angle*.

3. $\overrightarrow{BA}$ and $\overrightarrow{BC}$ 4. $\overrightarrow{AB}$ and $\overrightarrow{AC}$

Key Concept Angle

Definition	How to Name It	Diagram
An **angle** is formed by two rays with the same endpoint. The rays are the **sides** of the angle. The endpoint is the **vertex** of the angle.	You can name an angle by • its vertex • a point on each ray and the vertex • a number	

Chapter 1 14

ELL Support

Focus on Communication Pair students so there is a more proficient student with a less proficient student. Draw adjacent angles ∠*RSQ* and ∠*QST*. Write: If ∠*RSQ* has an angle measure of $(2x + 5)$ and ∠*QST* has a measure of $3x$, what is the measure of ∠*RST*? Have students ask each other to describe the steps to find the missing angle measure. Encourage students to ask questions like: What is the first thing you would do? What is that postulate? What is that called? Is there another way to do that?

5 Assess & Remediate

Lesson Quiz

1. What are two other names for ∠2?

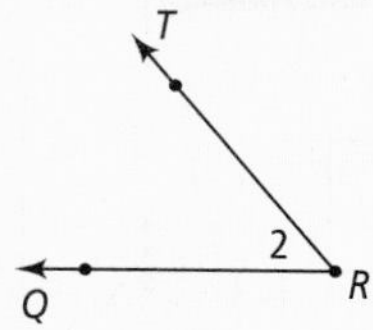

2. What are the measures of ∠*LKN*, ∠*HKL*, and ∠*HKN*? Classify each angle as acute, right, obtuse, or straight.

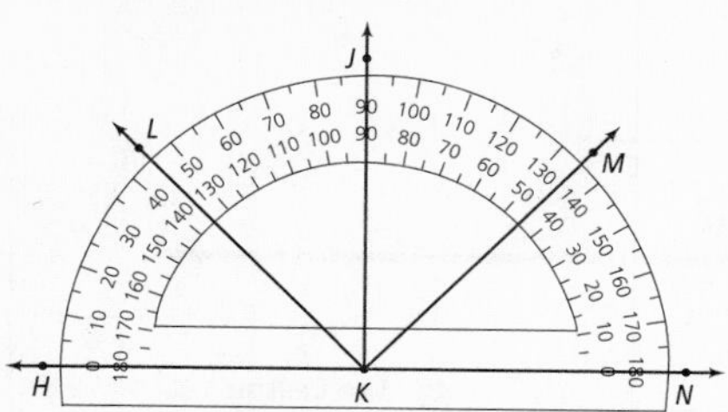

3. Do you UNDERSTAND? If $m\angle WXY = 160$, what are $m\angle WXZ$ and $m\angle ZXY$?

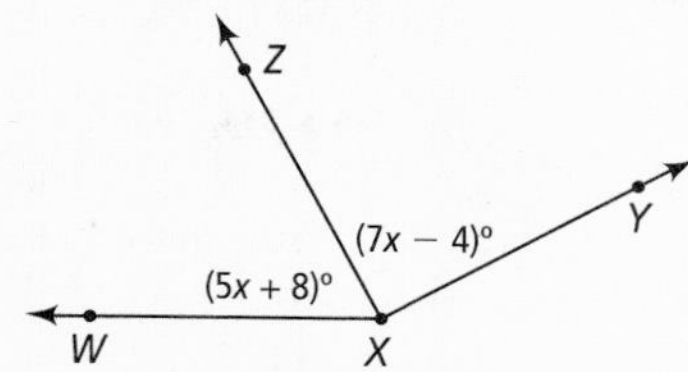

ANSWERS TO LESSON QUIZ

1. ∠*QRT* and ∠*TRQ*

2. $m\angle LKN = 135$, obtuse; $m\angle HKL = 45$, acute; $m\angle HKN = 180$, straight

3. $m\angle WXZ = 73$ and $m\angle ZXY = 87$

PRESCRIPTION FOR REMEDIATION

Use the student work on the Lesson Quiz to prescribe a differentiated review assignment.

Points	Differentiated Remediation
0–1	Intervention
2	On-level
3	Extension

PowerGeometry.com

5 Assess & Remediate

Assign the Lesson Quiz. Appropriate intervention, practice, or enrichment is automatically generated based on student performance.

Intervention

- **Reteaching** (2 pages) Provides reteaching and practice exercises for the key lesson concepts. Use with struggling students or absent students.
- **English Language Learner Support** Helps students develop and reinforce mathematical vocabulary and key concepts.

All-in-One Resources/Online

Reteaching

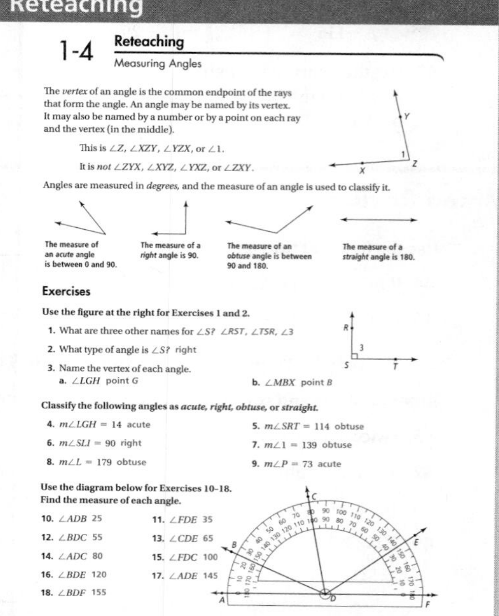

1-4 **Reteaching**
Measuring Angles

The *vertex* of an angle is the common endpoint of the rays that form the angle. An angle may be named by its vertex. It may also be named by a number or by a point on each ray and the vertex (in the middle).

This is ∠*Z*, ∠*XZY*, ∠*YZX*, or ∠1.

It is *not* ∠*ZYX*, ∠*XYZ*, ∠*YXZ*, or ∠*ZXY*.

Angles are measured in *degrees*, and the measure of an angle is used to classify it.

The measure of an *acute* angle is between 0 and 90. The measure of a *right* angle is 90. The measure of an *obtuse* angle is between 90 and 180. The measure of a *straight* angle is 180.

Exercises

Use the figure at the right for Exercises 1 and 2.

1. What are three other names for ∠*S*? ∠*RST*, ∠*TSR*, ∠3
2. What type of angle is ∠*S*? right
3. Name the vertex of each angle.
   a. ∠*LGH* point *G* b. ∠*MBX* point *B*

Classify the following angles as *acute, right, obtuse,* or *straight*.

4. $m\angle LGH = 14$ acute
5. $m\angle SRT = 114$ obtuse
6. $m\angle SLI = 90$ right
7. $m\angle 1 = 139$ obtuse
8. $m\angle L = 179$ obtuse
9. $m\angle P = 73$ acute

Use the diagram below for Exercises 10–18. Find the measure of each angle.

10. ∠*ADB* 25
11. ∠*FDE* 35
12. ∠*BDC* 55
13. ∠*CDE* 65
14. ∠*ADC* 80
15. ∠*FDC* 100
16. ∠*BDE* 120
17. ∠*ADE* 145
18. ∠*BDF* 155

All-in-One Resources/Online

English Language Learner Support

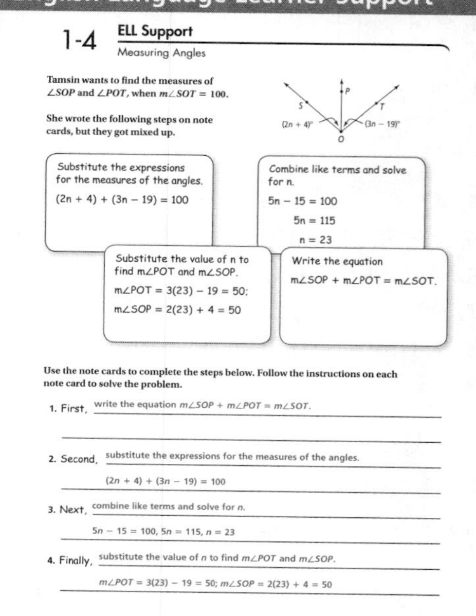

1-4 **ELL Support**
Measuring Angles

Tamsin wants to find the measures of ∠*SOP* and ∠*POT*, when $m\angle SOT = 100$.

She wrote the following steps on note cards, but they got mixed up.

Substitute the expressions for the measures of the angles. $(2n + 4) + (3n - 19) = 100$

Combine like terms and solve for n. $5n - 15 = 100$, $5n = 115$, $n = 23$

Substitute the value of n to find m∠POT and m∠SOP. $m\angle POT = 3(23) - 19 = 50$; $m\angle SOP = 2(23) + 4 = 50$

Write the equation $m\angle SOP + m\angle POT = m\angle SOT$.

Use the note cards to complete the steps below. Follow the instructions on each note card to solve the problem.

1. First, write the equation $m\angle SOP + m\angle POT = m\angle SOT$.
2. Second, substitute the expressions for the measures of the angles. $(2n + 4) + (3n - 19) = 100$
3. Next, combine like terms and solve for *n*. $5n - 15 = 100$, $5n = 115$, $n = 23$
4. Finally, substitute the value of *n* to find $m\angle POT$ and $m\angle SOP$. $m\angle POT = 3(23) - 19 = 50$; $m\angle SOP = 2(23) + 4 = 50$

Differentiated Remediation *continued*

On-Level

- **Practice** (2 pages) Provides extra practice for each lesson. For simpler practice exercises, use the Form K Practice pages found in the All-in-One Teaching Resources and online.
- **Think About a Plan** Helps students develop specific problem-solving skills and strategies by providing scaffolded guiding questions.
- **Standardized Test Prep** Focuses on all major exercises, all major question types, and helps students prepare for the high-stakes assessments.

Extension

- **Enrichment** Provides students with interesting problems and activities that extend the concepts of the lesson.
- **Activities, Games, and Puzzles** Worksheets that can be used for concepts development, enrichment, and for fun!

Practice and Problem Solving Wkbk/ All-in-One Resources/Online

Practice page 1

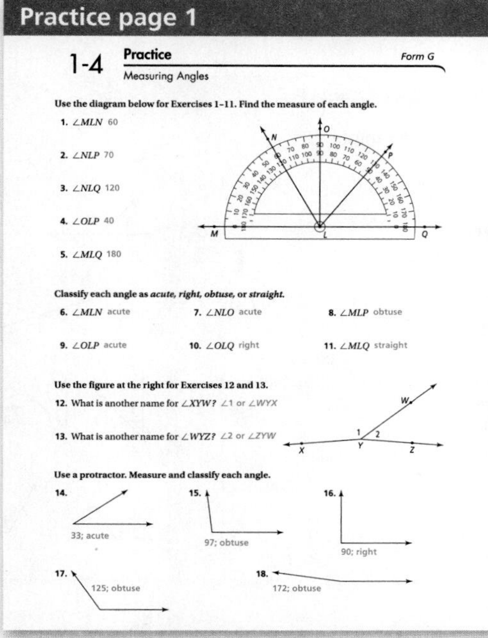

1-4 **Practice** — Measuring Angles — *Form G*

Use the diagram below for Exercises 1–11. Find the measure of each angle.

1. ∠*MLN* 60
2. ∠*NLP* 70
3. ∠*NLQ* 120
4. ∠*OLP* 40
5. ∠*MLQ* 180

Classify each angle as *acute, right, obtuse,* or *straight.*

6. ∠*MLN* acute
7. ∠*NLO* acute
8. ∠*MLP* obtuse
9. ∠*OLP* acute
10. ∠*OLQ* right
11. ∠*MLQ* straight

Use the figure at the right for Exercises 12 and 13.

12. What is another name for ∠*XYW*? ∠1 or ∠*WYX*
13. What is another name for ∠*WYZ*? ∠2 or ∠*ZYW*

Use a protractor. Measure and classify each angle.

14. 33; acute
15. 97; obtuse
16. 90; right
17. 125; obtuse
18. 172; obtuse

Practice and Problem Solving Wkbk/ All-in-One Resources/Online

Practice page 2

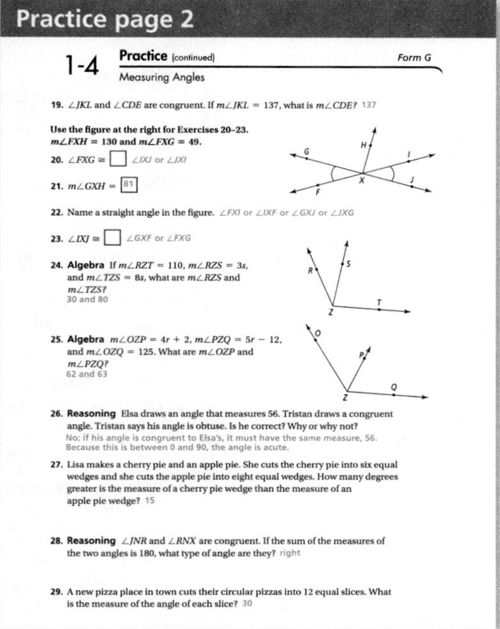

1-4 **Practice** (continued) — Measuring Angles — *Form G*

19. ∠*JKL* and ∠*CDE* are congruent. If *m*∠*JKL* = 137, what is *m*∠*CDE*? 137

Use the figure at the right for Exercises 20–23. *m*∠*FXH* = 130 and *m*∠*FXG* = 49.

20. ∠*FXG* ≅ ☐ ∠*IXJ* or ∠*JXI*
21. *m*∠*GXH* = ☐ 81
22. Name a straight angle in the figure. ∠*FXI* or ∠*IXF* or ∠*GXJ* or ∠*JXG*
23. ∠*IXJ* ≅ ☐ ∠*GXF* or ∠*FXG*
24. **Algebra** If *m*∠*RZT* = 110, *m*∠*RZS* = 3*s*, and *m*∠*TZS* = 8*s*, what are *m*∠*RZS* and *m*∠*TZS*? 30 and 80
25. **Algebra** *m*∠*OZP* = 4*r* + 2, *m*∠*PZQ* = 5*r* − 12, and *m*∠*OZQ* = 125. What are *m*∠*OZP* and *m*∠*PZQ*? 62 and 63
26. **Reasoning** Elsa draws an angle that measures 56. Tristan draws a congruent angle. Tristan says his angle is obtuse. Is he correct? Why or why not? No; if his angle is congruent to Elsa's, it must have the same measure, 56. Because this is between 0 and 90, the angle is acute.
27. Lisa makes a cherry pie and an apple pie. She cuts the cherry pie into six equal wedges and she cuts the apple pie into eight equal wedges. How many degrees greater is the measure of a cherry pie wedge than the measure of an apple pie wedge? 15
28. **Reasoning** ∠*JNR* and ∠*RNX* are congruent. If the sum of the measures of the two angles is 180, what type of angle are they? right
29. A new pizza place in town cuts their circular pizzas into 12 equal slices. What is the measure of the angle of each slice? 30

All-in-One Resources/Online

Enrichment

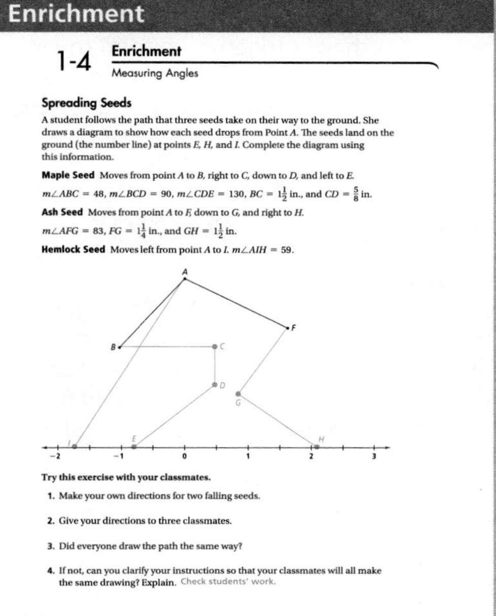

1-4 **Enrichment** — Measuring Angles

Spreading Seeds

A student follows the path that three seeds take on their way to the ground. She draws a diagram to show how each seed drops from Point *A*. The seeds land on the ground (the number line) at points *E*, *H*, and *I*. Complete the diagram using this information.

Maple Seed Moves from point *A* to *B*, right to *C*, down to *D*, and left to *E*.

m∠*ABC* = 48, *m*∠*BCD* = 90, *m*∠*CDE* = 130, *BC* = $1\frac{1}{2}$ in., and *CD* = $\frac{5}{8}$ in.

Ash Seed Moves from point *A* to *F*, down to *G*, and right to *H*.

m∠*AFG* = 83, *FG* = $1\frac{1}{4}$ in., and *GH* = $1\frac{1}{2}$ in.

Hemlock Seed Moves left from point *A* to *I*. *m*∠*AIH* = 59.

Try this exercise with your classmates.

1. Make your own directions for two falling seeds.
2. Give your directions to three classmates.
3. Did everyone draw the path the same way?
4. If not, can you clarify your instructions so that your classmates will all make the same drawing? Explain. Check students' work.

Practice and Problem Solving Wkbk/ All-in-One Resources/Online

Think About a Plan

1-4 **Think About a Plan** — Measuring Angles

Use the diagram at the right. Solve for *x*. Find the angle measures to check your work.

m∠*AOB* = 4*x* − 2, *m*∠*BOC* = 5*x* + 10, *m*∠*COD* = 2*x* + 14

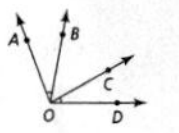

Understanding the Problem

1. The diagram shows that ∠*AOB* and ∠*COD* are congruent.
2. So, *m*∠*AOB* = *m*∠*COD*.

Planning the Solution

3. How can you use the information in Step 2 to write an equation for *x*? Substitute the given values of *m*∠*AOB* and *m*∠*COD* into the equation in Exercise 2.
4. Write an equation for *x*. 4*x* − 2 = 2*x* + 14

Getting an Answer

5. Solve for *x*. *x* = 8
6. Find the measures of the angles by substituting for *x*.
   m∠*AOB* = 30
   m∠*BOC* = 50
   m∠*COD* = 30
7. Measure the angles using a protractor to check your answers. Are they reasonable? yes

Practice and Problem Solving Wkbk/ All-in-One Resources/Online

Standardized Test Prep

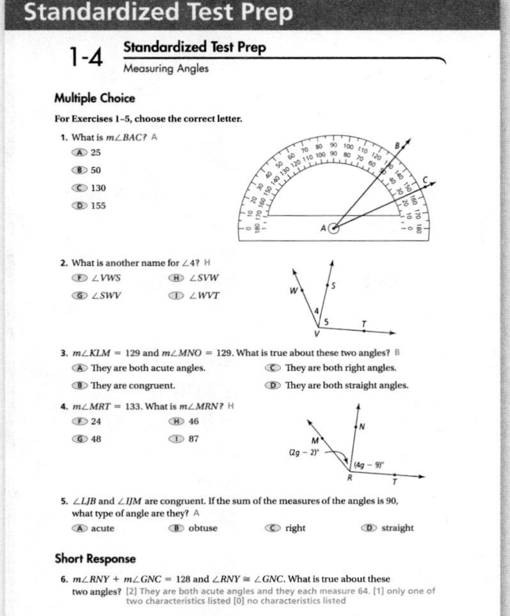

1-4 **Standardized Test Prep** — Measuring Angles

Multiple Choice

For Exercises 1–5, choose the correct letter.

1. What is *m*∠*BAC*? A
   (A) 25 (B) 50 (C) 130 (D) 155
2. What is another name for ∠4? H
   (F) ∠*VWS* (H) ∠*SVW* (G) ∠*SWV* (I) ∠*WVT*
3. *m*∠*KLM* = 129 and *m*∠*MNO* = 129. What is true about these two angles? B
   (A) They are both acute angles. (C) They are both right angles.
   (B) They are congruent. (D) They are both straight angles.
4. *m*∠*MRT* = 133. What is *m*∠*MRN*? H
   (F) 24 (H) 46 (G) 48 (I) 87
5. ∠*LJB* and ∠*IJM* are congruent. If the sum of the measures of the angles is 90, what type of angle are they? A
   (A) acute (B) obtuse (C) right (D) straight

Short Response

6. *m*∠*RNY* + *m*∠*GNC* = 128 and ∠*RNY* ≅ ∠*GNC*. What is true about these two angles? [2] They are both acute angles and they each measure 64. [1] only one of two characteristics listed [0] no characteristics listed

Online Teacher Resource Center

Activities, Games, and Puzzles

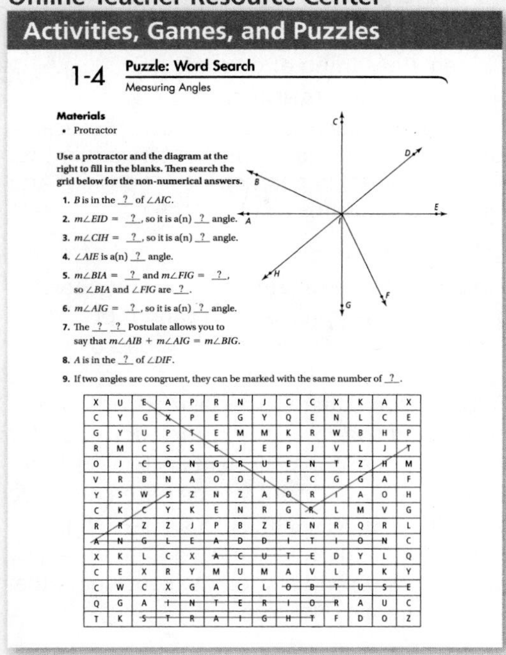

1-4 **Puzzle: Word Search** — Measuring Angles

Materials

- Protractor

Use a protractor and the diagram at the right to fill in the blanks. Then search the grid below for the non-numerical answers.

1. *B* is in the _?_ of ∠*AIC*.
2. *m*∠*EID* = _?_, so it is a(n) _?_ angle.
3. *m*∠*CIH* = _?_, so it is a(n) _?_ angle.
4. ∠*AIE* is a(n) _?_ angle.
5. *m*∠*BIA* = _?_ and *m*∠*FIG* = _?_, so ∠*BIA* and ∠*FIG* are _?_.
6. *m*∠*AIG* = _?_, so it is a(n) _?_ angle.
7. The _?_ _?_ Postulate allows you to say that *m*∠*AIB* + *m*∠*AIG* = *m*∠*BIG*.
8. *A* is in the _?_ of ∠*DIF*.
9. If two angles are congruent, they can be marked with the same number of _?_.

X	U	E	A	P	R	N	J	C	C	X	K	A	X
C	Y	G	X	P	E	G	Y	Q	E	N	L	C	E
G	Y	U	P	T	E	M	M	K	R	W	B	H	P
R	M	C	S	S	E	J	E	P	J	V	L	J	T
O	J	C	O	N	G	R	U	E	N	T	Z	H	M
V	R	B	N	A	O	O	I	F	C	G	G	A	F
Y	S	W	S	Z	N	Z	A	O	R	I	A	O	H
C	K	C	Y	K	E	N	R	G	R	L	M	V	G
R	R	Z	Z	J	P	B	Z	E	N	R	Q	R	L
A	N	G	L	E	A	D	D	I	T	I	O	N	C
X	K	L	C	X	A	C	U	T	E	D	Y	L	Q
C	E	X	R	Y	M	U	M	A	V	L	P	K	Y
C	W	C	X	G	A	C	L	O	B	T	U	S	E
Q	G	A	I	N	T	E	R	I	O	R	A	U	C
T	K	S	T	R	A	I	G	H	T	F	D	O	Z

1 Interactive Learning

Solve It!

PURPOSE To require students to find complements and supplements of angles that complete straight and right angles

PROCESS Students may use visual judgment or the process of elimination.

FACILITATE

Q How can you determine that the green triangle piece does not fit into the upper left-hand corner? **[Answers may vary. Sample: The sides of the triangle are too long to fit if the right corner of the triangle is placed in the corner of the box. If the triangle is placed so that the tip of the right angle is in the center of the top side, that leaves a gap in the upper left corner.]**

ANSWER See Solve It in Answers on next page.

CONNECT THE MATH In the Solve It angles are placed so that they fit together to form square corners and straight lines. In this lesson students learn that such angles have specific relationships and names.

2 Guided Instruction

Take Note

Adding a column of counterexamples into the summary table listed below can help students clarify the definitions of each angle pair. For example, the angles shown below would be an appropriate counterexample of angles that are not adjacent.

1-5 Exploring Angle Pairs

TN State Performance Indicator

SPI 3108.4.2 Define, identify, describe, and/or model plane figures using appropriate mathematical symbols (including collinear and non-collinear points, lines, segments, rays, angles, triangles, quadrilaterals, and other polygons).

Objective To identify special angle pairs and use their relationships to find angle measures

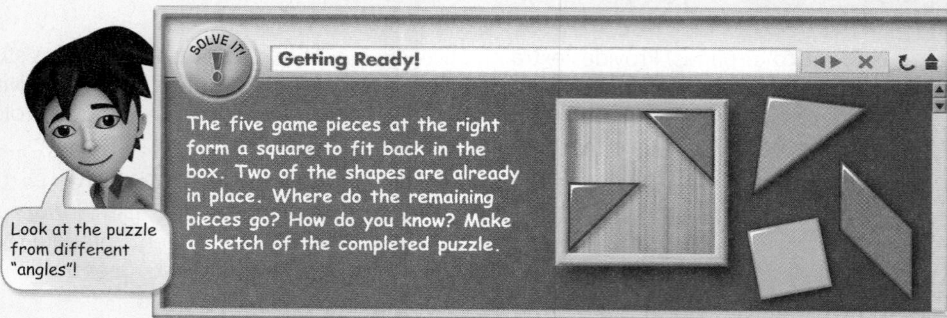
SOLVE IT!
Getting Ready!
The five game pieces at the right form a square to fit back in the box. Two of the shapes are already in place. Where do the remaining pieces go? How do you know? Make a sketch of the completed puzzle.
Look at the puzzle from different "angles"!

Lesson Vocabulary
- adjacent angles
- vertical angles
- complementary angles
- supplementary angles
- linear pair
- angle bisector

In this lesson, you will learn how to describe different kinds of angle pairs.

Essential Understanding Special angle pairs can help you identify geometric relationships. You can use these angle pairs to find angle measures.

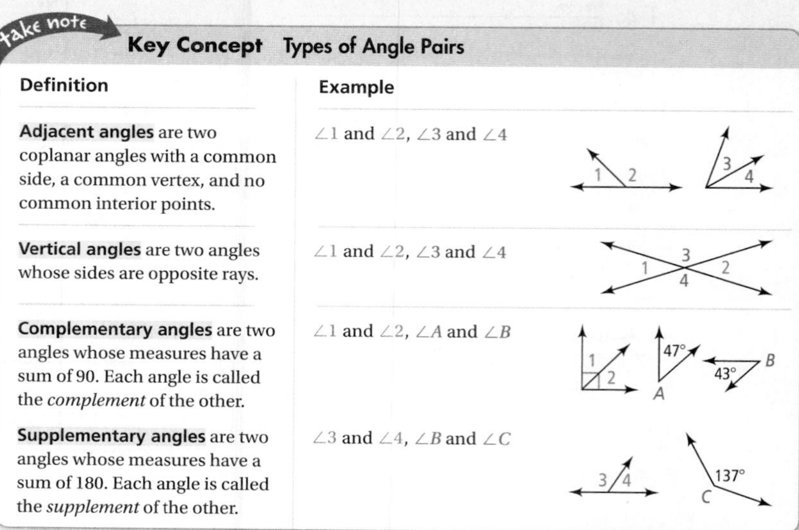

take note **Key Concept** Types of Angle Pairs

Definition	Example
Adjacent angles are two coplanar angles with a common side, a common vertex, and no common interior points.	$\angle 1$ and $\angle 2$, $\angle 3$ and $\angle 4$
Vertical angles are two angles whose sides are opposite rays.	$\angle 1$ and $\angle 2$, $\angle 3$ and $\angle 4$
Complementary angles are two angles whose measures have a sum of 90. Each angle is called the *complement* of the other.	$\angle 1$ and $\angle 2$, $\angle A$ and $\angle B$
Supplementary angles are two angles whose measures have a sum of 180. Each angle is called the *supplement* of the other.	$\angle 3$ and $\angle 4$, $\angle B$ and $\angle C$

1-5 Preparing to Teach

BIG idea Reasoning and Proof UbD

ESSENTIAL UNDERSTANDING
- Special angle pairs, such as adjacent, vertical, complementary, and supplementary angles, can be used to identify geometric relationships and to find angle measures.

Math Background

It is important in geometry to understand the information a diagram can and cannot provide. It is tempting to make assumptions based on the appearance of a diagram, but assumptions must be limited either to special markings or to knowledge of special geometric relationships. Many of the assumptions that students will make from diagrams in future lessons will be based on student knowledge of special angle pairs. For example, learning to recognize from a diagram that angles are vertical will eventually lead to concluding that the angles are also congruent.

Examine the diagram shown below.

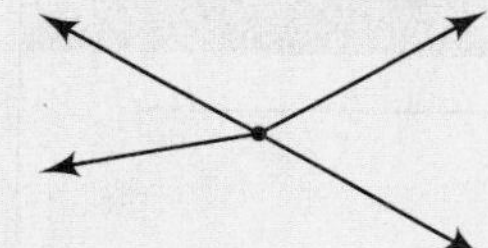

It is easy to see how a student may conclude that angles are congruent by vertical angles. However, a closer look at the diagram reveals that there is one line and two rays, and not just two intersecting lines.

Support Student Learning

Use the **Geometry Companion** to engage and support students during instructions. See Lesson Resources at the end of this lesson for details.

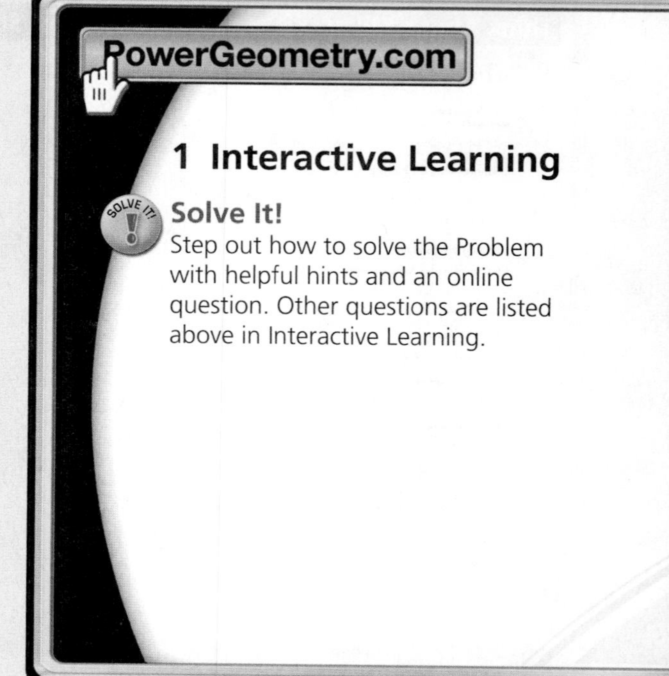
PowerGeometry.com
1 Interactive Learning
Solve It!
Step out how to solve the Problem with helpful hints and an online question. Other questions are listed above in Interactive Learning.

Plan

What should you look for in the diagram? For part (A), check whether the angle pair matches every part of the definition of adjacent angles.

Problem 1 Identifying Angle Pairs

Use the diagram at the right. Is the statement true? Explain.

A $\angle BFD$ **and** $\angle CFD$ **are adjacent angles.**

No. They have a common side ($\overrightarrow{FD}$) and a common vertex (F), but they also have common interior points. So $\angle BFD$ and $\angle CFD$ are not adjacent.

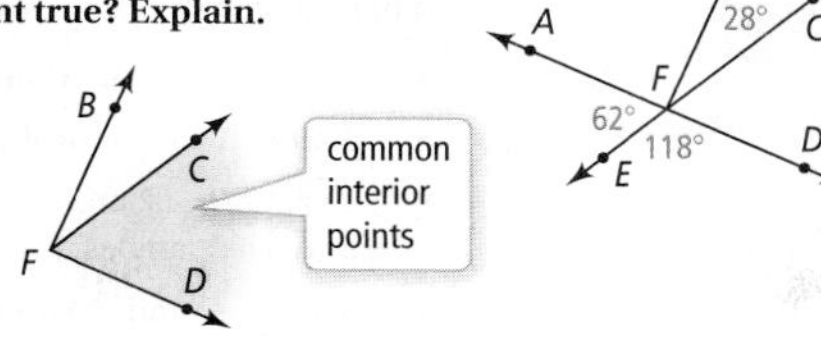

B $\angle AFB$ **and** $\angle EFD$ **are vertical angles.**

No. $\overrightarrow{FA}$ and $\overrightarrow{FD}$ are opposite rays, but $\overrightarrow{FE}$ and $\overrightarrow{FB}$ are not. So $\angle AFB$ and $\angle EFD$ are not vertical angles.

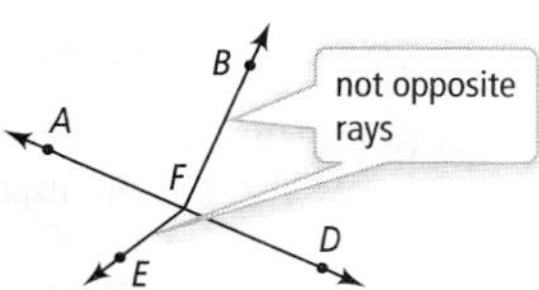

C $\angle AFE$ **and** $\angle BFC$ **are complementary.**

Yes. $m\angle AFE + m\angle BFC = 62 + 28 = 90$. The sum of the angle measures is 90, so $\angle AFE$ and $\angle BFC$ are complementary.

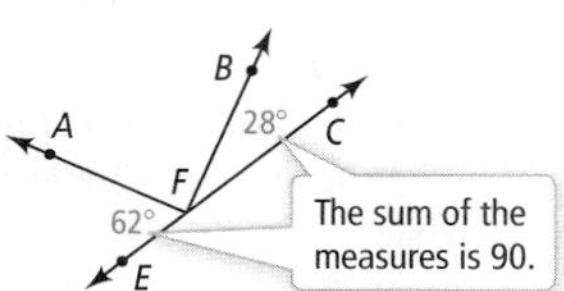

Got It? **1.** Use the diagram in Problem 1. Is the statement true? Explain.

a. $\angle AFE$ and $\angle CFD$ are vertical angles.

b. $\angle BFC$ and $\angle DFE$ are supplementary.

c. $\angle BFD$ and $\angle AFB$ are adjacent angles.

Take note — Concept Summary: Finding Information From a Diagram

There are some relationships you can assume to be true from a diagram that has no marks or measures. There are other relationships you cannot assume directly. For example, you *can* conclude the following from an unmarked diagram.

- Angles are adjacent.
- Angles are adjacent and supplementary.
- Angles are vertical angles.

You *cannot* conclude the following from an unmarked diagram.

- Angles or segments are congruent.
- An angle is a right angle.
- Angles are complementary.

Problem 1

Q What conditions must be met for two angles to be adjacent? **[They must have a common side, a common vertex, and no common interior points.]**

Q Do all vertical angles share a common vertex? Explain. **[Yes, the opposite rays all share the same endpoint, which is the vertex.]**

Q Are $\angle AFE$ and $\angle BFC$ adjacent? Explain. **[No, they do not share a common side.]**

Got It? VISUAL LEARNERS

Q What angle is supplementary to $\angle DFE$? Explain. **[$\angle AFE$ and $\angle CFD$ are supplementary to $\angle DFE$, because each forms a straight angle with $\angle DFE$, which by definition has a measure of 180.]**

Take Note

Q What are two ways to mark a right angle in a diagram? **[Indicate that the measure is 90 or include the right angle symbol in the corner of the angle.]**

Q Can a diagram be marked such that two angles can be assumed to be complementary without providing labels for the measures of the two angles? Explain. **[Yes, if two adjacent angles form a right angle that is marked with the right angle symbol, then you can assume that the angles are complementary.]**

2 Guided Instruction

Each Problem is worked out and supported online.

Problem 1
Identifying Angle Pairs
Animated

Problem 2
Making Conclusions From a Diagram
Animated

Problem 3
Finding Missing Angle Measures
Animated

Problem 4
Using an Angle Bisector to Find Angle Measures

Support in Geometry Companion

- Vocabulary
- Key Concepts
- Got It?

Answers

Solve It!

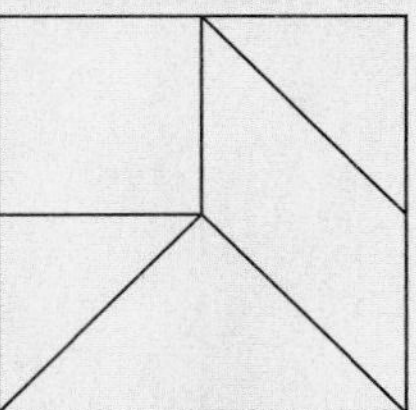

Check students' work.

Got It?

1a. Yes; $\angle AFE$ and $\angle CFD$ are formed by opposite rays $\overrightarrow{FA}$, $\overrightarrow{FD}$, $\overrightarrow{FC}$, and $\overrightarrow{FE}$.

b. No; $m\angle BFC = 28$ and $m\angle DFE = 118$, so $28 + 118 \neq 180$.

c. Yes; $\angle BFD$ and $\angle AFB$ share $\overrightarrow{FB}$, and they have no common interior points.

Problem 2

Q What is the relationship between ∠3 and ∠4? Explain. **[∠3 and ∠4 are adjacent supplementary angles, so the sum of the measure of the angles is 180.]**

Q Do any other pairs of angles in the diagram appear to be congruent? Can you assume that they are congruent based on appearance? **[∠3 and ∠5 appear congruent, but they are not marked as congruent. You cannot make the assumption that they are on the basis of appearance alone.]**

Got It? ERROR PREVENTION

Q In 2d, can you conclude that $\overline{PQ}$ bisects $\overline{TV}$? Explain. **[Yes, $\overline{PQ}$ divides $\overline{TV}$ into two congruent segments.]**

Take Note TACTILE LEARNERS

Have students use a ruler to construct a linear pair of angles. Students can then use a protractor to measure the angles and verify that the angles are indeed supplementary.

Problem 3 ERROR PREVENTION

Make sure that students realize that the position of $\overrightarrow{PL}$ in the sketch is arbitrary. With this in mind, emphasize that just because the calculated measures for ∠KPL and ∠JPL may not match the sketch as measured with a protractor, this does not indicate that the problem was done incorrectly.

Think

How can you get information from a diagram?
Look for relationships between angles. For example, look for congruent angles and adjacent angles.

Problem 2 Making Conclusions From a Diagram

What can you conclude from the information in the diagram?

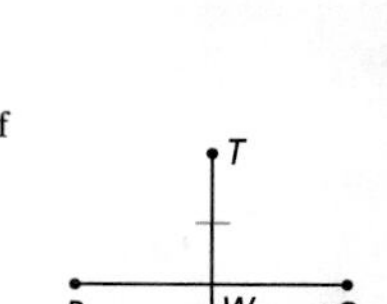

- ∠1 ≅ ∠2 by the markings.
- ∠3 and ∠5 are vertical angles.
- ∠1 and ∠2, ∠2 and ∠3, ∠3 and ∠4, ∠4 and ∠5, and ∠5 and ∠1 are adjacent angles.
- ∠3 and ∠4, and ∠4 and ∠5 are adjacent supplementary angles. So, $m\angle 3 + m\angle 4 = 180$ and $m\angle 4 + m\angle 5 = 180$ by the definition of supplementary angles.

Got It? **2.** Can you make each conclusion from the information in the diagram? Explain.

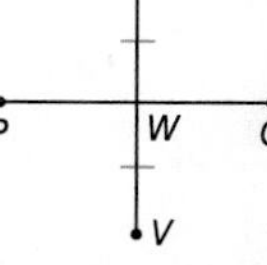

a. $\overline{TW} \cong \overline{WV}$ **b.** $\overline{PW} \cong \overline{WQ}$
c. ∠TWQ is a right angle. **d.** $\overline{TV}$ bisects $\overline{PQ}$.

A **linear pair** is a pair of adjacent angles whose noncommon sides are opposite rays. The angles of a linear pair form a straight angle.

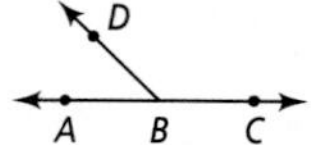

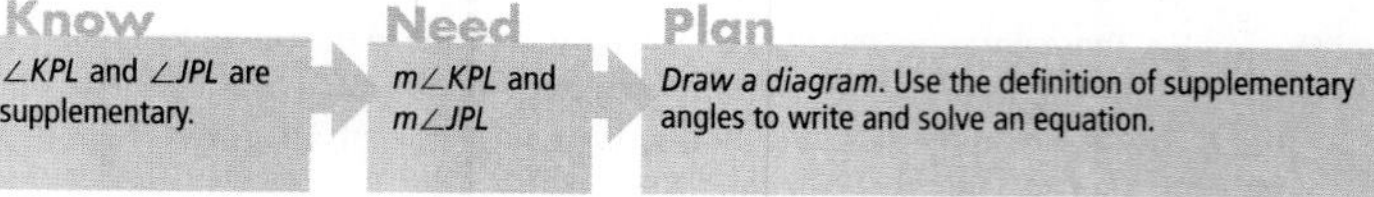

Postulate 1-9 Linear Pair Postulate

If two angles form a linear pair, then they are supplementary.

Problem 3 Finding Missing Angle Measures

Algebra **∠KPL and ∠JPL are a linear pair, $m\angle KPL = 2x + 24$, and $m\angle JPL = 4x + 36$. What are the measures of ∠KPL and ∠JPL?**

Know	Need	Plan
∠KPL and ∠JPL are supplementary.	m∠KPL and m∠JPL	*Draw a diagram.* Use the definition of supplementary angles to write and solve an equation.

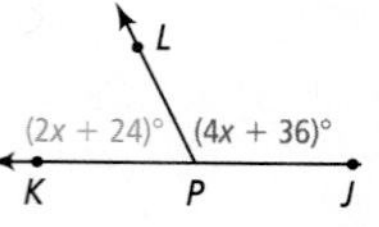

Step 1

$m\angle KPL + m\angle JPL = 180$	Def. of supplementary angles
$(2x + 24) + (4x + 36) = 180$	Substitute.
$6x + 60 = 180$	Combine like terms.
$6x = 120$	Subtract 60 from each side.
$x = 20$	Divide each side by 6.

Step 2 Evaluate the original expressions for $x = 20$.

$m\angle KPL = 2x + 24 = 2 \cdot 20 + 24 = 40 + 24 = 64$

$m\angle JPL = 4x + 36 = 4 \cdot 20 + 36 = 80 + 36 = 116$

Substitute 20 for *x*.

Additional Problems

1. Use the diagram below. Is each statement true? Explain.

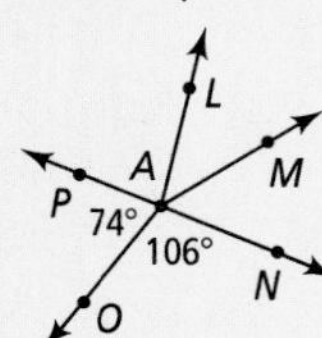

a. ∠PAL and ∠LAM are adjacent angles.
b. ∠PAO and ∠NAM are vertical angles.
c. ∠PAO and ∠NAO are supplementary.

ANSWER **a.** Yes, they have a common side, a common vertex, and share no interior points **b.** No, they do not share two pairs of opposite rays **c.** Yes, the sum of the angles is 180.

2. What can you conclude from the information in the diagram?

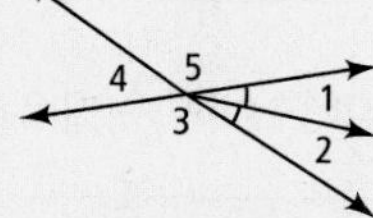

ANSWER angles 1 and 2 are congruent; angles 3 and 5 are vertical angles; the angle pairs 1 and 2, 2 and 3, 3 and 4, 4 and 5, 5 and 1 are all pairs of adjacent angles; angles 4 and 5 and angles 3 and 4 are adjacent supplementary angles

3. ∠ABC and ∠DBC are a linear pair, $m\angle ABC = 3x + 19$, and $m\angle DBC = 7x - 9$. What are the measures of ∠ABC and ∠DBC?

ANSWER $m\angle ABC = 70$, $m\angle DBC = 110$

4. $\overrightarrow{LM}$ bisects ∠JLN. If $m\angle JLM = 42$, what is $m\angle JLN$?

A. 21
B. 42
C. 60
D. 84

ANSWER D

Got It? 3. a. **Reasoning** How can you check your results in Problem 3?
b. $\angle ADB$ and $\angle BDC$ are a linear pair. $m\angle ADB = 3x + 14$ and $m\angle BDC = 5x - 2$. What are $m\angle ADB$ and $m\angle BDC$?

An **angle bisector** is a ray that divides an angle into two congruent angles. Its endpoint is at the angle vertex. Within the ray, a segment with the same endpoint is also an angle bisector. The ray or segment bisects the angle. In the diagram, $\overrightarrow{AY}$ is the angle bisector of $\angle XAZ$, so $\angle XAY \cong \angle YAZ$.

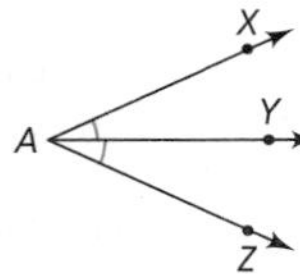

Problem 4 Using an Angle Bisector to Find Angle Measures

Multiple Choice $\overrightarrow{AC}$ **bisects** $\angle DAB$**. If** $m\angle DAC = 58$**, what is** $m\angle DAB$**?**

(A) 29 (B) 58 (C) 87 (D) 116

Plan
Draw a diagram to help you visualize what you are given and what you need to find.

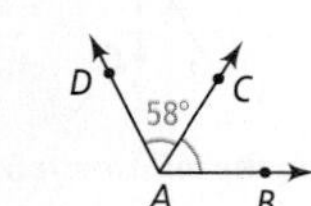

Draw a diagram.

$m\angle CAB = m\angle DAC$	Definition of angle bisector
$= 58$	Substitute.
$m\angle DAB = m\angle CAB + m\angle DAC$	Angle Addition Postulate
$= 58 + 58$	Substitute.
$= 116$	Simplify.

The measure of $\angle DAB$ is 116. The correct choice is D.

Got It? 4. $\overrightarrow{KM}$ bisects $\angle JKL$. If $m\angle JKL = 72$, what is $m\angle JKM$?

Lesson Check

Do you know HOW?

Name a pair of the following types of angle pairs.

1. vertical angles
2. complementary angles
3. linear pair

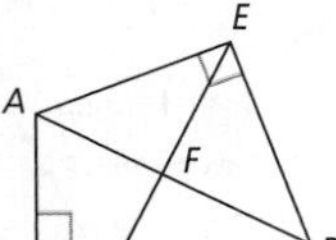

4. $\overrightarrow{PB}$ bisects $\angle RPT$ so that $m\angle RPB = x + 2$ and $m\angle TPB = 2x - 6$. What is $m\angle RPT$?

Do you UNDERSTAND?

5. **Vocabulary** How does the term *linear pair* describe how the angle pair looks?
6. **Error Analysis** Your friend calculated the value of *x* below. What is her error?

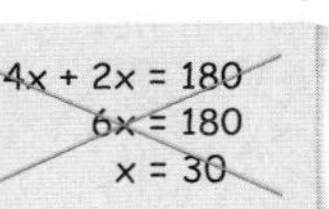

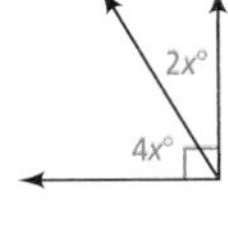

Got It? ERROR PREVENTION

Q In 3a, why is checking the value of *x* not the best way to check your results? **[If the equation is not written correctly, the solution to the equation is not the answer.]**

Problem 4

Q Why might choice B be the most common wrong answer given by students? **[Students think they should determine** $m\angle CAB$**, instead they should determine** $m\angle DAB$**.]**

Got It?

Q Using the information given in Problem 4, what congruence statement can you write? **[$\angle JKM \cong \angle MKL$]**

3 Lesson Check

Do you know HOW?

- For Exercise 3, ask students to verbalize all assumptions that can be made about the linear pair of angles that they identify.

Do you UNDERSTAND?

- For Exercise 6, ask students to state how the equation might be adjusted to correct the error.

Close

Q How can you remember that the sum of the measures of complementary angles is 90 and the sum of the measures of supplementary angles is 180? **[Answers may vary. Sample: Complementary angles can fit into a "Corner"; Supplementary angles fit along Straight lines.]**

Answers

Got It? (continued)

2a. Yes; they have corresponding ≅ tick marks.
b. No; they do not have corresponding ≅ tick marks.
c. No; it (or its supplements) do not have a right angle symbol.
d. No; $\overline{PW}$ and $\overline{WQ}$ do not have corresponding ≅ tick marks.
3a. Adding the measures of both ∡ should give 180.
b. $m\angle ADB = 77$, $m\angle BDC = 103$
4. 36

Lesson Check

1. Answers may vary. Sample: $\angle AFE$ and $\angle CFD$ (or $\angle AFC$ and $\angle EFD$)
2. Answers may vary. Sample: $\angle AEF$ and $\angle DEF$ (or $\angle AEC$ and $\angle DEC$)
3. Answers may vary. Sample: $\angle BCE$ and $\angle ECD$ (or any two adjacent ∡ with common vertex F)
4. 20
5. Answers may vary. Sample: The angles combine to form a line.
6. Since the ∡ are complementary, the sum of the two measures should be 90, not 180. So, $x = 15$.

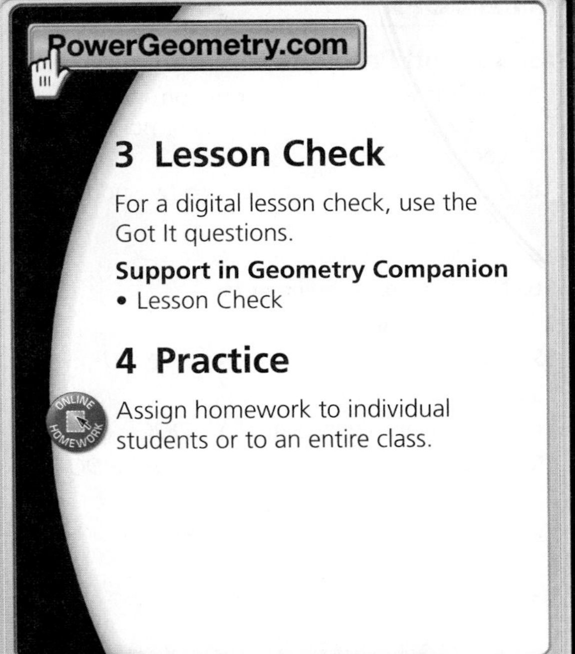

4 Practice

ASSIGNMENT GUIDE

Basic: 7–26 all, 28–30 even, 31, 34–38 even, 39–40

Average: 7–25 odd, 27–41

Advanced: 7–25 odd, 27–47

Standardized Test Prep: 48–50

Mixed Review: 51–59

Reasoning exercises have blue headings.

Applications exercises have red headings.

EXERCISE 39: Use the Think About a Plan worksheet in the **Practice and Problem Solving Workbook** (also available in the Teaching Resources in print and online) to further support students' development in becoming independent learners.

HOMEWORK QUICK CHECK

To check students' understanding of key skills and concepts, go over Exercises 11, 17, 31, 38, and 39.

Practice and Problem-Solving Exercises

A Practice

Use the diagram at the right. Is each statement true? Explain. See Problem 1.

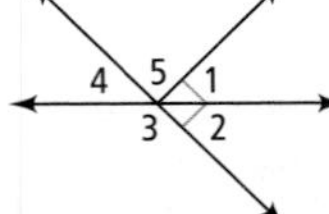

7. $\angle 1$ and $\angle 5$ are adjacent angles.

8. $\angle 3$ and $\angle 5$ are vertical angles.

9. $\angle 3$ and $\angle 4$ are complementary.

10. $\angle 1$ and $\angle 2$ are supplementary.

Name an angle or angles in the diagram described by each of the following.

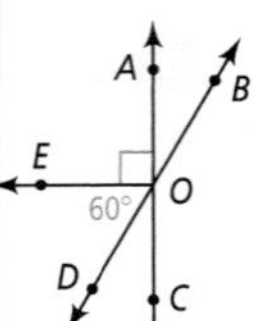

11. supplementary to $\angle AOD$

12. adjacent and congruent to $\angle AOE$

13. supplementary to $\angle EOA$

14. complementary to $\angle EOD$

15. a pair of vertical angles

For Exercises 16–23, can you make each conclusion from the information in the diagram? Explain. See Problem 2.

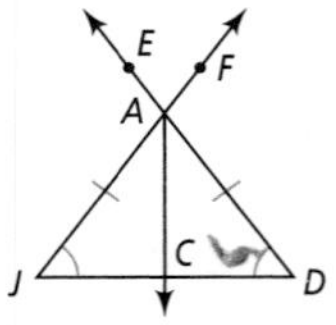

16. $\angle J \cong \angle D$

17. $\angle JAC \cong \angle DAC$

18. $m\angle JCA = m\angle DCA$

19. $m\angle JCA + m\angle ACD = 180$

20. $\overline{AJ} \cong \overline{AD}$

21. C is the midpoint of $\overline{JD}$.

22. $\angle JAE$ and $\angle EAF$ are adjacent and supplementary.

23. $\angle EAF$ and $\angle JAD$ are vertical angles.

See Problem 3.

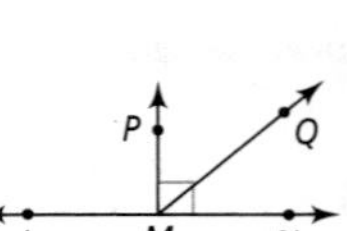

24. Name two pairs of angles that form a linear pair in the diagram at the right.

25. $\angle EFG$ and $\angle GFH$ are a linear pair, $m\angle EFG = 2n + 21$, and $m\angle GFH = 4n + 15$. What are $m\angle EFG$ and $m\angle GFH$?

See Problem 4.

26. Algebra In the diagram, $\overrightarrow{GH}$ bisects $\angle FGI$.

a. Solve for x and find $m\angle FGH$.

b. Find $m\angle HGI$.

c. Find $m\angle FGI$.

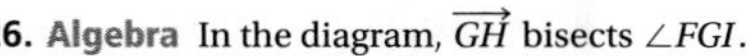

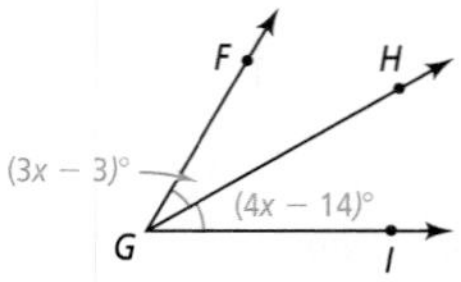

Answers

Practice and Problem-Solving Exercises

7. Yes, the angles share a common side and vertex, and have no interior points in common.

8. No, the angles are not formed by opposite rays.

9. No, they are supplementary.

10. No, they are complementary.

11. $\angle DOC$, $\angle AOB$

12. $\angle EOC$

13. $\angle EOC$

14. Answers may vary. Sample: $\angle DOC$

15. Answers may vary. Sample: $\angle AOB$, $\angle DOC$

16. Yes; they are marked as $\cong$.

17. No; they are not marked as $\cong$.

18. No; they are not marked as $\cong$.

19. Yes. Answers may vary. Sample: The two ∠s form a linear pair.

20. Yes; they are marked as $\cong$.

21. No; $\overline{JC}$ and $\overline{CD}$ are not marked as $\cong$.

22. Yes; they form a linear pair.

23. Yes; they are formed by $\overleftrightarrow{JF}$ and $\overleftrightarrow{ED}$.

24. $\angle LMP$ and $\angle PMN$, $\angle LMQ$ and $\angle QMN$

25. $m\angle EFG = 69$, $m\angle GFH = 111$

26a. $x = 11$, $m\angle FGH = 30$

b. 30

c. 60

B Apply

Algebra $\overrightarrow{BD}$ bisects $\angle ABC$. Solve for x and find $m\angle ABC$.

27. $m\angle ABD = 5x$, $m\angle DBC = 3x + 10$

28. $m\angle ABC = 4x - 12$, $m\angle ABD = 24$

29. $m\angle ABD = 4x - 16$, $m\angle CBD = 2x + 6$

30. $m\angle ABD = 3x + 20$, $m\angle CBD = 6x - 16$

Algebra Find the measure of each angle in the angle pair described.

31. Think About a Plan The measure of one angle is twice the measure of its supplement.
- How many angles are there? What is their relationship?
- How can you use algebra, such as using the variable x, to help you?

32. The measure of one angle is 20 less than the measure of its complement.

In the diagram at the right, $m\angle ACB = 65$. Find each of the following.

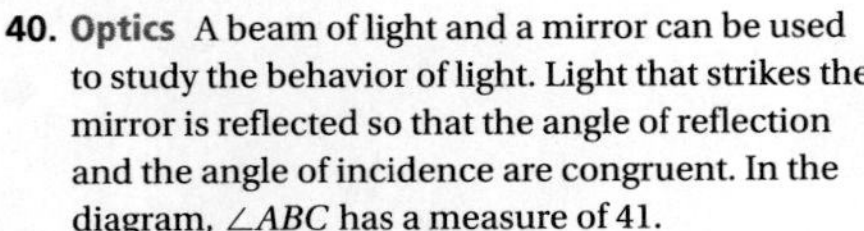

33. $m\angle ACD$ **34.** $m\angle BCD$

35. $m\angle ECD$ **36.** $m\angle ACE$

37. Algebra $\angle RQS$ and $\angle TQS$ are a linear pair where $m\angle RQS = 2x + 4$ and $m\angle TQS = 6x + 20$.

a. Solve for x.
b. Find $m\angle RQS$ and $m\angle TQS$.
c. Show how you can check your answer.

38. Writing In the diagram at the right, are $\angle 1$ and $\angle 2$ adjacent? Justify your reasoning.

39. Reasoning When $\overrightarrow{BX}$ bisects $\angle ABC$, $\angle ABX \cong \angle CBX$. One student claims there is always a related equation $m\angle ABX = \frac{1}{2}m\angle ABC$. Another student claims the related equation is $2m\angle ABX = m\angle ABC$. Who is correct? Explain.

40. Optics A beam of light and a mirror can be used to study the behavior of light. Light that strikes the mirror is reflected so that the angle of reflection and the angle of incidence are congruent. In the diagram, $\angle ABC$ has a measure of 41.

a. Name the angle of reflection and find its measure.
b. Find $m\angle ABD$.
c. Find $m\angle ABE$ and $m\angle DBF$.

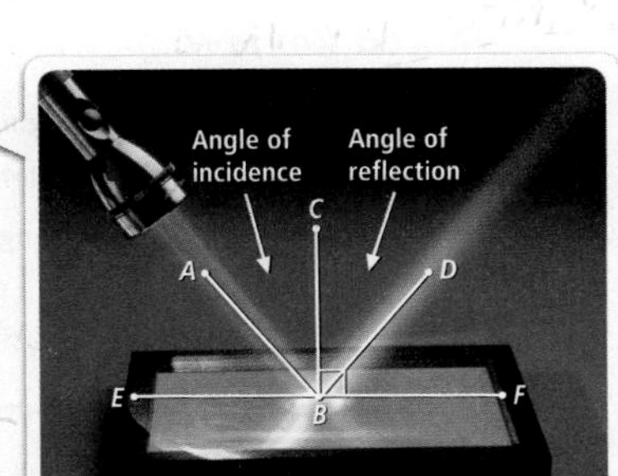

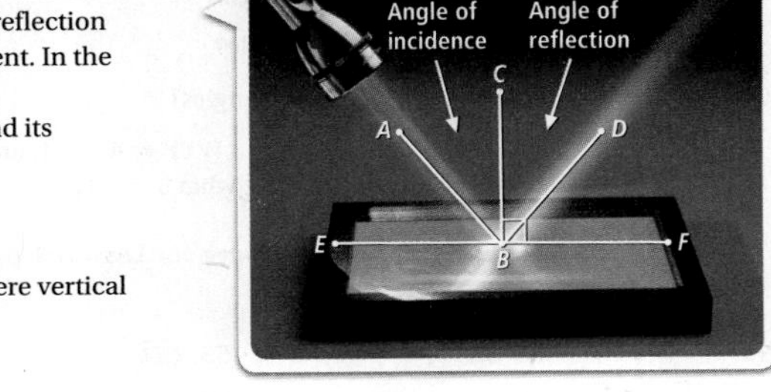

41. Reasoning Describe all situations where vertical angles are also supplementary.

PowerGeometry.com | Lesson 1-5 Exploring Angle Pairs | 39

27. $x = 5$, $m\angle ABC = 50$
28. $x = 15$, $m\angle ABC = 48$
29. $x = 11$, $m\angle ABC = 56$
30. $x = 12$, $m\angle ABC = 112$
31. 120; 60
32. 35, 55
33. 90
34. 25
35. 155
36. 115
37a. 19.5
b. $m\angle RQS = 43$, $m\angle TQS = 137$
c. Answers may vary. Sample: $43 + 137 = 180$

38. No; they do not have a common vertex.
39. Both are correct; if you multiply both sides of the equation $m\angle ABX = \frac{1}{2}m\angle ABC$ by 2, you get $2m\angle ABX = m\angle ABC$.
40a. $\angle CBD$; 41
b. 82
c. 49; 49
41. The four vertical angles are all right angles.

Answers

Practice and Problem-Solving Exercises (continued)

44. ∠KMQ, ∠KML, ∠NMR, ∠PMR, ∠MQP

43. ∠KML

44. ∠LMN, ∠PMQ

45. ∠PMR, ∠KML, ∠KMQ, ∠MQP

46. $y = x$

47. 30

48. C

49. I

50. [2] Answers may vary. Sample:

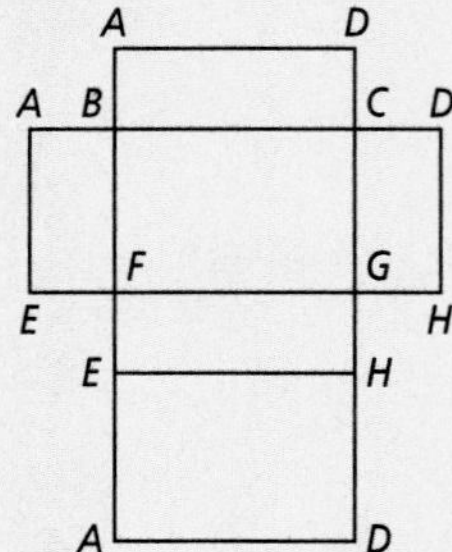

When the net is folded, the vertices with the same letter meet.

[1] error in net OR description

51. ∠WXY

52. ∠WXZ, ∠YXZ

53. 39

54. Answers may vary. Sample:

G H

55. Answers may vary. Sample:

56. Answers may vary. Sample:

57. Answers may vary. Sample:

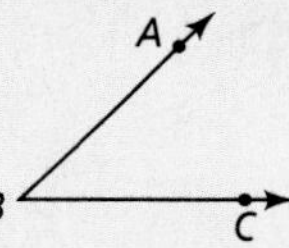

58. Answers may vary. Sample:

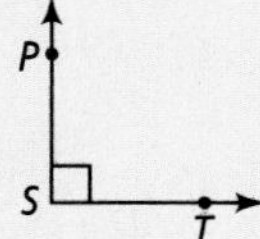

59. Answers may vary. Sample:

Challenge **Name all of the angle(s) in the diagram described by the following.**

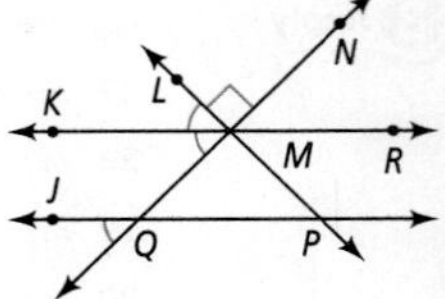

42. supplementary to ∠JQM **43.** adjacent and congruent to ∠KMQ

44. a linear pair with ∠LMQ **45.** complementary to ∠NMR

46. Coordinate Geometry The *x*- and *y*-axes of the coordinate plane form four right angles. The interior of each of the right angles is a quadrant of the coordinate plane. What is the equation for the line that contains the angle bisector of Quadrants I and III?

47. $\overrightarrow{XC}$ bisects ∠AXB, $\overrightarrow{XD}$ bisects ∠AXC, $\overrightarrow{XE}$ bisects ∠AXD, $\overrightarrow{XF}$ bisects ∠EXD, $\overrightarrow{XG}$ bisects ∠EXF, and $\overrightarrow{XH}$ bisects ∠DXB. If $m\angle DXC = 16$, find $m\angle GXH$.

Standardized Test Prep

SAT/ACT

48. Which statement is true?

(A) A right angle has a complement.
(B) An obtuse angle has a complement.
(C) The supplement of a right angle is a right angle.
(D) Every angle has a supplement.

49. The diagram shows distance in meters. How far, in meters, is it from the parking lot to your house?

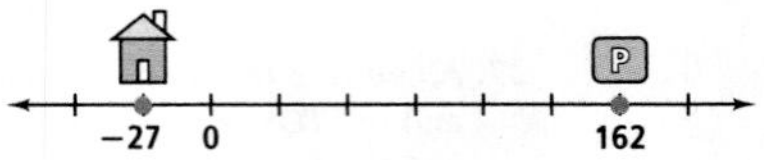

(F) 44 (H) 183
(G) 135 (I) 189

−27 0 162

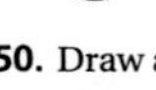

Short Response

50. Draw a net for the box at the right. Label each corner with its corresponding letter. Some letters will be repeated. How can the repeated letters on the net help you visualize how the net folds into the solid?

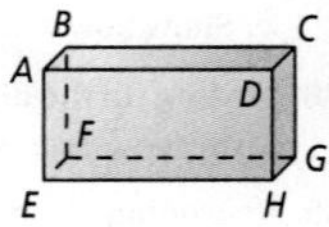

Mixed Review

Use the diagram at the right. See Lesson 1-4.

51. What is the acute angle?

52. What are the obtuse angles?

53. If $m\angle WXZ = 150$, $m\angle WXY = 8x - 1$, and $m\angle ZXY = 17x + 26$, what is $m\angle WXY$?

Get Ready! **To prepare for Lesson 1-6, do Exercises 54–59.**

Sketch each figure.

54. $\overrightarrow{GH}$ **55.** $\overline{CD}$ **56.** $\overleftrightarrow{AB}$ See Lesson 1-2.

57. acute ∠ABC **58.** right ∠PST **59.** straight ∠XYZ See Lesson 1-4.

1-5 Lesson Resources

Differentiated Remediation

Instructional Support

Geometry Companion

Students can use the **Geometry Companion** worktext (4 pages) . . .

- New Vocabulary
- Key Concepts
- Got It for each Problem
- Lesson Check

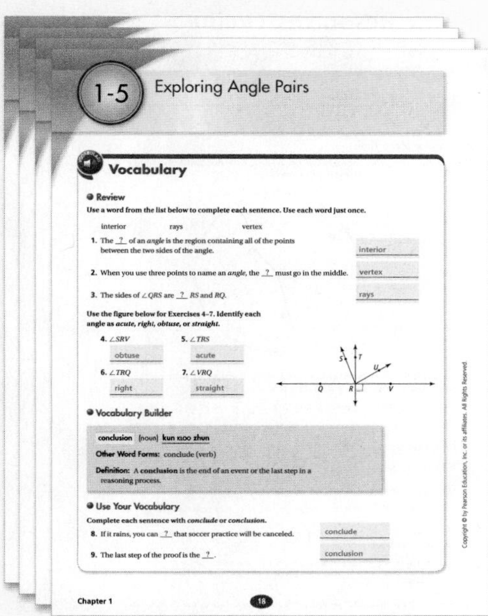

1-5 Exploring Angle Pairs

Vocabulary

Review

Use a word from the list below to complete each sentence. Use each word just once.

interior rays vertex

1. The _?_ of an angle is the region containing all of the points between the two sides of the angle. interior
2. When you use three points to name an angle, the _?_ must go in the middle. vertex
3. The sides of ∠QRS are _?_ RS and RQ. rays

Use the figure below for Exercises 4–7. Identify each angle as *acute, right, obtuse,* or *straight.*

4. ∠SRV obtuse
5. ∠TRS acute
6. ∠TRQ right
7. ∠VRQ straight

Vocabulary Builder

conclusion (noun) kun KLOO zhun

Other Word Forms: conclude (verb)

Definition: A conclusion is the end of an event or the last step in a reasoning process.

Use Your Vocabulary

Complete each sentence with *conclude* or *conclusion.*

8. If it rains, you can _?_ that soccer practice will be canceled. conclude
9. The last step of the proof is the _?_. conclusion

Chapter 1 16

ELL Support

Use Manipulatives Write the four types of angle pairs on the board. Draw an example of each in random order. Ask students to match the terms and angles. Discuss the definition of each angle pair as you use your finger to follow the angles from ray to vertex to angle. Point to the interior of each angle and convey where the interior is located.

Hand out sticky notes to each student. Have them draw an example of each, labeling the degrees of the angles. Tell them to stick their examples on the board next to the correct term. Discuss the results, using it as an opportunity for instruction.

5 Assess & Remediate

Lesson Quiz

1. Use the diagram below. Is each statement true?

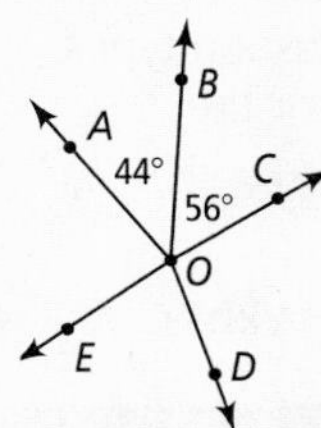

a. ∠*EOB* and ∠*AOC* are supplementary angles.

b. ∠*AOB* and ∠*BOC* are complementary angles.

c. ∠*EOD* and ∠*DOC* are adjacent angles.

2. Do you UNDERSTAND? ∠*RST* and ∠*VST* are a linear pair, $m\angle RST = 3x + 7$, and $m\angle VST = 9x + 17$. What are the measures of ∠*RST* and ∠*VST*?

3. $\overline{RS}$ bisects ∠*QRT*. If $m\angle QRT = 116$, what is $m\angle QRS$?

ANSWERS TO LESSON QUIZ

1. a. no, b. no, c. yes

2. 46, 134

3. 58

PRECRIPTION FOR REMEDIATION

Use the student work on the Lesson Quiz to prescribe a differentiated review assignment.

Points	Differentiated Remediation
0–1	Intervention
2	On-level
3	Extension

PowerGeometry.com

5 Assess & Remediate

Assign the Lesson Quiz. Appropriate intervention, practice, or enrichment is automatically generated based on student performance.

Intervention

- **Reteaching** (2 pages) Provides reteaching and practice exercises for the key lesson concepts. Use with struggling students or absent students.
- **English Language Learner Support** Helps students develop and reinforce mathematical vocabulary and key concepts.

All-in-One Resources/Online

Reteaching

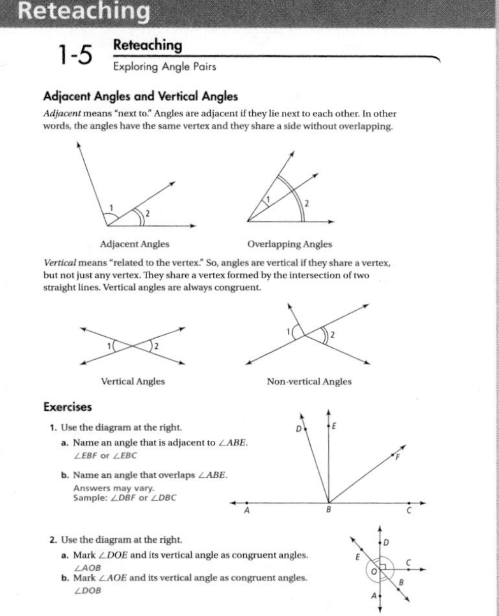

1-5 Reteaching

Exploring Angle Pairs

Adjacent Angles and Vertical Angles

Adjacent means "next to." Angles are adjacent if they lie next to each other. In other words, the angles have the same vertex and they share a side without overlapping.

Adjacent Angles Overlapping Angles

Vertical means "related to the vertex." So, angles are vertical if they share a vertex, but not just any vertex. They share a vertex formed by the intersection of two straight lines. Vertical angles are always congruent.

Vertical Angles Non-vertical Angles

Exercises

1. Use the diagram at the right.
   a. Name an angle that is adjacent to ∠ABE. ∠EBF or ∠EBC
   b. Name an angle that overlaps ∠ABE. Answers may vary. Sample: ∠DBF or ∠DBC
2. Use the diagram at the right.
   a. Mark ∠DOE and its vertical angle as congruent angles. ∠AOB
   b. Mark ∠AOE and its vertical angle as congruent angles. ∠DOB

All-in-One Resources/Online

English Language Learner Support

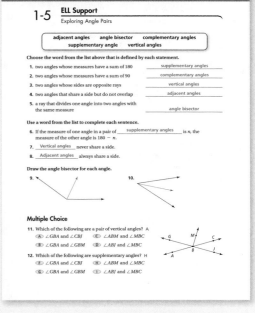

1-5 ELL Support

Exploring Angle Pairs

adjacent angles angle bisector complementary angles supplementary angle vertical angles

Choose the word from the list above that is defined by each statement.

1. two angles whose measures have a sum of 180 supplementary angles
2. two angles whose measures have a sum of 90 complementary angles
3. two angles whose sides are opposite rays vertical angles
4. two angles that share a side but do not overlap adjacent angles
5. a ray that divides one angle into two angles with the same measure angle bisector

Use a word from the list to complete each sentence.

6. If the measure of one angle in a pair of supplementary angles is *n*, the measure of the other angle is 180 − *n*.
7. Vertical angles never share a side.
8. Adjacent angles always share a side.

Draw the angle bisector for each angle.

9.
10.

Multiple Choice

11. Which of the following are a pair of vertical angles? A
    A ∠GBA and ∠CBJ C ∠ABM and ∠MBC
    B ∠GBA and ∠GBM D ∠ABJ and ∠MBC
12. Which of the following are supplementary angles? H
    F ∠GBA and ∠CBJ H ∠ABM and ∠MBC
    G ∠GBA and ∠GBM I ∠ABJ and ∠MBC

Differentiated Remediation *continued*

On-Level

- **Practice** (2 pages) Provides extra practice for each lesson. For simpler practice exercises, use the Form K Practice pages found in the All-in-One Teaching Resources and online.
- **Think About a Plan** Helps students develop specific problem-solving skills and strategies by providing scaffolded guiding questions.
- **Standardized Test Prep** Focuses on all major exercises, all major question types, and helps students prepare for the high-stakes assessments.

Practice and Problem Solving Wkbk/ All-in-One Resources/Online

Practice page 1

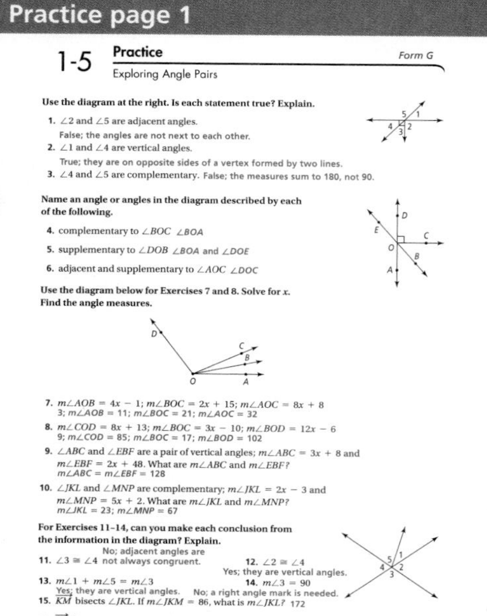

1-5 **Practice** *Form G*
Exploring Angle Pairs

Use the diagram at the right. Is each statement true? Explain.

1. $\angle 2$ and $\angle 5$ are adjacent angles. False; the angles are not next to each other.
2. $\angle 1$ and $\angle 4$ are vertical angles. True; they are on opposite sides of a vertex formed by two lines.
3. $\angle 4$ and $\angle 5$ are complementary. False; the measures sum to 180, not 90.

Name an angle or angles in the diagram described by each of the following.

4. complementary to $\angle BOC$ $\angle BOA$
5. supplementary to $\angle DOB$ $\angle BOA$ and $\angle DOE$
6. adjacent and supplementary to $\angle AOC$ $\angle DOC$

Use the diagram below for Exercises 7 and 8. Solve for x. Find the angle measures.

7. $m\angle AOB = 4x - 1$; $m\angle BOC = 2x + 15$; $m\angle AOC = 8x + 8$
3; $m\angle AOB = 11$; $m\angle BOC = 21$; $m\angle AOC = 32$
8. $m\angle COD = 8x + 13$; $m\angle BOC = 3x - 10$; $m\angle BOD = 12x - 6$
9; $m\angle COD = 85$; $m\angle BOC = 17$; $m\angle BOD = 102$
9. $\angle ABC$ and $\angle EBF$ are a pair of vertical angles; $m\angle ABC = 3x + 8$ and $m\angle EBF = 2x + 48$. What are $m\angle ABC$ and $m\angle EBF$?
$m\angle ABC = m\angle EBF = 128$
10. $\angle JKL$ and $\angle MNP$ are complementary; $m\angle JKL = 2x - 3$ and $m\angle MNP = 5x + 2$. What are $m\angle JKL$ and $m\angle MNP$?
$m\angle JKL = 23$; $m\angle MNP = 67$

For Exercises 11–14, can you make each conclusion from the information in the diagram? Explain.

11. $\angle 3 \cong \angle 4$ No; adjacent angles are not always congruent.
12. $\angle 2 \cong \angle 4$ Yes; they are vertical angles.
13. $m\angle 1 + m\angle 5 = m\angle 3$ Yes; they are vertical angles.
14. $m\angle 3 = 90$ No; a right angle mark is needed.
15. $\overrightarrow{KM}$ bisects $\angle JKL$. If $m\angle JKM = 86$, what is $m\angle JKL$? 172
16. $\overrightarrow{SV}$ bisects $\angle RST$. If $m\angle RST = 62$, what is $m\angle RSV$? 31

Practice and Problem Solving Wkbk/ All-in-One Resources/Online

Practice page 2

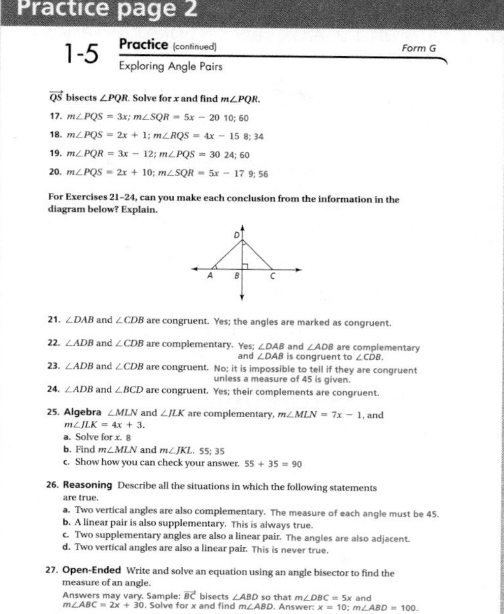

1-5 **Practice** (continued) *Form G*
Exploring Angle Pairs

$\overrightarrow{QS}$ bisects $\angle PQR$. Solve for x and find $m\angle PQR$.

17. $m\angle PQS = 3x$; $m\angle SQR = 5x - 20$ 10; 60
18. $m\angle PQS = 2x + 1$; $m\angle RQS = 4x - 15$ 8; 34
19. $m\angle PQR = 3x - 12$; $m\angle PQS = 30$ 24; 60
20. $m\angle PQS = 2x + 10$; $m\angle SQR = 5x - 17$ 9; 56

For Exercises 21–24, can you make each conclusion from the information in the diagram below? Explain.

21. $\angle DAB$ and $\angle CDB$ are congruent. Yes; the angles are marked as congruent.
22. $\angle ADB$ and $\angle CDB$ are complementary. Yes; $\angle DAB$ and $\angle ADB$ are complementary and $\angle DAB$ is congruent to $\angle CDB$.
23. $\angle ADB$ and $\angle CDB$ are congruent. No; it is impossible to tell if they are congruent unless a measure of 45 is given.
24. $\angle ADB$ and $\angle BCD$ are congruent. Yes; their complements are congruent.
25. **Algebra** $\angle MLN$ and $\angle JLK$ are complementary, $m\angle MLN = 7x - 1$, and $m\angle JLK = 4x + 3$.
    a. Solve for x. 8
    b. Find $m\angle MLN$ and $m\angle JKL$. 55; 35
    c. Show how you can check your answer. $55 + 35 = 90$
26. **Reasoning** Describe all the situations in which the following statements are true.
    a. Two vertical angles are also complementary. The measure of each angle must be 45.
    b. A linear pair is also supplementary. This is always true.
    c. Two supplementary angles are also a linear pair. The angles are also adjacent.
    d. Two vertical angles are also a linear pair. This is never true.
27. **Open-Ended** Write and solve an equation using an angle bisector to find the measure of an angle.
Answers may vary. Sample: $\overrightarrow{BC}$ bisects $\angle ABD$ so that $m\angle DBC = 5x$ and $m\angle ABC = 2x + 30$. Solve for x and find $m\angle ABD$. Answer: $x = 10$; $m\angle ABD = 100$.

Practice and Problem Solving Wkbk/ All-in-One Resources/Online

Think About a Plan

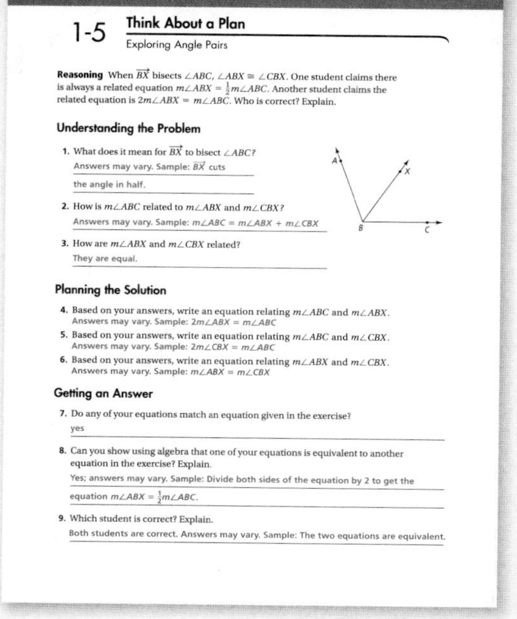

1-5 **Think About a Plan**
Exploring Angle Pairs

Reasoning When $\overrightarrow{BX}$ bisects $\angle ABC$, $\angle ABX \cong \angle CBX$. One student claims there is always a related equation $m\angle ABX = \frac{1}{2}m\angle ABC$. Another student claims the related equation is $2m\angle ABX = m\angle ABC$. Who is correct? Explain.

Understanding the Problem

1. What does it mean for $\overrightarrow{BX}$ to bisect $\angle ABC$?
Answers may vary. Sample: $\overrightarrow{BX}$ cuts the angle in half.
2. How is $m\angle ABC$ related to $m\angle ABX$ and $m\angle CBX$?
Answers may vary. Sample: $m\angle ABC = m\angle ABX + m\angle CBX$
3. How are $m\angle ABX$ and $m\angle CBX$ related?
They are equal.

Planning the Solution

4. Based on your answers, write an equation relating $m\angle ABC$ and $m\angle ABX$.
Answers may vary. Sample: $2m\angle ABX = m\angle ABC$
5. Based on your answers, write an equation relating $m\angle ABC$ and $m\angle CBX$.
Answers may vary. Sample: $2m\angle CBX = m\angle ABC$
6. Based on your answers, write an equation relating $m\angle ABX$ and $m\angle CBX$.
Answers may vary. Sample: $m\angle ABX = m\angle CBX$

Getting an Answer

7. Do any of your equations match an equation given in the exercise?
yes
8. Can you show using algebra that one of your equations is equivalent to another equation in the exercise? Explain.
Yes; answers may vary. Sample: Divide both sides of the equation by 2 to get the equation $m\angle ABX = \frac{1}{2}m\angle ABC$.
9. Which student is correct? Explain.
Both students are correct. Answers may vary. Sample: The two equations are equivalent.

Practice and Problem Solving Wkbk/ All-in-One Resources/Online

Standardized Test Prep

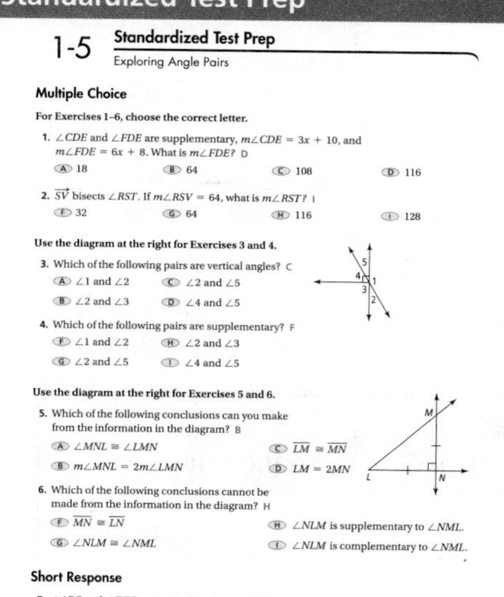

1-5 **Standardized Test Prep**
Exploring Angle Pairs

Multiple Choice

For Exercises 1–6, choose the correct letter.

1. $\angle CDE$ and $\angle FDE$ are supplementary, $m\angle CDE = 3x + 10$, and $m\angle FDE = 6x + 8$. What is $m\angle FDE$? D
(A) 18 (B) 64 (C) 108 (D) 116
2. $\overrightarrow{SV}$ bisects $\angle RST$. If $m\angle RSV = 64$, what is $m\angle RST$? I
(F) 32 (G) 64 (H) 116 (I) 128

Use the diagram at the right for Exercises 3 and 4.

3. Which of the following pairs are vertical angles? C
(A) $\angle 1$ and $\angle 2$ (B) $\angle 2$ and $\angle 3$ (C) $\angle 2$ and $\angle 5$ (D) $\angle 4$ and $\angle 5$
4. Which of the following pairs are supplementary? F
(F) $\angle 1$ and $\angle 2$ (G) $\angle 2$ and $\angle 5$ (H) $\angle 2$ and $\angle 3$ (I) $\angle 4$ and $\angle 5$

Use the diagram at the right for Exercises 5 and 6.

5. Which of the following conclusions can you make from the information in the diagram? B
(A) $\angle MNL \cong \angle LMN$ (B) $m\angle MNL = 2m\angle LMN$ (C) $\overline{LM} \cong \overline{MN}$ (D) $LM = 2MN$
6. Which of the following conclusions cannot be made from the information in the diagram? H
(F) $\overline{MN} \cong \overline{LN}$ (G) $\angle NLM \cong \angle NML$ (H) $\angle NLM$ is supplementary to $\angle NML$. (I) $\angle NLM$ is complementary to $\angle NML$.

Short Response

7. $\angle ABC$ and $\angle DBE$ are vertical angles, $m\angle ABC = 3x + 20$, and $m\angle DBE = 4x - 10$. Write and solve an equation to find $m\angle ABC$ and $m\angle DBE$.
[2] $3x + 20 = 4x - 10$; $m\angle ABC = m\angle DBE = 110$ [1] correct equation and wrong solution or correct answer with no equation [0] both equation and solution wrong

Extension

- **Enrichment** Provides students with interesting problems and activities that extend the concepts of the lesson.
- **Activities, Games, and Puzzles** Worksheets that can be used for concepts development, enrichment, and for fun!

All-in-One Resources/Online

Enrichment

1-5 **Enrichment**
Exploring Angle Pairs

Angling for More Time

Examine the analog clock shown below. Let the hour hand define $\overrightarrow{OA}$, the minute hand define $\overrightarrow{OB}$, and the second hand define $\overrightarrow{OC}$.

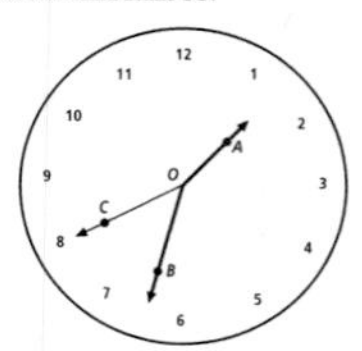

Make a sketch of a clock that matches the following descriptions. Estimate the time shown on each sketch. Show all three hands on each sketch.

1. $\angle AOB$ and $\angle BOC$ are supplementary. Answers may vary. Sample: 4:00:50
2. $\angle AOB$ and $\angle BOC$ are complementary. Answers may vary. Sample: 10:00:05
3. $\overrightarrow{OC}$ bisects $\angle AOB$ and $m\angle AOB = 60$. Answers may vary. Sample: 2:00:05
4. $\overrightarrow{OB}$ bisects $\angle AOC$ and $m\angle AOB = 60$. Answers may vary. Sample: 10:00:10
5. $\overrightarrow{OA}$ bisects $\angle BOC$, and $\angle BOC$ is a straight angle. Answers may vary. Sample: 3:00:30
6. $\angle AOB$, $\angle BOC$, and $\angle AOC$ are congruent. Answers may vary. Sample: 4:00:40

After you have answered Exercises 1–6, exchange answers with a partner. Check your partner's answers.

7. Explain why the exercises can have more than one answer.
The rays can always be rotated so that the hands point to a different time and still maintain their relationship.
8. Use only terms found in Chapter 1. Try to describe a clock face such that only one possible clock face matches the description. Then give your description to another student and see if that student can determine the correct time.
Check students' work.

Online Teacher Resource Center

Activities, Games, and Puzzles

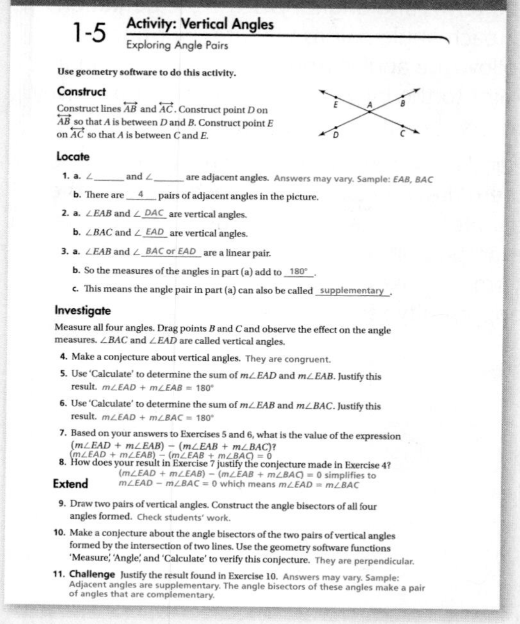

1-5 **Activity: Vertical Angles**
Exploring Angle Pairs

Use geometry software to do this activity.

Construct

Construct lines $\overleftrightarrow{AB}$ and $\overleftrightarrow{AC}$. Construct point D on $\overleftrightarrow{AB}$ so that A is between D and B. Construct point E on $\overleftrightarrow{AC}$ so that A is between C and E.

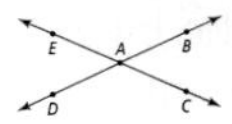

Locate

1. a. $\angle$ _____ and $\angle$ _____ are adjacent angles. Answers may vary. Sample: EAB, BAC
   b. There are 4 pairs of adjacent angles in the picture.
2. a. $\angle EAB$ and $\angle$ DAC are vertical angles.
   b. $\angle BAC$ and $\angle$ EAD are vertical angles.
3. a. $\angle EAB$ and $\angle$ BAC or EAD are a linear pair.
   b. So the measures of the angles in part (a) add to 180°.
   c. This means the angle pair in part (a) can also be called supplementary.

Investigate

Measure all four angles. Drag points B and C and observe the effect on the angle measures. $\angle BAC$ and $\angle EAD$ are called vertical angles.

4. Make a conjecture about vertical angles. They are congruent.
5. Use 'Calculate' to determine the sum of $m\angle EAD$ and $m\angle EAB$. Justify this result. $m\angle EAD + m\angle EAB = 180°$
6. Use 'Calculate' to determine the sum of $m\angle EAB$ and $m\angle BAC$. Justify this result. $m\angle EAD + m\angle BAC = 180°$
7. Based on your answers to Exercises 5 and 6, what is the value of the expression $(m\angle EAD + m\angle EAB) - (m\angle EAB + m\angle BAC)$?
$(m\angle EAD + m\angle EAB) - (m\angle EAB + m\angle BAC) = 0$
8. How does your result in Exercise 7 justify the conjecture made in Exercise 4?
$(m\angle EAD + m\angle EAB) - (m\angle EAB + m\angle BAC) = 0$ simplifies to $m\angle EAD - m\angle BAC = 0$ which means $m\angle EAD = m\angle BAC$

Extend

9. Draw two pairs of vertical angles. Construct the angle bisectors of all four angles formed. Check students' work.
10. Make a conjecture about the angle bisectors of the two pairs of vertical angles formed by the intersection of two lines. Use the geometry software functions 'Measure,' 'Angle,' and 'Calculate' to verify this conjecture. They are perpendicular.
11. **Challenge** Justify the result found in Exercise 10. Answers may vary. Sample: Adjacent angles are supplementary. The angle bisectors of these angles make a pair of angles that are complementary.

Mid-Chapter Quiz

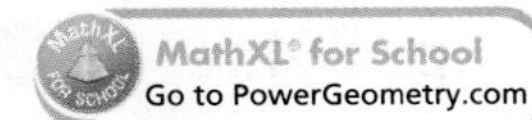

Do you know HOW?

Draw a net for each figure.

1. 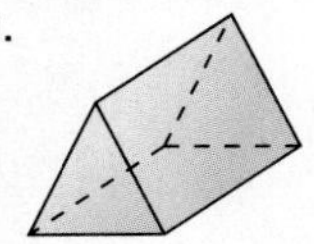
2. 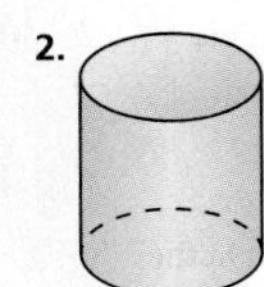

Determine whether the given points are coplanar. If *yes*, name the plane. If *no*, explain.

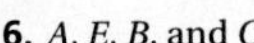

3. *A, E, F,* and *B*
4. *D, C, E,* and *F*
5. *H, G, F,* and *B*
6. *A, E, B,* and *C*
7. Use the figure from Exercises 3–6. Name the intersection of each pair of planes.
   a. plane *AEFB* and plane *CBFG*
   b. plane *EFGH* and plane *AEHD*

Use the figure below for Exercises 8–15.

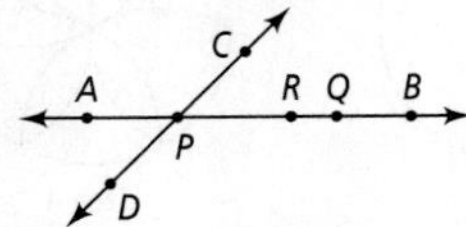

8. Give two other names for $\overleftrightarrow{AB}$.
9. Give two other names for $\overrightarrow{PR}$.
10. Give two other names for $\angle CPR$.
11. Name three collinear points.
12. Name two opposite rays.
13. Name three segments.
14. Name two angles that form a linear pair.
15. Name a pair of vertical angles.

16. a. **Algebra** Find the value of *x* in the diagram below.
    b. Classify $\angle ABC$ and $\angle CBD$ as *acute, right,* or *obtuse.*

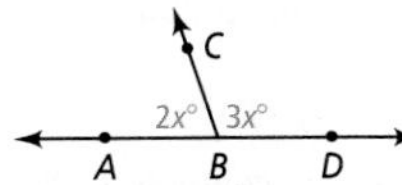

Find the length of each segment.

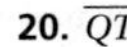

17. $\overline{PQ}$
18. $\overline{RS}$
19. $\overline{ST}$
20. $\overline{QT}$

Use the figure below for Exercises 21–23.

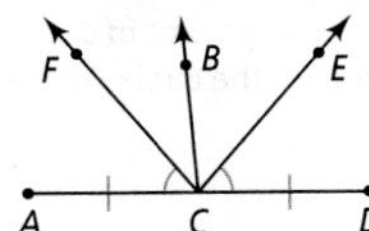

21. **Algebra** If $AC = 4x + 5$ and $DC = 3x + 8$, find *AD*.
22. If $m\angle FCD = 130$ and $m\angle BCD = 95$, find $m\angle FCB$.
23. If $m\angle FCA = 50$, find $m\angle FCE$.

Do you UNDERSTAND?

24. **Error Analysis** Suppose $PQ = QR$. Your friend says that *Q* is always the midpoint of $\overline{PR}$. Is he correct? Explain.
25. **Reasoning** Determine whether the following situation is possible. Explain your reasoning. Include a sketch.

    Collinear points *C, F,* and *G* lie in plane *M*. $\overleftrightarrow{AB}$ intersects plane *M* at *C*. $\overleftrightarrow{AB}$ and $\overleftrightarrow{GF}$ do not intersect.

Answers

Mid-Chapter Quiz

1. Answers may vary. Sample:

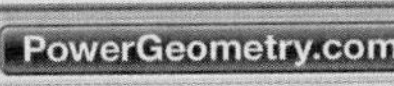

2. Answers may vary. Sample:

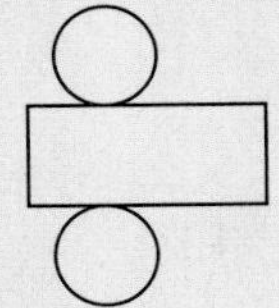

3. yes; plane *AEB*
4. yes, plane *DCE*
5. No; sample: Points *H, G,* and *F* are in plane *HGF*, and point *B* is not in that plane.
6. No; sample: Points *A, E,* and *B* are in plane *AEB*, and point *C* is not in that plane.

7a. $\overleftrightarrow{BF}$

b. $\overleftrightarrow{EH}$

8. Answers may vary. Sample: $\overleftrightarrow{AR}$, $\overleftrightarrow{AQ}$
9. $\overrightarrow{PQ}$, $\overrightarrow{PB}$
10. Answers may vary. Sample: $\angle CPQ$, $\angle CPB$
11. Answers may vary. Sample: *D, P, C*
12. Answers may vary. Sample: $\overrightarrow{PA}$ and $\overrightarrow{PB}$
13. Answers may vary. Sample: $\overline{AP}$, $\overline{PR}$, $\overline{RQ}$
14. Answers may vary. Sample: $\angle CPR$ and $\angle APC$
15. Answers may vary. Sample: $\angle APD$ and $\angle CPB$

16a. 36

b. $\angle ABC$ is acute, and $\angle CBD$ is obtuse.

17. 3
18. 3
19. 3
20. 7
21. 34
22. 35
23. 80
24. No; if *P, Q,* and *R* are not collinear, then *Q* is not on $\overline{PR}$, so it cannot be the midpoint of $\overline{PR}$.
25. No; *C, F,* and *G* are collinear, so $\overleftrightarrow{AB}$ must intersect $\overleftrightarrow{GF}$ at *C* in plane *M*.

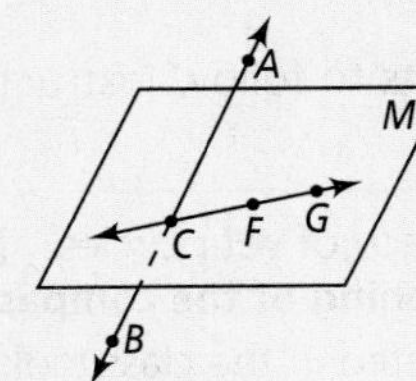

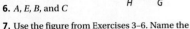

Guided Instruction

PURPOSE To introduce the idea that a compass can be used to construct geometric figures

PROCESS Students will construct an interesting design using a compass.

DISCUSS Before assigning the activity, you may want to assist students in getting started. Constructing the initial circle is straightforward, but getting started on the arcs may be confusing to some students. Be sure the piece of paper being used is large enough. A typical 8½ x 11 may not be quite large enough for this activity. However, if you do not want to supply a larger size paper, you could adjust the compass setting accordingly.

Activity

This Activity requires students to follow instructions to create a compass design.

Q What is the diameter of each of your circles? **[The diameter is twice the opening of the compass.]**

Q Should all the designs created in the class look the same? Explain. **[Yes; as long as the same directions were followed exactly.]**

Concept Byte — Compass Designs

Use With Lesson 1-6

ACTIVITY

In Lesson 1-6, you will use a compass to construct geometric figures. You can construct figures to show geometric relationships, to suggest new relationships, or simply to make interesting geometric designs.

Activity

Step 1 Open your compass to about 2 in. Make a circle and mark the point at the center of the circle. Keep the opening of your compass fixed. Place the compass point on the circle. With the pencil end, make a small arc to intersect the circle.

Step 2 Place the compass point on the circle at the arc. Mark another arc. Continue around the circle this way to draw four more arcs—six in all.

Step 3 Place your compass point on an arc you marked on the circle. Place the pencil end at the next arc. Draw a large arc that passes through the circle's center and continues to another point on the circle.

Step 4 Draw six large arcs in this manner, each centered at one of the six points marked on the circle. You may choose to color your design.

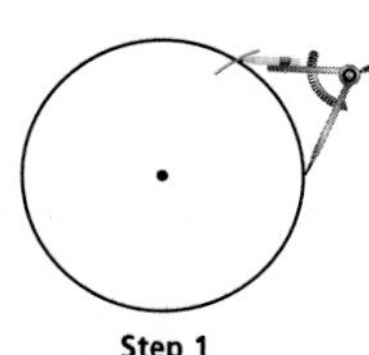
Step 1

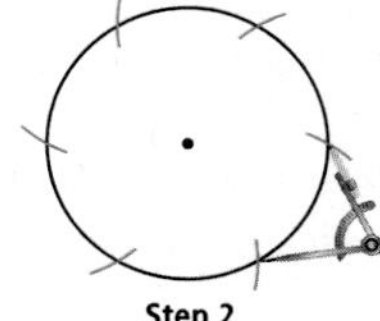
Step 2

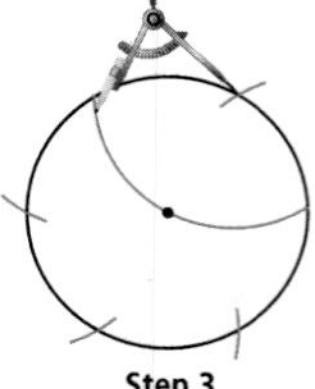
Step 3

Step 4

Exercises

1. In Step 2, did your sixth mark on the circle land precisely on the point where you first placed your compass on the circle?
   - **a.** Survey the class to find out how many did.
   - **b.** Explain why your sixth mark may not have landed on your starting point.
2. Extend your design by using one of the six points on the circle as the center for a new circle. Repeat Steps 1–4 with this circle. Repeat several times to make interlocking circles

Answers

Exercises

1a. Depending on students' accuracy, the sixth mark should be the location of the first compass point.

b. Answers may vary. Sample: The compass width may have changed accidentally while making the marks. Also, because a point has no size, it is very difficult to land on. So your compass point may not have landed exactly on the previous arc as you drew the next arc. The error could add up enough so that the sixth arc would not land on the starting point.

2. Check students' work.

1-6 Basic Constructions

Objective To make basic constructions using a straightedge and a compass

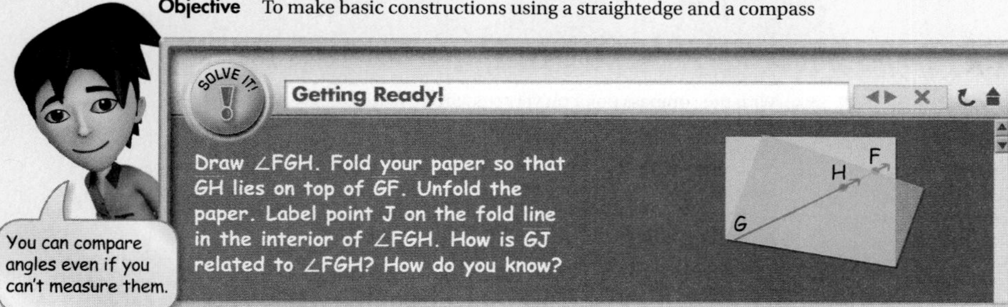

You can compare angles even if you can't measure them.
Getting Ready!
Draw ∠FGH. Fold your paper so that GH lies on top of GF. Unfold the paper. Label point J on the fold line in the interior of ∠FGH. How is GJ related to ∠FGH? How do you know?
H
F
G

In this lesson, you will learn another way to construct figures like the one above.

Lesson Vocabulary
- straightedge
- compass
- construction
- perpendicular lines
- perpendicular bisector

Essential Understanding You can use special geometric tools to make a figure that is congruent to an original figure without measuring. This method is more accurate than sketching and drawing.

A **straightedge** is a ruler with no markings on it. A **compass** is a geometric tool used to draw circles and parts of circles called *arcs*. A **construction** is a geometric figure drawn using a straightedge and a compass.

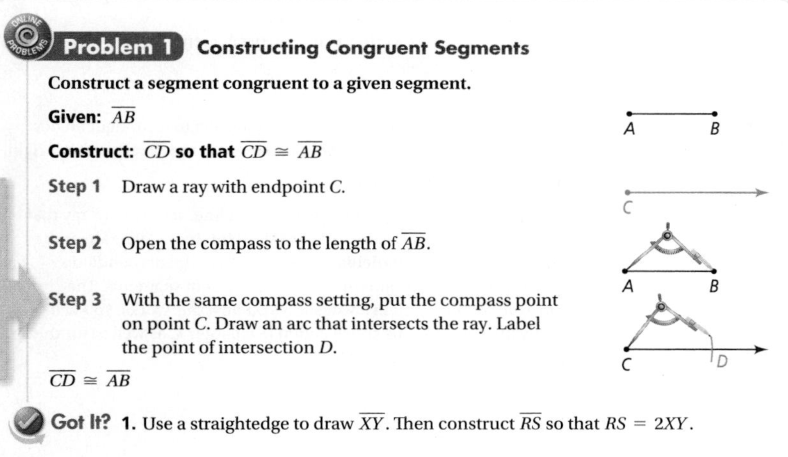

Problem 1 **Constructing Congruent Segments**

Construct a segment congruent to a given segment.

Given: $\overline{AB}$

Construct: $\overline{CD}$ **so that** $\overline{CD} \cong \overline{AB}$

Step 1 Draw a ray with endpoint C.

Step 2 Open the compass to the length of $\overline{AB}$.

Step 3 With the same compass setting, put the compass point on point C. Draw an arc that intersects the ray. Label the point of intersection D.

$\overline{CD} \cong \overline{AB}$

Think
Why must the compass setting stay the same?
Using the same compass setting keeps segments congruent. It guarantees that the lengths of $\overline{AB}$ and $\overline{CD}$ are exactly the same.

Got It? **1.** Use a straightedge to draw $\overline{XY}$. Then construct $\overline{RS}$ so that $RS = 2XY$.

1 Interactive Learning

Solve It!

PURPOSE To provide students with a method for constructing an angle bisector that requires only the use of a straightedge and compass

PROCESS Students may use visual judgment and their knowledge of congruent adjacent angles to determine the relationship in the question.

FACILITATE

Q How many angles exist in the diagram after the fold is made? What are the names of the angles? **[3; ∠*FGH*, ∠*FGJ*, and ∠*JGH*]**

ANSWER See Solve It in Answers on next page.

CONNECT THE MATH The method used in the Solve It for finding an angle bisector does not require the use of a measuring tool. This is one of the basic geometric constructions taught in this lesson.

2 Guided Instruction

Problem 1

Q In Step 1 can the distance between *C* and the arrowhead be shorter than the given segment? Explain. **[No, it needs to be longer than the given segment so that the arc will intersect the ray.]**

Got It? SYNTHESIZING

Point out to students that they are using the Segment Addition Postulate to complete this construction.

1-6 Preparing to Teach

ESSENTIAL UNDERSTANDINGS
- Special geometric tools can be used to make a figure that is congruent to an original figure without measuring.
- Construction with straightedge and compass is more accurate than sketching and drawing.

Math Background

Euclidean constructions employ a compass and a straightedge. Students need to become comfortable using a straightedge for the purpose of drawing a straight line and, if a ruler is used, learn not to rely on the scale markings.

The techniques for constructing congruent figures in this lesson will be important skills in future lessons. Just as learning to write letters is a prerequisite for learning to write words, learning to construct congruent angles and segments is a prerequisite for learning to construct parallel and perpendicular lines in Chapter 3.

Three famous construction problems intrigued ancient Greek geometers and many others in more recent times: trisecting an angle, constructing a cube with double the volume, and constructing a square whose area is that of a given circle. No solutions were ever found, and many years passed before mathematicians proved that solutions do not exist.

Support Student Learning

Use the **Geometry Companion** to engage and support students during instructions. See Lesson Resources at the end of this lesson for details.

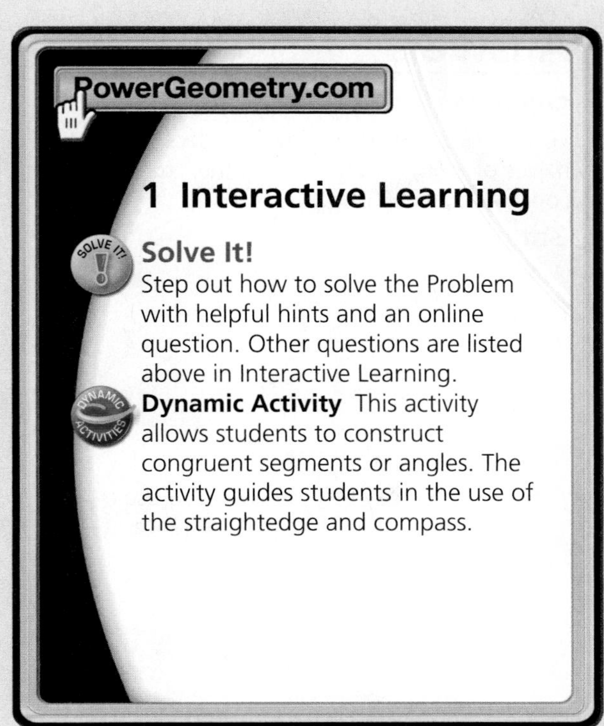

Problem 2

Q If you repeat Steps 2 and 3 using a different compass setting than used originally, where will the two arcs in Step 4 intersect? **[The arcs will intersect somewhere on ST.]**

Q How could you construct adjacent congruent angles? **[Instead of beginning with a new ray in Step 1, substitute AB for SR in the rest of the steps.]**

Got It?

Point out to students that the construction of the angle bisector of $\angle F$ is a by-product of the construction of $\angle F$.

Problem 2 Constructing Congruent Angles

Construct an angle congruent to a given angle.

Given: $\angle A$

Construct: $\angle S$ so that $\angle S \cong \angle A$

Step 1
Draw a ray with endpoint S.

Step 2
With the compass point on vertex A, draw an arc that intersects the sides of $\angle A$. Label the points of intersection B and C.

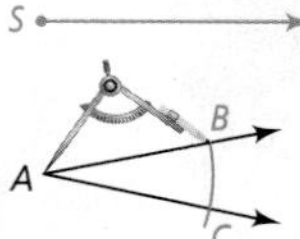

Think
Why do you need points like B and C?
B and C are reference points on the original angle. You can construct a congruent angle by locating corresponding points R and T on your new angle.

Step 3
With the same compass setting, put the compass point on point S. Draw an arc and label its point of intersection with the ray as R.

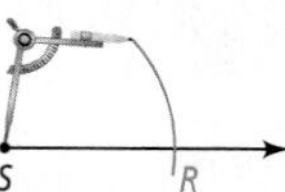

Step 4
Open the compass to the length BC. Keeping the same compass setting, put the compass point on R. Draw an arc to locate point T.

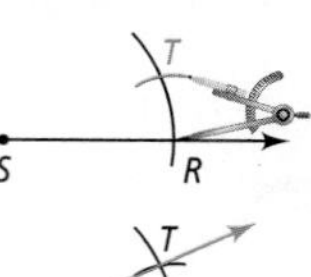

Step 5
Draw $\overrightarrow{ST}$.

$\angle S \cong \angle A$

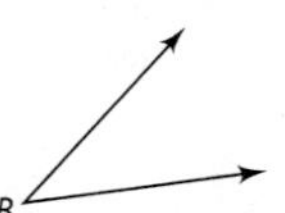

Got It? 2. a. Construct $\angle F$ so that $m\angle F = 2m\angle B$.

b. Reasoning How is constructing a congruent angle similar to constructing a congruent segment?

Dynamic Activity Constructing Congruent Segments and Angles

Perpendicular lines are two lines that intersect to form right angles. The symbol $\perp$ means "is perpendicular to." In the diagram at the right, $\overleftrightarrow{AB} \perp \overleftrightarrow{CD}$ and $\overleftrightarrow{CD} \perp \overleftrightarrow{AB}$.

A **perpendicular bisector** of a segment is a line, segment, or ray that is perpendicular to the segment at its midpoint. In the diagram at the right, $\overleftrightarrow{EF}$ is the perpendicular bisector of $\overline{GH}$. The perpendicular bisector bisects the segment into two congruent segments. The construction in Problem 3 will show you how this works. You will justify the steps for this construction in Chapter 4, as well as for the other constructions in this lesson.

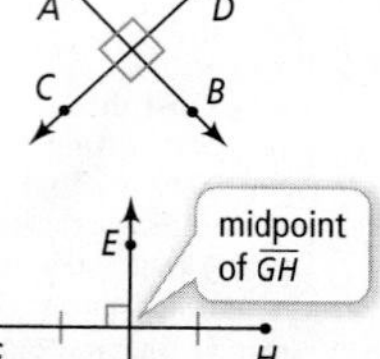

Answers

Solve It!

$\overline{GJ}$ divides $\angle FGH$ in exactly half; because the two halves of $\angle FGH$ overlap each other exactly, you can conclude that $\angle FGJ \cong \angle JGH$.

Got It?

1.

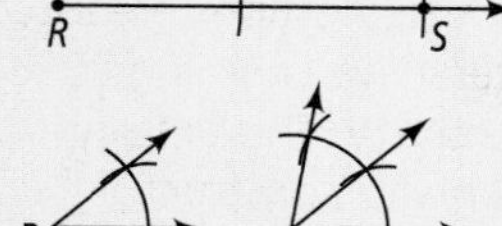

2a.

b. Answers may vary. Sample: You use a compass setting to copy a distance.

PowerGeometry.com

2 Guided Instruction

Each Problem is worked out and supported online.

Problem 1
Constructing Congruent Segments

Problem 2
Constructing Congruent Angles
Animated

Problem 3
Constructing the Perpendicular Bisector
Animated

Problem 4
Constructing the Angle Bisector
Animated

Support in Geometry Companion
- Vocabulary
- Key Concepts
- Got It?

Problem 3 Constructing the Perpendicular Bisector

Construct the perpendicular bisector of a segment.

Given: $\overline{AB}$

Construct: $\overleftrightarrow{XY}$ so that $\overleftrightarrow{XY}$ is the perpendicular bisector of $\overline{AB}$

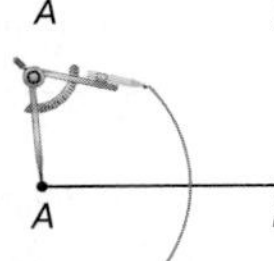

Step 1
Put the compass point on point A and draw a long arc as shown. Be sure the opening is greater than $\frac{1}{2}AB$.

Think
Why must the compass opening be greater than $\frac{1}{2}AB$?
If the opening is less than $\frac{1}{2}AB$, the two arcs will not intersect in Step 2.

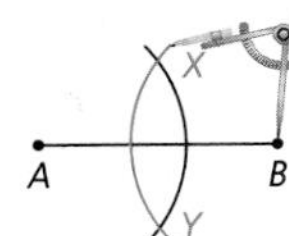

Step 2
With the same compass setting, put the compass point on point B and draw another long arc. Label the points where the two arcs intersect as X and Y.

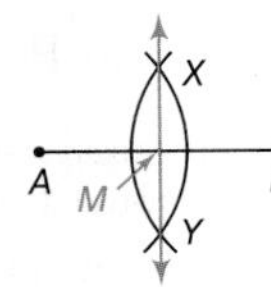

Step 3
Draw $\overleftrightarrow{XY}$. Label the point of intersection of $\overline{AB}$ and $\overleftrightarrow{XY}$ as M, the midpoint of $\overline{AB}$.

$\overleftrightarrow{XY} \perp \overline{AB}$ at midpoint M, so $\overleftrightarrow{XY}$ is the perpendicular bisector of $\overline{AB}$.

Got It? **3.** Draw $\overline{ST}$. Construct its perpendicular bisector.

Problem 4 Constructing the Angle Bisector

Construct the bisector of an angle.

Given: $\angle A$

Construct: $\overrightarrow{AD}$, the bisector of $\angle A$

Step 1
Put the compass point on vertex A. Draw an arc that intersects the sides of $\angle A$. Label the points of intersection B and C.

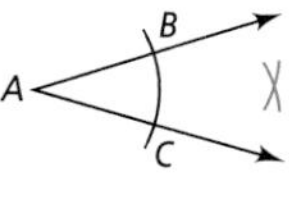

Step 2
Put the compass point on point C and draw an arc. With the same compass setting, draw an arc using point B. Be sure the arcs intersect. Label the point where the two arcs intersect as D.

Think
Why must the arcs intersect?
The arcs need to intersect so that you have a point through which to draw a ray.

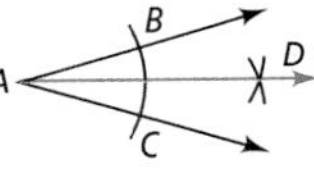

Step 3
Draw $\overrightarrow{AD}$.

$\overrightarrow{AD}$ is the bisector of $\angle CAB$.

Got It? **4.** Draw obtuse $\angle XYZ$. Then construct its bisector $\overrightarrow{YP}$.

Problem 3

Q What happens if you change the compass setting between Step 1 and Step 2? **[The intersections form a perpendicular line, but the line is not the bisector.]**

Q How can you use your compass to verify $\overline{AM} \cong \overline{MB}$? **[You can use your compass as a measuring tool to compare the lengths of the two segments.]**

Got It?
Encourage students to change the compass opening and repeat Steps 2 and 3 several times. Students will see that all of the pairs of arcs intersect on the perpendicular bisector.

Problem 4

Q How can you use your compass to verify $\angle BAD \cong \angle DAC$? **[You can use your compass as a measuring tool to compare the lengths of the two segments created by the intersections of the arc drawn in Step 1 with the bisector.]**

Q If the arcs in Step 2 are drawn such that the arcs lie to the left of vertex A, will their intersection also lie on the angle bisector? Explain. **[Yes, but it may be harder to draw an accurate angle bisector that way.]**

Got It? VISUAL LEARNERS
Students may find that they remember the construction steps more easily if they make a sketch of the desired outcome before beginning the construction.

Additional Problems

1. Construct $\overline{EF}$ so that $\overline{EF} \cong \overline{CD}$.

ANSWER

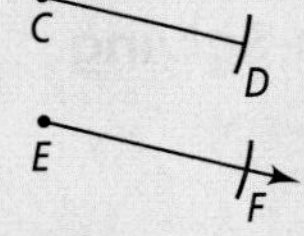

2. Construct $\angle R$ so that $\angle R \cong \angle T$.

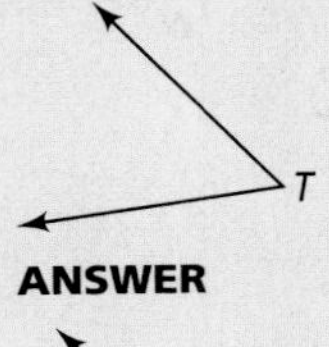

ANSWER

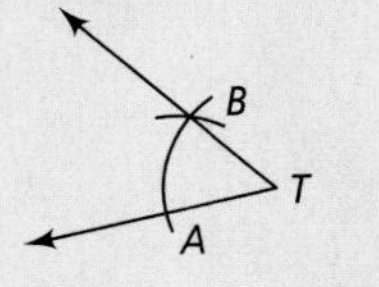

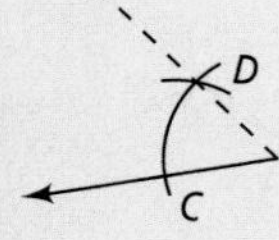

3. Construct line LM so that LM is the perpendicular bisector of $\overline{QR}$.

ANSWER

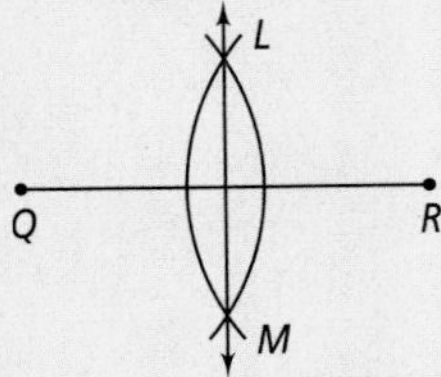

4. Construct DE, the bisector of $\angle D$.

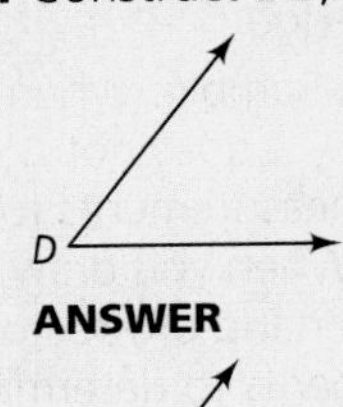

ANSWER

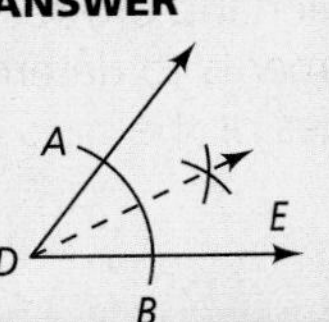

Answers

Got It? (continued)

3.

4.

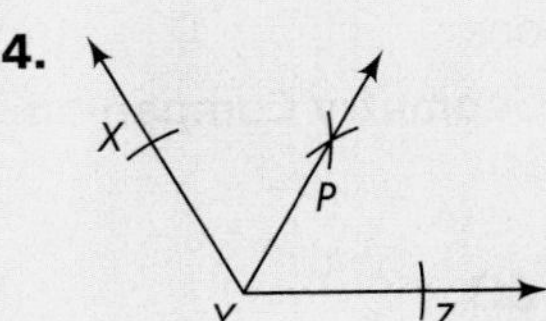

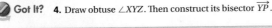

3 Lesson Check

Do you know HOW?

- If students have difficulty with Exercises 1, 2, and 3, then have them reference the steps in Problem 1, Problem 3, and Problem 4 respectively.

Do you UNDERSTAND?

- If students have difficulty with Exercise 5, then ask them to sketch, draw, and construct a perpendicular bisector and an angle bisector and measure the accuracy of the results.

Close

Q How can you use the constructions learned in this lesson to create a 45° angle? **[Begin with a segment and construct its perpendicular bisector. Next, construct the angle bisector of one of the 90° angles that was created in Step 1. Each of the angles created by the angle bisector will measure 45°.]**

Lesson Check

Do you know HOW?

For Exercises 1 and 2, draw $\overline{PQ}$. Use your drawing as the original figure for each construction.

1. Construct a segment congruent to $\overline{PQ}$.
2. Construct the perpendicular bisector of $\overline{PQ}$.
3. Draw an obtuse $\angle JKL$. Construct its bisector.

Do you UNDERSTAND?

4. **Vocabulary** What two tools do you use to make constructions?
5. **Compare and Contrast** Describe the difference in accuracy between sketching a figure, drawing a figure with a ruler and protractor, and constructing a figure. Explain.
6. **Error Analysis** Your friend constructs $\overleftrightarrow{XY}$ so that it is perpendicular to and contains the midpoint of $\overline{AB}$. He claims that $\overline{AB}$ is the perpendicular bisector of $\overline{XY}$. What is his error?

Practice and Problem-Solving Exercises

A Practice

For Exercises 7–14, draw a diagram similar to the given one. Then do the construction. Check your work with a ruler or a protractor.

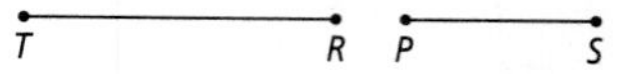

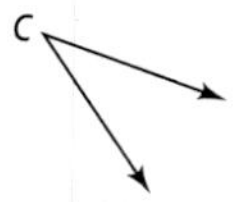

7. Construct $\overline{XY}$ congruent to $\overline{AB}$. See Problem 1.
8. Construct $\overline{VW}$ so that $VW = 2AB$.
9. Construct $\overline{DE}$ so that $DE = TR + PS$.
10. Construct $\overline{QJ}$ so that $QJ = TR - PS$.
11. Construct $\angle D$ so that $\angle D \cong \angle C$. See Problem 2.
12. Construct $\angle F$ so that $m\angle F = 2m\angle C$.
13. Construct the perpendicular bisector of $\overline{AB}$. See Problem 3.
14. Construct the perpendicular bisector of $\overline{TR}$.
15. Draw acute $\angle PQR$. Then construct its bisector. See Problem 4.
16. Draw obtuse $\angle XQZ$. Then construct its bisector.

B Apply

Sketch the figure described. Explain how to construct it. Then do the construction.

17. $\overleftrightarrow{XY} \perp \overleftrightarrow{YZ}$
18. $\overrightarrow{ST}$ bisects right $\angle PSQ$.
19. **Compare and Contrast** How is constructing an angle bisector similar to constructing a perpendicular bisector?

PowerGeometry.com

3 Lesson Check

For a digital lesson check, use the Got It questions.

Support in Geometry Companion
- Lesson Check

4 Practice

Assign homework to individual students or to an entire class.

Answers

Lesson Check

1.

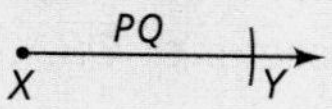

2.

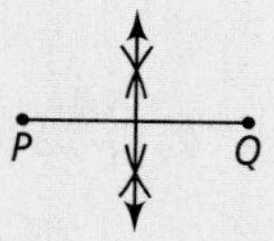

3.

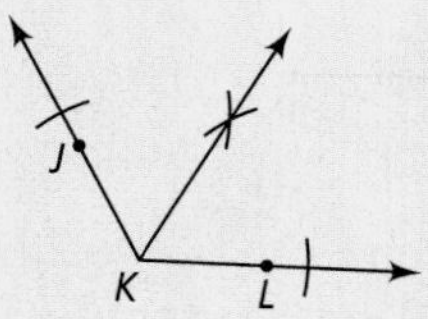

4. compass, straightedge
5. Answers may vary. Sample: When you sketch a figure, it does not require accurate measurements for angles and sides. When you draw a figure with a ruler and protractor, you use measurements to determine the lengths of sides or the sizes of angles. When you construct a figure, the only tools you use are a compass and straightedge.
6. Since $\overleftrightarrow{XY}$ is $\perp$ to and contains the midpoint of $\overline{AB}$, then $\overleftrightarrow{XY}$ is the $\perp$ bis. of $\overline{AB}$, not the other way around.

Practice and Problem-Solving Exercises

7.

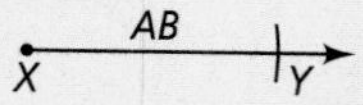

8.

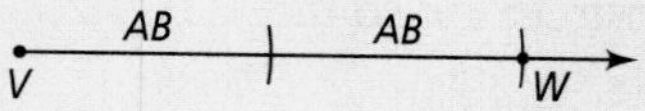

9.

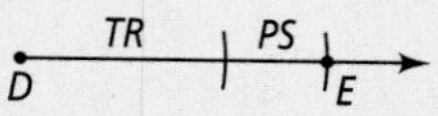

10.

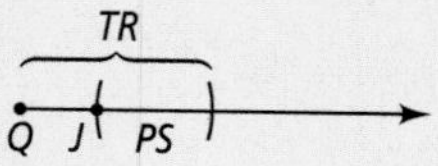

11.

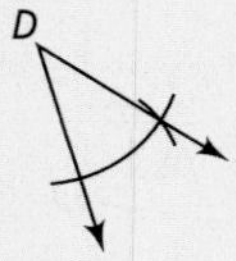

20. **Think About a Plan** Draw an $\angle A$. Construct an angle whose measure is $\frac{1}{4}m\angle A$.
- How is the angle you need to construct related to the angle bisector of $\angle A$?
- How can you use previous constructions to help you?

21. Answer the questions about a segment in a plane. Explain each answer.
   a. How many midpoints does the segment have?
   b. How many bisectors does it have?
   c. How many lines in the plane are its perpendicular bisectors?
   d. How many lines in space are its perpendicular bisectors?

For Exercises 22–24, copy $\angle 1$ and $\angle 2$. Construct each angle described.

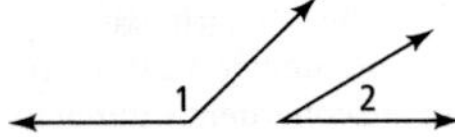

22. $\angle B$; $m\angle B = m\angle 1 + m\angle 2$

23. $\angle C$; $m\angle C = m\angle 1 - m\angle 2$

24. $\angle D$; $m\angle D = 2m\angle 2$

25. **Writing** Explain how to do each construction with a compass and straightedge.
   a. Draw a segment $\overline{PQ}$. Construct the midpoint of $\overline{PQ}$.
   b. Divide $\overline{PQ}$ into four congruent segments.

26. a. Draw a large triangle with three acute angles. Construct the bisectors of the three angles. What appears to be true about the three angle bisectors?
   b. Repeat the constructions with a triangle that has one obtuse angle.
   c. **Make a Conjecture** What appears to be true about the three angle bisectors of any triangle?

Use a ruler to draw segments of 2 cm, 4 cm, and 5 cm. Then construct each triangle with the given side measures, if possible. If it is not possible, explain why not.

27. 4 cm, 4 cm, and 5 cm

28. 2 cm, 5 cm, and 5 cm

29. 2 cm, 2 cm, and 5 cm

30. 2 cm, 2 cm, and 4 cm

31. a. Draw a segment, $\overline{XY}$. Construct a triangle with sides congruent to $\overline{XY}$.
   b. Measure the angles of the triangle.
   c. **Writing** Describe how to construct a 60° angle using what you know. Then describe how to construct a 30° angle.

32. Which steps best describe how to construct the pattern at the right?

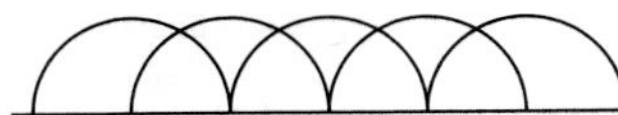

   (A) Use a straightedge to draw the segment and then a compass to draw five half circles.
   (B) Use a straightedge to draw the segment and then a compass to draw six half circles.
   (C) Use a compass to draw five half circles and then a straightedge to join their ends.
   (D) Use a compass to draw six half circles and then a straightedge to join their ends.

4 Practice

ASSIGNMENT GUIDE

Basic: 7–16 all, 18–19 all, 20–24 even, 25, 26–30 even
Average: 7–15 odd, 17–32
Advanced: 7–15 odd, 17–35
Standardized Test Prep: 36–38
Mixed Review: 39–47

Reasoning exercises have blue headings.
Applications exercises have red headings.

EXERCISE 26: Use the Think About a Plan worksheet in the **Practice and Problem Solving Workbook** (also available in the Teaching Resources in print and online) to further support students' development in becoming independent learners.

HOMEWORK QUICK CHECK

To check students' understanding of key skills and concepts, go over Exercises 11, 15, 20, 25, and 26.

12.

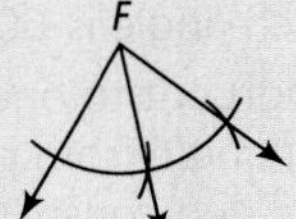

13.

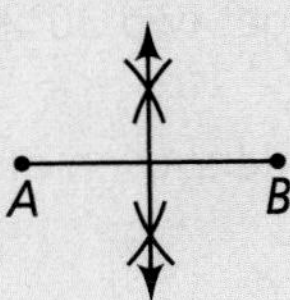

14.

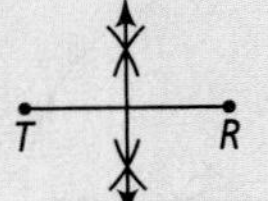

15.

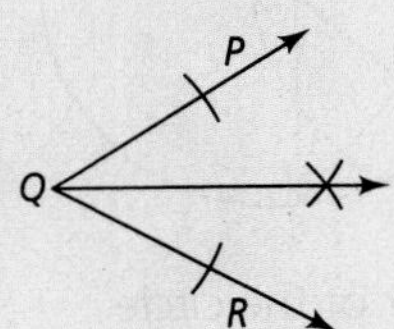

16.

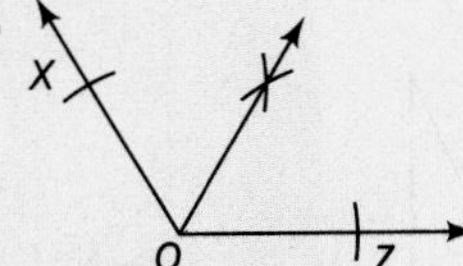

17. Answers may vary. Sample:

Z
X
Y

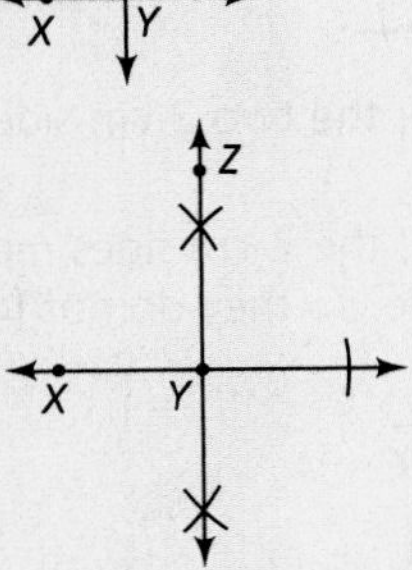

Find a segment on $\overleftrightarrow{XY}$ so that you can construct $\overleftrightarrow{YZ}$ as its perpendicular bisector.

18.

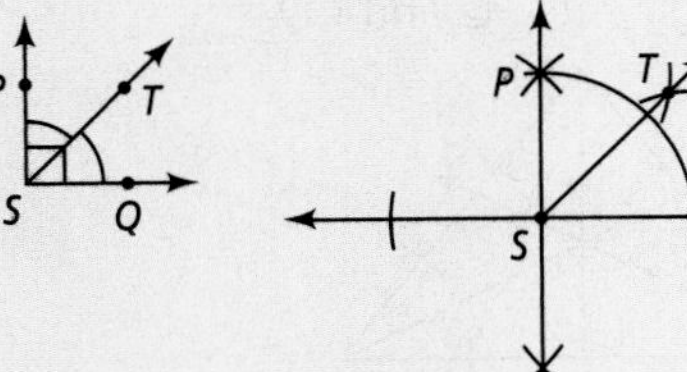

Find a segment on $\overleftrightarrow{SQ}$ so that you can construct $\overleftrightarrow{SP}$ as its perpendicular bisector. Then bisect $\angle PSQ$.

19. Answers may vary. Sample: Both constructions involve drawing arcs with the same radius from two different points, and using the point(s) of intersection of those arcs. Arcs must intersect at two points for the $\perp$ bis., but only one point for the $\angle$ bis.

20.

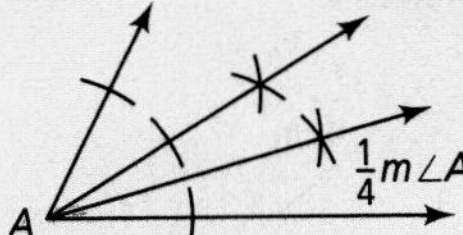

21–32. See next page.

Answers

Practice and Problem-Solving Exercises (continued)

21a. A segment has exactly one midpoint; using the ruler postulate (Post. 1-5), each point corresponds with exactly one number, and exactly one number represents half the length of a segment.

b. A segment has infinitely many bisectors because many lines can be drawn through the midpoint.

c. In the plane with the segment, there is one ⊥ bis. because only one line in that plane can be drawn through the midpoint so that it forms a right angle with the given segment.

d. Consider the plane that is the ⊥ bis. of the segment. Any line in that plane that contains the midpoint of the segment is a ⊥ bis. of the segment, and there are infinitely many such lines.

22.

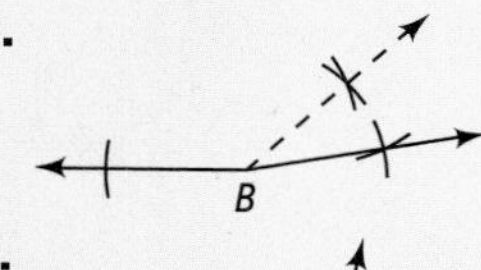

23.

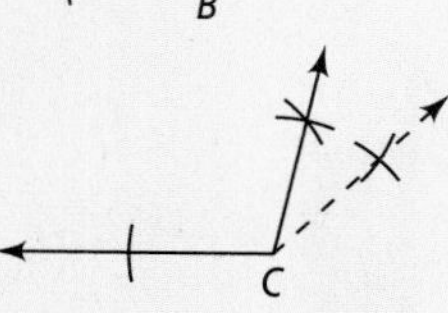

24.

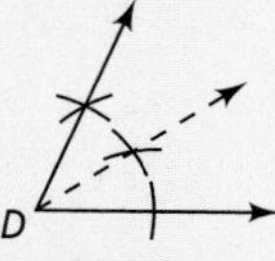

25a. With P as center, draw an arc with radius slightly more than $\frac{1}{2}PQ$. Keeping that radius, draw an arc with Q as center. Those two arcs meet at 2 points; the line through those 2 points intersects $\overline{PQ}$ at its midpoint.

b. Follow the steps in part (a) to find the midpoint C of $\overline{PQ}$. Then repeat the process for segments $\overline{PC}$ and $\overline{CQ}$.

26a.

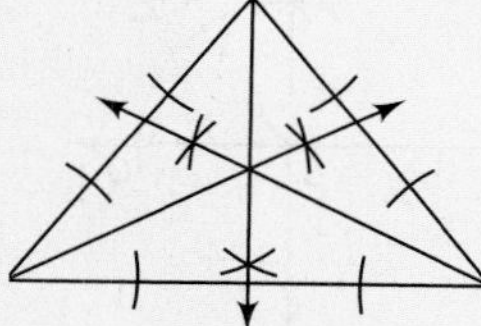

The three angle bisectors meet at a point.

b.

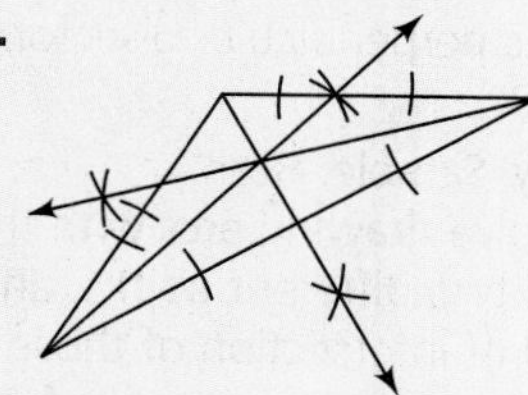

c. For any triangle, the three angle bisectors meet at a point.

27. possible

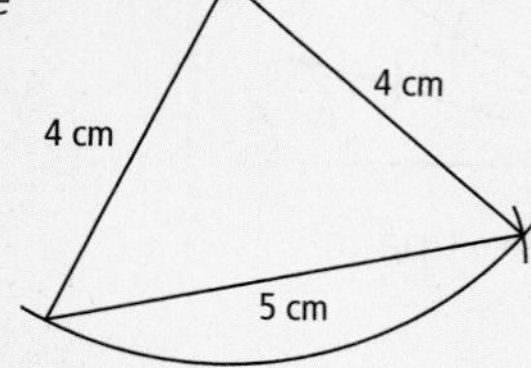

Challenge

33. Study the figures. Complete the definition of a line perpendicular to a plane: A line is perpendicular to a plane if it is __?__ to every line in the plane that __?__.

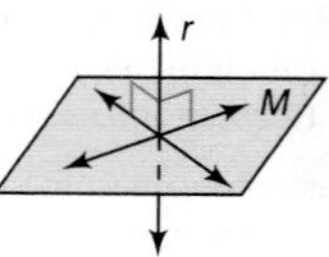

Line r ⊥ plane M.

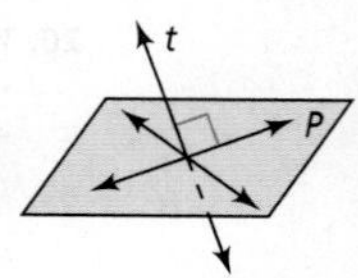

Line t is not ⊥ plane P.

34. a. Use your compass to draw a circle. Locate three points A, B, and C on the circle.

b. Draw $\overline{AB}$ and $\overline{BC}$. Then construct the perpendicular bisectors of $\overline{AB}$ and $\overline{BC}$.

c. Reasoning Label the intersection of the two perpendicular bisectors as point O. What do you think is true about point O?

35. Two triangles are *congruent* if each side and each angle of one triangle is congruent to a side or angle of the other triangle. In Chapter 4, you will learn that if each side of one triangle is congruent to a side of the other triangle, then you can conclude that the triangles are congruent without finding the angles. Explain how you can use congruent triangles to justify the angle bisector construction.

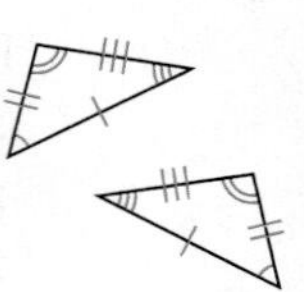

Standardized Test Prep

SAT/ACT

36. What must you do to construct the midpoint of a segment?

Ⓐ Measure half its length. Ⓒ Measure twice its length.

Ⓑ Construct an angle bisector. Ⓓ Construct a perpendicular bisector.

37. Given the diagram at the right, what is NOT a reasonable name for the angle?

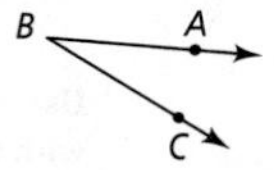

Ⓕ $\angle ABC$ Ⓗ $\angle CBA$

Ⓖ $\angle B$ Ⓘ $\angle ACB$

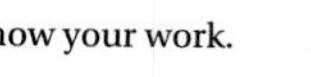

Short Response

38. M is the midpoint of $\overline{XY}$. Find the value of x. Show your work.

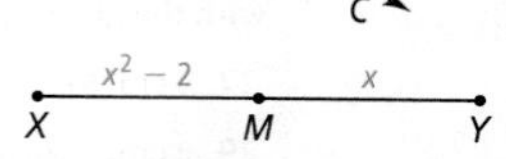

Mixed Review

39. $\angle DEF$ is the supplement of $\angle DEG$ with $m\angle DEG = 64$. What is $m\angle DEF$? See Lesson 1-5.

40. $m\angle TUV = 100$ and $m\angle VUW = 80$. Are $\angle TUV$ and $\angle VUW$ a linear pair? Explain.

Find the length of each segment. See Lesson 1-3.

41. $\overline{AC}$ **42.** $\overline{AD}$

43. $\overline{CD}$ **44.** $\overline{BC}$

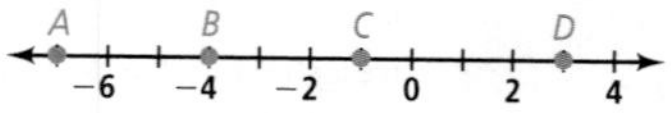

A B C D on a number line: −6 −4 −2 0 2 4

Get Ready! **To prepare for Lesson 1-7, do Exercises 45–47.**

Algebra Evaluate each expression for $a = 6$ and $b = -8$. See p. 830.

45. $(a - b)^2$ **46.** $\sqrt{a^2 + b^2}$ **47.** $\frac{a + b}{2}$

28. possible

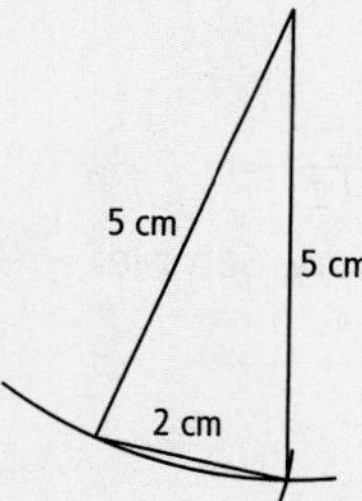

29. Not possible; the two 2-cm sides do not meet.

30. Not possible; the 2-cm sides meet on the 4-cm side, so they do not form a triangle.

31a.

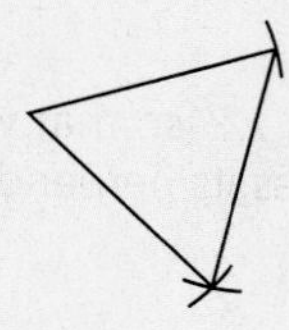

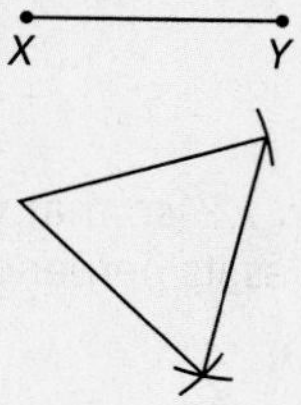

b. The measure of each angle is 60°.

c. Draw an angle congruent to one of the angles of the triangle from part (a) to get a 60° ∠. Then construct its angle bisector to get two 30° ∠s.

32. A

33. ⊥; contains the intersection of that line with the plane

34a–b.

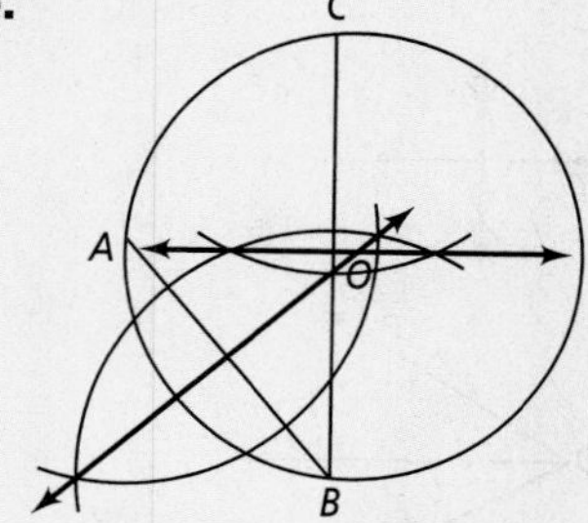

c. O is the center of the circle.

35–47. See back of book.

1-6 Lesson Resources

Differentiated Remediation

Instructional Support

Geometry Companion

Students can use the **Geometry Companion** worktext (4 pages) . . .

- New Vocabulary
- Key Concepts
- Got It for each Problem
- Lesson Check

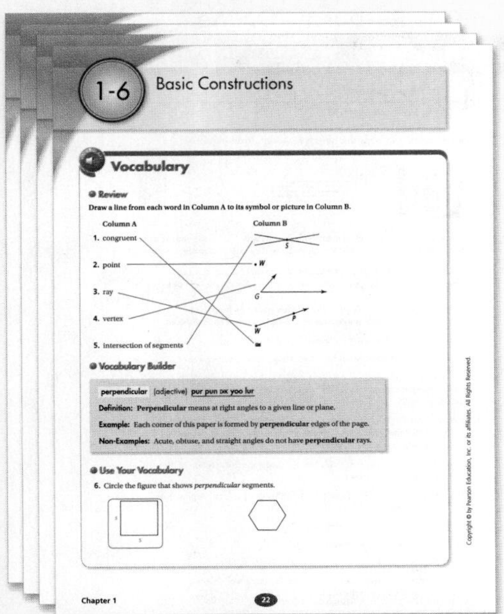

1-6 Basic Constructions

Vocabulary

Review

Draw a line from each word in Column A to its symbol or picture in Column B.

Column A	Column B
1. congruent	
2. point	W
3. ray	G
4. vertex	W, P
5. intersection of segments	

Vocabulary Builder

perpendicular (adjective) pur pun DIK yoo lur

Definition: **Perpendicular** means at right angles to a given line or plane.

Example: Each corner of this paper is formed by **perpendicular** edges of the page.

Non-Examples: Acute, obtuse, and straight angles do not have **perpendicular** rays.

Use Your Vocabulary

6. Circle the figure that shows *perpendicular* segments.

Chapter 1 22

ELL Support

Focus on Language Examine the word "perpendicular." As an adjective, perpendicular means straight up and down or upright. Ask students for examples of things that are upright. Then ask students for synonyms for *perpendicular*. Remind students that a synonym is a word that means the same thing. Examples are *vertical*, *on two legs*, *standing*, *erect*, or *plumb*. Ask for antonyms, such as *horizontal* or *on four legs*.

Perpendicular can also be a noun meaning a perpendicular position, perpendicular line, or perpendicular plane. The word comes from the Latin *perpendiculum* (plumb line) and from *perpendere* (balance carefully).

5 Assess & Remediate

Lesson Quiz

1. Construct $\angle Y$ so that $\angle Y \cong \angle Z$.

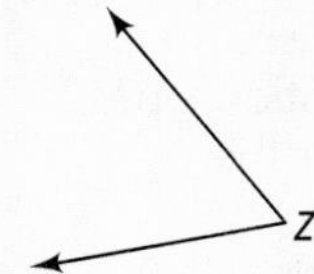

2. Construct the line CD so that CD is the perpendicular bisector of $\overline{EF}$.

3. Do you UNDERSTAND? Construct UV, the bisector of $\angle U$.

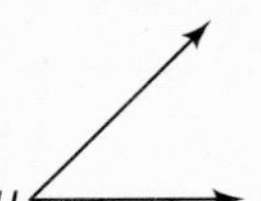

ANSWERS TO LESSON QUIZ

1.

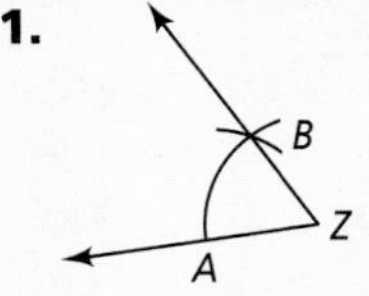

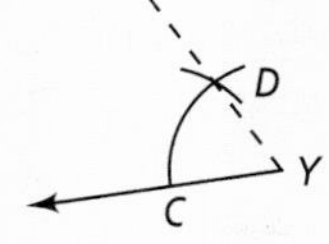

2.

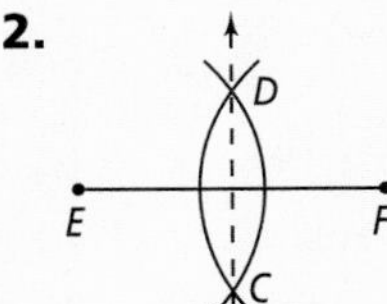

3.

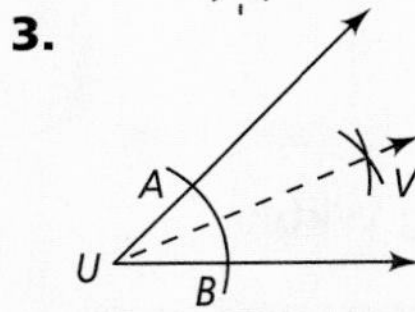

PRECRIPTION FOR REMEDIATION

Use the student work on the Lesson Quiz to prescribe a differentiated review assignment.

Points	Differentiated Remediation
0–1	Intervention
2	On-level
3	Extension

PowerGeometry.com

5 Assess & Remediate

Assign the Lesson Quiz. Appropriate intervention, practice, or enrichment is automatically generated based on student performance.

Intervention

- **Reteaching** (2 pages) Provides reteaching and practice exercises for the key lesson concepts. Use with struggling students or absent students.
- **English Language Learner Support** Helps students develop and reinforce mathematical vocabulary and key concepts.

All-in-One Resources/Online

Reteaching

1-6 **Reteaching**

Basic Constructions

Before you start the construction, THINK about the goal. Then SKETCH the segment or angle you are trying to construct. Next EXPLAIN the purpose of each step in the construction as you complete it.

Problem

Construct $\overline{AB}$ so that $\overline{AB}$ is congruent to $\overline{XY}$.

THINK: Can you describe what the problem is asking for in your own words?
You want to draw a line segment that has the same length as one you are given.

SKETCH: Sketch a segment and label it as $\overline{AB}$. Why do you start with a sketch?
A sketch helps you to see what you need to construct.

EXPLAIN: First, draw a ray. What is the purpose of drawing a ray?
The ray is a part of a line on which you can mark off the correct length of $\overline{AB}$.

Second, measure the length of $\overline{XY}$, using the compass. What is the purpose of measuring the length of $\overline{XY}$?
You need this measure to mark the same length on the ray.

Finally, mark the length of $\overline{XY}$ on the ray, using the compass. Why do you mark the length of $\overline{XY}$ on your ray?
This completes your construction of $\overline{AB}$, *which is congruent to* $\overline{XY}$.

Exercises

Analyze the construction of a congruent angle and bisectors.

1. Analyze the construction of a perpendicular bisector. First draw $\overline{XY}$.
   a. THINK about what it means to construct a perpendicular bisector. What is your goal? Answers may vary. Sample: to draw a segment that is perpendicular to $\overline{XY}$ and that divides it into two equal pieces
   b. SKETCH a perpendicular bisector to $\overline{XY}$. Check students' work.
   c. EXPLAIN the first two steps. What is the purpose of drawing an arc from each endpoint? Answers may vary. Sample: to form two intersections to become two points of the perpendicular bisector
   d. EXPLAIN the last step. What is the purpose of drawing the segment between the intersections of the arcs? Answers may vary. Sample: to draw the perpendicular bisector

All-in-One Resources/Online

English Language Learner Support

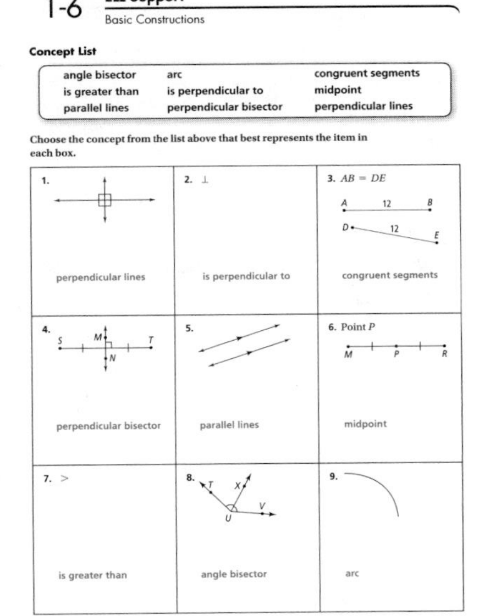

1-6 **ELL Support**

Basic Constructions

Concept List

angle bisector	arc	congruent segments
is greater than	is perpendicular to	midpoint
parallel lines	perpendicular bisector	perpendicular lines

Choose the concept from the list above that best represents the item in each box.

1. perpendicular lines	2. ⊥ is perpendicular to	3. $AB = DE$ (A 12 B; D 12 E) congruent segments
4. (S, M, N, T) perpendicular bisector	5. parallel lines	6. Point P (M, P, R) midpoint
7. > is greater than	8. (T, X, U, V) angle bisector	9. arc

Differentiated Remediation *continued*

On-Level

- **Practice** (2 pages) Provides extra practice for each lesson. For simpler practice exercises, use the Form K Practice pages found in the All-in-One Teaching Resources and online.
- **Think About a Plan** Helps students develop specific problem-solving skills and strategies by providing scaffolded guiding questions.
- **Standardized Test Prep** Focuses on all major exercises, all major question types, and helps students prepare for the high-stakes assessments.

Extension

- **Enrichment** Provides students with interesting problems and activities that extend the concepts of the lesson.
- **Activities, Games, and Puzzles** Worksheets that can be used for concepts development, enrichment, and for fun!

Practice and Problem Solving Wkbk/ All-in-One Resources/Online

Practice page 1

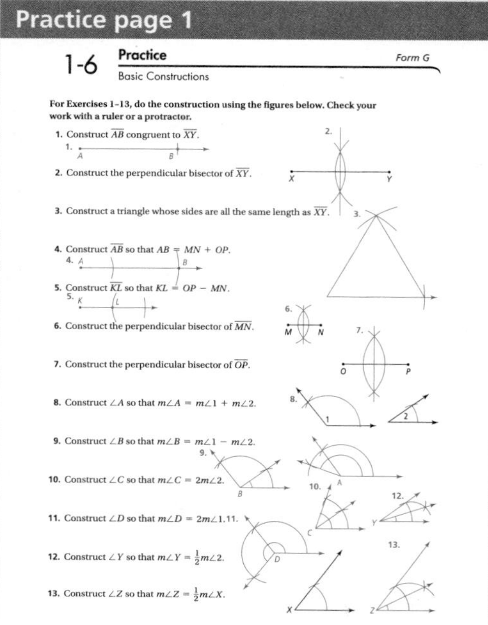

1-6 **Practice** — Basic Constructions — *Form G*

For Exercises 1–13, do the construction using the figures below. Check your work with a ruler or a protractor.

1. Construct $\overline{AB}$ congruent to $\overline{XY}$.
2. Construct the perpendicular bisector of $\overline{XY}$.
3. Construct a triangle whose sides are all the same length as $\overline{XY}$.
4. Construct $\overline{AB}$ so that $AB = MN + OP$.
5. Construct $\overline{KL}$ so that $KL = OP - MN$.
6. Construct the perpendicular bisector of $\overline{MN}$.
7. Construct the perpendicular bisector of $\overline{OP}$.
8. Construct $\angle A$ so that $m\angle A = m\angle 1 + m\angle 2$.
9. Construct $\angle B$ so that $m\angle B = m\angle 1 - m\angle 2$.
10. Construct $\angle C$ so that $m\angle C = 2m\angle 2$.
11. Construct $\angle D$ so that $m\angle D = 2m\angle 1$.
12. Construct $\angle Y$ so that $m\angle Y = \frac{1}{2}m\angle 2$.
13. Construct $\angle Z$ so that $m\angle Z = \frac{1}{2}m\angle X$.

Practice and Problem Solving Wkbk/ All-in-One Resources/Online

Practice page 2

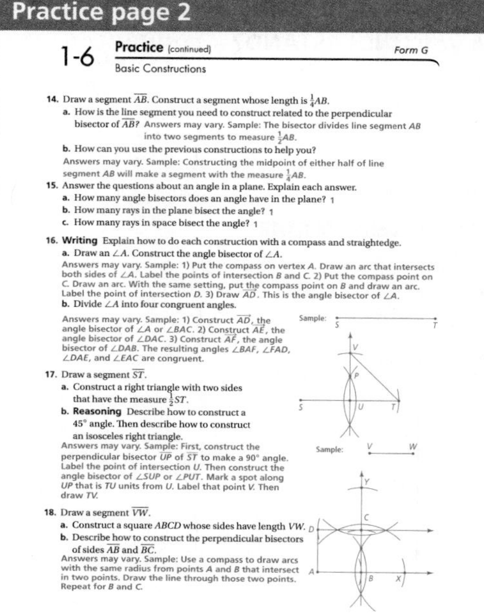

1-6 **Practice** (continued) — Basic Constructions — *Form G*

14. Draw a segment $\overline{AB}$. Construct a segment whose length is $\frac{1}{4}AB$.
    a. How is the line segment you need to construct related to the perpendicular bisector of $\overline{AB}$? Answers may vary. Sample: The bisector divides line segment *AB* into two segments to measure $\frac{1}{2}AB$.
    b. How can you use the previous constructions to help you?
    Answers may vary. Sample: Constructing the midpoint of either half of line segment *AB* will make a segment with the measure $\frac{1}{4}AB$.
15. Answer the questions about an angle in a plane. Explain each answer.
    a. How many angle bisectors does an angle have in the plane? 1
    b. How many rays in the plane bisect the angle? 1
    c. How many rays in space bisect the angle? 1
16. **Writing** Explain how to do each construction with a compass and straightedge.
    a. Draw an $\angle A$. Construct the angle bisector of $\angle A$.
    Answers may vary. Sample: 1) Put the compass on vertex *A*. Draw an arc that intersects both sides of $\angle A$. Label the points of intersection *B* and *C*. 2) Put the compass point on *C*. Draw an arc. With the same setting, put the compass point on *B* and draw an arc. Label the point of intersection *D*. 3) Draw $\overrightarrow{AD}$. This is the angle bisector of $\angle A$.
    b. Divide $\angle A$ into four congruent angles.
    Answers may vary. Sample: 1) Construct $\overrightarrow{AD}$, the angle bisector of $\angle A$ or $\angle BAC$. 2) Construct $\overrightarrow{AE}$, the angle bisector of $\angle DAC$. 3) Construct $\overrightarrow{AF}$, the angle bisector of $\angle DAB$. The resulting angles $\angle BAF$, $\angle FAD$, $\angle DAE$, and $\angle EAC$ are congruent.
17. Draw a segment $\overline{ST}$.
    a. Construct a right triangle with two sides that have the measure $\frac{1}{2}ST$.
    b. **Reasoning** Describe how to construct a 45° angle. Then describe how to construct an isosceles right triangle.
    Answers may vary. Sample: First, construct the perpendicular bisector $\overline{UP}$ of $\overline{ST}$ to make a 90° angle. Label the point of intersection *U*. Then construct the angle bisector of $\angle SUP$ or $\angle PUT$. Mark a spot along *UP* that is *TU* units from *U*. Label that point *V*. Then draw *TV*.
18. Draw a segment $\overline{VW}$.
    a. Construct a square *ABCD* whose sides have length *VW*.
    b. Describe how to construct the perpendicular bisectors of sides $\overline{AB}$ and $\overline{BC}$.
    Answers may vary. Sample: Use a compass to draw arcs with the same radius from points *A* and *B* that intersect in two points. Draw the line through those two points. Repeat for *B* and *C*.

All-in-One Resources/Online

Enrichment

1-6 **Enrichment** — Basic Constructions

An optical illusion is an image that often is misleading to the human eye. The following images are optical illusions. How do you view each image?

Do you see the cube from above or below? | How many balls are on each shelf? Which shelf are they on? | Are the inside vertical lines straight or curved?

The optical illusion at the right can be viewed in two ways. It can be viewed as a cube with another cube on its corner or as a cube with a corner cut out.

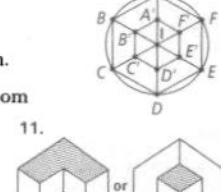

Use the following steps to make this optical illusion. Use a pencil for steps 1–6 so that your pencil marks can be erased when you have finished.

1. Use a compass to draw a circle and keep the compass settings.
2. Place a point on the circumference of the circle. Label this point *A*.
3. Place the tip of the compass at point *A*, and mark an arc on the circle counterclockwise from *A*. Label the point where the arc intersects the circle as point *B*.
4. Place the tip of the compass at point *B*, and mark a similar arc on the circle next to *B*. Label the point where the arc intersects the circle as point *C*. Repeat this step to mark *D*, *E*, and *F*.
5. Use a straightedge to draw $\overline{AD}$, $\overline{BE}$, and $\overline{CF}$. Label the intersection of these three line segments as point *I*.
6. Use a compass to find the midpoint of $\overline{AI}$. Label this point A'. Repeat this step to find midpoints of $\overline{BI}$, $\overline{CI}$, $\overline{DI}$, $\overline{EI}$, and $\overline{FI}$.
7. Use a straightedge to draw hexagon *ABCDEF*.
8. Use a straightedge to draw hexagon $A'B'C'D'E'F'$.
9. Name the two polygons you shade to make the optical illusion.
   hexagon $ABB'A'F'F$ and quadrilateral $IC'D'E'$
10. Name the two polygons you shade to cause the illusion of a room with a cube on the floor in the corner.
    hexagon $CDEE'D'C'$ and quadrilateral $A'F'IB'$
11. Shade the two polygons named in Step 9 or 10 to complete one of the optical illusions. Then erase all lines drawn with a pencil.

1–6. A, B, B', A', F', F, C', I, E', C, D', E, D

7–8. A, B, A', F', F, B', I, E', C, C', D', E, D

11. or

Practice and Problem Solving Wkbk/ All-in-One Resources/Online

Think About a Plan

1-6 **Think About a Plan** — Basic Constructions

a. Draw a large triangle with three acute angles. Construct the bisector of the three angles. What appears to be true about the three angle bisectors?
b. Repeat the constructions with a triangle that has one obtuse angle.
c. **Make a Conjecture** What appears to be true about the three angle bisectors of any triangle?

1. In this problem, you will draw three rays for each triangle. Each ray starts at a vertex and passes through the interior of the triangle.
   a. What is the maximum number of points of intersection between the rays? 3
   b. What is the minimum number? 1
2. On a separate piece of paper, draw $\triangle ABC$ such that all three angles are acute angles and the triangle takes up most of the paper.
   Check students' drawings of an acute $\triangle ABC$.
3. In your own words, what are the steps for drawing the angle bisector of $\angle A$?
   Answers may vary. Sample: Draw an arc centered at *A* that crosses its two rays at *X* and *Y*. Draw arcs with the same radius from *X* and *Y* that intersect at *Z*. Draw a ray from *A* through *Z*.
4. Draw the angle bisector of $\angle A$. Then draw the angle bisectors for $\angle B$ and $\angle C$.
   Answers may vary. Check students' drawings of angle bisectors drawn at $\angle A$, $\angle B$, and $\angle C$.
5. On a separate piece of paper, draw $\triangle DEF$ such that one of the three angles is an obtuse angle and the triangle takes up most of the paper. Construct the angle bisectors for $\angle D$, $\angle E$, and $\angle F$.
   Answers may vary. Check students' drawings of obtuse $\triangle DEF$ with angle bisectors at $\angle D$, $\angle E$, and $\angle F$.
6. How many points of intersection are there for the three angle bisectors of $\triangle ABC$? 1
7. How many points of intersection are there for the three angle bisectors of $\triangle DEF$? 1
8. Suppose a friend draws $\triangle DHI$. Without looking at the triangle, what do you think will be true of the three angle bisectors of its angles?
   They will intersect at a single point.

Practice and Problem Solving Wkbk/ All-in-One Resources/Online

Standardized Test Prep

1-6 **Standardized Test Prep** — Basic Constructions

Multiple Choice

For Exercises 1–4, choose the correct letter.

1. You are asked to construct a segment congruent to $\overline{AB}$. As a first step, you draw a ray. Which of the following, if true of the ray, would be most helpful? B
   A. The ray is drawn on the paper shorter than $\overline{AB}$.
   B. The ray is drawn on the paper longer than $\overline{AB}$.
   C. The ray is drawn parallel to $\overline{AB}$.
   D. The ray is drawn perpendicular to $\overline{AB}$.
2. Which of the following must be true about a perpendicular bisector and the segment it bisects? I
   F. The perpendicular bisector and the segment bisect each other.
   G. The angle of intersection depends on the length of the line segment.
   H. The perpendicular bisector intersects the segment at a 45° angle.
   I. The perpendicular bisector intersects the segment at a 90° angle.
3. Which of the following is true about the bisectors of a segment in a plane? C
   A. Every segment has exactly one bisector.
   B. Every segment has exactly two bisectors.
   C. Every segment has infinitely many bisectors.
   D. Every segment has infinitely many perpendicular bisectors.
4. Which of the following materials is not used when making basic constructions? F
   F. a ruler G. a compass H. a straightedge I. a pencil

Extended Response

5. How do you construct a perpendicular bisector of $\overline{AB}$? Use three steps.
   [4] 1) Put the compass point on *A*. Open the compass to wider than $\frac{1}{2}AB$. Then draw a long arc. 2) Put the compass point on *B*. Draw another long arc that intersects the first arc at two points. Label the points of intersection as *X* and *Y*. 3) Draw $\overline{XY}$. Label $\overline{XY}$ as the perpendicular bisector of $\overline{AB}$. [3] three steps but not all clear [2] two good steps and one wrong step [1] some steps shown [0] no steps shown

Online Teacher Resource Center

Activities, Games, and Puzzles

1-6 **Puzzle: Mystery Pictures** — Basic Constructions

Materials

- Compass
- Straight edge

Using only a compass and straight edge, follow the directions to construct the mystery picture.

1. Find and label *C*, the midpoint of $\overline{AB}$.
2. Draw $\overline{CD}$ such that point *D* is above *C* on the perpendicular bisector of $\overline{AB}$ and $CD = \frac{1}{2}AB$.
3. Draw $\overline{CE}$ such that point *E* is below *C* on the perpendicular bisector of $\overline{AB}$ and $CE = \frac{3}{4}AB$.
4. Draw $\overline{AD}$, $\overline{DB}$, $\overline{BE}$, and $\overline{AE}$.
5. Starting at point *E*, draw a curve through the intersections of each pair of equilateral triangles.

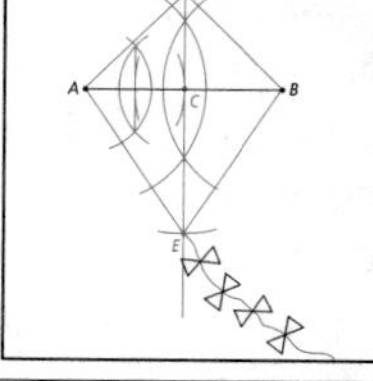

Constructions may vary. Sample is given.

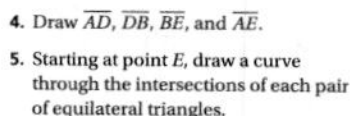

1. Construct $\angle RJI$ such that $m\angle RJI = m\angle HGF$ and $RJ = IJ$.
2. Construct $\angle SLK$ such that $m\angle SLK = \frac{3}{2}m\angle HGF$ and $SL = KL$.
3. Construct $\angle TNM$ such that $m\angle TNM = 2m\angle HGF$ and $TN = MN$.
4. Draw an arc with radius *JO* through the exterior points of $\angle RJI$.
5. Draw an arc with radius *LP* through the exterior points of $\angle SLK$.
6. Draw an arc with radius *NQ* through the exterior points of $\angle TNM$.

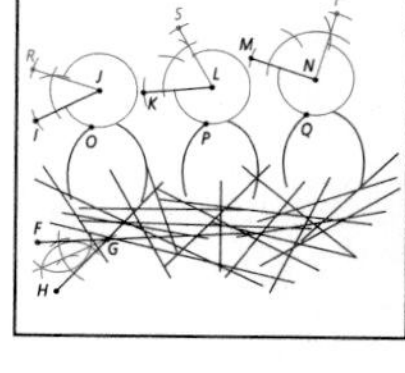

Challenge

Design your own mystery picture, and provide directions for its construction.
Check students' work.

Concept Byte

Use With Lesson 1-6

TECHNOLOGY

Exploring Constructions

You can use Draw tools or Construct tools in geometry software to make points, lines, and planes. A figure made by Draw has no constraints. When you manipulate, or try to change, a figure made by Draw, it moves or changes size freely. A figure made by Construct is related to an existing object. When you manipulate the existing object, the constructed object moves or resizes accordingly.

In this Activity, you will explore the difference between Draw and Construct.

Activity

Draw $\overline{AB}$ and Construct the perpendicular bisector $\overleftrightarrow{DC}$. Then Draw $\overline{EF}$ and Construct G, any point on $\overline{EF}$. Draw $\overleftrightarrow{HG}$.

1. Find EG, GF, and $m\angle HGF$. Try to drag G so that $EG = GF$. Try to drag H so that $m\angle HGF = 90$. Were you able to draw the perpendicular bisector of $\overline{EF}$? Explain.
2. Drag A and B. Observe AC, CB, and $m\angle DCB$. Is $\overleftrightarrow{DC}$ always the perpendicular bisector of $\overline{AB}$ no matter how you manipulate the figure?
3. Drag E and F. Observe EG, GF, and $m\angle HGF$. How is the relationship between $\overline{EF}$ and $\overleftrightarrow{HG}$ different from the relationship between $\overline{AB}$ and $\overleftrightarrow{DC}$?
4. Write a description of the general difference between Draw and Construct. Then use your description to explain why the relationship between $\overline{EF}$ and $\overleftrightarrow{HG}$ differs from the relationship between $\overline{AB}$ and $\overleftrightarrow{DC}$.

Exercises

5. a. Draw $\angle NOP$. Draw $\overrightarrow{OQ}$ in the interior of $\angle NOP$. Drag Q until $m\angle NOQ = m\angle QOP$.
   b. Manipulate the figure and observe the different angle measures. Is $\overrightarrow{OQ}$ always the angle bisector of $\angle NOP$?

6. a. Draw $\angle JKL$.
   b. Construct its angle bisector, $\overrightarrow{KM}$.
   c. Manipulate the figure and observe the different angle measures. Is $\overrightarrow{KM}$ always the angle bisector of $\angle JKL$?
   d. How can you manipulate the figure on the screen so that it shows a right angle? Justify your answer.

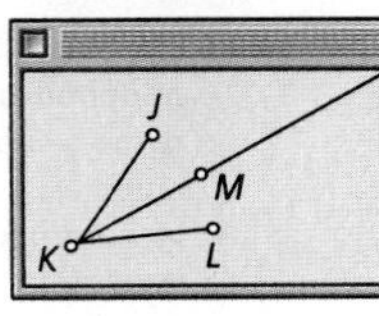

Guided Instruction

PURPOSE To use geometry software to make points, lines, and planes and complete constructions

PROCESS Students will

- construct figures using geometry software.
- make conjectures after manipulating their constructions.

DISCUSS In this Activity have students work with a partner to perform the exercises. Have partners analyze, evaluate, and form a consensus through discussion of the differences between the tools. Then have them join with other classmates to synthesize their ideas by organizing their thoughts on paper.

Activity

This Activity allows students to examine the difference between the Draw and Construct features of geometry software.

Q Before performing the activity, ask the students what differences, if any, they think there will be between the Construct and Draw tools. **[Answers will vary. Sample: The Construct tool will provide a more accurate drawing and will be based on existing figures.]**

Q What are some other geometry constructions you could use to examine the differences between these tools? **[Answers will vary. Sample: constructing a parallelogram]**

Answers

Activity

1. Yes. It is possible to make $m\angle HGF = 90$ and $EG = GF$. When these conditions are met, $\overleftrightarrow{HG}$ is a perpendicular bisector.
2. Yes.
3. The position of $\overline{EF}$ relative to $\overleftrightarrow{GH}$ can change, whereas the position of $\overline{AB}$ relative to $\overleftrightarrow{DC}$ is fixed.
4. The Construct tool fixes objects so that their relationship does not change. The Draw tool does not fix objects, so that the relationship between drawn objects can be changed.

Exercises

5a. Check students' work.

b. no

6a–b. Check students' work.

c. yes

d. Answers may vary. Sample: Adjust $\angle JKM$ or $\angle MKL$ until it is 45°.

1 Interactive Learning

Solve It!

PURPOSE To introduce students to the notion that distance between points has both a horizontal and a vertical component

PROCESS Students may use visualization, draw a segment between the two structures and construct its bisector, or use the horizontal and vertical components of distance.

FACILITATE

Q If you were to travel from the lower left structure to the second structure, how many vertical units would you travel? How many horizontal units would you travel? **[3 units; 5 units]**

Q If you were to travel from the lower left structure to the halfway point between the two structures, how many horizontal and vertical units would you travel? **[1.5 vertical units and 2.5 horizontal units]**

ANSWER See Solve It in Answers on next page.

CONNECT THE MATH Ask students how the Solve It would be different if the structures were lined up either horizontally or vertically rather than diagonally on the grid. In this lesson students learn about distances on a number line and the coordinate plane.

2 Guided Instruction

Take Note

VISUAL LEARNERS

The midpoint of two endpoints in a coordinate system is the point that lies at the intersection of the perpendicular bisectors of the segments that represent the horizontal and vertical distances between the two endpoints.

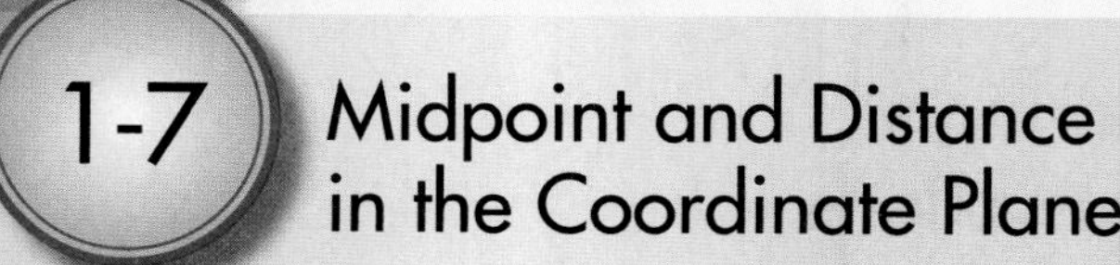

1-7 Midpoint and Distance in the Coordinate Plane

Objectives To find the midpoint of a segment
To find the distance between two points in the coordinate plane

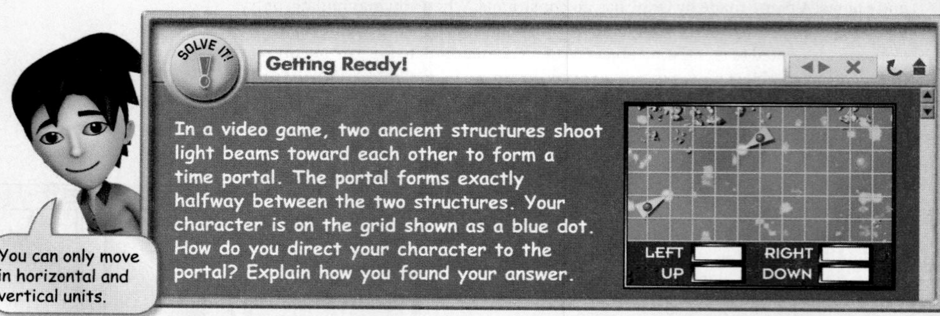

Solve It!
Getting Ready!
In a video game, two ancient structures shoot light beams toward each other to form a time portal. The portal forms exactly halfway between the two structures. Your character is on the grid shown as a blue dot. How do you direct your character to the portal? Explain how you found your answer.
LEFT
RIGHT
UP
DOWN
You can only move in horizontal and vertical units.

In this lesson, you will learn how to find midpoints and distance on a grid like the one in the Solve It.

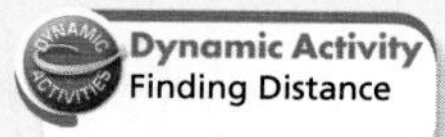

Essential Understanding You can use formulas to find the midpoint and length of any segment in the coordinate plane.

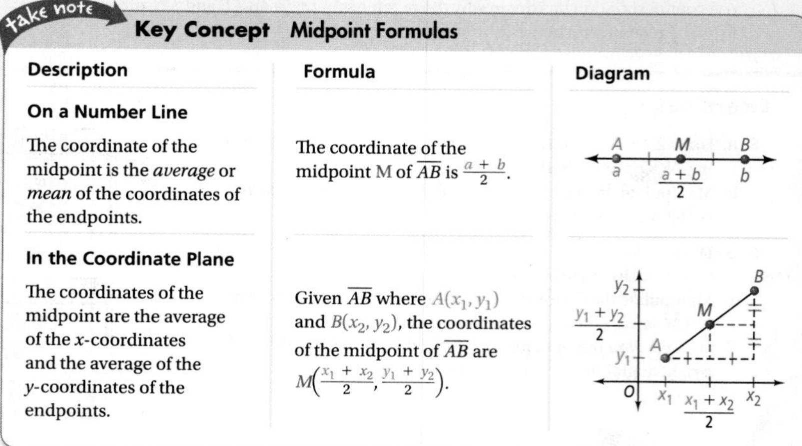

Take note **Key Concept** Midpoint Formulas

Description	Formula	Diagram
On a Number Line The coordinate of the midpoint is the *average* or *mean* of the coordinates of the endpoints.	The coordinate of the midpoint M of $\overline{AB}$ is $\frac{a+b}{2}$.	A, M, B; a, $\frac{a+b}{2}$, b
In the Coordinate Plane The coordinates of the midpoint are the average of the x-coordinates and the average of the y-coordinates of the endpoints.	Given $\overline{AB}$ where $A(x_1, y_1)$ and $B(x_2, y_2)$, the coordinates of the midpoint of $\overline{AB}$ are $M\left(\frac{x_1+x_2}{2}, \frac{y_1+y_2}{2}\right)$.	A, M, B; O; y_2, $\frac{y_1+y_2}{2}$, y_1; x_1, $\frac{x_1+x_2}{2}$, x_2

1-7 Preparing to Teach

BIG idea Measurement

UbD

ESSENTIAL UNDERSTANDING

- Formulas can be used to find the midpoint and length of any segment in the coordinate plane.

Math Background

This lesson provides students with their first of many exposures to analytic geometry. Analytic geometry is the branch of geometry in which points are represented using a coordinate system in two or more dimensions. Mathematician René Descartes was credited with early applications of algebra to geometry and thus the coordinate plane is called the Cartesian plane.

In this lesson, points are represented using two coordinates in the Cartesian plane. Because the endpoints of line segments are assigned two coordinates rather than just one coordinate as in Lesson 1-3, students need to reexamine the concepts of length, distance, and midpoint.

The Midpoint Formula and the Distance Formula are introduced, and students learn to relate familiar algebraic manipulations to geometry topics.

Support Student Learning

Use the **Geometry Companion** to engage and support students during instructions. See Lesson Resources at the end of this lesson for details.

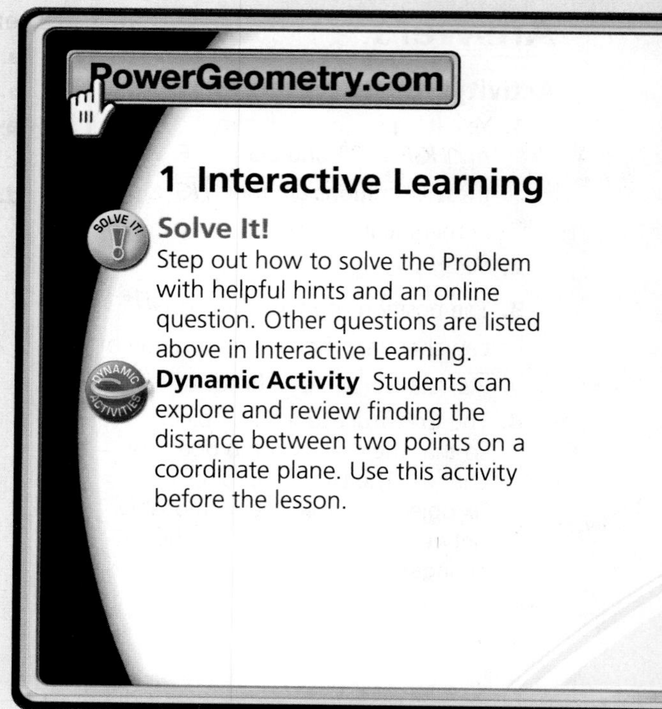

Problem 1 Finding the Midpoint

Think

Which Midpoint Formula do you use?
If the endpoints are real numbers, use the formula for the number line. If they are ordered pairs, use the formula for the coordinate plane.

A $\overline{AB}$ **has endpoints at −4 and 9. What is the coordinate of its midpoint?**

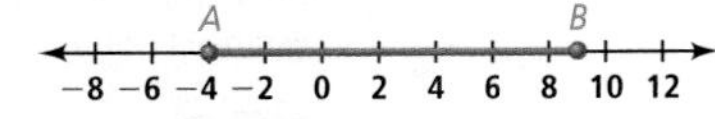

Let $a = -4$ and $b = 9$.

$$M = \frac{a+b}{2} = \frac{-4+9}{2} = \frac{5}{2} = 2.5$$

The coordinate of the midpoint of $\overline{AB}$ is 2.5.

B $\overline{EF}$ **has endpoints $E(7, 5)$ and $F(2, -4)$. What are the coordinates of its midpoint M?**

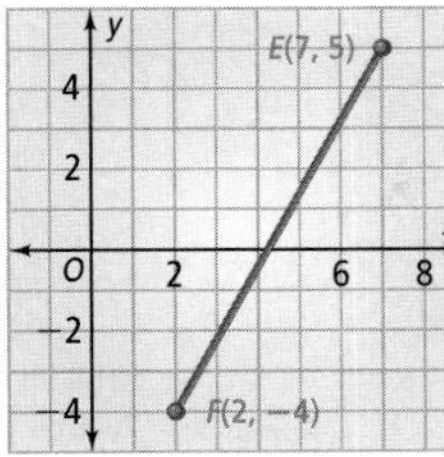

Let $E(7, 5)$ be (x_1, y_1) and $F(2, -4)$ be (x_2, y_2).

$$x\text{-coordinate of } M = \frac{x_1+x_2}{2} = \frac{7+2}{2} = \frac{9}{2} = 4.5$$

$$y\text{-coordinate of } M = \frac{y_1+y_2}{2} = \frac{5+(-4)}{2} = \frac{1}{2} = 0.5$$

The coordinates of the midpoint of $\overline{EF}$ are $M(4.5, 0.5)$.

Got It? 1. a. $\overline{JK}$ has endpoints at −12 and 4 on a number line. What is the coordinate of its midpoint?

b. What is the midpoint of $\overline{RS}$ with endpoints $R(5, -10)$ and $S(3, 6)$?

When you know the midpoint and an endpoint of a segment, you can use the Midpoint Formula to find the other endpoint.

Problem 2 Finding an Endpoint

Plan

How can you find the coordinates of *D*?
Use the Midpoint Formula to set up an equation. Split that equation into two equations: one for the *x*-coordinate and one for the *y*-coordinate.

The midpoint of $\overline{CD}$ is $M(-2, 1)$. One endpoint is $C(-5, 7)$. What are the coordinates of the other endpoint D?

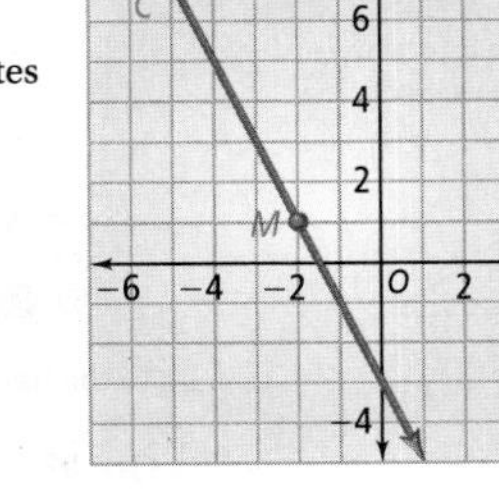

Let $M(-2, 1)$ be (x, y) and $C(-5, 7)$ be (x_1, y_1). Let the coordinates of D be (x_2, y_2).

$$(-2, 1) = \left(\frac{-5+x_2}{2}, \frac{7+y_2}{2}\right)$$

x		y
$-2 = \frac{-5+x_2}{2}$	Use the Midpoint Formula.	$1 = \frac{7+y_2}{2}$
$-4 = -5 + x_2$	Multiply each side by 2.	$2 = 7 + y_2$
$1 = x_2$	Simplify.	$-5 = y_2$

The coordinates of D are $(1, -5)$.

Got It? 2. The midpoint of $\overline{AB}$ has coordinates $(4, -9)$. Endpoint A has coordinates $(-3, -5)$. What are the coordinates of B?

Problem 1

Q How can you use the definition of distance learned in Lesson 1-3 to verify that you found the correct midpoint for 1A? **[You can use the distance formula to verify that the lengths of the two smaller segments are equal.]**

Q How can you use a visual estimate to check your calculated midpoint? **[Answers may vary. Sample: Your calculated answer should be close to the midpoint you determined by visual inspection.]**

Got It? SYNTHESIZING

If a student provides an answer of 8 for Question 1a, then the student likely took the absolute value of the sum of −12 and 4 and is confusing the Midpoint Formula with the definition of distance.

Problem 2

Q Does this problem involve the Midpoint Formula on a number line or on a coordinate plane? Explain. **[Because the midpoint and the given endpoint are ordered pairs, you know to use the Midpoint Formula for the coordinate plane.]**

Q How should you check your results? **[You should use the Midpoint Formula to verify that the midpoint of the given endpoint and the endpoint that you determined is actually the given midpoint.]**

Got It? VISUAL LEARNERS

Show students how they can use the vertical and horizontal components of the distance from point *A* to the midpoint to determine the coordinates of point *B*.

2 Guided Instruction

Each Problem is worked out and supported online.

Problem 1
Finding the Midpoint
Animated

Problem 2
Finding an Endpoint
Animated

Problem 3
Finding Distance

Problem 4
Real World Connection
Animated

Support in Geometry Companion

- Vocabulary
- Key Concepts
- Got It?

Answers

Solve It!

7 units left, 0.5 unit down; explanations may vary. Sample: The horizontal distance between the two structures is 5 units, and the vertical distance is 3 units. The portal will form at the point $\frac{5}{2}$, or 2.5, units to the right and $\frac{3}{2}$, or 1.5, units up from the leftmost structure. The point is 7 units to the left and 0.5 unit down from the character.

Got It?

1a. −4

b. (4, −2)

2. (11, −13

Take Note
Point out that the distance measurement using the Ruler Postulate introduced in Lesson 1-3 included absolute value brackets surrounding the difference expression, but that this Distance Formula does not. Elicit that the absolute value brackets are not necessary in this formula because the difference expressions are squared, which always results in a positive number.

In Lesson 1-3, you learned how to find the distance between two points on a number line. To find the distance between two points in a coordinate plane, you can use the Distance Formula.

Key Concept Distance Formula

The distance between two points $A(x_1, y_1)$ and $B(x_2, y_2)$ is

$$d = \sqrt{(x_2 - x_1)^2 + (y_2 - y_1)^2}.$$

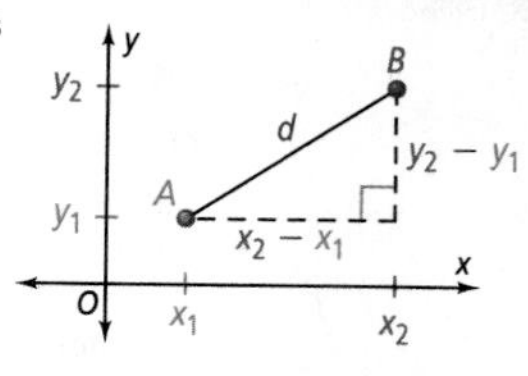

The Distance Formula is based on the *Pythagorean Theorem*, which you will study later in this book. When you use the Distance Formula, you are really finding the length of a side of a right triangle. You will verify the Distance Formula in Chapter 8.

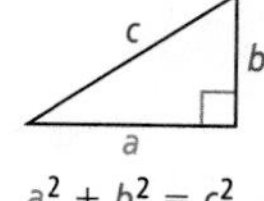

$a^2 + b^2 = c^2$

Problem 3

Q How do you know the correct order to perform the operations necessary to simplify the numerical expression? **[You must follow the order of operations.]**

Q Why is a calculator required to find $\sqrt{185}$? **[185 is not a perfect square.]**

Problem 3 Finding Distance — GRIDDED RESPONSE

What is the distance between $U(-7, 5)$ and $V(4, -3)$? Round to the nearest tenth.

Let $U(-7, 5)$ be (x_1, y_1) and $V(4, -3)$ be (x_2, y_2).

$d = \sqrt{(x_2 - x_1)^2 + (y_2 - y_1)^2}$	Use the Distance Formula.
$= \sqrt{(4 - (-7))^2 + (-3 - 5)^2}$	Substitute.
$= \sqrt{(11)^2 + (-8)^2}$	Simplify within the parentheses.
$= \sqrt{121 + 64}$	Simplify.
$= \sqrt{185}$	
185 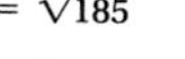 13.60147051	Use a calculator.

To the nearest tenth, $UV = 13.6$.

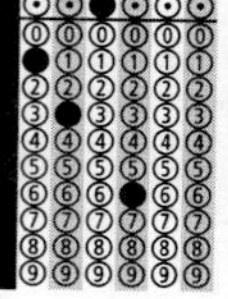

Think
What part of a right triangle is $\overline{UV}$?
$\overline{UV}$ is the hypotenuse of a right triangle with legs of length 11 and 8.

Got It? 3. a. $\overline{SR}$ has endpoints $S(-2, 14)$ and $R(3, -1)$. What is SR to the nearest tenth?

b. Reasoning In Problem 3, suppose you let $V(4, -3)$ be (x_1, y_1) and $U(-7, 5)$ be (x_2, y_2). Do you get the same result? Why?

Got It? **ERROR PREVENTION**
If students have difficulty arriving at the correct answer for Question 3a, suggest that they use parentheses with negative numbers when substituting into the formula.

Additional Problems

1. $\overline{FG}$ has endpoints at -3 and 7. What is the coordinate of its midpoint?

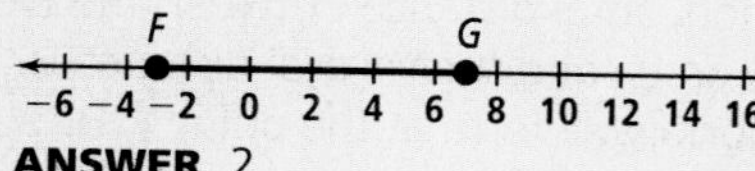

ANSWER 2

2. The midpoint of $\overline{LM}$ is $A(2, -1)$. One endpoint is $L(-3, -5)$. What are the coordinates of the other endpoint?

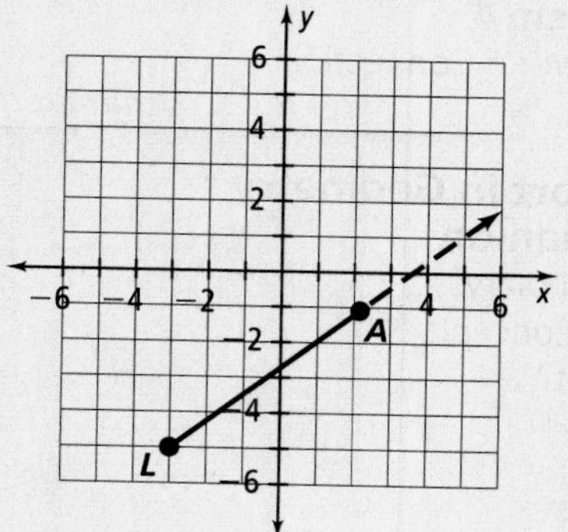

ANSWER (7, 3)

3. What is the distance between (6, −2) and (−5, 3)? Round to the nearest tenth.

ANSWER 12.1 units

4. On a zip-line course, you are harnessed to a cable that travels through the treetops. You start at Platform *A* and zip to each of the other platforms. How far do you travel from Platform *B* to Platform *C*?

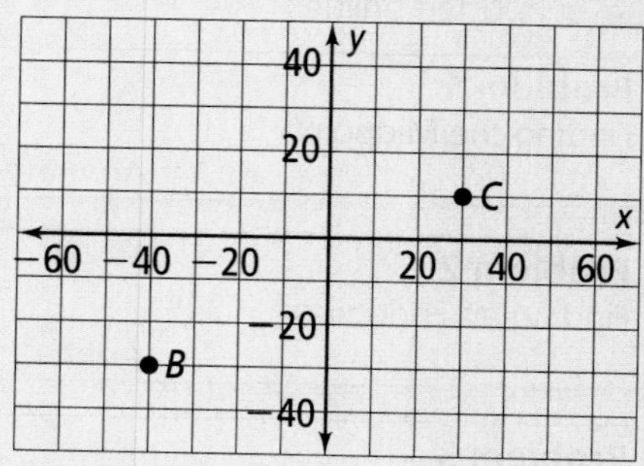

ANSWER 80.6 meters

Problem 4 Finding Distance

Recreation On a zip-line course, you are harnessed to a cable that travels through the treetops. You start at Platform A and zip to each of the other platforms. How far do you travel from Platform B to Platform C? Each grid unit represents 5 m.

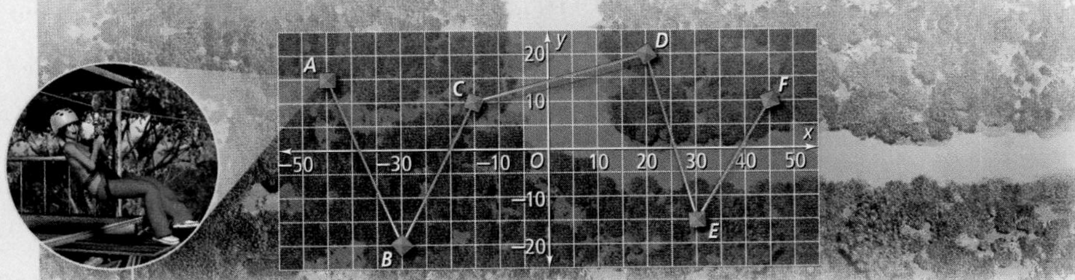

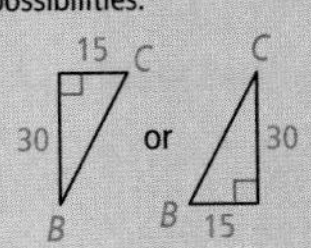

Think

Where's the right triangle?
The lengths of the legs of the right triangle are 15 and 30. There are two possibilities:

Let Platform $B(-30, -20)$ be (x_1, y_1) and Platform $C(-15, 10)$ be (x_2, y_2).

$d = \sqrt{(x_2 - x_1)^2 + (y_2 - y_1)^2}$ Use the Distance Formula.

$= \sqrt{(-15 - (-30))^2 + (10 - (-20))^2}$ Substitute.

$= \sqrt{15^2 + 30^2} = \sqrt{225 + 900} = \sqrt{1125}$ Simplify.

√ 1125 = 33.54101966 Use a calculator.

You travel about 33.5 m from Platform B to Platform C.

Got It? 4. How far do you travel from Platform D to Platform E?

Lesson Check

Do you know HOW?

1. $\overline{RS}$ has endpoints $R(2, 4)$ and $S(-1, 7)$. What are the coordinates of its midpoint M?
2. The midpoint of $\overline{BC}$ is $(5, -2)$. One endpoint is $B(3, 4)$. What are the coordinates of endpoint C?
3. What is the distance between points $K(-9, 8)$ and $L(-6, 0)$?

Do you UNDERSTAND?

4. **Reasoning** How does the Distance Formula ensure that the distance between two different points is positive?
5. **Error Analysis** Your friend calculates the distance between points $Q(1, 5)$ and $R(3, 8)$. What is his error?

$d = \sqrt{(1-8)^2 + (5-3)^2}$
$= \sqrt{(-7)^2 + 2^2}$
$= \sqrt{49 + 4}$
$= \sqrt{53} \approx 7.3$

Problem 4

Q Using the grid to count, what is the vertical distance from Platform B to Platform C? **[30 units × 5 m = 150 m]**

Q Using the grid to count, what is the horizontal distance from Platform B to Platform C? **[15 units × 5 m = 75 m]**

Q Are these distances substituted into the Distance Formula? Explain. **[Yes, you take the square root of the sum of the squares of these distances.]**

Got It?

Q What are the coordinates of Platform D? of Platform E? **[(20, 20), (30, −15)]**

3 Lesson Check

Do you know HOW?

- If students have difficulty with Exercise 2, then have them realize that they are given the midpoint, so solving an equation is necessary to find the other endpoint.

Do you UNDERSTAND?

- If students have difficulty with Exercise 5, then have them identify the values for x_1, x_2, y_1, and y_2 before reexamining the work as shown.

Close

Q How do you find the midpoint of a segment in the coordinate plane? **[After identifying the endpoints of the segment, you find the average of the x-coordinates and the average of the y-coordinates.]**

Answers

Got It? (continued)

3a. 15.8

b. Yes; the diff. of the coordinates are opposite, but their squares are the same. $VU = \sqrt{(-11)^2 + 8^2} = \sqrt{185} = 13.6$

4. $\sqrt{1325}$ m, or about 36.4 m

Lesson Check

1. (0.5, 5.5), or $\left(\frac{1}{2}, \frac{11}{2}\right)$
2. (7, −8)
3. $\sqrt{73}$, or about 8.5 units
4. Answers may vary. Sample: For two different points, the expression $(x_2 - x_1)^2 + (y_2 - y_1)^2$ in the Distance Formula is always positive. So the positive square root of a positive number is positive.
5. He did not keep the x-value and y-values together; so, $d = \sqrt{(1-3)^2 + (5-8)^2} = \sqrt{4 + 9} = \sqrt{13}$ units.

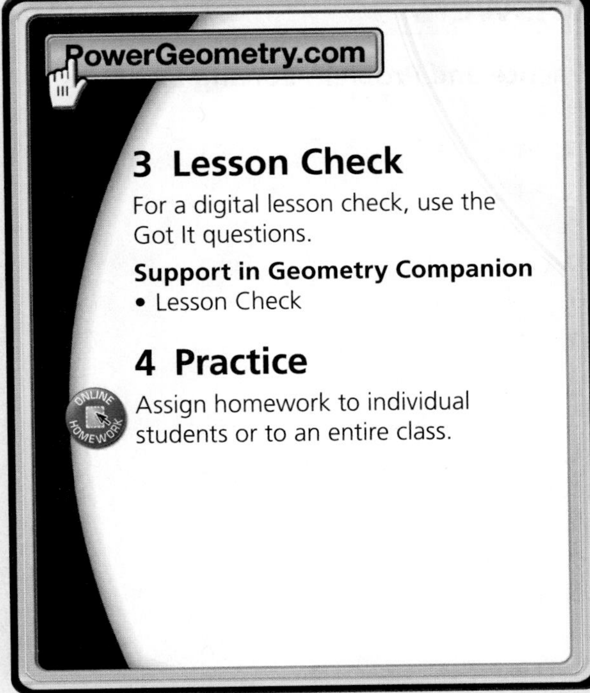

PowerGeometry.com

3 Lesson Check

For a digital lesson check, use the Got It questions.

Support in Geometry Companion
- Lesson Check

4 Practice

Assign homework to individual students or to an entire class.

4 Practice

ASSIGNMENT GUIDE

Basic: 6–35 all, 36–44 even, 45–47 all, 48–56 even
Average: 7–35 odd, 36–57
Advanced: 7–35 odd, 36–61
Standardized Test Prep: 62–64
Mixed Review: 65–72

Reasoning exercises have blue headings.
Applications exercises have red headings.

EXERCISE 47: Use the Think About a Plan worksheet in the **Practice and Problem Solving Workbook** (also available in the Teaching Resources in print and online) to further support students' development in becoming independent learners.

HOMEWORK QUICK CHECK

To check students' understanding of key skills and concepts, go over Exercises 11, 27, 45, 46, and 47.

Practice and Problem-Solving Exercises

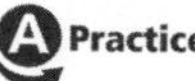

A Practice

Find the coordinate of the midpoint of the segment with the given endpoints. See Problem 1.

6. 2 and 4 **7.** −9 and 6 **8.** 2 and −5 **9.** −8 and −12

Find the coordinates of the midpoint of $\overline{HX}$.

10. $H(0, 0), X(8, 4)$ **11.** $H(-1, 3), X(7, -1)$ **12.** $H(13, 8), X(-6, -6)$

13. $H(7, 10), X(5, -8)$ **14.** $H(-6.3, 5.2), X(1.8, -1)$ **15.** $H\left(5\frac{1}{2}, -4\frac{3}{4}\right), X\left(2\frac{1}{4}, -1\frac{1}{4}\right)$

The coordinates of point T are given. The midpoint of $\overline{ST}$ is $(5, -8)$. Find the coordinates of point S. See Problem 2.

16. $T(0, 4)$ **17.** $T(5, -15)$ **18.** $T(10, 18)$

19. $T(-2, 8)$ **20.** $T(1, 12)$ **21.** $T(4.5, -2.5)$

Find the distance between each pair of points. If necessary, round to the nearest tenth. See Problem 3.

22. $J(2, -1), K(2, 5)$ **23.** $L(10, 14), M(-8, 14)$ **24.** $N(-1, -11), P(-1, -3)$

25. $A(0, 3), B(0, 12)$ **26.** $C(12, 6), D(-8, 18)$ **27.** $E(6, -2), F(-2, 4)$

28. $Q(12, -12), T(5, 12)$ **29.** $R(0, 5), S(12, 3)$ **30.** $X(-3, -4), Y(5, 5)$

Maps For Exercises 31–35, use the map below. Find the distance between the cities to the nearest tenth. See Problem 4.

31. Augusta and Brookline

32. Brookline and Charleston

33. Brookline and Davenport

34. Everett and Fairfield

35. List the cities in the order of least to greatest distance from Augusta.

B Apply

Find (a) PQ to the nearest tenth and (b) the coordinates of the midpoint of $\overline{PQ}$.

36. $P(3, 2), Q(6, 6)$ **37.** $P(0, -2), Q(3, 3)$ **38.** $P(-4, -2), Q(1, 3)$

39. $P(-5, 2), Q(0, 4)$ **40.** $P(-3, -1), Q(5, -7)$ **41.** $P(-5, -3), Q(-3, -5)$

42. $P(-4, -5), Q(-1, 1)$ **43.** $P(2, 3), Q(4, -2)$ **44.** $P(4, 2), Q(3, 0)$

45. Think About a Plan An airplane at $T(80, 20)$ needs to fly to both $U(20, 60)$ and $V(110, 85)$. What is the shortest possible distance for the trip? Explain.
- What type of information do you need to find the shortest distance?
- How can you use a diagram to help you?

Answers

Practice and Problem-Solving Exercises

6. 3
7. −1.5, or $-\frac{3}{2}$
8. −1.5, or $-\frac{3}{2}$
9. −10
10. (4, 2)
11. (3, 1)
12. (3.5, 1), or $\left(\frac{7}{2}, 1\right)$
13. (6, 1)
14. (−2.25, 2.1)
15. $\left(3\frac{7}{8}, -3\right)$
16. (10, −20)
17. (5, −1)
18. (0, −34)
19. (12, −24)
20. (9, −28)
21. (5.5, −13.5)
22. 6
23. 18
24. 8
25. 9
26. 23.3
27. 10
28. 25
29. 12.2
30. 12.0
31. 8.2
32. 5
33. 8.5
34. 9.4
35. Everett, Charleston, Brookline, Fairfield, Davenport
36a. 5
b. (4.5, 4), or $\left(\frac{9}{2}, 4\right)$
37a. 5.8
b. $\left(\frac{3}{2}, \frac{1}{2}\right)$, or (1.5, 0.5)
38a. 7.1
b. $\left(-\frac{3}{2}, \frac{1}{2}\right)$, or (−1.5, 0.5)
39a. 5.4
b. $\left(-\frac{5}{2}, 3\right)$, or (−2.5, 3)
40a. 10
b. (1, −4)
41a. 2.8
b. (−4, −4)
42a. 6.7
b. $\left(-\frac{5}{2}, -2\right)$, or (−2.5, −2)
43a. 5.4
b. $\left(3, \frac{1}{2}\right)$, or (3, 0.5)
44a. 2.2
b. $\left(\frac{7}{2}, 1\right)$, or (3.5, 1)
45. 165 units; flying T to V then to U is shortest distance.

46. **Reasoning** The midpoint of $\overline{TS}$ is the origin. Point T is located in Quadrant II. What quadrant contains point S? Explain.

47. Do you use the Midpoint Formula or the Distance Formula to find the following?
  a. Given points K and P, find the distance from K to the midpoint of $\overline{KP}$.
  b. Given point K and the midpoint of $\overline{KP}$, find KP.

For each graph, find (a) AB to the nearest tenth and (b) the coordinates of the midpoint of $\overline{AB}$.

48. 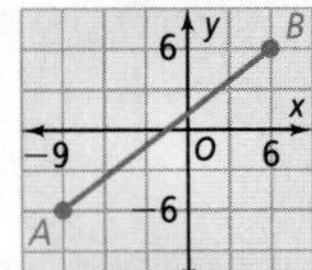

49. 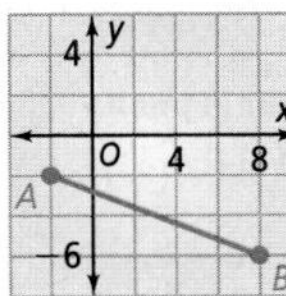

50. 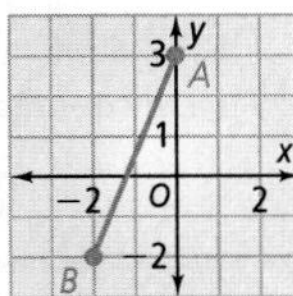

51. **Coordinate Geometry** Graph the points $A(2, 1)$, $B(6, -1)$, $C(8, 7)$, and $D(4, 9)$. Draw parallelogram $ABCD$, and diagonals $\overline{AC}$ and $\overline{BD}$.
  a. Find the midpoints of $\overline{AC}$ and $\overline{BD}$.
  b. What appears to be true about the diagonals of a parallelogram?

Travel The units of the subway map at the right are in miles. Suppose the routes between stations are straight. Find the distance you would travel between each pair of stations to the nearest tenth of a mile.

52. Oak Station and Jackson Station

53. Central Station and South Station

54. Elm Station and Symphony Station

55. Cedar Station and City Plaza Station

56. Maple Station is located 6 mi west and 2 mi north of City Plaza. What is the distance between Cedar Station and Maple Station?

57. **Open-Ended** Point $H(2, 2)$ is the midpoint of many segments.
  a. Find the coordinates of the endpoints of four noncollinear segments that have point H as their midpoint.
  b. You know that a segment with midpoint H has length 8. How many possible noncollinear segments match this description? Explain.

58. Points $P(-4, 6)$, $Q(2, 4)$, and R are collinear. One of the points is the midpoint of the segment formed by the other two points.
  a. What are the possible coordinates of R?
  b. **Reasoning** $RQ = \sqrt{160}$. Does this information affect your answer to part (a)? Explain.

46. S is in Quadrant IV; since (0, 0) is the midpoint, the coordinates of S are the opposites of the coordinates of T, so S is in Quadrant IV.

47a. Answers may vary. Sample: Distance Formula (Find KP, then divide it by 2.)

b. Answers may vary. Sample: Distance Formula (If M is the given midpoint, find KM, and then multiply it by 2.)

48a. 19.2

b. $\left(-\frac{3}{2}, 0\right)$, or $(-1.5, 0)$

49a. 10.7

b. $(3, -4)$

50a. 5.4

b. $\left(-1, \frac{1}{2}\right)$

51a. 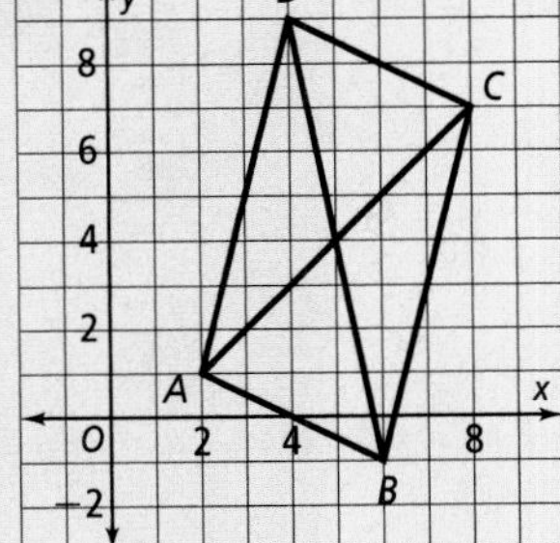

The midpoints are the same, (5, 4).

b. Answers may vary. Sample: The diagonals bisect each other.

52. 6.7 mi

53. 7 mi

54. 8.9 mi

55. 3.2 mi

56. 3.2 mi

57a. Answers may vary. Sample: (0, 2) and (4, 2); (2, 0) and (2, 4); (0, 4) and (4, 0); (0, 0) and (4, 4)

b. Infinitely many; draw a circle with center (2, 2) and radius 4. Any diameter of that circle has length 8 and midpoint (2, 2).

58a. $(-10, 8)$, $(-1, 5)$, $(8, 2)$

b. Yes; $PQ = \sqrt{40}$, so if $RQ = \sqrt{160}$, then $RQ = 2 \cdot PQ$. Therefore P must be the midpoint of $\overline{RQ}$, and the coordinates of R are $(-10, 8)$.

Answers

Practice and Problem-Solving Exercises (continued)

59. $A(0, 0, 0)$, $B(6, 0, 0)$, $C(6, -3, 0)$, $D(0, -3, 0)$, $E(0, 0, 9)$, $F(6, 0, 9)$, $G(0, -3, 9)$

60. 6.5 units

61. 11.7 units

62. D

63. F

64. [2] **a.** $(-8, 9)$
b. 17.9 units
[1] one part correct

65.

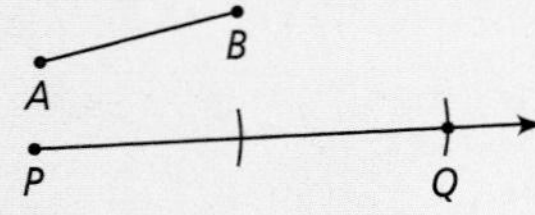

66.

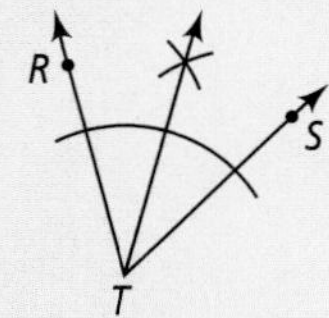

67. $\angle PQR$, $\angle RQP$

68. 150

69. $10\frac{5}{6}$

70. 504

71. 9

72. 10,560

Geometry in 3 Dimensions You can use three coordinates (x, y, z) to locate points in three dimensions.

59. Point P has coordinates $(6, -3, 9)$ as shown at the right. Give the coordinates of points $A, B, C, D, E, F,$ and G.

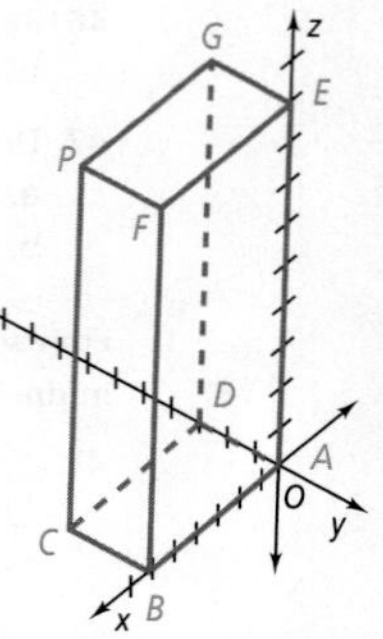

Distance in 3 Dimensions In a three-dimensional coordinate system, you can find the distance between two points (x_1, y_1, z_1) and (x_2, y_2, z_2) with this extension of the Distance Formula.

$$d = \sqrt{(x_2 - x_1)^2 + (y_2 - y_1)^2 + (z_2 - z_1)^2}$$

Find the distance between each pair of points to the nearest tenth.

60. $P(2, 3, 4)$, $Q(-2, 4, 9)$ **61.** $T(0, 12, 15)$, $V(-8, 20, 12)$

Standardized Test Prep

SAT/ACT

62. A segment has endpoints $(14, -8)$ and $(4, 12)$. What are the coordinates of its midpoint?

Ⓐ $(9, 10)$ Ⓑ $(-5, 10)$ Ⓒ $(5, -10)$ Ⓓ $(9, 2)$

63. Which of these is the first step in constructing a congruent segment?

Ⓕ Draw a ray. Ⓗ Label two points.
Ⓖ Find the midpoint. Ⓘ Measure the segment.

Short Response

64. The midpoint of $\overline{RS}$ is $N(-4, 1)$. One endpoint is $S(0, -7)$.
a. What are the coordinates of R?
b. What is the length of $\overline{RS}$ to the nearest tenth of a unit?

Mixed Review

Use a straightedge and a compass. See Lesson 1-6.

65. Draw $\overline{AB}$. Construct $\overline{PQ}$ so that $PQ = 2AB$.

66. Draw an acute $\angle RTS$. Construct the bisector of $\angle RTS$.

Use the diagram at the right. See Lesson 1-4.

S P 1 T Q R

67. Name $\angle 1$ two other ways.

68. If $m\angle PQR = 60$, what is $m\angle RQS$?

Get Ready! To prepare for Lesson 1-8, do Exercises 69–72.

Complete each statement. Use the conversion table on page 837. See p. 826.

69. 130 in. = ■ ft **70.** 14 yd = ■ in. **71.** 27 ft = ■ yd **72.** 2 mi = ■ ft

1-7 Lesson Resources

Differentiated Remediation

Instructional Support

Geometry Companion

Students can use the **Geometry Companion** worktext (4 pages) . . .

- New Vocabulary
- Key Concepts
- Got It for each Problem
- Lesson Check

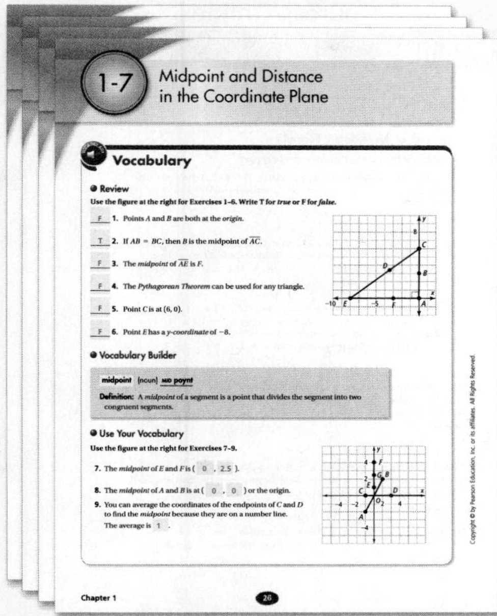

1-7 Midpoint and Distance in the Coordinate Plane

Vocabulary

Review

Use the figure at the right for Exercises 1–6. Write T for *true* or F for *false*.

F 1. Points A and B are both at the *origin*.

T 2. If $AB = BC$, then B is the midpoint of $\overline{AC}$.

F 3. The *midpoint* of $\overline{AE}$ is F.

F 4. The *Pythagorean Theorem* can be used for any triangle.

F 5. Point C is at (6, 0).

F 6. Point E has a *y-coordinate* of −8.

Vocabulary Builder

midpoint (noun) MID poynt

Definition: A *midpoint* of a segment is a point that divides the segment into two congruent segments.

Use Your Vocabulary

Use the figure at the right for Exercises 7–9.

7. The *midpoint* of E and F is (0 , 2.5).

8. The *midpoint* of A and B is at (0 , 0) or the origin.

9. You can average the coordinates of the endpoints of C and D to find the *midpoint* because they are on a number line. The average is 1 .

Chapter 1 26

ELL Support

Assess Understanding Divide the students into mixed pairs. Write the coordinates (−4, 0) and (−2, −6) on the board. Have one student in the pair find the distance between the coordinates. Have the other student find the midpoint between the coordinates. Have students trade papers and discuss their work.

Use Multiple Representations A mail carrier leaves the corner of Maple and Main Streets and walks along Main Street 6 blocks east to 2nd Street. She continues east another 3 blocks to 4th Street. Then she continues another 6 blocks to Laurel Street. Draw a picture to show the distance between Laurel Street and Maple Street.

5 Assess & Remediate

Lesson Quiz

1. $\overline{PB}$ has endpoints at −2 and 12. What is the coordinate of its midpoint?

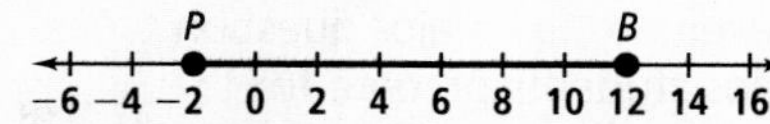

2. **Do you UNDERSTAND?** The midpoint of $\overline{CD}$ is $E(-1, 0)$. One endpoint is $C(5, 2)$. What are the coordinates of the other endpoint?

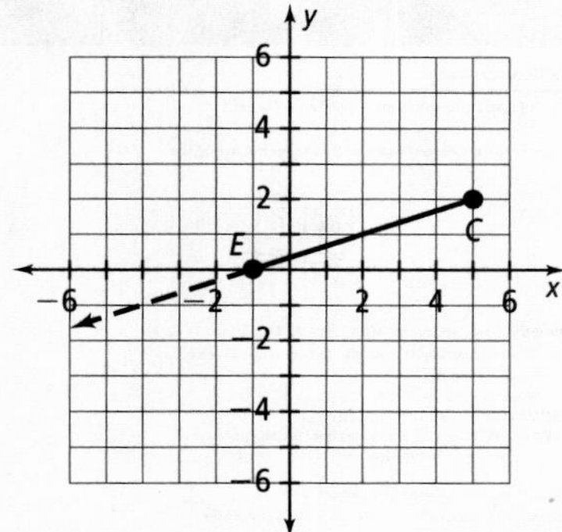

3. What is the distance between $P(-4, 3)$ and $Q(6, 1)$? Round to the nearest tenth.

ANSWERS TO LESSON QUIZ

1. 5
2. $D(-7, -2)$
3. 10.2

PRECRIPTION FOR REMEDIATION

Use the student work on the Lesson Quiz to prescribe a differentiated review assignment.

Points	Differentiated Remediation
0–1	Intervention
2	On-level
3	Extension

PowerGeometry.com

5 Assess & Remediate

Assign the Lesson Quiz. Appropriate intervention, practice, or enrichment is automatically generated based on student performance.

Intervention

- **Reteaching** (2 pages) Provides reteaching and practice exercises for the key lesson concepts. Use with struggling students or absent students.
- **English Language Learner Support** Helps students develop and reinforce mathematical vocabulary and key concepts.

All-in-One Resources/Online

Reteaching

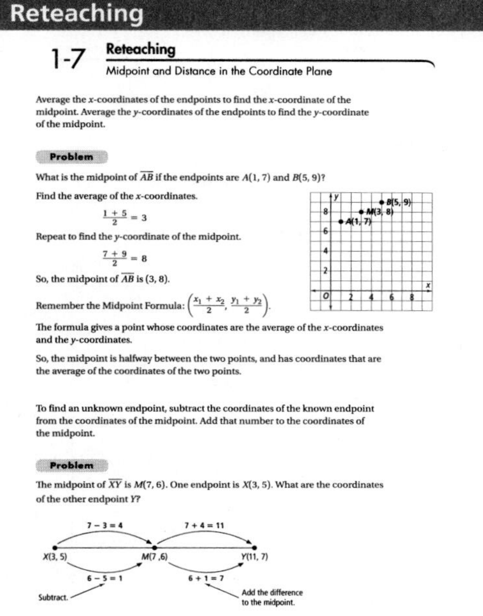

1-7 **Reteaching**

Midpoint and Distance in the Coordinate Plane

Average the x-coordinates of the endpoints to find the x-coordinate of the midpoint. Average the y-coordinates of the endpoints to find the y-coordinate of the midpoint.

Problem

What is the midpoint of $\overline{AB}$ if the endpoints are $A(1, 7)$ and $B(5, 9)$?

Find the average of the x-coordinates.

$$\frac{1+5}{2} = 3$$

Repeat to find the y-coordinate of the midpoint.

$$\frac{7+9}{2} = 8$$

So, the midpoint of $\overline{AB}$ is (3, 8).

Remember the Midpoint Formula: $\left(\frac{x_1 + x_2}{2}, \frac{y_1 + y_2}{2}\right)$.

The formula gives a point whose coordinates are the average of the x-coordinates and the y-coordinates.

So, the midpoint is halfway between the two points, and has coordinates that are the average of the coordinates of the two points.

To find an unknown endpoint, subtract the coordinates of the known endpoint from the coordinates of the midpoint. Add that number to the coordinates of the midpoint.

Problem

The midpoint of $\overline{XY}$ is $M(7, 6)$. One endpoint is $X(3, 5)$. What are the coordinates of the other endpoint Y?

All-in-One Resources/Online

English Language Learner Support

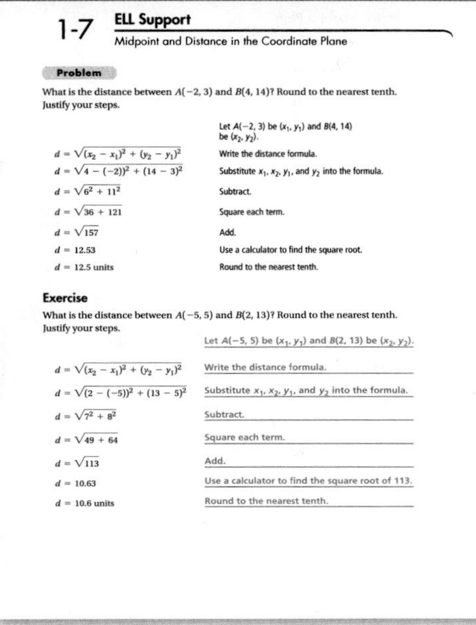

1-7 **ELL Support**

Midpoint and Distance in the Coordinate Plane

Problem

What is the distance between $A(-2, 3)$ and $B(4, 14)$? Round to the nearest tenth. Justify your steps.

	Let $A(-2, 3)$ be (x_1, y_1) and $B(4, 14)$ be (x_2, y_2).
$d = \sqrt{(x_2 - x_1)^2 + (y_2 - y_1)^2}$	Write the distance formula.
$d = \sqrt{4 - (-2))^2 + (14 - 3)^2}$	Substitute x_1, x_2, y_1, and y_2 into the formula.
$d = \sqrt{6^2 + 11^2}$	Subtract.
$d = \sqrt{36 + 121}$	Square each term.
$d = \sqrt{157}$	Add.
$d = 12.53$	Use a calculator to find the square root.
$d = 12.5$ units	Round to the nearest tenth.

Exercise

What is the distance between $A(-5, 5)$ and $B(2, 13)$? Round to the nearest tenth. Justify your steps.

	Let $A(-5, 5)$ be (x_1, y_1) and $B(2, 13)$ be (x_2, y_2).
$d = \sqrt{(x_2 - x_1)^2 + (y_2 - y_1)^2}$	Write the distance formula.
$d = \sqrt{(2 - (-5))^2 + (13 - 5)^2}$	Substitute x_1, x_2, y_1, and y_2 into the formula.
$d = \sqrt{7^2 + 8^2}$	Subtract.
$d = \sqrt{49 + 64}$	Square each term.
$d = \sqrt{113}$	Add.
$d = 10.63$	Use a calculator to find the square root of 113.
$d = 10.6$ units	Round to the nearest tenth.

Differentiated Remediation *continued*

On-Level

- **Practice** (2 pages) Provides extra practice for each lesson. For simpler practice exercises, use the Form K Practice pages found in the All-in-One Teaching Resources and online.
- **Think About a Plan** Helps students develop specific problem-solving skills and strategies by providing scaffolded guiding questions.
- **Standardized Test Prep** Focuses on all major exercises, all major question types, and helps students prepare for the high-stakes assessments.

Extension

- **Enrichment** Provides students with interesting problems and activities that extend the concepts of the lesson.
- **Activities, Games, and Puzzles** Worksheets that can be used for concepts development, enrichment, and for fun!

Practice and Problem Solving Wkbk/ All-in-One Resources/Online

Practice page 1

1-7 **Practice** *Form G*

Midpoint and Distance in the Coordinate Plane

Find the coordinate of the midpoint of the segment with the given endpoints.

1. 3 and 5 4
2. -7 and 4 $-\frac{3}{2}$
3. 5 and -9 -2
4. -6 and -10 -8

Find the coordinates of the midpoint of $\overline{AB}$.

5. $A(6, 7), B(4, 3)$ (5, 5)
6. $A(-1, 5), B(2, -3)$ $(\frac{1}{2}, 1)$
7. $A(14, -2), B(7, -8)$ $(10\frac{1}{2}, -5)$
8. $A(0, 0), B(-5, 12)$ $(-2\frac{1}{2}, 6)$
9. $A(2.8, 1.1), B(-3.4, 5.7)$ $(-0.3, 3.4)$
10. $A(2\frac{1}{2}, -\frac{1}{4}), B(3\frac{1}{4}, -1)$ $(2\frac{7}{8}, -\frac{5}{8})$

The coordinates of point Y are given. The midpoint of $\overline{XY}$ is $(3, -5)$. Find the coordinates of point X.

11. $Y(0, 2)$ $(6, -12)$
12. $Y(-10, 5)$ $(16, -15)$
13. $Y(7, 1)$ $(-1, -11)$
14. $Y(4, -8)$ $(2, -2)$
15. $Y(-1, -9)$ $(7, -1)$
16. $Y(2.5, -6.5)$ $(3.5, -3.5)$

Find the distance between each pair of points. If necessary, round to the nearest tenth.

17. $A(6, 7), B(-1, 7)$ 7
18. $C(5, -5), D(5, 3)$ 8
19. $E(-1, 0), F(12, 0)$ 13
20. $Q(2, -6), T(10, 0)$ 10
21. $H(20, -4), I(-4, 3)$ 25
22. $J(-5, 5), K(-3, -2)$ 7.3

The room shown below right is 14 ft by 10 ft. Find the dimensions of each piece of furniture to the nearest tenth.

23. length and width of the dresser 6 ft × 3 ft
24. length and width of the table 2.8 ft × 2.8 ft
25. length and width of the bed 7.1 ft × 5.7 ft 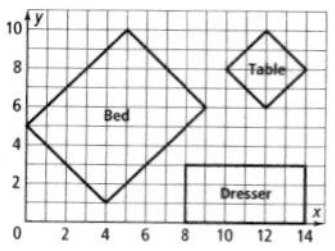
26. **Reasoning** The midpoint of $\overline{AB}$ is on the y-axis, and $\overline{AB}$ is parallel to the x-axis. Point A is located in Quadrant III. Which quadrant contains point B? Explain.
IV; Answers may vary. Sample: Suppose A is at $(-4, -5)$, which is a point in Quadrant III. Then B will be on the opposite side of the y-axis at $(4, -5)$ in Quadrant IV.

Practice and Problem Solving Wkbk/ All-in-One Resources/Online

Practice page 2

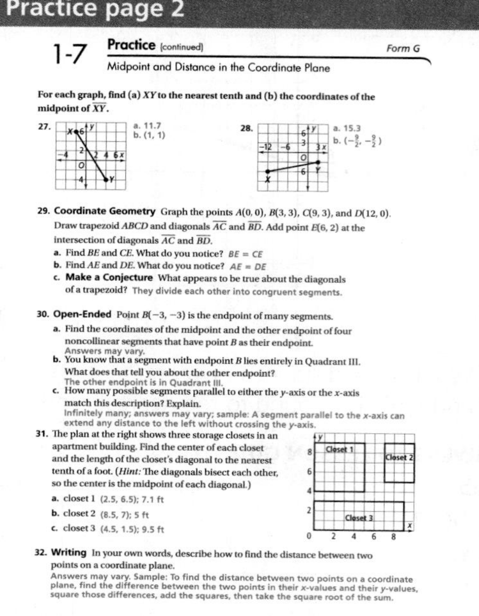

1-7 **Practice** (continued) *Form G*

Midpoint and Distance in the Coordinate Plane

For each graph, find (a) XY to the nearest tenth and (b) the coordinates of the midpoint of $\overline{XY}$.

27. a. 11.7 b. (1, 1)

28. a. 15.3 b. $(-\frac{9}{2}, -\frac{9}{2})$

29. **Coordinate Geometry** Graph the points $A(0, 0)$, $B(3, 3)$, $C(9, 3)$, and $D(12, 0)$. Draw trapezoid $ABCD$ and diagonals $\overline{AC}$ and $\overline{BD}$. Add point $E(6, 2)$ at the intersection of diagonals $\overline{AC}$ and $\overline{BD}$.
  a. Find BE and CE. What do you notice? $BE = CE$
  b. Find AE and DE. What do you notice? $AE = DE$
  c. **Make a Conjecture** What appears to be true about the diagonals of a trapezoid? They divide each other into congruent segments.

30. **Open-Ended** Point $B(-3, -3)$ is the endpoint of many segments.
  a. Find the coordinates of the midpoint and the other endpoint of four noncollinear segments that have point B as their endpoint. Answers may vary.
  b. You know that a segment with endpoint B lies entirely in Quadrant III. What does that tell you about the other endpoint? The other endpoint is in Quadrant III.
  c. How many possible segments parallel to either the y-axis or the x-axis match this description? Explain. Infinitely many; answers may vary; sample: A segment parallel to the x-axis can extend any distance to the left without crossing the y-axis.

31. The plan at the right shows three storage closets in an apartment building. Find the center of each closet and the length of the closet's diagonal to the nearest tenth of a foot. (*Hint:* The diagonals bisect each other, so the center is the midpoint of each diagonal.)
  a. closet 1 (2.5, 6.5); 7.1 ft
  b. closet 2 (8.5, 7); 5 ft
  c. closet 3 (4.5, 1.5); 9.5 ft

32. **Writing** In your own words, describe how to find the distance between two points on a coordinate plane.
Answers may vary. Sample: To find the distance between two points on a coordinate plane, find the difference between the two points in their x-values and their y-values, square those differences, add the squares, then take the square root of the sum.

All-in-One Resources/Online

Enrichment

1-7 **Enrichment**

Midpoint and Distance in the Coordinate Plane

A Closer Look at the Midpoint Formula

Find the Midpoint Formula by finding the halfway point.

1. What is the difference in the x-values between (1, 7) and (3, 11)? What is half that difference? How can you use half that difference to find the x-value of the midpoint? 2; 1; answers may vary. Sample: Add half that difference to 1.
2. What is the difference in the y-values between (1, 7) and (3, 11)? What is half that difference? How can you use half that difference to find the y-value of the midpoint? 4; 2; answers may vary. Sample: Add half that difference to 7.
3. If you add half the difference between the x-values of (1, 7) and (3, 11) to 1 to find the x-value of the midpoint, you get the expression $1 + \frac{1}{2}(3 - 1)$. What expression do you get if you add half the difference between the y-values of (1, 7) and (3, 11) to 7 to find the y-value of the midpoint? $7 + \frac{1}{2}(11 - 7)$
4. If you add half the difference between the x-values of (x_1, y_1) and (x_2, y_2) to x_1 to find the x-value of the midpoint, the resulting expression is $x_1 + \frac{1}{2}(x_2 - x_1)$. What expression can you use to find the y-value of the midpoint of (x_1, y_1) and (x_2, y_2)? $y_1 + \frac{1}{2}(y_2 - y_1)$
5. When you simplify the expression $x_1 + \frac{1}{2}(x_2 - x_1)$, you get $\frac{x_2 + x_1}{2}$. Can you simplify the expression $y_1 + \frac{1}{2}(y_2 - y_1)$? Show your work. Do these simplified expressions look like the Midpoint Formula?
yes; $y_1 + \frac{1}{2}(y_2 - y_1) = y_1 + \frac{1}{2}y_2 - \frac{1}{2}y_1 = \frac{1}{2}y_1 + \frac{1}{2}y_2 = \frac{y_1 + y_2}{2}$; yes
6. Do you prefer to use the process of finding the halfway point or to use the Midpoint Formula? What are the advantages and disadvantages of each method? Check students' responses.

Practice and Problem Solving Wkbk/ All-in-One Resources/Online

Think About a Plan

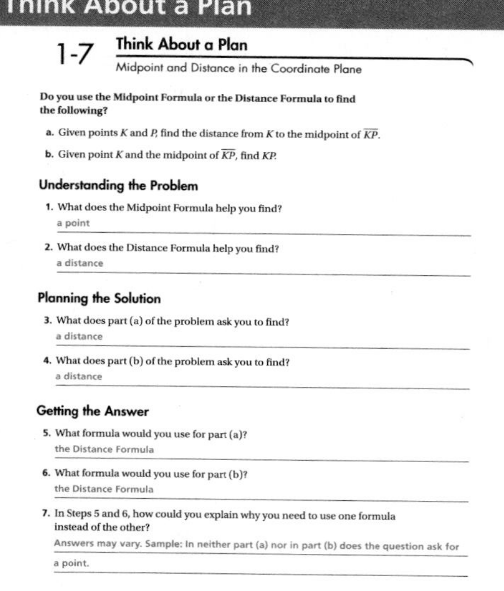

1-7 **Think About a Plan**

Midpoint and Distance in the Coordinate Plane

Do you use the Midpoint Formula or the Distance Formula to find the following?

a. Given points K and P, find the distance from K to the midpoint of $\overline{KP}$.

b. Given point K and the midpoint of $\overline{KP}$, find KP.

Understanding the Problem

1. What does the Midpoint Formula help you find?
a point
2. What does the Distance Formula help you find?
a distance

Planning the Solution

3. What does part (a) of the problem ask you to find?
a distance
4. What does part (b) of the problem ask you to find?
a distance

Getting the Answer

5. What formula would you use for part (a)?
the Distance Formula
6. What formula would you use for part (b)?
the Distance Formula
7. In Steps 5 and 6, how could you explain why you need to use one formula instead of the other?
Answers may vary. Sample: In neither part (a) nor in part (b) does the question ask for a point.

Practice and Problem Solving Wkbk/ All-in-One Resources/Online

Standardized Test Prep

1-7 **Standardized Test Prep**

Midpoint and Distance in the Coordinate Plane

Multiple Choice

For Exercises 1–7, choose the correct letter.

1. What is the other endpoint of the segment with midpoint -3 and endpoint -7? C
(A) -11 (B) -5 (C) 1 (D) 4
2. The endpoints of $\overline{ST}$ are $S(2, -2)$ and $T(4, 2)$. What are the coordinates of the midpoint of $\overline{ST}$? F
(F) (3, 0) (G) (0, 3) (H) (3, −2) (I) (3, 2)
3. What is the distance between $A(-8, 4)$ and $B(4, -1)$? C
(A) 7 (B) 10 (C) 13 (D) 17
4. The midpoint of $\overline{XZ}$ is Y. Which of the following is true? I
(F) $XZ = XY$ (G) $XZ = \frac{1}{2}XY$ (H) $YZ = \frac{1}{2}XY$ (I) $YZ = \frac{1}{2}XZ$

Use the graph at the right for Exercises 5 and 6.

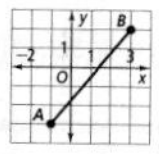

5. According to the graph, what is the midpoint of $\overline{AB}$? B
(A) (1, 0) (B) (1, −0.5) (C) (1, 0.5) (D) (1.5, −0.5)
6. According to the graph, what is AB to the nearest tenth? I
(F) 2.2 (G) 3 (H) 5 (I) 6.4
7. The midpoint of $\overline{CD}$ is $M(-3, -7)$. If the coordinates of C are $(-2, -10)$, what are the coordinates of D? A
(A) (−4, −4) (B) (−1, −13) (C) (−2.5, −8.5) (D) (−5, −17)

Short Response

8. The midpoint of $\overline{AB}$ is in Quadrant IV, and $\overline{AB}$ is parallel to the y-axis.
  a. What quadrant or quadrants cannot contain either point A or B? Explain.
  [2] II and III; the line segment is vertical and at the right of the origin, so it cannot be in Quadrant II or III.
  b. What else can you determine about points A and B?
  At least one point must be in Quadrant IV. [1] missing an answer or explanation [0] no correct answers or explanations

Online Teacher Resource Center

Activities, Games, and Puzzles

1-7 **Game: Cross the Ocean**

Midpoint and Distance in the Coordinate Plane

Materials

- Graphing calculator
- Ruler
- Number cube

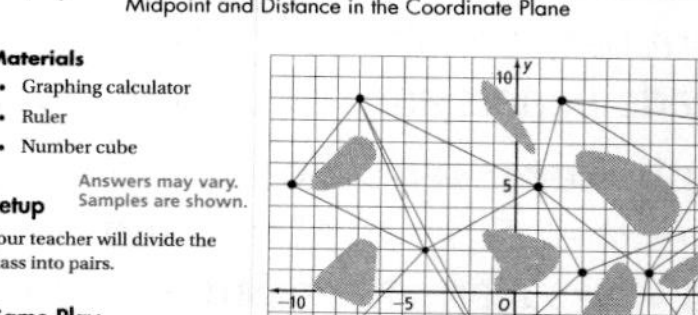

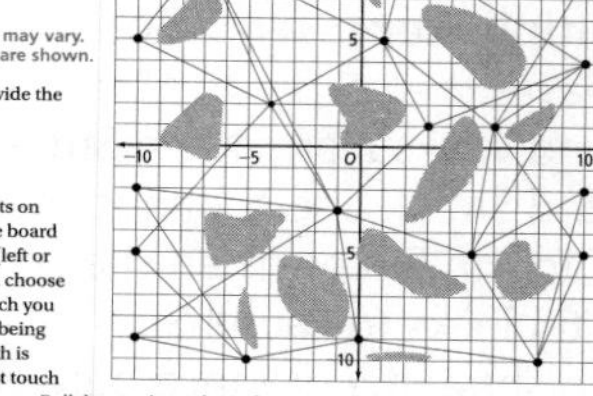

Answers may vary. Samples are shown.

Setup

Your teacher will divide the class into pairs.

Game Play

Players choose points on opposite sides of the board from which to start (left or right). On your turn, choose a target point to which you would like to move, being certain that your path is straight and does not touch an "island" in the ocean. Roll the number cube to determine what calculation to make, using the point you are on and the target point to which you would like to secure a path.

- Roll a 1, 2, or 3: Find the distance between the two points.
- Roll a 4 or 5: Find the midpoint of the segment between the two points.
- Roll a 6: Use your first point as one endpoint and your target point as the midpoint of a segment. You must find the other endpoint of this segment that may be on or across an island.

Do your calculations by hand. Your opponent can check your work using a graphing calculator. If you are correct, use a ruler to draw your path and "move" to the target point. Note that you always move to the point you selected, not to the midpoint or endpoint of a segment that you calculated. You may not attempt to connect two points if your opponent has already done so.

Ending the Game

The game ends when one player wins by securing a path from one side of the board to the other. Check students' work.

Review — Classifying Polygons

Use With Lesson 1-8

TN State Performance Indicators
SPI 3108.4.3 Identify, describe and/or apply the relationships and theorems involving different types of triangles, quadrilaterals and other polygons.
Also SPI 3108.4.2

In geometry, a figure that lies in a plane is called a *plane figure*.

A **polygon** is a closed plane figure formed by three or more segments. Each segment intersects exactly two other segments at their endpoints. No two segments with a common endpoint are collinear. Each segment is called a *side*. Each endpoint of a side is a *vertex*.

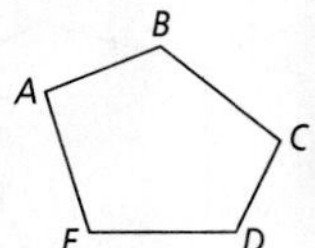

A polygon

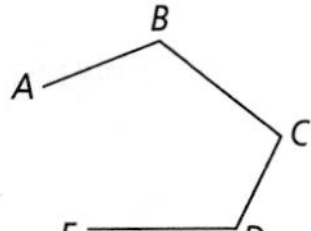

Not a polygon; not a closed figure

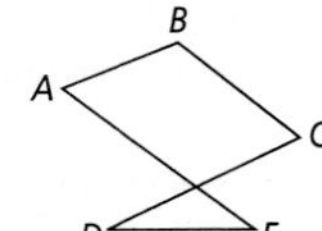

Not a polygon; two sides intersect between endpoints.

To name a polygon, start at any vertex and list the vertices consecutively in a clockwise or counterclockwise direction.

Example 1

Name the polygon. Then identify its sides and angles.

Two names for this polygon are *DHKMGB* and *MKHDBG*.

sides: $\overline{DH}$, $\overline{HK}$, $\overline{KM}$, $\overline{MG}$, $\overline{GB}$, $\overline{BD}$

angles: $\angle D$, $\angle H$, $\angle K$, $\angle M$, $\angle G$, $\angle B$

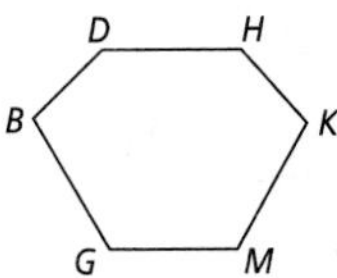

You can classify a polygon by its number of sides. The tables below show the names of some common polygons.

Names of Common Polygons

Sides	Name
3	Triangle, or trigon
4	Quadrilateral, or tetragon
5	Pentagon
6	Hexagon
7	Heptagon
8	Octagon

Sides	Name
9	Nonagon, or enneagon
10	Decagon
11	Hendecagon
12	Dodecagon
⋮	⋮
n	*n*-gon

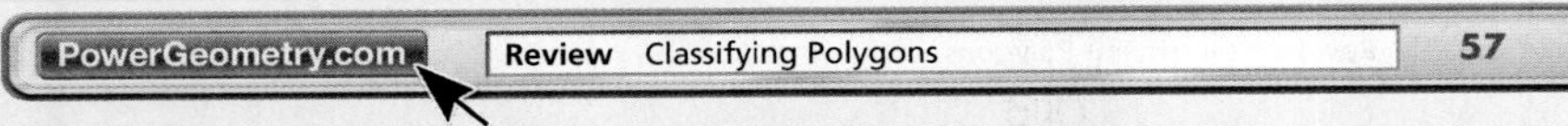

Guided Instruction

PURPOSE To review the definition of a polygon and the ways in which a polygon can be classified

PROCESS Students will

- define a polygon and name a polygon by its parts (its angles and sides).
- identify both examples and nonexamples of polygons and determine why a particular figure is not a polygon.
- classify a polygon by its number of sides.
- explain the difference between a convex and concave polygon.

DISCUSS Engage the class by giving a variety of examples of polygons and figures that are not polygons.

Example 1

This Example requires students to name polygons by their vertices.

ERROR PREVENTION

Explain that when naming polygons by their vertices, the order in which they can be named may vary. In other words, one student may write quadrilateral *ABCD*, and another may write quadrilateral *CDAB*. Both are correct.

Example 2

This Example requires students to classify polygons by their sides and tell whether a polygon is concave or convex.

Q Can a polygon be both concave and convex? Explain. **[No; when one diagonal has points outside the polygon, the polygon is concave.]**

Q Could the angle between any two sides of a polygon measure 180? Explain. **[No, that would be a straight angle, and both of those sides would be considered parts of a straight edge.]**

You can also classify a polygon as concave or convex, using the diagonals of the polygon. A **diagonal** is a segment that connects two nonconsecutive vertices.

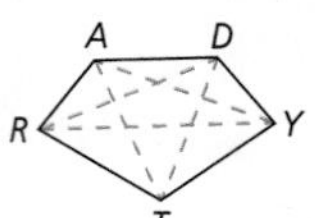

A **convex polygon** has no diagonal with points outside the polygon.

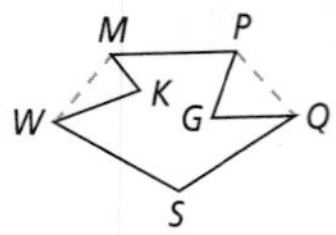

A **concave polygon** has at least one diagonal with points outside the polygon.

In this textbook, a polygon is convex unless otherwise stated.

Example 2

Classify the polygon by its number of sides. Tell whether the polygon is *convex* or *concave*.

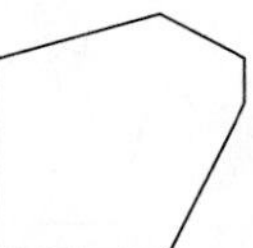

The polygon has six sides. Therefore, it is a hexagon.

No diagonal of the hexagon contains points outside the hexagon. The hexagon is convex.

Exercises

Is the figure a polygon? If not, explain why.

1. 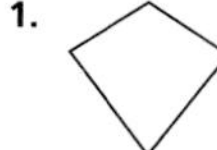
2. 
3. 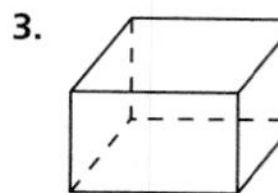
4. 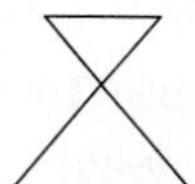

Name the polygon. Then identify its sides and angles.

5. 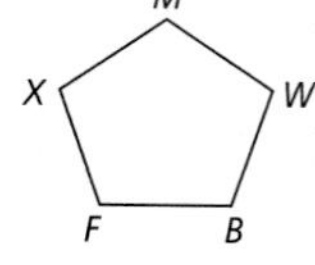

6. 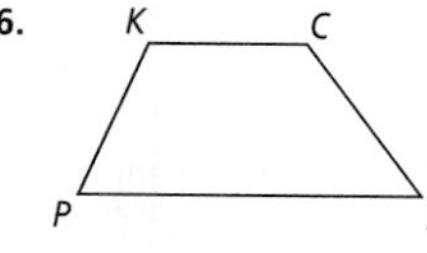

7. 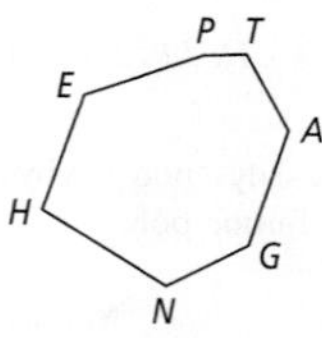

Classify the polygon by its number of sides. Tell whether the polygon is *convex* or *concave*.

8. 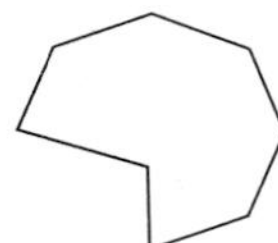
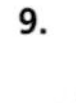
9. 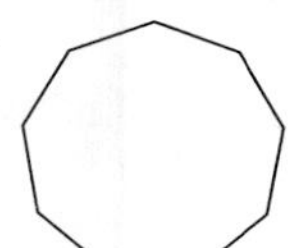
10. 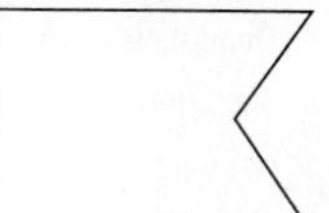

Answers

Exercises

1. yes
2. no; no sides and vertices
3. no; not a plane figure
4. no; intersecting sides
5. Sample: *FBWMX*; sides are $\overline{FB}$, $\overline{BW}$, $\overline{WM}$, $\overline{MX}$, $\overline{XF}$; angles are $\angle F$, $\angle B$, $\angle W$, $\angle M$, $\angle X$
6. Sample: *CLPK*; sides are $\overline{CL}$, $\overline{LP}$, $\overline{PK}$, $\overline{KC}$; angles are $\angle C$, $\angle L$, $\angle P$, $\angle K$
7. Sample: *AGNHEPT*; sides are $\overline{AG}$, $\overline{GN}$, $\overline{NH}$, $\overline{HE}$, $\overline{EP}$, $\overline{PT}$, $\overline{TA}$; angles are $\angle A$, $\angle G$, $\angle N$, $\angle H$, $\angle E$, $\angle P$, $\angle T$
8. octagon, concave
9. nonagon or enneagon, convex
10. pentagon, concave

Perimeter, Circumference, and Area

TN State Performance Indicators
SPI 3108.1.2 Determine areas of planar figures by decomposing them into simpler figures without a grid.
Also SPI 3108.4.7

Objectives To find the perimeter or circumference of basic shapes
To find the area of basic shapes

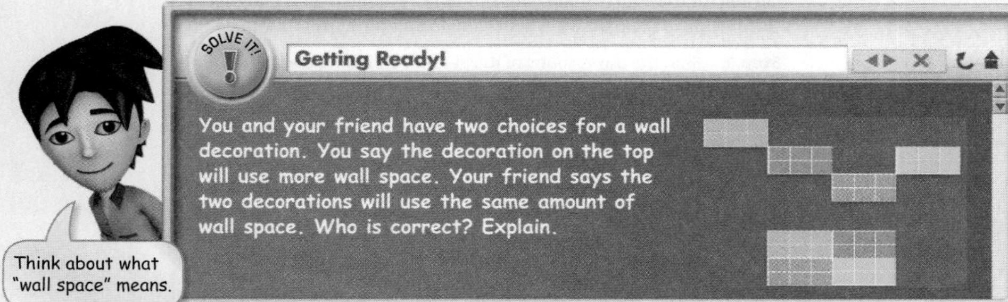

Getting Ready!
You and your friend have two choices for a wall decoration. You say the decoration on the top will use more wall space. Your friend says the two decorations will use the same amount of wall space. Who is correct? Explain.
Think about what "wall space" means.

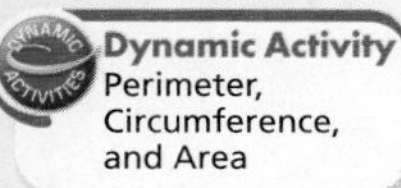

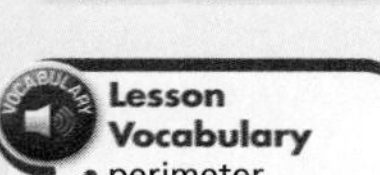

In the Solve It, you considered various ideas of what it means to take up space on a flat surface.

Essential Understanding Perimeter and area are two different ways of measuring geometric figures.

The **perimeter** P of a polygon is the sum of the lengths of its sides. The **area** A of a polygon is the number of square units it encloses. For figures such as squares, rectangles, triangles, and circles, you can use formulas for perimeter (or *circumference* C for circles) and area.

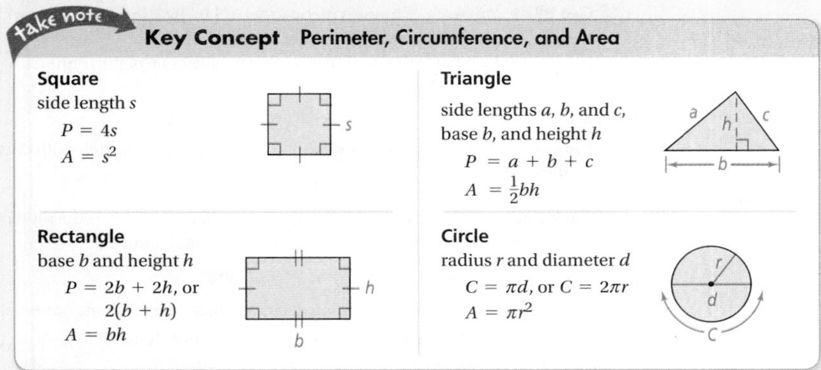

take note **Key Concept** Perimeter, Circumference, and Area

Square
side length s
$P = 4s$
$A = s^2$

Triangle
side lengths a, b, and c, base b, and height h
$P = a + b + c$
$A = \frac{1}{2}bh$

Rectangle
base b and height h
$P = 2b + 2h$, or $2(b + h)$
$A = bh$

Circle
radius r and diameter d
$C = \pi d$, or $C = 2\pi r$
$A = \pi r^2$

1 Interactive Learning

Solve It!

PURPOSE To introduce students to the notion of measuring two-dimensional shapes
PROCESS Students may
- use visual judgment.
- use the grid to quantify the amount of space.
- use prior knowledge of how to calculate area.

FACILITATE

Q Does wall space refer to the area covered by the design or the dimensions of the design? **[area]**

Q How can you visually determine the area of each design? **[Count the number of grid units in each design.]**

Q How could you have altered your statement so that it was true? **[Sample answer: The design on the top has a greater length and width than the design on the bottom.]**

ANSWER See Solve It in Answers on next page.
CONNECT THE MATH Ask students to conjecture how they would determine the amount of space covered by a shape if the shape were not displayed on a grid. Use their conjectures as motivation for learning the mathematical formulas for area.

2 Guided Instruction

Take Note

TACTILE LEARNERS
Use manipulatives to show students that the formula for the area of a triangle is derived from the formula for the area of a rectangle.

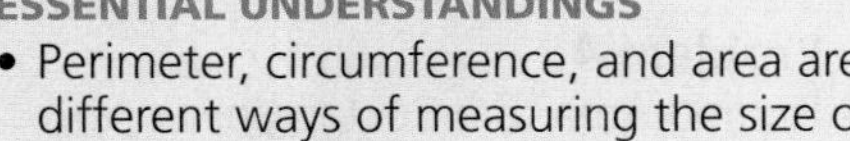

1-8 Preparing to Teach

BIG idea Measurement UbD
ESSENTIAL UNDERSTANDINGS
- Perimeter, circumference, and area are different ways of measuring the size of geometric figures.
- The area of a region is the sum of the areas of its nonoverlapping parts.

Math Background

As dimensions are added to the geometric figures studied, the notion of how to quantify their size needs to be addressed. A line segment, which has one dimension, can be examined using the Ruler Postulate to determine its length. The figures studied in this lesson have two dimensions. The size of two dimensional figures is quantified both through area and perimeter or circumference.

The study of the circumference of a circle, which can be thought of as the perimeter of a circle, provides an opportunity to investigate the meaning of the irrational number π. Help students understand that 3.14 or $\frac{22}{7}$ is only an approximation for π. To name an area or circumference of a circle using the symbol π is to provide an exact measurement.

Support Student Learning

Use the **Geometry Companion** to engage and support students during instructions. See Lesson Resources at the end of this lesson for details.

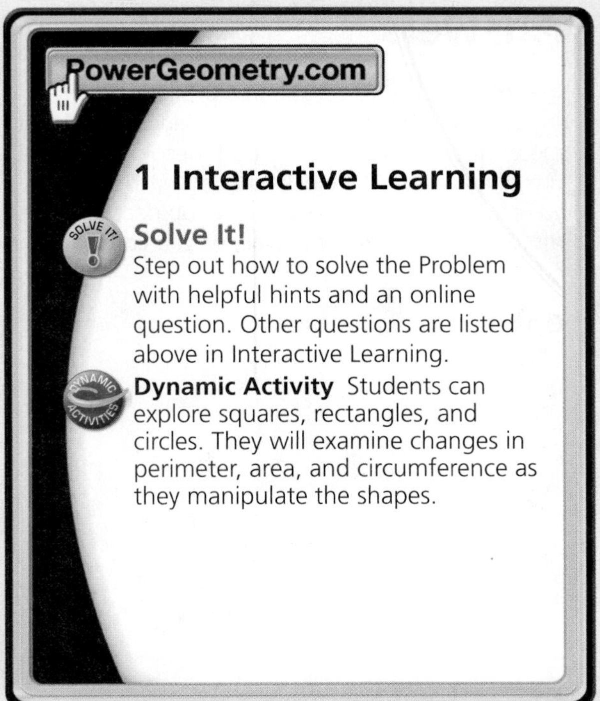

PowerGeometry.com
1 Interactive Learning
Solve It!
Step out how to solve the Problem with helpful hints and an online question. Other questions are listed above in Interactive Learning.
Dynamic Activity Students can explore squares, rectangles, and circles. They will examine changes in perimeter, area, and circumference as they manipulate the shapes.

Problem 1

Q Which unit of measurement is appropriate for this problem, feet or square feet? Explain. **[The appropriate unit is feet because it is a perimeter problem.]**

Q What is the numerical difference between the perimeter of the garden and the perimeter of the garden including the path? **[32 ft]**

Got It?

Q What is the perimeter of the inside edge of the frame? **[24 in.]**

The units of measurement for perimeter and circumference include inches, feet, yards, miles, centimeters, and meters. When measuring area, use square units such as square inches ($in.^2$), square feet (ft^2), square yards (yd^2), square miles (mi^2), square centimeters (cm^2), and square meters (m^2).

Problem 1 Finding the Perimeter of a Rectangle

Landscaping The botany club members are designing a rectangular garden for the courtyard of your school. They plan to place edging on the outside of the path. How much edging material will they need?

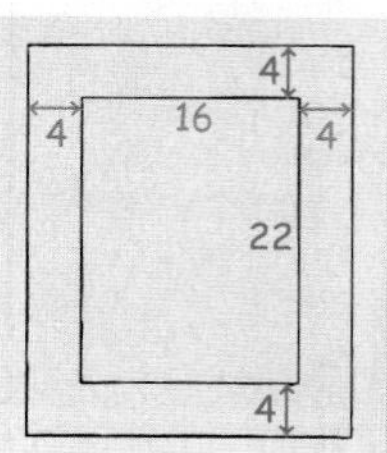

Plan

Why should you draw a diagram?
A diagram can help you see the larger rectangle formed by the garden and the path, and which lengths to add together.

Step 1 Find the dimensions of the garden, including the path.

For a rectangle, "length" and "width" are sometimes used in place of "base" and "height."

Width of the garden and path

$= 4 + 16 + 4 = 24$

Length of the garden and path

$= 4 + 22 + 4 = 30$

Step 2 Find the perimeter of the garden including the path.

$P = 2b + 2h$	Use the formula for the perimeter of a rectangle.
$= 2(24) + 2(30)$	Substitute 24 for b and 30 for h.
$= 48 + 60$	Simplify.
$= 108$	

You will need 108 ft of edging material.

Got It? **1.** You want to frame a picture that is 5 in. by 7 in. with a 1-in.-wide frame.
a. What is the perimeter of the picture?
b. What is the perimeter of the outside edge of the frame?

You can name a circle with the symbol ⊙. For example, the circle with center A is written $\odot A$.

The formulas for a circle involve the special number *pi* (π). Pi is the ratio of any circle's circumference to its diameter. Since π is an irrational number,

$$\pi = 3.1415926\ldots,$$

you cannot write it as a terminating decimal. For an approximate answer, you can use 3.14 or $\frac{22}{7}$ for π. You can also use the π key on your calculator to get a rounded decimal for π. For an exact answer, leave the result in terms of π.

Answers

Solve It!

Answers may vary. The answer depends on what it means to "use wall space." Both decorations have the same number of blocks that cover the wall, so your friend could be correct. The top decoration is more spread out over the wall, so you could also be correct.

Got It?

1a. 24 in.
b. 32 in.

PowerGeometry.com

2 Guided Instruction

Each Problem is worked out and supported online.

Problem 1
Finding the Perimeter of a Rectangle
Animated

Problem 2
Finding Circumference

Problem 3
Finding Perimeter in the Coordinate Plane
Animated

Problem 4
Finding Area of a Rectangle

Problem 5
Finding Area of a Circle

Problem 6
Finding Area of an Irregular Shape
Animated

Support in Geometry Companion
- Vocabulary
- Key Concepts
- Got It?

Problem 2 Finding Circumference

Plan

Which formula should you use?
You want to find circumference. Since you know the diameter in part (A), it would be easier to use the circumference formula that involves diameter.

What is the circumference of the circle in terms of π? What is the circumference of the circle to the nearest tenth?

A $\odot M$

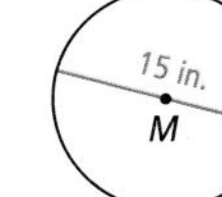

$C = \pi d$ Use the formula for circumference of a circle.

$= \pi(15)$ This is the exact answer.

≈ 47.1238898 Use a calculator.

The circumference of $\odot M$ is 15π in., or about 47.1 in.

B $\odot T$

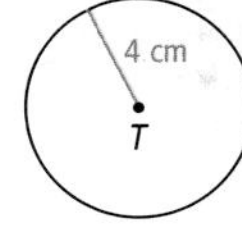

$C = 2\pi r$ Use the formula for circumference of a circle.

$= 2\pi(4)$ This is the exact answer.

$= 8\pi$ Simplify.

≈ 25.13274123 Use a calculator.

The circumference of $\odot T$ is 8π cm, or about 25.1 cm.

Got It? 2. **a.** What is the circumference of a circle with radius 24 m in terms of π?
b. What is the circumference of a circle with diameter 24 m to the nearest tenth?

Problem 3 Finding Perimeter in the Coordinate Plane

Plan

What do you need?
To find the perimeter of a figure, you need its side lengths. Use what you know about length on a number line and in the coordinate plane.

Coordinate Geometry **What is the perimeter of $\triangle EFG$?**

Step 1 Find the length of each side.

$EF = |6 - (-2)| = 8$
$FG = |3 - (-3)| = 6$ Use the Ruler Postulate.

$EG = \sqrt{(3 - (-3))^2 + (6 - (-2))^2}$ Use the Distance Formula.

$= \sqrt{6^2 + 8^2}$ Simplify within the parentheses.

$= \sqrt{36 + 64}$ Simplify.

$= \sqrt{100}$

$= 10$

E(3, 6), F(3, −2), G(−3, −2)

Step 2 Add the side lengths to find the perimeter.

$EF + FG + EG = 8 + 6 + 10 = 24$

The perimeter of $\triangle EFG$ is 24 units.

Got It? 3. Graph quadrilateral $JKLM$ with vertices $J(-3, -3)$, $K(1, -3)$, $L(1, 4)$, and $M(-3, 1)$. What is the perimeter of $JKLM$?

Problem 2

Q How do you identify a diameter of a circle? **[A diameter of a circle is a segment that has endpoints on the circle and intersects the center of the circle.]**

Q How do you identify a radius of a circle? **[A radius is a segment that has one endpoint as the center of the circle and one endpoint on the circle.]**

Q How are the diameter and the radius of a circle related? **[The diameter is twice the radius.]**

Got It? VISUAL LEARNERS

Help students to conceptualize the circumference by telling them to visualize a circle made of string, then cutting the string and straightening it out to form a segment.

Problem 3

Q Can you use the Distance Formula, rather than the Ruler Postulate, to determine *EF* and *FG*? Explain. **[Yes, one of the addends in the formula will be zero.]**

Q What is the relationship of the sum of the squares of *EF* and *FG* to the square of *GE*? **[They are equal.]**

Got It? ERROR PREVENTION

Q What is a quadrilateral? **[A figure with four sides.]**

Q Which segment will require the use of the Distance Formula in order to determine its length? **[*LM*]**

Got It? (continued)

2a. 48π m

b. 75.4 m

3.

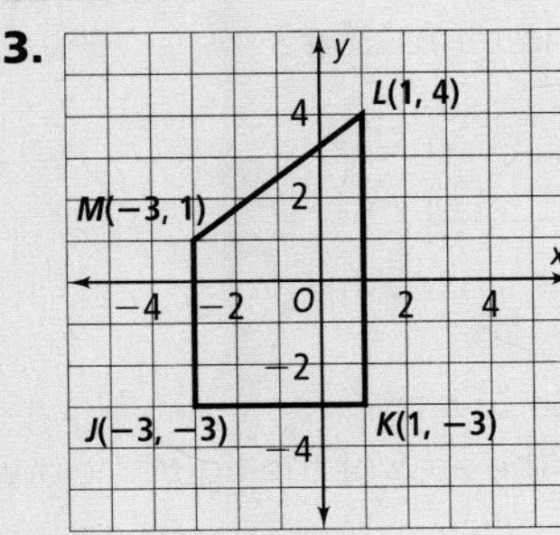

20 units

Problem 4

Q How many feet are in a yard? **[There are 3 feet in a yard.]**

Q How many square feet are in a square yard? Explain. **[9; A square yard measures 3 feet by 3 feet, so it contains 9 square feet.]**

Q Is it possible to substitute 4 for b and 2 for h? Explain. **[Yes, either side can be the base or the height.]**

Got It?

Q If the question did not specify the units for the answer, would you convert yards to feet or feet to yards? Explain. **[Answers may vary. Sample: It would be easier to convert 3 yards to feet, because converting 8 feet to yards would result in a decimal.]**

Problem 5

Q Is $2r$ the same as r^2? Explain. **[No, the first expression says to multiply r by 2, the second expression says to multiply r by r.]**

Q According to the order of operations, how do you simplify the numeric expression created by substituting into the area formula? **[First square the radius, then multiply by π.]**

Got It?

Help students to correctly recall the formulas for the area and circumference of a circle by pointing out that the area formula includes r "squared" and area is expressed in square units.

To find area, you should use the same unit for both dimensions.

Problem 4 Finding Area of a Rectangle

Banners **You want to make a rectangular banner similar to the one at the right. The banner shown is $2\frac{1}{2}$ ft wide and 5 ft high. To the nearest square yard, how much material do you need?**

Think
How can you check your conversion?
Yards are longer than feet, so the number you get in yards should be less than the given number in feet. Since $\frac{5}{6} < 2\frac{1}{2}$, the conversion checks.

Step 1 Convert the dimensions of the banner to yards. Use the conversion factor $\frac{1 \text{ yd}}{3 \text{ ft}}$.

Width: $\frac{5}{2}\cancel{\text{ft}} \cdot \frac{1 \text{ yd}}{3 \cancel{\text{ft}}} = \frac{5}{6}\text{yd}$ $\quad 2\frac{1}{2}\text{ ft} = \frac{5}{2}\text{ ft}$

Height: $5\cancel{\text{ft}} \cdot \frac{1 \text{ yd}}{3 \cancel{\text{ft}}} = \frac{5}{3}\text{yd}$

Step 2 Find the area of the banner.

$A = bh$ Use the formula for area of a rectangle.

$= \frac{5}{6} \cdot \frac{5}{3}$ Substitute $\frac{5}{6}$ for b and $\frac{5}{3}$ for h.

$= \frac{25}{18}$

The area of the banner is $\frac{25}{18}$, or $1\frac{7}{18}$ square yards (yd^2). You need 2 yd^2 of material.

Got It? **4.** You are designing a poster that will be 3 yd wide and 8 ft high. How much paper do you need to make the poster? Give your answer in square feet.

Problem 5 Finding Area of a Circle

What is the area of $\odot K$ in terms of π?

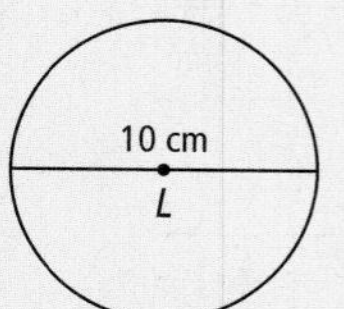

Plan
What are you given?
In circle problems, make it a habit to note whether you are given the radius or the diameter. In this case, you are given the diameter.

Step 1 Find the radius of $\odot K$.

$r = \frac{16}{2}$, or 8 The radius is half the diameter.

Step 2 Use the radius to find the area.

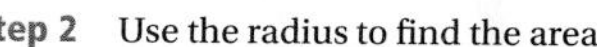
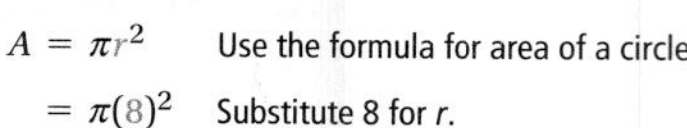

$A = \pi r^2$ Use the formula for area of a circle.

$= \pi(8)^2$ Substitute 8 for r.

$= 64\pi$ Simplify.

The area of $\odot K$ is 64π m^2.

Got It? **5.** The diameter of a circle is 14 ft.
a. What is the area of the circle in terms of π?
b. What is the area of the circle using an approximation of π?
c. **Reasoning** Which approximation of π did you use in part (b)? Why?

Additional Problems

1. To place a fence on the outside of the garden, how much material will you need?

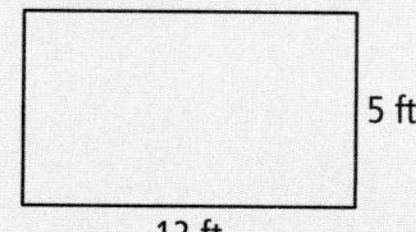

ANSWER 34 ft

2. What is the circumference of the circle in terms of π? What is the circumference of each circle to the nearest tenth?

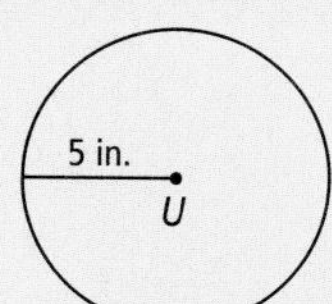

ANSWER 10π; 31.4 in.

3. What is the perimeter of triangle LMN?

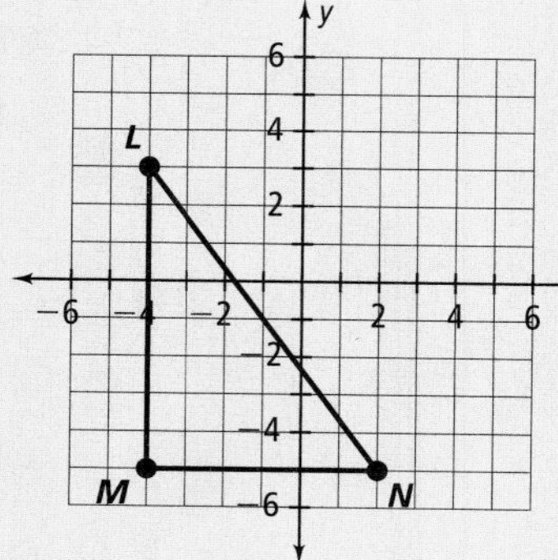

ANSWER 24 units

4. You are designing a rectangular flag for your city's museum. The flag will be 15 feet wide and 2 yards high. How many square yards of material do you need?

ANSWER 10 yd^2

5. The diameter of $\odot L$ is 10 cm. What is its area in terms of π?

ANSWER 25π cm^2

6. What is the area of the figure below?

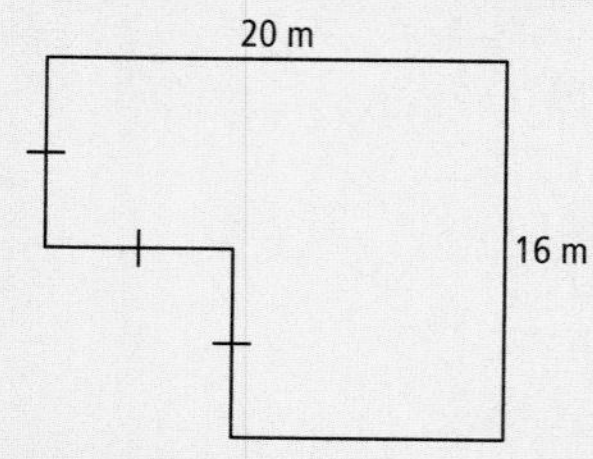

ANSWER 256 m^2

The following postulate is useful in finding areas of figures with irregular shapes.

take note

Postulate 1-10 Area Addition Postulate

The area of a region is the sum of the areas of its nonoverlapping parts.

Problem 6 Finding Area of an Irregular Shape

Multiple Choice **What is the area of the figure at the right? All angles are right angles.**

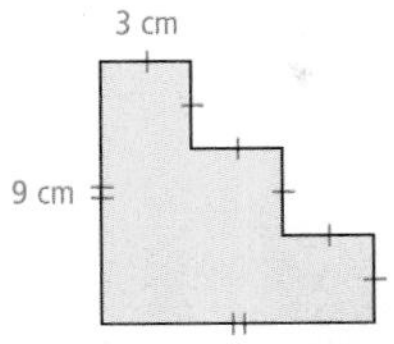

Ⓐ 27 cm^2 Ⓑ 36 cm^2 Ⓒ 45 cm^2 Ⓓ 54 cm^2

3 cm
9 cm

Step 1 Separate the figure into rectangles.

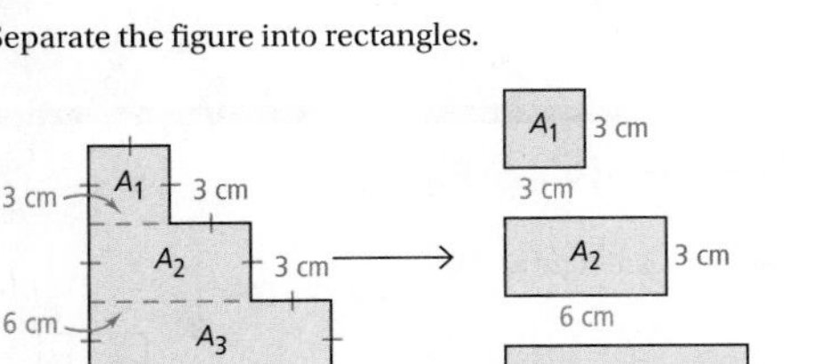

A_1 3 cm
3 cm
A_2 3 cm
6 cm
A_3 3 cm
9 cm

Step 2 Find A_1, A_2, and A_3.

Area $= bh$ Use the formula for the area of a rectangle.

$A_1 = 3 \cdot 3 = 9$ Substitute for the base and height.

$A_2 = 6 \cdot 3 = 18$

$A_3 = 9 \cdot 3 = 27$

Step 3 Find the total area of the figure.

Total Area $= A_1 + A_2 + A_3$ Use the Area Addition Postulate.

$= 9 + 18 + 27$

$= 54$

The area of the figure is 54 cm^2. The correct choice is D.

Got It? 6. a. **Reasoning** What is another way to separate the figure in Problem 6?

b. What is the area of the figure at the right?

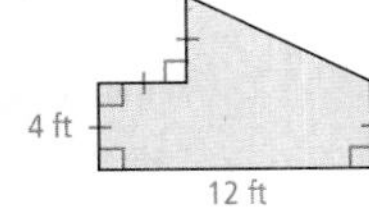

Think

What is another way to find the area?
Extend the figure to form a square. Then subtract the areas of basic shapes from the area of the square.

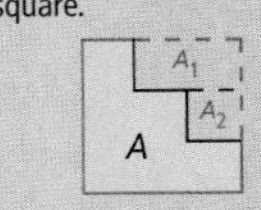

$A = A_{\text{square}} - A_1 - A_2$

Take Note VISUAL LEARNERS

Demonstrate this postulate by calculating the area of a rectangle, and then calculating the area of the triangles created by drawing in the diagonal of the rectangle. The sum of the areas of the triangles will be the area of the rectangle.

Problem 6

Demonstrate to students the following alternate method for determining the area of the figure:

1) Extend the top side and right side of the figure to form a square.
2) Determine the area of the square.
3) Determine the area of the figure created by extending the sides of the figure.
4) Subtract the area determined in step 3 from the area determined in step 2.

Got It?

Q Into what two shapes should the figure in Question 6b be separated? **[A rectangle and a triangle.]**

Q What is the length of the base of the triangle? Explain. **[8 ft; to determine the base of the triangle you subtract 4 ft from 12 ft.]**

Answers

Got It? (continued)

4. 72 ft^2

5a. $49\pi \text{ ft}^2$

b. 153.9 ft^2

c. Answers may vary. Sample: $\frac{22}{7}$; it gives a result without fractions or decimals.

6a.

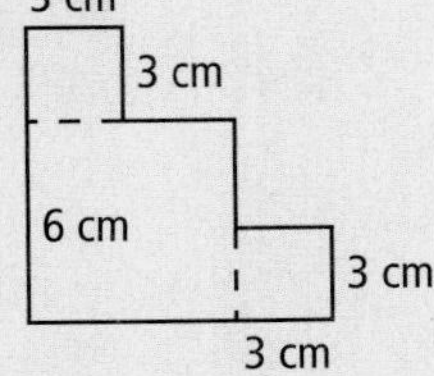

b. 64 ft^2

3 Lesson Check

Do you know HOW?

- Encourage students to check their answer for the area of the figure in Exercise 3 by counting the number of square units that are enclosed by the figure.

Do you UNDERSTAND?

- In Exercise 4, ask students to share their real-world situations with the class. As students describe the situations, make sure that they also provide a description of how they would calculate both the area and the perimeter.

Close

Q Which has greater area, a square with side of length 3 cm or a circle with a diameter of 3 cm? Which has a greater perimeter or circumference? **[The square has the greater area, and its perimeter is also greater than the circumference of the circle.]**

Lesson Check

Do you know HOW?

1. What is the perimeter and area of a rectangle with base 3 in. and height 7 in.?
2. What is the circumference and area of each circle to the nearest tenth?
   a. $r = 9$ in. **b.** $d = 7.3$ m
3. What is the perimeter and area of the figure at the right?

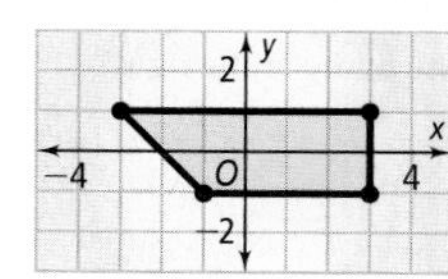

Do you UNDERSTAND?

4. **Writing** Describe a real-world situation in which you would need to find a perimeter. Then describe a situation in which you would need to find an area.
5. **Compare and Contrast** Your friend can't remember whether $2\pi r$ computes the circumference or the area of a circle. How would you help your friend? Explain.
6. **Error Analysis** A classmate finds the area of a circle with radius 30 in. to be 900 in.^{2}. What error did your classmate make?

Practice and Problem-Solving Exercises

Practice **Find the perimeter of each figure.** See Problem 1.

7.

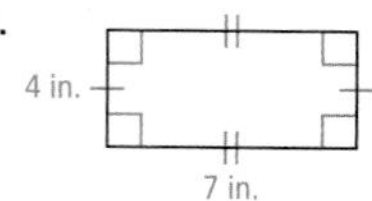

8. 9 cm

9. **Fencing** A garden that is 5 ft by 6 ft has a walkway 2 ft wide around it. What is the amount of fencing needed to surround the walkway?

Find the circumference of ⊙C in terms of π. See Problem 2.

10. C, 15 cm
11. 5 ft, C
12. C, 3.7 in.
13. $\frac{1}{4}$ m, C

Coordinate Geometry **Graph each figure in the coordinate plane. Find each perimeter.** See Problem 3.

14. $X(0, 2)$, $Y(4, -1)$, $Z(-2, -1)$
15. $A(-4, -1)$, $B(4, 5)$, $C(4, -2)$
16. $L(0, 1)$, $M(3, 5)$, $N(5, 5)$, $P(5, 1)$
17. $S(-5, 3)$, $T(7, -2)$, $U(7, -6)$, $V(-5, -6)$

Find the area of each rectangle with the given base and height. See Problem 4.

18. 4 ft, 4 in.
19. 30 in., 4 yd
20. 2 ft 3 in., 6 in.
21. 40 cm, 2 m

22. **Roads** What is the area of a section of pavement that is 20 ft wide and 100 yd long? Give your answer in square feet.

PowerGeometry.com

3 Lesson Check

For a digital lesson check, use the Got It questions.

Support in Geometry Companion

- Lesson Check

4 Practice

Assign homework to individual students or to an entire class.

Answers

Lesson Check

1. 20 in.; 21 in.^{2}

2a. 56.5 in.; 254.5 in.^{2}

b. 22.9 m; 41.9 m^2

3. $(12 + 2\sqrt{2})$ units; 10 square units

4. Answers may vary. Sample: To fence a garden you would find the perimeter; to determine the material needed to make a tablecloth you would find the area.

5. Answers may vary. Sample: Remind your friend that $2\pi r$ has only one variable, so it must compute the circumference. πr^2 has one variable squared, and square units indicate area.

6. The classmate seems to have forgotten to multiply r^2 by π. The correct answer is $A = \pi r^2 = \pi(30)^2 = 900\pi \approx 2827.4$ in.^{2}.

Practice and Problem-Solving Exercises

7. 22 in.

8. 36 cm

9. 38 ft

10. 15π cm

11. 10π ft

12. 3.7π in.

13. $\frac{\pi}{2}$ m

14. y, 3, X(0, 2), x, O, 6, Z(−2, −1), Y(4, −1)

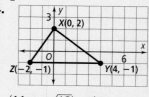

$(11 + \sqrt{13})$ units

Find the area of each circle in terms of π.

See Problem 5.

23. 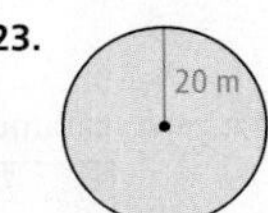

24. 

25.
6.3 ft

26.
0.1 m

Find the area of each circle using an approximation of π. If necessary, round to the nearest tenth.

27. $r = 7$ ft **28.** $d = 8.3$ m **29.** $d = 24$ cm **30.** $r = 12$ in.

Find the area of the shaded region. All angles are right angles.

See Problem 6.

31. 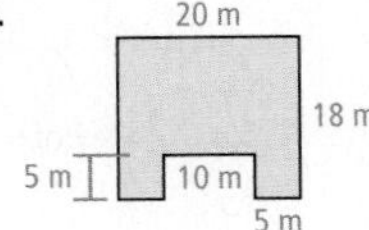

32.
4 in.
8 in.
4 in.
12 in.

33. 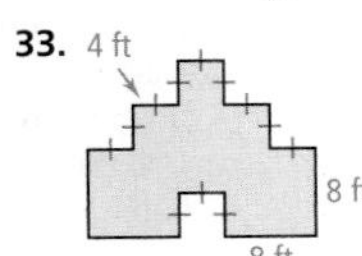

B Apply

34–37. Home Maintenance To determine how much of each item to buy, tell whether you need to know area or perimeter. Explain your choice.

34. wallpaper for a bedroom

35. crown molding for a ceiling

36. fencing for a backyard

37. paint for a basement floor

38. Think About a Plan A light-year unit describes the distance that one photon of light travels in one year. The Milky Way galaxy has a diameter of about 100,000 light-years. The distance to Earth from the center of the Milky Way galaxy is about 30,000 light-years. How many more light-years does a star on the outermost edge of the Milky Way travel in one full revolution around the galaxy compared to Earth?

- What do you know about the shape of each orbital path?
- Are you looking for circumference or area?
- How do you compare the paths using algebraic expressions?

39. a. What is the area of a square with sides 12 in. long? 1 ft long?
b. How many square inches are in a square foot?

40. a. Count squares at the right to find the area of the polygon outlined in blue.
b. Use a formula to find the area of each square outlined in red.
c. Writing How does the sum of your results in part (b) compare to your result in part (a)? Which postulate does this support?

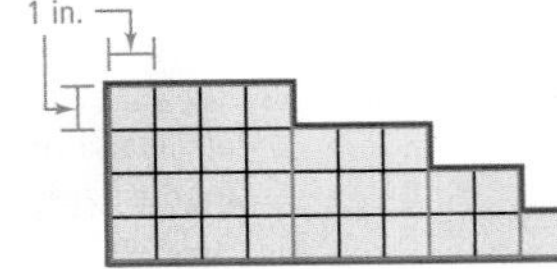

41. The area of an 11-cm-wide rectangle is 176 cm^2. What is its length?

42. A square and a rectangle have equal areas. The rectangle is 64 cm by 81 cm. What is the perimeter of the square?

4 Practice

ASSIGNMENT GUIDE

Basic: 7–33 all, 34–46 even, 47–48, 52, 55
Average: 7–33 odd, 34–56
Advanced: 7–33 odd, 34–59
Standardized Test Prep: 60–63
Mixed Review: 64–69

Reasoning exercises have blue headings.
Applications exercises have red headings.
EXERCISE 55: Use the Think About a Plan worksheet in the **Practice and Problem Solving Workbook** (also available in the Teaching Resources in print and online) to further support students' development in becoming independent learners.

HOMEWORK QUICK CHECK

To check students' understanding of key skills and concepts, go over Exercises 13, 15, 38, 39, and 55.

15. 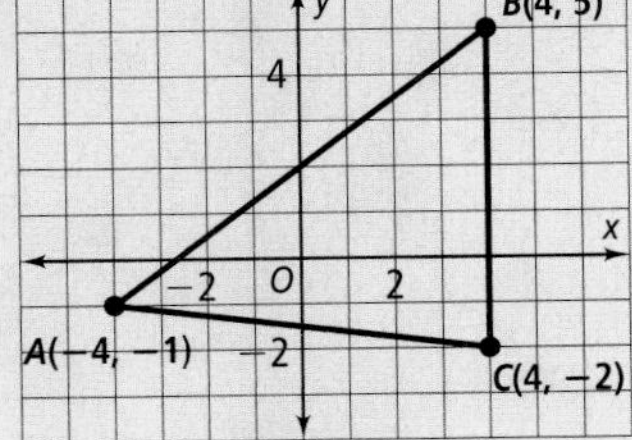

$(17 + \sqrt{65})$ units

16. 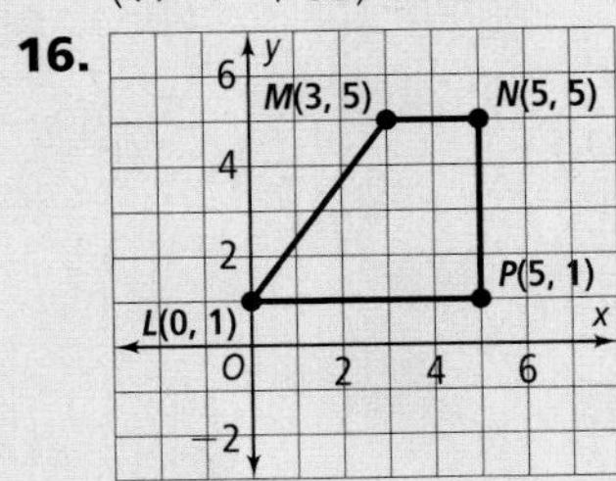

16 units

17. 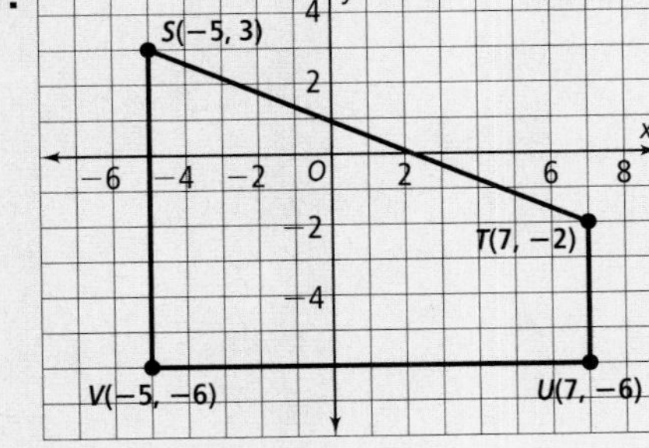

38 units

18. 192 in.^{2}, or $\frac{4}{3}$ ft^2
19. 4320 in.^{2}, or $3\frac{1}{3}$ yd^2
20. 162 in.^{2}, or $1\frac{1}{8}$ ft^2
21. 8000 cm^2, or 0.8 m^2
22. 6000 ft^2
23. 400π m^2
24. $\frac{9}{64}\pi$ in.^{2}
25. $\frac{3969}{400}\pi$ ft^2
26. $\frac{1}{100}\pi$ m^2
27. 153.9 ft^2
28. 54.1 m^2
29. 452.4 cm^2
30. 452.4 in.^{2}
31. 310 m^2
32. 80 in.^{2}
33. 208 ft^2
34. Area; the wall is a surface.
35. Perimeter; the crown molding must fit the edges of the ceiling.
36. Perimeter; the fencing must fit the edges of the backyard.
37. Area; the floor is a surface.
38. $40{,}000\pi$ or about 125,664 light-years
39a. 144 in.^{2}; 1 ft^2
b. 144
40a. 30 squares
b. 16; 9; 4; 1
c. They are equal by the Area Addition Postulate.
41. 16 cm
42. 288 cm

Answers

Practice and Problem-Solving Exercises (continued)

43. 96 cm^2

44. 2975π mm^2, or 9346.2 mm^2

45. 27 $in.^2$

46. 27 cm^2

47a. Yes; substitute s for each of a and b to get perimeter, $P = 2s + 2s$ or $P = 4s$.

b. No; we need to know the length and width of a rectangle to find its perimeter.

c. $A = \frac{P^2}{16}$

48. about 4326 m^2

49. $\frac{25}{4}\pi$ $units^2$

50. D

51.

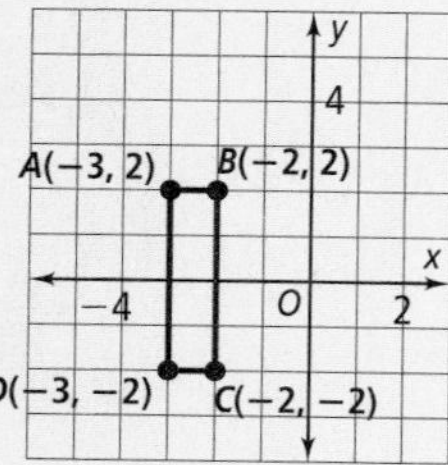

10 units, 4 square units

52.

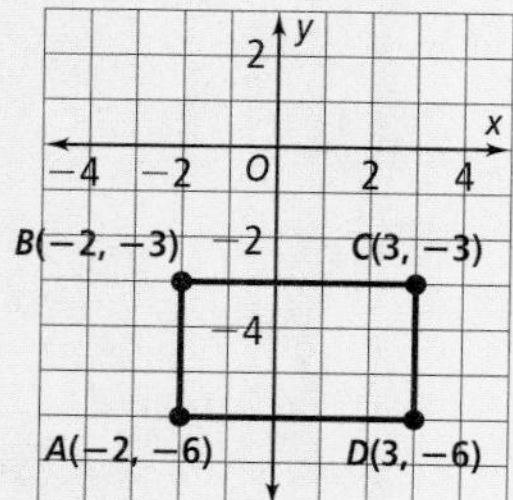

16 units, 15 square units

53a. Answers may vary. Sample:

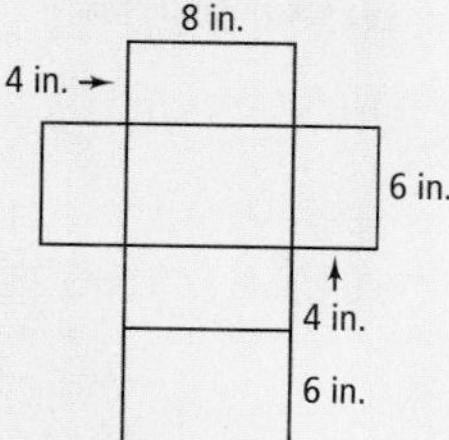

b. 208 $in.^2$; 208 $in.^2$

54.

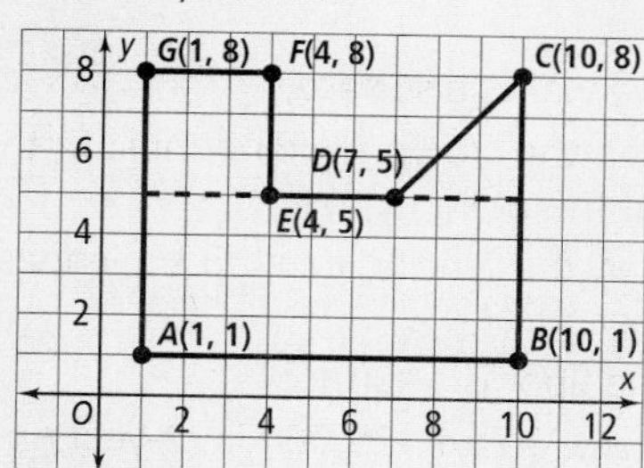

about 36.2 units; 49.5 square units

43. A rectangle has perimeter 40 cm and base 12 cm. What is its area?

Find the area of each shaded figure.

44. compact disc

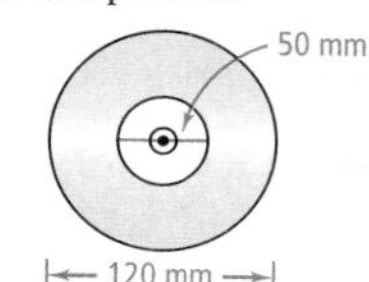

45. drafting triangle

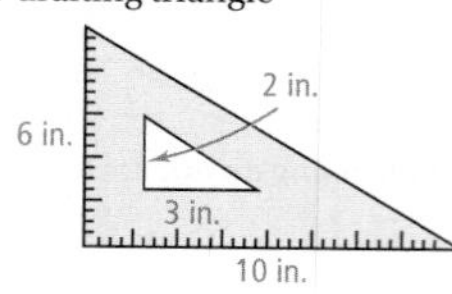

46. picture frame

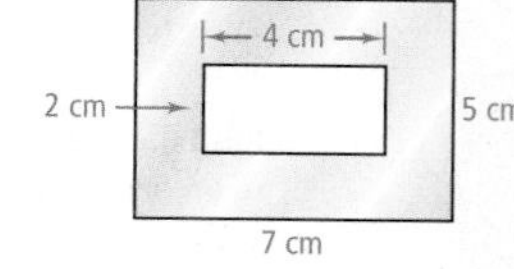

47. a. Reasoning Can you use the formula for the perimeter of a rectangle to find the perimeter of any square? Explain.

b. Can you use the formula for the perimeter of a square to find the perimeter of any rectangle? Explain.

c. Use the formula for the perimeter of a square to write a formula for the area of a square in terms of its perimeter.

48. Estimation On an art trip to England, a student sketches the floor plan of the main body of Salisbury Cathedral. The shape of the floor plan is called the building's "footprint." The student estimates the dimensions of the cathedral on her sketch at the right. Use the student's lengths to estimate the area of Salisbury Cathedral's footprint.

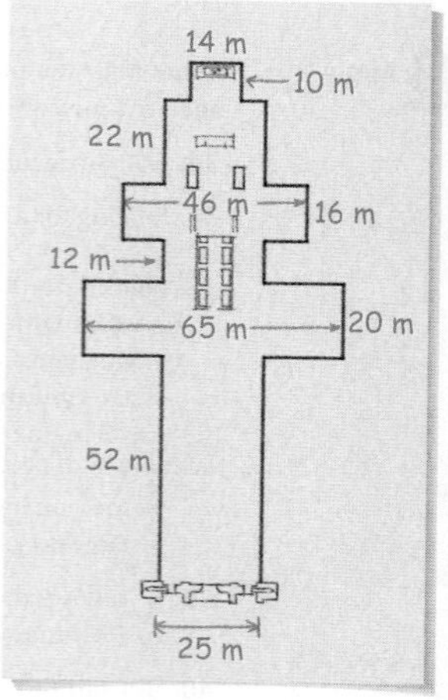

14 m, 10 m, 22 m, 46 m, 16 m, 12 m, 65 m, 20 m, 52 m, 25 m

49. Coordinate Geometry The endpoints of a diameter of a circle are $A(2, 1)$ and $B(5, 5)$. Find the area of the circle in terms of π.

50. Algebra A rectangle has a base of x units. The area is $(4x^2 - 2x)$ square units. What is the height of the rectangle in terms of x?

Ⓐ $(4 - x)$ units Ⓒ $(4x^3 - 2x^2)$ units

Ⓑ $(x - 2)$ units Ⓓ $(4x - 2)$ units

Coordinate Geometry Graph each rectangle in the coordinate plane. Find its perimeter and area.

51. $A(-3, 2)$, $B(-2, 2)$, $C(-2, -2)$, $D(-3, -2)$

52. $A(-2, -6)$, $B(-2, -3)$, $C(3, -3)$, $D(3, -6)$

53. The surface area of a three-dimensional figure is the sum of the areas of all of its surfaces. You can find the surface area by finding the area of a net for the figure.

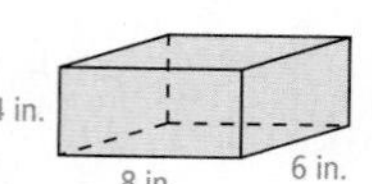

a. Draw a net for the solid shown. Label the dimensions.

b. What is the area of the net? What is the surface area of the solid?

54. Coordinate Geometry On graph paper, draw polygon $ABCDEFG$ with vertices $A(1, 1)$, $B(10, 1)$, $C(10, 8)$, $D(7, 5)$, $E(4, 5)$, $F(4, 8)$, and $G(1, 8)$. Find the perimeter and the area of the polygon.

55. Pet Care You want to adopt a puppy from your local animal shelter. First, you plan to build an outdoor playpen along the side of your house, as shown on the right. You want to lay down special dog grass for the pen's floor. If dog grass costs \$1.70 per square foot, how much will you spend?

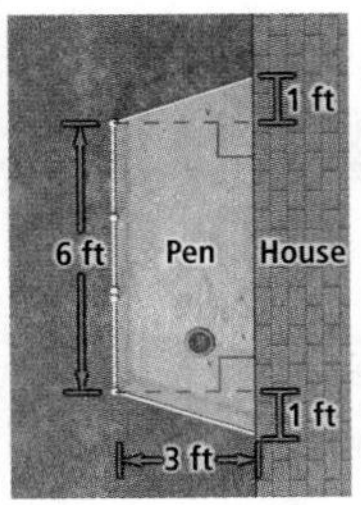

56. A rectangular garden has an 8-ft walkway around it. How many more feet is the outer perimeter of the walkway than the perimeter of the garden?

Challenge **Algebra** **Find the area of each figure.**

57. a rectangle with side lengths $\frac{2a}{5b}$ units and $\frac{3b}{8}$ units

58. a square with perimeter $10n$ units

59. a triangle with base $(5x - 2y)$ units and height $(4x + 3y)$ units

Standardized Test Prep

GRIDDED RESPONSE

SAT/ACT

60. An athletic field is a 100 yd-by-40 yd rectangle with a semicircle at each of the short sides. A running track 10 yd wide surrounds the field. Find the perimeter of the outside of the running track to the nearest tenth of a yard.

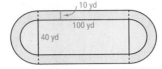

10 yd
100 yd
40 yd

61. A square garden has a 4-ft walkway around it. The garden has a perimeter of 260 ft. What is the area of the walkway in square feet?

62. $A(4, -1)$ and $B(-2, 3)$ are points in a coordinate plane. M is the midpoint of $\overline{AB}$. What is the length of $\overline{MB}$ to the nearest tenth of a unit?

63. Find CD to the nearest tenth if point C is at $(12, -8)$ and point D is at $(5, 19)$.

Mixed Review

Find (a) AB to the nearest tenth and (b) the midpoint coordinates of $\overline{AB}$. See Lesson 1-7.

64. $A(4, 1), B(7, 9)$ **65.** $A(0, 3), B(-3, 8)$ **66.** $A(-1, 1), B(-4, -5)$

$\overleftrightarrow{BG}$ is the perpendicular bisector of $\overline{WR}$ at point K. See Lesson 1-6.

67. What is $m\angle BKR$?

68. Name two congruent segments.

Get Ready! To prepare for Lesson 2-1, do Exercise 69.

69. a. Copy and extend this list to show the first 10 perfect squares. See p. 829.
$1^2 = 1, 2^2 = 4, 3^2 = 9, 4^2 = 16, \ldots$

b. Which do you think describes the square of any odd number?
It is odd. It is even.

55. \$35.70
56. 64 ft
57. $\frac{3a}{20}$ square units
58. $\frac{25}{4}n^2$ square units or $6.25n^2$ square units
59. $(10x^2 + \frac{7}{2}xy - 3y^2)$ square units
60. 388.5 yd
61. 1104 ft^2
62. 3.6 units
63. 27.9
64a. 8.5 units
b. $\left(\frac{11}{2}, 5\right)$ or (5.5, 5)
65a. 5.8 units
b. $\left(-\frac{3}{2}, \frac{11}{2}\right)$ or (−1.5, 5.5)
66a. 6.7 units
b. $\left(-\frac{5}{2}, -2\right)$ or (−2.5, −2)
67. 90
68. $\overline{WK}$, $\overline{KR}$

69a. $1^2 = 1, 2^2 = 4, 3^2 = 9, 4^2 = 16, 5^2 = 25, 6^2 = 36, 7^2 = 49, 8^2 = 64, 9^2 = 81, 10^2 = 100$
b. It is odd.

1-8 Lesson Resources

Differentiated Remediation

Instructional Support

Geometry Companion

Students can use the **Geometry Companion** worktext (4 pages) . . .

- New Vocabulary
- Key Concepts
- Got It for each Problem
- Lesson Check

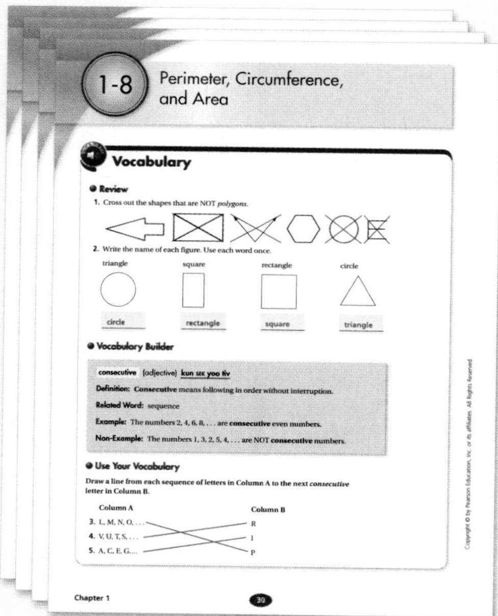

1-8 Perimeter, Circumference, and Area

Vocabulary

Review

1. Cross out the shapes that are NOT *polygons.*

2. Write the name of each figure. Use each word once.

triangle square rectangle circle

circle rectangle square triangle

Vocabulary Builder

consecutive (adjective) kun SEK yoo tiv

Definition: **Consecutive** means following in order without interruption.

Related Word: sequence

Example: The numbers 2, 4, 6, 8, . . . are **consecutive** even numbers.

Non-Example: The numbers 1, 3, 2, 5, 4, . . . are NOT **consecutive** numbers.

Use Your Vocabulary

Draw a line from each sequence of letters in Column A to the next *consecutive* letter in Column B.

Column A	Column B
3. L, M, N, O, . . .	R
4. V, U, T, S, . . .	I
5. A, C, E, G, . . .	P

Chapter 1 30

ELL Support

Assess Understanding Write the lesson objective on the board and read it aloud. Ask: What is the difference between perimeter and circumference? Have students read the text for the meaning of *area.* Guide students to rephrase the objective in their own words.

Draw a rectangle on the board and run your finger along its sides. Ask: What is the distance around the rectangle called? Shade the inside of the rectangle. Ask: What does this represent? Contrast the formulas for the area of a rectangle and a triangle. How are they similar? How are they different?

5 Assess & Remediate

Lesson Quiz

1. What is the circumference of the circle below in terms of π? What is the circumference of the circle to the nearest tenth?

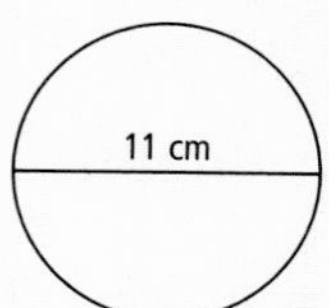

2. What is the perimeter of triangle PQR? Round to the nearest tenth if necessary.

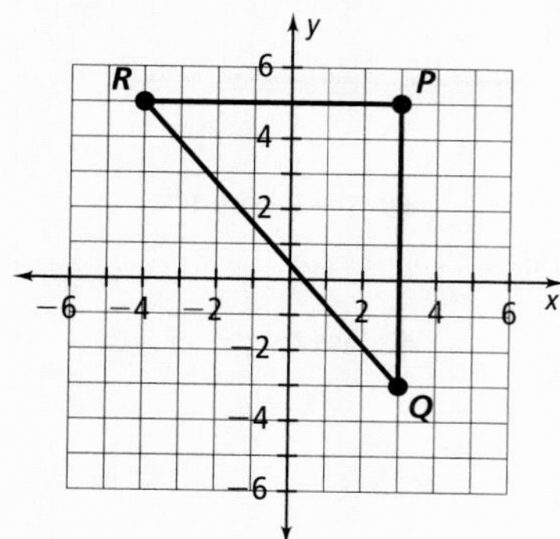

3. Do you UNDERSTAND? You are designing a rectangular sign for your school's football team. The sign will be 6 yd wide and 9 ft high. How many square yards of material do you need?

ANSWERS TO LESSON QUIZ

1. $11\pi \approx 34.6$ cm

2. 25.6 units

3. 18 yd^2

PRESCRIPTION FOR REMEDIATION

Use the student work on the Lesson Quiz to prescribe a differentiated review assignment.

Points	Differentiated Remediation
0–1	Intervention
2	On-level
3	Extension

PowerGeometry.com

5 Assess & Remediate

Assign the Lesson Quiz. Appropriate intervention, practice, or enrichment is automatically generated based on student performance.

Intervention

- **Reteaching** (2 pages) Provides reteaching and practice exercises for the key lesson concepts. Use with struggling students or absent students.
- **English Language Learner Support** Helps students develop and reinforce mathematical vocabulary and key concepts.

All-in-One Resources/Online

Reteaching

1-8 **Reteaching**

Perimeter, Circumference, and Area

The perimeter of a rectangle is the sum of the lengths of its sides. So, the perimeter is the distance around its outside. The formula for the perimeter of a rectangle is $P = 2(b + h)$.

The area of a rectangle is the number of square units contained within the rectangle. The formula for the area of a rectangle is $A = bh$.

Exercises

1. Fill in the missing information for each rectangle in the table below.

Dimensions	Perimeter, $P = 2(b + h)$	Area, $A = bh$
1 ft × 9 ft	2(1 ft + 9 ft) = 20 ft	1 ft × 9 ft = 9 ft^2
2 ft × 8 ft	2(2 ft + 8 ft) = 20 ft	2 ft × 8 ft = 16 ft^2
3 ft × 7 ft	2(3 ft + 7 ft) = 20 ft	3 ft × 7 ft = 21 ft^2
4 ft × 6 ft	2(4 ft + 6 ft) = 20 ft	4 ft × 6 ft = 24 ft^2

2. How does the perimeter vary as you move down the table? How does the area vary as you move down the table? The perimeter stays the same. The area increases.

3. What pattern in the dimensions of the rectangles explains your answer to Exercise 2? Answers may vary. Sample: The sum $b + h$ is always the same, while the product bh increases.

4. Fill in the missing information for each rectangle in the table below.

Dimensions	Perimeter, $P = 2(b + h)$	Area, $A = bh$
1 ft × 24 ft	2(1 ft + 24 ft) = 50 ft	1 ft × 24 ft = 24 ft^2
2 ft × 12 ft	2(2 ft + 12 ft) = 28 ft	2 ft × 12 ft = 24 ft^2
3 ft × 8 ft	2(3 ft + 8 ft) = 22 ft	3 ft × 8 ft = 24 ft^2
4 ft × 6 ft	2(4 ft + 6 ft) = 20 ft	4 ft × 6 ft = 24 ft^2

5. How does the perimeter vary as you move down the table? How does the area vary as you move down the table? The perimeter decreases. The area stays the same.

6. What pattern in the dimensions of the rectangles explains your answer to Exercise 5? Answers may vary. Sample: The product bh is always the same, while the sum $b + h$ decreases.

All-in-One Resources/Online

English Language Learner Support

1-8 **ELL Support**

Perimeter, Circumference, and Area

For Exercises 1–7, draw a line from each word in Column A to its definition in Column B. The first one is done for you.

Column A	Column B
1. perimeter	a polygon with three sides
2. radius	the sum of the lengths of the sides of a polygon, or the distance around a polygon
3. diameter	the distance from the center to a point on a circle
4. area	a polygon with four sides
5. circumference	the distance across a circle, through the center
6. triangle	the number of square units a figure encloses
7. quadrilateral	the distance around a circle

For Exercises 8–13, draw a line from each phrase in Column A to its formula in Column B.

Column A	Column B
8. perimeter of a square	$4s$
9. circumference of a circle	bh
10. area of a rectangle	$\frac{1}{2}bh$
11. area of a triangle	πd or $2\pi r$
12. perimeter of a rectangle	$2b + 2h$
13. area of a circle	πr^2

Differentiated Remediation *continued*

On-Level

- **Practice** (2 pages) Provides extra practice for each lesson. For simpler practice exercises, use the Form K Practice pages found in the All-in-One Teaching Resources and online.
- **Think About a Plan** Helps students develop specific problem-solving skills and strategies by providing scaffolded guiding questions.
- **Standardized Test Prep** Focuses on all major exercises, all major question types, and helps students prepare for the high-stakes assessments.

Extension

- **Enrichment** Provides students with interesting problems and activities that extend the concepts of the lesson.
- **Activities, Games, and Puzzles** Worksheets that can be used for concepts development, enrichment, and for fun!

Practice and Problem Solving Wkbk/ All-in-One Resources/Online

Practice page 1

1-8 **Practice** — Form G
Perimeter, Circumference, and Area

Find the perimeter of each figure.

1. 28 cm 2. 28 cm

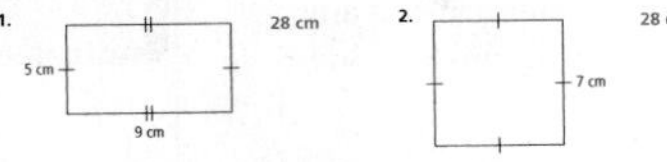

3. An 8-ft-by-10-ft rug leaves 1 ft of the bedroom floor exposed on all four sides. Find the perimeter of the bedroom floor. 44 ft

Find the circumference of each circle in terms of π.

4. 32π units 5. 16π units 6. 7.8π units

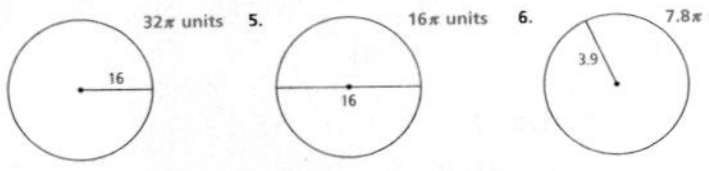

Graph each figure in the coordinate plane. Find the perimeter.

7. $X(-4, 2)$, $Y(2, 10)$, $Z(2, 2)$ 24; check students' work. Graphs should include $X(-4, 2)$, $Y(2, 10)$, and $Z(2, 2)$.
8. $R(1, 2)$, $S(1, -2)$, $T(4, -2)$ 12; check students' work. Graphs should include $R(1, 2)$, $S(1, -2)$, and $T(4, -2)$.
9. $A(0, 0)$, $B(0, 5)$, $C(6, 5)$, $D(6, 0)$ 22; check students' work. Graphs should include $A(0, 0)$, $B(0, 5)$, $C(6, 5)$, and $D(6, 0)$.
10. $L(-3, 2)$, $M(2, 14)$, $N(2, 20)$, $P(-3, 20)$ 42; check students' work. Graphs should include $L(-3, 2)$, $M(2, 14)$, $N(2, 20)$, and $P(-3, 20)$.

Find the area of the rectangle with the given base and height.

11. 4 ft, 15 in. 5 ft² 12. 90 in., 3 yd 7.5 yd² 13. 3 m, 130 cm 3.9 m²

Find the area of each circle in terms of π.

14. 156.25π units 15. $10{,}000\pi$ units 16. $\frac{1}{16}\pi^3$ units

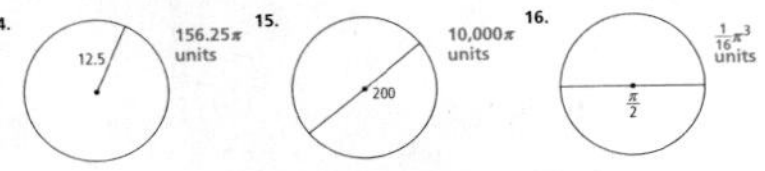

Practice and Problem Solving Wkbk/ All-in-One Resources/Online

Practice page 2

1-8 **Practice** (continued) — Form G
Perimeter, Circumference, and Area

Find the area of each shaded region. All angles are right angles.

17. 15 285 18. 7 22 19. 4 44

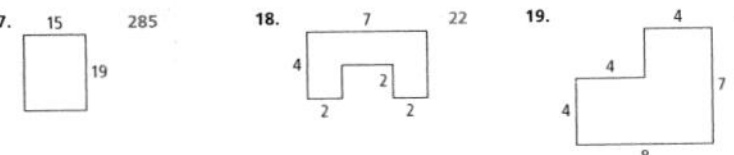

Find the circumference and area of each circle, using $\pi = 3.14$. If necessary, round to the nearest tenth.

20. $r = 5$ m 31.4 m; 78.5 m²
21. $d = 2.1$ in. 6.6 in.; 3.5 in.²
22. $d = 2$ m 6.3 m; 3.1 m²
23. $r = 4.7$ ft 29.5 ft; 69.4 ft²
24. The area of a circle is 25π in.². What is its radius? 5 in.
25. A rectangle has twice the area of a square. The rectangle is 18 in. by 4 in. What is the perimeter of the square? 24 in.
26. **Reasoning** If two circles have the same circumference, what do you know about their areas? Explain. They have the same area because they have the same radius.
27. **Coordinate Geometry** The center of a circle is $A(-3, 3)$, and $B(1, 6)$ is on the circle. Find the area of the circle in terms of π. 25π units²
28. **Algebra** Use the formula for the circumference of a circle to write a formula for the area of a circle in terms of its circumference. $A = \frac{C^2}{4\pi}$
29. **Coordinate Geometry** On graph paper, draw polygon *ABCDEF* with vertices $A(0, 0)$, $B(0, 10)$, $C(5, 10)$, $D(5, 7)$, $E(9, 7)$, and $F(9, 0)$. Find the perimeter and the area of the polygon. 38 units; 78 units²; check students' work.
30. The units of the floor plan at the right are in feet. Find the perimeter and area of each room.
   a. the kitchen 44 ft; 92 ft²
   b. the bedroom 40 ft; 96 ft²
   c. the bathroom 26 ft; 36 ft²
   d. the closet 28 ft; 48 ft²
   e. What is the area of the main hallway? Explain how you could find this area using the area of each room. 128 ft²; answers may vary. Sample: Add the room areas and subtract from 400 ft².

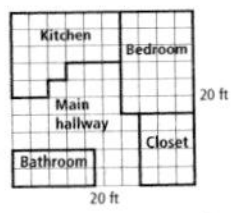

All-in-One Resources/Online

Enrichment

1-8 **Enrichment**
Perimeter, Circumference, and Area

Shape and Area

Compare the areas enclosed by different shapes.

1. You have 80 ft of fencing to enclose a rectangular yard. The yard is 10 ft wide by 30 ft long. What is the area of the rectangular yard? 300 ft²
2. Next, you use 80 ft of fencing to make a square yard that is 20 ft on each side. What is the area of the square yard? 400 ft²
3. Which of the two yards has the greater area: the rectangular yard or the square yard? How much greater is the area of the larger yard? square; 100 ft²
4. Repeat the steps above with 120 ft, 160 ft, and 200 ft of fencing. Copy the table below onto your own paper and fill in your results.

	Length of Fence		
	120 ft	160 ft	200 ft
Dimensions of Rectangle	20 ft × 40 ft	20 ft × 60 ft	45 ft × 55 ft
Area of Rectangle	800 ft²	1200 ft²	2475 ft²
Dimensions of Square	30 ft × 30 ft	40 ft × 40 ft	50 ft × 50 ft
Area of Square	900 ft²	1600 ft²	2500 ft²
Difference in Area	100 ft²	400 ft²	25 ft²
Shape with Greater Area	square	square	square

5. Finally, you make an approximately circular yard using 80 ft of fence. What is the area of the yard? (*Hint:* First find the radius of the yard.) 509 ft²
6. When you used 80 ft of fencing, which shape made the yard with the greatest area: the rectangle, the square, or the circle? Do you think this shape will always make the yard with the greatest area? Explain. Circle; answers may vary. Sample: a circle with perimeter $2\pi r$ has the same perimeter as a square with side length $\frac{\pi r}{2}$. The square's area is $\frac{\pi^2 r^2}{4}$, which is less than πr^2.

Practice and Problem Solving Wkbk/ All-in-One Resources/Online

Think About a Plan

1-8 **Think About a Plan**
Perimeter, Circumference, and Area

Pet Care You want to adopt a puppy from your local animal shelter. First, you plan to build an outdoor playpen along the side of your house, as shown on the right. You want to lay down special dog grass for the pen's floor. If dog grass costs $1.70 per square foot, how much will you spend?

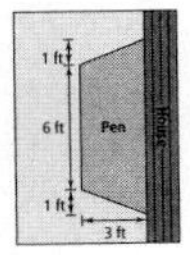

Understanding the Problem

1. What are you trying to find? What is the cost of the grass for the playpen?

Planning the Solution

2. What additional information do you need to know to answer the question? Answers may vary. Sample: the area of the playpen
3. How will you use that additional information to answer the question? Answers may vary. Sample: Multiply the area by $1.70 to find the cost.

Getting the Answer

4. How can you find the area of the playpen? First break it down into triangles and a rectangle. Find the areas of these figures and then add the areas. Multiply the length by the width (6 × 3) for the rectangle and add the area of the two triangles on the sides $(2 \times \frac{1}{2} \times 1 \times 3)$.
5. How do you find the total cost of the grass? Multiply the area by $1.70.
6. What is the total cost of the grass? Show your work. Area $= 6 \times 3 + 2[\frac{1}{2}(1)(3)] = 21$ ft²; cost $= 21 \times \$1.70 = \$35.70$

Practice and Problem Solving Wkbk/ All-in-One Resources/Online

Standardized Test Prep

1-8 **Standardized Test Prep**
Perimeter, Circumference, and Area

Multiple Choice

For Exercises 1–6, choose the correct letter.

1. A 12-ft-by-15-ft swimming pool has a 3-ft-wide no-slip surface around it. What is the outer perimeter of the no-slip surface? A
   A 78 ft B 78 ft² C 198 ft D 198 ft²
2. What is the circumference of the circle at the right in terms of π? I
   F 1.1π G 1.21π H 2.2π I 4.4π

3. What is the perimeter of $\triangle PQR$ with vertices $P(-2, 9)$, $Q(7, -3)$, and $R(-2, -3)$ in the coordinate plane? D
   A 21 units B 25 units C 34 units D 36 units
4. You are tiling a kitchen floor that is 10 ft wide by 4 yd long. How many square yards of tile do you need? F
   F $13\frac{1}{3}$ yd² G $13\frac{1}{2}$ yd² H 20 yd² I 40 yd²
5. The diameter of $\odot Z$ is 5 in. What is its area in terms of π? C
   A 2.5π in.² B 5π in.² C 6.25π in.² D 25π in.²
6. All angles in the figure at the right are right angles. What is the area of the figure? I
   F 14 G 18 H 28 I 36

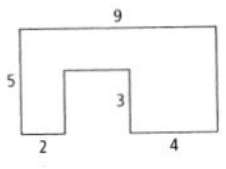

Short Response

7. a. If two squares have the same area, what do you know about the measures of their sides? Explain. The area of a square is the measure of the length of the side squared. So, the measures of both squares' sides are the same.
   b. If two rectangles have the same area, what do you know about the measures of their sides? Explain. The area of a rectangle is the product of the measures of their sides. So, the product of the measures of both rectangles' sides is the same. [2] Both answers and explanations are correct. [1] missing answer or explanation [0] both answers incorrect or missing explanations

Online Teacher Resource Center

Activities, Games, and Puzzles

1-8 **Puzzle: Cross-Number**
Perimeter, Circumference, and Area

Fill in the cross-number puzzle with your answers to the given clues. All answers should be rounded to the thousandths place when necessary. Each digit and decimal point of your answer goes in its own box.

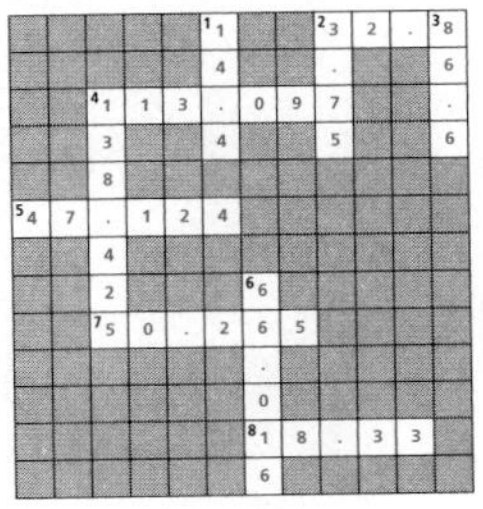

Across

2. perimeter of a triangle with side lengths of 13.9 in., 10.4 in., and 8.5 in.
4. area of a circle with a 12-ft diameter
5. circumference of a circle with a 7.5-cm radius
7. circumference of a circle with a 16-ft diameter
8. area of a rectangle with dimensions 4.7 m and 3.9 m

Down

1. perimeter of a square with side length 3.6 cm
2. area of a rectangle with dimensions 2.5 in. and 1.5 in.
3. perimeter of a rectangle with dimensions 32.4 m and 10.9 m
4. area of a triangle with a base of 24.5 cm and height of 11.3 cm
6. area of a square with side length 8.125 cm

Guided Instruction

PURPOSE To use a graphing calculator or spreadsheet software to find maximum values for the area and perimeter of a rectangular figure

PROCESS Students will

- solve a real-world problem that involves a given perimeter and varied areas.
- use a graphing calculator to make a table of values that can be analyzed to solve the problem.

DISCUSS Before assigning the activity, guide students through the process of making a table of values on their calculators, as well as displaying and tracing a graph on their graphing calculators.

Activity

In this Activity students will find the maximum area of a rectangle given a fixed perimeter.

Q While drawing the rectangular pens, when the base and height differ by a greater amount, what do you notice about the corresponding area? **[The area is a lesser amount.]**

Q Based upon the calculations you made with your sketches, what do you anticipate the calculator results to be? **[A pen with equal base and height will yield the greatest area.]**

Q What does Y_1 represent? **[Y_1 represents the height of the pen.]**

Q What does Y_2 represent? **[Y_2 represents the area of the pen.]**

Concept Byte

Use With Lesson 1-8

TECHNOLOGY

Comparing Perimeters and Areas

You can use a graphing calculator or spreadsheet software to find maximum and minimum values. These values help you solve real-world problems where you want to minimize or maximize a quantity such as cost or time. In this Activity, you will find minimum and maximum values for area and perimeter problems.

Activity

You have 32 yd of fencing. You want to make a rectangular horse pen with maximum area.

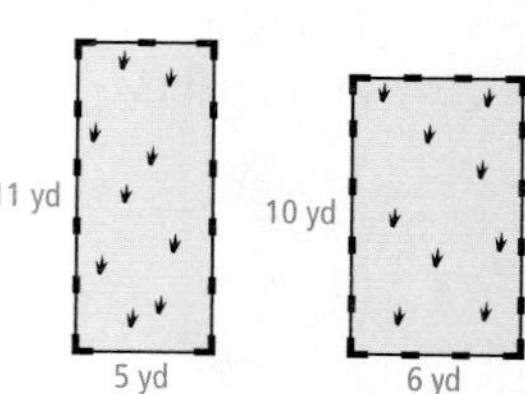

$A = 55$ yd^2 $A = 60$ yd^2

1. Draw some possible rectangular pens and find their areas. Use the examples at the right as models.
2. You plan to use all of your fencing. Let X represent the base of the pen. What is the height of the pen in terms of X? What is the area of the pen in terms of X?
3. Make a graphing calculator table to find area. Again, let X represent the base. For Y_1, enter the expression you wrote for the height in Question 2. For Y_2, enter the expression you wrote for the area in Question 2. Set the table so that X starts at 4 and changes by 1. Scroll down the table.
   a. What value of X gives you the maximum area?
   b. What is the maximum area?

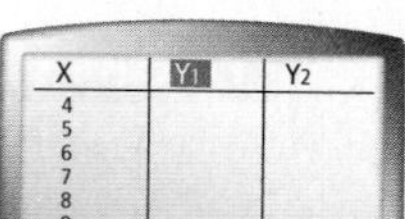

4. Use your calculator to graph Y_2. Describe the shape of the graph. Trace on the graph to find the coordinates of the highest point. What is the relationship, if any, between the coordinates of the highest point on the graph and your answers to Question 3? Explain.

Exercises

5. For a fixed perimeter, what rectangular shape will result in a maximum area?
6. Consider that the pen is not limited to polygon shapes. What is the area of a circular pen with circumference 32 yd? How does this result compare to the maximum area you found in the Activity?
7. You plan to make a rectangular garden with an area of 900 ft^2. You want to use a minimum amount of fencing to keep the cost low.
   a. List some possible dimensions for the garden. Find the perimeter of each.
   b. Make a graphing calculator table. Use integer values of the base b, and the corresponding values of the height h, to find values for P, the perimeter. What dimensions will give you a garden with the minimum perimeter?

Answers

Exercises

5. square
6. About 81.5 yd^2; the circular pen has greater area.

7a. Answers may vary. Sample:
25 ft by 36 ft; 122 ft
30 ft by 30 ft; 120 ft
10 ft by 90 ft; 200 ft

b. 30 ft-by-30 ft square

Pull It All Together

To solve these problems, you will pull together many concepts and skills that you learned in this chapter. They are the basic tools used to study geometry.

BIG idea Visualization

You can draw and construct figures to understand geometric relationships.

Task 1

Graph $\triangle ABC$ with $A(4, 7)$, $B(0,0)$, and $C(8, 1)$.

a. Which sides of $\triangle ABC$ are congruent? How do you know?

b. Construct the bisector of $\angle B$. Mark the intersection of the ray and $\overline{AC}$ as D.

c. What do you notice about AD and CD?

BIG idea Measurement

Measures of segments and angles give you ways to describe geometric figures.

Task 2

Using the design below, you plan to make a rectangular wall hanging to decorate your bedroom. The green rectangle is 16 ft by 10 ft, the blue square is 7 ft by 7 ft, the orange triangles have a height of 1.73 ft and a side length of 2 ft, and the yellow circle has a diameter of 3 ft. You plan to glue the pieces together and then outline each piece with black cord.

a. How much black cord does the design use?

b. How much fabric of each color does the design show?

c. At a craft store, fabric comes in bolts that are a fixed number of inches wide. You can only buy fabric by the whole yard. If each bolt is 48 in. wide, what is the least amount of each color that you need to buy? Explain.

Performance Task 

Pull It All Together

The concepts and skills required to solve these problems are from several lessons within this chapter and from the previous chapter. As students solve these problems, they will demonstrate their reasoning strategies and their growth as independent problem solvers.

The following questions are designed to:

- Help support students as they do the Tasks.
- Gauge the amount of support students need as they become independent problem solvers.

Task 1

- How can you show the sides are congruent?
- What two items do you need for the construction?

Task 2

- Is the amount of black cord used found by calculating perimeter or area?
- Is the amount of each color of fabric used found by calculating perimeter or area?
- Should you round each area up, or to the nearest unit?

Assess Performance UbD

Analytic Holistic Scoring

Holistic scoring provides feedback to students to help them become autonomous, confident problem solvers. Holistic scoring considers the entire solution to evaluate students' strategies, process, and answers. Use the rubric below to evaluate students' work for Pull It All Together and for Performance Tasks found in the Teaching Resources.

Understanding the Problem

Score	Description
2	complete understanding of the problem
1	part of the problem misunderstood or misinterpreted
0	complete misunderstanding of the problem

Planning a Solution

Score	Description
2	plan could lead to a correct solution if implemented properly
1	partially correct plan based on part of the problem interpreted correctly
0	no attempt or totally inappropriate plan

Getting an Answer

Score	Description
2	correct answer and correct label for the answer
1	copying error; computational error; partial answer for a problem with multiple answers
0	no answer or wrong answer based on an inappropriate plan

Developing Autonomy

Score	Description
2	completed the problem without help
1	needed one or two hints
0	could not work the problem without extensive guidance

Pull It All Together

SOLUTION OUTLINES

1a. Possible plan: Find the distance between each pair of points ($AB = \sqrt{65}$, $AC = \sqrt{52}$, $BC = \sqrt{65}$). Then compare the distances to determine which segments are congruent. (Answer: $\overline{AB} \cong \overline{BC}$)

b. Possible plan: Follow the steps in Lesson 1-6, Problem 4.

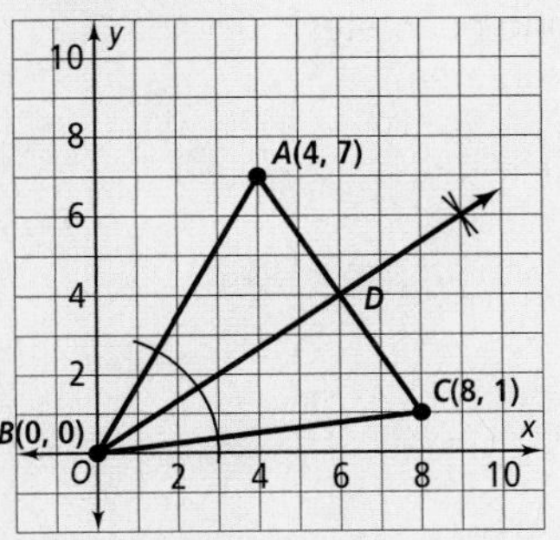

1c, 2a–c. See next page.

Essential Questions 

BIG idea Visualization

ESSENTIAL QUESTION How can you represent a three-dimensional figure with a two-dimensional drawing?

ANSWER You can represent a 3-D figure with a 2-D drawing by visualizing the surfaces of the figure and how they relate to each other.

BIG idea Reasoning

ESSENTIAL QUESTION What are the building blocks of geometry?

ANSWER Geometry is a mathematical system built on basic terms, definitions, and assumptions called postulates.

BIG idea Measurement

ESSENTIAL QUESTION How can you describe the attributes of a segment or angle?

ANSWER You can describe the attributes of a segment or angle by using unit amounts.

1 Chapter Review

Connecting BIG ideas and Answering the Essential Questions

1 Visualization
You can represent a 3-D figure with a 2-D drawing by visualizing the surfaces of the figure and how they relate to each other.

Lesson 1-1 Nets and Drawings

2 Reasoning
Geometry is a mathematical system built on basic terms, definitions, and assumptions called postulates.

Lesson 1-2 Points, Lines, and Planes

Lesson 1-5 Exploring Angle Pairs
You can conclude these relationships from an unmarked diagram.
- Angles are adjacent.
- Angles are adjacent supplementary.
- Angles are vertical angles.

3 Measurement
You can describe the attributes of a segment or angle by using unit amounts.

Lessons 1-3 and 1-4 Segments and Angles

$AB = 5$ $m\angle A = 45$

Lesson 1-7 Midpoint and Distance

Midpoint $= \left(\frac{x_1 + x_2}{2}, \frac{y_1 + y_2}{2}\right)$

Distance $= \sqrt{(x_2 - x_1)^2 + (y_2 - y_1)^2}$

Chapter Vocabulary

- acute, right, obtuse, straight angles (p. 29)
- adjacent angles (p. 34)
- angle bisector (p. 37)
- collinear points, coplanar (p. 12)
- complementary angles (p. 34)
- congruent angles (p. 29)
- congruent segments (p. 22)
- construction (p. 43)
- isometric drawing (p. 5)
- linear pair (p. 36)
- measure of an angle (p. 28)
- net (p. 4)
- orthographic drawing (p. 6)
- perpendicular bisector (p. 44)
- perpendicular lines (p. 44)
- point, line, plane (p. 11)
- postulate, axiom (p. 13)
- ray, opposite rays (p. 12)
- segment (p. 12)
- segment bisector (p. 22)
- space (p. 12)
- supplementary angles (p. 34)
- vertex of an angle (p. 27)
- vertical angles (p. 34)

Choose the correct term to complete each sentence.

1. A ray that divides an angle into two congruent angles is a(n) __?__.

2. __?__ are two lines that intersect to form right angles.

3. A(n) __?__ is a two-dimensional diagram that you can fold to form a 3-D figure.

4. __?__ are two angles with measures that have a sum of 90.

Summative Questions UbD

Use the following prompts as you review this chapter with your students. The prompts are designed to help you assess your students' understanding of the Big Ideas they have studied.

- How are points, lines, and planes represented?
- How can you measure segments?
- How can you measure angles?
- What angle pair relationships have you learned?
- How do you find perimeter?
- How do you find area?

SOLUTION OUTLINES (continued)

1c. Possible plan: Find the midpoint of $\overline{AC}$. Then compare the midpoint with point D. (Answer: The midpoint of $\overline{AC}$ coincides with D, so $AD = CD$.)

2a. Possible plan: Find the perimeter of each shape in the design (rectangle: 52 ft, square: 28 ft, four triangles: 6 ft each, circle: 3π, or about 9.42 ft). Add the perimeters to find the total amount of cord. (Answer: 113.42 ft)

b. Possible plan: Find the area of each shape (green: 160 ft^2; blue: 49 ft^2; orange: 6.92 ft^2; yellow: 7.07 ft^2). To find the amount of each color, subtract overlapping areas. (Answer: green: $160 - 49 = 111$ ft^2; blue: $49 - 6.92 - 7.07 = 35.01$ ft^2; orange: 6.92 ft^2; yellow: 7.07 ft^2)

2c. Possible plan: A bolt of material allows for 48 in. (or 4 ft) in one direction and any whole number of yards in the other direction.
Green rectangle: The width of the rectangle is divisible by 4. Glue four strips together that are each 10 ft long for a 16 ft-by-10 ft rectangle. Find the total length of the green material needed (40 ft). Find the length in yards ($13\frac{1}{3}$ yd). Then round up. (Answer: 14 yd)
Blue square: The blue square is 7 ft on each side. Since $7 \div 4 = 1\frac{3}{4}$ ft, you need about two strips that are each 7 ft long, or 14 ft. Convert to yards ($4\frac{2}{3}$ yd) and round up. (Answer: 5 yd)

1-1 Nets and Drawings for Visualizing Geometry

Quick Review

A **net** is a two-dimensional pattern that you can fold to form a three-dimensional figure. A net shows all surfaces of a figure in one view.

An **isometric drawing** shows a corner view of a three-dimensional object. It allows you to see the top, front, and side of the object in one view.

An **orthographic drawing** shows three separate views of a three-dimensional object: a top view, a front view, and a right-side view.

Example

Draw a net for the solid at the right.

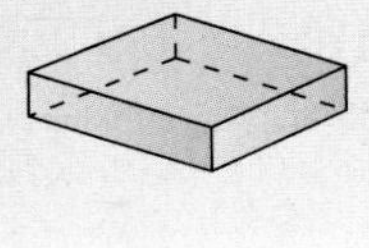

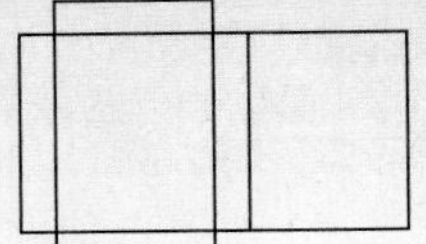

Exercises

5. The net below is for a number cube. What are the three sums of the numbers on opposite surfaces of the cube?

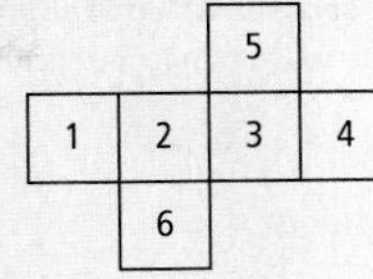

6. Make an orthographic drawing for the isometric drawing at the right. Assume there are no hidden cubes.

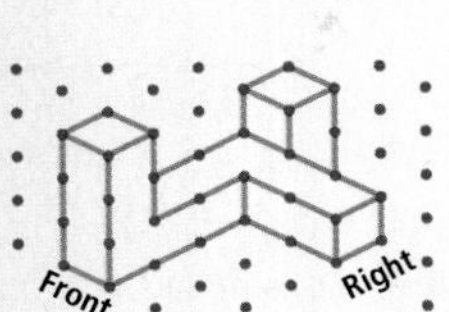

1-2 Points, Lines, and Planes

Quick Review

A **point** indicates a location and has no size.

A **line** is represented by a straight path that extends in two opposite directions without end and has no thickness.

A **plane** is represented by a flat surface that extends without end and has no thickness.

Points that lie on the same line are **collinear points.**

Points and lines in the same plane are **coplanar.**

Segments and **rays** are parts of lines.

Example

Name all the segments and rays in the figure.

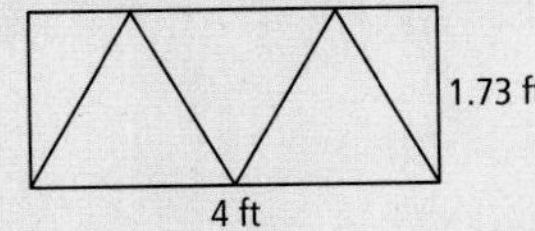

Segments: $\overline{AB}$, $\overline{AC}$, $\overline{BC}$, and $\overline{BD}$

Rays: $\overrightarrow{BA}$, $\overrightarrow{CA}$ or $\overrightarrow{CB}$, $\overrightarrow{AC}$ or $\overrightarrow{AB}$, $\overrightarrow{BC}$, and $\overrightarrow{BD}$

Exercises

Use the figure below for Exercises 7–9.

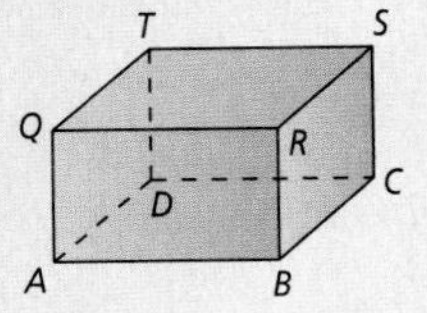

7. Name two intersecting lines.

8. Name the intersection of planes *QRBA* and *TSRQ*.

9. Name three noncollinear points.

Determine whether the statement is *true* or *false*. Explain your reasoning.

10. Two points are always collinear.

11. $\overrightarrow{LM}$ and $\overrightarrow{ML}$ are the same ray.

SOLUTION OUTLINES (continued)

Orange triangle: One side of each triangle is 2 ft. The most economical way to arrange the triangles is

1.73 ft

4 ft

with three whole triangles and two halves. You will need one strip of 1.73 ft (0.58 yd). (Answer: 1 yd)

Yellow circle: The diameter is 3 ft, so the circle fits in one 4-ft width of bolt. You need a 3-ft strip. (Answer: 1 yd)

Answers

Chapter Review

1. angle bisector

2. perpendicular lines

3. net

4. complementary angles

5. 4, 6, 11

6.

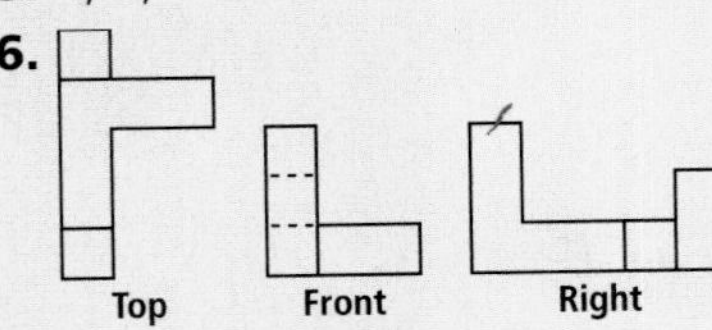

7. Answers may vary. Sample: $\overleftrightarrow{QA}$ and $\overleftrightarrow{AB}$

8. $\overleftrightarrow{QR}$

9. Answers may vary. Sample: *A*, *B*, *C*

10. True; Postulate 1-1 states, "Through any two points, there is exactly one line."

11. False; they have different endpoints.

Answers

Chapter Review (continued)

12. –7, 3

13. $\frac{1}{2}$ or 0.5

14. 15

15. $XY = 21$, $YZ = 29$

16. acute

17. right

18. 36

19. 14

1-3 Measuring Segments

Quick Review

The **distance** between two points is the length of the segment connecting those points. Segments with the same length are **congruent segments.** A **midpoint** of a segment divides the segment into two congruent segments.

Example

Are $\overline{AB}$ and $\overline{CD}$ congruent?

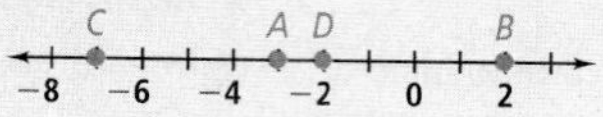

$AB = |-3 - 2| = |-5| = 5$

$CD = |-7 - (-2)| = |-5| = 5$

$AB = CD$, so $\overline{AB} \cong \overline{CD}$.

Exercises

For Exercises 12 and 13, use the number line below.

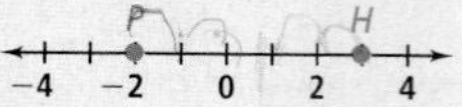

12. Find two possible coordinates of Q such that $PQ = 5$.

13. Use the number line above. Find the coordinate of the midpoint of $\overline{PH}$.

14. Find the value of m.

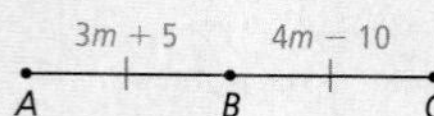

15. If $XZ = 50$, what are XY and YZ?

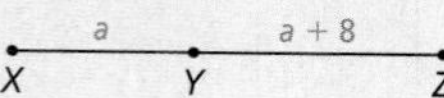

1-4 Measuring Angles

Quick Review

Two rays with the same endpoint form an **angle.** The endpoint is the **vertex** of the angle. You can classify angles as acute, right, obtuse, or straight. Angles with the same measure are **congruent angles.**

Example

If $m\angle AOB = 47$ and $m\angle BOC = 73$, find $m\angle AOC$.

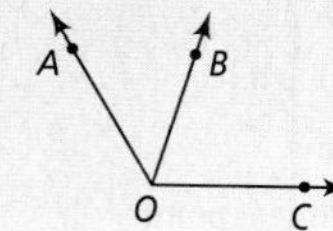

$m\angle AOC = m\angle AOB + m\angle BOC$

$= 47 + 73$

$= 120$

Exercises

Classify each angle as *acute, right, obtuse,* or *straight.*

16. **17.**

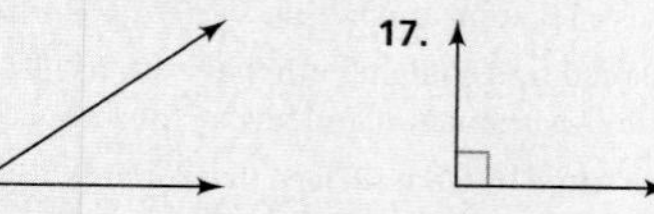

Use the diagram below for Exercises 18 and 19.

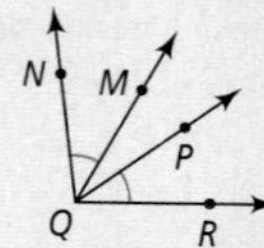

18. If $m\angle MQR = 61$ and $m\angle MQP = 25$, find $m\angle PQR$.

19. If $m\angle NQM = 2x + 8$ and $m\angle PQR = x + 22$, find the value of x.

1-5 Exploring Angle Pairs

Quick Review

Some pairs of angles have special names.

- **Adjacent angles:** coplanar angles with a common side, a common vertex, and no common interior points
- **Vertical angles:** sides are opposite rays
- **Complementary angles:** measures have a sum of 90
- **Supplementary angles:** measures have a sum of 180
- **Linear pair:** adjacent angles with noncommon sides as opposite rays

Angles of a linear pair are supplementary.

Example

Are $\angle ACE$ and $\angle BCD$ vertical angles? Explain.

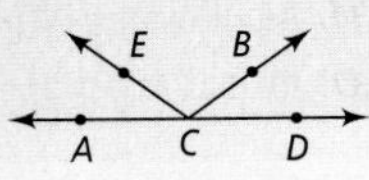

No. They have only one set of sides with opposite rays.

Exercises

Name a pair of each of the following.

20. complementary angles

21. supplementary angles

22. vertical angles

23. linear pair

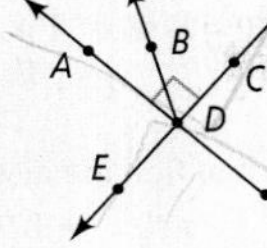

Find the value of x.

24.

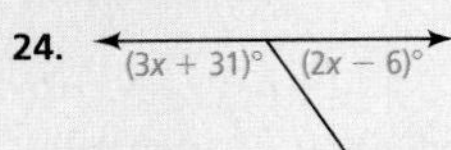

25.

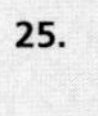
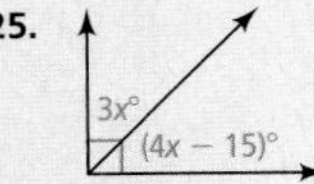

1-6 Basic Constructions

Quick Review

Construction is the process of making geometric figures using a **compass** and a **straightedge**. Four basic constructions involve congruent segments, congruent angles, and bisectors of segments and angles.

Example

Construct $\overline{AB}$ congruent to $\overline{EF}$.

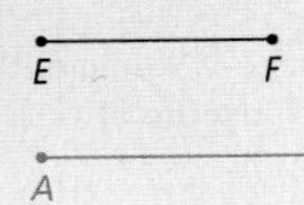

Step 1

Draw a ray with endpoint A.

Step 2

Open the compass to the length of $\overline{EF}$. Keep that compass setting and put the compass point on point A. Draw an arc that intersects the ray. Label the point of intersection B.

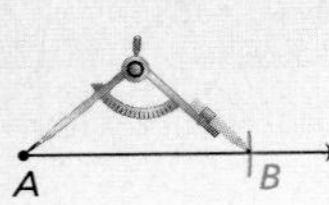

Exercises

26. Use a protractor to draw a 73° angle. Then construct an angle congruent to it.

27. Use a protractor to draw a 60° angle. Then construct the bisector of the angle.

28. Sketch $\overline{LM}$ on paper. Construct a line segment congruent to $\overline{LM}$. Then construct the perpendicular bisector of your line segment.

29. a. Sketch $\angle B$ on paper. Construct an angle congruent to $\angle B$.

b. Construct the bisector of your angle from part (a).

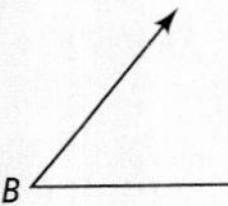

20. Answers may vary. Sample: $\angle ADB$ and $\angle BDC$

21. Answers may vary. Sample: $\angle ADB$ and $\angle BDF$

22. Answers may vary. Sample: $\angle ADC$ and $\angle EDF$

23. Answers may vary. Sample: $\angle ADC$ and $\angle ADE$

24. 31

25. 15

26.

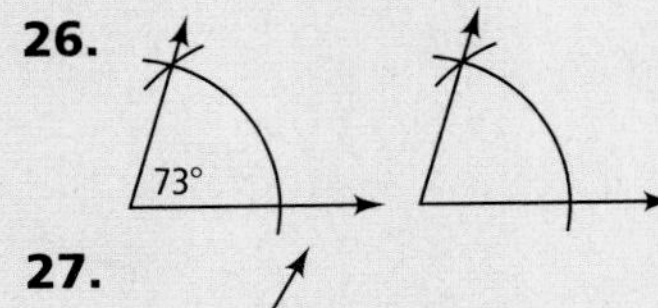

27.

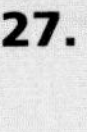
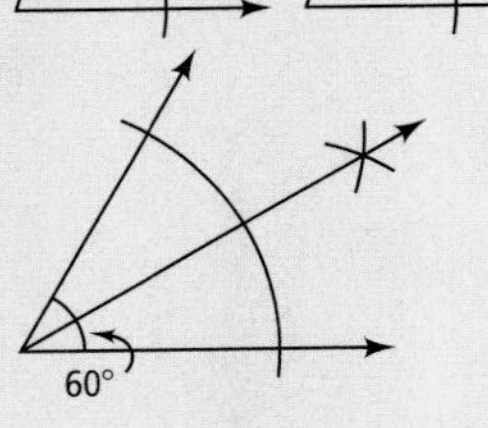

28.

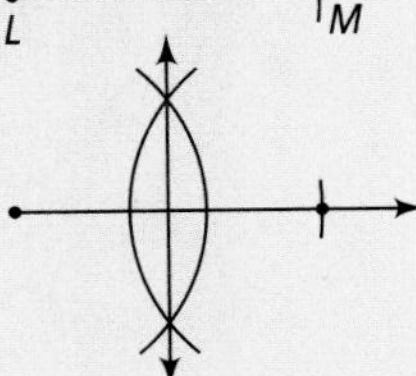

29a–b.

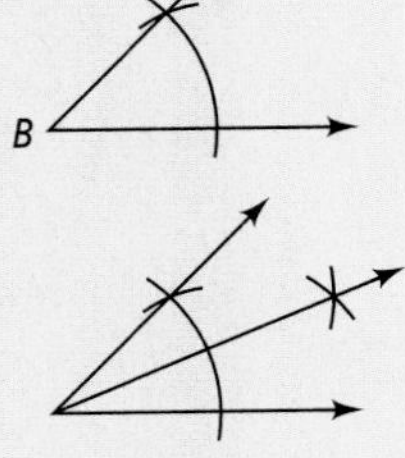

Answers

Chapter Review (continued)

30. 1.4 units
31. 7.6 units
32. 14.4 units
33. (0, 0)
34. 7.2 units
35. (6, −2)
36. (1, 1)
37. (−6, −7)
38. 32 cm; 64 cm^2
39. 32 in.; 40 $in.^2$
40. 6π in.; 9π $in.^2$
41. 15π m; $\frac{225}{4}\pi$ m^2

1-7 Midpoint and Distance in the Coordinate Plane

Quick Review

You can find the coordinates of the midpoint M of $\overline{AB}$ with endpoints $A(x_1, y_1)$ and $B(x_2, y_2)$ using the **Midpoint Formula.**

$$M\left(\frac{x_1 + x_2}{2}, \frac{y_1 + y_2}{2}\right)$$

You can find the distance d between two points $A(x_1, y_1)$ and $B(x_2, y_2)$ using the **Distance Formula.**

$$d = \sqrt{(x_2 - x_1)^2 + (y_2 - y_1)^2}$$

Example

$\overline{GH}$ has endpoints $G(-11, 6)$ and $H(3, 4)$. What are the coordinates of its midpoint M?

x-coordinate $= \frac{-11 + 3}{2} = -4$

y-coordinate $= \frac{6 + 4}{2} = 5$

The coordinates of the midpoint of $\overline{GH}$ are $M(-4, 5)$.

Exercises

Find the distance between the points to the nearest tenth.

30. $A(-1, 5), B(0, 4)$

31. $C(-1, -1), D(6, 2)$

32. $E(-7, 0), F(5, 8)$

$\overline{AB}$ has endpoints $A(-3, 2)$ and $B(3, -2)$.

33. Find the coordinates of the midpoint of $\overline{AB}$.

34. Find AB to the nearest tenth.

M is the midpoint of $\overline{JK}$. Find the coordinates of K.

35. $J(-8, 4), M(-1, 1)$

36. $J(9, -5), M(5, -2)$

37. $J(0, 11), M(-3, 2)$

1-8 Perimeter, Circumference, and Area

Quick Review

The perimeter P of a polygon is the sum of the lengths of its sides. Circles have a circumference C. The area A of a polygon or a circle is the number of square units it encloses.

Square: $P = 4s; A = s^2$

Rectangle: $P = 2b + 2h; A = bh$

Triangle: $P = a + b + c; A = \frac{1}{2}bh$

Circle: $C = \pi d$ or $C = 2\pi r; A = \pi r^2$

Example

Find the perimeter and area of a rectangle with $b = 12$ m and $h = 8$ m.

$P = 2b + 2h$ $A = bh$
$= 2(12) + 2(8)$ $= 12 \cdot 8$
$= 40$ $= 96$

The perimeter is 40 m and the area is 96 m^2.

Exercises

Find the perimeter and area of each figure.

38.

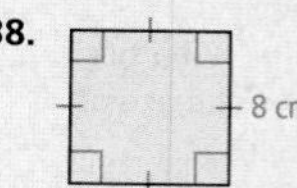

39.

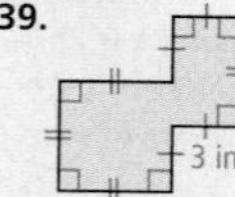

Find the circumference and the area for each circle in terms of π.

40. $r = 3$ in.

41. $d = 15$ m

Chapter Test

Do you know HOW?

1. Draw a net for a cube.

2. Draw an obtuse $\angle ABC$. Use a compass and a straightedge to bisect the angle.

Use the figure for Exercises 3–6.

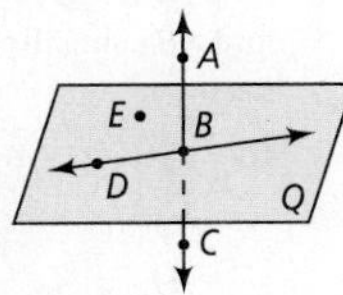

3. Name three collinear points.

4. Name four coplanar points.

5. What is the intersection of $\overleftrightarrow{AC}$ and plane Q?

6. How many planes contain the given line and point?

a. $\overleftrightarrow{DB}$ and point A

b. $\overleftrightarrow{BD}$ and point E

c. $\overleftrightarrow{AC}$ and point D

d. $\overleftrightarrow{EB}$ and point C

7. The running track at the right is a rectangle with a half circle on each end. $\overline{FI}$ and $\overline{GH}$ are diameters. Find the area inside the track to the nearest tenth.

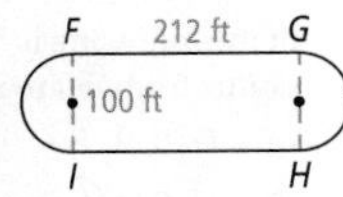

8. Algebra $M(x, y)$ is the midpoint of $\overline{CD}$ with endpoints $C(5, 9)$ and $D(17, 29)$.

a. Find the values of x and y.

b. Show that $MC = MD$.

9. Algebra If $JK = 48$, find the value of x.

J H K
$4x - 15$ $2x + 3$

10. To the nearest tenth, find the perimeter of $\triangle ABC$ with vertices $A(-2, -2)$, $B(0, 5)$, and $C(3, -1)$.

Use the figure to complete each statement.

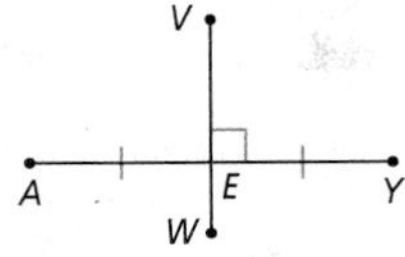

11. $\overline{VW}$ is the __?__ of $\overline{AY}$.

12. If $EY = 3.5$, then $AY =$ __?__.

13. $AE = \frac{1}{2}$ __?__

14. __?__ is the midpoint of __?__.

For the given dimensions, find the area of each figure. If necessary, round to the nearest hundredth.

15. rectangle with base 4 m and height 2 cm

16. square with side length 3.5 in.

17. circle with diameter 9 cm

Algebra **Find the value of the variable.**

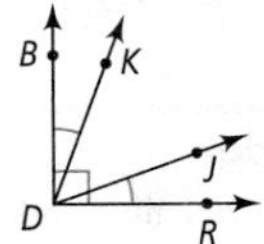

18. $m\angle BDK = 3x + 4$, $m\angle JDR = 5x - 10$

19. $m\angle BDJ = 7y + 2$, $m\angle JDR = 2y + 7$

Do you UNDERSTAND?

Determine whether each statement is *always*, *sometimes*, or *never* true.

20. $\overrightarrow{LJ}$ and $\overrightarrow{TJ}$ are opposite rays.

21. Angles that form a linear pair are supplementary.

22. The intersection of two planes is a point.

23. Complementary angles are congruent.

24. Writing Explain why it is useful to have more than one way to name an angle.

25. You have 30 yd^2 of carpet. You want to install carpeting in a room that is 20 ft long and 15 ft wide. Do you have enough carpet? Explain.

Answers

Chapter Test

1. Answers may vary. Sample:

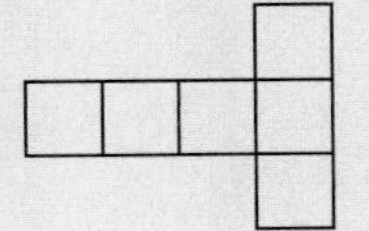

2.

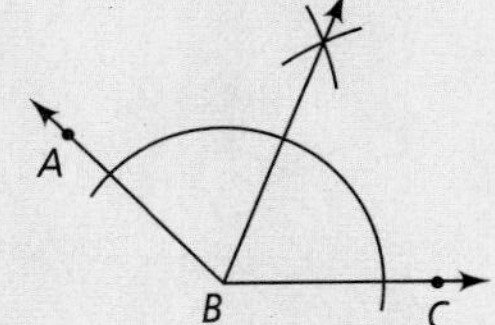

3. Answers may vary. Sample: A, B, C

4. Answers may vary. Sample: A, B, C, E

5. point B

6a. 1 plane

b. 1 plane

c. 1 plane

d. 1 plane

7. 29,054.0 ft^2

8a. $x = 11$, $y = 19$

b. $MC = \sqrt{(5 - 11)^2 + (9 - 19)^2} = \sqrt{36 + 100} = \sqrt{136}$; $MD = \sqrt{(17 - 11)^2 + (29 - 19)^2} = \sqrt{36 + 100} = \sqrt{136}$. So $MC = MD$.

9. 10

10. 19.1 units

11. $\perp$ bis.

12. 7

13. AY

14. E, $\overline{AY}$

15. 800 cm^2 or 0.08 m^2

16. 12.25 $in.^2$

17. 63.62 cm^2

18. 7

19. 9

20. never

21. always

22. never

23. sometimes

24. Answers may vary. Sample: If several $\angle$s have the same vertex, three letters are used to name each $\angle$.

25. No; you need $33\frac{1}{3}$ yd^2 of carpet.

Item	Lesson
1	1-2
2	1-8
3	1-6
4	1-8
5	1-5
6	1-8
7	1-5
8	1-6
9	1-7
10	1-4
11	1-7
12	1-2
13	1-7
14	1-5
15	1-8
16	1-5
17	1-8
18	1-3
19	1-8
20	1-5
21	1-8
22	1-7
23	1-8
24	1-8
25	1-8

1 Cumulative Test Prep

TIPS FOR SUCCESS

Some questions ask you to find a distance using coordinate geometry. Read the sample question at the right. Then follow the tips to answer it.

What is the distance from the midpoint of $\overline{AB}$ to endpoint B?

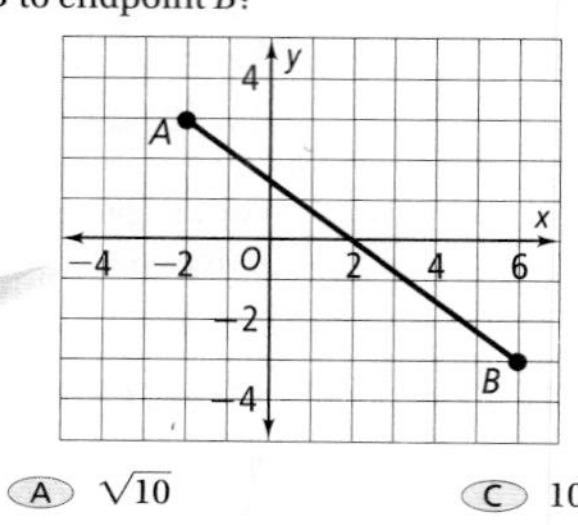

Ⓐ $\sqrt{10}$　Ⓒ 10
Ⓑ 5　Ⓓ 100

TIP 1

The midpoint divides the segment into two congruent segments that are each half of the total length.

TIP 2

Use the Distance Formula to find the length of the segment.

Think It Through

Find AB using the Distance Formula.

$$AB = \sqrt{(-2-6)^2 + [3-(-3)]^2}$$
$$= \sqrt{100}$$
$$= 10$$

The distance from the midpoint of $\overline{AB}$ to endpoint B is $\frac{1}{2}AB$, or 5. The correct answer is B.

Vocabulary Builder

As you solve test items, you must understand the meanings of mathematical terms. Match each term with its mathematical meaning.

A. segment
B. angle bisector
C. construction
D. net
E. congruent angles

I. angles with the same measure
II. a two-dimensional diagram of a three-dimensional figure
III. the part of a line consisting of two endpoints and all points between
IV. a ray that divides an angle into two congruent angles
V. a geometric figure made using a straightedge and compass

Multiple Choice

Read each question. Then write the letter of the correct answer on your paper.

1. Points $A, B, C, D,$ and E are collinear. A is to the right of B, E is to the right of D, and B is to the left of C. Which of the following is NOT a possible arrangement of the points from left to right?

Ⓐ D, B, A, E, C　Ⓒ B, D, E, C, A
Ⓑ D, B, A, C, E　Ⓓ B, A, E, C, D

2. A square and a rectangle have equal area. If the rectangle is 36 cm by 25 cm, what is the perimeter of the square?

Ⓕ 30 cm　Ⓗ 120 cm
Ⓖ 60 cm　Ⓘ 900 cm

Answers

Cumulative Test Prep

A. III
B. IV
C. V
D. II
E. I
1. D
2. H

3. Which construction requires drawing only one arc with a compass?

Ⓐ constructing congruent segments

Ⓑ constructing congruent angles

Ⓒ constructing the perpendicular bisector

Ⓓ constructing the angle bisector

4. Rick paints the four walls in a room that is 12 ft long and 10 ft wide. The ceiling in the room is 8 ft from the floor. The doorway is 3 ft by 7 ft, and the window is 6 ft by 5 ft. If Rick does NOT paint the doorway or window, what is the approximate area that he paints?

Ⓕ 301 ft^2 Ⓗ 331 ft^2

Ⓖ 322 ft^2 Ⓘ 352 ft^2

5. If $\angle A$ and $\angle B$ are supplementary angles, what angle relationship between $\angle A$ and $\angle B$ CANNOT be true?

Ⓐ $\angle A$ and $\angle B$ are right angles.

Ⓑ $\angle A$ and $\angle B$ are adjacent angles.

Ⓒ $\angle A$ and $\angle B$ are complementary angles.

Ⓓ $\angle A$ and $\angle B$ are congruent angles.

6. A net for a small rectangular gift box is shown below. What is the total area of the net?

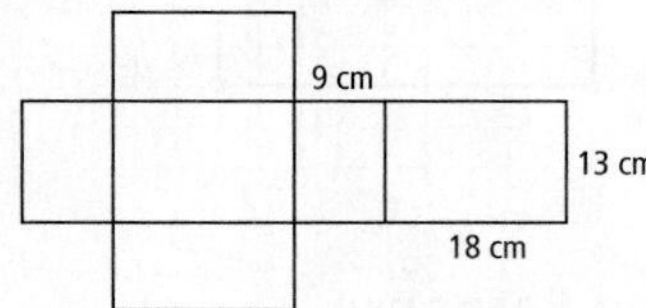

Ⓕ 468 cm^2 Ⓗ 1026 cm^2

Ⓖ 782 cm^2 Ⓘ 2106 cm^2

7. The measure of an angle is 12 less than twice the measure of its supplement. What is the measure of the angle?

Ⓐ 28 Ⓒ 64

Ⓑ 34 Ⓓ 116

8. Given: $\angle A$

What is the second step in constructing the angle bisector of $\angle A$?

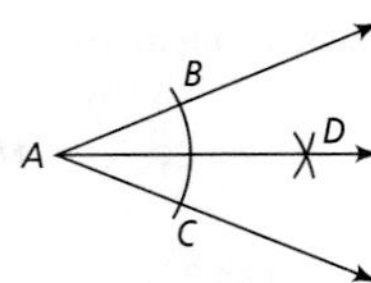

Ⓕ Draw $\overrightarrow{AD}$.

Ⓖ From points B and C, draw equal arcs that intersect at D.

Ⓗ Draw a line segment connecting points B and C.

Ⓘ From point A, draw an arc that intersects the sides of the angle at points B and C.

9. Which two segments are congruent?

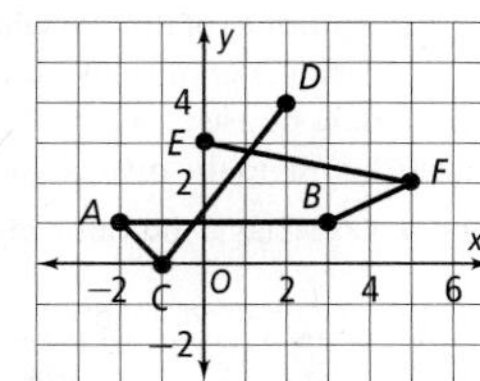

Ⓐ $\overline{AB}$ and $\overline{CD}$ Ⓒ $\overline{CD}$ and $\overline{EF}$

Ⓑ $\overline{EF}$ and $\overline{AB}$ Ⓓ $\overline{AC}$ and $\overline{BF}$

10. Which postulate most closely resembles the Angle Addition Postulate?

Ⓕ Ruler Postulate

Ⓖ Protractor Postulate

Ⓗ Segment Addition Postulate

Ⓘ Area Addition Postulate

11. What is the length of the segment with endpoints $A(1, 7)$ and $B(-3, -1)$?

Ⓐ $\sqrt{40}$ Ⓒ $\sqrt{80}$

Ⓑ 8 Ⓓ 40

3. A
4. F
5. C
6. H
7. D
8. G
9. A
10. H
11. C

Answers

Cumulative Test Prep (continued)

12. I
13. B
14. 6
15. 6.32
16. 45
17. 1361
18. 4.5
19. 9
20. 35
21. 30
22. 10
23. [2] The area of the front surface of the Provolone cheese is $25\pi \approx 78.5\text{ cm}^2$, and the area of the front surface of the American cheese is 81 cm^2. Since a slice of American has more cheese for the same price, American cheese is a better deal.

[1] incomplete OR incorrect explanation

24. [2]

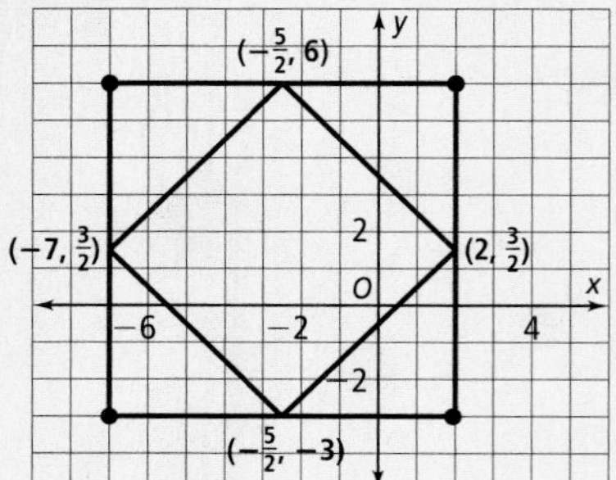

The vertices of the square are $(-7, 6)$, $(2, 6)$, $(2, -3)$, $(-7, -3)$. The midpoints of the top and left sides are $\left(\frac{-7+2}{2}, \frac{6+6}{2}\right) = (-2.5, 6)$ and $\left(\frac{2+2}{2}, \frac{6+(-3)}{2}\right) = (2, 1.5)$. So the length of one side of the "midpoints square" is $\sqrt{(-2.5-2)^2 + (6-1.5)^2} = \sqrt{(-4.5)^2 + (4.5)^2} = \sqrt{40.5}$ and the perimeter of the "midpoints square" is $4 \cdot \sqrt{40.5} \approx 25.46$ units.

[1] incomplete OR incorrect solution

25. [4] **a.** Area of bottom of box is $12\text{ cm} \times 16\text{ cm} = 192\text{ cm}^2$.

b. $6 \cdot 9\pi = 54\pi \approx 169.65\text{ cm}^2$

c. No; the diameter of each can is 6 cm, so three cans across need $3 \cdot 6 = 18$ cm. Since the box is only 16 cm across, the cans will not fit.

[3] a minor computation error, but a correct answer to part (c) OR missing units on parts (a) and (b)

[2] correct answer to part (a) or (b), and an incorrect answer to part (c)

[1] incomplete answer OR incorrect explanation

12. Which of the following does NOT extend forever in at least one direction?

Ⓕ line Ⓗ ray
Ⓖ plane Ⓘ segment

13. Which point is exactly 5 units from $(-10, 4)$?

Ⓐ $(-6, -7)$ Ⓒ $(6, -7)$
Ⓑ $(-6, 7)$ Ⓓ $(6, 7)$

GRIDDED RESPONSE

14. The measure of an angle is 78 less than the measure of its complement. What is the measure of the angle?

15. The face of a circular game token has an area of $10\pi\text{ cm}^2$. What is the diameter of the game token? Round to the nearest hundredth of a centimeter.

16. The measure of an angle is one third the measure of its supplement. What is the measure of the angle?

17. Bill's bike wheels have a 26-in. diameter. The odometer on his bike counts the number of times a wheel rotates during a trip. If the odometer counts 200 rotations during the trip from Bill's house to school, how many feet does Bill travel? Round to the nearest foot.

18. Y is the midpoint of $\overline{XZ}$. What is the value of b?

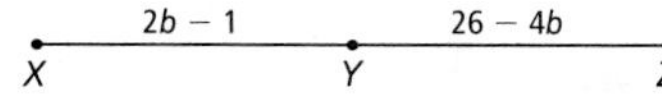

19. A rectangular garden has dimensions 8 ft by 16 ft. If you triple the length of each side of the garden, how many times greater than the original area will the resulting area be?

20. The sum of the measures of a complement and a supplement of an angle is 200. What is the measure of the angle?

21. What is the area in square units of a rectangle with vertices $(-2, 5)$, $(3, 5)$, $(3, -1)$, and $(-2, -1)$?

22. $\overline{AB}$ has endpoints $A(-4, 5)$ and $B(3, 5)$. What is the x-coordinate of a point C such that B is the midpoint of $\overline{AC}$?

Short Response

23. The two blocks of cheese shown below are cut into slices of equal thickness. If the cheese sells at the same cost per slice, which type of cheese slice is the better deal? Explain your reasoning.

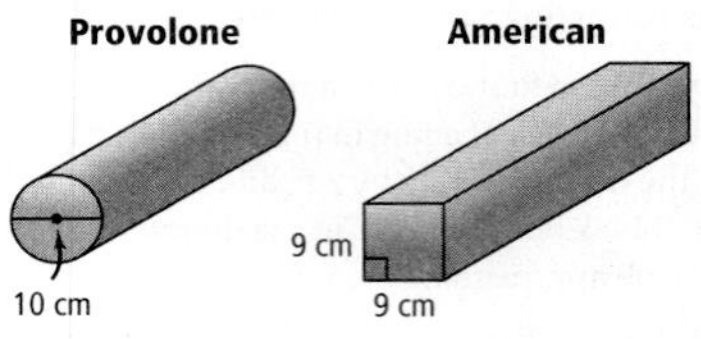

24. Copy the graph below. Connect the midpoints of the sides of the square consecutively. What is the perimeter of the new square? Show your work.

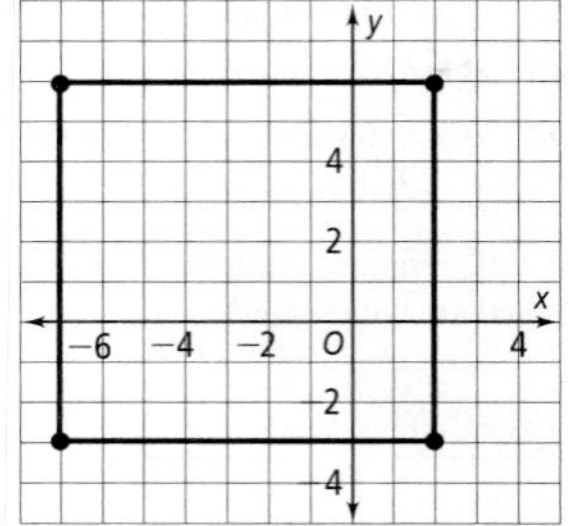

Extended Response

25. A packaging company wants to fit 6 energy-drink cans in a cardboard box, as shown below. The bottom of each can is a circle with an area of $9\pi\text{ cm}^2$.

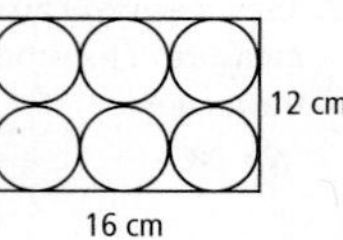

a. What is the area of the bottom of the box?

b. What is the total area taken up by the bottoms of the cans? Round to the nearest hundredth.

c. Will the cans fit in the bottom of the box? Explain.

CHAPTER 2

Get Ready!

Skills Handbook, p. 830

Evaluating Expressions

Algebra **Evaluate each expression for the given value of x.**

1. $9x - 13$ for $x = 7$ **2.** $90 - 3x$ for $x = 31$ **3.** $\frac{1}{2}x + 14$ for $x = 23$

Skills Handbook, p. 834

Solving Equations

Algebra **Solve each equation.**

4. $2x - 17 = 4$
5. $3x + 8 = 53$
6. $(10x + 5) + (6x - 1) = 180$
7. $14x = 2(5x + 14)$
8. $2(x + 4) = x + 13$
9. $7x + 5 = 5x + 17$
10. $(x + 21) + (2x + 9) = 90$
11. $2(3x - 4) + 10 = 5(x + 4)$

Lessons 1-3 through 1-5

Segments and Angles

Use the figure at the right.

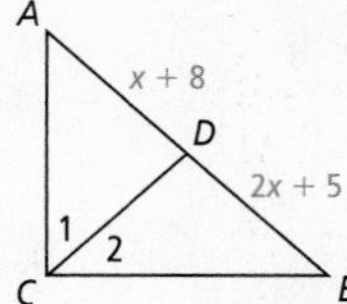

12. Name $\angle 1$ in two other ways.

13. If D is the midpoint of $\overline{AB}$, find the value of x.

14. If $\angle ACB$ is a right angle, $m\angle 1 = 4y$, and $m\angle 2 = 2y + 18$, find $m\angle 1$ and $m\angle 2$.

15. Name a pair of angles that form a linear pair.

16. Name a pair of adjacent angles that are not supplementary.

17. If $m\angle ADC + m\angle BDC = 180$, name the straight angle.

Looking Ahead Vocabulary

18. A scientist often makes an assumption, or *hypothesis*, about a scientific problem. Then the scientist uses experiments to test the *hypothesis* to see if it is true. How might a *hypothesis* in geometry be similar? How might it be different?

19. The *conclusion* of a novel answers questions raised by the story. How do you think the term *conclusion* applies in geometry?

20. A detective uses *deductive reasoning* to solve a case by gathering, combining, and analyzing clues. How might you use *deductive reasoning* in geometry?

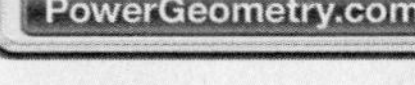

Answers

Get Ready!

1. 50 **2.** −3 **3.** 25.5
4. 10.5 **5.** 15 **6.** 11
7. 7 **8.** 5 **9.** 6
10. 20 **11.** 18
12. $\angle ACD$, $\angle DCA$ **13.** 3
14. $m\angle 1 = 48$, $m\angle 2 = 42$
15. $\angle ADC$ and $\angle CDB$
16. $\angle 1$ and $\angle 2$
17. $\angle ADB$ or $\angle BDA$
18. Answers may vary. Sample: Similar: They are both statements you start with. Different: In geometry you do not try to prove the hypothesis of a statement.
19. Answers may vary. Sample: A conclusion in geometry answers questions raised by the hypothesis.
20. Answers may vary. Sample: In geometry we use deductive reasoning to draw conclusions from other information.

Get Ready!

Assign this diagnostic assessment to determine if students have the prerequisite skills for Chapter 2.

Lesson	Skill
Skills Handbook, p. 830	Evaluating Expressions
Skills Handbook, p. 834	Solving Equations
1-3 through 1-5	Segments and Angles

To remediate students, select from these resources (available for every lesson).

- Online Problems (PowerGeometry.com)
- Reteaching (All-in-One Teaching Resources)
- Practice (All-in-One Teaching Resources)

Why Students Need These Skills

EVALUATING EXPRESSIONS Students will evaluate expressions to find counterexamples to conjectures.

SOLVING EQUATIONS Students will use equation solving skills to evaluate numeric patterns, to determine angle measures, to assess conditional statements, to apply properties of equality, and to develop proof.

SEGMENTS AND ANGLES Students will need to know basic information about segments and angles in order to prove conjectures related to them.

Looking Ahead Vocabulary

HYPOTHESIS Ask students to give examples of how scientists test their hypotheses.

CONCLUSION Have students name other examples in real life that have conclusions.

DEDUCTIVE REASONING Read students a story that involves a mystery. Have them gather clues as you read.

Chapter 2 Overview

UbD Understanding by Design

Chapter 2 introduces topics related to reasoning. Students will learn inductive and deductive reasoning. In this chapter, students will develop the answers to the Essential Questions posed on the opposite page as they learn the concepts and skills bulleted below.

BIG idea Reasoning and Proof

ESSENTIAL QUESTION How can you make a conjecture and prove that it is true?

- Students will observe patterns leading to making conjectures.
- Students will solve equations giving their reasons for each step and connect this to simple proofs.
- Students will prove geometric relationships using given information, definitions, properties, postulates, and theorems.

TN Checks for Understanding

3108.1.6 Use inductive reasoning to write conjectures and/or conditional statements.
3108.1.13 Use proofs to further develop and deepen the understanding of the study of geometry.
3108.1.14 Identify and explain the necessity of postulates, theorems, and corollaries in a mathematical system.
3108.4.2 Compare and contrast inductive reasoning and deductive reasoning for making predictions and valid conclusions based on contextual situations.
3108.4.5 Use vertical, adjacent, complementary, and supplementary angle pairs to solve problems and write proofs.
3108.4.15 Identify, write, and interpret conditional and bi-conditional statements along with the converse, inverse, and contra-positive of a conditional statement.
3108.4.16 Analyze and create truth tables to evaluate conjunctions, disjunctions, conditionals, inverses, contra-positives, and bi-conditionals.
3108.4.17 Use the Law of Detachment, Law of Syllogism, conditional statements, and bi-conditional statements to draw conclusions.
3108.4.18 Use counterexamples, when appropriate, to disprove a statement.

CHAPTER
2

Reasoning and Proof

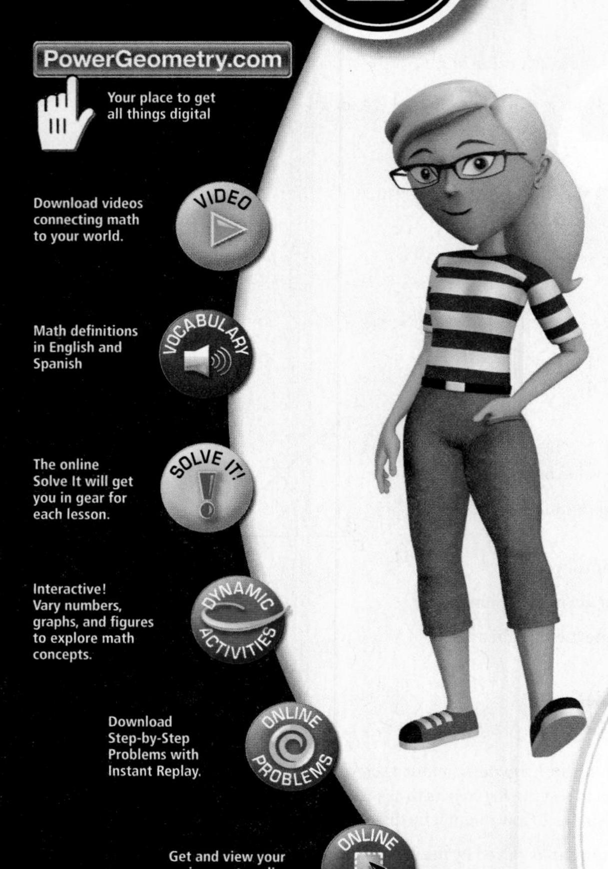

PowerGeometry.com
Your place to get all things digital
Download videos connecting math to your world.
VIDEO
Math definitions in English and Spanish
VOCABULARY
The online Solve It will get you in gear for each lesson.
SOLVE IT!
Interactive! Vary numbers, graphs, and figures to explore math concepts.
DYNAMIC ACTIVITIES
Download Step-by-Step Problems with Instant Replay.
ONLINE PROBLEMS
Get and view your assignments online.
ONLINE HOMEWORK
Extra practice and review online
MathXL FOR SCHOOL

Look at all the dominoes! Whether a domino falls depends on the dominoes before it. In a proof, each statement follows logically from the previous statements.

You'll learn about logical reasoning in this chapter.

Vocabulary

English/Spanish Vocabulary Audio Online:

English	Spanish
biconditional, *p. 98*	bicondicional
conclusion, *p. 89*	conclusión
conditional, *p. 89*	condicional
conjecture, *p. 83*	conjetura
contrapositive, *p. 91*	contrapositivo
converse, *p. 91*	recíproco
deductive reasoning, *p. 106*	razonamiento deductivo
hypothesis, *p. 89*	hipótesis
inductive reasoning, *p. 82*	razonamiento inductivo
inverse, *p. 91*	inverso
negation, *p. 91*	negación
theorem, *p. 120*	teorema

PowerGeometry.com

Chapter 2 Overview

Use these online assets to engage your students. These include support for the Solve It and step-by step solutions for Problems.

Show the student-produced video demonstrating relevant and engaging applications of the new concepts in the chapter.

Find online definitions for new terms in English and Spanish.

Start each lesson with an attention-getting Problem. View the Problem online with helpful hints.

BIG ideas

Reasoning and Proof

Essential Question How can you make a conjecture and prove that it is true?

Chapter Preview

Increase students' depth of knowledge with interactive online activities.

Show Problems from each lesson solved step by step. Instant replay allows students to go at their own pace when studying online.

Assign homework to individual students or to an entire class.

Prepare students for the Mid-Chapter Quiz and Chapter Test with online practice and review.

My Math Video

FACILITATE Use this photo to discuss the concept of "the domino effect." Students already understand that one action may affect other events. This concept will be used to build logical proofs in this chapter.

Q What is the point of the domino structure in the photo? **[The artist will set up the dominos and then knock the first one down. Each domino will then knock the next one down and so on.]**

Q How can the artist be sure that the dominos will all fall? **[The artist must be sure that he has set the dominos the right distances apart so that as one falls it touches the next one hard enough to make it fall.]**

Q Can you describe a situation in real life that you can relate to "domino effect"? **[Answers may vary. Sample: If I study, then I will do well in school. If I do well in school I will get a good job. If I get a good job, I will be able to support myself.]**

In this chapter you will start with facts and use them to logically deduce other true statements. As with dominos, one fact will lead to another.

ERROR PREVENTION

Many students struggle with proofs throughout geometry. Focus on the concept that each statement will logically lead to others. Have students question themselves with every statement: What does this information tell me?

CHAPTER 2

REASONING AND PROOF
Math Background

UbD

Reasoning and Proof

BIG idea Definitions establish meanings and remove possible misunderstanding. Other truths are more complex and difficult to see. It is often possible to verify complex truths by reasoning from simpler ones by using deductive reasoning.

ESSENTIAL UNDERSTANDINGS

2-1 Patterns in some number sequences and some sequences of geometric figures can be used to discover relationships.

2-2 Some mathematical relationships can be described using a variety of if-then statements.

2-3 A definition is good if it can be written as a biconditional.

2-4 Given true statements, deductive reasoning can be used to make a valid or true conclusion.

2-5 Algebraic properties of equality are used in geometry to solve problems and justify reasoning.

2-6 Given information, definitions, properties, postulates, and previously proven theorems can be used as reasons in a proof.

Inductive Reasoning

Inductive reasoning uses observed patterns to draw conclusions. With inductive reasoning you cannot be sure that your conclusion is valid. The patterns are assumed to continue. This is why the result of inductive reasoning is often called a conjecture.

For example, students might conjecture that the number sequence 1, 2, 4 will be continued with 8 and 16 ($1 \cdot 2 = 2$, $2 \cdot 2 = 4$, $4 \cdot 2 = 8$, $8 \cdot 2 = 16$). The sequence can also be continued with 7 and 11 ($1 + 1 = 2$, $2 + 2 = 4$, $4 + 3 = 7$, $7 + 4 = 11$).

A *counterexample* disproves an inductive conjecture. A *counterexample* is a single example that shows that the conjecture is not true.

Common Errors With Inductive Reasoning

Students might conjecture by inductive reasoning without considering possible counterexamples.

For example, if three lines are randomly generated on a coordinate plane, the three lines may form a triangle, as shown below.

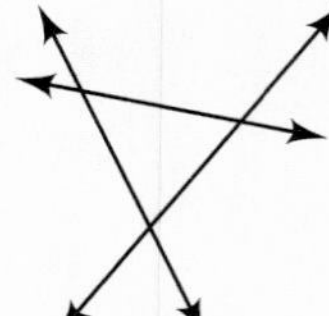

It is possible that such a triangle might be formed for each of thousands of attempts. It may be tempting to conjecture that three lines on the coordinate plane always form a triangle.

However the following counterexample is possible

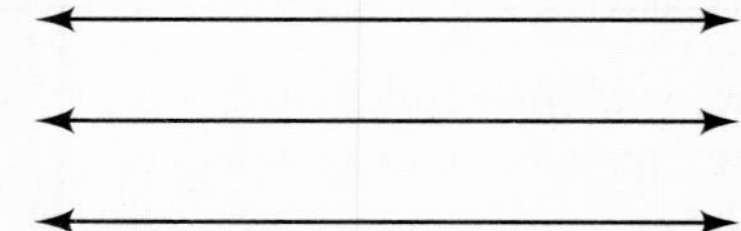

Deductive Reasoning

Deductive reasoning uses accepted properties, postulates, or theorems to create a string of logically connected statements. The conclusion of deductive reasoning is valid as long as the methods used to draw the conclusion are correct. There are two universally accepted Laws of Logic that are presented in this chapter.

Law of Syllogism	Law of Detachment
If $p \rightarrow q$ is true and $q \rightarrow r$ is true, then $p \rightarrow r$ is true	If $p \rightarrow q$ is true and p is true, then q is true

Valid Arguments

An argument is only valid if the logic it uses is correct. For example:

Premise: All rectangles are quadrilaterals.
Premise: A square is a rectangle.
Conclusion: A square is a quadrilateral.

This argument is valid because it uses the Law of Detachment.

Invalid Arguments

A conclusion that does not follow from the premises is invalid.

Premise: All rectangles are quadrilaterals.
Premise: A square is a rectangle.
Conclusion: A quadrilateral is a rectangle.

The Law of Detachment was not followed, and the conclusion is invalid: A quadrilateral is not necessarily a rectangle.

Common Errors With Deductive Reasoning

Students might incorrectly use the Law of Detachment. They may see that the conclusion of a statement is true and assume that the premise is true.

If two triangles are congruent, then they are similar.
Two triangles are similar.
Therefore, the two triangles are congruent.

This is not a valid conclusion. Similar triangles are not necessarily congruent.

Types of Proof

Proofs can be written in two-column, flow chart, or paragraph formats.

In a *two-column proof*, statements are listed in the first column and the reasons that justify them are listed in the second column.

Given: $-8x - 16 = 2x + 4$

Prove: $x = -2$

Statement	Reason
1) $-8x - 16 = 2x + 4$	**1)** Given
2) $-10x - 16 = 4$	**2)** Subtraction Property of Equality
3) $-10x = 20$	**3)** Addition Property of Equality
4) $x = -2$	**4)** Division Property of Equality

In a *flow proof*, statements are connected with arrows that indicate how one statement follows logically from another.

$-8x - 16 = 2x + 4$
Given

$-10x - 16 = 4$
Subtraction Property of Equality

$-10x = 20$
Addition Property of Equality

$x = -2$
Division Property of Equality

A *paragraph proof* is a proof in paragraph form.

$-8x - 16 = 2x + 4$ is given. Subtract $2x$ from both sides to get $-10x - 16 = 4$. Then add 16 to both sides to get $-10x = 20$. Divide both sides by -10. So $x = -2$.

Common Errors With Proofs

Working with proofs is often a daunting task for many students. The number of mathematical properties, theorems, definitions, etc. can be overwhelming. Some students may benefit from working backward. Have them start with the statement they'd like to prove and identify what information is needed to get to that statement.

CHAPTER 2

REASONING AND PROOF

Pacing and Assignment Guide

		TRADITIONAL			BLOCK
Lesson	**Teaching Day(s)**	**Basic**	**Average**	**Advanced**	**Block**
2-1	**1**	Problems 1–3 Exs. 6–30	Problems 1–3 Exs. 7–29 odd, 38–49	Problems 1–3 Exs. 7–29 odd, 38–49	**Day 1** Problems 1–5 Exs. 7–37 odd, 38–55, 59–66
	2	Problems 4–5 Exs. 31–40, 50, 53–54, 59–66	Problems 4–5 Exs. 31–37 odd, 50–55, 59–66	Problems 4–5 Exs. 31–37 odd, 50–66	
2-2	**1**	Problems 1–4 Exs. 5–24, 28–29, 35, 37, 39–40, 47–58	Problems 1–4 Exs. 5–23 odd, 25–42, 47–58	Problems 1–4 Exs. 5–23 odd, 25–58	**Day 2** Problems 1–4 Exs. 5–23 odd, 25–42, 47–58
2-3	**1**	Problems 1–4 Exs. 7–30, 33, 35–36, 43, 45, 49–57	Problems 1–4 Exs. 7–30, 33, 35–36, 43, 45, 49–57	Problems 1–4 Exs. 7–29 odd, 30–57	Problems 1–4 Exs. 7–30, 33, 35–36, 43, 45, 49–57
2-4	**1**	Problems 1–3 Exs. 6–21, 26, 28, 30, 33–39	Problems 1–3 Exs. 7–17 odd, 18–30, 33–39	Problems 1–3 Exs. 7–17 odd, 18–39	**Day 3** Problems 1–3 Exs. 7–17 odd, 18–30, 33–39
2-5	**1**	Problems 1–3 Exs. 5–17, 20, 22, 23, 29–41	Problems 1–3 Exs. 5–13 odd, 14–24, 29–41	Problems 1–3 Exs. 5–13 odd, 14–41	Problems 1–3 Exs. 5–13 odd, 14–24, 29–41
2-6	**1**	Problems 1–2 Exs. 6–12, 36–48	Problems 1–2 Exs. 7–11 odd, 36–48	Problems 1–2 Exs. 7–11 odd, 36–48	**Day 4** Problems 1–2 Exs. 7–13 odd, 14–30, 36–48
	2	Problem 3 Exs. 13–14, 16, 20–21, 25, 26, 28	Problem 3 Exs. 13–30	Problem 3 Exs. 13–35	
Review	**1**	Chapter 2 Review	Chapter 2 Review	Chapter 2 Review	**Day 5** Chapter 2 Review Chapter 2 Test
Assess	**1**	Chapter 2 Test	Chapter 2 Test	Chapter 2 Test	
Total		**10 Days**	**10 Days**	**10 Days**	**5 Days**

Note: Pacing does not include Concept Bytes and other feature pages.

Resources

KEY

I = Interactive asset at PowerGeometry.com
E = Editable master at PowerGeometry.com
P = Available in Print
T = Available as a Transparency
M = Master at PowerGeometry.com
✓= CD-ROM

	For the Chapter	2-1	2-2	2-3	2-4	2-5	2-6
Planning							
Teacher Center Online Planner & Grade Book	I	I	I	I	I	I	I
Interactive Learning & Guided Instruction							
My Math Video	I						
Solve It!		I TM	I TM	I TM	I TM	I TM	I TM
Student Companion (SP)*		P M	P M	P M	P M	P M	
Vocabulary Support		I P M	I P M	I P M	I P M	I P M	I P M
Got It? Support		I P	I P	I P	I P	I P	I P
Dynamic Activity			I	I			
Online Problems		I	I	I	I	I	I
Additional Problems		M	M	M	M	M	M
English Language Learner Support (TR)		E P M	E P M	E P M	E P M	E P M	E P M
Activities, Games, and Puzzles		E M	E M	E M	E M	E M	E M
Teaching With TI Technology With CD-ROM						✓ P	✓ P
TI-Nspire™ Support CD-ROM		✓	✓	✓	✓	✓	✓
Lesson Check & Practice							
Student Companion (SP)*		P M	P M	P M	P M	P M	P M
Lesson Check Support		I P	I P	I P	I P	I P	I P
Practice and Problem Solving Workbook (SP)		P	P	P	P	P	P
Think About a Plan (TR)*		E P M	E P M	E P M	E P M	E P M	E P M
Practice Form G (TR)*		E P M	E P M	E P M	E P M	E P M	E P M
Standardized Test Prep (TR)*		P M	P M	P M	P M	P M	P M
Practice *Form K* (TR)*		E P M	E P M	E P M	E P M	E P M	E P M
Extra Practice	E M						
Find the Errors!	M						
Enrichment (TR)		E P M	E P M	E P M	E P M	E P M	E P M
Answers and Solutions CD-ROM	✓	✓	✓	✓	✓	✓	✓
Assess & Remediate							
ExamView CD-ROM	✓	✓	✓	✓	✓	✓	✓
Lesson Quiz		I TM	I TM	I TM	I TM	I TM	I TM
Quizzes and Tests *Form G* (TR)*	E P M			E P M			E P M
Quizzes and Tests *Form K* (TR)*	E P M			E P M			E P M
Reteaching (TR)*		E P M	E P M	E P M	E P M	E P M	E P M
Performance Tasks (TR)*	P M						
Cumulative Review (TR)*	P M						
Progress Monitoring Assessments	I P M						

(TR) Available in All-In-One Teaching Resources * Spanish available

1 Interactive Learning

Solve It!

PURPOSE To solve a problem using inductive reasoning

PROCESS Students may collect data to identify and extrapolate a pattern.

FACILITATE

Q How many rectangles do you expect to get if you fold the paper a third time? Explain. **[Eight; the number of rectangles doubles with each fold.]**

Q How can you use your answer to the previous question to answer the Solve It? **[Test the pattern for four folds. Modify if necessary, and then use the pattern for eight folds.]**

ANSWER See Solve It in Answers on next page.

CONNECT THE MATH In the Solve It students identified and extrapolated a pattern. In this lesson, students will recognize patterns in numeric and geometric sequences.

2 Guided Instruction

Problem 1

Q Is there a way to determine the 12th term in the sequence for 1B without knowing the 11th term? Explain. **[Yes, the 12th term is a circle enclosing a polygon with 12 + 2 = 14 sides.]**

Got It?

Q How many quadrilaterals will be drawn to complete the 4th term for 1b? **[4]**

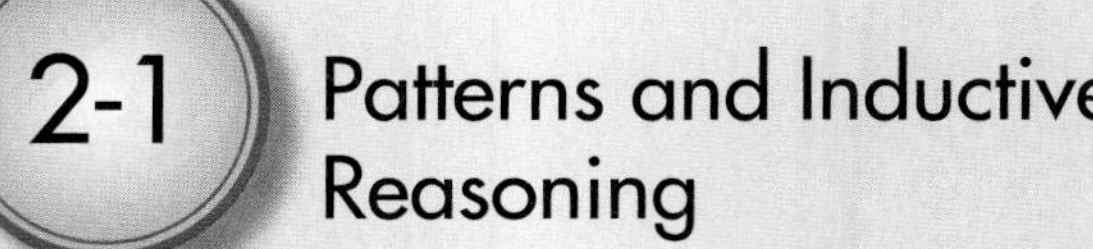

2-1 Patterns and Inductive Reasoning

Objective To use inductive reasoning to make conjectures

You could keep folding the paper, but there's an easier way.

Getting Ready!

Fold a piece of paper in half. When you unfold it, the paper is divided into two rectangles. Refold the paper, and then fold it in half again. This time when you unfold it, there are four rectangles. How many rectangles would you get if you folded a piece of paper in half eight times? Explain.

Lesson Vocabulary
- inductive reasoning
- conjecture
- counterexample

In the Solve It, you may have used inductive reasoning. **Inductive reasoning** is reasoning based on patterns you observe.

Essential Understanding You can observe patterns in some number sequences and some sequences of geometric figures to discover relationships.

Problem 1 Finding and Using a Pattern

Plan

How do you *look for a pattern* in a sequence? Look for a relationship between terms. Test that the relationship is consistent throughout the sequence.

Look for a pattern. What are the next two terms in each sequence?

A 3, 9, 27, 81, . . .

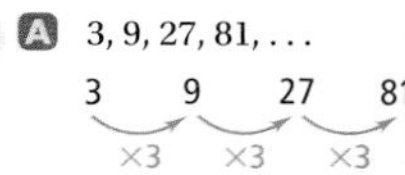

Each term is three times the previous term. The next two terms are $81 \times 3 = 243$ and $243 \times 3 = 729$.

B

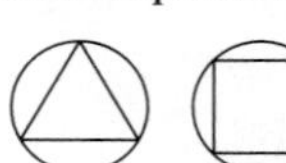

Each circle contains a polygon that has one more side than the preceding polygon. The next two circles contain a six-sided and a seven-sided polygon.

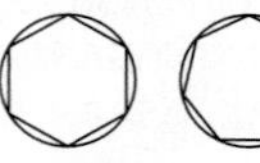

Got It? **1.** What are the next two terms in each sequence?

a. 45, 40, 35, 30, . . .

b. 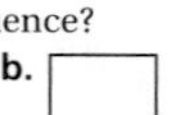  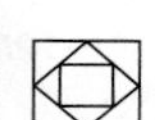

2-1 Preparing to Teach

BIG idea Reasoning and Proof

ESSENTIAL UNDERSTANDINGS
- Patterns in some number sequences and some sequences of geometric figures can be used to discover relationships.
- Conjectures are not valid unless they are proven true.
- One counterexample can prove that a conjecture is false.

Math Background

Inductive reasoning is the process of identifying a pattern based on limited data. Deductive reasoning, on the other hand, is the process of concluding that a relationship is true because it is a particular case of a general principle that is known to be true. Both types of reasoning are important to mathematical thinking. Mathematicians observe particular cases and then use inductive reasoning to make conjectures. Conjectures are proved to be true by means of deductive reasoning in a mathematical proof.

Support Student Learning

Use the **Geometry Companion** to engage and support students during instructions. See Lesson Resources at the end of this lesson for details.

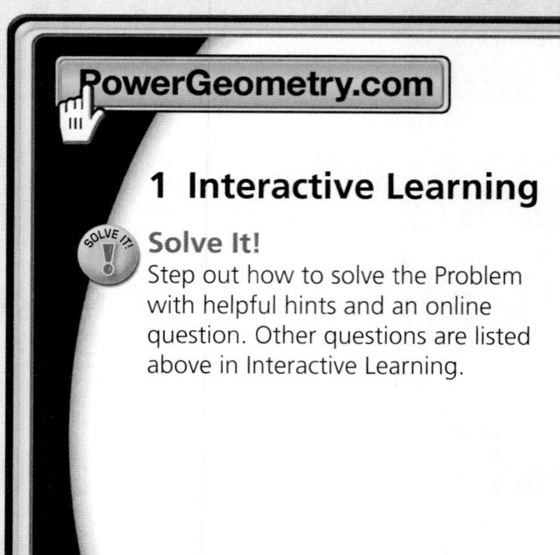

You may want to find the tenth or the one-hundredth term in a sequence. In this case, rather than find every previous term, you can look for a pattern and make a conjecture. A **conjecture** is a conclusion you reach using inductive reasoning.

Problem 2 Using Inductive Reasoning

Plan

Do you need to draw a circle with 20 diameters?
No. *Solve a simpler problem* by finding the number of regions formed by 1, 2, and 3 diameters. Then look for a pattern.

Look at the circles. What conjecture can you make about the number of regions 20 diameters form?

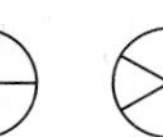

1 diameter forms 2 regions.

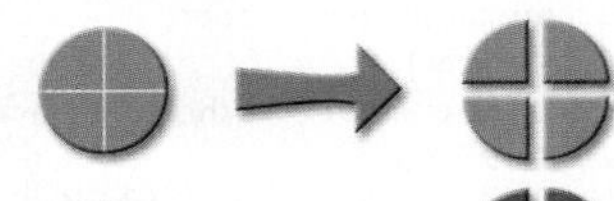
2 diameters form 4 regions.

3 diameters form 6 regions.

Each circle has twice as many regions as diameters. Twenty diameters form $20 \cdot 2$, or 40 regions.

Got It? **2.** What conjecture can you make about the twenty-first term in R, W, B, R, W, B, . . . ?

It is important to gather enough data before you make a conjecture. For example, you do not have enough information about the sequence 1, 3, . . . to make a reasonable conjecture. The next term could be $3 \cdot 3 = 9$ or $3 + 2 = 5$.

Problem 3 Collecting Information to Make a Conjecture

Plan

What's the first step?
Start by gathering data. You can organize your data by *making a table*.

What conjecture can you make about the sum of the first 30 even numbers?

Find the first few sums and look for a pattern.

Number of Terms	Sum
1	$2 = 2 = 1 \cdot 2$
2	$2 + 4 = 6 = 2 \cdot 3$
3	$2 + 4 + 6 = 12 = 3 \cdot 4$
4	$2 + 4 + 6 + 8 = 20 = 4 \cdot 5$

Each sum is the product of the number of terms and the number of terms plus one.

You can conclude that the sum of the first 30 even numbers is $30 \cdot 31$, or 930.

Got It? **3.** What conjecture can you make about the sum of the first 30 odd numbers?

Problem 2

Q How might you test the pattern you discover in the first four circles before making a conjecture about the 20th circle? **[Use the pattern to make a conjecture about a circle with five diameters, and then draw the circle and diameters to test the conjecture.]**

Q How is the number of regions of each successive circle related to the number of regions in the previous circle? **[There are two more regions in each circle than in the previous circle.]**

Got It?

Q How can you tell if a term will be an "R"? **[When divided by 3, the term number has a remainder of 1.]**

Problem 3

Q How are successive sums related to one another? **[The difference from one sum to the next increases by 2 each time.]**

Q How can you use the number of terms to determine the sum of the numbers? **[You multiply the number of terms by the number of terms plus one.]**

Got It?

Q What conjecture can you make about the sum of the first 30 natural numbers? **[The sum is $\frac{(30 \cdot 31)}{2} = 465$.]**

2 Guided Instruction

Each Problem is worked out and supported online.

Problem 1
Finding and Using a Pattern

Problem 2
Using Inductive Reasoning
Animated

Problem 3
Collecting Information to Make a Conjecture

Problem 4
Making a Prediction
Animated

Problem 5
Finding a Counterexample
Animated

Support in Geometry Companion
- Vocabulary
- Key Concepts
- Got It?

Answers

Solve It!

256; each fold produces twice as many rectangles as the previous fold.

Got It?

1a. 25, 20

b. 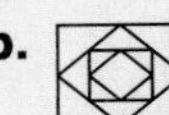 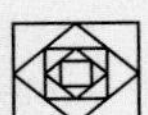

2. Every 3rd term is B, so the 21st term will be B.

3. The sum of the first 30 odd numbers is 30^2, or 900.

Problem 4

Q How could you use the April sales figure to estimate the May sales figure? **[Subtract 500 from the April sales figure.]**

Q How could you use the November sales figure to estimate the May sales figure? **[Subtract 500 times 6 from the November sales figure.]**

Got It?

Ask students to identify the *y*-intercept, slope, and an equation of the line. Have students estimate the June sales by using the equation of the line.

Problem 5

Q How can you modify the statement in 5B so that there are no counterexamples? **[You can connect any three noncollinear points to form a triangle.]**

Q If you replace the word "number" in 5C with "whole number," what number would provide the only counterexample to the statement? **[0, because $0 \cdot 2 = 0$, and 0 is not greater than 0.]**

Got It?

Make sure that students understand that while one counterexample can prove a conjecture false, no number of examples can prove a conjecture true.

Problem 4 Making a Prediction

Plan

How can you use the given data to make a prediction? *Look for a pattern* of points on the graph. Then make a prediction, based on the pattern, about where the next point will be.

Sales **Sales of backpacks at a nationwide company decreased over a period of six consecutive months. What conjecture can you make about the number of backpacks the company will sell in May?**

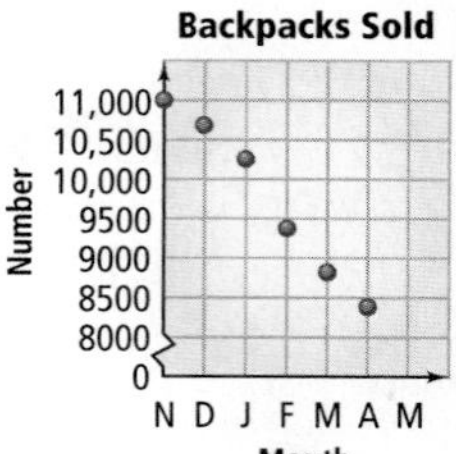

The points seem to fall on a line. The graph shows the number of sales decreasing by about 500 backpacks each month. By inductive reasoning, you can estimate that the company will sell approximately 8000 backpacks in May.

Got It? **4. a.** What conjecture can you make about backpack sales in June?

b. Reasoning Is it reasonable to use this graph to make a conjecture about sales in August? Explain.

Not all conjectures turn out to be true. You should test your conjecture multiple times. You can prove that a conjecture is false by finding *one* counterexample. A **counterexample** is an example that shows that a conjecture is incorrect.

Problem 5 Finding a Counterexample

What is a counterexample for each conjecture?

A **If the name of a month starts with the letter J, it is a summer month.**

Counterexample: January starts with J and it is a winter month.

B **You can connect any three points to form a triangle.**

Counterexample: If the three points lie on a line, you cannot form a triangle.

These three points support the conjecture . . . . . . but these three points are a counterexample to the conjecture.

Think

What numbers should you *guess-and-check*? Try positive numbers, negative numbers, fractions, and special cases like zero.

C **When you multiply a number by 2, the product is greater than the original number.**

The conjecture is true for positive numbers, but it is false for negative numbers and zero.

Counterexample: $-4 \cdot 2 = -8$ and $-8 \not> -4$.

Got It? **5.** What is a counterexample for each conjecture?

a. If a flower is red, it is a rose.

b. One and only one plane exists through any three points.

c. When you multiply a number by 3, the product is divisible by 6.

Additional Problems

1. Look for a pattern. What are the next two terms in each sequence?

a. 4, 8, 16, 32, . . .

b.

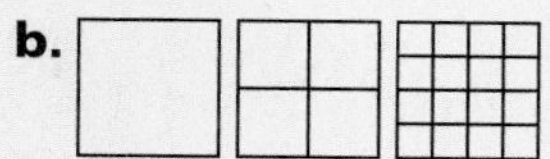

ANSWER **a.** 64, 128

b.

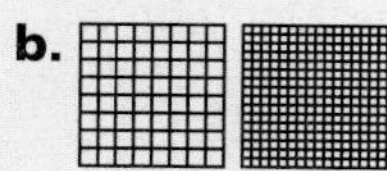

2. What conjecture can you make about the 25th term in 1, 2, 3, 1, 2, 3, . . .?

ANSWER The 25th term will be 1.

3. What conjecture can you make about the sum of the first 40 even numbers?

ANSWER The sum of the first 40 even numbers is 1640.

4. Sales of tickets at an amusement park increased over a period of four consecutive months. What conjecture can you make about the number of tickets the park will sell in February?

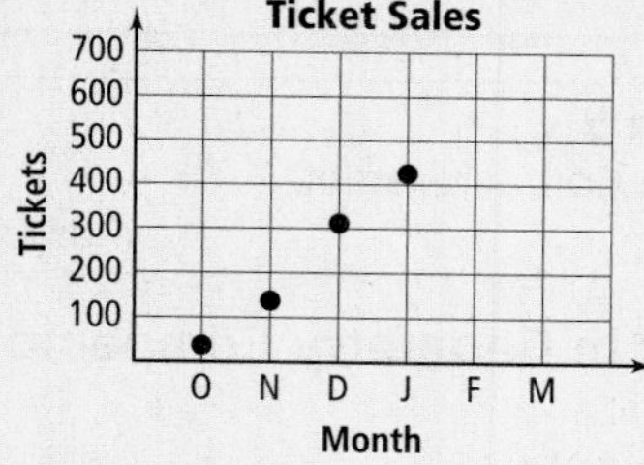

ANSWER The park will sell about 600 tickets in February.

5. What is a counterexample for each conjecture?

a. If an animal is green, it is a frog.

b. Any three segments form a triangle.

c. When you multiply a number by 2, the product is divisible by 4.

ANSWER **a.** Sample: A turtle is green, but a turtle is not a frog. **b.** Sample: Segments with lengths 3 in., 6 in., and 10 cm cannot form a triangle. If the 10 cm segment has the 3 in. segment on one end and the 6 in. segment on the other end, the two smaller segments will not touch. **c.** Sample: $3 \times 2 = 6$, but 6 is not divisible by 4.

Lesson Check

Do you know HOW?

What are the next two terms in each sequence?

1. 7, 13, 19, 25, . . .

2. 

3. What is a counterexample for the following conjecture?

All four-sided figures are squares.

Do you UNDERSTAND?

4. **Vocabulary** How does the word *counter* help you understand the term *counterexample*?

5. **Compare and Contrast** Clay thinks the next term in the sequence 2, 4, . . . is 6. Given the same pattern, Ott thinks the next term is 8, and Stacie thinks the next term is 7. What conjecture is each person making? Is there enough information to decide who is correct?

Practice and Problem-Solving Exercises

A Practice

Find a pattern for each sequence. Use the pattern to show the next two terms. See Problem 1.

6. 5, 10, 20, 40, . . .
7. 1, 4, 9, 16, 25, . . .
8. 1, −1, 2, −2, 3, . . .
9. $1, \frac{1}{2}, \frac{1}{4}, \frac{1}{8}, \ldots$
10. $1, \frac{1}{2}, \frac{1}{3}, \frac{1}{4}, \ldots$
11. 15, 12, 9, 6, . . .
12. O, T, T, F, F, S, S, E, . . .
13. J, F, M, A, M, . . .
14. 1, 2, 6, 24, 120, . . .
15. Washington, Adams, Jefferson, . . .
16. dollar coin, half dollar, quarter, . . .
17. AL, AK, AZ, AR, CA, . . .
18. Aquarius, Pisces, Aries, Taurus, . . .
19. 
20.

Use the sequence and inductive reasoning to make a conjecture. See Problem 2.

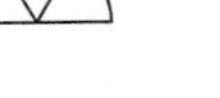

21. What is the color of the fifteenth figure?
22. What is the shape of the twelfth figure?
23. What is the color of the thirtieth figure?
24. What is the shape of the fortieth figure?

Make a conjecture for each scenario. Show your work. See Problem 3.

25. the sum of the first 100 positive odd numbers
26. the sum of the first 100 positive even numbers
27. the sum of two odd numbers
28. the sum of an even and odd number
29. the product of two even numbers
30. the product of two odd numbers

3 Lesson Check

Do you know HOW?

- If students have difficulty with Exercise 3, have them draw a figure that satisfies both conditions of the conjecture. Then have them draw a figure that satisfies the first condition, but not the second.

Do you UNDERSTAND?

- If students have difficulty with Exercise 4, then ask them to explain the difference between *clockwise* and *counterclockwise* or between *productive* and *counterproductive*.

Close

Q How do you use inductive reasoning to make a conjecture? **[Analyze a limited number of cases to find a pattern, then use the pattern to make a conjecture about other cases.]**

Answers

Got It? (continued)

4a. Sales will be about 500 fewer than 8000, or 7500.

b. No; explanations may vary. Sample: sales may increase because students may want backpacks for school.

5a–c. Answers may vary. Samples are given.

a. A carnation can be red, and it is not a rose.

b. When three points are collinear, the number of planes that can be drawn through them is infinite.

c. When you multiply 5 (or any odd number) by 3, the product is not divisible by 6.

Lesson Check

1. 31, 37

2.

G	P
B	R

B	G
R	P

3. Answers may vary. Sample: any nonsquare rectangle

4. One meaning of *counter* is "against," so a counterexample is an example that goes against a statement.

5. In the pattern 2, 4, . . . , the next term is 6 if the rule is "add 2"; the next term is 8 if the rule is "double the previous term"; and the next term is 7 if the rule is "add 2, then add 3, then add 4, . . ." Just giving the first 2 terms does not give enough information to describe the pattern.

Practice and Problem-Solving Exercises

6–30. See next page.

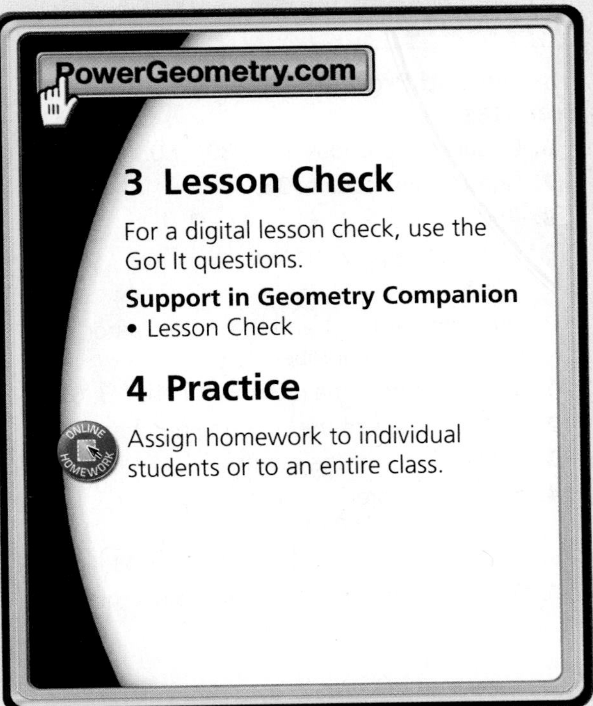

PowerGeometry.com

3 Lesson Check

For a digital lesson check, use the Got It questions.

Support in Geometry Companion

- Lesson Check

4 Practice

Assign homework to individual students or to an entire class.

4 Practice

ASSIGNMENT GUIDE
Basic: 6–40, 50, 53–54
Average: 7–37 odd, 38–55
Advanced: 7–37 odd, 38–58
Standardized Test Prep: 59–61
Mixed Review: 62–66
Reasoning exercises have blue headings.
Applications exercises have red headings.
EXERCISE 54: Use the Think About a Plan worksheet in the **Practice and Problem Solving Workbook** (also available in the Teaching Resources in print and online) to further support students' development in becoming independent learners.

HOMEWORK QUICK CHECK
To check students' understanding of key skills and concepts, go over Exercises 11, 35, 40, 50, and 54.

Weather **Use inductive reasoning to make a prediction about the weather.** See Problem 4.

31. Lightning travels much faster than thunder, so you see lightning before you hear thunder. If you count 5 s between the lightning and thunder, how far away is the storm?

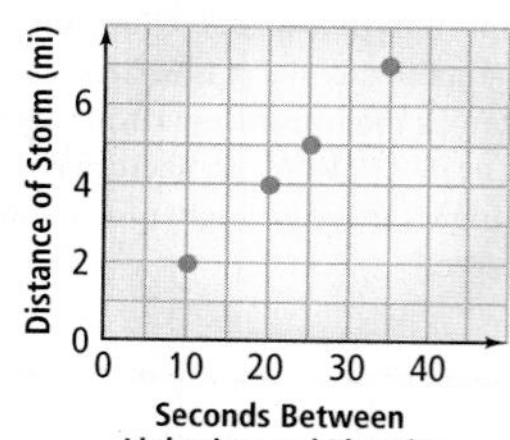

32. The speed at which a cricket chirps is affected by the temperature. If you hear 20 cricket chirps in 14 s, what is the temperature?

Number of Chirps per 14 Seconds	Temperature (°F)
5	45
10	55
15	65

Find one counterexample to show that each conjecture is false. See Problem 5.

33. $\angle 1$ and $\angle 2$ are supplementary, so one of the angles is acute.

34. $\triangle ABC$ is a right triangle, so $\angle A$ measures 90.

35. The sum of two numbers is greater than either number.

36. The product of two positive numbers is greater than either number.

37. The difference of two integers is less than either integer.

B Apply

Find a pattern for each sequence. Use inductive reasoning to show the next two terms.

38. 1, 3, 7, 13, 21, . . .

39. 1, 2, 5, 6, 9, . . .

40. 0.1, 0.01, 0.001, . . .

41. 2, 6, 7, 21, 22, 66, 67, . . .

42. 1, 3, 7, 15, 31, . . .

43. $0, \frac{1}{2}, \frac{3}{4}, \frac{7}{8}, \frac{15}{16}, \ldots$

Predict the next term in each sequence. Use your calculator to verify your answer.

44.
$12345679 \times 9 = 111111111$
$12345679 \times 18 = 222222222$
$12345679 \times 27 = 333333333$
$12345679 \times 36 = 444444444$
$12345679 \times 45 = \blacksquare$

45.
$1 \times 1 = 1$
$11 \times 11 = 121$
$111 \times 111 = 12321$
$1111 \times 1111 = 1234321$
$11111 \times 11111 = \blacksquare$

46. Patterns Draw the next figure in the sequence. Make sure you think about color and shape.

Answers

Practice and Problem-Solving Exercises

6. Double the previous term; 80, 160.
7. Find the next square; 36, 49.
8. Add −2, +3, −4, +5, . . . ; −3, 4.
9. Multiply the previous term by $\frac{1}{2}$; $\frac{1}{16}, \frac{1}{32}$.
10. The numerator is 1 and the denominator is the next whole number; $\frac{1}{5}, \frac{1}{6}$.
11. Subtract 3 from the previous number; 3, 0.
12. the first letters of the counting numbers; N, T
13. the first letter of the months; J, J
14. Multiply the previous number by 2, by 3, by 4, by 5, . . . ; 720, 5040.
15. the Presidents of the U.S.; Madison, Monroe
16. U.S. coins of descending value; dime, nickel
17. state postal abbreviations in alphabetical order; CO, CT
18. zodiac signs; Gemini, Cancer
19.

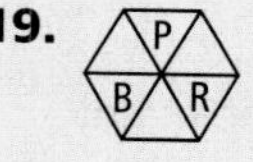

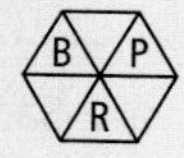

20.

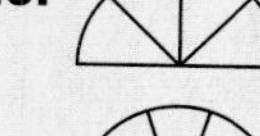

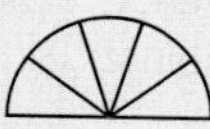

21. blue
22. star
23. blue
24. star
25–30. Answers may vary. Samples are given.
25. The sum of the first 100 positive odd numbers is 100^2, or 10,000.
26. The sum of the first 100 positive even numbers is 100 · 101, or 10,100.
27. The sum of two odd numbers is even.
28. The sum of an even number and an odd number is odd.
29. The product of two even numbers is even.
30. The product of two odd numbers is odd.

Draw the next figure in each sequence.

47.

48.

49. **Reasoning** Find the perimeter when 100 triangles are put together in the pattern shown. Assume that all triangle sides are 1 cm long.

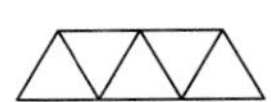

50. **Think About a Plan** Below are 15 points. Most of the points fit a pattern. Which does not? Explain.

$A(6, -2)$ $B(6, 5)$ $C(8, 0)$ $D(8, 7)$ $E(10, 2)$ $F(10, 6)$ $G(11, 4)$ $H(12, 3)$
$I(4, 0)$ $J(7, 6)$ $K(5, 6)$ $L(4, 7)$ $M(2, 2)$ $N(1, 4)$ $O(2, 6)$

- How can you draw a diagram to help you find a pattern?
- What pattern do the majority of the points fit?

51. **Language** Look for a pattern in the Chinese number system.
a. What is the Chinese name for the numbers 43, 67, and 84?
b. **Reasoning** Do you think that the Chinese number system is base 10? Explain.

Chinese Number System

Number	Chinese Word
1	yī
2	èr
3	sān
4	sì
5	wǔ
6	liù
7	qī
8	bā

Number	Chinese Word
9	jǐu
10	shí
11	shí-yī
12	shí-èr
⋮	⋮
20	èr-shí
21	èr-shí-yī
⋮	⋮
30	sān-shí

52. **Open-Ended** Write two different number sequences that begin with the same two numbers.

53. **Error Analysis** For each of the past four years, Paulo has grown 2 in. every year. He is now 16 years old and is 5 ft 10 in. tall. He figures that when he is 22 years old he will be 6 ft 10 in. tall. What would you tell Paulo about his conjecture?

54. **Bird Migration** During bird migration, volunteers get up early on Bird Day to record the number of bird species they observe in their community during a 24-h period. Results are posted online to help scientists and students track the migration.
a. Make a graph of the data.
b. Use the graph and inductive reasoning to make a conjecture about the number of bird species the volunteers in this community will observe in 2015.

Bird Count

Year	Number of Species
2004	70
2005	83
2006	80
2007	85
2008	90

55. **Writing** Describe a real-life situation in which you recently used inductive reasoning.

31. 1 mi **32.** 75°F

33–37. Answers may vary. Samples are given.

33. two right angles

34. $\triangle ABC$ with $m\angle B = 90$

35. -2 and -3 **36.** $\frac{1}{4}$ and $\frac{1}{2}$

37. -2 and -3

38. Add 2, add 4, add 6, . . . ; 31, 43.

39. Add 1 then add 3; add 1 then add 3; . . . ; 10, 13.

40. Divide the previous number by 10; 0.0001, 0.00001.

41. Multiply by 3, add 1; multiply by 3, add 1; . . . ; 201, 202.

42. Add 2, add 4, add 8, add 16, . . . ; 63, 127.

43. Add $\frac{1}{2}$, add $\frac{1}{4}$, add $\frac{1}{8}$ . . . ; $\frac{31}{32}$, $\frac{63}{64}$.

44. 555,555,555

45. 123,454,321

46.

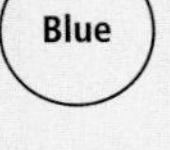

47.

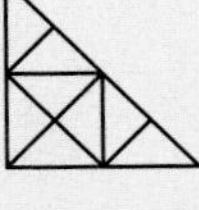

48.

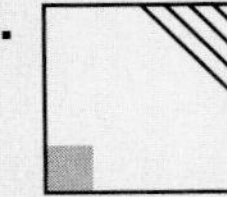

49. 102 cm

50. H; the rest of the points form the shape of a heart.

51a. sì-shí-sān; lìu-shí-qī; bā-shí-sì

b. Yes; the second part of the number repeats each ten numbers.

52. Answers may vary. Sample: 1, 2, 3, 4, 5, . . . and 1, 2, 4, 8, 16, . . .

53. His conjecture is probably false because most people's growth slows by 18 until they stop growing sometime between 18 and 22 years.

54a.

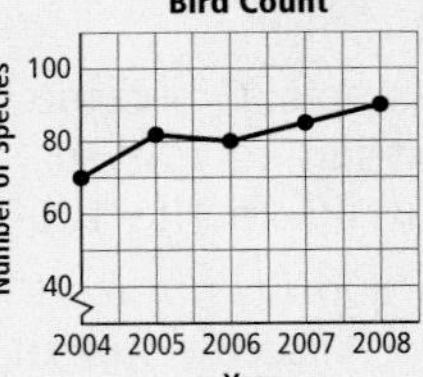

b. Answers may vary. Sample: Using just the data from 2005 to 2008, the gain is 7 species in 3 years, or between 2 and 3 species each year. The year 2015 is 7 years after 2008, so the number of new species will be between 14 and 21 more than 90; an estimate is 90 + 17 or 107 species.

55. Check students' work.

Answers

Practice and Problem-Solving Exercises (continued)

56. Answers may vary. Sample: Group the numbers in pairs that sum to 101, so the sum of the integers from 1 to 100 is $\frac{100 \cdot 101}{2} = 5050$; group the numbers in pairs that sum to $n + 1$, so the sum of the integers from 1 to n is $\frac{n(n + 1)}{2}$.

57. 1×1: 64 squares; 2×2: 49 squares; 3×3: 36 squares; 4×4: 25 squares; 5×5: 16 squares; 6×6: 9 squares; 7×7: 4 squares; 8×8: 1 square; total number of squares: 204

58a. 1, 3, 6, 10, 15, 21

b.

n	1	2	3	4	5	6
$\frac{n^2 + n}{2}$	1	3	6	10	15	21

The values are the same.

c. $\frac{n^2 + n}{2} = \frac{n(n + 1)}{2}$; since the diagram represents $n(n + 1)$, half of the diagram represents $\frac{n^2 + n}{2}$.

d.

59. C **60.** I

61. [2] No; since all four variables are positive, the two ordered pairs must be in Quadrant I, so the midpoint of the segment will also be in Quadrant I.
[1] incomplete OR incorrect explanation

62. 16π in.^{2} **63.** 20 m **64.** 2

65. True; explanations may vary. Sample: If the two even numbers are $2a$ and $2b$, the sum is $2a + 2b = 2(a + b)$, which is the form of an even number.

66. True; explanations may vary. Sample: if the three odd numbers are $2a + 1$, $2b + 1$, and $2c + 1$, the sum is $2(a + b + c) + 2 + 1 = 2(a + b + c + 1) + 1$, which is the form of an odd number.

Challenge

56. History When he was in the third grade, German mathematician Karl Gauss (1777–1855) took ten seconds to sum the integers from 1 to 100. Now it's your turn. Find a fast way to sum the integers from 1 to 100. Find a fast way to sum the integers from 1 to n. (*Hint:* Use patterns.)

57. Chess The small squares on a chessboard can be combined to form larger squares. For example, there are sixty-four 1×1 squares and one 8×8 square. Use inductive reasoning to determine how many 2×2 squares, 3×3 squares, and so on, are on a chessboard. What is the total number of squares on a chessboard?

58. a. Algebra Write the first six terms of the sequence that starts with 1, and for which the difference between consecutive terms is first 2, and then 3, 4, 5, and 6.

b. Evaluate $\frac{n^2 + n}{2}$ for $n = 1, 2, 3, 4, 5$, and 6. Compare the sequence you get with your answer for part (a).

c. Examine the diagram at the right and explain how it illustrates a value of $\frac{n^2 + n}{2}$.

d. Draw a similar diagram to represent $\frac{n^2 + n}{2}$ for $n = 5$.

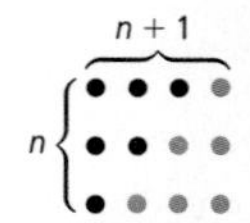

Standardized Test Prep

SAT/ACT

59. What is the next term in the sequence 1, 1, 2, 3, 5, 8, 13, . . . ?

(A) 17 (B) 20 (C) 21 (D) 24

60. A horse trainer wants to build three adjacent rectangular corrals as shown at the right. The area of each corral is 7200ft^2. If the length of each corral is 120 ft, how much fencing does the horse trainer need to buy in order to build the corrals?

120 ft

(F) 300 ft (G) 360 ft (H) 560 ft (I) 840 ft

Short Response

61. The coordinates x, y, a, and b are all positive integers. Could the points (x, y) and (a, b) have a midpoint in Quadrant III? Explain.

Mixed Review

62. What is the area of a circle with radius 4 in.? Leave your answer in terms of π. See Lesson 1-8.

63. What is the perimeter of a rectangle with side lengths 3 m and 7 m?

64. Solve for x if B is the midpoint of $\overline{AC}$. (A ——12x + 8—— B ——32—— C) See Lesson 1-3.

Get Ready! **To prepare for Lesson 2-2, do Exercises 65 and 66.**

Tell whether each conjecture is *true* or *false*. Explain. See Lesson 2-1.

65. The sum of two even numbers is even.

66. The sum of three odd numbers is odd.

2-1 Lesson Resources

Differentiated Remediation

Instructional Support

Geometry Companion

Students can use the **Geometry Companion** worktext (4 pages) . . .

- New Vocabulary
- Key Concepts
- Got It for each Problem
- Lesson Check

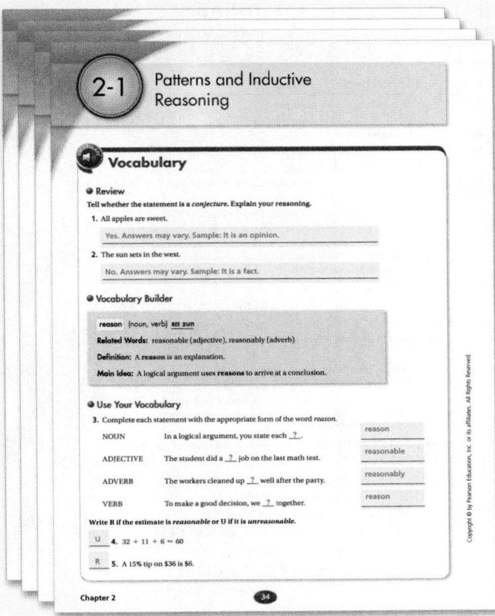

2-1 Patterns and Inductive Reasoning

Vocabulary

Review

Tell whether the statement is a *conjecture*. Explain your reasoning.

1. All apples are sweet.
   Yes. Answers may vary. Sample: It is an opinion.
2. The sun sets in the west.
   No. Answers may vary. Sample: It is a fact.

Vocabulary Builder

reason (noun, verb) REE zun

Related Words: reasonable (adjective), reasonably (adverb)

Definition: A **reason** is an explanation.

Main Idea: A logical argument uses **reasons** to arrive at a conclusion.

Use Your Vocabulary

3. Complete each statement with the appropriate form of the word *reason*.

NOUN	In a logical argument, you state each _?_.	reason
ADJECTIVE	The student did a _?_ job on the last math test.	reasonable
ADVERB	The workers cleaned up _?_ well after the party.	reasonably
VERB	To make a good decision, we _?_ together.	reason

Write R if the estimate is *reasonable* or U if it is *unreasonable*.

U 4. $32 + 11 + 6 \approx 60$

R 5. A 15% tip on \$36 is \$6.

Chapter 2 34

ELL Support

Focus on Communication Draw several scalene triangles on the board and write "scalene." Tell students these are scalene triangles and ask them what they can conclude about scalene triangles. You can use other examples. Then say, these are examples of *inductive reasoning*. Ask: What do you think inductive reasoning is? Guide students to conclude that inductive reasoning is based on relationships and patterns that you observe.

Focus on Language Examine the word *inductive*. What does the suffix -tive mean? (tending to) The root of inductive is induct or induce meaning to introduce or lead to.

5 Assess & Remediate

Lesson Quiz

1. Look for a pattern. What are the next two terms in the sequence: 55, 44, 33, 22, . . .?
2. What conjecture can you make about the 19th term in the pattern: A, B, B, A, B, B, A, . . .?
3. **Do you UNDERSTAND?** The graph shows the level of the Little Miami River over several hours during a rain storm. What conjecture can you make about the level of the river after 5 hours of rain? Explain.

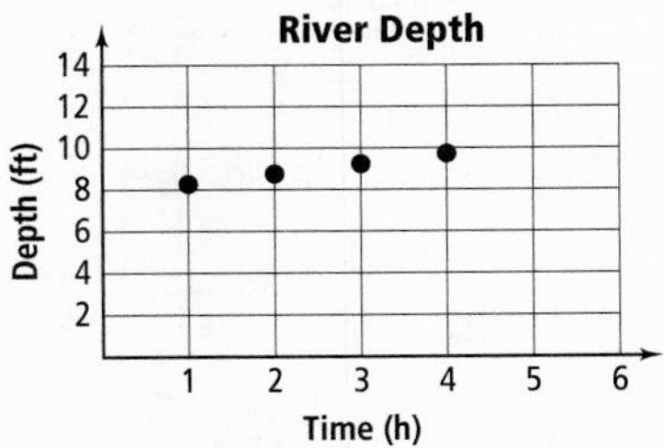

ANSWERS TO LESSON QUIZ

1. 11, 0
2. The 19th term is A.
3. The level of the river will be about 10 ft. The level is going up in a path that appears to be linear. The next point on the graph would be about (5, 10).

PRESCRIPTION FOR REMEDIATION

Use the student work on the Lesson Quiz to prescribe a differentiated review assignment.

Points	Differentiated Remediation
0–1	Intervention
2	On-level
3	Extension

PowerGeometry.com

5 Assess & Remediate

Assign the Lesson Quiz. Appropriate intervention, practice, or enrichment is automatically generated based on student performance.

Intervention

- **Reteaching** (2 pages) Provides reteaching and practice exercises for the key lesson concepts. Use with struggling students or absent students.
- **English Language Learner Support** Helps students develop and reinforce mathematical vocabulary and key concepts.

All-in-One Resources/Online

Reteaching

2-1 **Reteaching**
Patterns and Inductive Reasoning

Inductive reasoning is a type of reasoning in which you look at a pattern and then make some type of prediction based on the pattern. These predictions are also called conjectures. A *conjecture* is a statement about what you think will happen based on the pattern you observed.

Problem

Which conjectures below are reasonable? Which are not?

Pattern	Conjecture
Pattern 1: Every day for the two weeks that Alba visited Cairo, the weather was hot and dry.	Alba thought to herself, "The weather is always hot and dry in this city."
Pattern 2: 5, 10, 15, 20, 25, 30, 35, 40, 45, 50, . . .	Each number increases by 5. The next two numbers are most likely 55 and 60.
Pattern 3: Dani and Liz both examined this pattern of letters: A, BB, CCC, . . .	Dani was sure that the next two terms of the pattern would be DDDD and EEEEE. Liz wasn't so sure. She thought the pattern might repeat and the next two elements would be A and BB.

Pattern 1: The conjecture for Pattern 1 is probably not correct. In most cities, the weather will not be hot and dry all the time.

Pattern 2: You are given enough numbers in the pattern to assume that the numbers continue to increase by five. The conjecture is probably correct.

Pattern 3: Only three terms of the pattern are shown. This makes it difficult to determine what rule the pattern follows. Either Dani or Liz could be correct, or they could both be incorrect.

Remember that conjectures are never the final goal in a complete reasoning process. They are simply the first step to figuring out a problem.

Exercises

Make a conjecture about the rule these patterns follow.

1. 3, 6, 9, 12, 15, . . .
   The numbers increase by 3.
2. 9, 3, 1, $\frac{1}{3}$, $\frac{1}{9}$, . . .
   The numbers are divided by 3.
3. A, C, E, G, I, K, M, . . .
   One letter of the alphabet is skipped between each term.
4. 0, 5, −2, 3, −4, 1, −6, . . .
   Add 5, then subtract 7.
5. 4, 8, 16, 32, 64, 128, . . .
   The numbers are multiplied by 2.
6. 0.1, 0.01, 0.001, 0.0001, . . .
   The numbers are divided by 10.

All-in-One Resources/Online

English Language Learner Support

2-1 **ELL Support**
Patterns and Inductive Reasoning

Complete the vocabulary chart by filling in the missing information.

Word	Description	Picture or Example
conjecture	A *conjecture* is what you think might happen or might be true based on what you have observed.	Conjecture: The streets are wet, so I think it has been raining.
counterexample	1. Sample: A counterexample is a statement that shows that a conjecture is wrong by giving an example that does not agree with the conjecture.	All trees lose their leaves in the fall. Counterexample: Evergreen trees have needles and do not lose them in the fall.
inductive reasoning	2. Sample: Inductive reasoning is reasoning based on a pattern that is observed.	5, 10, 15, 20, . . . Based on the pattern, I think the next number is 25.
pattern	A *pattern* is an arrangement or ordering. You can extend a pattern if you know the rule for the pattern.	3. Sample: A C E G I K M O Q (Rule: skip every other letter.)
prediction	Similar to a conjecture, a *prediction* is something that you think might happen based on what you observe.	4. Sample: On Fridays, they usually serve beans in the cafeteria. Today is Friday, so they will serve beans today in the cafeteria.

Differentiated Remediation *continued*

On-Level

- **Practice** (2 pages) Provides extra practice for each lesson. For simpler practice exercises, use the Form K Practice pages found in the All-in-One Teaching Resources and online.
- **Think About a Plan** Helps students develop specific problem-solving skills and strategies by providing scaffolded guiding questions.
- **Standardized Test Prep** Focuses on all major exercises, all major question types, and helps students prepare for the high-stakes assessments.

Extension

- **Enrichment** Provides students with interesting problems and activities that extend the concepts of the lesson.
- **Activities, Games, and Puzzles** Worksheets that can be used for concepts development, enrichment, and for fun!

Practice and Problem Solving Wkbk/ All-in-One Resources/Online

Practice page 1

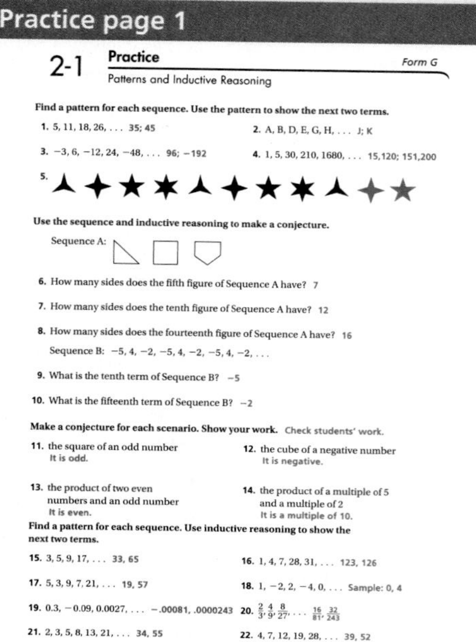

2-1 Practice — Form G
Patterns and Inductive Reasoning

Find a pattern for each sequence. Use the pattern to show the next two terms.

1. 5, 11, 18, 26, . . . 35; 45
2. A, B, D, E, G, H, . . . J; K
3. −3, 6, −12, 24, −48, . . . 96; −192
4. 1, 5, 30, 210, 1680, . . . 15,120; 151,200
5. [sequence of star figures]

Use the sequence and inductive reasoning to make a conjecture.

Sequence A: [figures]

6. How many sides does the fifth figure of Sequence A have? 7
7. How many sides does the tenth figure of Sequence A have? 12
8. How many sides does the fourteenth figure of Sequence A have? 16

Sequence B: −5, 4, −2, −5, 4, −2, −5, 4, −2, . . .

9. What is the tenth term of Sequence B? −5
10. What is the fifteenth term of Sequence B? −2

Make a conjecture for each scenario. Show your work. Check students' work.

11. the square of an odd number — It is odd.
12. the cube of a negative number — It is negative.
13. the product of two even numbers and an odd number — It is even.
14. the product of a multiple of 5 and a multiple of 2 — It is a multiple of 10.

Find a pattern for each sequence. Use inductive reasoning to show the next two terms.

15. 3, 5, 9, 17, . . . 33, 65
16. 1, 4, 7, 28, 31, . . . 123, 126
17. 5, 3, 9, 7, 21, . . . 19, 57
18. 1, −2, 2, −4, 0, . . . Sample: 0, 4
19. 0.3, −0.09, 0.0027, . . . −.00081, .0000243
20. $\frac{2}{3}, \frac{4}{9}, \frac{8}{27}, \ldots$ $\frac{16}{81}, \frac{32}{243}$
21. 2, 3, 5, 8, 13, 21, . . . 34, 55
22. 4, 7, 12, 19, 28, . . . 39, 52

Practice and Problem Solving Wkbk/ All-in-One Resources/Online

Practice page 2

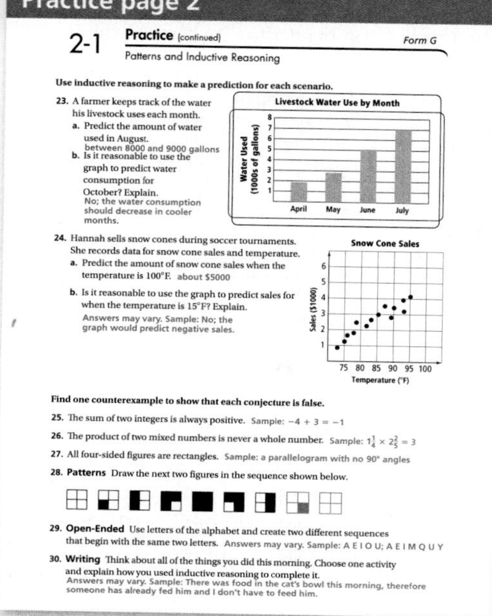

2-1 Practice (continued) — Form G
Patterns and Inductive Reasoning

Use inductive reasoning to make a prediction for each scenario.

23. A farmer keeps track of the livestock water use each month.
a. Predict the amount of water used in August. between 8000 and 9000 gallons
b. Is it reasonable to use the graph to predict water consumption for October? Explain. No; the water consumption should decrease in cooler months.

24. Hannah sells snow cones during soccer tournaments. She records data for snow cone sales and temperature.
a. Predict the amount of snow cone sales when the temperature is 100°F. about $5000
b. Is it reasonable to use the graph to predict sales for when the temperature is 15°F? Explain. Answers may vary. Sample: No; the graph would predict negative sales.

Find one counterexample to show that each conjecture is false.

25. The sum of two integers is always positive. Sample: −4 + 3 = −1
26. The product of two mixed numbers is never a whole number. Sample: $1\frac{1}{4} \times 2\frac{2}{5} = 3$
27. All four-sided figures are rectangles. Sample: a parallelogram with no 90° angles
28. Patterns Draw the next two figures in the sequence shown below.
29. Open-Ended Use letters of the alphabet and create two different sequences that begin with the same two letters. Answers may vary. Sample: A E I O U; A E I M Q U Y
30. Writing Think about all of the things you did this morning. Choose one activity and explain how you used inductive reasoning to complete it. Answers may vary. Sample: There was food in the cat's bowl this morning, therefore someone has already fed him and I don't have to feed him.

All-in-One Resources/Online

Enrichment

2-1 Enrichment
Patterns and Inductive Reasoning

Using an Area Model

How can you find the sum of the first 5 consecutive positive integers?

You can easily add the numbers mentally—the sum is 15. But what if you want to find the sum of the first *n* consecutive whole numbers? Keep this question in mind and make some conjectures about a formula.

You can use an area model to help develop a general formula for the sum. A model of 1 + 2 + 3 + 4 + 5 appears at the right.

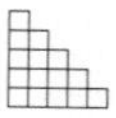

One way to find the area of this model directly is to count the number of squares. However, another way to find the area is to draw a duplicate of the model and rotate the duplicate so that together the two diagrams form a rectangle.

Duplicate and flip the model. Then place the two models together to form a rectangle as shown at the right.

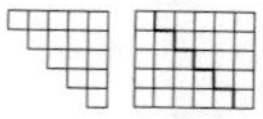

1. Write a multiplication expression that represents the area of the rectangle. 5 × 6
2. Use the expression in Exercise 1 to write an expression that represents the area of the original model. 5 × 6 ÷ 2
3. Suppose a 6th row of 6 blocks were added to the bottom of the first diagram to model the sum 1 + 2 + 3 + 4 + 5 + 6. Write a multiplication/division expression for the area of this model. 6 × 7 ÷ 2
4. Use inductive reasoning to write a formula for the sum of the first *n* consecutive positive integers. *n* × (*n* + 1) ÷ 2

Use your formula to find each sum.

5. Find the sum of the first 10 consecutive whole numbers. 55
6. Find the sum of the first 100 consecutive whole numbers. 5050
7. Find the sum of the first 1000 consecutive whole numbers. 500,500
8. Find the sum of the first 500 consecutive whole numbers. 125,250
9. Find the sum of the first 5000 consecutive whole numbers. 12,502,500
10. Find the sum of the first 50,000 consecutive whole numbers. 1,250,025,000
11. What patterns do you notice in Exercises 5–10? Answers may vary. Sample: As the number of numbers being added gets multiplied by 10 there are two zeroes added to the sum, one at the end and one in the middle of the number.

Practice and Problem Solving Wkbk/ All-in-One Resources/Online

Think About a Plan

2-1 Think About a Plan
Patterns and Inductive Reasoning

Bird Migration During bird migration, volunteers get up early on Bird Day to record the number of bird species they observe in their community during a 24-h period. Results are posted online to help scientists and students track the migration.

a. Make a graph of the data.
b. Use the graph and inductive reasoning to make a conjecture about the number of bird species the volunteers in this community will observe in 2015.

Bird Count

Year	Number of Species
2004	70
2005	83
2006	80
2007	85
2008	90

Understanding the Problem

1. What does the problem ask you to predict? the number of bird species volunteers will observe on Bird Day in 2015
2. What approach to organizing the data is suggested in the problem? The problem suggests using a graph of the data.

Planning the Solution

3. On your graph, what data should be represented by the horizontal axis? years
4. On your graph, what data should be represented by the vertical axis? number of bird species
5. Graph the data on the grid at the right. Don't forget to label the axes. Check students' graphs. Sample shown at the right.

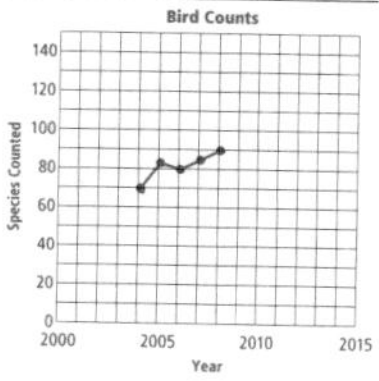

Bird Counts — Species Counted; Year (2000, 2005, 2010, 2015)

Getting an Answer

6. Look at the data points. Is there an upward or downward trend? What is the approximate increase or decrease in the number of bird species observed per year? upward; increases by about 5 species per year
7. Based on the pattern in the graph of the data, how many bird species do you think will be observed in 2015? about 125

Practice and Problem Solving Wkbk/ All-in-One Resources/Online

Standardized Test Prep

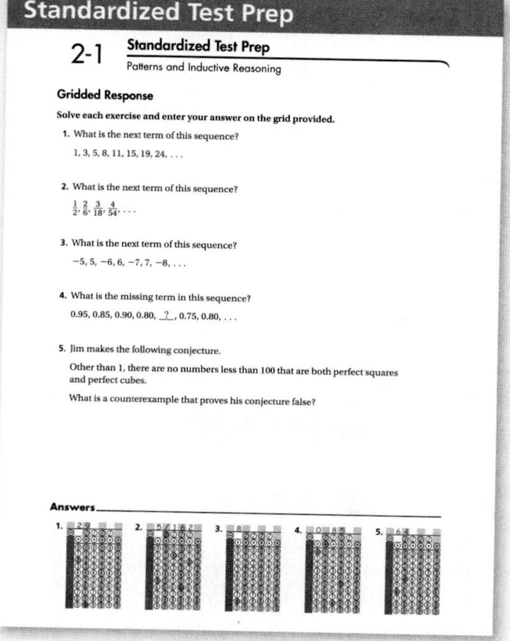

2-1 Standardized Test Prep
Patterns and Inductive Reasoning

Gridded Response

Solve each exercise and enter your answer on the grid provided.

1. What is the next term of this sequence?
1, 3, 5, 8, 11, 15, 19, 24, . . .
2. What is the next term of this sequence?
$\frac{1}{2}, \frac{2}{6}, \frac{3}{18}, \frac{4}{54}, \ldots$
3. What is the next term of this sequence?
−5, 5, −6, 6, −7, 7, −8, . . .
4. What is the missing term in this sequence?
0.95, 0.85, 0.90, 0.80, __?__, 0.75, 0.80, . . .
5. Jim makes the following conjecture.
Other than 1, there are no numbers less than 100 that are both perfect squares and perfect cubes.
What is a counterexample that proves his conjecture false?

Answers

Online Teacher Resource Center

Activities, Games, and Puzzles

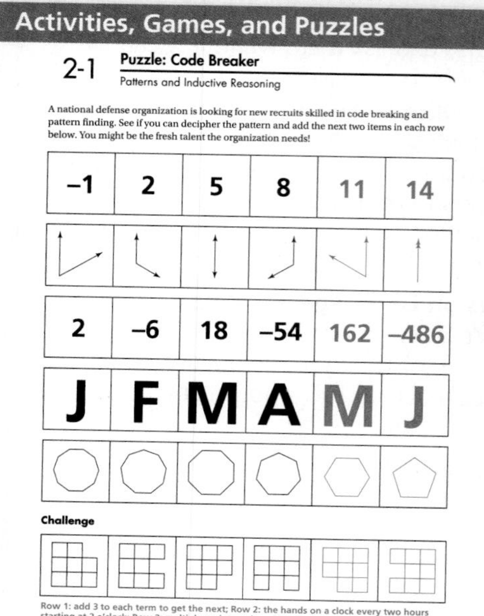

2-1 Puzzle: Code Breaker
Patterns and Inductive Reasoning

A national defense organization is looking for new recruits skilled in code breaking and pattern finding. See if you can decipher the pattern and add the next two items in each row below. You might be the fresh talent the organization needs!

−1	2	5	8	11	14
[clock]	[clock]	[clock]	[clock]	[clock]	[clock]
2	−6	18	−54	162	−486
J	F	M	A	M	J
[polygon]	[polygon]	[polygon]	[polygon]	[polygon]	[polygon]

Challenge

Row 1: add 3 to each term to get the next; Row 2: the hands on a clock every two hours starting at 2 o'clock; Row 3: multiply each term by −3 to get the next; Row 4: the initial letters of the first 6 months of the year; Row 5: regular polygons with the number of sides decreasing by 1; Challenge: the missing square rotates clockwise around outer edge of 3-by-3 grid.

2-2 Conditional Statements

Objectives To recognize conditional statements and their parts
To write converses, inverses, and contrapositives of conditionals

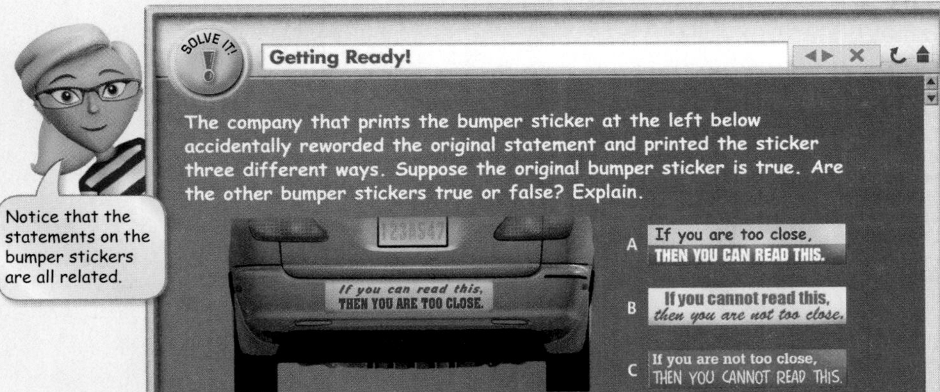

Getting Ready!
The company that prints the bumper sticker at the left below accidentally reworded the original statement and printed the sticker three different ways. Suppose the original bumper sticker is true. Are the other bumper stickers true or false? Explain.
If you can read this, THEN YOU ARE TOO CLOSE.
A If you are too close, THEN YOU CAN READ THIS.
B If you cannot read this, then you are not too close.
C If you are not too close, THEN YOU CANNOT READ THIS.
Notice that the statements on the bumper stickers are all related.

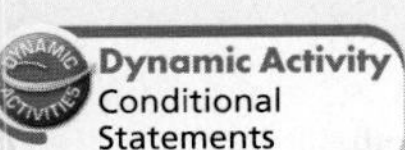
Dynamic Activity
Conditional Statements

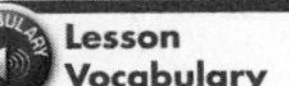
Lesson Vocabulary
- conditional
- hypothesis
- conclusion
- truth value
- negation
- converse
- inverse
- contrapositive
- equivalent statements

The study of *if-then* statements and their truth values is a foundation of reasoning.

Essential Understanding You can describe some mathematical relationships using a variety of *if-then* statements.

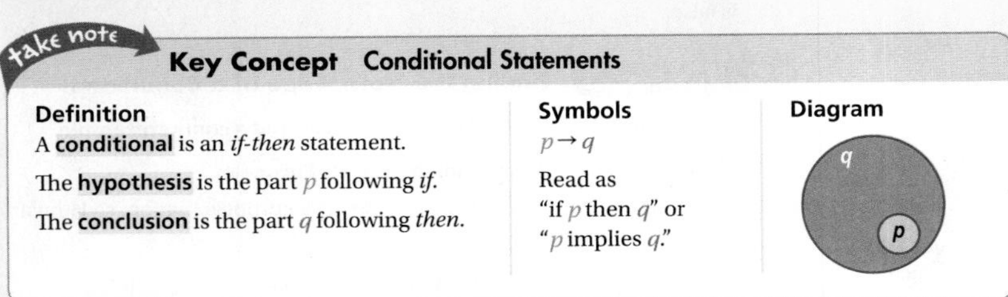

Key Concept Conditional Statements

Definition	Symbols	Diagram
A **conditional** is an *if-then* statement. The **hypothesis** is the part p following *if*. The **conclusion** is the part q following *then*.	$p \rightarrow q$ Read as "if p then q" or "p implies q."	(Venn diagram: circle p inside circle q)

The Venn diagram above illustrates how the set of things that satisfy the hypothesis lies inside the set of things that satisfy the conclusion.

1 Interactive Learning

Solve It!

PURPOSE To introduce students to conditional statements, their truth values, and related conditional statements

PROCESS Students may use the process of elimination and assume a statement is true unless they determine a counterexample.

FACILITATE

Q What circumstance would show the sticker "If you are too close, then you can read this" to be a false statement? **[Answers may vary. Sample: The driver is too close, but cannot read the bumper sticker.]**

Q What circumstance would show the sticker "If you cannot read this, then you are not too close" to be a false statement? **[Answers may vary. Sample: The driver is not wearing necessary reading glasses and cannot read the bumper sticker, but is driving too close.]**

ANSWER See Solve It in Answers on next page.

CONNECT THE MATH The bumper stickers in the Solve It demonstrate different conditional statements that have equivalent meanings and equivalent truth values. In this lesson, students study conditional statements and related conditional statements in the context of different situations.

2 Guided Instruction

Take Note

VISUAL LEARNERS

Have students fill in the Venn diagram with the hypothesis and conclusion from the correct bumper sticker to reinforce the relationship between parts of a conditional.

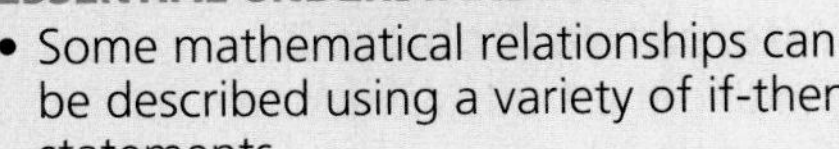

2-2 Preparing to Teach

BIG idea Reasoning and Proof UbD

ESSENTIAL UNDERSTANDINGS
- Some mathematical relationships can be described using a variety of if-then statements.
- Each conditional statement has a converse, an inverse, and a contrapositive.

Math Background

Postulates and theorems in geometry are written as conditional statements, and for that reason, it is important for students to understand these types of statements. Students will encounter many geometric definitions as they progress through the textbook, and each of these definitions is a true conditional statement whose converse is also true. It is critical to stress to students that converse statements may or may not be true, regardless of the truth of the original conditional statement.

Venn diagrams provide a powerful and intuitive tool for establishing the truth of some if-then statements. Emphasize that proving a conditional statement false requires only a single counterexample, in contrast to proving a conditional statement true. No number of supporting examples is sufficient to prove a conditional statement true. Conditional statements are proved by a series of logical arguments.

Support Student Learning

Use the **Geometry Companion** to engage and support students during instructions. See Lesson Resources at the end of this lesson for details.

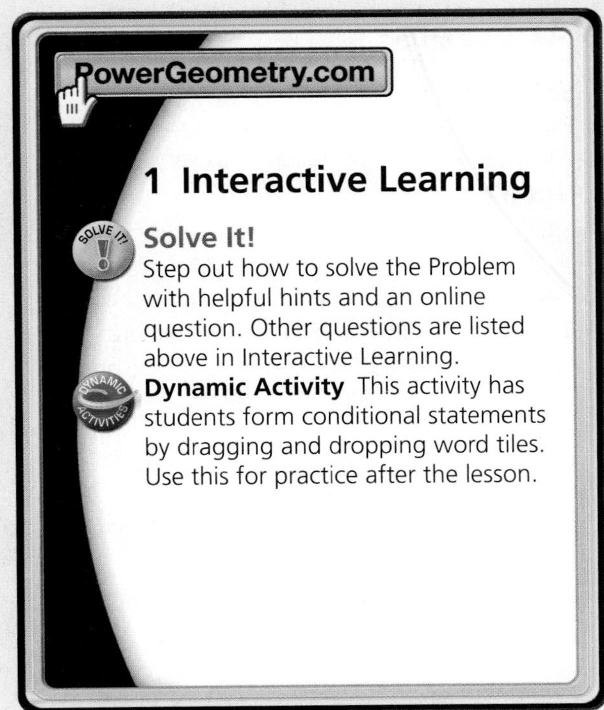

PowerGeometry.com

1 Interactive Learning

Solve It! Step out how to solve the Problem with helpful hints and an online question. Other questions are listed above in Interactive Learning.

Dynamic Activity This activity has students form conditional statements by dragging and dropping word tiles. Use this for practice after the lesson.

Problem 1

Q Write a variation of the conditional. What are the hypothesis and conclusion for this version? **[Answers may vary. Sample: If an animal is a bird, then it is a robin. Hypothesis: An animal is a bird; Conclusion: The animal is a robin.]**

Got It?

Q In a Venn diagram for the Got It problem, what phrase would you write in the inside circle? **[angles that measure 130 degrees]**

Problem 2 VISUAL LEARNERS

Ask students to sketch vertical angles and indicate the common vertex. Also ask students to sketch two angles that share a vertex but are not vertical angles.

Got It? VISUAL LEARNERS

Have students construct a Venn diagram to identify the hypothesis and conclusion of the conditional.

Problem 3

To help students understand the truth value of a conditional, show the following four cases and develop the truth table.

If it is your birthday, then you will have cake.

			Truth value
Case 1: It is your birthday, you have cake.	True	True	True
Case 2: It is your birthday, you do not have cake.	True	False	False
Case 3: It is not your birthday, you have cake.	False	True	True
Case 4: It is not your birthday, you do not have cake.	False	False	True

This should help students see that if the hypothesis is false, the truth value of the conditional is always true.

Think

What would a Venn diagram look like?
A robin is a kind of bird, so the set of robins (R) should be inside the set of birds (B).

Problem 1 Identifying the Hypothesis and the Conclusion

What are the hypothesis and the conclusion of the conditional?
If an animal is a robin, then the animal is a bird.

Hypothesis (p): An animal is a robin.

Conclusion (q): The animal is a bird.

Got It? 1. What are the hypothesis and the conclusion of the conditional?
If an angle measures 130, then the angle is obtuse.

Think

Which part of the statement is the hypothesis (*p*)?
For two angles to be vertical, they must share a vertex. So the set of vertical angles (*p*) is inside the set of angles that share a vertex (*q*).

Problem 2 Writing a Conditional

How can you write the following statement as a conditional?
Vertical angles share a vertex.

Step 1 Identify the hypothesis and the conclusion.

Vertical angles share a vertex.

Step 2 Write the conditional.

If two angles are vertical, then they share a vertex.

Got It? 2. How can you write "Dolphins are mammals" as a conditional?

The **truth value** of a conditional is either *true* or *false*. To show that a conditional is true, show that every time the hypothesis is true, the conclusion is also true. A counterexample can help you determine whether a conditional with a true hypothesis is true. To show that the conditional is false, if you find one counterexample for which the hypothesis is true and the conclusion is false, then the truth value of the conditional is false.

Plan

How do you find a counterexample?
Find an example where the hypothesis is true, but the conclusion is false. For part (B), find a number divisible by 3 that is not odd.

Problem 3 Finding the Truth Value of a Conditional

Is the conditional *true* or *false*? If it is false, find a counterexample.

A If a woman is Hungarian, then she is European.

The conditional is true. Hungary is a European nation, so Hungarians are European.

B If a number is divisible by 3, then it is odd.

The conditional is false. The number 12 is divisible by 3, but it is not odd.

Got It? 3. Is the conditional *true* or *false*? If it is false, find a counterexample.

a. If a month has 28 days, then it is February.

b. If two angles form a linear pair, then they are supplementary.

Answers

Solve It!

The first two bumper stickers are false, but the third one is true. Explanations may vary.

Got It?

1. Hypothesis: An angle measures 130. Conclusion: The angle is obtuse.

2. If an animal is a dolphin, then it is a mammal.

3a. False; January has 28 days, plus 3 more.

b. True; the sum of the measures of two angles that form a linear pair is 180.

PowerGeometry.com

2 Guided Instruction

Each Problem is worked out and supported online.

Problem 1
Identifying the Hypothesis and the Conclusion

Problem 2
Writing a Conditional
Animated

Problem 3
Finding the Truth Value of a Conditional

Alternative Problem 3
Finding the Truth Value of a Conditional
Animated

Problem 4
Writing and Finding Truth Values of Statements
Animated

Support in Geometry Companion
- Vocabulary
- Key Concepts
- Got It?

The **negation** of a statement p is the opposite of the statement. The symbol is $\sim p$ and is read "not p." The negation of the statement "The sky is blue" is "The sky is *not* blue." You can use negations to write statements related to a conditional. Every conditional has three related conditional statements.

take note

Key Concept Related Conditional Statements

Statement	How to Write It	Example	Symbols	How to Read It
Conditional	Use the given hypothesis and conclusion.	If $m\angle A = 15$, then $\angle A$ is acute.	$p \to q$	If p, then q.
Converse	Exchange the hypothesis and the conclusion.	If $\angle A$ is acute, then $m\angle A = 15$.	$q \to p$	If q, then p.
Inverse	Negate both the hypothesis and the conclusion of the conditional.	If $m\angle A \neq 15$, then $\angle A$ is not acute.	$\sim p \to \sim q$	If not p, then not q.
Contrapositive	Negate both the hypothesis and the conclusion of the converse.	If $\angle A$ is not acute, then $m\angle A \neq 15$.	$\sim q \to \sim p$	If not q, then not p.

Below are the truth values of the related statements above. **Equivalent statements** have the same truth value.

Statement	Example	Truth Value
Conditional	If $m\angle A = 15$, then $\angle A$ is acute.	True
Converse	If $\angle A$ is acute, then $m\angle A = 15$.	False
Inverse	If $m\angle A \neq 15$, then $\angle A$ is not acute.	False
Contrapositive	If $\angle A$ is not acute, then $m\angle A \neq 15$.	True

A conditional and its contrapositive are equivalent statements. They are either both true or both false. The converse and inverse of a statement are also equivalent statements.

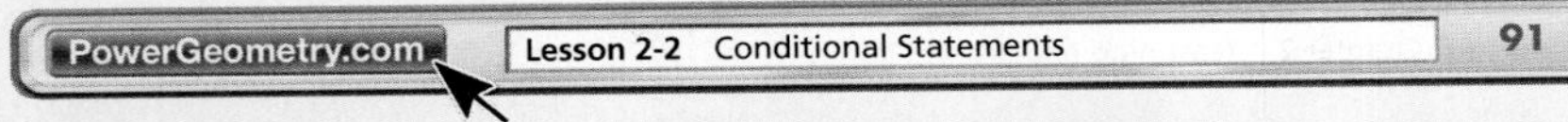

Take Note

Q What is the hypothesis, p, of the conditional? **[An angle measures 15°.]**

Q What is the conclusion, q, of the hypothesis? **[The angle is acute.]**

Use a graphic organizer to help students remember the forms of conditional statements and the relationships between the conditional statements.

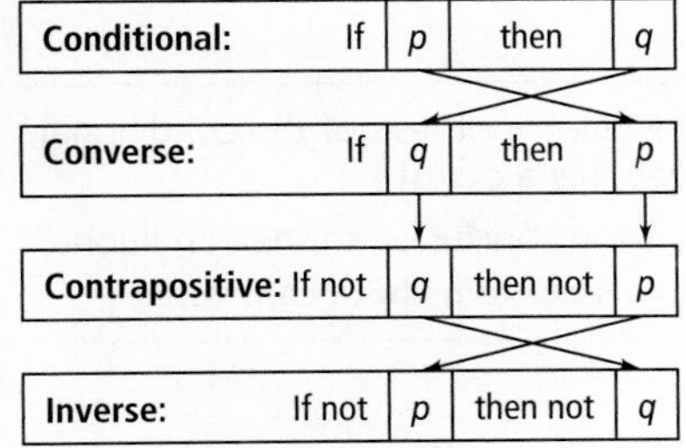

Q What is a counterexample that proves the converse false? **[Answers may vary. Sample: A 20° angle is acute, but it does not measure 15.]**

Q What is a counterexample that proves the inverse false? **[Answers may vary. Sample: A 20° angle does not measure 15, but it is acute.]**

Additional Problems

1. What are the hypothesis and the conclusion of the conditional? If a number is even, then it is divisible by 2.

ANSWER Hypothesis: A number is even. Conclusion: It is divisible by 2.

2. How can you write the following statement as a conditional? Adjacent angles share a side.

ANSWER If two angles are adjacent, then they share a side.

3. Is the conditional *true* or *false*? If it is false, find a counterexample.

a. If you live in Miami, then you live in Florida.

b. If a number is divisible by 5, then it is odd.

ANSWER a. true **b.** false; counterexample: 10 is divisible by 5, but is not odd.

4. What are the converse, inverse, and contrapositive of the conditional statement below? What are the truth values of each? If a statement is false, give a counterexample.

If a figure is a rectangle, then it is a parallelogram.

ANSWER Converse: If a figure is a parallelogram, then it is a rectangle. The converse is false. Inverse: If a figure is not a rectangle, then it is not a parallelogram. The inverse is false. Contrapositive: If a figure is not a parallelogram, then it is not a rectangle. The contrapositive is true. Counterexample: A rhombus is a parallelogram that is not a rectangle.

Problem 4

Q If the conditional is true, which other statement must also be true? Explain. **[The conditional and its contrapositive are equivalent statements, so the contrapositive must be true.]**

Q How are the truth values of the inverse and the converse related? **[The truth values of the inverse and the converse must be the same, because these statements are equivalent.]**

Got It?

Q What is the hypothesis of the conditional? **[The vegetable is a carrot.]**

Q What is the conclusion of the conditional? **[The vegetable contains beta carotene.]**

3 Lesson Check

Do you know HOW?

- If students have difficulty with Exercise 2, then refer students to the Take Note table on the top of page 91.

Do you UNDERSTAND?

- If students have difficulty with Exercise 4, then refer students to the Take Note table on the bottom of page 91.

Close

Q How can you conclude that a conditional statement is true? **[If you determine that every time the hypothesis is true, the conclusion is also true, you can conclude that a conditional statement is true.]**

Problem 4 Writing and Finding Truth Values of Statements

What are the converse, inverse, and contrapositive of the following conditional? What are the truth values of each? If a statement is false, give a counterexample.

If the figure is a square, then the figure is a quadrilateral.

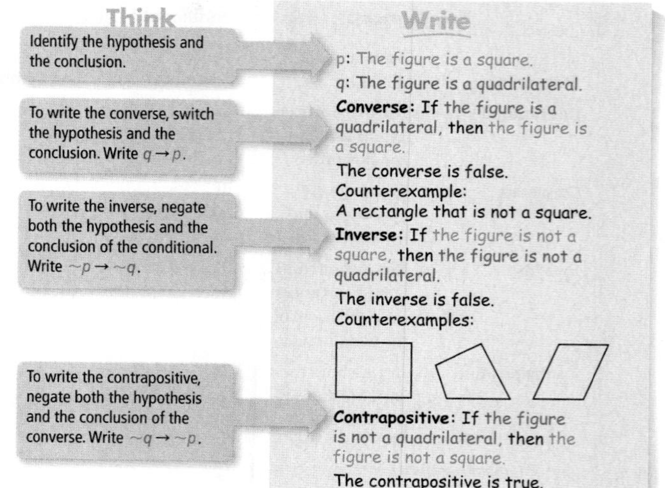

Think
Write
Identify the hypothesis and the conclusion.
p: The figure is a square.
q: The figure is a quadrilateral.
To write the converse, switch the hypothesis and the conclusion. Write q → p.
Converse: If the figure is a quadrilateral, then the figure is a square.
The converse is false. Counterexample:
A rectangle that is not a square.
To write the inverse, negate both the hypothesis and the conclusion of the conditional. Write ~p → ~q.
Inverse: If the figure is not a square, then the figure is not a quadrilateral.
The inverse is false. Counterexamples:
To write the contrapositive, negate both the hypothesis and the conclusion of the converse. Write ~q → ~p.
Contrapositive: If the figure is not a quadrilateral, then the figure is not a square.
The contrapositive is true.

Got It? 4. What are the converse, inverse, and contrapositive of the conditional statement below? What are the truth values of each? If a statement is false, give a counterexample.

If a vegetable is a carrot, then it contains beta carotene.

Lesson Check

Do you know HOW?

1. What are the hypothesis and the conclusion of the following statement? Write it as a conditional.
   Residents of Key West live in Florida.
2. What are the converse, inverse, and contrapositive of the statement? Which statements are true?
   If a figure is a rectangle with sides 2 cm and 3 cm, then it has a perimeter of 10 cm.

Do you UNDERSTAND?

3. **Error Analysis** Your classmate rewrote the statement "You jog every Sunday" as the following conditional. What is your classmate's error? Correct it.
   If you jog, then it is Sunday.
4. **Reasoning** Suppose a conditional statement and its converse are both true. What are the truth values of the contrapositive and inverse? How do you know?

3 Lesson Check

For a digital lesson check, use the Got It questions.

Support in Geometry Companion
- Lesson Check

4 Practice

Assign homework to individual students or to an entire class.

Answers

Got It? (continued)

4. Counterexamples may vary. Samples are given. Converse: If a vegetable contains beta carotene, then it is a carrot. Inverse: If a vegetable is not a carrot, then it does not contain beta carotene. Contrapositive: If a vegetable does not contain beta carotene, then it is not a carrot. The conditional and the contrapositive are true. The converse and inverse are false; counterexample: any vegetable, such as spinach, that contains beta carotene.

Lesson Check

1. Hypothesis: Someone is a resident of Key West. Conclusion: The person lives in Florida. Conditional: If someone is a resident of Key West, then that person lives in Florida.
2. Converse: If a figure has a perimeter of 10 cm, then it is a rectangle with sides 2 cm and 3 cm. Inverse: If a figure is not a rectangle with sides 2 cm and 3 cm, then it does not have a perimeter of 10 cm. Contrapositive: If a figure does not have a perimeter of 10 cm, then it is not a rectangle with sides 2 cm and 3 cm. The original conditional and the contrapositive are true.
3. The hypothesis and conclusion were exchanged. The conditional should be "If it is Sunday, then you jog."
4. Both are true because a conditional and its contrapositive have the same truth value, and a converse and an inverse have the same truth value.

Practice and Problem-Solving Exercises

A Practice

Identify the hypothesis and conclusion of each conditional. See Problem 1.

5. If you are an American citizen, then you have the right to vote.
6. If a figure is a rectangle, then it has four sides.
7. If you want to be healthy, then you should eat vegetables.

Write each sentence as a conditional. See Problem 2.

8. Hank Aaron broke Babe Ruth's home-run record.
9. **Algebra** $3x - 7 = 14$ implies that $3x = 21$.
10. Thanksgiving in the United States falls on the fourth Thursday of November.
11. A counterexample shows that a conjecture is false.
12. **Coordinate Geometry** A point in the first quadrant has two positive coordinates.

Write a conditional statement that each Venn diagram illustrates.

13.

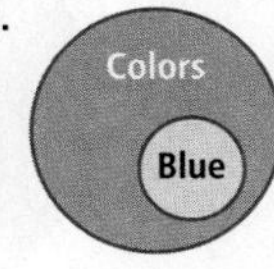

14.

Integers
Whole numbers

15.

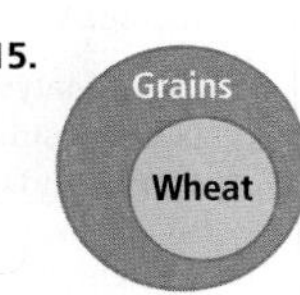

Determine if the conditional is *true* or *false*. If it is false, find a counterexample. See Problem 3.

16. If a polygon has eight sides, then it is an octagon.
17. If you live in a country that borders the United States, then you live in Canada.
18. If you play a sport with a ball and a bat, then you play baseball.
19. If an angle measures 80, then it is acute.

If the given statement is not in *if-then* form, rewrite it. Write the converse, inverse, and contrapositive of the given conditional statement. Determine the truth value of all four statements. If a statement is false, give a counterexample. See Problem 4.

20. If you are a quarterback, then you play football.
21. Pianists are musicians.
22. **Algebra** If $4x + 8 = 28$, then $x = 5$.
23. Odd natural numbers less than 8 are prime.
24. Two lines that lie in the same plane are coplanar.

4 Practice

ASSIGNMENT GUIDE

Basic: 5–24 all, 28–29, 31, 35, 37, 39–40
Average: 5–23 odd, 25–42
Advanced: 5–23 odd, 25–46
Standardized Test Prep: 47–50
Mixed Review: 51–58

Reasoning exercises have blue headings.
Applications exercises have red headings.

EXERCISE 31: Use the Think About a Plan worksheet in the **Practice and Problem Solving Workbook** (also available in the Teaching Resources in print and online) to further support students' development in becoming independent learners.

HOMEWORK QUICK CHECK

To check students' understanding of key skills and concepts, go over Exercises 11, 17, 28, 31, and 37.

Practice and Problem-Solving Exercises

5. Hypothesis: You are an American citizen. Conclusion: You have the right to vote.
6. Hypothesis: A figure is a rectangle. Conclusion: It has four sides.
7. Hypothesis: You want to be healthy. Conclusion: You should eat vegetables.
8. If a baseball player is Hank Aaron, then the player broke Babe Ruth's home-run record.
9. If $3x - 7 = 14$, then $3x = 21$.
10. If it is Thanksgiving in the United States, then it is the fourth Thursday in November.
11. If an object or example is a counterexample for a conjecture, then the object or example shows that the conjecture is false.
12. If a point is in the first quadrant of a coordinate plane, then both coordinates of that point are positive.
13. If something is blue, then it has a color.
14. If a number is a whole number, then it is an integer.
15. If something is wheat, then it is a grain.
16. true
17. false; Mexico
18. false; softball
19. true
20. Converse: If you play football, then you are a quarterback. Inverse: If you are not a quarterback, then you do not play football. Contrapositive: If you do not play football, then you are not a quarterback. The conditional and the contrapositive are true. The converse and inverse are false; counterexample: a person who is a tailback plays football.
21. Conditional: If a person is a pianist, then that person is a musician. Converse: If a person is a musician, then that person is a pianist. Inverse: If a person is not a pianist, then that person is not a musician. Contrapositive: If a person is not a musician, then that person is not a pianist. The conditional and contrapositive are true. The converse and inverse are false; counterexample: a percussionist is a musician.

22–24. See next page.

Answers

Practice and Problem-Solving Exercises (continued)

22. Converse: If $x = 5$, then $4x + 8 = 28$. Inverse: If $4x + 8 \neq 28$, then $x \neq 5$. Contrapositive: If $x \neq 5$, then $4x + 8 \neq 28$. All four statements are true.

23. Conditional: If a number is an odd natural number less than 8, then the number is prime. Converse: If a number is prime, then it is an odd natural number less than 8. Inverse: If a number is not an odd natural number less than 8, then the number is not prime. Contrapositive: If a number is not prime, then it is not an odd natural number less than 8. All four statements are false; counterexamples: 1 and 11.

24. Conditional: If two lines lie in the same plane, then they are coplanar. Converse: If two lines are coplanar, then they lie in the same plane. Inverse: If two lines do not lie in the same plane, then they are not coplanar. Contrapositive: If two lines are not coplanar, then they do not lie in the same plane. All four statements are true.

25. If a group is half the people, then that group should make up half the Congress.

26. If you have never made a mistake, then you have never tried anything new.

27. If an event has a probability of 1, then that event is certain to occur.

28. Yes, he is correct; both are true, because a conditional and its contrapositive have the same truth value.

29. Answers may vary. Sample: If an angle is acute, its measure is less than 90; if the measure of an angle is 85, then it is acute.

30. Answers may vary. Sample: If a person is a pitcher, then that person is a baseball player. If a person is a baseball player, then that person is an athlete. If a person is a pitcher, then that person is an athlete.

31. Natalie is correct because a conditional statement and its contrapositive have the same truth value.

32.

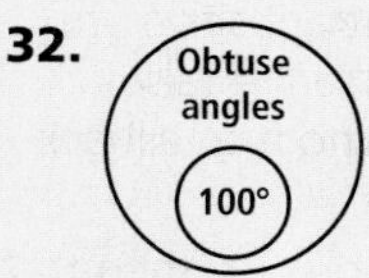

33.

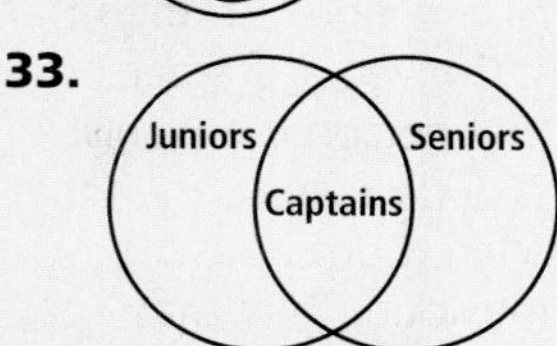

34.

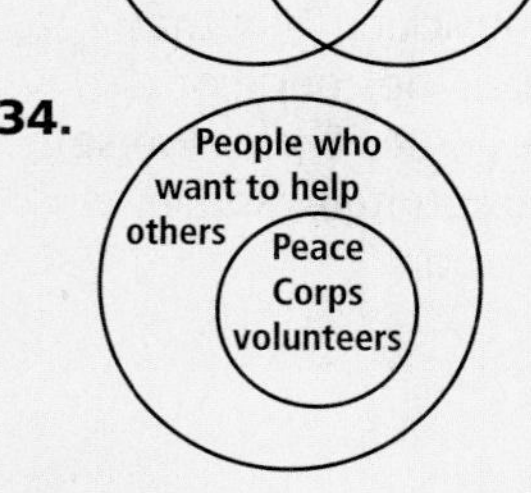

35. If $|x| = 6$, then $x = -6$; false, $x = 6$ is a counterexample.

36. If $-y$ is positive, then y is negative; true.

37. If $x^3 < 0$, then $x < 0$; true.

38. If $x^2 > 0$, then $x < 0$; false, a counterexample is $x = 1$.

39. If you wear Snazzy sneakers, then you will look cool.

40. If two lines intersect, then they meet in exactly one point.

41. If two figures are congruent, then they have equal areas.

42. If you identify any two (distinct) points, then exactly one line goes through those two points.

B Apply

Write each statement as a conditional.

25. "We're half the people; we should be half the Congress." —Jeanette Rankin, former U.S. congresswoman, calling for more women in office

26. "Anyone who has never made a mistake has never tried anything new." —Albert Einstein

27. Probability An event with probability 1 is certain to occur.

28. Think About a Plan Your classmate claims that the conditional and contrapositive of the following statement are both true. Is he correct? Explain.

If $x = 2$, then $x^2 = 4$.

- Can you find a counterexample of the conditional?
- Do you need to find a counterexample of the contrapositive to know its truth value?

29. Open-Ended Write a true conditional that has a true converse, and write a true conditional that has a false converse.

30. Multiple Representations Write three separate conditional statements that the Venn diagram illustrates.

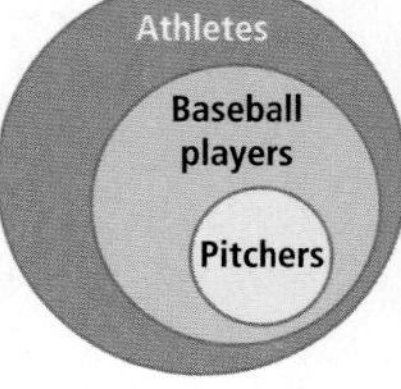

31. Error Analysis A given conditional is true. Natalie claims its contrapositive is also true. Sean claims its contrapositive is false. Who is correct and how do you know?

Draw a Venn diagram to illustrate each statement.

32. If an angle measures 100, then it is obtuse.

33. If you are the captain of your team, then you are a junior or senior.

34. Peace Corps volunteers want to help other people.

Algebra **Write the converse of each statement. If the converse is true, write *true*. If it is not true, provide a counterexample.**

35. If $x = -6$, then $|x| = 6$.

36. If y is negative, then $-y$ is positive.

37. If $x < 0$, then $x^3 < 0$.

38. If $x < 0$, then $x^2 > 0$.

39. Advertising Advertisements often suggest conditional statements. What conditional does the ad at the right imply?

Write each postulate as a conditional statement.

40. Two intersecting lines meet in exactly one point.

41. Two congruent figures have equal areas.

42. Through any two points there is exactly one line.

Challenge Write a statement beginning with *all, some,* or *no* to match each Venn diagram.

43.

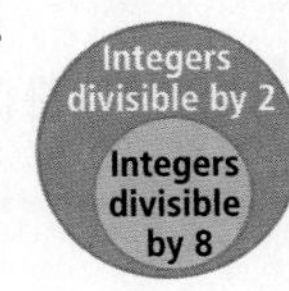

44.

45.

Students
Musicians

46. Let a represent an integer. Consider the five statements r, s, t, u, and v.

r: a is even. s: a is odd. t: $2a$ is even. u: $2a$ is odd. v: $2a + 1$ is odd.

How many statements of the form $p \rightarrow q$ can you make from these statements? Decide which are true, and provide a counterexample if they are false.

Standardized Test Prep

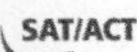

SAT/ACT

47. Which conditional and its converse are both true?

Ⓐ If $x = 1$, then $2x = 2$. Ⓒ If $x = 3$, then $x^2 = 6$.

Ⓑ If $x = 2$, then $x^2 = 4$. Ⓓ If $x^2 = 4$, then $x = 2$.

48. What is the midpoint of the segment with endpoints $(-3, 7)$ and $(9, 5)$?

Ⓕ (6, 12) Ⓖ (2, 4) Ⓗ (3, 6) Ⓘ (6, 6)

49. Which is the best description of the figure at the right?

Ⓐ convex pentagon Ⓒ convex polygon

Ⓑ concave octagon Ⓓ concave pentagon

Short Response

50. Describe how to form the Fibonacci sequence 1, 1, 2, 3, 5, 8, 13 . . .

Mixed Review

Find a counterexample to show that each statement is false. See Lesson 2-1.

51. You can connect any four points to form a rectangle.

52. The square of a number is always greater than the number.

Find the perimeter of each rectangle with the given base and height. See Lesson 1-8.

53. 6 in., 12 in. **54.** 3.5 cm, 7 cm **55.** $1\frac{3}{4}$ yd, 18 in. **56.** 11 m, 60 cm

Get Ready! **To prepare for Lesson 2-3, do Exercises 57 and 58.**

Write the converse of each statement. Then determine the truth value of the original statement and of the converse. See Lesson 2-2.

57. If today is September 30, then tomorrow is October 1.

58. If $\overline{AB}$ is the perpendicular bisector of $\overline{CD}$, then $\overline{AB}$ and $\overline{CD}$ are perpendicular.

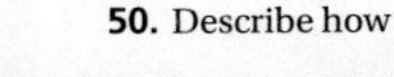

43. All integers divisible by 8 are divisible by 2.

44. No squares are triangles.

45. Some musicians are students.

46. 25 statements

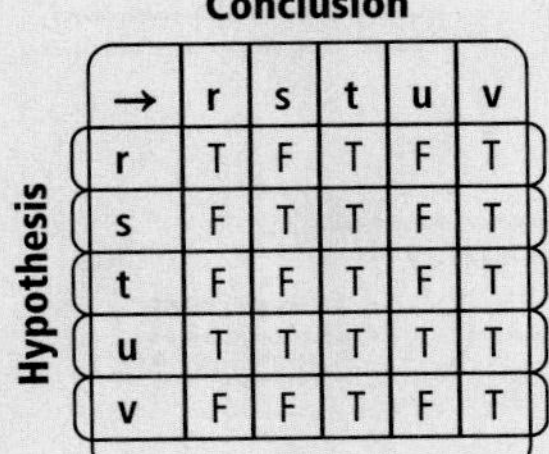

Conclusion (columns); Hypothesis (rows)

→	r	s	t	u	v
r	T	F	T	F	T
s	F	T	T	F	T
t	F	F	T	F	T
u	T	T	T	T	T
v	F	F	T	F	T

Sample counterexamples: for $r \rightarrow s$, $r \rightarrow u$, $t \rightarrow s$, and $v \rightarrow s$: $a = 2$; for $s \rightarrow r$, $s \rightarrow u$, $t \rightarrow r$, $t \rightarrow u$, $v \rightarrow r$, and $v \rightarrow u$: $a = 1$

47. A

48. H

49. D

50. [2] Answers may vary. Sample: Begin with 1 and 1 as the first two terms; after that, each term is the sum of the two preceding terms.
[1] incomplete OR inaccurate description

51. Answers may vary. Sample: 4 collinear points

52. Answers may vary. Sample: 0.5

53. 36 in.

54. 21 cm

55. 4.5 yd or 162 in.

56. 23.2 m or 2320 cm

57. If tomorrow is October 1, then today is September 30; both the statement and the converse are true.

58. If $\overline{AB}$ and $\overline{CD}$ are perpendicular, then $\overline{AB}$ is the perpendicular bisector of $\overline{CD}$; the statement is true and the converse is false.

2-2 Lesson Resources

Differentiated Remediation

Instructional Support

Geometry Companion

Students can use the **Geometry Companion** worktext (4 pages) . . .

- New Vocabulary
- Key Concepts
- Got It for each Problem
- Lesson Check

ELL Support

Focus on Language Write the objectives on the board and read them aloud as you point to each word. Ask: What does it mean to 'recognize' something? Ask students the meanings of key words. Have them read the text and find the definitions. After examining the objectives, ask students to rephrase them in their own words.

Use Graphic Organizers Model the Venn diagram in the Key Concept box, thinking aloud as you redraw it. Model another example like: If a polygon has 3 sides, then it is a triangle. Think aloud as you draw the diagram. Ask for volunteers to contribute other conditional statements for you to model. Then have students make Venn diagrams for conditional statements.

5 Assess & Remediate

Lesson Quiz

1. What are the hypothesis and the conclusion of the following conditional, "If a figure is a triangle, then it has 3 sides"?
2. How can you write the following statement as a conditional? All squares are rectangles.
3. Is the following conditional true or false? If it is false, find a counterexample. If two numbers are odd, then their sum is even.
4. **Do you UNDERSTAND?** What are the converse, inverse, and contrapositive of the following conditional statement? What are the truth values of each? "If today is Sunday, then tomorrow is Monday."

ANSWERS TO LESSON QUIZ

1. Hypothesis: A figure is a triangle. Conclusion: It has 3 sides.
2. If a figure is a square, then it is a rectangle.
3. true
4. Converse: If tomorrow is Monday, then today is Sunday. Inverse: If today is not Sunday, then tomorrow is not Monday. Contrapositive: If tomorrow is not Monday, then today is not Sunday. All three are true.

PRESCRIPTION FOR REMEDIATION

Use the student work on the Lesson Quiz to prescribe a differentiated review assignment.

Points	Differentiated Remediation
0–2	Intervention
3	On-level
4	Extension

PowerGeometry.com

5 Assess & Remediate

Assign the Lesson Quiz. Appropriate intervention, practice, or enrichment is automatically generated based on student performance.

Intervention

- **Reteaching** (2 pages) Provides reteaching and practice exercises for the key lesson concepts. Use with struggling students or absent students.
- **English Language Learner Support** Helps students develop and reinforce mathematical vocabulary and key concepts.

All-in-One Resources/Online

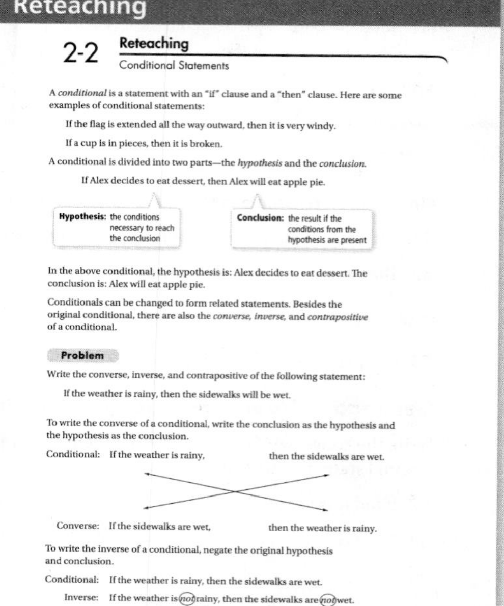

Reteaching

2-2 **Reteaching**

Conditional Statements

A *conditional* is a statement with an "if" clause and a "then" clause. Here are some examples of conditional statements:

If the flag is extended all the way outward, then it is very windy.

If a cup is in pieces, then it is broken.

A conditional is divided into two parts—the *hypothesis* and the *conclusion*.

If Alex decides to eat dessert, then Alex will eat apple pie.

Hypothesis: the conditions necessary to reach the conclusion

Conclusion: the result if the conditions from the hypothesis are present

In the above conditional, the hypothesis is: Alex decides to eat dessert. The conclusion is: Alex will eat apple pie.

Conditionals can be changed to form related statements. Besides the original conditional, there are also the *converse, inverse,* and *contrapositive* of a conditional.

Problem

Write the converse, inverse, and contrapositive of the following statement:

If the weather is rainy, then the sidewalks will be wet.

To write the converse of a conditional, write the conclusion as the hypothesis and the hypothesis as the conclusion.

Conditional: If the weather is rainy, then the sidewalks are wet.

Converse: If the sidewalks are wet, then the weather is rainy.

To write the inverse of a conditional, negate the original hypothesis and conclusion.

Conditional: If the weather is rainy, then the sidewalks are wet.

Inverse: If the weather is *not* rainy, then the sidewalks are *not* wet.

All-in-One Resources/Online

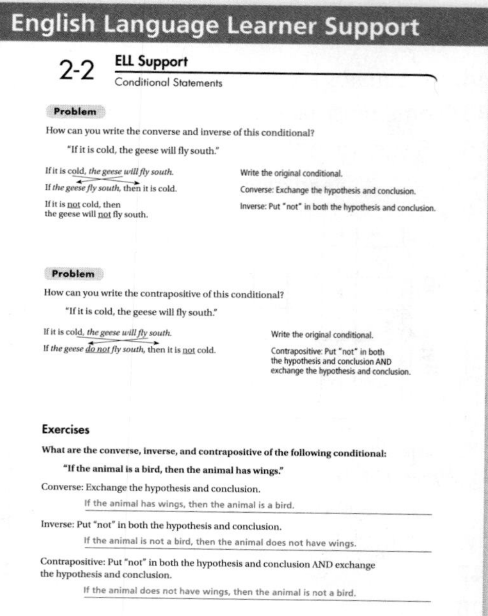

English Language Learner Support

2-2 **ELL Support**

Conditional Statements

Problem

How can you write the converse and inverse of this conditional?

"If it is cold, the geese will fly south."

If it is cold, *the geese will fly south.* — Write the original conditional.

If *the geese fly south,* then it is cold. — Converse: Exchange the hypothesis and conclusion.

If it is not cold, then the geese will not fly south. — Inverse: Put "not" in both the hypothesis and conclusion.

Problem

How can you write the contrapositive of this conditional?

"If it is cold, the geese will fly south."

If it is cold, *the geese will fly south.* — Write the original conditional.

If *the geese do not fly south,* then it is not cold. — Contrapositive: Put "not" in both the hypothesis and conclusion AND exchange the hypothesis and conclusion.

Exercises

What are the converse, inverse, and contrapositive of the following conditional:

"If the animal is a bird, then the animal has wings."

Converse: Exchange the hypothesis and conclusion.

If the animal has wings, then the animal is a bird.

Inverse: Put "not" in both the hypothesis and conclusion.

If the animal is not a bird, then the animal does not have wings.

Contrapositive: Put "not" in both the hypothesis and conclusion AND exchange the hypothesis and conclusion.

If the animal does not have wings, then the animal is not a bird.

Differentiated Remediation *continued*

On-Level

- **Practice** (2 pages) Provides extra practice for each lesson. For simpler practice exercises, use the Form K Practice pages found in the All-in-One Teaching Resources and online.
- **Think About a Plan** Helps students develop specific problem-solving skills and strategies by providing scaffolded guiding questions.
- **Standardized Test Prep** Focuses on all major exercises, all major question types, and helps students prepare for the high-stakes assessments.

Practice and Problem Solving Wkbk/ All-in-One Resources/Online

Practice page 1

2-2 Practice *Form G*
Conditional Statements

Identify the hypothesis and conclusion of each conditional.

1. If a number is divisible by 2, then the number is even.
   Hypothesis: A number is divisible by 2. Conclusion: The number is even.
2. If the sidewalks are wet, then it has been raining.
   Hypothesis: The sidewalks are wet. Conclusion: It has been raining.
3. The dog will bark if a stranger walks by the house.
   Hypothesis: A stranger walks by the house. Conclusion: The dog will bark.
4. If a triangle has three congruent angles, then the triangle is equilateral.
   Hypothesis: A triangle has three congruent angles. Conclusion: The triangle is equilateral.

Write each sentence as a conditional.

5. A regular pentagon has exactly five congruent sides.
   If the figure is a regular pentagon, then it has exactly five congruent sides.
6. All uranium is radioactive.
   If a substance is uranium, then it is radioactive.
7. Two complementary angles form a right angle.
   If two angles are complementary, then they form a right angle.
8. A catfish is a fish that has no scales.
   If the fish is a catfish, then it has no scales.

Write a conditional statement that each Venn diagram illustrates.

9. 

If a language is Italian, then it is a Romance language.

10. 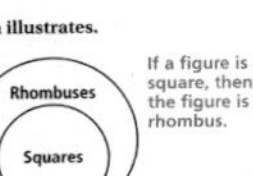

If a figure is a square, then the figure is a rhombus.

Determine if the conditional is *true* or *false*. If it is false, find a counterexample.

11. If the figure has four congruent angles, then the figure is a square.
    False; a rectangle that is not a square has four congruent angles.
12. If an animal barks, then it is a seal.
    False; dogs are animals that bark.

Practice and Problem Solving Wkbk/ All-in-One Resources/Online

Practice page 2

2-2 Practice (continued) *Form G*
Conditional Statements

Write the converse, inverse, and contrapositive of the given conditional statement. Determine the truth value of all three statements. If a statement is false, give a counterexample.

13. If two angles are complementary, then their measures sum to 90.
    Converse: If the measures of two angles sum to 90, then the angles are complementary; true. Inverse: If two angles are not complementary, then their measures do not sum to 90; true. Contrapositive: If the measures of two angles do not sum to 90, then the angles are not complementary; true.
14. If the temperature outside is below freezing, then ice can form on the sidewalks.
    Converse: If ice can form on the sidewalks, then the temperature outside is below freezing; true. Inverse: If the temperature outside is not below freezing, then ice cannot form on the sidewalks; true. Contrapositive: If ice cannot form on the sidewalks, then the temperature outside is not below freezing; true.
15. If a figure is a rectangle, then it has exactly four sides.
    Converse: If a figure has exactly four sides, then the figure is a rectangle; false, a trapezoid has four sides. Inverse: If a figure is not a rectangle, then it does not have exactly four sides; false, a trapezoid has four sides. Contrapositive: If a figure does not have exactly four sides, then the figure is not a rectangle; true.

Draw a Venn diagram to illustrate each statement.

16. If a figure is a square, then it is a rectangle.
    Rectangles
    Squares
17. If the game is rugby, then the game is a team sport.
    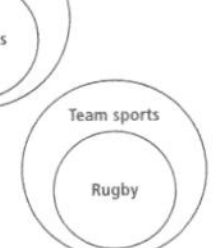

18. **Open-Ended** Write a conditional statement that is false and has a true converse. Then write the converse, inverse, and contrapositive. Determine the truth values for each statement.
    Answers may vary. Sample: conditional: If a figure is a rectangle, then it is a square. (false) Converse: If a figure is a square, then it is a rectangle. (true) Inverse: If a figure is not a rectangle, then it is not a square. (true) Contrapositive: If a figure is not a square, then it is not a rectangle. (false)
19. **Multiple Representations** Use the definitions of p, q, and r to write each conditional statement below in symbolic form.
    p: The weather is rainy. q: The sky is cloudy. r: The ground is wet.
    a. If the weather is not rainy, then the sky is not cloudy. $\sim p \to \sim q$
    b. If the ground is wet, then the weather is rainy. $r \to p$
    c. If the sky is not cloudy, then the ground is wet. $\sim q \to r$

Practice and Problem Solving Wkbk/ All-in-One Resources/Online

Think About a Plan

2-2 Think About a Plan
Conditional Statements

Error Analysis Natalie claims that a given conditional and its contrapositive are both true. Sean claims that the given conditional is true but its contrapositive is false. Who is correct and how do you know?

Understanding the Problem

1. What is the main point of disagreement between Natalie and Sean?
   Sample: Natalie thinks that a conditional and its contrapositive are both true. Sean thinks that only the conditional is true.
2. Do you think it is possible to write a conditional statement that is true, but has a false contrapositive? Explain.
   Sample: No; a conditional statement has the same truth value as its contrapositive.
3. How could you use examples of true and false conditionals to decide who is correct?
   Sample: You could write some conditional statements that you know are true and test whether the contrapositives are true. You could write some conditional statements that you know are false and test whether the contrapositives are false.

Planning the Solution

4. Use a table to test some conditional statements. Write several conditional statements and their contrapositives. Use the table to show their truth values. One example has been completed for you. Use additional paper if necessary. Answers may vary. Sample:

Conditional	True or false?	Contrapositive	True or false?
If a dog has spots, then the dog can fly.	false	If a dog cannot fly, then the dog does not have spots.	false
If a glass is half full, then the glass is half empty.	true	If a glass is not half empty, then the glass is not half full.	true

Getting an Answer

5. What does the pattern in your table tell you about whether Natalie or Sean is probably correct?
   Natalie is correct. If the original conditional is true, then its contrapositive must be true. Either both the conditional and contrapositive are true, or both are false.

Practice and Problem Solving Wkbk/ All-in-One Resources/Online

Standardized Test Prep

2-2 Standardized Test Prep
Conditional Statements

Multiple Choice

For Exercises 1–4, choose the correct letter.

1. What is the hypothesis of the given statement? A
   If pigs had wings, you could fly.
   A. Pigs have wings. C. Pigs do not have wings.
   B. You can fly. D. You cannot fly.
2. Which statement is the converse of the given statement? H
   If you make an insurance claim, then your rates will go up.
   F. If your insurance rates do not go up, then you have not made a claim.
   G. If you do not make an insurance claim, then your rates will not go up.
   H. If your insurance rates go up, then you have made an insurance claim.
   I. If you make an insurance claim, then your rates will not go up.
3. Which statement is the contrapositive of the given statement? A
   If a person is a banjo player, then the person is a musician.
   A. If a person is not a musician, then the person is not a banjo player.
   B. If a person is not a banjo player, then the person is a musician.
   C. If a person is not a banjo player, then the person is not a musician.
   D. If a person is a musician, then the person is a banjo player.
4. How are the two statements given below related to each other? H
   X: If you run for 10 minutes, then you will raise your heart rate.
   Z: If you do not run for 10 minutes, then you will not raise your heart rate.
   F. *Z* is the contrapositive of *X*. H. *Z* is the inverse of *X*.
   G. *Z* is the converse of *X*. I. *Z* is the retrograde of *X*.

Short Response

5. What are the inverse and the contrapositive of the following conditional?
   If a movie is a comedy, then it is funny.
   [2] Inverse: If a movie is not a comedy, then it is not funny. Contrapositive: If a movie is not funny, then it is not a comedy. [1] Only one answer is written correctly. [0] Neither answer is written correctly.

Extension

- **Enrichment** Provides students with interesting problems and activities that extend the concepts of the lesson.
- **Activities, Games, and Puzzles** Worksheets that can be used for concepts development, enrichment, and for fun!

All-in-One Resources/Online

Enrichment

2-2 Enrichment
Conditional Statements

Conditional Chains

You can string together several conditional statements to form a conditional chain or logic chain. If the first condition is met, then all the rest of the conditions will be met.

If the clock strikes 12, then it is time for a shift change.
If it is time for a shift change, then the machinery will shut down for 15 minutes.
If the machinery shuts down for 15 minutes, then the manufacturing plant will be quiet.
If it is quiet in the manufacturing plant, then you can hear other people talking.
Therefore, if the clock strikes 12, you will be able to hear other people talking in the manufacturing plant.

The contrapositive of a conditional chain negates all the statements and reverses the order of the statements. Just as with a simple conditional statement, the contrapositive has the same truth value as the conditional.

If you cannot hear other people talking, then it is not quiet in the manufacturing plant.
If it is not quiet, then the machinery has not been shut down for 15 minutes.
If the machinery is not shut down for 15 minutes, it is not time for a shift change.
If it is not time for a shift change, the clock has not struck 12.
Therefore, if you cannot hear people talking, the clock has not struck 12.

1. Write the contrapositive for the following conditional chain.
   If there is thunder, the cat is frightened. If the cat is frightened, it hisses and puffs up its tail. If the cat hisses and puffs up its tail, the dog runs into another room to get away from the cat. Therefore, if there is thunder, the dog runs into another room to get away from the cat. If the dog does not run into another room to get away from the cat, then the cat has not hissed and puffed up its tail. If the cat has not hissed and puffed up its tail, then the cat is not frightened. If the cat is not frightened, then there is not any thunder. Therefore, if the dog does not run into another room to get away from the cat, there is not any thunder.
2. **Algebra** You might recognize that the Transitive Property of Equality is a conditional chain. If $a = b$ and $b = c$, then $a = c$. Write a transitive property for congruence. (Use the $\cong$ sign.) Answers may vary. Sample: If $a \cong b$ and $b \cong c$, then $a \cong c$.
3. **Open-Ended** Write your own conditional chain with at least four conditionals. Then write the contrapositive of the conditional chain. Answers may vary. Sample: Conditional: If it is winter, then it is snowing. If it is snowing, everyone wears boots. If everyone wears boots, then no one buys sandals. If no one buys sandals, then the sandal store is closed. Therefore, if it is winter, then the sandal store is closed. Contrapositive: If the sandal store is not closed, then someone buys sandals. If someone buys sandals, then not everyone wears boots. If not everyone wears boots, then it is not snowing. If it is not snowing, then it is not winter. Therefore, if the sandal store is not closed, then it is not winter.

Online Teacher Resource Center

Activities, Games, and Puzzles

2-2 Activity: IF, THEN, GOTO...
Conditional Statements

In a computer program, a GOTO statement, along with an IF-THEN statement, tells the computer to go to a particular line in the program if a certain condition is met.

Given any two numbers, the program shown at the right displays the numbers in order according to size.

```
10 INPUT X
20 INPUT Y
30 IF X>Y THEN GOTO 60
40 IF X<Y THEN GOTO 70
50 IF X=Y THEN GOTO 80
60 PRINT Y,X:END
70 PRINT X,Y:END
80 PRINT X; "="; Y:END
```

Refer to the given program, and use the chart below.

Hypothesis (p)	T or F	Negation (~p)	T or F
X > Y (6 > 5)	T	X not greater than Y (6 ≤ 5)	F
X < Y (6 < 5)	F	X not less than Y (6 ≥ 5)	T
X = Y (6 = 5)	F	X ≠ Y (6 ≠ 5)	T

1. For each of the conditional statements used in the program, write the p clause (hypothesis) in the first column of your chart. Then write the negation (~p) in the third column of your chart.
2. Now suppose that X = 6 and Y = 5. Go back to the chart and fill in the truth values for each p and ~p.

In this computer program, the GOTO statement is a link between the hypothesis p and the conclusion q. For example, without the GOTO statement, the first conditional statement of the program would read:

```
30 IF X>Y THEN PRINT Y,X
```

3. Rewrite each of the other IF-THEN statements in the program without the GOTO statement. IF X>Y THEN PRINT Y,X; IF X<Y THEN PRINT X,Y; IF X=Y THEN PRINT X; "="; Y

Suppose that somebody scrambles the instructions in the program so that the second conditional statement reads:

```
40 IF X<Y THEN GOTO 80
```

4. Rewrite this statement without the GOTO statement for X = 3 and Y = 10. IF 3<10 THEN PRINT 3; "="; 10
5. Is the statement you wrote a true conditional or a false conditional? Explain. False; the hypothesis is true, and the conclusion is false.

Guided Instruction

PURPOSE To use logic and truth tables to determine truth values of compound statements

PROCESS Students will

- find truth values of compound statements without tables
- find truth values of compound statements with tables

DISCUSS A truth table shows all the possible truth values for a conditional statement and its related statements.

Q What is the everyday meaning of *compound*? **[more than one]**

Q What is a conjunction? **[more than one statement connected by the word *and*]**

Q What is a disjunction? **[more than one statement connected by the word *or*]**

Activity 1

This Activity requires students to determine truth values of given statements without using a table.

Q When is a conjunction true? **[A conjunction is true when both of its parts are true.]**

Q When is a disjunction true? **[A disjunction is true when at least one of its parts is true.]**

Concept Byte Logic and Truth Tables

Use With Lesson 2-2

ACTIVITY

A **compound statement** combines two or more statements.

take note

Key Concepts Compound Statements

Compound Statement	How to Form It	Example	Symbols
conjunction	Connect two or more statements with *and*.	You will eat a sandwich and you will drink juice.	$s \wedge j$ You say "*s* and *j*."
disjunction	Connect two or more statements with *or*.	You will eat a sandwich or you will drink juice.	$s \vee j$ You say "*s* or *j*."

A conjunction $s \wedge j$ is true only when both *s* and *j* are true.

A disjunction $s \vee j$ is false only when both *s* and *j* are false.

Activity 1

For Exercises 1–4, use the statements below to construct the following compound statements.

s: We will go to the beach.
j: We will go out to dinner.
t: We will go to the movies.

1. $s \wedge j$ **2.** $s \vee j$ **3.** $s \vee (j \wedge t)$ **4.** $(s \vee j) \wedge t$

5. Write three of your own statements and label them *s*, *j*, and *t*. Repeat Exercises 1–4 using your own statements.

For Exercises 6–9, use the statements below to determine the truth value of the compound statement.

x: Emperor penguins are black and white.
y: Polar bears are a threatened species.
z: Penguins wear tuxedos.

6. $x \wedge y$ **7.** $x \vee y$ **8.** $x \wedge z$ **9.** $x \vee z$

Answers

Activity 1

1. We will go to the beach and we will go out to dinner.
2. We will go to the beach or we will go out to dinner.
3. Either we will go to the beach or we will go out to dinner and go to the movies.
4. We either will go to the beach or out to dinner, and we will go to the movies.
5. Check students' work.
6. true
7. true
8. false
9. true

A **truth table** lists all the possible combinations of truth values for two or more statements.

Example	p	q	$p \to q$	$p \wedge q$	$p \vee q$
p: Ohio is a state. *q*: There are 50 states.	T	T	T	T	T
p: Georgia is a state. *q*: Miami is a state.	T	F	F	F	T
$p: 2 + 2 = 5$ $q: 2 \cdot 2 = 4$	F	T	T	F	T
$p: 2 + 1 = 4$ *q*: Dolphins are big fish.	F	F	T	F	F

Activity 2

To find the possible truth values of a complex statement such as $(s \wedge j) \vee {\sim}t$, you can make a truth table like the one below. You start with columns for the single statements and add columns to the right. Each column builds toward the final statement. The table below starts with columns for *s*, *j*, and *t* and builds to $(s \wedge j) \vee {\sim}t$. Copy the table and work with a partner to fill in the blanks.

s	j	t	${\sim}t$	$s \wedge j$	$(s \wedge j) \vee {\sim}t$
T	T	T	F	T	20. ?
T	T	F	13. ?	T	T
T	F	T	F	F	21. ?
T	F	F	T	17. ?	T
F	T	T	14. ?	F	22. ?
F	T	F	15. ?	F	23. ?
F	F	T	F	18. ?	F
10. ?	11. ?	12. ?	16. ?	19. ?	24. ?

25. Make a truth table for the statement $({\sim}p \vee q) \wedge {\sim}r$.

26. a. Make a truth table for ${\sim}(p \wedge q)$. Make another truth table for ${\sim}p \vee {\sim}q$.

b. Make a truth table for ${\sim}(p \vee q)$. Make another for ${\sim}p \wedge {\sim}q$.

c. DeMorgan's Law states that ${\sim}(p \wedge q) = {\sim}p \vee {\sim}q$ and that ${\sim}(p \vee q) = {\sim}p \wedge {\sim}q$. How do the truth tables you made in parts (a) and (b) show that DeMorgan's Law is true?

Activity 2

In this Activity, students are guided through the steps for showing all the columns of a truth table. They are then asked to fill in the blanks in a truth table that is partially finished. This Activity culminates by having students show DeMorgan's Law is true for any statements *p* and *q*.

Q How can you be sure you listed all the possible truth values for *s*, *j*, and *t*? **[There are 2 possible truth values for each individual statement, true or false. The Fundamental Counting Principle can be used to show there are 2 × 2 × 2, or 8 possible combinations of truth values.]**

Q Which column of the truth table shown is used to fill in the blanks in the fourth column (~*t*)? **[third]**

Q Which columns of the truth table shown are used to fill in the blanks in the fifth column (*s* and *j*)? **[first and second]**

Q Which columns of the truth table shown are used to fill in the blanks in the sixth column (*s* and *j* or ~*t*)? **[fourth and fifth]**

Q How do you know DeMorgan's law is true for any statements *p* and *q*? **[The truth tables in part (a) and part (b) have the same end result.]**

10. F
11. F
12. F
13. T
14. F
15. T
16. T
17. F
18. F
19. F
20. T
21. F
22. F
23. T
24. T

25.

p	q	r	${\sim}p$	${\sim}p \vee q$	${\sim}r$	$({\sim}p \vee q) \wedge {\sim}r$
T	T	T	F	T	F	F
T	T	F	F	T	T	T
T	F	T	F	F	F	F
T	F	F	F	F	T	F
F	T	T	T	T	F	F
F	T	F	T	T	T	T
F	F	T	T	T	F	F
F	F	F	T	T	T	T

26a.

p	q	$p \wedge q$	${\sim}(p \wedge q)$
T	T	T	F
T	F	F	T
F	T	F	T
F	F	F	T

p	q	${\sim}p$	${\sim}q$	${\sim}p \vee {\sim}q$
T	T	F	F	F
T	F	F	T	T
F	T	T	F	T
F	F	T	T	T

b.

p	q	$p \vee q$	${\sim}(p \vee q)$
T	T	T	F
T	F	T	F
F	T	T	F
F	F	F	T

p	q	${\sim}p$	${\sim}q$	${\sim}p \wedge {\sim}q$
T	T	F	F	F
T	F	F	T	F
F	T	T	F	F
F	F	T	T	T

c. Answers may vary. Sample: Since the last two columns in the truth tables are the same, DeMorgan's Law is true.

1 Interactive Learning

Solve It!

PURPOSE To have students write a conditional statement whose converse is also true, and thus to write a definition

PROCESS Students may make observations about the sets of insects and noninsects and use deductive reasoning.

FACILITATE

Q What characteristics do all the insects share? **[six legs and its body has three sections]**

Q Do any of the noninsects share these characteristics? Explain. **[No; none of the noninsects have six legs or bodies with three sections.]**

ANSWER See Solve It in Answers on next page.

CONNECT THE MATH Students will learn how to use conditional statements like those written in the Solve It to write biconditional statements and good definitions.

2 Guided Instruction

Problem 1

Q When writing a biconditional, is the order of the hypothesis and conclusion important? Explain. **[No, the converse and the conditional must both be true.]**

Got It?

Q Are the inverse and the contrapositive statements true? Explain. **[Yes, the contrapositive has the same truth value as the conditional, and the inverse has the same truth value as the converse.]**

2-3 Biconditionals and Definitions

Objective To write biconditionals and recognize good definitions

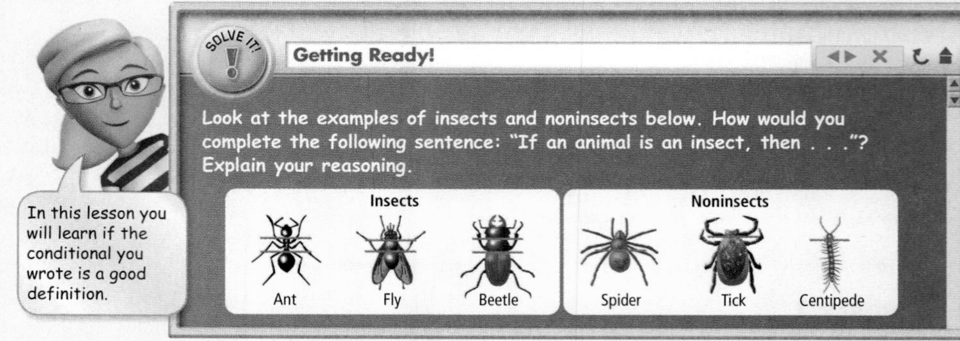

In this lesson you will learn if the conditional you wrote is a good definition.

Lesson Vocabulary
- biconditional

In the Solve It, you used conditional statements. A **biconditional** is a single true statement that combines a true conditional and its true converse. You can write a biconditional by joining the two parts of each conditional with the phrase *if and only if*.

Essential Understanding A definition is good if it can be written as a biconditional.

Problem 1 Writing a Biconditional

What is the converse of the following true conditional? If the converse is also true, rewrite the statements as a biconditional.

If the sum of the measures of two angles is 180, then the two angles are supplementary.

Think

How else can you write the biconditional?
You can also write the biconditional as "The sum of the measures of two angles is 180 if and only if the two angles are supplementary."

Converse: If two angles are supplementary, then the sum of the measures of the two angles is 180.

The converse is true. You can form a true biconditional by joining the true conditional and the true converse with the phrase *if and only if*.

Biconditional: Two angles are supplementary if and only if the sum of the measures of the two angles is 180.

Got It? 1. What is the converse of the following true conditional? If the converse is also true, rewrite the statements as a biconditional.

If two angles have equal measure, then the angles are congruent.

2-3 Preparing to Teach

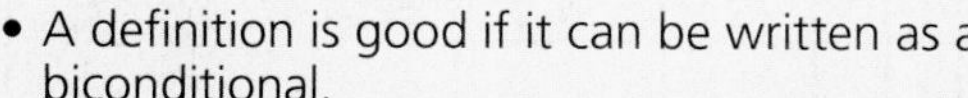

BIG idea Reasoning and Proof UbD

ESSENTIAL UNDERSTANDINGS

- A definition is good if it can be written as a biconditional.
- Every biconditional can be written as two conditionals that are converses of each other.

Math Background

Geometric knowledge can be described as a building-up process. The first terms learned in geometry must be understood and undefined; otherwise, all definitions in geometry would be circular. The terms that follow can be explained using only undefined terms or a combination of undefined terms and previously defined terms. The postulates and theorems that will be learned throughout the text follow the same progression as undefined terms and defined terms. Postulates are assumed to be true without proof, and theorems are proved using postulates and previously proved theorems.

Definitions in mathematics are biconditional statements. One way to help students learn to write mathematical definitions is to have them define everyday objects using the biconditional format. Emphasize the biconditional aspect of all definitions in geometry, because students will need to use both conditional statements in proofs.

Support Student Learning

Use the **Geometry Companion** to engage and support students during instructions. See Lesson Resources at the end of this lesson for details.

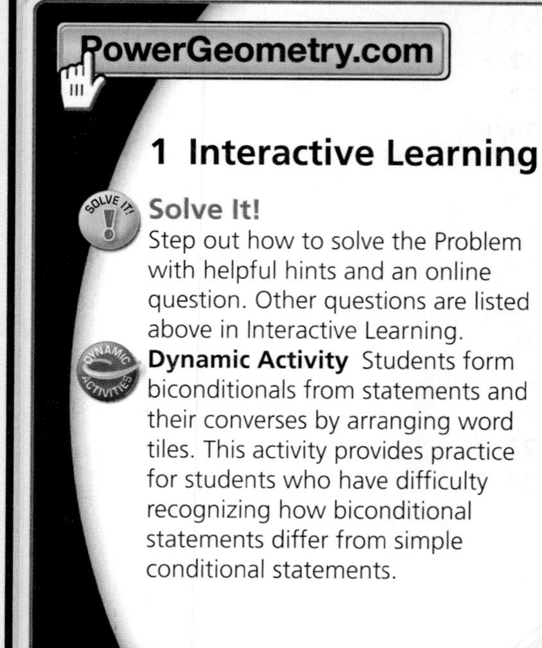

PowerGeometry.com

1 Interactive Learning

Solve It! Step out how to solve the Problem with helpful hints and an online question. Other questions are listed above in Interactive Learning.

Dynamic Activity Students form biconditionals from statements and their converses by arranging word tiles. This activity provides practice for students who have difficulty recognizing how biconditional statements differ from simple conditional statements.

Dynamic Activity
Biconditional Statements

Key Concept Biconditional Statements

A biconditional combines $p \rightarrow q$ and $q \rightarrow p$ as $p \leftrightarrow q$.

Example	Symbols	How to Read It
A point is a midpoint if and only if it divides a segment into two congruent segments.	$p \leftrightarrow q$	"p if and only if q"

You can write a biconditional as two conditionals that are converses.

Problem 2 Identifying the Conditionals in a Biconditional

Plan

How can you separate the biconditional into two parts?
Identify the part before and the part after the phrase *if and only if*.

What are the two conditional statements that form this biconditional?
A ray is an angle bisector if and only if it divides an angle into two congruent angles.

Let p and q represent the following:

p: A ray is an angle bisector.

q: A ray divides an angle into two congruent angles.

$p \rightarrow q$: If a ray is an angle bisector, then it divides an angle into two congruent angles.

$q \rightarrow p$: If a ray divides an angle into two congruent angles, then it is an angle bisector.

Got It? **2.** What are the two conditionals that form this biconditional?
Two numbers are reciprocals if and only if their product is 1.

As you learned in Lesson 1-2, undefined terms such as *point, line,* and *plane* are the building blocks of geometry. You understand the meanings of these terms intuitively. Then you use them to define other terms such as *segment.*

A good definition is a statement that can help you identify or classify an object. A good definition has several important components.

- ✔ A good definition uses clearly understood terms. These terms should be commonly understood or already defined.
- ✔ A good definition is precise. Good definitions avoid words such as *large, sort of,* and *almost.*
- ✔ A good definition is reversible. That means you can write a good definition as a true biconditional.

Take Note

Make sure students realize that the symbols $q \leftrightarrow p$ and the phrase "q if and only if p" are equivalent to those shown in the Key Concept box.

Problem 2

Q Why is the following Venn diagram not an accurate depiction of the biconditional? **[Because both p and q should be within the same circle.]**

rays that are angle bisectors

rays that divide an angle into two congruent angles

Got It?

Q What is the relationship between the two conditional statements? **[They are converses.]**

Ask students to consider definitions found in a science book. Ask students to determine if they have the three components necessary to classify them as *good* definitions.

2 Guided Instruction

Each Problem is worked out and supported online.

Problem 1
Writing a Biconditional
Animated

Problem 2
Identifying the Conditionals in a Biconditional
Animated

Problem 3
Writing a Definition as a Biconditional

Problem 4
Identifying Good Definitions
Animated

Support in Geometry Companion
- Vocabulary
- Key Concepts
- Got It?

Answers

Solve It!

". . . it has 6 legs." OR ". . . its body has 3 sections." OR ". . . it has 6 legs and its body has 3 sections." All of the insects have 6 legs and bodies with 3 sections, but none of the noninsects have 6 legs or bodies with 3 sections.

Got It?

1. Converse: If two angles are congruent, then the angles have equal measure; true. Biconditional: Two angles have equal measure if and only if the angles are congruent.
2. If two numbers are reciprocals, then their product is 1. If the product of two numbers is 1, then the numbers are reciprocals.

Problem 3

Q Which term in the definition of a quadrilateral is assumed to be clearly understood or already defined? **[The term polygon is assumed to be understood or already defined.]**

Q What is a polygon? **[A polygon is a closed plane figure with at least three sides that are segments.]**

Got It?

Make sure to elicit both versions of the biconditional from students in order to emphasize that the biconditional can be written as "*p* if and only if *q*" as well as "*q* if and only if *p*."

Problem 4

Q How can you revise choice A to make it a good definition? **[Answers may vary. Sample: A fish is an animal that breathes using gills.]**

Q How can you revise choice B to make it a good definition? **[Answers may vary. Sample: Quadrilaterals have four angles.]**

Got It?

Q Can you write the definition in 4a as a true biconditional? **[No, the conditional "If a figure has four right angles, then it is a square" is not true.]**

Problem 3 Writing a Definition as a Biconditional

Plan

How do you determine whether a definition is reversible?
Write the definition as a conditional and the converse of the conditional. If both are true, the definition is reversible.

Is this definition of *quadrilateral* reversible? If yes, write it as a true biconditional.
Definition: A quadrilateral is a polygon with four sides.

Think	Write
Write a conditional.	**Conditional:** If a figure is a quadrilateral, then it is a polygon with four sides.
Write the converse.	**Converse:** If a figure is a polygon with four sides, then it is a quadrilateral.
The conditional and its converse are both true. The definition is reversible. Write the conditional and its converse as a true biconditional.	**Biconditional:** A figure is a quadrilateral if and only if it is a polygon with four sides.

Got It? **3.** Is this definition of *straight angle* reversible? If yes, write it as a true biconditional.
A straight angle is an angle that measures 180.

One way to show that a statement is *not* a good definition is to find a counterexample.

Problem 4 Identifying Good Definitions

Plan

How can you eliminate answer choices?
You can eliminate an answer choice if the definition fails to meet any one of the components of a good definition.

Multiple Choice **Which of the following is a good definition?**

Ⓐ A fish is an animal that swims.
Ⓑ Rectangles have four corners.
Ⓒ Giraffes are animals with very long necks.
Ⓓ A penny is a coin worth one cent.

Choice A is not reversible. A whale is a counterexample. A whale is an animal that swims, but it is a mammal, not a fish. In Choice B, *corners* is not clearly defined. All quadrilaterals have four corners. In Choice C, *very long* is not precise. Also, Choice C is not reversible because ostriches also have long necks. Choice D is a good definition. It is reversible, and all of the terms in the definition are clearly defined and precise. The answer is D.

Got It? **4. a.** Is the following statement a good definition? Explain.
A square is a figure with four right angles.

b. Reasoning How can you rewrite the statement "Obtuse angles have greater measures than acute angles" so that it is a good definition?

Additional Problems

1. What is the converse of the following true conditional? If the converse is also true, rewrite the statements as a biconditional.
Conditional: If the sum of the measures of two angles is 90°, then the angles are complementary.

ANSWER Converse: If two angles are complementary, then the sum of their measures is 90°. Biconditional: The sum of the measures of two angles is 90° if and only if they are complementary.

2. What are the two conditional statements that form this biconditional? Two numbers are additive inverses if and only if their sum is 0.

ANSWER If two numbers are additive inverses, then their sum is 0; if the sum of two numbers is 0, then they are additive inverses.

3. Is this definition of an equilateral triangle reversible? If yes, write it as a true biconditional. An equilateral triangle is a triangle with 3 congruent sides.

ANSWER yes; A triangle is equilateral if and only if it has 3 congruent sides.

4. Which of the following is a good definition?
A. Dogs are animals with 4 paws.
B. Squares have 4 sides.
C. Tuesday is the day before Wednesday.
D. An acute angle has a small measure.

ANSWER C

Answers

Got It? (continued)

3. Yes, it is reversible; an angle is a straight angle if and only if its measure is 180.

4a. No, it is not reversible; a rectangle is also a figure with four right angles.

b. Answers may vary. Sample: Obtuse angles have measures between 90 and 180.

Lesson Check

Do you know HOW?

1. How can you write the following statement as two true conditionals?
   Collinear points are points that lie on the same line.
2. How can you combine the following statements as a biconditional?
   If this month is June, then next month is July.
   If next month is July, then this month is June.
3. Write the following definition as a biconditional.
   Vertical angles are two angles whose sides are opposite rays.

Do you UNDERSTAND?

4. **Vocabulary** Explain how the term *biconditional* is fitting for a statement composed of *two* conditionals.
5. **Error Analysis** Why is the following statement a poor definition?
   Elephants are gigantic animals.
6. **Compare and Contrast** Which of the following statements is a better definition of a linear pair? Explain.
   A linear pair is a pair of supplementary angles.
   A linear pair is a pair of adjacent angles with noncommon sides that are opposite rays.

Practice and Problem-Solving Exercises

A Practice

Each conditional statement below is true. Write its converse. If the converse is also true, combine the statements as a biconditional.

See Problem 1.

7. If two segments have the same length, then they are congruent.
8. **Algebra** If $x = 12$, then $2x - 5 = 19$.
9. If a number is divisible by 20, then it is even.
10. **Algebra** If $x = 3$, then $|x| = 3$.
11. In the United States, if it is July 4, then it is Independence Day.
12. If $p \to q$ is true, then $\sim q \to \sim p$ is true.

Write the two statements that form each biconditional.

See Problem 2.

13. A line bisects a segment if and only if the line intersects the segment only at its midpoint.
14. An integer is divisible by 100 if and only if its last two digits are zeros.
15. You live in Washington, D. C., if and only if you live in the capital of the United States.
16. A polygon is a triangle if and only if it has exactly three sides.
17. An angle is a right angle if and only if it measures 90.
18. **Algebra** $x^2 = 144$ if and only if $x = 12$ or $x = -12$.

3 Lesson Check

Do you know HOW?

- If students have difficulty with Exercise 3, have them review Problem 3.

Do you UNDERSTAND?

- If students have difficulty with Exercise 5, then refer students to the three components of a good definition listed on the bottom of page 99.

Close

Q What is the definition of a biconditional?
[A statement is a biconditional if and only if both the statement and its converse are true.]

Lesson Check

1. If points are collinear, then they lie on the same line. If points lie on the same line, then they are collinear.
2. This month is June if and only if next month is July.
3. Two angles are vertical angles if and only if their sides are opposite rays.
4. The prefix *bi-* means "two."
5. The word *gigantic* is not precise.
6. The second statement is a better definition. A counterexample for the first statement is any two nonadjacent right angles.

Practice and Problem-Solving Exercises

7. Converse: If two segments are congruent, then they have the same length; true. Biconditional: Two segments have the same length if and only if they are congruent.
8. Converse: If $2x - 5 = 19$, then $x = 12$; true.
   Biconditional: $x = 12$ if and only if $2x - 5 = 19$.
9. Converse: If a number is even, then it is divisible by 20; false.
10. Converse: If $|x| = 3$, then $x = 3$; false.
11. Converse: If it is Independence Day in the United States, then it is July 4; true. Biconditional: In the United States, it is July 4 if and only if it is Independence Day.
12. Converse: If $\sim q \to \sim p$ is true, then $p \to q$ is true; true.
    Biconditional: $p \to q$ if and only if $\sim q \to \sim p$.

13–18. See next page.

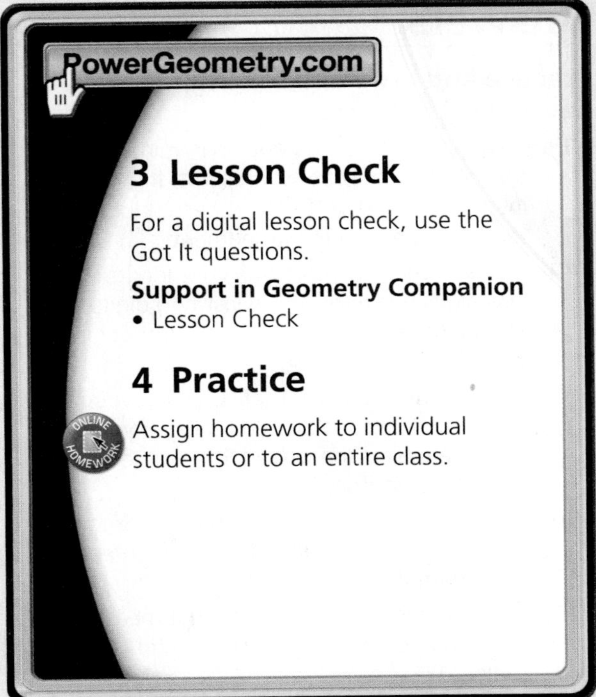
PowerGeometry.com
3 Lesson Check
For a digital lesson check, use the Got It questions.
Support in Geometry Companion
• Lesson Check
4 Practice
Assign homework to individual students or to an entire class.

4 Practice

ASSIGNMENT GUIDE

Basic: 7–30, 33, 35–36, 43, 45
Average: 7–29 odd, 30–46
Advanced: 7–29 odd, 30–48
Standardized Test Prep: 49–51
Mixed Review: 52–57

Reasoning exercises have blue headings.
Applications exercises have red headings.

EXERCISE 33: Use the Think About a Plan worksheet in the **Practice and Problem Solving Workbook** (also available in the Teaching Resources in print and online) to further support students' development in becoming independent learners.

HOMEWORK QUICK CHECK

To check students' understanding of key skills and concepts, go over Exercises 9, 25, 30, 33, and 43.

Test each statement below to see if it is reversible. If so, write it as a true biconditional. If not, write *not reversible.* See Problem 3.

19. A perpendicular bisector of a segment is a line, segment, or ray that is perpendicular to a segment at its midpoint.

20. Complementary angles are two angles with measures that have a sum of 90.

21. A Tarheel is a person who was born in North Carolina.

22. A rectangle is a four-sided figure with at least one right angle.

23. Two angles that form a linear pair are adjacent.

Is each statement below a good definition? If not, explain. See Problem 4.

24. A cat is an animal with whiskers.

25. The red wolf is an endangered animal.

26. A segment is part of a line.

27. A compass is a geometric tool.

28. Opposite rays are two rays that share the same endpoint.

29. Perpendicular lines are two lines that intersect to form right angles.

B Apply

30. Think About a Plan Is the following a good definition? Explain.
A ligament is a band of tough tissue connecting bones or holding organs in place.
- Can you write the statement as two true conditionals?
- Are the two true conditionals converses of each other?

31. Reasoning Is the following a good definition? Explain.
An obtuse angle is an angle with measure greater than 90.

32. Open-Ended Choose a definition from a dictionary or from a glossary. Explain what makes the statement a good definition.

33. Error Analysis Your friend defines a right angle as an angle that is greater than an acute angle. Use a biconditional to show that this is not a good definition.

34. Which conditional and its converse form a true biconditional?

(A) If $x > 0$, then $|x| > 0$.
(B) If $x = 3$, then $x^2 = 9$.
(C) If $x^3 = 5$, then $x = 125$.
(D) If $x = 19$, then $2x - 3 = 35$.

Write each statement as a biconditional.

35. Points in Quadrant III have two negative coordinates.

36. When the sum of the digits of an integer is divisible by 9, the integer is divisible by 9 and vice versa.

37. The whole numbers are the nonnegative integers.

38. A hexagon is a six-sided polygon.

Answers

Practice and Problem-Solving Exercises (continued)

13. If a line bisects a segment, then it intersects the segment only at its midpoint. If a line intersects a segment only at its midpoint, then the line bisects the segment.

14. If an integer is divisible by 100, then its last two digits are zeros. If the last two digits of an integer are zeros, then the integer is divisible by 100.

15. If you live in Washington, D.C., then you live in the capital of the United States. If you live in the capital of the United States, then you live in Washington, D.C.

16. If a polygon is a triangle, then it has exactly three sides. If a polygon has exactly three sides, then it is a triangle.

17. If an angle is a right angle, then it measures 90. If an angle measures 90, then it is a right angle.

18. If $x^2 = 144$, then $x = 12$ or $x = -12$. If $x = 12$ or $x = -12$, then $x^2 = 144$.

19. A line, segment, or ray is a perpendicular bisector of a segment if and only if it is perpendicular to the segment at its midpoint.

20. Two angles are complementary if and only if the measures of the angles have a sum of 90.

21. A person is a Tarheel if and only if the person was born in North Carolina.

22. not reversible

23. not reversible

24. No, it is not reversible; some animals with whiskers are not cats.

25. No, it is not reversible; some endangered animals are not red wolves.

26. No, it is not precise; a point or a ray can be part of a line.

27. No, it is not precise; straightedges and protractors are geometric tools.

28. No, it is not reversible; some pairs of rays that share the same endpoint are not opposite rays.

29. yes

30. Yes; it uses clearly understood terms, is precise, and is reversible. You can write the two statements as two true conditional statements that are converses: If a band of tough tissue connects bones or holds organs in place, then it is a ligament. If a band of tough tissue is a ligament, then it connects bones or holds organs in place.

31. No; a straight angle has a measure greater than 90, but it is not an obtuse angle.

32. Check students' work.

Language **For Exercises 39–42, use the chart below. Decide whether the description of each letter is a good definition. If not, provide a counterexample by giving another letter that could fit the definition.**

39. The letter *D* is formed by pointing straight up with the finger beside the thumb and folding the other fingers and the thumb so that they all touch.

40. The letter *K* is formed by making a *V* with the two fingers beside the thumb.

41. You have formed the letter *I* if and only if the smallest finger is sticking up and the other fingers are folded into the palm of your hand with your thumb folded over them and your hand is held still.

42. You form the letter *B* by holding all four fingers tightly together and pointing them straight up while your thumb is folded into the palm of your hand.

Reading Math **Let statements *p*, *q*, *r*, and *s* be as follows:**

p: $\angle A$ and $\angle B$ are a linear pair.
q: $\angle A$ and $\angle B$ are supplementary angles.
r: $\angle A$ and $\angle B$ are adjacent angles.
s: $\angle A$ and $\angle B$ are adjacent and supplementary angles.

Substitute for *p*, *q*, *r*, *s*, and write each statement the way you would read it.

43. $p \to q$ 44. $p \to r$ 45. $p \to s$ 46. $p \leftrightarrow s$

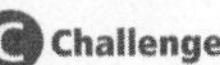 **Challenge**

47. **Writing** Use the figures to write a good definition of a *line* in spherical geometry.

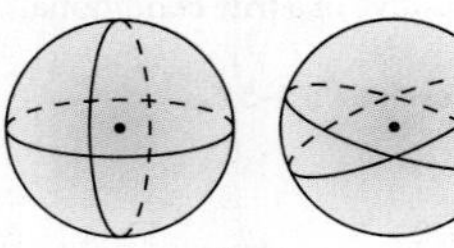
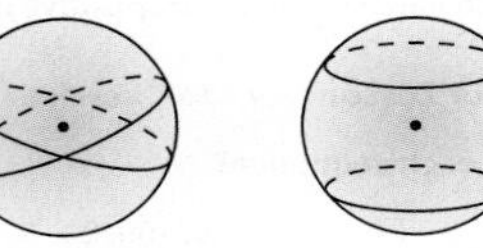
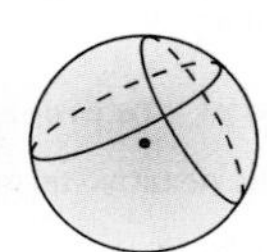

Lines Not Lines

33. That statement, as a biconditional, is "an angle is a right angle if and only if it is greater than an acute angle." Counterexamples to that statement are obtuse angles and straight angles.
34. D
35. A point is in Quadrant III if and only if it has two negative coordinates.
36. The sum of the digits of an integer is divisible by 9 if and only if the integer is divisible by 9.
37. A number is a whole number if and only if it is a nonnegative integer.
38. A figure is a hexagon if and only if it is a six-sided polygon.
39. good definition
40. No; V could fit that description.
41. good definition
42. good definition
43. If $\angle A$ and $\angle B$ are a linear pair, then $\angle A$ and $\angle B$ are supplementary.
44. If $\angle A$ and $\angle B$ are a linear pair, then $\angle A$ and $\angle B$ are adjacent angles.
45. If $\angle A$ and $\angle B$ are a linear pair, then $\angle A$ and $\angle B$ are adjacent and supplementary angles.
46. $\angle A$ and $\angle B$ are a linear pair if and only if $\angle A$ and $\angle B$ are adjacent and supplementary angles.
47. Answers may vary. Sample: A line is a circle on the sphere formed by the intersection of the sphere and a plane containing the center of the sphere.

Answers

Practice and Problem-Solving Exercises (continued)

48a. If an integer is divisible by 10, then its last digit is 0. If the last digit of an integer is 0, then the integer is divisible by 10.

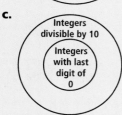

b. Integers with last digit of 0 (outer circle); Integers divisible by 10 (inner circle)

c. Integers divisible by 10 (outer circle); Integers with last digit of 0 (inner circle)

d. Integers divisible by 10; Integers with last digit of 0 (one circle)

e. Answers may vary. Sample: The two circles coincide.

f. Answers may vary. Sample: A good definition can be written as a biconditional because either of the coinciding circles of its Venn diagram can be the hypothesis, and the other the conclusion.

49. D

50. I

51. [4] **a.** If you go to the store, then you want to buy milk; false.

b. Answers may vary. Sample: A counterexample is going to the store because you want to buy juice.

[3] predominantly correct, but with 1 error

[2] at least 1 correct response, and some appropriate information for one other part

[1] some correct information

52. If your grades suffer, then you do not sleep enough.

53. If you have a good voice, then you are in the school chorus.

54. true

55. 60, 50

56. 4, $\frac{4}{5}$

57. 4, −2

48. Multiple Representations You have illustrated true conditional statements with Venn diagrams. You can do the same thing with true biconditionals. Consider the following statement.

An integer is divisible by 10 if and only if its last digit is 0.

a. Write the two conditional statements that make up this biconditional.
b. Illustrate the first conditional from part (a) with a Venn diagram.
c. Illustrate the second conditional from part (a) with a Venn diagram.
d. Combine your two Venn diagrams from parts (b) and (c) to form a Venn diagram representing the biconditional statement.
e. What must be true of the Venn diagram for any true biconditional statement?
f. Reasoning How does your conclusion in part (e) help to explain why you can write a good definition as a biconditional?

Standardized Test Prep

SAT/ACT

49. Which statement is a good definition?

(A) Rectangles are usually longer than they are wide.
(B) Squares are convex.
(C) Circles have no corners.
(D) Triangles are three-sided polygons.

50. What is the exact area of a circle with a diameter of 6 cm?

(F) 28.27 cm (G) 9π m^2 (H) 36π cm^2 (I) 9π cm^2

Extended Response

51. Consider this true conditional statement.

If you want to buy milk, then you go to the store.

a. Write the converse and determine whether it is *true* or *false*.
b. If the converse is false, give a counterexample to show that it is false. If the converse is true, combine the original statement and its converse as a biconditional.

Mixed Review

Write the converse of each statement. See Lesson 2-2.

52. If you do not sleep enough, then your grades suffer.

53. If you are in the school chorus, then you have a good voice.

54. Reasoning What is the truth value of the contrapositive of a true conditional?

Get Ready! **To prepare for Lesson 2-4, do Exercises 55–57.**

What are the next two terms in each sequence? See Lesson 2-1.

55. 100, 90, 80, 70, . . . **56.** 2500, 500, 100, 20, . . . **57.** 1, 2, 0, 3, −1, . . .

2-3 Lesson Resources

Differentiated Remediation

Instructional Support

Geometry Companion

Students can use the **Geometry Companion** worktext (4 pages) . . .

- New Vocabulary
- Key Concepts
- Got It for each Problem
- Lesson Check

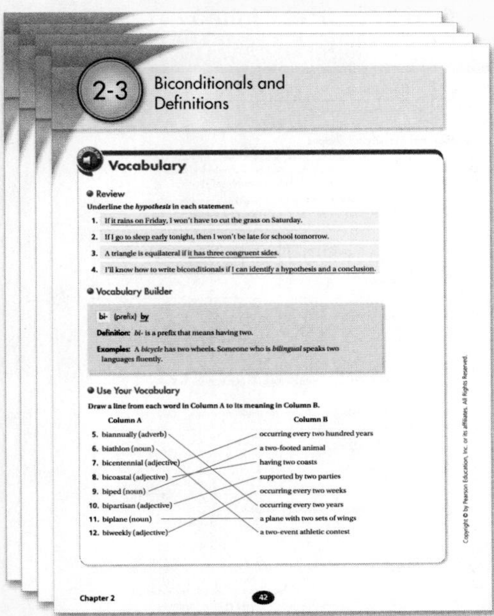

2-3 Biconditionals and Definitions

Vocabulary

Review

Underline the *hypothesis* in each statement.

1. If it rains on Friday, I won't have to cut the grass on Saturday.
2. If I go to sleep early tonight, then I won't be late for school tomorrow.
3. A triangle is equilateral if it has three congruent sides.
4. I'll know how to write biconditionals if I can identify a hypothesis and a conclusion.

Vocabulary Builder

bi- (prefix) by

Definition: *bi-* is a prefix that means having two.

Examples: A *bicycle* has two wheels. Someone who is *bilingual* speaks two languages fluently.

Use Your Vocabulary

Draw a line from each word in Column A to its meaning in Column B.

Column A	Column B
5. biannually (adverb)	occurring every two hundred years
6. biathlon (noun)	a two-footed animal
7. bicentennial (adjective)	having two coasts
8. bicoastal (adjective)	supported by two parties
9. biped (noun)	occurring every two weeks
10. bipartisan (adjective)	occurring every two years
11. biplane (noun)	a plane with two sets of wings
12. biweekly (adjective)	a two-event athletic contest

Chapter 2 42

ELL Support

Assess Understanding Have students list the differences between a conditional and a biconditional statement in their own words. Ask: What is a biconditional statement? How are a conditional statement and a biconditional statement related? How are they different? How do you know a statement is biconditional and not conditional? Tell them to write an example of each.

Focus on Communication Have students work in pairs of mixed abilities. Students can share their written work orally with each other. Invite students to discuss their ideas. When they are finished talking, allow time for students to make edits to their work.

5 Assess & Remediate

Lesson Quiz

1. What is the converse of the following true conditional? If the converse is also true, combine the statements as a biconditional. If a number is even, then it is divisible by 2.
2. **Do you UNDERSTAND?** What are the two conditional statements that form this biconditional? A quadrilateral is a trapezoid if and only if it has exactly one pair of parallel sides.
3. Is this definition of a rectangle reversible? If yes, write it as a true biconditional. A rectangle is a parallelogram with four right angles.

ANSWERS TO LESSON QUIZ

1. Converse: If a number is divisible by 2, then it is even. Biconditional: A number is even if and only if it is divisible by 2.
2. If a quadrilateral has exactly one pair of parallel sides, then it is a trapezoid. If a quadrilateral is a trapezoid, then it has exactly one pair of parallel sides.
3. yes; A parallelogram is a rectangle if and only if it has four right angles.

PRESCRIPTION FOR REMEDIATION

Use the student work on the Lesson Quiz to prescribe a differentiated review assignment.

Points	Differentiated Remediation
0–1	Intervention
2	On-level
3	Extension

PowerGeometry.com

5 Assess & Remediate

Assign the Lesson Quiz. Appropriate intervention, practice, or enrichment is automatically generated based on student performance.

Intervention

- **Reteaching** (2 pages) Provides reteaching and practice exercises for the key lesson concepts. Use with struggling students or absent students.
- **English Language Learner Support** Helps students develop and reinforce mathematical vocabulary and key concepts.

All-in-One Resources/Online

Reteaching

2-3 **Reteaching**
Biconditionals and Definitions

If a conditional statement and its converse are both true, we say the original conditional is reversible. It works both ways because both $p \rightarrow q$ and $q \rightarrow p$ are true.

If a conditional is reversible, you can write it as a **biconditional**. A biconditional uses the words "if and only if." A biconditional can be written as $p \leftrightarrow q$.

Conditional: If a triangle has three congruent sides, then the triangle is equilateral.

Converse: If a triangle is equilateral, then the triangle has three congruent sides.

The conditional is true. The converse is also true. Since the conditional and its converse are both true, the original statement is "reversible" and the biconditional will be true.

Biconditional: A triangle has three congruent sides if and only if it is an equilateral triangle.

Exercises

Test each statement below to see if it is reversible. If it is reversible, write it as a true biconditional. If not, write *not reversible*.

1. If a whole number is a multiple of 2, then the whole number is even.
   Reversible; a whole number is a multiple of 2 if and only if the whole number is even.
2. Rabbits are animals that eat carrots.
   not reversible
3. Two lines that intersect to form four 90° angles are perpendicular.
   Reversible; two lines intersect to form four 90° angles if and only if the two lines are perpendicular.
4. Mammals are warm-blooded animals.
   not reversible

Write the two conditionals that form each biconditional.

5. A parallelogram is a rectangle if and only if the diagonals are congruent.
   If a parallelogram is a rectangle, then the diagonals are congruent. If the diagonals of a parallelogram are congruent, then the parallelogram is a rectangle.
6. An animal is a giraffe if and only if the animal's scientific name is *Giraffa camelopardalis*.
   If an animal is a giraffe, then the animal's scientific name is *Giraffa camelopardalis*. If the animal's scientific name is *Giraffa camelopardalis*, then the animal is a giraffe.

All-in-One Resources/Online

English Language Learner Support

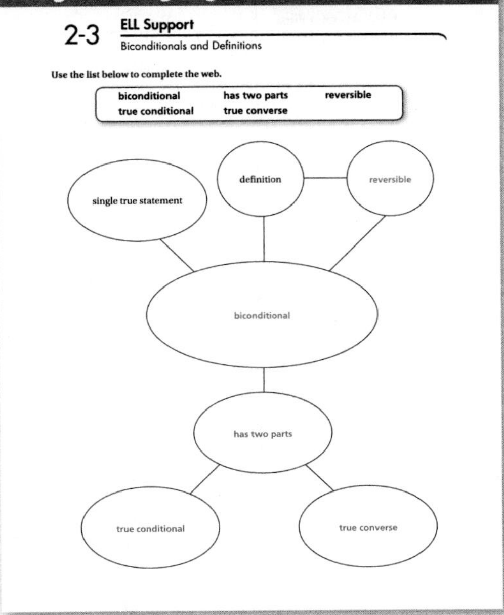

2-3 **ELL Support**
Biconditionals and Definitions

Use the list below to complete the web.

biconditional · has two parts · reversible · true conditional · true converse

Differentiated Remediation *continued*

On-Level

- **Practice** (2 pages) Provides extra practice for each lesson. For simpler practice exercises, use the Form K Practice pages found in the All-in-One Teaching Resources and online.
- **Think About a Plan** Helps students develop specific problem-solving skills and strategies by providing scaffolded guiding questions.
- **Standardized Test Prep** Focuses on all major exercises, all major question types, and helps students prepare for the high-stakes assessments.

Extension

- **Enrichment** Provides students with interesting problems and activities that extend the concepts of the lesson.
- **Activities, Games, and Puzzles** Worksheets that can be used for concepts development, enrichment, and for fun!

Practice and Problem Solving Wkbk/ All-in-One Resources/Online

Practice page 1

2-3 Practice *Form G*
Biconditionals and Definitions

Each conditional statement below is true. Write its converse. If the converse is also true, combine the statements as a biconditional.

1. If a number is divisible by 2, then the number is even.
   Converse: If a number is even, then the number is divisible by 2; Biconditional: A number is divisible by 2 if and only if it is even.
2. If two angles have the same measure, then the angles are congruent.
   Converse: If two angles are congruent, then the two angles have the same measure; Biconditional: Two angles have the same measure if and only if they are congruent.
3. If $x > 5$, then $|x| > 5$.
   Converse: If $|x| > 5$, then $x > 5$.
4. If a closed figure is a pentagon, then it has exactly five sides.
   Converse: If a closed figure has exactly five sides, then it is a pentagon; Biconditional: A closed figure is a pentagon if and only if it has exactly five sides.
5. If two numbers are both even, then the sum of the two numbers is even.
   Converse: If the sum of two numbers is even, then the numbers are both even.

Write the two statements that form each biconditional.

6. Two lines are perpendicular if and only if they intersect to form four right angles.
   If two lines are perpendicular, then they intersect to form four right angles. If two lines intersect to form four right angles, then the two lines are perpendicular.
7. A whole number is divisible by 3 if and only if the sum of the digits of the whole number is divisible by 3.
   If a whole number is divisible by 3, then the sum of the digits of the whole number is divisible by 3. If the sum of the digits of a whole number is divisible by 3, then the whole number is divisible by 3.
8. A whole number is an odd number if and only if it is not divisible by 2.
   If a whole number is an odd number, then it is not divisible by 2. If a whole number is not divisible by 2, then it is an odd number.
9. A person lives in Alaska if and only if the person lives in the northernmost state in the United States.
   If a person lives in Alaska, then the person lives in the northernmost state in the United States. If a person lives in the northernmost state in the United States, then the person lives in Alaska.

Practice and Problem Solving Wkbk/ All-in-One Resources/Online

Practice page 2

2-3 Practice (continued) *Form G*
Biconditionals and Definitions

Test each statement below to see if it is reversible. If so, write it as a true biconditional. If not, write *not reversible.*

10. If a quadrilateral is a square, then the quadrilateral has four congruent angles.
    not reversible
11. An isosceles triangle is a triangle with two congruent angles.
    Reversible; a triangle has two congruent angles if and only if it is isosceles.
12. A circle is a figure with no sides.
    not reversible
13. If a quadrilateral is a trapezoid, it has exactly two sides that are parallel.
    Reversible; a quadrilateral is a trapezoid if and only if it has exactly two sides that are parallel.
14. A person who lives in Miami is a person who lives in Florida.
    not reversible

Is each statement below a good definition? If not, explain.

15. Two rays intersect if and only if they lie in the same plane.
    No; the rays could be parallel.
16. A redwood tree is an evergreen tree that grows very tall.
    No; the statement is not reversible. There are many evergreen trees that grow very tall that are not redwoods.
17. A rectangle is a quadrilateral with four congruent angles.
    yes
18. A hexagon is a polygon with exactly six sides.
    yes

Write each statement as a biconditional.

19. A square is a rectangle with four congruent sides.
    A figure is a square if and only if it is a rectangle with four congruent sides.
20. An equilateral triangle is a triangle with three congruent angles.
    A figure is an equilateral triangle if and only if it is a triangle with three congruent angles.
21. A factor of a whole number is a whole number that divides evenly into the given number.
    A whole number is a factor of a given number if and only if the first whole number divides evenly into the given number.
22. **Open-Ended** Write a definition of your choice. Then write the definition as a biconditional.
    Answers may vary. Sample: A chair is a piece of furniture that is designed for one person to sit on. Biconditional: A piece of furniture is a chair if and only if it is designed for one person to sit on.

All-in-One Resources/Online

Enrichment

2-3 Enrichment
Biconditionals and Definitions

Defining and Classifying Shapes

One aspect of geometric thinking is the ability to look at a group of shapes and find some common features that define the group. For example, you know that rectangles are part of the set of figures called quadrilaterals.

At some point, you may be asked to classify objects based on examples and non-examples. Look at the two sets of objects below. ("Wamps" is a made-up name.)

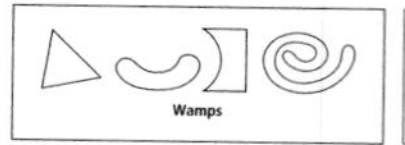

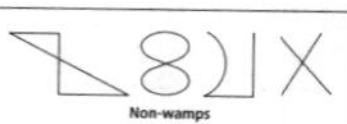

Which of the following objects are wamps?

A. B. C.

Notice that the wamps are all closed figures. The non-wamps are either open figures or two closed figures joined at a single point. So figures A and C above are wamps.

Look at the two sets of objects below. ("Flupes" is a made-up name.)

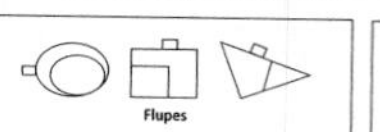

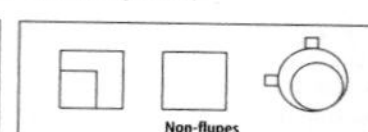

1. Which of the following figures are flupes? Explain.
   A. B. C.
   The figures in A and B are flupes. They have a closed shape that has a similar closed shape within. They also have one small rectangle attached to one side. The non-flupes may have some of these characteristics, but not all.
2. Create a group of figures with certain characteristics and give them a made-up name. Then create a set of figures that are non-examples for your group. Finally, write a definition for the figures in your group.
   Check students' work.

Practice and Problem Solving Wkbk/ All-in-One Resources/Online

Think About a Plan

2-3 Think About a Plan
Biconditionals and Definitions

Error Analysis Your friend defines a right angle as an angle that is greater than an acute angle. Use a biconditional to show that this is not a good definition.

1. What is your friend's statement?
   A right angle is an angle that is greater than an acute angle.
2. The exercise tells you to use a biconditional. What would be a good first step before you write a biconditional?
   Answers may vary. Sample: First write the definition as a conditional statement.
3. Rewrite your friend's statement as a biconditional.
   An angle is a right angle if and only if it is greater than an acute angle.
4. Now write the two conditionals that make up the biconditional. Fill in the blanks to complete the two conditional statements.
   a. If an angle is a(n) _right_ angle, then the measure of the angle is _greater_ than the measure of a(n) _acute_ angle.
   b. If the measure of an angle is _greater_ than the measure of a(n) _acute angle_, then the angle is a(n) _right angle_.
5. Look at the two conditionals. Are both conditionals true? Explain.
   The first of the two conditionals is true, but the second is not true. Obtuse angles also have measures that are greater than the measures of acute angles.
6. What would be the best way to explain that your friend's definition is not a good definition?
   The converse of the original definition is not true. Writing it as the two conditionals that make up a biconditional shows that it only works in one direction.

Practice and Problem Solving Wkbk/ All-in-One Resources/Online

Standardized Test Prep

2-3 Standardized Test Prep
Biconditionals and Definitions

Multiple Choice

For Exercises 1–3, choose the correct letter.

1. Which statement is a good definition of a rectangle? C
   A. A rectangle is a shape with four sides.
   B. A rectangle is a shape with two pairs of parallel sides.
   C. A rectangle is a quadrilateral with four congruent angles.
   D. A rectangle is a parallelogram with four congruent sides.
2. Conditional: If a triangle is scalene, then the triangle has no congruent sides. F
   Which statement shows the conditional written as a true biconditional?
   F. A triangle is scalene if and only if it has no congruent sides.
   G. If a triangle has no congruent sides, then the triangle is scalene.
   H. If a triangle has some congruent sides, then the triangle is not scalene.
   I. A triangle is equilateral if and only if it is not scalene.
3. Biconditional: A triangle is equilateral if and only if the triangle has three congruent angles.
   Which choice shows the two conditionals that make up the biconditional? B
   A. If a triangle has three sides, then it is equilateral. If the triangle is equilateral, then it has three sides.
   B. If a triangle is equilateral, then it has three congruent angles. If a triangle has three congruent angles, then it is equilateral.
   C. If a triangle is scalene, then the triangle is not equilateral. If a triangle is equilateral, then the triangle is not scalene.
   D. An equilateral triangle has symmetry. If a triangle has symmetry, it is equilateral.

Short Response

4. Write this definition as a true biconditional two different ways.
   Definition: A rhombus is a parallelogram with four congruent sides.
   [2] A figure is a rhombus if and only if it is a parallelogram with four congruent sides. A parallelogram has four congruent sides if and only if it is a rhombus.
   [1] The student writes just one form of the biconditional correctly.
   [0] The student writes no correct forms of the biconditional.

Online Teacher Resource Center

Activities, Games, and Puzzles

2-3 Activity: Definition Editor
Biconditionals and Definitions

You work for a publisher editing "My First Dictionary" for young students. For various reasons, each of the following definitions has been flagged for revision. First, explain what is wrong with the existing definition. Then, rewrite it so that it meets the requirements for a good definition.
Answers may vary. Samples are given.

Bat A bat is a long stick used in sports. 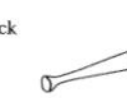 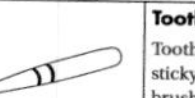 The definition is imprecise, using the word "long" and not describing what sports one plays with a bat. A good definition: A bat is a stick about three feet long used for hitting a ball in a sport such as baseball.	**Toothpaste** Toothpaste is the sticky stuff you use to brush your teeth. The definition is unclear and the word "stuff" is imprecise. A good definition: Toothpaste is the substance placed on a toothbrush to clean teeth.
Fork A fork is a pokey utensil you eat with. 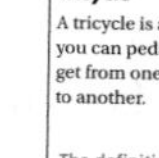 Young students do not commonly understand the word "utensil," and "pokey" is an imprecise word. A good definition: A fork is an eating tool with four separate points.	**Tricycle** A tricycle is a toy you can pedal to get from one place to another. 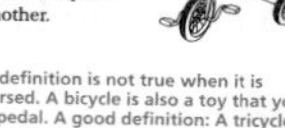 The definition is not true when it is reversed. A bicycle is also a toy that you can pedal. A good definition: A tricycle is a 3-wheeled toy you can pedal to get from one place to another.
Mittens Mittens are the clothes you wear on your hands to keep them warm. The definition is not true when it is reversed. Gloves are also clothes worn on the hands for warmth. A good definition: Mittens are clothes worn on the hands that are divided into a section for the fingers and another for the thumb.	**Wristwatch** A wristwatch is an object that tells you what time it is. The definition is imprecise, describing any clock. A good definition: A wristwatch is a clock that can be worn around the wrist.

Mid-Chapter Quiz

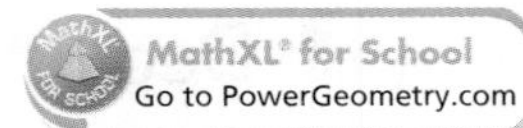
MathXL® for School
Go to PowerGeometry.com

Do you know HOW?

Use inductive reasoning to describe the pattern of each sequence. Then find the next two terms.

1. 1, 12, 123, 1234, . . .

2. 3, 4.5, 6.75, 10.125, . . .

3. 2, 3, 5, 7, 11, 13, . . .

Draw the next figure in each sequence.

4. 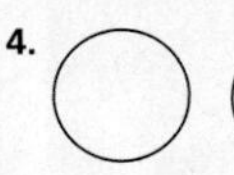  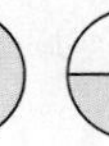

5. 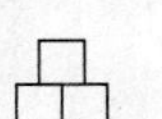 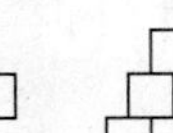

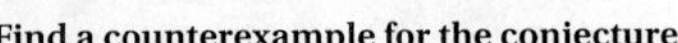

Find a counterexample for the conjecture.

6. Three coplanar lines always make a triangle.

7. All balls are spheres.

8. When it rains, it pours.

Identify the hypothesis and the conclusion of the conditional statements.

9. If the traffic light is red, then you must stop.

10. If $x > 5$, then $x^2 > 25$.

11. If you leave your house, then you must lock the door.

Rewrite the statements as conditional statements.

12. Roses are beautiful flowers.

13. Apples grow on trees.

14. Quadrilaterals have four sides.

15. The world's largest trees are giant sequoias.

For Exercises 16–19, write the converse, inverse, and contrapositive of each conditional statement. Determine the truth value of each statement. If it is false, provide a counterexample.

16. If a figure is a circle with radius r, then its circumference is $2\pi r$.

17. If an integer ends with 0, then it is divisible by 2.

18. If you win the league championship game, then you win the league trophy.

19. If a triangle has one right angle, then the other two angles are complementary.

20. Write the two conditionals that make up this biconditional: An angle is an acute angle if and only if its measure is between 0 and 90.

For Exercises 21–23, rewrite the definition as a biconditional.

21. Points that lie on the same line are collinear.

22. Figures with three sides are triangles.

23. The moon is the largest satellite of Earth.

24. Which of the following is a good definition?

Ⓐ Grass is green.

Ⓑ Dinosaurs are extinct.

Ⓒ A pound weighs less than a kilogram.

Ⓓ A yard is a unit of measure exactly 3 ft long.

Do you UNDERSTAND?

25. **Open-Ended** Describe a situation where you used a pattern to reach a conjecture.

26. How does the word *induce* relate to the term *inductive reasoning*?

27. **Error Analysis** Why is the following not a good definition? How could you improve it?
Rain is water.

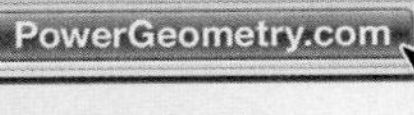
PowerGeometry.com

Answers

Mid-Chapter Quiz

1. Append the next digit; 12,345; 123,456.

2. Multiply the previous term by 1.5; 15.1875, 22.78125.

3. Write the next prime number; 17, 19.

4. 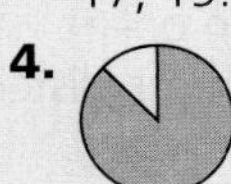

5.  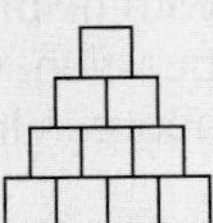

6. Three coplanar, nonparallel lines that intersect at a single point do not form a triangle.

7. a football

8. a light rain; a drizzle

9. Hypothesis: The traffic light is red.
Conclusion: You must stop.

10. Hypothesis: $x > 5$
Conclusion: $x^2 > 25$

11. Hypothesis: You leave your house.
Conclusion: You must lock the door.

12. If a flower is a rose, then it is beautiful.

13. If a fruit is an apple, then it grows on a tree.

14. If a figure is a quadrilateral, then it has four sides.

15. If a tree is the world's largest, then it is a giant sequoia.

16. Converse: If the circumference of a figure is $2\pi r$, then it is a circle with radius r. Inverse: If a figure is not a circle with radius r, then its circumference is not $2\pi r$. Contrapositive: If the circumference of a figure is not $2\pi r$, then it is not a circle with radius r. All four statements are true.

17. Converse: If an integer is divisible by 2, then it ends with 0. Inverse: If an integer does not end with 0, then it is not divisible by 2. Contrapositive: If an integer is not divisible by 2, then it does not end with 0. The conditional and contrapositive are true. The converse and inverse are false; counterexample: 4.

18. Converse: If you win the league trophy, then you win the league championship game. Inverse: If you do not win the league championship game, then you do not win the league trophy. Contrapositive: If you do not win the league trophy, then you do not win the league championship game. All four statements are true.

19. Converse: If two angles in a triangle are complementary, then the triangle has one right angle. Inverse: If a triangle does not have one right angle, then the other two angles are not complementary. Contrapositive: If a triangle does not have two complementary angles, then the triangle does not have a right angle. All four statements are true.

20. If an angle is an acute angle, then its measure is between 0 and 90. If the measure of an angle is between 0 and 90, then the angle is an acute angle.

21. Points lie on the same line if and only if the points are collinear.

22. A figure has three sides if and only if the figure is a triangle.

23. An object is the moon if and only if it is the largest satellite of Earth.

24. D

25. Check students' work.

26. Answers may vary. Sample: Inductive reasoning refers to reaching a general conclusion based on some specific examples, so *induce* refers to reaching a general conclusion based on some specific examples.

27. It is not reversible; rain is water that falls in drops from clouds.

PowerGeometry.com
MathXL for School
Prepare students for the Mid-Chapter Quiz and Chapter Test with online practice and review.

1 Interactive Learning

Solve It!

PURPOSE To have students use a conditional statement representing a real-world situation and the Law of Detachment to solve a problem

PROCESS Students may use trial and error, process of elimination, or logical reasoning.

FACILITATE

- **Q** Which three jeans would you choose to spend as little as possible? **[$24.99, $39.99, and $40.99]**
- **Q** Of these three pairs of jeans, which will you actually pay for? **[$39.99 and $40.99]**
- **Q** How do you find an "average amount? **[Add $39.99 and $40.99 and divide by 3.]**

ANSWER See Solve It in Answers on next page.

CONNECT THE MATH The Solve It requires that students draw conclusions based on a set of facts. They can reduce the thought process to a series of related conditionals.

- If I spend as little as possible, then I will use the coupon.
- If I use the coupon, then I will receive the lowest priced pair of jeans free.

Practicing these mental habits now sets the stage for problem-solving strategies and writing proofs.

2 Guided Instruction

Take Note

The Law of Detachment can be written using symbols as $[(p \to q) \text{ and } p] \to q$. Students may voice that this law is simple common sense. This is a good opportunity to discuss that all logic is basically common sense. The Law of Detachment is also referred to by its Latin name, *Modus Ponens*.

2-4 Deductive Reasoning

Objective To use the Law of Detachment and the Law of Syllogism

How do you know which pair of jeans you'll get free?

SOLVE IT! Getting Ready!

You want to use the coupon to buy three different pairs of jeans. You have narrowed your choices to four pairs. The costs of the different pairs are $24.99, $39.99, $40.99, and $50.00. If you spend as little as possible, what is the average amount per pair of jeans that you will pay? Explain.

BUY TWO PAIRS OF JEANS
Get a THIRD Free*
*Free jeans must be of equal or lesser value.

Lesson Vocabulary
- deductive reasoning
- Law of Detachment
- Law of Syllogism

In the Solve It, you drew a conclusion based on several facts. You used deductive reasoning. **Deductive reasoning** (sometimes called logical reasoning) is the process of reasoning logically from given statements or facts to a conclusion.

Essential Understanding Given true statements, you can use deductive reasoning to make a valid or true conclusion.

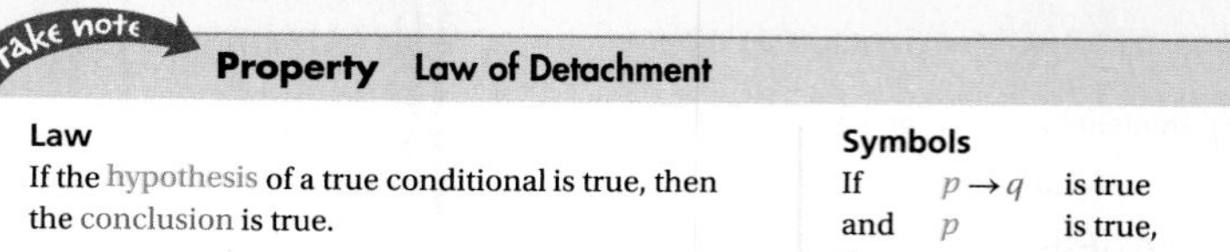

Take note — Property Law of Detachment

Law	Symbols
If the hypothesis of a true conditional is true, then the conclusion is true.	If $p \to q$ is true and p is true, then q is true.

To use the Law of Detachment, identify the hypothesis of the given true conditional. If the second given statement matches the hypothesis of the conditional, then you can make a valid conclusion.

2-4 Preparing to Teach

BIG idea Reasoning and Proof UbD

ESSENTIAL UNDERSTANDINGS

- Given true statements, deductive reasoning can be used to make a valid or true conclusion.
- Deductive reasoning often involves the Laws of Syllogism and Detachment.

Math Background

Students have used deduction (possibly unknowingly) when they have solved puzzles and played games. Among different types of reasoning, deductive reasoning stands out because conclusions reached are logically consistent and valid. With other forms of reasoning, such as inductive reasoning or analogy, conclusions have only the potential of holding true.

This lesson focuses on two rules of formal logic. The Law of Detachment uses a conditional statement (if p, then q) and given information "detached" from p to draw a conclusion. With a true conditional (if p, then q) and a given fact p, then the statement q may be deduced.

The Law of Syllogism is sometimes called the Law of Transitivity. A true conditional statement's conclusion becomes the hypothesis for another true conditional statement. The conclusion of the second conditional can in turn become the hypothesis of a third conditional statement. This process continues until the desired conclusion is reached.

Support Student Learning

Use the **Geometry Companion** to engage and support students during instructions. See Lesson Resources at the end of this lesson for details.

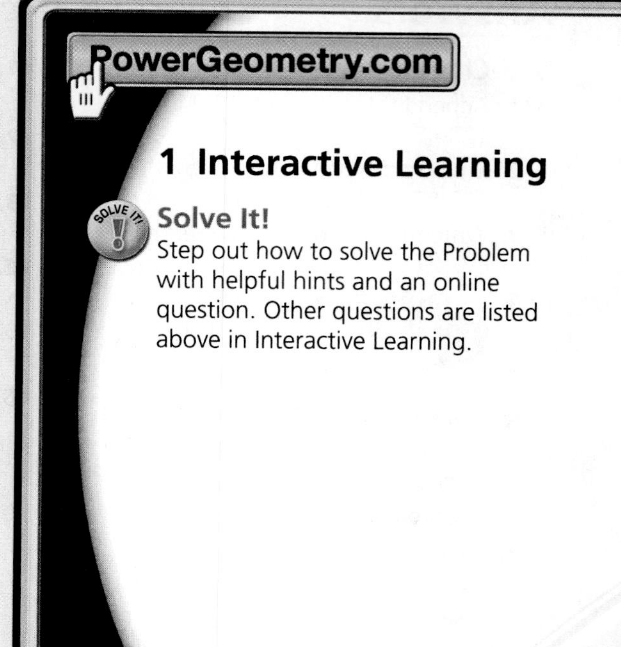

Problem 1 **Using the Law of Detachment**

What can you conclude from the given true statements?

A Given: If a student gets an A on a final exam, then the student will pass the course. Felicia got an A on her history final exam.

If a student gets an A on a final exam, **then** the student will pass the course.
Felicia got an A on her history final exam.

The second statement matches the hypothesis of the given conditional. By the Law of Detachment, you can make a conclusion.

You conclude: Felicia will pass her history course.

B Given: If a ray divides an angle into two congruent angles, then the ray is an angle bisector.
$\overrightarrow{RS}$ divides $\angle ARB$ so that $\angle ARS \cong \angle SRB$.

If a ray divides an angle into two congruent angles, **then** the ray is an angle bisector.
$\overrightarrow{RS}$ divides $\angle ARB$ so that $\angle ARS \cong \angle SRB$.

The second statement matches the hypothesis of the given conditional. By the Law of Detachment, you can make a conclusion.

You conclude: $\overrightarrow{RS}$ is an angle bisector.

Think
In part (C), the second statement is not a subset of the hypothesis. Instead, it is a subset of the conditional's conclusion.

C Given: If two angles are adjacent, then they share a common vertex.
$\angle 1$ and $\angle 2$ share a common vertex.

If two angles are adjacent, **then** they share a common vertex.
$\angle 1$ and $\angle 2$ share a common vertex.

The information in the second statement about $\angle 1$ and $\angle 2$ does not tell you if the angles are adjacent. The second statement does not match the hypothesis of the given conditional, so you cannot use the Law of Detachment. $\angle 1$ and $\angle 2$ could be vertical angles, since vertical angles also share a common vertex. You cannot make a conclusion.

Got It? **1.** What can you conclude from the given information?
a. If there is lightning, then it is not safe to be out in the open. Marla sees lightning from the soccer field.
b. If a figure is a square, then its sides have equal length. Figure *ABCD* has sides of equal length.

Problem 1

Q Could you make a valid conclusion if the second statement were "Felicia passed the course?" Explain. **[No, because the statement would not match the hypothesis of the conditional.]**

Q What is the converse of the conditional statement in B? Is it true? **[If a ray is an angle bisector, it divides an angle into two congruent angles. It is true.]**

Q In C, what second statement would allow you to make a valid conclusion? **[$\angle 1$ and $\angle 2$ are adjacent angles.]**

Got It? ERROR PREVENTION

If students draw an invalid conclusion from 1b, first ask students to identify a counterexample for their false conclusions. Further, have them verbalize the mistake they made when employing the Law of Detachment.

2 Guided Instruction

Each Problem is worked out and supported online.

Problem 1
Using the Law of Detachment
Animated

Problem 2
Using the Law of Syllogism
Animated

Problem 3
Using the Laws of Syllogism and Detachment
Animated

Support in Geometry Companion

- Vocabulary
- Key Concepts
- Got It?

Answers

Solve It!

$26.99; to spend as little as possible using the coupon, you should select the three lowest priced jeans. The lowest priced pair of the three is free and the average amount you spend is the sum of the two higher priced pairs divided by 3.

Got It?

1a. Marla is not safe out in the open.
b. No conclusion is possible.

Take Note

Students may recognize the Law of Syllogism as being similar to the Transitive Property introduced in a previous Algebra course.

A key difference to note between the Law of Syllogism and the Law of Detachment is that syllogism involves three statements, while detachment involves two statements.

The Law of Syllogism is also called the *Chain Rule*.

Problem 2

Q Could the statement that is concluded in A be written as a biconditional? Explain. **[No, the converse of the statement is not true.]**

Q How can you reword one of the statements in B such that the Law of Syllogism can be applied? **[Answers may vary. Sample answer: If you are flexible, then you spend time stretching your muscles.]**

Got It?

Q Prior to applying the Law of Syllogism, what examination should be made of both conditional statements? **[You should make sure both conditional statements are true.]**

Another law of deductive reasoning is the Law of Syllogism. The **Law of Syllogism** allows you to state a conclusion from two true conditional statements when the conclusion of one statement is the hypothesis of the other statement.

take note

Property **Law of Syllogism**

Symbols

If	$p \rightarrow q$	is true
and	$q \rightarrow r$	is true,
then	$p \rightarrow r$	is true.

Example

If it is July, then you are on summer vacation.

If you are on summer vacation, then you work at a smoothie shop.

You conclude: If it is July, then you work at a smoothie shop.

Problem 2 Using the Law of Syllogism

Plan

When can you use the Law of Syllogism?
You can use the Law of Syllogism when the conclusion of one statement is the hypothesis of the other.

What can you conclude from the given information?

A Given: If a figure is a square, then the figure is a rectangle.
If a figure is a rectangle, then the figure has four sides.

If a figure is a square, then the figure is a rectangle.
If a figure is a rectangle, then the figure has four sides.

The conclusion of the first statement is the hypothesis of the second statement, so you can use the Law of Syllogism to make a conclusion.

You conclude: If a figure is a square, then the figure has four sides.

B Given: If you do gymnastics, then you are flexible.
If you do ballet, then you are flexible.

If you do gymnastics, then you are flexible.
If you do ballet, then you are flexible.

The statements have the same conclusion. Neither conclusion is the hypothesis of the other statement, so you cannot use the Law of Syllogism. You cannot make a conclusion.

Got It? 2. What can you conclude from the given information? What is your reasoning?

a. If a whole number ends in 0, then it is divisible by 10.
If a whole number is divisible by 10, then it is divisible by 5.

b. If $\overrightarrow{AB}$ and $\overrightarrow{AD}$ are opposite rays, then the two rays form a straight angle.
If two rays are opposite rays, then the two rays form a straight angle.

Additional Problems

1. What can you conclude from the given true statements?

a. Given: If it is raining outside, then there are clouds in the sky. It is raining today.

b. Given: If Malcolm scores at least 85% on his final exam, then he will earn an A for the term. Malcolm scores a 90% on his final exam.

c. Given: If two angles are vertical, then they are congruent. Angles 3 and 4 are vertical angles.

ANSWER a. There are clouds in the sky. **b.** Malcolm will earn an A for the term. **c.** Angles 3 and 4 are congruent.

2. What can you conclude from the given information?

a. Given: If a number is divisible by 12, then it is divisible by 6. If a number is divisible by 6, then it is divisible by 3.

b. Given: If a figure is a square, then the figure is a parallelogram. If a figure is a rectangle, then the figure is a parallelogram.

ANSWER a. If a number is divisible by 12, then it is divisible by 3. **b.** No conclusion.

3. What can you conclude from the given information?

Given: If you live in Cincinnati, then you live in Ohio. If you live in Ohio, then you live in the United States. Ken lives in Cincinnati.

ANSWER Ken lives in the United States.

You can use the Law of Syllogism and the Law of Detachment together to make conclusions.

Problem 3 Using the Laws of Syllogism and Detachment

What can you conclude from the given information?

Given: If you live in Accra, then you live in Ghana. If you live in Ghana, then you live in Africa. Aissa lives in Accra.

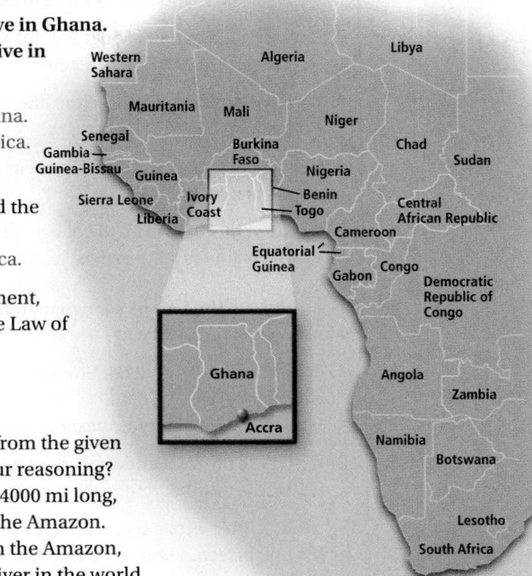

If you live in Accra, then you live in Ghana.
If you live in Ghana, then you live in Africa.
Aissa lives in Accra.

You can use the first two statements and the Law of Syllogism to conclude:
If you live in Accra, then you live in Africa.

You can use this new conditional statement, the fact that Aissa lives in Accra, and the Law of Detachment to make a conclusion.

You conclude: Aissa lives in Africa.

Think

Does the conclusion make sense?
Accra is a city in Ghana, which is an African nation. So if a person lives in Accra, then that person lives in Africa. The conclusion makes sense.

Got It? 3. a. What can you conclude from the given information? What is your reasoning?
If a river is more than 4000 mi long, then it is longer than the Amazon.
If a river is longer than the Amazon, then it is the longest river in the world.
The Nile is 4132 mi long.

b. Reasoning In Problem 3, does it matter whether you use the Law of Syllogism or the Law of Detachment first? Explain.

Lesson Check

Do You Know HOW?

If possible, make a conclusion from the given true statements. What reasoning did you use?

1. If it is Tuesday, then you will go bowling.
You go bowling.
2. If a figure is a three-sided polygon, then it is a triangle.
Figure ABC is a three-sided polygon.
3. If it is Saturday, then you walk to work.
If you walk to work, then you wear sneakers.

Do You UNDERSTAND?

4. **Error Analysis** What is the error in the reasoning below?

> Birds that weigh more than 50 pounds cannot fly. A kiwi cannot fly. So, a kiwi weighs more than 50 pounds.

5. **Compare and Contrast** How is deductive reasoning different from inductive reasoning?

Problem 3

Q To use the Law of Syllogism, what conditions must be satisfied? **[Both conditionals must be true, and the hypothesis of one of the conditionals must be equivalent to the conclusion of another conditional.]**

Q To use the Law of Detachment, what condition must be satisfied? **[The second given statement must match the hypothesis of the conditional statement.]**

Got It?

Q What new conditional statement can you construct using the Law of Syllogism with the information given in Question 3(a)? **[If a river is more than 4000 mi long, then it is the longest river in the world.]**

3 Lesson Check

Do you know HOW?

- If students have difficulty with Exercise 1, then ask students to identify the condition of the law that was not satisfied.

Do you UNDERSTAND?

- If students have difficulty with Exercise 4, then first make sure that students can accurately identify the hypothesis and conclusion presented in the conditional statement, and then refer them to Problem 1C.

Close

Q If only one of the laws is to be used to reach a conclusion, how can you quickly determine which to use? **[The Law of Syllogism is used when two conditionals are provided. The Law of Detachment is used when only one conditional is provided.]**

Answers

Got It? (continued)

2a. If a whole number ends in 0, then it is divisible by 5; Law of Syllogism.

b. No conclusion is possible.

3a. The Nile is the longest river in the world; Law of Syllogism and Law of Detachment.

b. Yes; if you use the Law of Detachment first, then you must use it again to reach the same conclusion. The Law of Syllogism is not used.

Lesson Check

1. No conclusion is possible.
2. Figure ABC is a triangle; Law of Detachment.
3. If it is Saturday, then you wear sneakers; Law of Syllogism.
4. The Law of Detachment cannot be applied because the hypothesis is not satisfied.
5. Answers may vary. Sample: Deductive reasoning uses logic to reach conclusions, while inductive reasoning bases conclusions on unproved (but possibly true) conjectures.

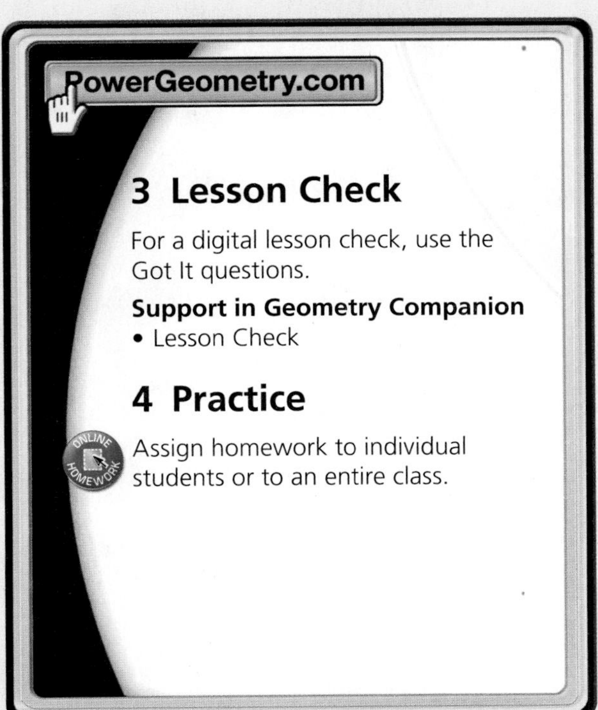

4 Practice

ASSIGNMENT GUIDE
Basic: 6–21, 26, 28, 30
Average: 7–17 odd, 18–30
Advanced: 7–17 odd, 18–32
Standardized Test Prep: 33–34
Mixed Review: 35–39
Reasoning exercises have blue headings.
Applications exercises have red headings.
EXERCISE 30: Use the Think About a Plan worksheet in the **Practice and Problem Solving Workbook** (also available in the Teaching Resources in print and online) to further support students' development in becoming independent learners.

HOMEWORK QUICK CHECK
To check students' understanding of key skills and concepts, go over Exercises 9, 17, 18, 28, and 30.

Practice and Problem-Solving Exercises

A Practice

If possible, use the Law of Detachment to make a conclusion. If it is not possible to make a conclusion, tell why. See Problem 1.

6. If a doctor suspects her patient has a broken bone, then she should take an X-ray.
Dr. Ngemba suspects Lilly has a broken arm.

7. If a rectangle has side lengths 3 cm and 4 cm, then it has area 12 cm^2.
Rectangle *ABCD* has area 12 cm^2.

8. If three points are on the same line, then they are collinear.
Points *X*, *Y*, and *Z* are on line *m*.

9. If an angle is obtuse, then it is not acute.
$\angle XYZ$ is not obtuse.

10. If a student wants to go to college, then the student must study hard.
Rashid wants to go to Pennsylvania State University.

If possible, use the Law of Syllogism to make a conclusion. If it is not possible to make a conclusion, tell why. See Problem 2.

11. Ecology If an animal is a Florida panther, then its scientific name is *Puma concolor coryi*.
If an animal is a *Puma concolor coryi*, then it is endangered.

12. If a whole number ends in 6, then it is divisible by 2.
If a whole number ends in 4, then it is divisible by 2.

13. If a line intersects a segment at its midpoint, then the line bisects the segment.
If a line bisects a segment, then it divides the segment into two congruent segments.

14. If you improve your vocabulary, then you will improve your score on a standardized test.
If you read often, then you will improve your vocabulary.

Use the Law of Detachment and the Law of Syllogism to make conclusions from the following statements. If it is not possible to make a conclusion, tell why. See Problem 3.

15. If a mountain is the highest in Alaska, then it is the highest in the United States.
If an Alaskan mountain is more than 20,300 ft high, then it is the highest in Alaska.
Alaska's Mount McKinley is 20,320 ft high.

16. If you live in the Bronx, then you live in New York.
Tracy lives in the Bronx.
If you live in New York, then you live in the eleventh state to enter the Union.

17. If you are studying botany, then you are studying biology.
If you are studying biology, then you are studying a science.
Shanti is taking science this year.

Answers

Practice and Problem-Solving Exercises

6. Dr. Ngemba should take an X-ray.
7. No conclusion is possible; the hypothesis has not been satisfied.
8. Points *X*, *Y*, and *Z* are collinear.
9. No conclusion is possible; the hypothesis has not been satisfied.
10. Rashid must study hard.
11. If an animal is a Florida panther, then it is endangered.
12. No conclusion is possible; the same statement does not appear as the conclusion of one conditional and as the hypothesis of the other conditional.
13. If a line intersects a segment at its midpoint, then it divides the segment into two congruent segments.
14. If you read often, then you will improve your score on a standardized test.
15. Alaska's Mount McKinley is the highest mountain in the U.S.
16. Tracy lives in the 11th state to enter the Union.
17. If you are studying botany, then you are studying a science. (Law of Syllogism only) No conclusion can be made about Shanti.

Apply

18. **Think About a Plan** If it is the night of your weekly basketball game, your family eats at your favorite restaurant. When your family eats at your favorite restaurant, you always get chicken fingers. If it is Tuesday, then it is the night of your weekly basketball game. How much do you pay for chicken fingers after your game? Use the specials board at the right to decide. Explain your reasoning.
    - How can you reorder and rewrite the sentences to help you?
    - How can you use the Law of Syllogism to answer the question?

Monday
salads $4.99
Tuesday
chicken fingers $5.99
Wednesday
burgers $6.99

Beverages **For Exercises 19–24, assume that the following statements are true.**

A. If Maria is drinking juice, then it is breakfast time.
B. If it is lunchtime, then Kira is drinking milk and nothing else.
C. If it is mealtime, then Curtis is drinking water and nothing else.
D. If it is breakfast time, then Julio is drinking juice and nothing else.
E. Maria is drinking juice.

Use only the information given above. For each statement, write *must be true*, *may be true*, or *is not true*. Explain your reasoning.

19. Julio is drinking juice.
20. Curtis is drinking water.
21. Kira is drinking milk.
22. Curtis is drinking juice.
23. Maria is drinking water.
24. Julio is drinking milk.

25. **Physics** Quarks are subatomic particles identified by electric charge and rest energy. The table shows how to categorize quarks by their flavors. Show how the Law of Detachment and the table are used to identify the flavor of a quark with a charge of $-\frac{1}{3}\,e$ and rest energy 540 MeV.

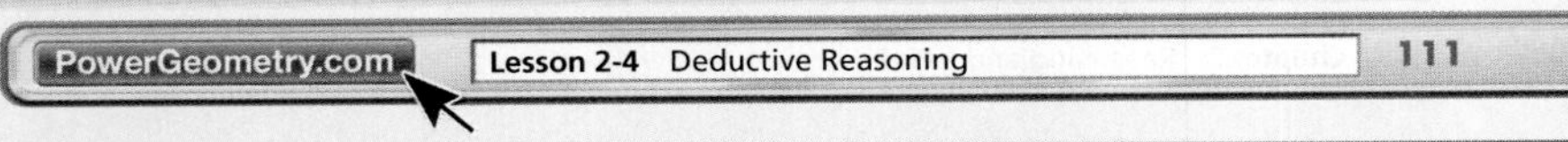

Rest Energy and Charge of Quarks

Rest Energy (MeV)	360	360	1500	540	173,000	5000
Electric Charge (e)	$+\frac{2}{3}$	$-\frac{1}{3}$	$+\frac{2}{3}$	$-\frac{1}{3}$	$+\frac{2}{3}$	$-\frac{1}{3}$
Flavor	Up	Down	Charmed	Strange	Top	Bottom

Write the first statement as a conditional. If possible, use the Law of Detachment to make a conclusion. If it is not possible to make a conclusion, tell why.

26. All national parks are interesting.
    Mammoth Cave is a national park.
27. All squares are rectangles.
    $ABCD$ is a square.
28. The temperature is always above 32°F in Key West, Florida.
    The temperature is 62°F.
29. Every high school student likes art.
    Ling likes art.

30. **Writing** Give an example of a rule used in your school that could be written as a conditional. Explain how the Law of Detachment is used in applying that rule.

18. $5.99; your family goes to your favorite restaurant on the night of your weekly game, which is on Tuesday. Chicken fingers are $5.99 on Tuesday.
19. Must be true; by E and A, it is breakfast time; by D, Julio is drinking juice.
20. Must be true; by E and A, it is breakfast time; by C, Curtis is drinking water.
21. May be true; by E and A, it is breakfast time. You don't know what Kira drinks at breakfast.
22. Is not true; by E and A, it is breakfast time; by C, Curtis drinks water and nothing else.
23. May be true; by E, Maria is drinking juice. You don't know if she also drinks water.
24. Is not true; by A and E, it is breakfast time; by D, Julio is drinking juice and nothing else.
25. strange
26. If a place is a national park, then it is an interesting place; Mammoth Cave is an interesting place.
27. If a figure is a square, then it is a rectangle; *ABCD* is a rectangle.
28. If you are in Key West, Florida, then the temperature is always above 32°F; no conclusion is possible because the hypothesis is not satisfied.
29. If a person is a high school student, then the person likes art; no conclusion is possible because the hypothesis is not satisfied.
30. Check students' work.

Answers

Practice and Problem-Solving Exercises (continued)

31a.

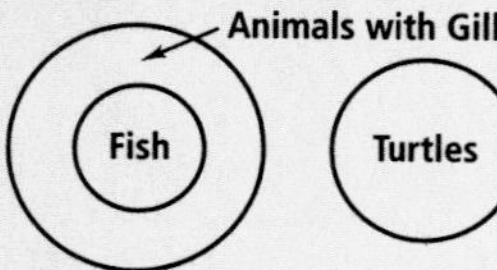

b. Turtles are not in the circle of animals with gills, so a turtle is not a fish.

32a. The result is two more than the chosen integer.

b. $x + 2$

c. The expression in part (b) is equivalent to the conjecture in part (a). In part (a) inductive reasoning was used to make a conjecture based on a pattern. In part (b) deductive reasoning was used in order to write and simplify an expression.

33. B

34. [2] **a.** Ben

b. Andrea, Ben, and Claire; if Dion is also reading it, then all four would be reading it.

[1] either part (a) or part (b) correct

35. A type of reasoning is called inductive if and only if it is based on patterns that you observe.

36. $\angle AOB$, $\angle BOA$

37. $\angle BOC$, $\angle COB$

38. $\overrightarrow{OB}$

39. acute

31. Biology Consider the following given statements and conclusion.

Given: If an animal is a fish, then it has gills.
A turtle does not have gills.
You conclude: A turtle is not a fish.

a. Make a Venn diagram to illustrate the given information.
b. Use the Venn diagram to help explain why the argument uses good reasoning.

32. Reasoning Use the following algorithm: Choose an integer. Multiply the integer by 3. Add 6 to the product. Divide the sum by 3.

a. Complete the algorithm for four different integers. Look for a pattern in the chosen integers and in the corresponding answers. Make a conjecture that relates the chosen integers to the answers.
b. Let the variable x represent the chosen integer. Apply the algorithm to x. Simplify the resulting expression.
c. How does your answer to part (b) confirm your conjecture in part (a)? Describe how inductive and deductive reasoning are exhibited in parts (a) and (b).

Standardized Test Prep

SAT/ACT

33. What can you conclude from the given true statements?
If you wake up late, then you miss the bus.
If you miss the bus, then you are late for school.

(A) If you are late for school, then you missed the bus.
(B) If you wake up late, then you are late for school.
(C) If you miss the bus, then you woke up late.
(D) If you are late for school, then you woke up late.

Short Response

34. Claire reads anything Andrea reads. Ben reads what Claire reads, and Claire reads what Ben reads. Andrea reads whatever Dion reads.

a. Claire is reading *Hamlet*. Who else, if anyone, must also be reading *Hamlet*?
b. Exactly three people are reading *King Lear*. Who are they? Explain.

Mixed Review

35. Write the following definition as a biconditional. See Lesson 2-3.
Inductive reasoning is reasoning based on patterns you observe.

Get Ready! **To Prepare for Lesson 2-5, do Exercises 36–39.**

Use the figure at the right. See Lessons 1-4 and 1-5.

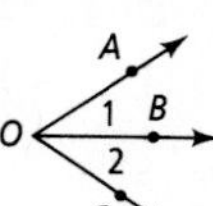

36. Name $\angle 1$ in two other ways.

37. Name $\angle 2$ in two other ways.

38. If $\angle 1 \cong \angle 2$, name the bisector of $\angle AOC$.

39. Classify $\angle AOC$.

2-4 Lesson Resources

Differentiated Remediation

Instructional Support

Geometry Companion

Students can use the **Geometry Companion** worktext (4 pages) . . .

- New Vocabulary
- Key Concepts
- Got It for each Problem
- Lesson Check

2-4 Deductive Reasoning

Vocabulary

Review

Write the converse of each conditional.

1. If I am thirsty, then I drink water.
   If I drink water, then I am thirsty.
2. If the car outside is wet, then it rained.
   If it rained, then the car outside is wet.

Vocabulary Builder

deduce (verb) dee DOOS

Related Words: deductive (adjective), deduction (noun)

Definition: To **deduce** is to use known facts to reach a conclusion.

Main Idea: When you use general principles and facts to come to a conclusion, you **deduce** the conclusion.

Example: Your friend is wearing red today. He wears red only when there is a home game. You use these facts to **deduce** that there is a home game today.

Use Your Vocabulary

Complete each statement with a word from the list. Use each word only once.

deduce deduction deductive

3. You use _?_ reasoning to draw a conclusion based on facts. deductive
4. The conclusion of your reasoning is a _?_. deduction
5. The teacher will not _?_ that a dog ate your homework. deduce

Chapter 2 46

ELL Support

Focus on Communication Project a transparency of the lesson on an overhead projector. Read the text as students follow along, pointing to each word. Think aloud as you highlight important ideas. Model how to paraphrase concepts or definitions to the right or left of the text. Model highlighting the hypothesis and conclusion of a conditional statement in different colors. As you proceed, ask students to identify each part and highlight accordingly.

Focus on Language Ask: What do you think *deductive* means? Have you heard the word before? Does the word deductive remind you of anything? The difference between the words *inductive* and *deductive* is the prefix. Because you already know *inductive* means to observe patterns to find a rule, what do you think *deductive* means?

5 Assess & Remediate

Lesson Quiz

1. What can you conclude from the given true statements?
   Given: If you want to buy the school lunch today, then you will need $2.50. You brought $2.50 to school today.
2. What can you conclude from the given information?
   Given: If Karl runs 1 mi, then he runs 1760 yd. If Karl runs 1760 yd, then he runs 5280 ft.
3. **Do you UNDERSTAND?** What can you conclude from the given information?
   Given: If a student is on the basketball team, then he has practice after school. If there is practice after school, then the student needs to find a ride home other than the bus. Jamal is on the basketball team.

ANSWERS TO LESSON QUIZ

1. no conclusion
2. If Karl runs 1 mile, then he runs 5280 ft.
3. Jamal needs to find a ride home other than the bus.

PRESCRIPTION FOR REMEDIATION

Use the student work on the Lesson Quiz to prescribe a differentiated review assignment.

Points	Differentiated Remediation
0–1	Intervention
2	On-level
3	Extension

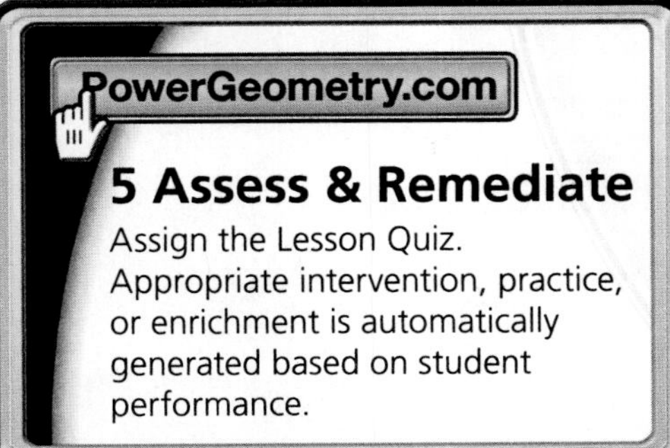
PowerGeometry.com
5 Assess & Remediate
Assign the Lesson Quiz. Appropriate intervention, practice, or enrichment is automatically generated based on student performance.

Intervention

- **Reteaching** (2 pages) Provides reteaching and practice exercises for the key lesson concepts. Use with struggling students or absent students.
- **English Language Learner Support** Helps students develop and reinforce mathematical vocabulary and key concepts.

All-in-One Resources/Online

Reteaching

2-4 **Reteaching**
Deductive Reasoning

The **Law of Detachment** states that if a conditional statement is true, then any time the conditions for the hypothesis exist, the conclusion is true.

If the conditional statement is not true, or the conditions of the hypothesis do not exist, then you cannot make a valid conclusion.

Problem

What can you conclude from the following series of statements?

If an animal has feathers and can fly, then it is a bird.
A crow has feathers and can fly.
Is the conditional statement true? Yes.
Do the conditions of the hypothesis exist? Yes.
Therefore, you can conclude that a crow is a bird.

If an animal has feathers and can fly, then it is a bird.
A bat can fly.
Is the conditional statement true? Yes.
Do the conditions of the hypothesis exist? No; a bat does not have feathers.
Therefore, no conclusions can be made with the given information.

Exercises

Use the Law of Detachment to make a valid conclusion based on each conditional. Assume the conditional statement is true.

1. If it is Monday, then Jim has tae kwon do practice.
   The date is Monday, August 25. Conclusion: Jim has tae kwon do practice.
2. If the animal is a whale, then the animal lives in the ocean.
   Daphne sees a beluga whale. Conclusion: The beluga whale lives in the ocean.
3. If you live in the city of Miami, then you live in the state of Florida.
   Jani lives in Florida. Conclusion: No conclusion is possible.
4. If a triangle has an angle with a measure greater than 90, then the triangle is obtuse.
   In $\triangle GHI$, $m\angle HGI = 110$. Conclusion: $\triangle GHI$ is obtuse.
5. A parallelogram is a rectangle if its diagonals are congruent.
   Lincoln draws a parallelogram on a piece of paper. Conclusion: No conclusion is possible.

All-in-One Resources/Online

English Language Learner Support

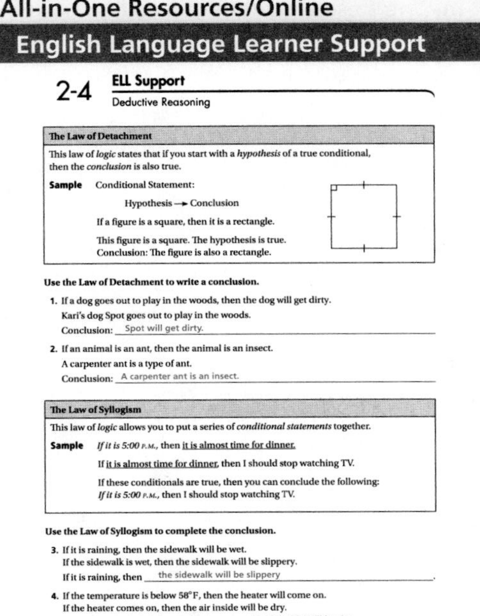
2-4 **ELL Support**
Deductive Reasoning

The Law of Detachment

This law of *logic* states that if you start with a *hypothesis* of a true conditional, then the *conclusion* is also true.

Sample Conditional Statement:
Hypothesis → Conclusion
If a figure is a square, then it is a rectangle.
This figure is a square. The hypothesis is true.
Conclusion: The figure is also a rectangle.

Use the Law of Detachment to write a conclusion.

1. If a dog goes out to play in the woods, then the dog will get dirty.
   Kari's dog Spot goes out to play in the woods.
   Conclusion: Spot will get dirty.
2. If an animal is an ant, then the animal is an insect.
   A carpenter ant is a type of ant.
   Conclusion: A carpenter ant is an insect.

The Law of Syllogism

This law of *logic* allows you to put a series of *conditional statements* together.

Sample *If it is 5:00 P.M.*, then it is almost time for dinner.
If it is almost time for dinner, then I should stop watching TV.
If these conditionals are true, then you can conclude the following:
If it is 5:00 P.M., then I should stop watching TV.

Use the Law of Syllogism to complete the conclusion.

3. If it is raining, then the sidewalk will be wet.
   If the sidewalk is wet, then the sidewalk will be slippery.
   If it is raining, then the sidewalk will be slippery.
4. If the temperature is below 58°F, then the heater will come on.
   If the heater comes on, then the air inside will be dry.
   If the temperature is below 58°F, then the air inside will be dry.

Differentiated Remediation *continued*

On-Level

- **Practice** (2 pages) Provides extra practice for each lesson. For simpler practice exercises, use the Form K Practice pages found in the All-in-One Teaching Resources and online.
- **Think About a Plan** Helps students develop specific problem-solving skills and strategies by providing scaffolded guiding questions.
- **Standardized Test Prep** Focuses on all major exercises, all major question types, and helps students prepare for the high-stakes assessments.

Practice and Problem Solving Wkbk/ All-in-One Resources/Online

Practice page 1

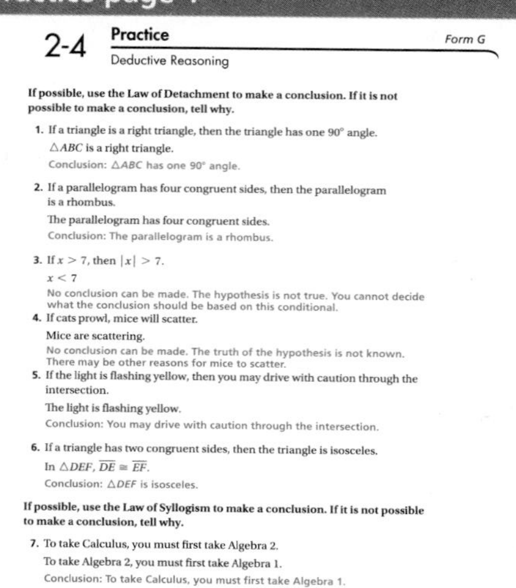

2-4 **Practice** — Deductive Reasoning — *Form G*

If possible, use the Law of Detachment to make a conclusion. If it is not possible to make a conclusion, tell why.

1. If a triangle is a right triangle, then the triangle has one 90° angle.
   $\triangle ABC$ is a right triangle.
   Conclusion: $\triangle ABC$ has one 90° angle.
2. If a parallelogram has four congruent sides, then the parallelogram is a rhombus.
   The parallelogram has four congruent sides.
   Conclusion: The parallelogram is a rhombus.
3. If $x > 7$, then $|x| > 7$.
   $x < 7$
   No conclusion can be made. The hypothesis is not true. You cannot decide what the conclusion should be based on this conditional.
4. If cats prowl, mice will scatter.
   Mice are scattering.
   No conclusion can be made. The truth of the hypothesis is not known. There may be other reasons for mice to scatter.
5. If the light is flashing yellow, then you may drive with caution through the intersection.
   The light is flashing yellow.
   Conclusion: You may drive with caution through the intersection.
6. If a triangle has two congruent sides, then the triangle is isosceles.
   In $\triangle DEF$, $\overline{DE} \cong \overline{EF}$.
   Conclusion: $\triangle DEF$ is isosceles.

If possible, use the Law of Syllogism to make a conclusion. If it is not possible to make a conclusion, tell why.

7. To take Calculus, you must first take Algebra 2.
   To take Algebra 2, you must first take Algebra 1.
   Conclusion: To take Calculus, you must first take Algebra 1.
8. If a tree has ragged bark, then the tree is unhealthy.
   If a tree has ragged bark, then the tree might be a birch tree.
   The Law of Syllogism cannot be used. The identical hypothesis is presented twice with two different results.
9. A quadrilateral has four congruent sides if and only if it is a rhombus.
   A square is a rhombus.
   Conclusion: A square is a quadrilateral with four congruent sides.

Practice and Problem Solving Wkbk/ All-in-One Resources/Online

Practice page 2

2-4 **Practice** (continued) — Deductive Reasoning — *Form G*

If possible, use the Law of Syllogism to make a conclusion. If it is not possible to make a conclusion, tell why.

10. If you like to snow ski, then you will like Colorado.
    If you like to wakeboard, then you will like Florida.
    No conclusion can be made. The two statements are not related to each other.
11. If it is Tuesday, then the cafeteria is serving meat loaf.
    When the cafeteria serves meat loaf, Harlan brings a sack lunch.
    Conclusion: If it is Tuesday, then Harlan brings a sack lunch.
12. If a polygon is a square, then it has exactly four congruent angles.
    If a polygon has exactly four congruent angles, then it is a rectangle.
    Conclusion: If a polygon is a square, then it is a rectangle.

Use the Law of Detachment and the Law of Syllogism to make conclusions from the following statements. If it is not possible to make a conclusion, tell why.

13. If you live in Fairbanks, then you live in Alaska. If you live in Alaska, then you live in the largest state in the United States. Alan lives in Fairbanks.
    Conclusion: Alan lives in the largest state in the United States.
14. A rectangle is a quadrilateral with four congruent angles. A rectangle is a parallelogram with four congruent angles. A square is a rectangle.
    Conclusions: A square is a quadrilateral with four congruent angles. A square is a parallelogram with four congruent angles.
15. If it is summer, the days will be warm. If people are swimming, the days are warm. If the air conditioning is turned on inside, then it is warm outside.
    No conclusions can be drawn. The statements do not connect in a way that allows you to use a syllogism to make a valid conclusion.
16. If it is raining, the temperature is greater than 32°F. If the temperature is greater than 32°F, then it is not freezing outside. It is raining.
    Conclusion: It is not freezing outside.
17. During the school week, if it does not rain, the soccer team will have practice. If the soccer team has practice, the team members will warm up by jogging two miles. It does not rain on Wednesday.
    Conclusions: The soccer team will have practice on Wednesday. The soccer team will warm up by jogging two miles.
18. **Open-Ended** Write a set of statements that uses the Law of Syllogism to make a conclusion.
    Check students' work.
19. **Writing** Give an example of how a police officer uses the Law of Detachment.
    Sample: If a car is traveling over the speed limit, the driver of the car should get a ticket. When a police officer observes someone speeding, the officer applies the Law of Detachment and gives the driver a ticket.

Practice and Problem Solving Wkbk/ All-in-One Resources/Online

Think About a Plan

2-4 **Think About a Plan** — Deductive Reasoning

Writing Give an example of a rule used in your school that could be written as a conditional. Explain how the Law of Detachment is used in applying that rule.

Understanding the Problem

1. What is the problem asking you to do?
   Answers may vary. Sample: Write a school rule as a conditional. Then show how the rule is applied using the Law of Detachment.

Planning the Solution

2. List a school rule that could be written as a conditional.
   Example: Do not park your car in spaces marked "reserved" or your car will be towed.
   Sample: You will be given a 30-minute detention after getting three tardy slips.

Getting an Answer

3. Rewrite the school rule as a conditional.
   Example: If you park your car in a space marked "reserved," then your car will be towed.
   Sample: If you are tardy to class three times, then you will be given a 30-minute detention.
4. Identify the hypothesis and the conclusion of the conditional you wrote for the school rule.
   Example: Hypothesis: You park your car in a space marked "reserved."
   Conclusion: Your car will be towed.
   Sample: Hypothesis: You are tardy to class three times. Conclusion: You will be given a 30-minute detention.
5. The Law of Detachment states that if the hypothesis of a true conditional is true, then the conclusion is true. Explain how the Law of Detachment is used when applying your school rule.
   Sample: The conclusion of the rule is the consequence for breaking the rule. So, when the conditions of the hypothesis are met, then the consequence will result. So, when you get a third tardy slip, the consequence will be that you get a 30-minute detention.

Practice and Problem Solving Wkbk/ All-in-One Resources/Online

Standardized Test Prep

2-4 **Standardized Test Prep** — Deductive Reasoning

Multiple Choice

For Exercises 1–3, choose the correct letter.

1. Which statement is a valid conclusion based on the argument? C
   If a polygon is a regular pentagon, then the polygon has exactly five congruent angles.
   The polygon is a regular pentagon.
   (A) Therefore, the polygon is a rectangle.
   (B) Therefore, the polygon is a regular quadrilateral.
   (C) Therefore, the polygon has exactly five congruent angles.
   (D) Therefore, the polygon has congruent sides.
2. Using the Law of Syllogism, which of the following completes the statement to form a valid conclusion? G
   If it is snowing heavily, then school will be canceled.
   If school is canceled, the big test will not be given today.
   It is snowing heavily, therefore
   (F) look out for the snowplows while driving to school.
   (G) the big test will not be given today.
   (H) the roads will be hard to drive on.
   (I) you should call the school to see if school is canceled.
3. Using the Law of Detachment, which statement is a valid conclusion? B
   If Jordin has a temperature of 100° or more, then Jordin should stay home from school.
   Jordin has a temperature of 101°.
   (A) Jordin should see the school nurse.
   (B) Jordin should stay home from school.
   (C) Jordin should take his temperature again.
   (D) Jordin has a temperature of 100° or more.

Short Response

4. Use the Law of Syllogism to make a valid conclusion.
   If a blub is screaming, then a frot is swimming.
   If a frot is swimming, then a greep is flinging.

[2] The student writes the complete conclusion: If a blub is screaming, then a greep is flinging. [1] The student writes, "A greep is flinging." [0] The student writes no correct conclusions.

Extension

- **Enrichment** Provides students with interesting problems and activities that extend the concepts of the lesson.
- **Activities, Games, and Puzzles** Worksheets that can be used for concepts development, enrichment, and for fun!

All-in-One Resources/Online

Enrichment

2-4 **Enrichment** — Deductive Reasoning

Forms of Logical Argument

The study of logic as a discipline has existed for thousands of years. Greek mathematicians and philosophers as far back as 600 BCE attempted to define how to argue logically. Two types of argument forms come from ancient times and have Latin names—*modus ponens* and *modus tollens*.

Modus Ponens		Modus Tollens	
Given:	$p \rightarrow q$	Given:	$p \rightarrow q$
	p		$\sim q$
Conclusion:	q	Conclusion:	$\sim p$

For Exercises 1–6, identify whether the argument is of the form *modus ponens, modus tollens,* or *neither.*

1. If it rains in Spain, then it rains on the plain.
   It is raining in Spain. Therefore, it is raining on the plain.
   modus ponens
2. If the scissor-tail swallows have returned, then it is not freezing outside.
   It is freezing outside. Therefore, the scissor-tail swallows have not returned.
   modus tollens
3. You cannot get a speeding ticket if you do not speed.
   You do not speed. Therefore, you cannot get a speeding ticket.
   modus ponens
4. If the animal is a dog, then the animal barks.
   The animal barks, therefore it is a dog.
   neither; not a valid argument
5. If the train is on time, I will get to work on time.
   If I get to work on time, I get to take a full hour for lunch.
   I didn't get to take a full hour for lunch. Therefore, the train wasn't on time.
   modus tollens
6. If I think, then I am.
   I think, therefore I am.
   modus ponens
7. **Open-Ended** Write an argument that uses *modus ponens.*
   Answers may vary. Sample: If it is spring, then it is not January. It is spring. Therefore, it is not January.
8. **Open-Ended** Write an argument that uses *modus tollens.*
   Answers may vary. Sample: If it is spring, then it is not January. It is January. Therefore, it is not spring.

Online Teacher Resource Center

Activities, Games, and Puzzles

2-4 **Puzzle: Statement-Conclusion Match-up** — Deductive Reasoning

Match pairs of statements with a valid conclusion based on the Laws of Detachment and Syllogism. Record your findings in the table at the bottom of the page. Choices may be used more than once or not at all. One is done for you. How many can you find in 2 minutes? 5 minutes?

A	B	C	D	E
If a person is a gimble, then he is a quimble.	Jim is not a gimble.	If a person is a quimble, then he is a swimble.	Jim is not a quimble.	If a person is not a quimble, then he is not a swimble.
F	**G**	**H**	**I**	**J**
If a person is a quimble, then he is a gimble.	Jim is a gimble.	If a person is a swimble, then he is a quimble.	Jim is a swimble.	Jim is not a swimble.
K	**L**	**M**	**N**	**O**
If a person is not a swimble, then he is not a gimble.	If a person is a swimble, then he is a gimble.	Jim is a quimble.	If a person is not a swimble, then he is not a quimble.	If a person is not a gimble, then he is a quimble.

Law of Detachment		
Statements		**Conclusion**
A	G	M
C	M	I
E	D	J
F	M	G
H	I	M
K	J	B
L	I	G
N	J	D
O	B	M

Law of Syllogism		
Statements		**Conclusion**
C	L	F
H	F	L
L	A	H

2-5 Reasoning in Algebra and Geometry

TN State Performance Indicators
SPI 3108.1.4 Use definitions, basic postulates, and theorems about points, lines, angles, and planes to write/complete proofs and/or to solve problems.
SPI 3108.4.4 Analyze different types and formats of proofs.

Objective To connect reasoning in algebra and geometry

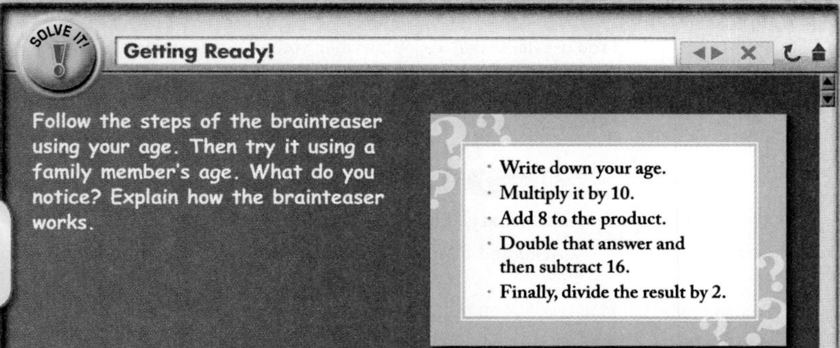

Getting Ready!
Follow the steps of the brainteaser using your age. Then try it using a family member's age. What do you notice? Explain how the brainteaser works.
Write down your age.
Multiply it by 10.
Add 8 to the product.
Double that answer and then subtract 16.
Finally, divide the result by 2.

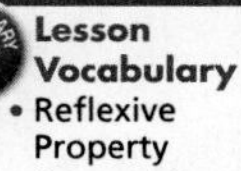

Lesson Vocabulary
- Reflexive Property
- Symmetric Property
- Transitive Property
- proof
- two-column proof

In the Solve It, you logically examined a series of steps. In this lesson, you will apply logical reasoning to algebraic and geometric situations.

Essential Understanding Algebraic properties of equality are used in geometry. They will help you solve problems and justify each step you take.

In geometry you accept postulates and properties as true. Some of the properties that you accept as true are the properties of equality from algebra.

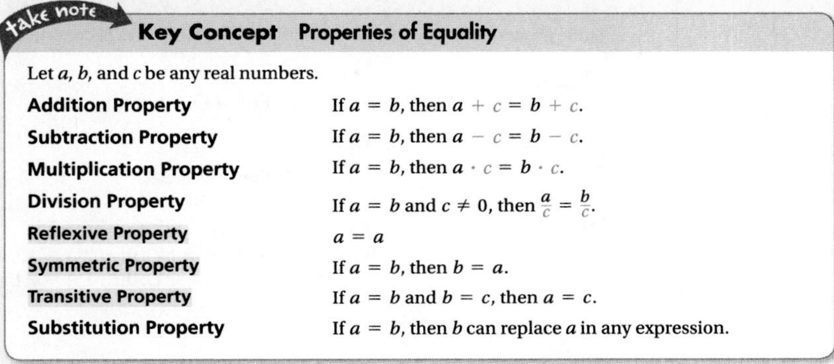

Key Concept Properties of Equality

Let a, b, and c be any real numbers.

Addition Property	If $a = b$, then $a + c = b + c$.
Subtraction Property	If $a = b$, then $a - c = b - c$.
Multiplication Property	If $a = b$, then $a \cdot c = b \cdot c$.
Division Property	If $a = b$ and $c \neq 0$, then $\frac{a}{c} = \frac{b}{c}$.
Reflexive Property	$a = a$
Symmetric Property	If $a = b$, then $b = a$.
Transitive Property	If $a = b$ and $b = c$, then $a = c$.
Substitution Property	If $a = b$, then b can replace a in any expression.

1 Interactive Learning

Solve It!

PURPOSE To analyze a series of steps which can logically lead to a consistent result

PROCESS Students may use several numbers to determine how each step of the brainteaser is affecting the original age. Students may also recognize from analyzing the steps that each operation except one is inverted.

FACILITATE

Q Can you do the steps in any order and get the same result? Explain. **[No; changing the order results in different answers.]**

Q What is an inverse operation? Provide an example. **[An operation that is the opposite of, or undoes, another operation. Adding 6 and subtracting 6 are inverse operations.]**

ANSWER See Solve It in Answers on next page.

CONNECT THE MATH Elicit from students that while you cannot show that the brainteaser always works by trying numeric examples, you could prove that the brainteaser always works by allowing a variable to represent all real numbers. Show students that, if you begin with x as the age, the result will be $10x$ after all of the steps are applied.

2 Guided Instruction

Take Note

Q Could the Addition, Subtraction, Multiplication, and Division Properties all be written as biconditionals? Explain. **[Yes, the converse of each of the properties is true.]**

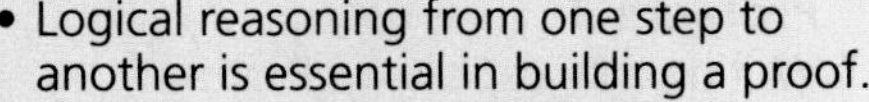

2-5 Preparing to Teach

BIG idea Reasoning and Proof UbD

ESSENTIAL UNDERSTANDINGS
- Logical reasoning from one step to another is essential in building a proof.
- Reasons in a proof include given information, definitions, properties, postulates, and previously proven theorems.

Math Background

The properties of equality reviewed in the beginning of this lesson add to the students' "toolbox" for writing proofs using deductive reasoning. It is important to make a connection between the algebraic proofs that students unknowingly completed throughout all of algebra and the proofs that students will complete in geometry. Students should have a clear understanding that the process of solving an equation is an algebraic proof, although the justifications for each step are not generally written down and often not even discussed. Students should realize from this lesson that proofs are not unique to geometry.

Support Student Learning

Use the **Geometry Companion** to engage and support students during instructions. See Lesson Resources at the end of this lesson for details.

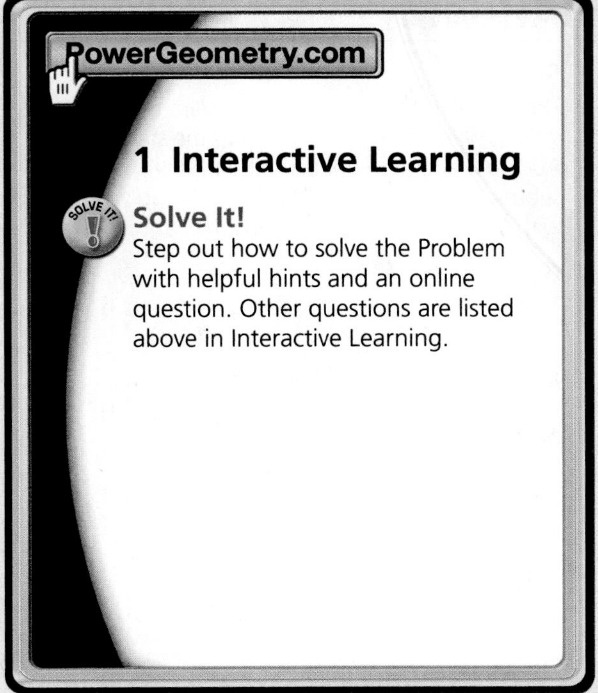

Take Note

Point out to students that the Distributive Property is the only property in this lesson that involves a combination of two operations. Show students that the Distributive Property can also be applied to a problem such as $a\left(\frac{1}{b} + \frac{1}{c} - \frac{1}{d}\right) = \frac{a}{b} + \frac{a}{c} - \frac{a}{d}$.

Problem 1

Q How could you use the Addition Property of Equality in place of the Subtraction Property? **[You can add (–30) to each side instead of subtracting 30 from each side.]**

Q How can you check the solution to the equation for accuracy? **[Substitute the value for x into the algebraic expressions in the diagram and check to make sure that the angles add up to 180.]**

Got It? ERROR PREVENTION

Q If $\overrightarrow{AB}$ bisects $\angle RAN$, what is true about $\angle RAB$ and $\angle BAN$? Justify your answer. **[The angles have equal measure by the definition of an angle bisector.]**

Take Note

Students may not understand why the Transitive, Symmetric, and Reflexive Properties are being repeated. Make sure that students understand that the properties of equality on page 113 are true for any numbers, while the congruence properties are true for geometric figures.

take note

Key Concept The Distributive Property

Use multiplication to distribute a to each term of the sum or difference within the parentheses.

Sum: $a(b + c) = a(b + c) = ab + ac$

Difference: $a(b - c) = a(b - c) = ab - ac$

You use deductive reasoning when you solve an equation. You can justify each step with a postulate, a property, or a definition. For example, you can use the Distributive Property to justify combining like terms. If you think of the Distributive Property as $ab + ac = a(b + c)$ or $ab + ac = (b + c)a$, then $2x + x = (2 + 1)x = 3x$.

Plan

How can you use the given information? Use what you know about linear pairs to relate the two angles.

Problem 1 Justifying Steps When Solving an Equation

Algebra What is the value of x? Justify each step.

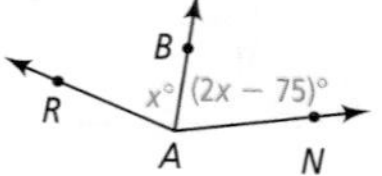

$\angle AOM$ and $\angle MOC$ are supplementary.	$\angle$s that form a linear pair are supplementary.
$m\angle AOM + m\angle MOC = 180$	Definition of supplementary $\angle$s
$(2x + 30) + x = 180$	Substitution Property
$3x + 30 = 180$	Distributive Property
$3x = 150$	Subtraction Property of Equality
$x = 50$	Division Property of Equality

Got It? 1. What is the value of x? Justify each step.
Given: $\overrightarrow{AB}$ bisects $\angle RAN$.

B, R, A, N, x°, (2x − 75)°

Some properties of equality have corresponding properties of congruence.

take note

Key Concept Properties of Congruence

Reflexive Property	$\overline{AB} \cong \overline{AB}$ $\quad \angle A \cong \angle A$
Symmetric Property	If $\overline{AB} \cong \overline{CD}$, then $\overline{CD} \cong \overline{AB}$. If $\angle A \cong \angle B$, then $\angle B \cong \angle A$.
Transitive Property	If $\overline{AB} \cong \overline{CD}$ and $\overline{CD} \cong \overline{EF}$, then $\overline{AB} \cong \overline{EF}$. If $\angle A \cong \angle B$ and $\angle B \cong \angle C$, then $\angle A \cong \angle C$. If $\angle B \cong \angle A$ and $\angle B \cong \angle C$, then $\angle A \cong \angle C$.

Answers

Solve It!

The leftmost digit(s) of the result is/are the one(s) you started with; the result is 10 times the starting age. Adding 8 and then doubling the sum is undone by subtracting 16 and then dividing by 2. So you end up with the product of the age and 10.

Got It?

1. 75; $x = 2x - 75$ (Def. of an $\angle$ bis.); $x + 75 = 2x$ (Add. Prop. of Eq.); $75 = 2x - x$ (Subtr. Prop. of Eq.); $75 = x$ (Distr. Prop.)

PowerGeometry.com

2 Guided Instruction

Each Problem is worked out and supported online.

Problem 1
Justifying Steps When Solving an Equation
Animated

Problem 2
Using Properties of Equality and Congruence
Animated

Problem 3
Writing a Two-Column Proof
Animated

Support in Geometry Companion
- Vocabulary
- Key Concepts
- Got It?

Think

Is the justification a property of equality or congruence?
Numbers are equal (=) and you can perform operations on them, so (A) and (C) are properties of equality. Figures and their corresponding parts are congruent (≅), so (B) is a property of congruence.

Problem 2 Using Properties of Equality and Congruence

What is the name of the property of equality or congruence that justifies going from the first statement to the second statement?

A $2x + 9 = 19$
$2x = 10$ — Subtraction Property of Equality

B $\angle O \cong \angle W$ and $\angle W \cong \angle L$
$\angle O \cong \angle L$ — Transitive Property of Congruence

C $m\angle E = m\angle T$
$m\angle T = m\angle E$ — Symmetric Property of Equality

Got It? 2. For parts (a)–(c), what is the name of the property of equality or congruence that justifies going from the first statement to the second statement?

a. $\overline{AR} \cong \overline{TY}$, $\overline{TY} \cong \overline{AR}$ b. $3(x + 5) = 9$, $3x + 15 = 9$ c. $\frac{1}{4}x = 7$, $x = 28$

d. **Reasoning** What property justifies the statement $m\angle R = m\angle R$?

A **proof** is a convincing argument that uses deductive reasoning. A proof logically shows why a conjecture is true. A **two-column proof** lists each statement on the left. The justification, or the reason for each statement, is on the right. Each statement must follow logically from the steps before it. The diagram below shows the setup for a two-column proof. You will find the complete proof in Problem 3.

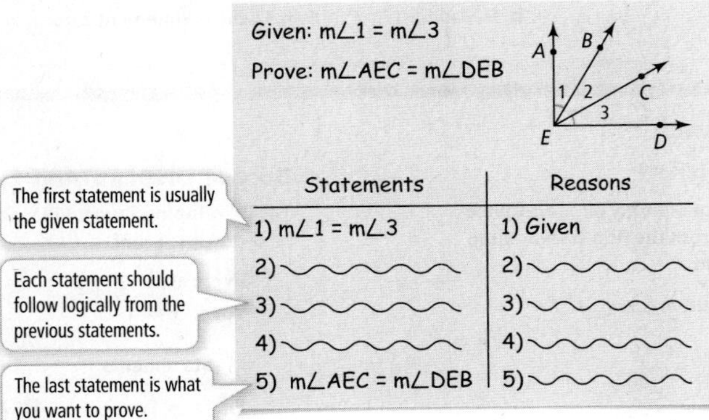

Statements	Reasons
1) $m\angle 1 = m\angle 3$	1) Given
2)	2)
3)	3)
4)	4)
5) $m\angle AEC = m\angle DEB$	5)

Problem 2

Q To find the value of x, which properties could you apply to the equation $2x = 10$? **[Multiplication or Division Property of Equality.]**

Q Why is 2C justified by the Symmetric Property of Equality rather than the Symmetric Property of Congruence? **[$\angle E$ is a geometric figure, but $m\angle E$ is a number.]**

Got It?

Q How could you solve the equation in 2b for x without using the Distributive Property? **[Divide by 3 using the Division Property of Equality and subtract 5 using the Subtraction Property of Equality.]**

Additional Problems

1. What is the value of x?

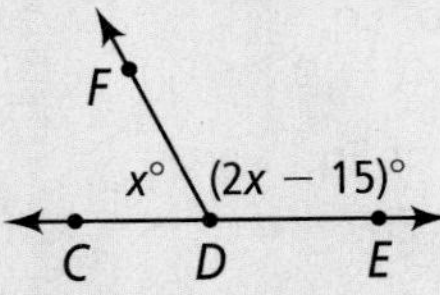

ANSWER $x = 65$

2. What is the name of the property of equality or congruence that justifies going from the first statement to the second statement?

a. $7x + 3 = 24$
$7x = 21$

b. $RS = ST$ and $ST = TU$
$RS = TU$

c. $5x = 10$
$10 = 5x$

ANSWER **a.** Subtraction Property of Equality **b.** Transitive Property of Equality **c.** Symmetric Property of Equality

3. Write a two-column proof.

A B C D

Given: $AC = BD$
Prove: $AB = CD$

ANSWER 1. $AC = BD$, given; 2. $BC = BC$, Reflexive Property; 3. $AC = AB + BC$, Segment Addition Postulate; 4. $BD = BC + CD$, Segment Addition Postulate; 5. $AB + BC = BC + CD$, Substitution; 6. $AB = CD$, Subtraction Property of Equality

Answers

Got It? (continued)

2a. Sym. Prop. of ≅
b. Distr. Prop.
c. Mult. Prop. of Eq.
d. Refl. Prop. of Eq.

Problem 3

Students benefit from considering the path of the proof informally before they begin writing the formal proof. Ask these questions prior to beginning the formal proof process.

Q What postulate relates the measure of two smaller angles to the measure of a larger angle comprising the smaller angles? **[Angle Addition Postulate]**

Q Which two angles compose $\angle AEC$? Which two angles compose $\angle DEB$? **[$\angle 1$ and $\angle 2$; $\angle 3$ and $\angle 2$]**

Got It?

Encourage students to use the proof from Problem 3 as a template for completing this proof.

3 Lesson Check

Do you know HOW?

- If students have difficulty identifying the Distributive Property in Exercise 2, remind them that the process of combining like terms would not be possible without it.

Do you UNDERSTAND?

- If students have difficulty with Exercise 4, have them show the arithmetic that is done to change one statement to the next statement. The arithmetic operation used should lead students to the property of equality that justifies it.

Close

Q What is the main difference between a Property of Equality and a Property of Congruence? **[A property of equality is used to justify equal numbers, while a property of congruence is used to justify congruent geometric figures.]**

Proof 

Problem 3 Writing a Two-Column Proof

Write a two-column proof.

Given: $m\angle 1 = m\angle 3$

Prove: $m\angle AEC = m\angle DEB$

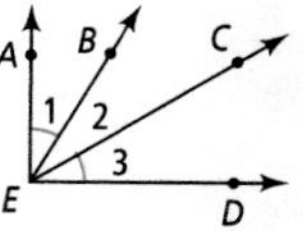

Know	Need	Plan
$m\angle 1 = m\angle 3$	To prove that $m\angle AEC = m\angle DEB$	Add $m\angle 2$ to both $m\angle 1$ and $m\angle 3$. The resulting angles will have equal measure.

Statements	Reasons
1) $m\angle 1 = m\angle 3$	1) Given
2) $m\angle 2 = m\angle 2$	2) Reflexive Property of Equality
3) $m\angle 1 + m\angle 2 = m\angle 3 + m\angle 2$	3) Addition Property of Equality
4) $m\angle 1 + m\angle 2 = m\angle AEC$ $m\angle 3 + m\angle 2 = m\angle DEB$	4) Angle Addition Postulate
5) $m\angle AEC = m\angle DEB$	5) Substitution Property

Got It? 3. a. Write a two-column proof.

Given: $\overline{AB} \cong \overline{CD}$

Prove: $\overline{AC} \cong \overline{BD}$

A B C D

b. **Reasoning** In Problem 3, why is Statement 2 necessary in the proof?

Lesson Check

Do you know HOW?

Name the property of equality or congruence that justifies going from the first statement to the second statement.

1. $m\angle A = m\angle S$ and $m\angle S = m\angle K$
   $m\angle A = m\angle K$
2. $3x + x + 7 = 23$
   $4x + 7 = 23$
3. $4x + 5 = 17$
   $4x = 12$

Do you UNDERSTAND?

4. **Developing Proof** Fill in the reasons for this algebraic proof.

Given: $5x + 1 = 21$

Prove: $x = 4$

Statements	Reasons
1) $5x + 1 = 21$	1) a. ?
2) $5x = 20$	2) b. ?
3) $x = 4$	3) c. ?

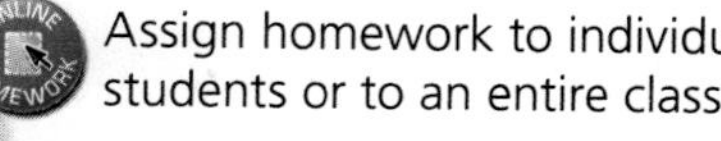

3 Lesson Check

For a digital lesson check, use the Got It questions.

Support in Geometry Companion
- Lesson Check

4 Practice

Assign homework to individual students or to an entire class.

Answers

Got It? (continued)

3a. Answers may vary. Sample: $\overline{AB} \cong \overline{CD}$ (Given); $AB = CD$ ($\cong$ segments have $=$ length.); $BC = BC$ (Refl. Prop. of Eq.); $AB + BC = BC + CD$ (Add. Prop. of $=$); $AB + BC = AC$, $BC + CD = BD$ (Seg. Add. Post.); $AC = BD$ (Subst. Prop. of Eq.); $\overline{AC} \cong \overline{BD}$ (Segments with $=$ length are $\cong$.)

b. Answers may vary. Sample: You need to establish equality in order to add the same quantity ($m\angle 2$) to each side of the equation in Statement 3.

Lesson Check

1. Trans. Prop. of Eq.
2. Distr. Prop.
3. Subtr. Prop of Eq.

4a. Given
b. Subtr. Prop. of Eq.
c. Div. Prop. of Eq.

Practice and Problem-Solving Exercises

A Practice

Algebra Fill in the reason that justifies each step. See Problem 1.

5. $\frac{1}{2}x - 5 = 10$ Given
$2\left(\frac{1}{2}x - 5\right) = 20$ **a.** ?
$x - 10 = 20$ **b.** ?
$x = 30$ **c.** ?

6. $5(x + 3) = -4$ Given
$5x + 15 = -4$ **a.** ?
$5x = -19$ **b.** ?
$x = -\frac{19}{5}$ **c.** ?

7. $\angle CDE$ and $\angle EDF$ are supplementary. ⦞ that form a linear pair are supplementary
$m\angle CDE + m\angle EDF = 180$ **a.** ?
$x + (3x + 20) = 180$ **b.** ?
$4x + 20 = 180$ **c.** ?
$4x = 160$ **d.** ?
$x = 40$ **e.** ?

E, $x°$, $(3x + 20)°$, C, D, F

8. $XY = 42$ Given
$XZ + ZY = XY$ **a.** ?
$3(n + 4) + 3n = 42$ **b.** ?
$3n + 12 + 3n = 42$ **c.** ?
$6n + 12 = 42$ **d.** ?
$6n = 30$ **e.** ?
$n = 5$ **f.** ?

$3(n + 4)$, $3n$, X, Z, Y

Name the property of equality or congruence that justifies going from the first statement to the second statement. See Problem 2.

9. $2x + 1 = 7$
$2x = 6$

10. $5x = 20$
$x = 4$

11. $\overline{ST} \cong \overline{QR}$
$\overline{QR} \cong \overline{ST}$

12. $AB - BC = 12$
$AB = 12 + BC$

13. Developing Proof Fill in the missing statements or reasons for the following two-column proof. See Problem 3.

Given: C is the midpoint of $\overline{AD}$.
Prove: $x = 6$

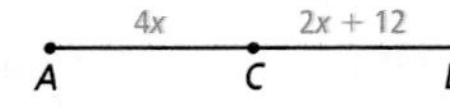

Statements	Reasons
1) C is the midpoint of $\overline{AD}$.	1) **a.** ?
2) $\overline{AC} \cong \overline{CD}$	2) **b.** ?
3) $AC = CD$	3) ≅ segments have equal length.
4) $4x = 2x + 12$	4) **c.** ?
5) **d.** ?	5) Subtraction Property of Equality
6) $x = 6$	6) **e.** ?

4 Practice

ASSIGNMENT GUIDE
Basic: 5–17, 20, 22, 23
Average: 5–13 odd, 14–24
Advanced: 5–13 odd, 14–28
Standardized Test Prep: 29–33
Mixed Review: 34–41
Reasoning exercises have blue headings.
Applications exercises have red headings.
EXERCISE 23: Use the Think About a Plan worksheet in the **Practice and Problem Solving Workbook** (also available in the Teaching Resources in print and online) to further support students' development in becoming independent learners.

HOMEWORK QUICK CHECK
To check students' understanding of key skills and concepts, go over Exercises 5, 11, 20, 22, and 23.

Practice and Problem-Solving Exercises

5a. Mult. Prop. of Eq.
b. Distr. Prop.
c. Add. Prop. of Eq.
6a. Distr. Prop.
b. Subtr. Prop. of Eq.
c. Div. Prop. of Eq.
7a. def. of suppl. ⦞
b. Subst. Prop.
c. Distr. Prop.
d. Subtr. Prop. of Eq.
e. Div. Prop. of Eq.
8a. Seg. Add. Post.
b. Subst. Prop.
c. Distr. Prop.
d. Distr. Prop.
e. Subtr. Prop. of Eq.
f. Div. Prop. of Eq.
9. Subtr. Prop. of Eq.
10. Div. Prop. of Eq.
11. Sym. Prop. of ≅
12. Add. Prop. of Eq.
13a. Given
b. A midpt. divides a seg. into two ≅ segments.
c. Substitution
d. $2x = 12$
e. Div. Prop. of Eq.

Answers

Practice and Problem-Solving Exercises (continued)

14. $YU = AB$

15. $\angle K$

16. $\angle POR$

17. 3

18. $EF + 7$

19. $\angle XYZ \cong \angle WYT$

20. Samples: $\angle 1$ and $\angle 2$ are a linear pair, $m\angle 1 + m\angle 2 = 180$, $DB = EB$

21. Since $\overline{LR}$ and $\overline{RL}$ are two ways to name the same segment and $\angle CBA$ and $\angle ABC$ are two ways to name the same $\angle$, then both statements are examples of saying that something is $\cong$ to itself.

22. Domino C; Law of Syllogism

23. $KM = 35$ (Given); $KL + LM = KM$ (Seg. Add. Post.); $(2x - 5) + 2x = 35$ (Subst. Prop.); $4x - 5 = 35$ (Distr. Prop.); $4x = 40$ (Add. Prop. of Eq.); $x = 10$ (Div. Prop. of Eq.); $KL = 2x - 5$ (Given); $KL = 2(10) - 5$ (Subst. Prop.); $KL = 15$ (Simplify.)

24. $m\angle GFI = 128$ (Given); $m\angle GFE + m\angle EFI = m\angle GFI$ ($\angle$ Add. Post.); $(9x - 2) + 4x = 128$ (Subst. Prop.); $13x - 2 = 128$ (Distr. Prop.); $13x = 130$ (Add. Prop. of Eq.); $x = 10$ (Div. Prop. of Eq.); $m\angle EFI = 4x$ (Given); $m\angle EFI = 4(10)$ (Subst. Prop.); $m\angle EFI = 40$ (Simplify.)

25. The error is in the 5th step when both sides of the equation are divided by $b - a$, which is 0, and division by 0 is not defined.

Use the given property to complete each statement.

14. Symmetric Property of Equality
If $AB = YU$, then __?__.

15. Symmetric Property of Congruence
If $\angle H \cong \angle K$, then __?__ $\cong \angle H$.

16. Reflexive Property of Congruence
$\angle POR \cong$ __?__

17. Distributive Property
$3(x - 1) = 3x -$ __?__

18. Substitution Property
If $LM = 7$ and $EF + LM = NP$, then __?__ $= NP$.

19. Transitive Property of Congruence
If $\angle XYZ \cong \angle AOB$ and $\angle AOB \cong \angle WYT$, then __?__.

20. Think About a Plan A very important part in writing proofs is analyzing the diagram for key information. What true statements can you make based on the diagram at the right?
- What theorems or definitions relate to the geometric figures in the diagram?
- What types of markings show relationships between parts of geometric figures?

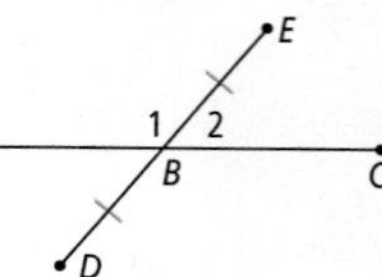

21. Writing Explain why the statements $\overline{LR} \cong \overline{RL}$ and $\angle CBA \cong \angle ABC$ are both true by the Reflexive Property of Congruence.

22. Reasoning Complete the following statement. Describe the reasoning that supports your answer.

The Transitive Property of Falling Dominoes: If Domino A causes Domino B to fall, and Domino B causes Domino C to fall, then Domino A causes Domino __?__ to fall.

Write a two-column proof.

23. Proof **Given:** $KM = 35$
Prove: $KL = 15$

24. Proof **Given:** $m\angle GFI = 128$
Prove: $m\angle EFI = 40$

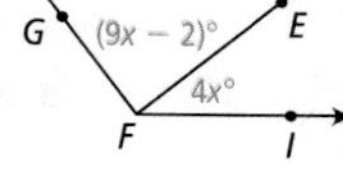

25. Error Analysis The steps below "show" that $1 = 2$. Describe the error.

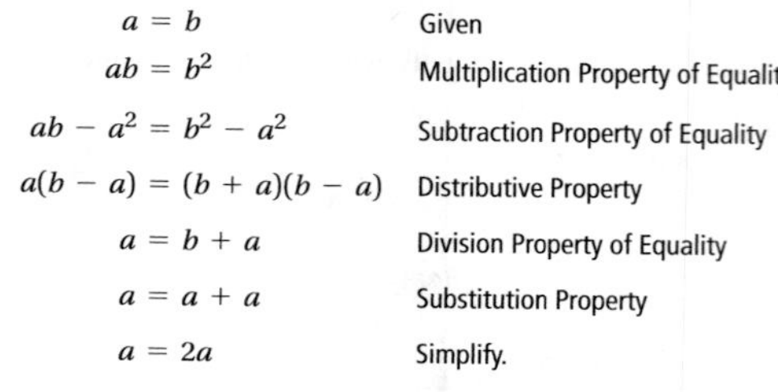

$a = b$	Given
$ab = b^2$	Multiplication Property of Equality
$ab - a^2 = b^2 - a^2$	Subtraction Property of Equality
$a(b - a) = (b + a)(b - a)$	Distributive Property
$a = b + a$	Division Property of Equality
$a = a + a$	Substitution Property
$a = 2a$	Simplify.
$1 = 2$	Division Property of Equality

Relationships Consider the following relationships among people. Tell whether each relationship is *reflexive, symmetric, transitive,* or *none of these.* Explain.

Sample: The relationship "is younger than" is not reflexive because Sue is not younger than herself. It is not symmetric because if Sue is younger than Fred, then Fred is not younger than Sue. It is transitive because if Sue is younger than Fred and Fred is younger than Alana, then Sue is younger than Alana.

26. has the same birthday as **27.** is taller than **28.** lives in a different state than

Standardized Test Prep

GRIDDED RESPONSE

SAT/ACT

29. You are typing a one-page essay for your English class. You set 1-in. margins on all sides of the page as shown in the figure at the right. How many square inches of the page will contain your essay?

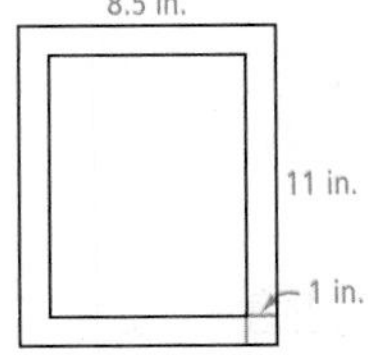

30. Given $2(m\angle A) + 17 = 45$ and $m\angle B = 2(m\angle A)$, what is $m\angle B$?

31. A circular flowerbed has circumference 14π m. What is its area in square meters? Use 3.14 for π.

32. The measure of the supplement of $\angle 1$ is 98. What is $m\angle 1$?

33. What is the next term in the sequence 2, 4, 8, 14, 22, 32, 44, . . . ?

Mixed Review

34. Reasoning Use logical reasoning to draw a conclusion.

See Lesson 2-4.

If a student is having difficulty in class, then that student's teacher is concerned.

Walt is having difficulty in science class.

Use the diagram at the right. Find each measure.

See Lesson 1-4.

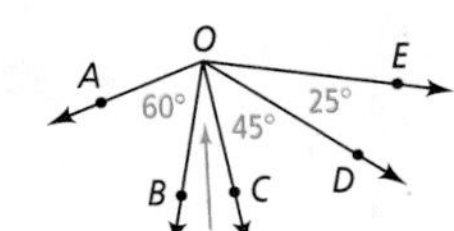

35. $m\angle AOC$ **36.** $m\angle DOB$

37. $m\angle AOD$ **38.** $m\angle BOE$

Get Ready! To prepare for Lesson 2-6, do Exercises 39–41.

Find the value of each variable.

See Lesson 1-5.

39.

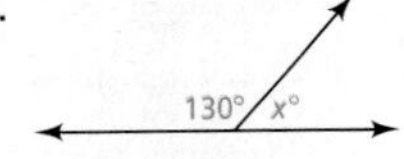

40.

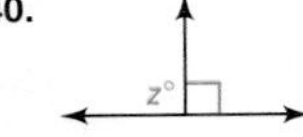

41.

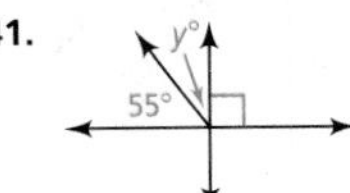

26. reflexive, symmetric, and transitive; because "has the same birthday as" satisfies all three properties

27. Transitive only; A cannot be taller than A; if A is taller than B, then B is not taller than A.

28. Symmetric only; A cannot live in a different state than A, and if A lives in a different state than B and B lives in a different state than C, then it is possible that A and C live in the same state.

29. 58.5 **30.** 28 **31.** 153.86

32. 82 **33.** 58

34. Walt's science teacher is concerned.

35. 80 **36.** 65 **37.** 125

38. 90 **39.** 50 **40.** 90

41. 35

2-5 Lesson Resources

Instructional Support

Geometry Companion

Students can use the **Geometry Companion** worktext (4 pages) . . .

- New Vocabulary
- Key Concepts
- Got It for each Problem
- Lesson Check

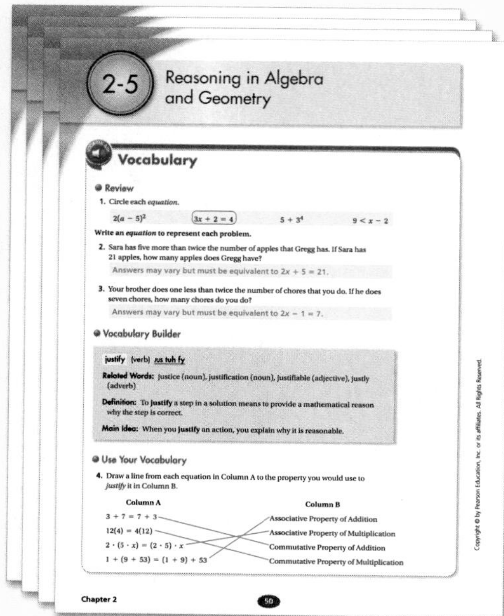

2-5 Reasoning in Algebra and Geometry

Vocabulary

Review

1. Circle each *equation*.

$2(a-5)^2$ $\quad$ $3x+2=4$ $\quad$ $5+3^4$ $\quad$ $9<x-2$

Write an *equation* to represent each problem.

2. Sara has five more than twice the number of apples that Gregg has. If Sara has 21 apples, how many apples does Gregg have?

Answers may vary but must be equivalent to $2x+5=21$.

3. Your brother does one less than twice the number of chores that you do. If he does seven chores, how many chores do you do?

Answers may vary but must be equivalent to $2x-1=7$.

Vocabulary Builder

justify (verb) JUS tuh fy

Related Words: justice (noun), justification (noun), justifiable (adjective), justly (adverb)

Definition: To **justify** a step in a solution means to provide a mathematical reason why the step is correct.

Main Idea: When you **justify** an action, you explain why it is reasonable.

Use Your Vocabulary

4. Draw a line from each equation in Column A to the property you would use to *justify* it in Column B.

Column A	Column B
$3+7=7+3$	Associative Property of Addition
$12(4)=4(12)$	Associative Property of Multiplication
$2\cdot(5\cdot x)=(2\cdot5)\cdot x$	Commutative Property of Addition
$1+(9+53)=(1+9)+53$	Commutative Property of Multiplication

Chapter 2 50

ELL Support

Use Graphic Organizers Have students fold a sheet of paper in half three times to form eight equal sections. Tell students to label each section with a Property of Equality from the Key Concept box. Discuss the meanings of the properties. Write examples of each randomly on the board and ask for volunteers to give the property and explain their reasoning. Students can write the example in the correct section of their organizers.

Focus on Language Invite students to provide a verbal example of each Property of Equality. For example, for *Transitive Property* an example might be: Tom is Jay's brother and Jay's brother is Kayla's cousin, so Tom is Kayla's cousin. Group students with similar language learners to share their work.

5 Assess & Remediate

Lesson Quiz

1. What is the value of x?

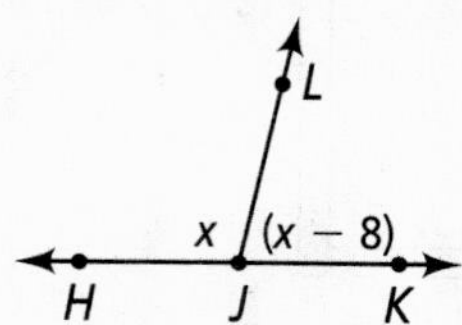

2. Do you UNDERSTAND? What is the name of the property of equality or congruence that justifies going from the first statement to the second statement?

a. $6a = 30$

$a = 5$

b. $\angle ABC \cong \angle LMN$

$\angle LMN \cong \angle ABC$

3. Write a two-column proof.

Given: $\frac{2}{3}(x-6) = 8$

Prove: $x = 18$

ANSWERS TO LESSON QUIZ

1. $x = 94$

2. a. Division Property of Equality

b. Symmetric Property of Congruence

3. 1. $\frac{2}{3}(x-6) = 8$, given

2. $2(x-6) = 24$, Multiplication Property of Equality

3. $2x - 12 = 24$, Distributive Property

4. $2x = 36$, Addition Property of Equality

5. $x = 18$, Division Property of Equality

PRESCRIPTION FOR REMEDIATION

Use the student work on the Lesson Quiz to prescribe a differentiated review assignment.

Points	Differentiated Remediation
0–1	Intervention
2	On-level
3	Extension

PowerGeometry.com

5 Assess & Remediate

Assign the Lesson Quiz. Appropriate intervention, practice, or enrichment is automatically generated based on student performance.

Differentiated Remediation

Intervention

- **Reteaching** (2 pages) Provides reteaching and practice exercises for the key lesson concepts. Use with struggling students or absent students.
- **English Language Learner Support** Helps students develop and reinforce mathematical vocabulary and key concepts.

All-in-One Resources/Online

Reteaching

2-5 **Reteaching**

Reasoning in Algebra and Geometry

When you solve equations you use the Properties of Equality.

Property	Words	Example
Addition Property	You can add the same number to each side of an equation.	If $x = 2$, then $x + 2 = 4$.
Subtraction Property	You can subtract the same number from each side of an equation.	If $y = 8$, then $y - 3 = 5$.
Multiplication Property	You can multiply by the same number on each side of an equation.	If $z = 2$, then $5z = 10$.
Division Property	You can divide each side of an equation by the same number.	If $6m = 12$, then $m = 2$.
Substitution Property	You can exchange a part of an expression with an equivalent value.	If $3x + 5 = 3$ and $x = 2$, then $3(2) + 5 = 3$.

Exercises

Support each conclusion with a reason.

1. Given: $6x + 2 = 12$

Conclusion: $6x = 10$
Subtraction Property

2. Given: $m\angle 1 + m\angle 2 = 90$

Conclusion: $m\angle 1 = 90 - m\angle 2$
Subtraction Property

3. Given: $x = m\angle C$

Conclusion: $2x = m\angle C + x$
Addition Property

4. Given: $q - x = r$

Conclusion: $4(q - x) = 4r$
Multiplication Property

5. Given: $m\angle Q - m\angle R = 90$,

$m\angle Q = 4m\angle R$

Conclusion: $4m\angle R - m\angle R = 90$
Substitution Property

6. Given: $CD = AF - 2CD$

Conclusion: $3CD = AF$
Addition Property

7. Given: $5(y - x) = 20$

Conclusion: $5y - 5x = 20$
Distributive Prop.

8. Given: $m\angle AOX = 2m\angle XOB$

$2m\angle XOB = 140$

Conclusion: $m\angle AOX = 140$
Substitution Prop.

9. Order the steps below to complete the proof.

Given: $m\angle P + m\angle Q = 90$, $m\angle Q = 5m\angle P$

Prove: $m\angle Q = 75$ d, a, c, b

a) $6m\angle P = 90$ by the Distributive Property

b) $m\angle Q = 5 \cdot 15 = 75$ by the Substitution Property

c) $m\angle P = 15$ by the Division Property

d) $m\angle P + 5m\angle P = 90$ by the Substitution Property

All-in-One Resources/Online

English Language Learner Support

2-5 **ELL Support**

Reasoning in Algebra and Geometry

Concept List

Addition Property of Equality	Distributive Property
Division Property of Equality	Multiplication Property of Equality
Reflexive Property of Equality	Substitution Property
Subtraction Property of Equality	Symmetric Property of Equality
Transitive Property of Equality	

Choose the concept from the list above that best represents the item in each box.

1. If $a = b$, then $a + c = b + c$ Addition Property of Equality	2. If $a = b$, and $c \neq 0$, then $\frac{a}{c} = \frac{b}{c}$ Division Property of Equality	3. $12.5 = 12.5$ Reflexive Property of Equality
4. If $a = b$, and $b = c$, then $a = c$ Transitive Property of Equality	5. If $a = b$, then $b = a$ Symmetric Property of Equality	6. If $a = b$, then $a \cdot c = b \cdot c$ Multiplication Property of Equality
7. $3(12 - 4) = (3)(12) - (3)(4)$ Distributive Property	8. If $a = b$, then $a - c = b - c$ Subtraction Property of Equality	9. $a = -4$ $6a + 2 = 6(-4) + 2$ Substitution Property of Equality

Differentiated Remediation *continued*

On-Level

- **Practice** (2 pages) Provides extra practice for each lesson. For simpler practice exercises, use the Form K Practice pages found in the All-in-One Teaching Resources and online.
- **Think About a Plan** Helps students develop specific problem-solving skills and strategies by providing scaffolded guiding questions.
- **Standardized Test Prep** Focuses on all major exercises, all major question types, and helps students prepare for the high-stakes assessments.

Extension

- **Enrichment** Provides students with interesting problems and activities that extend the concepts of the lesson.
- **Activities, Games, and Puzzles** Worksheets that can be used for concepts development, enrichment, and for fun!

Practice and Problem Solving Wkbk/ All-in-One Resources/Online

Practice page 1

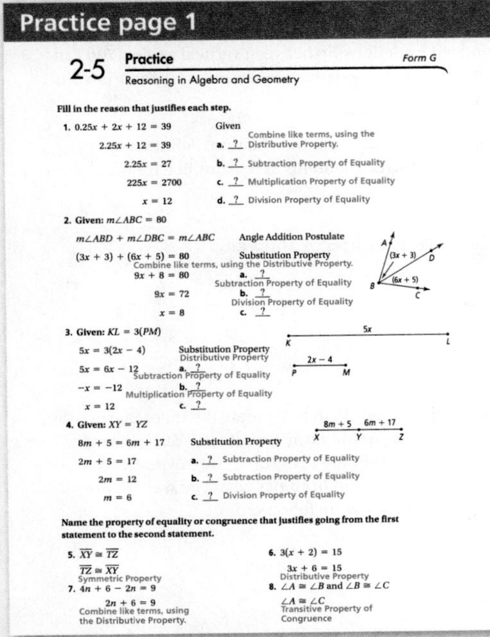

2-5 Practice — Form G
Reasoning in Algebra and Geometry

Fill in the reason that justifies each step.

1. $0.25x + 2x + 12 = 39$ Given
$2.25x + 12 = 39$ a. ? Combine like terms, using the Distributive Property.
$2.25x = 27$ b. ? Subtraction Property of Equality
$225x = 2700$ c. ? Multiplication Property of Equality
$x = 12$ d. ? Division Property of Equality

2. Given: $m\angle ABC = 80$
$m\angle ABD + m\angle DBC = m\angle ABC$ Angle Addition Postulate
$(3x + 3) + (6x + 5) = 80$ Substitution Property
$9x + 8 = 80$ a. ? Combine like terms, using the Distributive Property.
$9x = 72$ b. ? Subtraction Property of Equality
$x = 8$ c. ? Division Property of Equality

3. Given: $KL = 3(PM)$
$5x = 3(2x - 4)$ Substitution Property
$5x = 6x - 12$ a. ? Distributive Property
$-x = -12$ b. ? Subtraction Property of Equality
$x = 12$ c. ? Multiplication Property of Equality

4. Given: $XY = YZ$
$8m + 5 = 6m + 17$ Substitution Property
$2m + 5 = 17$ a. ? Subtraction Property of Equality
$2m = 12$ b. ? Subtraction Property of Equality
$m = 6$ c. ? Division Property of Equality

Name the property of equality or congruence that justifies going from the first statement to the second statement.

5. $\overline{XY} \cong \overline{TZ}$; $\overline{TZ} \cong \overline{XY}$ Symmetric Property
6. $3(x + 2) = 15$; $3x + 6 = 15$ Distributive Property
7. $4n + 6 - 2n = 9$; $2n + 6 = 9$ Combine like terms, using the Distributive Property.
8. $\angle A \cong \angle B$ and $\angle B \cong \angle C$; $\angle A \cong \angle C$ Transitive Property of Congruence

Practice and Problem Solving Wkbk/ All-in-One Resources/Online

Practice page 2

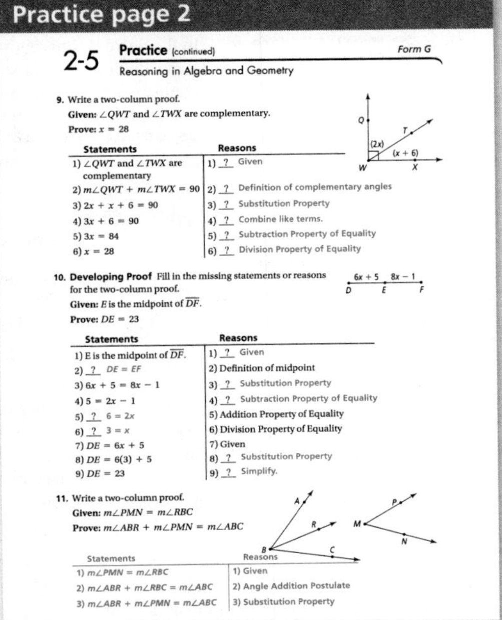

2-5 Practice (continued) — Form G
Reasoning in Algebra and Geometry

9. Write a two-column proof.
Given: $\angle QWT$ and $\angle TWX$ are complementary.
Prove: $x = 28$

Statements	Reasons
1) $\angle QWT$ and $\angle TWX$ are complementary	1) ? Given
2) $m\angle QWT + m\angle TWX = 90$	2) ? Definition of complementary angles
3) $2x + x + 6 = 90$	3) ? Substitution Property
4) $3x + 6 = 90$	4) ? Combine like terms.
5) $3x = 84$	5) ? Subtraction Property of Equality
6) $x = 28$	6) ? Division Property of Equality

10. **Developing Proof** Fill in the missing statements or reasons for the two-column proof.
Given: E is the midpoint of $\overline{DF}$.
Prove: $DE = 23$

Statements	Reasons
1) E is the midpoint of $\overline{DF}$.	1) ? Given
2) ? $DE = EF$	2) Definition of midpoint
3) $6x + 5 = 8x - 1$	3) ? Substitution Property
4) $5 = 2x - 1$	4) ? Subtraction Property of Equality
5) ? $6 = 2x$	5) Addition Property of Equality
6) ? $3 = x$	6) Division Property of Equality
7) $DE = 6x + 5$	7) Given
8) $DE = 6(3) + 5$	8) ? Substitution Property
9) $DE = 23$	9) ? Simplify.

11. Write a two-column proof.
Given: $m\angle PMN = m\angle RBC$
Prove: $m\angle ABR + m\angle PMN = m\angle ABC$

Statements	Reasons
1) $m\angle PMN = m\angle RBC$	1) Given
2) $m\angle ABR + m\angle RBC = m\angle ABC$	2) Angle Addition Postulate
3) $m\angle ABR + m\angle PMN = m\angle ABC$	3) Substitution Property

All-in-One Resources/Online

Enrichment

2-5 Enrichment
Reasoning in Algebra and Geometry

False Proofs

One of the reasons that justifying each step in a proof is important is because it allows you to find mistakes or inconsistencies in complicated chains of reasoning. For example, here is a false proof about line segments. See if you can find the mistake.

Given: $\overline{AB}$ with midpoint C
Prove: $AB = 0$

Statements	Reasons
$\overline{AB}$ has midpoint C	1) Given
$AC = BC$	2) ? Definition of midpoint
$(AC)(AC) = (AC)(BC)$	3) ? Multiplication Property of Equality
$(AC)^2 = (AC)(BC)$	4) Simplify.
$(AC)^2 + (AC)^2 = (AC)^2 + (AC)(BC)$	5) ? Addition Property of Equality
$2(AC)^2 = (AC)^2 + (AC)(BC)$	6) Simplify.
$2(AC)^2 - 2(AC)(BC) = (AC)^2 + (AC)(BC) - 2(AC)(BC)$	7) ? Subtraction Property of Equality
$2(AC)^2 - 2(AC)(BC) = (AC)^2 - (AC)(BC)$	8) ? Simplify.
$2[(AC)^2 - (AC)(BC)] = (AC)^2 - (AC)(BC)$	9) ? Distributive Property
$2(AC)[(AC) - (BC)] = (AC)[(AC) - (BC)]$	10) Distributive Property
$\frac{2(AC)[(AC) - (BC)]}{(AC) - (BC)} = \frac{(AC)[(AC) - (BC)]}{(AC) - (BC)}$	11) Division Property of Equality
$2(AC) = (AC)$	12) Simplify.
$2(AC) - AC = AC - AC$	13) ? Subtraction Property of Equality
$AC = 0$	14) Simplify.
$BC = 0$	15) ? Substitution Property of Equality
$AB = AC + BC$	16) Definition of midpoint
$AB = 0 + 0$	17) ? Substitution Property
$AB = 0$	18) ? Simplify.

1. Fill in the missing reasons in the proof above.
2. Examine the reasons. One property or definition has not been applied properly. Which one is it? (*Hint:* Choose a value for *AB* and step through the proof substituting actual values.)
Step 11 is incorrect. For any value of *AB*, $(AC)^2 = (AC)(BC)$, so $(AC)^2 - (AC)(BC) = 0$. This means that zero divides both sides of the equation. The Division Property of Equality is invalid for division by zero.

Practice and Problem Solving Wkbk/ All-in-One Resources/Online

Think About a Plan

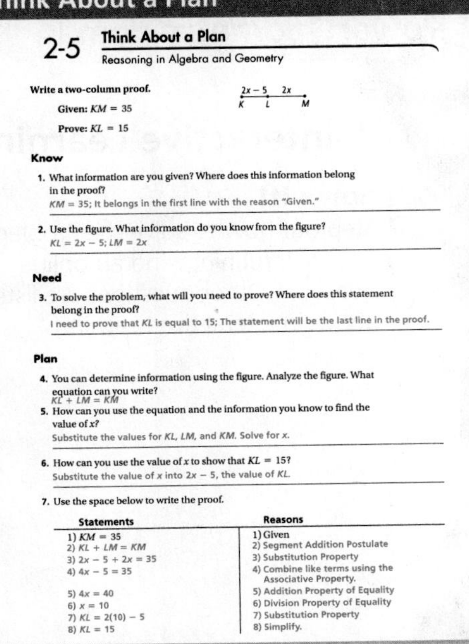

2-5 Think About a Plan
Reasoning in Algebra and Geometry

Write a two-column proof.
Given: $KM = 35$
Prove: $KL = 15$

Know

1. What information are you given? Where does this information belong in the proof?
$KM = 35$; It belongs in the first line with the reason "Given."
2. Use the figure. What information do you know from the figure?
$KL = 2x - 5$; $LM = 2x$

Need

3. To solve the problem, what will you need to prove? Where does this statement belong in the proof?
I need to prove that *KL* is equal to 15; The statement will be the last line in the proof.

Plan

4. You can determine information using the figure. Analyze the figure. What equation can you write?
$KL + LM = KM$
5. How can you use the equation and the information you know to find the value of *x*?
Substitute the values for *KL*, *LM*, and *KM*. Solve for *x*.
6. How can you use the value of *x* to show that $KL = 15$?
Substitute the value of *x* into $2x - 5$, the value of *KL*.
7. Use the space below to write the proof.

Statements	Reasons
1) $KM = 35$	1) Given
2) $KL + LM = KM$	2) Segment Addition Postulate
3) $2x - 5 + 2x = 35$	3) Substitution Property
4) $4x - 5 = 35$	4) Combine like terms using the Associative Property.
5) $4x = 40$	5) Addition Property of Equality
6) $x = 10$	6) Division Property of Equality
7) $KL = 2(10) - 5$	7) Substitution Property
8) $KL = 15$	8) Simplify.

Practice and Problem Solving Wkbk/ All-in-One Resources/Online

Standardized Test Prep

2-5 Standardized Test Prep
Reasoning in Algebra and Geometry

Multiple Choice

For Exercises 1–6, choose the correct letter.

1. According to the Transitive Property of Equality, if $TX = XY$, and $XY = YZ$, then $TX = \square$. C
A. TX B. XY C. YZ D. TZ
2. What property is illustrated by the statement, if $KL = LM$, then $LM = KL$? G
F. Reflexive Property of Equality H. Transitive Property of Equality
G. Symmetric Property of Equality I. Division Property of Equality

Use the list of reasons below for Exercises 3–6. Choose the correct reason for each algebraic statement.

A. Subtraction Property of Equality C. Distributive Property
B. Combine like terms. D. Division Property of Equality

Statements	Reasons
$3(x + 2) + 1 = 8$	Given
$6x + 6 + 1 = 8$	3) ? C
$6x + 7 = 8$	4) ? B
$6x = 1$	5) ? A
$x = \frac{1}{6}$	6) ? D

Extended Response

7. Write a two-column proof.
Given: A is the midpoint of $\overline{ZP}$.
$XY = ZA$
Prove: $XY = AP$

[4] Statements | Reasons
1) A is the midpoint of *ZP* and $XY = ZA$. | 1) Given
2) $ZA = AP$ | 2) Definition of midpoint
3) $XY = AP$ | 3) Transitive Property of Equality

[3] The student provides a thorough proof but a minimal number of statements, or fails to provide reasons or provides incomplete reasons; [2] The student provides a logical proof but fails to provide reasons or provides incomplete reasons; [1] The student provides a two-column proof format with the given included in the proof. [0] The student does not provide a proof that shows reasons.

Online Teacher Resource Center

Activities, Games, and Puzzles

2-5 Game: Property Password
Reasoning in Algebra and Geometry

Materials
- Paper
- Pencil

Setup

Your teacher will divide the class into teams of two (partner A and partner B). Sit facing your partner with a desk or another writing surface between you. Your teacher will give each of you a list. Make sure to take the A list if you are partner A, or the B list if you are partner B.

Game Play

Your teacher will call out a letter of the alphabet. The letter will correspond to one of the properties below.
- Addition Property of Equality
- Subtraction Property of Equality
- Multiplication Property of Equality
- Division Property of Equality
- Reflexive Property of Equality
- Symmetric Property of Equality
- Transitive Property of Equality
- Distributive Property
- Reflexive Property of Congruence
- Symmetric Property of Congruence
- Transitive Property of Congruence

Write a clue for your partner. The clue should be an equation or a series of equations that illustrate the property. Your partner should write down their guess. Properties will repeat.

Variation

Your teacher may decide not to use the letters of the alphabet to call out the properties. He or she may say for example, "the third property from the bottom." In this case, you and your partner write a clue for the given property. Then guess your partner's property.

Ending the Game

The game ends when time runs out or when your teacher has exhausted the list. Your teacher will reveal the answers. You earn two points for each correct answer and one point for each correct clue. The team(s) with the most points wins.

1 Interactive Learning

Solve It!

PURPOSE To use inductive reasoning to make a conjecture about vertical angles

PROCESS Students may use knowledge of supplementary angles, inductive reasoning to make a conjecture, knowledge of congruent angles, or logical reasoning.

FACILITATE

Q What is $m\angle 4$? Explain. **[$m\angle 4$ is 30; $180 - (60 + 90) = 30$]**

Q If two angles are congruent, what conclusion can you make about the measures of the angles? **[If two angles are congruent, they have the same measure.]**

ANSWER See Solve It in Answers on next page.

CONNECT THE MATH After students have completed the Solve It, ask them to state their conjecture about vertical angles. Remind students that they used inductive reasoning to make a conjecture about vertical angles, but deductive reasoning is necessary to prove that the conjecture is always true.

2 Guided Instruction

Take Note

Remind students that this theorem is a conditional statement that can be proven true. Let students know that each theorem introduced in the text will be followed with a proof using postulates, definitions, properties, and previously proved theorems. Ask students to provide a description for each component of a proof.

2-6 Proving Angles Congruent

TN State Performance Indicators

SPI 3108.1.4 Use definitions, basic postulates, and theorems about points, lines, angles, and planes to write/complete proofs and/or to solve problems.

SPI 3108.1.4 Analyze different types and formats of proofs.

Objective To prove and apply theorems about angles

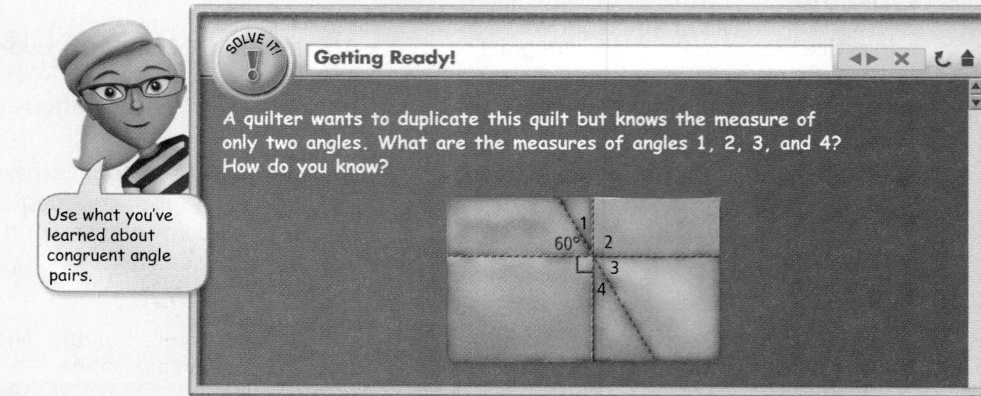

SOLVE IT!
Getting Ready!
A quilter wants to duplicate this quilt but knows the measure of only two angles. What are the measures of angles 1, 2, 3, and 4? How do you know?
60°
1
2
3
4
Use what you've learned about congruent angle pairs.

- theorem
- paragraph proof

In the Solve It, you may have noticed a relationship between vertical angles. You can prove that this relationship is always true using deductive reasoning. A **theorem** is a conjecture or statement that you prove true.

Essential Understanding You can use given information, definitions, properties, postulates, and previously proven theorems as reasons in a proof.

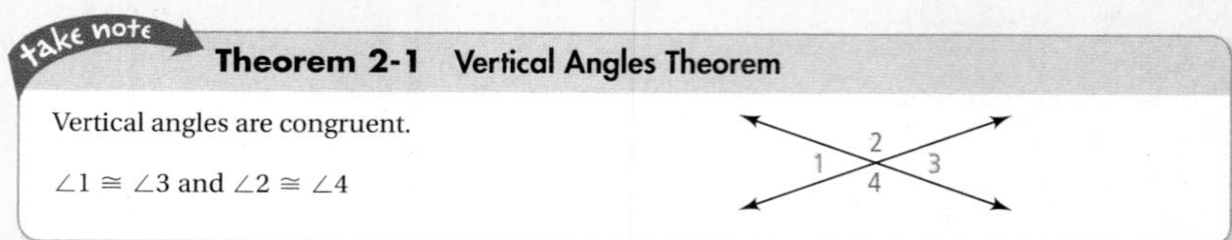

take note **Theorem 2-1 Vertical Angles Theorem**

Vertical angles are congruent.

$\angle 1 \cong \angle 3$ and $\angle 2 \cong \angle 4$

When you are writing a geometric proof, it may help to separate the theorem you want to prove into a hypothesis and conclusion. Another way to write the Vertical Angles Theorem is "If two angles are vertical, then they are congruent." The hypothesis becomes the given statement, and the conclusion becomes what you want to prove. A two-column proof of the Vertical Angles Theorem follows.

2-6 Preparing to Teach

BIG idea Reasoning and Proof 

ESSENTIAL UNDERSTANDING

- Given information, definitions, properties, postulates, and previously proven theorems can be used as reasons in a proof.

Math Background

Students use two forms of proofs in this lesson: the two-column proof and the paragraph proof. While these proofs might look different on the written page, they are both considered direct proofs that logically progress from a given condition to the desired conclusion. Many other forms of proof are also employed in the study of mathematics.

In a sense, proofs are problems in which the answer is already known and the focus is on demonstrating how the answer is derived using principles of deductive reasoning and related definitions, postulates, and theorems.

Support Student Learning

Use the **Geometry Companion** to engage and support students during instructions. See Lesson Resources at the end of this lesson for details.

PowerGeometry.com

1 Interactive Learning

Solve It!

Step out how to solve the Problem with helpful hints and an online question. Other questions are listed above in Interactive Learning.

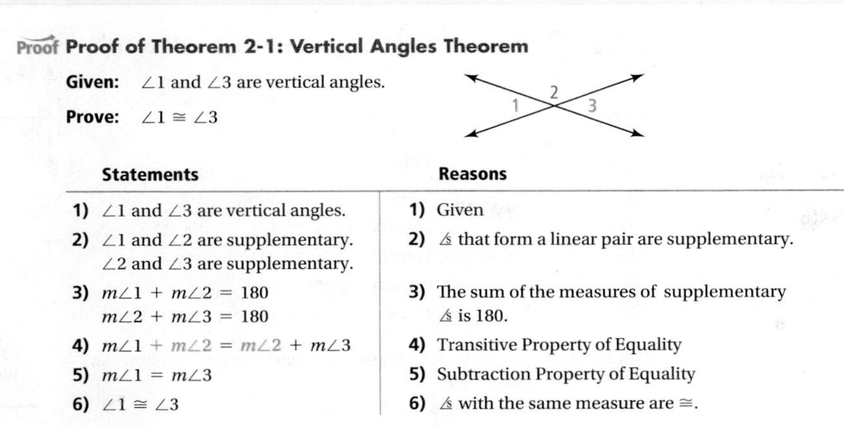

Proof Proof of Theorem 2-1: Vertical Angles Theorem

Given: $\angle 1$ and $\angle 3$ are vertical angles.

Prove: $\angle 1 \cong \angle 3$

Statements	Reasons
1) $\angle 1$ and $\angle 3$ are vertical angles.	**1)** Given
2) $\angle 1$ and $\angle 2$ are supplementary. $\angle 2$ and $\angle 3$ are supplementary.	**2)** $\angle$s that form a linear pair are supplementary.
3) $m\angle 1 + m\angle 2 = 180$ $m\angle 2 + m\angle 3 = 180$	**3)** The sum of the measures of supplementary $\angle$s is 180.
4) $m\angle 1 + m\angle 2 = m\angle 2 + m\angle 3$	**4)** Transitive Property of Equality
5) $m\angle 1 = m\angle 3$	**5)** Subtraction Property of Equality
6) $\angle 1 \cong \angle 3$	**6)** $\angle$s with the same measure are $\cong$.

Point out to students that the formal proof of the Vertical Angles Theorem likely resembles the logical reasoning that they used to complete the Solve It.

Problem 1 Using the Vertical Angles Theorem GRIDDED RESPONSE

What is the value of x?

(2x + 21)° 4x°

Plan

How do you get started?
Look for a relationship in the diagram that allows you to *write an equation* with the variable.

Think	Write
The two labeled angles are vertical angles, so set them equal.	$2x + 21 = 4x$
Solve for x by subtracting $2x$ from each side and then dividing by 2.	$21 = 2x$ $\frac{21}{2} = x$
Grid the answer as 21/2 or 10.5.	2 1 / 2

Got It? **1.** What is the value of x?

3x° (2x + 40)°

Problem 1

Q How can you check the solution to the equation for accuracy? **[Substitute the value for *x* into the algebraic expressions in the diagram and check to make sure that the angles are equal.]**

Q What are the measures of the labeled vertical angles? **[42]**

Q What are the measures of the unlabeled vertical angles? Explain. **[Using the definition of supplementary angles, the angles each measure 138.]**

Got It?

Q What is one first step for solving the equation for *x*? What is the justification for the step? **[Answers may vary. Sample: The Subtraction Property of Equality justifies subtracting 2*x* from both sides.]**

2 Guided Instruction

Each Problem is worked out and supported online.

Problem 1
Using the Vertical Angles Theorem
Animated

Problem 2
Proof Using the Vertical Angles Theorem
Animated

Problem 3
Writing a Paragraph Proof
Animated

Support in Geometry Companion
- Vocabulary
- Key Concepts
- Got It?

Answers

Solve It!

$m\angle 1 = 30$; $m\angle 2 = 90$; $m\angle 3 = 60$; $m\angle 4 = 30$; $m\angle 1$ can be found by subtracting the sum of 60 and 90 from 180. The other measures can also be found by finding three angles with a sum of 180.

Got It?

1. 40

Problem 2

Q If the given data for the proof were changed to $m\angle 1 = m\angle 4$, how would you modify the proof? **[Answers may vary. Sample: The second statement would be $\angle 1 \cong \angle 4$, justified by the definition of congruent angles.]**

Q Can you use this proof to draw a conclusion concerning the congruence of adjacent angles? Explain. **[No, the pairs in this diagram are congruent because of the given for the proof. Not all adjacent angles are congruent.]**

Got It?

Tell students to use the proof for Problem 2 as a template for the proof for 2a.

Let students know that each sentence in a paragraph proof can be worded in many ways, but the order of the sentences generally cannot change.

For example, the second sentence in the paragraph proof given could read "Because vertical angles are congruent, $\angle 4 \cong \angle 2$." However, you could not reverse the order of the second and third sentences.

Take Note — VISUAL LEARNERS

Ask students to make a sketch of two sets of linear angle pairs that would illustrate the Congruent Supplements Theorem. Have students label the angles with actual degree measures to make the illustrations as concrete as possible.

Proof **Problem 2 Proof Using the Vertical Angles Theorem**

Given: $\angle 1 \cong \angle 4$

Prove: $\angle 2 \cong \angle 3$

Think
Why does the Transitive Property work for statements 3 and 5?
In each case, an angle is congruent to two other angles, so the two angles are congruent to each other.

Statements	Reasons
1) $\angle 1 \cong \angle 4$	1) Given
2) $\angle 4 \cong \angle 2$	2) Vertical angles are $\cong$.
3) $\angle 1 \cong \angle 2$	3) Transitive Property of Congruence
4) $\angle 1 \cong \angle 3$	4) Vertical angles are $\cong$.
5) $\angle 2 \cong \angle 3$	5) Transitive Property of Congruence

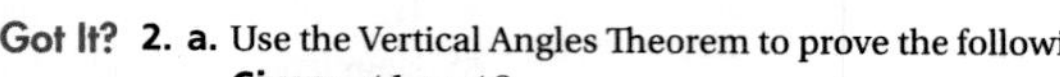

Got It? 2. a. Use the Vertical Angles Theorem to prove the following.

Given: $\angle 1 \cong \angle 2$

Prove: $\angle 1 \cong \angle 2 \cong \angle 3 \cong \angle 4$

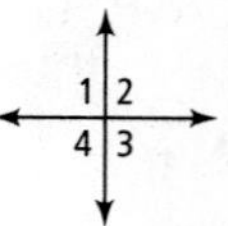

b. Reasoning How can you prove $\angle 1 \cong \angle 2 \cong \angle 3 \cong \angle 4$ without using the Vertical Angles Theorem? Explain.

The proof in Problem 2 is two-column, but there are many ways to display a proof. A **paragraph proof** is written as sentences in a paragraph. Below is the proof from Problem 2 in paragraph form. Each statement in the Problem 2 proof is red in the paragraph proof.

Proof **Given:** $\angle 1 \cong \angle 4$

Prove: $\angle 2 \cong \angle 3$

Proof: $\angle 1 \cong \angle 4$ is given. $\angle 4 \cong \angle 2$ because vertical angles are congruent. By the Transitive Property of Congruence, $\angle 1 \cong \angle 2$. $\angle 1 \cong \angle 3$ because vertical angles are congruent. By the Transitive Property of Congruence, $\angle 2 \cong \angle 3$.

The Vertical Angles Theorem is a special case of the following theorem.

take note

Theorem 2-2 Congruent Supplements Theorem

Theorem	If . . .	Then . . .
If two angles are supplements of the same angle (or of congruent angles), then the two angles are congruent.	$\angle 1$ and $\angle 3$ are supplements and $\angle 2$ and $\angle 3$ are supplements	$\angle 1 \cong \angle 2$

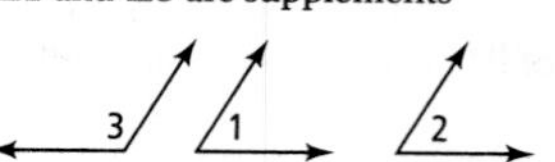

You will prove Theorem 2-2 in Problem 3.

Additional Problems

1. What is the value of x?

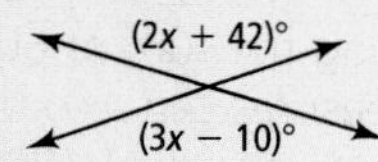

ANSWER $x = 52$

2.

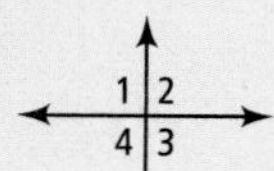

Given: $\angle 2 \cong \angle 3$

Prove: $\angle 1 \cong \angle 2$

ANSWER 1. $\angle 2 \cong \angle 3$, given; 2. $\angle 1 \cong \angle 3$, vertical angles are congruent; 3. $\angle 1 \cong \angle 2$, Transitive Property of Congruence

3. Given:
$\angle 1$ and $\angle 2$ are complementary
$\angle 2$ and $\angle 3$ are complementary
Prove: $\angle 1 \cong \angle 3$

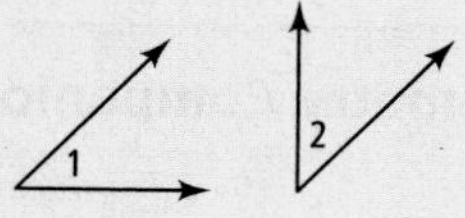

ANSWER It is given that $\angle 1$ and $\angle 2$ are complementary and $\angle 2$ and $\angle 3$ are complementary. So, $m\angle 1 + m\angle 2 = 90$ and $m\angle 2 + m\angle 3 = 90$ by the definition of complementary angles. By the Transitive Property of Equality, $m\angle 1 + m\angle 2 = m\angle 2 + m\angle 3$. Subtract $m\angle 2$ from each side. By the Subtraction Property of Equality, $m\angle 1 = m\angle 3$. Angles with the same measure are congruent, so $\angle 1 \cong \angle 3$.

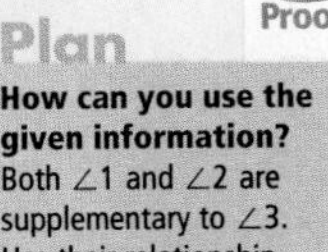

Plan

How can you use the given information?
Both ∠1 and ∠2 are supplementary to ∠3. Use their relationship with ∠3 to relate ∠1 and ∠2 to each other.

Proof

Problem 3 Writing a Paragraph Proof

Given: ∠1 and ∠3 are supplementary.
∠2 and ∠3 are supplementary.

Prove: ∠1 ≅ ∠2

Proof: ∠1 and ∠3 are supplementary because it is given. So $m\angle 1 + m\angle 3 = 180$ by the definition of supplementary angles. ∠2 and ∠3 are supplementary because it is given, so $m\angle 2 + m\angle 3 = 180$ by the same definition. By the Transitive Property of Equality, $m\angle 1 + m\angle 3 = m\angle 2 + m\angle 3$. Subtract $m\angle 3$ from each side. By the Subtraction Property of Equality, $m\angle 1 = m\angle 2$. Angles with the same measure are congruent, so ∠1 ≅ ∠2.

Got It? 3. Write a paragraph proof for the Vertical Angles Theorem.

The following theorems are similar to the Congruent Supplements Theorem.

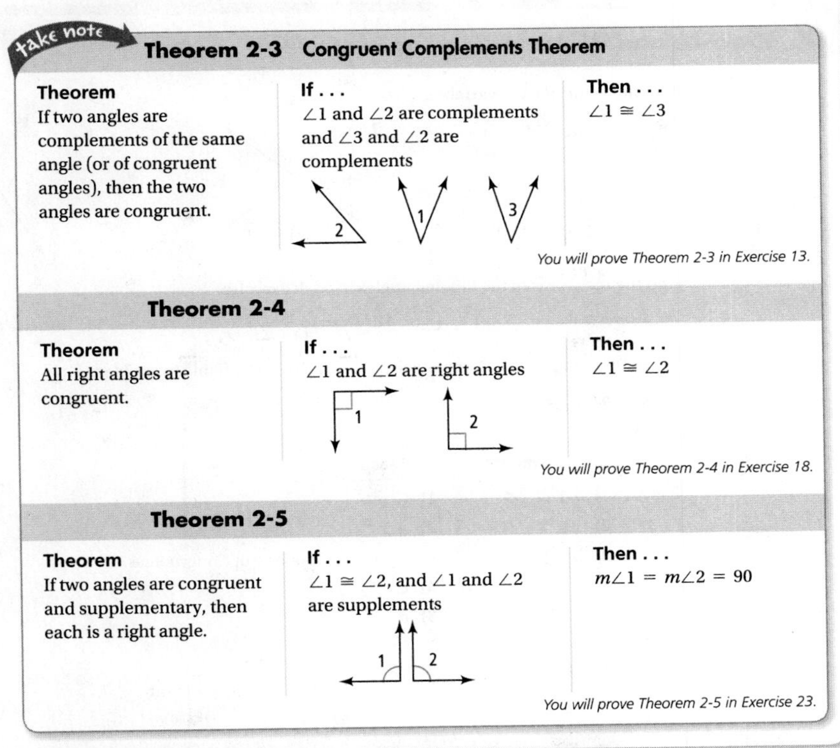

take note

Theorem 2-3 Congruent Complements Theorem

Theorem	If . . .	Then . . .
If two angles are complements of the same angle (or of congruent angles), then the two angles are congruent.	∠1 and ∠2 are complements and ∠3 and ∠2 are complements	∠1 ≅ ∠3

You will prove Theorem 2-3 in Exercise 13.

Theorem 2-4

Theorem	If . . .	Then . . .
All right angles are congruent.	∠1 and ∠2 are right angles	∠1 ≅ ∠2

You will prove Theorem 2-4 in Exercise 18.

Theorem 2-5

Theorem	If . . .	Then . . .
If two angles are congruent and supplementary, then each is a right angle.	∠1 ≅ ∠2, and ∠1 and ∠2 are supplements	$m\angle 1 = m\angle 2 = 90$

You will prove Theorem 2-5 in Exercise 23.

Problem 3

To provide students with reinforcement, ask them to write the paragraph proof for Problem 3 as a two-column proof.

Got It? TACTILE LEARNERS

To reinforce the necessary logical order of proofs, provide students with strips of paper that each contain one line of the proof of the Vertical Angles Theorem. Students will need to put the strips in order first before they write the steps in paragraph form.

Take Note

Students will be constructing proofs for these theorems in their homework. It would be beneficial to help students plan the proofs now. Elicit from students the following plans:

Theorem 2-3: Because both ∠1 and ∠3 are complementary to ∠2, use their relationship with ∠2 to deduce the relationship between ∠1 and ∠3.

Theorem 2-4: Use the definition of a right angle and the definition of congruent angles to conclude that ∠1 ≅ ∠3.

Theorem 2-5: Use the definition of supplementary angles and the Substitution Property to create an equation which can be solved for either $m\angle 1$ or $m\angle 2$.

Answers

Got It? (continued)

2a. ∠1 ≅ ∠2 (Given); ∠1 ≅ ∠3, ∠2 ≅ ∠4 (Vert. ∡ are ≅); ∠1 ≅ ∠4, ∠2 ≅ ∠3 (Trans. Prop. of ≅); ∠1 ≅ ∠2 ≅ ∠3 ≅ 4 (Trans. Prop. of ≅)

b. Answers may vary. Sample: $m\angle 1 + m\angle 2 = 180$ because they form a linear pair. So $m\angle 1 = 90$ and $m\angle 2 = 90$ because ∠1 ≅ ∠2. Then, using the relationship that $m\angle 2 + m\angle 3 = 180$ and $m\angle 1 + m\angle 4 = 180$, you can show that $m\angle 3 = m\angle 4 = 90$ by the Subtr. Prop. of Eq. Then ∠1 ≅ ∠2 ≅ ∠3 ≅ ∠4 because their measures are =.

3. Answers may vary. Sample: ∠1 and ∠3 are vert. ∡ because it is given. ∠1 and ∠2 are suppl. and ∠2 and ∠3 are suppl. because ∡ that form a linear pair are suppl. So, $m\angle 1 + m\angle 2 = 180$ and $m\angle 2 + m\angle 3 = 180$ by the def. of suppl. ∡. By the Trans. Prop. of Eq., $m\angle 1 + m\angle 2 = m\angle 2 + m\angle 3$. By the Subtr. Prop. of Eq., $m\angle 1 = m\angle 3$. So, ∠1 ≅ ∠3 because ∡ with the same measure are ≅.

3 Lesson Check

Do you know HOW?

- If students have difficulty with Exercise 1, then ask students to redraw the figure with letters for each vertex and ray. Ask them to list supplementary angles, complementary angles, and vertical angles.

Do you UNDERSTAND?

- If students have difficulty understanding the relationship between a postulate and a theorem, have them compare that relationship with the notions of primary, secondary, and tertiary colors. The primary colors of red, yellow, and blue cannot be mixed from any other color and are the starting point for every other color. Secondary colors are colors made by mixing two primaries, and tertiary colors are made by mixing a primary and a secondary.

Close

Q What three equations could be used to determine the value of x in the figure below?

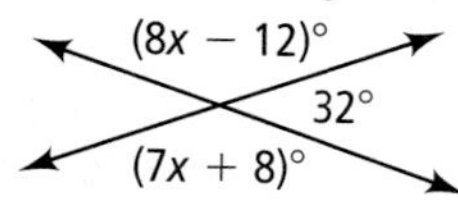

[$8x - 12 = 7x + 8$, $8x - 12 + 32 = 180$, $7x + 8 + 32 = 180$]

Lesson Check

Do you know HOW?

1. What are the measures of $\angle 1$, $\angle 2$, and $\angle 3$?

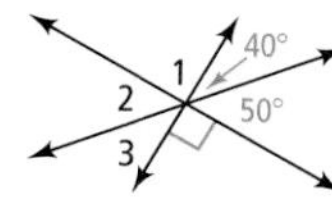

2. What is the value of x?

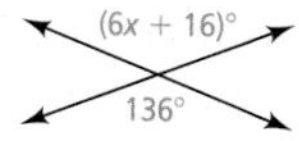

Ⓐ 12 Ⓒ 120

Ⓑ 20 Ⓓ 136

Do you UNDERSTAND?

3. **Reasoning** If $\angle A$ and $\angle B$ are supplements, and $\angle A$ and $\angle C$ are supplements, what can you conclude about $\angle B$ and $\angle C$? Explain.

4. **Error Analysis** Your friend knows that $\angle 1$ and $\angle 2$ are complementary and that $\angle 1$ and $\angle 3$ are complementary. He concludes that $\angle 2$ and $\angle 3$ must be complementary. What is his error in reasoning?

5. **Compare and Contrast** How is a theorem different from a postulate?

Practice and Problem-Solving Exercises

A Practice

Find the value of each variable.

See Problem 1.

6. 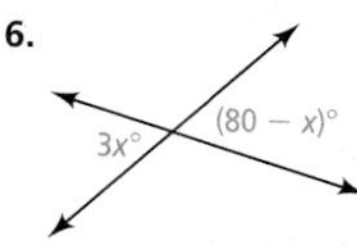

7. 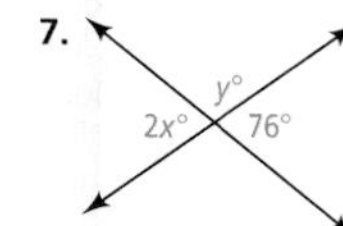

8. 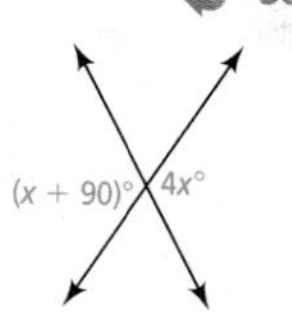

Find the measures of the labeled angles in each exercise.

9. Exercise 6

10. Exercise 7

11. Exercise 8

12. **Developing Proof** Complete the following proof by filling in the blanks.

See Problem 2.

Given: $\angle 1 \cong \angle 3$

Prove: $\angle 6 \cong \angle 4$

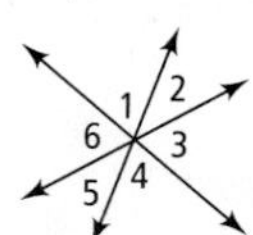

Statements	Reasons
1) $\angle 1 \cong \angle 3$	1) Given
2) $\angle 3 \cong \angle 6$	2) a. ?
3) b. ?	3) Transitive Property of Congruence
4) $\angle 1 \cong \angle 4$	4) c. ?
5) $\angle 6 \cong \angle 4$	5) d. ?

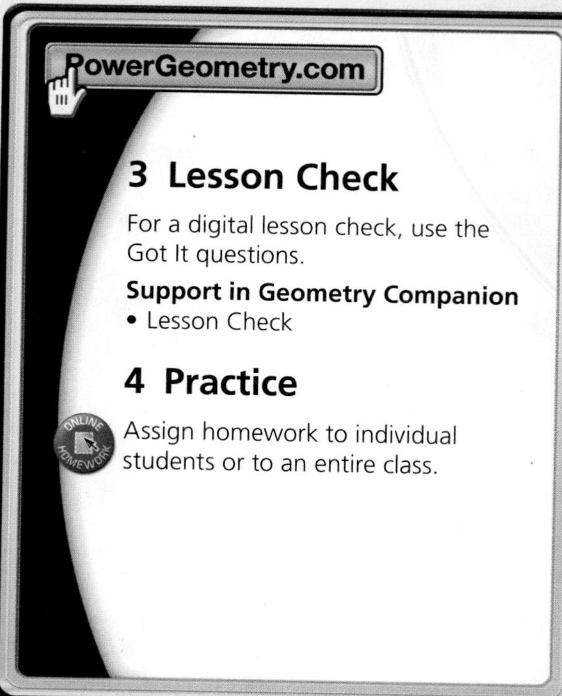

PowerGeometry.com

3 Lesson Check

For a digital lesson check, use the Got It questions.

Support in Geometry Companion

- Lesson Check

4 Practice

Assign homework to individual students or to an entire class.

Answers

Lesson Check

1. $m\angle 1 = 90$, $m\angle 2 = 50$, $m\angle 3 = 40$
2. B
3. $\angle B \cong \angle C$ because both are suppl. to $\angle A$ and if two ∠s are suppl. to the same ∠, then they are ≅.
4. He used the Trans. Prop. of ≅, which does not apply here. $\angle 2$ and $\angle 3$ are ≅, not compl. If two ∠s are compl. to the same ∠, then they are ≅ to each other.
5. Answers may vary. Sample: A postulate is a statement that is assumed to be true, while a theorem is a statement that is proved to be true.

Practice and Problem-Solving Exercises

6. 20
7. $x = 38$, $y = 104$
8. 30
9. 60, 60
10. 76, 104, 76
11. 120, 120

12a. Vert. ∠s Thm.
b. $\angle 1 \cong \angle 6$
c. Vert. ∠s Thm.
d. Trans. Prop. of ≅

13. **Developing Proof** Fill in the blanks to complete this proof of the Congruent Complements Theorem (Theorem 2-3). See Problem 3.

If two angles are complements of the same angle, then the two angles are congruent.

Given: $\angle 1$ and $\angle 2$ are complementary. $\angle 3$ and $\angle 2$ are complementary.

Prove: $\angle 1 \cong \angle 3$

Proof: $\angle 1$ and $\angle 2$ are complementary and $\angle 3$ and $\angle 2$ are complementary because it is given. By the definition of complementary angles, $m\angle 1 + m\angle 2 =$ **a.** ? and $m\angle 3 + m\angle 2 =$ **b.** ? . Then $m\angle 1 + m\angle 2 = m\angle 3 + m\angle 2$ by the Transitive Property of Equality. Subtract $m\angle 2$ from each side. By the Subtraction Property of Equality, you get $m\angle 1 =$ **c.** ? . Angles with the same measure are **d.** ? , so $\angle 1 \cong \angle 3$.

14. **Think About a Plan** What is the measure of the angle formed by Park St. and 116th St.?
   - Can you make a connection between the angle you need to find and the labeled angle?
   - How are angles that form a right angle related?

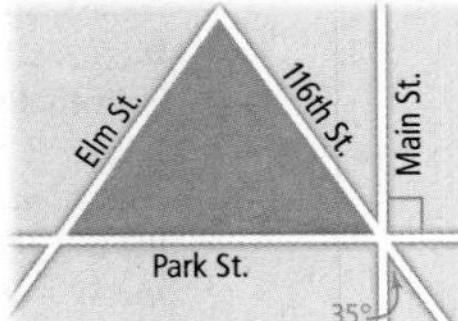

15. **Open-Ended** Give an example of vertical angles in your home or classroom.

Algebra Find the value of each variable and the measure of each labeled angle.

16. 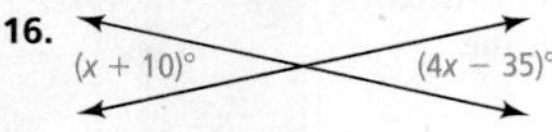

17. 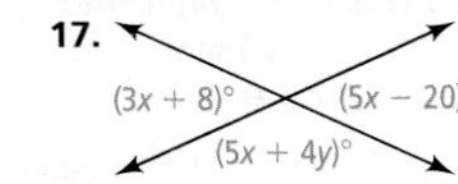

18. **Developing Proof** Fill in the blanks to complete this proof of Theorem 2-4.

All right angles are congruent.

Given: $\angle X$ and $\angle Y$ are right angles.

Prove: $\angle X \cong \angle Y$

Proof: $\angle X$ and **a.** ? are right angles because it is given. By the definition of **b.** ? , $m\angle X = 90$ and $m\angle Y = 90$. By the Transitive Property of Equality, $m\angle X =$ **c.** ? . Because angles of equal measure are congruent, **d.** ? .

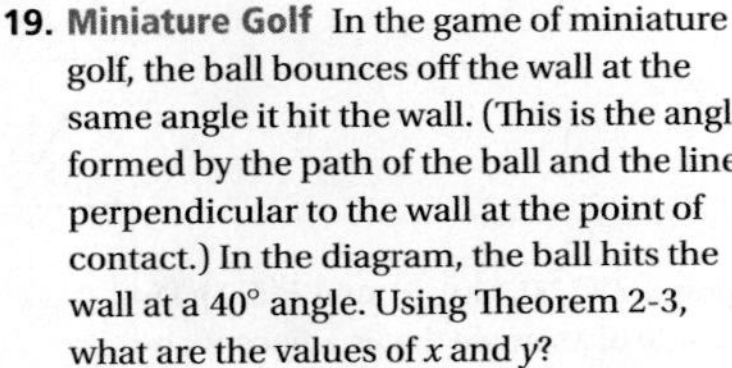

19. **Miniature Golf** In the game of miniature golf, the ball bounces off the wall at the same angle it hit the wall. (This is the angle formed by the path of the ball and the line perpendicular to the wall at the point of contact.) In the diagram, the ball hits the wall at a 40° angle. Using Theorem 2-3, what are the values of x and y?

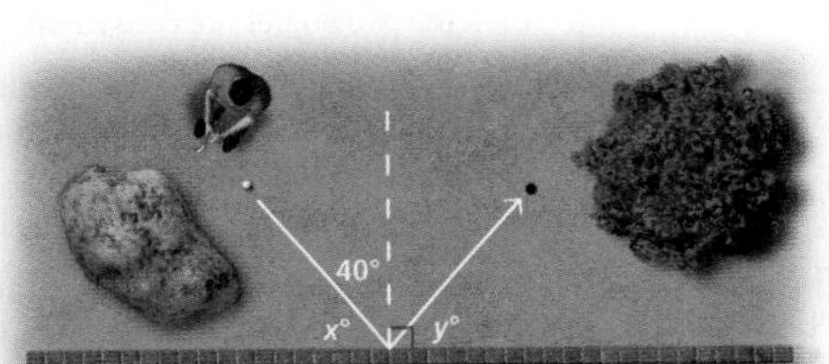

13a. 90 **b.** 90
c. $m\angle 3$ **d.** $\cong$

14. 55

15. Answers may vary. Sample: scissors

16. $x = 15$, $x + 10 = 25$, $4x - 35 = 25$

17. $x = 14$, $y = 15$; $3x + 8 = 50$, $5x - 20 = 50$, $5x + 4y = 130$

18a. $\angle Y$ **b.** right $\angle$
c. $m\angle Y$ **d.** $\angle X \cong \angle Y$

19. $x = 50$, $y = 50$

4 Practice

ASSIGNMENT GUIDE

Basic: 6–14, 16, 20–21, 25, 26, 28
Average: 7–13 odd, 14–30
Advanced: 7–13 odd, 14–35
Standardized Test Prep: 36–39
Mixed Review: 40–48

Reasoning exercises have blue headings.
Applications exercises have red headings.

EXERCISE 25: Use the Think About a Plan worksheet in the **Practice and Problem Solving Workbook** (also available in the Teaching Resources in print and online) to further support students' development in becoming independent learners.

HOMEWORK QUICK CHECK

To check students' understanding of key skills and concepts, go over Exercises 7, 13, 14, 25, and 26.

Answers

Practice and Problem-Solving Exercises (continued)

20. $\angle AOD \cong \angle BOC$, $\angle AOB \cong \angle DOC$ because vert. ∠s are ≅. (Also, all of the straight ∠s are ≅ because each one has measure 180.)

21. $\angle EIG \cong \angle FIH$ because all rt. ∠s are ≅; $\angle EIF \cong \angle HIG$ because each one is compl. to $\angle FIG$ and compl. of the same ∠ are ≅.

22. $\angle KPJ \cong \angle MPJ$ (Given in the diagram); $\angle KPL \cong \angle MPL$ because each is suppl. to one of two ≅ ∠s. (Also, the two straight ∠s are ≅.)

23a. it is given **b.** $m\angle V$ **c.** 180 **d.** Division **e.** right

24. If two ∠s are suppl. to ≅ ∠s, then the two ∠s are ≅ to each other.

25. By Theorem 2-5: If two ∠s are ≅ and suppl., then each is a right ∠.

26. $m\angle A = 60$, $m\angle B = 30$

27. $m\angle A = 30$, $m\angle B = 60$

28. $m\angle A = 120$, $m\angle B = 60$

29. $m\angle A = 90$, $m\angle B = 90$

30. ∠1 and ∠2 are suppl., ∠3 and ∠4 are suppl. (Given); $m\angle 1 + m\angle 2 = 180$, $m\angle 3 + m\angle 4 = 180$ (If two ∠s are suppl., then the sum of their measures is 180.); $m\angle 1 + m\angle 2 = m\angle 3 + m\angle 4$ (Subst. Prop.); $\angle 2 \cong \angle 4$ (Given); $m\angle 2 = m\angle 4$ (If two ∠s are ≅, their measures are =.); $m\angle 1 = m\angle 3$ (Subtr. Prop. of Eq.); $\angle 1 \cong \angle 3$ (If two ∠s have the same measure, then they are ≅.)

31. Answers may vary. Sample: (−5, −1)

Name two pairs of congruent angles in each figure. Justify your answers.

20.

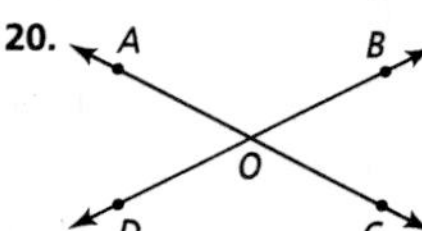

21.

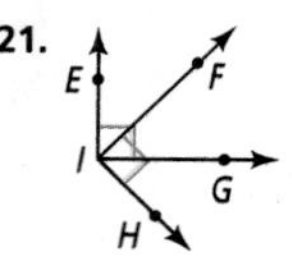

22.

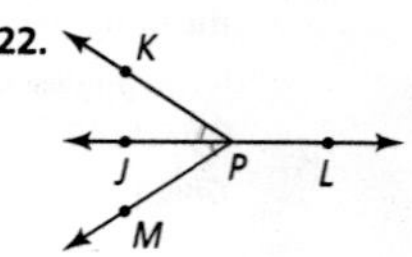

23. Developing Proof Fill in the blanks to complete this proof of Theorem 2-5. If two angles are congruent and supplementary, then each is a right angle.

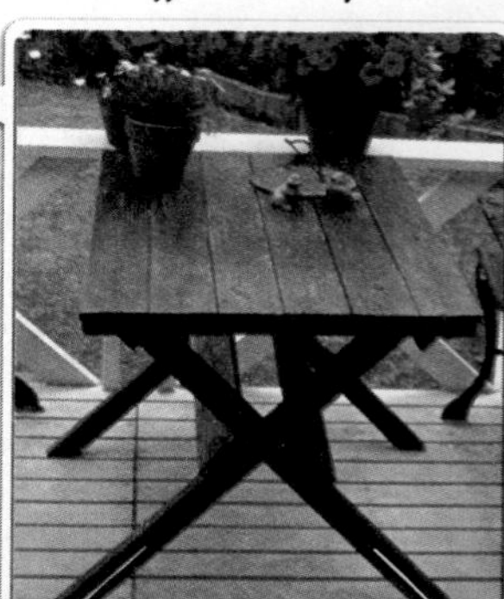

Given: ∠W and ∠V are congruent and supplementary.

Prove: ∠W and ∠V are right angles.

Proof: ∠W and ∠V are congruent because **a.** _?_. Because congruent angles have the same measure, $m\angle W =$ **b.** _?_. ∠W and ∠V are supplementary because it is given. By the definition of supplementary angles, $m\angle W + m\angle V =$ **c.** _?_. Substituting $m\angle W$ for $m\angle V$, you get $m\angle W + m\angle W = 180$, or $2m\angle W = 180$. By the **d.** _?_ Property of Equality, $m\angle W = 90$. Since $m\angle W = m\angle V$, $m\angle V = 90$ by the Transitive Property of Equality. Both angles are **e.** _?_ angles by the definition of right angles.

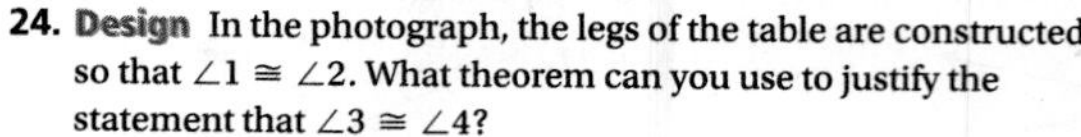

24. Design In the photograph, the legs of the table are constructed so that $\angle 1 \cong \angle 2$. What theorem can you use to justify the statement that $\angle 3 \cong \angle 4$?

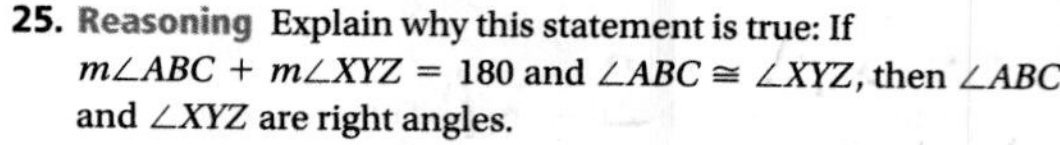

25. Reasoning Explain why this statement is true: If $m\angle ABC + m\angle XYZ = 180$ and $\angle ABC \cong \angle XYZ$, then ∠ABC and ∠XYZ are right angles.

Algebra **Find the measure of each angle.**

26. ∠A is twice as large as its complement, ∠B.

27. ∠A is half as large as its complement, ∠B.

28. ∠A is twice as large as its supplement, ∠B.

29. ∠A is half as large as twice its supplement, ∠B.

30. Write a proof for this form of Theorem 2-2.

Proof

If two angles are supplements of congruent angles, then the two angles are congruent.

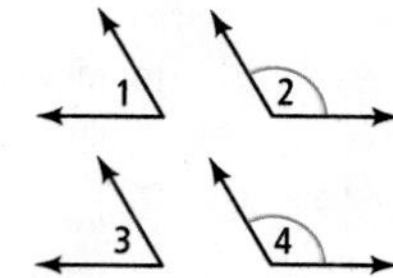

Given: ∠1 and ∠2 are supplementary.
∠3 and ∠4 are supplementary.
$\angle 2 \cong \angle 4$

Prove: $\angle 1 \cong \angle 3$

Challenge

31. Coordinate Geometry ∠DOE contains points $D(2, 3)$, $O(0, 0)$, and $E(5, 1)$. Find the coordinates of a point F so that $\overrightarrow{OF}$ is a side of an angle that is adjacent and supplementary to ∠DOE.

32. **Coordinate Geometry** $\angle AOX$ contains points $A(1, 3)$, $O(0, 0)$, and $X(4, 0)$.
  a. Find the coordinates of a point B so that $\angle BOA$ and $\angle AOX$ are adjacent complementary angles.
  b. Find the coordinates of a point C so that $\overrightarrow{OC}$ is a side of a different angle that is adjacent and complementary to $\angle AOX$.

Algebra **Find the value of each variable and the measure of each angle.**

33. 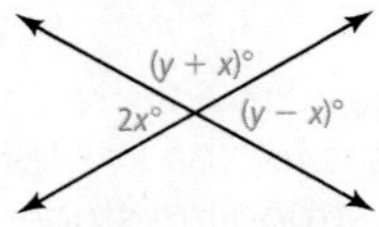

34. 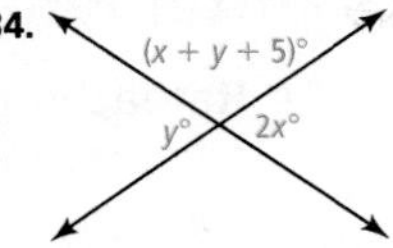

35. 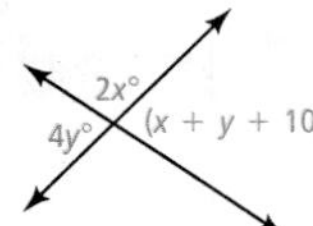

Standardized Test Prep

GRIDDED RESPONSE

SAT/ACT

36. $\angle 1$ and $\angle 2$ are vertical angles. If $m\angle 1 = 63$ and $m\angle 2 = 4x - 9$, what is the value of x?

37. What is the area in square centimeters of a triangle with a base of 5 cm and a height of 8 cm?

38. In the figure at the right, $m\angle 1 = \frac{1}{2}(m\angle 2)$, $m\angle 2 = \frac{2}{3}(m\angle 3)$. If $m\angle 3 = 72$, what is $m\angle 4$?

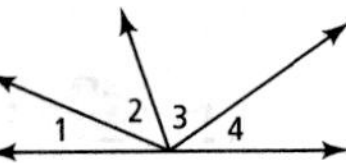

39. What is the measure of an angle with a supplement that is four times its complement?

Mixed Review

Which property of equality or congruence justifies going from the first statement to the second?

See Lesson 2-5.

40. $3x + 7 = 19$
$3x = 12$

41. $4x = 20$
$x = 5$

42. $\angle 1 \cong \angle 2$ and $\angle 3 \cong \angle 2$
$\angle 1 \cong \angle 3$

Get Ready! To prepare for Lesson 3-1, do Exercises 43–48.

See Lesson 1-2.

Refer to the figure at the right.

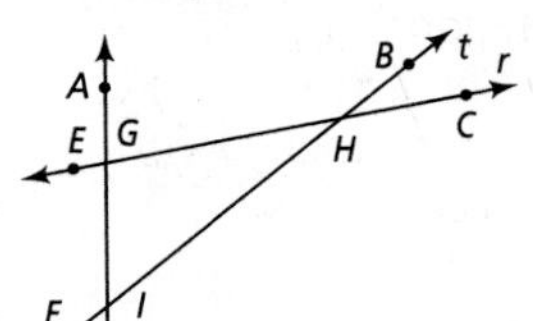

43. Name four points on line t.
44. Are points G, A, and B collinear?
45. Are points F, I, and H collinear?
46. Name the line on which point E lies.
47. Name line t in three other ways.
48. Name the point at which lines t and r intersect.

32a. B can be any point on the positive y-axis. Sample: (0, 5)
b. Answers may vary. Sample: (3, −1)
33. $x = 30$, $y = 90$; 60, 120, 60
34. $x = 35$, $y = 70$; 70, 110, 70
35. $x = 50$, $y = 20$; 80, 100, 80
36. 18 **37.** 20
38. 36 **39.** 60
40. Subtr. Prop. of Eq.
41. Div. Prop. of Eq.
42. Trans. Prop. of $\cong$
43. points F, I, H, B
44. no
45. yes
46. line r (or $\overleftrightarrow{EG}$, $\overleftrightarrow{GH}$, $\overleftrightarrow{HC}$, and so on)
47. any three of $\overleftrightarrow{FI}$ (or $\overleftrightarrow{IF}$), $\overleftrightarrow{FH}$, $\overleftrightarrow{FB}$, $\overleftrightarrow{IH}$, $\overleftrightarrow{IB}$, $\overleftrightarrow{HB}$
48. point H

2-6 Lesson Resources

Differentiated Remediation

Instructional Support

Geometry Companion

Students can use the **Geometry Companion** worktext (4 pages) . . .

- New Vocabulary
- Key Concepts
- Got It for each Problem
- Lesson Check

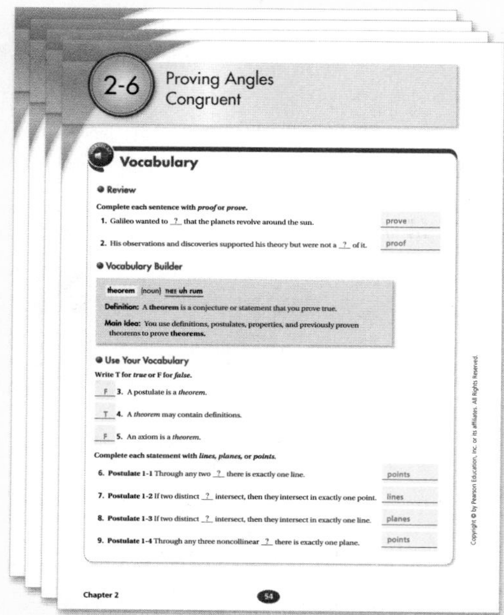

2-6 Proving Angles Congruent

Vocabulary

Review

Complete each sentence with *proof* or *prove*.

1. Galileo wanted to _?_ that the planets revolve around the sun. prove
2. His observations and discoveries supported his theory but were not a _?_ of it. proof

Vocabulary Builder

theorem (noun) THEE uh rum

Definition: A **theorem** is a conjecture or statement that you prove true.

Main Idea: You use definitions, postulates, properties, and previously proven theorems to prove **theorems.**

Use Your Vocabulary

Write T for *true* or F for *false*.

F 3. A postulate is a *theorem*.

T 4. A *theorem* may contain definitions.

F 5. An axiom is a *theorem*.

Complete each statement with *lines, planes,* or *points.*

6. **Postulate 1-1** Through any two _?_ there is exactly one line. points
7. **Postulate 1-2** If two distinct _?_ intersect, then they intersect in exactly one point. lines
8. **Postulate 1-3** If two distinct _?_ intersect, then they intersect in exactly one line. planes
9. **Postulate 1-4** Through any three noncollinear _?_ there is exactly one plane. points

Chapter 2 54

ELL Support

Focus on Communication Arrange students into pairs of mixed abilities. Write the following statements on the board: The sum of $m\angle ABC$ and $m\angle DBC$ is 90. The sum of $m\angle RST$ and $m\angle DBC$ is 90. Prove that $m\angle ABC = m\angle RST$. Have one student write a two-column proof and the other write a paragraph proof. They can trade papers and check their work. Write another statement and have students switch tasks.

Assess Understanding Write on the board: $\angle 1$ is one-fourth the size of its complement, $\angle 2$. Draw a picture to model the measure of each angle.

5 Assess & Remediate

Lesson Quiz

1. What is the value of x?

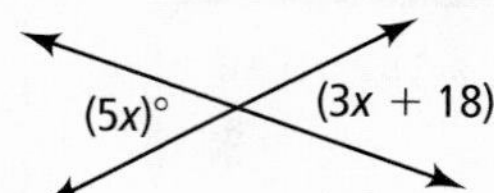

(5x)°
(3x + 18)°

2. **Do you UNDERSTAND?** Write a paragraph proof that validates $x = 14$ as the solution in the figure below.

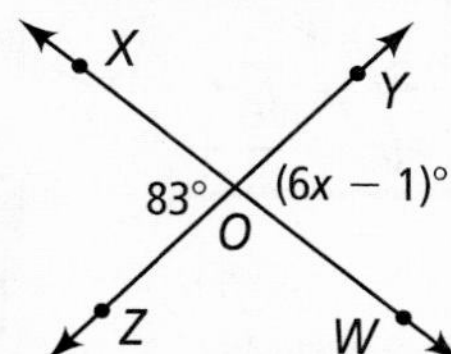

X
Y
83°
(6x − 1)°
O
Z
W

ANSWERS TO LESSON QUIZ

1. $x = 9$
2. Angles XOZ and YOW are congruent because they are vertical angles. So, their measures are equal by the definition of congruence and $83 = 6x - 1$. You can add 1 to each side of the equation by the Addition Property of Equality, which results in $84 = 6x$. Then by the Division Property of Equality $x = \frac{84}{6}$, or $x = 14$.

PRESCRIPTION FOR REMEDIATION

Use the student work on the Lesson Quiz to prescribe a differentiated review assignment.

Points	Differentiated Remediation
0	Intervention
1	On-level
2	Extension

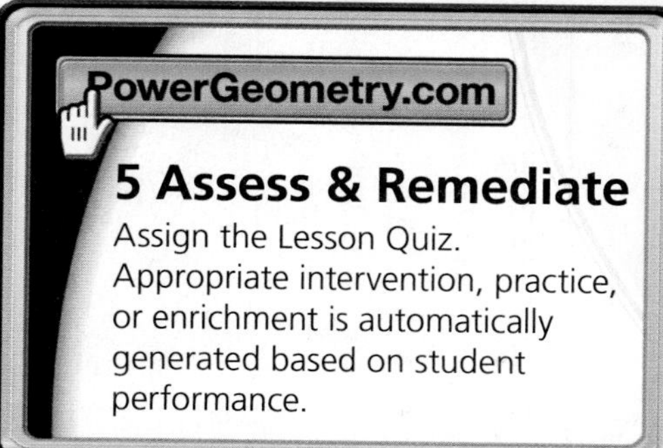

PowerGeometry.com
5 Assess & Remediate
Assign the Lesson Quiz.
Appropriate intervention, practice, or enrichment is automatically generated based on student performance.

Intervention

- **Reteaching** (2 pages) Provides reteaching and practice exercises for the key lesson concepts. Use with struggling students or absent students.
- **English Language Learner Support** Helps students develop and reinforce mathematical vocabulary and key concepts.

All-in-One Resources/Online

Reteaching

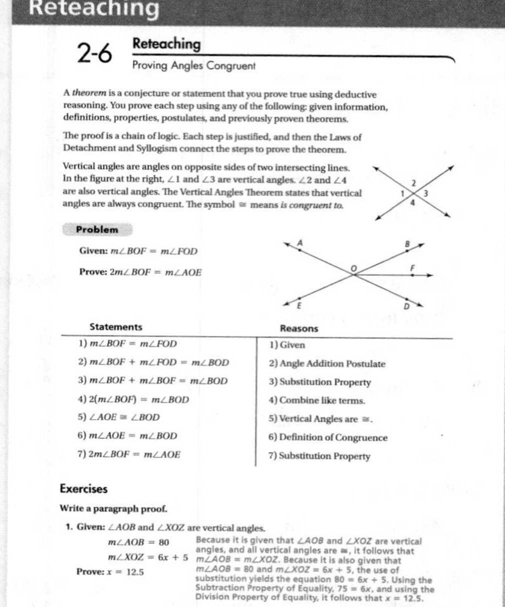

2-6 Reteaching
Proving Angles Congruent

A *theorem* is a conjecture or statement that you prove true using deductive reasoning. You prove each step using any of the following: given information, definitions, properties, postulates, and previously proven theorems.

The proof is a chain of logic. Each step is justified, and then the Laws of Detachment and Syllogism connect the steps to prove the theorem.

Vertical angles are angles on opposite sides of two intersecting lines. In the figure at the right, $\angle 1$ and $\angle 3$ are vertical angles. $\angle 2$ and $\angle 4$ are also vertical angles. The Vertical Angles Theorem states that vertical angles are always congruent. The symbol $\cong$ means *is congruent to.*

Problem

Given: $m\angle BOF = m\angle FOD$

Prove: $2m\angle BOF = m\angle AOE$

Statements	Reasons
1) $m\angle BOF = m\angle FOD$	1) Given
2) $m\angle BOF + m\angle FOD = m\angle BOD$	2) Angle Addition Postulate
3) $m\angle BOF + m\angle BOF = m\angle BOD$	3) Substitution Property
4) $2(m\angle BOF) = m\angle BOD$	4) Combine like terms.
5) $\angle AOE \cong \angle BOD$	5) Vertical Angles are $\cong$.
6) $m\angle AOE = m\angle BOD$	6) Definition of Congruence
7) $2m\angle BOF = m\angle AOE$	7) Substitution Property

Exercises

Write a paragraph proof.

1. **Given:** $\angle AOB$ and $\angle XOZ$ are vertical angles.
$m\angle AOB = 80$
$m\angle XOZ = 6x + 5$
Prove: $x = 12.5$

Because it is given that $\angle AOB$ and $\angle XOZ$ are vertical angles, and all vertical angles are $\cong$, it follows that $m\angle AOB = m\angle XOZ$. Because it is also given that $m\angle AOB = 80$ and $m\angle XOZ = 6x + 5$, the use of substitution yields the equation $80 = 6x + 5$. Using the Subtraction Property of Equality, $75 = 6x$, and using the Division Property of Equality, it follows that $x = 12.5$.

All-in-One Resources/Online

English Language Learner Support

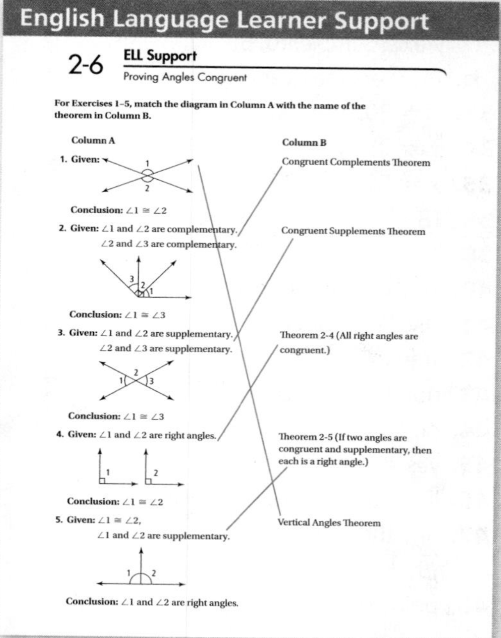

2-6 ELL Support
Proving Angles Congruent

For Exercises 1–5, match the diagram in Column A with the name of the theorem in Column B.

Column A

1. **Given:** (diagram) **Conclusion:** $\angle 1 \cong \angle 2$
2. **Given:** $\angle 1$ and $\angle 2$ are complementary. $\angle 2$ and $\angle 3$ are complementary. **Conclusion:** $\angle 1 \cong \angle 3$
3. **Given:** $\angle 1$ and $\angle 2$ are supplementary. $\angle 2$ and $\angle 3$ are supplementary. **Conclusion:** $\angle 1 \cong \angle 3$
4. **Given:** $\angle 1$ and $\angle 2$ are right angles. **Conclusion:** $\angle 1 \cong \angle 2$
5. **Given:** $\angle 1 \cong \angle 2$, $\angle 1$ and $\angle 2$ are supplementary. **Conclusion:** $\angle 1$ and $\angle 2$ are right angles.

Column B

- Congruent Complements Theorem
- Congruent Supplements Theorem
- Theorem 2-4 (All right angles are congruent.)
- Theorem 2-5 (If two angles are congruent and supplementary, then each is a right angle.)
- Vertical Angles Theorem

Differentiated Remediation *continued*

On-Level

- **Practice** (2 pages) Provides extra practice for each lesson. For simpler practice exercises, use the Form K Practice pages found in the All-in-One Teaching Resources and online.
- **Think About a Plan** Helps students develop specific problem-solving skills and strategies by providing scaffolded guiding questions.
- **Standardized Test Prep** Focuses on all major exercises, all major question types, and helps students prepare for the high-stakes assessments.

Extension

- **Enrichment** Provides students with interesting problems and activities that extend the concepts of the lesson.
- **Activities, Games, and Puzzles** Worksheets that can be used for concepts development, enrichment, and for fun!

Practice and Problem Solving Wkbk/ All-in-One Resources/Online

Practice page 1

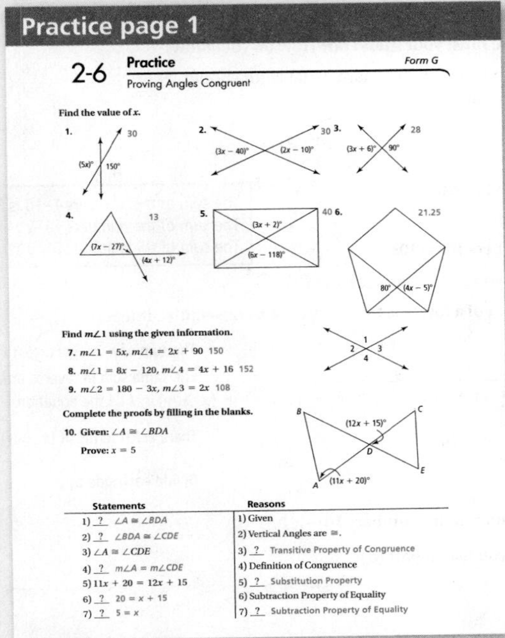

2-6 Practice *Form G*
Proving Angles Congruent

Find the value of x.

1. 30
2. 30
3. 28
4. 13
5. 40
6. 21.25

Find $m\angle 1$ using the given information.

7. $m\angle 1 = 5x$, $m\angle 4 = 2x + 90$ 150
8. $m\angle 1 = 8x - 120$, $m\angle 4 = 4x + 16$ 152
9. $m\angle 2 = 180 - 3x$, $m\angle 3 = 2x$ 108

Complete the proofs by filling in the blanks.

10. Given: $\angle A \cong \angle BDA$
Prove: $x = 5$

Statements	Reasons
1) ? $\angle A \cong \angle BDA$	1) Given
2) ? $\angle BDA \cong \angle CDE$	2) Vertical Angles are ≅.
3) $\angle A \cong \angle CDE$	3) ? Transitive Property of Congruence
4) ? $m\angle A = m\angle CDE$	4) Definition of Congruence
5) $11x + 20 = 12x + 15$	5) ? Substitution Property
6) ? $20 = x + 15$	6) Subtraction Property of Equality
7) ? $5 = x$	7) ? Subtraction Property of Equality

Practice and Problem Solving Wkbk/ All-in-One Resources/Online

Practice page 2

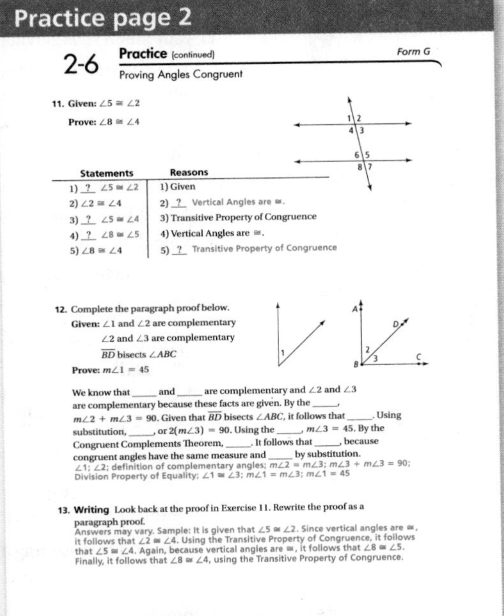

2-6 Practice (continued) *Form G*
Proving Angles Congruent

11. Given: $\angle 5 \cong \angle 2$
Prove: $\angle 8 \cong \angle 4$

Statements	Reasons
1) ? $\angle 5 \cong \angle 2$	1) Given
2) $\angle 2 \cong \angle 4$	2) ? Vertical Angles are ≅.
3) ? $\angle 5 \cong \angle 4$	3) Transitive Property of Congruence
4) ? $\angle 8 \cong \angle 5$	4) Vertical Angles are ≅.
5) $\angle 8 \cong \angle 4$	5) ? Transitive Property of Congruence

12. Complete the paragraph proof below.
Given: $\angle 1$ and $\angle 2$ are complementary
$\angle 2$ and $\angle 3$ are complementary
$\overline{BD}$ bisects $\angle ABC$
Prove: $m\angle 1 = 45$

We know that _____ and _____ are complementary and $\angle 2$ and $\angle 3$ are complementary because these facts are given. By the _____, $m\angle 2 + m\angle 3 = 90$. Given that $\overline{BD}$ bisects $\angle ABC$, it follows that _____. Using substitution, _____, or $2(m\angle 3) = 90$. Using the _____, $m\angle 3 = 45$. By the Congruent Complements Theorem, _____. It follows that _____, because congruent angles have the same measure and _____ by substitution.
$\angle 1$; $\angle 2$; definition of complementary angles; $m\angle 2 = m\angle 3$; $m\angle 3 + m\angle 3 = 90$; Division Property of Equality; $\angle 1 \cong \angle 3$; $m\angle 1 = m\angle 3$; $m\angle 1 = 45$

13. **Writing** Look back at the proof in Exercise 11. Rewrite the proof as a paragraph proof.
Answers may vary. Sample: It is given that $\angle 5 \cong \angle 2$. Since vertical angles are ≅, it follows that $\angle 2 \cong \angle 4$. Using the Transitive Property of Congruence, it follows that $\angle 5 \cong \angle 4$. Again, because vertical angles are ≅, it follows that $\angle 8 \cong \angle 5$. Finally, it follows that $\angle 8 \cong \angle 4$, using the Transitive Property of Congruence.

All-in-One Resources/Online

Enrichment

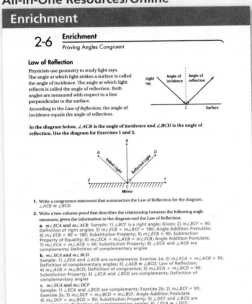

2-6 Enrichment
Proving Angles Congruent

Law of Reflection

Physicists use geometry to study light rays. The angle at which light strikes a surface is called the angle of incidence. The angle at which light reflects is called the angle of reflection. Both angles are measured with respect to a line perpendicular to the surface.

According to the *Law of Reflection,* the angle of incidence equals the angle of reflection.

Light ray | Angle of incidence | Angle of reflection | C | Surface

In the diagram below, $\angle ACB$ is the angle of incidence and $\angle BCD$ is the angle of reflection. Use the diagram for Exercises 1 and 2.

A | B | D | Indent Light | Reflected Light | E | C | F | Mirror

1. Write a congruence statement that summarizes the Law of Reflection for the diagram.
$\angle ACB \cong \angle BCD$
2. Write a two-column proof that describes the relationship between the following angle measures, given the information in the diagram and the Law of Reflection.
  a. $m\angle ECA$ and $m\angle ACB$ Sample: 1) $\angle BCF$ is a right angle; Given; 2) $m\angle BCF = 90$; Definition of right angles; 3) $m\angle ECB + m\angle BCF = 180$; Angle Addition Postulate; 4) $m\angle ECB + 90 = 180$; Substitution Property; 5) $m\angle ECB = 90$; Subtraction Property of Equality; 6) $m\angle ECA + m\angle ACB = m\angle ECB$; Angle Addition Postulate; 7) $m\angle ECA + m\angle ACB = 90$; Substitution Property; 8) $\angle ECA$ and $\angle ACB$ are complements; Definition of complementary angles
  b. $m\angle ECA$ and $m\angle BCD$
  Sample: 1) $\angle ECA$ and $\angle ACB$ are complements; Exercise 2a; 2) $m\angle ECA + m\angle ACB = 90$; Definition of complementary angles; 3) $\angle ACB \cong \angle BCD$; Law of Reflection; 4) $m\angle ACB = m\angle BCD$; Definition of congruence; 5) $m\angle ECA + m\angle BCD = 90$; Substitution Property; 6) $\angle ECA$ and $\angle BCD$ are complements; Definition of complementary angles
  c. $m\angle ECA$ and $m\angle DCF$
  Sample: 1) $\angle ECA$ and $\angle BCD$ are complements; Exercise 2b; 2) $m\angle BCF = 90$; Exercise 2a; 3) $m\angle DCF + m\angle BCD = m\angle BCF$; Angle Addition Postulate 4) $m\angle DCF + m\angle BCD = 90$; Substitution Property; 5) $\angle DCF$ and $\angle BCD$ are complements; Definition of complementary angles; 6) $\angle ECA \cong \angle DCF$; Congruent Complements Theorem

Practice and Problem Solving Wkbk/ All-in-One Resources/Online

Think About a Plan

2-6 Think About a Plan
Proving Angles Congruent

Reasoning Explain why this statement is true:
If $m\angle ABC + m\angle XYZ = 180$ and $\angle ABC \cong \angle XYZ$, then $\angle ABC$ and $\angle XYZ$ are right angles.

Understanding the Problem

1. The statement is a conditional. Break the conditional down into its parts. What is the hypothesis?
$m\angle ABC + m\angle XYZ = 180$ and $\angle ABC \cong \angle XYZ$
2. What is the conclusion of the conditional?
$\angle ABC$ and $\angle XYZ$ are right angles.
3. What makes an angle a right angle? It has a measure of 90.
4. What does the symbol ≅ mean about the angles? It means that they are congruent.

Planning the Solution

5. For the statement to be true, the sum of the measures of the two angles must equal 180 and the angles must have the same measure.
6. Write an equation to represent the hypothesis. Because $\angle ABC \cong \angle XYZ$, they have the same measure, so use the same variable m to represent the measure of each angle. $m + m = 180$
7. Simplify the equation. $2m = 180$

Getting an Answer

8. What is the value of m? 90
9. Does this value of m mean that $\angle ABC$ and $\angle XYZ$ are right angles?
yes
10. How can you explain why the statement is true?
Since both angles have the same measure, if you multiply that measure by 2, you get 180. The number 90 is the only number which when added to itself, equals 180. Since right angles have a measure of 90, then the statement must be true.

Practice and Problem Solving Wkbk/ All-in-One Resources/Online

Standardized Test Prep

2-6 Standardized Test Prep
Proving Angles Congruent

Multiple Choice

For Exercises 1–5, choose the correct letter.

1. $\angle A$ and $\angle B$ are supplementary, and $\angle A$ and $\angle C$ are supplementary. Which conclusion is valid? D
  A. $\angle B$ and $\angle C$ are supplementary.
  B. $\angle B$ and $\angle C$ are complementary.
  C. $\angle B$ and $\angle C$ are acute.
  D. $\angle B$ and $\angle C$ are congruent.
2. The measure of $\angle B$ is one-half the measure of its complement. What is the measure of $\angle B$? F
  F. 30 G. 45 H. 60 I. 90
3. $\angle T$ and $\angle R$ are vertical angles. $m\angle T = 3x + 36$ and $m\angle R = 6x - 9$. What is the measure of $\angle T$? B
  A. 15 B. 81 C. 87 D. 99

Use the figure at the right for Exercises 4 and 5.

$(6x - 5)°$ | $(2y + 30)°$ | $(3y + 20)°$ | $(8x - 50)°$

4. What is the value of x? G
  F. 8.9 H. 16.8
  G. 22.5 I. 27.5
5. What is the value of y? D
  A. −10 C. 2
  B. −2 D. 10
6. $\angle A$ and $\angle B$ are complementary angles. If $m\angle A = 5x - 2$, and $m\angle B = 3x + 4$, what is the value of x? H
  F. 3 G. 6 H. 11 I. 22.25

Short Response

7. In the figure at the right, if $m\angle 1 = 37$, and $\angle 1 \cong \angle 3$, what is $m\angle 4$? Explain.
[2] 53; $m\angle 1 = m\angle 3$, and $m\angle 3 + m\angle 4 = 90$.
So, $m\angle 4 = 90 - m\angle 3 = 90 - m\angle 1 = 90 - 37 = 53$.
[1] missing answer or explanation [0] answer and explanation both missing

Online Teacher Resource Center

Activities, Games, and Puzzles

2-6 Puzzle: Crossword
Proving Angles Congruent

Each clue below describes a vocabulary word from this chapter. Write the vocabulary word in the appropriate place in the crossword puzzle.

Across

3. this part of a conditional statement comes after the "if" in "if-then" form
6. a conditional statement that exchanges the hypothesis and conclusion
7. this variation of a conditional statement always shares the same truth value as the original conditional statement
9. also known as an "if-then" statement
10. a statement that negates both the hypothesis and the conclusion of a given conditional statement

Down

1. a conclusion one reaches using inductive reasoning
2. a true statement that combines a true conditional statement and its true converse
4. an example that shows why a conjecture is wrong
5. When you change the truth value of a given conditional statement, you get a ? .
8. a logically constructed argument that shows why a conjecture is true

Performance Task 

Pull It All Together

The concepts and skills required to solve these problems are from several lessons within this chapter and from the previous chapter. As students solve these problems, they will demonstrate their reasoning strategies and their growth as independent problem solvers.

The following questions are designed to:
- Help support students as they do the Tasks.
- Gauge the amount of support students need as they become independent problem solvers.

Task 1
- What determines how many spaces to move?
- What color space did your brother land on?
- How can you determine the color of the roll-again box?

Task 2
- What is the pattern in the given number range?
- What is the pattern in the sum?
- How can you test your conjectures?

2 Pull It All Together

To solve these problems, you will pull together ideas about inductive and deductive reasoning.

BIG idea Reasoning and Proof

You can observe patterns to make a conjecture; you can prove a conjecture is true by using given information, definitions, properties, postulates, and theorems.

Task 1

You have the yellow game piece, your friend has the red game piece, and your brother has the blue game piece. Read the rules of the board game and then answer the questions.

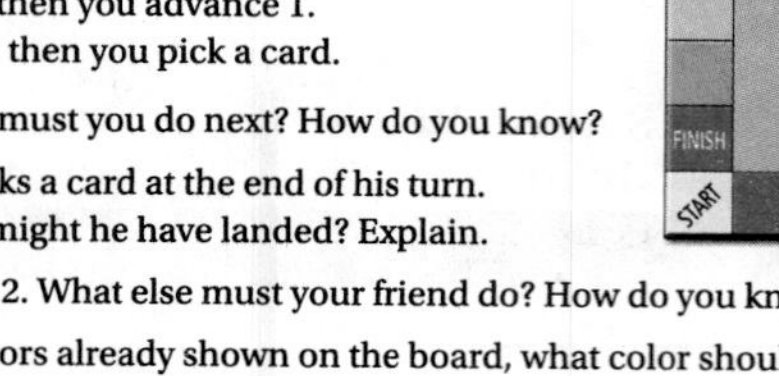

Rules
- You play counterclockwise.
- If you land on red, then you go back 1.
- If you land on green, then you advance 1.
- If you land on yellow, then you pick a card.

a. You roll 3. What must you do next? How do you know?

b. Your brother picks a card at the end of his turn. On what colors might he have landed? Explain.

c. Your friend rolls 2. What else must your friend do? How do you know?

d. Based on the colors already shown on the board, what color should the roll-again box be? Justify your answer.

Task 2

Consider the number pattern at the right.

The sum of the numbers 1–10 is 55.
The sum of the numbers 11–20 is 155.
The sum of the numbers 21–30 is 255.

a. What is the sum of the numbers 31–40?

b. What is the sum of the numbers 101–110?

c. What kind of reasoning did you use in parts (a) and (b)?

d. Following is the development of a formula for the sum of n consecutive integers.

$S = x + (x + 1) + (x + 2) + \dots + (y - 2) + (y - 1) + y$	The sum of n integers from x to y
$+ \quad S = y + (y - 1) + (y - 2) + \dots + (x + 2) + (x + 1) + x$	The same sum in reverse order
$2S = (x + y) + (x + y) + (x + y) + \dots + (x + y) + (x + y) + (x + y)$	Add the equations.
$2S = n(x + y)$	There are n terms of $(x + y)$.
$S = \frac{n(x + y)}{2}$	Divide each side by 2.

Use the formula to find the sum of the numbers 101–110.

e. What kind of reasoning did you use in part (d)?

Assess Performance UbD

Pull It All Together

See p. 69 for a holistic scoring rubric to gauge a student's progress on Understanding the Problem, Planning a Solution, Getting an Answer, and Assessing Autonomy.

SOLUTION OUTLINES

1a–c. Possible plan: Use the number rolled and the rules of the game to determine where each player ends their turn and what they must do. (Answers: a. pick a card; b. advance 1 space and then pick a card; c. green or yellow)

d. First step: Identify the pattern of colors on the game board. (Answer: orange)

2a–b. Possible plan: Identify the pattern and use it to find each sum. (Answers: a. 355; b. 1055)

c. (Answer: inductive reasoning)

d. First step: Substitute 10 for n, 101 for x, and 110 for y in the formula. (Answer: 1055)

e. (Answer: deductive reasoning)

Chapter Review

Connecting BIG ideas and Answering the Essential Questions

Reasoning and Proof
You can observe patterns to make a conjecture; you can prove it is true using given information, definitions, properties, postulates, and theorems.

Inductive Reasoning (Lesson 2-1)
Inductive reasoning is the process of making conjectures based on patterns.

3 9 27 81
×3 ×3 ×3

Deductive Reasoning (Lessons 2-2, 2-3, 2-4)
Deductive reasoning is the process of making logical conclusions from given statements or facts.

Law of Detachment	Law of Syllogism
If $p \rightarrow q$ is true	If $p \rightarrow q$ is true
and p is true,	and $q \rightarrow r$ is true,
then q is true.	then $p \rightarrow r$ is true.

Proofs (Lessons 2-5 and 2-6)
A two-column proof lists the statements to the right and the corresponding reasons to the left. In a paragraph proof, the statements and reasons are written as sentences.

Statements	Reasons
• given information • information from a diagram • logical reasoning • statement to prove	• definitions • properties • postulates • previously proven theorems

Chapter Vocabulary

- biconditional (p. 98)
- conclusion (p. 89)
- conditional (p. 89)
- conjecture (p. 83)
- contrapositive (p. 91)
- converse (p. 91)
- counterexample (p.84)
- deductive reasoning (p. 106)
- equivalent statements (p. 91)
- hypothesis (p. 89)
- inductive reasoning (p. 82)
- inverse (p. 91)
- Law of Detachment (p. 106)
- Law of Syllogism (p. 108)
- negation (p. 91)
- paragraph proof (p. 122)
- proof (p. 115)
- theorem (p. 120)
- truth value (p. 90)
- two-column proof (p. 115)

Choose the correct vocabulary term to complete each sentence.

1. The part of a conditional that follows "then" is the _?_.
2. Reasoning logically from given statements to a conclusion is _?_.
3. A conditional has a(n) _?_ of true or false.
4. The _?_ of a conditional switches the hypothesis and conclusion.
5. When a conditional and its converse are true, you can write them as a single true statement called a(n) _?_.
6. A statement that you prove true is a(n) _?_.
7. The part of a conditional that follows "if" is the _?_.

Essential Questions UbD

BIG idea Reasoning and Proof

ESSENTIAL QUESTION How can you make a conjecture and prove that it is true?

ANSWER You can observe patterns to make a conjecture; you can prove it is true using given information, definitions, properties, postulates, and theorems.

Answers

Chapter Review

1. conclusion
2. deductive reasoning
3. truth value
4. converse
5. biconditional
6. theorem
7. hypothesis

Summative Questions UbD

Use the following prompts as you review this chapter with your students. The prompts are designed to help you assess your students' understanding of the Big Ideas they have studied.

- What is inductive reasoning?
- What is deductive reasoning?
- How do you write a conditional?

Answers

Chapter Review (continued)

8. Divide the previous term by 10; 1, 0.1.

9. Multiply the previous term by −1; 5, −5.

10. Subtract 7 from the previous term; 6, −1.

11. Multiply the previous term by 4; 1536, 6144.

12. Answers may vary. Sample: $-1 \cdot 2 = -2$, and −2 is not greater than 2

13. Answers may vary. Sample: Portland, Maine

14. If a person is a motorcyclist, then that person wears a helmet.

15. If two nonparallel lines intersect, then they intersect in one point.

16. If two ∠s form a linear pair, then the ∠s are supplementary.

17. If today is a certain holiday, then school is closed.

18. Converse: If the measure of an ∠ is greater than 90 and less than 180, then the ∠ is obtuse. Inverse: If an angle is not obtuse, then it is not true that its measure is greater than 90 and less than 180. Contrapositive: If it is not true that the measure of an ∠ is greater than 90 and less than 180, then the ∠ is not obtuse. All four statements are true.

19. Converse: If a figure has four sides, then the figure is a square. Inverse: If a figure is not a square, then it does not have four sides. Contrapositive: If a figure does not have four sides, then it is not a square. The conditional and the contrapositive are true. The converse and inverse are false.

20. Converse: If you play an instrument, then you play the tuba. Inverse: If you do not play the tuba, then you do not play an instrument. Contrapositive: If you do not play an instrument, then you do not play the tuba. The conditional and the contrapositive are true. The converse and inverse are false.

21. Converse: If you are busy on Saturday night, then you baby-sit. Inverse: If you do not baby-sit, then you are not busy on Saturday night. Contrapositive: If you are not busy on Saturday night, then you do not baby-sit. The conditional and the contrapositive are true. The converse and inverse are false.

2-1 Patterns and Inductive Reasoning

Quick Review

You use **inductive reasoning** when you make conclusions based on patterns you observe. A **conjecture** is a conclusion you reach using inductive reasoning. A **counterexample** is an example that shows a conjecture is incorrect.

Example

Describe the pattern. What are the next two terms in the sequence?

1, −3, 9, −27, ...

Each term is −3 times the previous term. The next two terms are $-27 \times (-3) = 81$ and $81 \times (-3) = -243$.

Exercises

Find a pattern for each sequence. Describe the pattern and use it to show the next two terms.

8. 1000, 100, 10, ...

9. 5, −5, 5, −5, ...

10. 34, 27, 20, 13, ...

11. 6, 24, 96, 384, ...

Find a counterexample to show that each conjecture is false.

12. The product of any integer and 2 is greater than 2.

13. The city of Portland is in Oregon.

2-2 Conditional Statements

Quick Review

A **conditional** is an *if-then* statement. The symbolic form of a conditional is $p \rightarrow q$, where p is the **hypothesis** and q is the **conclusion.**

- To find the **converse,** switch the hypothesis and conclusion of the conditional ($q \rightarrow p$).
- To find the **inverse,** negate the hypothesis and the conclusion of the conditional ($\sim p \rightarrow \sim q$).
- To find the **contrapositive,** negate the hypothesis and the conclusion of the converse ($\sim q \rightarrow \sim p$).

Example

What is the converse of the conditional statement below? What is its truth value?

If you are a teenager, then you are younger than 20.

Converse: If you are younger than 20, then you are a teenager.

A 7-year-old is not a teenager. The converse is false.

Exercises

Rewrite each sentence as a conditional statement.

14. All motorcyclists wear helmets.

15. Two nonparallel lines intersect in one point.

16. Angles that form a linear pair are supplementary.

17. School is closed on certain holidays.

Write the converse, inverse, and contrapositive of the given conditional. Then determine the truth value of each statement.

18. If an angle is obtuse, then its measure is greater than 90 and less than 180.

19. If a figure is a square, then it has four sides.

20. If you play the tuba, then you play an instrument.

21. If you baby-sit, then you are busy on Saturday night.

2-3 Biconditionals and Definitions

Quick Review

When a conditional and its converse are true, you can combine them as a true **biconditional** using the phrase *if and only if*. The symbolic form of a biconditional is $p \leftrightarrow q$. You can write a good **definition** as a true biconditional.

Example

Is the following definition reversible? If yes, write it as a true biconditional.

A hexagon is a polygon with exactly six sides.

Yes. The conditional is true: If a figure is a hexagon, then it is a polygon with exactly six sides. Its converse is also true: If a figure is a polygon with exactly six sides, then it is a hexagon.

Biconditional: A figure is a hexagon *if and only if* it is a polygon with exactly six sides.

Exercises

Determine whether each statement is a good definition. If not, explain.

22. A newspaper has articles you read.

23. A linear pair is a pair of adjacent angles whose noncommon sides are opposite rays.

24. An angle is a geometric figure.

25. Write the following definition as a biconditional.

An oxymoron is a phrase that contains contradictory terms.

26. Write the following biconditional as two statements, a conditional and its converse.

Two angles are complementary if and only if the sum of their measures is 90.

2-4 Deductive Reasoning

Quick Review

Deductive reasoning is the process of reasoning logically from given statements to a conclusion.

Law of Detachment: If $p \rightarrow q$ is true and p is true, then q is true.

Law of Syllogism: If $p \rightarrow q$ and $q \rightarrow r$ are true, then $p \rightarrow r$ is true.

Example

What can you conclude from the given information?
Given: If you play hockey, then you are on the team. If you are on the team, then you are a varsity athlete.

The conclusion of the first statement matches the hypothesis of the second statement. Use the Law of Syllogism to conclude: If you play hockey, then you are a varsity athlete.

Exercises

Use the Law of Detachment to make a conclusion.

27. If you practice tennis every day, then you will become a better player. Colin practices tennis every day.

28. $\angle 1$ and $\angle 2$ are supplementary. If two angles are supplementary, then the sum of their measures is 180.

Use the Law of Syllogism to make a conclusion.

29. If two angles are vertical, then they are congruent. If two angles are congruent, then their measures are equal.

30. If your father buys new gardening gloves, then he will work in his garden. If he works in his garden, then he will plant tomatoes.

22. No; it is not reversible; a magazine is a counterexample.

23. yes

24. No; it is not reversible; a line is a counterexample.

25. A phrase is an oxymoron if and only if it contains contradictory terms.

26. If two ∠s are complementary, then the sum of their measures is 90; if the sum of the measures of two ∠s is 90, then the ∠s are complementary.

27. Colin will become a better player.

28. $m\angle 1 + m\angle 2 = 180$

29. If two angles are vertical, then their measures are equal.

30. If your father buys new gardening gloves, then he will plant tomatoes.

Answers

Chapter Review (continued)

31a. Given
b. Seg. Add. Post.
c. Subst. Prop.
d. Distr. Prop.
e. Subtr. Prop. of Eq.
f. Div. Prop. of Eq.

32. BY

33. $p - 2q$

34. 18

35. 74

36. 74

37. 106

38. $\angle 1$ is compl. to $\angle 2$, $\angle 3$ is compl. to $\angle 4$, and $\angle 2 \cong \angle 4$ are all given. $m\angle 2 = m\angle 4$ by the def. of $\cong$. $\angle 1$ and $\angle 4$ are compl. by the Subst. Post. $\angle 1 \cong \angle 3$ by the $\cong$ Compl. Thm.

2-5 Reasoning in Algebra and Geometry

Quick Review

You use deductive reasoning and properties to solve equations and justify your reasoning.

A **proof** is a convincing argument that uses deductive reasoning. A **two-column proof** lists each statement on the left and the justification for each statement on the right.

Example

What is the name of the property that justifies going from the first line to the second line?

$\angle A \cong \angle B$ and $\angle B \cong \angle C$
$\angle A \cong \angle C$

Transitive Property of Congruence

Exercises

31. Algebra Fill in the reason that justifies each step.

Given: $QS = 42$
Prove: $x = 13$

Q —— $x + 3$ —— R —— $2x$ —— S

Statements	Reasons
1) $QS = 42$	1) a. ___?___
2) $QR + RS = QS$	2) b. ___?___
3) $(x + 3) + 2x = 42$	3) c. ___?___
4) $3x + 3 = 42$	4) d. ___?___
5) $3x = 39$	5) e. ___?___
6) $x = 13$	6) f. ___?___

Use the given property to complete the statement.

32. Division Property of Equality
If $2(AX) = 2(BY)$, then $AX =$ ___?___.

33. Distributive Property: $3p - 6q = 3($___?___$)$

2-6 Proving Angles Congruent

Quick Review

A statement that you prove true is a **theorem.** A proof written as a paragraph is a **paragraph proof.** In geometry, each statement in a proof is justified by given information, a property, postulate, definition, or theorem.

Example

Write a paragraph proof.

Given: $\angle 1 \cong \angle 4$
Prove: $\angle 2 \cong \angle 3$

$\angle 1 \cong \angle 4$ because it is given. $\angle 1 \cong \angle 2$ because vertical angles are congruent. $\angle 4 \cong \angle 2$ by the Transitive Property of Congruence. $\angle 4 \cong \angle 3$ because vertical angles are congruent. $\angle 2 \cong \angle 3$ by the Transitive Property of Congruence.

Exercises

Use the diagram for Exercises 34–37.

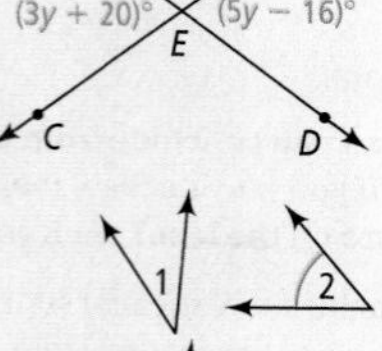

34. Find the value of y.

35. Find $m\angle AEC$.

36. Find $m\angle BED$.

37. Find $m\angle AEB$.

38. Given: $\angle 1$ and $\angle 2$ are complementary. $\angle 3$ and $\angle 4$ are complementary. $\angle 2 \cong \angle 4$
Prove: $\angle 1 \cong \angle 3$

2 Chapter Test

Do you know HOW?

Use inductive reasoning to describe each pattern and find the next two terms of each sequence.

1. $-16, 8, -4, 2, \dots$
2. $1, 4, 9, 16, 25, \dots$

For Exercises 3 and 4, find a counterexample.

3. All snakes are poisonous.
4. If two angles are complementary, then they are not congruent.
5. Identify the hypothesis and conclusion:
   If $x + 9 = 11$, then $x = 2$.
6. Write "all puppies are cute" as a conditional.

Write the converse, inverse, and contrapositive for each statement. Determine the truth value of each.

7. If a figure is a square, then it has at least two right angles.
8. If a square has side length 3 m, then its perimeter is 12 m.

Writing Explain why each statement is not a good definition.

9. A pen is a writing instrument.
10. Supplementary angles are angles that form a straight line.
11. Vertical angles are angles that are congruent.

Name the property that justifies each statement.

12. If $UV = KL$ and $KL = 6$, then $UV = 6$.
13. If $m\angle 1 + m\angle 2 = m\angle 4 + m\angle 2$, then $m\angle 1 = m\angle 4$.
14. $\angle ABC \cong \angle ABC$
15. If $\angle DEF \cong \angle HJK$, then $\angle HJK \cong \angle DEF$.
16. The measure of an angle is 52 more than the measure of its complement. What is the measure of the angle?
17. Rewrite this biconditional as two conditionals.
    A fish is a bluegill if and only if it is a bluish, freshwater sunfish.

For each diagram, state two pairs of angles that are congruent. Justify your answers.

18.

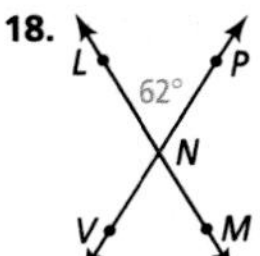

19.

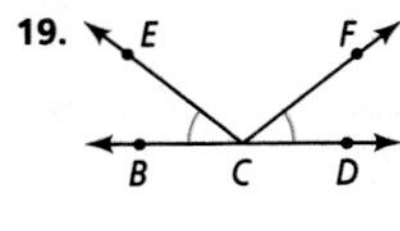

Use the Law of Detachment and the Law of Syllogism to make any possible conclusion. Write *not possible* if you cannot make any conclusion.

20. People who live in glass houses should not throw stones. Emily should not throw stones.
21. James wants to be a chemical engineer. If a student wants to be a chemical engineer, then that student must graduate from college.

Do you UNDERSTAND?

22. **Open-Ended** Write two different sequences whose first three terms are 1, 2, 4. Describe each pattern.
23. **Developing Proof** Complete this proof by filling in the blanks.

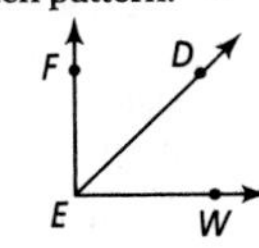

Given: $\angle FED$ and $\angle DEW$ are complementary.
Prove: $\angle FEW$ is a right angle.

$\angle FED$ and $\angle DEW$ are complementary because it is given. By the Definition of Complementary Angles, $m\angle FED + m\angle DEW =$ **a.** __?__.
$m\angle FED + m\angle DEW = m\angle FEW$ by the **b.** __?__.
$90 = m\angle FEW$ by the **c.** __?__ Property of Equality.
Then $\angle FEW$ is a right angle by the **d.** __?__.

Answers

Chapter Test

1. Divide the previous term by -2, or multiply by -0.5; -1, 0.5.
2. Find the square of 1, 2, 3, 4, . . . ; 36, 49.
3. Answers may vary. Sample: a garter snake
4. two 45° ∠s
5. Hypothesis: $x + 9 = 11$
   Conclusion: $x = 2$
6. If an animal is a puppy, then the animal is cute.
7. Converse: If a figure has at least two right angles, then it is a square; inverse: If a figure is not a square, then it does not have at least two right angles; contrapositive: If a figure does not have at least two right angles, then it is not a square. The converse and the inverse are false. The contrapositive is true.
8. Converse: If a square's perimeter is 12 m, then the square has side length 3 m; inverse: If a square does not have side length 3 m, then its perimeter is not 12 m; contrapositive: If a square's perimeter is not 12 m, then the square does not have side length 3 m. All three statements are true.
9. It is not reversible.
10. The statement "If two ∠s are suppl., then they form a straight line" is not true; a counterexample is any two ∠s of a rectangle.
11. It is not reversible.
12. Trans. Prop. of Eq., or Subst. Prop. of Eq.
13. Subtr. Prop. of Eq.
14. Refl. Prop. of ≅
15. Sym. Prop. of ≅
16. 71
17. If a fish is a bluegill, then it is a bluish, freshwater sunfish. If a fish is a bluish, freshwater sunfish, then it is a bluegill.
18. $\angle LNP \cong \angle VNM$, $\angle LNV \cong \angle PNM$ (Vert. ∠s Thm); also, any pair of straight ∠s are ≅.
19. $\angle BCE \cong \angle DCF$ (given in the diagram); $\angle BCF \cong \angle DCE$ (Two ∠s suppl. to ≅ ∠s are ≅.)
20. not possible
21. James must graduate from college.
22. Answers may vary. Sample: 1, 2, 4, 8, 16, 32, . . . (Each term is two times the previous term.); 1, 2, 4, 7, 11, 16, 22, . . . (Add 1, add 2, add 3, add 4, . . .)

23a. 90
   b. ∠ Add. Post.
   c. Subst.
   d. def. of right ∠

Item Number	Lesson
1	2-6
2	1-2
3	1-6
4	2-2
5	1-5
6	2-2
7	2-1
8	2-4
9	1-8
10	2-2
11	1-8
12	2-1
13	1-8
14	1-1
15	1-5
16	1-8
17	2-6
18	1-7
19	2-2
20	1-7
21	2-1
22	2-6

2 Cumulative Test Prep

TIPS FOR SUCCESS

Some questions ask you to extend a pattern. Read the sample question at the right. Then follow the tips to answer it.

TIP 1

Look for a relationship between consecutive figures. Make sure the relationship holds for each pair of consecutive figures, not just the first two figures.

The first four figures in a sequence are shown below. How many dots will be in the sixth figure of this sequence?

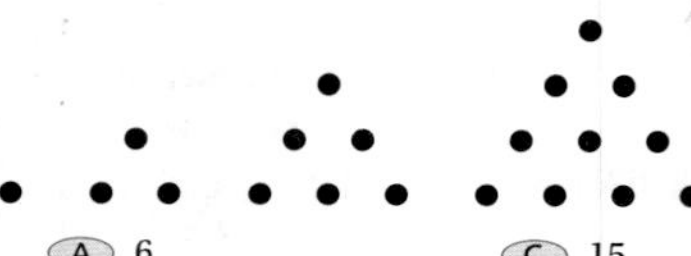

(A) 6
(B) 11
(C) 15
(D) 21

TIP 2

Use the relationship between the figures to extend the pattern.

Think It Through

The second figure has 2 more dots than the first figure, the third figure has 3 more dots than the second figure, and the fourth figure has 4 more dots than the third figure. So, the fifth figure will have 5 more dots than the fourth figure, or $10 + 5 = 15$ dots. The sixth figure will have 6 more dots than the fifth figure, or $15 + 6 = 21$ dots.
The correct answer is D.

Vocabulary Builder

As you solve test items, you must understand the meanings of mathematical terms. Choose the correct term to complete each sentence.

I. Reasoning that is based on patterns you observe is called (*inductive, deductive*) reasoning.

II. The (*Law of Syllogism, Law of Detachment*) allows you to state a conclusion from two true conditional statements when the conclusion of one statement is the hypothesis of the other statement.

III. A conditional, or *if-then*, statement has two parts. The part following *if* is the (*conclusion, hypothesis*).

IV. The (*Reflexive Property, Symmetric Property*) says that if $a = b$, then $b = a$.

V. The (*inverse, converse*) of a conditional negates both the hypothesis and the conclusion.

Multiple Choice

Read each question. Then write the letter of the correct answer on your paper.

1. Which pair of angles must be congruent?
(A) supplementary angles
(B) complementary angles
(C) adjacent angles
(D) vertical angles

2. Which of the following best defines a postulate?
(F) a statement accepted without proof
(G) a conclusion reached using inductive reasoning
(H) an example that proves a conjecture false
(I) a statement that you prove true

Answers

Cumulative Test Prep

I. inductive
II. Law of Syllogism
III. hypothesis
IV. Symmetric Property
V. inverse
1. D
2. F

3. What is the second step in constructing $\angle S$, an angle congruent to $\angle A$?

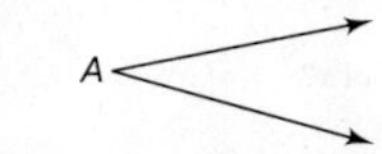

Ⓐ S

Ⓑ

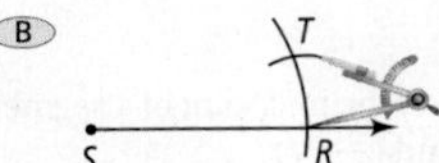

Ⓒ

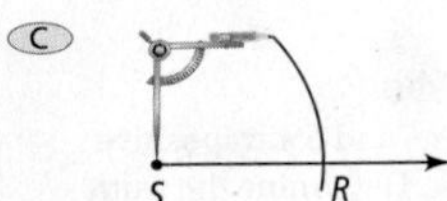

Ⓓ

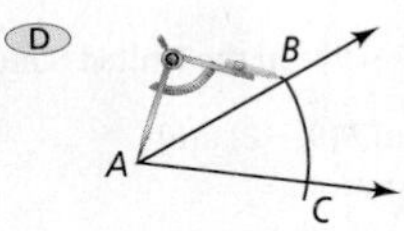

4. What is the converse of the following statement?

If a whole number has 0 as its last digit, then the number is evenly divisible by 10.

Ⓕ If a number is evenly divisible by 10, then it is a whole number.

Ⓖ If a whole number is divisible by 10, then it is an even number.

Ⓗ If a whole number is evenly divisible by 10, then it has 0 as its last digit.

Ⓘ If a whole number has 0 as its last digit, then it must be evenly divisible by 10.

5. The sum of the measures of the complement and the supplement of an angle is 114. What is the measure of the angle?

Ⓐ 12 Ⓒ 78

Ⓑ 66 Ⓓ 102

6. Which counterexample shows that the following conjecture is false?

Every perfect square number has exactly three factors.

Ⓕ The factors of 2 are 1, 2.

Ⓖ The factors of 4 are 1, 2, 4.

Ⓗ The factors of 8 are 1, 2, 4, 8.

Ⓘ The factors of 16 are 1, 2, 4, 8, 16.

7. How many rays are in the next two terms in the sequence?

Ⓐ 16 and 33 rays Ⓒ 17 and 34 rays

Ⓑ 17 and 33 rays Ⓓ 18 and 34 rays

8. Which of the statements could be a conclusion based on the following information?

If a polygon is a pentagon, then it has one more side than a quadrilateral. If a polygon has one more side than a quadrilateral, then it has two more sides than a triangle.

Ⓕ If a polygon is a pentagon, then it has many sides.

Ⓖ If a polygon has two more sides than a quadrilateral, then it is a hexagon.

Ⓗ If a polygon has more sides than a triangle, then it is a pentagon.

Ⓘ If a polygon is a pentagon, then it has two more sides than a triangle.

9. The radius of each of the circular sections in the dumbbell-shaped table below is 3 ft. The rectangular portion has an area of 32 ft^2 and the length is twice the width. What is the area of the entire table to the nearest tenth?

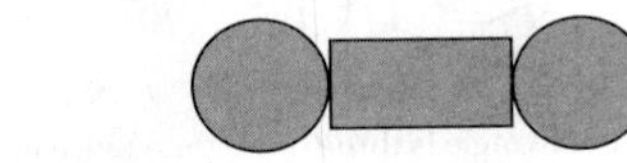

Ⓐ 88.5 ft^2 Ⓒ 132.5 ft^2

Ⓑ 124.5 ft^2 Ⓓ 166.5 ft^2

3. D
4. H
5. C
6. I
7. B
8. I
9. A

Answers

Cumulative Test Prep (continued)

10. H
11. 522.6
12. 25
13. 20
14. 8
15. 121
16. 96
17. 45
18. 1.5
19. [2] Converse: If you live in the United States, then you live in Oregon; false.
Inverse: If you do not live in Oregon, then you do not live in the United States; false.
Contrapositive: If you do not live in the United States, then you do not live in Oregon; true.
[1] one incorrect or incomplete response
20. [2] **a.** Using the definition of midpoint, the coordinates of point M are $\left(\frac{3+9}{2}, \frac{6+(-2)}{2}\right) = \left(\frac{12}{2}, \frac{4}{2}\right) = (6, 2)$.
b. Using the Distance Formula, $AB = \sqrt{(3-9)^2 + (6-(-2))^2} = \sqrt{(-6)^2 + 8^2} = \sqrt{36+64} = \sqrt{100} = 10$.
[1] incomplete or incorrect response
21. [4] **a.**

Power	Ones Place Digit
7^1	7
7^2	9
7^3	3
7^4	1
7^5	7
7^6	9
7^7	3
7^8	1

b. 9; the ones digit has four repeating digits (7, 9, 3, 1). Since 34 divided by 4 has a remainder of 2, the ones digit in 7^{34} is the same as the ones digit in 7^2.
[3] appropriate methods, but one computational error in table
[2] incorrect table OR incorrect analysis for part (b)
[1] some correct answers OR without explanation
22. [4] ∠1 and ∠2 are suppl. (Given); ∠1 ≅ ∠2 (Vert. ∠s Thm.); ∠1 and ∠2 are right ∠s (If two ∠s are ≅ and suppl., then each is a right ∠.)
[3] one incorrect reason
[2] one step missing in the proof
[1] incorrect reasons given or two missing steps

10. Which of the following statements does NOT have a counterexample?
(F) Every month has at least 30 days.
(G) The product of two fractions is an integer.
(H) The sum of any two whole numbers is a whole number.
(I) All United States coins are silver-colored.

GRIDDED RESPONSE

11. An athletic field is a rectangle, 120 yd by 60 yd, with a semicircle at each of the ends. A running track 15 yd wide surrounds the field. How many yards of fencing do you need to surround the outside edge of the track? Round your answer to the nearest tenth of a yard. Use 3.14 for π.

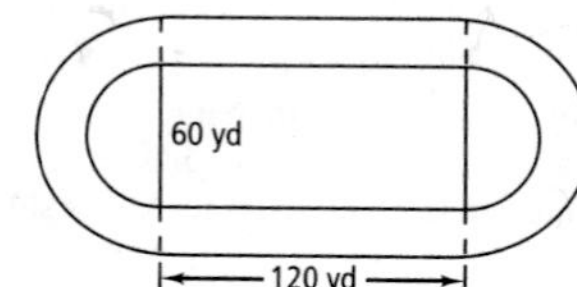

12. What is the next number in the pattern?

1, −4, 9, −16, . . .

13. The base of a rectangle is 7 cm less than three times its height. If the base is 5 cm, what is the area of the rectangle in square centimeters?

14. How many cubes would you need to build the structure shown below?

15. The measure of an angle is three more than twice its supplement. What is the measure of the angle?

16. A square and rectangle have equal area. The rectangle is 32 cm by 18 cm. What is the perimeter of the square in centimeters?

17. What is the value of x?

18. What is the y-coordinate of the midpoint of a segment with endpoints (0, −4) and (−4, 7)?

Short Response

19. Write the converse, inverse, and contrapositive of the following statement. Determine the truth value of each.

If you live in Oregon, then you live in the United States.

20. $\overline{AB}$ has endpoints $A(3, 6)$ and $B(9, -2)$ and midpoint M. Justify each response.
a. What are the coordinates of M?
b. What is AB?

Extended Response

21. The sequence below lists the first eight powers of 7.

$7^1, 7^2, 7^3, 7^4, 7^5, 7^6, 7^7, 7^8, \ldots$

a. Make a table that lists the digit in the ones place for each of the first eight powers of 7. For example, $7^4 = 2401$. The 1 is in the ones place.
b. What number is in the ones place of 7^{34}? Explain your reasoning.

22. Write a proof.
Given: ∠1 and ∠2 are supplementary.
Prove: ∠1 and ∠2 are right angles.

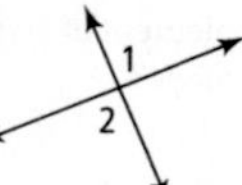

CHAPTER 3

Get Ready!

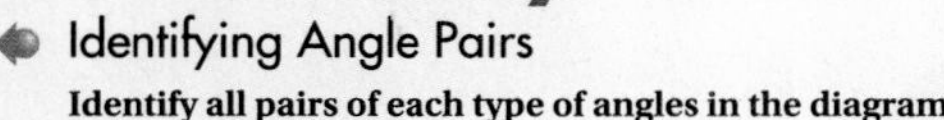

Lesson 1-5

Identifying Angle Pairs

Identify all pairs of each type of angles in the diagram.

1. linear pair

2. complementary angles

3. vertical angles

4. supplementary angles

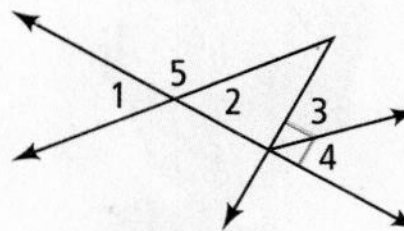

Lesson 2-5

Justifying Statements

Name the property that justifies each statement.

5. If $3x = 6$, then $x = 2$.

6. If $\angle 1 \cong \angle 2$ and $\angle 2 \cong \angle 3$, then $\angle 1 \cong \angle 3$.

Skills Handbook, p. 834

Solving Equations

Algebra Solve each equation.

7. $3x + 11 = 7x - 5$ **8.** $(x - 4) + 52 = 109$ **9.** $(2x + 5) + (3x - 10) = 70$

Lesson 1-7

Finding Distances in the Coordinate Plane

Find the distance between the points.

10. (1, 3) and (5, 0) **11.** (−4, 2) and (4, 4) **12.** (3, −1) and (7, −2)

Looking Ahead Vocabulary

13. The core of an apple is in the *interior* of the apple. The peel is on the *exterior*. How can the terms *interior* and *exterior* apply to geometric figures?

14. A ship sailing from the United States to Europe makes a transatlantic voyage. What does the prefix *trans-* mean in this situation? A *transversal* is a special type of line in geometry. What might a *transversal* do? Explain.

15. People in many jobs use *flow*charts to describe the logical steps of a particular process. How do you think you can use a *flow proof* in geometry?

Answers

Get Ready!

1. $\angle 1$ and $\angle 5$, $\angle 5$ and $\angle 2$

2. $\angle 3$ and $\angle 4$

3. $\angle 1$ and $\angle 2$

4. $\angle 1$ and $\angle 5$, $\angle 5$ and $\angle 2$

5. Div. Prop. of =

6. Trans. Prop. of $\cong$

7. 4

8. 61

9. 15

10. 5

11. $2\sqrt{17}$

12. $\sqrt{17}$

13. Answers may vary. Sample: A figure divides a plane or space into three parts: the figure itself, the region inside the figure—called its interior—and the region outside the figure—called its exterior.

14. Answers may vary. Sample: *Trans-* means "cross"; a transversal crosses other lines.

15. Answers may vary. Sample: A flow proof shows the individual steps of the proof and how each step is related to the other steps.

Get Ready!

Assign this diagnostic assessment to determine if students have the prerequisite skills for Chapter 3.

Lesson	Skill
1-5	Identifying Angle Pairs
2-5	Justifying Statements
Skills Handbook, p. 834	Solving Equations
1-7	Finding Distances in the Coordinate Plane

To remediate students, select from these resources (available for every lesson).

- Online Problems (PowerGeometry.com)
- Reteaching (All-in-One Teaching Resources)
- Practice (All-in-One Teaching Resources)

Why Students Need These Skills

IDENTIFYING ANGLE PAIRS Angle relationships will be extended to triangles and quadrilaterals.

JUSTIFYING STATEMENTS Students will use statements to prove relationships among lines in triangles and in quadrilaterals.

SOLVING EQUATIONS Equations will be used to find unknown angle measures in triangles and quadrilaterals.

FINDING DISTANCES IN THE COORDINATE PLANE Students will find equations of lines in the coordinate plane.

Looking Ahead Vocabulary

INTERIOR AND EXTERIOR Ask students to name objects that are in the interior of the classroom and objects that are in the exterior of the classroom.

TRANSVERSAL Have students name other words that use *trans-* as a prefix.

FLOW PROOF Show examples of flowcharts from various industries.

Chapter 3 Overview

UbD Understanding by Design

Chapter 3 expands on students' understandings and skills related to parallel and perpendicular lines. In this chapter, students will develop the answers to the Essential Questions posed on the opposite page as they learn the concepts and skills bulleted below.

BIG idea Reasoning and Proof

ESSENTIAL QUESTION How do you prove that two lines are parallel or perpendicular?

- Students will use postulates and theorems to explore lines in a plane.
- Students will use coordinate geometry to examine the slopes of parallel and perpendicular lines.

BIG idea Measurement

ESSENTIAL QUESTION What is the sum of the measures of the angles of a triangle?

- Students will use the Triangle-Angle Sum Theorem.

BIG idea Coordinate Geometry

ESSENTIAL QUESTION How do you write an equation of a line in the coordinate plane?

- Students will write equations using slope-intercept form.
- Students will write equations using point-slope form.

TN Checks for Understanding

3108.1.13 Use proofs to further develop and deepen the understanding of the study of geometry.
3108.3.1 Prove two lines are parallel, perpendicular, or oblique using coordinate geometry.
3108.3.2 Describe the intersection of lines (in the plane and in space), a line and a plane, or of two planes.
3108.4.1 Recognize that there are geometries, other than Euclidean geometry, in which the parallel postulate is not true and discuss unique properties of each.
3108.4.6 Describe the intersection of lines (in the plane and in space), a line and a plane, or of two planes.
3108.4.7 Identify perpendicular planes, parallel planes, a line parallel to a plane, skew lines, and a line perpendicular to a plane.
3108.4.8 Apply properties and theorems about angles associated with parallel and perpendicular lines to solve problems.
3108.4.20 Prove key basic theorems in geometry.
3108.4.21 Use properties of and theorems about parallel lines, perpendicular lines, and angles to prove basic theorems in Euclidean geometry.
Also 3108.1.5 and 3108.4.22

CHAPTER 3
PowerGeometry.com
Your place to get all things digital
Download videos connecting math to your world.
VIDEO
Math definitions in English and Spanish
VOCABULARY
The online Solve It will get you in gear for each lesson.
SOLVE IT!
Interactive! Vary numbers, graphs, and figures to explore math concepts.
DYNAMIC ACTIVITIES
Download Step-by-Step Problems with Instant Replay.
ONLINE PROBLEMS
Get and view your assignments online.
ONLINE HOMEWORK
Extra practice and review online
MathXL FOR SCHOOL

Parallel and Perpendicular Lines

Check out the gymnast on the parallel bars! Why do you think they are called parallel bars?

You'll learn about properties of parallel lines in this chapter.

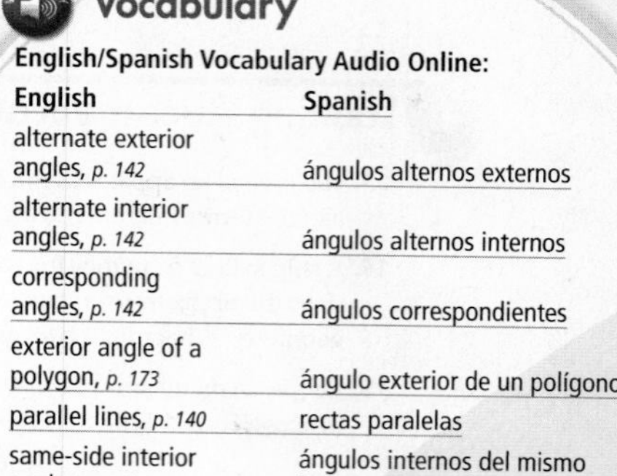

Vocabulary

English/Spanish Vocabulary Audio Online:

English	Spanish
alternate exterior angles, *p. 142*	ángulos alternos externos
alternate interior angles, *p. 142*	ángulos alternos internos
corresponding angles, *p. 142*	ángulos correspondientes
exterior angle of a polygon, *p. 173*	ángulo exterior de un polígono
parallel lines, *p. 140*	rectas paralelas
same-side interior angles, *p. 142*	ángulos internos del mismo lado
skew lines, *p. 140*	rectas cruzadas
transversal, *p. 141*	transversal

PowerGeometry.com

Chapter 3 Overview

Use these online assets to engage your students. These include support for the Solve It and step-by-step solutions for Problems.

Show the student-produced video demonstrating relevant and engaging applications of the new concepts in the chapter.

Find online definitions for new terms in English and Spanish.

Start each lesson with an attention-getting problem. View the Problem online with helpful hints.

BIG ideas

1 **Reasoning and Proof**
Essential Question How do you prove that two lines are parallel?

2 **Measurement**
Essential Question What is the sum of the measures of the angles of a triangle?

3 **Coordinate Geometry**
Essential Question How do you write an equation of a line in the coordinate plane?

Chapter Preview

 Increase students' depth of knowledge with interactive online activities.

 Show Problems from each lesson solved step by step. Instant replay allows students to go at their own pace when studying online.

 Assign homework to individual students or to an entire class.

 Prepare students for the Mid-Chapter Quiz and Chapter Test with online practice and review.

My Math Video

FACILITATE Use this photo to discuss the concept of parallel lines. In this lesson, students will learn about properties of parallel lines and how to prove that lines are parallel. Parallel lines can be seen in the real world frequently.

Q What is the name of the equipment used in the photo? **[parallel bars]**

Q How are these bars used in gymnastics? **[They are used in artistic gymnastic routines that involve swinging, arm stands, and flips.]**

Q Why do you think these bars are used in gymnastics? **[Answers may vary. Sample: the bars are always the same distance apart, so flips and turns are easier.]**

EXTENSION

Have students research the uses of parallel lines in other disciplines. Some examples include art, architecture, and science. Have students present a report that details why parallel lines are used in these cases and what properties make them useful.

ERROR PREVENTION

Students should understand that parallel lines must be in the same plane. Ask students to identify the plane in which the parallel bars in the photo lie. They should visualize a plane that is parallel to the ground or perpendicular to the stands of the parallel bars.

CHAPTER 3

PARALLEL AND PERPENDICULAR LINES

Math Background

UbD

Reasoning and Proof

BIG idea Definitions establish meanings and remove possible misunderstanding. Other truths are more complex and difficult to see. It is often possible to verify complex truths by reasoning from simpler ones by using deductive reasoning.

ESSENTIAL UNDERSTANDINGS

3-1 Not all lines and not all planes intersect. When a line intersects two or more lines, the angles formed at the intersection points create special angle pairs.

3-2 The special angle pairs formed by parallel lines and a transversal are either congruent or supplementary.

3-3 Certain angle pairs can be used to decide whether two lines are parallel.

3-4 The relationships of two lines to a third line can be used to decide whether two lines are parallel or perpendicular to each other.

Measurement

BIG idea Some attributes of geometric figures, such as length, area, volume, and angle measure, are measurable. Units are used to describe these attributes.

ESSENTIAL UNDERSTANDING

3-5 The sum of the angle measures of a triangle is always the same.

Coordinate Geometry

BIG idea A coordinate system on a line is a number line on which points are labeled, corresponding to the real numbers. A coordinate system in a plane is formed by two perpendicular number lines, called the *x*- and *y*- axes, and the quadrants they form. The coordinate plane can be used to graph many functions. It is possible to verify some complex truths using deductive reasoning in combination with Distance, Midpoint, and Slope formulas.

ESSENTIAL UNDERSTANDINGS

3-7 A line can be graphed and its equation written when certain facts about the line, such as its slope and a point on the line, are known.

3-8 Comparing the slopes of two lines can show whether the lines are parallel or perpendicular.

Angle Relationships Given Parallel Lines

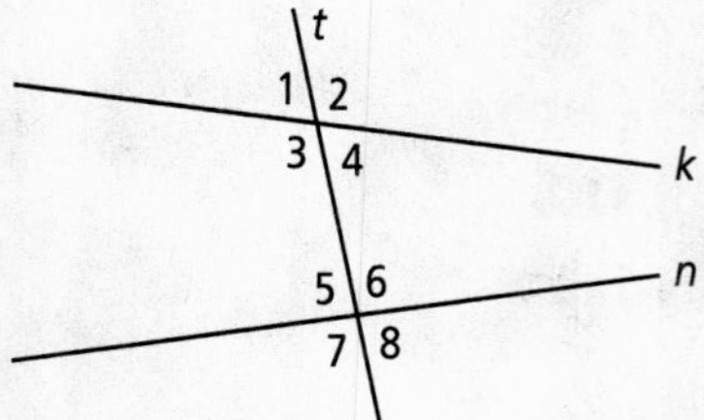

When two lines, such as *k* and *n* above, are intersected by a third line, such as *t*, the third line is called a transversal. There are special names for certain pairs of the eight angles that are formed. Students are likely to remember the terms and relationships better if they look closely at the reason why each term is applied.

Students need to understand that the word *linear* in linear pairs (such as $\angle 1$ and $\angle 2$ above) means "forming a line". Students should also understand that the angles between (or "inside") the two intersected lines ($\angle 3$, $\angle 4$, $\angle 5$, and $\angle 6$) are called *interior* angles. The words *interior* and *exterior* concern the relationship of an angle to the two intersected lines. The words *same-side* and *alternate* apply to two angles and their relationship to the transversal. Finally, students must understand that the word *corresponding* applies to both the intersected lines and the transversal: two corresponding angles (such as $\angle 1$ and $\angle 5$ or $\angle 4$ and $\angle 8$) are both above or both below the intersected lines and both to the left or both to the right of the transversal. The term *vertical angles* (such as $\angle 1$ and $\angle 4$) is harder to justify, but you can point out that such angles are never side by side.

Common Errors With Angle Relationships

Students may assume that the relations of corresponding angles, same-side interior angles, and alternate interior and exterior angles do not exist at all when the two intersected lines are not parallel. Students need to understand that the angle-pair relations exist when two lines are intersected by a transversal, whether the lines are parallel or not. Likewise, they need to understand that some of the angle-pair relations can be used to find angle measures only when the intersected lines are parallel.

Slopes of Parallel and Perpendicular Lines

Slopes can determine whether or not two lines are parallel or whether two lines are perpendicular. Students need to use their prior knowledge of how to determine slope of a line given two points: $m = \frac{y_2 - y_1}{x_2 - x_1}$. Slope is often described as the ratio comparing the change in the rise of the line as compared to the change in the run of the line. Students should realize that the smaller the absolute value of the slope, the flatter or less steep is the graph of the line.

If students are confused by dealing with the four x and y values, sketch a line on a grid with large squares and ask: How many units does the line move up when it moves one unit to the right?

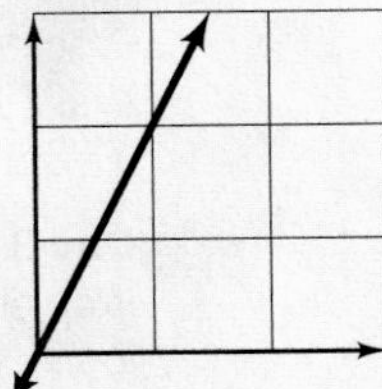

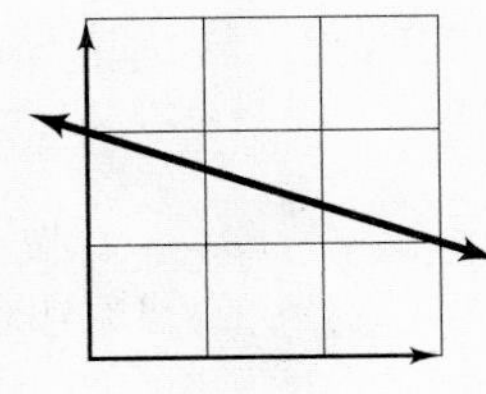

In the graph on the left, the line moves two units up for every unit it moves to the right, indicating a slope of 2. In the graph on the right, the line moves one-third a unit *down* for every unit it moves to the right, for a slope of $-\frac{1}{3}$.

Given the equations of lines, students can determine if the lines are parallel simply by looking at the slope in the equation. To determine whether or not lines are perpendicular, students must find the product of the slopes. If the lines are perpendicular, the product of their slopes equals -1.

Common Errors With Slopes of Parallel and Perpendicular Lines

Students may attempt to read the slope directly from equations not given in slope-intercept form or point-slope form. Given an equation such as $3y = 2x + 6$, for example, students may assume that the slope is 2 without first solving the equation for y.

When drawing and identifying perpendicular lines, students may forget that the two slopes of perpendicular lines must be both opposite and reciprocal: they need to understand that lines with slopes of 2 and -2 are not perpendicular, nor lines with slopes of 2 and $\frac{1}{2}$. Properties of parallel and perpendicular lines are integral parts of many geometric proofs. In order to use these concepts with the necessary rigor, students must learn early on that lines may look roughly parallel or perpendicular in a diagram, but that is not enough to go on: to be sure that lines are really parallel or perpendicular, students should look for parallel or right-angle markings in a diagram or examine the slopes algebraically.

Connecting Algebra and Geometry

This chapter illustrates the close connection between algebra and geometry. Students learn to write equations of lines and find equations of lines that are parallel or perpendicular to the given line. This enables students to describe geometric shapes in terms of the linear equations represented by their graphs. For example, students can determine whether the quadrilateral, *ABCD*, contains four right angles. The coordinates of the vertices are $A\,(1, 3)$, $B\,(4, 0)$, $C\,(1, -3)$, and $D\,(-2, 0)$.

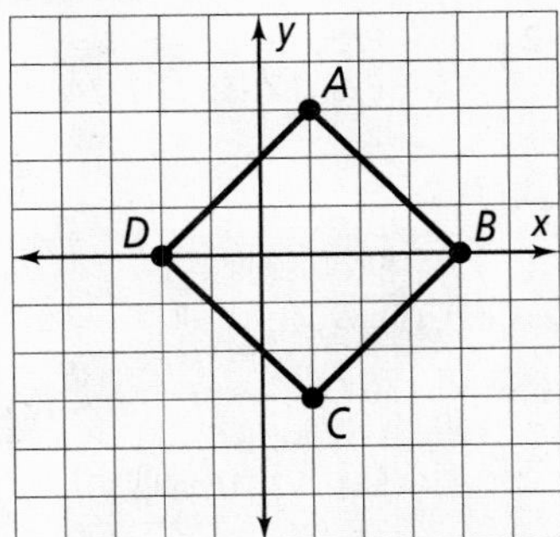

Students can determine whether $\overline{AB} \perp \overline{BC}$ by finding the product of the slopes of the two lines. Similarly, they can determine whether $\overline{BC} \perp \overline{CD}$. The products of the slopes for both sets of lines are equal to -1 and therefore, the lines are perpendicular. By establishing $\overline{AD} \perp \overline{CD}$, the students can draw the conclusion that the figure does indeed have four right angles. When students learn the method for determining distance along a line, they will be able to determine whether the quadrilateral is a square.

Common Errors Connecting Algebra and Geometry

Many situations call for the merging of algebraic and geometric skills. If students try to memorize methods or procedures, the knowledge is fragile and can be easily confused with other information. Students need to work for a deeper understanding so that they know when and how to apply the necessary skills. Many opportunities to solve multi-step problems based on familiar contexts will help strengthen their understanding.

PARALLEL AND PERPENDICULAR LINES

Pacing and Assignment Guide

TRADITIONAL | **BLOCK**

Lesson	Teaching Day(s)	Basic	Average	Advanced	Block
3-1	1	Problems 1–3 Exs. 11–29 all, 30–44 even, 49–60	Problems 1–3 Exs. 11–23 odd, 25–45, 49–60	Problems 1–3 Exs. 11–23 odd, 25–60	**Day 1** Problems 1–3 Exs. 11–23 odd, 25–45, 49–60
3-2	1	Problems 1–2 Exs. 7–11, 29–39	Problems 1–2 Exs. 7–11 odd, 29–39	Problems 1–2 Exs. 7–11 odd, 29–39	Problems 1–2 Exs. 7–11 odd, 29–39
	2	Problems 3–4 Exs. 12–18, 20–24	Problems 3–4 Exs. 13–17 odd, 18–26	Problems 3–4 Exs. 13–17 odd, 18–28	**Day 2** Problems 3–4 Exs. 13–17 odd, 18–26
3-3	1	Problems 1–2 Exs. 7–11 all, 18–28 even	Problems 1–2 Exs. 7–11 odd, 17–28	Problems 1–2 Exs. 7–11 odd, 17–28	Problems 1–2 Exs. 7–11 odd, 17–28
	2	Problems 3–4 Exs. 12–16 all, 30–34 even, 35, 36, 38, 47–57	Problems 3–4 Exs. 13–15 odd, 29–41, 47–57	Problems 3–4 Exs. 13–15 odd, 28–57	**Day 3** Problems 1–2 Exs. 13–15 odd, 29–41, 47–57
3-4	1	Problems 1–2 Exs. 6–9 all, 12–16 even, 17–18, 27–39	Problems 1–2 Exs. 6–18, 27–39	Problems 1–2 Exs. 6–39	Problems 1–2 Exs. 6–18, 27–39
3-5	1	Problems 1–2 Exs. 9–14 all, 43–53	Problems 1–2 Exs. 9–13 odd, 43–53	Problems 1–3 Exs. 9–21 odd, 22–53	**Day 4** Problems 1–3 Exs. 9–21 odd, 22–35, 43–53
	2	Problem 3 Exs. 15–22 all, 24–25 all, 27, 30–34 even, 35	Problem 3 Exs. 15–21 odd, 22–35		
3-6	1	Problems 1–2 Exs. 7–13, 40–47	Problems 1–2 Exs. 7–13 odd, 40–47	Problems 1–4 Exs. 7–17 odd, 19–47	**Day 5** Problems 1–4 Exs. 7–17 odd, 19–29, 40–47
	2	Problems 3–4 Exs. 14–27	Problems 3–4 Exs. 7–17 odd, 19–29		
3-7	1	Problems 1–2 Exs. 8–23 all, 64–77	Problems 1–2 Exs. 9–23 odd, 64–77	Problems 1–2 Exs. 9–23 odd, 64–77	**Day 6** Problems 1–5 Exs. 9–37 odd, 38–57, 64–77
	2	Problems 3–4 Exs. 24–37 all, 40, 42–44 all, 46–52 even, 53, 56	Problems 3–4 Exs. 25–37 odd, 38–57	Problems 3–4 Exs. 25–37 odd, 38–63	
3-8	1	Problems 1–2 Exs. 7–14 all, 27, 48–62	Problems 1–2 Exs. 7–13 odd, 27, 48–62	Problems 1–2 Exs. 7–21 odd, 27, 48–62	**Day 7** Problems 1–2 Exs. 7–21 odd, 23–43, 48–62
	2	Problems 3–4 Exs. 15–22 all, 24, 29, 30–40 even, 41	Problems 3–4 Exs. 15–21 odd, 23–28, 30–43	Problems 3–4 Exs. 7–21 odd, 23–28, 30–47	
Review	1	Chapter 3 Review	Chapter 3 Review	Chapter 3 Review	**Day 8** Chapter 3 Review
Assess	1	Chapter 3 Test	Chapter 3 Test	Chapter 3 Test	Chapter 3 Test
Total		**16 Days**	**16 Days**	**15 Days**	**8 Days**

Note: Pacing does not include Concept Bytes and other feature pages.

Resources

KEY
- I = Interactive asset at PowerGeometry.com
- E = Editable master at PowerGeometry.com
- P = Available in Print
- T = Available as a Transparency
- M = Master at PowerGeometry.com
- ✓ = CD-ROM

	For the Chapter	3–1	3–2	3–3	3–4	3–5	3–6	3–7	3–8
Planning									
Teacher Center Online Planner & Grade Book	I	I	I	I	I	I	I	I	I
Interactive Learning & Guided Instruction									
My Math Video	I								
Solve It!		I TM	I TM	I TM	I TM	I TM	I TM	I TM	I TM
Student Companion (SP)*		P M	P M	P M	P M	P M	P M	P M	P M
Vocabulary Support		I P M	I P M	I P M	I P M	I P M	I P M	I P M	I P M
Got It? Support		I P	I P	I P	I P	I P	I P	I P	I P
Dynamic Activity						I	I		
Online Problems		I	I	I	I	I	I	I	I
Additional Problems		M	M	M	M	M	M	M	M
English Language Learner Support (TR)		E P M	E P M	E P M	E P M	E P M	E P M	E P M	E P M
Activities, Games, and Puzzles		E M	E M	E M	E M	E M	E M	E M	E M
Teaching With TI Technology With CD-ROM			✓ P			✓ P			
TI-Nspire™ Support CD-ROM		✓	✓	✓	✓	✓	✓	✓	✓
Lesson Check & Practice									
Student Companion (SP)*		P M	P M	P M	P M	P M	P M	P M	P M
Lesson Check Support		I P	I P	I P	I P	I P	I P	I P	I P
Practice and Problem Solving Workbook (SP)		P	P	P	P	P	P	P	P
Think About a Plan (TR)*		E P M	E P M	E P M	E P M	E P M	E P M	E P M	E P M
Practice Form G (TR)*		E P M	E P M	E P M	E P M	E P M	E P M	E P M	E P M
Standardized Test Prep (TR)*		P M	P M	P M	P M	P M	P M	P M	P M
Practice *Form K* (TR)*		E P M	E P M	E P M	E P M	E P M	E P M	E P M	E P M
Extra Practice	E M								
Find the Errors!	M								
Enrichment (TR)		E P M	E P M	E P M	E P M	E P M	E P M	E P M	E P M
Answers and Solutions CD-ROM	✓	✓	✓	✓	✓	✓	✓	✓	✓
Assess & Remediate									
ExamView CD-ROM	✓	✓	✓	✓	✓	✓	✓	✓	✓
Lesson Quiz		I TM	I TM	I TM	I TM	I TM	I TM	I TM	I TM
Quizzes and Tests *Form G* (TR)*	E P M					E P M			E P M
Quizzes and Tests *Form K* (TR)*	E P M					E P M			E P M
Reteaching (TR)*		E P M	E P M	E P M	E P M	E P M	E P M	E P M	E P M
Performance Tasks (TR)*	P M								
Cumulative Review (TR)*	P M								
Progress Monitoring Assessments	I P M								

(TR) Available in All-In-One Teaching Resources   * Spanish available

1 Interactive Learning

Solve It!

PURPOSE To become familiar with parallel planes using a three-dimensional object

PROCESS Students may visualize the assembled bookcase or make a paper model of the bookcase. Directions may include defined terms or descriptions of undefined terms.

FACILITATE

Q Which pieces are the sides of the bookcase? Explain. **[A and D; They are longer than the other four pieces and are congruent to one another.]**

Q What is the relationship of pieces B, C, E and F to the sides of the assembled bookcase? **[Pieces B, C, E, and F form right angles with the sides of the bookcase.]**

ANSWER See Solve It in Answers on next page.

CONNECT THE MATH Discuss the relationship between the two sides of the bookcase and the relationship between the shelves and the top of the bookcase. In this lesson, students will study the concepts associated with parallel lines and planes.

2 Guided Instruction

Take Note

VISUAL LEARNERS

Ask students to identify objects in the classroom that model parallel lines, skew lines, and parallel planes.

3-1 Lines and Angles

TN State Performance Indicator

SPI 3108.1.4 Use geometric understanding and spatial visualization of geometric solids to solve problems and/or create drawings.

Objectives To identify relationships between figures in space
To identify angles formed by two lines and a transversal

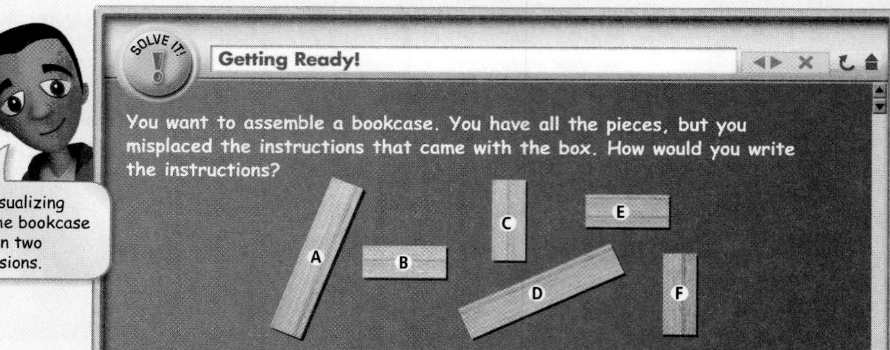

Getting Ready!
You want to assemble a bookcase. You have all the pieces, but you misplaced the instructions that came with the box. How would you write the instructions?
A
B
C
D
E
F
Try visualizing how the bookcase looks in two dimensions.

Lesson Vocabulary
- parallel lines
- skew lines
- parallel planes
- transversal
- alternate interior angles
- same-side interior angles
- corresponding angles
- alternate exterior angles

In the Solve It, you used relationships among planes in space to write the instructions. In Chapter 1, you learned about intersecting lines and planes. In this lesson, you will explore relationships of nonintersecting lines and planes.

Essential Understanding Not all lines and not all planes intersect.

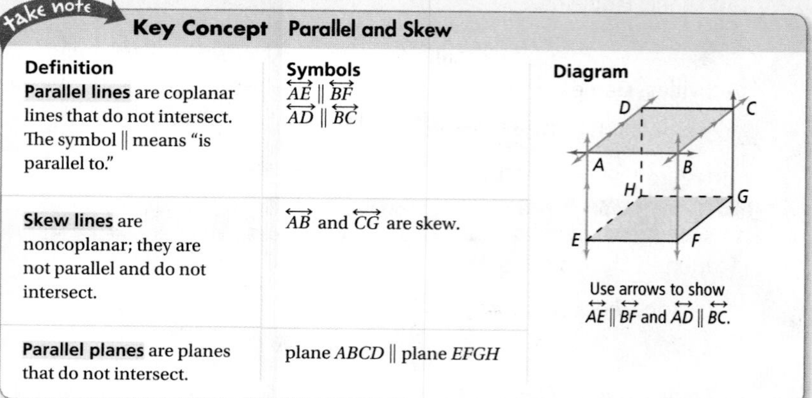

take note **Key Concept** Parallel and Skew

Definition	Symbols	Diagram
Parallel lines are coplanar lines that do not intersect. The symbol ∥ means "is parallel to."	$\overleftrightarrow{AE} \parallel \overleftrightarrow{BF}$ $\overleftrightarrow{AD} \parallel \overleftrightarrow{BC}$	Use arrows to show $\overleftrightarrow{AE} \parallel \overleftrightarrow{BF}$ and $\overleftrightarrow{AD} \parallel \overleftrightarrow{BC}$.
Skew lines are noncoplanar; they are not parallel and do not intersect.	$\overleftrightarrow{AB}$ and $\overleftrightarrow{CG}$ are skew.	
Parallel planes are planes that do not intersect.	plane $ABCD \parallel$ plane $EFGH$	

3-1 Preparing to Teach

BIG idea **Reasoning and Proof** UbD

ESSENTIAL UNDERSTANDINGS
- Not all lines and not all planes intersect.
- When a line intersects two or more lines, the angles formed at the intersection points create special angle pairs.

Math Background

The concepts presented in this lesson will provide students with the vocabulary necessary to study the properties of parallel lines. The naming conventions for the special pairs of angles that are formed when a transversal intersects two lines are a foundation for many geometry topics. Students will need to confidently identify these relationships so that they can learn the theorems or postulates that relate to each of the four special pairs of angles. These relationships appear in problems concerning special quadrilaterals, angles of elevation and depression (triangle trigonometry), and congruent and similar triangles.

Support Student Learning

Use the **Geometry Companion** to engage and support students during instructions. See Lesson Resources at the end of this lesson for details.

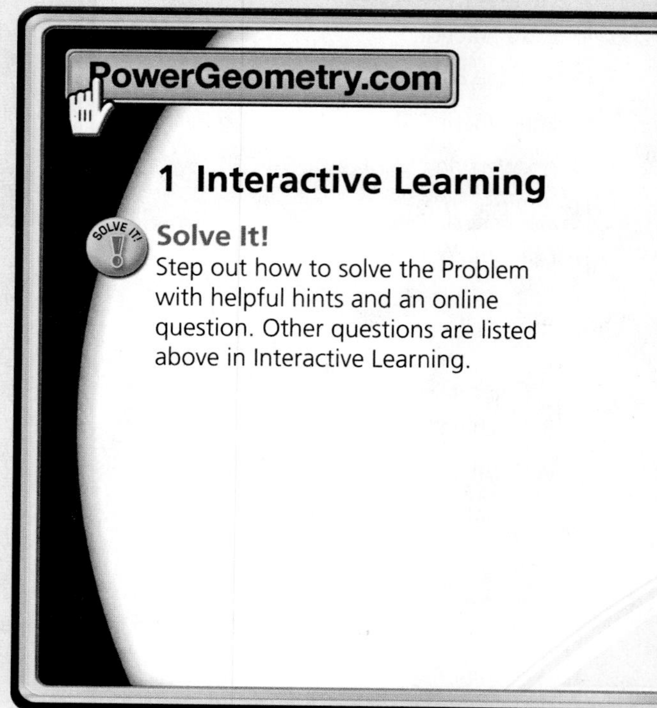

A line and a plane that do not intersect are parallel. Segments and rays can also be parallel or skew. They are parallel if they lie in parallel lines and skew if they lie in skew lines.

Think

Parallel lines are coplanar. Which planes contain $\overline{AB}$? Planes *ABCD*, *ABFE*, and *ABGH* contain $\overline{AB}$. You need to visualize plane *ABGH*.

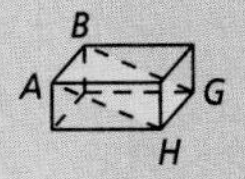

Problem 1 Identifying Nonintersecting Lines and Planes

In the figure, assume that lines and planes that appear to be parallel are parallel.

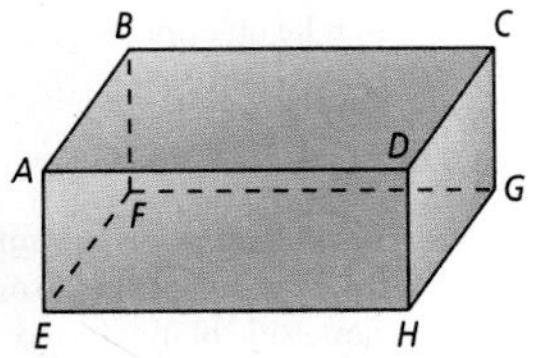

A Which segments are parallel to $\overline{AB}$?

$\overline{EF}$, $\overline{DC}$, and $\overline{HG}$

B Which segments are skew to $\overline{CD}$?

$\overline{BF}$, $\overline{AE}$, $\overline{EH}$, and $\overline{FG}$

C What are two pairs of parallel planes?

plane $ABCD \parallel$ plane $EFGH$

plane $DCG \parallel$ plane ABF

D What are two segments parallel to plane *BCGF*?

$\overline{AD}$ and $\overline{DH}$

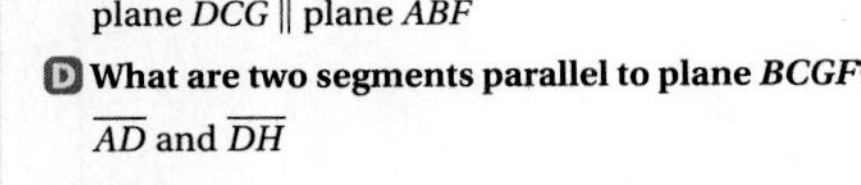

Got It? **1.** Use the figure in Problem 1.

a. Which segments are parallel to $\overline{AD}$?

b. Reasoning Explain why $\overline{FE}$ and $\overline{CD}$ are *not* skew.

c. What is another pair of parallel planes?

d. What are two segments parallel to plane *DCGH*?

Essential Understanding When a line intersects two or more lines, the angles formed at the intersection points create special angle pairs.

A **transversal** is a line that intersects two or more coplanar lines at distinct points. The diagram below shows the eight angles formed by a transversal *t* and two lines ℓ and *m*.

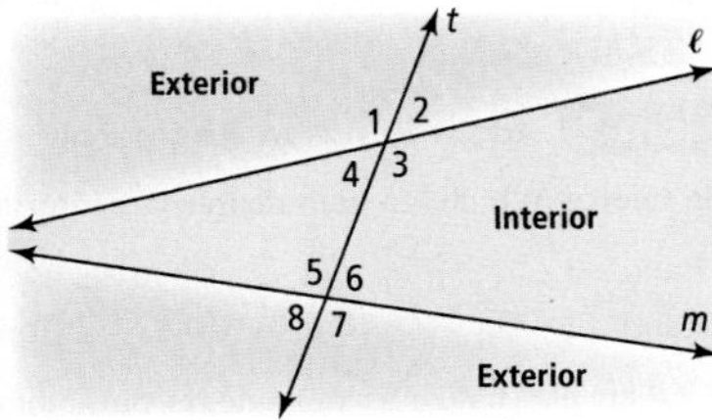

Notice that angles 3, 4, 5, and 6 lie between ℓ and *m*. They are *interior* angles. Angles 1, 2, 7, and 8 lie outside of ℓ and *m*. They are *exterior* angles.

Problem 1

Q What planes can be constructed with the vertices shown that do not contain sides of the figure? **[*ABGH*, *CDEF*, *ADGF*, *BCHE*, *BFHD*, *AEGC*]**

Q How many planes can be constructed containing $\overline{AB}$ and at least one other segment in the diagram? **[3]**

Q Of the three planes that contain $\overline{AB}$ and at least one other segment, which does not also contain a face of the prism? **[plane *ABGH*]**

Q For a segment to be skew to $\overline{CD}$, what conditions must be true? **[The segment must not be in the same plane as $\overline{CD}$ and must not be parallel to $\overline{CD}$.]**

Q How many pairs of parallel planes are shown in the diagram? Identify each pair. **[3; top and bottom, front and back sides, left and right sides]**

Got It? TACTILE LEARNERS

Have students hold a model of a rectangular prism, such as a shoebox, to visualize the planes. Students can label the corners and edges of the box and use pieces of paper to model the different planes. The *ABGH* plane and other diagonal planes can be illustrated after removing the top of the box.

2 Guided Instruction

Each Problem is worked out and supported online.

Problem 1
Identifying Nonintersecting Lines and Planes
Animated

Problem 2
Identifying an Angle Pair
Animated

Problem 3
Classifying an Angle Pair
Animated

Support in Geometry Companion
- Vocabulary
- Key Concepts
- Got It?

Answers

Solve It!

Pieces A and D are the sides of the bookcase. Pieces B, C, E, and F are the shelves; instructions may vary. Sample: Arrange pieces A and D so that a pair of flat faces are across from each other, and each piece stands upright with its long edges $\perp$ to the floor. Place piece B flat on the floor between A and D so that its long edge is $\perp$ to the long edges of both A and D. Attach one short edge of B to each of pieces A and D. Place piece C in between and at the top of A and D so that its long edge is $\perp$ to the long edges of both A and D. Attach one short edge of C to each of pieces A and D. Attach pieces E and F in a similar manner in between pieces B and C.

Got It?

1a–d. See next page.

Take Note — VISUAL LEARNERS

Use the following suggestions to help students learn the names of the angles formed by two lines and a transversal.

- Students may use a colored pencil to lightly shade the interior angles to match the color of the numeric labels.
- Students should draw several variations for each of the diagrams that are presented in the text. The variations should change the slopes of the lines, the orientation of the transversal, or both. Make certain that students label the pairs of angles on their additional diagrams.
- Students should paraphrase the definitions for each of the angle pairs. For example, a student might write "Corresponding angles: Two angles, both above a line and to the right of the transversal, etc."
- Students should note how many pairs of angles satisfy each of the four types of angle pairs.

Problem 2

Q Which line is the transversal? Explain. **[*r* is the transversal, because it intersects both line *m* and line *n*.]**

Q Why is choice B incorrect? **[∠6 and ∠7 are not on opposite sides of the transversal.]**

Got It?

Q How can you determine which angles are corresponding angles? **[The angles are on the same side of the transversal and are in exactly the same positions.]**

Pairs of the eight angles have special names as suggested by their positions.

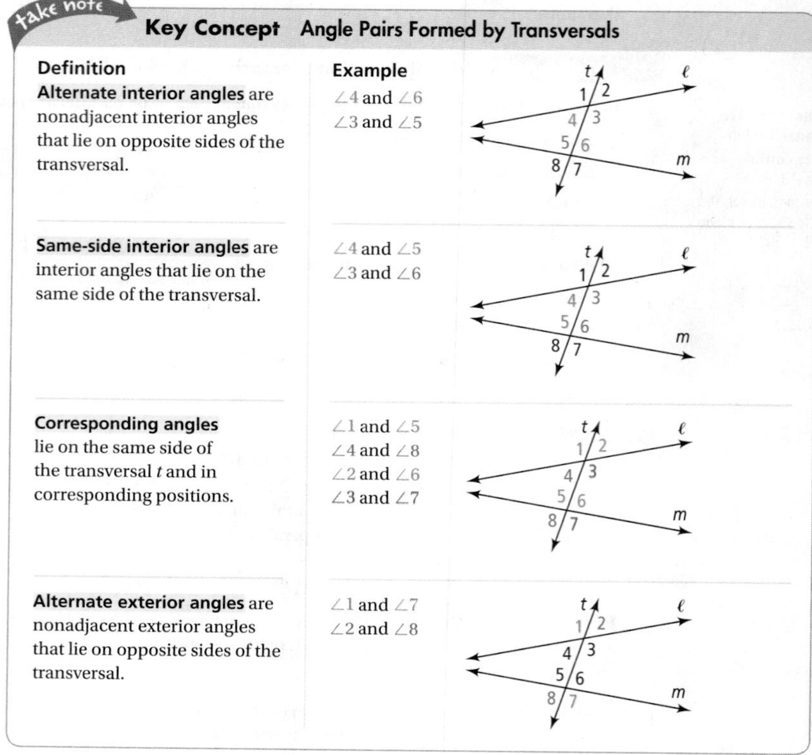

take note **Key Concept** Angle Pairs Formed by Transversals

Definition	Example
Alternate interior angles are nonadjacent interior angles that lie on opposite sides of the transversal.	∠4 and ∠6 ∠3 and ∠5
Same-side interior angles are interior angles that lie on the same side of the transversal.	∠4 and ∠5 ∠3 and ∠6
Corresponding angles lie on the same side of the transversal *t* and in corresponding positions.	∠1 and ∠5 ∠4 and ∠8 ∠2 and ∠6 ∠3 and ∠7
Alternate exterior angles are nonadjacent exterior angles that lie on opposite sides of the transversal.	∠1 and ∠7 ∠2 and ∠8

Problem 2 Identifying an Angle Pair

Think

Which choices can you eliminate? You need a pair of interior angles. ∠1, ∠4, and ∠8 are exterior angles. You can eliminate choices A and D.

Multiple Choice Which is a pair of alternate interior angles?

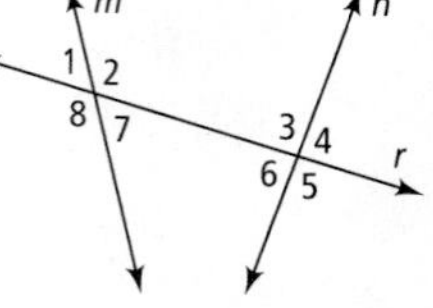

(A) ∠1 and ∠3 (B) ∠6 and ∠7 (C) ∠2 and ∠6 (D) ∠4 and ∠8

∠2 and ∠6 are alternate interior angles because they lie on opposite sides of the transversal *r* and in between *m* and *n*. The correct answer is C.

Got It? **2.** Use the figure in Problem 2. What are three pairs of corresponding angles?

Additional Problems

1.

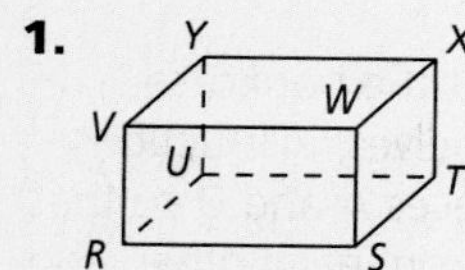

a. Which segments are parallel to $\overline{RU}$?

b. Which segments are skew to $\overline{SW}$?

c. What are two pairs of parallel planes?

d. What are two segments parallel to plane *RUYV*?

ANSWER a. $\overline{ST}$, $\overline{VY}$, $\overline{WX}$ **b.** $\overline{RU}$, $\overline{VY}$, $\overline{XY}$, $\overline{TU}$ **c.** planes *RUYV* and *STXW*, planes *RSWV* and *UTXY* planes *RUTS* and *VYXW* **d.** $\overline{ST}$, $\overline{TX}$, $\overline{SW}$, $\overline{WX}$

2. Which is a pair of alternate interior angles?

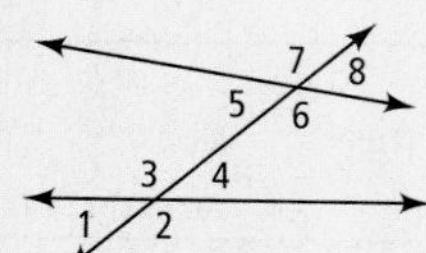

A. ∠1 and ∠2
B. ∠3 and ∠6
C. ∠2 and ∠7
D. ∠4 and ∠8

ANSWER B

3. In the figure above, are ∠3 and ∠7 alternate interior angles, same-side interior angles, corresponding angles, or alternate exterior angles?

ANSWER corresponding angles

Answers

Got It?

1a. $\overline{EH}$, $\overline{BC}$, $\overline{FG}$

b. Sample: They are both in plane *FEDC*, so they are coplanar.

c. plane *BCG* ∥ plane *ADH*

d. any two of $\overline{AB}$, $\overline{BF}$, $\overline{EF}$, and $\overline{AE}$

2. any three of ∠1 and ∠3, ∠2 and ∠4, ∠8 and ∠6, ∠7 and ∠5

Problem 3 Classifying an Angle Pair

Architecture **The photo below shows the Royal Ontario Museum in Toronto, Canada. Are angles 2 and 4 *alternate interior angles, same-side interior angles, corresponding angles,* or *alternate exterior angles*?**

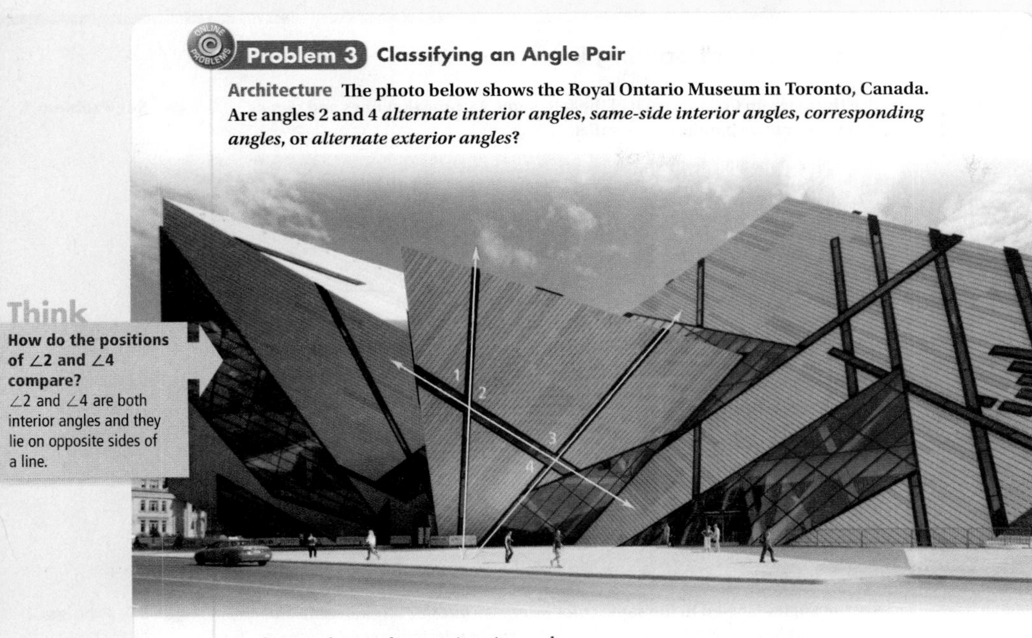

1
2
3
4

Think

How do the positions of ∠2 and ∠4 compare?

∠2 and ∠4 are both interior angles and they lie on opposite sides of a line.

Angles 2 and 4 are alternate interior angles.

Got It? 3. In Problem 3, are angles 1 and 3 *alternate interior angles, same-side interior angles, corresponding angles,* or *alternate exterior angles*?

Lesson Check

Do you know HOW?

Name one pair each of the segments, planes, or angles. Lines and planes that appear to be parallel are parallel.

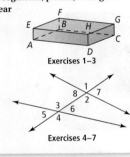

1. parallel segments
2. skew segments
3. parallel planes
4. alternate interior
5. same-side interior
6. corresponding
7. alternate exterior

Exercises 1–3

Exercises 4–7

Do you UNDERSTAND?

8. **Vocabulary** Why is the word *coplanar* included in the definition for parallel lines?
9. **Vocabulary** How does the phrase *alternate interior angles* describe the positions of the two angles?
10. **Error Analysis** In the figure at the right, lines and planes that appear to be parallel are parallel. Carly says $\overline{AB} \parallel \overline{HG}$. Juan says $\overline{AB}$ and $\overline{HG}$ are skew. Who is correct? Explain.

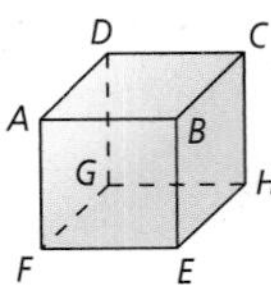

Problem 3

Q Are ∠2 and ∠4 interior or exterior angles? **[interior]**

Q Are ∠2 and ∠4 on opposite sides or the same side of the transversal? **[opposite sides]**

Got It?

Q Are ∠1 and ∠3 interior or exterior angles? **[∠1 is exterior and ∠3 is interior.]**

Q Are ∠1 and ∠3 in corresponding positions? Explain. **[Yes, both angles are above the transversal and to the left of the lines.]**

3 Lesson Check

Do you know HOW?

- To reinforce the definitions and their visual representations, ask students to name a pair of segments, planes, or angles that do not match the descriptions in Exercises 1–7, such as linear pairs or vertical angles.

Do you UNDERSTAND? ERROR PREVENTION

- If students have difficulty with Exercise 9, then have them use a checklist of questions to identify what the angles have in common. They can also draw a diagram.

Close

Q Given the diagram in Problem 2 in this lesson, list a pair of same-side exterior angles **[∠1 and ∠4, or ∠5 and ∠8]**, a pair of same-side interior angles **[∠2 and ∠3, or ∠6 and ∠7]**, and pairs of corresponding angles **[∠1 and ∠3, ∠2 and ∠4, ∠5 and ∠7, ∠6 and ∠8]**.

Got It? (continued)

3. corresp. ∠s

Lesson Check

1–7. Answers may vary. Samples are given.

1. $\overline{EF}$ and $\overline{HG}$
2. $\overline{EF}$ and $\overline{GC}$
3. plane *ABF* ∥ plane *DCG*
4. ∠8 and ∠6
5. ∠3 and ∠8
6. ∠1 and ∠3
7. ∠1 and ∠4
8. Although lines that are not coplanar do not intersect, they are not parallel.
9. Alt. int. ∠s are ∠s between two lines on opposite sides of a transversal.
10. Carly; the lines are coplanar since they are both in plane *ABH*, so $\overline{AB} \parallel \overline{HG}$.

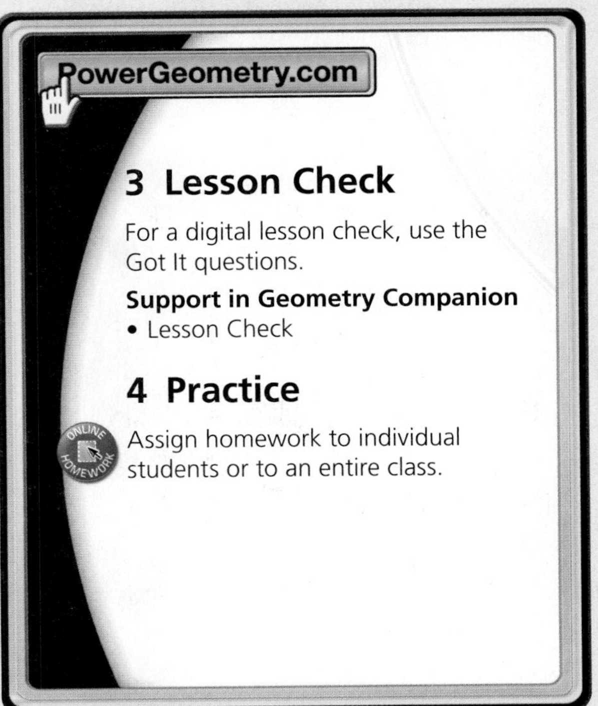

PowerGeometry.com
3 Lesson Check
For a digital lesson check, use the Got It questions.
Support in Geometry Companion
• Lesson Check
4 Practice
Assign homework to individual students or to an entire class.

4 Practice

ASSIGNMENT GUIDE
Basic: 11–29 all, 30–44 even
Average: 11–23 odd, 25–45
Advanced: 11–23 odd, 25–48
Standardized Test Prep: 49–52
Mixed Review: 53–60
Reasoning exercises have blue headings.
Applications exercises have red headings.
EXERCISE 29: Use the Think About a Plan worksheet in the **Practice and Problem Solving Workbook** (also available in the Teaching Resources in print and online) to further support students' development in becoming independent learners.

HOMEWORK QUICK CHECK
To check students' understanding of key skills and concepts, go over Exercises 13, 23, 29, 36, and 44.

Practice and Problem-Solving Exercises

Use the diagram to name each of the following. Assume that lines and planes that appear to be parallel are parallel.

See Problem 1.

11. a pair of parallel planes
12. all lines that are parallel to $\overleftrightarrow{AB}$
13. all lines that are parallel to $\overleftrightarrow{DH}$
14. two lines that are skew to $\overleftrightarrow{EJ}$
15. all lines that are parallel to plane *JFAE*
16. a plane parallel to $\overleftrightarrow{LH}$

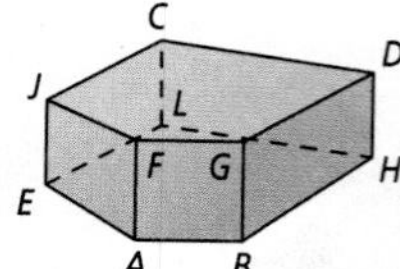

Identify all pairs of each type of angles in the diagram. Name the two lines and the transversal that form each pair.

See Problem 2.

17. corresponding angles
18. alternate interior angles
19. same-side interior angles
20. alternate exterior angles

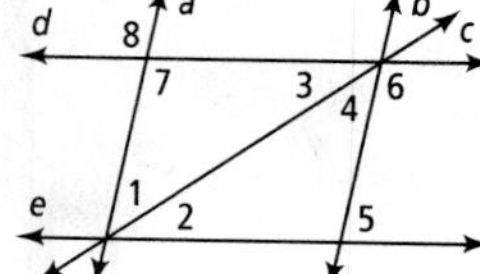

Are the angles labeled in the same color *alternate interior angles, same-side interior angles, corresponding angles,* or *alternate exterior angles?*

See Problem 3.

21.

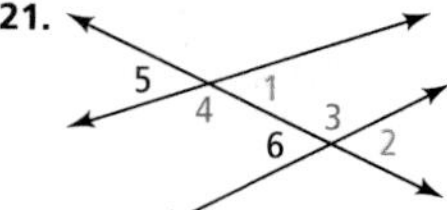

22.

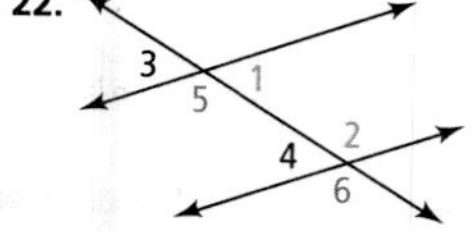

23.

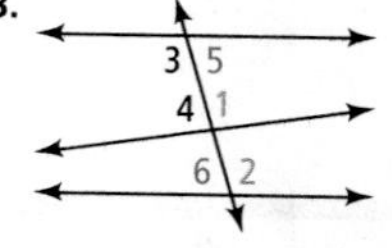

24. **Aviation** The photo shows an overhead view of airport runways. Are ∠1 and ∠2 *alternate interior angles, same-side interior angles, corresponding angles,* or *alternate exterior angles?*

Answers

Practice and Problem-Solving Exercises

11. plane *JCD* ∥ plane *ELH*
12. $\overleftrightarrow{FG}$
13. $\overleftrightarrow{GB}$, $\overleftrightarrow{JE}$, $\overleftrightarrow{CL}$, $\overleftrightarrow{FA}$
14. Answers may vary. Sample: $\overleftrightarrow{AB}$, $\overleftrightarrow{BH}$
15. $\overleftrightarrow{GB}$, $\overleftrightarrow{DH}$, $\overleftrightarrow{CL}$
16. plane *JCD*
17. ∠7 and ∠6 (lines *a* and *b* with transversal *d*); ∠2 and ∠5 (lines *b* and *c* with transversal *e*)
18. ∠2 and ∠3 (lines *d* and *e* with transversal *c*); ∠1 and ∠4 (lines *a* and *b* with transversal *c*); ∠4 and ∠5 (lines *c* and *e* with transversal *b*)
19. ∠5 and ∠6 (lines *d* and *e* with transversal *b*); ∠2 and ∠4 (lines *b* and *e* with transversal *c*)
20. ∠6 and ∠8 (lines *a* and *b* with transversal *d*)
21. ∠1 and ∠2 are corresp. ∠s; ∠3 and ∠4 are alt. int. ∠s; ∠5 and ∠6 are corresp. ∠s.
22. ∠1 and ∠2 are same-side int. ∠s; ∠3 and ∠4 are corresp. ∠s; ∠5 and ∠6 are corresp. ∠s.
23. ∠1 and ∠2 are corresp. ∠s; ∠3 and ∠4 are same-side int. ∠s; ∠5 and ∠6 are alt. int. ∠s.
24. corresp. ∠s

 **Apply**

How many pairs of each type of angles do two lines and a transversal form?

25. alternate interior angles

26. corresponding angles

27. alternate exterior angles

28. vertical angles

29. Recreation You and a friend are driving go-karts on two different tracks. As you drive on a straight section heading east, your friend passes above you on a straight section heading south. Are these sections of the two tracks *parallel, skew,* or *neither*? Explain.

In Exercises 30–35, describe the statement as *true* or *false*. If false, explain. Assume that lines and planes that appear to be parallel are parallel.

30. $\overleftrightarrow{CB} \parallel \overleftrightarrow{HG}$

31. $\overleftrightarrow{ED} \parallel \overleftrightarrow{HG}$

32. plane *AED* ∥ plane *FGH*

33. plane *ABH* ∥ plane *CDF*

34. $\overleftrightarrow{AB}$ and $\overleftrightarrow{HG}$ are skew lines.

35. $\overleftrightarrow{AE}$ and $\overleftrightarrow{BC}$ are skew lines.

36. Think About a Plan A rectangular rug covers the floor in a living room. One of the walls in the same living room is painted blue. Are the rug and the blue wall parallel? Explain.

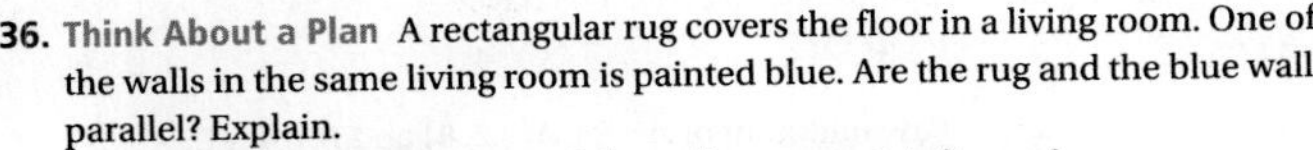

- Can you visualize the rug and the wall as geometric figures?
- What must be true for these geometric figures to be parallel?

In Exercises 37–42, determine whether each statement is *always, sometimes,* or *never* true.

37. Two parallel lines are coplanar.

38. Two skew lines are coplanar.

39. Two planes that do not intersect are parallel.

40. Two lines that lie in parallel planes are parallel.

41. Two lines in intersecting planes are skew.

42. A line and a plane that do not intersect are skew.

43. a. Writing Describe the three ways in which two lines may be related.
b. Give examples from the real world to illustrate each of the relationships you described in part (a).

44. Open-Ended The letter Z illustrates alternate interior angles. Find at least two other letters that illustrate pairs of angles presented in this lesson. Draw the letters. Then mark and describe the angles.

45. a. Reasoning Suppose two parallel planes *A* and *B* are each intersected by a third plane *C*. Make a conjecture about the intersection of planes *A* and *C* and the intersection of planes *B* and *C*.
b. Find examples in your classroom to illustrate your conjecture in part (a).

25. 2 pairs **26.** 4 pairs

27. 2 pairs **28.** 4 pairs

29. Skew; answers may vary. Sample: Since the paths are not coplanar, they are skew.

30. true

31. False; $\overleftrightarrow{ED}$ and $\overleftrightarrow{HG}$ are skew.

32. true

33. False; the planes intersect.

34. true

35. False; both lines are in plane *ABC*.

36. No; the floor and the wall intersect, so figures on those planes are not parallel.

37. always **38.** never

39. always **40.** sometimes

41. sometimes **42.** never

43a. Lines may be intersecting, parallel, or skew.

b. Answers may vary. Sample: In a classroom, two adjacent edges of the floor are intersecting, two opposite edges of the floor are parallel, and one edge of the floor is skew to each of the vertical edges of the opposite wall.

44. Answers may vary. Sample: E illustrates corresp. ∠s; Z illustrates alt. int. ∠s and same-side int. ∠s.

45a. The lines of intersection are ∥.

b. Sample: the lines of intersection of a wall with the ceiling and floor (or the lines of intersection of any of the 6 planes with two different, opposite faces)

Answers

Practice and Problem-Solving Exercises (continued)

46. No; if two planes intersect, then their intersection is a single line, and the intersection of planes A and B is $\overleftrightarrow{CD}$.

47. Yes;

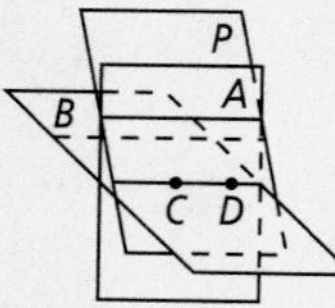

48. Answers may vary. Sample:

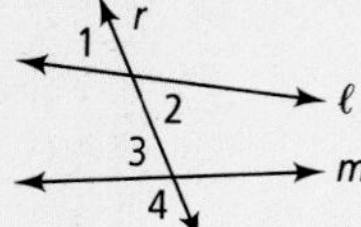

49. B **50.** G **51.** C

52. [2]

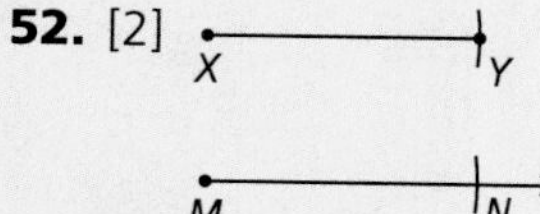

[1] incorrect explanation or inaccurate diagram

53. 121 **54.** 59 **55.** 29.5

56. 16, −32

57. corresp. ∠s

58. alt. int. ∠s

59. alt. ext. ∠s

60. same-side int. ∠s

Challenge Use the figure at the right for Exercises 46 and 47.

46. Do planes A and B have other lines in common that are parallel to $\overleftrightarrow{CD}$? Explain.

47. **Visualization** Are there planes that intersect planes A and B in lines parallel to $\overleftrightarrow{CD}$? Draw a sketch to support your answer.

48. **Draw a Diagram** A transversal r intersects lines ℓ and m. If ℓ and r form $\angle 1$ and $\angle 2$ and m and r form $\angle 3$ and $\angle 4$, sketch a diagram that meets the following conditions.

- $\angle 1 \cong \angle 2$
- $\angle 3$ is an interior angle.
- $\angle 4$ is an exterior angle.
- $\angle 3$ and $\angle 4$ are supplementary.
- $\angle 2$ and $\angle 4$ lie on opposite sides of r.

Standardized Test Prep

SAT/ACT

49. How many pairs of parallel planes does a cereal box have?

(A) 2 (B) 3 (C) 4 (D) 6

50. What are the coordinates of the midpoint of $\overline{AB}$ for $A(-2, 8)$ and $B(-4, 4)$?

(F) $(-6, 12)$ (G) $(-3, 6)$ (H) $(1, 2)$ (I) $(1, 6)$

51. Which of the following is NOT the net of a cube?

(A) 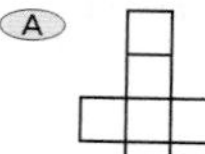 (B) 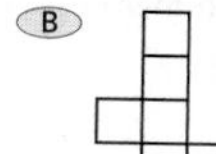 (C) 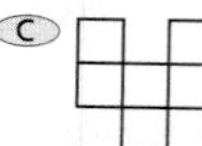 (D) 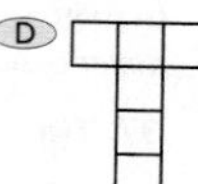

Short Response

52. Construct $\overline{MN}$ congruent to $\overline{XY}$.

Mixed Review

If $m\angle YDF = 121$ and $\overrightarrow{DR}$ bisects $\angle FDI$, find the measure of each angle. See Lesson 2-6.

53. $\angle IDA$

54. $\angle YDA$

55. $\angle RDI$

56. What are the next two terms in the sequence 1, −2, 4, −8, . . .? See Lesson 2-1.

Get Ready! **To prepare for Lesson 3-2, do Exercises 57–60.**

Classify each pair of angles. See Lesson 3-1.

57. $\angle 4$ and $\angle 2$ **58.** $\angle 6$ and $\angle 3$

59. $\angle 4$ and $\angle 5$ **60.** $\angle 6$ and $\angle 7$

3-1 Lesson Resources

Differentiated Remediation

Instructional Support

Geometry Companion

Students can use the **Geometry Companion** worktext (4 pages) . . .

- New Vocabulary
- Key Concepts
- Got It for each Problem
- Lesson Check

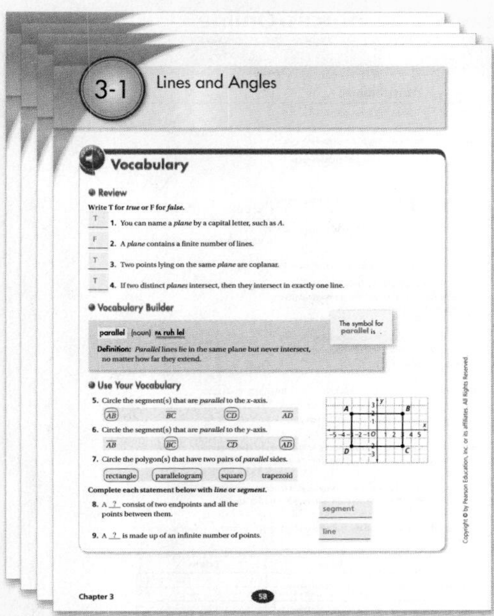

3-1 Lines and Angles

Vocabulary

Review

Write T for *true* or F for *false*.

T 1. You can name a *plane* by a capital letter, such as *A*.

F 2. A *plane* contains a finite number of lines.

T 3. Two points lying on the same *plane* are coplanar.

T 4. If two distinct *planes* intersect, then they intersect in exactly one line.

Vocabulary Builder

parallel (noun) PA ruh lel

The symbol for parallel is .

Definition: *Parallel* lines lie in the same plane but never intersect, no matter how far they extend.

Use Your Vocabulary

5. Circle the segment(s) that are *parallel* to the *x*-axis.

$\overline{AB}$ $\overline{BC}$ $\overline{CD}$ $\overline{AD}$

6. Circle the segment(s) that are *parallel* to the *y*-axis.

$\overline{AB}$ $\overline{BC}$ $\overline{CD}$ $\overline{AD}$

7. Circle the polygon(s) that have two pairs of *parallel* sides.

rectangle parallelogram square trapezoid

Complete each statement below with *line* or *segment*.

8. A _?_ consist of two endpoints and all the points between them. segment

9. A _?_ is made up of an infinite number of points. line

Chapter 3 58

ELL Support

Focus on Language Have students make a card file with one card for each key concept and each postulate and theorem in the chapter. Have the students write in math symbols and in English using their own words. They may include illustrations for each postulate or theorem. Have students refer to the card file as they do problems throughout the chapter.

Focus on Communication Discuss the meaning of the prefixes in the words *interior* and *exterior*. **[*In* means inside and *ex* means outside.]** Have students identify the interior and exterior of a box, a building, and a triangle. Then discuss the meaning of the word *remote*. Have students identify an exterior angle and its remote interior angles in various triangles.

5 Assess & Remediate

Lesson Quiz

1. Name a plane parallel to plane *ABCD*.

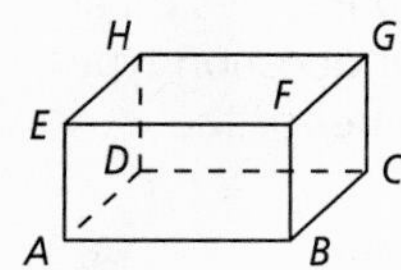

2. Name a pair of same-side interior angles in the figure below.

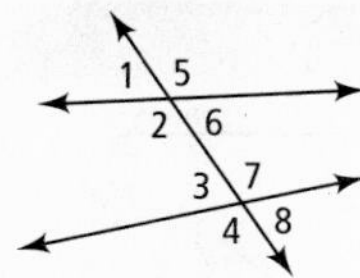

3. In the figure above, are ∠1 and ∠8 alternate interior angles, same-side interior angles, corresponding angles, or alternate exterior angles?
4. **Do you UNDERSTAND?** Why are alternate interior angles and alternate exterior angles both called "alternate"?

ANSWERS TO LESSON QUIZ

1. plane *EFGH*
2. ∠2 and ∠3 or ∠6 and ∠7
3. alternate exterior angles
4. Both alternate interior and alternate exterior angle pairs lie on opposite sides of the transversal.

PRECRIPTION FOR REMEDIATION

Use the student work on the Lesson Quiz to prescribe a differentiated review assignment.

Points	Differentiated Remediation
0–2	Intervention
3	On-level
4	Extension

PowerGeometry.com

5 Assess & Remediate

Assign the Lesson Quiz. Appropriate intervention, practice, or enrichment is automatically generated based on student performance.

Intervention

- **Reteaching** (2 pages) Provides reteaching and practice exercises for the key lesson concepts. Use with struggling students or absent students.
- **English Language Learner Support** Helps students develop and reinforce mathematical vocabulary and key concepts.

All-in-One Resources/Online

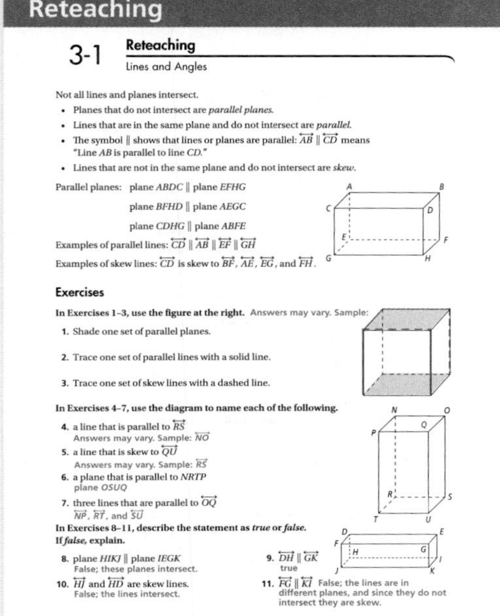

Reteaching

3-1 **Reteaching**
Lines and Angles

Not all lines and planes intersect.

- Planes that do not intersect are *parallel planes*.
- Lines that are in the same plane and do not intersect are *parallel*.
- The symbol ∥ shows that lines or planes are parallel: $\overleftrightarrow{AB} \parallel \overleftrightarrow{CD}$ means "Line *AB* is parallel to line *CD*."
- Lines that are not in the same plane and do not intersect are *skew*.

Parallel planes: plane *ABDC* ∥ plane *EFHG*
plane *BFHD* ∥ plane *AEGC*
plane *CDHG* ∥ plane *ABFE*

Examples of parallel lines: $\overleftrightarrow{CD} \parallel \overleftrightarrow{AB} \parallel \overleftrightarrow{EF} \parallel \overleftrightarrow{GH}$

Examples of skew lines: $\overleftrightarrow{CD}$ is skew to $\overleftrightarrow{BF}$, $\overleftrightarrow{AE}$, $\overleftrightarrow{EG}$, and $\overleftrightarrow{FH}$.

Exercises

In Exercises 1–3, use the figure at the right. Answers may vary. Sample:

1. Shade one set of parallel planes.
2. Trace one set of parallel lines with a solid line.
3. Trace one set of skew lines with a dashed line.

In Exercises 4–7, use the diagram to name each of the following.

4. a line that is parallel to $\overleftrightarrow{RS}$
Answers may vary. Sample: $\overleftrightarrow{NO}$
5. a line that is skew to $\overleftrightarrow{QU}$
Answers may vary. Sample: $\overleftrightarrow{RS}$
6. a plane that is parallel to *NRTP*
plane *OSUQ*
7. three lines that are parallel to $\overleftrightarrow{OQ}$
$\overleftrightarrow{NP}$, $\overleftrightarrow{RT}$, and $\overleftrightarrow{SU}$

In Exercises 8–11, describe the statement as *true* or *false*. If *false*, explain.

8. plane *HIKJ* ∥ plane *IEGK*
False; these planes intersect.
9. $\overleftrightarrow{DH} \parallel \overleftrightarrow{GK}$
true
10. $\overleftrightarrow{HJ}$ and $\overleftrightarrow{HD}$ are skew lines.
False; the lines intersect.
11. $\overleftrightarrow{FG} \parallel \overleftrightarrow{KI}$ False; the lines are in different planes, and since they do not intersect they are skew.

All-in-One Resources/Online

English Language Learner Support

3-1 **ELL Support**
Lines and Angles

Concept List

alternate exterior angles	alternate interior angles	corresponding angles
parallel lines	parallel planes	plane
same-side interior angles	skew lines	transversal

Choose the concept from the list above that best represents the item in each box.

1. parallel planes	2. alternate exterior angles	3. plane
4. same-side interior angles	5. skew lines	6. corresponding angles
7. transversal	8. parallel lines	9. alternate interior angles

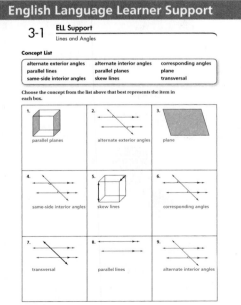

Differentiated Remediation *continued*

On-Level

- **Practice** (2 pages) Provides extra practice for each lesson. For simpler practice exercises, use the Form K Practice pages found in the All-in-One Teaching Resources and online.
- **Think About a Plan** Helps students develop specific problem-solving skills and strategies by providing scaffolded guiding questions.
- **Standardized Test Prep** Focuses on all major exercises, all major question types, and helps students prepare for the high-stakes assessments.

Extension

- **Enrichment** Provides students with interesting problems and activities that extend the concepts of the lesson.
- **Activities, Games, and Puzzles** Worksheets that can be used for concepts development, enrichment, and for fun!

Practice and Problem Solving Wkbk/ All-in-One Resources/Online

Practice page 1

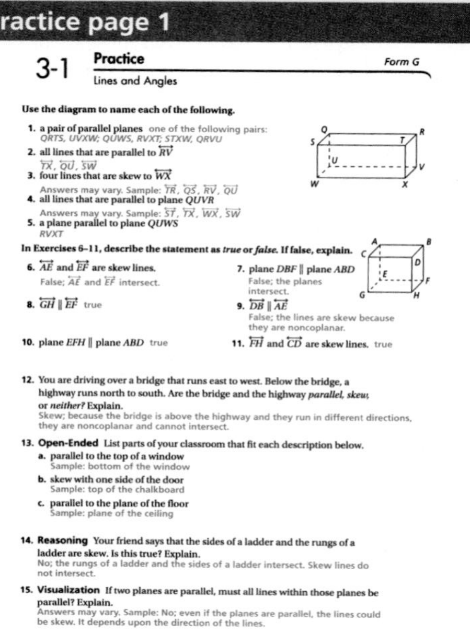

3-1 **Practice** — Lines and Angles — *Form G*

Use the diagram to name each of the following.

1. a pair of parallel planes one of the following pairs: *QRTS, UVXW; QUWS, RVXT; STXW, QRVU*
2. all lines that are parallel to $\overleftrightarrow{RV}$ $\overleftrightarrow{TX}$, $\overleftrightarrow{QU}$, $\overleftrightarrow{SW}$
3. four lines that are skew to $\overleftrightarrow{WX}$ Answers may vary. Sample: $\overleftrightarrow{TR}$, $\overleftrightarrow{QS}$, $\overleftrightarrow{RV}$, $\overleftrightarrow{QU}$
4. all lines that are parallel to plane *QUVR* Answers may vary. Sample: $\overleftrightarrow{ST}$, $\overleftrightarrow{TX}$, $\overleftrightarrow{WX}$, $\overleftrightarrow{SW}$
5. a plane parallel to plane *QUWS* *RVXT*

In Exercises 6–11, describe the statement as *true* or *false*. If false, explain.

6. $\overleftrightarrow{AE}$ and $\overleftrightarrow{EF}$ are skew lines. False; $\overleftrightarrow{AE}$ and $\overleftrightarrow{EF}$ intersect.
7. plane *DBF* ∥ plane *ABD* False; the planes intersect.
8. $\overleftrightarrow{GH} \parallel \overleftrightarrow{EF}$ true
9. $\overleftrightarrow{DB} \parallel \overleftrightarrow{AE}$ False; the lines are skew because they are noncoplanar.
10. plane *EFH* ∥ plane *ABD* true
11. $\overleftrightarrow{FH}$ and $\overleftrightarrow{CD}$ are skew lines. true
12. You are driving over a bridge that runs east to west. Below the bridge, a highway runs north to south. Are the bridge and the highway *parallel, skew,* or *neither?* Explain. Skew; because the bridge is above the highway and they run in different directions, they are noncoplanar and cannot intersect.
13. **Open-Ended** List parts of your classroom that fit each description below.
    a. parallel to the top of a window Sample: bottom of the window
    b. skew with one side of the door Sample: top of the chalkboard
    c. parallel to the plane of the floor Sample: plane of the ceiling
14. **Reasoning** Your friend says that the sides of a ladder and the rungs of a ladder are skew. Is this true? Explain. No; the rungs of a ladder and the sides of a ladder intersect. Skew lines do not intersect.
15. **Visualization** If two planes are parallel, must all lines within those planes be parallel? Explain. Answers may vary. Sample: No; even if the planes are parallel, the lines could be skew. It depends upon the direction of the lines.

Practice and Problem Solving Wkbk/ All-in-One Resources/Online

Practice page 2

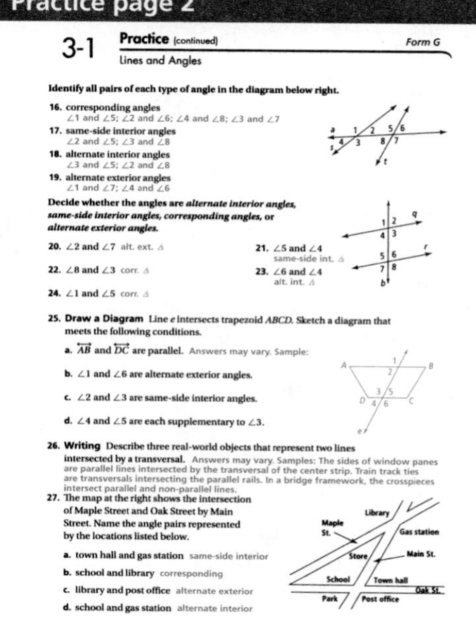

3-1 **Practice** (continued) — Lines and Angles — *Form G*

Identify all pairs of each type of angle in the diagram below right.

16. corresponding angles $\angle 1$ and $\angle 5$; $\angle 2$ and $\angle 6$; $\angle 4$ and $\angle 8$; $\angle 3$ and $\angle 7$
17. same-side interior angles $\angle 2$ and $\angle 5$; $\angle 3$ and $\angle 8$
18. alternate interior angles $\angle 3$ and $\angle 5$; $\angle 2$ and $\angle 8$
19. alternate exterior angles $\angle 1$ and $\angle 7$; $\angle 4$ and $\angle 6$

Decide whether the angles are *alternate interior angles, same-side interior angles, corresponding angles,* or *alternate exterior angles.*

20. $\angle 2$ and $\angle 7$ alt. ext. ∡
21. $\angle 5$ and $\angle 4$ same-side int. ∡
22. $\angle 8$ and $\angle 3$ corr. ∡
23. $\angle 6$ and $\angle 4$ alt. int. ∡
24. $\angle 1$ and $\angle 5$ corr. ∡
25. **Draw a Diagram** Line *e* intersects trapezoid *ABCD*. Sketch a diagram that meets the following conditions.
    a. $\overleftrightarrow{AB}$ and $\overleftrightarrow{DC}$ are parallel. Answers may vary. Sample:
    b. $\angle 1$ and $\angle 6$ are alternate exterior angles.
    c. $\angle 2$ and $\angle 3$ are same-side interior angles.
    d. $\angle 4$ and $\angle 5$ are each supplementary to $\angle 3$.
26. **Writing** Describe three real-world objects that represent two lines intersected by a transversal. Answers may vary. Samples: The sides of window panes are parallel lines intersected by the transversal of the center strip. Train track ties are transversals intersecting the parallel rails. In a bridge framework, the crosspieces intersect parallel and non-parallel lines.
27. The map at the right shows the intersection of Maple Street and Oak Street by Main Street. Name the angle pairs represented by the locations listed below.
    a. town hall and gas station same-side interior
    b. school and library corresponding
    c. library and post office alternate exterior
    d. school and gas station alternate interior

All-in-One Resources/Online

Enrichment

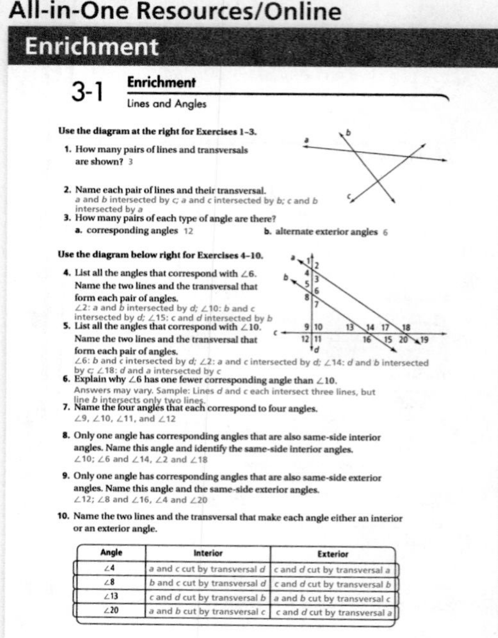

3-1 **Enrichment** — Lines and Angles

Use the diagram at the right for Exercises 1–3.

1. How many pairs of lines and transversals are shown? 3
2. Name each pair of lines and their transversal. *a* and *b* intersected by *c*; *a* and *c* intersected by *b*; *c* and *b* intersected by *a*
3. How many pairs of each type of angle are there?
    a. corresponding angles 12
    b. alternate exterior angles 6

Use the diagram below right for Exercises 4–10.

4. List all the angles that correspond with $\angle 6$. Name the two lines and the transversal that form each pair of angles. $\angle 2$: *a* and *b* intersected by *d*; $\angle 10$: *b* and *c* intersected by *d*; $\angle 15$: *c* and *d* intersected by *b*
5. List all the angles that correspond with $\angle 10$. Name the two lines and the transversal that form each pair of angles. $\angle 6$: *b* and *c* intersected by *d*; $\angle 2$: *a* and *c* intersected by *d*; $\angle 14$: *d* and *b* intersected by *c*; $\angle 18$: *d* and *a* intersected by *c*
6. Explain why $\angle 6$ has one fewer corresponding angle than $\angle 10$. Answers may vary. Sample: Lines *d* and *c* each intersect three lines, but line *b* intersects only two lines.
7. Name the four angles that each correspond to four angles. $\angle 9$, $\angle 10$, $\angle 11$, and $\angle 12$
8. Only one angle has corresponding angles that are also same-side interior angles. Name this angle and identify the same-side interior angles. $\angle 10$; $\angle 6$ and $\angle 14$, $\angle 2$ and $\angle 18$
9. Only one angle has corresponding angles that are also same-side exterior angles. Name this angle and the same-side exterior angles. $\angle 12$; $\angle 8$ and $\angle 16$, $\angle 4$ and $\angle 20$
10. Name the two lines and the transversal that make each angle either an interior or an exterior angle.

Angle	Interior	Exterior
$\angle 4$	*a* and *c* cut by transversal *d*	*c* and *d* cut by transversal a
$\angle 8$	*b* and *c* cut by transversal *d*	*c* and *d* cut by transversal *b*
$\angle 13$	*c* and *d* cut by transversal *b*	*a* and *b* cut by transversal *c*
$\angle 20$	*a* and *b* cut by transversal *c*	*c* and *d* cut by transversal *a*

Practice and Problem Solving Wkbk/ All-in-One Resources/Online

Think About a Plan

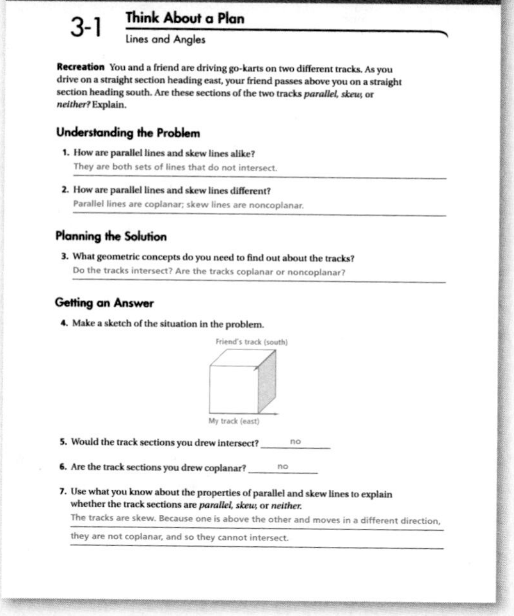

3-1 **Think About a Plan** — Lines and Angles

Recreation You and a friend are driving go-karts on two different tracks. As you drive on a straight section heading east, your friend passes above you on a straight section heading south. Are these sections of the two tracks *parallel, skew,* or *neither?* Explain.

Understanding the Problem

1. How are parallel lines and skew lines alike? They are both sets of lines that do not intersect.
2. How are parallel lines and skew lines different? Parallel lines are coplanar; skew lines are noncoplanar.

Planning the Solution

3. What geometric concepts do you need to find out about the tracks? Do the tracks intersect? Are the tracks coplanar or noncoplanar?

Getting an Answer

4. Make a sketch of the situation in the problem.

Friend's track (south)

My track (east)

5. Would the track sections you drew intersect? no
6. Are the track sections you drew coplanar? no
7. Use what you know about the properties of parallel and skew lines to explain whether the track sections are *parallel, skew,* or *neither.* The tracks are skew. Because one is above the other and moves in a different direction, they are not coplanar, and so they cannot intersect.

Practice and Problem Solving Wkbk/ All-in-One Resources/Online

Standardized Test Prep

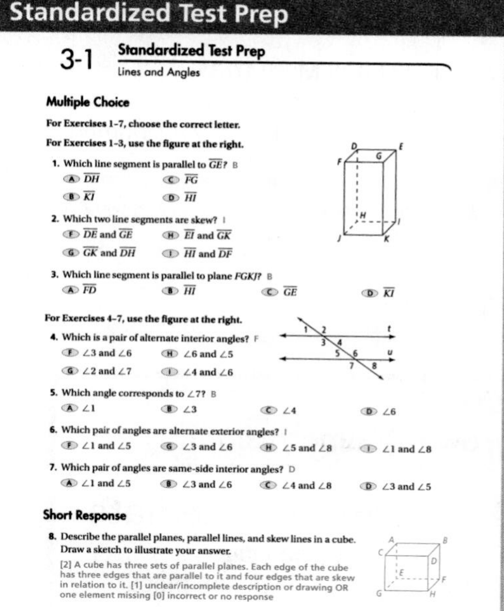

3-1 **Standardized Test Prep** — Lines and Angles

Multiple Choice

For Exercises 1–7, choose the correct letter.

For Exercises 1–3, use the figure at the right.

1. Which line segment is parallel to $\overline{GE}$? B
    A. $\overline{DH}$ C. $\overline{FG}$
    B. $\overline{KI}$ D. $\overline{HI}$
2. Which two line segments are skew? I
    F. $\overline{DE}$ and $\overline{GE}$ H. $\overline{EI}$ and $\overline{GK}$
    G. $\overline{GK}$ and $\overline{DH}$ I. $\overline{HI}$ and $\overline{DF}$
3. Which line segment is parallel to plane *FGKJ*? B
    A. $\overline{FD}$ B. $\overline{HI}$ C. $\overline{GE}$ D. $\overline{KI}$

For Exercises 4–7, use the figure at the right.

4. Which is a pair of alternate interior angles? F
    F. $\angle 3$ and $\angle 6$ H. $\angle 6$ and $\angle 5$
    G. $\angle 2$ and $\angle 7$ I. $\angle 4$ and $\angle 6$
5. Which angle corresponds to $\angle 7$? B
    A. $\angle 1$ B. $\angle 3$ C. $\angle 4$ D. $\angle 6$
6. Which pair of angles are alternate exterior angles? I
    F. $\angle 1$ and $\angle 5$ G. $\angle 3$ and $\angle 6$ H. $\angle 5$ and $\angle 8$ I. $\angle 1$ and $\angle 8$
7. Which pair of angles are same-side interior angles? D
    A. $\angle 1$ and $\angle 5$ B. $\angle 3$ and $\angle 6$ C. $\angle 4$ and $\angle 8$ D. $\angle 3$ and $\angle 5$

Short Response

8. Describe the parallel planes, parallel lines, and skew lines in a cube. Draw a sketch to illustrate your answer.
    [2] A cube has three sets of parallel planes. Each edge of the cube has three edges that are parallel to it and four edges that are skew in relation to it. [1] unclear/incomplete description or drawing OR one element missing [0] incorrect or no response

Online Teacher Resource Center

Activities, Games, and Puzzles

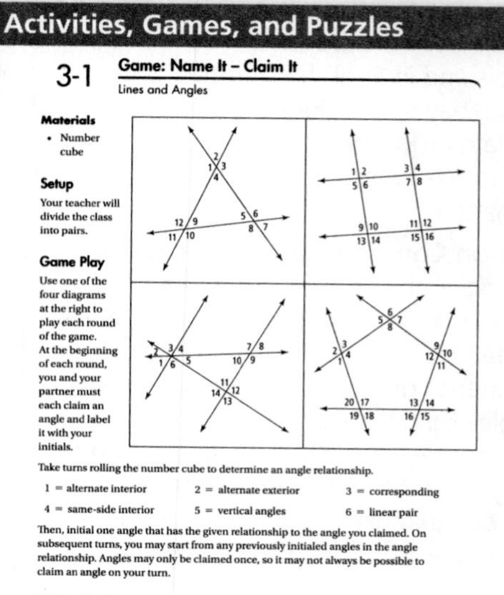

3-1 **Game: Name It – Claim It** — Lines and Angles

Materials

- Number cube

Setup

Your teacher will divide the class into pairs.

Game Play

Use one of the four diagrams at the right to play each round of the game. At the beginning of each round, you and your partner must each claim an angle and label it with your initials.

Take turns rolling the number cube to determine an angle relationship.

1 = alternate interior 2 = alternate exterior 3 = corresponding
4 = same-side interior 5 = vertical angles 6 = linear pair

Then, initial one angle that has the given relationship to the angle you claimed. On subsequent turns, you may start from any previously initialed angles in the angle relationship. Angles may only be claimed once, so it may not always be possible to claim an angle on your turn.

Ending the Game

The round ends when all of the angles have been claimed. The player with the most angles claimed wins the round. The player who wins the most rounds wins the game.

Concept Byte

Use With Lesson 3-2

TECHNOLOGY

Parallel Lines and Related Angles

Activity

Use geometry software to construct two parallel lines. Check that the lines remain parallel as you manipulate them. Construct a point on each line. Then construct the transversal through these two points.

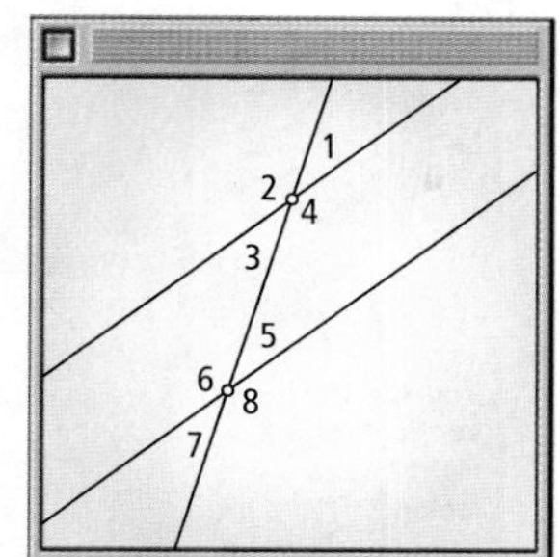

1. Measure each of the eight angles formed by the parallel lines and the transversal. Record the measurements.
2. Manipulate the lines. Record the new measurements.
3. When a transversal intersects parallel lines, what are the relationships among the angle pairs formed? Make as many conjectures as possible.

Exercises

4. Construct three or more parallel lines. Then construct a line that intersects all the parallel lines.
   a. What relationships can you find among the angles formed?
   b. How many different angle measures are there?
5. Construct two parallel lines and a transversal perpendicular to one of the parallel lines. What angle does the transversal form with the second line?
6. Construct two lines and a transversal, making sure that the two lines are *not* parallel. Locate a pair of alternate interior angles. Manipulate the lines so that these angles have the same measure.
   a. Make a conjecture about the relationship between the two lines.
   b. How is this conjecture different from the conjecture(s) you made in the Activity?
7. Again, construct two lines and a transversal, making sure that the two lines are *not* parallel. Locate a pair of same-side interior angles. Manipulate the lines so that these angles are supplementary.
   a. Make a conjecture about the relationship between the two lines.
   b. How is this conjecture different from the conjecture(s) you made in the Activity?
8. Construct perpendicular lines a and b. At a point that is not the intersection of a and b, construct line c perpendicular to line a. Make a conjecture about lines b and c.

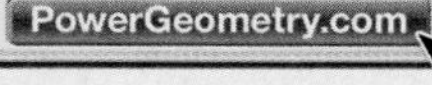

Guided Instruction

PURPOSE To use geometry software to create, manipulate, and make conjectures about angles formed by two parallel lines and a transversal

PROCESS Students will

- use geometry software to construct two parallel lines and a transversal and measure the angles formed.
- make conjectures about the angle pairs formed by two parallel lines and a transversal.

DISCUSS After students measure the angles and make conjectures, they will use the geometry software to manipulate the size of the angles and verify their conjectures.

Activity

VISUAL LEARNERS

In addition to geometry software or as an alternate, students may complete this lab with compasses and protractors. They should construct two parallel lines and a transversal and measure their angles. Students may color the angle pairs that have special relationships.

Q Is it necessary for the lines to be parallel in order for congruent angle pair relationships to exist? **[Yes. When the lines are not parallel, the angle pairs are not congruent.]**

Answers

Activity

1. Check students' work.
2. Check students' work.
3. Answers may vary. Sample: When a transversal intersects two $\parallel$ lines, the $\angle$s formed are $\cong$ or suppl.

Exercises

4a. Sample: Pairs of corresp., alt. int., and alt. ext. $\angle$s have equal measures; pairs of same-side int. $\angle$s are supplementary.

b. two

5. rt. $\angle$s

6a. The lines are $\parallel$.

b. Sample: This conjecture is about lines, while the conjectures in the activity are about $\angle$s.

7a. Sample: The lines are $\parallel$.

b. Sample: This conjecture is about lines, while the conjectures in the activity are about $\angle$s.

8. line $c \parallel$ line b

1 Interactive Learning

Solve It!

PURPOSE To become familiar with the angles formed by a transversal and two parallel lines

PROCESS Students may use informal logical reasoning or cite previous theorems pertaining to angles.

FACILITATE

Q Which angles form vertical pairs? **[∠1 and ∠3, ∠2 and ∠4, ∠5 and ∠7, ∠6 and ∠8, ∠9 and ∠11, ∠10 and ∠12]**

Q Which street is a transversal in the diagram? Explain. **[N. Garden Avenue is a transversal, because it intersects the streets that have numbered angles.]**

Q Does the direction of N. Garden Avenue affect the relationship that the intersections of the angles form? **[No, the angle measures change, but the relationships remain the same.]**

ANSWER See Solve It in Answers on next page.

CONNECT THE MATH In the Solve It, students looked for angles that appeared congruent. In this lesson, they will use measures of angles to find measures of related angles.

2 Guided Instruction

Take Note VISUAL LEARNERS

In geometry, postulates are accepted without justification in the formal sense, although students know there is very strong evidence for them.

3-2 Properties of Parallel Lines

TN State Performance Indicator

SPI 3108.1.4 Use definitions, basic postulates, and theorems about points, lines, angles, and planes to write/complete proofs and/or to solve problems.

Objectives To prove theorems about parallel lines
To use properties of parallel lines to find angle measures

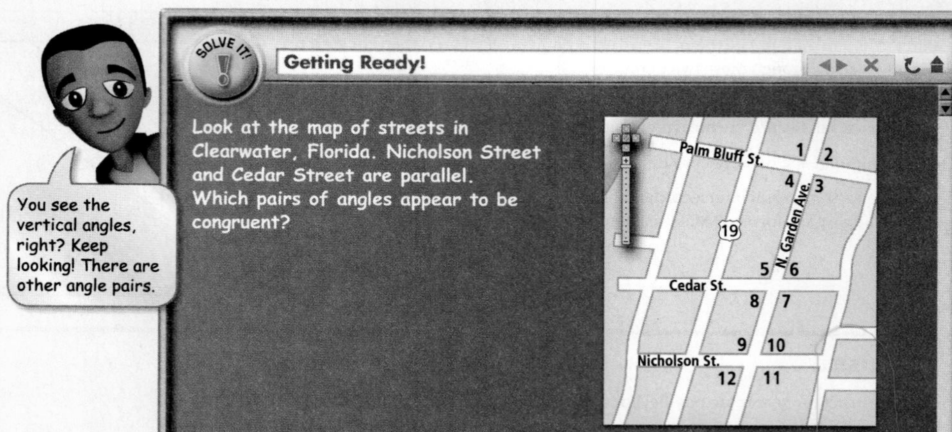

Getting Ready!
Look at the map of streets in Clearwater, Florida. Nicholson Street and Cedar Street are parallel. Which pairs of angles appear to be congruent?
You see the vertical angles, right? Keep looking! There are other angle pairs.
Palm Bluff St.
N. Garden Ave.
Cedar St.
Nicholson St.
19

In the Solve It, you identified several pairs of angles that appear congruent. You already know the relationship between vertical angles. In this lesson, you will explore the relationships between the angles you learned about in Lesson 3-1 when they are formed by *parallel* lines and a transversal.

Essential Understanding The special angle pairs formed by parallel lines and a transversal are congruent, supplementary, or both.

Postulate 3-1 Corresponding Angles Postulate

Postulate
If a transversal intersects two parallel lines, then corresponding angles are congruent.

If . . . $\ell \parallel m$

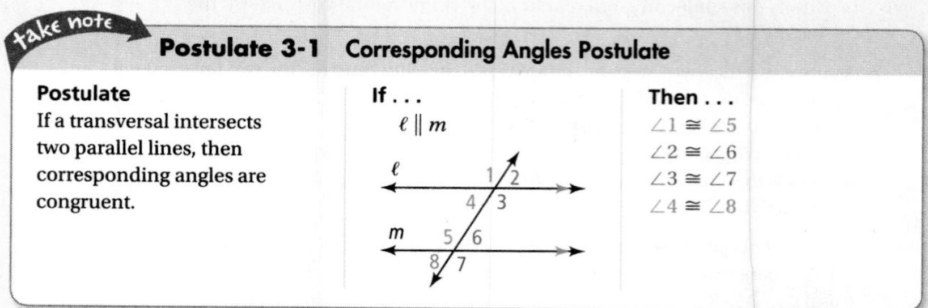

Then . . . $\angle 1 \cong \angle 5$, $\angle 2 \cong \angle 6$, $\angle 3 \cong \angle 7$, $\angle 4 \cong \angle 8$

3-2 Preparing to Teach

BIG idea Reasoning and Proof UbD

ESSENTIAL UNDERSTANDINGS

- The special angle pairs formed by parallel lines and a transversal are either congruent or supplementary.
- Geometric postulates and theorems can be combined with algebra to find some angle measures.

Math Background

The theorems in this lesson illustrate how a postulate is used as the starting point for the development of theorems. The Corresponding Angles Postulate is a variation of Euclid's famous Parallel Postulate. For thousands of years, mathematicians tried to prove this postulate because they felt that it was less obviously true than Euclid's other four postulates. Mathematicians eventually realized that the Parallel Postulate is necessary for the development of Euclidean geometry and cannot be proved from the other four postulates. Other mathematicians found that systems of geometry (such as spherical geometry) exist for which the Parallel Postulate does not hold (see pp. 179–180). (Students will learn the Parallel Postulate in an upcoming lesson, so you should not mention it at this point.) Note that if any of the theorems 3-1, 3-2, or 3-3 had been the "postulate," the remaining theorems and Postulate 3-1 could be proved from that first assumed theorem.

Support Student Learning

Use the **Geometry Companion** to engage and support students during instructions. See Lesson Resources at the end of this lesson for details.

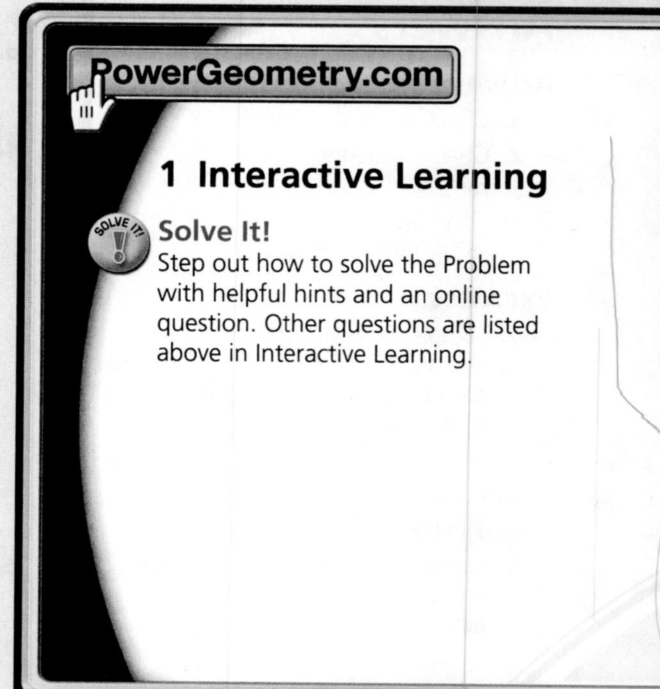

Problem 1 Identifying Congruent Angles

Think

How do you find angles congruent to the given 55° angle?
Look for angles that are corresponding and vertical to the given angle.

Which angles measure 55? How do you know?

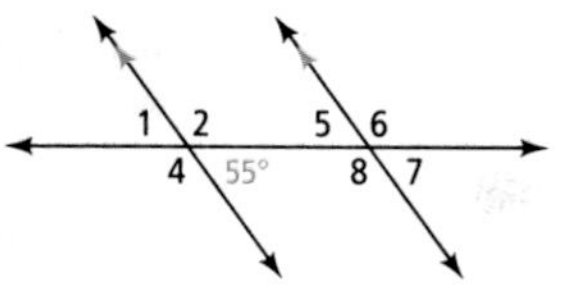

$m\angle 7 = 55$ by the Corresponding Angles Postulate.

$m\angle 1 = 55$ by the Vertical Angles Theorem.

$m\angle 5 = 55$ by the Corresponding Angles Postulate because $\angle 1$ and $\angle 5$ are corresponding angles.

Got It? **1. a. Reasoning** In Problem 1, can you find another way to justify $m\angle 5 = 55$? Explain.

b. Using linear pairs, find $m\angle 4$. Which other angles have that measure? How do you know?

You can use the Corresponding Angles Postulate to prove other angle relationships.

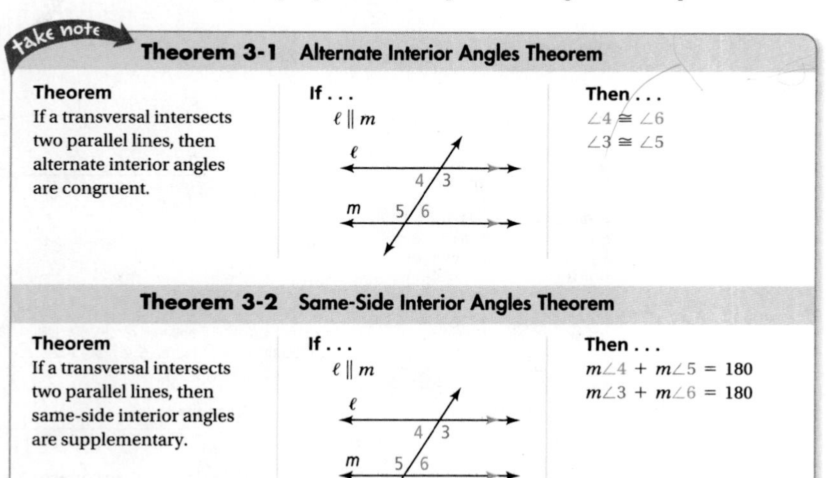

take note

Theorem 3-1 Alternate Interior Angles Theorem

Theorem	If . . .	Then . . .
If a transversal intersects two parallel lines, then alternate interior angles are congruent.	$\ell \parallel m$	$\angle 4 \cong \angle 6$ $\angle 3 \cong \angle 5$

Theorem 3-2 Same-Side Interior Angles Theorem

Theorem	If . . .	Then . . .
If a transversal intersects two parallel lines, then same-side interior angles are supplementary.	$\ell \parallel m$	$m\angle 4 + m\angle 5 = 180$ $m\angle 3 + m\angle 6 = 180$

You will prove Theorem 3-2 in Exercise 25.

Problem 1

Q What angle corresponds to the angle labeled 55°? **[∠7]**

Q What angle forms a vertical pair with the angle labeled 55°? **[∠1]**

Got It? VISUAL LEARNERS

Have students use tracing paper to copy the diagram. They should use a straightedge to extend the lines in the diagram. Have students use a protractor to verify their conjectures.

Take Note

Ask students how the Alternate Interior Angles Theorem will lead to the Alternate Exterior Angles Theorem. Show students that once it is known that alternate interior angles are congruent, the Vertical Angles Theorem and the Transitive Property of Congruence can be used to show that alternate exterior angles are congruent.

Students will be proving the Same-Side Interior Angles Theorem in Exercise 25. Help students plan for the proof by using techniques from proofs of related theorems.

2 Guided Instruction

Each Problem is worked out and supported online.

Problem 1
Identifying Congruent Angles

Alternative Problem 1
Identifying Congruent Angles

Problem 2
Proving an Angle Relationship
Animated

Problem 3
Finding Measures of Angles

Alternative Problem 3
Finding Measures of Angles
Animated

Problem 4
Finding an Angle Measure
Animated

Answers

Solve It!

∠1 and ∠3, ∠2 and ∠4, ∠5 and ∠7, ∠6 and ∠8, ∠9 and ∠11, ∠10 and ∠12, ∠5 and ∠9, ∠8 and ∠12, ∠6 and ∠10, ∠7 and ∠11, ∠8 and ∠10, ∠7 and ∠9, ∠5 and ∠11, ∠6 and ∠12

Got It?

1a. Sample: $m\angle 7 = 55$, so $m\angle 5 = 55$ by the Vert. ∠s Thm.

b. 125; sample: $m\angle 2 = 125$ by the Vert. ∠s Thm.; $m\angle 8 = 125$ by the Corresp. ∠s Post.; $m\angle 6 = 125$ by the Vert. ∠s Thm.

Q What is meant by "alternate"? **[Answers may vary. Samples: to change back and forth, to take turns, one after another]**

Have students restate the proof of the Alternate Interior Angles Theorem in their own words.

Problem 2

Q What is the purpose of Statement and Reason 3 in the proof? **[The purpose is to convert a known relationship into a form that can be used for calculations.]**

Q Can Statements 4, 5, and 6 be presented in any other order? Explain. **[No; statement 4 establishes a relationship that can be seen from the diagram. Statement 5 associates the relationship with a term that indicates a known measure. Statement 6 quantifies that relationship.]**

Q Which statements make the substitution in Statement 6 possible? **[Statements 3 and 5]**

Got It?

Q What theorem not used in the proof for Problem 2, will need to be used in this proof? Explain. **[The Vertical Angles Theorem will need to be used, because ∠5 and ∠7 form a vertical pair and ∠5 and ∠1 are corresponding angles.]**

Proof **Proof of Theorem 3-1: Alternate Interior Angles Theorem**

Given: $\ell \parallel m$

Prove: $\angle 4 \cong \angle 6$

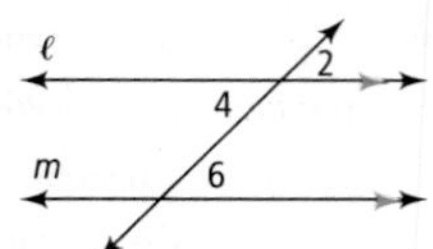

Statement	Reasons
1) $\ell \parallel m$	1) Given
2) $\angle 2 \cong \angle 6$	2) If lines are ∥, then corresponding ∡ are ≅.
3) $\angle 4 \cong \angle 2$	3) Vertical ∡ are ≅.
4) $\angle 4 \cong \angle 6$	4) Transitive Prop. of ≅

Proof **Problem 2 Proving an Angle Relationship**

Given: $a \parallel b$

Prove: ∠1 and ∠8 are supplementary.

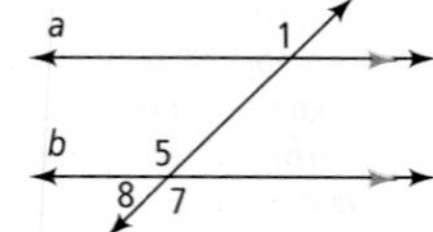

Know
- $a \parallel b$

From the diagram you know
- ∠1 and ∠5 are corresponding
- ∠5 and ∠8 form a linear pair

Need
∠1 and ∠8 are supplementary, or $m\angle 1 + m\angle 8 = 180$.

Plan
Show that $\angle 1 \cong \angle 5$ and that $m\angle 5 + m\angle 8 = 180$. Then substitute $m\angle 1$ for $m\angle 5$ to prove that ∠1 and ∠8 are supplementary.

Statements	Reasons
1) $a \parallel b$	1) Given
2) $\angle 1 \cong \angle 5$	2) If lines are ∥, then corresp. ∡ are ≅.
3) $m\angle 1 = m\angle 5$	3) Congruent ∡ have equal measures.
4) ∠5 and ∠8 are supplementary.	4) ∡ that form a linear pair are suppl.
5) $m\angle 5 + m\angle 8 = 180$	5) Def. of suppl. ∡
6) $m\angle 1 + m\angle 8 = 180$	6) Substitution Property
7) ∠1 and ∠8 are supplementary.	7) Def. of suppl. ∡

Got It? 2. Using the same given information and diagram in Problem 2, prove that $\angle 1 \cong \angle 7$.

Additional Problems

1. Which angles measure 130?

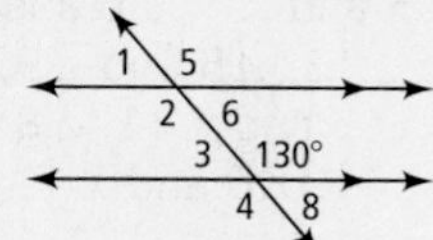

ANSWER ∠2, ∠4, ∠5

2. Given: $a \parallel b$

Prove: ∠1 and ∠3 are supplementary.

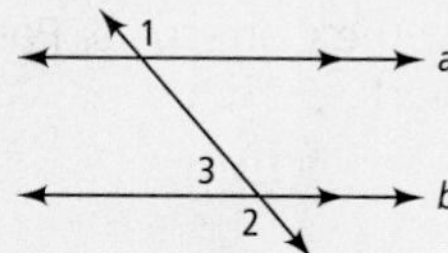

ANSWER It is given that $a \parallel b$. So, ∠1 is congruent to ∠2 because they are alternate exterior angles. ∠3 and ∠2 are supplementary because they form a linear pair. So, ∠1 and ∠3 are supplementary by the Congruent Supplements Theorem.

3. What are the measures of ∠8 and ∠4? Explain.

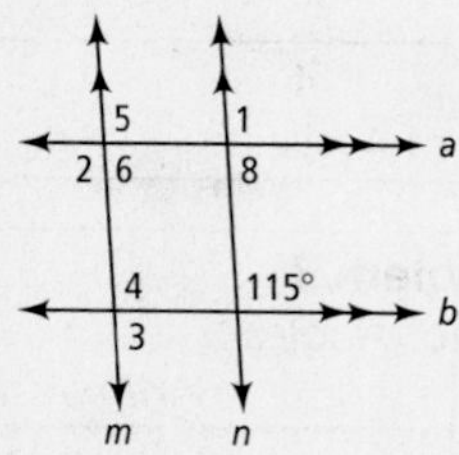

ANSWER $m\angle 8 = 65$ because $a \parallel b$ and same side interior angles of parallel lines are supplementary angles. $m\angle 4 = 115$ because $m \parallel n$ and corresponding angles of parallel lines are equal.

4. What is the value of y?

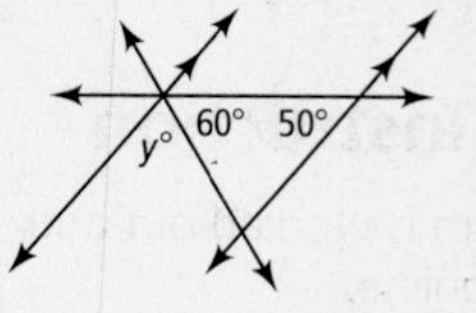

ANSWER 70

In the diagram for Problem 2, $\angle 1$ and $\angle 7$ are alternate exterior angles. In Got It 2, you proved the following theorem.

take note

Theorem 3-3 Alternate Exterior Angles Theorem

Theorem	If . . .	Then . . .
If a transversal intersects two parallel lines, then alternate exterior angles are congruent.	$\ell \parallel m$ 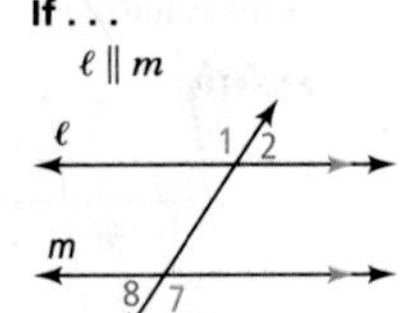	$\angle 1 \cong \angle 7$ $\angle 2 \cong \angle 8$

If you know the measure of one of the angles formed by two parallel lines and a transversal, you can use theorems and postulates to find the measures of the other angles.

Problem 3 Finding Measures of Angles

What are the measures of $\angle 3$ and $\angle 4$? Which theorem or postulate justifies each answer?

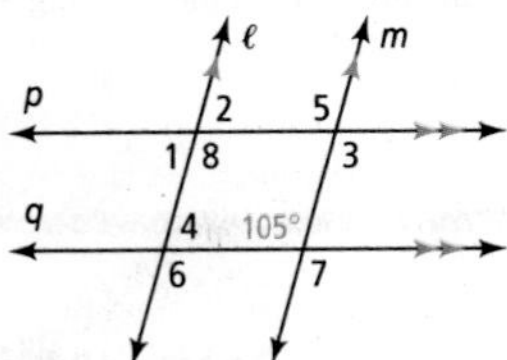

Think

How do $\angle 3$ and $\angle 4$ relate to the given 105° angle?
$\angle 3$ and the given angle are alternate interior angles. $\angle 4$ and the given angle are same-side interior angles.

Since $p \parallel q$, $m\angle 3 = 105$ by the Alternate Interior Angles Theorem.

Since $\ell \parallel m$, $m\angle 4 + 105 = 180$ by the Same-Side Interior Angles Theorem.
So, $m\angle 4 = 180 - 105 = 75$.

 **Got It?** **3.** Use the diagram in Problem 3. What is the measure of each angle? Justify each answer.

a. $\angle 1$ **b.** $\angle 2$
c. $\angle 5$ **d.** $\angle 6$
e. $\angle 7$ **f.** $\angle 8$

Take Note

Discuss with students why their work in the Got It was a proof of Theorem 3-3.

Problem 3

SYNTHESIZING

Q What are the angles that are equal to $\angle 3$? Justify each answer. **[$\angle 5$ by Vertical Angles, $\angle 7$ and $\angle 8$ by Corresponding Angles Postulate, $\angle 6$ by Transitive Property of Equality (first find $\angle 6 = \angle 7$ or $\angle 6 = \angle 8$ by Corresponding Angles Postulate)]**

Got It?

Q What angles do not have a measure of 105? **[$\angle 1$, $\angle 2$, $\angle 4$]**

Q What is the relationship of $\angle 1$, $\angle 2$ and $\angle 4$ to any of the other angles in the diagram? **[They are supplements.]**

EXTENSION

Q The quadrilateral formed by the two pairs of parallel lines is a parallelogram. What conjecture can you make about the measures of the four angles of the parallelogram? **[The measures of the opposite angles in a parallelogram are congruent, and the consecutive angles are supplementary.]**

Answers

Got It? (continued)

2. (1) $a \parallel b$ (Given)
(2) $\angle 1 \cong \angle 5$ (If lines are $\parallel$, then corresp. $\angle$s are $\cong$.)
(3) $\angle 5 \cong \angle 7$ (Vert. $\angle$s are $\cong$.)
(4) $\angle 1 \cong \angle 7$ (Trans. Prop. of $\cong$)

3a. 75; $m\angle 1 = m\angle 4$ by the Alt. Int. $\angle$s Thm.

b. 75; $m\angle 2 = m\angle 4$ by the Corresp. $\angle$s Post.

c. 105; $m\angle 5 = 105$ by the Corresp. $\angle$s Post.

d. 105; Alt. Int. $\angle$s Thm.

e. 105; Vert. $\angle$s. Thm.

f. 105; $\angle 8 \cong \angle 6$ by the Corresp. $\angle$s Post.

Problem 4

Q How can you find the value of y using the Corresponding Angles Postulate? **[$y + 40 + 80 = 180$, using the angle to the left of the 40° angle.]**

Got It?

VISUAL LEARNERS

Students should extend the segments that form the trapezoid to identify the pair of parallel lines and the transversals. Remind students to write and solve an equation for x and an equation for y.

3 Lesson Check

Do you know HOW?

- If students have difficulty with Exercise 3, then tell them that they can find the answer using the Alternate Exterior Angles Theorem, or by using a combination of the Vertical Angles Theorem with either the Corresponding Angles Postulate or the Alternate Interior Angles Theorem.

Do you UNDERSTAND?

- If students have difficulty with Exercise 6, then ask them how this pair of angles is similar to other angle pairs for which they know the terms.

Close

Q How is a diagram of any two lines intersected by a transversal the same as a diagram of two parallel lines intersected by a transversal? How are they different? **[Both diagrams contain the special pairs of angles; the theorems apply only when the lines intersected by the transversal are parallel.]**

You can combine theorems and postulates with your knowledge of algebra to find angle measures.

Problem 4 Finding an Angle Measure

GRIDDED RESPONSE

Algebra What is the value of y?

Think

What do you know from the diagram?
You have one pair of parallel lines. The 80° angle and the angle formed by the 40° and y° angles are same-side interior angles.

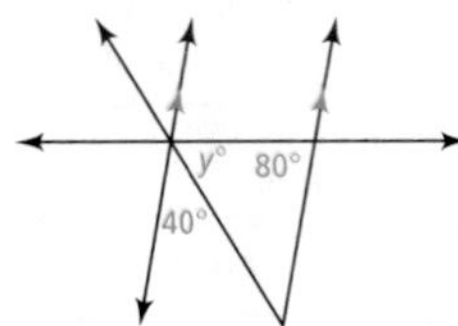

By the Angle Addition Postulate, $y + 40$ is the measure of an interior angle.

$(y + 40) + 80 = 180$	Same-side interior ∠s of ∥ lines are suppl.
$y + 120 = 180$	Simplify.
$y = 60$	Subtract 120 from each side.

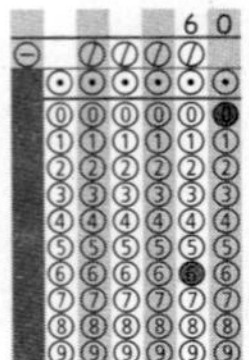

Got It? **4. a.** In the figure at the right, what are the values of x and y?

b. What are the measures of the four angles in the figure?

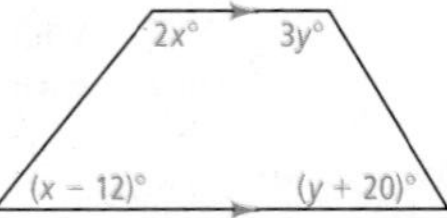

Lesson Check

Do you know HOW?

Use the diagram for Exercises 1–4.

1. Identify four pairs of congruent angles. (Exclude vertical angle pairs.)
2. Identify two pairs of supplementary angles. (Exclude linear pairs.)
3. If $m\angle 1 = 70$, what is $m\angle 8$?
4. If $m\angle 4 = 70$ and $m\angle 7 = 2x$, what is the value of x?

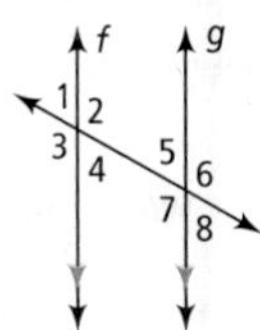

Do you UNDERSTAND?

5. **Compare and Contrast** How are the Alternate Interior Angles Theorem and the Alternate Exterior Angles Theorem alike? How are they different?
6. In Problem 2, you proved that ∠1 and ∠8, in the diagram below, are supplementary. What is a good name for this pair of angles? Explain.

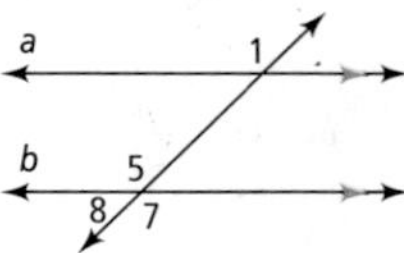

PowerGeometry.com

3 Lesson Check

For a digital lesson check, use the Got It questions.

Support in Geometry Companion

- Lesson Check

4 Practice

Assign homework to individual students or to an entire class.

Answers

Got It? (continued)

4a. $x = 64$, $y = 40$

b. Clockwise from the bottom left, the measures are 52, 128, 120, 60.

Lesson Check

1–2. Answer may vary. Samples are given.

1. ∠4 and ∠5, ∠2 and ∠6, ∠3 and ∠7, ∠4 and ∠8

2. ∠2 and ∠5, ∠4 and ∠7

3. 70

4. 55

5. Alike: Two parallel lines are cut by a transversal and the angles are congruent; different: The int. ∠s are between the two parallel lines, while the ext. ∠s are not between the two parallel lines.

6. same-side ext. ∠s, because they are ext. ∠s on the same side of the transversal

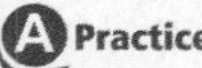

Practice and Problem-Solving Exercises

A Practice

Identify all the numbered angles that are congruent to the given angle. Justify your answers.

See Problem 1.

7. 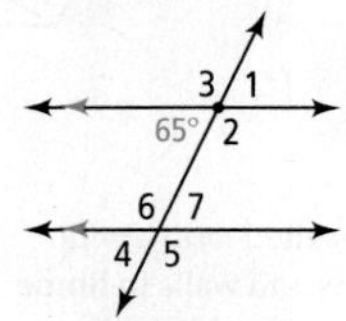

8. 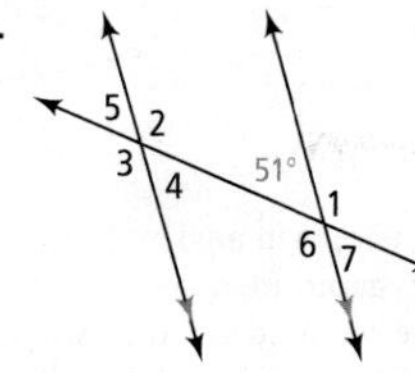

9. 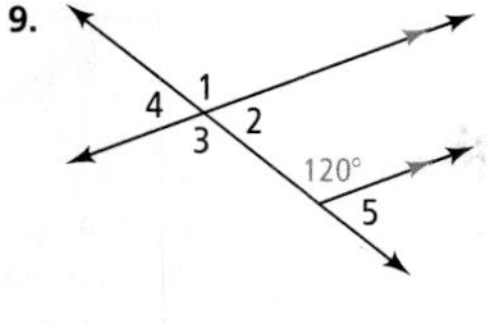

10. Developing Proof Supply the missing reasons in the two-column proof.

See Problem 2.

Given: $a \parallel b, c \parallel d$

Prove: $\angle 1 \cong \angle 3$

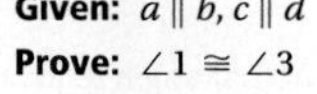
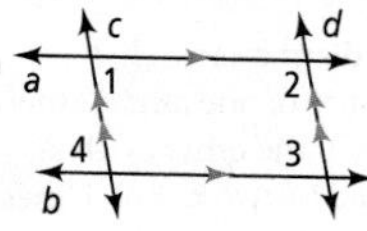

Statements	Reasons
1) $a \parallel b$	1) Given
2) $\angle 3$ and $\angle 2$ are supplementary.	2) **a.** ?
3) $c \parallel d$	3) Given
4) $\angle 1$ and $\angle 2$ are supplementary.	4) **b.** ?
5) $\angle 1 \cong \angle 3$	5) **c.** ?

11. Write a two-column proof for Exercise 10 that does not use $\angle 2$.
Proof

Find $m\angle 1$ and $m\angle 2$. Justify each answer.

See Problem 3.

12. 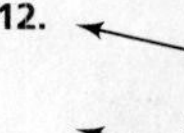
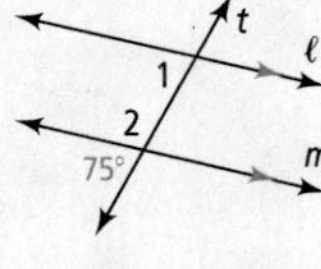

13. 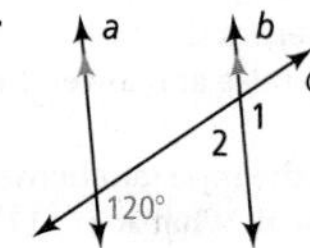

14. 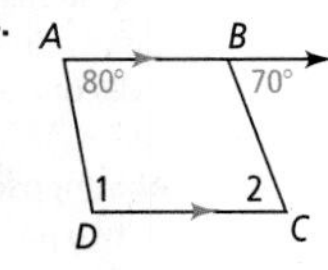

Algebra Find the value of x. Then find the measure of each labeled angle.

See Problem 4.

15. 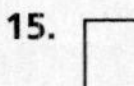
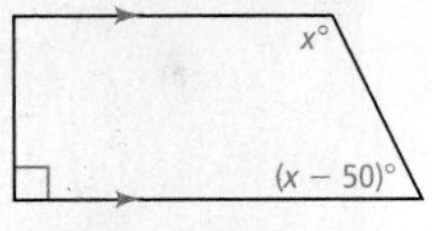

16. 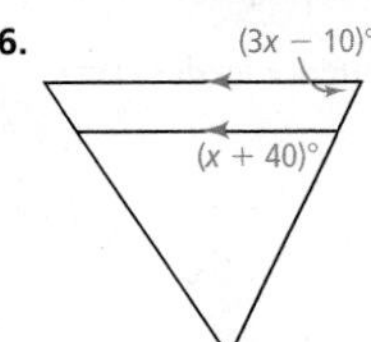

17. 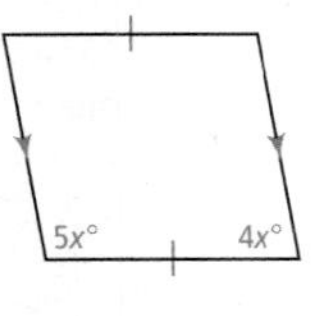

4 Practice

ASSIGNMENT GUIDE

Basic: 7–17, 18, 20–24
Average: 7–17 odd, 18–26
Advanced: 7–17 odd, 18–28
Standardized Test Prep: 29–32
Mixed Review: 33–39

Reasoning exercises have blue headings.
Applications exercises have red headings.

EXERCISE 23: Use the Think About a Plan worksheet in the **Practice and Problem Solving Workbook** (also available in the Teaching Resources in print and online) to further support students' development in becoming independent learners.

HOMEWORK QUICK CHECK

To check students' understanding of key skills and concepts, go over Exercises 9, 15, 21, 22, and 23.

Practice and Problem-Solving Exercises

7. $\angle 1$ (vert. ∡), $\angle 7$ (alt. int. ∡), $\angle 4$ (corresp. ∡)

8. $\angle 7$ (vert. ∡), $\angle 4$ (alt. int. ∡), $\angle 5$ (corresp. ∡)

9. $\angle 3$ (alt. int. ∡), $\angle 1$ (corresp. ∡)

10a. If two $\parallel$ lines are cut by a transversal, then the same-side int. ∡ are suppl.

b. If two $\parallel$ lines are cut by a transversal, then the same-side int. ∡ are suppl.

c. If two ∡ are suppl. to the same $\angle$, then they are $\cong$.

11. (1) $a \parallel b$; $c \parallel d$ (Given)
(2) $\angle 1 \cong \angle 4$ (Alt. int. ∡ are $\cong$.)
(3) $\angle 4 \cong \angle 3$ (Corresp. ∡ are $\cong$.)
(4) $\angle 1 \cong \angle 3$ (Trans. Prop. of $\cong$)

12. $m\angle 1 = 75$ because corresp. ∡ are $\cong$; $m\angle 2 = 105$ because $\angle 2$ forms a linear pair with the given $\angle$.

13. $m\angle 1 = 120$ because corresp. ∡ are $\cong$; $m\angle 2 = 60$ because $\angle 2$ forms a linear pair with the given $\angle$.

14. $m\angle 2 = 70$ because alt. int. ∡ are $\cong$; $m\angle 1 = 100$ because same-side int. ∡ are suppl.

15. $x = 115$, $x - 50 = 65$

16. 25; $x + 40 = 65$, $3x - 10 = 65$

17. 20; $5x = 100$, $4x = 80$

Answers

Practice and Problem-Solving Exercises (continued)

18. 32

19. $x = 135$, $y = 45$

20. $x = 87$, $y = 31$, $w = 20$, $v = 42$

21. 90; all the ∠s are ≅ because each pair form vert. ∠s, corresp. ∠s, or suppl. ∠s.

22. A; the marked ∠s are same-side int. ∠s, so they are suppl.

23a. 117

b. same-side int. ∠s

24. Yes; same-side int. ∠s are ≅ if they are both rt. ∠s because two rt. ∠s are suppl.

Algebra Find the values of the variables.

18.

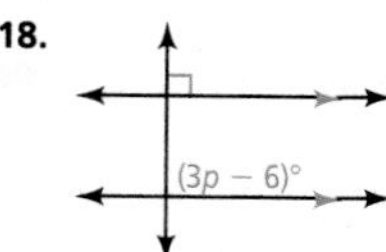

19.

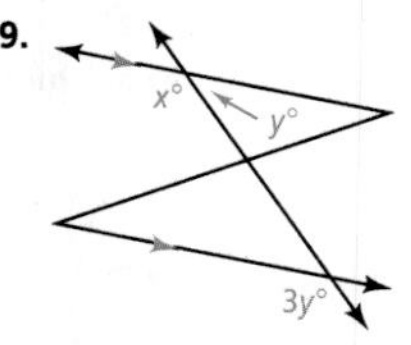

20.

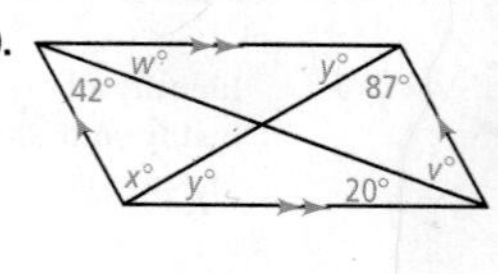

21. Think About a Plan People in ancient Rome played a game called *terni lapilli.* The exact rules of this game are not known. Etchings on floors and walls in Rome suggest that the game required a grid of two intersecting pairs of parallel lines, similar to the modern game tick-tack-toe. The measure of one of the angles formed by the intersecting lines is 90°. Find the measure of each of the other 15 angles. Justify your answers.

- How can you use a diagram to help?
- You know the measure of one angle. How does the position of that angle relate to the position of each of the other angles?
- Which angles formed by two parallel lines and a transversal are congruent? Which angles are supplementary?

22. Error Analysis Which solution for the value of x in the figure at the right is incorrect? Explain.

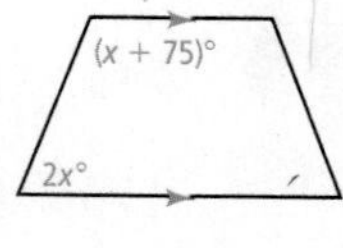

A.

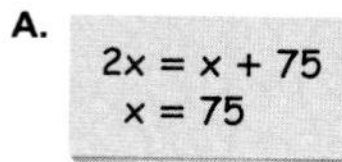

$2x = x + 75$
$x = 75$

B.

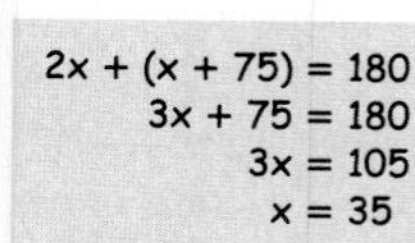

$2x + (x + 75) = 180$
$3x + 75 = 180$
$3x = 105$
$x = 35$

23. Outdoor Recreation Campers often use a "bear bag" at night to avoid attracting animals to their food supply. In the bear bag system at the right, a camper pulls one end of the rope to raise and lower the food bag.

a. Suppose a camper pulls the rope taut between the two parallel trees, as shown. What is $m\angle 1$?

b. Are ∠1 and the given angle *alternate interior angles, same-side interior angles,* or *corresponding angles*?

24. Writing Are same-side interior angles ever congruent? Explain.

25. Write a two-column proof to prove the Same-Side Interior Angles Theorem (Theorem 3-2).
Proof
Given: $\ell \parallel m$
Prove: $\angle 3$ and $\angle 6$ are supplementary.

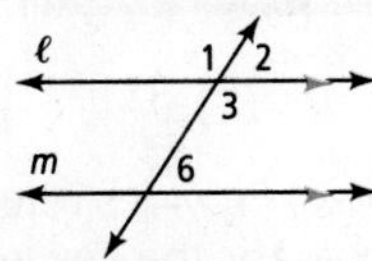

26. Write a two-column proof.
Proof
Given: $a \parallel b$, $\angle 1 \cong \angle 4$
Prove: $\angle 2 \cong \angle 3$

Challenge Use the diagram at the right for Exercises 27 and 28.

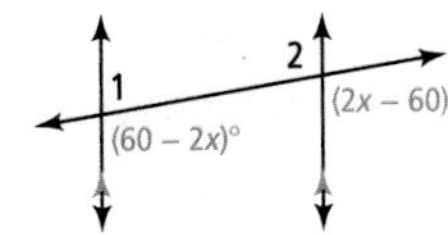

27. **Algebra** Suppose the measures of $\angle 1$ and $\angle 2$ are in a 4 : 11 ratio. Find their measures. (Diagram is not to scale.)

28. **Error Analysis** The diagram contains contradictory information. What is it? Why is it contradictory?

Standardized Test Prep

GRIDDED RESPONSE

SAT/ACT

29. $\angle 1$ and $\angle 2$ are same-side interior angles formed by two parallel lines and a transversal. If $m\angle 1 = 115$, what is $m\angle 2$?

30. The rectangular swimming pool shown at the right has an area of 1500 ft^2. A rectangular walkway surrounds the pool. How many feet of fencing do you need to surround the walkway?

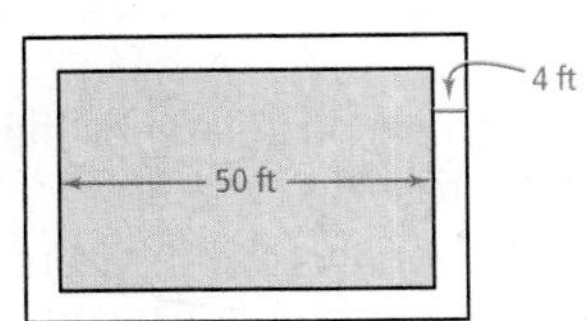

31. The measure of an angle is two times the measure of its complement. What is the measure of the angle?

32. $\angle 1$ and $\angle 2$ are vertical angles. If $m\angle 1 = 4x$ and $m\angle 2 = 56$, what is the value of x?

Mixed Review

Determine whether each statement is *always, sometimes,* or *never* true.

See Lesson 3-1.

33. Skew lines are coplanar.
34. Skew lines intersect.
35. Parallel planes intersect.
36. Rays are parallel.

Get Ready! **To prepare for Lesson 3-3, do Exercises 37–39.**

Write the converse and determine its truth value.

See Lesson 2-2.

37. If a triangle is a right triangle, then it has a 90° angle.
38. If two angles are vertical angles, then they are congruent.
39. If two angles are same-side interior angles, then they are supplementary.

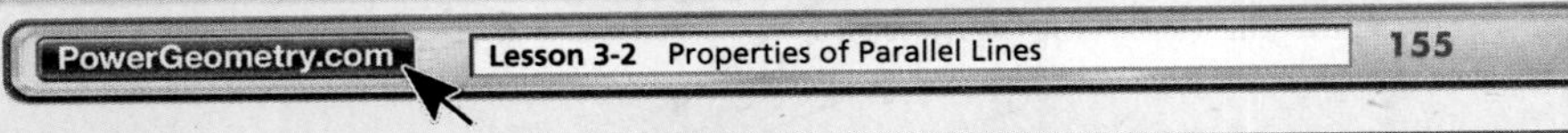

25. (1) $\ell \parallel m$ (Given)
(2) $\angle 2 \cong \angle 6$ (Corresp. $\angle$s are $\cong$.)
(3) $m\angle 2 + m\angle 3 = 180$ ($\angle$s that form a linear pair are suppl.)
(4) $m\angle 2 = m\angle 6$ (Def. of $\cong$)
(5) $m\angle 6 + m\angle 3 = 180$ (Substitution)
(6) $\angle 6$ and $\angle 3$ are suppl. (If the sum of the measures of two $\angle$s is 180, then the $\angle$s are suppl.)

26. (1) $a \parallel b$ (Given)
(2) $m\angle 1 + m\angle 2 = 180$ and $m\angle 3 + m\angle 4 = 180$ (Same-side int. $\angle$s are suppl.)
(3) $\angle 1 \cong \angle 4$ (Given)
(4) $\angle 2 \cong \angle 3$ (If two $\angle$s are suppl. to $\cong$ $\angle$s, then the $\angle$s are $\cong$.)

27. $m\angle 1 = 48$, $m\angle 2 = 132$

28. Sample: The labels $(60 - 2x)°$ and $(2x - 60)°$ contain contradictory information because those $\angle$s are corresp. $\angle$s. If $60 - 2x = 2x - 60$, then $x = 30$ and the measure of each $\angle$ is 0.

29. 65 **30.** 192 ft
31. 60 **32.** 14
33. never **34.** never
35. never **36.** sometimes

37. If a $\triangle$ has a 90° angle, then it is a right $\triangle$; true.

38. If two $\angle$s are $\cong$, then they are vert. $\angle$s; false.

39. If two $\angle$s are suppl., then they are same-side int. $\angle$s; false.

3-2 Lesson Resources

Differentiated Remediation

Instructional Support

Geometry Companion

Students can use the **Geometry Companion** worktext (4 pages) . . .

- New Vocabulary
- Key Concepts
- Got It for each Problem
- Lesson Check

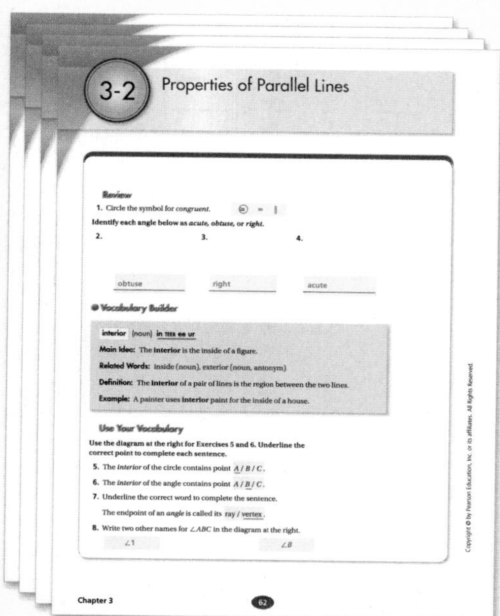

3-2 Properties of Parallel Lines

Review

1. Circle the symbol for *congruent*. ≅ = ∥

Identify each angle below as *acute, obtuse,* or *right*.

2. obtuse 3. right 4. acute

Vocabulary Builder

interior (noun) in TEER ee ur

Main Idea: The **interior** is the inside of a figure.

Related Words: inside (noun), exterior (noun, antonym)

Definition: The **interior** of a pair of lines is the region between the two lines.

Example: A painter uses **interior** paint for the inside of a house.

Use Your Vocabulary

Use the diagram at the right for Exercises 5 and 6. Underline the correct point to complete each sentence.

5. The *interior* of the circle contains point *A* / *B* / *C*.
6. The *interior* of the angle contains point *A* / *B* / *C*.
7. Underline the correct word to complete the sentence.

   The endpoint of an *angle* is called its ray / vertex.
8. Write two other names for ∠*ABC* in the diagram at the right.

   ∠1 ∠*B*

Chapter 3 62

ELL Support

Connect to Prior Knowledge Ask: Where do you see parallel lines in our classroom? **[sides of a bookshelf, opposite sides of floor tiles]** Have two students hold pencils so that they model skew lines. Ask: Where do you see skew lines in our classroom? **[edge of ceiling with one wall and edge of floor with an adjacent wall]** Ask: Where do you see parallel planes in our classroom? **[opposite walls or the floor and ceiling]**

Use Manipulatives Have small groups use books and pencils to model parallel and perpendicular lines and planes. (Students may use protractors to measure right angles.) Students should describe the models made by other groups. Have the students return to their groups and model skew lines. Each student should draw a picture of one of the models and write a description of it.

5 Assess & Remediate

Lesson Quiz

1. Use the figure to answer each question.

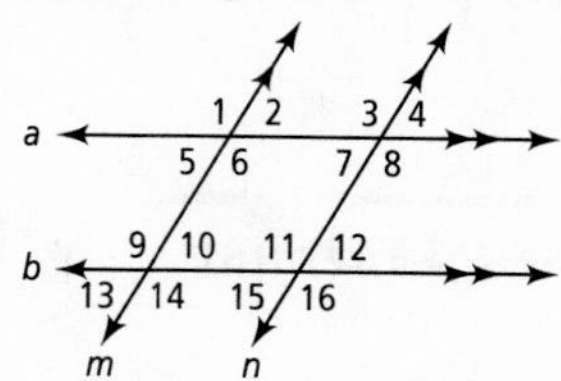

1. If $m\angle 11 = 118$, what is the measure of $\angle 8$?
2. Which theorem or postulate justifies your answer to Exercise 1?
3. If $m\angle 4 = 62$, what is the measure of $\angle 5$?
4. Which theorem or postulate justifies your answer to Exercise 3?
5. **Do you UNDERSTAND?** Which of the following does *not* prove two angles to be congruent: Vertical Angles Theorem, Corresponding Angles Postulate, Alternate Interior Angles Theorem, Same-Side Interior Angles Theorem?

ANSWERS TO LESSON QUIZ

1. 118
2. Alternate Interior Angles Theorem
3. 62
4. Alternate Exterior Angles Theorem
5. The Same-Side Interior Angles Theorem proves two angles to be supplementary, not congruent.

PRESCRIPTION FOR REMEDIATION

Use the student work on the Lesson Quiz to prescribe a differentiated review assignment.

Points	Differentiated Remediation
0–2	Intervention
3–4	On-level
5	Extension

PowerGeometry.com

5 Assess & Remediate

Assign the Lesson Quiz. Appropriate intervention, practice, or enrichment is automatically generated based on student performance.

Intervention

- **Reteaching** (2 pages) Provides reteaching and practice exercises for the key lesson concepts. Use with struggling students or absent students.
- **English Language Learner Support** Helps students develop and reinforce mathematical vocabulary and key concepts.

All-in-One Resources/Online

Reteaching

3-2 **Reteaching**

Properties of Parallel Lines

When a transversal intersects parallel lines, special congruent and supplementary angle pairs are formed.

Congruent angles formed by a transversal intersecting parallel lines:

- corresponding angles (Postulate 3-1)

  $\angle 1 \cong \angle 5$ $\angle 2 \cong \angle 6$

  $\angle 4 \cong \angle 7$ $\angle 3 \cong \angle 8$
- alternate interior angles (Theorem 3-1)

  $\angle 4 \cong \angle 6$ $\angle 3 \cong \angle 5$
- alternate exterior angles (Theorem 3-3)

  $\angle 1 \cong \angle 8$ $\angle 2 \cong \angle 7$

Supplementary angles formed by a transversal intersecting parallel lines:

- same-side interior angles (Theorem 3-2)

  $m\angle 4 + m\angle 5 = 180$ $m\angle 3 + m\angle 6 = 180$

Identify all the numbered angles congruent to the given angle. Explain.

1. ∠6; vert. ∠s are ≅; ∠2; corresp. ∠s are ≅; ∠4; alt. ext. ∠s are ≅.
2. ∠2; vert. ∠s are ≅; ∠5; alt. int. ∠s are ≅; ∠7; corresp. ∠s are ≅.
3. ∠2; vert. ∠s are ≅; ∠4; alt. ext. ∠s are ≅.
4. Supply the missing reasons in the two-column proof.

   Given: $g \parallel h$, $i \parallel j$

   Prove: ∠1 is supplementary to ∠16.

Statements	Reasons
1) ∠1 ≅ ∠3	1) ? Vertical angles are congruent.
2) $g \parallel h$; $i \parallel j$	2) Given
3) ∠3 ≅ ∠11	3) ? Corresponding angles are congruent.
4) ∠11 and ∠16 are supplementary.	4) ? Same-side interior angles are supplementary.
5) ∠1 and ∠16 are supplementary.	5) ? Substitution property

All-in-One Resources/Online

English Language Learner Support

3-2 **ELL Support**

Properties of Parallel Lines

Complete the vocabulary chart by filling in the missing information.

Word or Word Phrase	Definition	Picture or Example
angle pairs	*Angle pairs* are two angles that are related in some way.	congruent angles, supplementary angles, corresponding angles, exterior angles, interior angles, vertical angles
parallel lines	1. *Parallel lines* are lines found in the same plane that do not intersect. They are always the same distance apart.	
transversal	2. A *transversal* is a line that intersects two lines in the same plane at two different points.	
congruent	Two angles are *congruent* if the angles have the same measure.	3. 42° 42°
supplementary angles	The sum of the measures of two *supplementary angles* is 180.	4. 60° 120°
complementary angles	5. The sum of the measures of two *complementary angles* is 90.	60° 30°
corresponding angles	6. When two lines are intersected by a transversal, angles that are on the same side of the transversal and are in the same position are *corresponding angles*.	

Differentiated Remediation *continued*

On-Level

- **Practice** (2 pages) Provides extra practice for each lesson. For simpler practice exercises, use the Form K Practice pages found in the All-in-One Teaching Resources and online.
- **Think About a Plan** Helps students develop specific problem-solving skills and strategies by providing scaffolded guiding questions.
- **Standardized Test Prep** Focuses on all major exercises, all major question types, and helps students prepare for the high-stakes assessments.

Extension

- **Enrichment** Provides students with interesting problems and activities that extend the concepts of the lesson.
- **Activities, Games, and Puzzles** Worksheets that can be used for concepts development, enrichment, and for fun!

Practice and Problem Solving Wkbk/ All-in-One Resources/Online

Practice page 1

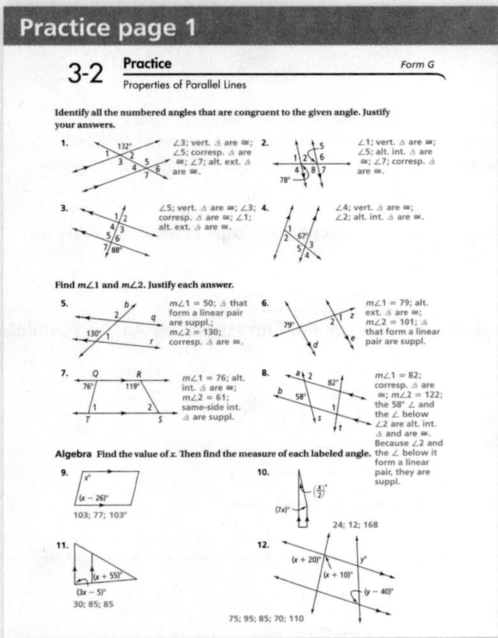

3-2 **Practice** *Form G*

Properties of Parallel Lines

Identify all the numbered angles that are congruent to the given angle. Justify your answers.

1. ∠3; vert. ∠s are ≅; ∠5; corresp. ∠s are ≅; ∠7; alt. ext. ∠s are ≅.
2. ∠1; vert. ∠s are ≅; ∠5; alt. int. ∠s are ≅; ∠7; corresp. ∠s are ≅.
3. ∠5; vert. ∠s are ≅; ∠3; corresp. ∠s are ≅; ∠1; alt. ext. ∠s are ≅.
4. ∠4; vert. ∠s are ≅; ∠2; alt. int. ∠s are ≅.

Find $m\angle 1$ and $m\angle 2$. Justify each answer.

5. $m\angle 1 = 50$; ∠s that form a linear pair are suppl.; $m\angle 2 = 130$; corresp. ∠s are ≅.
6. $m\angle 1 = 79$; alt. ext. ∠s are ≅; $m\angle 2 = 101$; ∠s that form a linear pair are suppl.
7. $m\angle 1 = 76$; alt. int. ∠s are ≅; $m\angle 2 = 61$; same-side int. ∠s are suppl.
8. $m\angle 1 = 82$; corresp. ∠s are ≅; $m\angle 2 = 122$; the 58° ∠ and the ∠ below ∠2 are alt. int. ∠s and are ≅. Because ∠2 and the ∠ below it form a linear pair, they are suppl.

Algebra **Find the value of x. Then find the measure of each labeled angle.**

9. 103; 77; 103°
10. 24; 12; 168
11. 30; 85; 85
12. 75; 95; 85; 70; 110

Practice and Problem Solving Wkbk/ All-in-One Resources/Online

Practice page 2

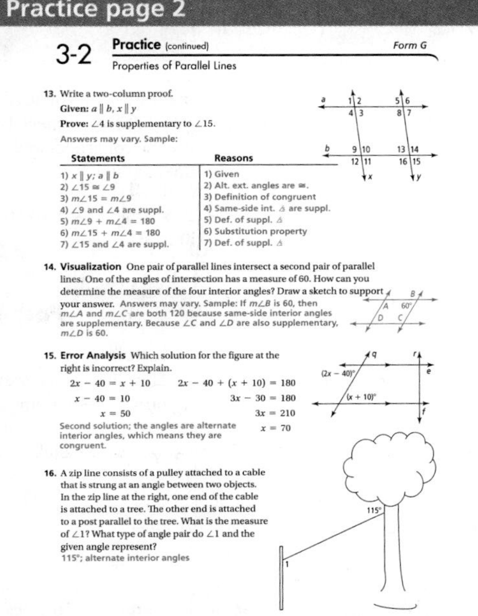

3-2 **Practice** (continued) *Form G*

Properties of Parallel Lines

13. Write a two-column proof.

Given: $a \parallel b$, $x \parallel y$

Prove: ∠4 is supplementary to ∠15.

Answers may vary. Sample:

Statements	Reasons
1) $x \parallel y$; $a \parallel b$	1) Given
2) ∠15 ≅ ∠9	2) Alt. ext. angles are ≅.
3) $m\angle 15 = m\angle 9$	3) Definition of congruent
4) ∠9 and ∠4 are suppl.	4) Same-side int. ∠s are suppl.
5) $m\angle 9 + m\angle 4 = 180$	5) Def. of suppl. ∠s
6) $m\angle 15 + m\angle 4 = 180$	6) Substitution property
7) ∠15 and ∠4 are suppl.	7) Def. of suppl. ∠s

14. **Visualization** One pair of parallel lines intersect a second pair of parallel lines. One of the angles of intersection has a measure of 60. How can you determine the measure of the four interior angles? Draw a sketch to support your answer. Answers may vary. Sample: If $m\angle B$ is 60, then $m\angle A$ and $m\angle C$ are both 120 because same-side interior angles are supplementary. Because ∠C and ∠D are also supplementary, $m\angle D$ is 60.

15. **Error Analysis** Which solution for the figure at the right is incorrect? Explain.

$2x - 40 = x + 10$ | $2x - 40 + (x + 10) = 180$

$x - 40 = 10$ | $3x - 30 = 180$

$x = 50$ | $3x = 210$

$x = 70$

Second solution; the angles are alternate interior angles, which means they are congruent.

16. A zip line consists of a pulley attached to a cable that is strung at an angle between two objects. In the zip line at the right, one end of the cable is attached to a tree. The other end is attached to a post parallel to the tree. What is the measure of ∠1? What type of angle pair do ∠1 and the given angle represent? 115°; alternate interior angles

All-in-One Resources/Online

Enrichment

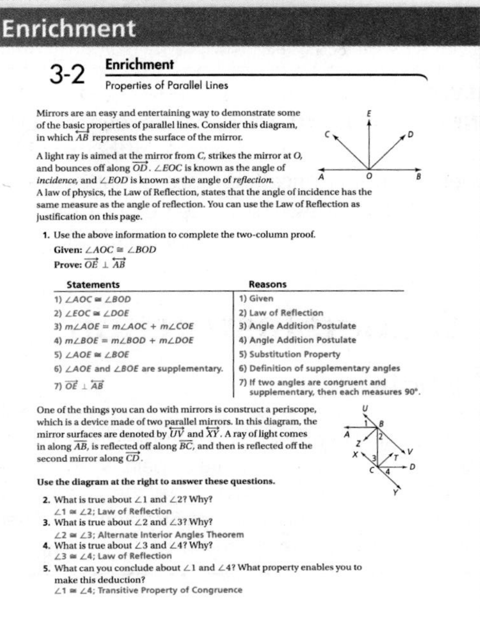

3-2 **Enrichment**

Properties of Parallel Lines

Mirrors are an easy and entertaining way to demonstrate some of the basic properties of parallel lines. Consider this diagram, in which $\overleftrightarrow{AB}$ represents the surface of the mirror.

A light ray is aimed at the mirror from C, strikes the mirror at O, and bounces off along $\overrightarrow{OD}$. ∠EOC is known as the angle of *incidence*, and ∠EOD is known as the angle of *reflection*.

A law of physics, the Law of Reflection, states that the angle of incidence has the same measure as the angle of reflection. You can use the Law of Reflection as justification on this page.

1. Use the above information to complete the two-column proof.

Given: ∠AOC ≅ ∠BOD

Prove: $\overrightarrow{OE} \perp \overleftrightarrow{AB}$

Statements	Reasons
1) ∠AOC ≅ ∠BOD	1) Given
2) ∠EOC ≅ ∠DOE	2) Law of Reflection
3) $m\angle AOE = m\angle AOC + m\angle COE$	3) Angle Addition Postulate
4) $m\angle BOE = m\angle BOD + m\angle DOE$	4) Angle Addition Postulate
5) ∠AOE ≅ ∠BOE	5) Substitution Property
6) ∠AOE and ∠BOE are supplementary.	6) Definition of supplementary angles
7) $\overrightarrow{OE} \perp \overleftrightarrow{AB}$	7) If two angles are congruent and supplementary, then each measures 90°.

One of the things you can do with mirrors is construct a periscope, which is a device made of two parallel mirrors. In this diagram, the mirror surfaces are denoted by $\overleftrightarrow{UV}$ and $\overleftrightarrow{XY}$. A ray of light comes in along $\overline{AB}$, is reflected off along $\overline{BC}$, and then is reflected off the second mirror along $\overrightarrow{CD}$.

Use the diagram at the right to answer these questions.

2. What is true about ∠1 and ∠2? Why? ∠1 ≅ ∠2; Law of Reflection
3. What is true about ∠2 and ∠3? Why? ∠2 ≅ ∠3; Alternate Interior Angles Theorem
4. What is true about ∠3 and ∠4? Why? ∠3 ≅ ∠4; Law of Reflection
5. What can you conclude about ∠1 and ∠4? What property enables you to make this deduction? ∠1 ≅ ∠4; Transitive Property of Congruence

Practice and Problem Solving Wkbk/ All-in-One Resources/Online

Think About a Plan

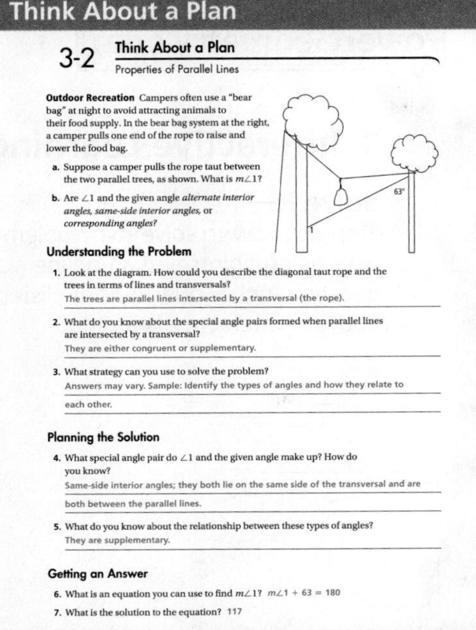

3-2 **Think About a Plan**

Properties of Parallel Lines

Outdoor Recreation Campers often use a "bear bag" at night to avoid attracting animals to their food supply. In the bear bag system at the right, a camper pulls one end of the rope to raise and lower the food bag.

a. Suppose a camper pulls the rope taut between the two parallel trees, as shown. What is $m\angle 1$?

b. Are ∠1 and the given angle *alternate interior angles, same-side interior angles,* or *corresponding angles?*

Understanding the Problem

1. Look at the diagram. How could you describe the diagonal taut rope and the trees in terms of lines and transversals? The trees are parallel lines intersected by a transversal (the rope).
2. What do you know about the special angle pairs formed when parallel lines are intersected by a transversal? They are either congruent or supplementary.
3. What strategy can you use to solve the problem? Answers may vary. Sample: Identify the types of angles and how they relate to each other.

Planning the Solution

4. What special angle pair do ∠1 and the given angle make up? How do you know? Same-side interior angles; they both lie on the same side of the transversal and are both between the parallel lines.
5. What do you know about the relationship between these types of angles? They are supplementary.

Getting an Answer

6. What is an equation you can use to find $m\angle 1$? $m\angle 1 + 63 = 180$
7. What is the solution to the equation? 117

Practice and Problem Solving Wkbk/ All-in-One Resources/Online

Standardized Test Prep

3-2 **Standardized Test Prep**

Properties of Parallel Lines

Multiple Choice

For Exercises 1–6, choose the correct letter.

For Exercises 1–4, use the figure at the right.

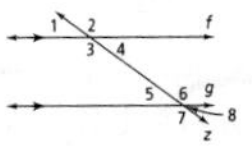

1. Which angle is congruent to ∠1? B
   - A ∠2
   - C ∠6
   - B ∠5
   - D ∠7
2. Which angle is not supplementary to ∠6? F
   - F ∠2
   - G ∠4
   - H ∠5
   - I ∠8
3. Which can be used to prove directly that ∠1 ≅ ∠8? D
   - A Alternate Interior Angles Theorem
   - B Corresponding Angles Postulate
   - C Same-Side Interior Angles Theorem
   - D Alternate Exterior Angles Theorem
4. If $m\angle 5 = 42$, what is $m\angle 4$? F
   - F 42
   - G 48
   - H 128
   - I 138

For Exercises 5 and 6, use the figure at the right.

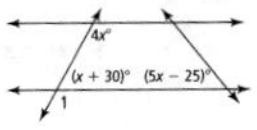

5. What is the value of x? C
   - A 10
   - C 30
   - B 25
   - D 120
6. What is the measure of ∠1? H
   - F 45
   - G 60
   - H 120
   - I 125

Short Response

7. Write a two-column proof of the Alternate Exterior Angles Theorem (Theorem 3-2).

Given: $r \parallel s$

Prove: ∠1 ≅ ∠8

[2] $r \parallel s$; given; ∠1 ≅ ∠6; if lines are ∥, then corresp. ∠s are ≅; ∠6 ≅ ∠8; vert. ∠s are ≅; ∠1 ≅ ∠8; trans. prop. of ≅. [1] some steps correct [0] proof incorrect or absent

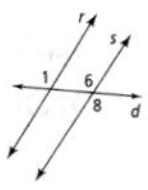

Online Teacher Resource Center

Activities, Games, and Puzzles

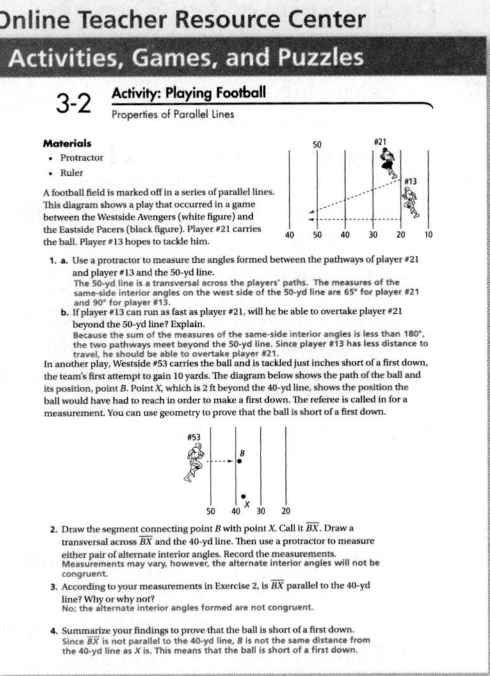

3-2 **Activity: Playing Football**

Properties of Parallel Lines

Materials

- Protractor
- Ruler

A football field is marked off in a series of parallel lines. This diagram shows a play that occurred in a game between the Westside Avengers (white figure) and the Eastside Pacers (black figure). Player #21 carries the ball. Player #13 hopes to tackle him.

1. a. Use a protractor to measure the angles formed between the pathways of player #21 and player #13 and the 50-yd line. The 50-yd line is a transversal across the players' paths. The measures of the same-side interior angles on the west side of the 50-yd line are 65° for player #21 and 90° for player #13.

   b. If player #13 can run as fast as player #21, will he be able to overtake player #21 beyond the 50-yd line? Explain. Because the sum of the measures of the same-side interior angles is less than 180°, the two pathways meet beyond the 50-yd line. Since player #13 has less distance to travel, he should be able to overtake player #21.

In another play, Westside #53 carries the ball and is tackled just inches short of a first down, the team's first attempt to gain 10 yards. The diagram below shows the path of the ball and its position, point B. Point X, which is 2 ft beyond the 40-yd line, shows the position the ball would have had to reach in order to make a first down. The referee is called in for a measurement. You can use geometry to prove that the ball is short of a first down.

2. Draw the segment connecting point B with point X. Call it $\overline{BX}$. Draw a transversal across $\overline{BX}$ and the 40-yd line. Then use a protractor to measure either pair of alternate interior angles. Record the measurements. Measurements may vary, however, the alternate interior angles will not be congruent.
3. According to your measurements in Exercise 2, is $\overline{BX}$ parallel to the 40-yd line? Why or why not? No; the alternate interior angles formed are not congruent.
4. Summarize your findings to prove that the ball is short of a first down. Since $\overline{BX}$ is not parallel to the 40-yd line, B is not the same distance from the 40-yd line as X is. This means that the ball is short of a first down.

1 Interactive Learning

Solve It!

PURPOSE To visualize and investigate angle relationships when parallel lines are crossed by transversals

PROCESS Students may use visual judgment or previously learned definitions and theorems pertaining to angles.

FACILITATE

Q How can you determine the measure of ∠1? **[∠1 is supplementary to the angle that measures 60]**

Q What are the two possible degree measures for each turn? Explain. **[60 and 120; because all the lines are parallel, all the special pairs will involve these two measurements only.]**

Q How could you instruct the mouse to follow the path shown? **[1 block, turn 120°; 2 blocks, turn 240°; 1 block, turn 300°; 1 block, turn 60°; 1 block, turn 300°; proceed to cheese.]**

ANSWER See Solve It in Answers on next page.

CONNECT THE MATH Students can identify vertical angles and supplementary angles in the maze. Students should notice the maze is made of several pairs of parallel lines. This maze demonstrates conditions used to prove two lines parallel.

2 Guided Instruction

Take Note

Q If one pair of corresponding angles in the diagram is given to be congruent, are all pairs of corresponding angles congruent? Explain. **[Yes, the Vertical Angles Theorem and the Congruent Supplements Theorem show that they are congruent.]**

3-3 Proving Lines Parallel

TN State Performance Indicators

SPI 3108.1.4 Use definitions, basic postulates, and theorems about points, lines, angles, and planes to write/complete proofs and/or to solve problems.

SPI 3108.4.4 Analyze different types and formats of proofs.

Objective To determine whether two lines are parallel

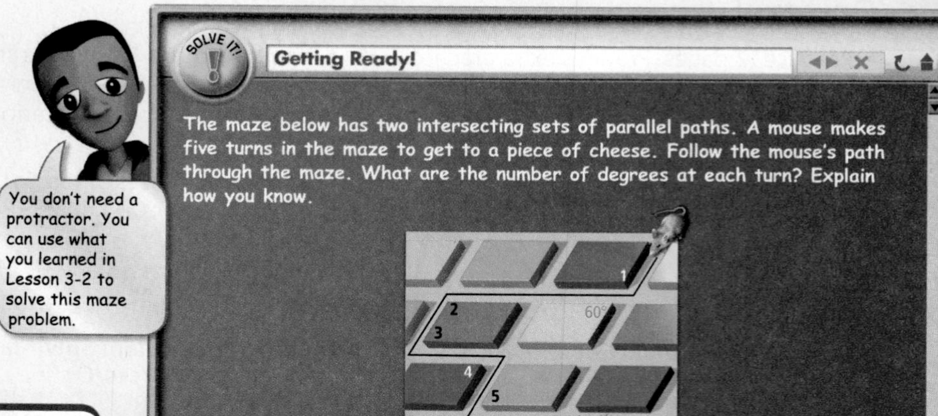

SOLVE IT!
Getting Ready!
The maze below has two intersecting sets of parallel paths. A mouse makes five turns in the maze to get to a piece of cheese. Follow the mouse's path through the maze. What are the number of degrees at each turn? Explain how you know.
You don't need a protractor. You can use what you learned in Lesson 3-2 to solve this maze problem.
1
2
3
4
5
60°

Lesson Vocabulary
- flow proof

In the Solve It, you used parallel lines to find congruent and supplementary relationships of special angle pairs. In this lesson you will do the converse. You will use the congruent and supplementary relationships of the special angle pairs to prove lines parallel.

Essential Understanding You can use certain angle pairs to decide whether two lines are parallel.

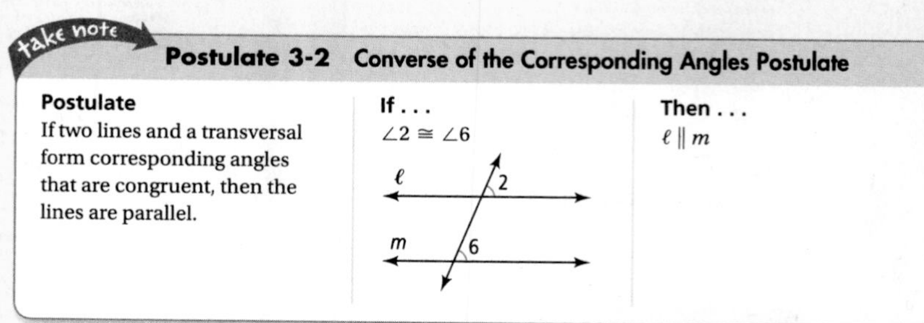

take note **Postulate 3-2 Converse of the Corresponding Angles Postulate**

Postulate	If . . .	Then . . .
If two lines and a transversal form corresponding angles that are congruent, then the lines are parallel.	∠2 ≅ ∠6	ℓ ∥ m

3-3 Preparing to Teach

BIG idea Reasoning and Proof UbD

ESSENTIAL UNDERSTANDINGS

- Certain angle pairs can be used to decide whether two lines are parallel.
- Paragraph, two-column, and flow proofs are three forms of proof.

Math Background

Teaching students to write proofs, whether two-column, paragraph, or flow proofs, is an exercise in getting students to map out a process. Students skilled in writing proofs work step by step, not assuming any relationship or taking any knowledge for granted.

Students should be encouraged to consider all the postulates, definitions, and theorems related to parallel lines when making a list of how to get from the given statement to the statement to be proved.

Proofs should be looked upon as problems where the answer is already known and the task is to demonstrate how the answer is derived. For the proofs in this lesson, students often overlook that they must prove lines parallel before using postulates and theorems involving parallel lines. They simply skip right to conditions related to the angles. Stress that although lines may appear parallel in a diagram, that fact cannot be assumed, but must be included in the logic that leads to the proof.

Support Student Learning

Use the **Geometry Companion** to engage and support students during instructions. See Lesson Resources at the end of this lesson for details.

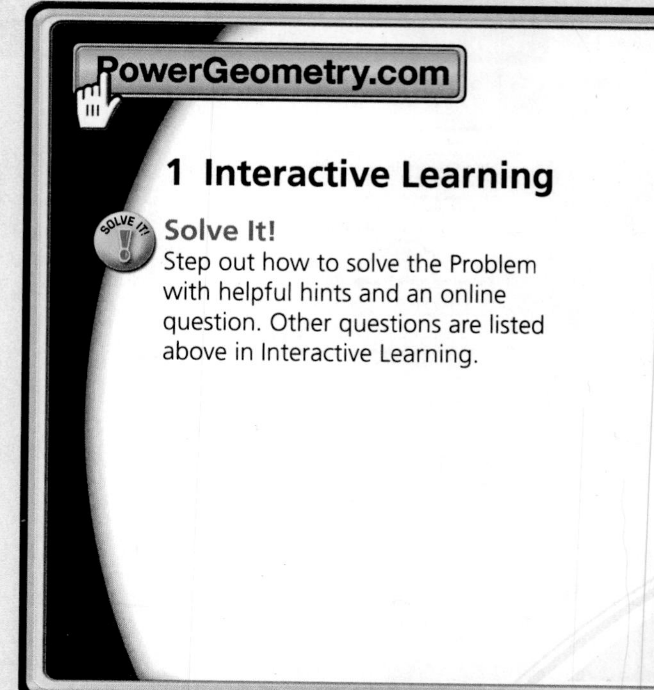

Think
Which line is the transversal for ∠1 and ∠2?
Line *m* is the transversal because it forms one side of both angles.

Problem 1 Identifying Parallel Lines

Which lines are parallel if ∠1 ≅ ∠2? Justify your answer.

∠1 and ∠2 are corresponding angles. If ∠1 ≅ ∠2, then $a \parallel b$ by the Converse of the Corresponding Angles Postulate.

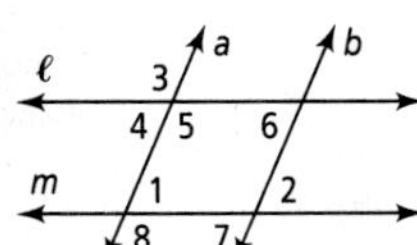

Got It? 1. Which lines are parallel if ∠6 ≅ ∠7? Justify your answer.

In Lesson 3-2 you proved theorems based on the Corresponding Angles Postulate. You can use the Converse of the Corresponding Angles Postulate to prove converses of the theorems you learned in Lesson 3-2.

take note

Theorem 3-4 Converse of the Alternate Interior Angles Theorem

Theorem	If . . .	Then . . .
If two lines and a transversal form alternate interior angles that are congruent, then the two lines are parallel.	∠4 ≅ ∠6 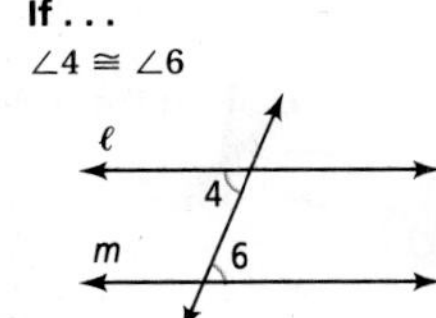	$\ell \parallel m$

Theorem 3-5 Converse of the Same-Side Interior Angles Theorem

Theorem	If . . .	Then . . .
If two lines and a transversal form same-side interior angles that are supplementary, then the two lines are parallel.	$m\angle 3 + m\angle 6 = 180$ 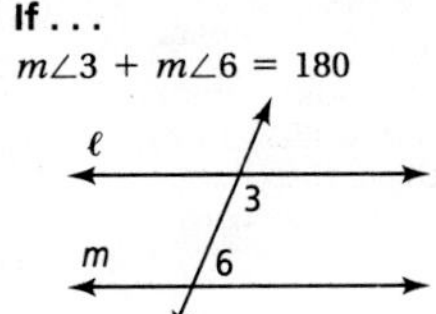	$\ell \parallel m$

You will prove Theorem 3-5 in Exercise 29.

Theorem 3-6 Converse of the Alternate Exterior Angles Theorem

Theorem	If . . .	Then . . .
If two lines and a transversal form alternate exterior angles that are congruent, then the two lines are parallel.	∠1 ≅ ∠7 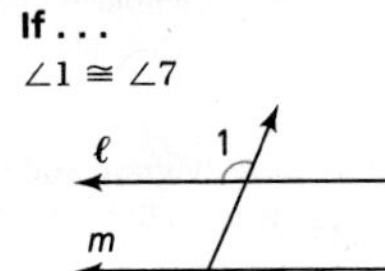	$\ell \parallel m$

Problem 1

Q Which lines form ∠1? Which lines form ∠2? **[lines *a* and *m*; lines *b* and *m*]**

Got It? ERROR PREVENTION
Recommend that students try covering up one line, so that only two parallel lines and one transversal are visible at a time.

Take Note

Q How can you tell that the interior angles which form linear pairs with ∠4 and ∠6 are also congruent? **[Because they are both supplementary to congruent angles, they are also congruent by the Congruent Suppl. Thm.]**

Q What does the phrase "same-side" refer to in the diagram? **[It means the same side of the transversal, either the right side or the left side.]**

Q How many pairs of same-side interior angles are in the diagram? **[2]**

In future proofs, students may struggle to determine when to use the Alternate Exterior Angles Theorem and when to use its converse. Explain to students that the converse is used when they need to prove the lines are parallel. The theorem is used when they already know that the lines are parallel and they need to prove the alternate exterior angles are congruent.

2 Guided Instruction

Each Problem is worked out and supported online.

Problem 1
Identifying Parallel Lines

Problem 2
Writing a Flow Proof of Theorem 3-6
Animated

Problem 3
Determining Whether Lines are Parallel
Animated

Problem 4
Using Algebra
Animated

Support in Geometry Companion
- Vocabulary
- Key Concepts
- Got It?

Answers

Solve It!
Turn 1: 120°, turn 2: 120°, turn 3: 60°, turn 4: 60°, turn 5: 60°; explanations may vary. Sample: When a transversal intersects two ∥ lines, the ∠s formed are ≅ or suppl. If you know the measure of one of those ∠s, you can use the properties of ∥ lines to find the measures of the other seven ∠s.

Got It?
1. $\ell \parallel m$ by the Converse of the Corresp. ∠s Post.

The two forms of proof students have used thus far, two-column and paragraph proofs, are deductive proofs. A third type of deductive proof is a flow proof, which is modeled after flowcharts. A flowchart, which is often used to show workflows in the business environment, is a schematic representation of a process. Flow proofs are a visual representation of a proof using statements and reasons in a logical order.

Problem 2

Q What statements could replace the statements listed in the lower left and middle section of the proof? **[lower left: $\angle 5 \cong \angle 7$; middle: $\angle 5 \cong \angle 1$]**

Q How could you use this proof to prove that $\angle 6$ and $\angle 3$ are supplementary? **[Once you have proven the lines parallel, you can use the Same-Side Interior Angles Theorem.]**

Got It? SYNTHESIZING

Remind students the proof written in Problem 2 can be used to prove lines ℓ and m parallel before proving that $\angle 3 \cong \angle 5$.

The proof of the Converse of the Alternate Interior Angles Theorem below looks different than any proof you have seen so far in this course. You know two forms of proof—paragraph and two-column. In a third form, called **flow proof**, arrows show the logical connections between the statements. Reasons are written below the statements.

Proof Proof of Theorem 3-4: Converse of the Alternate Interior Angles Theorem

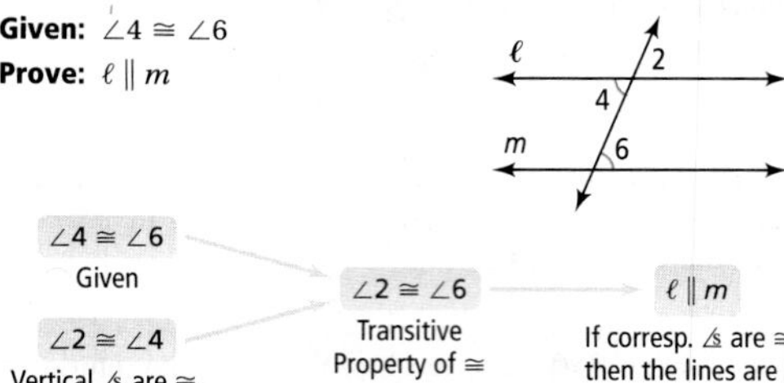

Given: $\angle 4 \cong \angle 6$

Prove: $\ell \parallel m$

$\angle 4 \cong \angle 6$ — Given

$\angle 2 \cong \angle 4$ — Vertical ∠s are ≅.

→ $\angle 2 \cong \angle 6$ — Transitive Property of ≅

→ $\ell \parallel m$ — If corresp. ∠s are ≅, then the lines are ∥.

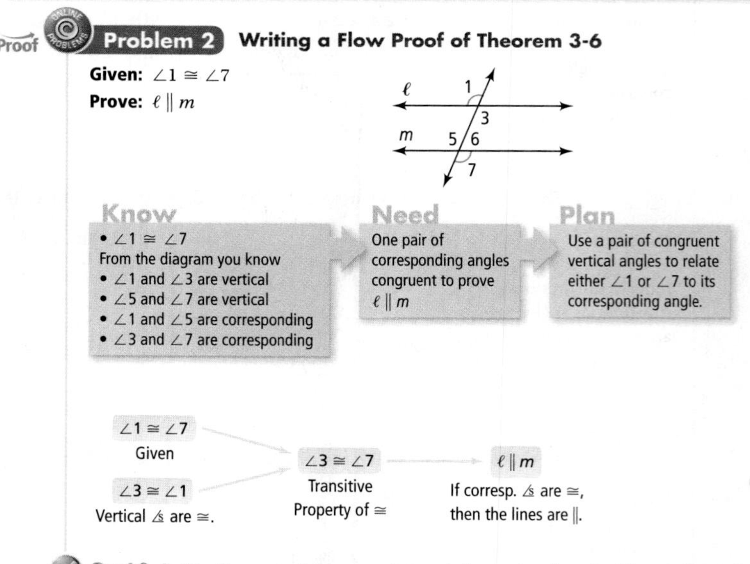

Proof Problem 2 Writing a Flow Proof of Theorem 3-6

Given: $\angle 1 \cong \angle 7$

Prove: $\ell \parallel m$

Know
- $\angle 1 \cong \angle 7$

From the diagram you know
- $\angle 1$ and $\angle 3$ are vertical
- $\angle 5$ and $\angle 7$ are vertical
- $\angle 1$ and $\angle 5$ are corresponding
- $\angle 3$ and $\angle 7$ are corresponding

Need
One pair of corresponding angles congruent to prove $\ell \parallel m$

Plan
Use a pair of congruent vertical angles to relate either $\angle 1$ or $\angle 7$ to its corresponding angle.

$\angle 1 \cong \angle 7$ — Given

$\angle 3 \cong \angle 1$ — Vertical ∠s are ≅.

→ $\angle 3 \cong \angle 7$ — Transitive Property of ≅

→ $\ell \parallel m$ — If corresp. ∠s are ≅, then the lines are ∥.

Got It? 2. Use the same diagram and given information from Problem 2. Prove that $\angle 3 \cong \angle 5$ using a flow proof.

Additional Problems

1. Which lines are parallel if $\angle 2 \cong \angle 3$? Justify your answer.

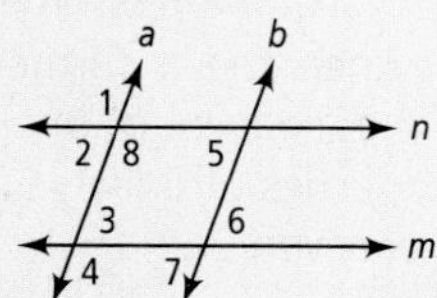

ANSWER m and n by the Converse of the Alt. Int. Angles Thm.

2. Use the diagram below. Write a flow proof.

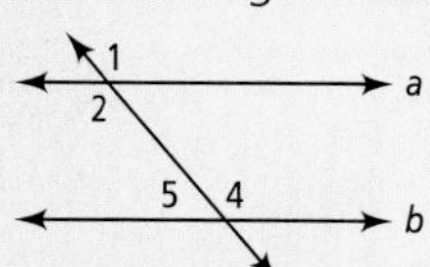

Given: $m\angle 5 = 40$, $m\angle 2 = 140$

Prove: $a \parallel b$

ANSWER

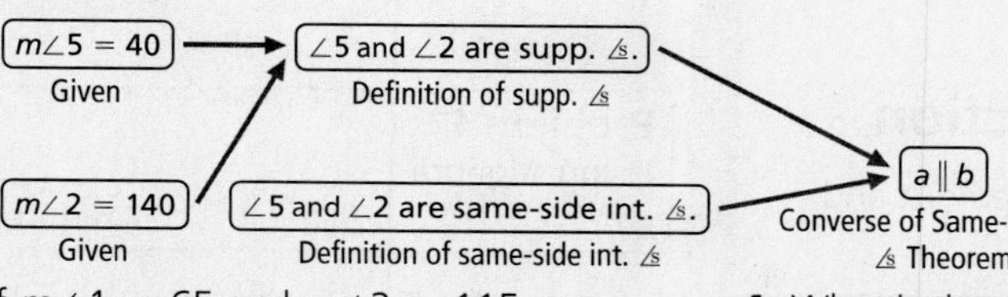

$m\angle 5 = 40$ — Given

$m\angle 2 = 140$ — Given

→ $\angle 5$ and $\angle 2$ are supp. ∠s. — Definition of supp. ∠s

$\angle 5$ and $\angle 2$ are same-side int. ∠s. — Definition of same-side int. ∠s

→ $a \parallel b$ — Converse of Same-Side Int. ∠s Theorem

3. If $m\angle 1 = 65$ and $m\angle 2 = 115$, are lines a and b parallel? Explain.

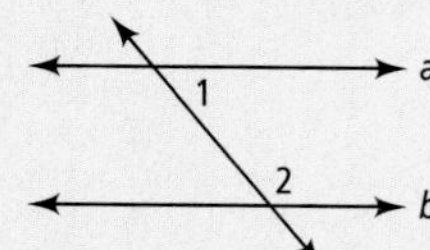

ANSWER Yes, they are same-side interior angles and are suppl., so lines a and b are parallel.

4. What is the value of x for which $a \parallel b$?

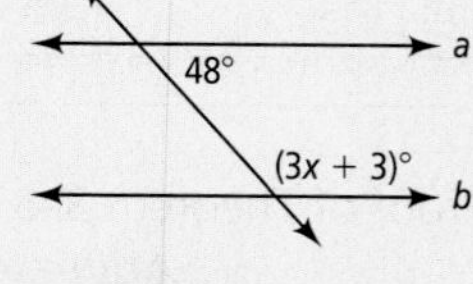

ANSWER 43

The postulate and three theorems you have just learned provide you with four ways to determine if two lines are parallel.

Think

How do ∠1 and ∠2 relate to each other in the diagram?
∠1 and ∠2 are both exterior angles and they lie on opposite sides of *t*.

Problem 3 Determining Whether Lines are Parallel

The fence gate at the right is made up of pieces of wood arranged in various directions. Suppose ∠1 ≅ ∠2. Are lines *r* and *s* parallel? Explain.

Yes, $r \parallel s$. ∠1 and ∠2 are alternate exterior angles. If two lines and a transversal form congruent alternate exterior angles, then the lines are parallel (Converse of the Alternate Exterior Angles Theorem).

Got It? 3. In Problem 3, what is another way to explain why $r \parallel s$? Justify your answer.

You can use algebra along with the postulates and theorems from Lesson 3-2 and Lesson 3-3 to help you solve problems involving parallel lines.

Think

Work backward.
Think about what must be true of the given angles for *a* and *b* to be parallel.

Problem 4 Using Algebra

Algebra What is the value of *x* for which $a \parallel b$?

a
(2x + 9)°
b
111°

The two angles are same-side interior angles. By the Converse of the Same-Side Interior Angles Theorem, $a \parallel b$ if the angles are supplementary.

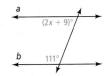

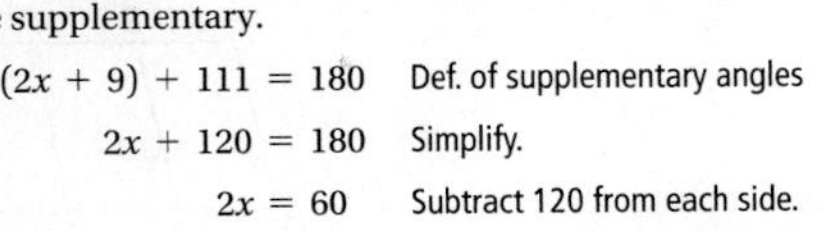
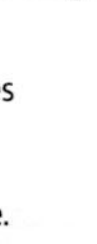

$(2x + 9) + 111 = 180$	Def. of supplementary angles
$2x + 120 = 180$	Simplify.
$2x = 60$	Subtract 120 from each side.
$x = 30$	Divide each side by 2.

Got It? 4. What is the value of *w* for which $c \parallel d$?

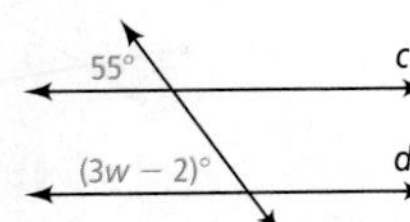

Problem 3

Q What piece on the gate represents the transversal in this diagram? **[the diagonal piece of wood that runs from the lower left corner of the gate to the upper right corner]**

Q Are ∠1 and ∠2 on the same side of the transversal? **[no]**

Q What labeled angle is on the same side of the transversal as ∠1? **[∠3]**

Got It?

Q What is the relationship between ∠2 and ∠3? **[They are vertical angles.]**

Q What congruence statement is a result of this relationship? **[∠2 ≅ ∠3]**

Q Using angles on the same side of the transversal, what congruence statement do you need to prove the lines parallel? **[∠1 ≅ ∠3]**

Problem 4

Q What kind of special angles are the labeled angles in the diagram? **[They are same-side interior angles.]**

Q Given what you know about same-side interior angles, what other measure is used to write the equation to solve for *x*? **[180]**

Q If $x = 60$, will lines *a* and *b* intersect to the left or to the right of the transversal? **[They will intersect to the right of the transversal.]**

Q If $x = 10$, will lines *a* and *b* intersect to the left or to the right of the transversal? **[They will intersect to the left of the transversal.]**

Got It? VISUAL LEARNERS

Q In order for *c* and *d* to be parallel, what relationship must be true for the given angles? **[The measures of corresponding angles must be equal.]**

Answers

Got It? (continued)

2. Answers may vary. Sample:

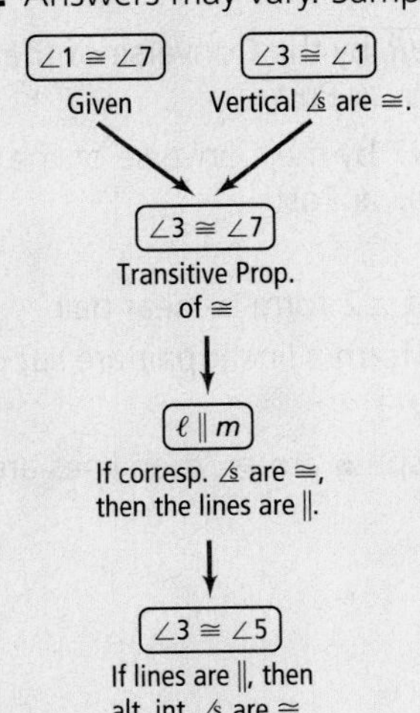

3. ∠2 ≅ ∠3 (Vert. ∠s are ≅.), so ∠1 ≅ ∠3 (Trans. Prop. of ≅). So $r \parallel s$ by the Converse of the Corresp. ∠s Post.

4. 19

3 Lesson Check

Do you know HOW?

- If students have difficulty with Exercises 1–2, then tell them to first identify the relationship of the indicated angles.

Do you UNDERSTAND?

- If students have difficulty with Exercise 6, then discuss that same-side interior angles both lie along one side of the transversal, not along one of the parallel lines.

Close

Q List all the different ways that you can prove that two lines are parallel. **[Show that same-side interior angles are supplementary or show that one of the following pairs of angles is congruent: alternate interior, alternate exterior, or corresponding.]**

Lesson Check

Do you know HOW?

State the theorem or postulate that proves $a \parallel b$.

1.

2.

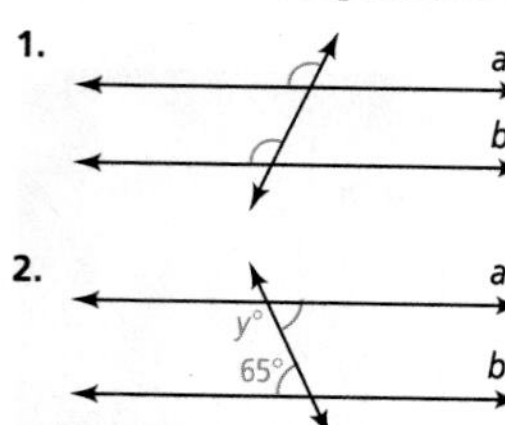

3. What is the value of y for which $a \parallel b$ in Exercise 2?

Do you UNDERSTAND?

4. Explain how you know when to use the Alternate Interior Angles Theorem and when to use the Converse of the Alternate Interior Angles Theorem.

5. Compare and Contrast How are flow proofs and two-column proofs alike? How are they different?

6. Error Analysis A classmate says that $\overleftrightarrow{AB} \parallel \overleftrightarrow{DC}$ based on the diagram at the right. Explain your classmate's error.

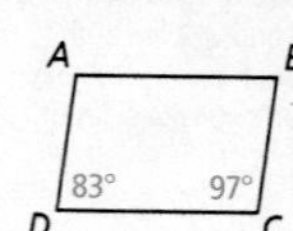

Practice and Problem-Solving Exercises

A Practice

Which lines or segments are parallel? Justify your answer.

See Problem 1.

7.

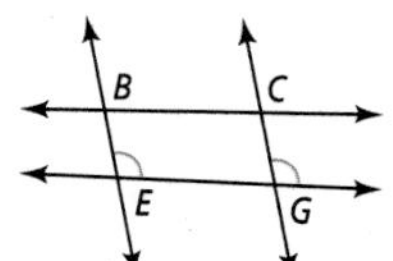

8.

P Q S T

9.

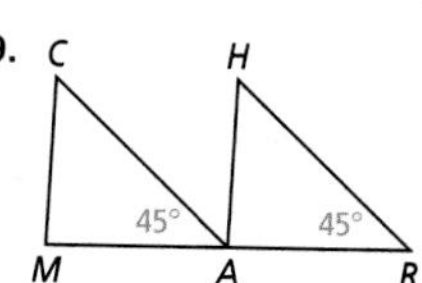

10.

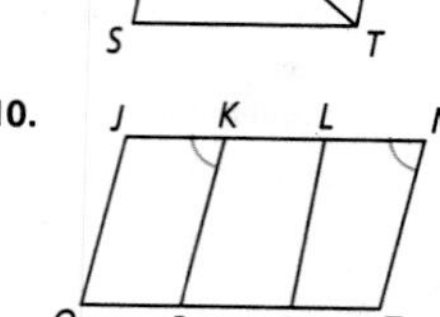

11. Developing Proof Complete the flow proof below.

See Problem 2.

Given: $\angle 1$ and $\angle 3$ are supplementary.
Prove: $a \parallel b$

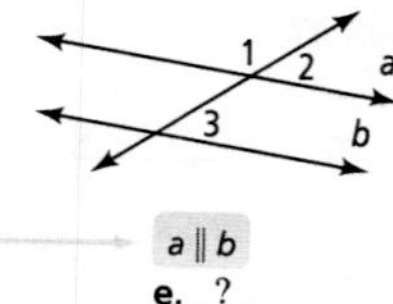

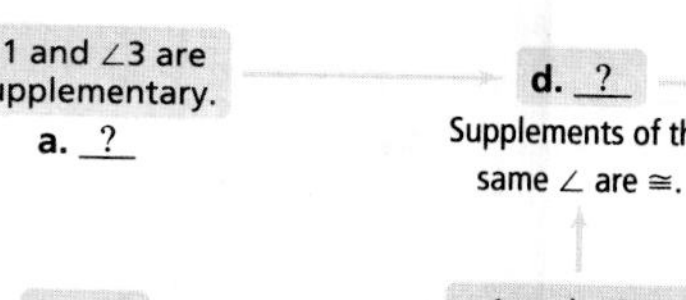

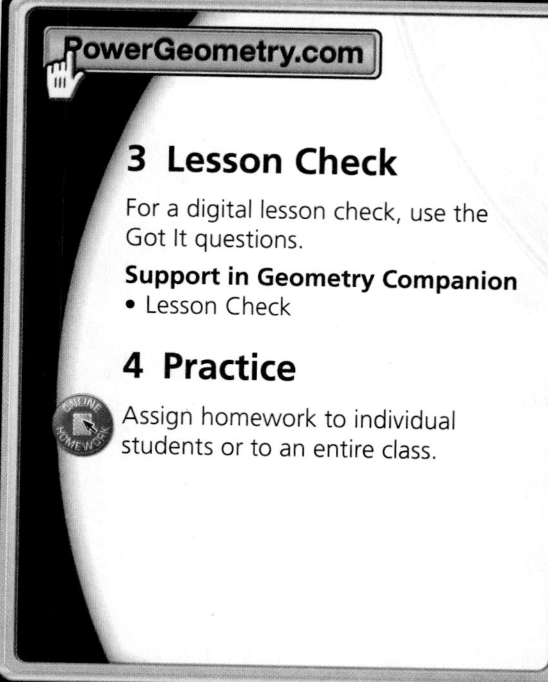

Answers

Lesson Check

1. Conv. of Corresp. ⦠ Post.

2. Conv. of Alt. Int. ⦠ Thm.

3. 115

4. If you want to prove that alt. int. ⦠ are ≅, use the Alt. Int. ⦠ Thm.; if you want to prove that two lines are parallel, use the Converse of the Alt. Int. ⦠ Thm.

5. Alike: Both give statements and reasons; different: The proofs use different formats.

6. $\overleftrightarrow{DC}$ is the transversal, so the two same-side int. ⦠ show that $\overleftrightarrow{AD}$ and $\overleftrightarrow{BC}$ are parallel.

Practice and Problem-Solving Exercises

7. $\overleftrightarrow{BE} \parallel \overleftrightarrow{CG}$ by the Converse of the Corresp. ⦠ Post.

8. $\overleftrightarrow{PS} \parallel \overleftrightarrow{QT}$ by the Converse of the Corresp. ⦠ Post.

9. $\overleftrightarrow{CA} \parallel \overleftrightarrow{HR}$ by the Converse of the Corresp. ⦠ Post.

10. $\overline{KR} \parallel \overline{MT}$ by the Converse of the Corresp. ⦠ Post.

11a. Given

b. $\angle 1$ and $\angle 2$ form a linear pair.

c. ⦠ that form a linear pair are suppl.

d. $\angle 2 \cong \angle 3$

e. If corresp. ⦠ are ≅, then lines are ∥.

12. Parking Two workers paint lines for angled parking spaces. One worker paints a line so that $m\angle 1 = 65$. The other worker paints a line so that $m\angle 2 = 65$. Are their lines parallel? Explain.

See Problem 3.

Algebra Find the value of x for which $\ell \parallel m$.

See Problem 4.

13.

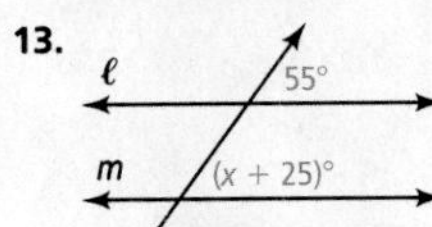

14.

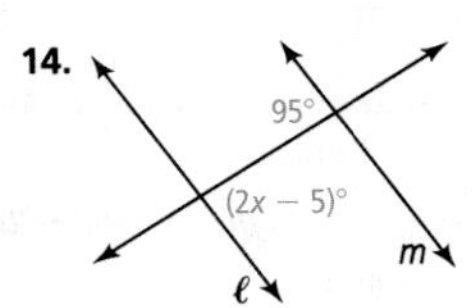

15.

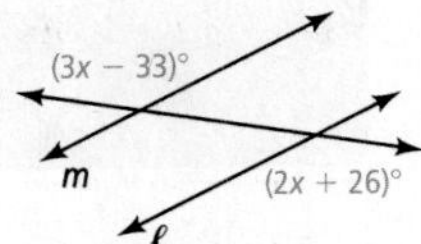

16.

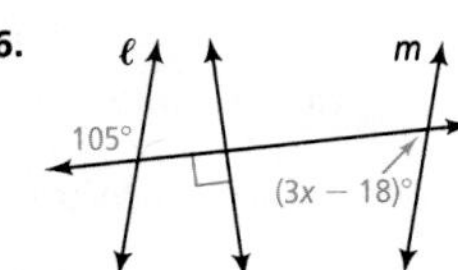

B Apply

Developing Proof Use the given information to determine which lines, if any, are parallel. Justify each conclusion with a theorem or postulate.

17. $\angle 2$ is supplementary to $\angle 3$.

18. $\angle 1 \cong \angle 3$

19. $\angle 6$ is supplementary to $\angle 7$.

20. $\angle 9 \cong \angle 12$

21. $m\angle 7 = 65$, $m\angle 9 = 115$

22. $\angle 2 \cong \angle 10$

23. $\angle 1 \cong \angle 8$

24. $\angle 8 \cong \angle 6$

25. $\angle 11 \cong \angle 7$

26. $\angle 5 \cong \angle 10$

Algebra Find the value of x for which $\ell \parallel m$.

27.

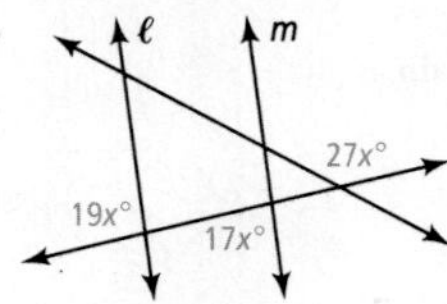

28.

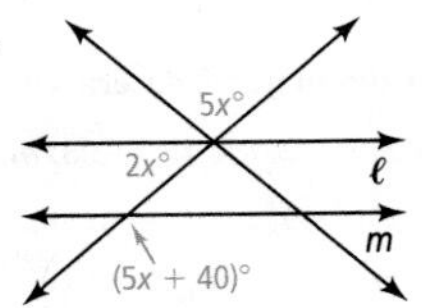

29. Prove the Converse of the Same-Side Interior Angles Theorem (Theorem 3-5).
Proof

Given: $m\angle 3 + m\angle 6 = 180$

Prove: $\ell \parallel m$

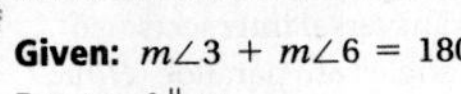

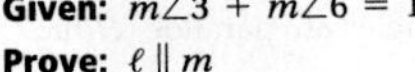

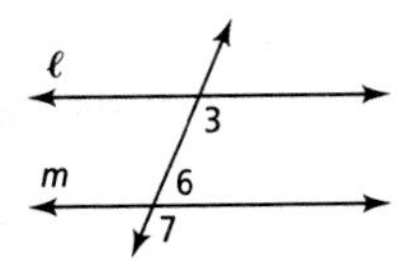

4 Practice

ASSIGNMENT GUIDE

Basic: 7–16 all, 18–34 even, 35, 36, 38
Average: 7–15 odd, 17–41
Advanced: 7–15 odd, 17–46
Standardized Test Prep: 47–51
Mixed Review: 52–57

Reasoning exercises have blue headings.
Applications exercises have red headings.

EXERCISE 34: Use the Think About a Plan worksheet in the **Practice and Problem Solving Workbook** (also available in the Teaching Resources in print and online) to further support students' development in becoming independent learners.

HOMEWORK QUICK CHECK

To check students' understanding of key skills and concepts, go over Exercises 9, 15, 30, 34, and 35.

12. Yes; $\angle 1$ and $\angle 2$ are alt. ext. ∠s, and if alt. ext. ∠s are ≅, then the lines are ∥.

13. 30 **14.** 50

15. 59 **16.** 31

17. $a \parallel b$; if same-side int. ∠s are suppl., then the lines are ∥.

18. $a \parallel b$; Converse of Corresp. ∠s Post.

19. $a \parallel b$; if same-side int. ∠s are suppl., then the lines are ∥.

20. none

21. none

22. $\ell \parallel m$ (Conv. of Corresp. ∠s Post.)

23. $a \parallel b$ (Conv. of the Alt. Ext. ∠s Thm.)

24. $a \parallel b$ (Conv. of Corresp. ∠s Post)

25. none

26. $\ell \parallel m$ (Conv. of the Alt. Int. ∠s Thm.)

27. 5 **28.** 20

29. $m\angle 3 + m\angle 6 = 180$ (Given) and $m\angle 6 + m\angle 7 = 180$ ($\angle 6$ and $\angle 7$ form a linear pair). Then $\angle 3 \cong \angle 7$ (∠s suppl. to the same ∠ are ≅.), and $\ell \parallel m$ (Converse of Corresp. ∠s Post.)

Answers

Practice and Problem-Solving Exercises (continued)

30. The corresp. ⦞ are ≅, so the oars are ∥ by the Conv. of Corresp. ⦞ Post.

31. $x = 10$; $m\angle 1 = m\angle 2 = 70$

32. $x = 5$; $m\angle 1 = m\angle 2 = 50$

33. $x = 2.5$; $m\angle 1 = m\angle 2 = 30$

34. $x = 1.25$; $m\angle 1 = m\angle 2 = 10$

35. Answers may vary. Sample: If $\angle 3 \cong \angle 5$, then $\ell \parallel n$ by the Converse of Corresp. ⦞ Post.

36. Answers may vary. Sample: If $m\angle 8 = m\angle 4$, then $\ell \parallel n$ because corresp. ⦞ are ≅ and $j \parallel k$ because same-side int. ⦞ are suppl.

37. Answers may vary. Sample: If $\angle 5 \cong \angle 3$, then $j \parallel k$ by the Converse of the Corresp. ⦞ Post.

38. Answers may vary. Sample: If $\angle 11 \cong \angle 3$, then $j \parallel k$ by the Converse of the Corresp. ⦞ Post.

39. If alt. ext. ⦞ are ≅, then the lines are ∥.

40. Answers may vary. Sample:

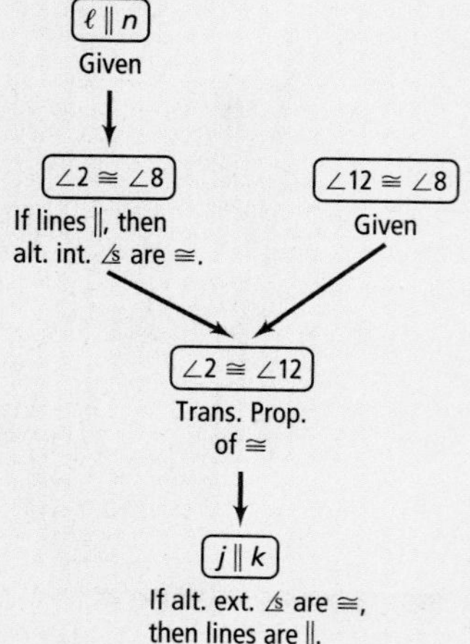

41. Answers may vary. Sample:

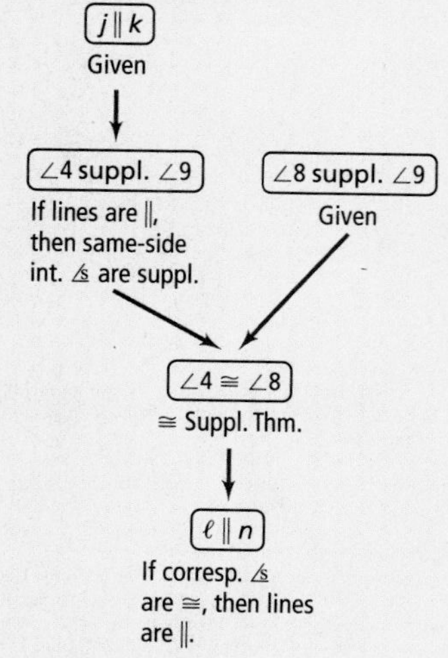

42. $\overline{PL} \parallel \overline{NA}$; $\overline{PN} \parallel \overline{LA}$; if same-side int. ⦞ are suppl., then the lines are ∥.

43. $\overline{PL} \parallel \overline{NA}$; if same-side int. ⦞ are suppl., then the lines are ∥.

---

30. Think About a Plan If the rowing crew at the right strokes in unison, the oars sweep out angles of equal measure. Explain why the oars on each side of the shell stay parallel.

- What type of information do you need to prove lines parallel?
- How do the positions of the angles of equal measure relate?

Algebra **Determine the value of x for which $r \parallel s$. Then find $m\angle 1$ and $m\angle 2$.**

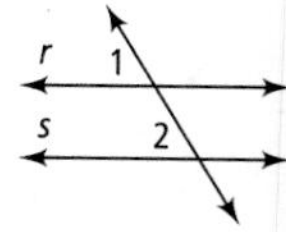

31. $m\angle 1 = 80 - x$, $m\angle 2 = 90 - 2x$

32. $m\angle 1 = 60 - 2x$, $m\angle 2 = 70 - 4x$

33. $m\angle 1 = 40 - 4x$, $m\angle 2 = 50 - 8x$

34. $m\angle 1 = 20 - 8x$, $m\angle 2 = 30 - 16x$

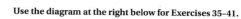

Use the diagram at the right below for Exercises 35–41.

Open-Ended **Use the given information. State another fact about one of the given angles that will guarantee two lines are parallel. Tell which lines will be parallel and why.**

35. $\angle 1 \cong \angle 3$

36. $m\angle 8 = 110$, $m\angle 9 = 70$

37. $\angle 5 \cong \angle 11$

38. $\angle 11$ and $\angle 12$ are supplementary.

39. Reasoning If $\angle 1 \cong \angle 7$, what theorem or postulate can you use to show that $\ell \parallel n$?

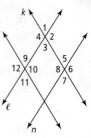

Write a flow proof.

40. Proof **Given:** $\ell \parallel n$, $\angle 12 \cong \angle 8$
Prove: $j \parallel k$

41. Proof **Given:** $j \parallel k$, $m\angle 8 + m\angle 9 = 180$
Prove: $\ell \parallel n$

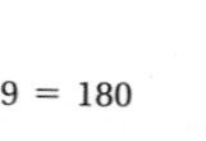

Challenge **Which sides of quadrilateral *PLAN* must be parallel? Explain.**

42. $m\angle P = 72$, $m\angle L = 108$, $m\angle A = 72$, $m\angle N = 108$

43. $m\angle P = 59$, $m\angle L = 37$, $m\angle A = 143$, $m\angle N = 121$

44. $m\angle P = 67$, $m\angle L = 120$, $m\angle A = 73$, $m\angle N = 100$

45. $m\angle P = 56$, $m\angle L = 124$, $m\angle A = 124$, $m\angle N = 56$

46. Proof Write a two-column proof to prove the following: If a transversal intersects two parallel lines, then the bisectors of two corresponding angles are parallel. (*Hint:* Start by drawing and marking a diagram.)

162 **Chapter 3** Parallel and Perpendicular Lines

---

44. none

45. $\overline{PN} \parallel \overline{LA}$; if same-side int. ⦞ are suppl., then the lines are ∥.

46. Answers may vary. Sample:

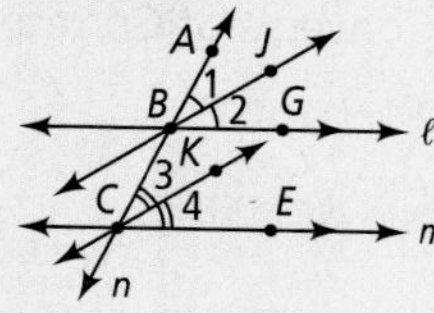

1. $\ell \parallel m$ (Given)
2. $\angle ABG \cong \angle ACE$ (If lines are ∥, then corresp. ⦞ are ≅.)
3. $\overline{BJ}$ bisects $\angle ABG$, $\overline{CK}$ bisects $\angle ACE$ (Given)
4. $m\angle 1 = \frac{1}{2} m\angle ABG$, $m\angle 3 = \frac{1}{2} m\angle ACE$ (A bis. divides an ∠ in half.)
5. $\frac{1}{2} m\angle ABG = \frac{1}{2} m\angle ACE$ (Mult. Prop. of Equality)
6. $m\angle 1 = m\angle 3$ (Substitution)
7. $\overline{CK} \parallel \overline{BJ}$ (If corresp. ⦞ are ≅, then the lines are ∥.)

Standardized Test Prep

SAT/ACT

Use the diagram for Exercises 47 and 48.

47. For what value of x is $c \parallel d$?

Ⓐ 21 Ⓑ 23 Ⓒ 43 Ⓓ 53

48. If $c \parallel d$, what is $m\angle 1$?

Ⓕ 24 Ⓖ 44 Ⓗ 136 Ⓘ 146

49. Which of the following is always a valid conclusion for the hypothesis?
If two angles are congruent, then __?__.

Ⓐ they are right angles
Ⓑ they share a vertex
Ⓒ they have the same measure
Ⓓ they are acute angles

50. What is the value of x in the diagram at the right?

Ⓕ $1.\overline{6}$ Ⓖ 10 Ⓗ 17 Ⓘ 19

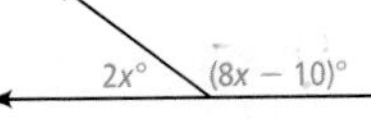

Short Response

51. Draw a pentagon. Is your pentagon convex or concave? Explain.

Mixed Review

Find $m\angle 1$ and $m\angle 2$. Justify each answer. See Lesson 3-2.

52.

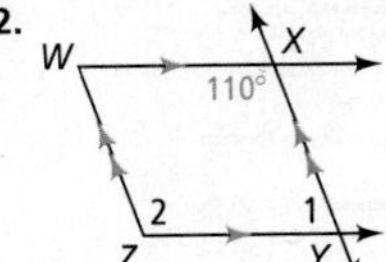

53.

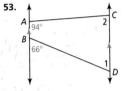

Get Ready! **To prepare for Lesson 3-4, do Exercises 54–57.**

Determine whether each statement is *always, sometimes,* or *never* true. See Lessons 1-6 and 3-1.

54. Perpendicular lines meet at right angles.

55. Two lines in intersecting planes are perpendicular.

56. Two lines in the same plane are parallel.

57. Two lines in parallel planes are perpendicular.

47. A **48.** G
49. C **50.** I

51. [2] A sketch of a closed plane figure consisting of 5 segments (sides); the pentagon is convex because all diagonals are inside the pentagon OR the pentagon is concave because at least one diagonal has points outside the pentagon.
[1] correct sketch with incorrect explanation OR no explanation

52. $m\angle 1 = 70$ ($\angle 1$ is suppl. to a $110°$ $\angle$.); $m\angle 2 = 110$ ($\angle 2$ is suppl. to $\angle 1$, which is a $70°$ angle.)

53. $m\angle 1 = 66$ (Alt. int. $\angle$s are $\cong$.); $m\angle 2 = 86$ ($\angle 2$ is suppl. to a $94°$ angle.)

54. always **55.** sometimes
56. sometimes **57.** never

Lesson Resources

Instructional Support

Geometry Companion

Students can use the **Geometry Companion** worktext (4 pages) . . .

- New Vocabulary
- Key Concepts
- Got It for each Problem
- Lesson Check

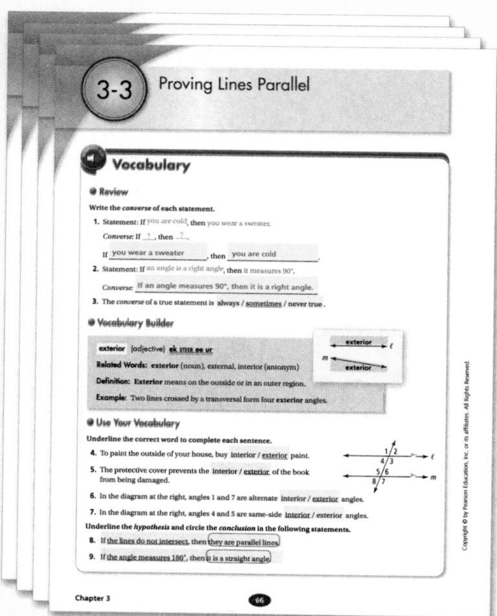

3-3 Proving Lines Parallel

Vocabulary

Review

Write the *converse* of each statement.

1. Statement: If you are cold, then you wear a sweater.

   Converse: If _?_, then _?_.

   If you wear a sweater, then you are cold.

2. Statement: If an angle is a right angle, then it measures 90°.

   Converse: If an angle measures 90°, then it is a right angle.

3. The *converse* of a true statement is always / sometimes / never true.

Vocabulary Builder

exterior (adjective) ek STEER ee ur

Related Words: exterior (noun), external, interior (antonym)

Definition: Exterior means on the outside or in an outer region.

Example: Two lines crossed by a transversal form four exterior angles.

Use Your Vocabulary

Underline the correct word to complete each sentence.

4. To paint the outside of your house, buy interior / exterior paint.
5. The protective cover prevents the interior / exterior of the book from being damaged.
6. In the diagram at the right, angles 1 and 7 are alternate interior / exterior angles.
7. In the diagram at the right, angles 4 and 5 are same-side interior / exterior angles.

Underline the *hypothesis* and circle the *conclusion* in the following statements.

8. If the lines do not intersect, then they are parallel lines.
9. If the angle measures 180°, then it is a straight angle.

Chapter 3 66

ELL Support

Use Role Playing Draw two parallel lines on the board. Say: Today you are detectives. Are these lines parallel? We will find out together. Each student may draw one line on the board. Each student may measure one distance or one angle. Have students take turns either drawing a line or making a measurement. Have the students record their measurements, but they should not share information with one another.

After each student has had a turn, form groups of four to five students. Have the students compare the information that they have about the two lines on the board. Ask: Does your group have enough information to prove that these lines are parallel? Have groups that do not have enough information take turns asking questions of the other students until they can prove the lines are parallel. When the group has enough information, have them write down an explanation of their proof.

5 Assess & Remediate

Lesson Quiz

Use the figure to answer each question.

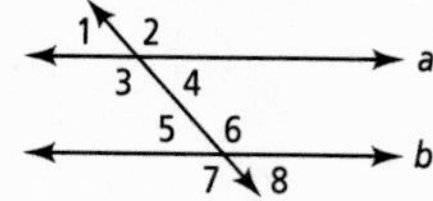

1. If $m\angle 1 = 42$, what must the measure of $\angle 7$ be in order to prove $a \parallel b$?
2. **Do you UNDERSTAND?** Suppose $m\angle 3 = 128$ and $m\angle 6 = (10x + 8)$. What value of x would result in $a \parallel b$?
3. Which theorem or postulate would you use in Exercise 2 to prove that $a \parallel b$?

Use the figure for Questions 4 and 5.

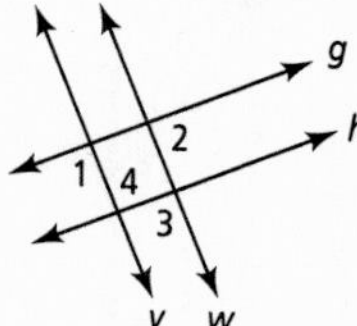

4. If $g \parallel h$ and $m\angle 2 = 88$, what is $m\angle 3$?
5. If $v \parallel w$ and $m\angle 1 = 120$, what is $m\angle 2$?

ANSWERS TO LESSON QUIZ

1. 138
2. 12
3. Converse of the Alternate Interior Angles Theorem
4. 92
5. 60

PRECRIPTION FOR REMEDIATION

Use the student work on the Lesson Quiz to prescribe a differentiated review assignment.

Points	Differentiated Remediation
0–2	Intervention
3–4	On-level
5	Extension

PowerGeometry.com

5 Assess & Remediate

Assign the Lesson Quiz. Appropriate intervention, practice, or enrichment is automatically generated based on student performance.

Differentiated Remediation

Intervention

- **Reteaching** (2 pages) Provides reteaching and practice exercises for the key lesson concepts. Use with struggling students or absent students.
- **English Language Learner Support** Helps students develop and reinforce mathematical vocabulary and key concepts.

All-in-One Resources/Online

Reteaching

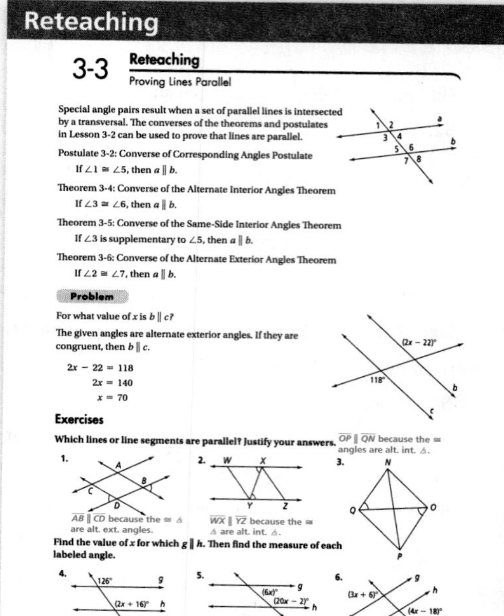

3-3 Reteaching

Proving Lines Parallel

Special angle pairs result when a set of parallel lines is intersected by a transversal. The converses of the theorems and postulates in Lesson 3-2 can be used to prove that lines are parallel.

Postulate 3-2: Converse of Corresponding Angles Postulate

If $\angle 1 \cong \angle 5$, then $a \parallel b$.

Theorem 3-4: Converse of the Alternate Interior Angles Theorem

If $\angle 3 \cong \angle 6$, then $a \parallel b$.

Theorem 3-5: Converse of the Same-Side Interior Angles Theorem

If $\angle 3$ is supplementary to $\angle 5$, then $a \parallel b$.

Theorem 3-6: Converse of the Alternate Exterior Angles Theorem

If $\angle 2 \cong \angle 7$, then $a \parallel b$.

Problem

For what value of x is $b \parallel c$?

The given angles are alternate exterior angles. If they are congruent, then $b \parallel c$.

$$2x - 22 = 118$$
$$2x = 140$$
$$x = 70$$

(2x − 22)°, 118°, b, c

Exercises

Which lines or line segments are parallel? Justify your answers.

1. $\overline{AB} \parallel \overline{CD}$ because the ≅ ∠s are alt. ext. angles.
2. $\overline{WX} \parallel \overline{YZ}$ because the ≅ ∠s are alt. int. ∠s.
3. $\overline{OP} \parallel \overline{QN}$ because the ≅ angles are alt. int. ∠s.

Find the value of x for which $g \parallel h$. Then find the measure of each labeled angle.

4. 126°, (2x + 16)° — 55; 126
5. (6x)°, (20x − 2)° — 7; 42; 138
6. (3x + 6)°, (4x − 18)° — 24; 78; 78

All-in-One Resources/Online

English Language Learner Support

3-3 ELL Support

Proving Lines Parallel

The column on the left shows the steps for proving lines parallel. Use the column on the left to answer each question in the column on the right.

Problem **Proving Lines Parallel** How can you prove the Converse of the Same-Side Interior Angles Theorem? Given: ∠3 and ∠5 are supplementary. Prove: $a \parallel b$	1. What does *converse* mean? The converse of a statement is formed when you switch the hypothesis and the conclusion of the original statement.
Start with the given information. ∠3 and ∠5 are supplementary.	2. What does *given* mean? Given is information listed in the problem statement.
Use the definition of supplementary angles. ∠3 and ∠1 are supplementary.	3. What are supplementary angles? Supplementary angles have a sum of 180 or form a straight angle.
Recognize that supplements of the same angle are congruent. ∠5 ≅ ∠1	4. What does the symbol ≅ stand for? ≅ means congruent.
Recall that if corresponding ∠s are congruent, lines are parallel. a and b are parallel.	5. How do corresponding angles correspond with each other? They are in corresponding locations where the parallel lines meet the transversal.

Differentiated Remediation *continued*

On-Level

- **Practice** (2 pages) Provides extra practice for each lesson. For simpler practice exercises, use the Form K Practice pages found in the All-in-One Teaching Resources and online.
- **Think About a Plan** Helps students develop specific problem-solving skills and strategies by providing scaffolded guiding questions.
- **Standardized Test Prep** Focuses on all major exercises, all major question types, and helps students prepare for the high-stakes assessments.

Extension

- **Enrichment** Provides students with interesting problems and activities that extend the concepts of the lesson.
- **Activities, Games, and Puzzles** Worksheets that can be used for concepts development, enrichment, and for fun!

Practice and Problem Solving Wkbk/ All-in-One Resources/Online

Practice page 1

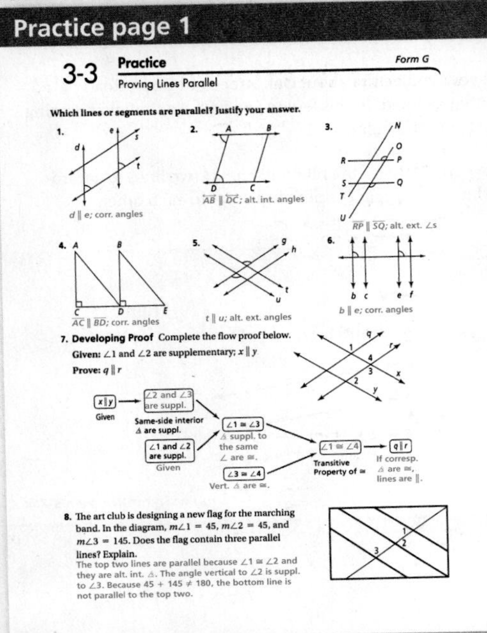

3-3 Practice — Form G
Proving Lines Parallel

Which lines or segments are parallel? Justify your answer.

1. $d \parallel e$; corr. angles
2. $\overline{AB} \parallel \overline{DC}$; alt. int. angles
3. $\overleftrightarrow{RP} \parallel \overleftrightarrow{SQ}$; alt. ext. ∠s
4. $\overline{AC} \parallel \overline{BD}$; corr. angles
5. $t \parallel u$; alt. ext. angles
6. $b \parallel e$; corr. angles

7. **Developing Proof** Complete the flow proof below.
Given: ∠1 and ∠2 are supplementary; $x \parallel y$
Prove: $q \parallel r$

8. The art club is designing a new flag for the marching band. In the diagram, m∠1 = 45, m∠2 = 45, and m∠3 = 145. Does the flag contain three parallel lines? Explain.
The top two lines are parallel because ∠1 ≅ ∠2 and they are alt. int. ∠s. The angle vertical to ∠2 is suppl. to ∠3. Because 45 + 145 ≠ 180, the bottom line is not parallel to the top two.

Practice and Problem Solving Wkbk/ All-in-One Resources/Online

Practice page 2

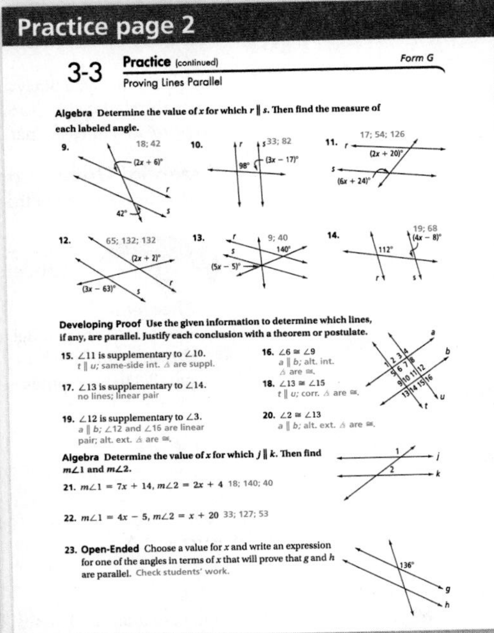

3-3 Practice (continued) — Form G
Proving Lines Parallel

Algebra Determine the value of x for which $r \parallel s$. Then find the measure of each labeled angle.

9. 18; 42
10. 33; 82
11. 17; 54; 126
12. 65; 132; 132
13. 9; 40
14. 19; 68

Developing Proof Use the given information to determine which lines, if any, are parallel. Justify each conclusion with a theorem or postulate.

15. ∠11 is supplementary to ∠10. $t \parallel u$; same-side int. ∠s are suppl.
16. ∠6 ≅ ∠9 $a \parallel b$; alt. int. ∠s are ≅.
17. ∠13 is supplementary to ∠14. no lines; linear pair
18. ∠13 ≅ ∠15 $t \parallel u$; corr. ∠s are ≅.
19. ∠12 is supplementary to ∠3. $a \parallel b$; ∠12 and ∠16 are linear pair; alt. ext. ∠s are ≅.
20. ∠2 ≅ ∠13 $a \parallel b$; alt. ext. ∠s are ≅.

Algebra Determine the value of x for which $j \parallel k$. Then find m∠1 and m∠2.

21. m∠1 = 7x + 14, m∠2 = 2x + 4 18; 140; 40
22. m∠1 = 4x − 5, m∠2 = x + 20 33; 127; 53

23. **Open-Ended** Choose a value for x and write an expression for one of the angles in terms of x that will prove that g and h are parallel. Check students' work.

All-in-One Resources/Online

Enrichment

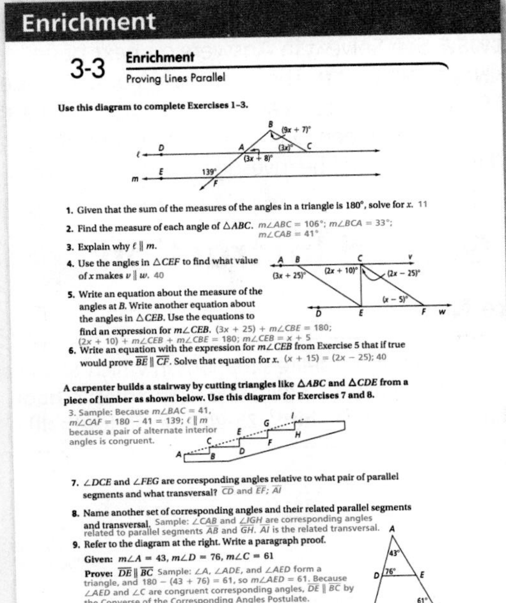

3-3 Enrichment
Proving Lines Parallel

Use this diagram to complete Exercises 1–3.

1. Given that the sum of the measures of the angles in a triangle is 180°, solve for x. 11
2. Find the measure of each angle of △ABC. m∠ABC = 106°; m∠BCA = 33°; m∠CAB = 41°
3. Explain why $\ell \parallel m$.
4. Use the angles in △CEF to find what value of x makes $v \parallel w$. 40
5. Write an equation about the measure of the angles at B. Write another equation about the angles in △CEB. Use the equations to find an expression for m∠CEB. (3x + 25) + m∠CBE = 180; (2x + 10) + m∠CEB + m∠CBE = 180; m∠CEB = x + 5
6. Write an equation with the expression for m∠CEB from Exercise 5 that if true would prove $\overline{BE} \parallel \overline{CF}$. Solve that equation for x. (x + 15) = (2x − 25); 40

A carpenter builds a stairway by cutting triangles like △ABC and △CDE from a piece of lumber as shown below. Use this diagram for Exercises 7 and 8.

3. Sample: Because m∠BAC = 41, m∠CAF = 180 − 41 = 139; $\ell \parallel m$ because a pair of alternate interior angles is congruent.

7. ∠DCE and ∠FEG are corresponding angles relative to what pair of parallel segments and what transversal? $\overline{CD}$ and $\overline{EF}$; $\overline{AI}$
8. Name another set of corresponding angles and their related parallel segments and transversal. Sample: ∠CAB and ∠IGH are corresponding angles related to parallel segments $\overline{AB}$ and $\overline{GH}$. $\overline{AI}$ is the related transversal.
9. Refer to the diagram at the right. Write a paragraph proof.
Given: m∠A = 43, m∠D = 76, m∠C = 61
Prove: $\overline{DE} \parallel \overline{BC}$ Sample: ∠A, ∠ADE, and ∠AED form a triangle, and 180 − (43 + 76) = 61, so m∠AED = 61. Because ∠AED and ∠C are congruent corresponding angles, $\overline{DE} \parallel \overline{BC}$ by the Converse of the Corresponding Angles Postulate.

Practice and Problem Solving Wkbk/ All-in-One Resources/Online

Think About a Plan

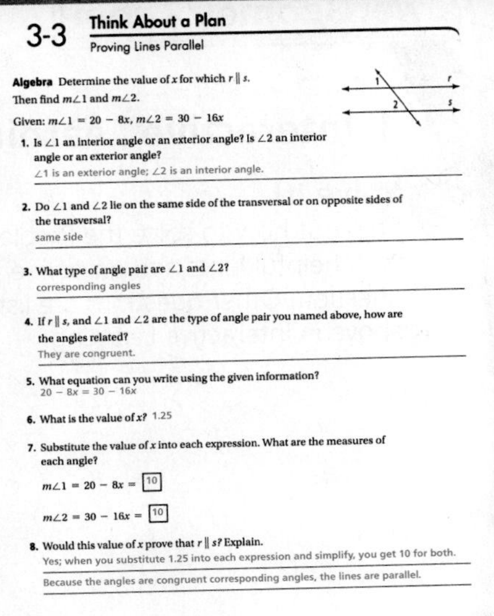

3-3 Think About a Plan
Proving Lines Parallel

Algebra Determine the value of x for which $r \parallel s$. Then find m∠1 and m∠2.
Given: m∠1 = 20 − 8x, m∠2 = 30 − 16x

1. Is ∠1 an interior angle or an exterior angle? Is ∠2 an interior angle or an exterior angle?
∠1 is an exterior angle; ∠2 is an interior angle.
2. Do ∠1 and ∠2 lie on the same side of the transversal or on opposite sides of the transversal?
same side
3. What type of angle pair are ∠1 and ∠2?
corresponding angles
4. If $r \parallel s$, and ∠1 and ∠2 are the type of angle pair you named above, how are the angles related?
They are congruent.
5. What equation can you write using the given information?
20 − 8x = 30 − 16x
6. What is the value of x? 1.25
7. Substitute the value of x into each expression. What are the measures of each angle?
m∠1 = 20 − 8x = 10
m∠2 = 30 − 16x = 10
8. Would this value of x prove that $r \parallel s$? Explain.
Yes; when you substitute 1.25 into each expression and simplify, you get 10 for both. Because the angles are congruent corresponding angles, the lines are parallel.

Practice and Problem Solving Wkbk/ All-in-One Resources/Online

Standardized Test Prep

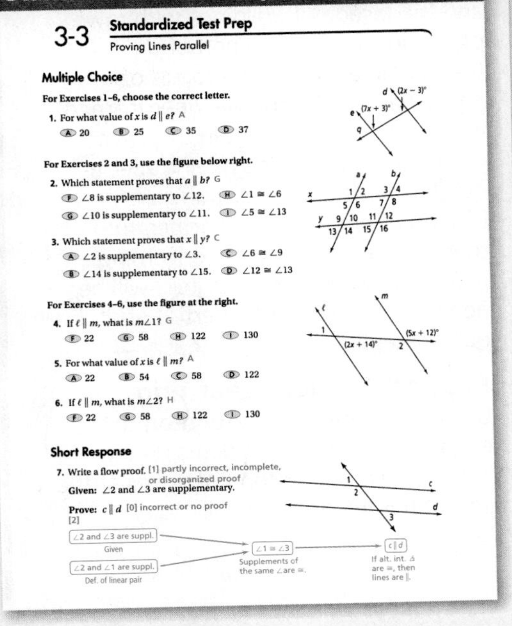

3-3 Standardized Test Prep
Proving Lines Parallel

Multiple Choice

For Exercises 1–6, choose the correct letter.

1. For what value of x is $d \parallel e$? A
A 20 B 25 C 35 D 37

For Exercises 2 and 3, use the figure below right.

2. Which statement proves that $a \parallel b$? G
F ∠8 is supplementary to ∠12. H ∠1 ≅ ∠6
G ∠10 is supplementary to ∠11. I ∠5 ≅ ∠13
3. Which statement proves that $x \parallel y$? C
A ∠2 is supplementary to ∠3. C ∠6 ≅ ∠9
B ∠14 is supplementary to ∠15. D ∠12 ≅ ∠13

For Exercises 4–6, use the figure at the right.

4. If $\ell \parallel m$, what is m∠1? G
F 22 G 58 H 122 I 130
5. For what value of x is $\ell \parallel m$? A
A 22 B 54 C 58 D 122
6. If $\ell \parallel m$, what is m∠2? H
F 22 G 58 H 122 I 130

Short Response

7. Write a flow proof. [1] partly incorrect, incomplete, or disorganized proof
Given: ∠2 and ∠3 are supplementary.
Prove: $c \parallel d$ [0] incorrect or no proof
[2]

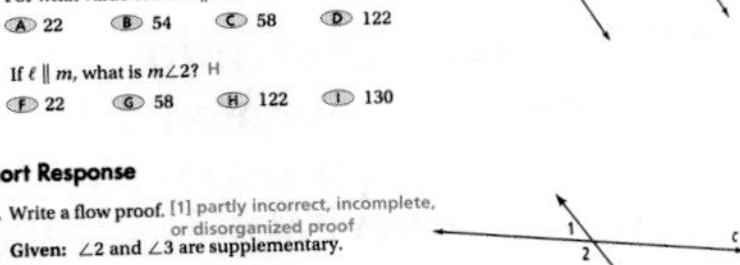

Online Teacher Resource Center

Activities, Games, and Puzzles

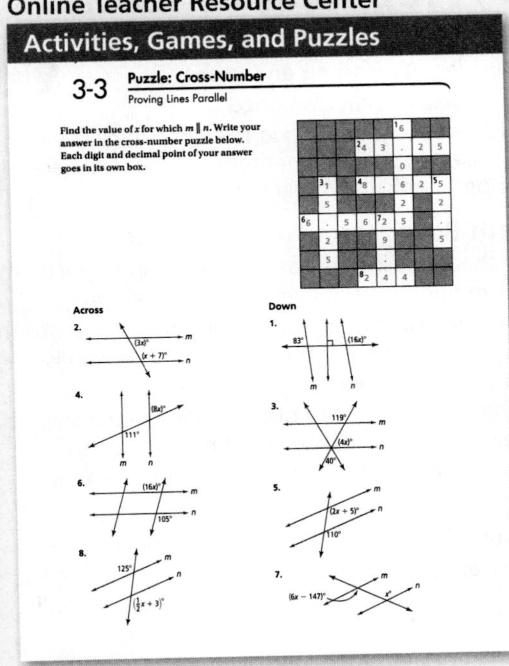

3-3 Puzzle: Cross-Number
Proving Lines Parallel

Find the value of x for which $m \parallel n$. Write your answer in the cross-number puzzle below. Each digit and decimal point of your answer goes in its own box.

Across

Down

1 Interactive Learning

Solve It!

PURPOSE To provide a situation in which students can make a conjecture that relates parallel and perpendicular lines

PROCESS Students may use visual judgment or previously learned theorems about angles.

FACILITATE

Q What is the relationship between Oak Street and Schoolhouse Road? Explain. **[They are parallel, because a pair of alternate interior angles is congruent.]**

Q How can extending the paths help to determine the relationship between Oak Street and Court Road? **[If one of the paths intersects both roads, then you might use the congruent and supplementary relationships of special angle pairs to prove lines parallel.]**

ANSWER See Solve It in Answers on next page.

CONNECT THE MATH The relationship of Oak Street and Schoolhouse Road can be used to determine the relationship between Oak Street and Court Road. Similar patterns will be investigated in this lesson.

2 Guided Instruction

Take Note

Q What are some real-life situations in which two lines are both parallel to a third line? **[Samples: school hallways, striped shirts, 25-yd lines in football]**

3-4 Parallel and Perpendicular Lines

TN State Performance Indicator
SPI 3108.1.4 Use definitions, basic postulates, and theorems about points, lines, angles, and planes to write/complete proofs and/or to solve problems.

Objective To relate parallel and perpendicular lines

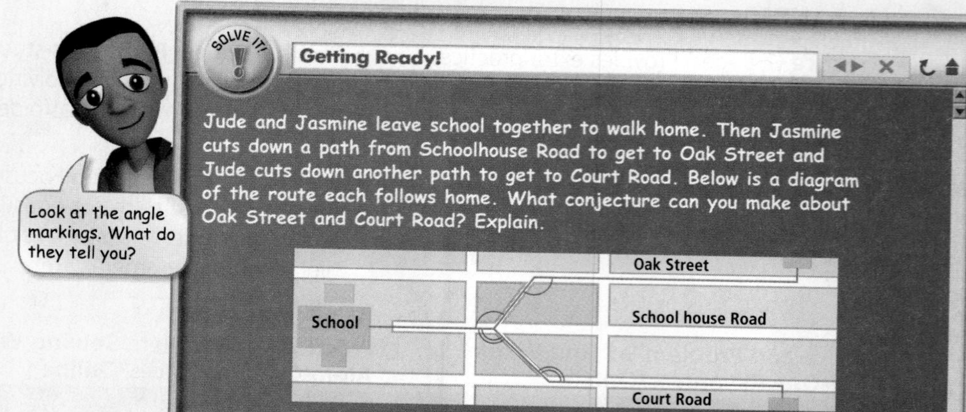

Look at the angle markings. What do they tell you?
Getting Ready!
Jude and Jasmine leave school together to walk home. Then Jasmine cuts down a path from Schoolhouse Road to get to Oak Street and Jude cuts down another path to get to Court Road. Below is a diagram of the route each follows home. What conjecture can you make about Oak Street and Court Road? Explain.
Oak Street
School
School house Road
Court Road

In the Solve It, you likely made your conjecture about Oak Street and Court Road based on their relationships to Schoolhouse Road. In this lesson you will use similar reasoning to prove that lines are parallel or perpendicular.

Essential Understanding You can use the relationships of two lines to a third line to decide whether the two lines are parallel or perpendicular to each other.

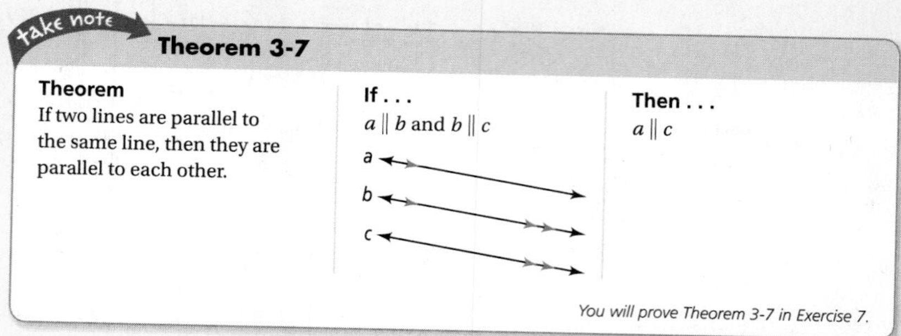

take note

Theorem 3-7

Theorem	If . . .	Then . . .
If two lines are parallel to the same line, then they are parallel to each other.	$a \parallel b$ and $b \parallel c$	$a \parallel c$

You will prove Theorem 3-7 in Exercise 7.

3-4 Preparing to Teach

BIG idea Reasoning and Proof UbD

ESSENTIAL UNDERSTANDING

- The relationships of two lines to a third line can be used to decide whether two lines are parallel or perpendicular to each other.

Math Background

The theorems in this lesson provide an opportunity to continue the study and use of transitive relationships. One significant difference to highlight when presenting the theorems in this lesson is the inclusion of the phrase "in a plane" in only two of the theorems. Point out that the relationship involving all parallel lines does not include this phrase because this relationship is true in a plane and also in space.

The use of these relationships is abundantly visible in the area of architectural design and can lead to many fruitful class discussions where examples of these applications can be demonstrated. Applications include high-rise buildings with many floors, all of which are parallel (an illustration of the theorem in space) and the façade of buildings with rows of windows (an illustration of the theorem in a plane). The topics of parallel and perpendicular lines learned in this and other lessons in this chapter will be the basis for classifying special quadrilaterals and other polygons in subsequent chapters. Further, the theorems and postulates concerning parallel and perpendicular lines will be needed to prove the properties of special quadrilaterals.

Support Student Learning

Use the **Geometry Companion** to engage and support students during instructions. See Lesson Resources at the end of this lesson for details.

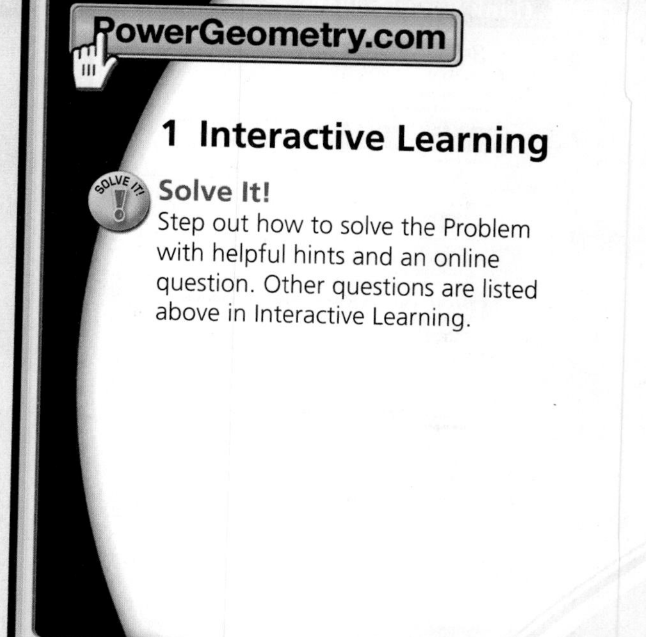

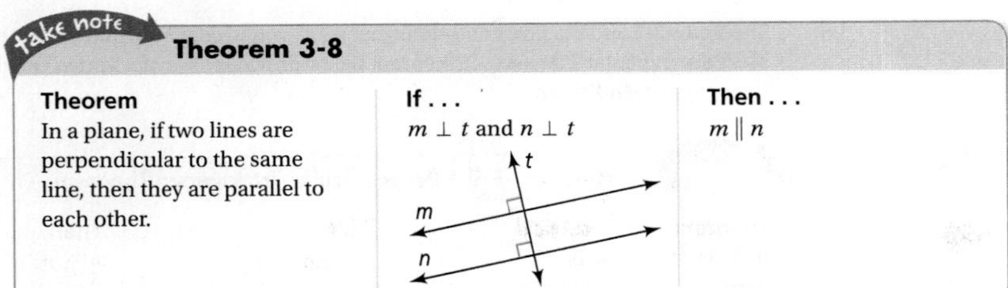

Notice that Theorem 3-8 includes the phrase *in a plane*. In Exercise 17, you will consider why this phrase is necessary.

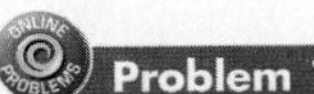

Proof of Theorem 3-8

Given: In a plane, $r \perp t$ and $s \perp t$.

Prove: $r \parallel s$

Proof: $\angle 1$ and $\angle 2$ are right angles by the definition of perpendicular. So, $\angle 1 \cong \angle 2$. Since corresponding angles are congruent, $r \parallel s$.

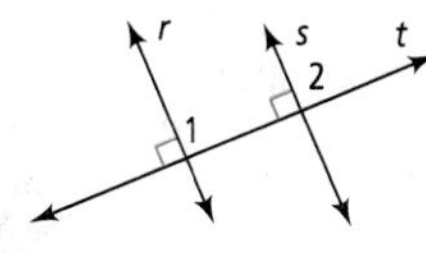

Problem 1 **Solving a Problem With Parallel Lines**

Carpentry **A carpenter plans to install molding on the sides and the top of a doorway. The carpenter cuts the ends of the top piece and one end of each of the side pieces at 45° angles as shown. Will the side pieces of molding be parallel? Explain.**

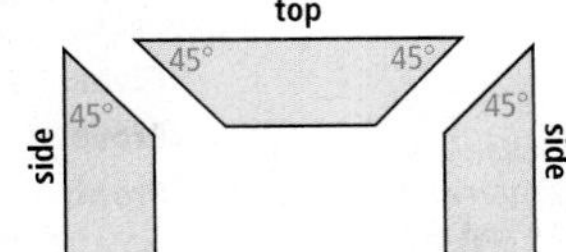

Know
The angles at the connecting ends are 45°.

Need
Determine whether the side pieces of molding are parallel.

Plan
Visualize fitting the pieces together to form new angles. Use information about the new angles to decide whether the sides are parallel.

Yes, the sides are parallel. When the pieces fit together, they form 45° + 45°, or 90°, angles. So, each side is perpendicular to the top. If two lines (the sides) are perpendicular to the same line (the top), then they are parallel to each other.

Got It? **1.** Can you assemble the pieces at the right to form a picture frame with opposite sides parallel? Explain.

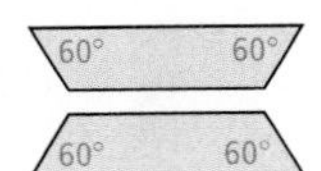

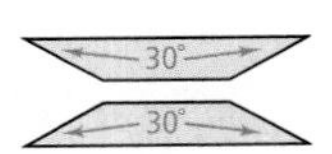

Take Note

Remind students of the definition of perpendicular lines prior to introducing this theorem.

Problem 1

Q When the three pieces of molding are put into place, what does the diagram look like? Label the measures of any angles known.

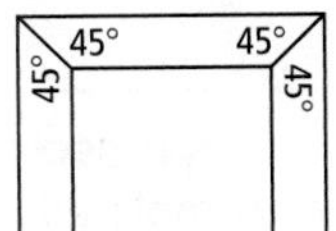

Q How can you show the angles formed on the outer sides of the doorway are right angles? **[A right angle measures 90. 45 + 45 = 90]**

Got It?

ERROR PREVENTION

Q Will it be enough to use Theorem 3-8 only one time when determining if the opposite sides are parallel? Explain. **[No, you will have to prove separately that each pair of opposite sides is parallel.]**

2 Guided Instruction

Each Problem is worked out and supported online.

Problem 1
Solving a Problem with Parallel Lines
Animated

Problem 2
Proving a Relationship Between Two Lines
Animated

Support in Geometry Companion

- Vocabulary
- Key Concepts
- Got It?

Answers

Solve It!

Oak Street and Court Road are ∥. The pairs of ≅ alt. int. ∠s show that both Oak Street and Court Road are ∥ to Schoolhouse Road.

Got It?

1. Yes; place the pieces with 60° ∠s opposite each other and place the pieces with 30° ∠s opposite each other. All four corners will be 90°, so opposite sides will be ∥.

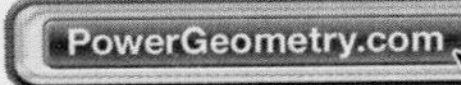

Take Note

VISUAL LEARNERS

Using a counterexample, demonstrate to students that the theorem is not true without the phrase "in a plane." Draw a pair of parallel lines on the chalkboard. At one point on one of the lines, hold a meter stick perpendicular to the chalkboard. Students should recognize that the meter stick is not perpendicular to both lines, because the three lines are not coplanar.

Problem 2

Q Is it possible to determine the measures of the other angles in the diagram prior to proving the relationship between the lines? Explain. **[Yes, you can determine the other measures by the definition of linear pairs and the Vertical Angles Theorem.]**

Q Which parallel lines must you use when planning the steps to this proof? **[lines *a* and *b*]**

Q Which line will you use as the transversal to use the Perpendicular Transversal Theorem with the lines named above? **[line *c*]**

Got It?

SYNTHESIZING

Point out to students that the proofs completed in Problem 2 and Got It can be used to define the characteristics of a rectangle: All four angles measure 90° and the opposite sides are parallel.

Theorems 3-7 and 3-8 give conditions that allow you to conclude that lines are parallel. The Perpendicular Transversal Theorem below provides a way for you to conclude that lines are perpendicular.

take note

Theorem 3-9 Perpendicular Transversal Theorem

Theorem	If . . .	Then . . .
In a plane, if a line is perpendicular to one of two parallel lines, then it is also perpendicular to the other.	$n \perp \ell$ and $\ell \parallel m$	$n \perp m$

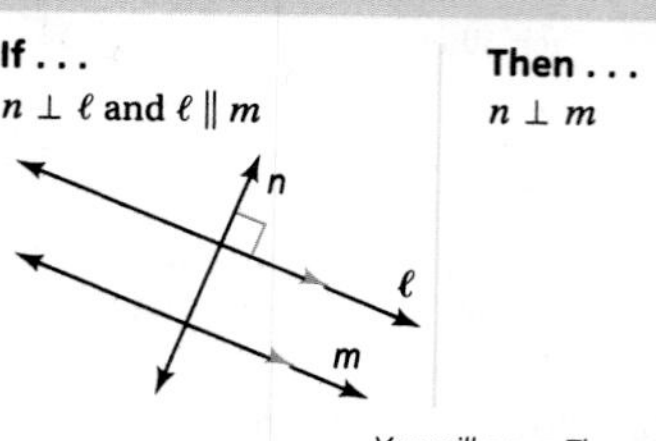

You will prove Theorem 3-9 in Exercise 10.

The Perpendicular Transversal Theorem states that the lines must be *in a plane.* The diagram at the right shows why. In the rectangular solid, $\overleftrightarrow{AC}$ and $\overleftrightarrow{BD}$ are parallel. $\overleftrightarrow{EC}$ is perpendicular to $\overleftrightarrow{AC}$, but it is not perpendicular to $\overleftrightarrow{BD}$. In fact, $\overleftrightarrow{EC}$ and $\overleftrightarrow{BD}$ are skew because they are not in the same plane.

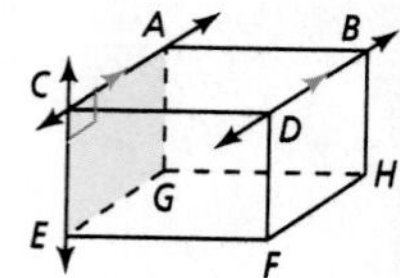

Proof

Problem 2 Proving a Relationship Between Two Lines

Think

Which line has a relationship to both lines *c* and *d*?

You know $c \perp b$ and $b \perp d$. So, line *b* relates to both lines *c* and *d*.

Given: In a plane, $c \perp b$, $b \perp d$, and $d \perp a$.

Prove: $c \perp a$

Proof: Lines *c* and *d* are both perpendicular to line *b*, so $c \parallel d$ because two lines perpendicular to the same line are parallel. It is given that $d \perp a$. Therefore, $c \perp a$ because a line that is perpendicular to one of two parallel lines is also perpendicular to the other (Perpendicular Transversal Theorem).

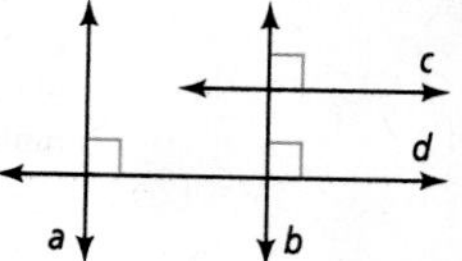

Got It? **2.** In Problem 2, could you also conclude $a \parallel b$? Explain.

Additional Problems

1. What is the relationship between segments *AB* and *CD*? Explain.

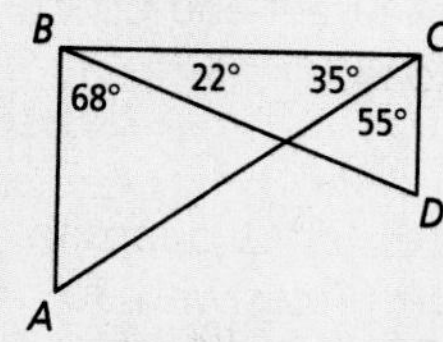

ANSWER They are parallel, because they are both perpendicular to $\overline{BC}$.

2. In a plane, $c \perp b$, $b \perp d$, and $d \perp a$. Prove that $c \parallel d$.

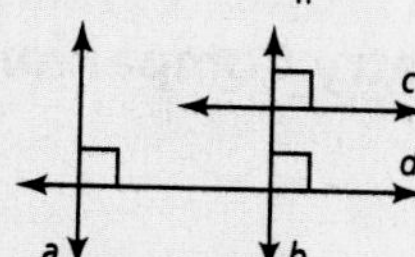

ANSWER Because $c \perp b$, the lines form right angles. Also, because $b \perp d$, those lines form right angles. So, there are corresponding congruent angles where *c* intersects *b* and where *d* intersects *b*. Therefore, $c \parallel d$ by Theorem 3-8.

Answers

Got It? (continued)

2. Yes: $a \parallel b$ because they are both $\perp$ to *d*, and in a plane, two lines $\perp$ to the same line are $\parallel$.

Lesson Check

Do you know HOW?

1. Main Street intersects Avenue A and Avenue B. Avenue A is parallel to Avenue B. Avenue A is also perpendicular to Main Street. How are Avenue B and Main Street related? Explain.

2. In the diagram below, lines a, b, and c are coplanar. What conclusion can you make about lines a and b? Explain.

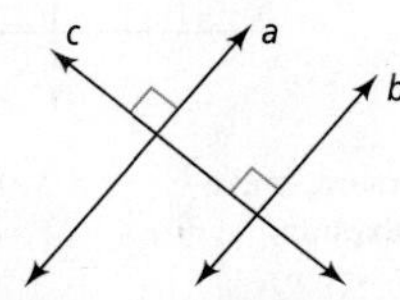

c
a
b

Do you UNDERSTAND?

3. Explain why the phrase *in a plane* is not necessary in Theorem 3-7.

4. Which theorem or postulate from earlier in the chapter supports the conclusion in Theorem 3-8? In the Perpendicular Transversal Theorem? Explain.

5. **Error Analysis** Shiro sketched coplanar lines m, n, and r on his homework paper. He claims that it shows that lines m and n are parallel. What other information do you need about line r in order for Shiro's claim to be true? Explain.

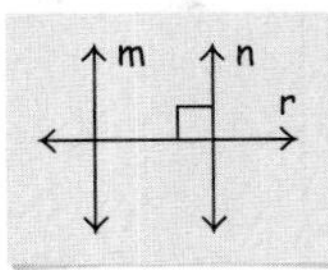

m
n
r

Practice and Problem-Solving Exercises

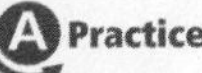

Practice

See Problem 1.

6. A carpenter is building a trellis for vines to grow on. The completed trellis will have two sets of diagonal pieces of wood that overlap each other.
   a. If pieces A, B, and C must be parallel, what must be true of $\angle 1$, $\angle 2$, and $\angle 3$?
   b. The carpenter attaches piece D so that it is perpendicular to piece A. If your answer to part (a) is true, is piece D perpendicular to pieces B and C? Justify your answer.

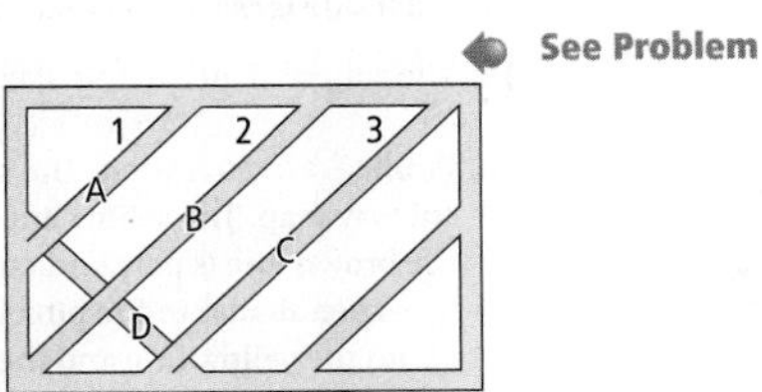

1
2
3
A
B
C
D

See Problem 2.

7. **Developing Proof** Copy and complete this paragraph proof of Theorem 3-7 for three coplanar lines.

   Given: $\ell \parallel k$ and $m \parallel k$

   Prove: $\ell \parallel m$

   Proof: Since $\ell \parallel k$, $\angle 2 \cong \angle 1$ by the **a.** __?__ Postulate. Since $m \parallel k$, **b.** __?__ $\cong$ **c.** __?__ for the same reason. By the Transitive Property of Congruence, $\angle 2 \cong \angle 3$. By the **d.** __?__ Postulate, $\ell \parallel m$.

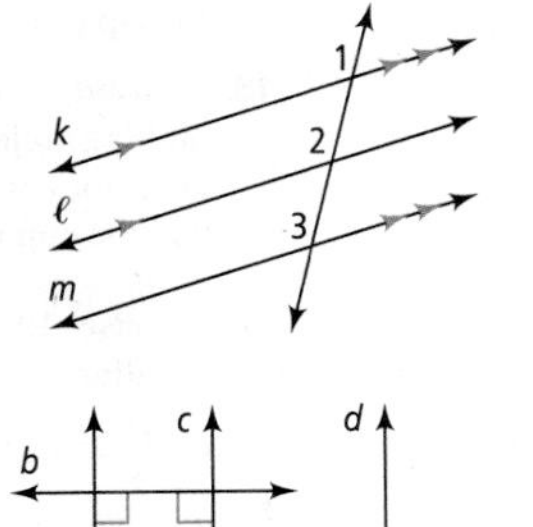

1
2
3
k
ℓ
m

8. Write a paragraph proof.
   Proof
   Given: In a plane, $a \perp b$, $b \perp c$, and $c \parallel d$.
   Prove: $a \parallel d$

3 Lesson Check

Do you know HOW?

- If students have difficulty with Exercise 1, then encourage them to make a sketch and label all given angles to represent the information provided in the question.

Do you UNDERSTAND?

- If students have difficulty with Exercise 3, then have them try to find a counterexample using a line not in the same plane.

Close

Q What methods introduced in this lesson can be used to prove that two lines are parallel? **[If two lines are parallel to the same line or if two lines are perpendicular to the same line, then they are parallel to each other.]**

Lesson Check

1. They are $\perp$; using Main Street as a transversal, Avenue B $\perp$ Main Street by Thm. 3-9.
2. $a \parallel b$; in a plane, if two lines are $\perp$ to the same line, then they are $\parallel$.
3. Sample: Even if the 3 lines are not in the same plane, each line is parallel to the other 2 lines.
4. Thm. 3-8 uses the Converse of the Corresp. ∠s Post.; the $\perp$ Trans. Thm. uses the Corresp. ∠s Post.
5. The diagram should show that m and r are $\perp$.

Practice and Problem-Solving Exercises

6a. $\angle 1 \cong \angle 2 \cong \angle 3$

b. Yes; pieces B and C are $\parallel$, and if a line is $\perp$ to one of several $\parallel$ lines, it is $\perp$ to all of the $\parallel$ lines.

7a. corresp. ∠s

b. $\angle 1$

c. $\angle 3$

d. Converse of Corresp. ∠s Post.

8. Since a and c are both $\perp$ to b, then $a \parallel c$ because, in a plane, if two lines are $\perp$ to the same line, they are $\parallel$. It is given that $c \parallel d$, so $a \parallel d$ because, if two lines are $\parallel$ to the same line, they are $\parallel$.

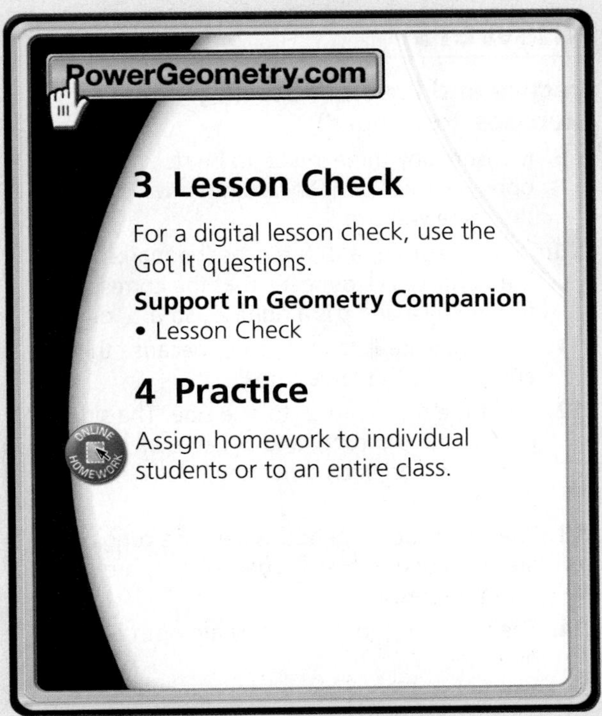

PowerGeometry.com
3 Lesson Check
For a digital lesson check, use the Got It questions.
Support in Geometry Companion
• Lesson Check
4 Practice
Assign homework to individual students or to an entire class.

4 Practice

ASSIGNMENT GUIDE

Basic: 6–8 all, 9, 12–16 even, 17–18
Average: 6–18
Advanced: 6–26
Standardized Test Prep: 27–30
Mixed Review: 31–39
Reasoning exercises have blue headings.
Applications exercises have red headings.
EXERCISE 18: Use the Think About a Plan worksheet in the **Practice and Problem Solving Workbook** (also available in the Teaching Resources in print and online) to further support students' development in becoming independent learners.

HOMEWORK QUICK CHECK

To check students' understanding of key skills and concepts, go over Exercises 6, 8, 9, 17, and 18.

Apply

9. Think About a Plan One traditional type of log cabin is a single rectangular room. Suppose you begin building a log cabin by placing four logs in the shape of a rectangle. What should you measure to guarantee that the logs on opposite walls are parallel? Explain.
- What type of information do you need to prove lines parallel?
- How can you use a diagram to help you?
- What do you know about the angles of the geometric shape?

10. Proof Prove the Perpendicular Transversal Theorem (Theorem 3-9): In a plane, if a line is perpendicular to one of two parallel lines, then it is also perpendicular to the other.

Given: In a plane, $a \perp b$ and $b \parallel c$.
Prove: $a \perp c$

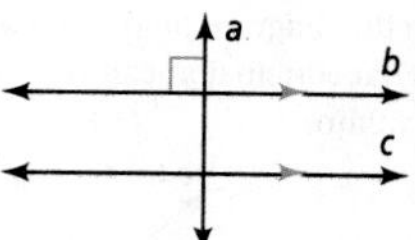

The following statements describe a ladder. Based only on the statement, make a conclusion about the rungs, one side, or both sides of the ladder. Explain.

11. The rungs are each perpendicular to one side.
12. The rungs are parallel and the top rung is perpendicular to one side.
13. The sides are parallel. The rungs are perpendicular to one side.
14. Each side is perpendicular to the top rung.
15. The rungs are perpendicular to one side. The sides are not parallel.

16. Public Transportation The map at the right is a section of a subway map. The yellow line is perpendicular to the brown line, the brown line is perpendicular to the blue line, and the blue line is perpendicular to the pink line. What conclusion can you make about the yellow line and the pink line? Explain.

17. Writing Theorem 3-8 states that in a plane, two lines perpendicular to the same line are parallel. Explain why the phrase *in a plane* is needed. (*Hint:* Refer to a rectangular solid to help you visualize the situation.)

18. Quilting You plan to sew two triangles of fabric together to make a square for a quilting project. The triangles are both right triangles and have the same side and angle measures. What must also be true about the triangles in order to guarantee that the opposite sides of the fabric square are parallel? Explain.

Challenge

For Exercises 19–24, *a*, *b*, *c*, and *d* are distinct lines in the same plane. For each combination of relationships, tell how *a* and *d* relate. Justify your answer.

19. $a \parallel b, b \parallel c, c \parallel d$
20. $a \parallel b, b \parallel c, c \perp d$
21. $a \parallel b, b \perp c, c \parallel d$
22. $a \perp b, b \parallel c, c \parallel d$
23. $a \parallel b, b \perp c, c \perp d$
24. $a \perp b, b \parallel c, c \perp d$

Answers

Practice and Problem-Solving Exercises (continued)

9. Measure any three int. ∠s to be rt. ∠s and opp. walls will be ∥ because two walls ⊥ to the same wall are ∥.
10. In the diagram, $a \perp b$ means the marked ∠ is a right ∠. $b \parallel c$ means that the corresp. ∠ formed by a and c is a right ∠, so $a \perp c$.
11. The rungs are ∥ to each other because they are all ⊥ to the same side.
12. All of the rungs are ⊥ to one side. The side is ⊥ to the top rung, and because all of the rungs are ∥ to each other, the side is ⊥ to all of the rungs.
13. The rungs are ⊥ to both sides. The rungs are ⊥ to one of two ∥ sides, so they are ⊥ to both sides.
14. The sides are ∥ because they are both ⊥ to one rung.
15. The rungs are ∥ because they are all ⊥ to one side.
16. They are ⊥; answers may vary. Sample: The yellow and blue lines are ∥ because they are both ⊥ to the brown line. Since the pink line is ⊥ to one of those two ∥ lines, it must also be ⊥ to the other.
17. Sample: Using the diagram underneath Thm. 3-9, $\overleftrightarrow{EC}$ and $\overleftrightarrow{AB}$ are both ⊥ to $\overleftrightarrow{AC}$, but $\overleftrightarrow{EC}$ and $\overleftrightarrow{AB}$ are skew, so they cannot be ∥.
18. The rt. ∆s must have acute ∠s that measure 45.
19. $a \parallel d$ by Thm. 3-7
20. $a \perp d$ by Thms. 3-7 and 3-9
21. $a \perp d$ by Thm. 3-9
22. $a \perp d$ by Thm. 3-9
23. $a \parallel d$ by Thms. 3-7 and 3-8
24. $a \parallel d$ by Thms. 3-8 and 3-9

25. Reasoning Review the reflexive, symmetric, and transitive properties for congruence in Lesson 2-5. Write reflexive, symmetric, and transitive statements for "is parallel to" ($\|$). Tell whether each statement is *true* or *false*. Justify your answer.

26. Reasoning Repeat Exercise 25 for "is perpendicular to" ($\perp$).

Standardized Test Prep

SAT/ACT

27. In a plane, line e is parallel to line f, line f is parallel to line g, and line h is perpendicular to line e. Which of the following MUST be true?

Ⓐ $e \| g$ Ⓑ $h \| f$ Ⓒ $g \| h$ Ⓓ $e \| h$

28. Which point lies nearest to (5, 2) in the coordinate plane?

Ⓕ $(-1, 3)$ Ⓖ $(0, -2)$ Ⓗ $(4, -5)$ Ⓘ $(4, 10)$

29. Which of the following is NOT a reason for proving two lines parallel.

Ⓐ The lines are both $\perp$ to the same line.
Ⓑ Corresponding angles are congruent.
Ⓒ Vertical angles are congruent.
Ⓓ The lines are both $\|$ to the same line.

Short Response

30. The diameter of a circle is the same length as the side of a square. The perimeter of the square is 16 cm. Find the diameter of the circle. Then find the circumference of the circle in terms of π.

Mixed Review

Algebra Determine the value of x for which $a \| b$.

See Lesson 3-3.

31.

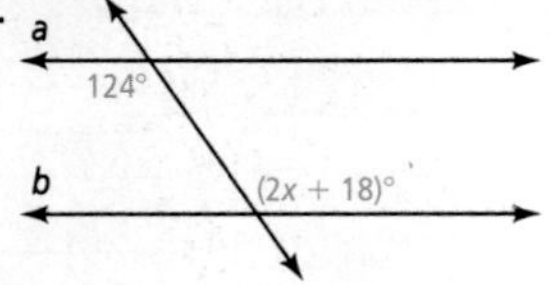

32.

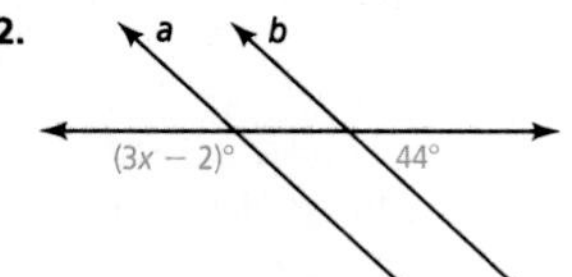

Use a protractor. Classify each angle as *acute*, *right*, or *obtuse*.

See Lesson 1-4.

33.

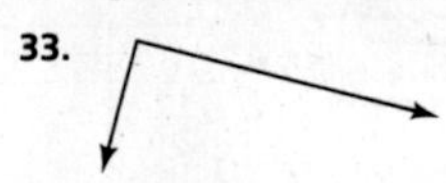

34.

35.

Get Ready! **To prepare for Lesson 3-5, do Exercises 36–39.**

Solve each equation.

See p. 834.

36. $30 + 90 + x = 180$

37. $55 + x + 105 = 180$

38. $x + 50 = 90$

39. $32 + x = 90$

25. Reflexive: $a \| a$; false; every line intersects itself. Symmetric: If $a \| b$ then $b \| a$; true; lines a and b are coplanar and do not meet. Transitive: If $a \| b$ and $b \| c$, then $a \| c$; true; that is Thm. 3-7.

flexive: $a \perp a$; false; a line does intersect itself at a rt. ∠. etric: If $a \perp b$, then $b \perp a$; es a and b form rt. ∠s. : If $a \perp b$ and $b \perp c$, then e; if a and c are both $\perp$ to c or a and c are skew.

F **29.** C

30. [2] The perimeter of the square is 16 cm so each side is 4 cm. That is the same as the diameter of the circle, so using the formula $C = \pi d$, you get 4π cm for the circumference.

[1] correct diameter, but incorrect circumference

31. 53 **32.** 46 **33.** right
34. obtuse **35.** acute **36.** 60
37. 20 **38.** 40 **39.** 58

3-4 Lesson Resources

Differentiated Remediation

Instructional Support

Geometry Companion

Students can use the **Geometry Companion** worktext (4 pages) . . .

- New Vocabulary
- Key Concepts
- Got It for each Problem
- Lesson Check

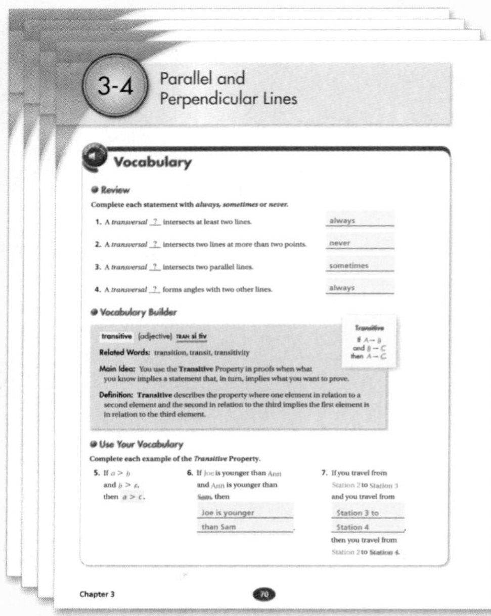
3-4 Parallel and Perpendicular Lines

Vocabulary

Review

Complete each statement with *always, sometimes* or *never.*

1. A *transversal* _?_ intersects at least two lines. always
2. A *transversal* _?_ intersects two lines at more than two points. never
3. A *transversal* _?_ intersects two parallel lines. sometimes
4. A *transversal* _?_ forms angles with two other lines. always

Vocabulary Builder

transitive (adjective) TRAN si tiv

Transitive: If A → B and B → C then A → C

Related Words: transition, transit, transitivity

Main Idea: You use the **Transitive** Property in proofs when what you know implies a statement that, in turn, implies what you want to prove.

Definition: Transitive describes the property where one element in relation to a second element and the second in relation to the third implies the first element is in relation to the third element.

Use Your Vocabulary

Complete each example of the *Transitive* Property.

5. If $a > b$ and $b > c$, then $a > c$.
6. If Joe is younger than Ann and Ann is younger than Sam, then Joe is younger than Sam.
7. If you travel from Station 2 to Station 3 and you travel from Station 3 to Station 4, then you travel from Station 2 to Station 4.

Chapter 3 70

ELL Support

Use Graphic Organizers Have groups of students make a poster about parallel and perpendicular lines. Say: Show right angles and intersections on your poster. Explain what *parallel* and *perpendicular* mean. Tell how you can prove lines are parallel or perpendicular. Have students draw or collect pictures to illustrate their posters. Have them use familiar language as well as appropriate mathematical terms.

Have each group explain its poster to another group. Then allow the groups to add to their posters or change them to include what they learned from the other group. Have each student in the group copy his or her own version of the poster onto a page to be kept in his or her chapter notebook.

5 Assess & Remediate

Lesson Quiz

1. What value of x results in $\overline{AB} \parallel \overline{CD}$?

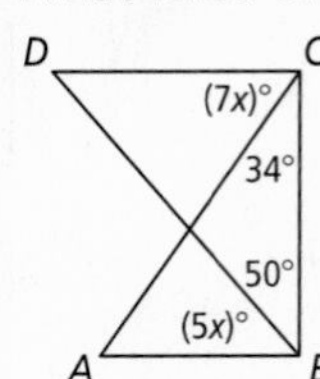
D
C
(7x)°
34°
50°
(5x)°
A
B

2. In a plane, if $\ell \perp n$ and $\ell \parallel m$, prove that $m \perp n$.

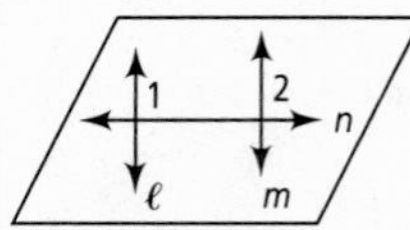
1
2
n
ℓ
m

3. **Do you UNDERSTAND?** A fly and an ant are sitting in the middle of a floor. If the fly starts moving along a straight path of his choice, will the ant be able to move along a parallel path?

ANSWERS TO LESSON QUIZ

1. 8
2. Since $\ell \parallel m$, $\angle 1 \cong \angle 2$ because they are corresponding angles. $m\angle 1 = m\angle 2$ by definition of congruent angles. Because $\angle 1$ is a right angle, $m\angle 1 = 90$. By substitution, $m\angle 2 = 90$. By definition of right angles, $\angle 2$ is a right angle. So, by the definition of perpendicular lines, $m \perp n$.
3. Not necessarily; if the fly's path goes straight up, for instance, the ant cannot move in a parallel path.

PRECRIPTION FOR REMEDIATION

Use the student work on the Lesson Quiz to prescribe a differentiated review assignment.

Points	Differentiated Remediation
0–1	Intervention
2	On-level
3	Extension

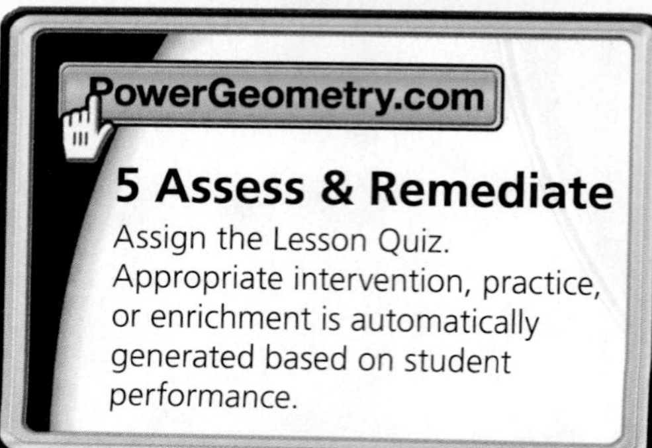
PowerGeometry.com
5 Assess & Remediate
Assign the Lesson Quiz.
Appropriate intervention, practice, or enrichment is automatically generated based on student performance.

Intervention

- **Reteaching** (2 pages) Provides reteaching and practice exercises for the key lesson concepts. Use with struggling students or absent students.
- **English Language Learner Support** Helps students develop and reinforce mathematical vocabulary and key concepts.

All-in-One Resources/Online

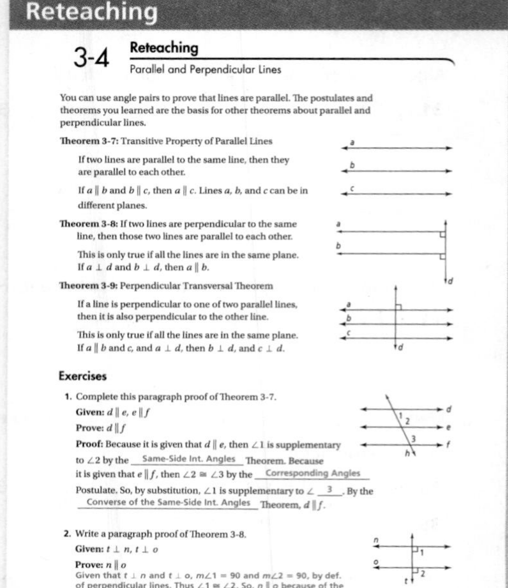
Reteaching

3-4 **Reteaching**
Parallel and Perpendicular Lines

You can use angle pairs to prove that lines are parallel. The postulates and theorems you learned are the basis for other theorems about parallel and perpendicular lines.

Theorem 3-7: Transitive Property of Parallel Lines

If two lines are parallel to the same line, then they are parallel to each other.

If $a \parallel b$ and $b \parallel c$, then $a \parallel c$. Lines a, b, and c can be in different planes.

Theorem 3-8: If two lines are perpendicular to the same line, then those two lines are parallel to each other.

This is only true if all the lines are in the same plane. If $a \perp d$ and $b \perp d$, then $a \parallel b$.

Theorem 3-9: Perpendicular Transversal Theorem

If a line is perpendicular to one of two parallel lines, then it is also perpendicular to the other line.

This is only true if all the lines are in the same plane. If $a \parallel b$ and c, and $a \perp d$, then $b \perp d$, and $c \perp d$.

Exercises

1. Complete this paragraph proof of Theorem 3-7.
   Given: $d \parallel e$, $e \parallel f$
   Prove: $d \parallel f$
   Proof: Because it is given that $d \parallel e$, then $\angle 1$ is supplementary to $\angle 2$ by the Same-Side Int. Angles Theorem. Because it is given that $e \parallel f$, then $\angle 2 \cong \angle 3$ by the Corresponding Angles Postulate. So, by substitution, $\angle 1$ is supplementary to $\angle$ 3. By the Converse of the Same-Side Int. Angles Theorem, $d \parallel f$.

2. Write a paragraph proof of Theorem 3-8.
   Given: $t \perp n$, $t \perp o$
   Prove: $n \parallel o$
   Given that $t \perp n$ and $t \perp o$, $m\angle 1 = 90$ and $m\angle 2 = 90$, by def. of perpendicular lines. Thus $\angle 1 \cong \angle 2$. So, $n \parallel o$ because of the Converse of the Corr. ∠s Post.

All-in-One Resources/Online

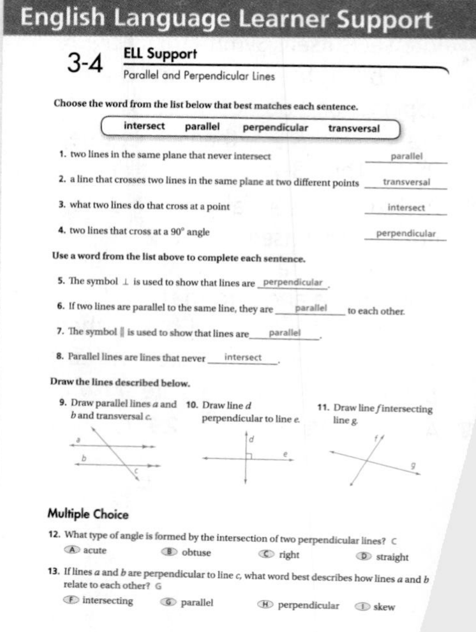
English Language Learner Support

3-4 **ELL Support**
Parallel and Perpendicular Lines

Choose the word from the list below that best matches each sentence.

intersect parallel perpendicular transversal

1. two lines in the same plane that never intersect parallel
2. a line that crosses two lines in the same plane at two different points transversal
3. what two lines do that cross at a point intersect
4. two lines that cross at a 90° angle perpendicular

Use a word from the list above to complete each sentence.

5. The symbol ⊥ is used to show that lines are perpendicular.
6. If two lines are parallel to the same line, they are parallel to each other.
7. The symbol ∥ is used to show that lines are parallel.
8. Parallel lines are lines that never intersect.

Draw the lines described below.

9. Draw parallel lines a and b and transversal c.
10. Draw line d perpendicular to line e.
11. Draw line f intersecting line g.

Multiple Choice

12. What type of angle is formed by the intersection of two perpendicular lines? C
    Ⓐ acute Ⓑ obtuse Ⓒ right Ⓓ straight
13. If lines a and b are perpendicular to line c, what word best describes how lines a and b relate to each other? G
    Ⓕ intersecting Ⓖ parallel Ⓗ perpendicular Ⓘ skew

Differentiated Remediation *continued*

On-Level

- **Practice** (2 pages) Provides extra practice for each lesson. For simpler practice exercises, use the Form K Practice pages found in the All-in-One Teaching Resources and online.
- **Think About a Plan** Helps students develop specific problem-solving skills and strategies by providing scaffolded guiding questions.
- **Standardized Test Prep** Focuses on all major exercises, all major question types, and helps students prepare for the high-stakes assessments.

Extension

- **Enrichment** Provides students with interesting problems and activities that extend the concepts of the lesson.
- **Activities, Games, and Puzzles** Worksheets that can be used for concepts development, enrichment, and for fun!

Practice and Problem Solving Wkbk/ All-in-One Resources/Online

Practice page 1

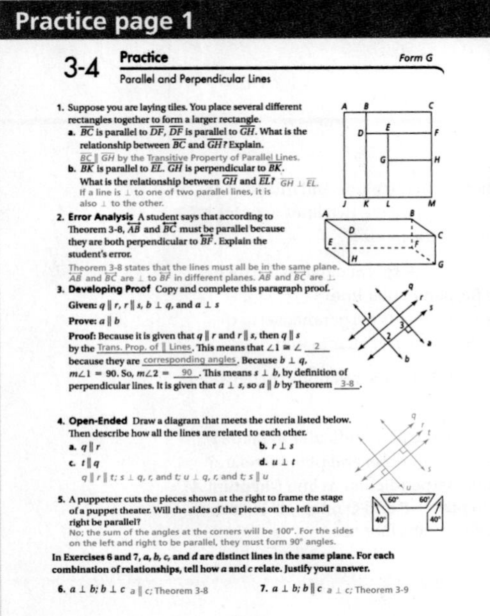

3-4 Practice — Form G
Parallel and Perpendicular Lines

1. Suppose you are laying tiles. You place several different rectangles together to form a larger rectangle.
 a. $\overline{BC}$ is parallel to $\overline{DF}$, $\overline{DF}$ is parallel to $\overline{GH}$. What is the relationship between $\overline{BC}$ and $\overline{GH}$? Explain. $\overline{BC} \parallel \overline{GH}$ by the Transitive Property of Parallel Lines.
 b. $\overline{BK}$ is parallel to $\overline{EL}$. $\overline{GH}$ is perpendicular to $\overline{BK}$. What is the relationship between $\overline{GH}$ and $\overline{EL}$? Explain. $\overline{GH} \perp \overline{EL}$. If a line is $\perp$ to one of two parallel lines, it is also $\perp$ to the other.
2. **Error Analysis** A student says that according to Theorem 3-8, $\overline{AB}$ and $\overline{BC}$ must be parallel because they are both perpendicular to $\overline{BF}$. Explain the student's error. Theorem 3-8 states that the lines must all be in the same plane. $\overline{AB}$ and $\overline{BC}$ are $\perp$ to $\overline{BF}$ in different planes. $\overline{AB}$ and $\overline{BC}$ are $\perp$.
3. **Developing Proof** Copy and complete this paragraph proof.
 Given: $q \parallel r$, $r \parallel s$, $b \perp q$, and $a \perp s$
 Prove: $a \parallel b$
 Proof: Because it is given that $q \parallel r$ and $r \parallel s$, then $q \parallel s$ by the Trans. Prop. of $\parallel$ Lines. This means that $\angle 1 \cong \angle$ 2 because they are corresponding angles. Because $b \perp q$, $m\angle 1 = 90$. So, $m\angle 2 =$ 90. This means $s \perp b$, by definition of perpendicular lines. It is given that $a \perp s$, so $a \parallel b$ by Theorem 3-8.
4. **Open-Ended** Draw a diagram that meets the criteria listed below. Then describe how all the lines are related to each other.
 a. $q \parallel r$ b. $r \perp s$
 c. $t \parallel q$ d. $u \perp t$
 $q \parallel r \parallel t$; $s \perp q$, r, and t; $u \perp q$, r, and t; $s \parallel u$
5. A puppeteer cuts the pieces shown at the right to frame the stage of a puppet theater. Will the sides of the pieces on the left and right be parallel? No; the sum of the angles at the corners will be 100°. For the sides on the left and right to be parallel, they must form 90° angles.

In Exercises 6 and 7, a, b, c, and d are distinct lines in the same plane. For each combination of relationships, tell how a and c relate. Justify your answer.

6. $a \perp b$; $b \perp c$ $a \parallel c$; Theorem 3-8
7. $a \perp b$; $b \parallel c$ $a \perp c$; Theorem 3-9

Practice and Problem Solving Wkbk/ All-in-One Resources/Online

Practice page 2

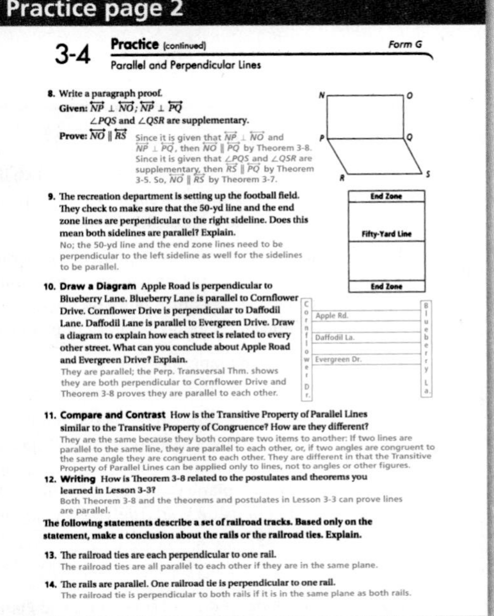

3-4 Practice (continued) — Form G
Parallel and Perpendicular Lines

8. Write a paragraph proof.
 Given: $\overline{NP} \perp \overline{NO}$; $\overline{NP} \perp \overline{PQ}$; $\angle PQS$ and $\angle QSR$ are supplementary.
 Prove: $\overline{NO} \parallel \overline{RS}$
 Since it is given that $\overline{NP} \perp \overline{NO}$ and $\overline{NP} \perp \overline{PQ}$, then $\overline{NO} \parallel \overline{PQ}$ by Theorem 3-8. Since it is given that $\angle PQS$ and $\angle QSR$ are supplementary, then $\overline{RS} \parallel \overline{PQ}$ by Theorem 3-5. So, $\overline{NO} \parallel \overline{RS}$ by Theorem 3-7.
9. The recreation department is setting up the football field. They check to make sure that the 50-yd line and the end zone lines are perpendicular to the right sideline. Does this mean both sidelines are parallel? Explain. No; the 50-yd line and the end zone lines need to be perpendicular to the left sideline as well for the sidelines to be parallel.
10. **Draw a Diagram** Apple Road is perpendicular to Blueberry Lane. Blueberry Lane is parallel to Cornflower Drive. Cornflower Drive is perpendicular to Daffodil Lane. Daffodil Lane is parallel to Evergreen Drive. Draw a diagram to explain how each street is related to every other street. What can you conclude about Apple Road and Evergreen Drive? Explain. They are parallel; the Perp. Transversal Thm. shows they are both perpendicular to Cornflower Drive and Theorem 3-8 proves they are parallel to each other.
11. **Compare and Contrast** How is the Transitive Property of Parallel Lines similar to the Transitive Property of Congruence? How are they different? They are the same because they both compare two items to another: If two lines are parallel to the same line, they are parallel to each other, or, if two angles are congruent to the same angle they are congruent to each other. They are different in that the Transitive Property of Parallel Lines can be applied only to lines, not to angles or other figures.
12. **Writing** How is Theorem 3-8 related to the postulates and theorems you learned in Lesson 3-3? Both Theorem 3-8 and the theorems and postulates in Lesson 3-3 can prove lines are parallel.

The following statements describe a set of railroad tracks. Based only on the statement, make a conclusion about the rails or the railroad ties. Explain.

13. The railroad ties are each perpendicular to one rail. The railroad ties are all parallel to each other if they are in the same plane.
14. The rails are parallel. One railroad tie is perpendicular to one rail. The railroad tie is perpendicular to both rails if it is in the same plane as both rails.

All-in-One Resources/Online

Enrichment

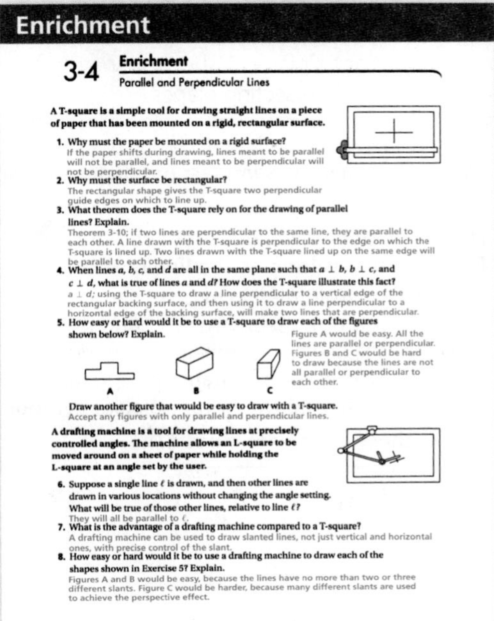

3-4 Enrichment
Parallel and Perpendicular Lines

A T-square is a simple tool for drawing straight lines on a piece of paper that has been mounted on a rigid, rectangular surface.

1. Why must the paper be mounted on a rigid surface? If the paper shifts during drawing, lines meant to be parallel will not be parallel, and lines meant to be perpendicular will not be perpendicular.
2. Why must the surface be rectangular? The rectangular shape gives the T-square two perpendicular guide edges on which to line up.
3. What theorem does the T-square rely on for the drawing of parallel lines? Explain. Theorem 3-10; if two lines are perpendicular to the same line, they are parallel to each other. A line drawn with the T-square is perpendicular to the edge on which the T-square is lined up. Two lines drawn with the T-square lined up on the same edge will be parallel to each other.
4. When lines a, b, c, and d are all in the same plane such that $a \perp b$, $b \perp c$, and $c \perp d$, what is true of lines a and d? How does the T-square illustrate this fact? $a \perp d$; using the T-square to draw a line perpendicular to a vertical edge of the rectangular backing surface, and then using it to draw a line perpendicular to a horizontal edge of the backing surface, will make two lines that are perpendicular.
5. How easy or hard would it be to use a T-square to draw each of the figures shown below? Explain. Figure A would be easy. All the lines are parallel or perpendicular. Figures B and C would be hard to draw because the lines are not all parallel or perpendicular to each other.

Draw another figure that would be easy to draw with a T-square. Accept any figures with only parallel and perpendicular lines.

A drafting machine is a tool for drawing lines at precisely controlled angles. The machine allows an L-square to be moved around on a sheet of paper while holding the L-square at an angle set by the user.

6. Suppose a single line ℓ is drawn, and then other lines are drawn in various locations without changing the angle setting. What will be true of those other lines, relative to line ℓ? They will all be parallel to ℓ.
7. What is the advantage of a drafting machine compared to a T-square? A drafting machine can be used to draw slanted lines, not just vertical and horizontal ones, with precise control of the slant.
8. How easy or hard would it be to use a drafting machine to draw each of the shapes shown in Exercise 5? Explain. Figures A and B would be easy, because the lines have no more than two or three different slants. Figure C would be harder, because many different slants are used to achieve the perspective effect.

Practice and Problem Solving Wkbk/ All-in-One Resources/Online

Think About a Plan

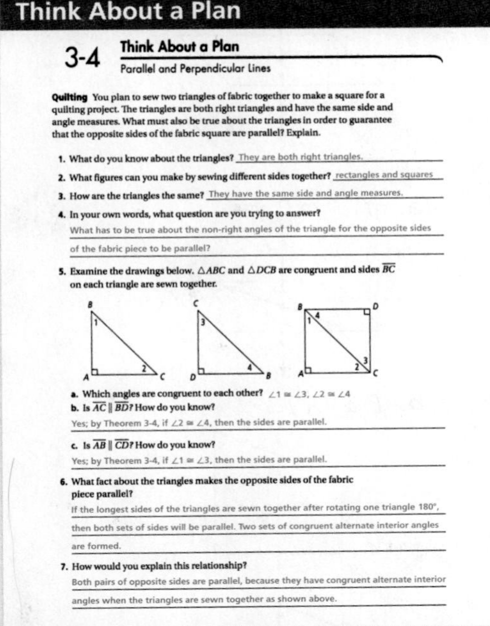

3-4 Think About a Plan
Parallel and Perpendicular Lines

Quilting You plan to sew two triangles of fabric together to make a square for a quilting project. The triangles are both right triangles and have the same side and angle measures. What must also be true about the triangles in order to guarantee that the opposite sides of the fabric square are parallel? Explain.

1. What do you know about the triangles? They are both right triangles.
2. What figures can you make by sewing different sides together? rectangles and squares
3. How are the triangles the same? They have the same side and angle measures.
4. In your own words, what question are you trying to answer? What has to be true about the non-right angles of the triangle for the opposite sides of the fabric piece to be parallel?
5. Examine the drawings below. $\triangle ABC$ and $\triangle DCB$ are congruent and sides $\overline{BC}$ on each triangle are sewn together.
 a. Which angles are congruent to each other? $\angle 1 \cong \angle 3$, $\angle 2 \cong \angle 4$
 b. Is $\overline{AC} \parallel \overline{BD}$? How do you know? Yes; by Theorem 3-4, if $\angle 2 \cong \angle 4$, then the sides are parallel.
 c. Is $\overline{AB} \parallel \overline{CD}$? How do you know? Yes; by Theorem 3-4, if $\angle 1 \cong \angle 3$, then the sides are parallel.
6. What fact about the triangles makes the opposite sides of the fabric piece parallel? If the longest sides of the triangles are sewn together after rotating one triangle 180°, then both sets of sides will be parallel. Two sets of congruent alternate interior angles are formed.
7. How would you explain this relationship? Both pairs of opposite sides are parallel, because they have congruent alternate interior angles when the triangles are sewn together as shown above.

Practice and Problem Solving Wkbk/ All-in-One Resources/Online

Standardized Test Prep

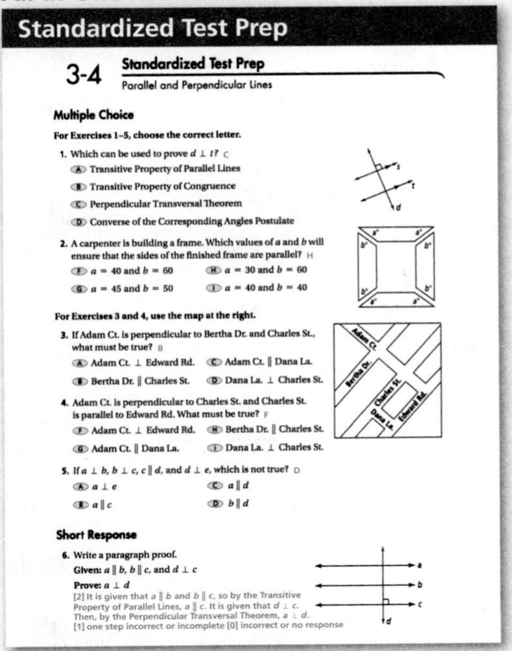

3-4 Standardized Test Prep
Parallel and Perpendicular Lines

Multiple Choice

For Exercises 1–5, choose the correct letter.

1. Which can be used to prove $d \perp t$? C
 A Transitive Property of Parallel Lines
 B Transitive Property of Congruence
 C Perpendicular Transversal Theorem
 D Converse of the Corresponding Angles Postulate
2. A carpenter is building a frame. Which values of a and b will ensure that the sides of the finished frame are parallel? H
 F $a = 40$ and $b = 60$ H $a = 30$ and $b = 60$
 G $a = 45$ and $b = 50$ I $a = 40$ and $b = 40$

For Exercises 3 and 4, use the map at the right.

3. If Adam Ct. is perpendicular to Bertha Dr. and Charles St., what must be true? B
 A Adam Ct. $\perp$ Edward Rd. C Adam Ct. $\parallel$ Dana La.
 B Bertha Dr. $\parallel$ Charles St. D Dana La. $\perp$ Charles St.
4. Adam Ct. is perpendicular to Charles St. and Charles St. is parallel to Edward Rd. What must be true? F
 F Adam Ct. $\perp$ Edward Rd. H Bertha Dr. $\parallel$ Charles St.
 G Adam Ct. $\parallel$ Dana La. I Dana La. $\perp$ Charles St.
5. If $a \perp b$, $b \perp c$, $c \parallel d$, and $d \perp e$, which is not true? D
 A $a \perp e$ C $a \parallel d$
 B $a \parallel c$ D $b \parallel d$

Short Response

6. Write a paragraph proof.
 Given: $a \parallel b$, $b \parallel c$, and $d \perp c$
 Prove: $a \perp d$
 [2] It is given that $a \parallel b$ and $b \parallel c$, so by the Transitive Property of Parallel Lines, $a \parallel c$. It is given that $d \perp c$. Then, by the Perpendicular Transversal Theorem, $a \perp d$.
 [1] one step incorrect or incomplete [0] incorrect or no response

Online Teacher Resource Center

Activities, Games, and Puzzles

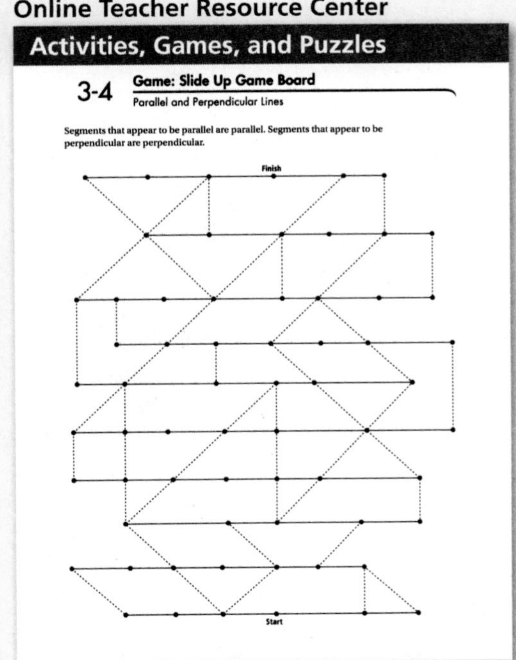

3-4 Game: Slide Up Game Board
Parallel and Perpendicular Lines

Segments that appear to be parallel are parallel. Segments that appear to be perpendicular are perpendicular.

Guided Instruction

PURPOSE To make discoveries about the relationships of perpendicular planes and lines contained in those planes

PROCESS Students will
- discover that perpendicular planes intersect in a line.
- sketch specific planes and lines and draw conclusions about their relationships based upon the sketches.

DISCUSS Students will further explore how perpendicular planes intersect in a line by drawing specific examples of planes, points, and lines in space.

Activity

VISUAL LEARNERS

Provide students with physical objects that can be used to illustrate points, lines, and planes—for example, marbles to represent points, a piece of string or yarn to represent a line, and a sheet of paper or a poster board to represent a plane. A shoebox shows a good representation of intersecting planes.

Q What shape will you draw to represent plane *A*? **[Answers will vary. Samples: parallelogram or rectangle]**

Q Does it matter where in plane *A* you draw $\overleftrightarrow{CD}$? Explain. **[No, as long as the line is entirely contained within plane *A*.]**

Q How can you draw segments through points *C* and *D* so that the segments appear perpendicular to plane *A*? **[Draw the segments to appear vertical. You could also add the perpendicular symbol where these segments meet $\overleftrightarrow{CD}$.]**

Concept Byte
Use With Lesson 3-4
ACTIVITY

Perpendicular Lines and Planes

As you saw in Chapter 1, you can use a polygon to represent a plane in space. You can sketch overlapping polygons to suggest how two perpendicular planes intersect in a line.

Activity

Draw perpendicular planes *A* and *B* intersecting in $\overleftrightarrow{CD}$.

Step 1 Draw plane *A* and $\overleftrightarrow{CD}$ in plane *A*.

Step 2 Draw two segments that are perpendicular to $\overleftrightarrow{CD}$. One segment should pass through point *C*. The other segment should pass through point *D*. The segments represent two lines in plane *B* that are perpendicular to plane *A*.

Step 3 Connect the segment endpoints to draw plane *B*. Plane *B* is perpendicular to plane *A* because plane *B* contains lines perpendicular to plane *A*.

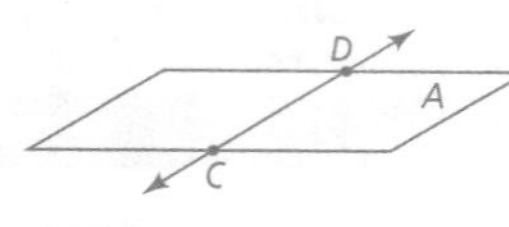

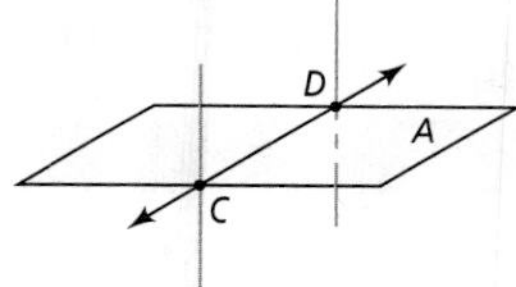

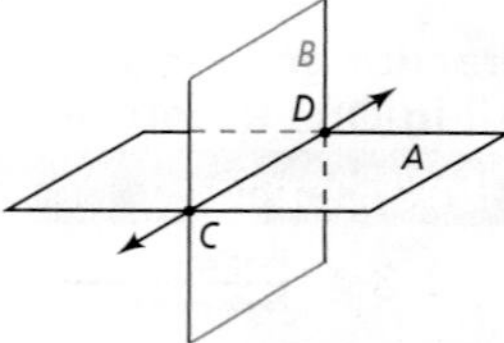

Exercises

1. Draw a plane in space. Then draw two lines that are in the plane and intersect at point *A*. Draw a third line that is perpendicular to each of the two lines at point *A*. What is the relationship between the third line and the plane?
2. a. Draw a plane and a point in the plane. Draw a line perpendicular to the plane at that point. Can you draw more than one perpendicular line?
   b. Draw a line and a point on the line. Draw a plane that is perpendicular to the line at that point. Can you draw more than one perpendicular plane?
3. Draw two planes perpendicular to the same line. What is the relationship between the planes?
4. Draw line ℓ through plane *P* at point *A*, so that line ℓ is perpendicular to plane *P*.
   a. Draw line *m* perpendicular to line ℓ at point *A*. How do *m* and plane *P* relate? Does this relationship hold true for every line perpendicular to line ℓ at point *A*?
   b. Draw a plane *Q* that contains line ℓ. How do planes *P* and *Q* relate? Does this relationship hold true for every plane *Q* that contains line ℓ?

Answers

Exercises

1. The third line is $\perp$ to the plane.

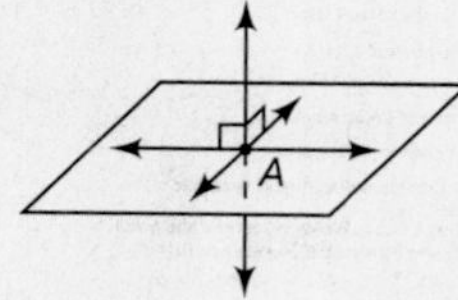

2a. No; there is only one line perpendicular to a plane at a given point.

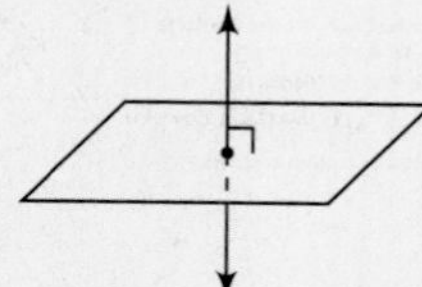

b. No; there is only one perpendicular plane to a line at a given point.

3. The planes are $\parallel$.

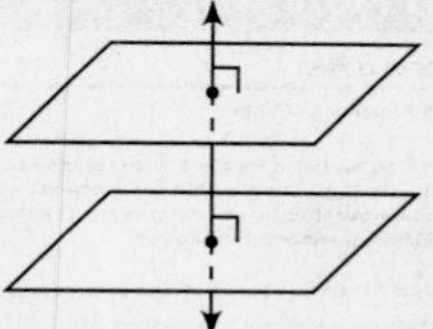

4a. *m* lies in *P*; yes.

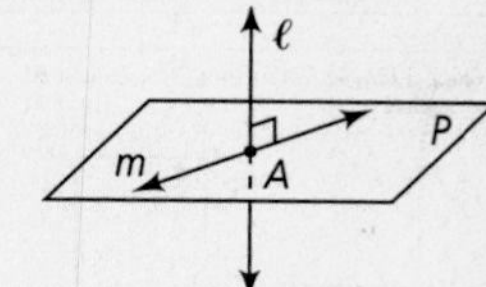

b. $P \perp Q$; yes

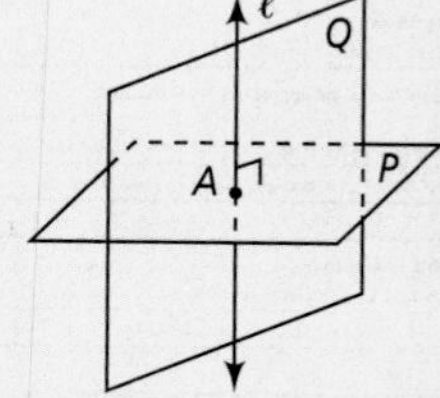

3-5 Parallel Lines and Triangles

TN State Performance Indicator
SPI 3108.1.4 Use definitions, basic postulates, and theorems about points, lines, angles, and planes to write/complete proofs and/or to solve problems.

Objectives To use parallel lines to prove a theorem about triangles
To find measures of angles of triangles

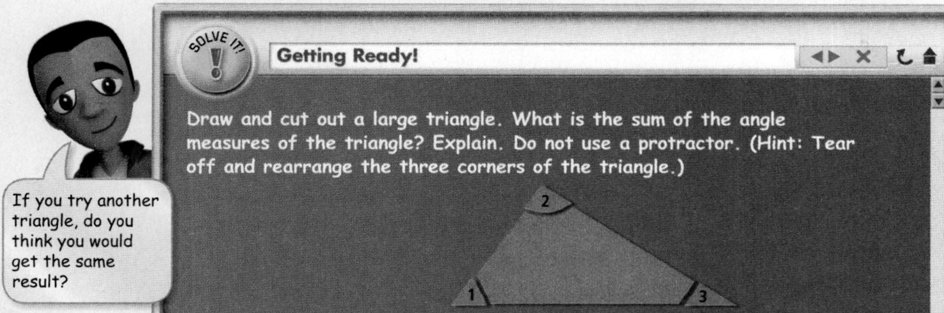

Getting Ready!
Draw and cut out a large triangle. What is the sum of the angle measures of the triangle? Explain. Do not use a protractor. (Hint: Tear off and rearrange the three corners of the triangle.)
If you try another triangle, do you think you would get the same result?

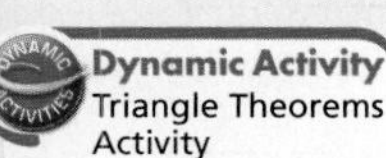
Dynamic Activity Triangle Theorems Activity

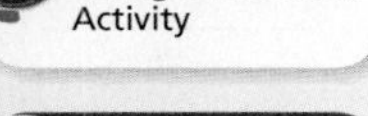
Lesson Vocabulary
- auxiliary line
- exterior angle of a polygon
- remote interior angles

In the Solve It, you may have discovered that you can rearrange the corners of the triangle to form a straight angle. You can do this for any triangle.

Essential Understanding The sum of the angle measures of a triangle is always the same.

The Solve It suggests an important theorem about triangles. To prove this theorem, you will need to use parallel lines.

take note

Postulate 3-3 Parallel Postulate

Through a point not on a line, there is one and only one line parallel to the given line.

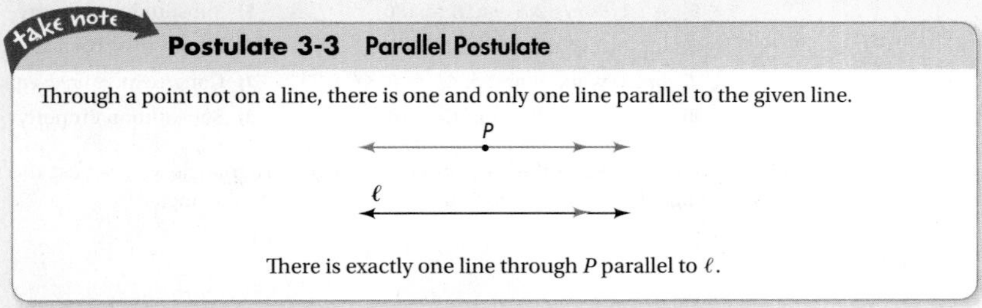

There is exactly one line through P parallel to ℓ.

1 Interactive Learning

Solve It!

PURPOSE To discover that the angles of any triangle can form a straight angle

PROCESS Students use visual judgment and knowledge of straight angles.

FACILITATE

Q Does the measure of the angle formed by the corner of the triangle depend on where you make the tear in the paper? Explain. **[No, the place you tear the paper only affects the length of the sides of the angle.]**

Q If you cut out a right triangle, what is true about the measures of the two acute angles? **[The measures of the two acute angles add to 90°. They form a right angle when they are adjacent.]**

ANSWER See Solve It in Answers on next page.

CONNECT THE MATH The angles of any triangle can be cut apart and rearranged to form a straight angle. There is no way to draw all possible triangles to test this conjecture. Students must prove the Triangle Angle-Sum Theorem deductively, thus the need to introduce the Parallel Postulate at this time.

2 Guided Instruction

Take Note

Demonstrate to students that there are an infinite number of lines through P, but that only one of those lines is parallel to ℓ.

3-5 Preparing to Teach

BIG idea Measurement UbD

ESSENTIAL UNDERSTANDINGS

- The sum of the angle measures of a triangle is always the same.
- Any exterior angle of a triangle has a special relationship with the two remote interior angles of a triangle.

Math Background

It is important that students know that the geometry studied in the course is Euclidean geometry and that its formulation depends on the parallel postulate put forth by Euclid. The conjecture (through a point not on a line, there is one and only one line parallel to a given line) put forth in the postulate is assumed to be true, and provides a framework for all of the other theorems and postulates in Euclidean geometry. Mathematicians have developed other geometries by modifying the assumption of the parallel postulate. For example, hyperbolic geometry was developed by assuming that for a point not on a line, there are an infinite number of lines though the point that are parallel to the given line. Projective geometry was developed by assuming that for a point not on a line there are no lines through the point that are parallel to the given line. Many students find the introduction of other geometries interesting, but more importantly, the study of such geometries often helps to solidify an understanding of Euclidean geometry.

Support Student Learning

Use the **Geometry Companion** to engage and support students during instructions. See Lesson Resources at the end of this lesson for details.

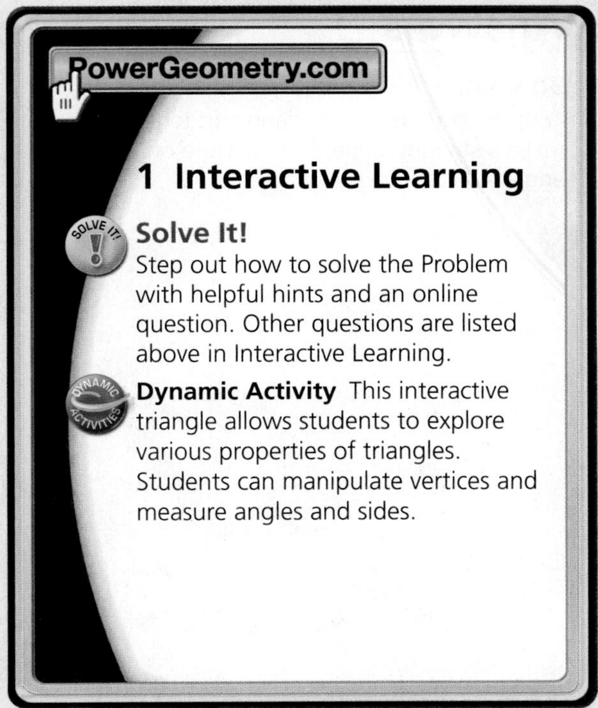

Take Note

Q Is this theorem true for all sizes and classifications of triangles? Explain. **[Yes, when the angles of any triangle are placed so that they share a common vertex and adjacent sides, but not interior points, they form a straight angle.]**

Q Does the order in which you add the measures of the angles affect the sum? Explain. **[No, addition is commutative, even when the addends are degrees.]**

Make sure that students understand that the auxiliary line in the diagram can be drawn through any of the vertices of the triangle. Draw two additional diagrams to illustrate this statement; one for each of the vertices not used in the Take Note diagram.

It may help students to visualize the use of the Alternate Interior Angles Theorem if the segment AC is extended to show the rest of the line containing it.

take note

Theorem 3-10 Triangle Angle-Sum Theorem

The sum of the measures of the angles of a triangle is 180.

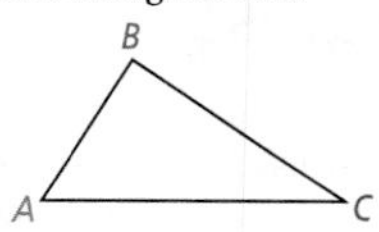

$$m\angle A + m\angle B + m\angle C = 180$$

The proof of the Triangle Angle-Sum Theorem requires an *auxiliary line.* An **auxiliary line** is a line that you add to a diagram to help explain relationships in proofs. The red line in the diagram below is an auxiliary line.

Proof **Proof of Theorem 3-10: Triangle Angle-Sum Theorem**

Given: $\triangle ABC$

Prove: $m\angle A + m\angle 2 + m\angle C = 180$

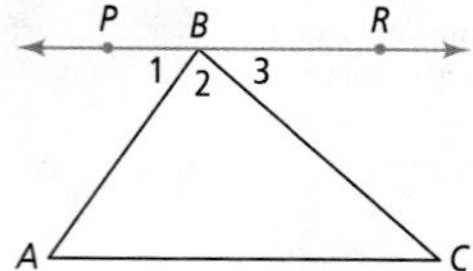

Statements	Reasons
1) Draw $\overleftrightarrow{PR}$ through B, parallel to $\overline{AC}$.	**1)** Parallel Postulate
2) $\angle PBC$ and $\angle 3$ are supplementary.	**2)** ∠s that form a linear pair are suppl.
3) $m\angle PBC + m\angle 3 = 180$	**3)** Definition of suppl. ∠s
4) $m\angle PBC = m\angle 1 + m\angle 2$	**4)** Angle Addition Postulate
5) $m\angle 1 + m\angle 2 + m\angle 3 = 180$	**5)** Substitution Property
6) $\angle 1 \cong \angle A$ and $\angle 3 \cong \angle C$	**6)** If lines are $\parallel$, then alternate interior ∠s are $\cong$.
7) $m\angle 1 = m\angle A$ and $m\angle 3 = m\angle C$	**7)** Congruent ∠s have equal measure.
8) $m\angle A + m\angle 2 + m\angle C = 180$	**8)** Substitution Property

When you know the measures of two angles of a triangle, you can use the Triangle Angle-Sum Theorem to find the measure of the third angle.

Answers

Solve It!

180; the corners of the triangle fit together to make a straight angle. The measure of a straight angle is 180.

PowerGeometry.com

2 Guided Instruction

Each Problem is worked out and supported online.

Problem 1
Using the Triangle Angle-Sum Theorem
Animated

Problem 2
Using the Triangle Exterior Angle Theorem
Animated

Problem 3
Applying the Triangle Theorems
Animated

Support in Geometry Companion

- Vocabulary
- Key Concepts
- Got It?

Problem 1 Using the Triangle Angle-Sum Theorem

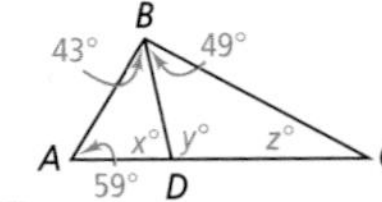

Plan

Which variable should you solve for first?
From the diagram, you know two angle measures in $\triangle ADB$. The third angle is labeled $x°$. So use what you know about the angle measures in a triangle to solve for x first.

Algebra What are the values of x and y in the diagram at the right?

Think	Write
Use the Triangle Angle-Sum Theorem to write an equation involving x.	$59 + 43 + x = 180$
Solve for x by simplifying and then subtracting 102 from each side.	$102 + x = 180$ $x = 78$
$\angle ADB$ and $\angle CDB$ form a linear pair, so they are supplementary.	$m\angle ADB + m\angle CDB = 180$
Substitute 78 for $m\angle ADB$ and y for $m\angle CDB$ in the above equation.	$x + y = 180$ $78 + y = 180$
Solve for y by subtracting 78 from each side.	$y = 102$

Got It? 1. Use the diagram in Problem 1. What is the value of z?

An **exterior angle of a polygon** is an angle formed by a side and an extension of an adjacent side. For each exterior angle of a triangle, the two nonadjacent interior angles are its **remote interior angles.** In each triangle below, $\angle 1$ is an exterior angle and $\angle 2$ and $\angle 3$ are its remote interior angles.

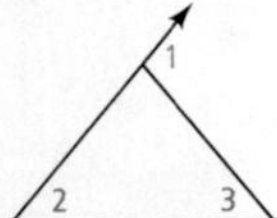

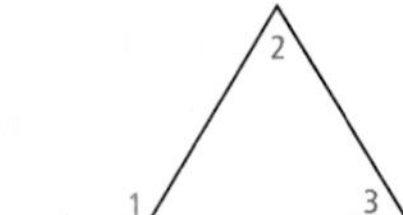

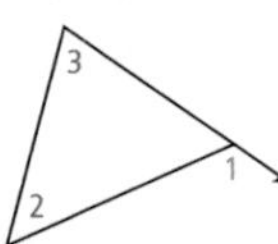

The theorem below states the relationship between an exterior angle and its two remote interior angles.

Theorem 3-11 Triangle Exterior Angle Theorem

The measure of each exterior angle of a triangle equals the sum of the measures of its two remote interior angles.

$$m\angle 1 = m\angle 2 + m\angle 3$$

You will prove Theorem 3-11 in Exercise 33.

Problem 1

Q How many distinct triangles are represented in the diagram? Name each triangle. **[3; $\triangle ABC$, $\triangle ABD$ and $\triangle BDC$]**

Q How is the measure of $\angle BDC$ related to the measures of $\angle BAC$ and $\angle ABD$? **[$m\angle BAC + m\angle ABD = m\angle BDC$]**

Got It? ERROR PREVENTION

Q What two equations can you use to determine the value of z? **[$49 + 102 + z = 180$ or $59 + 92 + z = 180$]**

Take Note TACTILE LEARNERS

Complete an activity similar to the Solve It activity to explore this theorem. Make two copies of a triangle, numbering all interior angles with 1a, 2a, 3a, and all exterior angles with 1b, 2b, and 3b. On the first triangle, extend the segments beyond the vertices. Cut out the second triangle and tear off the corners. Compare the torn-off corners with the exterior angles created in the first triangle.

Additional Problems

1. Solve for x, y, and z in the figure below.

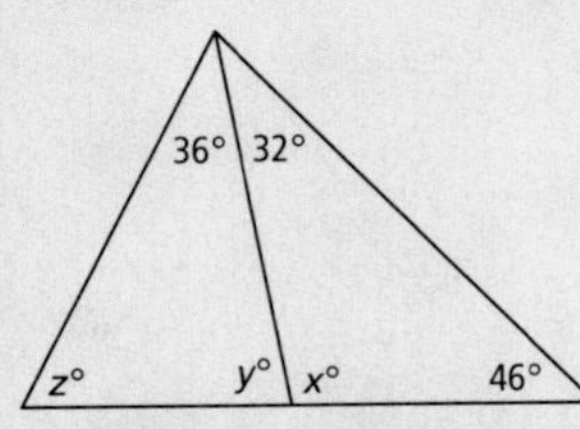

ANSWER $x = 102$, $y = 78$, $z = 66$

2. a. What is the measure of $\angle 1$?

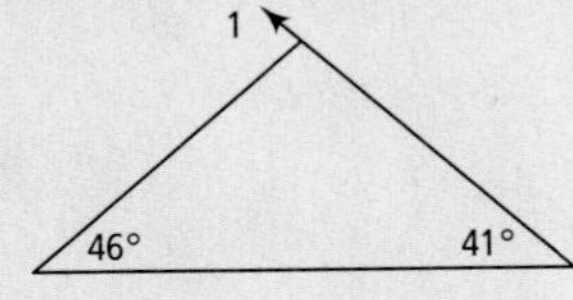

b. What is the measure of $\angle 2$?

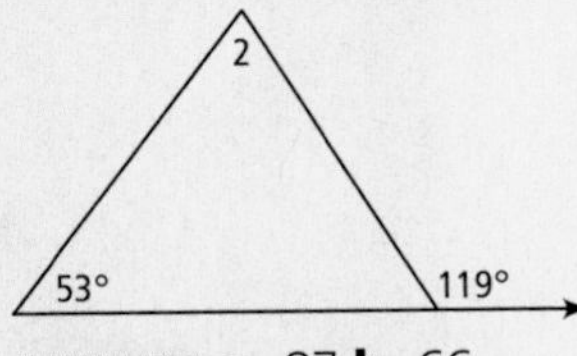

ANSWER a. 87 **b.** 66

3. What is the value of x?

x°
110°
60°

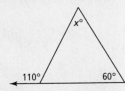

A. 170 **C.** 70
B. 110 **D.** 50

ANSWER D

Answers

Got It?

1. 29

Problem 2

Q How could you determine the measure of $\angle 1$ without using the Triangle Exterior Angles Theorem? **[You first determine the measure of the third angle of the triangle using the Triangle Angle-Sum Theorem. Then use the definitions of linear and supplementary angles.]**

Q How could you determine the measure of $\angle 2$ without using the Exterior Angles Theorem? **[You first determine the measure of the angle adjacent to the exterior angle through the definitions of linear and supplementary angles. Then use the Triangle Angle-Sum Theorem.]**

Got It? VISUAL LEARNERS

Have students make a sketch of the triangle prior to beginning the problem. Students should realize that an exterior angle can be formed at a vertex by extending either of the sides of the triangle at that vertex; which side is chosen will not affect the measure of the exterior angle.

Problem 3

Q What equation containing x can be justified by the Exterior Angles Theorem? **[$x + 30 = 80$]**

Q What is the measure of the third angle of the triangle? Explain. **[The third angle measures 100, because $180 - 30 - 50 = 100$.]**

Got It? VISUAL LEARNERS

Q Which angle forms a linear pair with the exterior angle that measures 80? What is its measure? **[The unlabeled vertex of the triangle; 100]**

You can use the Triangle Exterior Angle Theorem to find angle measures.

Problem 2 Using the Triangle Exterior Angle Theorem

Plan

What information can you get from the diagram?
The diagram shows you which angles are interior or exterior.

A **What is the measure of $\angle 1$?**

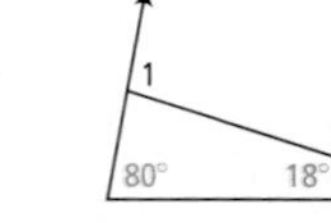

$m\angle 1 = 80 + 18$ Triangle Exterior Angle Theorem

$m\angle 1 = 98$ Simplify.

B **What is the measure of $\angle 2$?**

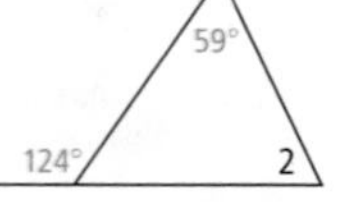

$124 = 59 + m\angle 2$ Triangle Exterior Angle Theorem

$65 = m\angle 2$ Subtract 59 from each side.

Got It? 2. Two angles of a triangle measure 53. What is the measure of an exterior angle at each vertex of the triangle?

Problem 3 Applying the Triangle Theorems

Plan

How can you apply your skills from Problem 2 here?
Look at the diagram. Notice that you have a triangle and information about interior and exterior angles.

Multiple Choice **When radar tracks an object, the reflection of signals off the ground can result in clutter. Clutter causes the receiver to confuse the real object with its reflection, called a ghost. At the right, there is a radar receiver at *A*, an airplane at *B*, and the airplane's ghost at *D*. What is the value of *x*?**

Ⓐ 30 Ⓒ 70

Ⓑ 50 Ⓓ 80

$m\angle A + m\angle B = m\angle BCD$	Triangle Exterior Angle Theorem
$x + 30 = 80$	Substitute.
$x = 50$	Subtract 30 from each side.

The value of x is 50. The correct answer is B.

Got It? 3. Reasoning In Problem 3, can you find $m\angle A$ without using the Triangle Exterior Angle Theorem? Explain.

Answers

Got It? (continued)

2. 127, 127, 106

3. Yes; answers may vary. Sample: $m\angle ACB$ must $= 100$, so by the $\triangle\angle$-Sum Thm., $m\angle A + 30 + 100 = 180$, and $m\angle A = 50$.

Lesson Check

Do you know HOW?

Find the measure of the third angle of a triangle given the measures of two angles.

1. 34 and 88
2. 45 and 90
3. 10 and 102
4. x and 50

In a triangle, $\angle 1$ is an exterior angle and $\angle 2$ and $\angle 3$ are its remote interior angles. Find the missing angle measure.

5. $m\angle 2 = 24$ and $m\angle 3 = 106$
6. $m\angle 1 = 70$ and $m\angle 2 = 32$

Do you UNDERSTAND?

7. Explain how the Triangle Exterior Angle Theorem makes sense based on the Triangle Angle-Sum Theorem.
8. **Error Analysis** The measures of the interior angles of a triangle are 30, x, and $3x$. Which of the following methods for solving for x is incorrect? Explain.

A.
$x + 3x = 30$
$4x = 30$
$x = 7.5$

B.
$x + 3x + 30 = 180$
$4x + 30 = 180$
$4x = 150$
$x = 37.5$

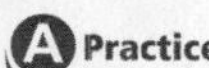

Practice and Problem-Solving Exercises

A Practice Find $m\angle 1$. See Problem 1.

9. 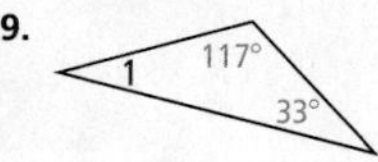

10. 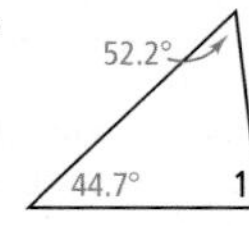

11. 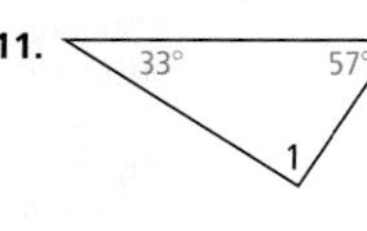

Algebra Find the value of each variable.

12. 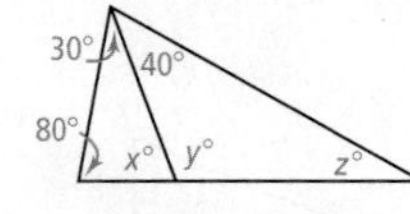

13. 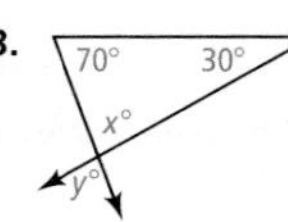

14. 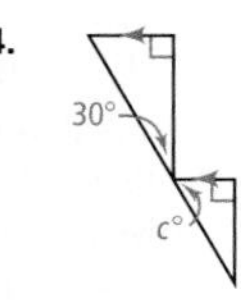

Use the diagram at the right for Exercises 15 and 16. See Problem 2.

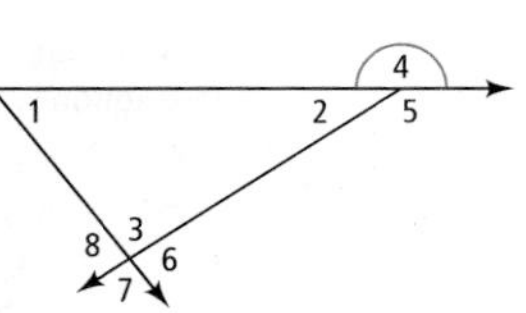

15. **a.** Which of the numbered angles are exterior angles?
    b. Name the remote interior angles for each exterior angle.
    c. How are exterior angles 6 and 8 related?
16. **a.** How many exterior angles are at each vertex of the triangle?
    b. How many exterior angles does a triangle have in all?

3 Lesson Check

Do you know HOW?

- If students have difficulty with Exercises 5–6, then have them review Problem 2.

Do you UNDERSTAND? ERROR INTERVENTION

- If students have difficulty with Exercise 8, then ask them to try to justify each step for the correct solution method.

Close

Q What is always true about the interior angles of any triangle? **[The sum of the measures of the angles equals 180.]**

Answers

Lesson Check

1. 58
2. 45
3. 68
4. $130 - x$
5. $m\angle 1 = 130$
6. $m\angle 3 = 38$
7. Answers may vary. Sample: Consider the int. $\angle A$ of $\triangle ABC$. By the $\triangle\angle$-Sum Thm., the sum of the measures of angles A, B, and C is 180°. $\angle A$ is suppl. to its ext. $\angle$. So the sum of the measures of angles B and C is equal to the measure of the ext. $\angle$ of $\angle A$.
8. A; all 3 ∡ are int. ∡, so the solution should use the $\triangle\angle$-Sum Thm.

Practice and Problem-Solving Exercises

9. 30
10. 83.1
11. 90
12. $x = 70$, $y = 110$, $z = 30$
13. $x = y = 80$
14. $c = 60$

15a. $\angle 5$, $\angle 6$, $\angle 8$
b. For $\angle 5$: $\angle 1$ and $\angle 3$; for $\angle 6$: $\angle 1$ and $\angle 2$; for $\angle 8$: $\angle 1$ and $\angle 2$
c. $\angle 6 \cong \angle 8$

16a. 2
b. 6

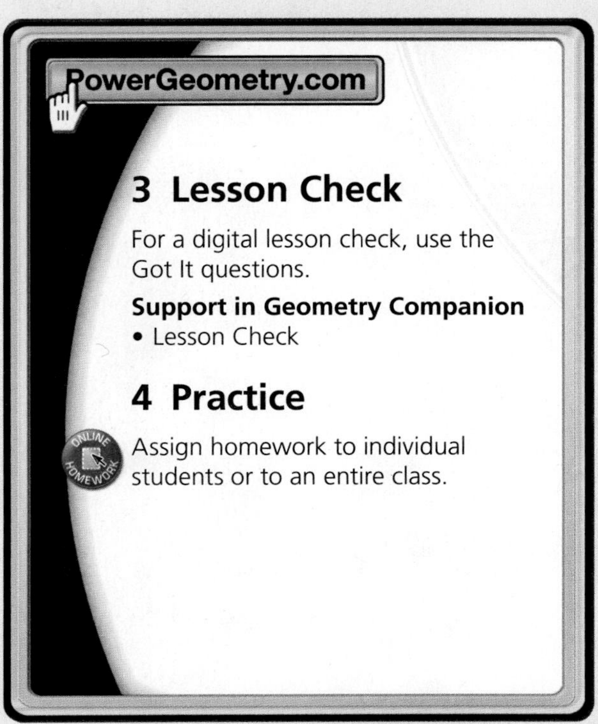

4 Practice

ASSIGNMENT GUIDE

Basic: 9–22 all, 24–25 all, 27, 30–34 even, 35
Average: 9–21 odd, 22–35
Advanced: 9–21 odd, 22–42
Standardized Test Prep: 43–46
Mixed Review: 47–53

Reasoning exercises have blue headings.
Applications exercises have red headings.

EXERCISE 35: Use the Think About a Plan worksheet in the **Practice and Problem Solving Workbook** (also available in the Teaching Resources in print and online) to further support students' development in becoming independent learners.

HOMEWORK QUICK CHECK

To check students' understanding of key skills and concepts, go over Exercises 11, 17, 25, 27, and 35.

Algebra **Find each missing angle measure.**

17.

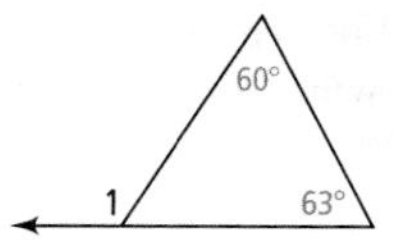

18.

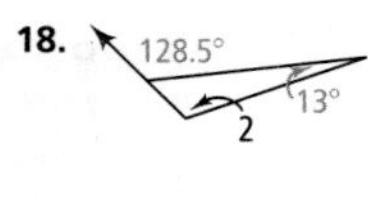

19.

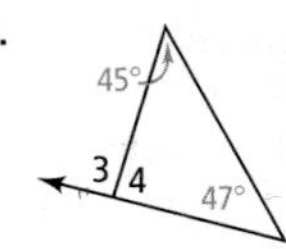

20. A ramp forms the angles shown at the right. What are the values of a and b?

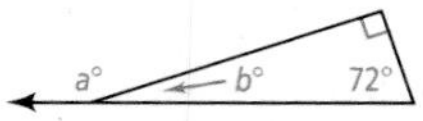

See Problem 3.

21. A lounge chair has different settings that change the angles formed by its parts. Suppose $m\angle 2 = 71$ and $m\angle 3 = 43$. Find $m\angle 1$.

B Apply

Algebra **Use the given information to find the unknown angle measures in the triangle.**

22. The ratio of the angle measures of the acute angles in a right triangle is $1 : 2$.

23. The measure of one angle of a triangle is 40. The measures of the other two angles are in a ratio of $3 : 4$.

24. The measure of one angle of a triangle is 108. The measures of the other two angles are in a ratio of $1 : 5$.

25. **Think About a Plan** The angle measures of $\triangle RST$ are represented by $2x$, $x + 14$, and $x - 38$. What are the angle measures of $\triangle RST$?
- How can you use the Triangle Angle-Sum Theorem to write an equation?
- How can you check your answer?

26. Proof Prove the following theorem: The acute angles of a right triangle are complementary.

Given: $\triangle ABC$ with right angle C

Prove: $\angle A$ and $\angle B$ are complementary.

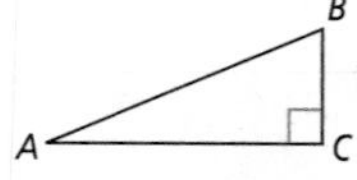

27. **Reasoning** What is the measure of each angle of an equiangular triangle? Explain.

28. **Draw a Diagram** Which diagram below correctly represents the following description? Explain your reasoning.

Draw any triangle. Label it $\triangle ABC$. Extend two sides of the triangle to form two exterior angles at vertex A.

I.

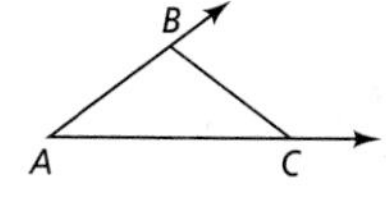

II.

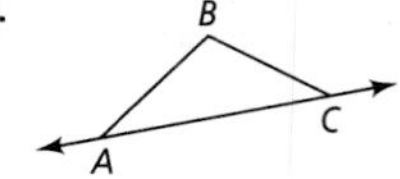

III.

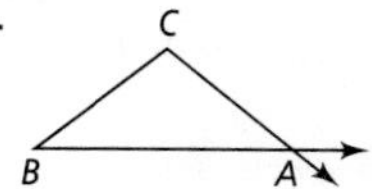

Answers

Practice and Problem-Solving Exercises (continued)

17. 123 **18.** 115.5

19. $m\angle 3 = 92$, $m\angle 4 = 88$

20. $a = 162$, $b = 18$

21. 114 **22.** 30, 60

23. 60, 80 **24.** 12, 60

25. 102, 65, 13

26. Answers may vary. Sample: $m\angle A + m\angle B + m\angle C = 180$ by the Triangle Angle-Sum Thm. It is given that $m\angle C = 90$, so $m\angle A + m\angle B + 90 = 180$. By the Subtr. Prop. of Equality, $m\angle A + m\angle B = 90$. Thus $\angle A$ and B are compl. by the def. of compl. ∠s.

27. 60; answers may vary. Sample: $180 \div 3 = 60$, so each ∠ is 60.

28. III; I does not have any ext. ∠s at A. II has only one ext. ∠ at A and only one side of the △ extended.

Find the values of the variables and the measures of the angles.

29.

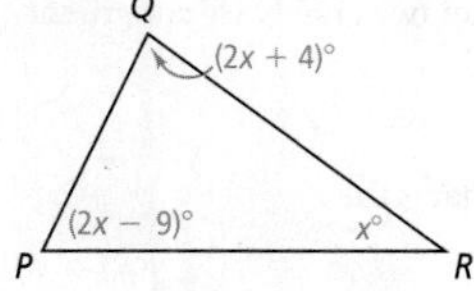

30.

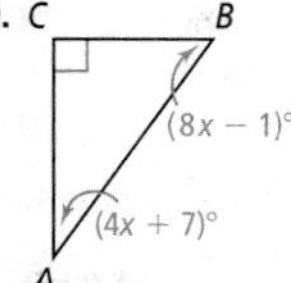

31.

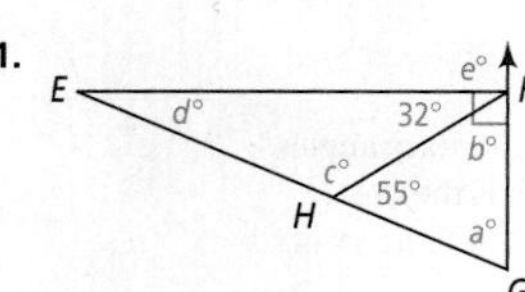

32.

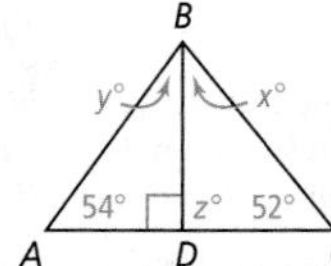

33. Prove the Triangle Exterior Angle Theorem (Theorem 3-11).
Proof
The measure of each exterior angle of a triangle equals the sum of the measures of its two remote interior angles.

Given: $\angle 1$ is an exterior angle of the triangle.

Prove: $m\angle 1 = m\angle 2 + m\angle 3$

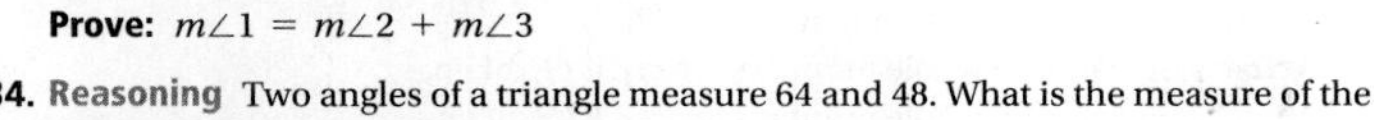

34. Reasoning Two angles of a triangle measure 64 and 48. What is the measure of the largest exterior angle of the triangle? Explain.

35. Algebra A right triangle has exterior angles at each of its acute angles with measures in the ratio 13 : 14. Find the measures of the two acute angles of the right triangle.

Challenge

Probability In Exercises 36–40, you know only the given information about the measures of the angles of a triangle. Find the probability that the triangle is equiangular.

36. Each is a multiple of 30.

37. Each is a multiple of 20.

38. Each is a multiple of 60.

39. Each is a multiple of 12.

40. One angle is obtuse.

41. In the figure at the right, $\overline{CD} \perp \overline{AB}$ and $\overline{CD}$ bisects $\angle ACB$. Find $m\angle DBF$.

42. If the remote interior angles of an exterior angle of a triangle are congruent, what can you conclude about the bisector of the exterior angle? Justify your answer.

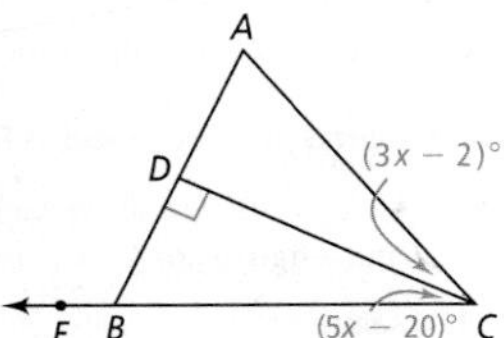

29. $x = 37$; $m\angle P = 65$, $m\angle Q = 78$, $m\angle R = 37$

30. $x = 7$; $m\angle A = 35$, $m\angle B = 55$, $m\angle C = 90$

31. $a = 67$, $b = 58$, $c = 125$, $d = 23$, $e = 90$

32. $x = 38$; $y = 36$, $z = 90$; $m\angle ABC = 74$

33. $\angle 1$ is an ext. $\angle$ of the $\triangle$. (Given); $\angle 1$ and $\angle 4$ are suppl. (⦣ that form a straight $\angle$ are suppl.); $m\angle 1 + m\angle 4 = 180$ (Def. of suppl.); $m\angle 2 + m\angle 3 + m\angle 4 = 180$ ($\triangle$ $\angle$-Sum Thm.); $m\angle 1 + m\angle 4 = m\angle 2 + m\angle 3 + m\angle 4$ (Subst. Prop.); $m\angle 1 = m\angle 2 + m\angle 3$ (Subtr. Prop. of =)

34. 132; the smallest interior $\angle$ is adjacent to the largest ext. $\angle$, so the largest ext. $\angle$ has measure $180 - 48 = 132$.

35. 40, 50

36. $\frac{1}{3}$

37. $\frac{1}{7}$

38. 1

39. $\frac{1}{19}$

40. 0

41. 115

42. The bisector is $\parallel$ to the side common to the $\cong$ ⦣. If the measure of each $\cong$ $\angle$ is x, then the measure of the ext. $\angle$ is $2x$ so the bisector forms 2 ⦣ of measure x. Alt. int. ⦣ are $\cong$, so the bisector is $\parallel$ to the side common to the $\cong$ int. ⦣.

Answers

Practice and Problem-Solving Exercises (continued)

43. A **44.** H **45.** C

46. [4] **a.** 159; $m\angle A + m\angle B + m\angle C = 180$, but $m\angle A = 21$ and $180 - 21 = 159$.

b. $1 \leq m\angle C \leq 68$; $\angle C$ is acute, so $m\angle B > 90$ and $m\angle A + m\angle C < 90$. Thus, $21 + m\angle C < 90$, or $m\angle C < 69$. Also $m\angle C > 0$.

c. $91 \leq m\angle B \leq 158$; $\angle B$ is obtuse, so $m\angle B > 90$. $m\angle B + m\angle C = 159$, so $m\angle B < 159$.

[3] two parts correct with complete explanations

[2] one part correct with a complete explanation

[1] correct answers with no explanations

47. $a \parallel c$; if 2 same-side ext. ∠s are suppl., then the lines are ∥.

48. $a \parallel b$; if 2 lines are ∥ to the same line, they are ∥ to each other.

49. 32

50. $m\angle 1 = m\angle 2 = 90$; sample: If the sum of two equal numbers is 180, then each number is 90.

51. X Y

52.

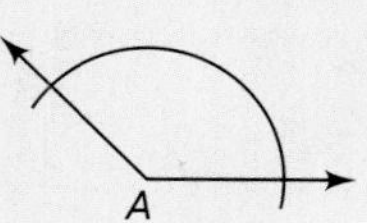

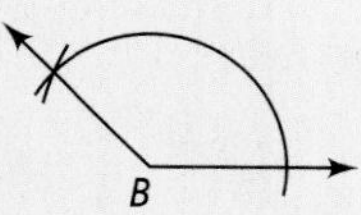

53.

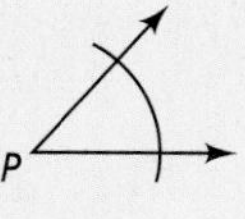

Q

Standardized Test Prep

SAT/ACT

43. The measure of one angle of a triangle is 115. The other two angles are congruent. What is the measure of each of the congruent angles?

(A) 32.5 (B) 57.5 (C) 65 (D) 115

44. The center of the circle at the right is at the origin. What is the approximate length of its diameter?

(F) 2 (H) 5.6
(G) 2.8 (I) 8

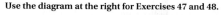

45. One statement in a proof is "∠1 and ∠2 are supplementary angles." The next statement is "$m\angle 1 + m\angle 2 = 180$." Which is the best justification for the second statement based on the first statement?

(A) The sum of the measures of two right angles is 180.

(B) Angles that form a linear pair are supplementary.

(C) Definition of supplementary angles

(D) The measure of a straight angle is 180.

Extended Response

46. $\triangle ABC$ is an obtuse triangle with $m\angle A = 21$ and $\angle C$ is acute.

a. What is $m\angle B + m\angle C$? Explain.

b. What is the range of whole numbers for $m\angle C$? Explain.

c. What is the range of whole numbers for $m\angle B$? Explain.

Mixed Review

Use the diagram at the right for Exercises 47 and 48. See Lesson 3-4.

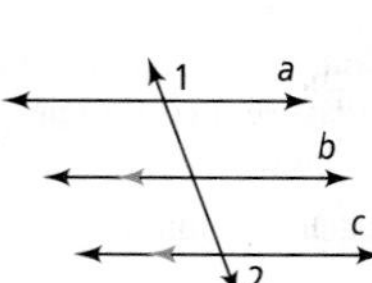

47. If ∠1 and ∠2 are supplementary, what can you conclude about lines *a* and *c*? Justify your answer.

48. If $a \parallel c$, what can you conclude about lines *a* and *b*? Justify your answer.

49. ∠ABC and ∠CBD form a linear pair. If $m\angle ABC = 3x + 20$ and $m\angle CBD = x + 32$, find the value of *x*. See Lesson 1-5.

50. ∠1 and ∠2 are supplementary. If $\angle 1 \cong \angle 2$, find $m\angle 1$ and $m\angle 2$. Explain.

Get Ready! **To prepare for Lesson 3-6, do Exercises 51–53.**

Use a straightedge to draw each figure. Then use a straightedge and compass to construct a figure congruent to it. See Lesson 1-6.

51. a segment **52.** an obtuse angle **53.** an acute angle

3-5 Lesson Resources

Differentiated Remediation

Instructional Support

Geometry Companion

Students can use the **Geometry Companion** worktext (4 pages) . . .

- New Vocabulary
- Key Concepts
- Got It for each Problem
- Lesson Check

3-5 Parallel Lines and Triangles

Vocabulary

Review

Identify the part of speech for the word *alternate* in each sentence below.

1. You vote for one winner and one *alternate*. noun
2. Your two friends *alternate* serves during tennis. verb
3. You and your sister babysit on *alternate* nights. adjective
4. Write the *converse* of the statement.

Statement: If it is raining, then I need an umbrella.

Converse: If I need an umbrella, then it is raining.

Vocabulary Builder

tri- (prefix) try

Related Word: triple

Main Idea: Tri- is a prefix meaning three that is used to form compound words.

Examples: triangle, tricycle, tripod

Use Your Vocabulary

Write T for *true* or F for *false*.

T 5. A *tri*pod is a stand that has three legs.

F 6. A *tri*angle is a polygon with three or more sides.

F 7. A *tri*atholon is a race with two events — swimming and bicycling.

T 8. In order to *tri*ple an amount, multiply it by three.

Chapter 3 74

ELL Support

Use Manipulatives Have the students form mixed-ability groups of three or four students each. Ask students to show examples of right, acute, obtuse, isosceles, and equilateral triangles. Have each group draw different kinds of triangles. Say: Label each of your triangles. Have each group measure the interior angles of its triangles. Say: Write the sum of the interior angles of each triangle next to the triangle. Ask: Is each of your sums 180°? Have groups that answer Yes check their triangles again more carefully. Have groups that answer No find reasons why the sum of the angles is not equal to 180°. [inaccuracies in measurement]

Have the groups exchange triangles with another group and measure the exterior angles of the other group's triangles. Ask: What is the sum of the exterior angles of the triangles? Have each group suggest a reason for their results.

5 Assess & Remediate

Lesson Quiz

1. Solve for x, y, and z in the figure below.

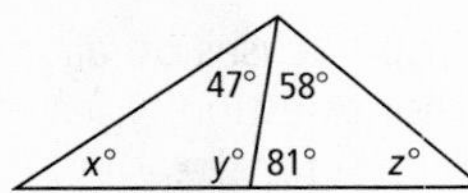

2. What are the measures of $\angle 1$ and $\angle 2$?

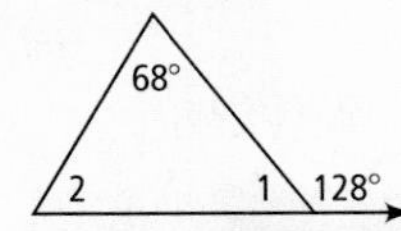

3. Do you UNDERSTAND? Neko made a triangular flag shown below. He wanted to attach it to the stick and then trim off the extra fabric so the flag would form an isosceles triangle. By how many degrees was he off when he attached the triangle to the stick?

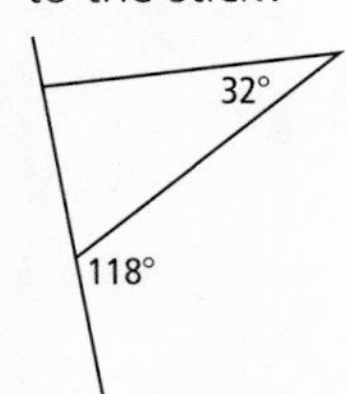

ANSWERS TO LESSON QUIZ

1. $x = 34, y = 99, z = 41$

2 $m\angle 1 = 52, m\angle 2 = 60$

3. Neko's flag ended up with base angles of 86° and 62°, so his stick was 12° out of alignment from the correct position (both angles 74°).

PRESCRIPTION FOR REMEDIATION

Use the student work on the Lesson Quiz to prescribe a differentiated review assignment.

Points	Differentiated Remediation
0–1	Intervention
2	On-level
3	Extension

PowerGeometry.com

5 Assess & Remediate

Assign the Lesson Quiz. Appropriate intervention, practice, or enrichment is automatically generated based on student performance.

Intervention

- **Reteaching** (2 pages) Provides reteaching and practice exercises for the key lesson concepts. Use with struggling students or absent students.
- **English Language Learner Support** Helps students develop and reinforce mathematical vocabulary and key concepts.

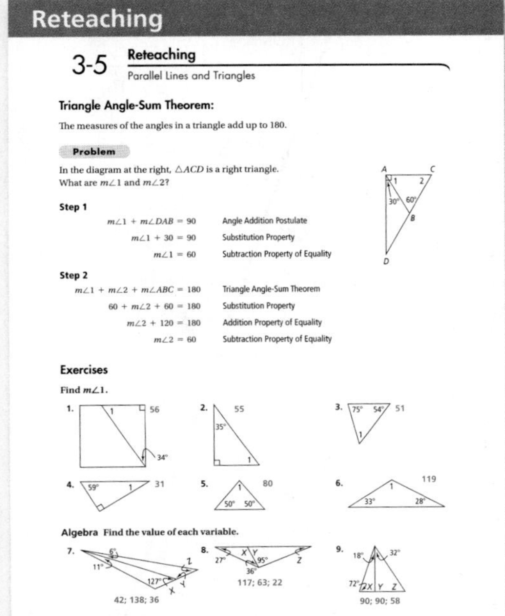

All-in-One Resources/Online

Reteaching

3-5 **Reteaching**

Parallel Lines and Triangles

Triangle Angle-Sum Theorem:

The measures of the angles in a triangle add up to 180.

Problem

In the diagram at the right, $\triangle ACD$ is a right triangle. What are $m\angle 1$ and $m\angle 2$?

Step 1

$m\angle 1 + m\angle DAB = 90$	Angle Addition Postulate
$m\angle 1 + 30 = 90$	Substitution Property
$m\angle 1 = 60$	Subtraction Property of Equality

Step 2

$m\angle 1 + m\angle 2 + m\angle ABC = 180$	Triangle Angle-Sum Theorem
$60 + m\angle 2 + 60 = 180$	Substitution Property
$m\angle 2 + 120 = 180$	Addition Property of Equality
$m\angle 2 = 60$	Subtraction Property of Equality

Exercises

Find $m\angle 1$.

1. 56
2. 55
3. 51
4. 31
5. 80
6. 119

Algebra Find the value of each variable.

7. 42; 138; 36
8. 117; 63; 22
9. 90; 90; 58

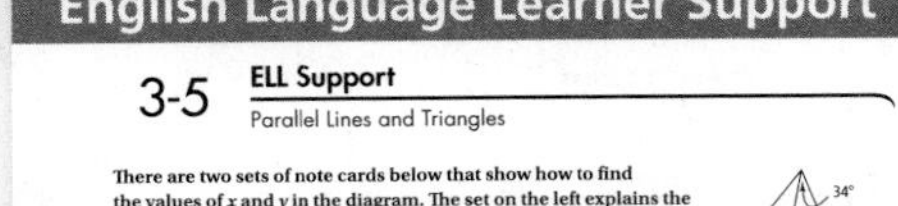

All-in-One Resources/Online

English Language Learner Support

3-5 **ELL Support**

Parallel Lines and Triangles

There are two sets of note cards below that show how to find the values of x and y in the diagram. The set on the left explains the thinking and the set on the right shows the steps. Write the thinking and the steps in the correct order.

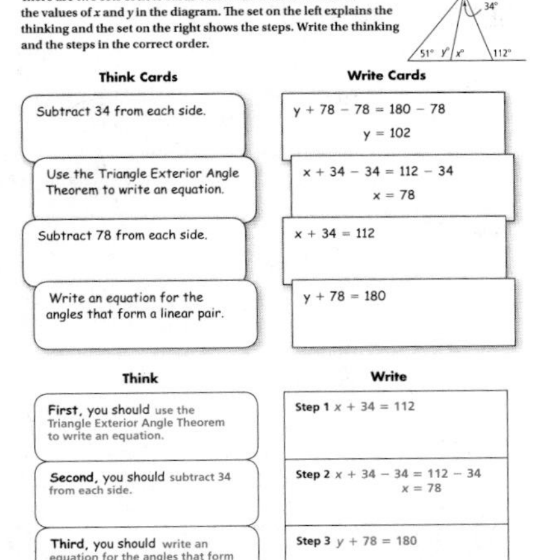

Think Cards	Write Cards
Subtract 34 from each side.	$y + 78 - 78 = 180 - 78$; $y = 102$
Use the Triangle Exterior Angle Theorem to write an equation.	$x + 34 - 34 = 112 - 34$; $x = 78$
Subtract 78 from each side.	$x + 34 = 112$
Write an equation for the angles that form a linear pair.	$y + 78 = 180$

Think	Write
First, you should use the Triangle Exterior Angle Theorem to write an equation.	**Step 1** $x + 34 = 112$
Second, you should subtract 34 from each side.	**Step 2** $x + 34 - 34 = 112 - 34$; $x = 78$
Third, you should write an equation for the angles that form a linear pair.	**Step 3** $y + 78 = 180$
Finally, you should subtract 78 from each side.	**Step 4** $y + 78 - 78 = 180 - 78$; $y = 102$

Differentiated Remediation *continued*

On-Level

- **Practice** (2 pages) Provides extra practice for each lesson. For simpler practice exercises, use the Form K Practice pages found in the All-in-One Teaching Resources and online.
- **Think About a Plan** Helps students develop specific problem-solving skills and strategies by providing scaffolded guiding questions.
- **Standardized Test Prep** Focuses on all major exercises, all major question types, and helps students prepare for the high-stakes assessments.

Practice and Problem Solving Wkbk/ All-in-One Resources/Online

Practice page 1

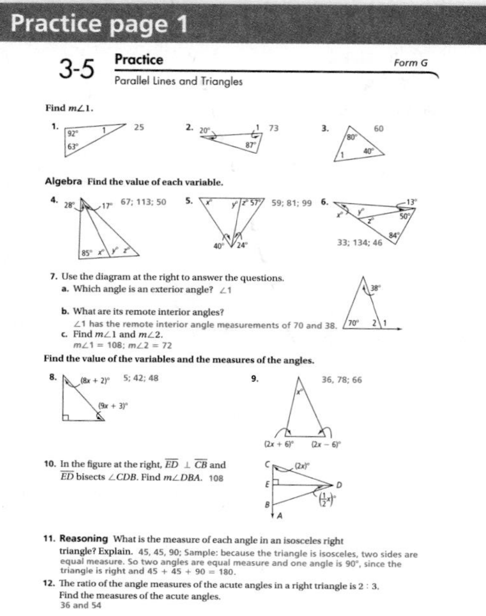

3-5 Practice — Form G
Parallel Lines and Triangles

Find $m\angle 1$.

1. 25 2. 73 3. 60

Algebra Find the value of each variable.

4. 67; 113; 50 5. 59; 81; 99 6. 33; 134; 46

7. Use the diagram at the right to answer the questions.
a. Which angle is an exterior angle? ∠1
b. What are its remote interior angles? ∠1 has the remote interior angle measurements of 70 and 38.
c. Find $m\angle 1$ and $m\angle 2$. $m\angle 1 = 108$; $m\angle 2 = 72$

Find the value of the variables and the measures of the angles.

8. 5; 42; 48 9. 36, 78; 66

10. In the figure at the right, $\overline{ED} \perp \overline{CB}$ and $\overline{ED}$ bisects $\angle CDB$. Find $m\angle DBA$. 108

11. Reasoning What is the measure of each angle in an isosceles right triangle? Explain. 45, 45, 90; Sample: because the triangle is isosceles, two sides are equal measure. So two angles are equal measure and one angle is 90°, since the triangle is right and 45 + 45 + 90 = 180.

12. The ratio of the angle measures of the acute angles in a right triangle is 2 : 3. Find the measures of the acute angles. 36 and 54

Practice and Problem Solving Wkbk/ All-in-One Resources/Online

Practice page 2

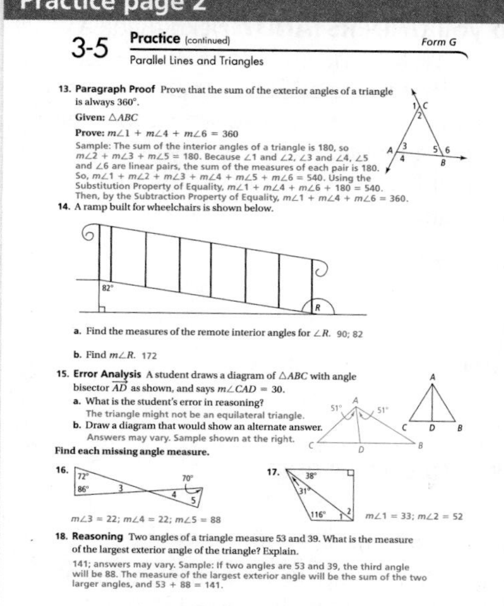

3-5 Practice (continued) — Form G
Parallel Lines and Triangles

13. Paragraph Proof Prove that the sum of the exterior angles of a triangle is always 360°.
Given: △ABC
Prove: $m\angle 1 + m\angle 4 + m\angle 6 = 360$
Sample: The sum of the interior angles of a triangle is 180, so $m\angle 2 + m\angle 3 + m\angle 5 = 180$. Because ∠1 and ∠2, ∠3 and ∠4, ∠5 and ∠6 are linear pairs, the sum of the measures of each pair is 180. So, $m\angle 1 + m\angle 2 + m\angle 3 + m\angle 4 + m\angle 5 + m\angle 6 = 540$. Using the Substitution Property of Equality, $m\angle 1 + m\angle 4 + m\angle 6 + 180 = 540$. Then, by the Subtraction Property of Equality, $m\angle 1 + m\angle 4 + m\angle 6 = 360$.

14. A ramp built for wheelchairs is shown below.
a. Find the measures of the remote interior angles for ∠R. 90; 82
b. Find $m\angle R$. 172

15. Error Analysis A student draws a diagram of △ABC with angle bisector $\overline{AD}$ as shown, and says $m\angle CAD = 30$.
a. What is the student's error in reasoning? The triangle might not be an equilateral triangle.
b. Draw a diagram that would show an alternate answer. Answers may vary. Sample shown at the right.

Find each missing angle measure.

16. $m\angle 3 = 22$; $m\angle 4 = 22$; $m\angle 5 = 88$ 17. $m\angle 1 = 33$; $m\angle 2 = 52$

18. Reasoning Two angles of a triangle measure 53 and 39. What is the measure of the largest exterior angle of the triangle? Explain. 141; answers may vary. Sample: If two angles are 53 and 39, the third angle will be 88. The measure of the largest exterior angle will be the sum of the two larger angles, and 53 + 88 = 141.

Practice and Problem Solving Wkbk/ All-in-One Resources/Online

Think About a Plan

3-5 Think About a Plan
Parallel Lines and Triangles

Algebra A right triangle has exterior angles at each of its acute angles with measures in the ratio 13 : 14. Find the measures of the two acute angles of the right triangle.

Know

1. What is the sum of all the interior angles in a right triangle? 180
2. One angle in a right triangle measures 90. What is the sum of the other two angles? 90
3. What is the sum of an interior angle and its adjacent exterior angle? 180

Need

4. What strategy can you use to keep track of the interior and exterior angles of the triangle? Sample: A diagram will help me keep track of the relationships between angles and what is already known.
5. Draw a diagram, labeling the interior acute angles ∠1 and ∠2 and their corresponding exterior angles ∠3 and ∠4.

Plan

6. Use what you know to find the following sums:
a. $m\angle 1 + m\angle 2 + m\angle 3 + m\angle 4$ 360
b. $m\angle 3 + m\angle 4$ 270
7. The ratio of $m\angle 3$ to $m\angle 4$ is 13 : 14. Use this to find the measures of ∠3 and ∠4. Explain your work. 130; 140; Sample: I used the ratio to set up proportions: $\frac{m\angle 3}{13} = \frac{270}{13 + 14}$ and $\frac{m\angle 4}{14} = \frac{270}{13 + 14}$.
8. How can you use $m\angle 3$ and $m\angle 4$ to find the measures of the interior angles? What are the interior angle measures? 50; 40; Sample: I subtracted the measure of the corresponding exterior angle from 180.

Practice and Problem Solving Wkbk/ All-in-One Resources/Online

Standardized Test Prep

3-5 Standardized Test Prep
Parallel Lines and Triangles

Gridded Response

1. What is the value of w?
2. What is the value of z?
3. What is the value of s?
4. What is the value of e?
5. What is the value of t on the truss of the bridge?

Answers

Extension

- **Enrichment** Provides students with interesting problems and activities that extend the concepts of the lesson.
- **Activities, Games, and Puzzles** Worksheets that can be used for concepts development, enrichment, and for fun!

All-in-One Resources/Online

Enrichment

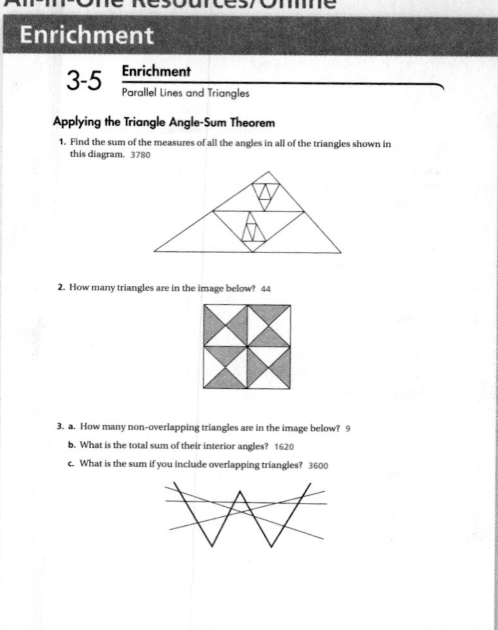

3-5 Enrichment
Parallel Lines and Triangles

Applying the Triangle Angle-Sum Theorem

1. Find the sum of the measures of all the angles in all of the triangles shown in this diagram. 3780
2. How many triangles are in the image below? 44
3. a. How many non-overlapping triangles are in the image below? 9
b. What is the total sum of their interior angles? 1620
c. What is the sum if you include overlapping triangles? 3600

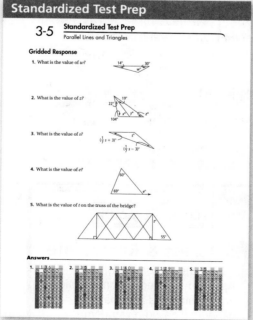

Online Teacher Resource Center

Activities, Games, and Puzzles

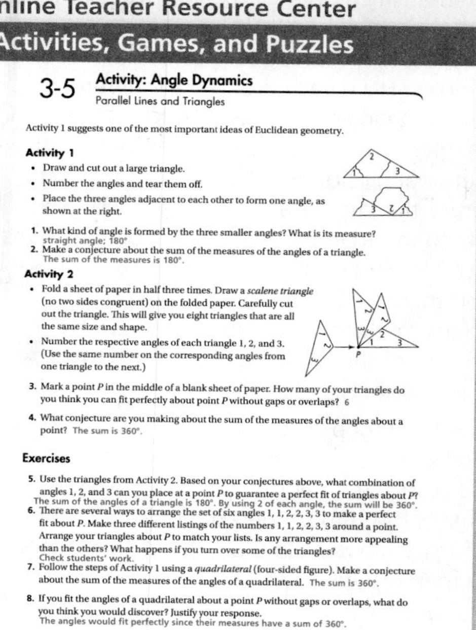

3-5 Activity: Angle Dynamics
Parallel Lines and Triangles

Activity 1 suggests one of the most important ideas of Euclidean geometry.

Activity 1
- Draw and cut out a large triangle.
- Number the angles and tear them off.
- Place the three angles adjacent to each other to form one angle, as shown at the right.

1. What kind of angle is formed by the three smaller angles? What is its measure? straight angle; 180°
2. Make a conjecture about the sum of the measures of the angles of a triangle. The sum of the measures is 180°.

Activity 2
- Fold a sheet of paper in half three times. Draw a *scalene triangle* (no two sides congruent) on the folded paper. Carefully cut out the triangle. This will give you eight triangles that are all the same size and shape.
- Number the respective angles of each triangle 1, 2, and 3. (Use the same number on the corresponding angles from one triangle to the next.)

3. Mark a point P in the middle of a blank sheet of paper. How many of your triangles do you think you can fit perfectly about point P without gaps or overlaps? 6
4. What conjecture are you making about the sum of the measures of the angles about a point? The sum is 360°.

Exercises

5. Use the triangles from Activity 2. Based on your conjectures above, what combination of angles 1, 2, and 3 can you place at a point P to guarantee a perfect fit of triangles about P? The sum of the angles of a triangle is 180°. By using 2 of each angle, the sum will be 360°.
6. There are several ways to arrange the set of six angles 1, 1, 2, 2, 3, 3 to make a perfect fit about P. Make three different listings of the numbers 1, 1, 2, 2, 3, 3 around a point. Arrange your triangles about P to match your lists. Is any arrangement more appealing than the others? What happens if you turn over some of the triangles? Check students' work.
7. Follow the steps of Activity 1 using a *quadrilateral* (four-sided figure). Make a conjecture about the sum of the measures of the angles of a quadrilateral. The sum is 360°.
8. If you fit the angles of a quadrilateral about a point P without gaps or overlaps, what do you think you would discover? Justify your response. The angles would fit perfectly since their measures have a sum of 360°.

Concept Byte
Use With Lesson 3-5
ACTIVITY

Exploring Spherical Geometry

TN State Performance Indicator
SPI 3108.4.1 Differentiate between Euclidean and non-Euclidean geometries.

Euclid was a Greek mathematician who identified many of the definitions, postulates, and theorems of high school geometry. Euclidean geometry is the geometry of flat planes, straight lines, and points.

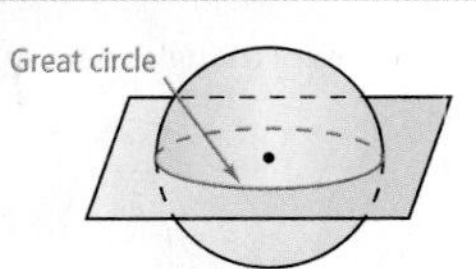

In spherical geometry, the curved surface of a sphere is studied. A "line" is a great circle. A *great circle* is the intersection of a sphere and a plane that contains the center of the sphere.

Activity 1

You can use latitude and longitude to identify positions on Earth. Look at the latitude and longitude markings on the globe.

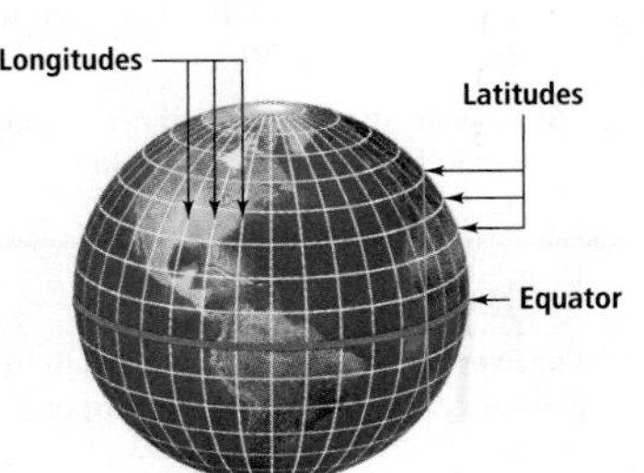

1. Think about "slicing" the globe with a plane at each latitude. Do any of your "slices" contain the center of the globe?
2. Think about "slicing" the globe with a plane at each longitude. Do any of your "slices" contain the center of the globe?
3. Which latitudes, if any, suggest great circles? Which longitudes, if any, suggest great circles? Explain.

You learned in Lesson 3.5 that through any point not on a line, there is one and only one line parallel to the given line (Parallel Postulate). That statement is not true in spherical geometry. In spherical geometry,

through a point not on a line, there is no line parallel to the given line.

Since lines are great circles in spherical geometry, two lines always intersect. In fact, any two lines on a sphere intersect at *two* points, as shown at the right.

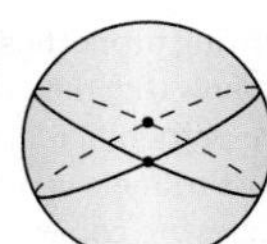

Guided Instruction

PURPOSE To explore spherical geometry
PROCESS Students will
- identify a plane in spherical geometry.
- identify a line in spherical geometry.
- define a great circle in spherical geometry.
- be able to describe a spherical triangle.

DISCUSS Spherical models can be used to examine the foundation of spherical geometry.

Q What are some spheres that can be used to explore spherical geometry? **[Answers will vary. Samples: globe, baseball, basketball, etc.]**

Activity 1

This Activity focuses on the relationships between spherical geometry and Earth's surface, using a globe as a reference. It refers to "slicing" the globe at the lines of latitude and longitude.

Q What is a line of latitude, and what is a line of longitude? **[A line of latitude contains all points that are an equal distance north or south of the equator. A line of longitude contains all points that are an equal distance east or west of the prime meridian.]**

Q How many great circles are there on the globe? **[infinitely many]**

Q What do you suppose a "small circle" refers to? **[Small circles are the "slices" that do not contain the center of the sphere.]**

Answers

Activity 1

1. yes, the slice at the equator
2. yes, all of them
3. The equator; all of them; a plane that intersects the sphere at the equator or at any longitude contains the center of the sphere.

Activity 2

In this Activity, students use three pieces of string and a sphere to create arcs that form a spherical triangle. They also measure the angles and make comparisons between the sums of these angle measures and the Triangle Angle-Sum Theorem of Euclidean geometry.

Q What does the Triangle Angle-Sum Theorem of Euclidean geometry state? **[The sum of the measures of the interior angles of any triangle is 180 degrees.]**

Q Before measuring the angles on your sphere, how do you suppose their sum will compare to those of a planar triangle? **[The angles look as if their sum will be greater than 180 degrees.]**

One result of the Parallel Postulate in Euclidean geometry is the Triangle Angle-Sum Theorem. The spherical geometry Parallel Postulate gives a very different result.

Activity 2

Hold a string taut between any two points on a sphere. The string forms a "segment" that is part of a great circle. Connect three such segments to form a triangle on the sphere.

Below are examples of triangles on a sphere.

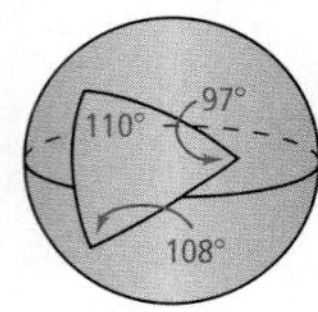

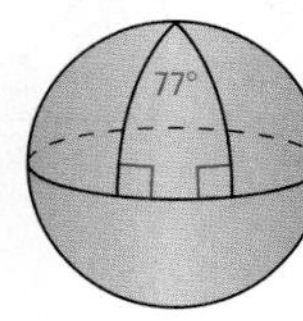

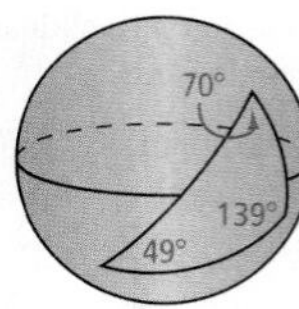

4. What is the sum of the angle measures in the first triangle? The second triangle? The third triangle?
5. How are these results different from the Triangle Angle-Sum Theorem in Euclidean geometry? Explain.

Exercises

For Exercises 6 and 7, draw a sketch to illustrate each property of spherical geometry. Explain how each property compares to what is true in Euclidean geometry.

6. There are pairs of points on a sphere through which you can draw more than one line.
7. Two equiangular triangles can have different angle measures.
8. For each of the following properties of Euclidean geometry, draw a counterexample to show that the property is *not* true in spherical geometry.
   a. Two lines that are perpendicular to the same line do not intersect.
   b. If two angles of one triangle are congruent to two angles of another triangle, then the third angles are congruent.
9. a. The figure at the right appears to show parallel lines on a sphere. Explain why this is not the case.
   b. Explain why a piece of the top circle in the figure is *not* a line segment. (*Hint:* What must be true of line segments in spherical geometry?)

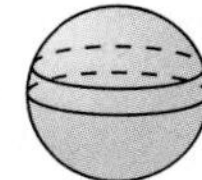

10. In Euclidean geometry, vertical angles are congruent. Does this seem to be true in spherical geometry? Explain. Make figures on a globe, ball, or balloon to support your answer.

Answers

Activity 2

4. 315; 257; 258
5. In spherical geometry, the sum of the measures of the int. ∠s of a △ is not constant.

Exercises

6. Answers may vary. Sample: In Euclidean geometry, there is exactly one line through two points.

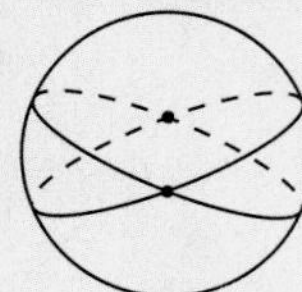

7. Answers may vary. Sample: In Euclidean geometry, the only possible equiangular △ has three 60° ∠s.

8a. Answers may vary. Sample:

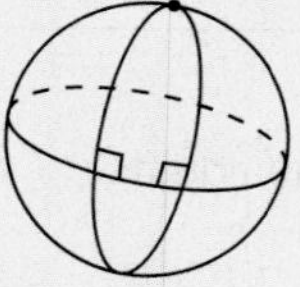

b.

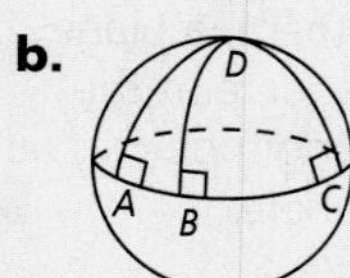

$\angle ADB \not\cong \angle ADC$

9a. At least one of the 2 curves is not a great circle, so it is not a line.

b. The top circle is not a line, so a piece of the top circle cannot be a line segment.

10. true

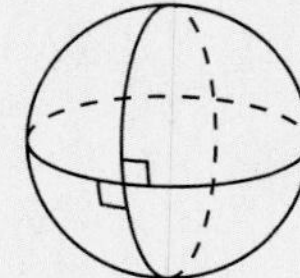

3 Mid-Chapter Quiz

Do you know HOW?

Identify the following. Lines and planes that appear to be parallel are parallel.

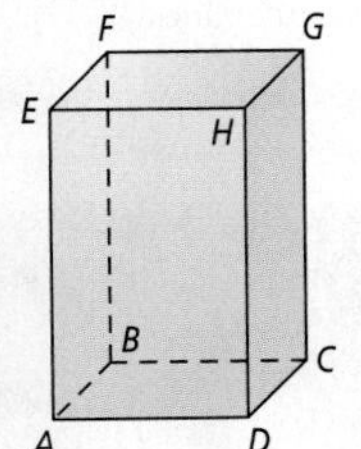

1. all segments parallel to $\overline{HG}$
2. a plane parallel to plane EFB
3. all segments skew to $\overline{EA}$
4. all segments parallel to plane $ABCD$

Use the diagram below for Exercises 5–14.

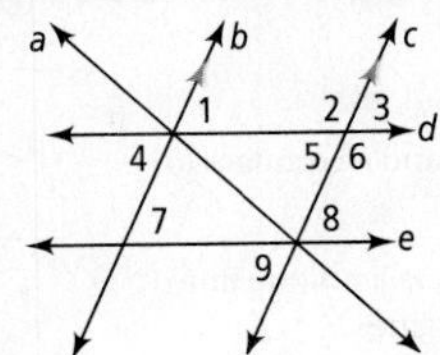

Name two pairs of each angle type.

5. corresponding angles
6. alternate interior angles
7. same-side interior angles

State the theorem or postulate that justifies each statement.

8. $\angle 7 \cong \angle 9$
9. $\angle 4 \cong \angle 5$
10. $m\angle 1 + m\angle 2 = 180$

Complete each statement.

11. If $\angle 5 \cong \angle 9$, then __?__ $\parallel$ __?__.
12. If $\angle 4 \cong$ __?__, then $d \parallel e$.
13. If $e \perp b$, then $e \perp$ __?__.
14. If $c \perp d$, then $b \perp$ __?__.

Find $m\angle 1$.

15.

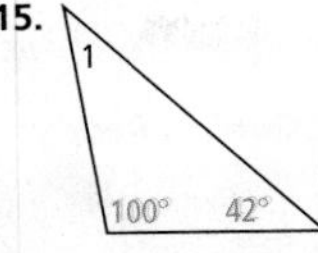

16.

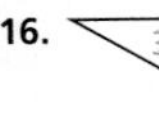

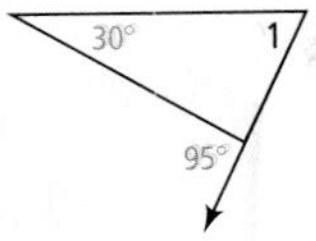

Find the value of x for which $a \parallel b$.

17.

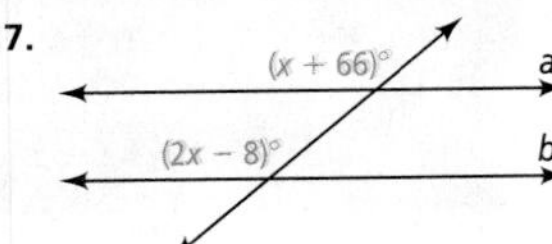

18.

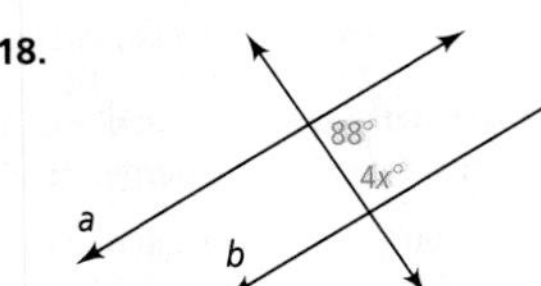

19. What is the value of x?

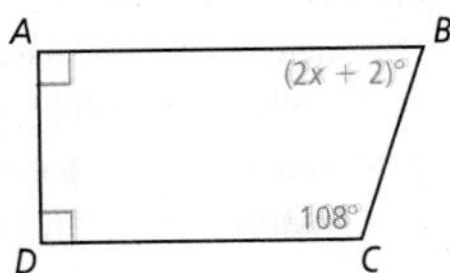

Do you UNDERSTAND?

20. **Reasoning** Can a pair of lines be both parallel and skew? Explain.
21. **Open-Ended** Give an example of parallel lines in the real world. Then describe how you could prove that the lines are parallel.
22. **Reasoning** Lines ℓ, r, and s are coplanar. Suppose ℓ is perpendicular to r and r is perpendicular to s. Is ℓ perpendicular to s? Explain.

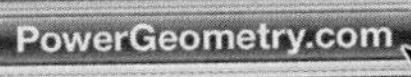

Answers

Mid-Chapter Quiz

1. $\overline{EF}$, $\overline{AB}$, $\overline{DC}$
2. plane HGC
3. $\overline{FG}$, $\overline{HG}$, $\overline{BC}$, $\overline{DC}$
4. $\overline{EF}$, $\overline{FG}$, $\overline{GH}$, $\overline{EH}$
5. any two of $\angle 1$ and $\angle 3$, $\angle 3$ and $\angle 8$, $\angle 4$ and $\angle 5$, $\angle 5$ and $\angle 9$, $\angle 7$ and $\angle 8$, $\angle 1$ and $\angle 7$
6. any two of $\angle 1$ and $\angle 5$, $\angle 4$ and $\angle 7$, $\angle 5$ and $\angle 8$, $\angle 7$ and $\angle 9$
7. $\angle 1$ and $\angle 2$, $\angle 6$ and $\angle 8$
8. Alt. Int. ∠s Thm.
9. Corresp. ∠s Post.
10. Same-side Int. ∠s Thm.
11. $d \parallel e$
12. $\angle 7$
13. c
14. d
15. 38
16. 65
17. 74
18. 23
19. 35
20. No; sample: Parallel lines are coplanar and skew lines are noncoplanar.
21. Answers may vary. Sample: A referee signaling a goal or touchdown has forearms that are parallel; a proof could use the fact that both forearms are $\perp$ to the line from elbow to elbow, and in a plane, two lines $\perp$ to the same line are $\parallel$.
22. No; ℓ and s are both $\perp$ to r, so they are $\parallel$.

1 Interactive Learning

Solve It!

PURPOSE To put together a paper-folding construction for parallel and perpendicular lines
PROCESS Students use paper folding and spatial reasoning using known definitions and theorems.

FACILITATE

Q What is true about two lines that are perpendicular to the same line in a plane? **[They are the same line or they are parallel to each other.]**

ANSWER See Solve It in Answers on next page.
CONNECT THE MATH Guide students to see the difference between a drawing and a construction. A drawing is a sketch used as an aid for understanding. A construction is a method of accurately creating a figure using specified tools.

2 Guided Instruction

Problem 1

Q What is the first step necessary to construct $\angle 1$? **[Put the compass point on vertex *H*, and draw an arc that intersects the sides of $\angle NHJ$.]**

Q What do you do next, keeping the compass open to the same width? **[Put the compass point on vertex *N* and draw an arc that intersects $\overleftrightarrow{HN}$.]**

Got It?

ERROR PREVENTION
Students should use the Converse of the Corresponding Angles Postulate rather than the Corresponding Angles Postulate.

3-6 Constructing Parallel and Perpendicular Lines

Objective To construct parallel and perpendicular lines

Check out the angles formed by the folded lines.

Getting Ready!

Draw a line m on a sheet of paper. Fold your paper so that line m falls on itself. Label your fold line n. Fold your paper again so that n falls on itself. Label your new fold line p. How are m and p related? How do you know?

In the Solve It, you used paper-folding to construct lines.

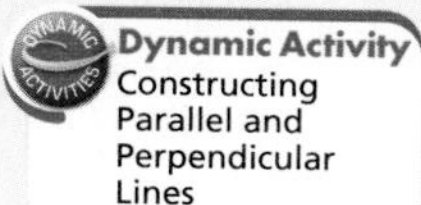

Essential Understanding You can also use a straightedge and a compass to construct parallel and perpendicular lines.

In Lesson 3-5, you learned that through a point not on a line, there is a unique line parallel to the given line. Problem 1 shows the construction of this line.

Problem 1 Constructing Parallel Lines

Construct the line parallel to a given line and through a given point that is not on the line.

Given: line ℓ and point N not on ℓ
Construct: line m through N with $m \parallel \ell$

Step 1 Label two points H and J on ℓ. Draw $\overleftrightarrow{HN}$.

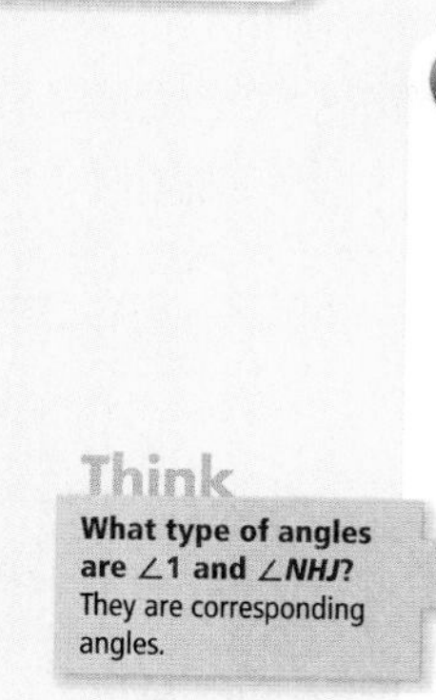

Think
What type of angles are ∠1 and ∠NHJ?
They are corresponding angles.

Step 2 At N, construct $\angle 1$ congruent to $\angle NHJ$. Label the new line m.

$m \parallel \ell$

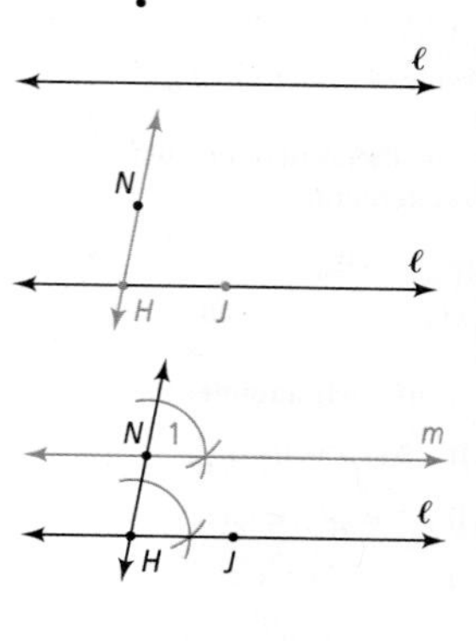

Got It? 1. Reasoning Why must lines ℓ and m be parallel?

3-6 Preparing to Teach

ESSENTIAL UNDERSTANDINGS

- Parallel and perpendicular lines can be constructed with a straightedge and compass.
- Special quadrilaterals can be constructed with a straightedge and compass.

Math Background

Constructions are often a difficult topic for students to understand. They fail to grasp that drawings can be made more precisely when they do not rely on marked measuring devices. You can demonstrate the discrepancies introduced when a ruler or protractor is used by creating two of the same diagram, one using a finely sharpened pencil and one using a pencil that needs to be sharpened. Once students see the precision achieved through constructions, it is important to offer different methods for performing constructions, including paper folding, straightedge and compass, and geometric software. Students should also realize that there are different steps and different theorems to use. Just as lines can be proven parallel through the use of multiple theorems, parallel lines can be constructed using multiple methods. The paper-folding activity at the beginning of the lesson is based on the theorem "In a plane, if two lines are perpendicular to the same line, then they are parallel to each other." The straightedge-and-compass construction shown in the lesson is based on the Converse of the Corresponding Angles Postulate. Another method for constructing parallel lines could be based on the Converse of the Alternate Interior Angles Theorem.

Support Student Learning

Use the **Geometry Companion** to engage and support students during instructions. See Lesson Resources at the end of this lesson for details.

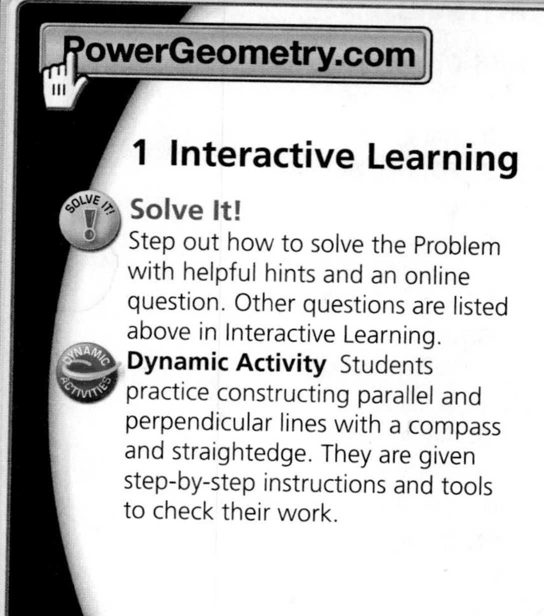

Problem 2 Constructing a Special Quadrilateral

Plan

How do you know which constructions to use?
Try sketching the final figure. This can help you visualize the construction steps you will need.

Construct a quadrilateral with one pair of parallel sides of lengths *a* and *b*.

Given: segments of lengths *a* and *b*

Construct: quadrilateral *ABYZ* with $AZ = a$, $BY = b$, and $\overleftrightarrow{AZ} \parallel \overleftrightarrow{BY}$

Think

You need a pair of parallel sides, so construct parallel lines as you did in Problem 1. Start by drawing a ray with endpoint *A*. Then draw $\overrightarrow{AB}$ such that point *B* is not on the first ray.

Construct congruent corresponding angles to finish your parallel lines.

Now you need sides of lengths *a* and *b*. In Lesson 1-6, you learned how to construct congruent segments. Construct *Y* and *Z* so that $BY = b$ and $AZ = a$.

Draw $\overline{YZ}$.

Write

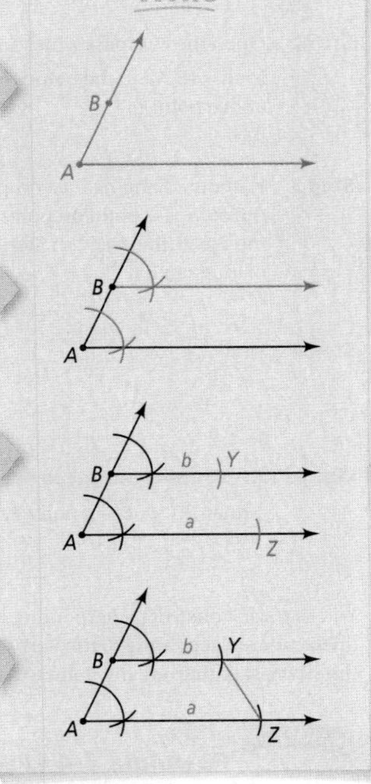

ABYZ is a quadrilateral with parallel sides of lengths *a* and *b*.

 **Got It? 2. a.** Draw a segment. Label its length *m*. Construct quadrilateral *ABCD* with $\overleftrightarrow{AB} \parallel \overleftrightarrow{CD}$, so that $AB = m$ and $CD = 2m$.

b. Reasoning Suppose you and a friend both use the steps in Problem 2 to construct *ABYZ* independently. Will your quadrilaterals necessarily have the same angle measures and side lengths? Explain.

Problem 2

Q What biconditional serves as a definition for congruent segments? **[Answers may vary. Sample: Two segments are congruent if and only if the two segments have the same length.]**

Q Why is a compass used to construct congruent segments rather than a ruler? **[Using a compass to construct congruent segments is more accurate than using a ruler, because the compass can match the length exactly, while the ruler can only match it to the nearest mark.]**

Q Will the lines that contain $\overline{AB}$ and $\overline{YZ}$ intersect? Explain. **[Yes, the lines will intersect because they are not parallel.]**

Got It? VISUAL LEARNERS

Q What conditions must be met for two quadrilaterals to be congruent? **[The corresponding segments must be congruent and the corresponding angles must be congruent.]**

2 Guided Instruction

Each Problem is worked out and supported online.

Problem 1
Constructing Parallel Lines

Alternative Problem 1
Constructing Parallel Lines

Problem 2
Constructing a Special Quadrilateral
Animated

Problem 3
Perpendicular at a Point on a Line
Animated

Problem 4
Perpendicular From a Point to a Line

Support in Geometry Companion
- Vocabulary
- Key Concepts
- Got It?

Answers

Solve It!

$m \parallel p$; both *m* and *p* are perpendicular to *n*.

Got It?

1. $\angle 1$ and $\angle NHJ$ are corresp. $\angle$s for lines *m* and ℓ. Since $\angle 1 \cong \angle NHJ$, then $m \parallel \ell$.

2a. Answers may vary. Sample:

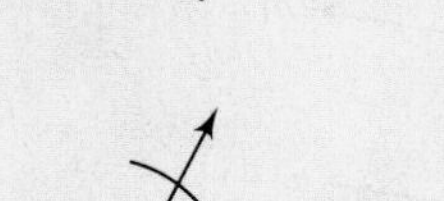

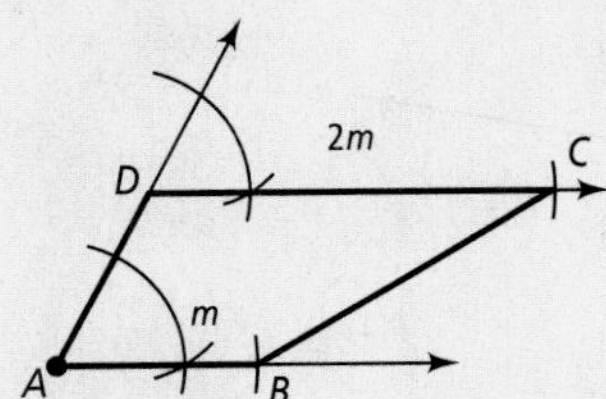

b. No; the length of $\overline{AB}$ and $m\angle A$ are not determined.

Problem 3

Q How could this construction be completed using paper folding? **[Fold line ℓ onto itself creating a new line (crease) that contains point *P*.]**

Q What segment measures exactly $\frac{1}{2}AB$? **[$\overline{AP}$ or $\overline{PB}$.]**

Q If you open the compass wider and repeat steps 2 and 3, what will happen? **[The arcs will also intersect at a point on $\overleftrightarrow{CP}$.]**

Q What is the measure of $\angle CPA$? of $\angle CPB$? Explain. **[Both angles measure 90 because the lines are perpendicular.]**

Got It?

VISUAL LEARNERS

Students will need to use the compass to add an auxiliary point on the line in order to complete the construction using the steps given in Problem 3.

TACTILE LEARNERS

Students who struggle to use a compass and straightedge efficiently will benefit from performing this construction using patty paper.

Take Note

SYNTHESIZING

Ask students to compare and contrast the Parallel Postulate with the Perpendicular Postulate.

Problem 3 Perpendicular at a Point on a Line

Construct the perpendicular to a given line at a given point on the line.

Given: point *P* on line ℓ

Construct: $\overleftrightarrow{CP}$ with $\overleftrightarrow{CP} \perp \ell$

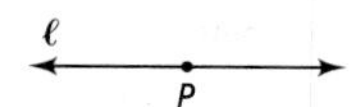

Think

Why is it important to open your compass wider?
If you don't, you won't be able to draw intersecting arcs above point *P*.

Step 1 Construct two points on ℓ that are equidistant from *P*. Label the points *A* and *B*.

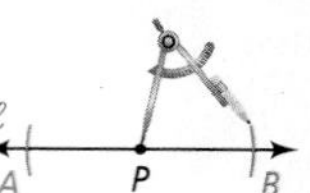

Step 2 Open the compass wider so the opening is greater than $\frac{1}{2}AB$. With the compass tip on *A*, draw an arc above point *P*.

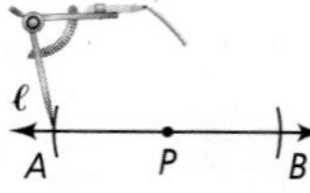

Step 3 Without changing the compass setting, place the compass point on point *B*. Draw an arc that intersects the arc from Step 2. Label the point of intersection *C*.

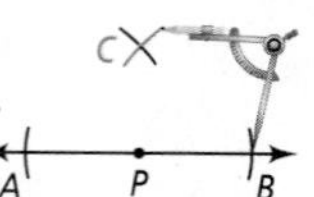

Step 4 Draw $\overleftrightarrow{CP}$.

$\overleftrightarrow{CP} \perp \ell$

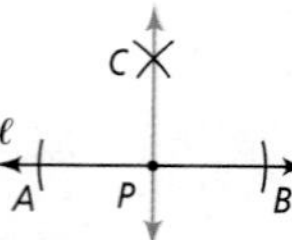

Got It? 3. Use a straightedge to draw $\overleftrightarrow{EF}$. Construct $\overleftrightarrow{FG}$ so that $\overleftrightarrow{FG} \perp \overleftrightarrow{EF}$ at point *F*.

You can also construct a perpendicular line from a point to a line. This perpendicular line is unique according to the Perpendicular Postulate. You will prove in Chapter 5 that the shortest path from any point to a line is along this unique perpendicular line.

take note

Postulate 3-4 Perpendicular Postulate

Through a point not on a line, there is one and only one line perpendicular to the given line.

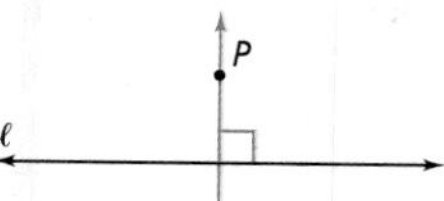

There is exactly one line through *P* perpendicular to ℓ.

Additional Problems

1. Construct line *m* through *P* with $m \parallel n$.

P
n

ANSWER

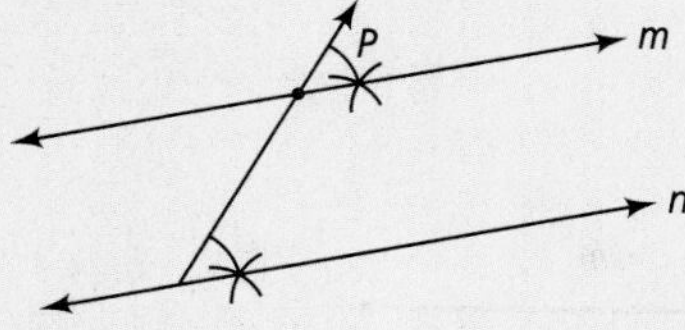

2. Construct *ABCD* with $AB = a$, $\overline{AB} \parallel \overline{CD}$, and $CD = b$.

ANSWER

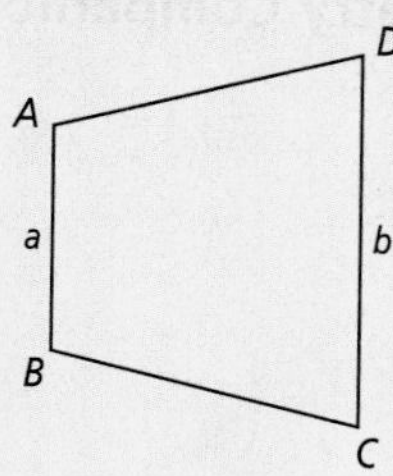

3. Construct $\overline{RS}$ with $\overline{RS} \perp m$.

S
m

ANSWER

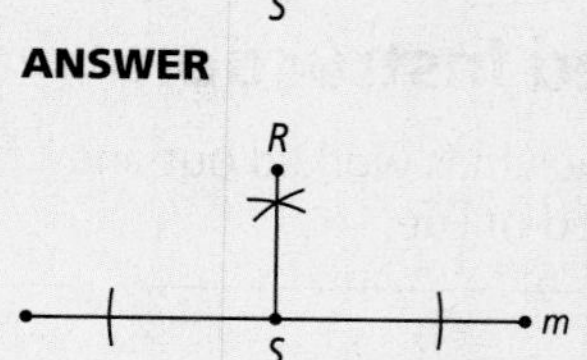

4. Construct $\overline{CD}$ with $\overline{CD} \perp \ell$.

C
ℓ

ANSWER

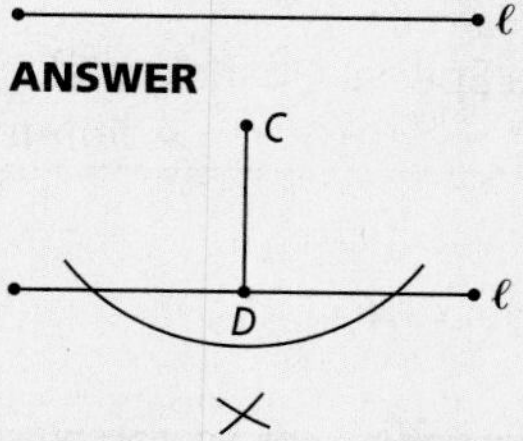

Problem 4 Perpendicular From a Point to a Line

Construct the perpendicular to a given line through a given point not on the line.

Given: line ℓ and point R not on ℓ

Construct: $\overleftrightarrow{RG}$ with $\overleftrightarrow{RG} \perp \ell$

Plan

Can you use similar steps for this problem as in Problem 3?
Yes. Mark two points on ℓ that are equidistant from the given point. Then draw two intersecting arcs.

Step 1 Open your compass to a size greater than the distance from R to ℓ. With the compass on point R, draw an arc that intersects ℓ at two points. Label the points E and F.

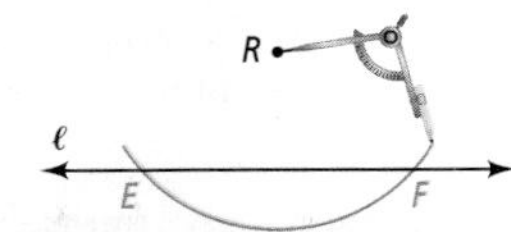

Step 2 Place the compass point on E and make an arc.

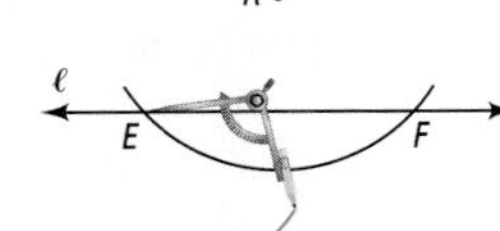

Step 3 Keep the same compass setting. With the compass tip on F, draw an arc that intersects the arc from Step 2. Label the point of intersection G.

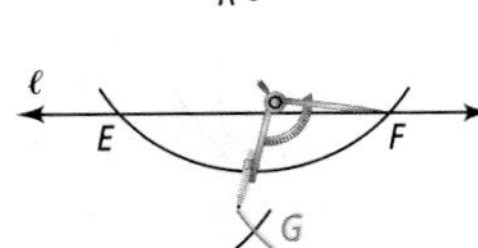

Step 4 Draw $\overleftrightarrow{RG}$.

$\overleftrightarrow{RG} \perp \ell$

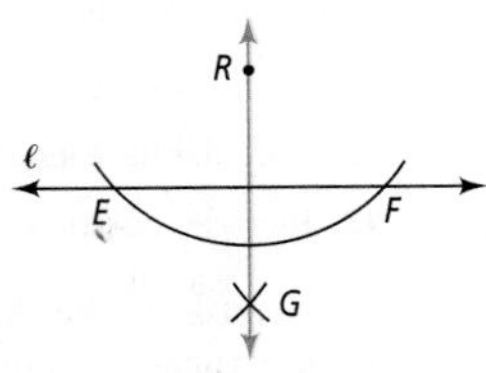

Got It? 4. Draw $\overleftrightarrow{CX}$ and a point Z not on $\overleftrightarrow{CX}$. Construct $\overleftrightarrow{ZB}$ so that $\overleftrightarrow{ZB} \perp \overleftrightarrow{CX}$.

Problem 4

Q Is every point on line ℓ equidistant from point R? Explain. **[No, segments connecting point R to various points on line ℓ are not congruent.]**

Q If you do not change the width of the compass setting from Step 1 to Step 2, where will the two new arcs intersect? **[They will intersect at point R and at a point below the arc drawn in Step 1.]**

Q If a point, H, is created on the opposite side of line ℓ by repeating Step 3, what is the relationship of H to $\overleftrightarrow{RG}$? Explain. **[The point lies on $\overleftrightarrow{RG}$.]**

Got It? ERROR PREVENTION

Many students are whole-part learners, which means they do not learn in step-by-step sequence. For these students, seeing a sketch of the final product before beginning the construction process can be crucial in helping them to understand the construction and the geometry being demonstrated.

Answers

Got It? (continued)

3.

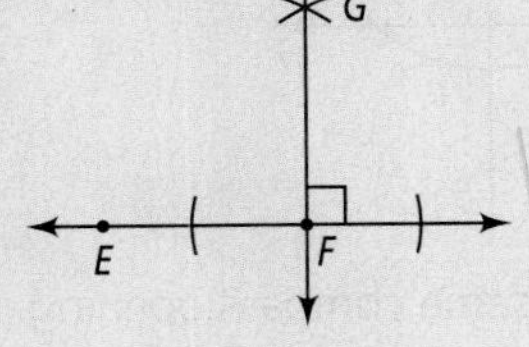

4.

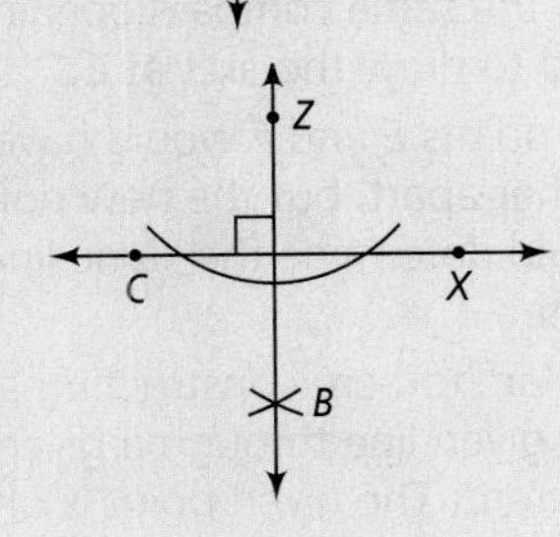

3 Lesson Check

Do you know HOW?

- If students have difficulty with Exercise 2, then have them review the steps shown in Problem 3.

Do you UNDERSTAND?

- If students have difficulty with Exercise 4, then have them review the definition of congruent segments discussed in Lesson 1-3. They can verify their answer by using their compass as a measuring tool.

Close

Q How could you use the construction of two perpendicular lines to construct a line parallel to a given line? Explain. **[Construct a line perpendicular to the given line; then construct another line perpendicular to the line created.]**

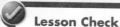

Lesson Check

Do you know HOW?

1. Draw a line ℓ and a point P not on the line. Construct the line through P parallel to line ℓ.
2. Draw $\overleftrightarrow{QR}$ and a point S on the line. Construct the line perpendicular to $\overleftrightarrow{QR}$ at point S.
3. Draw a line w and a point X not on the line. Construct the line perpendicular to line w at point X.

Do you UNDERSTAND?

4. In Problem 3, is $\overline{AC}$ congruent to $\overline{BC}$? Explain.
5. Suppose you use a wider compass setting in Step 1 of Problem 4. Will you construct a different perpendicular line? Explain.
6. **Compare and Contrast** How are the constructions in Problems 3 and 4 similar? How are they different?

Practice and Problem-Solving Exercises

A Practice

For Exercises 7–10, draw a figure like the given one. Then construct the line through point J that is parallel to $\overleftrightarrow{AB}$.

 See Problem 1.

7.

8. 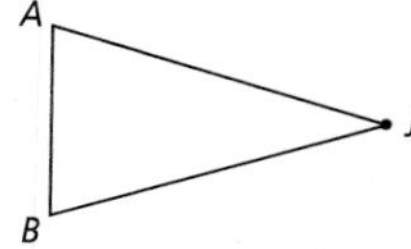

9. 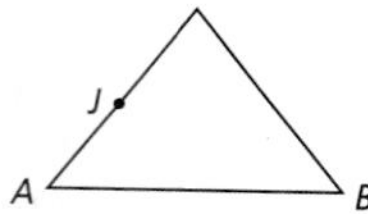

10. 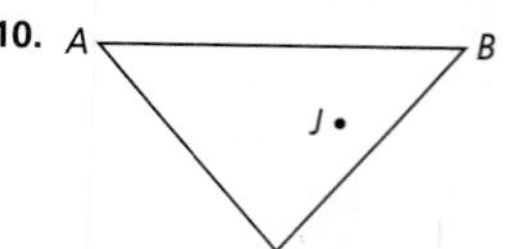

For Exercises 11–13, draw two segments. Label their lengths a and b. Construct a quadrilateral with one pair of parallel sides as described.

See Problem 2.

11. The sides have length a and b.
12. The sides have length $2a$ and b.
13. The sides have length a and $\frac{1}{2}b$.

For Exercises 14 and 15, draw a figure like the given one. Then construct the line that is perpendicular to ℓ at point P.

See Problem 3.

14.

15.

PowerGeometry.com

3 Lesson Check

For a digital lesson check, use the Got It questions.

Support in Geometry Companion

- Lesson Check

4 Practice

Assign homework to individual students or to an entire class.

Answers

Lesson Check

1. 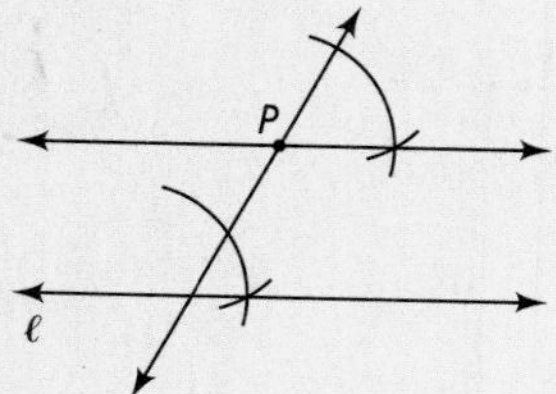

2. 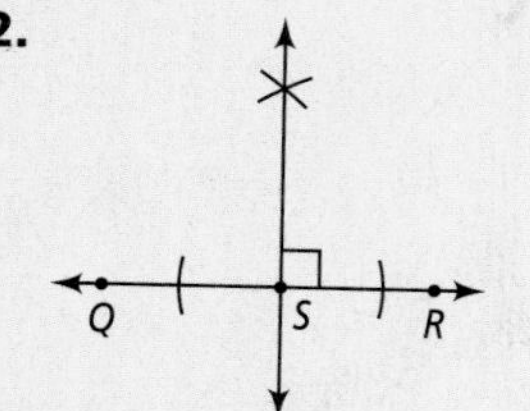

3. 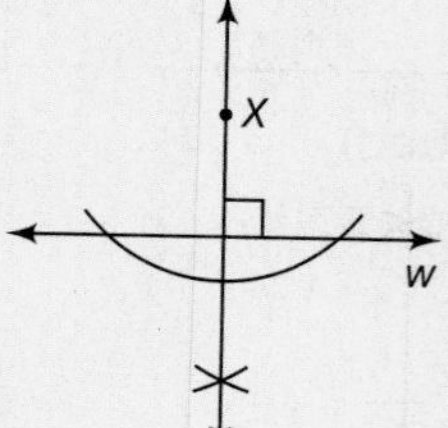

4. Yes; the same compass opening is used to draw the arcs at C.
5. No; points E and F would have been further apart, but the new point G would determine the same line $\overleftrightarrow{RG}$ as in Step 4.
6. Similar: You are constructing a line $\perp$ to a given line through a given point; different: The given point is on the given line in Problem 3 and is not on the given line in Problem 4.

Practice and Problem-Solving Exercises

7–20. See back of book.

For Exercises 16–18, draw a figure like the given one. Then construct the line through point P that is perpendicular to $\overleftrightarrow{RS}$.

See Problem 4.

16. 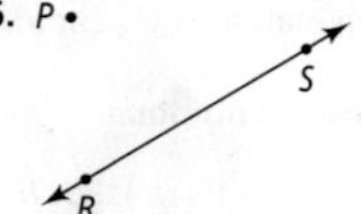

17. 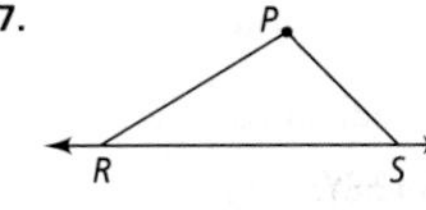

18. 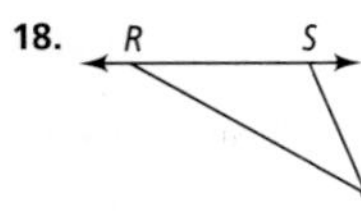

B Apply

19. **Think About a Plan** Draw an acute angle. Construct an angle congruent to your angle so that the two angles are alternate interior angles.
   - What does a sketch of the angle look like?
   - Which construction(s) should you use?

20. **Constructions** Construct a square with side length p.

21. **Writing** Explain how to use the Converse of the Alternate Interior Angles Theorem to construct a line parallel to the given line through a point not on the line. (*Hint:* See Exercise 19.)

For Exercises 22–28, use the segments at the right.

22. Draw a line m. Construct a segment of length b that is perpendicular to line m.
23. Construct a rectangle with base b and height c.
24. Construct a square with sides of length a.
25. Construct a rectangle with one side of length a and a diagonal of length b.
26. a. Construct a quadrilateral with a pair of parallel sides of length c.
    b. **Make a Conjecture** What appears to be true about the other pair of sides in the quadrilateral you constructed?
    c. Use a protractor, a ruler, or both to check the conjecture you made in part (b).
27. Construct a right triangle with legs of lengths a and b.
28. a. Construct a triangle with sides of lengths a, b, and c.
    b. Construct the midpoint of each side of the triangle.
    c. Form a new triangle by connecting the midpoints.
    d. **Make a Conjecture** How do the sides of the smaller triangle and the sides of the larger triangle appear to be related?
    e. Use a protractor, ruler, or both to check the conjecture you made in part (d).
29. **Constructions** The diagrams below show steps for a parallel line construction.

I. 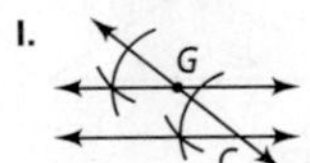

II. 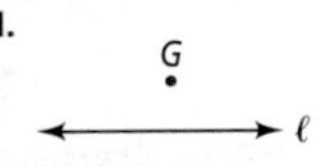

III. 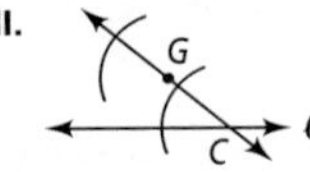

IV. 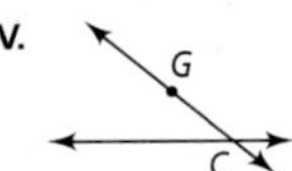

    a. List the construction steps in the correct order.
    b. For the steps that use a compass, describe the location(s) of the compass point.

4 Practice

ASSIGNMENT GUIDE

Basic: 7–21 all, 22–26 even, 27
Average: 7–17 odd, 19–29
Advanced: 7–17 odd, 19–39
Standardized Test Prep: 40–42
Mixed Review: 43–47

Reasoning exercises have blue headings.
Applications exercises have red headings.

EXERCISE 27: Use the Think About a Plan worksheet in the **Practice and Problem Solving Workbook** (also available in the Teaching Resources in print and online) to further support students' development in becoming independent learners.

HOMEWORK QUICK CHECK

To check students' understanding of key skills and concepts, go over Exercises 11, 17, 19, 21, and 27.

21. Construct a ≅ alt. int. ∠, then draw the ∥ line.

22. 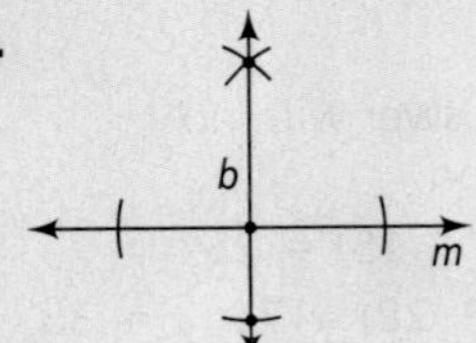

23. 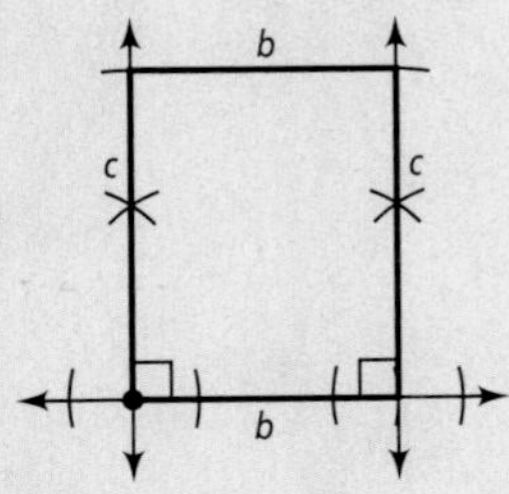

24. 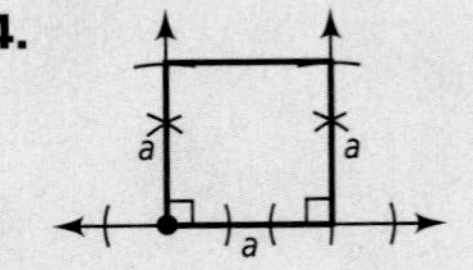

25. 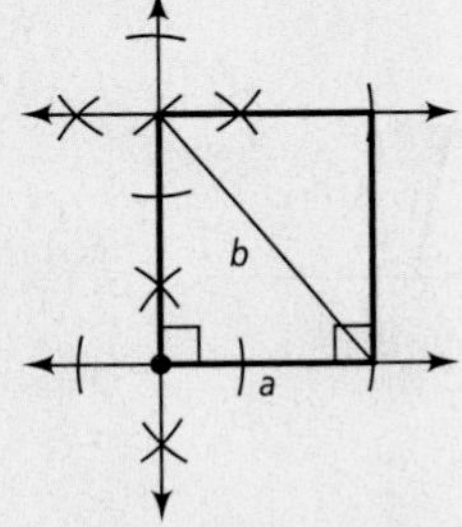

26a. Answers may vary. Sample:

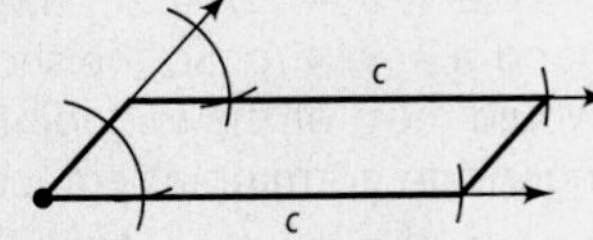

b. Sample: The sides are ∥ and ≅.
c. Check students' work.

27.

28a–c. 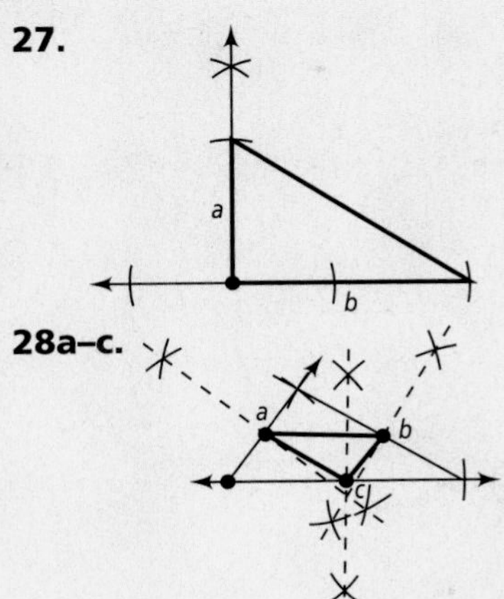

d. Sample: The sides of the smaller △ are half the length and ∥ to the sides of the larger △.
e. Check students' work.

29a. II, IV, III, I

b. III: points C and G; I: the intersection of $\overleftrightarrow{GC}$ with the arcs from Step III

Answers

Practice and Problem-Solving Exercises (continued)

30–39. Constructions may vary. Samples are given.

30.

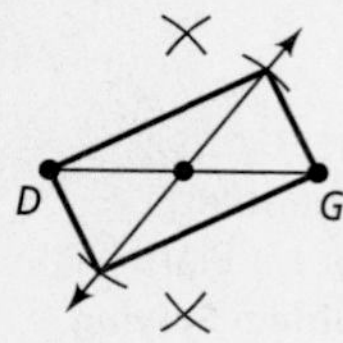

rectangle

31.

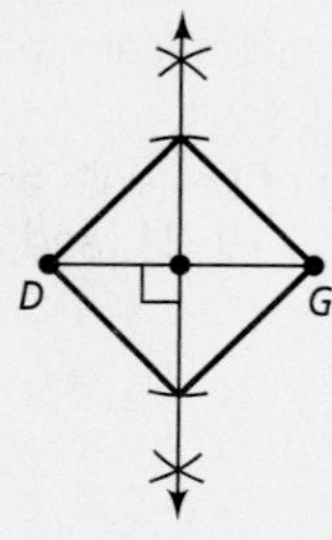

square

32.

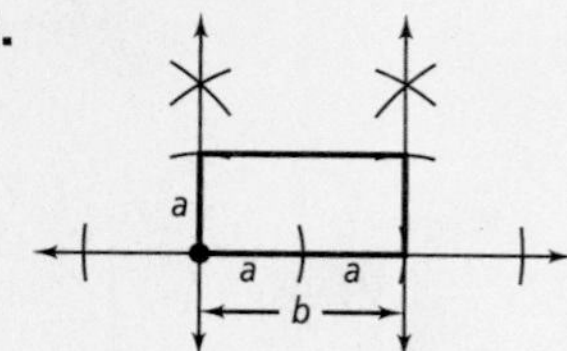

33.

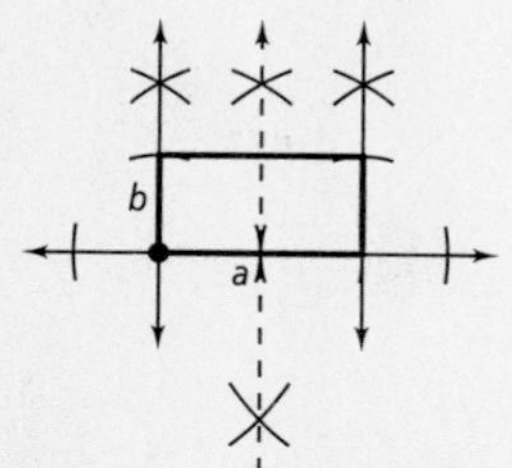

34.

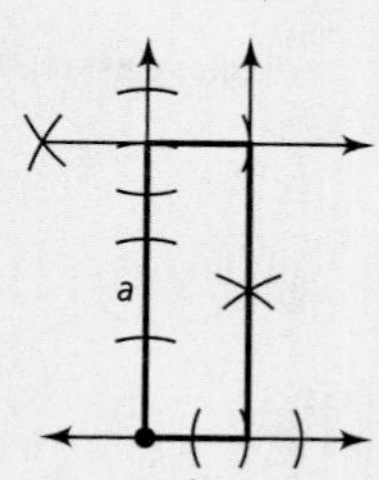

35.

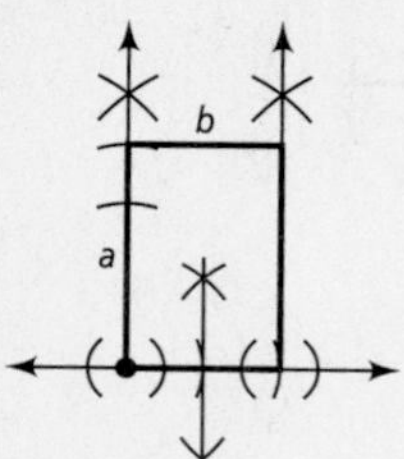

36.

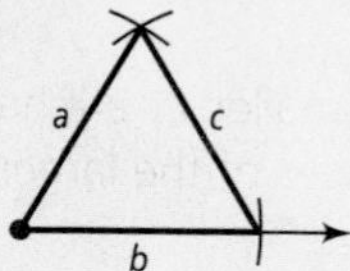

Challenge **Draw $\overline{DG}$. Construct a quadrilateral with diagonals that are congruent to $\overline{DG}$, bisect each other, and meet the given conditions. Describe the figure.**

30. The diagonals are not perpendicular. **31.** The diagonals are perpendicular.

Construct a rectangle with side lengths a and b that meets the given condition.

32. $b = 2a$ **33.** $b = \frac{1}{2}a$ **34.** $b = \frac{1}{3}a$ **35.** $b = \frac{2}{3}a$

Construct a triangle with side lengths a, b, and c that meets the given conditions. If such a triangle is not possible, explain.

36. $a = b = c$ **37.** $a = b = 2c$ **38.** $a = 2b = 2c$ **39.** $a = b + c$

Standardized Test Prep

SAT/ACT

40. The diagram at the right shows the construction of $\overleftrightarrow{CP}$ perpendicular to line ℓ through point P. Which of the following *must* be true?

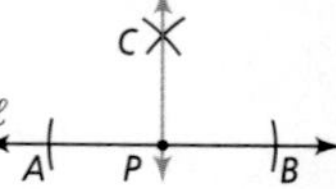

A $\overleftrightarrow{CB} \parallel \overleftrightarrow{AB}$

B $CP = \frac{1}{2}AB$

C $\overleftrightarrow{AC} \parallel \overleftrightarrow{CB}$

D $\overline{AC} \cong \overline{BC}$

41. Suppose you construct lines ℓ, m, and n so that $\ell \perp m$ and $\ell \parallel n$. Which of the following is true?

F $m \parallel n$ G $m \parallel \ell$ H $n \perp \ell$ I $n \perp m$

Short Response

42. For any two points, you can draw one segment. For any three noncollinear points, you can draw three segments. For any four noncollinear points, you can draw six segments. How many segments can you draw for eight noncollinear points? Explain your reasoning.

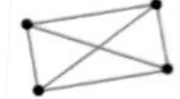

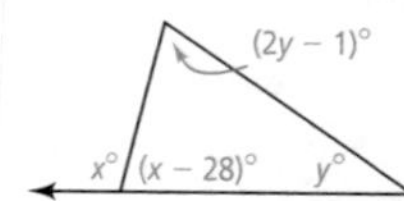

Mixed Review

Find each missing angle measure. See Lesson 3-5.

43. 35° $(y - 15)°$ $3y°$

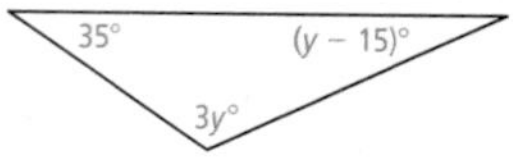

44. $(2y - 1)°$ $x°$ $(x - 28)°$ $y°$

Get Ready! **To prepare for Lesson 3-7, do Exercises 45–47.**

Simplify each ratio. See p. 831.

45. $\frac{2 - (-3)}{6 - (-4)}$ **46.** $\frac{1 - 4}{-2 - 1}$ **47.** $\frac{12 - 6}{2 - 5}$

37.

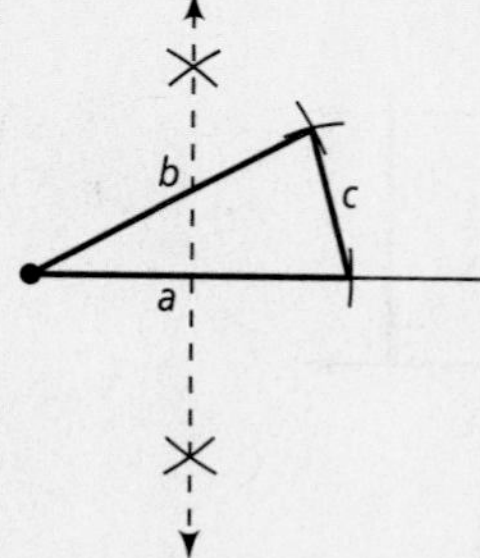

38. Not possible; if $a = 2b = 2c$, then $b = c$ and $a = b + c$. So the shorter sides would meet at the midpoint of the longer side, forming a segment.

39. Not possible; the shorter sides would meet at a point on the longer side, forming a segment.

40. D

41. I

42. [2] 28; if n is the number of points, then $\frac{n(n-1)}{2}$ is the number of segments.
[1] correct answer with no explanation

43. $3y = 120$, $(y - 15) = 25$

44. $x = 104$, $(x - 28) = 76$, $y = 35$, $(2y - 1) = 69$

45. $\frac{1}{2}$

46. 1

47. -2

3-6 Lesson Resources

Differentiated Remediation

Instructional Support

Geometry Companion

Students can use the **Geometry Companion** worktext (4 pages) . . .

- New Vocabulary
- Key Concepts
- Got It for each Problem
- Lesson Check

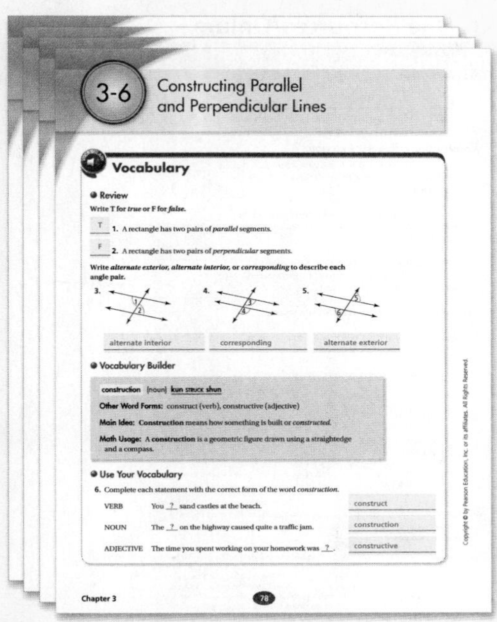

3-6 Constructing Parallel and Perpendicular Lines

Vocabulary

Review

Write T for *true* or F for *false*.

T 1. A rectangle has two pairs of *parallel* segments.

F 2. A rectangle has two pairs of *perpendicular* segments.

Write *alternate exterior, alternate interior,* or *corresponding* to describe each angle pair.

3. alternate interior 4. corresponding 5. alternate exterior

Vocabulary Builder

construction (noun) kun STRUCK shun

Other Word Forms: construct (verb), constructive (adjective)

Main Idea: **Construction** means how something is built or *constructed*.

Math Usage: A **construction** is a geometric figure drawn using a straightedge and a compass.

Use Your Vocabulary

6. Complete each statement with the correct form of the word *construction*.

VERB You _?_ sand castles at the beach. construct

NOUN The _?_ on the highway caused quite a traffic jam. construction

ADJECTIVE The time you spent working on your homework was _?_. constructive

Chapter 3 78

ELL Support

Focus on Communication Model using a straightedge and compass to construct parallel lines. Use sentences like the following: Draw a line with the straightedge; use the compass to draw an arc; use the straightedge to draw a line through the two points; the lines are parallel. Have the students repeat each sentence and imitate each action after you demonstrate it.

Now arrange students into pairs of mixed abilities. Have one student in each pair read the directions for constructing perpendicular lines while the other student uses a compass and straightedge to construct the lines. Have each pair of students compare their construction with another pair. Help the students decide which constructions are most accurate. Have the students switch roles so that students who were reading now do the construction. The students who did the construction should now read the directions. Display the best example from each pair on a bulletin board.

5 Assess & Remediate

Lesson Quiz

1. Construct line k through D with $k \parallel \ell$.

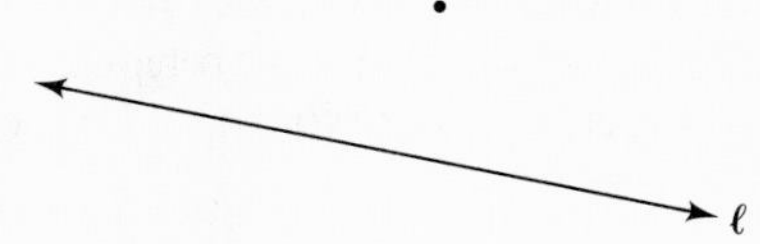

2. Construct $\overline{FG}$ with $\overline{FG} \perp h$.

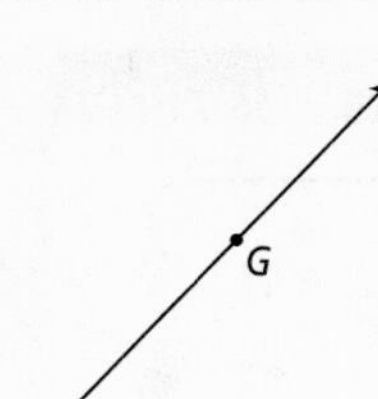

ANSWERS TO LESSON QUIZ

1.

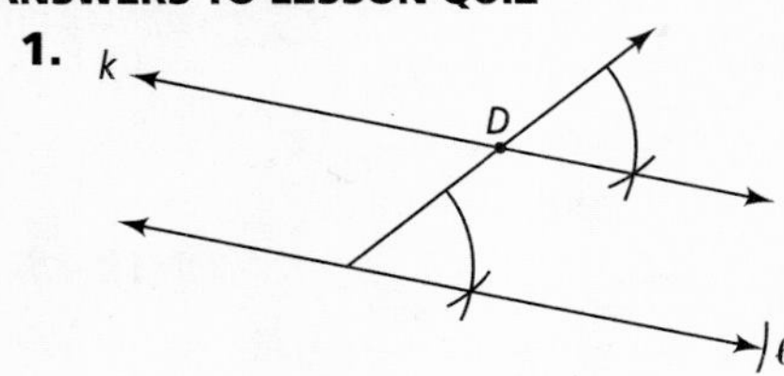

2.

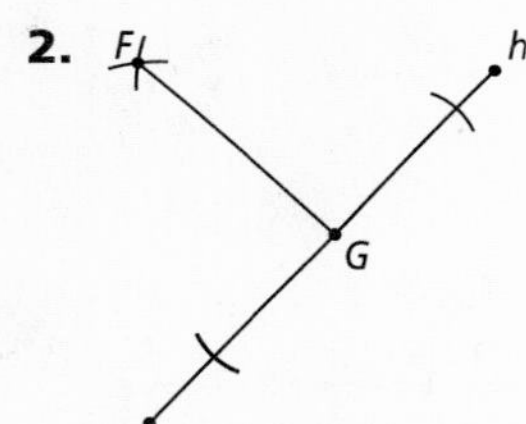

PRECRIPTION FOR REMEDIATION

Use the student work on the Lesson Quiz to prescribe a differentiated review assignment.

Points	Differentiated Remediation
0	Intervention
1	On-level
2	Extension

PowerGeometry.com

5 Assess & Remediate

Assign the Lesson Quiz. Appropriate intervention, practice, or enrichment is automatically generated based on student performance.

Intervention

- **Reteaching** (2 pages) Provides reteaching and practice exercises for the key lesson concepts. Use with struggling students or absent students.
- **English Language Learner Support** Helps students develop and reinforce mathematical vocabulary and key concepts.

All-in-One Resources/Online

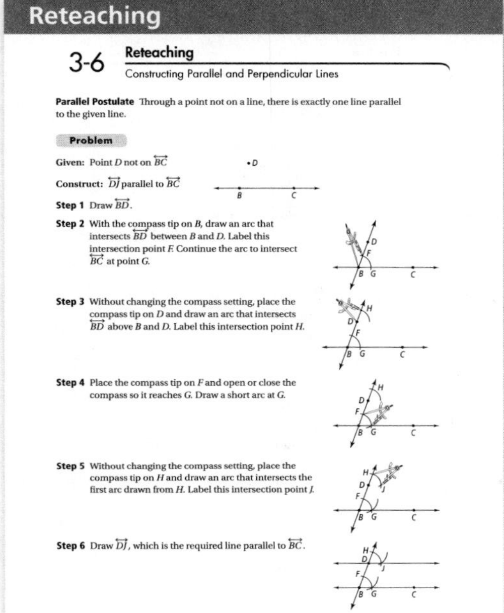

Reteaching

3-6 Reteaching
Constructing Parallel and Perpendicular Lines

Parallel Postulate Through a point not on a line, there is exactly one line parallel to the given line.

Problem

Given: Point D not on $\overleftrightarrow{BC}$

Construct: $\overleftrightarrow{DJ}$ parallel to $\overleftrightarrow{BC}$

Step 1 Draw $\overleftrightarrow{BD}$.

Step 2 With the compass tip on B, draw an arc that intersects $\overleftrightarrow{BD}$ between B and D. Label this intersection point F. Continue the arc to intersect $\overleftrightarrow{BC}$ at point G.

Step 3 Without changing the compass setting, place the compass tip on D and draw an arc that intersects $\overleftrightarrow{BD}$ above B and D. Label this intersection point H.

Step 4 Place the compass tip on F and open or close the compass so it reaches G. Draw a short arc at G.

Step 5 Without changing the compass setting, place the compass tip on H and draw an arc that intersects the first arc drawn from H. Label this intersection point J.

Step 6 Draw $\overleftrightarrow{DJ}$, which is the required line parallel to $\overleftrightarrow{BC}$.

All-in-One Resources/Online

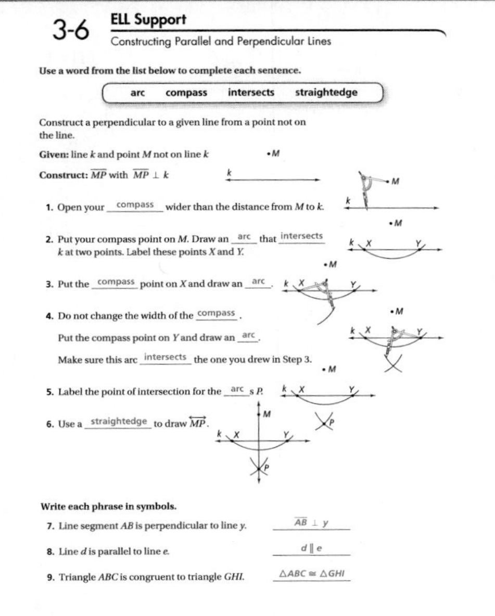

English Language Learner Support

3-6 ELL Support
Constructing Parallel and Perpendicular Lines

Use a word from the list below to complete each sentence.

arc compass intersects straightedge

Construct a perpendicular to a given line from a point not on the line.

Given: line k and point M not on line k

Construct: $\overline{MP}$ with $\overline{MP} \perp k$

1. Open your compass wider than the distance from M to k.
2. Put your compass point on M. Draw an arc that intersects k at two points. Label these points X and Y.
3. Put the compass point on X and draw an arc.
4. Do not change the width of the compass. Put the compass point on Y and draw an arc. Make sure this arc intersects the one you drew in Step 3.
5. Label the point of intersection for the arcs P.
6. Use a straightedge to draw $\overleftrightarrow{MP}$.

Write each phrase in symbols.

7. Line segment AB is perpendicular to line y. $\overline{AB} \perp y$
8. Line d is parallel to line e. $d \parallel e$
9. Triangle ABC is congruent to triangle GHI. $\triangle ABC \cong \triangle GHI$

Differentiated Remediation *continued*

On-Level

- **Practice** (2 pages) Provides extra practice for each lesson. For simpler practice exercises, use the Form K Practice pages found in the All-in-One Teaching Resources and online.
- **Think About a Plan** Helps students develop specific problem-solving skills and strategies by providing scaffolded guiding questions.
- **Standardized Test Prep** Focuses on all major exercises, all major question types, and helps students prepare for the high-stakes assessments.

Practice and Problem Solving Wkbk/ All-in-One Resources/Online

Practice page 1

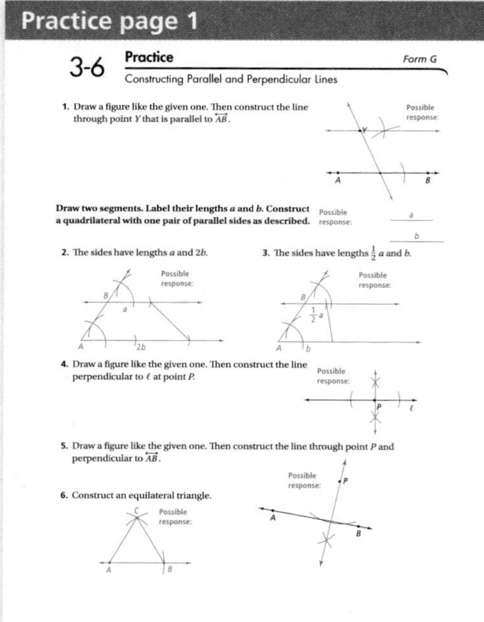
3-6 **Practice** *Form G*
Constructing Parallel and Perpendicular Lines

1. Draw a figure like the given one. Then construct the line through point Y that is parallel to $\overleftrightarrow{AB}$. Possible response:

Draw two segments. Label their lengths a and b. Construct a quadrilateral with one pair of parallel sides as described. Possible response:

2. The sides have lengths a and $2b$. Possible response:
3. The sides have lengths $\frac{1}{2}a$ and b. Possible response:
4. Draw a figure like the given one. Then construct the line perpendicular to ℓ at point P. Possible response:
5. Draw a figure like the given one. Then construct the line through point P and perpendicular to $\overleftrightarrow{AB}$. Possible response:
6. Construct an equilateral triangle. Possible response:

Practice and Problem Solving Wkbk/ All-in-One Resources/Online

Practice page 2

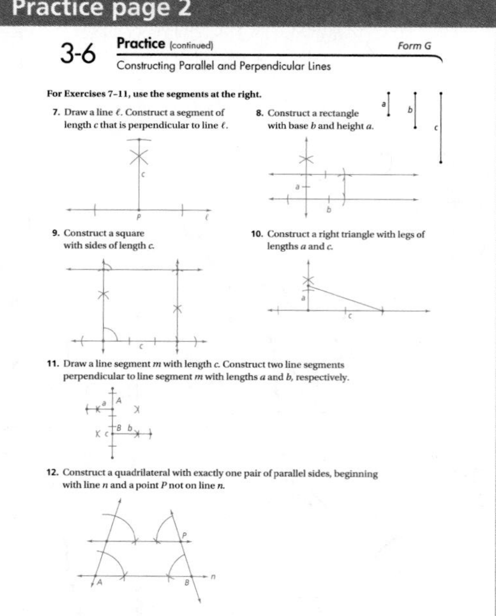
3-6 **Practice** (continued) *Form G*
Constructing Parallel and Perpendicular Lines

For Exercises 7–11, use the segments at the right.

7. Draw a line ℓ. Construct a segment of length c that is perpendicular to line ℓ.
8. Construct a rectangle with base b and height a.
9. Construct a square with sides of length c.
10. Construct a right triangle with legs of lengths a and c.
11. Draw a line segment m with length c. Construct two line segments perpendicular to line segment m with lengths a and b, respectively.
12. Construct a quadrilateral with exactly one pair of parallel sides, beginning with line n and a point P not on line n.

Extension

- **Enrichment** Provides students with interesting problems and activities that extend the concepts of the lesson.
- **Activities, Games, and Puzzles** Worksheets that can be used for concepts development, enrichment, and for fun!

All-in-One Resources/Online

Enrichment

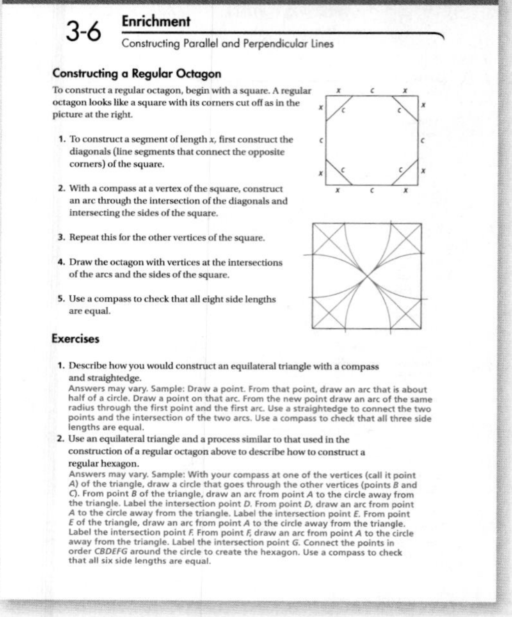

3-6 **Enrichment**
Constructing Parallel and Perpendicular Lines

Constructing a Regular Octagon

To construct a regular octagon, begin with a square. A regular octagon looks like a square with its corners cut off as in the picture at the right.

1. To construct a segment of length x, first construct the diagonals (line segments that connect the opposite corners) of the square.
2. With a compass at a vertex of the square, construct an arc through the intersection of the diagonals and intersecting the sides of the square.
3. Repeat this for the other vertices of the square.
4. Draw the octagon with vertices at the intersections of the arcs and the sides of the square.
5. Use a compass to check that all eight side lengths are equal.

Exercises

1. Describe how you would construct an equilateral triangle with a compass and straightedge.
Answers may vary. Sample: Draw a point. From that point, draw an arc that is about half of a circle. Draw a point on that arc. From the new point draw an arc of the same radius through the first point and the first arc. Use a straightedge to connect the two points and the intersection of the two arcs. Use a compass to check that all three side lengths are equal.
2. Use an equilateral triangle and a process similar to that used in the construction of a regular octagon above to describe how to construct a regular hexagon.
Answers may vary. Sample: With your compass at one of the vertices (call it point A) of the triangle, draw a circle that goes through the other vertices (points B and C). From point B of the triangle, draw an arc from point A to the circle away from the triangle. Label the intersection point D. From point D, draw an arc from point A to the circle away from the triangle. Label the intersection point E. From point E of the triangle, draw an arc from point A to the circle away from the triangle. Label the intersection point F. From point F, draw an arc from point A to the circle away from the triangle. Label the intersection point G. Connect the points in order $CBDEFG$ around the circle to create the hexagon. Use a compass to check that all six side lengths are equal.

Practice and Problem Solving Wkbk/ All-in-One Resources/Online

Think About a Plan

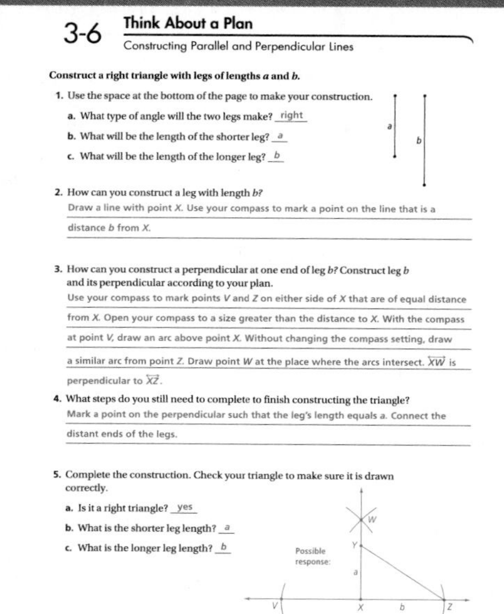
3-6 **Think About a Plan**
Constructing Parallel and Perpendicular Lines

Construct a right triangle with legs of lengths a and b.

1. Use the space at the bottom of the page to make your construction.
   a. What type of angle will the two legs make? right
   b. What will be the length of the shorter leg? a
   c. What will be the length of the longer leg? b
2. How can you construct a leg with length b?
Draw a line with point X. Use your compass to mark a point on the line that is a distance b from X.
3. How can you construct a perpendicular at one end of leg b? Construct leg b and its perpendicular according to your plan.
Use your compass to mark points V and Z on either side of X that are of equal distance from X. Open your compass to a size greater than the distance to X. With the compass at point V, draw an arc above point X. Without changing the compass setting, draw a similar arc from point Z. Draw point W at the place where the arcs intersect. $\overleftrightarrow{XW}$ is perpendicular to $\overleftrightarrow{XZ}$.
4. What steps do you still need to complete to finish constructing the triangle?
Mark a point on the perpendicular such that the leg's length equals a. Connect the distant ends of the legs.
5. Complete the construction. Check your triangle to make sure it is drawn correctly.
   a. Is it a right triangle? yes
   b. What is the shorter leg length? a
   c. What is the longer leg length? b

Possible response:

Practice and Problem Solving Wkbk/ All-in-One Resources/Online

Standardized Test Prep

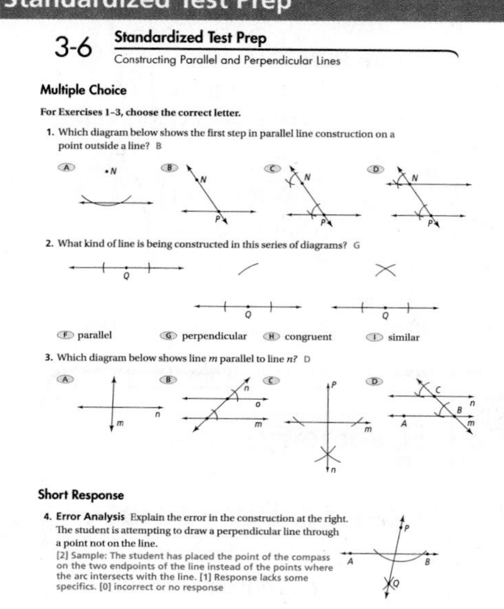
3-6 **Standardized Test Prep**
Constructing Parallel and Perpendicular Lines

Multiple Choice

For Exercises 1–3, choose the correct letter.

1. Which diagram below shows the first step in parallel line construction on a point outside a line? B
2. What kind of line is being constructed in this series of diagrams? G
   F parallel G perpendicular H congruent I similar
3. Which diagram below shows line m parallel to line n? D

Short Response

4. **Error Analysis** Explain the error in the construction at the right. The student is attempting to draw a perpendicular line through a point not on the line.
[2] Sample: The student has placed the point of the compass on the two endpoints of the line instead of the points where the arc intersects with the line. [1] Response lacks some specifics. [0] incorrect or no response

Online Teacher Resource Center

Activities, Games, and Puzzles

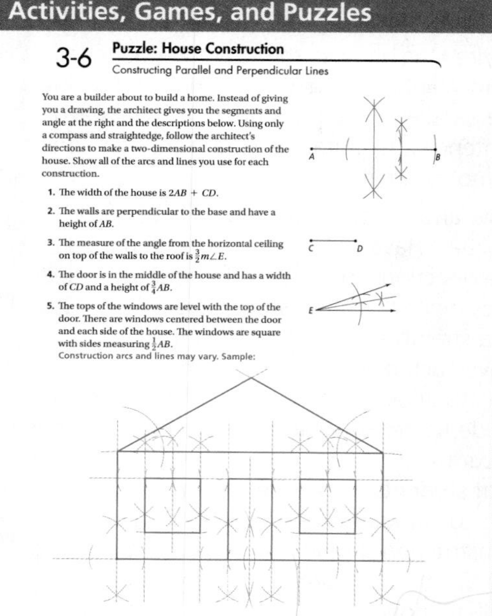
3-6 **Puzzle: House Construction**
Constructing Parallel and Perpendicular Lines

You are a builder about to build a home. Instead of giving you a drawing, the architect gives you the segments and angle at the right and the descriptions below. Using only a compass and straightedge, follow the architect's directions to make a two-dimensional construction of the house. Show all of the arcs and lines you use for each construction.

1. The width of the house is $2AB + CD$.
2. The walls are perpendicular to the base and have a height of AB.
3. The measure of the angle from the horizontal ceiling on top of the walls to the roof is $\frac{3}{2}m\angle E$.
4. The door is in the middle of the house and has a width of CD and a height of $\frac{3}{4}AB$.
5. The tops of the windows are level with the top of the door. There are windows centered between the door and each side of the house. The windows are square with sides measuring $\frac{1}{2}AB$.
Construction arcs and lines may vary. Sample:

3-7 Equations of Lines in the Coordinate Plane

Objective To graph and write linear equations

Think back! What did you learn in algebra that relates to steepness?

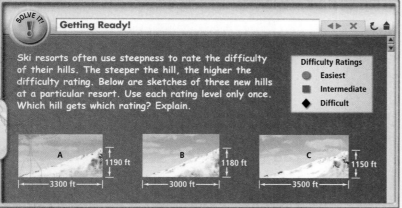

Getting Ready!

Ski resorts often use steepness to rate the difficulty of their hills. The steeper the hill, the higher the difficulty rating. Below are sketches of three new hills at a particular resort. Use each rating level only once. Which hill gets which rating? Explain.

Difficulty Ratings
- ● Easiest
- ■ Intermediate
- ◆ Difficult

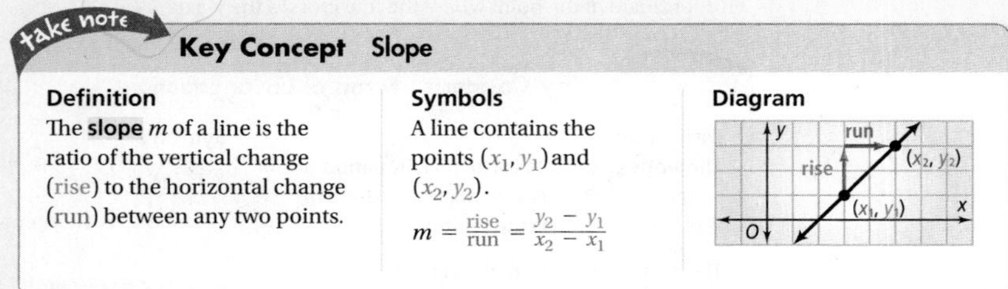

A
1190 ft
3300 ft
B
1180 ft
3000 ft
C
1150 ft
3500 ft

Lesson Vocabulary
- slope
- slope-intercept form
- point-slope form

The Solve It involves using vertical and horizontal distances to determine steepness. The steepest hill has the greatest *slope*. In this lesson you will explore the concept of slope and how it relates to both the graph and the equation of a line.

Essential Understanding You can graph a line and write its equation when you know certain facts about the line, such as its slope and a point on the line.

take note **Key Concept** **Slope**

Definition	Symbols	Diagram
The **slope** m of a line is the ratio of the vertical change (rise) to the horizontal change (run) between any two points.	A line contains the points (x_1, y_1) and (x_2, y_2). $m = \frac{\text{rise}}{\text{run}} = \frac{y_2 - y_1}{x_2 - x_1}$	y, run, rise, (x_2, y_2), (x_1, y_1), x, O

1 Interactive Learning

Solve It!

PURPOSE To examine the steepness of lines as a quantity in order to facilitate comparisons

PROCESS Students quantify the slopes of lines using visualization, counting grid squares, or using ratios.

FACILITATE

Q How can the attribute of steepness be calculated? **[by comparing the rate of vertical distance to the horizontal distance]**

Q How many feet of vertical distance are covered for each foot of horizontal distance on Hill A? On Hill B? On Hill C? Explain. **[0.361: 1190 divided by 3300; 0.393: 1180 divided by 3000; 0.329: 1150 divided by 3500.]**

ANSWER See Solve It in Answers on next page.

CONNECT THE MATH Ask students to create and label a sketch of a hill that covers a horizontal distance of 2000 ft and is more difficult than the three hills in the Solve It.

2 Guided Instruction

Take Note

ERROR PREVENTION

There are two common errors that students make when calculating slope:

- subtracting the *x*-coordinates in the reverse order from the *y*-coordinates.
- writing the difference of the *x*-coordinates in the numerator instead of the denominator.
- subtracting an *x*-coordinate from a *y*-coordinate in both numerator and denominator.

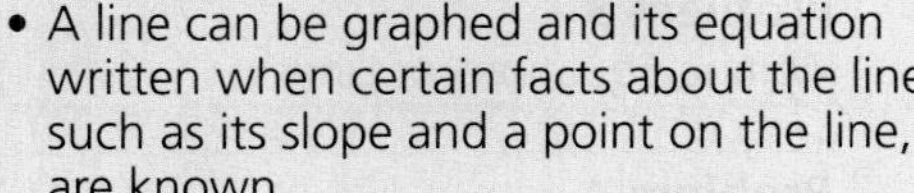

3-7 Preparing to Teach

BIG idea **Coordinate Geometry** UbD

ESSENTIAL UNDERSTANDINGS

- A line can be graphed and its equation written when certain facts about the line, such as its slope and a point on the line, are known.
- The equation of a line can be written in various forms.

Math Background

This lesson is a perfect example of how branches of mathematics are intertwined. Students should recall the concepts of slope and *y*-intercepts, as well as the slope-intercept form and point-slope form, from algebra. Point out that the mathematics being presented here is the same as that presented in algebra courses. Analytic geometry (the proper mathematical name for this lesson) is the branch of geometry in which points are represented by coordinates in the Cartesian plane. Lines, curves and planes are represented algebraically using 2 or 3 variables. These representations allow geometry to be represented algebraically and algebra to be represented geometrically. Analytic geometry is the foundation on which calculus was developed by Sir Isaac Newton and G. W. Leibniz in the late seventeenth century.

Support Student Learning

Use the **Geometry Companion** to engage and support students during instructions. See Lesson Resources at the end of this lesson for details.

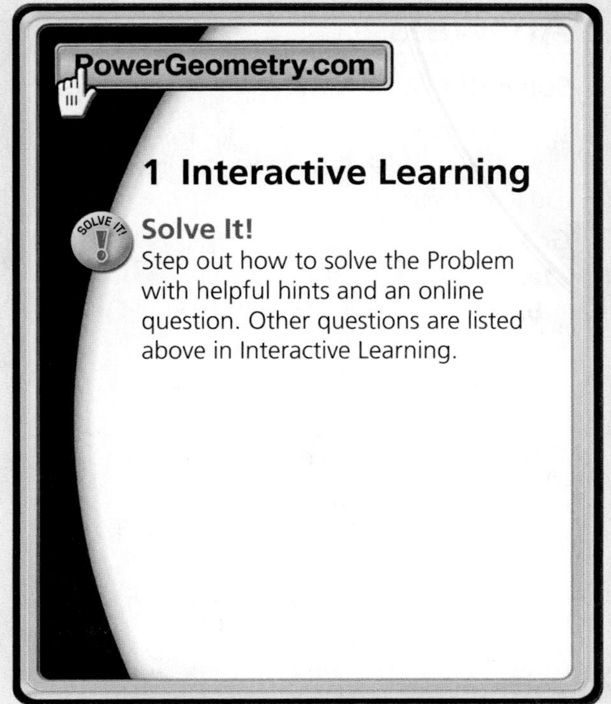

PowerGeometry.com
1 Interactive Learning
Solve It!
Step out how to solve the Problem with helpful hints and an online question. Other questions are listed above in Interactive Learning.

Problem 1

Q What do the physical characteristics of line b suggest about the slope? **[The line descends from left to right, so the vertical distance would be a negative number.]**

Q What is another integral point that is on line b but not visible on the coordinate grid? **[Answers may vary. Sample: (9, −6)]**

Q What do all of the points on line d have in common? **[They have an x-coordinate of 4.]**

Got It? — VISUAL LEARNERS

Make sure that students understand that you can "count" the rise and run to determine slope.

In 1a, students can count a horizontal distance of 3 and a vertical distance of 4 for line a.

In 1b, students should realize that there is no vertical distance to count and therefore the numerator of the slope ratio is 0.

Take Note — ERROR PREVENTION

Have students state the formula to themselves each time they write an equation using the slope-intercept form. The repetition will help them memorize the formula and reinforce the facts that m represents the slope and b represents the y-intercept.

EXTENSION

Ask students to explore and determine the relationship between the slope formula and the point-slope form of a line.

Plan

How do you know which numbers go where in a formula? For slope, you can choose either point's y-coordinate as y_2. Just be sure to use the same point's x-coordinate as x_2.

Problem 1 Finding Slopes of Lines

A What is the slope of line b?

$$m = \frac{2 - (-2)}{-1 - 4} = \frac{4}{-5} = -\frac{4}{5}$$

B What is the slope of line d?

$$m = \frac{0 - (-2)}{4 - 4} = \frac{2}{0} \quad \text{Undefined}$$

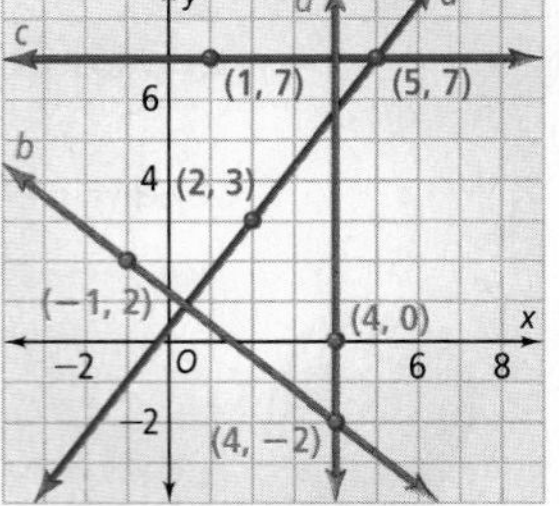

Got It? 1. Use the graph in Problem 1.
a. What is the slope of line a?
b. What is the slope of line c?

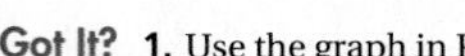

As you saw in Problem 1 and Got It 1 the slope of a line can be positive, negative, zero, or undefined. The sign of the slope tells you whether the line rises or falls to the right. A slope of zero tells you that the line is horizontal. An undefined slope tells you that the line is vertical.

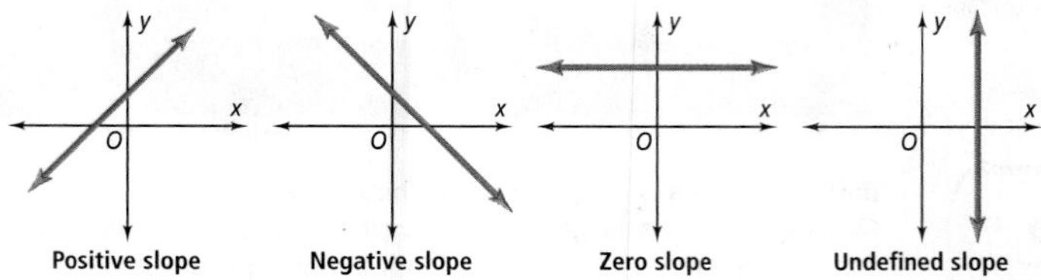

You can graph a line when you know its equation. The equation of a line has different forms. Two forms are shown below. Recall that the y-intercept of a line is the y-coordinate of the point where the line crosses the y-axis.

take note

Key Concept Forms of Linear Equations

Definition	Symbols
The **slope-intercept form** of an equation of a nonvertical line is $y = mx + b$, where m is the slope and b is the y-intercept.	$y = mx + b$ (↑ slope, ↑ y-intercept)
The **point-slope form** of an equation of a nonvertical line is $y - y_1 = m(x - x_1)$, where m is the slope and (x_1, y_1) is a point on the line.	$y - y_1 = m(x - x_1)$ (↑ y-coordinate, ↑ slope, ↑ x-coordinate)

Answers

Solve It!

The slopes of A, B, and C are $\frac{119}{330}$, $\frac{59}{150}$, and $\frac{23}{70}$. $\frac{23}{70} < \frac{119}{330} < \frac{59}{150}$, so C is easiest, A is intermediate, and B is difficult.

Got It?

1a. $\frac{4}{3}$
b. 0

PowerGeometry.com

2 Guided Instruction

Each Problem is worked out and supported online.

Problem 1
Finding Slopes of Lines

Alternative Problem 1
Finding Slopes of Lines
Animated

Problem 2
Graphing Lines
Animated

Problem 3
Writing Equations of Lines

Problem 4
Using Two Points to Write an Equation
Animated

Problem 5
Writing Equations of Horizontal and Vertical Lines

Plan

What do you do first?
Determine which form of linear equation you have. Then use the equation to identify the slope and a starting point.

Problem 2 Graphing Lines

A What is the graph of $y = \frac{2}{3}x + 1$?

The equation is in slope-intercept form, $y = mx + b$. The slope m is $\frac{2}{3}$ and the y-intercept b is 1.

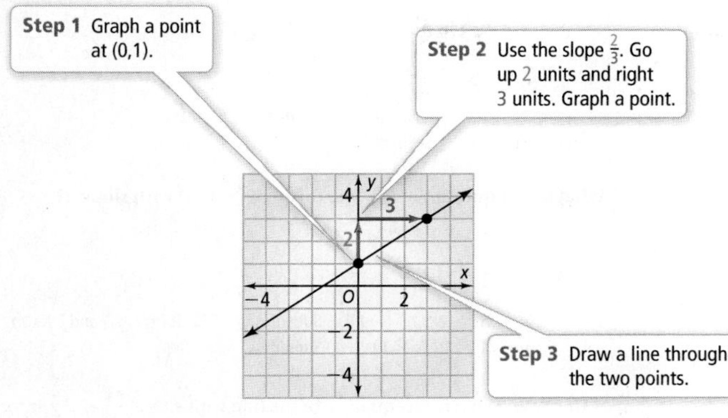

Step 1 Graph a point at (0,1).
Step 2 Use the slope $\frac{2}{3}$. Go up 2 units and right 3 units. Graph a point.
Step 3 Draw a line through the two points.
y
x
4
3
2
−4
O
2
−2
−4

Think

What do you do when the slope is not a fraction?
A rise always needs a run. So, write the integer as a fraction with 1 as the denominator.

B What is the graph of $y - 3 = -2(x + 3)$?

The equation is in point-slope form, $y - y_1 = m(x - x_1)$. The slope m is -2 and a point (x_1, y_1) on the line is $(-3, 3)$.

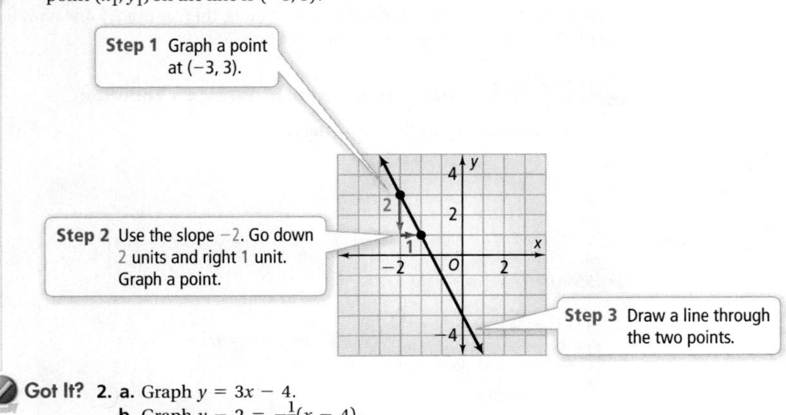

Step 1 Graph a point at (−3, 3).
Step 2 Use the slope −2. Go down 2 units and right 1 unit. Graph a point.
Step 3 Draw a line through the two points.
y
x
4
2
1
−2
O
2
−4

Got It? 2. a. Graph $y = 3x - 4$.
b. Graph $y - 2 = -\frac{1}{3}(x - 4)$.

Problem 2

Q In 2A, what ordered pair corresponds to a y-intercept of 1? **[(0, 1)]**

Q In 2A, how can you determine a point on the line to the left of the y-intercept rather than to the right of the y-intercept as shown in the diagram? **[From the y-intercept, rise the opposite number of units and run the opposite number of units; rise −2 (that is, go down 2) and run −3 (that is, go left 3).]**

Q In 2B, can you determine the y-intercept of a line whose equation is written in point-slope form by just looking at the equation? Explain. **[No, the numbers in the equation represent a point and the slope.]**

Q In 2B, if a student indicated that the point on the line was (3, −3) instead of (−3, 3), what advice would you give him or her? **[Answers may vary. Sample: Tell the student to rewrite the equation as $y - (3) = -2(x - (-3))$.]**

Got It? SYNTHESIZING

Have students name the slope and a point on the line before they graph each line. For 2a, students should name the point (0, −4) and a slope of 3. For 2b, students should realize that if they prefer, they can convert the equation to slope-intercept form. Students can graph the original form (point-slope form) and the new form (slope-intercept) to see that they result in the same line. Because 2b has a fractional y-intercept, this is a good opportunity to show students an advantage of point-slope form (graphing (4, 2) is easier than graphing $\left(0, \frac{10}{3}\right)$).

Answers

Got It? (continued)

2a.

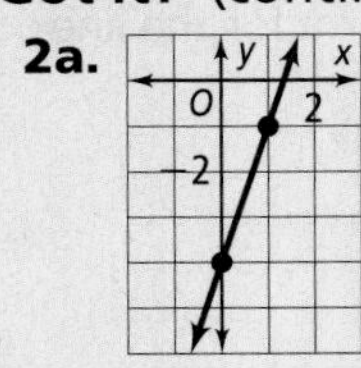

b.

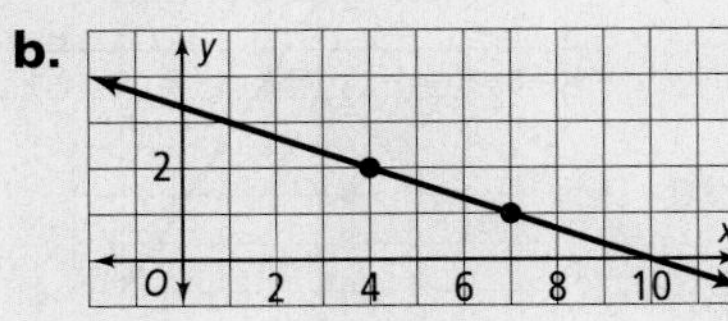

Problem 3

Q How could you use the point-slope form of a line to write the equation in 3A? **[You could substitute the point (0, −5) and the slope into the point-slope form.]**

Q What is the equation in 3B when it is solved for y? **[$y = 2x + 7$]**

Got It? ERROR PREVENTION

If students make a sign error in 3b, tell them to begin the problem by writing $y - (4) = -3(x - (-1))$. Remind students that the minus sign before the (−1) is part of the formula. Tell students to substitute values for x and y which will make both sides of the equation equal to 0.

Problem 4

Q Based on visual inspection, should your calculated slope be positive or negative? Explain. **[The slope should be positive. It rises from left to right.]**

Q Why is it not convenient to use the slope-intercept formula for writing the equation of this line? **[because you do not know the y-intercept]**

You can write an equation of a line when you know its slope and at least one point on the line.

Plan

Which linear equation form should you use?
When you know the slope and the y-intercept, use slope-intercept form. When you know the slope and a point on the line, use point-slope form.

Problem 3 Writing Equations of Lines

A What is an equation of the line with slope 3 and y-intercept −5?

$y = mx + b$

$m = 3$ $b = -5$

$y = 3x + (-5)$ Substitute 3 for m and −5 for b.

$y = 3x - 5$ Simplify.

B What is an equation of the line through (−1, 5) with slope 2?

$y - y_1 = m(x - x_1)$

$y_1 = 5$ $m = 2$ $x_1 = -1$

$y - 5 = 2[x - (-1)]$ Substitute (−1, 5) for (x_1, y_1) and 2 for m.

$y - 5 = 2(x + 1)$ Simplify.

Got It? 3. a. What is an equation of the line with slope $-\frac{1}{2}$ and y-intercept 2?
b. What is an equation of the line through (−1, 4) with slope −3?

Postulate 1-1 states that through any two points, there is exactly one line. So, you need only two points to write the equation of a line.

Plan

What is the first thing you need to know?
It doesn't matter yet what form of linear equation you plan to use. You'll need the slope for *both* slope-intercept form and point-slope form.

Problem 4 Using Two Points to Write an Equation

What is an equation of the line at the right?

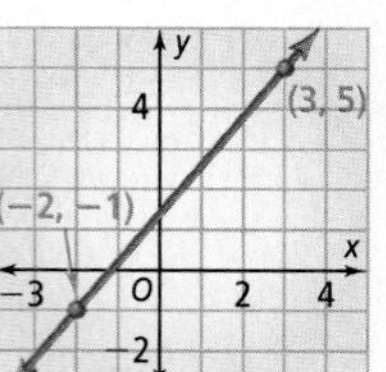

Think	Write
Start by finding the slope m of the line through the given points.	$m = \frac{y_2 - y_1}{x_2 - x_1} = \frac{5 - (-1)}{3 - (-2)} = \frac{6}{5}$
You have the slope and you know two points on the line. Use point-slope form.	$y - y_1 = m(x - x_1)$
Use either point for (x_1, y_1). For example, you can use (3, 5).	$y - 5 = \frac{6}{5}(x - 3)$

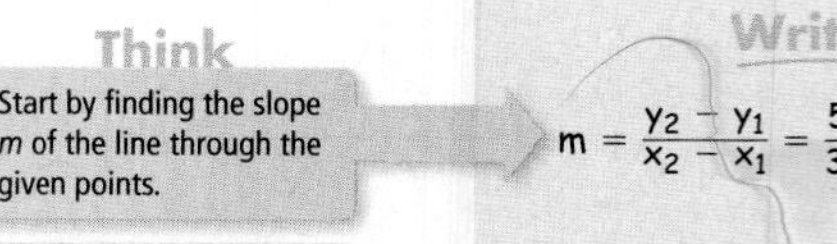

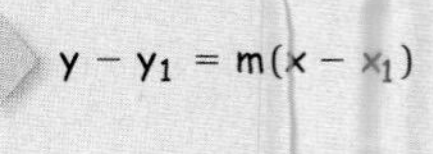

Additional Problems

1. a. What is the slope of line a?
b. What is the slope of line b?

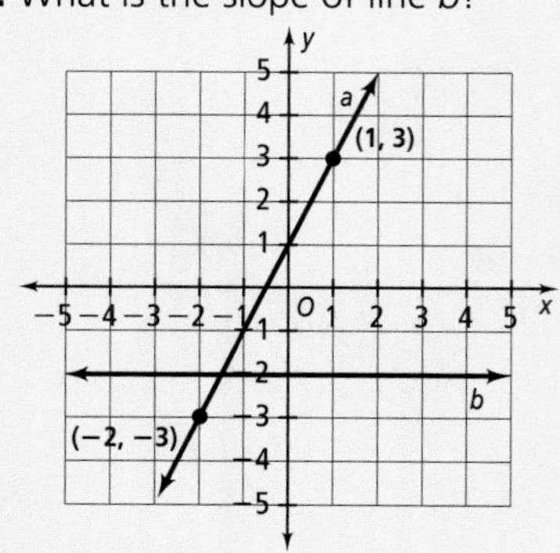

ANSWER a. 2 b. 0

2. a. Graph $y = \frac{1}{2}x - 1$.
b. Graph $y - 2 = -\frac{2}{3}(x + 4)$.

ANSWER

a.

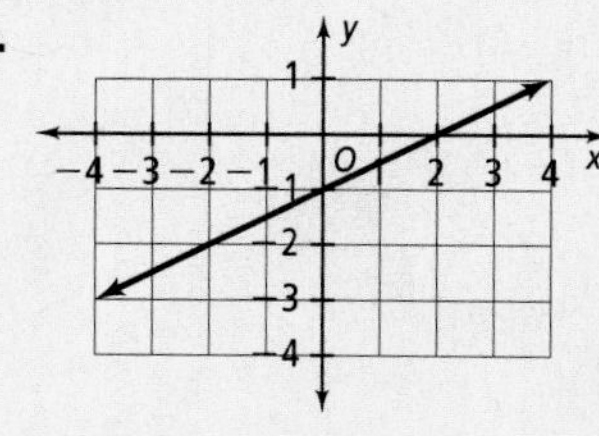

b.

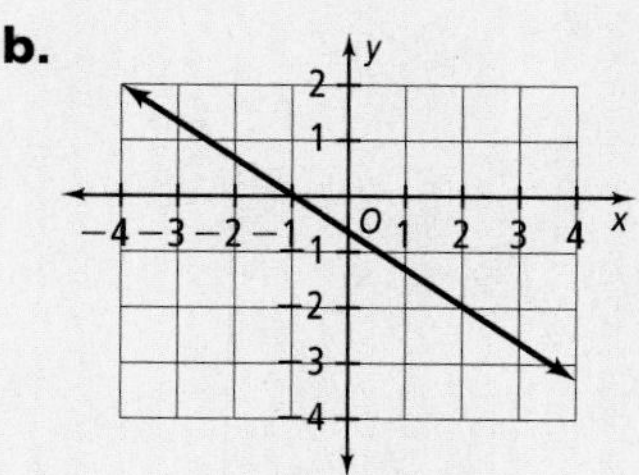

3. a. What is an equation in slope-intercept form of the line with slope 2 and y-intercept 4?
b. What is an equation in point-slope form of the line that passes through (3, −7) with slope −1?

ANSWER a. $y = 2x + 4$
b. $y + 7 = -1(x - 3)$

4. What is an equation in point-slope form for the line graphed?

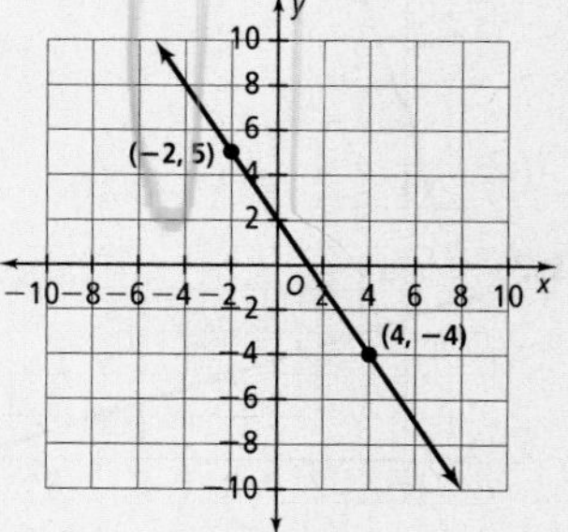

ANSWER $y - 5 = -\frac{3}{2}(x + 2)$ or $y + 4 = -\frac{3}{2}(x - 4)$

5. What are the equations for the horizontal and vertical lines through (1, 7)?

ANSWER Horizontal: $y = 7$, Vertical: $x = 1$

Got It? 4. a. What is the equation of the line in Problem 4 if you use $(-2, -1)$ instead of $(3, 5)$ in the last step?

b. Rewrite the equations in Problem 4 and part (a) in slope-intercept form and compare them. What can you conclude?

You know that the slope of a horizontal line is 0 and the slope of a vertical line is undefined. Thus, horizontal and vertical lines have easily recognized equations.

Problem 5 **Writing Equations of Horizontal and Vertical Lines**

Think

How is this different from writing other linear equations?
You don't need the slope. Just locate the point where the line crosses the *x*-axis (for vertical) or *y*-axis (for horizontal).

What are the equations for the horizontal and vertical lines through (2, 4)?

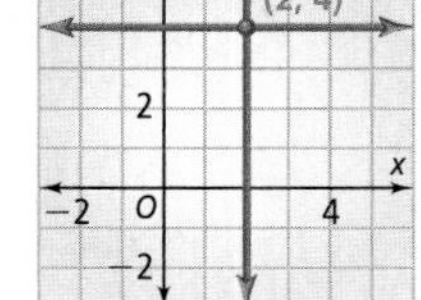

Every point on the horizontal line through (2, 4) has a *y*-coordinate of 4. The equation of the line is $y = 4$. It crosses the *y*-axis at (0, 4).

Every point on the vertical line through (2, 4) has an *x*-coordinate of 2. The equation of the line is $x = 2$. It crosses the *x*-axis at (2, 0).

Got It? 5. a. What are the equations for the horizontal and vertical lines through $(4, -3)$?

b. **Reasoning** Can you write the equation of a vertical line in slope-intercept form? Explain.

Lesson Check

Do you know HOW?

For Exercises 1 and 2, find the slope of the line passing through the given points.

1. (4, 5) and (6, 15)

2.

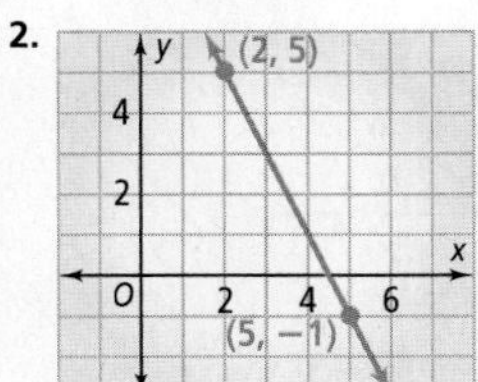

3. What is an equation of a line with slope 8 and *y*-intercept 10?

4. What is an equation of a line passing through (3, 3) and (4, 7)?

Do you UNDERSTAND?

5. **Vocabulary** Explain why you think *slope-intercept form* makes sense as a name for $y = mx + b$. Explain why you think *point-slope form* make sense as a name for $y - y_1 = m(x - x_1)$.

6. **Compare and Contrast** Graph $y = 2x + 5$ and $y = -\frac{1}{3}x + 5$. Describe how these lines are alike and how they are different.

7. **Error Analysis** A classmate found the slope of the line passing through $(8, -2)$ and $(8, 10)$, as shown at the right. Describe your classmate's error. Then find the correct slope of the line passing through the given points.

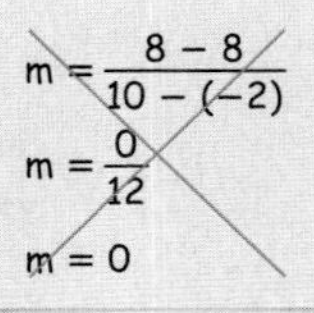

Got It? SYNTHESIZING

Show students the following alternate method for writing the equation of a line given two points. Use one of the points and the calculated slope to write the following: $-1 = \frac{6}{5}(-2) + b$. Solve the equation for $b : b = \frac{7}{5}$. Write the equation of the line in slope-intercept form: $y = \frac{6}{5}x + \frac{7}{5}$.

Problem 5

Q What is the slope of the vertical line? the horizontal line? **[The vertical line has undefined slope; the horizontal line has zero slope.]**

Got It? SYNTHESIZING

Q How can you write the equation of the horizontal line in slope-intercept form? **[$y = 0x + 4$]**

3 Lesson Check

Do you know HOW?

- If students have difficulty with Exercise 2, then remind them they can count units of rise and run or substitute the points into the formulas.

Do you UNDERSTAND?

- If students have difficulty with Exercise 7, then remind them that slope is the ratio of the vertical change (*y*-coordinates) to the horizontal change (*x*-coordinates).

Close

Q Is it always necessary to identify both the slope and *y*-intercept of a line when writing its equation? Explain. **[You must always find the slope. You do not have to identify the *y*-intercept when writing an equation in point-slope form.]**

Answers

Got It? (continued)

3a. $y = -\frac{1}{2}x + 2$

b. $y - 4 = -3(x + 1)$

4a. $y + 1 = \frac{6}{5}(x + 2)$

b. $y = \frac{6}{5}x + \frac{7}{5}$; $y = \frac{6}{5}x + \frac{7}{5}$; they represent the same line.

5a. horizontal: $y = -3$; vertical: $x = 4$

b. No; the slope is undefined for a vertical line, so you cannot use the slope-intercept form because that requires a value for the slope.

Lesson Check

1. 5
2. −2
3. $y = 8x + 10$
4. $y - 3 = 4(x - 3)$ or $y - 7 = 4(x - 4)$
5. Answers may vary. Sample: The slope-intercept form $y = mx + b$ uses the slope *m* and the *y*-intercept *b*; the point-slope form $y - y_1 = m(x - x_1)$ uses a point (x_1, y_1) on the line and the slope *m*.
6. The lines have the same *y*-int., but one line has a steep positive slope and the other has a less steep negative slope.
7. Your classmate switched the *x*- and *y*-values in the formula for slope. The slope of the line is undefined.

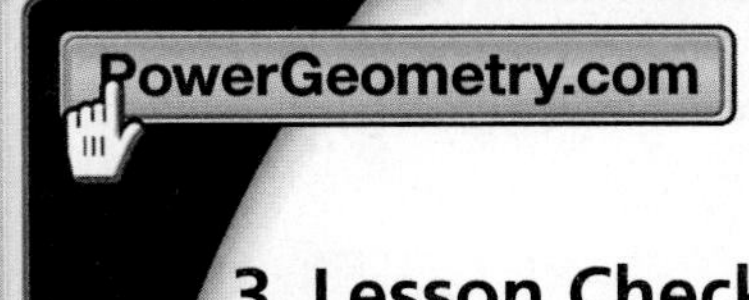

3 Lesson Check

For a digital lesson check, use the Got It questions.

Support in Geometry Companion
- Lesson Check

4 Practice

Assign homework to individual students or to an entire class.

4 Practice

ASSIGNMENT GUIDE

Basic: 8–38 all, 40, 42–44 all, 46–52 even, 53, 56
Average: 9–37 odd, 38–57
Advanced: 9–37 odd, 38–63
Standardized Test Prep: 64–68
Mixed Review: 69–77

Reasoning exercises have blue headings.
Applications exercises have red headings.

EXERCISE 53: Use the Think About a Plan worksheet in the **Practice and Problem Solving Workbook** (also available in the Teaching Resources in print and online) to further support students' development in becoming independent learners.

HOMEWORK QUICK CHECK

To check students' understanding of key skills and concepts, go over Exercises 9, 25, 43, 53, and 56.

Practice and Problem-Solving Exercises

A Practice

Find the slope of the line passing through the given points. See Problem 1.

8.

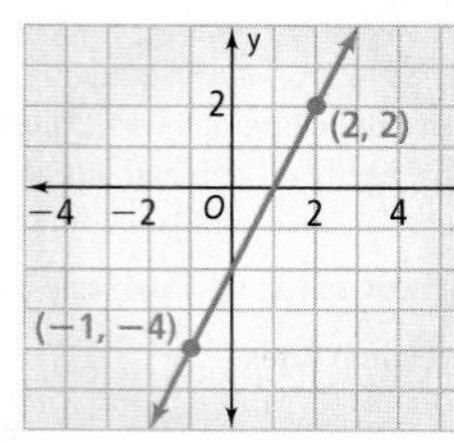

9. (−3, 4), (3, −1)

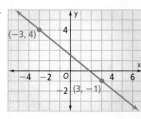

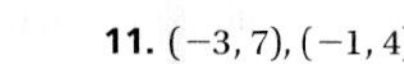

10. (4, −6), (7, 2) **11.** (−3, 7), (−1, 4) **12.** (−8, 3), (−11, 4)

13. (−6, 2), (−7, 10) **14.** (3, 2), (−6, 2) **15.** (5, 9), (5, −6)

Graph each line. See Problem 2.

16. $y = x + 2$ **17.** $y = 3x + 4$

18. $y = \frac{1}{2}x - 1$ **19.** $y = -\frac{5}{3}x + 2$

20. $y - 3 = \frac{1}{3}(x - 3)$ **21.** $y - 1 = -3(x + 2)$

22. $y + 4 = (x - 5)$ **23.** $y + 1 = -\frac{2}{3}(x + 4)$

Use the given information to write an equation of each line. See Problems 3 and 4.

24. slope 3, y-intercept 6 **25.** slope $\frac{1}{2}$, y-intercept −5

26. slope $\frac{2}{3}$, passes through (−2, −6) **27.** slope −3, passes through (4, −1)

28.

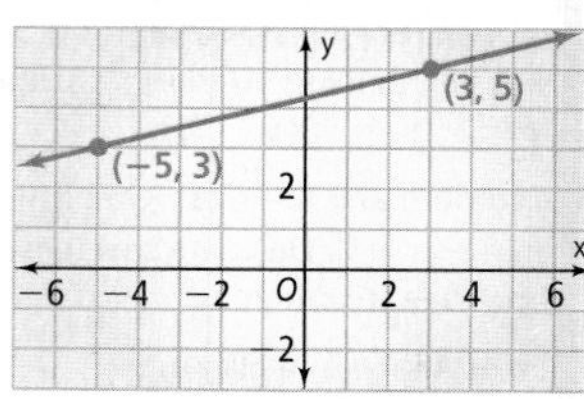

29. (−2, 6), (1, 3)

30. passes through (0, 5) and (5, 8) **31.** passes through (6, 2) and (2, 4)

32. passes through (−4, 4) and (2, 10) **33.** passes through (−1, 0) and (−3, −1)

Write the equation of the horizontal and vertical lines though the given point. See Problem 5.

34. (4, 7) **35.** (3, −2) **36.** (0, −1) **37.** (6, 4)

Answers

Practice and Problem-Solving Exercises

8. 2
9. $-\frac{5}{6}$
10. $\frac{8}{3}$
11. $-\frac{3}{2}$
12. $-\frac{1}{3}$
13. −8
14. 0
15. undefined
16.

17.

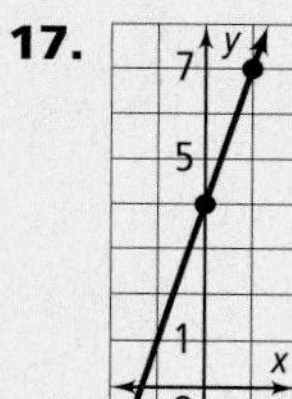

18.

19.

20.

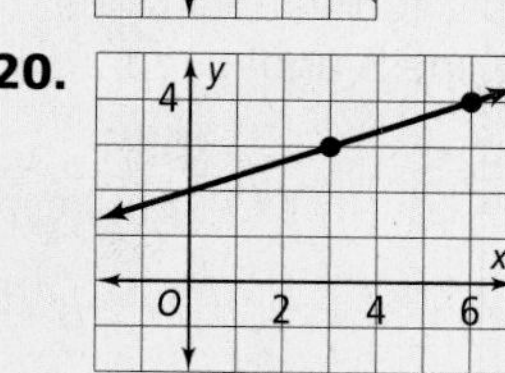

21.

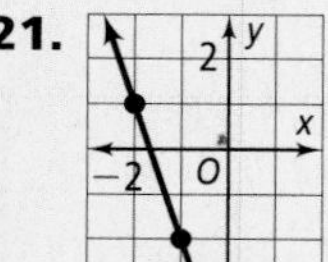

22.

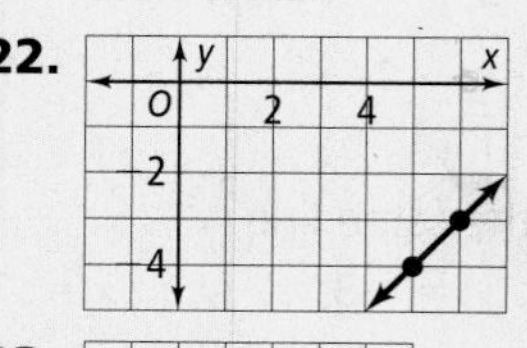

23.

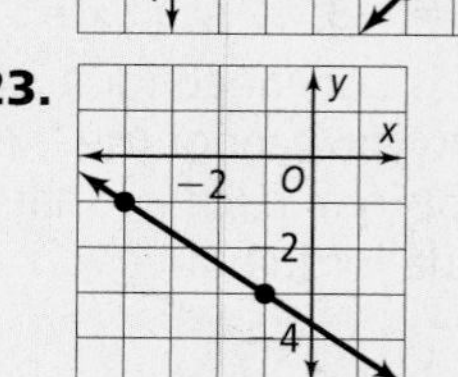

24. $y = 3x + 6$
25. $y = \frac{1}{2}x - 5$
26. $y + 6 = \frac{2}{3}(x + 2)$
27. $y + 1 = -3(x - 4)$

B Apply

Graph each line.

38. $x = 3$ **39.** $y = -2$ **40.** $x = 9$ **41.** $y = 4$

42. Open-Ended Write equations for three lines that contain the point (5, 6).

43. Think About a Plan You want to construct a "funbox" at a local skate park. The skate park's safety regulations allow for the ramp on the funbox to have a maximum slope of $\frac{4}{11}$. If you use the funbox plan at the right, can you build the ramp to meet the safety regulations? Explain.

- What information do you have that you can use to find the slope?
- How can you compare slopes?

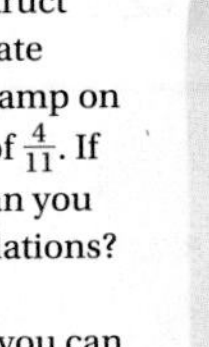
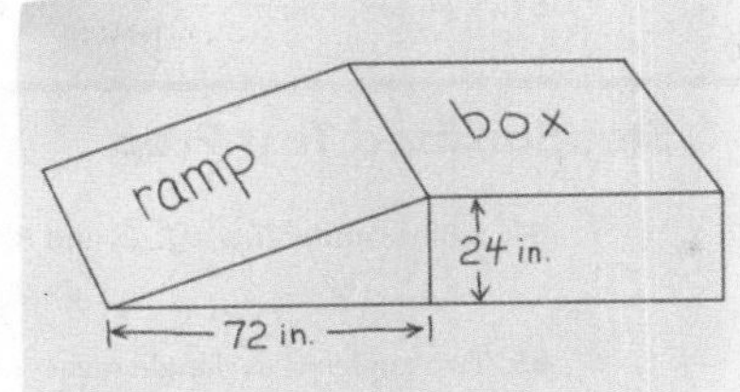

Write each equation in slope-intercept form.

44. $y - 5 = 2(x + 2)$ **45.** $y + 2 = -(x - 4)$ **46.** $-5x + y = 2$ **47.** $3x + 2y = 10$

48. Science The equation $P = -\frac{1}{33}d + 1$ represents the pressure P in atmospheres a scuba diver feels d feet below the surface of the water.

a. What is the slope of the line?
b. What does the slope represent in this situation?
c. What is the y-intercept (P-intercept)?
d. What does the y-intercept represent in this situation?

Graph each pair of lines. Then find their point of intersection.

49. $y = -4, x = 6$ **50.** $x = 0, y = 0$ **51.** $x = -1, y = 3$ **52.** $y = 5, x = 4$

53. Accessibility By law, the maximum slope of an access ramp in new construction is $\frac{1}{12}$. The plan for the new library shows a 3-ft height from the ground to the main entrance. The distance from the sidewalk to the building is 10 ft. If you assume the ramp does not have any turns, can you design a ramp that complies with the law? Explain.

54. a. What is the slope of the x-axis? Explain.
b. Write an equation for the x-axis.

55. a. What is the slope of the y-axis? Explain.
b. Write an equation for the y-axis.

56. Reasoning The x-intercept of a line is 2 and the y-intercept is 4. Use this information to write an equation for the line.

57. Coordinate Geometry The vertices of a triangle are $A(0, 0)$, $B(2, 5)$, and $C(4, 0)$.

a. Write an equation for the line through A and B.
b. Write an equation for the line through B and C.
c. Compare the slopes and the y-intercepts of the two lines.

28. $y - 3 = \frac{1}{4}(x + 5)$ or $y - 5 = \frac{1}{4}(x - 3)$

29. $y - 6 = -(x + 2)$ or $y - 3 = -(x - 1)$

30. $y = \frac{3}{5}x + 5$

31. $y - 2 = -\frac{1}{2}(x - 6)$ or $y - 4 = -\frac{1}{2}(x - 2)$

32. $y - 4 = x + 4$ or $y - 10 = x - 2$

33. $y = \frac{1}{2}(x + 1)$ or $y + 1 = \frac{1}{2}(x + 3)$

34. horizontal: $y = 7$; vertical: $x = 4$

35. horizontal: $y = -2$; vertical: $x = 3$

36. horizontal: $y = -1$; vertical: $x = 0$

37. horizontal: $y = 4$; vertical: $x = 6$

38.
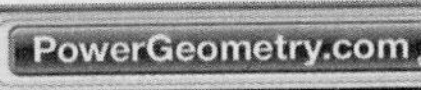

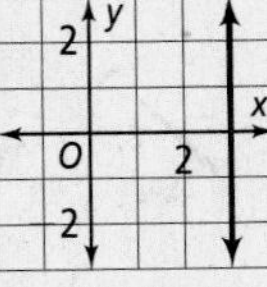

39.

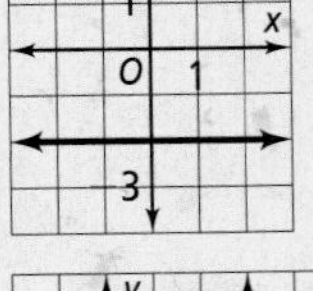

40.

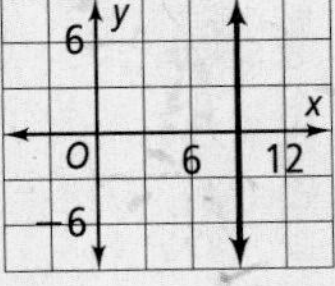

41.
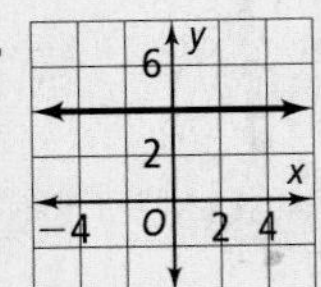

42. Answers may vary. Sample: $x = 5$, $y = 6$, $y = \frac{6}{5}x$, $y - 6 = \frac{6}{5}(x - 5)$

43. Yes; if the ramp is 24 in. high and 72 in. long, the slope will be $\frac{24}{72} = 0.\overline{3}$, which is less than the maximum slope of $\frac{4}{11} = 0.\overline{36}$.

44. $y = 2x + 9$

45. $y = -x + 2$

46. $y = 5x + 2$

47. $y = -\frac{3}{2}x + 5$

48a. $-\frac{1}{33}$

b. The slope represents the rate at which the pressure changes for each foot of a dive.

c. 1

d. The y-intercept is the value of the pressure when the depth of the dive is 0.

49. (6, −4)
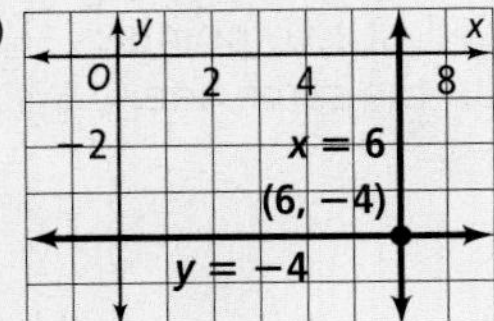

50. (0, 0)
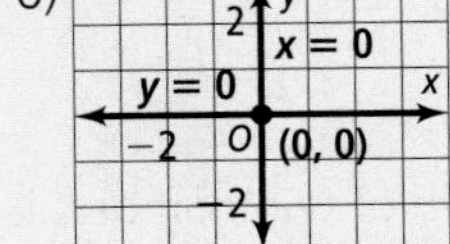

51. (−1, 3)
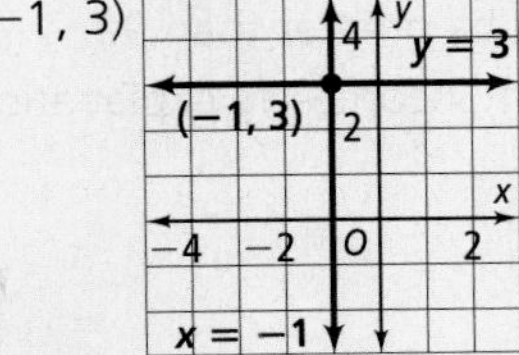

52. (4, 5)
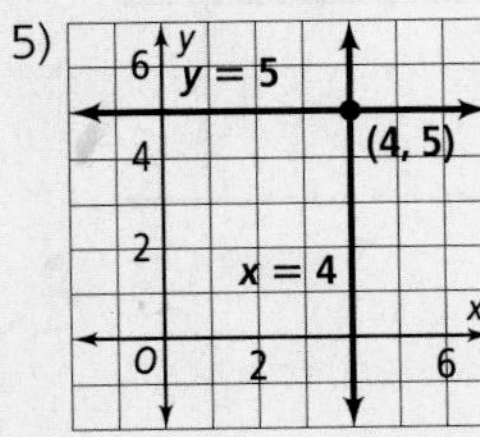

53. No; answers may vary. Sample: $\frac{1}{12} < \frac{3}{10}$ so the ramp would need to zigzag to comply with the law.

54a. 0; the x-axis is a horizontal line, and the slope of a horizontal line is 0.

b. $y = 0$

55a. Undefined; the y-axis is a vertical line, and the slope of a vertical line is undefined.

b. $x = 0$

56. $y = -2x + 4$

57a. $y = \frac{5}{2}x$

b. $y - 5 = -\frac{5}{2}(x - 2)$ or $y = -\frac{5}{2}x + 10$

c. The abs. value of the slopes is the same, but one slope is pos. and the other is neg. One y-int. is 0 and the other is 10.

Answers

Practice and Problem-Solving Exercises (continued)

58. Yes; the slope of the line through the first two points is 2 and the slope of the line through the last two points is 2, so the points lie on the same line.

59. No; the slope of the line through the first two points is $-\frac{1}{3}$ and the slope of the line through the last two points is -1, so the points do not lie on the same line.

60. Yes; the slope of the line through the first two points is $-\frac{7}{3}$ and the slope of the line through the last two points is $-\frac{7}{3}$, so the points lie on the same line.

61. 9

62. $-\frac{1}{6}$

63. $\frac{1}{6}$

64. B

65. G

66. D

67. G

68. [2] Yes; if the sum of two numbers is 180 and one of them is less than 90, then the other must be greater than 90.
[1] incorrect OR incomplete explanation

69.

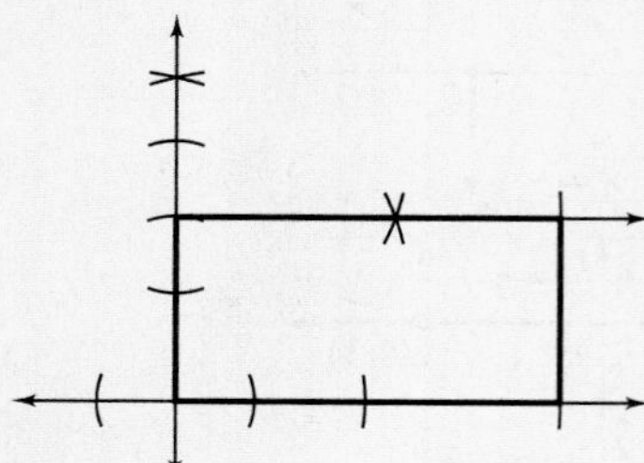

70.

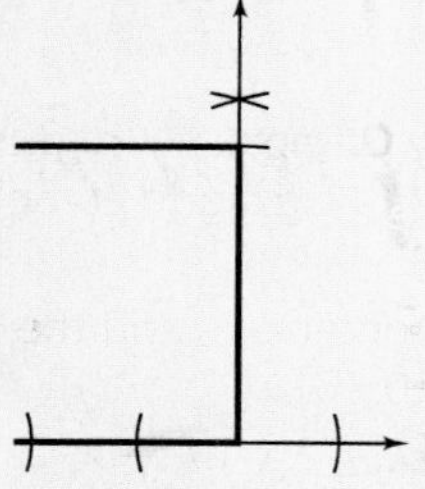

71. Distr. Prop.

72. Substitution

73. Reflexive Prop. of ≅

74. Symmetric Prop. of ≅

75. $\frac{1}{2}$

76. $\frac{5}{2}$

77. -5

Challenge **Do the three points lie on one line? Justify your answer.**

58. (5, 6), (3, 2), (6, 8) **59.** (−2, −2), (4, −4), (0, 0) **60.** (5, −4), (2, 3), (−1, 10)

Find the value of a such that the graph of the equation has the given slope.

61. $y = \frac{2}{9}ax + 6; m = 2$ **62.** $y = -3ax - 4; m = \frac{1}{2}$ **63.** $y = -4ax - 10; m = -\frac{2}{3}$

Standardized Test Prep

SAT/ACT

64. $\overline{AB}$ has endpoints $A(8, k)$ and $B(7, -3)$. The slope of $\overline{AB}$ is 5. What is k?

(A) 1 (B) 2 (C) 5 (D) 8

65. Two angles of a triangle measure 68 and 54. What is the measure of the third angle?

(F) 14 (G) 58 (H) 122 (I) 180

66. Which of the following CANNOT be true?

(A) plane $ABCD \parallel$ plane $EFGH$

(B) Planes $ABCD$ and $CDHG$ intersect in $\overleftrightarrow{CD}$.

(C) $ABCD$ and ABC represent the same plane.

(D) plane $ADHE \parallel$ plane DCG

67. The length of a rectangle is $(x - 2)$ inches and the width is $5x$ inches. Which expression represents the perimeter of the rectangle in inches?

(F) $6x - 2$ (G) $12x - 4$ (H) $5x^2 - 10x$ (I) $10x^2 - 20x$

Short Response

68. One of the angles in a certain linear pair is acute. Your friend says the other angle must be obtuse. Is your friend's conjecture reasonable? Explain.

Mixed Review

For Exercises 69 and 70, construct the geometric figure. See Lesson 3-6.

69. a rectangle with a length twice its width **70.** a square

Name the property that justifies each statement. See Lesson 2-5.

71. $4(2a - 3) = 8a - 12$ **72.** If $b + c = 7$ and $b = 2$, then $2 + c = 7$.

73. $\overline{RS} \cong \overline{RS}$ **74.** If $\angle 1 \cong \angle 4$, then $\angle 4 \cong \angle 1$.

Get Ready! **To prepare for Lesson 3-8, do Exercises 75–77.**

Find the slope of the line passing through the given points. See Lesson 3-7.

75. (2, 5), (−2, 3) **76.** (0, −5), (2, 0) **77.** (1, 1), (2, −4)

3-7 Lesson Resources

Differentiated Remediation

Instructional Support

Geometry Companion

Students can use the **Geometry Companion** worktext (4 pages) . . .

- New Vocabulary
- Key Concepts
- Got It for each Problem
- Lesson Check

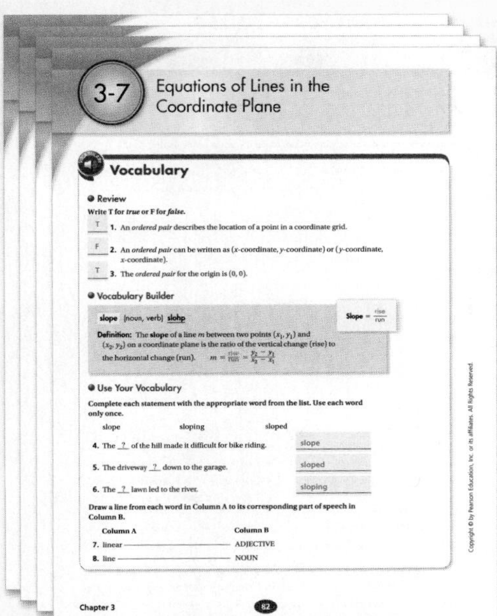

3-7 Equations of Lines in the Coordinate Plane

Vocabulary

Review

Write T for *true* or F for *false*.

T 1. An *ordered pair* describes the location of a point in a coordinate grid.

F 2. An *ordered pair* can be written as (x-coordinate, y-coordinate) or (y-coordinate, x-coordinate).

T 3. The *ordered pair* for the origin is (0, 0).

Vocabulary Builder

slope (noun, verb) **slohp**

Slope = $\frac{\text{rise}}{\text{run}}$

Definition: The **slope** of a line m between two points (x_1, y_1) and (x_2, y_2) on a coordinate plane is the ratio of the vertical change (rise) to the horizontal change (run). $m = \frac{\text{rise}}{\text{run}} = \frac{y_2 - y_1}{x_2 - x_1}$

Use Your Vocabulary

Complete each statement with the appropriate word from the list. Use each word only once.

slope sloping sloped

4. The _?_ of the hill made it difficult for bike riding. slope
5. The driveway _?_ down to the garage. sloped
6. The _?_ lawn led to the river. sloping

Draw a line from each word in Column A to its corresponding part of speech in Column B.

Column A	Column B
7. linear	ADJECTIVE
8. line	NOUN

Chapter 3 82

ELL Support

Assess Understanding Have a student draw a line with positive slope in a coordinate plane. Ask: What do we call the steepness of the line? Have another student draw a line with a negative slope. Ask: How are the lines different? Have a student draw two points on the positive line. Have students count off the horizontal distance between the points from left to right. Have a volunteer write that number as the denominator of a fraction. Have students count off the vertical distance between the points and a volunteer write that number as the numerator of the fraction. Write slope next to the fraction. Have students repeat after you the sentence: Slope equals rise over run. Repeat the activity for the negative slope line.

Connect to Prior Knowledge Have small groups of students collect or draw pictures of objects with slopes. Have the groups use a ruler to mark lines and label distances on the pictures. Have the groups calculate the slope and write it on each picture.

5 Assess & Remediate

Lesson Quiz

1. What is the slope of the line below?

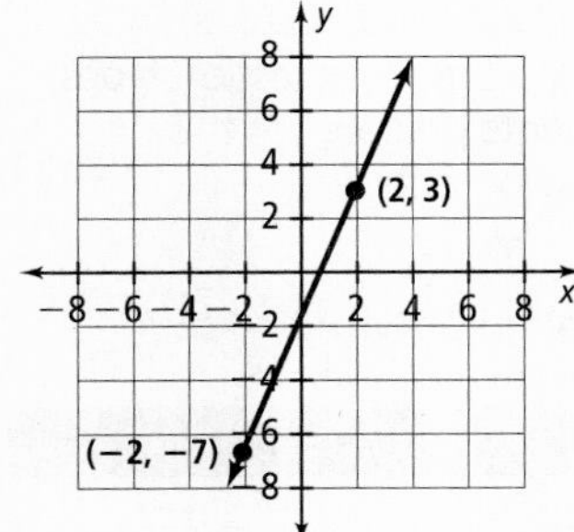

2. Write the equation of the line shown in Exercise 1. Express your answer in point-slope form.

3. What is an equation of the line with slope −3 and y-intercept 6? Express your answer in slope-intercept form.

4. What are the equations for the horizontal and vertical lines through (−2, 0)?

5. Do you UNDERSTAND? Which has a greater slope, a horizontal line or a vertical line?

ANSWERS TO LESSON QUIZ

1. 2.5 or $\frac{5}{2}$

2. $y - 3 = 2.5(x - 2)$

3. $y = -3x + 6$

4. horizontal $y = 0$, vertical $x = -2$

5. A vertical line has no defined slope, so th comparison cannot be made.

PRECRIPTION FOR REMEDIATION

Use the student work on the Lesson Quiz to prescribe a differentiated review assignment.

Points	Differentiated Remediation
0–2	Intervention
3–4	On-level
5	Extension

PowerGeometry.com

5 Assess & Remediate

Assign the Lesson Quiz. Appropriate intervention, practice, or enrichment is automatically generated based on student performance.

Intervention

- **Reteaching** (2 pages) Provides reteaching and practice exercises for the key lesson concepts. Use with struggling students or absent students.
- **English Language Learner Support** Helps students develop and reinforce mathematical vocabulary and key concepts.

All-in-One Resources/Online

Reteaching

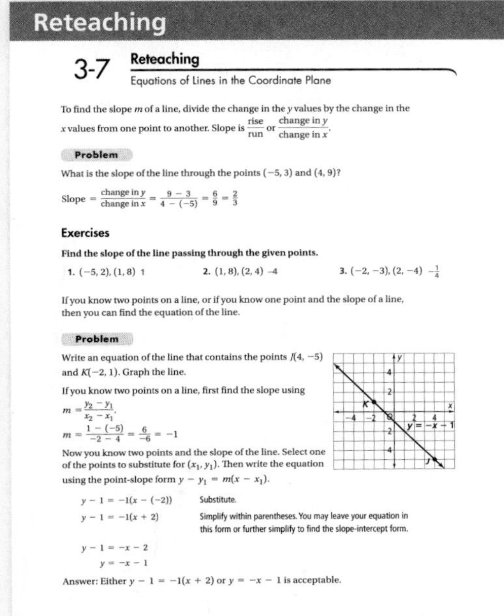

3-7 **Reteaching**

Equations of Lines in the Coordinate Plane

To find the slope m of a line, divide the change in the y values by the change in the x values from one point to another. Slope is $\frac{\text{rise}}{\text{run}}$ or $\frac{\text{change in } y}{\text{change in } x}$.

Problem

What is the slope of the line through the points (−5, 3) and (4, 9)?

$\text{Slope} = \frac{\text{change in } y}{\text{change in } x} = \frac{9 - 3}{4 - (-5)} = \frac{6}{9} = \frac{2}{3}$

Exercises

Find the slope of the line passing through the given points.

1. (−5, 2), (1, 8) 1
2. (1, 8), (2, 4) −4
3. (−2, −3), (2, −4) $-\frac{1}{4}$

If you know two points on a line, or if you know one point and the slope of a line, then you can find the equation of the line.

Problem

Write an equation of the line that contains the points $J(4, -5)$ and $K(-2, 1)$. Graph the line.

If you know two points on a line, first find the slope using $m = \frac{y_2 - y_1}{x_2 - x_1}$.

$m = \frac{1 - (-5)}{-2 - 4} = \frac{6}{-6} = -1$

Now you know two points and the slope of the line. Select one of the points to substitute for (x_1, y_1). Then write the equation using the point-slope form $y - y_1 = m(x - x_1)$.

$y - 1 = -1(x - (-2))$ Substitute.

$y - 1 = -1(x + 2)$ Simplify within parentheses. You may leave your equation in this form or further simplify to find the slope-intercept form.

$y - 1 = -x - 2$

$y = -x - 1$

Answer: Either $y - 1 = -1(x + 2)$ or $y = -x - 1$ is acceptable.

All-in-One Resources/Online

English Language Learner Support

3-7 **ELL Support**

Equations of Lines in the Coordinate Plane

Use the chart below to review vocabulary. These vocabulary words will help you complete this page.

Related Words	Explanations	Examples
coordinates koh AWR din its	Two numbers used to locate points on a coordinate plane	An ordered pair (x, y) lists the coordinates of a point.
point-slope form poynt slohp fawrm	The equation of a line in the form $y - y_1 = m(x - x_1)$; the variable m is the slope and x_1 and y_1 are coordinates of a point (x_1, y_1).	The equation $y - 7 = 3(x - 1)$ is in point-slope form.
slope-intercept form slohp IN tur sept fawrm	The equation of a line in the form $y = mx + b$; the variable m is the slope and variable b is the y-intercept.	The equation $y = 3x + 4$ is in slope-intercept form.
***x*-axis, *y*-axis** eks AK sis wy AK sis	The number lines on a coordinate plane; the x-axis is horizontal. The y-axis is vertical.	The x-axis is perpendicular to the y-axis.
***y*-intercept** wy IN tur sept	The point where a line crosses the y-axis	(0, 4) is the y-intercept of the graph of $y = x + 4$.

Circle or underline the correct answer.

1. Circle the equations that are in slope-intercept form. Underline the equations that are in point-slope form.
   $y = 3x + 6$ $y - 8 = -5(x + 2)$ $y + 1 = 2(x - 4)$ $y = -x - 9$
2. Circle the y-intercept in the equation. $y = -4x + 1$

Use the words to label the diagram below.

3.

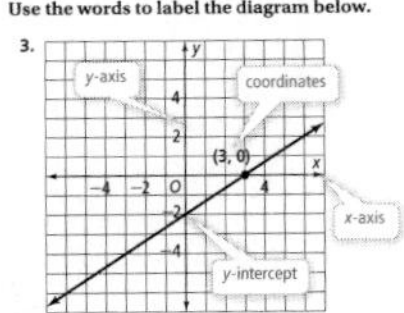

Differentiated Remediation *continued*

On-Level

- **Practice** (2 pages) Provides extra practice for each lesson. For simpler practice exercises, use the Form K Practice pages found in the All-in-One Teaching Resources and online.
- **Think About a Plan** Helps students develop specific problem-solving skills and strategies by providing scaffolded guiding questions.
- **Standardized Test Prep** Focuses on all major exercises, all major question types, and helps students prepare for the high-stakes assessments.

Extension

- **Enrichment** Provides students with interesting problems and activities that extend the concepts of the lesson.
- **Activities, Games, and Puzzles** Worksheets that can be used for concepts development, enrichment, and for fun!

Practice and Problem Solving Wkbk/ All-in-One Resources/Online

Practice page 1

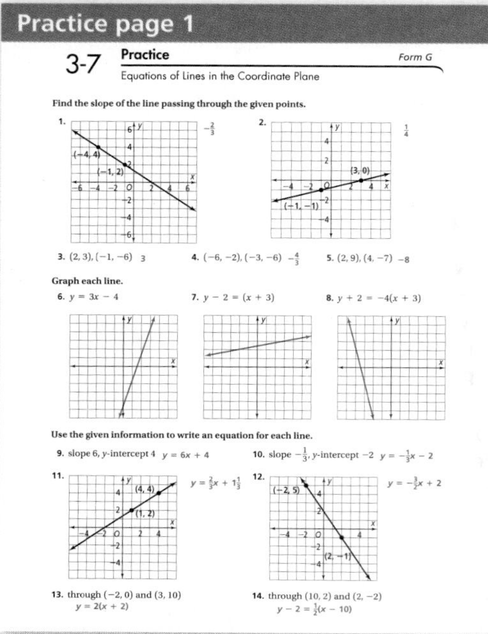

3-7 Practice — Form G

Equations of Lines in the Coordinate Plane

Find the slope of the line passing through the given points.

1. $-\frac{2}{3}$
2. $\frac{1}{4}$
3. (2, 3), (−1, −6) 3
4. (−6, −2), (−3, −6) $-\frac{4}{3}$
5. (2, 9), (4, −7) −8

Graph each line.

6. $y = 3x - 4$
7. $y - 2 = (x + 3)$
8. $y + 2 = -4(x + 3)$

Use the given information to write an equation for each line.

9. slope 6, y-intercept 4 $y = 6x + 4$
10. slope $-\frac{1}{3}$, y-intercept −2 $y = -\frac{1}{3}x - 2$
11. $y = \frac{3}{4}x + 1\frac{1}{2}$
12. $y = -\frac{5}{3}x + 2$
13. through (−2, 0) and (3, 10) $y = 2(x + 2)$
14. through (10, 2) and (2, −2) $y - 2 = \frac{1}{2}(x - 10)$

Practice and Problem Solving Wkbk/ All-in-One Resources/Online

Practice page 2

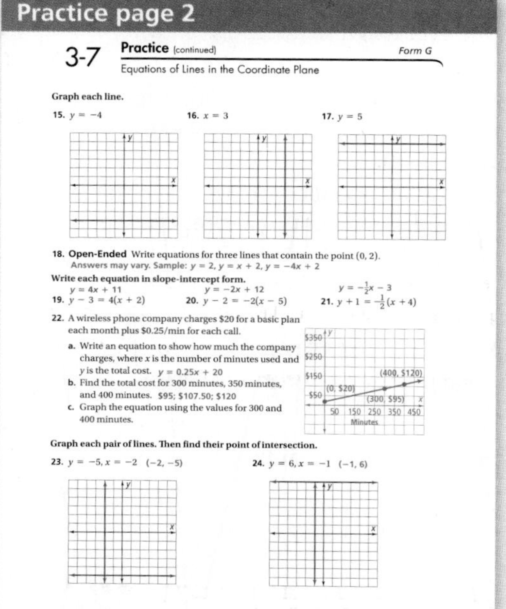

3-7 Practice (continued) — Form G

Equations of Lines in the Coordinate Plane

Graph each line.

15. $y = -4$
16. $x = 3$
17. $y = 5$

18. Open-Ended Write equations for three lines that contain the point (0, 2). Answers may vary. Sample: $y = 2$, $y = x + 2$, $y = -4x + 2$

Write each equation in slope-intercept form.

19. $y - 3 = 4(x + 2)$ $y = 4x + 11$
20. $y - 2 = -2(x - 5)$ $y = -2x + 12$
21. $y + 1 = -\frac{1}{2}(x + 4)$ $y = -\frac{1}{2}x - 3$

22. A wireless phone company charges $20 for a basic plan each month plus $0.25/min for each call.
  a. Write an equation to show how much the company charges, where x is the number of minutes used and y is the total cost. $y = 0.25x + 20$
  b. Find the total cost for 300 minutes, 350 minutes, and 400 minutes. $95; $107.50; $120
  c. Graph the equation using the values for 300 and 400 minutes.

Graph each pair of lines. Then find their point of intersection.

23. $y = -5$, $x = -2$ (−2, −5)
24. $y = 6$, $x = -1$ (−1, 6)

All-in-One Resources/Online

Enrichment

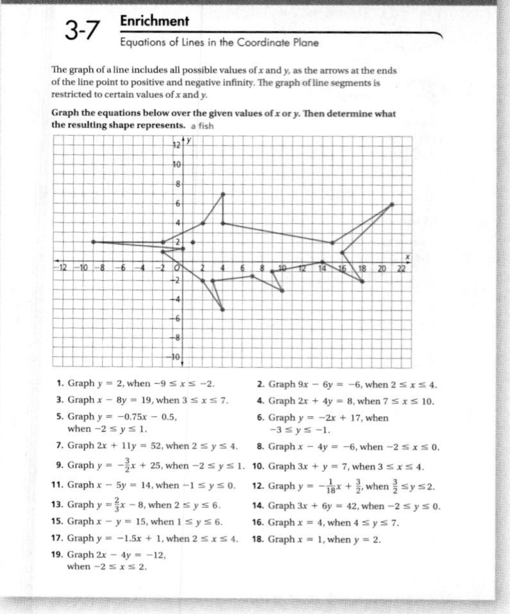

3-7 Enrichment

Equations of Lines in the Coordinate Plane

The graph of a line includes all possible values of x and y, as the arrows at the ends of the line point to positive and negative infinity. The graph of line segments is restricted to certain values of x and y.

Graph the equations below over the given values of x or y. Then determine what the resulting shape represents. a fish

1. Graph $y = 2$, when $-9 \le x \le -2$.
2. Graph $9x - 6y = -6$, when $2 \le x \le 4$.
3. Graph $x - 8y = 19$, when $3 \le x \le 7$.
4. Graph $2x + 4y = 8$, when $7 \le x \le 10$.
5. Graph $y = -0.75x - 0.5$, when $-2 \le y \le 1$.
6. Graph $y = -2x + 17$, when $-3 \le y \le -1$.
7. Graph $2x + 11y = 52$, when $2 \le y \le 4$.
8. Graph $x - 4y = -6$, when $-2 \le x \le 0$.
9. Graph $y = -\frac{3}{2}x + 25$, when $-2 \le y \le 1$.
10. Graph $3x + y = 7$, when $3 \le x \le 4$.
11. Graph $x - 5y = 14$, when $-1 \le y \le 0$.
12. Graph $y = -\frac{1}{18}x + \frac{3}{2}$, when $\frac{3}{2} \le y \le 2$.
13. Graph $y = \frac{2}{3}x - 8$, when $2 \le y \le 6$.
14. Graph $3x + 6y = 42$, when $-2 \le y \le 0$.
15. Graph $x - y = 15$, when $1 \le y \le 6$.
16. Graph $x = 4$, when $4 \le y \le 7$.
17. Graph $y = -1.5x + 1$, when $2 \le x \le 4$.
18. Graph $x = 1$, when $y = 2$.
19. Graph $2x - 4y = -12$, when $-2 \le x \le 2$.

Practice and Problem Solving Wkbk/ All-in-One Resources/Online

Think About a Plan

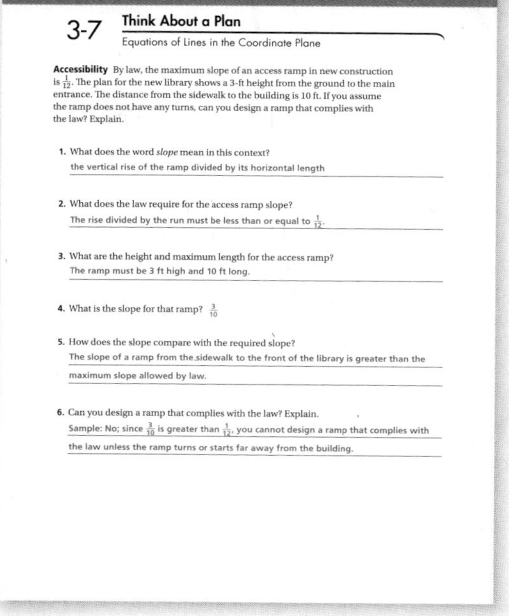

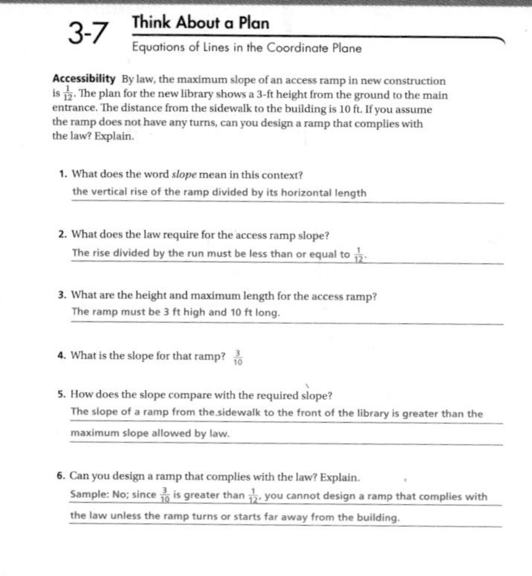

3-7 Think About a Plan

Equations of Lines in the Coordinate Plane

Accessibility By law, the maximum slope of an access ramp in new construction is $\frac{1}{12}$. The plan for the new library shows a 3-ft height from the ground to the main entrance. The distance from the sidewalk to the building is 10 ft. If you assume the ramp does not have any turns, can you design a ramp that complies with the law? Explain.

1. What does the word *slope* mean in this context? the vertical rise of the ramp divided by its horizontal length
2. What does the law require for the access ramp slope? The rise divided by the run must be less than or equal to $\frac{1}{12}$.
3. What are the height and maximum length for the access ramp? The ramp must be 3 ft high and 10 ft long.
4. What is the slope for that ramp? $\frac{3}{10}$
5. How does the slope compare with the required slope? The slope of a ramp from the sidewalk to the front of the library is greater than the maximum slope allowed by law.
6. Can you design a ramp that complies with the law? Explain. Sample: No; since $\frac{3}{10}$ is greater than $\frac{1}{12}$, you cannot design a ramp that complies with the law unless the ramp turns or starts far away from the building.

Practice and Problem Solving Wkbk/ All-in-One Resources/Online

Standardized Test Prep

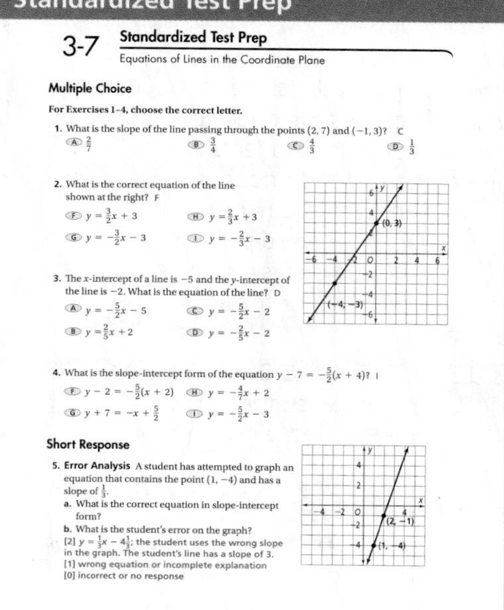

3-7 Standardized Test Prep

Equations of Lines in the Coordinate Plane

Multiple Choice

For Exercises 1–4, choose the correct letter.

1. What is the slope of the line passing through the points (2, 7) and (−1, 3)? C
 A. $\frac{2}{7}$ B. $\frac{3}{4}$ C. $\frac{4}{3}$ D. $\frac{1}{3}$
2. What is the correct equation of the line shown at the right? F
 F. $y = \frac{3}{2}x + 3$ H. $y = \frac{2}{3}x + 3$
 G. $y = -\frac{3}{2}x - 3$ I. $y = -\frac{2}{3}x - 3$
3. The x-intercept of a line is −5 and the y-intercept of the line is −2. What is the equation of the line? D
 A. $y = -\frac{5}{2}x - 5$ C. $y = -\frac{5}{2}x - 2$
 B. $y = \frac{2}{5}x + 2$ D. $y = -\frac{2}{5}x - 2$
4. What is the slope-intercept form of the equation $y - 7 = -\frac{5}{2}(x + 4)$? I
 F. $y - 2 = -\frac{5}{2}(x + 2)$ H. $y = -\frac{4}{5}x + 2$
 G. $y + 7 = -x + \frac{5}{2}$ I. $y = -\frac{5}{2}x - 3$

Short Response

5. Error Analysis A student has attempted to graph an equation that contains the point (1, −4) and has a slope of $\frac{1}{3}$.
 a. What is the correct equation in slope-intercept form?
 b. What is the student's error on the graph?
 [2] $y = \frac{1}{3}x - 4\frac{1}{3}$; the student uses the wrong slope in the graph. The student's line has a slope of 3.
 [1] wrong equation or incomplete explanation
 [0] incorrect or no response

Online Teacher Resource Center

Activities, Games, and Puzzles

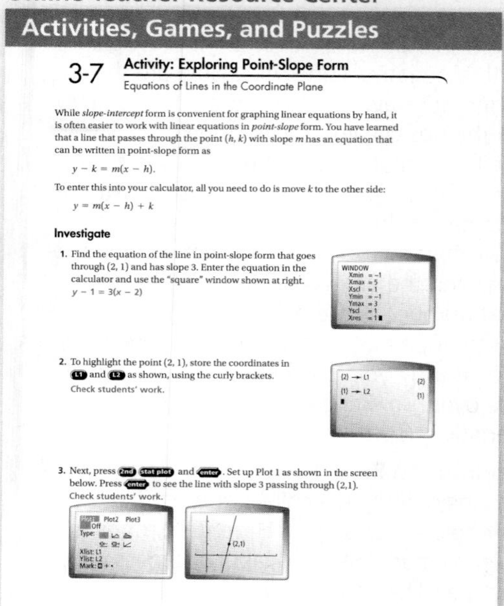

3-7 Activity: Exploring Point-Slope Form

Equations of Lines in the Coordinate Plane

While *slope-intercept* form is convenient for graphing linear equations by hand, it is often easier to work with linear equations in *point-slope* form. You have learned that a line that passes through the point (h, k) with slope m has an equation that can be written in point-slope form as

$y - k = m(x - h)$.

To enter this into your calculator, all you need to do is move k to the other side:

$y = m(x - h) + k$

Investigate

1. Find the equation of the line in point-slope form that goes through (2, 1) and has slope 3. Enter the equation in the calculator and use the "square" window shown at right. $y - 1 = 3(x - 2)$
2. To highlight the point (2, 1), store the coordinates in L1 and L2 as shown, using the curly brackets. Check students' work.
3. Next, press 2nd STAT PLOT and ENTER. Set up Plot 1 as shown in the screen below. Press ENTER to see the line with slope 3 passing through (2,1). Check students' work.

3-8 Slopes of Parallel and Perpendicular Lines

Objective To relate slope to parallel and perpendicular lines

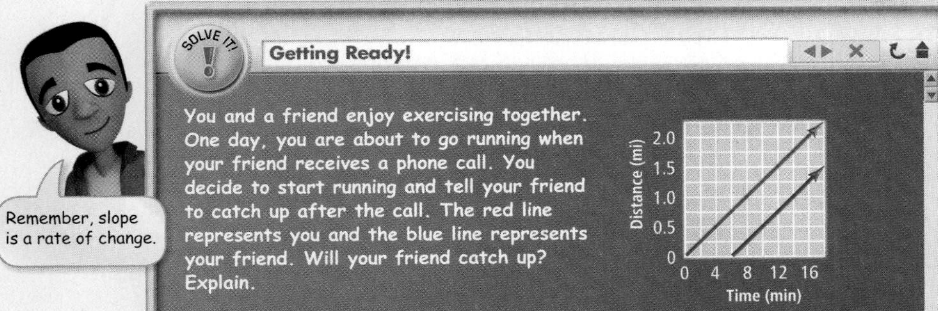

Getting Ready!
You and a friend enjoy exercising together. One day, you are about to go running when your friend receives a phone call. You decide to start running and tell your friend to catch up after the call. The red line represents you and the blue line represents your friend. Will your friend catch up? Explain.
Remember, slope is a rate of change.
Distance (mi)
Time (min)

In the Solve It, slope represents the running rate, or speed. According to the graph, you and your friend run at the same speed, so the slopes of the lines are the same. In this lesson, you will learn how to use slopes to determine how two lines relate graphically to each other.

Essential Understanding You can determine whether two lines are parallel or perpendicular by comparing their slopes.

When two lines are parallel, their slopes are the same.

Key Concept Slopes of Parallel Lines

- If two nonvertical lines are parallel, then their slopes are equal.
- If the slopes of two distinct nonvertical lines are equal, then the lines are parallel.
- Any two vertical lines or horizontal lines are parallel.

1 Interactive Learning

Solve It!

PURPOSE To introduce students to the characteristics of the equations of parallel lines

PROCESS Students may
- use visual judgment.
- observe the pattern shown in the graph and use inductive reasoning to make a conjecture.

FACILITATE

Q In miles per minute, what is your speed? What is your friend's speed? **[0.125 mi/min; 0.125 mi/min]**

Q How far are you ahead of your friend when she starts running? **[0.75 mi]**

Q If your friend runs the same distance as you, how many minutes will she continue to run after you have finished? **[6 min]**

ANSWER See Solve It in Answers on next page.

CONNECT THE MATH Students can see from the graph that lines with the same slope but different *y*-intercepts will never intersect and are therefore parallel.

2 Guided Instruction

Take Note

ERROR PREVENTION

Q Why must two parallel lines have different *y*-intercepts? **[Because if they had both the same slope and the same *y*-intercept, then they would be the same line.]**

Q Do all horizontal lines have the same slope? Explain. **[Yes, they all have a slope of 0.]**

3-8 Preparing to Teach

BIG idea **Coordinate Geometry**

ESSENTIAL UNDERSTANDINGS
- Comparing the slopes of two lines can show whether the lines are parallel or perpendicular.
- The relationship between parallel or perpendicular lines can sometimes be used to write the equation of a line.

Math Background

Slope is a fixed ratio that characterizes any nonvertical line.

Students will learn that the slopes of parallel lines must be equal. Students need to realize that equal slopes can be written as equivalent ratios. The lines $x + 2y = 9$ and $2x + 4y = 10$ are parallel lines because the ratios $-\frac{1}{2}$ and $-\frac{2}{4}$ are equivalent.

Students will learn that the slopes of perpendicular lines must be opposite reciprocals of each other. Students need to realize that the slopes do not have to appear as fractions with the numerators and denominators in reversed positions to be reciprocals. The numbers simply need to have a product of -1 for the lines to be perpendicular.

The lines $0.5x + y = 4$ and $2x - y = 6$ are perpendicular lines because the slopes of the two lines are -0.5 and 2, which have a product of -1.

Support Student Learning

Use the **Geometry Companion** to engage and support students during instructions. See Lesson Resources at the end of this lesson for details.

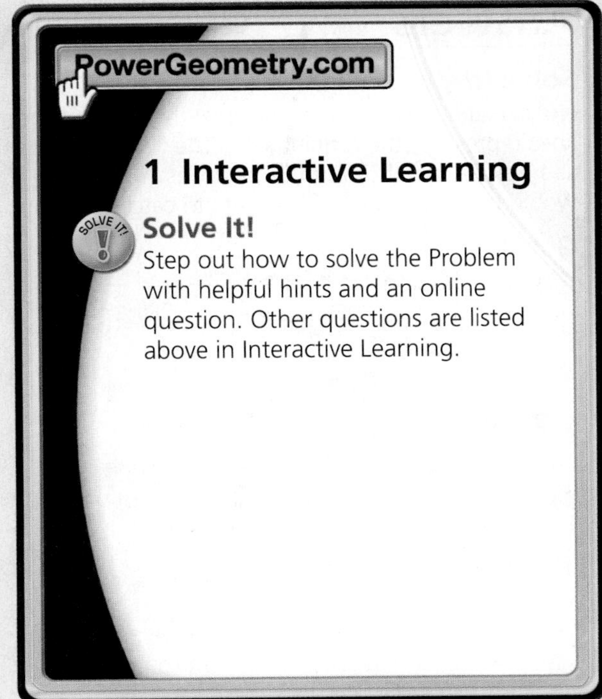

Problem 1

Q How could you determine the point of intersection for the two lines? **[Answers may vary. Sample: You could use the slopes to extend each line in both directions until the intersection point is found. You could also use algebra to solve the equations for both lines as a system of equations.]**

Got It? VISUAL LEARNERS

You can use the zoom function on a graphing utility to show students they cannot determine if lines are parallel by visual inspection alone. Let them see how lines may appear parallel in one viewing window but show a point of intersection when the viewing window is enlarged to show more of the lines.

Problem 2

Q Does the given information provide the *y*-intercept for the new line? Explain. **[No, it only provides the slope of the new line and a point on the new line.]**

Q How could you determine the *y*-intercept of the new line? **[Answers may vary. Sample: Solve the point-slope form for *y*.]**

Got It? SYNTHESIZING

Point out to students that once the slope of the given line is identified, this problem becomes a repeat of the problems studied in Lesson 1-7.

Take Note ERROR PREVENTION

Remind students that when the product of two slopes is −1, the lines are perpendicular.

Think

Can you tell from the diagram whether the lines are parallel?
No. The lines may look parallel, but you only see a small portion of their graphs. Compare their slopes to know for sure.

Problem 1 Checking for Parallel Lines

Are lines ℓ_1 and ℓ_2 parallel? Explain.

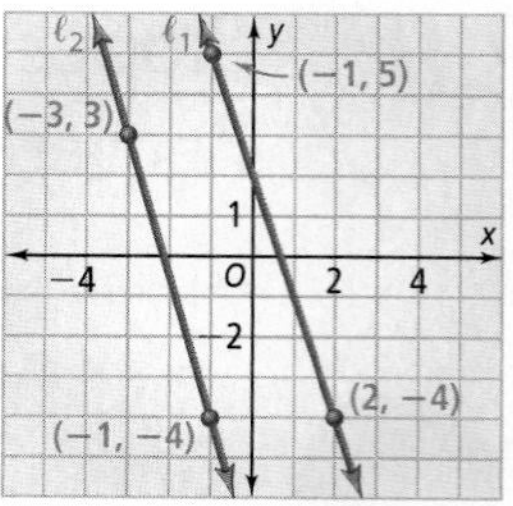

Step 1 Find the slope of each line.

$$\text{slope of } \ell_1 = \frac{5 - (-4)}{-1 - 2} = \frac{9}{-3} = -3$$

$$\text{slope of } \ell_2 = \frac{3 - (-4)}{-3 - (-1)} = \frac{7}{-2} = -\frac{7}{2}$$

Step 2 Compare the slopes.

Since $-3 \neq -\frac{7}{2}$, ℓ_1 and ℓ_2 are not parallel.

Got It? 1. Line ℓ_3 contains $A(-13, 6)$ and $B(-1, 2)$. Line ℓ_4 contains $C(3, 6)$ and $D(6, 7)$. Are ℓ_3 and ℓ_4 parallel? Explain.

Plan

How does the given line help you?
Parallel lines have the same slope. Once you know the slope of the given line, you know the slope you need to write an equation.

Problem 2 Writing Equations of Parallel Lines

What is an equation of the line parallel to $y = -3x - 5$ that contains $(-1, 8)$?

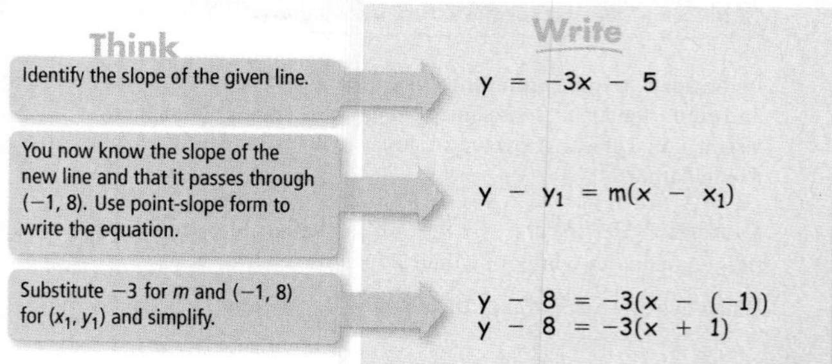

Think	Write
Identify the slope of the given line.	$y = -3x - 5$
You now know the slope of the new line and that it passes through (−1, 8). Use point-slope form to write the equation.	$y - y_1 = m(x - x_1)$
Substitute −3 for *m* and (−1, 8) for (x_1, y_1) and simplify.	$y - 8 = -3(x - (-1))$ $y - 8 = -3(x + 1)$

Got It? 2. What is an equation of the line parallel to $y = -x - 7$ that contains $(-5, 3)$?

When two lines are perpendicular, the product of their slopes is −1. Numbers with product −1 are opposite reciprocals.

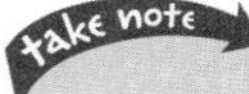

take note

Key Concept Slopes of Perpendicular Lines

- If two nonvertical lines are perpendicular, then the product of their slopes is −1.
- If the slopes of two lines have a product of −1, then the lines are perpendicular.
- Any horizontal line and vertical line are perpendicular.

Answers

Solve It!

No; explanations may vary. Sample: the slope of the lines represents the running rate. The lines have the same slope. You both run 8-min miles. Your friend would need to run at a faster rate to catch up.

Got It?

1. No; the slope of ℓ_3 is $\frac{6 - 2}{-13 - (-1)} = \frac{4}{-12} = -\frac{1}{3}$ and the slope of ℓ_4 is $\frac{6 - 7}{3 - 6} = \frac{-1}{-3} = \frac{1}{3}$. The slopes are not equal.
2. $y - 3 = -(x + 5)$
3. No; the slope of ℓ_3 is $\frac{7 - (-1)}{2 - 3} = \frac{8}{-1} = -8$ and the slope of ℓ_4 is $\frac{6 - 7}{-2 - 8} = \frac{-1}{-10} = \frac{1}{10}$. Since the product of the slopes is not −1, the lines are not ⊥.
4. $y - 7 = \frac{1}{3}(x + 3)$

PowerGeometry.com

2 Guided Instruction

Each Problem is worked out and supported online.

Problem 1
Checking for Parallel Lines

Problem 2
Writing Equations of Parallel Lines
Animated

Problem 3
Checking for Perpendicular Lines

Problem 4
Writing Equations of Perpendicular Lines

Problem 5
Writing Equations of Lines
Animated

Support in Geometry Companion
- Vocabulary
- Key Concepts
- Got It?

Plan

Can you tell from the diagram whether the lines are perpendicular?
No. You can tell that the lines intersect, but not necessarily at right angles. So, you need to compare their slopes.

Problem 3 Checking for Perpendicular Lines

Lines ℓ_1 and ℓ_2 are neither horizontal nor vertical. Are they perpendicular? Explain.

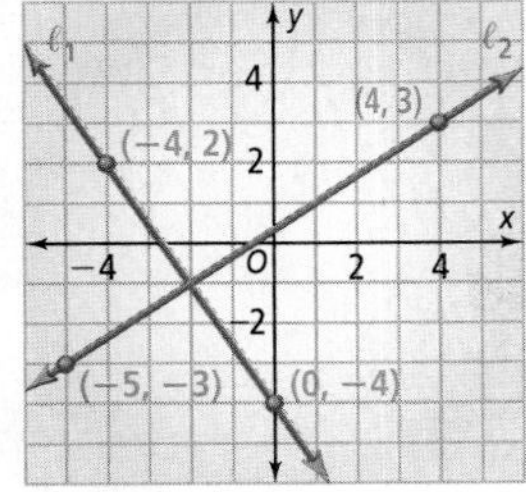

Step 1 Find the slope of each line.

$$m_1 = \text{slope of } \ell_1 = \frac{2 - (-4)}{-4 - 0} = \frac{6}{-4} = -\frac{3}{2}$$

$$m_2 = \text{slope of } \ell_2 = \frac{3 - (-3)}{4 - (-5)} = \frac{6}{9} = \frac{2}{3}$$

Step 2 Find the product of the slopes.

$$m_1 \cdot m_2 = -\frac{3}{2} \cdot \frac{2}{3} = -1$$

Lines ℓ_1 and ℓ_2 are perpendicular because the product of their slopes is -1.

Got It? 3. Line ℓ_3 contains $A(2, 7)$ and $B(3, -1)$. Line ℓ_4 contains $C(-2, 6)$ and $D(8, 7)$. Are ℓ_3 and ℓ_4 perpendicular? Explain.

Think

How is this similar to writing equations of parallel lines?
You follow the same process. The only difference here is that the slopes of perpendicular lines have product −1.

Problem 4 Writing Equations of Perpendicular Lines

What is an equation of the line perpendicular to $y = \frac{1}{5}x + 2$ that contains $(15, -4)$?

Step 1 Identify the slope of the given line.

$$y = \frac{1}{5}x + 2$$

↑ slope

Step 2 Find the slope of the line perpendicular to the given line.

$m_1 \cdot m_2 = -1$ The product of the slopes of ⊥ lines is −1.

$\frac{1}{5} \cdot m_2 = -1$ Substitute $\frac{1}{5}$ for m_1.

$m_2 = -5$ Multiply each side by 5.

Step 3 Use point-slope form to write an equation of the new line.

$y - y_1 = m(x - x_1)$

$y - (-4) = -5(x - 15)$ Substitute −5 for m and (15, −4) for (x_1, y_1).

$y + 4 = -5(x - 15)$ Simplify.

Got It? 4. What is an equation of the line perpendicular to $y = -3x - 5$ that contains $(-3, 7)$?

Problem 3

Q What is the product of the slopes of ℓ_1 and ℓ_2? **[−1]**

Q How is the slope of ℓ_1 related to the slope of ℓ_2? **[The slope of ℓ_1 is the opposite reciprocal of the slope of ℓ_2.]**

Got It? SYNTHESIZING

Q Will ℓ_3 intersect ℓ_4? Explain. **[Yes, they will intersect, because the slopes are not equal.]**

Problem 4

Q What is a shortcut for determining the slope in Step 2? **[Find the opposite reciprocal of $\frac{1}{5}$.]**

Q What postulate states that there is only one line perpendicular to the given line through the point (15, −4)? **[Perpendicular Postulate]**

Got It?

Q What is an equation of the line perpendicular to $y = -3x - 5$ that has the same y-intercept? **[$y = \frac{1}{3}x - 5$]**

Additional Problems

1. Are the lines shown in the graph parallel? Explain.

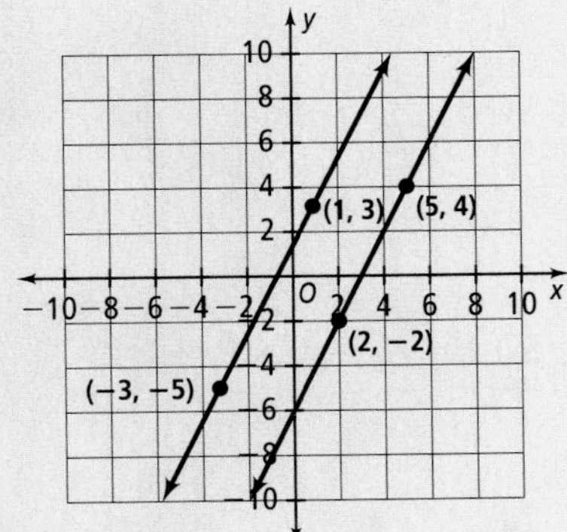

ANSWER Yes, they have the same slope.

2. What is an equation in slope-intercept form for the line parallel to $y = 4x - 2$ that contains $(-2, -2)$?

ANSWER $y = 4x + 6$

3. Are the lines shown in the graph perpendicular? Explain.

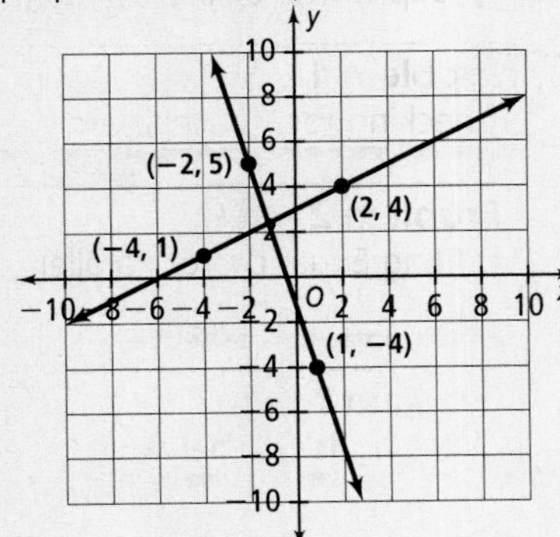

ANSWER No, their slopes are not opposite reciprocals. The product of the slopes is not −1.

4. What is an equation in slope-intercept form for the line perpendicular to $y = 3x + 2$ that contains $(6, 2)$?

ANSWER $y = -\frac{1}{3}x + 4$

5. What is an equation for a line perpendicular to the one shown that contains $(5, -1)$?

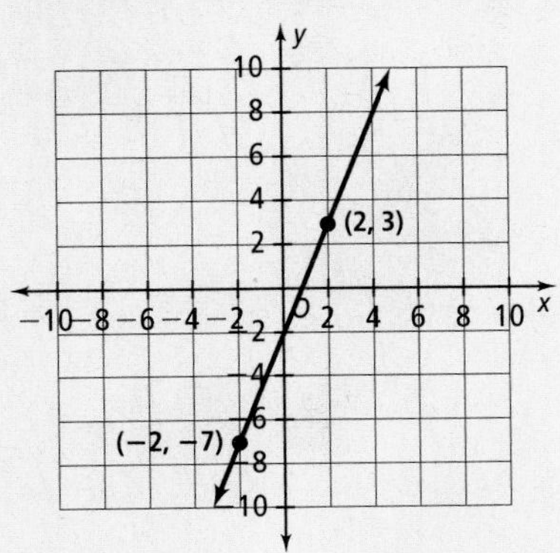

ANSWER $y = -\frac{2}{5}x + 1$

Problem 5

Q What information is needed in order to find the slope of the baseball's path? **[You must know two points on the path.]**

Q If you know the slope of the baseball's path, how do you determine the slope of the outfielder's path? **[You find the number that when multiplied by the slope of the baseball's path gives a product of -1.]**

Q What information is needed in order to write the equation of the outfielder's path? **[You must know the slope of the path as well as either the *y*-intercept or a point on the path.]**

Got It?

Q What is the relationship between the path of the second player and the path of the first player? Explain. **[Perpendicular; the players are in the same plane. So, if a line is perpendicular to one of two parallel lines, it is also perpendicular to the other (Theorem 3-9).]**

Problem 5 Writing Equations of Lines

Sports The baseball field below is on a coordinate grid with home plate at the origin. A batter hits a ground ball along the line shown. The player at (110, 70) runs along a path perpendicular to the path of the baseball. What is an equation of the line on which the player runs?

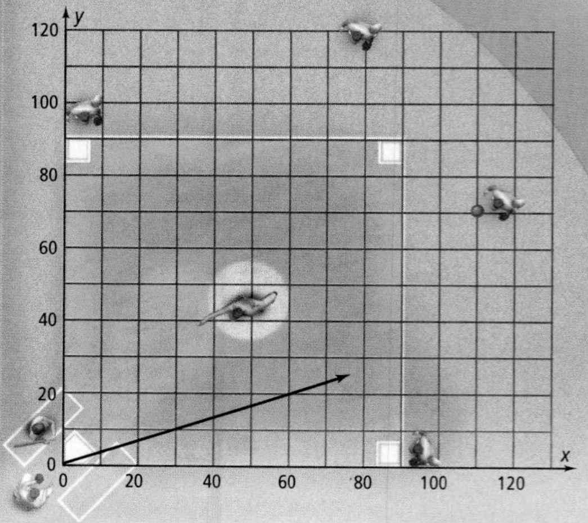

Step 1 Find the slope of the baseball's path.

$m_1 = \frac{y_2 - y_1}{x_2 - x_1} = \frac{20 - 10}{60 - 30} = \frac{10}{30} = \frac{1}{3}$ Points (30, 10) and (60, 20) are on the baseball's path.

Step 2 Find the slope of a line perpendicular to the baseball's path.

$m_1 \cdot m_2 = -1$ The product of the slopes of $\perp$ lines is -1.

$\frac{1}{3} \cdot m_2 = -1$ Substitute $\frac{1}{3}$ for m_1.

$m_2 = -3$ Multiply each side by 3.

Think

Which linear equation form should you use? You know the slope. The player is located at a point on the line. Use point-slope form.

Step 3 Write an equation of the line on which the player runs. The slope is -3 and a point on the line is (110, 70).

$y - y_1 = m(x - x_1)$ Point-slope form

$y - 70 = -3(x - 110)$ Substitute -3 for m and (110, 70) for (x_1, y_1).

Got It? 5. Suppose a second player standing at (90, 40) misses the ball, turns around, and runs on a path parallel to the baseball's path. What is an equation of the line representing this player's path?

Answers

Got It? (continued)

5. $y - 40 = \frac{1}{3}(x - 90)$

Lesson Check

Do you know HOW?

$\overleftrightarrow{AB}$ contains points A and B. $\overleftrightarrow{CD}$ contains points C and D. Are $\overleftrightarrow{AB}$ and $\overleftrightarrow{CD}$ *parallel, perpendicular,* or *neither*? Explain.

1. $A(-8, 3), B(-4, 11), C(-1, 3), D(1, 2)$
2. $A(3, 5), B(2, -1), C(7, -2), D(10, 16)$
3. $A(3, 1), B(4, 1), C(5, 9), D(2, 6)$
4. What is an equation of the line perpendicular to $y = -4x + 1$ that contains $(2, -3)$?

Do you UNDERSTAND?

5. **Error Analysis** Your classmate tries to find an equation for a line parallel to $y = 3x - 5$ that contains $(-4, 2)$. What is your classmate's error?

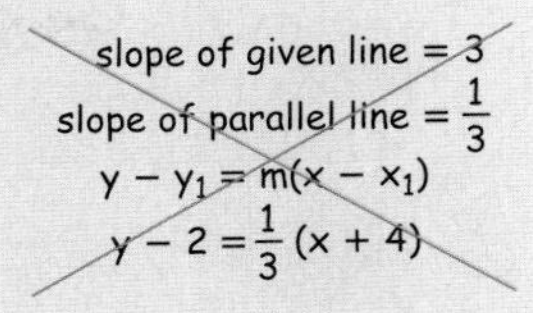

6. **Compare and Contrast** What are the differences between the equations of parallel lines and the equations of perpendicular lines? Explain.

Practice and Problem-Solving Exercises

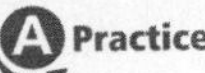

A Practice For Exercises 7–10, are lines ℓ_1 and ℓ_2 parallel? Explain. See Problem 1.

7. 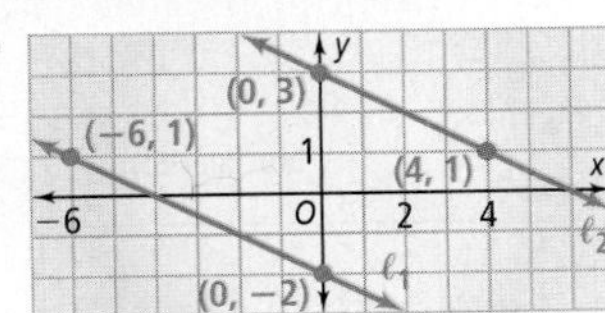 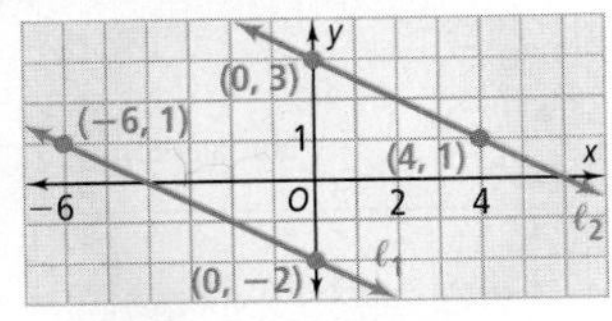

8. 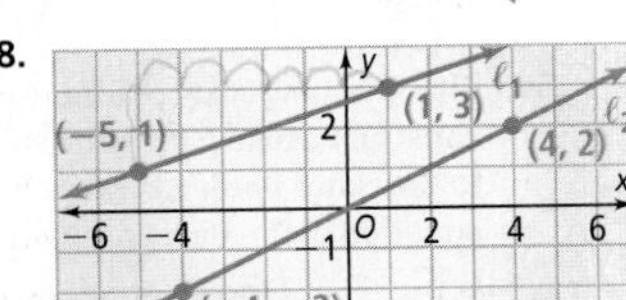

9. 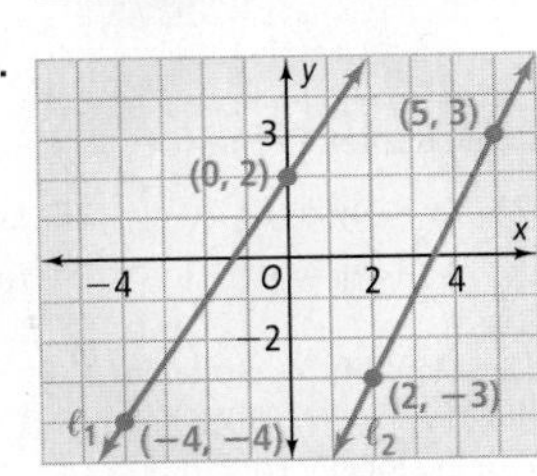

10. 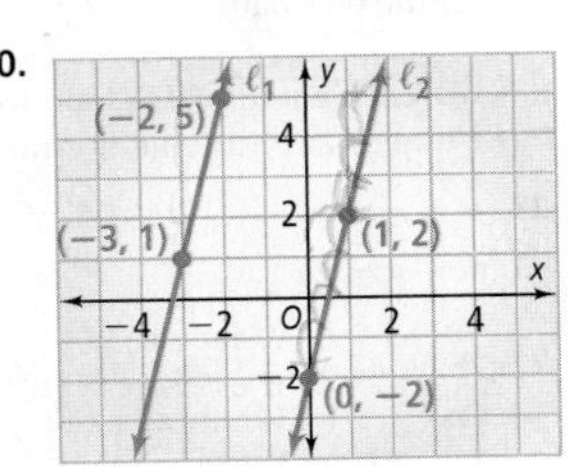

Write an equation of the line parallel to the given line that contains C. See Problem 2.

11. $C(0, 3); y = -2x + 1$
12. $C(6, 0); y = \frac{1}{3}x$
13. $C(-2, 4); y = \frac{1}{2}x + 2$
14. $C(6, -2); y = -\frac{3}{2}x + 6$

3 Lesson Check

Do you know HOW?

- If students have difficulty with Exercises 1–3, then have them review Problem 1.

Do you UNDERSTAND?

- If students have difficulty with Exercise 6, then remind them that while parallel lines cannot share the same y-intercept, perpendicular lines can share the same y-intercept.

Close

Q How can you determine if two lines will intersect? **[Determine the slopes of both lines. If the slopes are not equal, the lines will intersect.]**

Lesson Check

1. ⊥; the slope of $\overleftrightarrow{AB}$ is 2 and the slope of $\overleftrightarrow{CD}$ is $-\frac{1}{2}$. Since $(2)\left(-\frac{1}{2}\right) = -1$, the lines are ⊥.
2. ∥; the slope of $\overleftrightarrow{AB}$ is 6 and the slope of $\overleftrightarrow{CD}$ is 6. Since the slopes are equal, the lines are ∥.
3. Neither; the slope of $\overleftrightarrow{AB}$ is 0 and the slope of $\overleftrightarrow{CD}$ is 1. Since the slopes are not equal and their product is not −1, the lines are neither ∥ nor ⊥.
4. Answers may vary. Sample: $y + 3 = \frac{1}{4}(x - 2)$
5. The second line should say "slope of parallel line = 3" because ∥ lines have equal slopes.
6. Sample: ∥ line equations have equal slopes. ⊥ line equations have slopes with product −1.

Practice and Problem-Solving Exercises

7. Yes; the slope of ℓ_1 is $-\frac{1}{2}$ and the slope of ℓ_2 is $-\frac{1}{2}$, and two lines with the same slope are ∥.
8. No; the slope of ℓ_1 is $\frac{1}{3}$ and the slope of ℓ_2 is $\frac{1}{2}$. The slopes are not equal so the lines are not ∥.
9. No; the slope of ℓ_1 is $\frac{3}{2}$ and the slope of ℓ_2 is 2. Since the slopes are not equal the lines are not ∥.
10. Yes; the slope of ℓ_1 is 4 and the slope of ℓ_2 is 4, and two lines with the same slope are ∥.
11. $y = -2x + 3$
12. $y = \frac{1}{3}(x - 6)$
13. $y - 4 = \frac{1}{2}(x + 2)$
14. $y + 2 = -\frac{3}{2}(x - 6)$

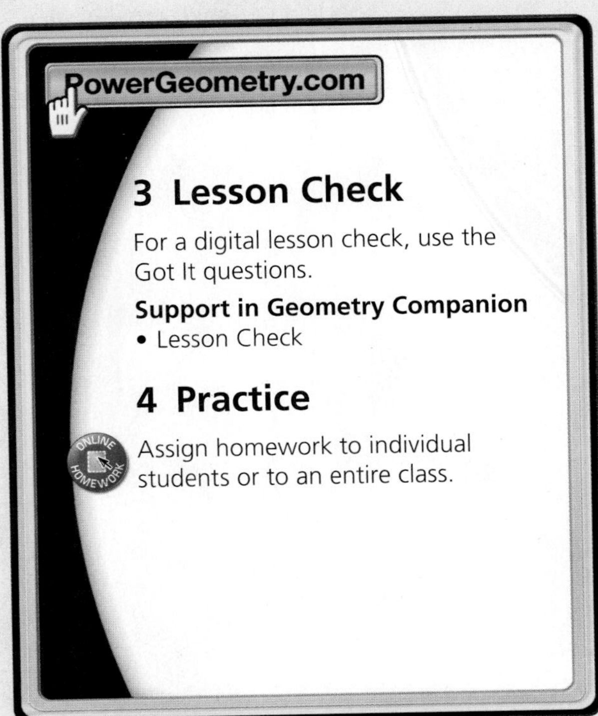

PowerGeometry.com

3 Lesson Check

For a digital lesson check, use the Got It questions.

Support in Geometry Companion

- Lesson Check

4 Practice

Assign homework to individual students or to an entire class.

4 Practice

ASSIGNMENT GUIDE

Basic: 7–22 all, 24, 27, 29, 30–40 even, 41
Average: 7–21 odd, 23–43
Advanced: 7–21 odd, 23–47
Standardized Test Prep: 48–52
Mixed Review: 53–62

Reasoning exercises have blue headings.
Applications exercises have red headings.

EXERCISE 41: Use the Think About a Plan worksheet in the **Practice and Problem Solving Workbook** (also available in the Teaching Resources in print and online) to further support students' development in becoming independent learners.

HOMEWORK QUICK CHECK

To check students' understanding of key skills and concepts, go over Exercises 9, 15, 27, 29, and 41.

For Exercises 15–18, are lines ℓ_1 and ℓ_2 perpendicular? Explain. See Problem 3.

15.
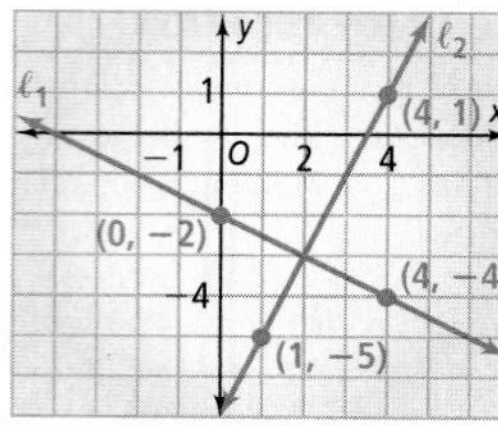

16.
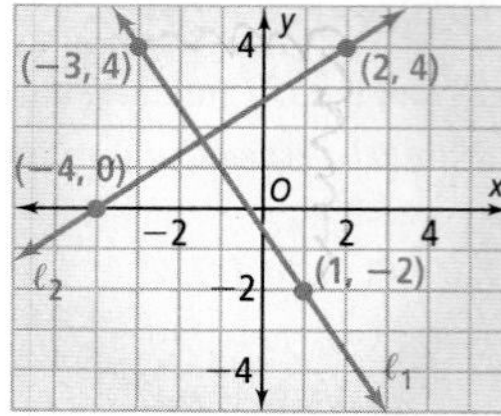

17.
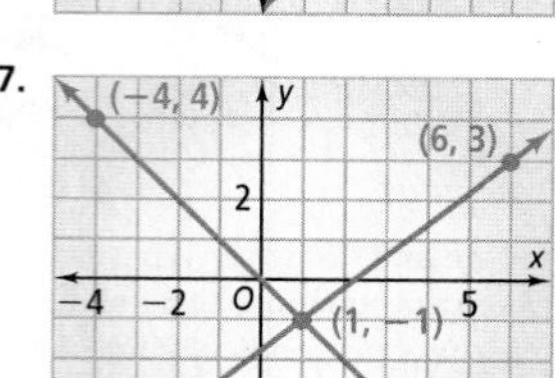

18.
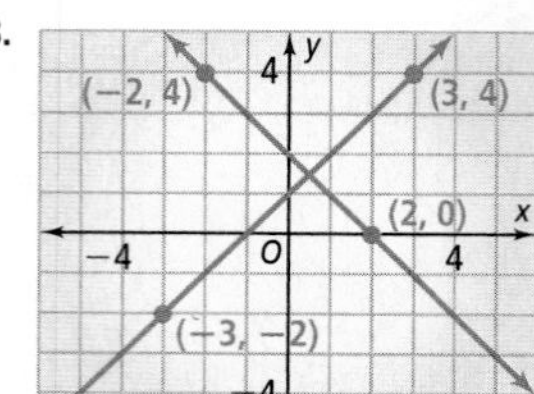

Write an equation of the line perpendicular to the given line that contains *P*. See Problem 4.

19. $P(6, 6); y = \frac{2}{3}x$

20. $P(4, 0); y = \frac{1}{2}x - 5$

21. $P(4, 4); y = -2x - 8$

22. **City Planning** City planners want to construct a bike path perpendicular to Bruckner Boulevard at point *P*. An equation of the Bruckner Boulevard line is $y = -\frac{3}{4}x$. Find an equation of the line for the bike path. See Problem 5.

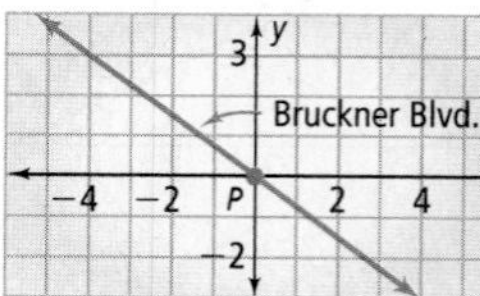

Apply

Rewrite each equation in slope-intercept form, if necessary. Then determine whether the lines are parallel. Explain.

23. $y = -x + 6$
$x + y = 20$

24. $y - 7x = 6$
$y + 7x = 8$

25. $3x + 4y = 12$
$6x + 2y = 6$

26. $2x + 5y = -1$
$10y = -4x - 20$

27. **Think About a Plan** Line ℓ_1 contains $(-4, 1)$ and $(2, 5)$ and line ℓ_2 contains $(3, 0)$ and $(-3, k)$. What value of k makes ℓ_1 and ℓ_2 parallel?
- For ℓ_1 and ℓ_2 to be parallel, what must be true of their slopes?
- What expressions represent the slopes of ℓ_1 and ℓ_2?

28. **Open-Ended** Write equations for two perpendicular lines that have the same *y*-intercept and do not pass through the origin.

29. **Writing** Can the *y*-intercepts of two nonvertical parallel lines be the same? Explain.

Answers

Practice and Problem-Solving Exercises (continued)

15. Yes; the slope of ℓ_1 is $-\frac{1}{2}$ and the slope of ℓ_2 is 2. Since the product of the slopes is -1, the lines are $\perp$.

16. Yes; the slope of ℓ_1 is $-\frac{3}{2}$ and the slope of ℓ_2 is $\frac{2}{3}$. Since the product of the slopes is -1, the lines are $\perp$.

17. No; the slope of ℓ_1 is -1 and the slope of ℓ_2 is $\frac{4}{5}$. Since the product of the slopes is not -1, the lines are not $\perp$.

18. Yes; the slope of ℓ_1 is -1 and the slope of ℓ_2 is 1. Since the product of the slopes is -1, the lines are $\perp$.

19. $y - 6 = -\frac{3}{2}(x - 6)$

20. $y = -2(x - 4)$

21. $y - 4 = \frac{1}{2}(x - 4)$

22. $y = \frac{4}{3}x$

23. Yes; both slopes are -1 so the lines are $\parallel$.

24. No; the slopes are 7 and -7, so the lines are not $\parallel$.

25. No; the slope of the first line is $-\frac{3}{4}$ and the slope of the second line is -3. Since the slopes are not equal, the lines are not $\parallel$.

26. Yes; both slopes are $-\frac{2}{5}$, so the lines are $\parallel$.

27. -4

28. Answers may vary. Samples:
$y = x + 1$ and $y = -x + 1$;
$y = 2x + 1$ and $y = -\frac{1}{2}x + 1$

29. No; if two equations represent lines with the same slope and the same *y*-intercept, the equations must represent the same line.

Use slopes to determine whether the opposite sides of quadrilateral $ABCD$ are parallel.

30. $A(0, 2), B(3, 4), C(2, 7), D(-1, 5)$

31. $A(-3, 1), B(1, -2), C(0, -3), D(-4, 0)$

32. $A(1, 1), B(5, 3), C(7, 1), D(3, 0)$

33. $A(1, 0), B(4, 0), C(3, -3), D(-1, -3)$

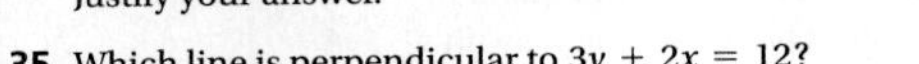

34. Reasoning Are opposite sides of hexagon $RSTUVW$ at the right parallel? Justify your answer.

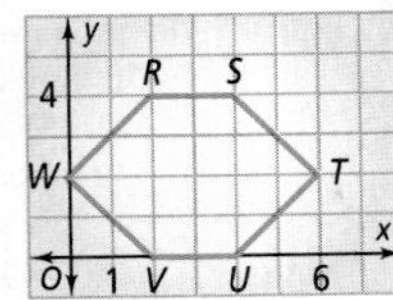

35. Which line is perpendicular to $3y + 2x = 12$?

Ⓐ $6x - 4y = 24$

Ⓑ $y + 3x = -2$

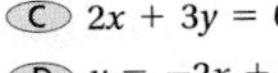

Ⓒ $2x + 3y = 6$

Ⓓ $y = -2x + 6$

Rewrite each equation in slope-intercept form, if necessary. Then determine whether the lines are perpendicular. Explain.

36. $y = -x - 7$
$y - x = 20$

37. $y = 3$
$x = -2$

38. $2x - 7y = -42$
$4y = -7x - 2$

Developing Proof **Explain why each theorem is true for three lines in the coordinate plane.**

39. Theorem 3-7: If two lines are parallel to the same line, then they are parallel to each other.

40. Theorem 3-8: In a plane, if two lines are perpendicular to the same line, then they are parallel to each other.

41. Rail Trail A community recently converted an old railroad corridor into a recreational trail. The graph at the right shows a map of the trail on a coordinate grid. They plan to construct a path to connect the trail to a parking lot. The new path will be perpendicular to the recreational trail.

a. Write an equation of the line representing the new path.

b. What are the coordinates of the point at which the path will meet the recreational trail?

c. If each grid space is 25 yd by 25 yd, how long is the path to the nearest yard?

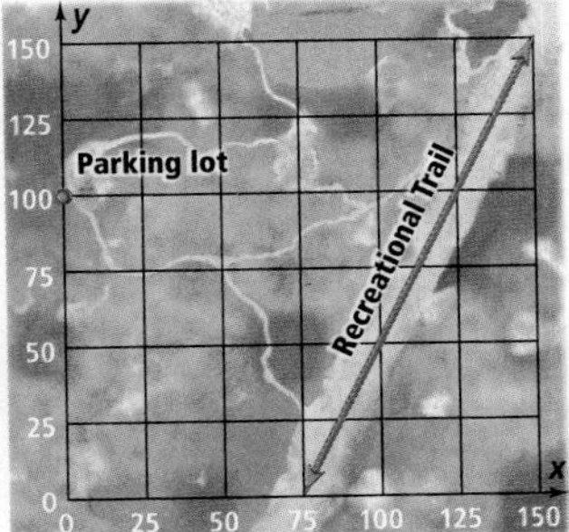

42. Reasoning Is a triangle with vertices $G(3, 2)$, $H(8, 5)$, and $K(0, 10)$ a right triangle? Justify your answer.

43. Graphing Calculator $\overleftrightarrow{AB}$ contains points $A(-3, 2)$ and $B(5, 1)$. $\overleftrightarrow{CD}$ contains points $C(2, 7)$ and $D(1, -1)$. Use your graphing calculator to find the slope of $\overleftrightarrow{AB}$. Enter the x-coordinates of A and B into the L1 list of your list editor. Enter the y-coordinates into the L2 list. In your stat CALC menu select **LinReg ($ax + b$)**. Press enter to find the slope a. Repeat to find the slope of $\overleftrightarrow{CD}$. Are $\overleftrightarrow{AB}$ and $\overleftrightarrow{CD}$ *parallel*, *perpendicular*, or *neither*?

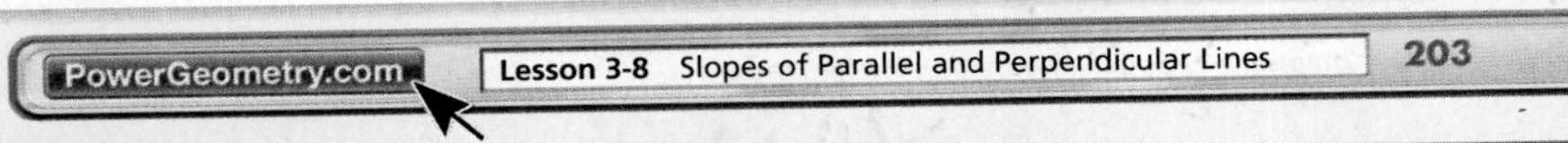

30. slope of $\overline{AB}$ = slope of $\overline{CD} = \frac{2}{3}$, $\overline{AB} \parallel \overline{CD}$; slope of $\overline{BC}$ = slope of $\overline{AD} = -3$, $\overline{BC} \parallel \overline{AD}$

31. slope of $\overline{AB}$ = slope of $\overline{CD} = -\frac{3}{4}$, $\overline{AB} \parallel \overline{CD}$; slope of $\overline{BC}$ = slope of $\overline{AD} = 1$, $\overline{BC} \parallel \overline{AD}$

32. slope of $\overline{AB} = \frac{1}{2}$, slope of $\overline{CD} = \frac{1}{4}$, $\overline{AB} \nparallel \overline{CD}$; slope of $\overline{BC} = -1$, slope of $\overline{AD} = -\frac{1}{2}$, $\overline{BC} \nparallel \overline{AD}$

33. slope of $\overline{AB}$ = slope of $\overline{CD} = 0$, $\overline{AB} \parallel \overline{CD}$; slope of $\overline{BC} = 3$, slope of $\overline{AD} = \frac{3}{2}$, $\overline{BC} \nparallel \overline{AD}$

34. Yes; $\overline{RS}$ and $\overline{VU}$ both have slope 0; $\overline{ST}$ and $\overline{WV}$ both have slope -1; $\overline{RW}$ and $\overline{TU}$ both have slope 1. Therefore, opposite sides of the figure are $\parallel$.

35. A

36. Yes; the slopes are -1 and 1 and their product is -1.

37. Yes; the equations represent a horizontal line and a vertical line, and every horizontal line is $\perp$ to every vertical line.

38. No; the slopes are $\frac{2}{7}$ and $-\frac{7}{4}$ and their product is not -1.

39. Answers may vary. Sample: The three lines must have the same slope or undefined slope, so all three lines are $\parallel$.

40. Answers may vary. Sample: Suppose the "same line" has slope $\frac{p}{q}$. Then each $\perp$ line has slope $-\frac{q}{p}$. Since those two lines have the same slope, they must be $\parallel$ to each other.

41a. $y = -\frac{1}{2}x + 100$

b. (100, 50)

c. 112 yd

42. No; the slope of $\overline{GH}$ is $\frac{3}{5}$, the slope of $\overline{HK}$ is $-\frac{5}{8}$, and the slope of $\overline{GK}$ is $-\frac{8}{3}$. Since no pair of slopes have a product of -1, no two lines are $\perp$ and the $\triangle$ is not a rt. $\triangle$.

43. Check students' work. Sample: slope of $\overline{AB}$ is $-\frac{1}{8}$; slope of $\overline{CD}$ is 8; the lines are $\perp$.

Answers

Practice and Problem-Solving Exercises (continued)

44. $AC = \sqrt{(7-9)^2 + (11-1)^2} = \sqrt{4 + 100}$
$= \sqrt{104}$ and $BD = \sqrt{(13-3)^2 + (7-5)^2}$
$= \sqrt{100 + 4} = \sqrt{104}$. Thus $AC = BD$.

45. The slope of $\overline{AC}$ is $\frac{10}{-2} = -5$ and the slope of $\overline{BD}$ is $\frac{2}{10} = \frac{1}{5}$. Since the product of the slopes is -1, the diagonals are $\perp$. The midpoint of $\overline{AC}$ is $\left(\frac{7+9}{2}, \frac{11+1}{2}\right) = (8, 6)$ and the midpoint of $\overline{BD}$ is $\left(\frac{13+3}{2}, \frac{7+5}{2}\right) = (8, 6)$. Since the two diagonals have the same midpoint, they bisect each other.

46a–c. Answers may vary. Sample:

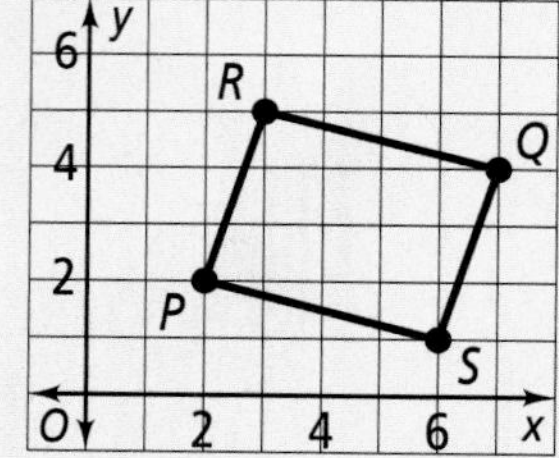

Students can show any two of these three possible locations for point S: (6, 1), (−2, 3), and (8, 7).

47. $y - 5 = \frac{1}{3}(x - 4)$

48. $\frac{1}{2}$

49. 6

50. 8.9

51. 7

52. 25

53. $y = -\frac{1}{2}x + 3$

54. $y - 2 = \frac{5}{3}(x + 4)$ or $y - 7 = \frac{5}{3}(x + 1)$

55. $y + 2 = \frac{3}{4}(x - 3)$ or $y + 8 = \frac{3}{4}(x + 5)$

56. Reflexive Prop. of ≅

57. Mult. Prop. of Equality

58. Distr. Prop.

59. Symmetric Prop. of ≅

60. Yes; ∠1 and ∠2 are vert. ⦞, and vert. ⦞ are ≅.

61. Yes; ∠1 and ∠2 are both rt. ⦞, and all rt. ⦞ are ≅.

62. No; $m\angle 1 = 54$ (Given) and $m\angle 2 = 90 - 54 = 36$ (because ∠1 and ∠2 are compl.)

For Exercises 44 and 45, use the graph at the right.

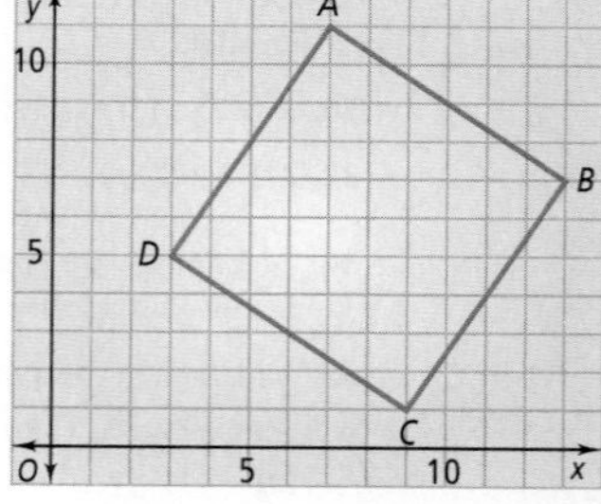

44. Show that the diagonals of the figure are congruent.

45. Show that the diagonals of the figure are perpendicular bisectors of each other.

46. a. Graph the points $P(2, 2)$, $Q(7, 4)$, and $R(3, 5)$.
b. Find the coordinates of a point S that, along with points P, Q, and R, will form the vertices of a quadrilateral with opposite sides parallel. Graph the quadrilateral.
c. Repeat part (b) to find a different point S. Graph the new quadrilateral.

47. Algebra A triangle has vertices $L(-5, 6)$, $M(-2, -3)$, and $N(4, 5)$. Write an equation for the line perpendicular to $\overline{LM}$ that contains point N.

Standardized Test Prep

GRIDDED RESPONSE

SAT/ACT

48. $\triangle ABC$ is right with right angle C. The slope of $\overline{AC}$ is -2. What is the slope of $\overline{BC}$?

49. In the diagram at the right, M is the midpoint of $\overline{AB}$. What is AB?

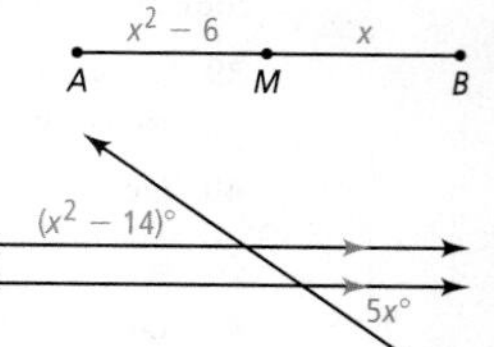

50. What is the distance between (−4.5, 1.2) and (3.5, −2.8) to the nearest tenth?

51. What is the value of x in the diagram at the right?

52. The perimeter of a square is 20 ft. What is the area of the square in square feet?

Mixed Review

Algebra **Write an equation for the line containing the given points.** See Lesson 3-7.

53. $A(0, 3)$, $B(6, 0)$ **54.** $C(-4, 2)$, $D(-1, 7)$ **55.** $E(3, -2)$, $F(-5, -8)$

Name the property that justifies each statement. See Lesson 2-5.

56. $\angle 4 \cong \angle 4$

57. If $m\angle B = 8$, then $2m\angle B = 16$.

58. $-3x + 6 = 3(-x + 2)$

59. If $\overline{RS} \cong \overline{MN}$, then $\overline{MN} \cong \overline{RS}$.

Get Ready! **To prepare for Lesson 4-1, do Exercises 60–62.**

Are ∠1 and ∠2 congruent? Explain. See Lessons 1-5 and 2-6.

60. **61.** 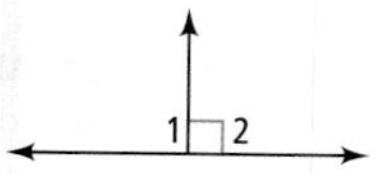 **62.**

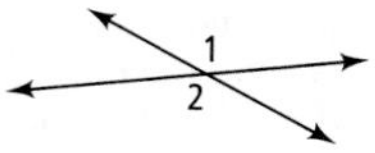

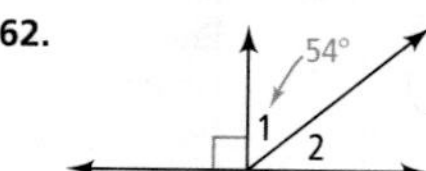

3-8 Lesson Resources

Differentiated Remediation

Instructional Support

Geometry Companion

Students can use the **Geometry Companion** worktext (4 pages) . . .

- New Vocabulary
- Key Concepts
- Got It for each Problem
- Lesson Check

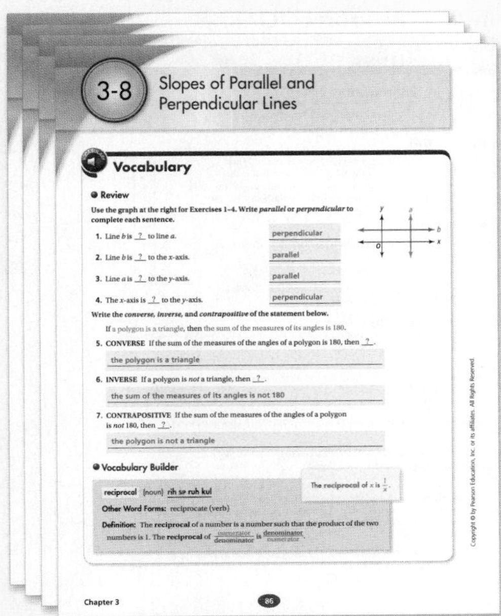

3-8 Slopes of Parallel and Perpendicular Lines

Vocabulary

Review

Use the graph at the right for Exercises 1–4. Write *parallel* or *perpendicular* to complete each sentence.

1. Line b is _?_ to line a. perpendicular
2. Line b is _?_ to the x-axis. parallel
3. Line a is _?_ to the y-axis. parallel
4. The x-axis is _?_ to the y-axis. perpendicular

Write the *converse, inverse,* and *contrapositive* of the statement below.

If a polygon is a triangle, then the sum of the measures of its angles is 180.

5. CONVERSE If the sum of the measures of the angles of a polygon is 180, then _?_.
the polygon is a triangle
6. INVERSE If a polygon is *not* a triangle, then _?_.
the sum of the measures of its angles is not 180
7. CONTRAPOSITIVE If the sum of the measures of the angles of a polygon is *not* 180, then _?_.
the polygon is not a triangle

Vocabulary Builder

reciprocal (noun) rih sɪ ruh kul

Other Word Forms: reciprocate (verb)

Definition: The **reciprocal** of a number is a number such that the product of the two numbers is 1. The **reciprocal** of $\frac{\text{numerator}}{\text{denominator}}$ is $\frac{\text{denominator}}{\text{numerator}}$.

The reciprocal of x is $\frac{1}{x}$.

Chapter 3 86

ELL Support

Use Graphic Organizers Have students divide a sheet of paper into three columns and two rows. Have the students write "Given" above the first column, "Example" above the second, and "Practice" above the third. Tell the students to write "Equation of a Parallel Line and a Point" in the first row and first column. Write the equation of a line on the board and the coordinates of a point on the board. Have the students copy these into the first row and first column of their graphic organizers.

Say: Copy the slope as you write the slope for the equation into $y - y_1 = m(x - x_1)$. Say: Copy x as you write the volunteer's x–coordinate into the equation. Say: Copy y as you write the volunteer's y-coordinate. Have the students copy the finished equation into the second row and first column of their graphic organizer. Have the students work in small groups to write their own example in the third column. Use a similar process to model "Equation of a Perpendicular Line and a Point" in the second row.

5 Assess & Remediate

Lesson Quiz

Use the graph below for Questions 1 and 2.

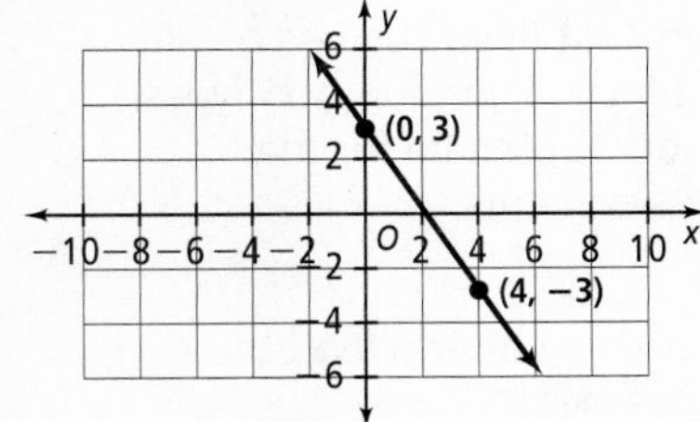

1. What is an equation of the line that is parallel to the one shown and passes through (6, −5)?
2. **Do you UNDERSTAND?** What is an equation of the line perpendicular to the one shown that passes through (−3, −4)?
3. Are the lines shown below parallel? Explain.

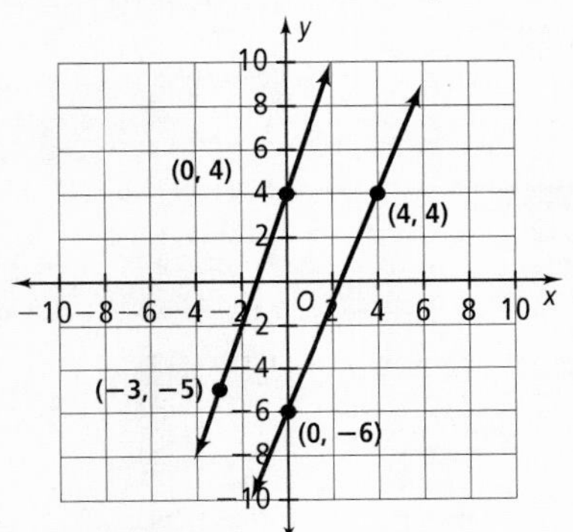

ANSWERS TO LESSON QUIZ

1. $y = -\frac{3}{2}x + 4$
2. $y = \frac{2}{3}x - 2$
3. No, the slopes are not the same.

PRESCRIPTION FOR REMEDIATION

Use the student work on the Lesson Quiz to prescribe a differentiated review assignment.

Points	Differentiated Remediation
0–1	Intervention
2	On-level
3	Extension

PowerGeometry.com

5 Assess & Remediate

Assign the Lesson Quiz. Appropriate intervention, practice, or enrichment is automatically generated based on student performance.

Intervention

- **Reteaching** (2 pages) Provides reteaching and practice exercises for the key lesson concepts. Use with struggling students or absent students.
- **English Language Learner Support** Helps students develop and reinforce mathematical vocabulary and key concepts.

All-in-One Resources/Online

Reteaching

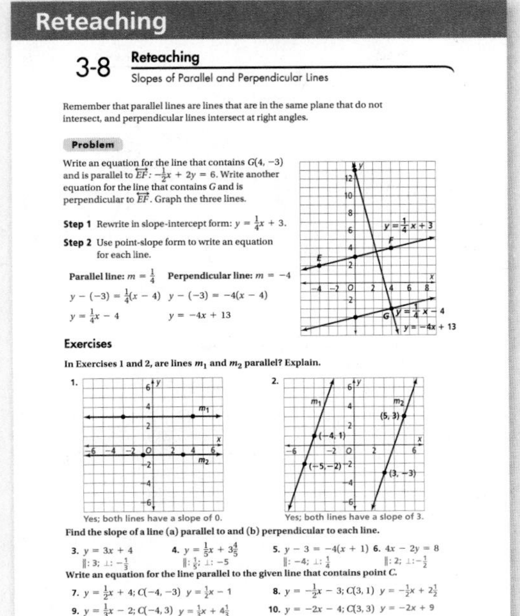

3-8 Reteaching
Slopes of Parallel and Perpendicular Lines

Remember that parallel lines are lines that are in the same plane that do not intersect, and perpendicular lines intersect at right angles.

Problem

Write an equation for the line that contains $G(4, -3)$ and is parallel to $\overleftrightarrow{EF}$: $-\frac{1}{2}x + 2y = 6$. Write another equation for the line that contains G and is perpendicular to $\overleftrightarrow{EF}$. Graph the three lines.

Step 1 Rewrite in slope-intercept form: $y = \frac{1}{4}x + 3$.

Step 2 Use point-slope form to write an equation for each line.

Parallel line: $m = \frac{1}{4}$ — $y - (-3) = \frac{1}{4}(x - 4)$ — $y = \frac{1}{4}x - 4$

Perpendicular line: $m = -4$ — $y - (-3) = -4(x - 4)$ — $y = -4x + 13$

Exercises

In Exercises 1 and 2, are lines m_1 and m_2 parallel? Explain.

1. Yes; both lines have a slope of 0.
2. Yes; both lines have a slope of 3.

Find the slope of a line (a) parallel to and (b) perpendicular to each line.

3. $y = 3x + 4$ — $\parallel$: 3; $\perp$: $-\frac{1}{3}$
4. $y = \frac{1}{5}x + 3\frac{4}{5}$ — $\parallel$: $\frac{1}{5}$; $\perp$: −5
5. $y - 3 = -4(x + 1)$ — $\parallel$: −4; $\perp$: $\frac{1}{4}$
6. $4x - 2y = 8$ — $\parallel$: 2; $\perp$: $-\frac{1}{2}$

Write an equation for the line parallel to the given line that contains point C.

7. $y = \frac{1}{2}x + 4$; $C(-4, -3)$ $y = \frac{1}{2}x - 1$
8. $y = -\frac{1}{2}x - 3$; $C(3, 1)$ $y = -\frac{1}{2}x + 2\frac{1}{2}$
9. $y = \frac{1}{3}x - 2$; $C(-4, 3)$ $y = \frac{1}{3}x + 4\frac{1}{3}$
10. $y = -2x - 4$; $C(3, 3)$ $y = -2x + 9$

All-in-One Resources/Online

English Language Learner Support

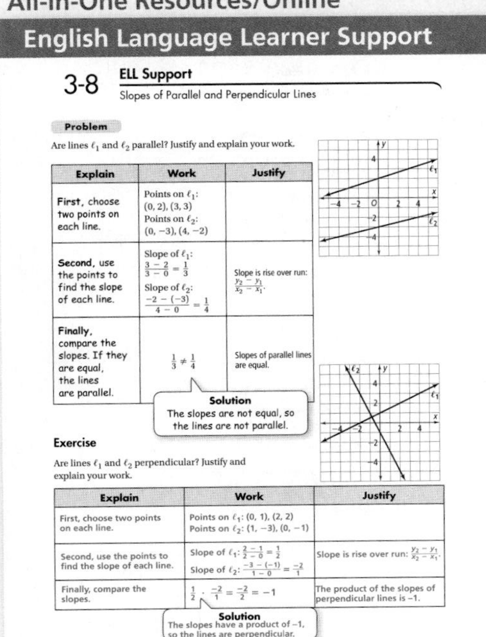

3-8 ELL Support
Slopes of Parallel and Perpendicular Lines

Problem

Are lines ℓ_1 and ℓ_2 parallel? Justify and explain your work.

Explain	Work	Justify
First, choose two points on each line.	Points on ℓ_1: (0, 2), (3, 3) Points on ℓ_2: (0, −3), (4, −2)	
Second, use the points to find the slope of each line.	Slope of ℓ_1: $\frac{3-2}{3-0} = \frac{1}{3}$ Slope of ℓ_2: $\frac{-2-(-3)}{4-0} = \frac{1}{4}$	Slope is rise over run: $\frac{y_2 - y_1}{x_2 - x_1}$.
Finally, compare the slopes. If they are equal, the lines are parallel.	$\frac{1}{3} \neq \frac{1}{4}$	Slopes of parallel lines are equal.

Solution The slopes are not equal, so the lines are not parallel.

Exercise

Are lines ℓ_1 and ℓ_2 perpendicular? Justify and explain your work.

Explain	Work	Justify
First, choose two points on each line.	Points on ℓ_1: (0, 1), (2, 2) Points on ℓ_2: (1, −3), (0, −1)	
Second, use the points to find the slope of each line.	Slope of ℓ_1: $\frac{2-1}{2-0} = \frac{1}{2}$ Slope of ℓ_2: $\frac{-3-(-1)}{1-0} = \frac{-2}{1}$	Slope is rise over run: $\frac{y_2 - y_1}{x_2 - x_1}$.
Finally, compare the slopes.	$\frac{1}{2} \cdot \frac{-2}{1} = \frac{-2}{2} = -1$	The product of the slopes of perpendicular lines is −1.

Solution The slopes have a product of −1, so the lines are perpendicular.

Differentiated Remediation *continued*

On-Level

- **Practice** (2 pages) Provides extra practice for each lesson. For simpler practice exercises, use the Form K Practice pages found in the All-in-One Teaching Resources and online.
- **Think About a Plan** Helps students develop specific problem-solving skills and strategies by providing scaffolded guiding questions.
- **Standardized Test Prep** Focuses on all major exercises, all major question types, and helps students prepare for the high-stakes assessments.

Practice and Problem Solving Wkbk/ All-in-One Resources/Online

Practice page 1

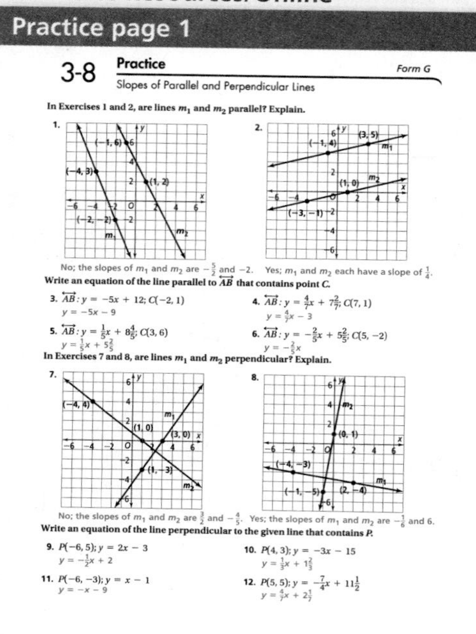

3-8 Practice — Form G
Slopes of Parallel and Perpendicular Lines

In Exercises 1 and 2, are lines m_1 and m_2 parallel? Explain.

No; the slopes of m_1 and m_2 are $-\frac{5}{2}$ and -2. Yes; m_1 and m_2 each have a slope of $\frac{1}{4}$.

Write an equation of the line parallel to $\overleftrightarrow{AB}$ that contains point *C*.

3. $\overleftrightarrow{AB}: y = -5x + 12$; $C(-2, 1)$ $y = -5x - 9$
4. $\overleftrightarrow{AB}: y = \frac{4}{5}x + 7\frac{3}{5}$; $C(7, 1)$ $y = \frac{4}{5}x - 3$
5. $\overleftrightarrow{AB}: y = \frac{1}{2}x + 8\frac{4}{5}$; $C(3, 6)$ $y = \frac{1}{2}x + 5\frac{1}{2}$
6. $\overleftrightarrow{AB}: y = -\frac{2}{5}x + 5\frac{2}{5}$; $C(5, -2)$ $y = -\frac{2}{5}x$

In Exercises 7 and 8, are lines m_1 and m_2 perpendicular? Explain.

No; the slopes of m_1 and m_2 are $\frac{3}{2}$ and $-\frac{4}{5}$. Yes; the slopes of m_1 and m_2 are $-\frac{1}{6}$ and 6.

Write an equation of the line perpendicular to the given line that contains *P*.

9. $P(-6, 5)$; $y = 2x - 3$ $y = -\frac{1}{2}x + 2$
10. $P(4, 3)$; $y = -3x - 15$ $y = \frac{1}{3}x + 1\frac{2}{3}$
11. $P(-6, -3)$; $y = x - 1$ $y = -x - 9$
12. $P(5, 5)$; $y = -\frac{7}{2}x + 11\frac{1}{2}$ $y = \frac{2}{7}x + 2\frac{1}{7}$

Practice and Problem Solving Wkbk/ All-in-One Resources/Online

Practice page 2

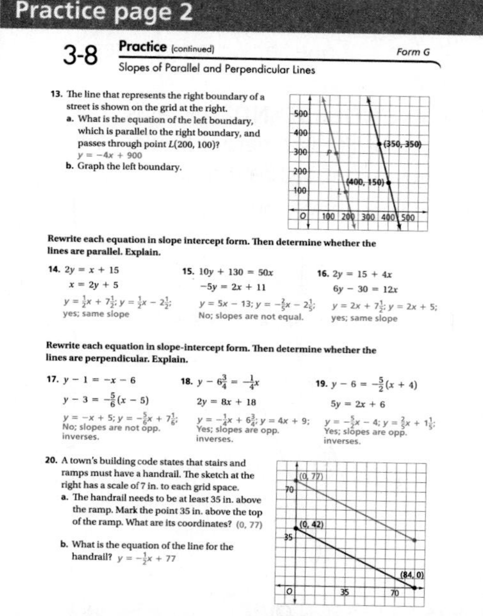

3-8 Practice (continued) — Form G
Slopes of Parallel and Perpendicular Lines

13. The line that represents the right boundary of a street is shown on the grid at the right.
   a. What is the equation of the left boundary, which is parallel to the right boundary, and passes through point $L(200, 100)$? $y = -4x + 900$
   b. Graph the left boundary.

Rewrite each equation in slope intercept form. Then determine whether the lines are parallel. Explain.

14. $2y = x + 15$; $x = 2y + 5$ — $y = \frac{1}{2}x + 7\frac{1}{2}$; $y = \frac{1}{2}x - 2\frac{1}{2}$; yes; same slope
15. $10y + 130 = 50x$; $-5y = 2x + 11$ — $y = 5x - 13$; $y = -\frac{2}{5}x - 2\frac{1}{5}$; No; slopes are not equal.
16. $2y = 15 + 4x$; $6y - 30 = 12x$ — $y = 2x + 7\frac{1}{2}$; $y = 2x + 5$; yes; same slope

Rewrite each equation in slope-intercept form. Then determine whether the lines are perpendicular. Explain.

17. $y - 1 = -x - 6$; $y - 3 = -\frac{5}{6}(x - 5)$ — $y = -x + 5$; $y = -\frac{5}{6}x + 7\frac{1}{6}$; No; slopes are not opp. inverses.
18. $y - 6\frac{3}{4} = -\frac{1}{4}x$; $2y = 8x + 18$ — $y = -\frac{1}{4}x + 6\frac{3}{4}$; $y = 4x + 9$; Yes; slopes are opp. inverses.
19. $y - 6 = -\frac{5}{2}(x + 4)$; $5y = 2x + 6$ — $y = -\frac{5}{2}x - 4$; $y = \frac{2}{5}x + 1\frac{1}{5}$; Yes; slopes are opp. inverses.

20. A town's building code states that stairs and ramps must have a handrail. The sketch at the right has a scale of 7 in. to each grid space.
   a. The handrail needs to be at least 35 in. above the ramp. Mark the point 35 in. above the top of the ramp. What are its coordinates? (0, 77)
   b. What is the equation of the line for the handrail? $y = -\frac{1}{2}x + 77$

Extension

- **Enrichment** Provides students with interesting problems and activities that extend the concepts of the lesson.
- **Activities, Games, and Puzzles** Worksheets that can be used for concepts development, enrichment, and for fun!

All-in-One Resources/Online

Enrichment

3-8 Enrichment
Slopes of Parallel and Perpendicular Lines

Miniature Golf

The dotted line shows the entrance to a hole of miniature golf. Where along the dotted line should you place your ball so that if you hit it at a 45° angle, you can bounce it off walls, not hit any of the obstructions, and have it go directly into the hole? The ball will bounce off the walls at $(180 - x)°$ where $x°$ is the angle at which the ball hits the wall.

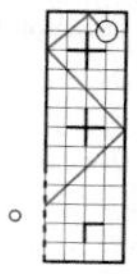

1. What are the possible slopes of a line that shows a ball hit at a 45° angle? 1 or −1
2. Where along the dotted line should you place the ball to get it directly into the hole? Explain. Intersections of lines; the hole is at an intersection of lines and the slope of the path of the ball is 1 or −1.
3. Try different points along the dotted line until you find the one that will allow the ball to go into the hole without hitting any of the obstructions.
4. How many different walls does the ball hit and how many times will it hit each wall before it goes into the hole? three walls: right, left, then back; each once only
5. Draw the path of the ball from where you hit it until it goes into the hole.
6. Are there other points that will allow you to get the ball into the hole without hitting any of the obstructions? Explain. No; using any other starting point will either hit an obstruction, or not go into a hole since we are hitting the ball at a 45° angle.
7. If the lower left corner of the grid is the origin and each square represents 1, write an equation of the line at which you should hit the ball to get the ball directly into the hole without hitting any obstructions. $y = x + 3$
8. Write an equation of each of the other lines that represent part of the path of the ball on its way to the hole. $y = -x + 11$; $y = x + 11$; $y = -x + 15$

Practice and Problem Solving Wkbk/ All-in-One Resources/Online

Think About a Plan

3-8 Think About a Plan
Slopes of Parallel and Perpendicular Lines

Rail Trail A community recently converted an old railroad corridor into a recreational trail. The graph at the right shows a map of the trail on a coordinate grid. They plan to construct a path to connect the trail to a parking lot. The new path will be perpendicular to the recreational trail.

a. Write an equation of the line representing the new path.
b. What are the coordinates of the point at which the path will meet the recreational trail?
c. If each grid space is 25 yd by 25 yd, how long is the path to the nearest yard?

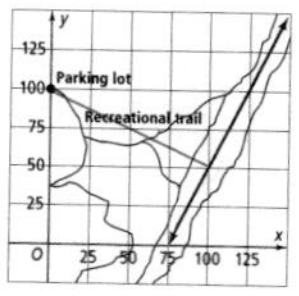

1. How can you tell whether two lines are perpendicular, given their equations? The slope of one line will be the opposite of the reciprocal of the slope of the other line.
2. What is the slope of the line representing the existing trail? 2
3. What is the slope of the line representing the new path? $-\frac{1}{2}$
4. What is the *y*-intercept of the line representing the new path? 100
5. Write an equation for the line representing the new path, and then graph it. $y = -\frac{1}{2}x + 100$
6. Name the point at which the path meets the recreational trail. (100, 50)
7. How long is the path in units of the coordinate grid? (*Hint:* Use the distance formula.) $2\sqrt{5}$ or about 4.47 units
8. How long is the path in yards? About 112 yd

Practice and Problem Solving Wkbk/ All-in-One Resources/Online

Standardized Test Prep

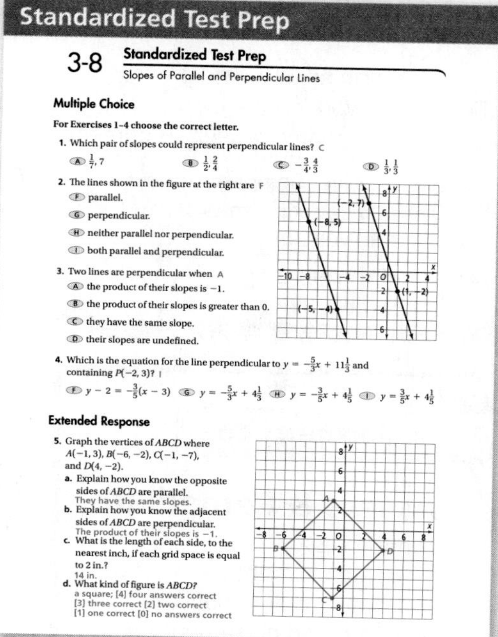

3-8 Standardized Test Prep
Slopes of Parallel and Perpendicular Lines

Multiple Choice

For Exercises 1–4 choose the correct letter.

1. Which pair of slopes could represent perpendicular lines? C
   A. $\frac{1}{7}, 7$ B. $\frac{1}{2}, \frac{2}{4}$ C. $-\frac{3}{4}, \frac{4}{3}$ D. $\frac{1}{3}, \frac{1}{3}$
2. The lines shown in the figure at the right are F
   F. parallel.
   G. perpendicular.
   H. neither parallel nor perpendicular.
   I. both parallel and perpendicular.
3. Two lines are perpendicular when A
   A. the product of their slopes is −1.
   B. the product of their slopes is greater than 0.
   C. they have the same slope.
   D. their slopes are undefined.
4. Which is the equation for the line perpendicular to $y = -\frac{5}{3}x + 11\frac{1}{3}$ and containing $P(-2, 3)$? I
   F. $y - 2 = -\frac{3}{5}(x - 3)$ G. $y = -\frac{5}{3}x + 4\frac{1}{5}$ H. $y = -\frac{3}{5}x + 4\frac{1}{5}$ I. $y = \frac{3}{5}x + 4\frac{1}{5}$

Extended Response

5. Graph the vertices of *ABCD* where $A(-1, 3)$, $B(-6, -2)$, $C(-1, -7)$, and $D(4, -2)$.
   a. Explain how you know the opposite sides of *ABCD* are parallel. They have the same slopes.
   b. Explain how you know the adjacent sides of *ABCD* are perpendicular. The product of their slopes is −1.
   c. What is the length of each side, to the nearest inch, if each grid space is equal to 2 in.? 14 in.
   d. What kind of figure is *ABCD*? a square; [4] four answers correct [3] three correct [2] two correct [1] one correct [0] no answers correct

Online Teacher Resource Center

Activities, Games, and Puzzles

3-8 Puzzle: On the Cutting Edge!
Slopes of Parallel and Perpendicular Lines

Cut out the squares below. Arrange squares 1–9 to form a 3-by-3 square so that the equations touching each other at the edges are equations of *parallel* lines. Then, arrange squares 10–18 to form a 3-by-3 square so that the equations touching each other at the edges are the equations of *perpendicular* lines.

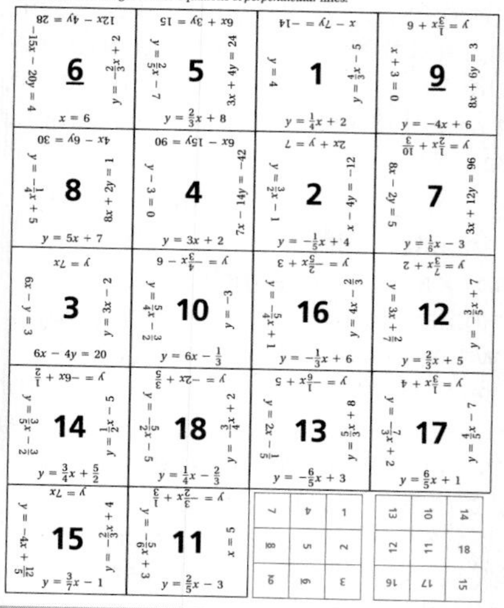

Pull It All Together

To solve these problems, you will pull together many concepts and skills that you have studied about parallel lines.

BIG idea Reasoning and Proof

You can prove that lines are parallel if you know that certain pairs of angles formed by the lines and a transversal are congruent.

Task 1

You want to put tape on the ground to mark the lines for a volleyball court. What is the most efficient way to make sure that the opposite sides of the court are parallel? Support your answer with a diagram.

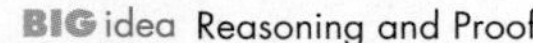

BIG idea Reasoning and Proof

You can prove that lines are parallel if you know that certain pairs of angles formed by the lines and a transversal are congruent.

BIG idea Measurement

You can find missing angle measures in triangles by using the fact that the sum of the measures of the angles of a triangle is 180.

Task 2

In the diagram below, $a \parallel b$. For lines p and q to be parallel, what is $m\angle 4$? Explain.

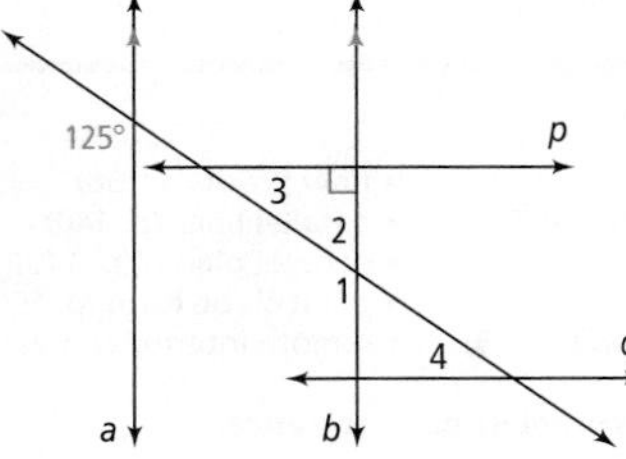

BIG idea Coordinate Geometry

You can write the equation of a line by using its slope and y-intercept.

Task 3

$\overleftrightarrow{AB}$ contains points $A(-6, -1)$ and $B(1, 4)$. $\overleftrightarrow{CD}$ contains point $D(7, 2)$. If $\angle ABC \cong \angle BCD$ and $m\angle ABC = 90$, what is an equation of $\overleftrightarrow{CD}$? (*Hint:* Sketch a graph.)

Performance Task 

Pull It All Together

The concepts and skills required to solve these problems are from several lessons within this chapter and from the previous chapter. As students solve these problems, they will demonstrate their reasoning strategies and their growth as independent problem solvers.

The following questions are designed to:

- Help support students as they do the Tasks.
- Gauge the amount of support students need as they become independent problem solvers.

Task 1

- What polygon represents the shape of a volleyball court?
- Which angles should you measure?

Task 2

- What angle measure forms a linear pair with an angle that measures 125?
- What is the measure of angle 1?
- What is the measure of angle 2?

Task 3

- What is the slope of $\overleftrightarrow{AB}$?
- What is the slope of $\overleftrightarrow{CD}$?
- How can you find the location of C?
- What do you need to write the equation for $\overleftrightarrow{CD}$?

Assess Performance 

Pull It All Together

See p. 69 for a holistic scoring rubric to gauge a student's progress on Understanding the Problem, Planning a Solution, Getting an Answer, and Assessing Autonomy.

SOLUTION OUTLINES

1. Possible plan: Using a side of the volleyball court as a transversal, locate the opposite sides so they form ≅ corresp. rt. ∠s with that transversal. If corresp. ∠s are ≅, then the lines are ∥.
2. Possible plan: Since ∠1 and the 125° angle are corresp. ∠s and $a \parallel b$, $m\angle 1 = 125$. If $p \parallel q$, then $q \perp b$ because a line ⊥ to one of two ∥ lines is ⊥ to the other line. So ∠4 and a rt. ∠ are the remote interior ∠s for ext. ∠1. Solve the equation $m\angle 4 + 90 = 125$ to find $m\angle 4$. (Answer: 35)
3. Possible plan: Sketch a graph of $\overleftrightarrow{AB}$ and point D. Since $\angle ABC \cong \angle BCD$ and $m\angle ABC = 90$, $m\angle BCD$ is also 90. So $\angle ABC$ and $\angle BCD$ are ≅ alt. int. ∠s and $\overleftrightarrow{AB} \parallel \overleftrightarrow{CD}$. Use the slope of $\overleftrightarrow{AB}$ and point D to write an equation of $\overleftrightarrow{CD}$. (Answer: $y - 2 = \frac{5}{7}(x - 7)$)

Essential Questions 

BIG idea Reasoning and Proof

ESSENTIAL QUESTION How do you prove that two lines are parallel or perpendicular?

ANSWER You can prove that two lines are parallel or perpendicular by using special angle relationships and the relationships of two lines to a third line.

BIG idea Measurement

ESSENTIAL QUESTION What is the sum of the measures of the angles of a triangle?

ANSWER The sum of the measures of the angles of a triangle is 180.

BIG idea Coordinate Geometry

ESSENTIAL QUESTION How do you write an equation of a line in the coordinate plane?

ANSWER You can write the equation of a line by using its slope and a point on the line.

3 Chapter Review

Connecting BIG ideas and Answering the Essential Questions

1 Reasoning and Proof
You can prove that two lines are parallel by using special angle relationships and the relationships of two lines to a third line.

Parallel Lines and Angle Pairs (Lessons 3-2 and 3-3)
$\angle 1 \cong \angle 5$
$\angle 4 \cong \angle 6$
$m\angle 4 + m\angle 5 = 180$
$\angle 2 \cong \angle 8$

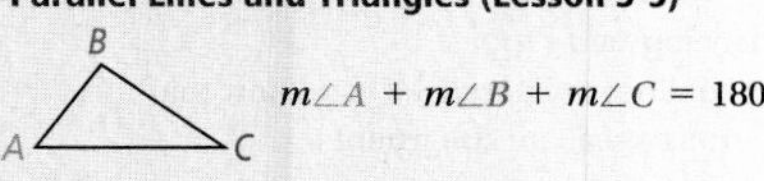

Parallel and Perpendicular Lines (Lesson 3-4)
$a \parallel b$ and $b \parallel c \rightarrow a \parallel c$
$a \perp b$ and $a \perp c \rightarrow b \parallel c$

2 Measurement
The sum of the measures of the angles of a triangle is 180.

Parallel Lines and Triangles (Lesson 3-5)
$m\angle A + m\angle B + m\angle C = 180$

3 Coordinate Geometry
You can write the equation of a line by using its slope and a point on the line.

Lines in the Coordinate Plane (Lesson 3-7)
Slope-intercept form: $y = mx + b$
Point-slope form: $y - y_1 = m(x - x_1)$

Slopes of Parallel and Perpendicular Lines (Lesson 3-8)
Parallel lines: equal slopes
Perpendicular lines: product of slopes is -1

Chapter Vocabulary

- alternate exterior angles (p. 142)
- alternate interior angles (p. 142)
- auxiliary line (p. 172)
- corresponding angles (p. 142)
- exterior angle of a polygon (p. 173)
- flow proof (p. 158)
- parallel lines (p. 140)
- parallel planes (p. 140)
- point-slope form (p. 190)
- remote interior angles (p. 173)
- same-side interior angles (p. 142)
- skew lines (p. 140)
- slope (p. 189)
- slope-intercept form (p. 190)
- transversal (p. 141)

Choose the correct term to complete each sentence.

1. A(n) _?_ intersects two or more coplanar lines at distinct points.

2. The measure of a(n) _?_ of a triangle is equal to the sum of the measures of its two remote interior angles.

3. The linear equation $y - 3 = 4(x + 5)$ is in _?_ form.

4. When two coplanar lines are cut by a transversal, the angles formed between the two lines and on opposite sides of the transversal are _?_.

5. Noncoplanar lines that do not intersect are _?_.

6. The linear equation $y = 3x - 5$ is in _?_ form.

Summative Questions UbD

Use the following prompts as you review this chapter with your students. The prompts are designed to help you assess your students' understanding of the BIG Ideas they have studied.

- What are the names for the relationships of angles formed by two lines and a transversal?
- What does it mean for two lines to be parallel?
- What does it mean for two lines to be perpendicular?
- What is true about the slopes of two parallel lines?

Answers

Chapter Review

1. transversal
2. ext. ∠
3. point-slope
4. alt. int. ∠s
5. skew lines
6. slope-intercept

3-1 Lines and Angles

Quick Review

A **transversal** is a line that intersects two or more coplanar lines at distinct points.

$\angle 1$ and $\angle 3$ are **corresponding angles.**

$\angle 2$ and $\angle 6$ are **alternate interior angles.**

$\angle 2$ and $\angle 3$ are **same-side interior angles.**

$\angle 4$ and $\angle 8$ are **alternate exterior angles.**

Example

Name two other pairs of corresponding angles in the diagram above.

$\angle 5$ and $\angle 7$
$\angle 2$ and $\angle 4$

Exercises

Identify all numbered angle pairs that form the given type of angle pair. Then name the two lines and transversal that form each pair.

7. alternate interior angles

8. same-side interior angles

9. corresponding angles

10. alternate exterior angles

Classify the angle pair formed by $\angle 1$ and $\angle 2$.

11.

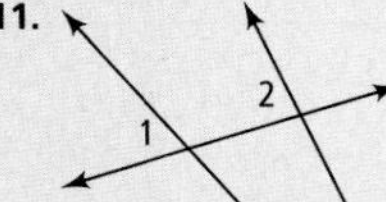

12.

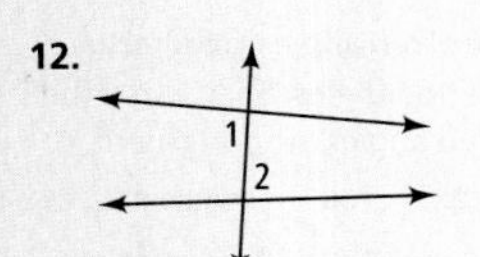

3-2 Properties of Parallel Lines

Quick Review

If two parallel lines are cut by a transversal, then

- corresponding angles, alternate interior angles, and alternate exterior angles are congruent
- same-side interior angles are supplementary

Example

Which other angles measure 110?

$\angle 6$ (corresponding angles)
$\angle 3$ (alternate interior angles)
$\angle 8$ (vertical angles)

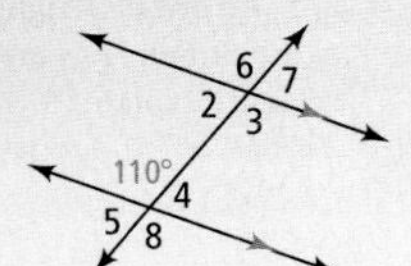

Exercises

Find $m\angle 1$ and $m\angle 2$. Justify your answers.

13.

14.

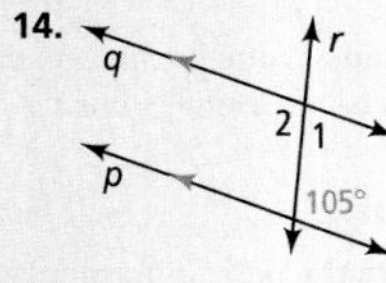

15. Find the values of x and y in the diagram below.

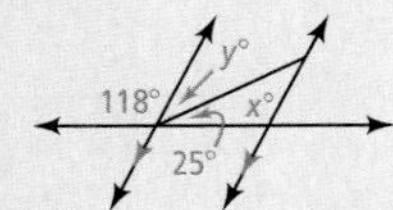

7. $\angle 2$ and $\angle 7$, *a* and *b*, transversal *d*; $\angle 3$ and $\angle 6$, *c* and *d*, transversal *e*; $\angle 3$ and $\angle 8$, *b* and *e*, transversal *c*

8. $\angle 5$ and $\angle 8$, lines *a* and *b*, transversal *c*; $\angle 2$ and $\angle 6$, *a* and *e*, transversal *d*

9. $\angle 1$ and $\angle 4$, lines *c* and *d*, transversal *b*; $\angle 2$ and $\angle 4$, lines *a* and *b*, transversal *d*; $\angle 2$ and $\angle 5$, lines *c* and *d*, transversal *a*; $\angle 1$ and $\angle 5$, lines *a* and *b*, transversal *c*; $\angle 3$ and $\angle 4$, *b* and *c*, transversal *e*

10. $\angle 1$ and $\angle 7$, lines *c* and *d*, transversal *b*

11. corresp. $\angle$s

12. alt. int. $\angle$s

13. $m\angle 1 = 120$ because corresp. $\angle$s are $\cong$; $m\angle 2 = 120$ because $\angle 1$ and $\angle 2$ are vert. $\angle$s.

14. $m\angle 1 = 75$ because same-side int. $\angle$s are suppl.; $m\angle 2 = 105$ because alt. int. $\angle$s are $\cong$.

15. $x = 118$, $y = 37$

Answers

Chapter Review (continued)

16. 20 **17.** 20

18. $n \parallel p$; if corresp. ∡ are ≅, then the lines are ∥.

19. none; ∠3 and ∠6 form a linear pair.

20. $\ell \parallel m$; if same-side int. ∡ are suppl., then the lines are ∥.

21. $n \parallel p$; if alt. int. ∡ are ≅, then the lines are ∥.

22. ∥ **23.** a

24. 1st Street and 3rd Street are ∥ because they are both ⊥ to Morris Avenue. Since 1st Street and 5th street are both ∥ to 3rd Street, 1st Street and 5th Street are ∥ to each other.

3-3 Proving Lines Parallel

Quick Review

If two lines and a transversal form
- congruent corresponding angles,
- congruent alternate interior angles,
- congruent alternate exterior angles, or
- supplementary same-side interior angles,

then the two lines are parallel.

Example

What is the value of x for which $\ell \parallel m$?

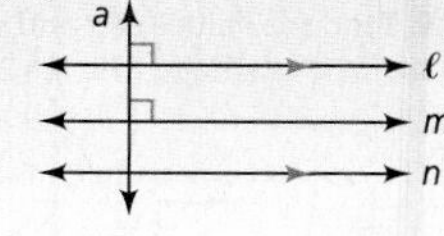

The given angles are alternate interior angles. So, $\ell \parallel m$ if the given angles are congruent.

$2x = 106$ Congruent ∡ have equal measures.

$x = 53$ Divide each side by 2.

Exercises

Find the value of x for which $\ell \parallel m$.

16.

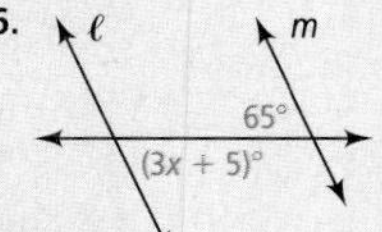

17.

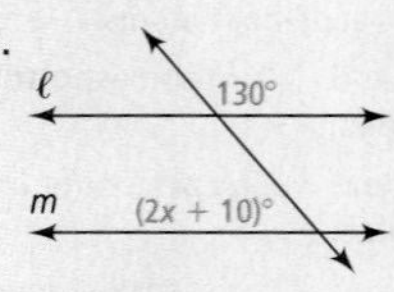

Use the given information to decide which lines, if any, are parallel. Justify your conclusion.

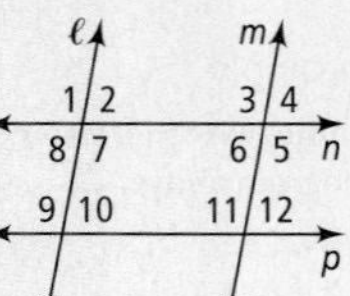

18. $\angle 1 \cong \angle 9$

19. $m\angle 3 + m\angle 6 = 180$

20. $m\angle 2 + m\angle 3 = 180$

21. $\angle 5 \cong \angle 11$

3-4 Parallel and Perpendicular Lines

Quick Review

- Two lines ∥ to the same line are ∥ to each other.
- In a plane, two lines ⊥ to the same line are ∥.
- In a plane, if one line is ⊥ to one of two ∥ lines, then it is ⊥ to both ∥ lines.

Example

What are the pairs of parallel and perpendicular lines in the diagram?

$\ell \parallel n$, $\ell \parallel m$, and $m \parallel n$.

$a \perp \ell$, $a \perp m$, and $a \perp n$.

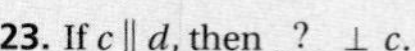

Exercises

Use the diagram at the right to complete each statement.

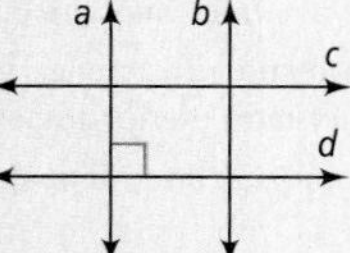

22. If $b \perp c$ and $b \perp d$, then c __?__ d.

23. If $c \parallel d$, then __?__ $\perp c$.

24. Maps Morris Avenue intersects both 1st Street and 3rd Street at right angles. 3rd Street is parallel to 5th Street. How are 1st Street and 5th Street related? Explain.

3-5 Parallel Lines and Triangles

Quick Review

The sum of the measures of the angles of a triangle is 180.

The measure of each **exterior angle** of a triangle equals the sum of the measures of its two **remote interior angles.**

Example

What are the values of x and y?

$x + 50 = 125$ Exterior Angle Theorem

$x = 75$ Simplify.

$x + y + 50 = 180$ Triangle Angle-Sum Theorem

$75 + y + 50 = 180$ Substitute 75 for x.

$y = 55$ Simplify.

Exercises

Find the values of the variables.

25.

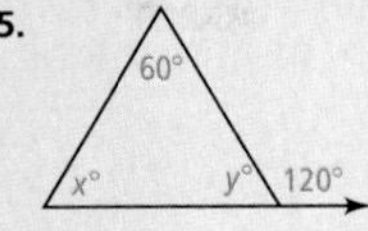

26.

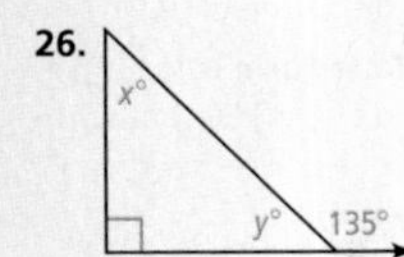

The measures of the three angles of a triangle are given. Find the value of x.

27. $x, 2x, 3x$

28. $x + 10, x - 20, x + 25$

29. $20x + 10, 30x - 2, 7x + 1$

3-6 Constructing Parallel and Perpendicular Lines

Quick Review

You can use a compass and a straightedge to construct

- a line parallel to a given line through a point not on the line
- a line perpendicular to a given line through a point on the line, or through a point not on the line

Example

Which step of the parallel lines construction guarantees the lines are parallel?

The parallel lines construction involves constructing a pair of congruent angles. Since the congruent angles are corresponding angles, the lines are parallel.

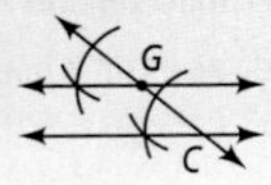

Exercises

30. Draw a line m and point Q not on m. Construct a line perpendicular to m through Q.

Use the segments below.

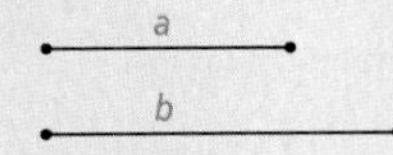

31. Construct a rectangle with side lengths a and b.

32. Construct a rectangle with side lengths a and $2b$.

33. Construct a quadrilateral with one pair of parallel opposite sides, each side of length $2a$.

25. $x = 60, y = 60$

26. $x = 45, y = 45$

27. 30 **28.** 55 **29.** 3

30.

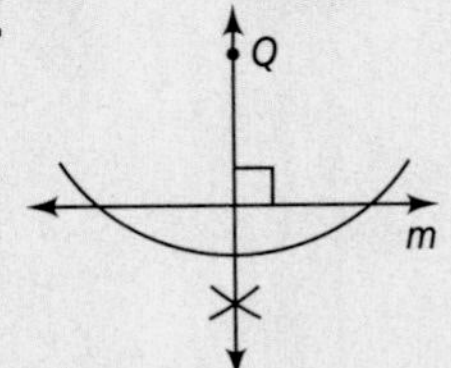

31.

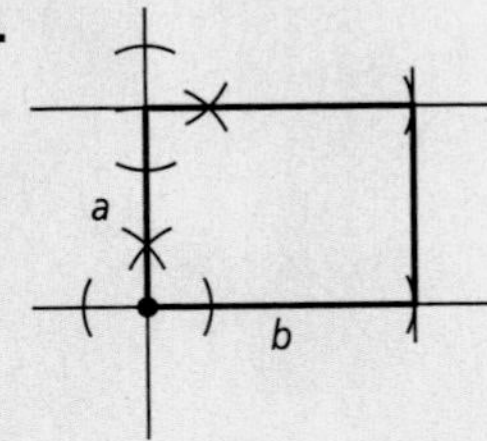

32.

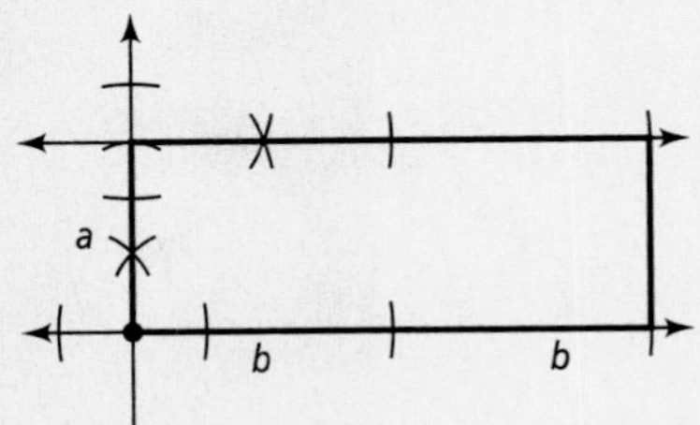

33.

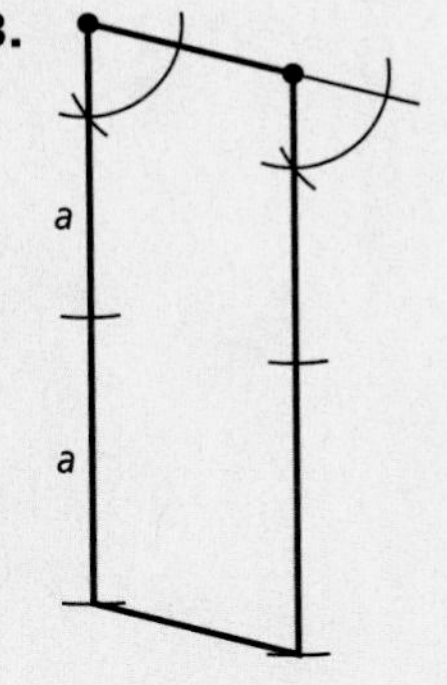

Answers

Chapter Review (continued)

34. −1

35. undefined

36. slope: 2; y-intercept: −1

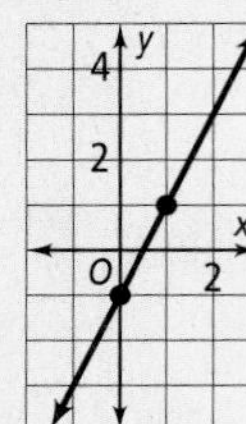

37. slope: −2; point: (−5, 3)

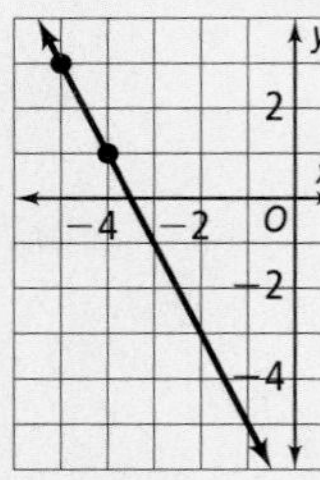

38. $y = -\frac{1}{2}x + 12$

39. $y + 9 = 3(x - 1)$

40. $y - 2 = 4(x - 4)$ or $y + 2 = 4(x - 3)$

41. neither

42. ∥

43. ⊥

44. ∥

45. $y - 2 = 8(x + 6)$

46. $y + 3 = -6(x - 3)$

3-7 Equations of Lines in the Coordinate Plane

Quick Review

Slope-intercept form is $y = mx + b$, where m is the slope and b is the y-intercept.

Point-slope form is $y - y_1 = m(x - x_1)$, where m is the slope and (x_1, y_1) is a point on the line.

Example

What is an equation of the line with slope −5 and y-intercept 6?

Use slope-intercept form: $y = -5x + 6$.

Example

What is an equation of the line through (−2, 8) with slope 3?

Use point-slope form: $y - 8 = 3(x + 2)$.

Exercises

Find the slope of the line passing through the points.

34. (6, −2), (1, 3)

35. (−7, 2), (−7, −5)

36. Name the slope and y-intercept of $y = 2x - 1$. Then graph the line.

37. Name the slope of and a point on $y - 3 = -2(x + 5)$. Then graph the line.

Write an equation of the line.

38. slope $-\frac{1}{2}$, y-intercept 12

39. slope 3, passes through (1, −9)

40. passes through (4, 2) and (3, −2)

3-8 Slopes of Parallel and Perpendicular Lines

Quick Review

Parallel lines have the same slopes.

The product of the slopes of two perpendicular lines is −1.

Example

What is an equation of the line perpendicular to $y = 2x - 5$ that contains (1, −3)?

Step 1 Identify the slope of $y = 2x - 5$.
The slope of the given line is 2.

Step 2 Find the slope of a line perpendicular to $y = 2x - 5$.
The slope is $-\frac{1}{2}$, because $2\left(-\frac{1}{2}\right) = -1$.

Step 3 Use point-slope form to write $y + 3 = -\frac{1}{2}(x - 1)$.

Exercises

Determine whether $\overleftrightarrow{AB}$ and $\overleftrightarrow{CD}$ are *parallel*, *perpendicular*, or *neither*.

41. $A(-1, -4)$, $B(2, 11)$, $C(1, 1)$, $D(4, 10)$

42. $A(2, 8)$, $B(-1, -2)$, $C(3, 7)$, $D(0, -3)$

43. $A(-3, 3)$, $B(0, 2)$, $C(1, 3)$, $D(-2, -6)$

44. $A(-1, 3)$, $B(4, 8)$, $C(-6, 0)$, $D(2, 8)$

45. Write an equation of the line parallel to $y = 8x - 1$ that contains (−6, 2).

46. Write an equation of the line perpendicular to $y = \frac{1}{6}x + 4$ that contains (3, −3).

3 Chapter Test

Do you know HOW?

Find the measure of the third angle of a triangle given the measures of two angles.

1. 57 and 101

2. 72 and 72

3. x and 20

Find $m\angle 1$ and $m\angle 2$. Justify each answer.

4.

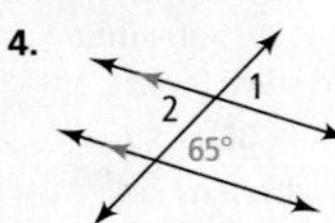

5.

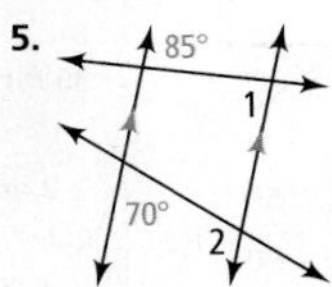

6.

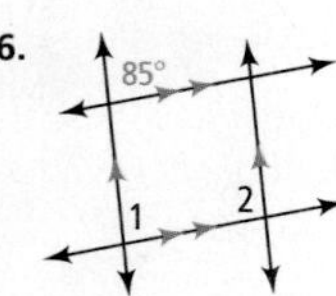

7.

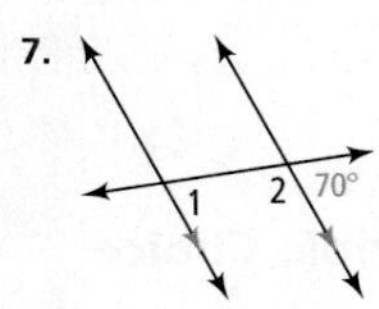

8. Draw a line m and a point T not on the line. Construct the line through T perpendicular to m.

9. Draw any $\angle ABC$. Then construct line m through A so that $m \parallel \overleftrightarrow{BC}$.

10. The measures of the angles of a triangle are $2x$, $x + 24$, and $x - 4$. Find the value of x. Then find the measures of the angles.

Determine whether the following are *parallel lines*, *skew lines*, or *neither*.

11. opposite sides of a rectangular picture frame

12. the center line of a soccer field and a sideline of the field

13. the path of an airplane flying north at 15,000 ft and the path of an airplane flying west at 10,000 ft

Use the given information to write an equation of each line.

14. slope -5, y-intercept -2

15. slope $\frac{1}{2}$, passes through $(4, -1)$

16. passes through $(1, 5)$ and $(3, 11)$

Algebra Find the value of x for which $\ell \parallel m$.

17.

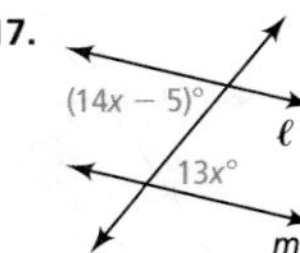

18.

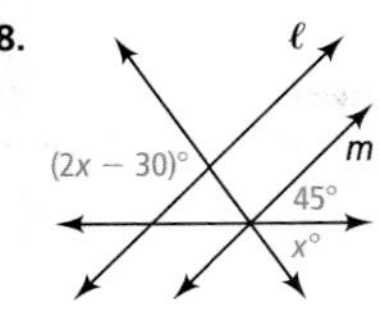

Graph each pair of lines. Tell whether they are *parallel*, *perpendicular*, or *neither*.

19. $y = 4x + 7$ and $y = -\frac{1}{4}x - 3$

20. $y = 3x - 4$ and $y = 3x + 1$

21. $y = x + 5$ and $y = -5x - 1$

Do you UNDERSTAND?

22. Developing Proof Provide the reason for each step.

Given: $\ell \parallel m$, $\angle 2 \cong \angle 4$

Prove: $n \parallel p$

Statements	Reasons
1) $\ell \parallel m$	1) a. ?
2) $\angle 1 \cong \angle 2$	2) b. ?
3) $\angle 2 \cong \angle 4$	3) c. ?
4) $\angle 1 \cong \angle 4$	4) d. ?
5) $n \parallel p$	5) e. ?

23. Reasoning Suppose a line intersecting two planes A and B forms a right angle at exactly one point in each plane. What must be true about planes A and B? (*Hint:* Draw a picture.)

Answers

Chapter Test

1. 22

2. 36

3. $160 - x$

4. $m\angle 1 = 65$ because corresp. ∠s are ≅. $m\angle 2 = 65$ because alt. int. ∠s are ≅.

5. $m\angle 1 = 85$ because alt. int. ∠s are ≅. $m\angle 2 = 110$ because same-side int. ∠s are suppl.

6. $m\angle 1 = 85$ because corresp. ∠s are ≅. $m\angle 2 = 95$ because same-side int. ∠s are suppl.

7. $m\angle 1 = 70$ because corresp. ∠s are ≅. $m\angle 2 = 110$ because it forms a linear pair with a 70°∠.

8.

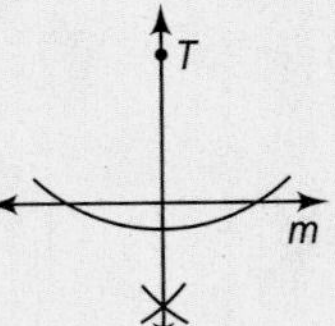

9.

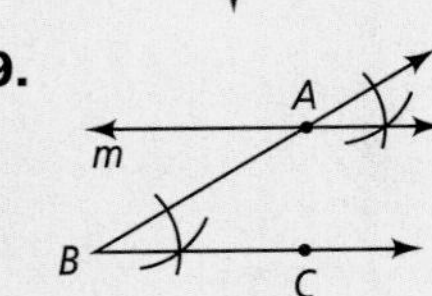

10. 40; 80, 64, 36

11. parallel lines

12. neither

13. skew lines

14. $y = -5x - 2$

15. $y + 1 = \frac{1}{2}(x - 4)$

16. $y - 5 = 3(x - 1)$ or $y - 11 = 3(x - 3)$

17. 5

18. 75

19. $\perp$

20. $\parallel$

21. neither

22a. Given

b. Corresp. ∠s Post.

c. Given

d. Trans. Prop. of ≅

e. Converse of Corresp. ∠s Post.

23. They are $\parallel$; planes A and B are $\perp$ to the same line.

PowerGeometry.com

MathXL for School

Prepare students for the Mid-Chapter Quiz and Chapter Test with online practice and review.

Item	Lesson
1	1-8
2	1-8
3	3-3
4	1-8
5	2-2
6	1-7
7	1-5
8	3-5
9	2-5
10	3-2
11	2-4
12	1-8
13	1-7
14	3-3
15	3-5
16	3-5
17	3-5
18	3-7
19	1-9
20	1-6
21	1-8
22	2-4
23	1-6
24	1-6
25	2-3

3 Cumulative Test Prep

TIPS FOR SUCCESS

Some test questions ask you to analyze a diagram. Read the sample question at the right. Then follow the tips to answer it.

In the diagram, $q \parallel r$ and $s \perp t$. If $m\angle 1 = 35$, what is $m\angle 3$?

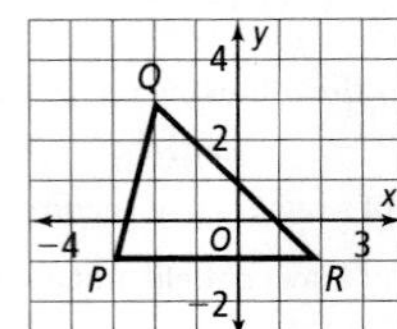

Ⓐ 35 Ⓑ 45 Ⓒ 55 Ⓓ 90

TIP 1

Use $m\angle 1$ and what you know about the measures of angles formed by perpendicular lines to find $m\angle 2$.

TIP 2

Use the diagram to find the relationship between $\angle 2$ and $\angle 3$.

Think It Through

Since $s \perp t$, the angle formed by $\angle 1$ and $\angle 2$ is a right angle. So $m\angle 1 + m\angle 2 = 90$. Substitute 35 for $m\angle 1$ and solve for $m\angle 2$.

$$m\angle 2 = 90 - 35 = 55$$

$\angle 2$ and $\angle 3$ are alternate exterior angles. Since $q \parallel r$, $\angle 2 \cong \angle 3$. So $m\angle 3 = 55$. The correct answer is C.

Vocabulary Builder

As you solve test items, you must understand the meanings of mathematical terms. Match each term with its mathematical meaning.

A. transversal
B. complementary angles
C. conditional
D. midpoint
E. supplementary angles

I. two angles whose measures have sum 90
II. a point that divides a segment into two congruent segments
III. an *if-then* statement
IV. a line that intersects two coplanar lines at two distinct points
V. two angles whose measures have sum 180

Multiple Choice

Read each question. Then write the letter of the correct answer on your paper.

1. Which expression describes the area of a square that has side lengths $7n^3$?

Ⓐ $14n^6$ Ⓑ $14n^9$ Ⓒ $49n^6$ Ⓓ $49n^9$

2. What is the area of $\triangle PQR$?

Ⓕ 10 units^2 Ⓖ 15 units^2 Ⓗ 20 units^2 Ⓘ 25 units^2

Answers

Cumulative Test Prep

A. IV
B. I
C. III
D. II
E. V
1. C
2. F

3. Which condition(s) will allow you to prove that $\ell \parallel m$?

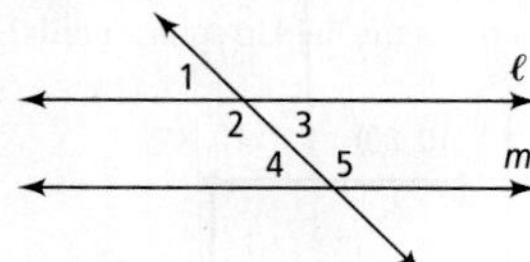

I. $\angle 1 \cong 4$

II. $\angle 2 \cong \angle 5$

III. $\angle 3 \cong \angle 4$

IV. $m\angle 2 + m\angle 4 = 180$

A III only
B I and IV only
C II and III only
D I, II, III, and IV

4. The length of your rectangular vegetable garden is 15 times its width. You used 160 ft of fencing to surround the garden. How much area do you have for planting?

F 150 ft^2
G 375 ft^2
H 800 ft^2
I 1600 ft^2

5. What is the converse of the statement, "If a strawberry is red, then it is ripe"?

A If a strawberry is not red, then it is not ripe.
B If a strawberry is ripe, then it is red.
C A strawberry is ripe if and only if it is red.
D If a strawberry is red, then it is ripe.

6. Which point lies farthest from the origin?

F (0, −7)
G (−3, 8)
H (−4, −3)
I (5, 1)

7. $\angle A$ and $\angle B$ are supplementary vertical angles. What is $m\angle B$?

A 45
B 90
C 135
D 180

8. Which types of angles can an obtuse triangle have?

I. a right angle
II. two acute angles
III. an obtuse angle
IV. two vertical angles

F I and II
G II and III
H III and IV
I I and IV

9. Ken went shopping and spent $14.00 on a book, $6.50 on lunch, and $2.50 on bus fare. On the way home he collected $10 from a friend who owed him money. When he returned home he had $15.00. He guessed that he started with $25.00. How can he verify this?

A Compute 25 − 14 − 6.5 − 2.5 + 10 to see if it equals 0.
B Compute 25 − 14 − 6.5 − 2.5 + 10 to see if it equals 15.
C Compute 14 + 6.50 + 2.50 − 10 to see if it equals 25.
D Compute 15 − (14 + 6.50 + 2.50) + 10 to see if it equals 25.

10. What is the value of x in the figure?

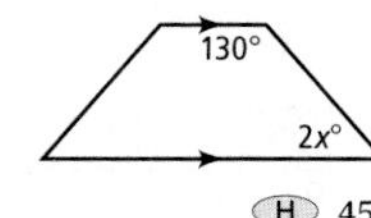

F 20
G 25
H 45
I 50

11. If Deb gets an A on the test, then she will go to the movies. If Deb goes to the movies, then she will get popcorn. Deb does not get popcorn. What can you conclude?

A Deb went to the movies.
B Deb got a C on the test.
C Deb got a soft pretzel.
D Deb did not get an A on the test.

12. The net for a cylindrical container that holds a stack of DVDs is shown below. What is the total area of the net?

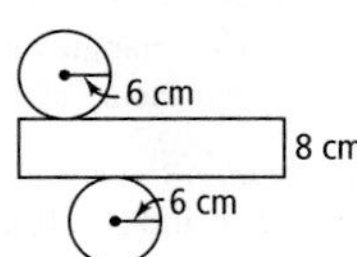

F 226 cm^2
G 302 cm^2
H 528 cm^2
I 582 cm^2

3. D
4. G
5. B
6. G
7. B
8. G
9. B
10. G
11. D
12. H

Answers

Cumulative Test Prep (continued)

13. A **14.** G **15.** D
16. I **17.** 54.5 **18.** 1
19. 31.4 **20.** 34 **21.** 6000

22. [2] The logic is not valid. You may have received the free month as a gift or through a coupon, without buying a one-year membership.
[1] incorrect OR incomplete explanation

23. [2]

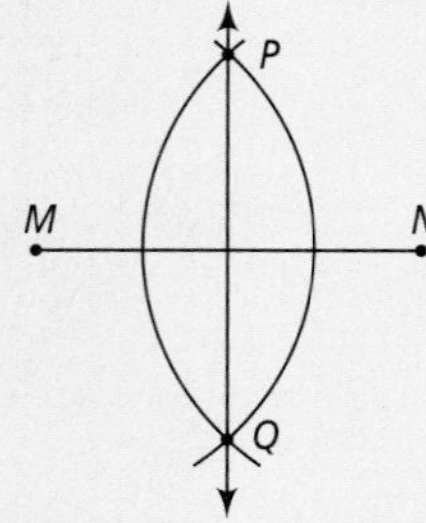

[1] incomplete construction

24. [4] Using $C(5, 7)$ and $D(10, -5)$, the coordinates of the midpoint are $\left(\frac{5+10}{2}, \frac{7+(-5)}{2}\right) = (7.5, 1)$. The length CD is $\sqrt{25 + 144} = \sqrt{169} = 13$.
[3] appropriate formulas and methods, but with one computational error
[2] incorrect formula used for midpoint and/ or distance, but subsequent steps are correct
[1] correct midpoint and distance, but without work shown

25. [4] **a.** No; answers may vary. Sample: The characteristics of a bleeble are that the outside shape is a noncircular oval and lines parallel to the longer axis divide the oval into sections, each of which contains a dot. The figure in question has lines ⊥ to the longer axis, so it is not a bleeble.
b. Answers may vary. Sample: A bleeble is a noncircular oval, divided into sections by lines parallel to the longer axis of the oval, with one dot in each section.
[3] no errors, but not a complete explanation or definition
[2] correct explanation of just one attribute in description and/or definition
[1] no correct characteristics of any attributes

13. What are the coordinates of the midpoint of a segment with endpoints $(-1, 2)$ and $(5, 6)$?
Ⓐ (2, 4) Ⓒ (6, 4)
Ⓑ (4, 8) Ⓓ (3, 4)

14. Which of the following angle relationships can you use to prove that two lines are parallel?
Ⓕ supplementary corresponding angles
Ⓖ congruent alternate interior angles
Ⓗ congruent vertical angles
Ⓘ congruent same-side interior angles

15. In $\triangle ABC$, $\angle ABC$ and $\angle ADB$ are right angles. Which of the following is NOT a true statement?

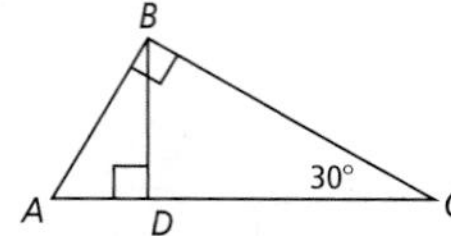

Ⓐ $\angle CBD \cong \angle DAB$
Ⓑ $\angle ABD \cong \angle BCD$
Ⓒ $\angle DBC$ and $\angle BCD$ are complementary.
Ⓓ $\angle DAB \cong \angle ABD$

16. What is the measure of any exterior angle of an equiangular triangle?
Ⓕ 30 Ⓗ 90
Ⓖ 60 Ⓘ 120

GRIDDED RESPONSE

17. Two angles of an isosceles triangle have measures 54.5 and 71. What is the measure of the third angle?

18. In the coordinate plane, $\overleftrightarrow{AB}$ contains $(-2, -4)$ and $(6, 8)$. $\overleftrightarrow{CD}$ contains $(6, y)$ and $(12, 10)$. For what value of y are the lines parallel?

19. A circular wading pool has a diameter of 10 ft. What is the circumference of the wading pool in feet? Use 3.14 for π.

20. What is the measure of the complement of a 56° angle?

21. A new athletic field is being constructed, as shown below. The given coordinates are in terms of yards. What is the area of the field in square yards?

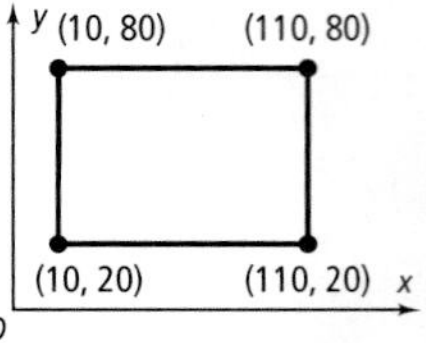

Short Response

22. Is your friend's argument for the following situation valid? Explain.
Given: If you buy a one-year membership at the gym, then you get one month free. You got a free month at the gym.
Your friend's conclusion: You bought a one-year membership.

23. Draw $\overline{MN}$. Then construct the perpendicular bisector of $\overline{MN}$.

Extended Response

24. $\overline{CD}$ has endpoints $C(5, 7)$ and $D(10, -5)$. What are the coordinates of the midpoint of $\overline{CD}$? What is CD? Show your work.

25. Examples and nonexamples of *bleebles* are shown.

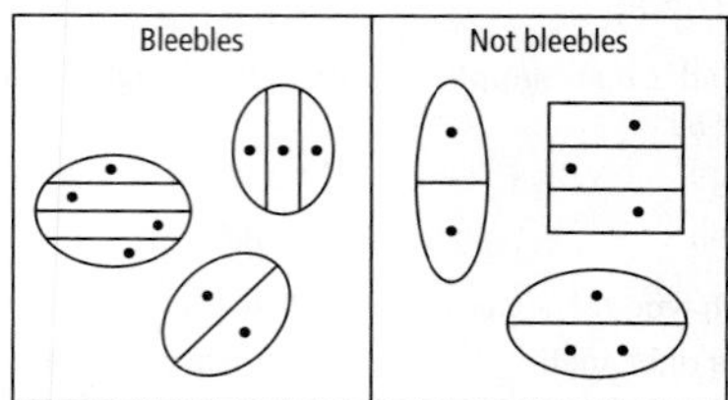

a. Is the figure at the right a *bleeble*? Explain your reasoning.
b. What is a definition for *bleeble*?

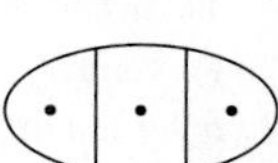

CHAPTER 4

Get Ready!

Lesson 1-7

The Distance Formula

Find the side lengths of $\triangle ABC$.

1. $A(3, 1), B(-1, 1), C(-1, -2)$

2. $A(-3, 2), B(-3, -6), C(8, 6)$

3. $A(-1, -2), B(6, 1), C(2, 5)$

Lesson 2-6

Proving Angles Congruent

Draw a conclusion based on the information given.

4. $\angle J$ is supplementary to $\angle K$; $\angle L$ is supplementary to $\angle K$.

5. $\angle M$ is supplementary to $\angle N$; $\angle M \cong \angle N$.

6. $\angle 1$ is complementary to $\angle 2$.

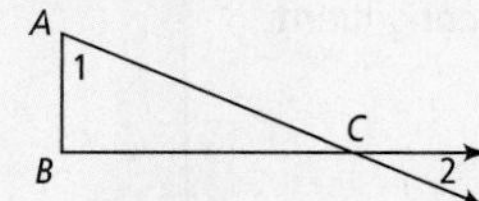

7. $\overrightarrow{FA} \perp \overrightarrow{FC}, \overrightarrow{FB} \perp \overrightarrow{FD}$

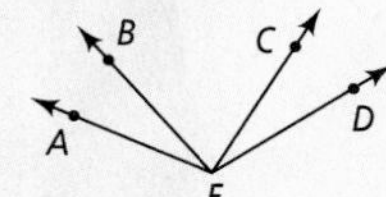

Lessons 3-2 and 3-5

Parallel Lines and the Triangle Angle-Sum Theorem

What can you conclude about the angles in each diagram?

8.

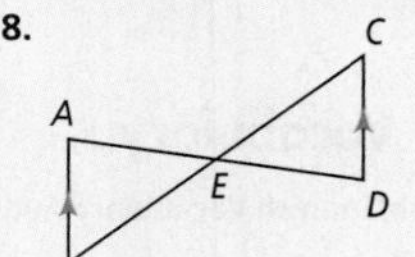

9.

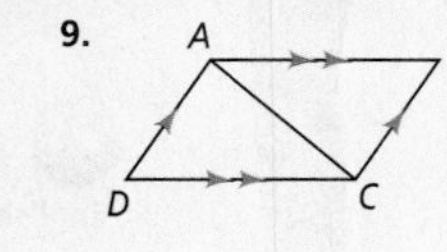

10.

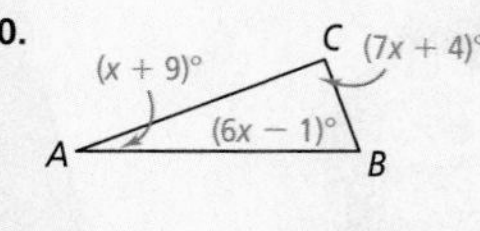

Looking Ahead Vocabulary

11. The foundation of a building is the *base* of the building. How would you describe the *base of an isosceles triangle* in geometry?

12. The *legs* of a table support the tabletop and are equal in length. How might they be similar to the *legs of an isosceles triangle*?

13. A postal worker delivers each piece of mail to the mailbox that *corresponds* to the address on the envelope. What might the term *corresponding parts* of geometric figures mean?

Get Ready!

Assign this diagnostic assessment to determine if students have the prerequisite skills for Chapter 4.

Lesson	Skill
1-7	The Distance Formula
2-6	Proving Angles Congruent
3-2 and 3-5	Parallel Lines and the Triangle Angle-Sum Theorem

To remediate students, select from these resources (available for every lesson).

- Online Problems (PowerGeometry.com)
- Reteaching (All-in-One Teaching Resources)
- Practice (All-in-One Teaching Resources)

Why Students Need These Skills

THE DISTANCE FORMULA Students will use the distance formula to show that sides of triangles on the coordinate plane are congruent.

PROVING ANGLES CONGRUENT Congruent angles will be used to prove triangles congruent.

PARALLEL LINES AND THE TRIANGLE ANGLE-SUM THEOREM Students will use deductive reasoning to show that angles are congruent and to find missing measures of angles to prove triangles congruent.

Looking Ahead Vocabulary

BASE OF AN ISOSCELES TRIANGLE Show examples of isosceles triangles in different orientations and have students identify the base.

LEGS OF AN ISOSCELES TRIANGLE Have students describe how their own legs may help them remember the definition.

CORRESPONDING PARTS Have students examine other uses of the word *corresponding*.

Answers

Get Ready!

1. $AB = 4$, $BC = 3$, $AC = 5$

2. $AB = 8$, $BC = \sqrt{265}$, $AC = \sqrt{137}$

3. $AB = \sqrt{58}$, $BC = \sqrt{32}$, $AC = \sqrt{58}$

4. $\angle J \cong \angle L$

5. $m\angle M = m\angle N = 90$

6. $\angle B$ is a rt. $\angle$.

7. $\angle AFB \cong \angle CFD$

8. $\angle B \cong \angle C$, $\angle A \cong \angle D$, $\angle AEB \cong \angle CED$

9. $\angle DAC \cong \angle BCA$, $\angle DCA \cong \angle BAC$, $\angle DAB \cong \angle BCD$, $\angle B \cong \angle D$

10. $m\angle A = 21$, $m\angle B = 71$, $m\angle C = 88$

11. Answers may vary. Sample: The base is the side that meets each of the two $\cong$ sides of the $\triangle$.

12. Answers may vary. Sample: The legs are the $\cong$ sides of an isosc. $\triangle$.

13. Answers may vary. Sample: Corresp. parts are the sides or $\angle$s that are in the same relative position in each figure.

Chapter 4 Overview

UbD Understanding by Design

Chapter 4 builds on students' understanding and skills related to angles and triangles. In this chapter, students will develop the answers to the Essential Questions posed on the opposite page as they learn the concepts and skills bulleted below.

BIG idea Visualization

ESSENTIAL QUESTION How do you identify corresponding parts of congruent triangles?

- Students will visualize the triangles placed on top of each other.
- Students will use tick marks and angle marks to label corresponding sides and corresponding angles.

BIG idea Reasoning and Proof

ESSENTIAL QUESTION How do you show that two triangles are congruent?

- Students will use the Side-Side-Side Postulate, the Side-Angle-Side Postulate, the Angle-Side-Angle Postulate, the Angle-Angle-Side Theorem, and the Hypotenuse-Leg Theorem.

BIG idea Reasoning and Proof

ESSENTIAL QUESTION How can you tell whether a triangle is isosceles or equilateral?

- Students will use the definitions and look at the number of congruent sides and angles.

TN Checks for Understanding

3108.1.5 Use technology, hands-on activities, and manipulatives to develop the language and the concepts of geometry, including specialized vocabulary.

3108.1.10 Use visualization, spatial reasoning, and geometric modeling to solve problems.

3108.1.13 Use proofs to further develop and deepen the understanding of the study of geometry.

3108.4.9 Classify triangles, quadrilaterals, and polygons (regular, non-regular, convex and concave) using their properties.

3108.4.10 Identify and apply properties and relationships of special figures.

3108.4.20 Prove key basic theorems in geometry.

3108.4.35 Prove that two triangles are congruent by applying the SSS, SAS, ASA, AAS, and HL congruence statements.

3108.4.38 Use the principle that corresponding parts of congruent triangles are congruent to solve problems.

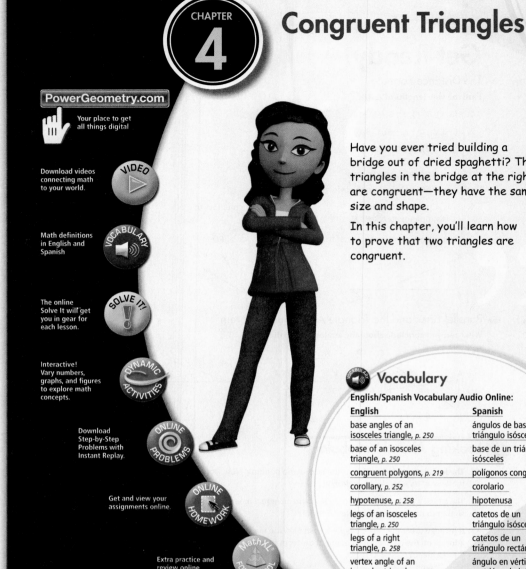

CHAPTER 4
PowerGeometry.com
Your place to get all things digital
Download videos connecting math to your world.
VIDEO
Math definitions in English and Spanish
VOCABULARY
The online Solve It will get you in gear for each lesson.
SOLVE IT!
Interactive! Vary numbers, graphs, and figures to explore math concepts.
DYNAMIC ACTIVITIES
Download Step-by-Step Problems with Instant Replay.
ONLINE PROBLEMS
Get and view your assignments online.
ONLINE HOMEWORK
Extra practice and review online
MathXL FOR SCHOOL

Congruent Triangles

Have you ever tried building a bridge out of dried spaghetti? The triangles in the bridge at the right are congruent—they have the same size and shape.

In this chapter, you'll learn how to prove that two triangles are congruent.

Vocabulary

English/Spanish Vocabulary Audio Online:

English	Spanish
base angles of an isosceles triangle, *p. 250*	ángulos de base de un triángulo isósceles
base of an isosceles triangle, *p. 250*	base de un triángulo isósceles
congruent polygons, *p. 219*	polígonos congruentes
corollary, *p. 252*	corolario
hypotenuse, *p. 258*	hipotenusa
legs of an isosceles triangle, *p. 250*	catetos de un triángulo isósceles
legs of a right triangle, *p. 258*	catetos de un triángulo rectángulo
vertex angle of an isosceles triangle, *p. 250*	ángulo en vértice de un triángulo isósceles

PowerGeometry.com

Chapter 4 Overview

Use these online assets to engage your students. These include support for the Solve It and step-by-step solutions for Problems.

Show the student-produced video demonstrating relevant and engaging applications of the new concepts in the chapter.

Find online definitions for new terms in English and Spanish.

Start each lesson with an attention-getting problem. View the Problem online with helpful hints.

BIG ideas

1 **Visualization**
Essential Question How do you identify corresponding parts of congruent triangles?

2 **Reasoning and Proof**
Essential Question How do you show that two triangles are congruent?

3 **Reasoning and Proof**
Essential Question How can you tell whether a triangle is isosceles or equilateral?

Chapter Preview

Increase students' depth of knowledge with interactive online activities.

Show Problems from each lesson solved step by step. Instant replay allows students to go at their own pace when studying online.

Assign homework to individual students or to an entire class.

Prepare students for the Mid-Chapter Quiz and Chapter Test with online practice and review.

My Math Video

FACILITATE Use this photo to discuss congruent triangles. In this chapter, students will learn to identify congruent triangles and prove two triangles congruent. Properties of congruent triangles help strengthen the bridge shown in the picture.

Q What figures do you see in the spaghetti bridge in the photo? **[There is an arc or semicircle, angles, and triangles.]**

Q How are the triangles used in the bridge? **[They are used to strengthen the arc of the bridge.]**

Q How are the triangles related to each other? **[There are matching triangles on the two sides of the bridge that are the same size and shape.]**

Q Are the triangles next to each other on one side of the bridge the same size and shape? How do you know? **[No, as you move from vertex to vertex on the arc of the bridge, note how the angles at the bottom change in size.]**

Q The triangles on each side of the bridge form congruent pairs. Based on the photo, what do you think congruent means? **[same size and shape]**

ERROR PREVENTION

If students have difficulty examining the triangles in the photo, provide them with tracing paper. Have students trace each triangle from the center to one side separately so that they can see how the triangles change based on their positions.

CHAPTER 4 CONGRUENT TRIANGLES
Math Background

Visualization

BIG idea Visualization can help you connect properties of real objects with two-dimensional drawings of these objects.

ESSENTIAL UNDERSTANDING

4–1 Comparing the corresponding parts of two figures can show whether the figures are congruent.

Reasoning and Proof

BIG idea Definitions establish meanings and remove possible misunderstanding. Other truths are more complex and difficult to see. It is often possible to verify complex truths by reasoning from simpler ones by using deductive reasoning.

ESSENTIAL UNDERSTANDINGS

4–2, 4–3, & 4–6 Two triangles can be proven to be congruent without having to show that all corresponding parts are congruent. Triangles can be proven to be congruent by using (1) three pairs of corresponding sides, (2) two pairs of corresponding sides and one pair of corresponding angles, (3) one pair of corresponding sides and two pairs of corresponding angles, or (4) one pair of right angles, a pair of hypotenuses, and a pair of legs.

4–4 If two triangles are congruent, then every pair of their corresponding parts is also congruent.

4–5 The angles and sides of isosceles and equilateral triangles have special relationships.

4–7 Congruent corresponding parts of one pair of congruent triangles can sometimes be used to prove another pair of triangles congruent. This often involves overlapping triangles.

Proving Triangles Congruent

Congruent triangles are the same shape and the same size. Geometrically, congruent triangles have all corresponding parts congruent.

Congruent triangles have six pairs of congruent parts, three pairs of angles and three pairs of sides.

$\triangle ABC \cong \triangle DEF$

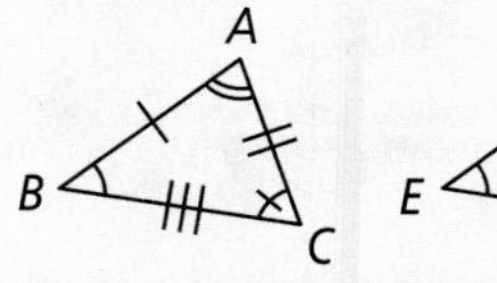

$\angle A \cong \angle D$, $\angle B \cong \angle E$, $\angle C \cong \angle F$

$\overline{AB} \cong \overline{DE}$, $\overline{BC} \cong \overline{EF}$, $\overline{AC} \cong \overline{DF}$

You can also prove that two triangles are congruent by using one of the following:

Side-Side-Side (SSS) Postulate

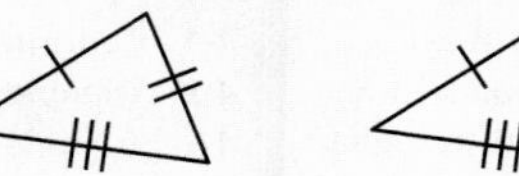

Side-Angle-Side (SAS) Postulate

Angle-Side-Angle (ASA) Postulate

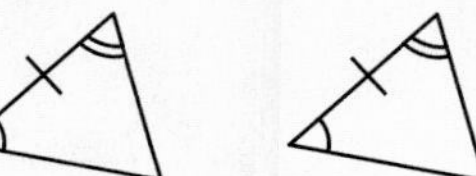

Angle-Angle-Side (AAS) Theorem

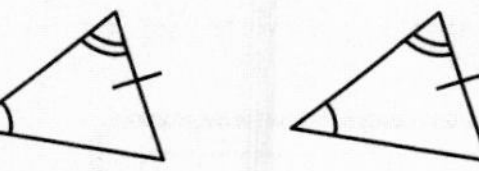

(See p. 217B for another way to prove right triangles congruent.)

Common Errors With Proving Triangles Congruent

Students will often try to use Side-Side-Angle and Angle-Angle-Angle corresponding parts to prove that two triangles are congruent. These are not valid methods.

Proving Right Triangles Congruent

There is a special theorem that can be used to prove right triangles congruent. In order to understand this theorem, look at the following proof.

Two triangles cannot be proven congruent by Side-Side-Angle (SSA). This can be demonstrated by giving a counterexample.

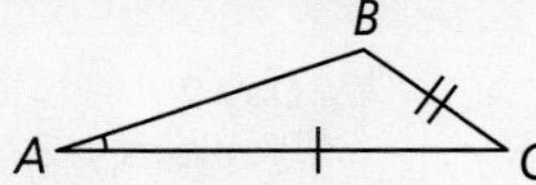

Start with $\triangle ABC$ above. Draw $\overrightarrow{AB}$ as shown below and rotate $\overline{BC}$—without changing its length—until point B touches a point B' on $\overrightarrow{AB}$.

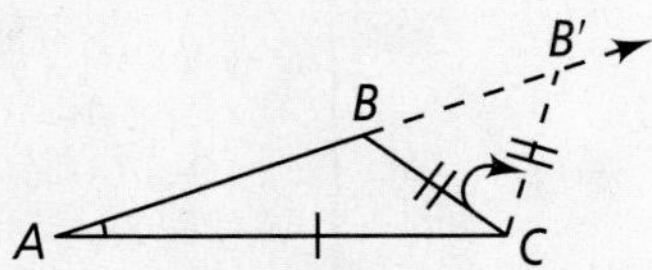

$\angle A \cong \angle A'$, $\overline{AC} \cong \overline{A'C'}$ and $\overline{CB} \cong \overline{C'B'}$ but $\triangle ABC$ is not congruent to $\triangle A'B''C''$.

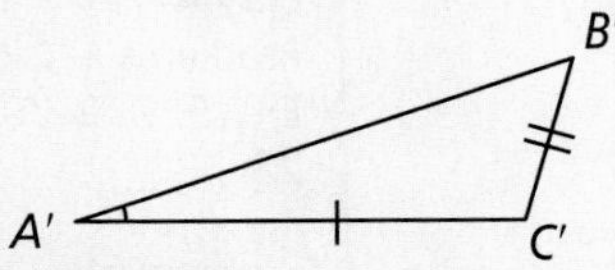

However, you can prove two right triangles congruent by Side-Side-Angle. This is the Hypotenuse-Leg Theorem (HL). The angle is the right angle and the sides are the hypotenuse and one of the legs.

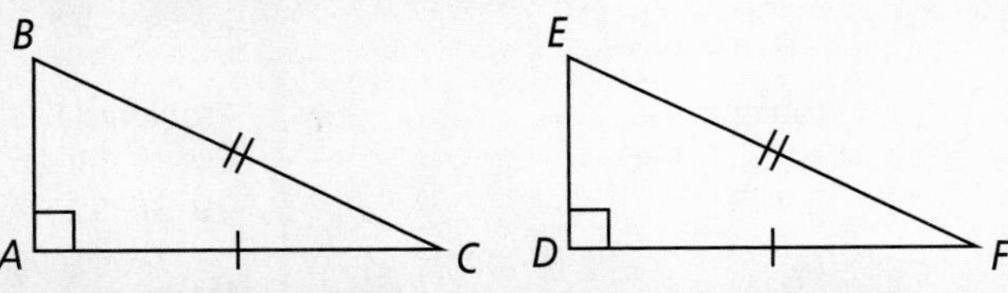

Common Errors With Proving Right Triangles Congruent

Students cannot use the Hypotenuse-Leg (HL) Theorem if they know only that the legs are congruent. In this case they can still prove that the triangles are congruent by Side-Angle-Side (SAS).

Overlapping Triangles

Sometimes triangles share one or more parts. In this case, it may be helpful to redraw the triangles separately to see which parts are corresponding.

Triangles That Share an Angle

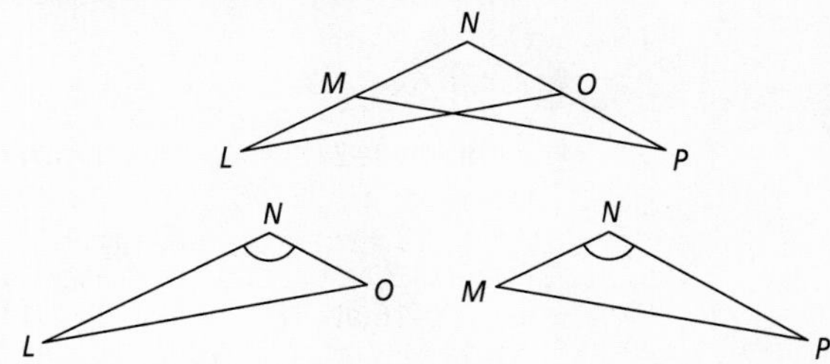

Triangles That Share a Side

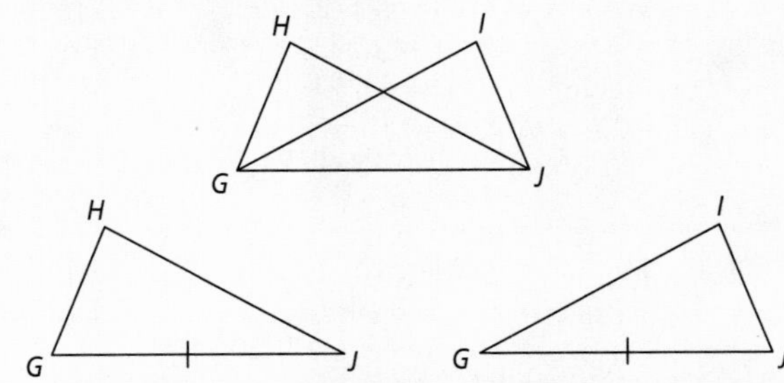

Common Errors With Overlapping Triangles

Students may struggle to distinguish the triangles in the diagram. Have students use their fingers to trace the triangle they are trying to draw, then cover the segments and points that they do not need.

CONGRUENT TRIANGLES

Pacing and Assignment Guide

		TRADITIONAL			BLOCK
Lesson	**Teaching Day(s)**	**Basic**	**Average**	**Advanced**	**Block**
4–1	**1**	Problems 1–2 Exs. 8–29 all, 50–61	Problems 1–4 Exs. 9–29 odd, 50–61	Problems 1–4 Exs. 9–29 odd, 50–61	**Day 1** Problems 1–4 Exs. 9–31 odd, 33–46, 50–61
	2	Problems 3–4 Exs. 30–32 all, 34–38 even, 39–43	Problems 1–4 Exs. 31, 33–46	Problems 1–4 Exs. 31, 33–49	
4–2	**1**	Problems 1–2 Exs. 8–12 all, 35–46	Problems 1–2 Exs. 9, 35–46	Problems 1–3 Exs. 9–13 odd, 15–46	**Day 2** Problems 1–3 Exs. 9–13 odd, 15–31, 35–46
	2	Problem 3 Exs. 13–16 all, 18, 20–22 all, 24–28 even	Problem 3 Exs. 11, 13 odd, 15–31		
4–3	**1**	Problems 1–2 Exs. 8–12 all, 32–39	Problems 1–2 Exs. 9–11 odd, 32–39	Problems 1–2 Exs. 9–11 odd, 32–39	**Day 3** Problems 1–4 Exs. 9–17 odd, 19–28, 32–39
	2	Problems 3–4 Exs. 13–18 all, 21, 22–28 even	Problems 3–4 Exs. 13–17 odd, 19–28	Problems 3–4 Exs. 13–17 odd, 19–31	
4–4	**1**	Problems 1–2 Exs. 5–8 all, 10–16 even, 17, 20, 23–32	Problems 1–2 Exs. 5, 7, 9–20, 23–32	Problems 1–2 Exs. 5, 7, 9–32	**Day 4** Problems 1–2 Exs. 5, 7, 9–20, 23–32
4–5	**1**	Problems 1–2 Exs. 6–12 all, 37–44	Problems 1–2 Exs. 7–11 odd, 37–44	Problems 1–3 Exs. 7–13 odd, 14–44	Problems 1–2 Exs. 7–11 odd, 37–44
	2	Problem 3 Exs. 13, 15, 16–24 even, 28–32 even	Problem 3 Exs. 13–32		**Day 5** Problem 3 Exs. 13–32
4–6	**1**	Problems 1–2 Exs. 8–16, 20, 22, 25, 29–36	Problems 1–2 Exs. 9, 11–26, 29–36	Problems 1–2 Exs. 9, 11–36	Problems 1–2 Exs. 9, 11–26, 29–36
4–7	**1**	Problems 1–2 Exs. 8–16 all, 29–37	Problems 1–2 Exs. 9–15 odd, 29–37	Problems 1–2 Exs. 9–15 odd, 29–37	**Day 6** Problems 1–4 Exs. 9–17 odd, 19–26, 29–37
	2	Problems 3–4 Exs. 17–20 all, 22–26 even	Problems 3–4 Exs. 17, 19–26	Problems 3–4 Exs. 17, 19–28	
Review	**1**	Chapter 4 Review	Chapter 4 Review	Chapter 4 Review	**Day 7** Chapter 4 Review Chapter 4 Test
Assess	**1**	Chapter 4 Test	Chapter 4 Test	Chapter 4 Test	
Total		**14 Days**	**14 Days**	**12 Days**	**7 Days**

Note: Pacing does not include Concept Bytes and other feature pages.

Resources

KEY

I = Interactive asset at PowerGeometry.com
E = Editable master at PowerGeometry.com
P = Available in Print
T = Available as a Transparency
M = Master at PowerGeometry.com
✓= CD-ROM

	For the Chapter	4-1	4-2	4-3	4-4	4-5	4-6	4-7
Planning								
Teacher Center Online Planner & Grade Book	I	I	I	I	I	I	I	I
Interactive Learning & Guided Instruction								
My Math Video	I							
Solve It!		I TM	I TM	I TM	I TM	I TM	I TM	I TM
Student Companion (SP)*		P M	P M	P M	P M	P M	P M	
Vocabulary Support		I P M	I P M	I P M	I P M	I P M	I P M	I P M
Got It? Support		I P	I P	I P	I P	I P	I P	I P
Dynamic Activity			I			I	I	
Animated Problems		I	I	I	I	I	I	I
Additional Problems		M	M	M	M	M	M	M
English Language Learner Support (TR)		E P M	E P M	E P M	E P M	E P M	E P M	E P M
Activities, Games, and Puzzles		E M	E M	E M	E M	E M	E M	E M
Teaching With TI Technology With CD-ROM						✓ P		
TI-Nspire™ Support CD-ROM		✓	✓	✓	✓	✓	✓	✓
Lesson Check & Practice								
Student Companion (SP)*		P M	P M	P M	P M	P M	P M	P M
Lesson Check Support		I P	I P	I P	I P	I P	I P	I P
Practice and Problem Solving Workbook (SP)		P	P	P	P	P	P	P
Think About a Plan (TR)*		E P M	E P M	E P M	E P M	E P M	E P M	E P M
Practice Form G (TR)*		E P M	E P M	E P M	E P M	E P M	E P M	E P M
Standardized Test Prep (TR)*		P M	P M	P M	P M	P M	P M	P M
Practice *Form K* (TR)*		E P M	E P M	E P M	E P M	E P M	E P M	E P M
Extra Practice	E M							
Find the Errors!	M							
Enrichment (TR)		E P M	E P M	E P M	E P M	E P M	E P M	E P M
Answers and Solutions CD-ROM	✓	✓	✓	✓	✓	✓	✓	✓
Assess & Remediate								
ExamView CD-ROM	✓	✓	✓	✓	✓	✓	✓	✓
Lesson Quiz		I TM	I TM	I TM	I TM	I TM	I TM	I TM
Quizzes and Tests *Form G* (TR)*	E P M			E P M				E P M
Quizzes and Tests *Form K* (TR)*	E P M			E P M				E P M
Reteaching (TR)*		E P M	E P M	E P M	E P M	E P M	E P M	E P M
Performance Tasks (TR)*	P M							
Cumulative Review (TR)*	P M							
Progress Monitoring Assessments	I P M							

(TR) Available in All-In-One Teaching Resources   * Spanish available

1 Interactive Learning

Solve It!

PURPOSE To recognize the characteristics of congruent figures

PROCESS Students can

- visually compare the remaining pieces with the spaces in the diagram.
- copy the page and cut out the pieces to determine which piece fits each space.

FACILITATE

Q How would you describe the piece that goes into space A? **[It should have three indentations on three sides, and one protrusion.]**

Q What characteristics are the same between the space and the piece that fits it? **[The size and shape should be the same.]**

ANSWER See Solve It in Answers on next page.

CONNECT THE MATH The Solve It introduces the concept of congruent figures. In this lesson, students learn to identify congruent polygons.

4-1 Congruent Figures

Objective To recognize congruent figures and their corresponding parts

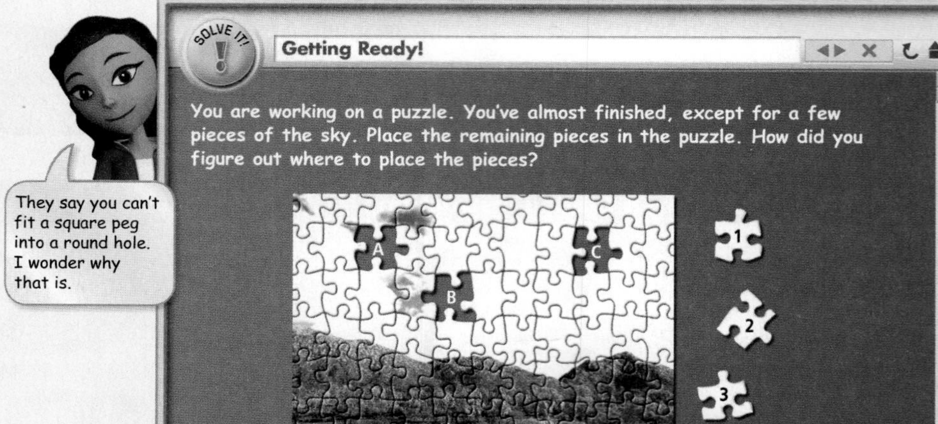

Getting Ready!
You are working on a puzzle. You've almost finished, except for a few pieces of the sky. Place the remaining pieces in the puzzle. How did you figure out where to place the pieces?
A
B
C
1
2
3

They say you can't fit a square peg into a round hole. I wonder why that is.

Lesson Vocabulary
- congruent polygons

Congruent figures have the same size and shape. When two figures are congruent, you can slide, flip, or turn one so that it fits exactly on the other one, as shown below. In this lesson, you will learn how to determine if geometric figures are congruent.

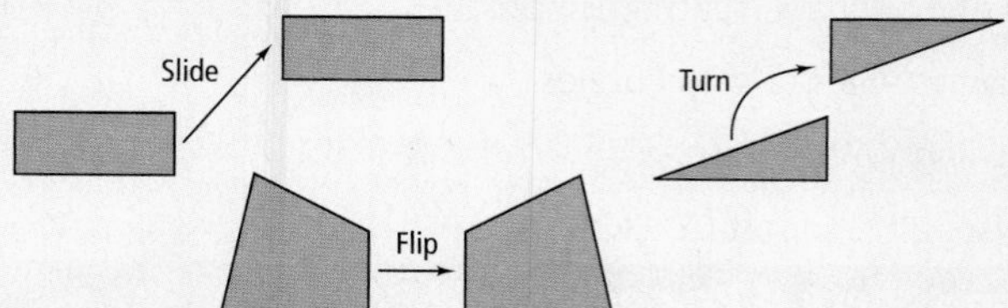

Essential Understanding You can determine whether two figures are congruent by comparing their corresponding parts.

4-1 Preparing to Teach

BIG ideas **Visualization**
Reasoning and Proof

UbD

ESSENTIAL UNDERSTANDING

- Comparing the corresponding parts of two figures can show whether the figures are congruent.

Math Background

Congruent figures are found in nature and in structures made by humans. Architects, surveyors, and doctors are among the many professionals that rely on properties of congruent figures to perform their jobs.

For figures to be congruent, corresponding parts must be congruent. For n-gons with n sides and n angles, $2n$ congruence statements can be written to show two of the figures are congruent.

To shorten the number of steps needed to prove figures are congruent, the Third Angles Theorem (presented in this lesson), and more theorems and postulates presented in upcoming lessons make it possible to write proofs without proving $2n$ congruence statements.

Support Student Learning

Use the **Geometry Companion** to engage and support students during instructions. See Lesson Resources at the end of this lesson for details.

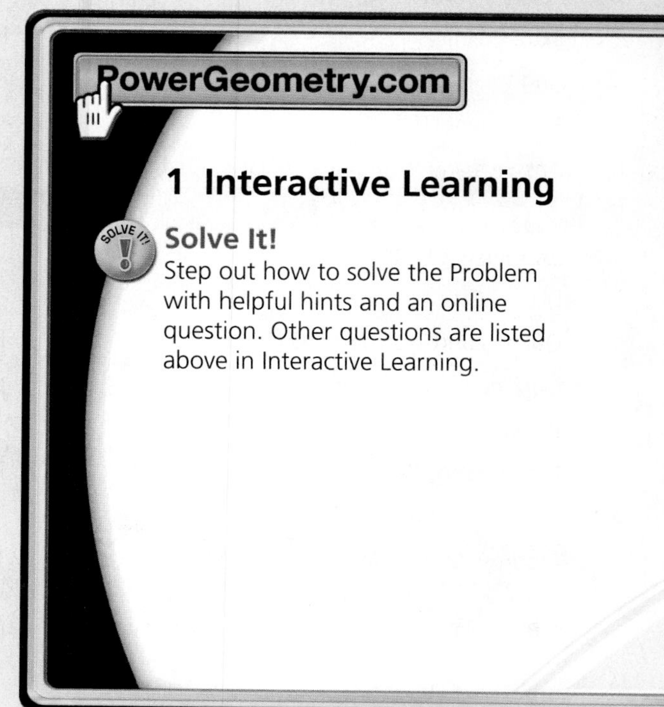

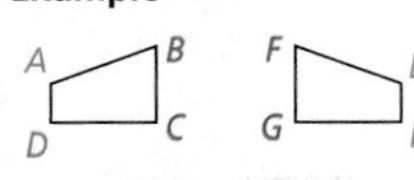

Key Concept Congruent Figures

Definition

Congruent polygons have congruent corresponding parts—their matching sides and angles. When you name congruent polygons, you must list corresponding vertices in the same order.

Example

$ABCD \cong EFGH$

$\overline{AB} \cong \overline{EF}$ $\overline{BC} \cong \overline{FG}$
$\overline{CD} \cong \overline{GH}$ $\overline{DA} \cong \overline{HE}$

$\angle A \cong \angle E$ $\angle B \cong \angle F$
$\angle C \cong \angle G$ $\angle D \cong \angle H$

Plan

How do you know which sides and angles correspond?
The congruence statement $HIJK \cong LMNO$ tells you which parts correspond.

Problem 1 Finding Congruent Parts

If $HIJK \cong LMNO$, what are the congruent corresponding parts?

Sides: $\overline{HI} \cong \overline{LM}$ $\overline{IJ} \cong \overline{MN}$ $\overline{JK} \cong \overline{NO}$ $\overline{KH} \cong \overline{OL}$

Angles: $\angle H \cong \angle L$ $\angle I \cong \angle M$ $\angle J \cong \angle N$ $\angle K \cong \angle O$

Got It? 1. If $\triangle WYS \cong \triangle MKV$, what are the congruent corresponding parts?

Plan

You know two angle measures in $\triangle ABC$. How can they help?
In the congruent triangles, $\angle D$ corresponds to $\angle A$, so you know that $\angle D \cong \angle A$. You can find $m\angle D$ by first finding $m\angle A$.

Problem 2 Using Congruent Parts

Multiple Choice The wings of an SR-71 Blackbird aircraft suggest congruent triangles. What is $m\angle D$?

(A) 30 (B) 75 (C) 105 (D) 150

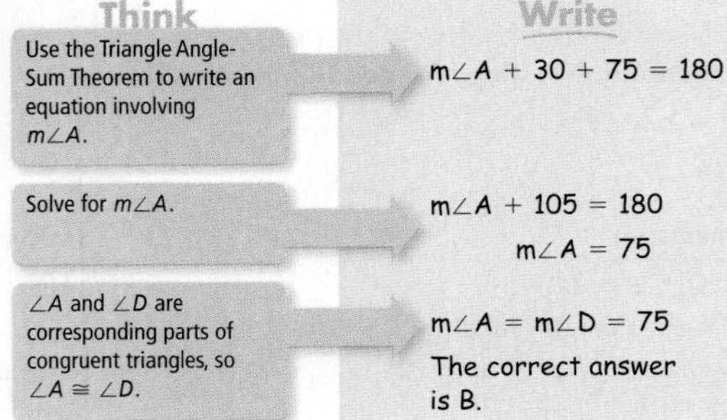

Think	Write
Use the Triangle Angle-Sum Theorem to write an equation involving $m\angle A$.	$m\angle A + 30 + 75 = 180$
Solve for $m\angle A$.	$m\angle A + 105 = 180$ $m\angle A = 75$
$\angle A$ and $\angle D$ are corresponding parts of congruent triangles, so $\angle A \cong \angle D$.	$m\angle A = m\angle D = 75$ The correct answer is B.

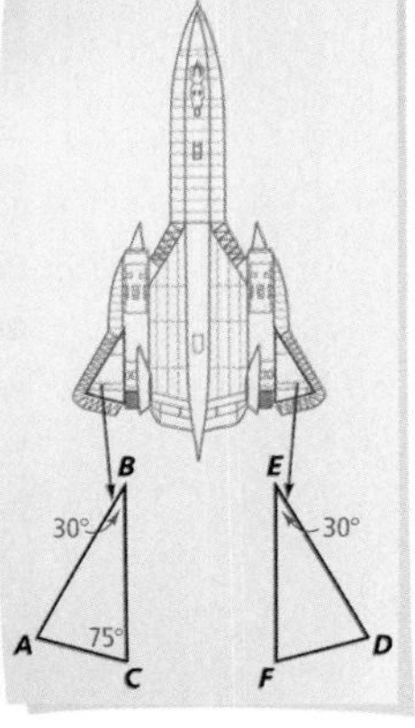

Got It? 2. Suppose that $\triangle WYS \cong \triangle MKV$. If $m\angle W = 62$ and $m\angle Y = 35$, what is $m\angle V$? Explain.

2 Guided Instruction

Take Note

Have students redraw quadrilateral $EFGH$ so that it is oriented the same way as $ABCD$. Students should be able to identify corresponding vertices.

Problem 1

Q How can you use the order of the congruence statement to identify corresponding sides? **[The vertices are listed in corresponding order, so the sides can be listed in the order they appear in the congruence statement.]**

Q What can you do with the diagram to help identify corresponding parts? **[Redraw one figure so that the orientation is the same for both figures.]**

Got It? ERROR PREVENTION

Have students draw the triangles and label the vertices in the same order in which they appear in the congruence statement.

Problem 2

Q How can you find the missing angle measure in $\triangle ABC$? **[Use the Triangle Angle-Sum Theorem. Subtract the known angle measures from 180°.]**

Q Which angle is congruent to $\angle D$? **[$\angle A$]**

Got It? VISUAL LEARNERS

Students should draw congruent triangles and label them according to the congruence statement.

2 Guided Instruction

Each Problem is worked out and supported online.

Problem 1
Finding Congruent Parts

Problem 2
Using Congruent Parts
Animated

Problem 3
Finding Congruent Triangles
Animated

Problem 4
Proving Triangles Congruent
Animated

Support in Geometry Companion

- Vocabulary
- Key Concepts
- Got It?

Answers

Solve It!

Piece 1 fits in A, piece 2 in B, and piece 3 in C; explanations may vary. Sample: You can match up the parts that stick out with the parts that "go in" based on their size and location.

Got It?

1. $\overline{WY} \cong \overline{MK}$, $\overline{YS} \cong \overline{KV}$, $\overline{WS} \cong \overline{MV}$, $\angle W \cong \angle M$, $\angle Y \cong \angle K$, $\angle S \cong \angle V$
2. $m\angle V = 83$; $\angle W \cong \angle M$ and $\angle Y \cong \angle K$ because they are corresp. parts of $\cong$ △s. By the Triangle Angle-Sum Theorem, $m\angle M + m\angle K + m\angle V = 180$. By substitution, $62 + 35 + m\angle V = 180$. So by subtraction, $m\angle V = 83$.

Problem 3

Q How many conditions must be proved to show that two triangles are congruent? **[The definition states that the figures must have congruent sides and angles. There are 3 pairs of angles and 3 pairs of sides that must be shown to be congruent.]**

Q There is one pair of unmarked angles in the diagram. What special name and relationship describes these angles? **[They are vertical angles and they are congruent.]**

Q What do the marks on the sides of the triangles mean? **[The sides with the matching marks are congruent.]**

Q How are congruent segments defined? **[Congruent segments have the same length.]**

Got It?

Q Other than the pair of sides that are marked congruent, which pair of sides is congruent? Justify your answer. **[$\overline{DB} \cong \overline{DB}$ by the Reflexive Property of Congruence.]**

Take Note

When completing a proof, many students benefit from thinking through the problem backwards. Have them begin with the desired conclusion and work backward to identify the information given and needed.

Q You can find equations involving $m\angle C$ and $m\angle F$ using which theorem? **[Triangle Angle-Sum Theorem]**

Q What is true about those equations? **[They both include other angle measures that are equal.]**

Plan

How do you determine whether two triangles are congruent?
Compare each pair of corresponding parts. If all six pairs are congruent, then the triangles are congruent.

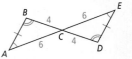

Problem 3 Finding Congruent Triangles

Are the triangles congruent? Justify your answer.

$\overline{AB} \cong \overline{ED}$	Given
$\overline{BC} \cong \overline{DC}$	$BC = 4 = DC$
$\overline{AC} \cong \overline{EC}$	$AC = 6 = EC$
$\angle A \cong \angle E, \angle B \cong \angle D$	Given
$\angle BCA \cong \angle DCE$	Vertical angles are congruent.

$\triangle ABC \cong \triangle EDC$ by the definition of congruent triangles.

Got It? 3. Is $\triangle ABD \cong \triangle CBD$? Justify your answer.

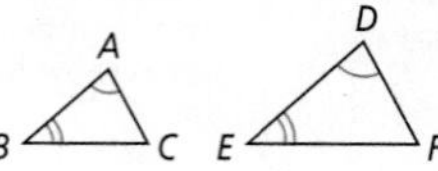

Recall the Triangle Angle-Sum Theorem: The sum of the measures of the angles in a triangle is 180. The next theorem follows from the Triangle Angle-Sum Theorem.

take note

Theorem 4-1 Third Angles Theorem

Theorem	If . . .	Then . . .
If two angles of one triangle are congruent to two angles of another triangle, then the third angles are congruent.	$\angle A \cong \angle D$ and $\angle B \cong \angle E$	$\angle C \cong \angle F$

Proof **Proof of Theorem 4-1: Third Angles Theorem**

Given: $\angle A \cong \angle D, \angle B \cong \angle E$

Prove: $\angle C \cong \angle F$

Statements	Reasons
1) $\angle A \cong \angle D, \angle B \cong \angle E$	1) Given
2) $m\angle A = m\angle D, m\angle B = m\angle E$	2) Def. of $\cong$ ∡
3) $m\angle A + m\angle B + m\angle C = 180$, $m\angle D + m\angle E + m\angle F = 180$	3) △ Angle-Sum Thm.
4) $m\angle A + m\angle B + m\angle C = m\angle D + m\angle E + m\angle F$	4) Subst. Prop.
5) $m\angle D + m\angle E + m\angle C = m\angle D + m\angle E + m\angle F$	5) Subst. Prop.
6) $m\angle C = m\angle F$	6) Subtraction Prop. of =
7) $\angle C \cong \angle F$	7) Def. of $\cong$ ∡

Additional Problems

1. If $RSTU \cong WXYZ$, what are the congruent corresponding parts?

ANSWER Sides: $\overline{RS} \cong \overline{WX}$, $\overline{ST} \cong \overline{XY}$, $\overline{TU} \cong \overline{YZ}$, $\overline{RU} \cong \overline{WZ}$; Angles: $\angle R \cong \angle W$, $\angle S \cong \angle X$, $\angle T \cong \angle Y$, $\angle U \cong \angle Z$

2. The sides of a roof suggest congruent triangles. What is $m\angle 1$?

A. 90
B. 48
C. 42
D. 32

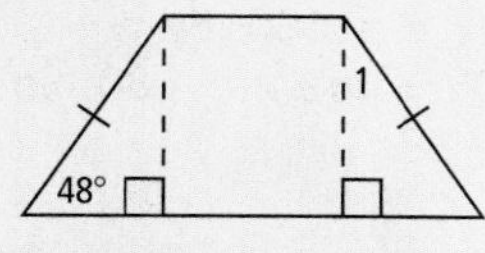

ANSWER C

3. Are the triangles congruent? Justify your answer.

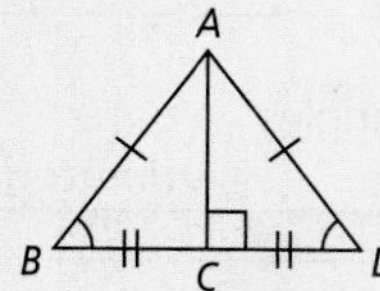

ANSWER $\triangle ACB \cong \triangle ACD$ by the Third Angles Theorem, the Reflexive Property of Congruence, and the definition of congruent triangles.

4. Given: $\overline{RS} \cong \overline{RU}$, $\overline{TS} \cong \overline{TU}$, $\angle S \cong \angle U$, $\angle SRT \cong \angle URT$

Prove: $\triangle RST \cong \triangle RUT$

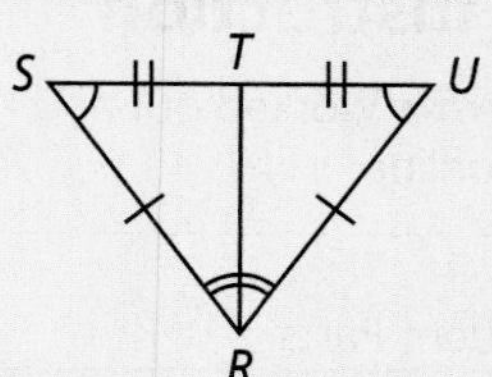

ANSWER It is given that $\overline{RS} \cong \overline{RU}$ and $\overline{TS} \cong \overline{TU}$. $\overline{RT} \cong \overline{RT}$ by the Reflexive Property of Congruence. It is also given that $\angle S \cong \angle U$ and $\angle SRT \cong \angle URT$. $\angle STR \cong \angle UTR$ by the Third Angles Theorem. So, $\triangle RST \cong \triangle RUT$ by the definition of congruent triangles.

Plan

You know four pairs of congruent parts. What else do you need to prove the triangles congruent? You need a third pair of congruent sides and a third pair of congruent angles.

Proof

Problem 4 Proving Triangles Congruent

Given: $\overline{LM} \cong \overline{LO}$, $\overline{MN} \cong \overline{ON}$, $\angle M \cong \angle O$, $\angle MLN \cong \angle OLN$

Prove: $\triangle LMN \cong \triangle LON$

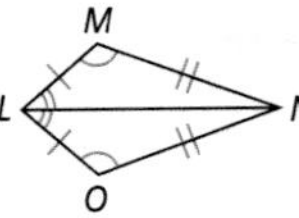

M
L
N
O

Statements	Reasons
1) $\overline{LM} \cong \overline{LO}$, $\overline{MN} \cong \overline{ON}$	1) Given
2) $\overline{LN} \cong \overline{LN}$	2) Reflexive Property of ≅
3) $\angle M \cong \angle O$, $\angle MLN \cong \angle OLN$	3) Given
4) $\angle MNL \cong \angle ONL$	4) Third Angles Theorem
5) $\triangle LMN \cong \triangle LON$	5) Definition of ≅ triangles

Got It? 4. Given: $\angle A \cong \angle D$, $\overline{AE} \cong \overline{DC}$, $\overline{EB} \cong \overline{CB}$, $\overline{BA} \cong \overline{BD}$

Prove: $\triangle AEB \cong \triangle DCB$

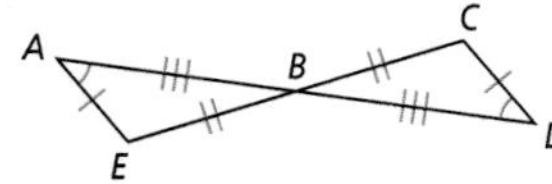

A
B
C
D
E

Lesson Check

Do you know HOW?

Complete the following statements.

1. **Given:** $\triangle QXR \cong \triangle NYC$
   a. $\overline{QX} \cong$?
   b. $\angle Y \cong$?
2. **Given:** $\triangle BAT \cong \triangle FOR$
   a. $\overline{TA} \cong$?
   b. $\angle R \cong$?
3. **Given:** $BAND \cong LUCK$
   a. $\angle U \cong$?
   b. $\overline{DB} \cong$?
   c. $NDBA \cong$?
4. In $\triangle MAP$ and $\triangle TIE$, $\angle A \cong \angle I$ and $\angle P \cong \angle E$.
   a. What is the relationship between $\angle M$ and $\angle T$?
   b. If $m\angle A = 52$ and $m\angle P = 36$, what is $m\angle T$?

Do you UNDERSTAND?

5. **Open-Ended** When do you think you might need to know that things are congruent in your everyday life?
6. If each angle in one triangle is congruent to its corresponding angle in another triangle, are the two triangles congruent? Explain.
7. **Error Analysis** Walter sketched the diagram below. He claims it shows that the two polygons are congruent. What information is missing to support his claim?

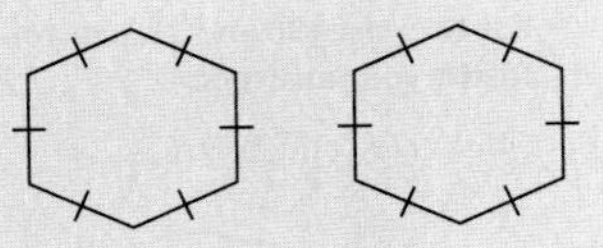

Problem 4

Q What property of congruence verifies that $\overline{LN} \cong \overline{LN}$? **[Reflexive Property of Congruence]**

Q How many pairs of angles are marked congruent? **[2]**

Q Is there a theorem that allows you to state that the third angles are congruent? If so, what is it? **[Yes, the Third Angles Theorem]**

Got It?

Ask students to list the pairs of congruent corresponding parts. Then have students identify the missing congruence statement that leads to the proof.

3 Lesson Check

Do you know HOW?

- If students have difficulty with Exercises 1-3, then have them review Problem 1.

Do you UNDERSTAND?

- If students have difficulty with Exercise 6, then have them try to draw a counterexample.

Close

Q How many statements must be proved to show that two n-gons are congruent? **[$2n$]**

Q Based on the definition of congruent triangles, how many pairs of angles must be shown to be congruent when proving two triangles congruent? **[3]**

Q Based on the Third Angles Theorem, how many pairs of angles must be shown to be congruent when proving two triangles congruent? **[2]**

Answers

Got It? (continued)

3. Answers may vary. Sample: You know that $\overline{AD} \cong \overline{CD}$ (Given) and $\overline{BD} \cong \overline{BD}$ (Reflexive Prop. of ≅), but you have no other information about the sides and ∠s of the △, so you cannot conclude that $\triangle ABD \cong \triangle CBD$.
4. $\angle A \cong \angle D$ (Given), and $\angle ABE \cong \angle DBC$ because vertical ∠s are ≅. Also, $\angle AEB \cong \angle DCB$ (Third ∠s Theorem). The three pairs of sides are ≅ (Given), so $\triangle AEB \cong \triangle DCB$ by the def. of ≅ △s.

Lesson Check

1a. $\overline{NY}$ b. $\angle X$

2a. $\overline{RO}$ b. $\angle T$

3a. $\angle A$ b. $\overline{KL}$ c. $CKLU$

4a. $\angle M = \angle T$ b. 92

5. Answers may vary. Sample: finding the correct top for a food container
6. No; the △s could be the same shape but not necessarily the same size.
7. He has not shown that corresp. ∠s are ≅.

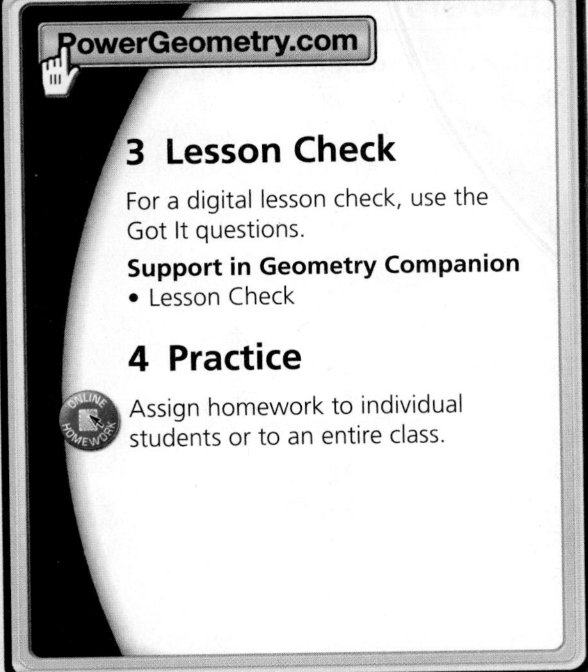

PowerGeometry.com
3 Lesson Check
For a digital lesson check, use the Got It questions.
Support in Geometry Companion
• Lesson Check
4 Practice
Assign homework to individual students or to an entire class.

4 Practice

ASSIGNMENT GUIDE
Basic: 8–32 all, 34–38 even, 39–43
Average: 9–31 odd, 33–46
Advanced: 9–31 odd, 33–49
Standardized Test Prep: 50–53
Mixed Review: 54–61
Reasoning exercises have blue headings.
Applications exercises have red headings.
EXERCISE 40: Use the Think About a Plan worksheet in the **Practice and Problem Solving Workbook** (also available in the Teaching Resources in print and online) to further support students' development in becoming independent learners.

HOMEWORK QUICK CHECK
To check students' understanding of key skills and concepts, go over Exercises 13, 31, 39, 40, and 43.

Practice and Problem-Solving Exercises

A Practice

8. Construction Builders use the king post truss (below left) for the top of a simple structure. In this truss, $\triangle ABC \cong \triangle ABD$. List the congruent corresponding parts. See Problem 1.

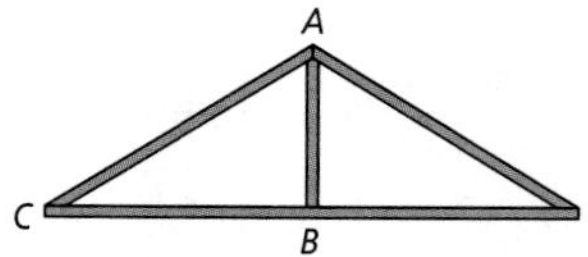

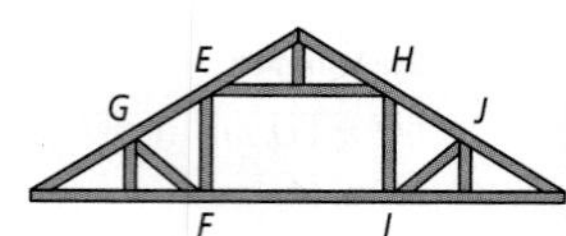

9. The attic frame truss (above right) provides open space in the center for storage. In this truss, $\triangle EFG \cong \triangle HIJ$. List the congruent corresponding parts.

$\triangle LMC \cong \triangle BJK$. Complete the congruence statements.

10. $\overline{LC} \cong$ _?_	**11.** $\overline{KJ} \cong$ _?_
12. $\overline{JB} \cong$ _?_	**13.** $\angle L \cong$ _?_
14. $\angle K \cong$ _?_	**15.** $\angle M \cong$ _?_
16. $\triangle CML \cong$ _?_	**17.** $\triangle KBJ \cong$ _?_
18. $\triangle MLC \cong$ _?_	**19.** $\triangle JKB \cong$ _?_

$POLY \cong SIDE$. List each of the following.

20. four pairs of congruent sides

21. four pairs of congruent angles

At an archeological site, the remains of two ancient step pyramids are congruent. If $ABCD \cong EFGH$, find each of the following. (Diagrams are not to scale.) See Problem 2.

22. AD	**23.** GH
24. $m\angle GHE$	**25.** $m\angle BAD$
26. EF	**27.** BC
28. $m\angle DCB$	**29.** $m\angle EFG$

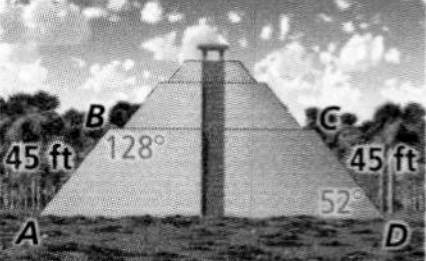

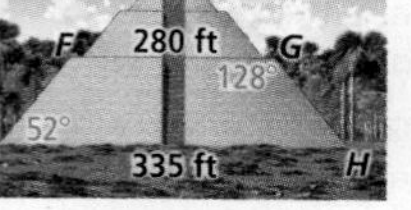

For Exercises 30 and 31, can you conclude that the triangles are congruent? Justify your answers. See Problem 3.

30. $\triangle TRK$ and $\triangle TUK$

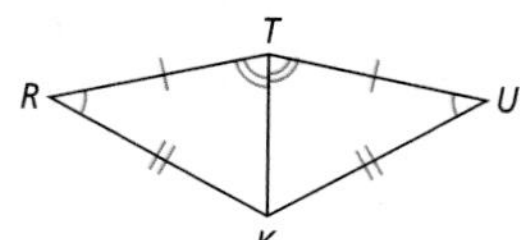

31. $\triangle SPQ$ and $\triangle TUV$

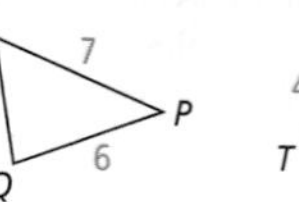

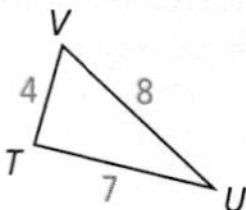

Answers

Practice and Problem-Solving Exercises

8. $\overline{AB} \cong \overline{AB}$, $\overline{BC} \cong \overline{BD}$, $\overline{AC} \cong \overline{AD}$, $\angle CAB \cong \angle DAB$, $\angle C \cong \angle D$, $\angle ABC \cong \angle ABD$

9. $\overline{EF} \cong \overline{HI}$, $\overline{FG} \cong \overline{IJ}$, $\overline{EG} \cong \overline{HJ}$, $\angle EFG \cong \angle HIJ$, $\angle FGE \cong \angle IJH$, $\angle FEG \cong \angle IHJ$

10. $\overline{BK}$	**11.** $\overline{CM}$
12. $\overline{ML}$	**13.** $\angle B$
14. $\angle C$	**15.** $\angle J$
16. $\triangle KJB$	**17.** $\triangle CLM$
18. $\triangle JBK$	**19.** $\triangle MCL$

20. $\overline{PO} \cong \overline{SI}$, $\overline{OL} \cong \overline{ID}$, $\overline{LY} \cong \overline{DE}$, $\overline{YP} \cong \overline{ES}$

21. $\angle P \cong \angle S$, $\angle O \cong \angle I$, $\angle L \cong \angle D$, $\angle Y \cong \angle E$

22. 335 ft	**23.** 45 ft
24. 52	**25.** 52
26. 45 ft	**27.** 280 ft
28. 128	**29.** 128

30. Yes; two pairs of sides and two pairs of ∠s are marked as ≅; the third pair of sides are ≅ by the Refl. Prop. of ≅, and the third pair of ∠s are ≅ by the Third ∠s Theorem.

31. No; there are not three pairs of ≅ corresp. sides.

See Problem 4.

32. **Given:** $\overline{AB} \parallel \overline{DC}$, $\angle B \cong \angle D$, $\overline{AB} \cong \overline{DC}$, $\overline{BC} \cong \overline{AD}$
Proof
Prove: $\triangle ABC \cong \triangle CDA$

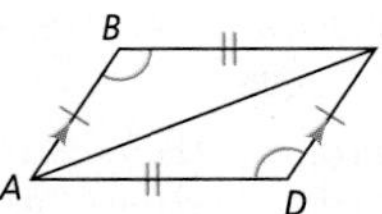

B Apply

33. If $\triangle DEF \cong \triangle LMN$, which of the following must be a correct congruence statement?

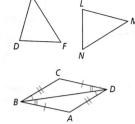

Ⓐ $\overline{DE} \cong \overline{LN}$ Ⓒ $\angle N \cong \angle F$
Ⓑ $\overline{FE} \cong \overline{NL}$ Ⓓ $\angle M \cong \angle F$

34. **Reasoning** Randall says he can use the information in the figure to prove $\triangle BCD \cong \triangle DAB$. Is he correct? Explain.

Algebra **$\triangle ABC \cong \triangle DEF$. Find the measures of the given angles or the lengths of the given sides.**

35. $m\angle A = x + 10$, $m\angle D = 2x$ 36. $m\angle B = 3y$, $m\angle E = 6y - 12$

37. $BC = 3z + 2$, $EF = z + 6$ 38. $AC = 7a + 5$, $DF = 5a + 9$

39. **Think About a Plan** $\triangle ABC \cong \triangle DBE$. Find the value of x.
- What does it mean for two triangles to be congruent?
- Which angle measures do you already know?
- How can you find the missing angle measure in a triangle?

Algebra **Find the values of the variables.**

40.

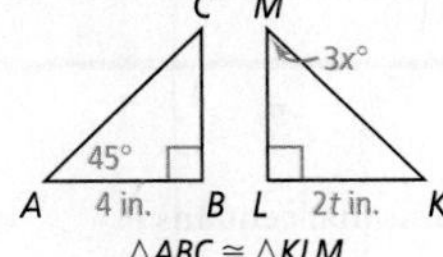

$\triangle ABC \cong \triangle KLM$

41.

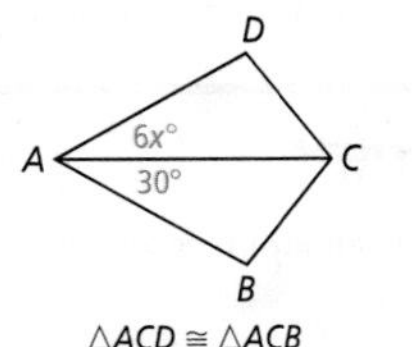

$\triangle ACD \cong \triangle ACB$

42. Complete in two different ways:
$\triangle JLM \cong$ __?__.

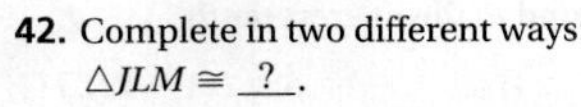

43. **Open-Ended** Write a congruence statement for two triangles. List the congruent sides and angles.

44. **Given:** $\overline{AB} \perp \overline{AD}$, $\overline{BC} \perp \overline{CD}$, $\overline{AB} \cong \overline{CD}$, $\overline{AD} \cong \overline{CB}$, $\overline{AB} \parallel \overline{CD}$
Proof
Prove: $\triangle ABD \cong \triangle CDB$

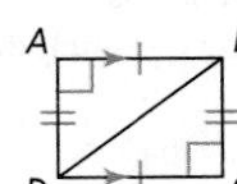

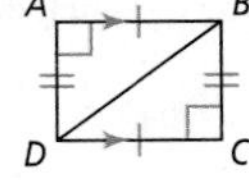

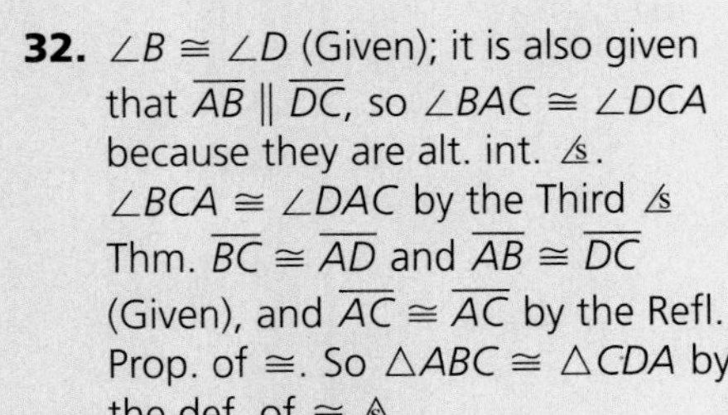

32. $\angle B \cong \angle D$ (Given); it is also given that $\overline{AB} \parallel \overline{DC}$, so $\angle BAC \cong \angle DCA$ because they are alt. int. ∠s. $\angle BCA \cong \angle DAC$ by the Third ∠s Thm. $\overline{BC} \cong \overline{AD}$ and $\overline{AB} \cong \overline{DC}$ (Given), and $\overline{AC} \cong \overline{AC}$ by the Refl. Prop. of ≅. So $\triangle ABC \cong \triangle CDA$ by the def. of ≅ △s.

33. C

34. Yes. The diagram shows that $\angle CBD \cong \angle ADB$ and $\angle CDB \cong \angle ABD$. By the Third ∠s Theorem, $\angle C \cong \angle A$. The diagram shows that $\overline{CD} \cong \overline{AB}$ and $\overline{CB} \cong \overline{AD}$. $\overline{BD} \cong \overline{BD}$ by the Refl. Prop. of ≅. So $\triangle BCD \cong \triangle DAB$ by the def. of ≅ △s.

35. $m\angle A = m\angle D = 20$

36. $m\angle B = m\angle E = 12$

37. $BC = EF = 8$

38. $AC = DF = 19$

39. 43

40. $x = 15$, $t = 2$

41. 5

42. $\triangle NRZ$, $\triangle ZRN$ (also $\triangle MLJ$)

43. Answers may vary. Sample: If $\triangle PQR \cong \triangle XYZ$, then $\overline{PQ} \cong \overline{XY}$, $\overline{QR} \cong \overline{YZ}$, $\overline{PR} \cong \overline{XZ}$, $\angle P \cong \angle X$, $\angle Q \cong \angle Y$, and $\angle R \cong \angle Z$.

44. Two pairs of sides are given as ≅, and the third pair of sides are ≅ by the Refl. Prop. of ≅. $\angle A \cong \angle C$ because ⊥ lines form rt. ∠s, and all rt. ∠s are ≅. $\angle ABD \cong \angle CDB$ by the Alt. Int. ∠s Thm., and $\angle ADB \cong \angle CBD$ by the Third ∠s Thm. So $\triangle ABD \cong \triangle CDB$ by the def. of ≅ △s.

Answers

Practice and Problem-Solving Exercises (continued)

45. Two pairs of ≅ sides are given, and the third pair of sides are ≅ because $\overline{PQ}$ bisects $\overline{RT}$, so $\overline{TS} \cong \overline{RS}$. $\overline{PR} \parallel \overline{TQ}$, so $\angle P \cong \angle Q$ and $\angle R \cong \angle T$ because they are alt. int. ∠s; the third pair of ∠s are vertical ∠s, so they are ≅. Thus $\triangle PRS \cong \triangle QTS$ by the def. of ≅ △s.

46. Answers may vary. Sample: Sort ≅ cards into three piles.

47. $KL = 4$, $LM = 3$, $KM = 5$

48. two; (3, 1) or (3, −7)

49a. 15 quadrilaterals

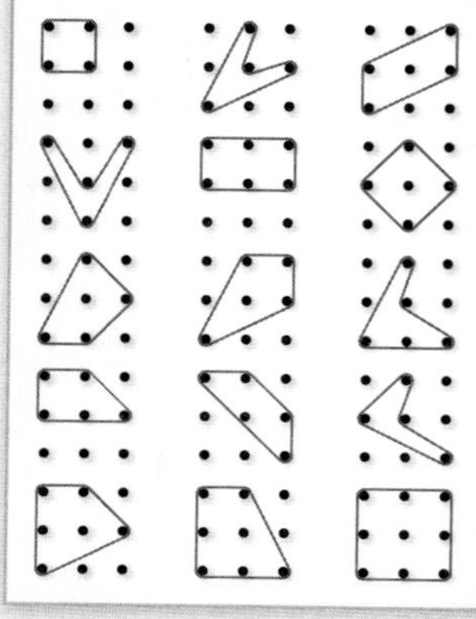

b. 11 convex, 4 concave

50. 72 **51.** 50

52. 13 **53.** 28

54. $y = -\frac{2}{3}x + \frac{25}{3}$

55. $y = -\frac{1}{4}x + \frac{5}{4}$

56. 5 **57.** 18 **58.** 10

59. $\overline{AB} \cong \overline{DE}$, $\angle C \cong \angle F$

60. $\angle Q \cong \angle S$, $\angle QPR \cong \angle SRP$, $\angle QPR$ and $\angle SPR$ are adjacent, $\angle QRP$ and $\angle SRP$ are adjacent.

61. $\angle M \cong \angle U$, $\overline{TO} \cong \overline{NV}$, $\overline{TV} \cong \overline{NO}$, $\angle MOT$ and $\angle MON$ are adjacent and suppl., $\angle UVT$ and $\angle UVN$ are adjacent and suppl.

---

45. Given: $\overline{PR} \parallel \overline{TQ}$, $\overline{PR} \cong \overline{TQ}$, $\overline{PS} \cong \overline{QS}$, $\overline{PQ}$ bisects $\overline{RT}$
Proof **Prove:** $\triangle PRS \cong \triangle QTS$

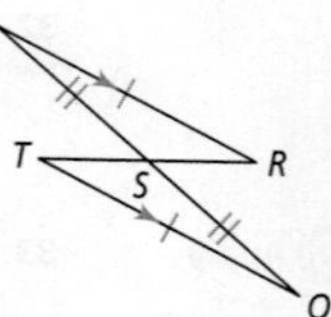

46. Writing The 225 cards in Tracy's sports card collection are rectangles of three different sizes. How could Tracy quickly sort the cards?

Challenge **Coordinate Geometry** **The vertices of $\triangle GHJ$ are $G(-2, -1)$, $H(-2, 3)$, and $J(1, 3)$.**

47. $\triangle KLM \cong \triangle GHJ$. Find KL, LM, and KM.

48. If L and M have coordinates $L(3, -3)$ and $M(6, -3)$, how many pairs of coordinates are possible for K? Find one such pair.

49. a. How many quadrilaterals (convex and concave) with different shapes or sizes can you make on a three-by-three geoboard? Sketch them. One is shown at the right.
b. How many quadrilaterals of each type are there?

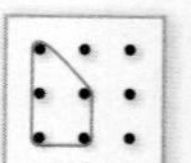

Standardized Test Prep

GRIDDED RESPONSE

SAT/ACT

50. $\triangle HLN \cong \triangle GST$, $m\angle H = 66$, and $m\angle S = 42$. What is $m\angle T$?

51. The measure of one angle in a triangle is 80. The other two angles are congruent. What is the measure of each?

52. Given $A(2, -6)$ and $B(-3, 6)$, what is AB?

53. What is the number of feet in the perimeter of a square with side length 7 ft?

Mixed Review

Write an equation for the line perpendicular to the given line that contains *P*. See Lesson 3-8.

54. $P(2, 7)$; $y = \frac{3}{2}x - 2$ **55.** $P(1, 1)$; $y = 4x + 3$

Find the distance between the points. If necessary, round to the nearest tenth. See Lesson 1-7.

56. $A(0, 0)$, $B(4, 3)$ **57.** $X(11, 24)$, $Y(-7, 24)$ **58.** $E(1, -12)$, $F(1, -2)$

Get Ready! **To prepare for Lesson 4-2, do Exercises 59–61.**

What can you conclude from each diagram? See Lessons 1-4 and 3-2.

59.

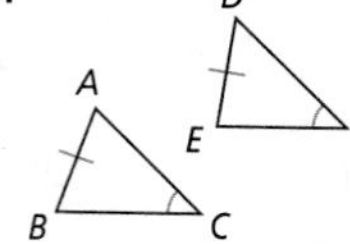

60.

61.

4-1 Lesson Resources

Differentiated Remediation

Instructional Support

Geometry Companion

Students can use the **Geometry Companion** worktext (4 pages) . . .

- New Vocabulary
- Key Concepts
- Got It for each Problem
- Lesson Check

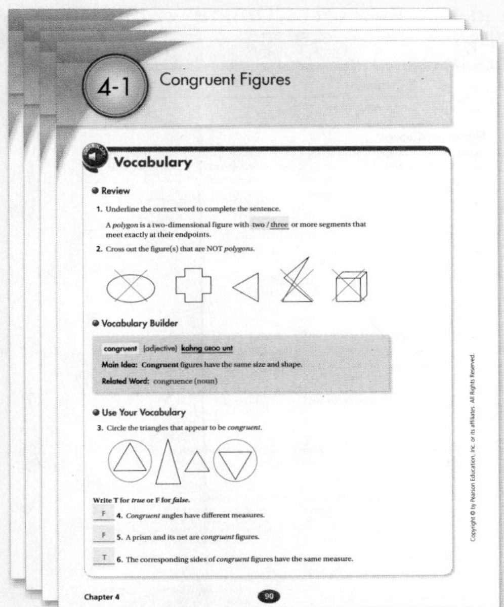

4-1 Congruent Figures

Vocabulary

Review

1. Underline the correct word to complete the sentence.

   A *polygon* is a two-dimensional figure with two / three or more segments that meet exactly at their endpoints.

2. Cross out the figure(s) that are NOT *polygons*.

Vocabulary Builder

congruent (adjective) kahng GROO unt

Main Idea: **Congruent** figures have the same size and shape.

Related Word: congruence (noun)

Use Your Vocabulary

3. Circle the triangles that appear to be *congruent*.

Write T for *true* or F for *false*.

F 4. *Congruent* angles have different measures.

F 5. A prism and its net are *congruent* figures.

T 6. The corresponding sides of *congruent* figures have the same measure.

Chapter 4 90

ELL Support

Assess Understanding Pair more proficient students with less proficient students. Then draw the following diagram on the board.

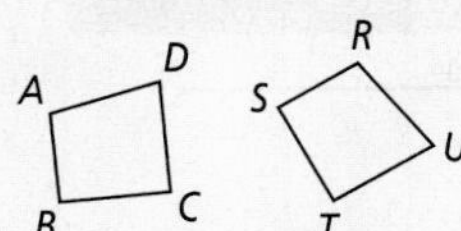

$ABCD \cong RSTU$

Touch the congruency symbol and ask: What does this symbol mean? Working in pairs, students will write congruency statements for the corresponding parts. Give another example without a diagram.

5 Assess & Remediate

Lesson Quiz

1. If $CDEF \cong KLMN$, what are the congruent corresponding parts?
2. If $\triangle UVW \cong \triangle EFC$, what is the measure of $\angle FEC$?

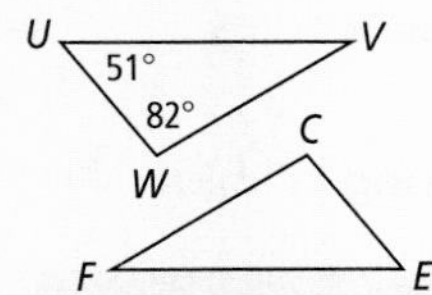

3. **Do you UNDERSTAND?** Suppose it is given that $\angle C \cong \angle B$, $\angle D \cong \angle A$, $\overline{AE} \cong \overline{BE}$, and $\overline{CE} \cong \overline{DE}$. Does that prove that the triangles are congruent? Justify your answer.

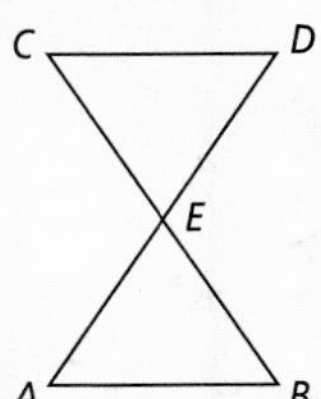

ANSWERS TO LESSON QUIZ

1. Sides: $\overline{CD} \cong \overline{KL}$, $\overline{DE} \cong \overline{LM}$, $\overline{EF} \cong \overline{MN}$, $\overline{CF} \cong \overline{KN}$; Angles: $\angle C \cong \angle K$, $\angle D \cong \angle L$, $\angle E \cong \angle M$, $\angle F \cong \angle N$
2. 51
3. No, the two triangles have congruent angles but not necessarily congruent sides.

PRESCRIPTION FOR REMEDIATION

Use the student work on the Lesson Quiz to prescribe a differentiated review assignment.

Points	Differentiated Remediation
0–1	Intervention
2	On-level
3	Extension

PowerGeometry.com

5 Assess & Remediate

Assign the Lesson Quiz. Appropriate intervention, practice, or enrichment is automatically generated based on student performance.

Intervention

- **Reteaching** (2 pages) Provides reteaching and practice exercises for the key lesson concepts. Use with struggling students or absent students.
- **English Language Learner Support** Helps students develop and reinforce mathematical vocabulary and key concepts.

All-in-One Resources/Online

Reteaching

4-1 Reteaching

Congruent Figures

Given $ABCD \cong QRST$, find corresponding parts using the names. Order matters.

For example, ABCD / QRST — This shows that $\angle A$ corresponds to $\angle Q$. Therefore, $\angle A \cong \angle Q$.

For example, ABCD / QRST — This shows that $\overline{BC}$ corresponds to $\overline{RS}$. Therefore, $\overline{BC} \cong \overline{RS}$.

Exercises

Find corresponding parts using the order of the letters in the names.

1. Identify the remaining three pairs of corresponding angles and sides between $ABCD$ and $QRST$ using the circle technique shown above.
   $\angle B \cong \angle R$, $\angle C \cong \angle S$, $\angle D \cong \angle T$, $\overline{AB} \cong \overline{QR}$, $\overline{CD} \cong \overline{ST}$, and $\overline{DA} \cong \overline{TQ}$
   Angles: ABCD ABCD ABCD / QRST QRST QRST — Sides: ABCD ABCD ABCD / QRST QRST QRST
2. Which pair of corresponding sides is hardest to identify using this technique?
   Answers may vary. Sample: $\overline{AD}$ and $\overline{QT}$

Find corresponding parts by redrawing figures.

3. The two congruent figures below at the left have been redrawn at the right. Why are the corresponding parts easier to identify in the drawing at the right?
   Answers may vary. Sample: The drawing at the right shows figures in same orientation.
4. Redraw the congruent polygons at the right in the same orientation. Identify all pairs of corresponding sides and angles. Check students' work. $\angle A$ and $\angle P$, $\angle B$ and $\angle Q$, $\angle C$ and $\angle R$, $\angle D$ and $\angle S$, $\angle E$ and $\angle T$, $\overline{AB}$ and $\overline{PQ}$, $\overline{BC}$ and $\overline{QR}$, $\overline{CD}$ and $\overline{RS}$, $\overline{DE}$ and $\overline{ST}$, and $\overline{EA}$ and $\overline{TP}$ all correspond.
5. $MNOP \cong QRST$. Identify all pairs of congruent sides and angles.
   $\angle M \cong \angle Q$, $\angle N \cong \angle R$, $\angle O \cong \angle S$, $\angle P \cong \angle T$, $\overline{MN} \cong \overline{QR}$, $\overline{NO} \cong \overline{RS}$, $\overline{OP} \cong \overline{ST}$, and $\overline{PM} \cong \overline{TQ}$

All-in-One Resources/Online

English Language Learner Support

4-1 ELL Support

Congruent Figures

Concept List

algebraic equation	angle measure	congruency statement
congruent angles	congruent polygons	congruent segments
congruent triangles	proof	segment measure

Choose the concept from the list above that best represents the item in each box.

1. $\overline{GH} \cong \overline{ST}$ congruency statement	2. $m\angle A = 45$ angle measure	3. congruent polygons
4. $YZ = MN$ congruent segments	5. $\triangle ABC \cong \triangle XYZ$ congruent triangles	6. Given: $\overline{BD}$ is the angle bisector of $\angle ABC$, and $\overline{BD}$ is the perpendicular bisector of $\overline{AC}$. Prove: $\triangle ADB \cong \triangle CDB$ proof
7. $m\angle H = 5x$, $m\angle W = x + 28$. Solve $5x = x + 28$ to find the measures of $\angle H$ and $\angle W$. algebraic equation	8. $BC = 3$ cm segment measure	9. $\angle ADB$ and $\angle SDT$ are vertical angles. So, $\angle ADB \cong \angle SDT$. congruent angles

Differentiated Remediation *continued*

On-Level

- **Practice** (2 pages) Provides extra practice for each lesson. For simpler practice exercises, use the Form K Practice pages found in the All-in-One Teaching Resources and online.
- **Think About a Plan** Helps students develop specific problem-solving skills and strategies by providing scaffolded guiding questions.
- **Standardized Test Prep** Focuses on all major exercises, all major question types, and helps students prepare for the high-stakes assessments.

Practice and Problem Solving Wkbk/ Resources/Online

Practice page 1

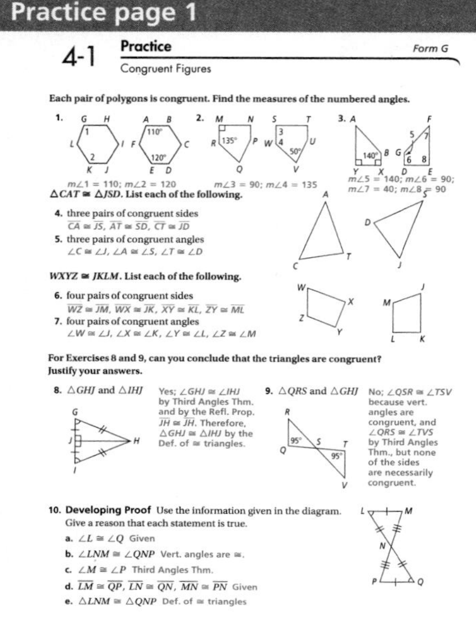

4-1 Practice — Form G
Congruent Figures

Each pair of polygons is congruent. Find the measures of the numbered angles.

1. $m\angle 1 = 110$; $m\angle 2 = 120$
2. $m\angle 3 = 90$; $m\angle 4 = 135$
3. $m\angle 5 = 140$; $m\angle 6 = 90$; $m\angle 7 = 40$; $m\angle 8 = 90$

$\triangle CAT \cong \triangle JSD$. List each of the following.

4. three pairs of congruent sides $\overline{CA} \cong \overline{JS}$, $\overline{AT} \cong \overline{SD}$, $\overline{CT} \cong \overline{JD}$
5. three pairs of congruent angles $\angle C \cong \angle J$, $\angle A \cong \angle S$, $\angle T \cong \angle D$

$WXYZ \cong JKLM$. List each of the following.

6. four pairs of congruent sides $\overline{WZ} \cong \overline{JM}$, $\overline{WX} \cong \overline{JK}$, $\overline{XY} \cong \overline{KL}$, $\overline{ZY} \cong \overline{ML}$
7. four pairs of congruent angles $\angle W \cong \angle J$, $\angle X \cong \angle K$, $\angle Y \cong \angle L$, $\angle Z \cong \angle M$

For Exercises 8 and 9, can you conclude that the triangles are congruent? Justify your answers.

8. $\triangle GHJ$ and $\triangle IHJ$ Yes; $\angle GHJ \cong \angle IHJ$ by Third Angles Thm. and by the Refl. Prop. $\overline{JH} \cong \overline{JH}$. Therefore, $\triangle GHJ \cong \triangle IHJ$ by the Def. of $\cong$ triangles.
9. $\triangle QRS$ and $\triangle QHJ$ No; $\angle QSR \cong \angle TSV$ because vert. angles are congruent, and $\angle QRS \cong \angle TVS$ by Third Angles Thm., but none of the sides are necessarily congruent.
10. **Developing Proof** Use the information given in the diagram. Give a reason that each statement is true.
    a. $\angle L \cong \angle Q$ Given
    b. $\angle LNM \cong \angle QNP$ Vert. angles are $\cong$.
    c. $\angle M \cong \angle P$ Third Angles Thm.
    d. $\overline{LM} \cong \overline{QP}$, $\overline{LN} \cong \overline{QN}$, $\overline{MN} \cong \overline{PN}$ Given
    e. $\triangle LNM \cong \triangle QNP$ Def. of $\cong$ triangles

Practice and Problem Solving Wkbk/ Resources/Online

Practice page 2

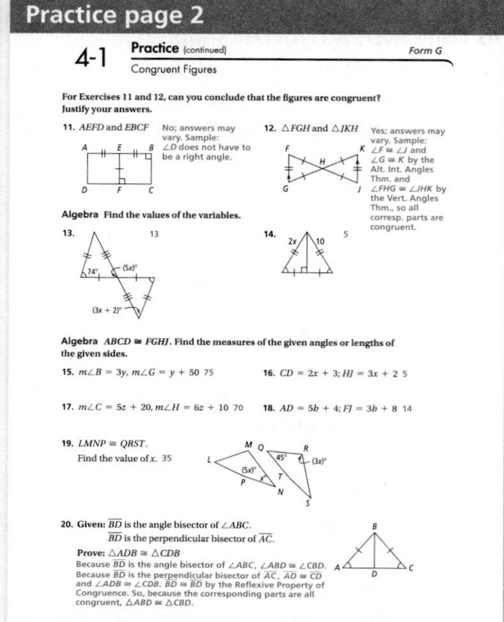

4-1 Practice (continued) — Form G
Congruent Figures

For Exercises 11 and 12, can you conclude that the figures are congruent? Justify your answers.

11. $AEFD$ and $EBCF$ No; answers may vary. Sample: $\angle D$ does not have to be a right angle.
12. $\triangle FGH$ and $\triangle JKH$ Yes; answers may vary. Sample: $\angle F \cong \angle J$ and $\angle G \cong K$ by the Alt. Int. Angles Thm. and $\angle FHG \cong \angle JHK$ by the Vert. Angles Thm., so all corresp. parts are congruent.

Algebra Find the values of the variables.

13. 13
14. 5

Algebra $ABCD \cong FGHJ$. Find the measures of the given angles or lengths of the given sides.

15. $m\angle B = 3y$, $m\angle G = y + 50$ 75
16. $CD = 2x + 3$; $HJ = 3x + 2$ 5
17. $m\angle C = 5z + 20$, $m\angle H = 6z + 10$ 70
18. $AD = 5b + 4$; $FJ = 3b + 8$ 14
19. $LMNP \cong QRST$. Find the value of x. 35
20. **Given:** $\overline{BD}$ is the angle bisector of $\angle ABC$. $\overline{BD}$ is the perpendicular bisector of $\overline{AC}$.
    Prove: $\triangle ADB \cong \triangle CDB$
    Because $\overline{BD}$ is the angle bisector of $\angle ABC$, $\angle ABD \cong \angle CBD$. Because $\overline{BD}$ is the perpendicular bisector of $\overline{AC}$, $\overline{AD} \cong \overline{CD}$ and $\angle ADB \cong \angle CDB$. $\overline{BD} \cong \overline{BD}$ by the Reflexive Property of Congruence. So, because the corresponding parts are all congruent, $\triangle ABD \cong \triangle CBD$.

Practice and Problem Solving Wkbk/ Resources/Online

Think About a Plan

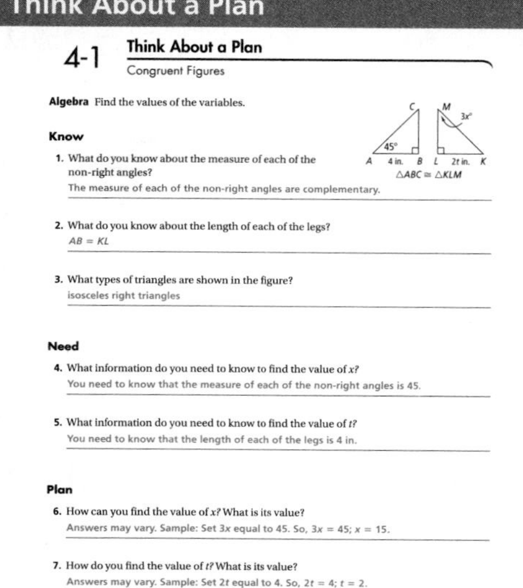

4-1 Think About a Plan
Congruent Figures

Algebra Find the values of the variables.

$\triangle ABC \cong \triangle KLM$

Know

1. What do you know about the measure of each of the non-right angles? The measure of each of the non-right angles are complementary.
2. What do you know about the length of each of the legs? $AB = KL$
3. What types of triangles are shown in the figure? isosceles right triangles

Need

4. What information do you need to know to find the value of x? You need to know that the measure of each of the non-right angles is 45.
5. What information do you need to know to find the value of t? You need to know that the length of each of the legs is 4 in.

Plan

6. How can you find the value of x? What is its value? Answers may vary. Sample: Set $3x$ equal to 45. So, $3x = 45$; $x = 15$.
7. How do you find the value of t? What is its value? Answers may vary. Sample: Set $2t$ equal to 4. So, $2t = 4$; $t = 2$.

Practice and Problem Solving Wkbk/ Resources/Online

Standardized Test Prep

4-1 Standardized Test Prep
Congruent Figures

Multiple Choice

For Exercises 1–6, choose the correct letter.

1. The pair of polygons at the right is congruent. What is $m\angle J$? A
   (A) 45 (B) 90 (C) 135 (D) 145
2. The triangles at the right are congruent. Which of the following statements must be true? I
   (F) $\angle A \cong \angle D$ (G) $\angle B \cong \angle E$ (H) $\overline{AB} \cong \overline{DE}$ (I) $\overline{BC} \cong \overline{DF}$
3. Given the diagram at the right, which of the following must be true? B
   (A) $\triangle XSF \cong \triangle XTG$ (B) $\triangle SXF \cong \triangle GXT$ (C) $\triangle FXS \cong \triangle XGT$ (D) $\triangle FXS \cong \triangle GXT$
4. If $\triangle RST \cong \triangle XYZ$, which of the following need not be true? I
   (F) $\angle R \cong \angle X$ (G) $\angle T \cong \angle Z$ (H) $\overline{RT} \cong \overline{XZ}$ (I) $\overline{SR} \cong \overline{YZ}$
5. If $\triangle ABC \cong \triangle DEF$, $m\angle A = 50$, and $m\angle E = 30$, what is $m\angle C$? C
   (A) 30 (B) 50 (C) 100 (D) 120
6. If $ABCD \cong QRST$, $m\angle A = x - 10$, and $m\angle Q = 2x - 30$, what is $m\angle A$? F
   (F) 10 (G) 20 (H) 30 (I) 40

Short Response

7. **Given:** $\overline{AB} \parallel \overline{DC}$, $\overline{AD} \parallel \overline{BC}$, $\overline{AB} \cong \overline{CD}$, $\overline{AD} \cong \overline{CB}$
   Prove: $\triangle ABD \cong \triangle CDB$
   [2] $\angle ABD \cong \angle CDB$ and $\angle ADB \cong \angle CBD$, both by the Alt. Int Angles Thm. So, by Third Angles Thm., $\angle A \cong \angle C$. Because $\overline{DB} \cong \overline{BD}$ by the Refl. Prop. of Congruence, and we know $\overline{AB} \cong \overline{CD}$ and $\overline{AD} \cong \overline{CB}$, then $\triangle ABD \cong \triangle CDB$. [1] incomplete proof [0] no proof or incorrect proof

Extension

- **Enrichment** Provides students with interesting problems and activities that extend the concepts of the lesson.
- **Activities, Games, and Puzzles** Worksheets that can be used for concepts development, enrichment, and for fun!

All-in-One Resources/Online

Enrichment

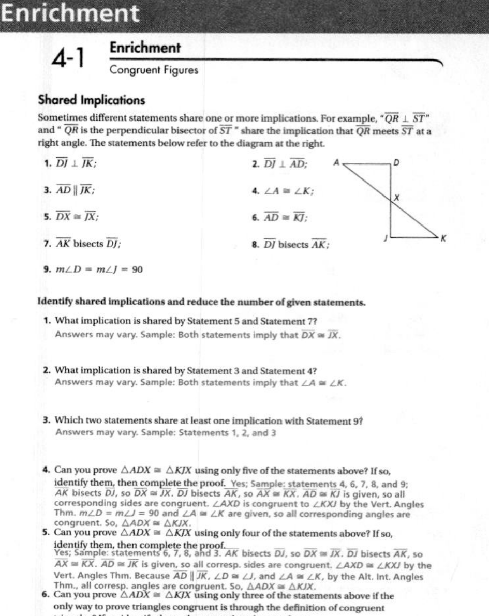

4-1 Enrichment
Congruent Figures

Shared Implications

Sometimes different statements share one or more implications. For example, "$\overline{QR} \perp \overline{ST}$" and "$\overline{QR}$ is the perpendicular bisector of $\overline{ST}$" share the implication that $\overline{QR}$ meets $\overline{ST}$ at a right angle. The statements below refer to the diagram at the right.

1. $\overline{DJ} \perp \overline{JK}$;
2. $\overline{DJ} \perp \overline{AD}$;
3. $\overline{AD} \parallel \overline{JK}$;
4. $\angle A \cong \angle K$;
5. $\overline{DX} \cong \overline{JX}$;
6. $\overline{AD} \cong \overline{KJ}$;
7. $\overline{AK}$ bisects $\overline{DJ}$;
8. $\overline{DJ}$ bisects $\overline{AK}$;
9. $m\angle D = m\angle J = 90$

Identify shared implications and reduce the number of given statements.

1. What implication is shared by Statement 5 and Statement 7? Answers may vary. Sample: Both statements imply that $\overline{DX} \cong \overline{JX}$.
2. What implication is shared by Statement 3 and Statement 4? Answers may vary. Sample: Both statements imply that $\angle A \cong \angle K$.
3. Which two statements share at least one implication with Statement 9? Answers may vary. Sample: Statements 1, 2, and 3
4. Can you prove $\triangle ADX \cong \triangle KJX$ using only five of the statements above? If so, identify them, then complete the proof. Yes; Sample: statements 4, 6, 7, 8, and 9; $\overline{AK}$ bisects $\overline{DJ}$, so $\overline{DX} \cong \overline{JX}$. $\overline{DJ}$ bisects $\overline{AK}$, so $\overline{AX} \cong \overline{KX}$. $\overline{AD} \cong \overline{KJ}$ is given, so all corresponding sides are congruent. $\angle AXD$ is congruent to $\angle KXJ$ by the Vert. Angles Thm. $m\angle D = m\angle J = 90$ and $\angle A \cong \angle K$ are given, so all corresponding angles are congruent. So, $\triangle ADX \cong \triangle KJX$.
5. Can you prove $\triangle ADX \cong \triangle KJX$ using only four of the statements above? If so, identify them, then complete the proof. Yes; Sample: statements 6, 7, 8, and 3. $\overline{AK}$ bisects $\overline{DJ}$, so $\overline{DX} \cong \overline{JX}$. $\overline{DJ}$ bisects $\overline{AK}$, so $\overline{AX} \cong \overline{KX}$. $\overline{AD} \cong \overline{JK}$ is given, so all corresp. sides are congruent. $\angle AXD \cong \angle KXJ$ by the Vert. Angles Thm. Because $\overline{AD} \parallel \overline{JK}$, $\angle D \cong \angle J$, and $\angle A \cong \angle K$, by the Alt. Int. Angles Thm., all corresp. angles are congruent. So, $\triangle ADX \cong \triangle KJX$.
6. Can you prove $\triangle ADX \cong \triangle KJX$ using only three of the statements above if the only way to prove triangles congruent is through the definition of congruent triangles? If so, identify them, then complete the proof. no

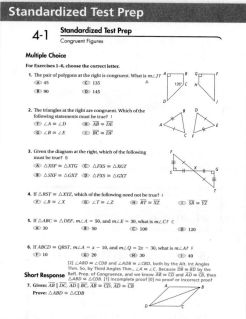

Online Teacher Resource Center

Activities, Games, and Puzzles

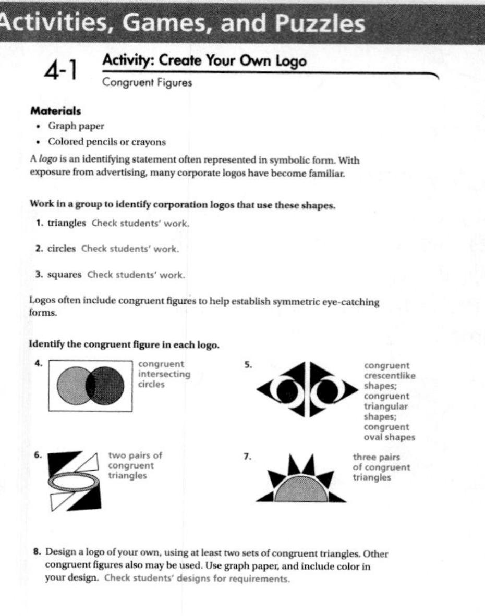

4-1 Activity: Create Your Own Logo
Congruent Figures

Materials

- Graph paper
- Colored pencils or crayons

A *logo* is an identifying statement often represented in symbolic form. With exposure from advertising, many corporate logos have become familiar.

Work in a group to identify corporation logos that use these shapes.

1. triangles Check students' work.
2. circles Check students' work.
3. squares Check students' work.

Logos often include congruent figures to help establish symmetric eye-catching forms.

Identify the congruent figure in each logo.

4. congruent intersecting circles
5. congruent crescentlike shapes; congruent triangular shapes; congruent oval shapes
6. two pairs of congruent triangles
7. three pairs of congruent triangles
8. Design a logo of your own, using at least two sets of congruent triangles. Other congruent figures also may be used. Use graph paper, and include color in your design. Check students' designs for requirements.

Concept Byte
Use With Lesson 4-2
ACTIVITY

Building Congruent Triangles

Can you use shortcuts to find congruent triangles? Find out by building and comparing triangles.

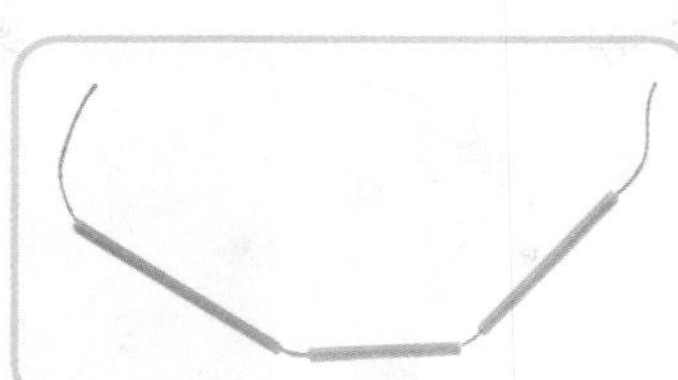

Activity 1

Step 1 Cut straws into three pieces of lengths 4 in., 5 in., and 6 in. Thread a string through the three pieces of straw. The straw pieces can be in any order.

Step 2 Bring the two ends of the string together to make a triangle. Tie the ends to hold your triangle in place.

Step 3 Compare your triangle with your classmates' triangles. Try to make your triangle fit exactly on top of the other triangles.

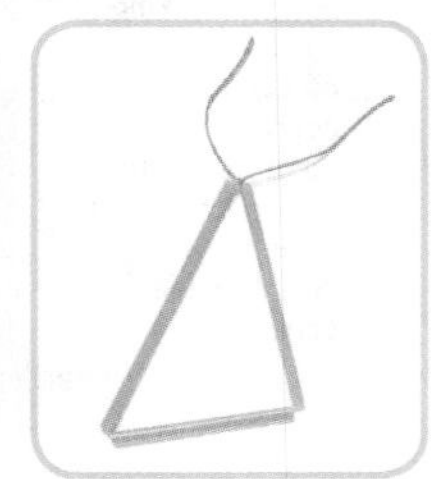

1. Is your triangle congruent to your classmates' triangles?
2. **Make a Conjecture** What seems to be true about two triangles in which three sides of one are congruent to three sides of another?
3. As a class, choose three different lengths and repeat Steps 1–3. Are all the triangles congruent? Does this support your conjecture from Question 2?

Activity 2

Step 1 Use a straightedge to draw and label any $\triangle ABC$ on tracing paper.

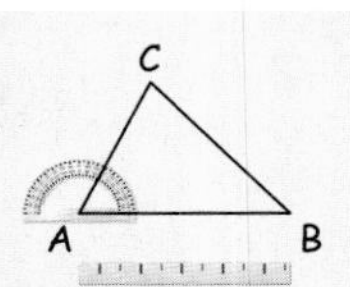

Step 2 Use a ruler. Carefully measure $\overline{AB}$ and $\overline{AC}$. Use a protractor to measure the angle between them, $\angle A$.

Step 3 Write the measurements on an index card and swap cards with a classmate. Draw a triangle using only your classmate's measurements.

Step 4 Compare your new triangle to your classmate's original $\triangle ABC$. Try to make your classmate's $\triangle ABC$ fit exactly on top of your new triangle.

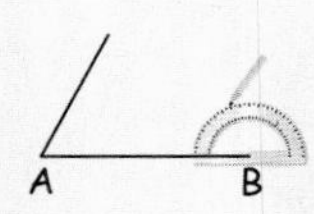

4. Is your new triangle congruent to your classmate's original $\triangle ABC$?
5. **Make a Conjecture** What seems to be true about two triangles when they have two congruent sides and a congruent angle between them?
6. **Make a Conjecture** At least how many triangle measurements must you know in order to guarantee that all triangles built with those measurements will be congruent?

Answers

Activity 1

1. yes
2. The ⚠ are ≅.
3. As long as the three lengths can form a △, all the ⚠ will be ≅; yes.

Activity 2

4. yes
5. In two ⚠, if two pairs of sides are ≅ and the angles contained between those sides are ≅, then the ⚠ are ≅.
6. three

Guided Instruction

PURPOSE To build and compare triangles in an effort to find shortcuts in identifying congruent triangles

PROCESS Students will
- form a triangle with drinking straws and tie the ends of the string that is threading them.
- compare their triangles to their classmates' triangles.
- use a protractor to measure angles and a ruler to measure sides.
- make comparisons between triangles.

DISCUSS Show students examples of congruent segments and angles and discuss how to construct them.

Q What does it mean for two triangles to be congruent? **[Answers will vary. Sample: the triangles have the same size and shape.]**

Q What is a visual way to determine whether two triangles are congruent? **[Place one directly on top of the other to see whether they match exactly.]**

Activity 1

In this Activity students build and compare triangles based on specific lengths of the triangles' three sides. (This sets up the SSS Postulate.)

Q What conjecture can you make based on the results of this Activity? **[Triangles that have the same side lengths are congruent.]**

Activity 2

In this Activity students build and compare triangles having two congruent sides and their included angle congruent. (This sets up the SAS Postulate.)

Q If you did not have tracing paper, what is another way you could determine whether your two triangles are congruent? **[Sample: you could cut them out with scissors and try to fit one on top of the other.]**

1 Interactive Learning

Solve It!

PURPOSE To prove that two triangles are congruent using the definition of congruence

PROCESS Students can

- use the Third Angles Theorem to show that the remaining angles of two triangles are congruent.
- use the Distance Formula to find the lengths of the sides of the triangles.

FACILITATE

Q What theorem will allow you to conclude that the last pair of angles is congruent? **[Third Angles Theorem]**

Q To prove the triangles congruent, what must you know about the sides of the triangles? **[Their lengths are equal.]**

Q What formula can you use to find the lengths of segments that are not horizontal or vertical? Write the formula. **[Distance Formula; $d = \sqrt{(x_1 - x_2)^2 + (y_1 - y_2)^2}$]**

ANSWER See Solve It in Answers on next page.

CONNECT THE MATH Two congruent triangles have corresponding angles that are congruent and corresponding sides that are congruent. But it is not necessary to know all six pairs are congruent. In this lesson, students will use the Side-Side-Side and Side-Angle-Side Postulates to prove that triangles are congruent without knowing that all six corresponding pairs are congruent.

4-2 Triangle Congruence by SSS and SAS

TN State Performance Indicators

SPI 3108.4.11 Use basic theorems about similar and congruent triangles to solve problems.

SPI 3108.4.12 Solve problems involving congruence, similarity, proportional reasoning and/or scale factor of two similar figures or solids.

Objective To prove two triangles congruent using the SSS and SAS Postulates

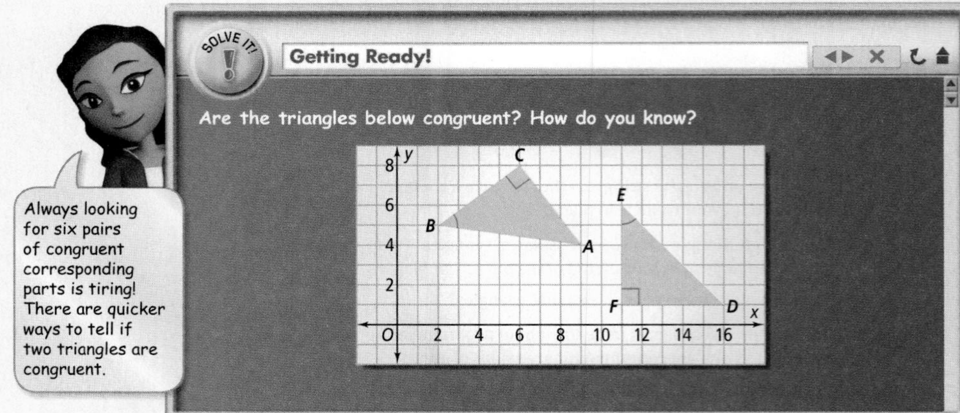

Getting Ready!
Are the triangles below congruent? How do you know?
Always looking for six pairs of congruent corresponding parts is tiring! There are quicker ways to tell if two triangles are congruent.

In the Solve It, you looked for relationships between corresponding sides and angles. In Lesson 4-1, you learned that if two triangles have three pairs of congruent corresponding angles and three pairs of congruent corresponding sides, then the triangles are congruent.

If you know . . .

$\angle F \cong \angle J$	$\overline{FG} \cong \overline{JK}$
$\angle G \cong \angle K$	$\overline{GH} \cong \overline{KL}$
$\angle H \cong \angle L$	$\overline{FH} \cong \overline{JL}$

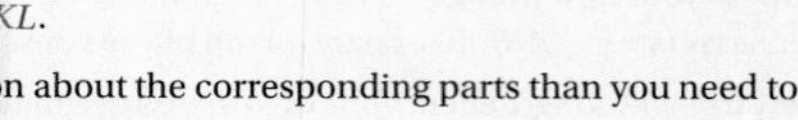

. . . then you know $\triangle FGH \cong \triangle JKL$.

However, this is more information about the corresponding parts than you need to prove triangles congruent.

Essential Understanding You can prove that two triangles are congruent without having to show that *all* corresponding parts are congruent. In this lesson, you will prove triangles congruent by using (1) three pairs of corresponding sides and (2) two pairs of corresponding sides and one pair of corresponding angles.

4-2 Preparing to Teach

BIG idea Reasoning and Proof 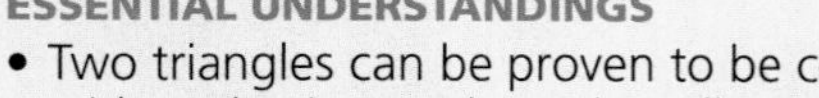

ESSENTIAL UNDERSTANDINGS

- Two triangles can be proven to be congruent without having to show that all corresponding parts are congruent.
- Two ways triangles can be proven to be congruent are by using three pairs of corresponding sides or by using two pairs of corresponding sides and one pair of corresponding angles.

Math Background

To prove triangles congruent using the definition, you must prove that three pairs of sides are congruent and three pairs of angles are congruent. However, there are postulates and theorems that shorten this process. The SSS and SAS Postulates allow you to prove two triangles are congruent by showing only three conditions are true.

Students quickly learn that S stands for side and A stands for angle in the triangle congruence postulates. Stress to students that the names of these postulates and theorems are reminders, in and of themselves, of the relative positions of the sides and angles. The A in the SAS Postulate is between the two letters S, which indicates that the congruent angles must be between the corresponding congruent sides. Students should specify that SSS and SAS are postulates and not theorems to differentiate them from results that follow in later sections (AAS, HL).

Support Student Learning

Use the **Geometry Companion** to engage and support students during instructions. See Lesson Resources at the end of this lesson for details.

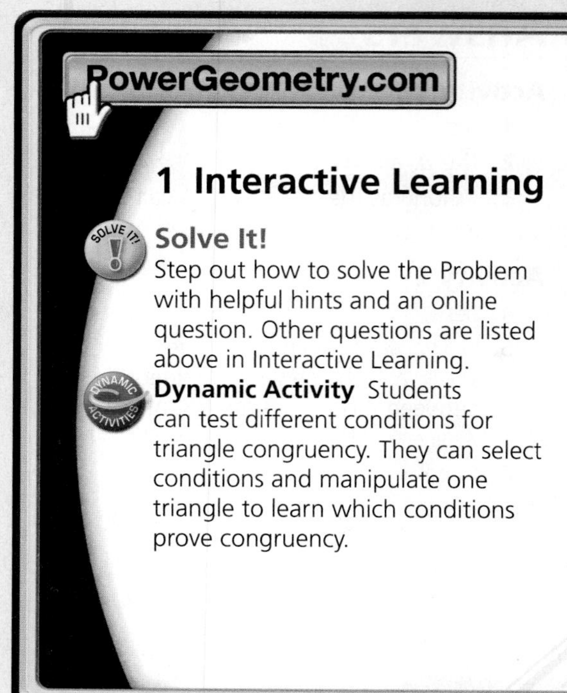

PowerGeometry.com
1 Interactive Learning
Solve It!
Step out how to solve the Problem with helpful hints and an online question. Other questions are listed above in Interactive Learning.
Dynamic Activity Students can test different conditions for triangle congruency. They can select conditions and manipulate one triangle to learn which conditions prove congruency.

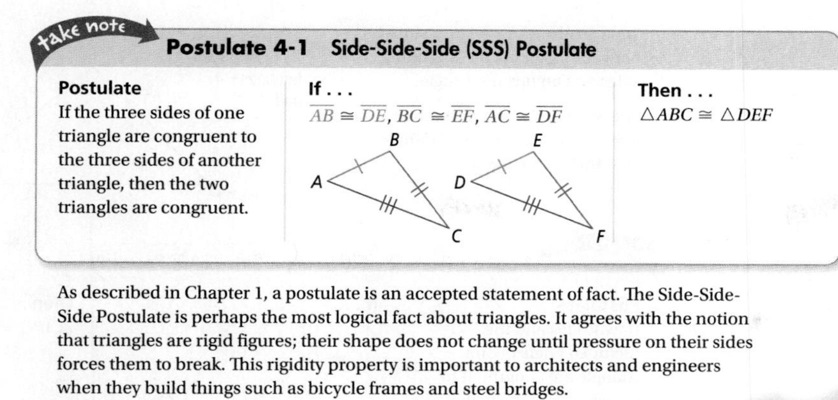

Take note
Postulate 4-1 Side-Side-Side (SSS) Postulate
Postulate
If the three sides of one triangle are congruent to the three sides of another triangle, then the two triangles are congruent.
If . . .
$\overline{AB} \cong \overline{DE}$, $\overline{BC} \cong \overline{EF}$, $\overline{AC} \cong \overline{DF}$
Then . . .
$\triangle ABC \cong \triangle DEF$

As described in Chapter 1, a postulate is an accepted statement of fact. The Side-Side-Side Postulate is perhaps the most logical fact about triangles. It agrees with the notion that triangles are rigid figures; their shape does not change until pressure on their sides forces them to break. This rigidity property is important to architects and engineers when they build things such as bicycle frames and steel bridges.

Plan

You have two pairs of congruent sides. What else do you need?
You need a third pair of congruent corresponding sides. Notice that the triangles share a common side, $\overline{LN}$.

Proof **Problem 1** **Using SSS**

Given: $\overline{LM} \cong \overline{NP}$, $\overline{LP} \cong \overline{NM}$

Prove: $\triangle LMN \cong \triangle NPL$

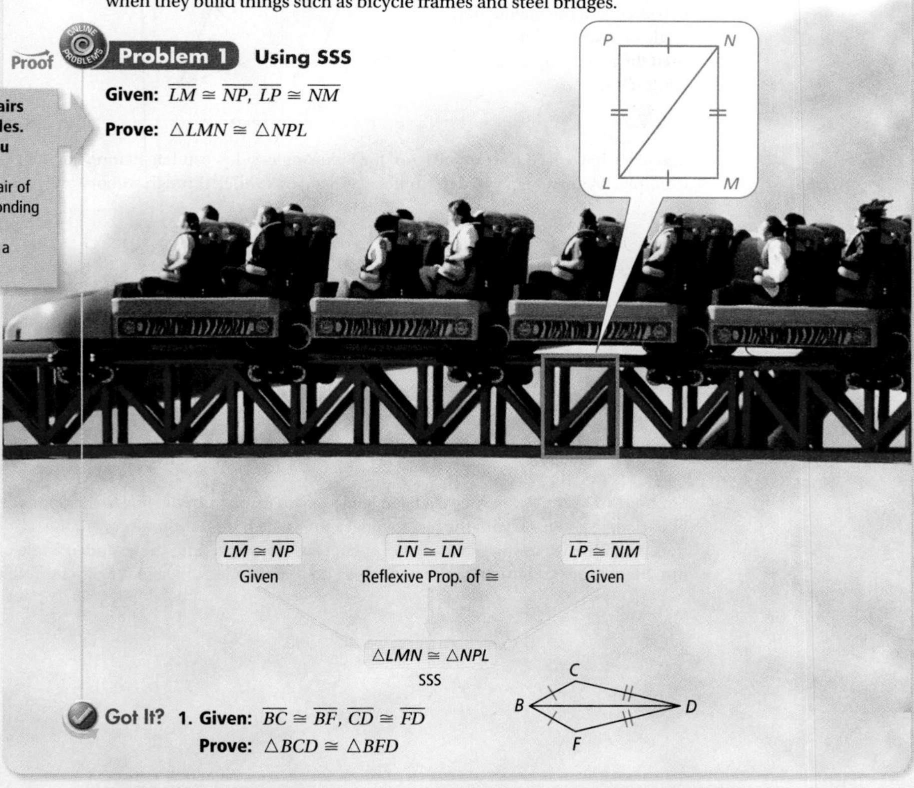

$\overline{LM} \cong \overline{NP}$ Given

$\overline{LN} \cong \overline{LN}$ Reflexive Prop. of $\cong$

$\overline{LP} \cong \overline{NM}$ Given

$\triangle LMN \cong \triangle NPL$ SSS

Got It? **1. Given:** $\overline{BC} \cong \overline{BF}$, $\overline{CD} \cong \overline{FD}$
Prove: $\triangle BCD \cong \triangle BFD$

2 Guided Instruction

Take Note

Ask students to identify the minimum number of congruence statements needed to prove two triangles are congruent. Have them draw a set of congruent triangles with vertices labeled and congruent parts marked. Identify the statements necessary to prove them congruent using this postulate.

Problem 1

Q Which side of each triangle is not named in the given statement? **[$\overline{LN}$ of $\triangle LMN$ and $\overline{LN}$ of $\triangle NPL$]**

Q What three pairs of congruent sides are needed to use the SSS Postulate? **[$\overline{LP}$ and $\overline{NM}$, $\overline{NP}$ and $\overline{LM}$, $\overline{LN}$ and $\overline{NL}$]**

Q What property of congruence confirms the third pair of sides to be congruent? **[Reflexive Property of Congruence]**

Got It?

ERROR PREVENTION

Have students name the two sides they need to show are congruent to prove that the triangles are congruent. Ask them to describe the similarities between this diagram and the one in Problem 1. **[$\overline{BD} \cong \overline{BD}$. The triangles in each diagram share a side. In both proofs, the Reflexive Property of Congruence is used.]**

2 Guided Instruction

Each Problem is worked out and supported online.

Problem 1
Using SSS
Animated

Problem 2
Using SAS
Animated

Problem 3
Identifying Congruent Triangles
Animated

Support in Geometry Companion

- Vocabulary
- Key Concepts
- Got It?

Answers

Solve It!

Answers may vary. Sample: Yes, $\triangle ABC \cong \triangle DEF$. $\angle B \cong \angle E$ (Given) and $\angle C \cong \angle F$ (All rt. ∠s are ≅.). By the Third Angles Theorem, $\angle A \cong \angle D$. By the Distance Formula, $AB = DE = \sqrt{50}$, $BC = EF = 5$, and $AC = DF = 5$. So the two △s are ≅ by def. of ≅ △s.

Got It?

1. Two pairs of sides are given as ≅, and $\overline{BD} \cong \overline{BD}$ by the Refl. Prop. of ≅. So $\triangle BCD \cong \triangle BFD$ by SSS.

Take Note

Have students practice identifying included angles given two sides. When drawing a diagram of the SAS Postulate, have students mark the sides and angles that are congruent. Students should understand that congruent sides are marked with one, two, or three very short segments made perpendicular to the sides of the triangle. The corresponding sides will have matching congruence markings. Congruent angles are marked using one, two, or three arcs inside the angle. Again, the corresponding angles will have matching congruence markings. Note that there is no relationship between the sides with one mark and sides with two marks; they are intended only to signify different lengths.

Ask students to identify the congruent sides and angles in the example at the bottom of the page. The arms represent congruent sides and the angles between them are the included congruent angles.

You can also show relationships between a pair of corresponding sides and an *included* angle.

The word *included* refers to the angles and the sides of a triangle as shown at the right.

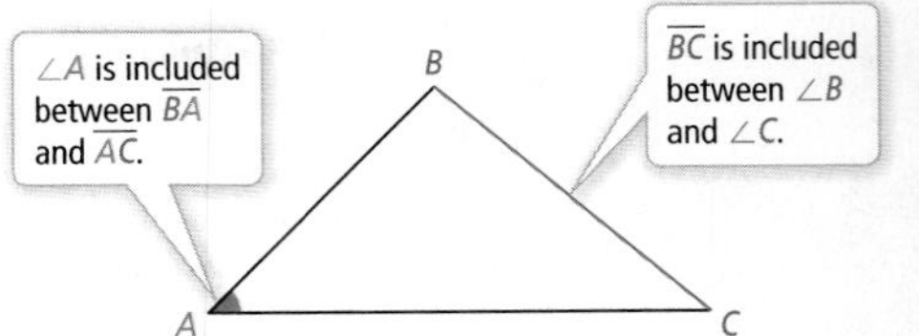

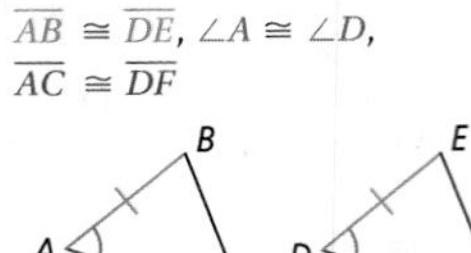

Postulate 4-2 Side-Angle-Side (SAS) Postulate

Postulate	If . . .	Then . . .
If two sides and the included angle of one triangle are congruent to two sides and the included angle of another triangle, then the two triangles are congruent.	$\overline{AB} \cong \overline{DE}$, $\angle A \cong \angle D$, $\overline{AC} \cong \overline{DF}$	$\triangle ABC \cong \triangle DEF$

You likely have used the properties of the Side-Angle-Side Postulate before. For example, SAS can help you determine whether a box will fit through a doorway.

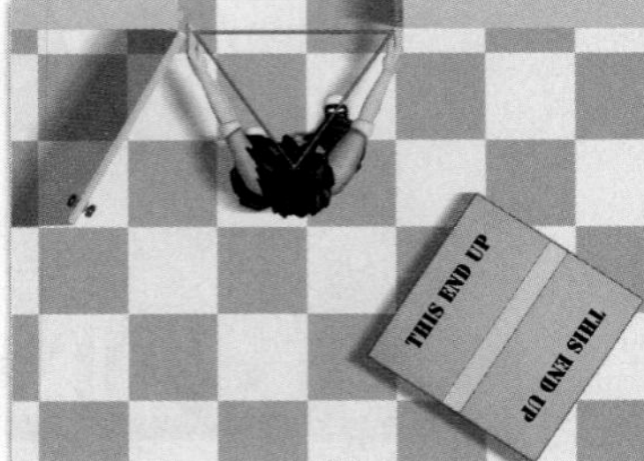

Suppose you keep your arms at a fixed angle as you move from the box to the doorway. The triangle you form with the box is congruent to the triangle you form with the doorway. The two triangles are congruent because two sides and the included angle of one triangle are congruent to the two sides and the included angle of the other triangle.

Additional Problems

1. Given: $\overline{RS} \cong \overline{UT}$, $\overline{RT} \cong \overline{SU}$

Prove: $\triangle RST \cong \triangle UTS$

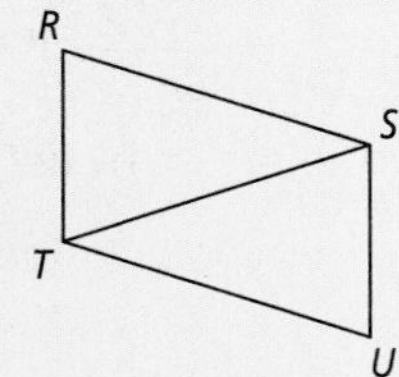

ANSWER It is given that $\overline{RS} \cong \overline{UT}$ and $\overline{RT} \cong \overline{SU}$. $\overline{ST} \cong \overline{ST}$ by the Reflexive Property of Congruence. So, $\triangle RST \cong \triangle UTS$ by the SSS Postulate.

2. What other information do you need to prove $\triangle ABC \cong \triangle ADC$ by SAS? Explain your answer.

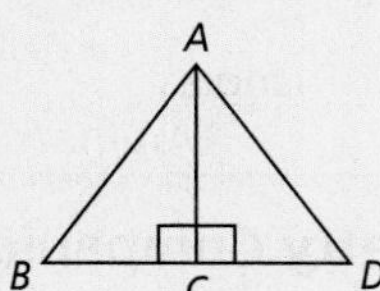

ANSWER $\overline{BC} \cong \overline{CD}$

3. Would you use SSS or SAS to prove the triangles congruent? If there is not enough information to prove the triangles congruent by SSS or SAS, write *not enough information*. Explain your answer.

a.

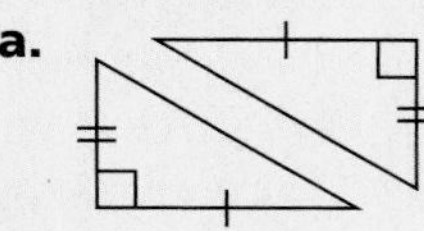

b.

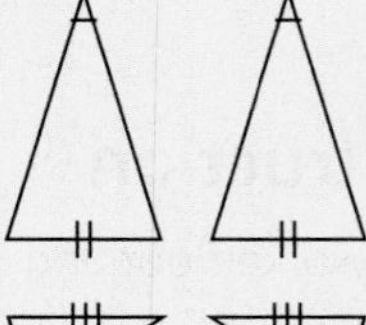

c.

d.

ANSWER a. SAS because two pairs of corresponding sides and their included angle are congruent.
b. not enough information
c. SSS because three pairs of corresponding sides are congruent.
d. not enough information

Problem 2 Using SAS

Plan

Do you need another pair of congruent sides?
Look at the diagram. The triangles share $\overline{DF}$. So you already have two pairs of congruent sides.

What other information do you need to prove $\triangle DEF \cong \triangle FGD$ by SAS? Explain.

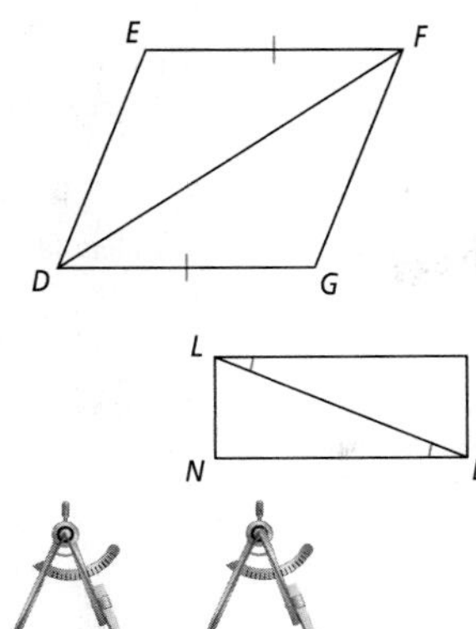

The diagram shows that $\overline{EF} \cong \overline{GD}$. Also, $\overline{DF} \cong \overline{DF}$ by the Reflexive Property of Congruence. To prove that $\triangle DEF \cong \triangle FGD$ by SAS, you must have congruent included angles. You need to know that $\angle EFD \cong \angle GDF$.

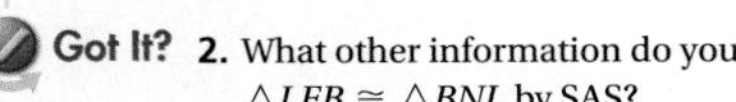

Got It? 2. What other information do you need to prove $\triangle LEB \cong \triangle BNL$ by SAS?

Recall that, in Lesson 1-6, you learned to construct segments using a compass open to a fixed angle. Now you can show that it works. Similar to the situation with the box and the doorway, the Side-Angle-Side Postulate tells you that the triangles outlined at the right are congruent. So, $\overline{AB} \cong \overline{CD}$.

Problem 3 Identifying Congruent Triangles

Plan

What should you look for first, sides or angles?
Start with sides. If you have three pairs of congruent sides, use SSS. If you have two pairs of congruent sides, look for a pair of congruent included angles.

Would you use SSS or SAS to prove the triangles congruent? If there is not enough information to prove the triangles congruent by SSS or SAS, write *not enough information*. Explain your answer.

A

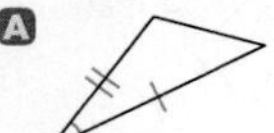

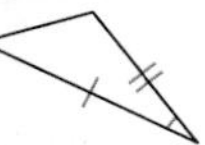

Use SAS because two pairs of corresponding sides and their included angles are congruent.

B

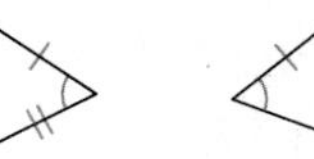

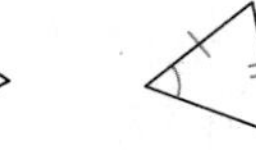

There is not enough information; two pairs of corresponding sides are congruent, but one of the angles is not the included angle.

C

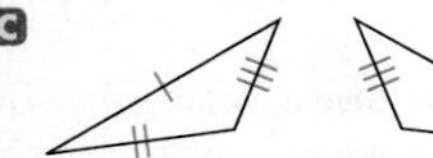

Use SSS because three pairs of corresponding sides are congruent.

D

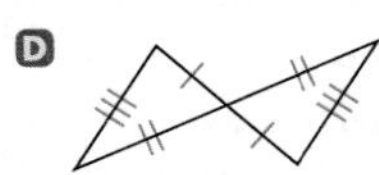

Use SSS or SAS because all three pairs of corresponding sides and a pair of included angles (the vertical angles) are congruent.

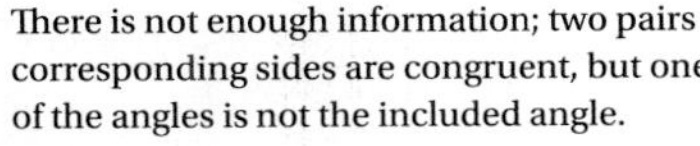

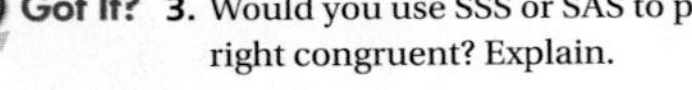

Got It? 3. Would you use SSS or SAS to prove the triangles at the right congruent? Explain.

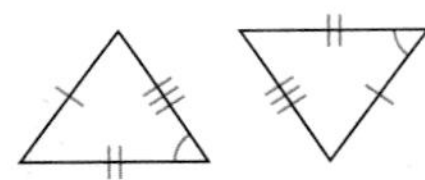

Problem 2

Q Which sides are marked congruent? **[$\overline{EF} \cong \overline{DG}$]**

Q For what other sides of the triangles can you write a congruence statement and give a justification? **[$\overline{DF} \cong \overline{DF}$; Reflexive Property of Congruence]**

Q Which angle in each triangle is the included angle between the two sides? **[$\angle GDF$ in $\triangle FGD$ and $\angle EFD$ in $\triangle DEF$]**

Got It?

Have students list the sides that form the marked angles. Remind them of the definition of included angle.

Problem 3

Q What corresponding parts are labeled congruent in 3A? **[There are two pairs of sides and the included angle.]**

Q In 3B, what is the relationship between the sides and angles that are marked congruent? **[In the first triangle, the angle is included between the marked sides. In the second triangle, the angle is not included between the marked sides.]**

Q What corresponding parts are labeled congruent in 3C? **[There are three pairs of congruent sides.]**

Q How can you prove at least one pair of angles congruent in 3D? **[The angles that share a vertex are congruent because they are vertical angles.]**

Got It? AUDITORY LEARNERS

The triangles are congruent by SSS only. SAS cannot be used because the sides marked on either side of the angle are not congruent. Have students explain this aloud to the class.

Answers

Got It? (continued)

2. $\overline{LE} \cong \overline{BN}$

3. SSS; three pairs of corresp. sides are $\cong$.

3 Lesson Check

Do you know HOW?

- If students have difficulty with Exercises 1-2, then have them draw each triangle and label the vertices in order.

Do you UNDERSTAND?

- If students have difficulty with Exercise 6, then have them review Problem 3B.

Close

Q What is the minimum number of conditions necessary to prove that two triangles are congruent? **[Three conditions must be proved.]**

Q Name two postulates that can be used to show that two triangles are congruent. **[SSS Postulate and SAS Postulate]**

Lesson Check

Do you know HOW?

1. In $\triangle PEN$, name the angle that is included between the given sides.

a. $\overline{PE}$ and $\overline{EN}$ **b.** $\overline{NP}$ and $\overline{PE}$

2. In $\triangle HAT$, between which sides is the given angle included?

a. $\angle H$ **b.** $\angle T$

Name the postulate you would use to prove the triangles congruent.

3.

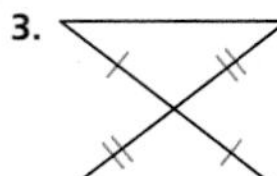

4.

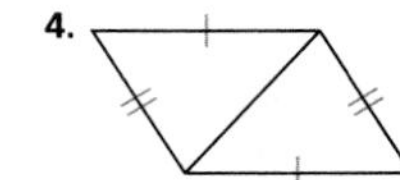

Do you UNDERSTAND?

5. Compare and Contrast How are the SSS Postulate and the SAS Postulate alike? How are they different?

6. Error Analysis Your friend thinks that the triangles shown below are congruent by SAS. Is your friend correct? Explain.

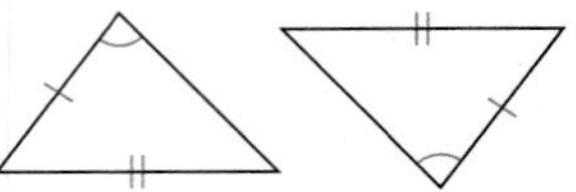

7. Reasoning A carpenter trims a triangular peak of a house with three 7-ft pieces of molding. The carpenter uses 21 ft of molding to trim a second triangular peak. Are the two triangles formed congruent? Explain.

Practice and Problem-Solving Exercises

A Practice

See Problem 1.

8. Developing Proof Copy and complete the flow proof.

Given: $\overline{JK} \cong \overline{LM}$, $\overline{JM} \cong \overline{LK}$

Prove: $\triangle JKM \cong \triangle LMK$

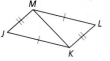

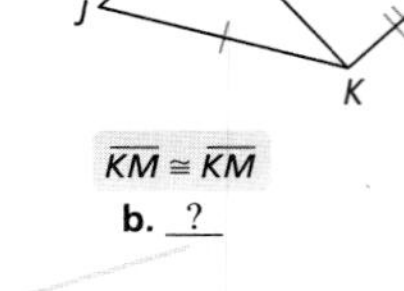

$\overline{JK} \cong \overline{LM}$ — Given

$\overline{JM} \cong \overline{LK}$ — a. ?

$\overline{KM} \cong \overline{KM}$ — b. ?

c. ? ≅ d. ? — SSS

9. Given: $\overline{IE} \cong \overline{GH}$, $\overline{EF} \cong \overline{HF}$, F is the midpoint of $\overline{GI}$

Proof

Prove: $\triangle EFI \cong \triangle HFG$

E G F I H

10. Given: $\overline{WZ} \cong \overline{ZS} \cong \overline{SD} \cong \overline{DW}$

Proof

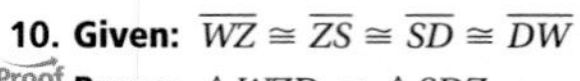

Prove: $\triangle WZD \cong \triangle SDZ$

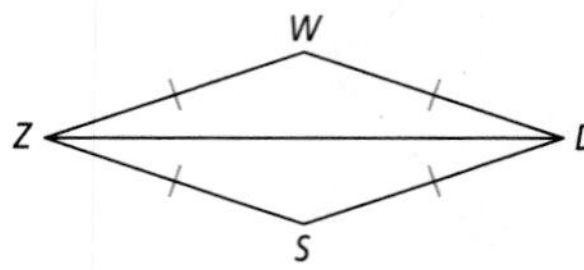

PowerGeometry.com

3 Lesson Check

For a digital lesson check, use the Got It questions.

Support in Geometry Companion

- Lesson Check

4 Practice

Assign homework to individual students or to an entire class.

Answers

Lesson Check

1a. $\angle PEN$ (or $\angle E$)

b. $\angle NPE$ (or $\angle P$)

2a. $\overline{HA}$ and $\overline{HT}$

b. $\overline{TH}$ and $\overline{TA}$

3. SAS

4. SSS

5. Answers may vary. Sample: Alike: Both use three pairs of ≅ parts to prove △s ≅. Different: SSS uses three pairs of ≅ sides, while SAS uses two pairs of ≅ sides and their ≅ included ∠s.

6. No; the ≅ ∠s are not included between the pairs of ≅ sides.

7. No; the △s have the same perimeter, but the three side lengths of one △ are not necessarily = to the three side lengths of the other △, so you cannot use SSS. There is no information about the ∠s of the △s, so you cannot use SAS.

Practice and Problem-Solving Exercises

8a. Given

b. Refl. Prop. of ≅

c. $\triangle JKM$

d. $\triangle LMK$

9. F is the midpt. of $\overline{GI}$ (Given), so $\overline{IF} \cong \overline{GF}$ because a midpt. divides a segment into two ≅ segments. The other two pairs of sides are given as ≅, so $\triangle EFI \cong \triangle HFG$ by SSS.

10. $\overline{ZD} \cong \overline{ZD}$ by the Refl. Prop. of ≅, and it is given that $\overline{ZW} \cong \overline{ZS} \cong \overline{SD} \cong \overline{DW}$. So $\triangle WZD \cong \triangle SDZ$ by SSS.

What other information, if any, do you need to prove the two triangles congruent by SAS? Explain.

See Problem 2.

11.

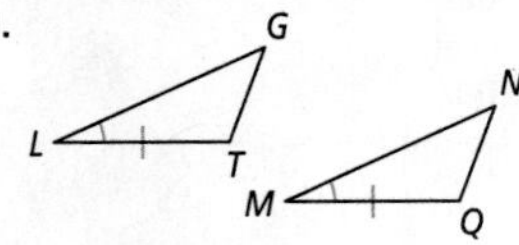

12. T U R W S V

Would you use SSS or SAS to prove the triangles congruent? If there is not enough information to prove the triangles congruent by SSS or SAS, write *not enough information*. Explain your answer.

See Problem 3.

13.

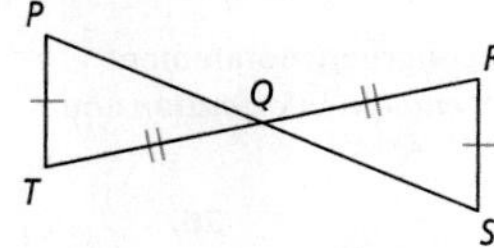

14.

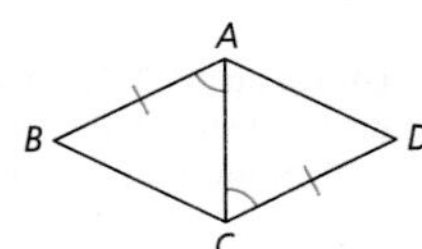

B Apply

15. Think About a Plan You and a friend are cutting triangles out of felt for an art project. You want all the triangles to be congruent. Your friend tells you that each triangle should have two 5-in. sides and a 40° angle. If you follow this rule, will all your felt triangles be congruent? Explain.

- How can you use diagrams to help you?
- Which postulate, SSS or SAS, are you likely to apply to the given situation?

16. Proof **Given:** $\overline{BC} \cong \overline{DA}$, $\angle CBD \cong \angle ADB$
Prove: $\triangle BCD \cong \triangle DAB$

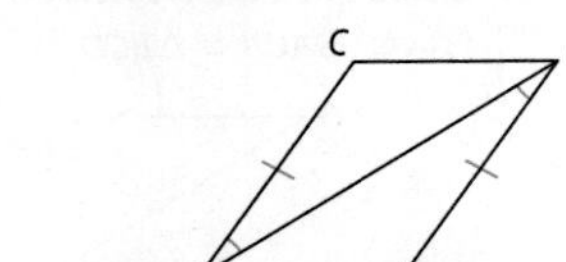

17. Proof **Given:** X is the midpoint of $\overline{AG}$ and $\overline{NR}$.
Prove: $\triangle ANX \cong \triangle GRX$

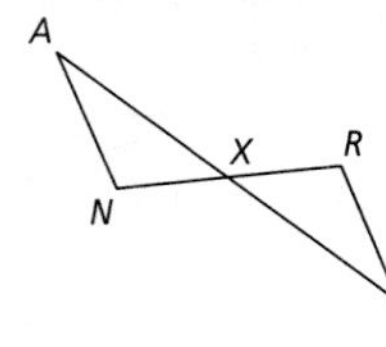

Use the Distance Formula to determine whether $\triangle ABC$ and $\triangle DEF$ are congruent. Justify your answer.

18. $A(1, 4), B(5, 5), C(2, 2)$; $D(-5, 1), E(-1, 0), F(-4, 3)$

19. $A(3, 8), B(8, 12), C(10, 5)$; $D(3, -1), E(7, -7), F(12, -2)$

20. $A(2, 9), B(2, 4), C(5, 4)$; $D(1, -3), E(1, 2), F(-2, 2)$

21. Writing List three real-life uses of congruent triangles. For each real-life use, describe why you think congruence is necessary.

4 Practice

ASSIGNMENT GUIDE

Basic: 8–16 all, 18, 20–22 all, 24–28 even
Average: 9–13 odd, 15–31
Advanced: 9–13 odd, 15–34
Standardized Test Prep: 35–38
Mixed Review: 39–46

Reasoning exercises have blue headings.
Applications exercises have red headings.

EXERCISE 18: Use the Think About a Plan worksheet in the **Practice and Problem Solving Workbook** (also available in the Teaching Resources in print and online) to further support students' development in becoming independent learners.

HOMEWORK QUICK CHECK

To check students' understanding of key skills and concepts, go over Exercises 9, 13, 15, 18, and 21.

11. You need to know $\overline{LG} \cong \overline{MN}$; the diagram shows that $\overline{LT} \cong \overline{MQ}$ and $\angle L \cong \angle M$. $\angle L$ is included between $\overline{LG}$ and $\overline{LT}$, and $\angle M$ is included between $\overline{MN}$ and $\overline{MQ}$.

12. You need to know $\overline{RS} \cong \overline{WU}$; the diagram shows that $\angle R \cong \angle W$ and $\overline{RT} \cong \overline{WV}$. $\angle R$ is included between $\overline{RT}$ and $\overline{RS}$, and $\angle W$ is included between $\overline{WV}$ and $\overline{WU}$.

13. Not enough information; the congruent vertical angles TQP and RQS are not included by the pairs of $\cong$ sides.

14. SAS; the $\cong$ angles BAC and DCA are included by the pairs of sides $\overline{AB} \cong \overline{CD}$ (Given) and $\overline{AC} \cong \overline{AC}$ (Refl. Prop. of $\cong$).

15. If the 40° $\angle$ is *always* included between the two 5-in. sides, then all the ▵ will be $\cong$ by SAS. If the 40° $\angle$ is *never* included between the two 5-in. sides, then the angles of the $\triangle$ will be 40°, 40°, and 100°, with the 100° angle included between the 5-in. sides, so all the ▵ will be $\cong$ by SAS. But a $\triangle$ with the 40° angle included between the 5-in. sides will NOT be $\cong$ to a $\triangle$ with the 40° angle not included between the 5-in. sides.

16. $\overline{BC} \cong \overline{DA}$ and $\angle CBD \cong \angle ADB$ (Given). $\overline{BD} \cong \overline{BD}$ (Refl. Prop. of $\cong$), so $\triangle BCD \cong \triangle DAB$ by SAS.

17. X is the midpt. of $\overline{AG}$ and $\overline{NR}$ (Given), so $\overline{AX} \cong \overline{GX}$ and $\overline{NX} \cong \overline{RX}$ by the def. of midpt. Also, $\angle AXN \cong \angle GXR$ because they are vertical ∡, so $\triangle ANX \cong \triangle GRX$ by SAS.

18. $AB = \sqrt{16 + 1} = \sqrt{17}$ and $DE = \sqrt{16 + 1} = \sqrt{17}$; $BC = \sqrt{9 + 9} = \sqrt{18}$ and $EF = \sqrt{9 + 9} = \sqrt{18}$; $AC = \sqrt{1 + 4} = \sqrt{5}$ and $DF = \sqrt{1 + 4} = \sqrt{5}$; so $\triangle ABC \cong \triangle DEF$ by SSS.

19. $AB = \sqrt{25 + 16} = \sqrt{41}$ and $DE = \sqrt{16 + 36} = \sqrt{52}$, so $\triangle ABC \ncong \triangle DEF$.

20. $AB = 5$, $BC = 3$, $AC = \sqrt{9 + 25} = \sqrt{34}$; $DE = 5$, $EF = 3$, $DF = \sqrt{9 + 25} = \sqrt{34}$; $\triangle ABC \cong \triangle DEF$ by SSS.

21. Answers may vary. Sample: roof trusses for a house, sections of a ferris wheel, sawhorses used by a carpenter; explanations will vary.

Answers

Practice and Problem-Solving Exercises (continued)

22. Yes; two sides of the original △ are ≅, and finding successive midpts. of ≅ segments results in pairs of (smaller) ≅ segments. The base ∡ of the original isosc. △ are ≅, so the ▵ outlined in red are ≅ by SAS.

23a. Answers may vary. Sample:

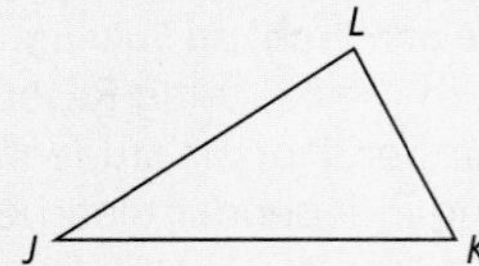

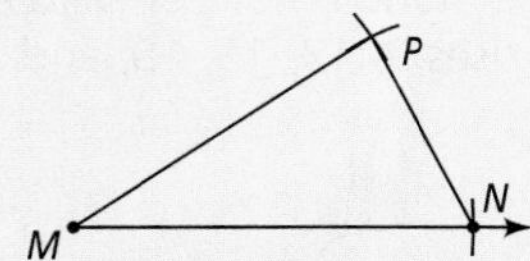

b. Answers may vary. Sample:

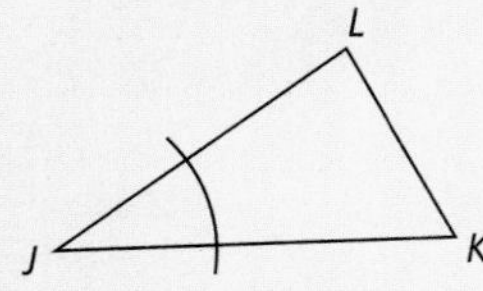

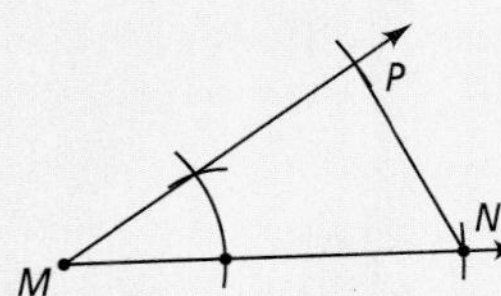

24. $\triangle ANG \cong \triangle RWT$ by SAS.

25. Not enough information; you need $\overline{DY} \cong \overline{TK}$ to show the ▵ are ≅ by SSS, or you need $\angle H \cong \angle P$ to show the ▵ are ≅ by SAS.

26. $\triangle JEF \cong \triangle SFV$ (or $\triangle JEF \cong \triangle SFV$) by SSS

27. Not necessarily; the ≅ ∡ are not included between the pairs of ≅ sides.

28. $\overline{GK}$ bisects $\angle JGM$ (Given), so $\angle JGK \cong \angle MGK$ (Def. of ∠ bisector). $\overline{GJ} \cong \overline{GM}$ (Given) and $\overline{GK} \cong \overline{GK}$ (Refl. Prop. of ≅), so $\triangle GJK \cong \triangle GMK$ by SAS.

29. $\overline{AE}$ and $\overline{BD}$ bisect each other (Given), so $\overline{AC} \cong \overline{EC}$ and $\overline{DC} \cong \overline{BC}$ (Def. of seg. bisector). $\angle ACB \cong \angle ECD$ (Vert. ∡ are ≅.), so $\triangle ACB \cong \triangle ECD$ by SAS.

30. $\overline{FG} \parallel \overline{KL}$ (Given), so $\angle GFK \cong \angle LKF$ because they are alt. int. ∡. $\overline{FG} \cong \overline{KL}$ (Given) and $\overline{KF} \cong \overline{KF}$ (Refl. Prop. of ≅), so $\triangle FGK \cong \triangle KLF$ by SAS.

31. Given the ⊥ segments, $\angle B \cong \angle CMA$ because all rt. ∡ are ≅. M is the midpt. of $\overline{AB}$ (Given), so $\overline{AM} \cong \overline{MB}$ by the def. of midpt. Since $\overline{DB} \cong \overline{CM}$ (Given), then $\triangle AMC \cong \triangle MBD$ by SAS.

22. Sierpinski's Triangle Sierpinski's triangle is a famous geometric pattern. To draw Sierpinski's triangle, start with a single triangle and connect the midpoints of the sides to draw a smaller triangle. If you repeat this pattern over and over, you will form a figure like the one shown. This particular figure started with an isosceles triangle. Are the triangles outlined in red congruent? Explain.

23. Constructions Use a straightedge to draw any triangle JKL. Then construct $\triangle MNP \cong \triangle JKL$ using the given postulate.

a. SSS

b. SAS

Can you prove the triangles congruent? If so, write the congruence statement and name the postulate you would use. If not, write *not enough information* and tell what other information you would need.

24.

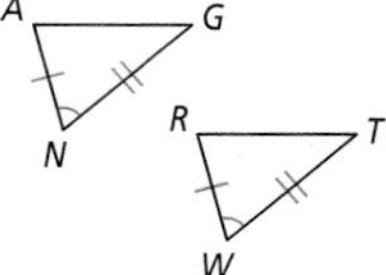

25.

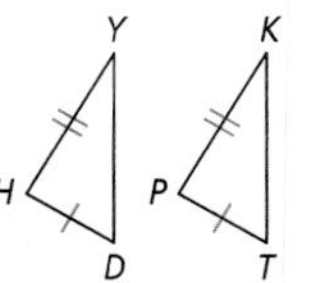

26.

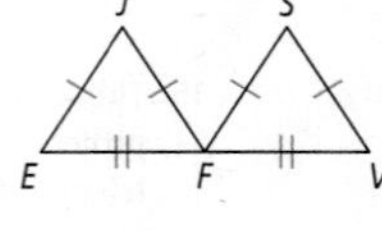

27. Reasoning Suppose $\overline{GH} \cong \overline{JK}$, $\overline{HI} \cong \overline{KL}$, and $\angle I \cong \angle L$. Is $\triangle GHI$ congruent to $\triangle JKL$? Explain.

28. Given: $\overline{GK}$ bisects $\angle JGM$, $\overline{GJ} \cong \overline{GM}$
Proof **Prove:** $\triangle GJK \cong \triangle GMK$

J
G K
M

29. Given: $\overline{AE}$ and $\overline{BD}$ bisect each other.
Proof **Prove:** $\triangle ACB \cong \triangle ECD$

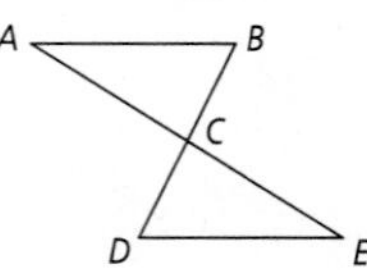

30. Given: $\overline{FG} \parallel \overline{KL}$, $\overline{FG} \cong \overline{KL}$
Proof **Prove:** $\triangle FGK \cong \triangle KLF$

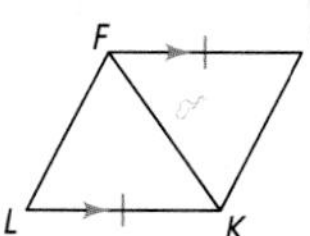

31. Given: $\overline{AB} \perp \overline{CM}$, $\overline{AB} \perp \overline{DB}$, $\overline{CM} \cong \overline{DB}$, M is the midpoint of $\overline{AB}$
Proof **Prove:** $\triangle AMC \cong \triangle MBD$

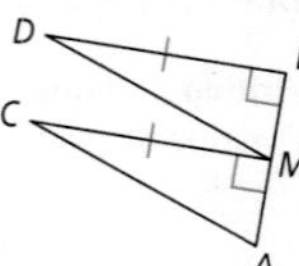

Challenge

32. **Reasoning** Four sides of polygon *ABCD* are congruent, respectively, to the four sides of polygon *EFGH*. Are *ABCD* and *EFGH* congruent? Is a quadrilateral a rigid figure? If not, what could you add to make it a rigid figure? Explain.

33. **Given:** $\overline{HK} \cong \overline{LG}$, $\overline{HF} \cong \overline{LJ}$, $\overline{FG} \cong \overline{JK}$
Proof **Prove:** $\triangle FGH \cong \triangle JKL$

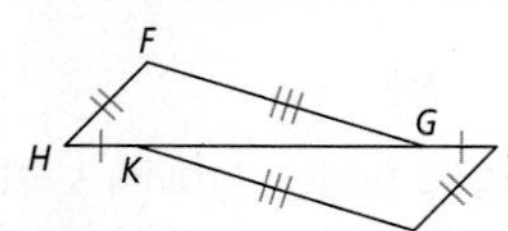

34. **Given:** $\angle N \cong \angle L$, $\overline{MN} \cong \overline{OL}$, $\overline{NO} \cong \overline{LM}$
Proof **Prove:** $\overline{MN} \parallel \overline{OL}$

Standardized Test Prep

SAT/ACT

35. What additional information do you need to prove that $\triangle VWY \cong \triangle VWZ$ by SAS?

A $\overline{YW} \cong \overline{ZW}$
B $\angle WVY \cong \angle WVZ$
C $\angle Y \cong \angle Z$
D $\overline{VZ} \cong \overline{VY}$

36. The measures of two angles of a triangle are 43 and 38. What is the measure of the third angle?

F 9 G 81 H 99 I 100

37. Which method would you use to find the inverse of a conditional statement?

A Switch the hypothesis and conclusion.
B Negate the hypothesis only.
C Negate the conclusion only.
D Negate both the hypothesis and conclusion.

Short Response

38. A segment has a midpoint at (1, 1) and an endpoint at (−3, 4). What are the coordinates of the other endpoint of the segment? Show your work.

Mixed Review

***ABCD* ≅ *EFGH*. Name the angle or side that corresponds to each part.** See Lesson 4-1.

39. $\angle A$ 40. $\overline{EF}$ 41. $\overline{BC}$ 42. $\angle G$

Write the converse of each statement. Determine whether the statement and its converse are true or false. See Lesson 2-2.

43. If $x = 3$, then $2x = 6$.
44. If $x = 3$, then $x^2 = 9$.

Get Ready! **To prepare for Lesson 4-3, do Exercises 45 and 46.** See Lesson 4-2.

45. In $\triangle JHK$, name the side that is included between $\angle J$ and $\angle H$.

46. In $\triangle NLM$, name the angle that is included between $\overline{NM}$ and $\overline{LN}$.

39. $\angle E$ **40.** $\overline{AB}$
41. $\overline{FG}$ **42.** $\angle C$
43. If $2x = 6$, then $x = 3$; both are true.
44. If $x^2 = 9$, then $x = 3$; the statement is true and its converse is false.
45. $\overline{JH}$
46. $\angle MNL$ (or $\angle N$)

32. Answers may vary. Sample: Given 4 pairs of ≅ sides, the two quadrilaterals do not have to be ≅ because the ∠s of the quadrilaterals may be different. To make the quadrilaterals rigid, add a diagonal to each figure. If corresponding diagonals are ≅, then the quadrilaterals form two pairs of ≅ △s (each by SSS), and so the quadrilaterals will be ≅.

33. $\overline{KG} \cong \overline{KG}$ by the Refl. Prop. of ≅. Since $\overline{HK} \cong \overline{LG}$ (Given), $HK + KG = LG + KG$ by the Seg. Add. Post. So, $\overline{HG} \cong \overline{LK}$. $\overline{HF} \cong \overline{LJ}$ and $\overline{FG} \cong \overline{JK}$ (Given), so $\triangle FGH \cong \triangle JKL$ by SSS.

34. Answers may vary. Sample: $\angle N \cong \angle L$, $\overline{MN} \cong \overline{OL}$, and $\overline{NO} \cong \overline{LM}$ (Given), so $\triangle MNO \cong \triangle OLM$ by SAS. $\angle NMO \cong \angle LOM$ (Corresp. parts of ≅ △s are ≅.) So $\overline{MN} \parallel \overline{OL}$ because if alt. int. ∠s are ≅, then the lines are ∥.

35. A **36.** H **37.** D

38. [2] Let the other endpoint be (x, y). Then $\left(\frac{-3 + x}{2}, \frac{4 + y}{2}\right) = (1, 1)$. So $\frac{-3 + x}{2} = 1$ and $\frac{4 + y}{2} = 1$, or $x = 5$ and $y = -2$. The coordinates of the other endpoint are $(5, -2)$.
[1] ordered pair only, without explanation, or incomplete or incorrect explanation

4-2 Lesson Resources

Differentiated Remediation

Instructional Support

Geometry Companion

Students can use the **Geometry Companion** worktext (4 pages) . . .

- New Vocabulary
- Key Concepts
- Got It for each Problem
- Lesson Check

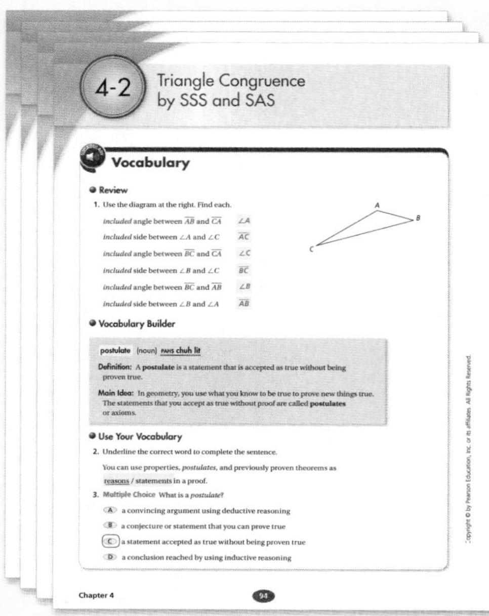

4-2 Triangle Congruence by SSS and SAS

Vocabulary

Review

1. Use the diagram at the right. Find each.

included angle between $\overline{AB}$ and $\overline{CA}$ — $\angle A$

included side between $\angle A$ and $\angle C$ — $\overline{AC}$

included angle between $\overline{BC}$ and $\overline{CA}$ — $\angle C$

included side between $\angle B$ and $\angle C$ — $\overline{BC}$

included angle between $\overline{BC}$ and $\overline{AB}$ — $\angle B$

included side between $\angle B$ and $\angle A$ — $\overline{AB}$

Vocabulary Builder

postulate (noun) PAHS chuh lit

Definition: A **postulate** is a statement that is accepted as true without being proven true.

Main Idea: In geometry, you use what you know to be true to prove new things true. The statements that you accept as true without proof are called **postulates** or axioms.

Use Your Vocabulary

2. Underline the correct word to complete the sentence.

You can use properties, *postulates*, and previously proven theorems as reasons / statements in a proof.

3. **Multiple Choice** What is a *postulate*?

(A) a convincing argument using deductive reasoning

(B) a conjecture or statement that you can prove true

(C) a statement accepted as true without being proven true

(D) a conclusion reached by using inductive reasoning

ELL Support

Use Manipulatives Divide students into small groups. Hand out pre-measured wooden sticks of three different lengths. Students can use markers or pencils to color the sticks so each size is a different color. Ask students to form two triangles using one of each color for each side. Ask students if their triangles are congruent. Discuss reasons.

5 Assess & Remediate

Lesson Quiz

1. What other information do you need to prove $\triangle GHK \cong \triangle KLG$ by SAS? Explain.

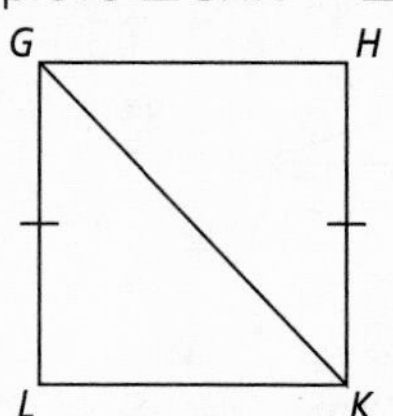

2. **Do you UNDERSTAND?** Would you use SSS or SAS to prove the triangles congruent? If there is not enough information to prove the triangles congruent by SSS or SAS, write *not enough information*. Explain your answer.

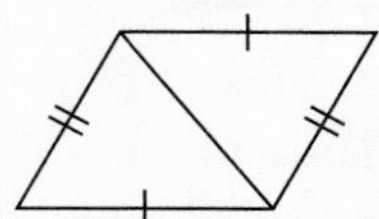

ANSWERS TO LESSON QUIZ

1. $\angle HKG \cong \angle LGK$
2. SSS; 2 congruent sides are given and the 3rd side is congruent by the Reflexive Property of Congruence.

PRESCRIPTION FOR REMEDIATION

Use the student work on the Lesson Quiz to prescribe a differentiated review assignment.

Points	Differentiated Remediation
0	Intervention
1	On-level
2	Extension

PowerGeometry.com

5 Assess & Remediate

Assign the Lesson Quiz. Appropriate intervention, practice, or enrichment is automatically generated based on student performance.

Intervention

- **Reteaching** (2 pages) Provides reteaching and practice exercises for the key lesson concepts. Use with struggling students or absent students.
- **English Language Learner Support** Helps students develop and reinforce mathematical vocabulary and key concepts.

All-in-One Resources/Online

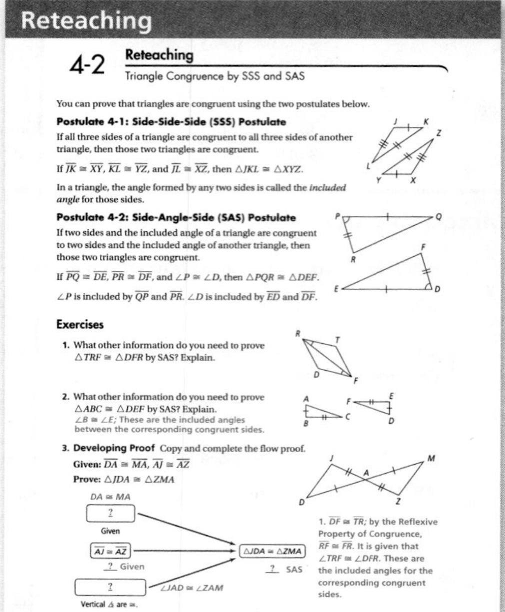

Reteaching

4-2 Reteaching

Triangle Congruence by SSS and SAS

You can prove that triangles are congruent using the two postulates below.

Postulate 4-1: Side-Side-Side (SSS) Postulate

If all three sides of a triangle are congruent to all three sides of another triangle, then those two triangles are congruent.

If $\overline{JK} \cong \overline{XY}$, $\overline{KL} \cong \overline{YZ}$, and $\overline{JL} \cong \overline{XZ}$, then $\triangle JKL \cong \triangle XYZ$.

In a triangle, the angle formed by any two sides is called the *included angle* for those sides.

Postulate 4-2: Side-Angle-Side (SAS) Postulate

If two sides and the included angle of a triangle are congruent to two sides and the included angle of another triangle, then those two triangles are congruent.

If $\overline{PQ} \cong \overline{DE}$, $\overline{PR} \cong \overline{DF}$, and $\angle P \cong \angle D$, then $\triangle PQR \cong \triangle DEF$.

$\angle P$ is included by $\overline{QP}$ and $\overline{PR}$. $\angle D$ is included by $\overline{ED}$ and $\overline{DF}$.

Exercises

1. What other information do you need to prove $\triangle TRF \cong \triangle DFR$ by SAS? Explain.

2. What other information do you need to prove $\triangle ABC \cong \triangle DEF$ by SAS? Explain.
$\angle B \cong \angle E$; These are the included angles between the corresponding congruent sides.

3. **Developing Proof** Copy and complete the flow proof.

Given: $\overline{DA} \cong \overline{MA}$, $\overline{AJ} \cong \overline{AZ}$

Prove: $\triangle JDA \cong \triangle ZMA$

$DA \cong MA$ — ? — Given

$\overline{AJ} \cong \overline{AZ}$ — ? Given

? — Vertical $\angle$s are $\cong$. — $\angle JAD \cong \angle ZAM$

$\triangle JDA \cong \triangle ZMA$ — ? SAS

1. $\overline{DF} \cong \overline{TR}$; by the Reflexive Property of Congruence, $\overline{RF} \cong \overline{FR}$. It is given that $\angle TRF \cong \angle DFR$. These are the included angles for the corresponding congruent sides.

All-in-One Resources/Online

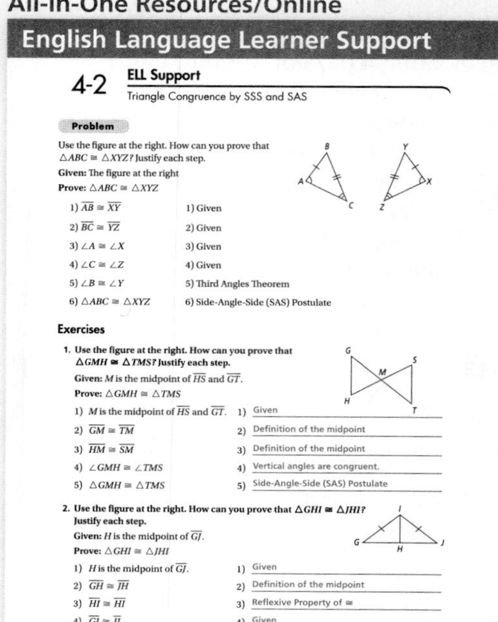

English Language Learner Support

4-2 ELL Support

Triangle Congruence by SSS and SAS

Problem

Use the figure at the right. How can you prove that $\triangle ABC \cong \triangle XYZ$? Justify each step.

Given: The figure at the right

Prove: $\triangle ABC \cong \triangle XYZ$

1) $\overline{AB} \cong \overline{XY}$ — 1) Given
2) $\overline{BC} \cong \overline{YZ}$ — 2) Given
3) $\angle A \cong \angle X$ — 3) Given
4) $\angle C \cong \angle Z$ — 4) Given
5) $\angle B \cong \angle Y$ — 5) Third Angles Theorem
6) $\triangle ABC \cong \triangle XYZ$ — 6) Side-Angle-Side (SAS) Postulate

Exercises

1. **Use the figure at the right. How can you prove that $\triangle GMH \cong \triangle TMS$? Justify each step.**

Given: M is the midpoint of $\overline{HS}$ and $\overline{GT}$.

Prove: $\triangle GMH \cong \triangle TMS$

1) M is the midpoint of $\overline{HS}$ and $\overline{GT}$. — 1) Given
2) $\overline{GM} \cong \overline{TM}$ — 2) Definition of the midpoint
3) $\overline{HM} \cong \overline{SM}$ — 3) Definition of the midpoint
4) $\angle GMH \cong \angle TMS$ — 4) Vertical angles are congruent.
5) $\triangle GMH \cong \triangle TMS$ — 5) Side-Angle-Side (SAS) Postulate

2. **Use the figure at the right. How can you prove that $\triangle GHI \cong \triangle JHI$? Justify each step.**

Given: H is the midpoint of $\overline{GJ}$.

Prove: $\triangle GHI \cong \triangle JHI$

1) H is the midpoint of $\overline{GJ}$. — 1) Given
2) $\overline{GH} \cong \overline{JH}$ — 2) Definition of the midpoint
3) $\overline{HI} \cong \overline{HI}$ — 3) Reflexive Property of $\cong$
4) $\overline{GI} \cong \overline{JI}$ — 4) Given
5) $\triangle GHI \cong \triangle JHI$ — 5) Side-Side Side (SSS) Postulate

Differentiated Remediation *continued*

On-Level

- **Practice** (2 pages) Provides extra practice for each lesson. For simpler practice exercises, use the Form K Practice pages found in the All-in-One Teaching Resources and online.
- **Think About a Plan** Helps students develop specific problem-solving skills and strategies by providing scaffolded guiding questions.
- **Standardized Test Prep** Focuses on all major exercises, all major question types, and helps students prepare for the high-stakes assessments.

Practice and Problem Solving Wkbk/ All-in-One Resources/Online

Practice page 1

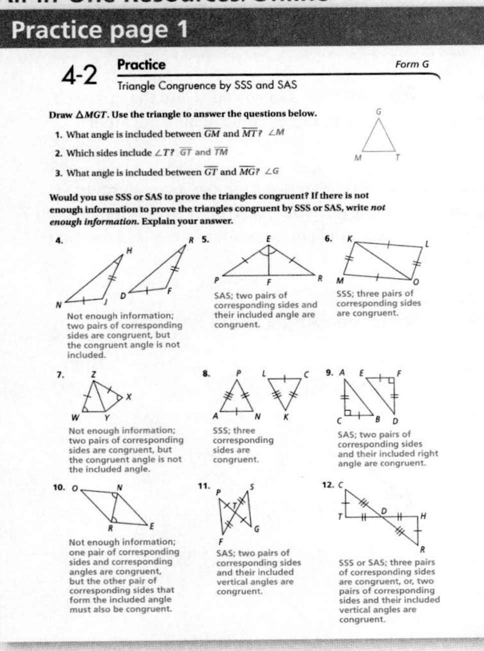

4-2 Practice — Form G
Triangle Congruence by SSS and SAS

Draw $\triangle MGT$. Use the triangle to answer the questions below.

1. What angle is included between $\overline{GM}$ and $\overline{MT}$? ∠M
2. Which sides include ∠T? $\overline{GT}$ and $\overline{TM}$
3. What angle is included between $\overline{GT}$ and $\overline{MG}$? ∠G

Would you use SSS or SAS to prove the triangles congruent? If there is not enough information to prove the triangles congruent by SSS or SAS, write *not enough information*. Explain your answer.

4. Not enough information; two pairs of corresponding sides are congruent, but the congruent angle is not included.
5. SAS; two pairs of corresponding sides and their included angle are congruent.
6. SSS; three pairs of corresponding sides are congruent.
7. Not enough information; two pairs of corresponding sides are congruent, but the congruent angle is not the included angle.
8. SSS; three corresponding sides are congruent.
9. SAS; two pairs of corresponding sides and their included right angle are congruent.
10. Not enough information; one pair of corresponding sides and corresponding angles are congruent, but the other pair of corresponding sides that form the included angle must also be congruent.
11. SAS; two pairs of corresponding sides and their included vertical angles are congruent.
12. SSS or SAS; three pairs of corresponding sides are congruent, or, two pairs of corresponding sides and their included vertical angles are congruent.

Practice and Problem Solving Wkbk/ All-in-One Resources/Online

Practice page 2

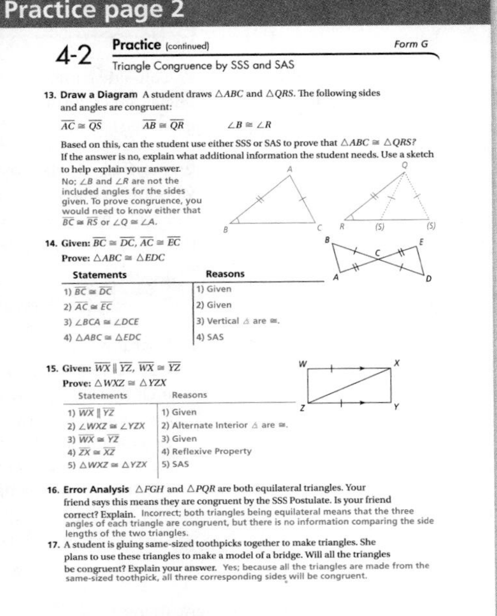

4-2 Practice (continued) — Form G
Triangle Congruence by SSS and SAS

13. **Draw a Diagram** A student draws $\triangle ABC$ and $\triangle QRS$. The following sides and angles are congruent:
$\overline{AC} \cong \overline{QS}$ $\quad$ $\overline{AB} \cong \overline{QR}$ $\quad$ $\angle B \cong \angle R$
Based on this, can the student use either SSS or SAS to prove that $\triangle ABC \cong \triangle QRS$? If the answer is no, explain what additional information the student needs. Use a sketch to help explain your answer.
No; ∠B and ∠R are not the included angles for the sides given. To prove congruence, you would need to know either that $\overline{BC} \cong \overline{RS}$ or $\angle Q \cong \angle A$.

14. Given: $\overline{BC} \cong \overline{DC}$, $\overline{AC} \cong \overline{EC}$
Prove: $\triangle ABC \cong \triangle EDC$

Statements	Reasons
1) $\overline{BC} \cong \overline{DC}$	1) Given
2) $\overline{AC} \cong \overline{EC}$	2) Given
3) $\angle BCA \cong \angle DCE$	3) Vertical ∠ are ≅.
4) $\triangle ABC \cong \triangle EDC$	4) SAS

15. Given: $\overline{WX} \parallel \overline{YZ}$, $\overline{WX} \cong \overline{YZ}$
Prove: $\triangle WXZ \cong \triangle YZX$

Statements	Reasons
1) $\overline{WX} \parallel \overline{YZ}$	1) Given
2) $\angle WXZ \cong \angle YZX$	2) Alternate Interior ∠ are ≅.
3) $\overline{WX} \cong \overline{YZ}$	3) Given
4) $\overline{ZX} \cong \overline{XZ}$	4) Reflexive Property
5) $\triangle WXZ \cong \triangle YZX$	5) SAS

16. **Error Analysis** $\triangle FGH$ and $\triangle PQR$ are both equilateral triangles. Your friend says this means they are congruent by the SSS Postulate. Is your friend correct? Explain. Incorrect; both triangles being equilateral means that the three angles of each triangle are congruent, but there is no information comparing the side lengths of the two triangles.
17. A student is gluing same-sized toothpicks together to make triangles. She plans to use these triangles to make a model of a bridge. Will all the triangles be congruent? Explain your answer. Yes; because all the triangles are made from the same-sized toothpick, all three corresponding sides will be congruent.

Practice and Problem Solving Wkbk/ All-in-One Resources/Online

Think About a Plan

4-2 Think About a Plan
Triangle Congruence by SSS and SAS

Use the Distance Formula to determine whether $\triangle ABC$ and $\triangle DEF$ are congruent. Justify your answer.
$A(1, 4), B(5, 5), C(2, 2)$
$D(-5, 1), E(-1, 0), F(-4, 3)$

Understanding the Problem

1. You need to determine if $\triangle ABC \cong \triangle DEF$. What are the three ways you know to prove triangles congruent?
If all corresponding parts are congruent, if all three sides are congruent, or, if two sides and the included angle are congruent, then the triangles are congruent.
2. What information is given in the problem?
the coordinates for each vertex of each triangle

Planning the Solution

3. If you use the SSS Postulate to determine whether the triangles are congruent, what information do you need to find?
the lengths of the three sides of each triangle
4. How can you find distances on a coordinate plane without measuring?
Use the Distance Formula.
5. In an ordered pair, which number is the *x*-coordinate? Which is the *y*-coordinate?
The *x*-coordinate is the first number and the *y*-coordinate is the second number.

Getting an Answer

6. Find the length of each segment using the Distance Formula, $D = \sqrt{(y_1 - y_2)^2 + (x_1 - x_2)^2}$. Your answers may be in simplest radical form.
$\overline{AB}$ $\sqrt{17}$ $\quad$ $\overline{BC}$ $3\sqrt{2}$ $\quad$ $\overline{CA}$ $\sqrt{5}$
$\overline{DE}$ $\sqrt{17}$ $\quad$ $\overline{EF}$ $3\sqrt{2}$ $\quad$ $\overline{FD}$ $\sqrt{5}$
7. Using the SSS Postulate, are the triangles congruent? Explain.
Yes; the triangles are congruent, because three pairs of sides are congruent.

Practice and Problem SolvingWkbk/ All-in-One Resources/Online

Standardized Test Prep

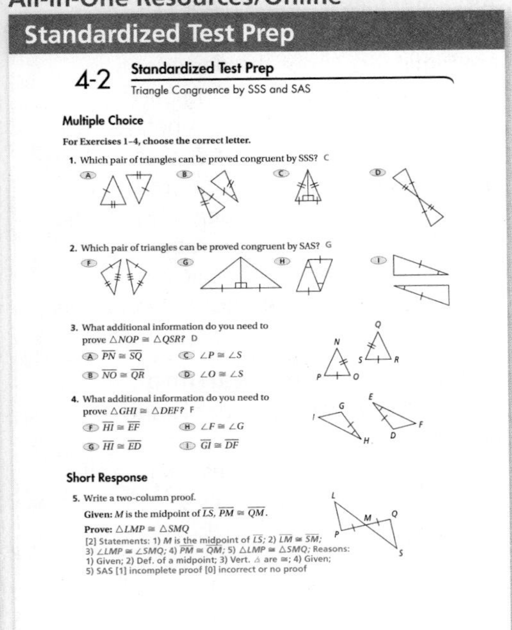

4-2 Standardized Test Prep
Triangle Congruence by SSS and SAS

Multiple Choice

For Exercises 1–4, choose the correct letter.

1. Which pair of triangles can be proved congruent by SSS? C
2. Which pair of triangles can be proved congruent by SAS? G
3. What additional information do you need to prove $\triangle NOP \cong \triangle QSR$? D
A. $\overline{PN} \cong \overline{SQ}$ $\quad$ C. $\angle P \cong \angle S$
B. $\overline{NO} \cong \overline{QR}$ $\quad$ D. $\angle O \cong \angle S$
4. What additional information do you need to prove $\triangle GHI \cong \triangle DEF$? F
F. $\overline{HI} \cong \overline{EF}$ $\quad$ H. $\angle F \cong \angle G$
G. $\overline{HI} \cong \overline{ED}$ $\quad$ I. $\overline{GI} \cong \overline{DF}$

Short Response

5. Write a two-column proof.
Given: *M* is the midpoint of $\overline{LS}$, $\overline{PM} \cong \overline{QM}$.
Prove: $\triangle LMP \cong \triangle SMQ$
[2] Statements: 1) *M* is the midpoint of $\overline{LS}$; 2) $\overline{LM} \cong \overline{SM}$; 3) $\angle LMP \cong \angle SMQ$; 4) $\overline{PM} \cong \overline{QM}$; 5) $\triangle LMP \cong \triangle SMQ$; Reasons: 1) Given; 2) Def. of a midpoint; 3) Vert. ∠ are ≅; 4) Given; 5) SAS [1] incomplete proof [0] incorrect or no proof

Extension

- **Enrichment** Provides students with interesting problems and activities that extend the concepts of the lesson.
- **Activities, Games, and Puzzles** Worksheets that can be used for concepts development, enrichment, and for fun!

All-in-One Resources/Online

Enrichment

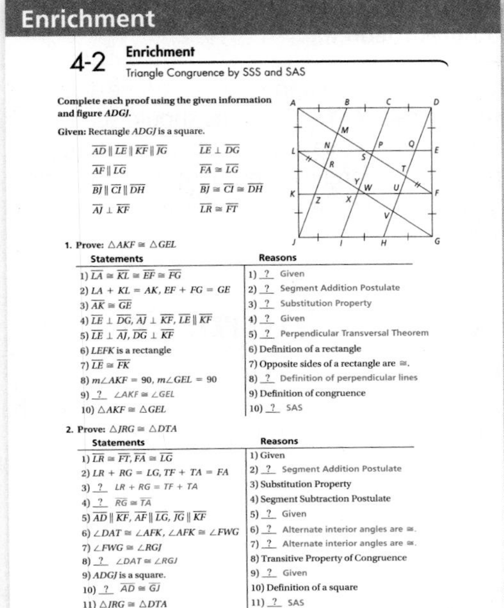

4-2 Enrichment
Triangle Congruence by SSS and SAS

Complete each proof using the given information and figure *ADGJ*.

Given: Rectangle *ADGJ* is a square.
$\overline{AD} \parallel \overline{LE} \parallel \overline{KF} \parallel \overline{JG}$ $\quad$ $\overline{LE} \perp \overline{DG}$
$\overline{AF} \parallel \overline{LG}$ $\quad$ $\overline{FA} \cong \overline{LG}$
$\overline{BJ} \parallel \overline{CI} \parallel \overline{DH}$ $\quad$ $\overline{BJ} \cong \overline{CI} \cong \overline{DH}$
$\overline{AJ} \perp \overline{KF}$ $\quad$ $\overline{LR} \cong \overline{FT}$

1. Prove: $\triangle AKF \cong \triangle GEL$

Statements	Reasons
1) $\overline{LA} \cong \overline{KL} \cong \overline{EF} \cong \overline{FG}$	1) ? Given
2) $LA + KL = AK$, $EF + FG = GE$	2) ? Segment Addition Postulate
3) $\overline{AK} \cong \overline{GE}$	3) ? Substitution Property
4) $\overline{LE} \perp \overline{DG}$, $\overline{AJ} \perp \overline{KF}$, $\overline{LE} \parallel \overline{KF}$	4) ? Given
5) $\overline{LE} \perp \overline{AJ}$, $\overline{DG} \perp \overline{KF}$	5) ? Perpendicular Transversal Theorem
6) *LEFK* is a rectangle	6) Definition of a rectangle
7) $\overline{LE} \cong \overline{FK}$	7) Opposite sides of a rectangle are ≅.
8) $m\angle AKF = 90$, $m\angle GEL = 90$	8) ? Definition of perpendicular lines
9) ? $\angle AKF \cong \angle GEL$	9) Definition of congruence
10) $\triangle AKF \cong \triangle GEL$	10) ? SAS

2. Prove: $\triangle JRG \cong \triangle DTA$

Statements	Reasons
1) $\overline{LR} \cong \overline{FT}$, $\overline{FA} \cong \overline{LG}$	1) Given
2) $LR + RG = LG$, $TF + TA = FA$	2) ? Segment Addition Postulate
3) ? $LR + RG = TF + TA$	3) Substitution Property
4) ? $\overline{RG} \cong \overline{TA}$	4) Segment Subtraction Postulate
5) $\overline{AD} \parallel \overline{KF}$, $\overline{AF} \parallel \overline{LG}$, $\overline{JG} \parallel \overline{KF}$	5) ? Given
6) $\angle DAT \cong \angle AFK$, $\angle AFK \cong \angle FWG$	6) ? Alternate interior angles are ≅.
7) $\angle FWG \cong \angle RGJ$	7) ? Alternate interior angles are ≅.
8) ? $\angle DAT \cong \angle RGJ$	8) Transitive Property of Congruence
9) *ADGJ* is a square.	9) ? Given
10) ? $\overline{AD} \cong \overline{GJ}$	10) Definition of a square
11) $\triangle JRG \cong \triangle DTA$	11) ? SAS

Online Teacher Resource Center

Activities, Games, and Puzzles

4-2 Game: Hidden Triangles
Triangle Congruence by SSS and SAS

Materials
- Protractor
- Compass
- Metric ruler

Game Play

Your teacher will divide the class into teams of three. Your teacher has hidden a triangle in a box or envelope. Your team's goal is to ask as few questions as possible in order to construct a triangle that is congruent to the one that is hidden. When you think you have enough information, construct the triangle and raise your hand. Your teacher will take the triangle out of the box and attempt to lay it directly over your construction. If the two triangles match, you are ready for the next round. If not, wait for your next turn and ask another question.

There are four possible ways to ask just three questions in order to be able to draw the triangle. If you discover one way in one round, try to find a different way in the next round.

Ending the Game

The team that correctly constructs the triangle with the fewest number of questions in each round wins 3 points, and the second team earns 1 point. In the event of a tie, more than one team can earn the set number of points.

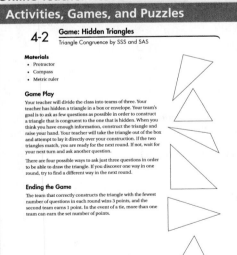

1 Interactive Learning

Solve It!

PURPOSE To prove that two triangles are congruent using methods learned in previous lessons

PROCESS Students may draw diagrams of the triangles by combining the information on both copies, use the Third Angles Theorem to identify a third pair of congruent angles, or use the SAS Postulate to prove that two triangles are congruent.

FACILITATE

Q Can you draw a complete diagram of each triangle? Explain. **[Yes, by combining the information in both copies.]**

Q Do any of the triangles have enough information to indicate congruence by SSS or SAS? **[No]**

Q What theorem will allow you to determine that all three pairs of angles in a triangle are congruent when two congruent pairs are known? **[Third Angles Theorem]**

ANSWER See Solve It in Answers on next page.

CONNECT THE MATH Students should see that the SAS and SSS Postulates are not always enough to prove two triangles congruent. In this lesson they will learn two more options for proving congruence.

2 Guided Instruction

Take Note

Have students use the ASA Postulate to show that the triangles in the Solve It are congruent.

4-3 Triangle Congruence by ASA and AAS

TN State Performance Indicators

SPI 3108.4.11 Use basic theorems about similar and congruent triangles to solve problems.

SPI 3108.4.12 Solve problems involving congruence, similarity, proportional reasoning and/or scale factor of two similar figures or solids.

Objective To prove two triangles congruent using the ASA Postulate and the AAS Theorem

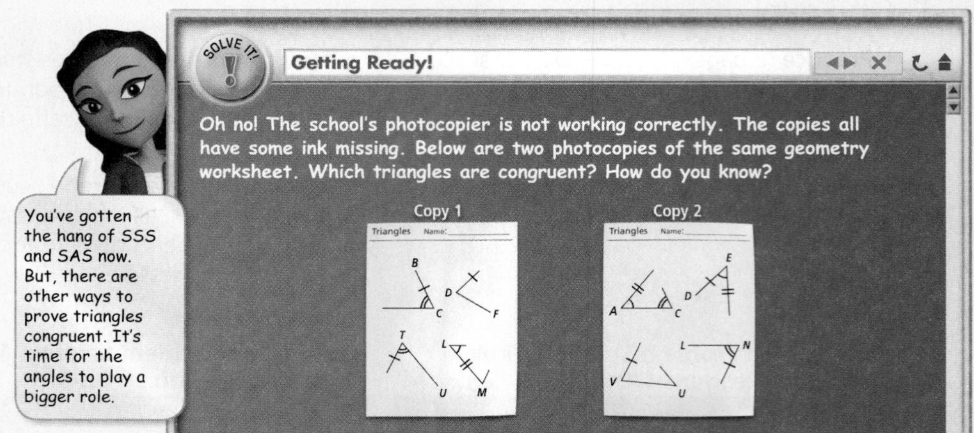

You already know that triangles are congruent if two pairs of sides and the included angles are congruent (SAS). You can also prove triangles congruent using other groupings of angles and sides.

Essential Understanding You can prove that two triangles are congruent without having to show that *all* corresponding parts are congruent. In this lesson, you will prove triangles congruent by using one pair of corresponding sides and two pairs of corresponding angles.

take note **Postulate 4-3 Angle-Side-Angle (ASA) Postulate**

Postulate	If . . .	Then . . .
If two angles and the included side of one triangle are congruent to two angles and the included side of another triangle, then the two triangles are congruent.	$\angle A \cong \angle D$, $\overline{AC} \cong \overline{DF}$, $\angle C \cong \angle F$ 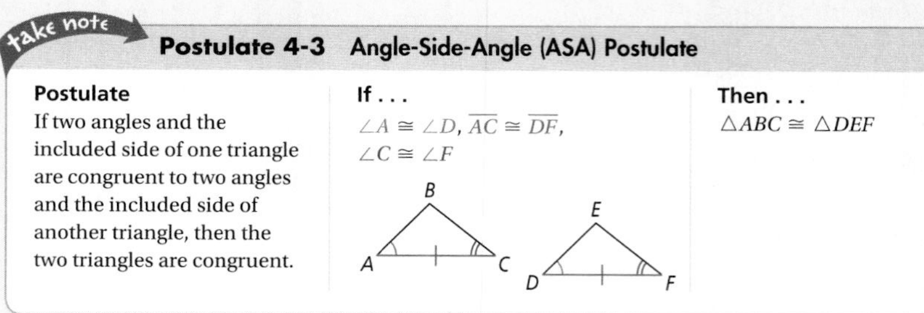	$\triangle ABC \cong \triangle DEF$

4-3 Preparing to Teach

BIG idea Reasoning and Proof UbD

ESSENTIAL UNDERSTANDINGS

- Two triangles can be proven to be congruent without having to show that all corresponding parts are congruent.
- Another way triangles can be proven to be congruent is by using one pair of corresponding sides and two pairs of corresponding angles.

Math Background

The postulate and theorem in this lesson allow students to prove that two triangles are congruent based on two pairs of congruent angles and one pair of congruent sides. This adds to the collection of methods students have to prove triangles congruent. These postulates and theorem represent the minimum number of conditions necessary to prove triangle congruence. In the next lesson, students will have the opportunity to use the postulates and theorem from this and previous lessons to determine whether triangles are congruent.

As in other lessons, the names of congruence postulates and theorems are reminders about the position of the congruent corresponding parts. The S in the ASA Postulate is between the two letters A, which indicates that the congruent sides must be between the corresponding congruent angles. The S in the AAS Theorem is **not** between the two letters A, which indicates that the congruent sides are **not** between the corresponding congruent angles.

Support Student Learning

Use the **Geometry Companion** to engage and support students during instructions. See Lesson Resources at the end of this lesson for details.

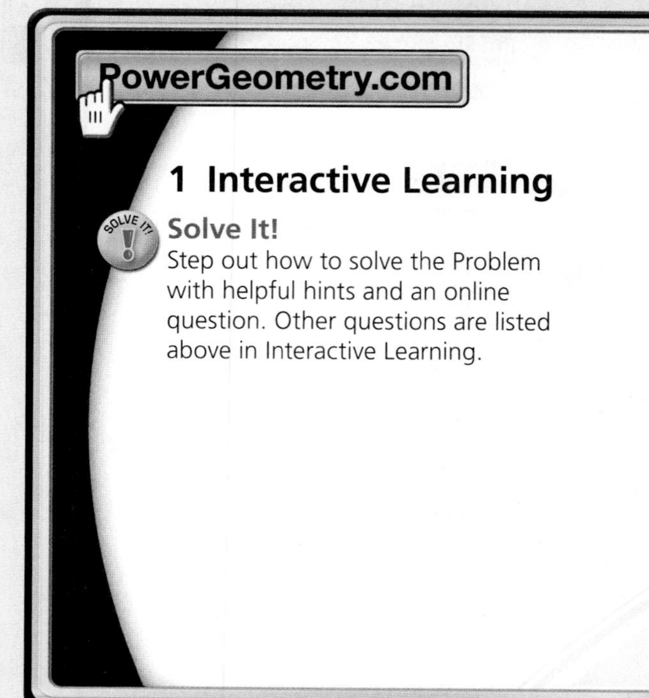

Problem 1 Using ASA

Which two triangles are congruent by ASA? Explain.

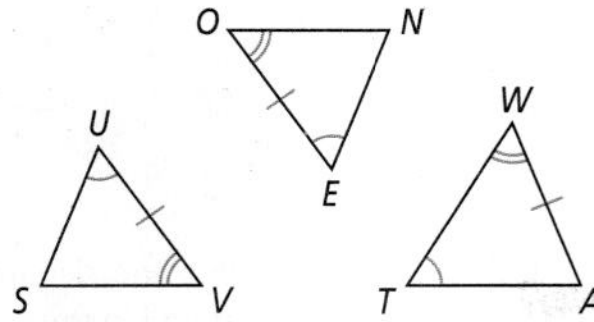

Know

From the diagram you know
- $\angle U \cong \angle E \cong \angle T$
- $\angle V \cong \angle O \cong \angle W$
- $\overline{UV} \cong \overline{EO} \cong \overline{AW}$

Need

To use ASA, you need two pairs of congruent angles and a pair of included congruent sides.

Plan

You already have pairs of congruent angles. So, identify the included side for each triangle and see whether it has a congruence marking.

In $\triangle SUV$, $\overline{UV}$ is included between $\angle U$ and $\angle V$ and has a congruence marking. In $\triangle NEO$, $\overline{EO}$ is included between $\angle E$ and $\angle O$ and has a congruence marking. In $\triangle ATW$, $\overline{TW}$ is included between $\angle T$ and $\angle W$ but does *not* have a congruence marking.

Since $\angle U \cong \angle E$, $\overline{UV} \cong \overline{EO}$, and $\angle V \cong \angle O$, $\triangle SUV \cong \triangle NEO$.

Got It? **1.** Which two triangles are congruent by ASA? Explain.

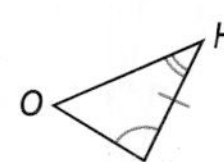

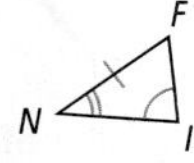

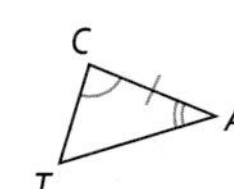

Proof

Problem 2 Writing a Proof Using ASA

Recreation **Members of a teen organization are building a miniature golf course at your town's youth center. The design plan calls for the first hole to have two congruent triangular bumpers. Prove that the bumpers on the first hole, shown at the right, meet the conditions of the plan.**

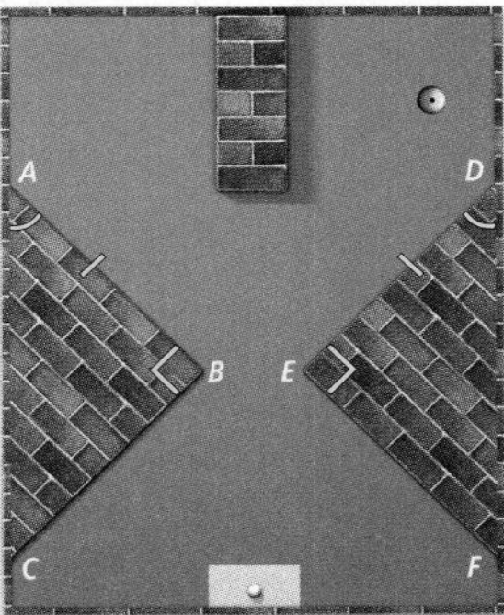

Plan

Can you use a plan similar to the plan in Problem 1?

Yes. Use the diagram to identify the included side for the marked angles in each triangle.

Given: $\overline{AB} \cong \overline{DE}$, $\angle A \cong \angle D$, $\angle B$ and $\angle E$ are right angles

Prove: $\triangle ABC \cong \triangle DEF$

Proof: $\angle B \cong \angle E$ because all right angles are congruent, and you are given that $\angle A \cong \angle D$. $\overline{AB}$ and $\overline{DE}$ are included sides between the two pairs of congruent angles. You are given that $\overline{AB} \cong \overline{DE}$. Thus, $\triangle ABC \cong \triangle DEF$ by ASA.

Problem 1

Q In each pair of triangles, how many pairs of congruent angles are shown? **[There are two pairs of angles that are congruent in each pair of triangles.]**

Q Which sides are included between the pairs of congruent angles? **[$\overline{UV}$, $\overline{EO}$, and $\overline{WT}$]**

Q Of the three triangles, which have two pairs of congruent angles and one pair of congruent included sides? **[$\triangle SUV$ and $\triangle NEO$]**

Got It? VISUAL LEARNERS

Students can reproduce the three triangles complete with the congruence markings on their own papers. Have them use three different colored highlighter markers to mark one congruent angle pair in each triangle. Draw over the side in each triangle that is congruent with a third color. Students can identify the congruent triangles because both will have the same color pattern marking the included side between two colored angles.

Problem 2

To complete the proof have students work backward. Ask them to identify information they need and then identify theorems or postulates that will support the statements.

Q Which two pairs of angles are congruent? Justify your answer. **[It is given that $\angle A \cong \angle D$. $\angle B \cong \angle E$ because they are both right angles.]**

Q Which sides are included between these two angles? **[$\overline{AB}$ and $\overline{DE}$]**

2 Guided Instruction

Each Problem is worked out and supported online.

Problem 1
Using ASA
Animated

Problem 2
Writing a Proof Using ASA

Problem 3
Writing a Proof Using AAS
Animated

Problem 4
Determining Whether Triangles Are Congruent
Animated

Support in Geometry Companion
- Vocabulary
- Key Concepts
- Got It?

Answers

Solve It!

The markings indicate that $\angle L \cong \angle A \cong \angle E$, $\angle C \cong \angle T \cong \angle N$, $\angle B \cong \angle M$ by Third Angles Theorem, $\overline{BC} \cong \overline{DE} \cong \overline{VT} \cong \overline{MN}$, and $\overline{LM} \cong \overline{AB} \cong \overline{EF}$. So $\triangle ABC \cong \triangle LMN$ by SAS.

Got It?

1. $\triangle HGO \cong \triangle ACT$ because $\overline{HG} \cong \overline{AC}$ and the $\cong$ segments are included between two pairs of $\cong$ $\angle$s.

Got It?

Q What are the similarities between the diagram for Problem 2 and the Got It diagram? **[Both pairs of triangles contain right angles, which are congruent. Both diagrams contain two pairs of congruent angles, one given and one implied. Both diagrams show the congruence of the given included sides.]**

Take Note

Discuss the similarities and differences between the ASA Postulate and the AAS Theorem. Have students discuss the location of the side needed for each statement.

Q Can you draw two triangles that have two pairs of congruent angles and one pair of congruent sides, but cannot be proved congruent using ASA or AAS? Explain. **[Yes; one triangle would need the included side marked congruent to a non-included side of the other triangle.]**

Proof of Theorem 4-2

This proof uses the ASA Postulate to prove the theorem. Discuss the ramifications of using a postulate (which can be assumed true) to prove a theorem. If students have difficulty understanding the flow proof, have them transfer the proof into a two-column format.

Got It? 2. Given: $\angle CAB \cong \angle DAE$, $\overline{BA} \cong \overline{EA}$, $\angle B$ and $\angle E$ are right angles

Prove: $\triangle ABC \cong \triangle AED$

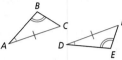

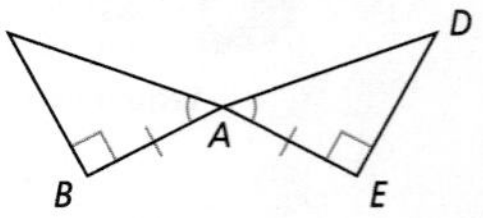

You can also prove triangles congruent by using two angles and a nonincluded side, as stated in the theorem below.

take note

Theorem 4-2 Angle-Angle-Side (AAS) Theorem

Theorem	If . . .	Then . . .
If two angles and a nonincluded side of one triangle are congruent to two angles and the corresponding nonincluded side of another triangle, then the triangles are congruent.	$\angle A \cong \angle D$, $\angle B \cong \angle E$, $\overline{AC} \cong \overline{DF}$ 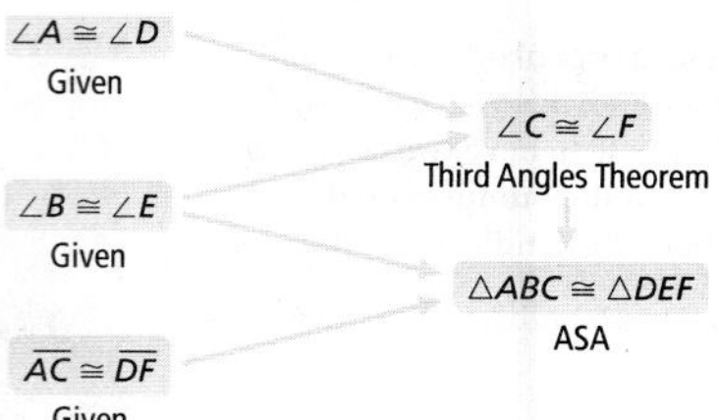	$\triangle ABC \cong \triangle DEF$

Proof Proof of Theorem 4-2: Angle-Angle-Side Theorem

Given: $\angle A \cong \angle D$, $\angle B \cong \angle E$, $\overline{AC} \cong \overline{DF}$

Prove: $\triangle ABC \cong \triangle DEF$

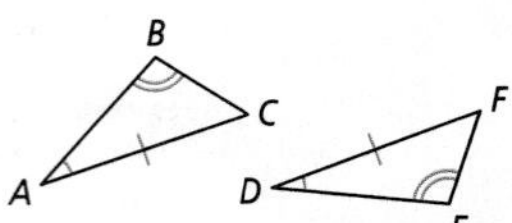

$\angle A \cong \angle D$ (Given)

$\angle B \cong \angle E$ (Given)

$\overline{AC} \cong \overline{DF}$ (Given)

$\angle C \cong \angle F$ (Third Angles Theorem)

$\triangle ABC \cong \triangle DEF$ (ASA)

You have seen and used three methods of proof in this book—two-column, paragraph, and flow proof. Each method is equally as valid as the others. Unless told otherwise, you can choose any of the three methods to write a proof. Just be sure your proof always presents logical reasoning with justification.

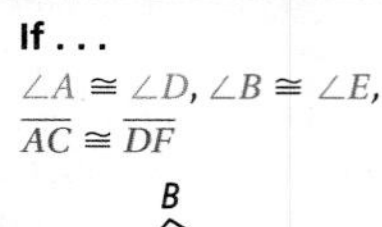

Additional Problems

1. Which two triangles are congruent by ASA?

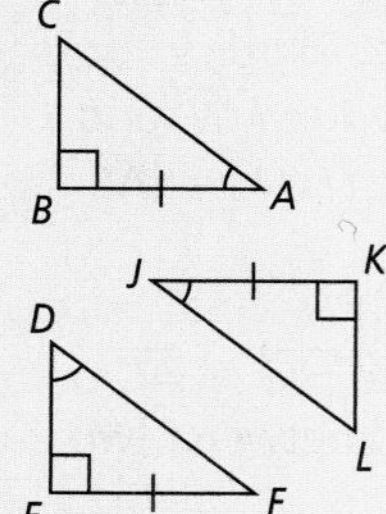

ANSWER $\triangle ABC \cong \triangle JKL$

2. Given: $\overline{LM} \cong \overline{PO}$, $\angle L \cong \angle P$, $\angle M$ and $\angle O$ are both right angles

Prove: $\triangle LMN \cong \triangle PON$

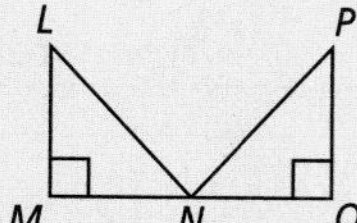

ANSWER It is given that $\overline{LM} \cong \overline{PO}$, $\angle L \cong \angle P$, $\angle M$ and $\angle O$ are both right angles. So $\angle M \cong \angle O$ because all right angles are congruent. $\triangle LMN \cong \triangle PON$ by the ASA Postulate.

3. Given: $\overline{AB} \cong \overline{AD}$, $\angle B \cong \angle D$, $\angle ACB$ and $\angle ACD$ are both right angles

Prove: $\triangle ABC \cong \triangle ADC$

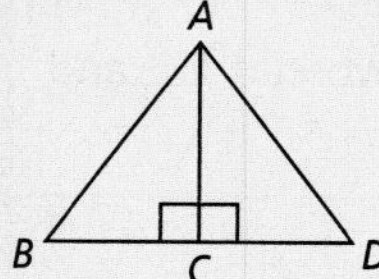

ANSWER It is given that $\overline{AB} \cong \overline{AD}$, $\angle B \cong \angle D$, and $\angle ACB$ and $\angle ACD$ are both right angles. So, $\angle ACB \cong \angle ACD$ because all right angles are congruent. $\triangle ABC \cong \triangle ADC$ by AAS.

Plan

How does information about parallel sides help?
You will need another pair of congruent angles to use AAS. Think back to what you learned in Chapter 3. $\overline{WR}$ is a transversal here.

Proof

Problem 3 Writing a Proof Using AAS

Given: $\angle M \cong \angle K$, $\overline{WM} \parallel \overline{RK}$

Prove: $\triangle WMR \cong \triangle RKW$

Statements	Reasons
1) $\angle M \cong \angle K$	1) Given
2) $\overline{WM} \parallel \overline{RK}$	2) Given
3) $\angle MWR \cong \angle KRW$	3) If lines are $\parallel$, then alternate interior $\angle$s are $\cong$.
4) $\overline{WR} \cong \overline{WR}$	4) Reflexive Property of Congruence
5) $\triangle WMR \cong \triangle RKW$	5) AAS

Got It? **3. a. Given:** $\angle S \cong \angle Q$, $\overline{RP}$ bisects $\angle SRQ$

Prove: $\triangle SRP \cong \triangle QRP$

b. Reasoning In Problem 3, how could you prove that $\triangle WMR \cong \triangle RKW$ by ASA? Explain.

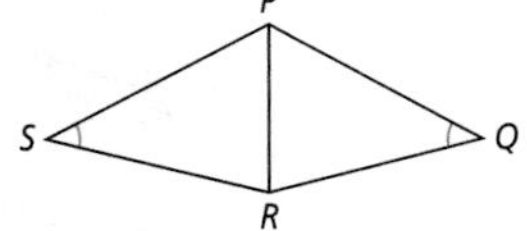

Problem 4 Determining Whether Triangles Are Congruent

Multiple Choice **Use the diagram at the right. Which of the following statements best represents the answer and justification to the question, "Is $\triangle BIF \cong \triangle UTO$?"**

Ⓐ Yes, the triangles are congruent by ASA.

Ⓑ No, $\overline{FB}$ and $\overline{OT}$ are not corresponding sides.

Ⓒ Yes, the triangles are congruent by AAS.

Ⓓ No, $\angle B$ and $\angle U$ are not corresponding angles.

The diagram shows that two pairs of angles and one pair of sides are congruent. The third pair of angles are congruent by the Third Angles Theorem. To prove these triangles congruent, you need to satisfy ASA or AAS.

ASA and AAS both fail because $\overline{FB}$ and $\overline{TO}$ are not included between the same pair of congruent corresponding angles, so they are not corresponding sides. The triangles are not necessarily congruent. The correct answer is B.

Think

Can you eliminate any of the choices?
Yes. If $\triangle BIF \cong \triangle UTO$ then $\angle B$ and $\angle U$ would be corresponding angles. You can eliminate choice D.

Got It? **4.** Are $\triangle PAR$ and $\triangle SIR$ congruent? Explain.

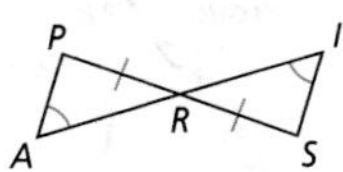

Problem 3

Once students understand this proof, challenge them to prove the triangles congruent using the ASA Postulate.

Q In order to use the AAS Theorem, what information do you need that is not directly given? **[one pair of congruent angles and one pair of congruent sides that is not included]**

Q What property of congruence can you use to prove that two of the triangles' sides are congruent? Write the congruence statement. **[Reflexive Property of Congruence; $\overline{WR} \cong \overline{WR}$]**

Q Which pair of angles do you need to use the AAS Theorem? **[$\angle KRW$ and $\angle MWR$ or $\angle KWR$ and $\angle MRW$]**

Got It?

ELL SUPPORT

Review the word *bisect* and its meaning. Remind students of the meaning of the prefix "bi." Discuss the significance of the statement that $\overline{RP}$ bisects $\angle SRQ$ and the congruence statement that follows from this fact.

Problem 4

Q What is the order in which corresponding parts are marked congruent in $\triangle FBI$? **[$\overline{FB}$, $\angle B$, $\angle I$]**

Q What is the order in which corresponding parts are marked congruent in $\triangle OUT$? **[$\angle U$, $\angle T$, $\overline{OT}$]**

Q Is there a postulate or theorem that proves the triangles congruent with the corresponding parts in this order? **[No.]**

Got It?

Have students identify a pair of congruent angles which are not marked in the diagram. Then ask students to list the sides and angles that are congruent in the order that they are marked.

4. Which of the following best represents the answer and justification to the question, "Are the triangles congruent?"

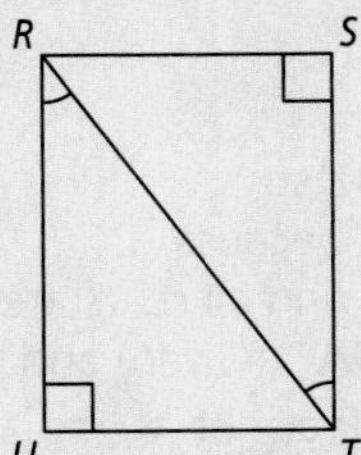

A. Yes, by ASA.

B. Yes, by SSS.

C. Yes, by AAS.

D. No, $\overline{RU}$ and $\overline{ST}$ are not necessarily congruent.

ANSWER C

Answers

Got It? (continued)

2. $\angle B \cong \angle E$ because all rt. $\angle$s are $\cong$. $\overline{AB} \cong \overline{AE}$ and $\angle CAB \cong \angle DAE$ (Given), so $\triangle ABC \cong \triangle AED$ by ASA.

3a. $\overline{RP}$ bisects $\angle SRQ$ (Given), so $\angle SRP \cong \angle QRP$ by the def. of $\angle$ bisector. $\angle S \cong \angle Q$ (Given) and $\overline{RP} \cong \overline{RP}$ (Refl. Prop. of $\cong$), so $\triangle SRP \cong \triangle QRP$ by AAS.

b. After Step 3 in the proof, state that $\angle MRW \cong \angle KWR$ by the Third $\angle$s Theorem and write Step 4, so $\triangle WMR \cong \triangle RKW$ by ASA.

4. Yes; $\overline{PR} \cong \overline{SR}$ and $\angle A \cong \angle I$ (Given). $\angle ARP \cong \angle IRS$ (Vert. $\angle$s are $\cong$.), so $\triangle PAR \cong \triangle SIR$ by AAS.

3 Lesson Check

Do you know HOW?

- If students have difficulty with Exercises 3 and 4, then have them review Problems 2 and 3.

Do you UNDERSTAND?

- If students have difficulty with Exercise 6, then have them redraw the triangles so that they have the same orientation.

Close

Q The theorem and the postulate in this lesson allow you to prove triangles are congruent based on what conditions? **[There are two pairs of congruent angles and one pair of congruent sides.]**

Q How do these two methods of proving congruence differ? **[In one case, the congruent sides are included between the congruent angles; in the other case, they are not.]**

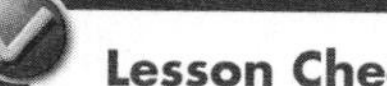

Lesson Check

Do you know HOW?

1. In $\triangle RST$, which side is included between $\angle R$ and $\angle S$?

2. In $\triangle NOM$, $\overline{NO}$ is included between which angles?

Which postulate or theorem could you use to prove $\triangle ABC \cong \triangle DEF$?

3.

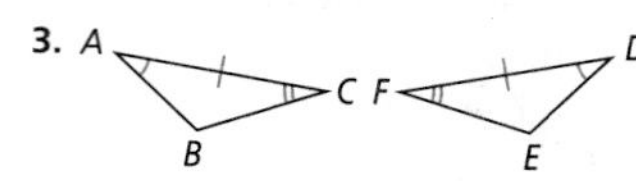

4.

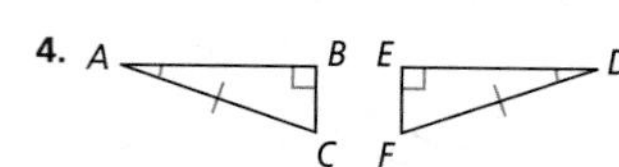

Do you UNDERSTAND?

5. Compare and Contrast How are the ASA Postulate and the SAS Postulate alike? How are they different?

6. Error Analysis Your friend asks you for help on a geometry exercise. Below is your friend's paper. What error did your friend make? Explain.

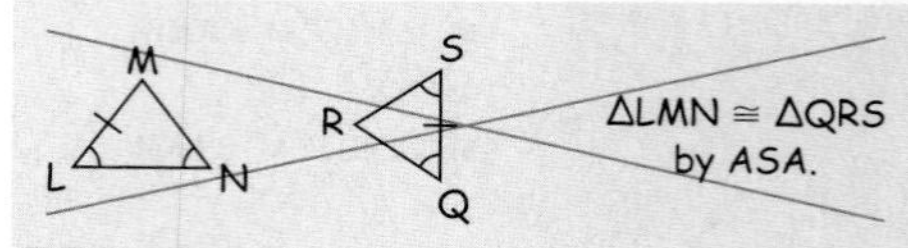

7. Reasoning Suppose $\angle E \cong \angle I$ and $\overline{FE} \cong \overline{GI}$. What else must you know in order to prove $\triangle FDE \cong \triangle GHI$ by ASA? By AAS?

Practice and Problem-Solving Exercises

Name two triangles that are congruent by ASA.

See Problem 1.

8.

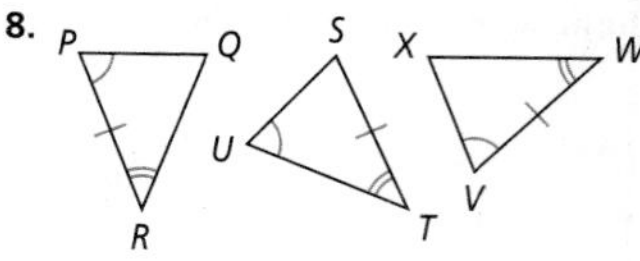

9.

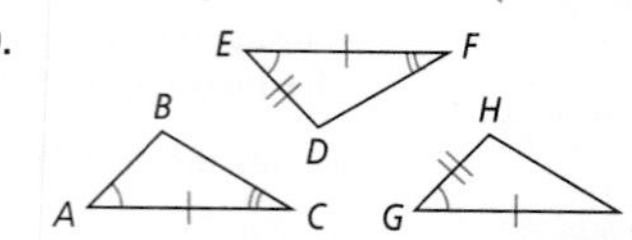

10. Developing Proof Complete the paragraph proof by filling in the blanks.

See Problem 2.

Given: $\angle LKM \cong \angle JKM$,
$\angle LMK \cong \angle JMK$

Prove: $\triangle LKM \cong \triangle JKM$

Proof: $\angle LKM \cong \angle JKM$ and $\angle LMK \cong \angle JMK$ are given. $\overline{KM} \cong \overline{KM}$ by the **a.** _?_ Property of Congruence. So, $\triangle LKM \cong \triangle JKM$ by **b.** _?_.

11. Proof **Given:** $\angle BAC \cong \angle DAC$, $\overline{AC} \perp \overline{BD}$

Prove: $\triangle ABC \cong \triangle ADC$

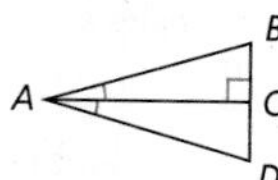

12. Proof **Given:** $\overline{QR} \cong \overline{TS}$, $\overline{QR} \parallel \overline{TS}$

Prove: $\triangle QRT \cong \triangle TSQ$

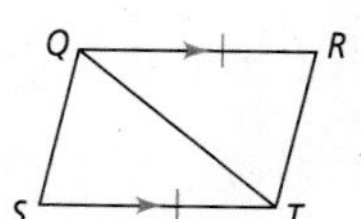

PowerGeometry.com

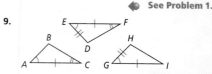

3 Lesson Check

For a digital lesson check, use the Got It questions.

Support in Geometry Companion

- Lesson Check

4 Practice

Assign homework to individual students or to an entire class.

Answers

Lesson Check

1. $\overline{RS}$

2. $\angle N$, $\angle O$

3. ASA

4. AAS

5. Answers may vary. Sample: Alike: Both postulates use three pairs of ≅ corresp. parts. Different: To use the ASA Postulate, the sides must be included between the pairs of corresp. ∠s, while to use the SAS Postulate, the ∠s must be included between the pairs of corresp. sides.

6. $\overline{LM}$ is not included between the pairs of ≅ corresp. ∠s.

7. $\angle F \cong \angle G$; $\angle D \cong \angle H$

Practice and Problem-Solving Exercises

8. $\triangle PRQ \cong \triangle VWX$

9. $\triangle ABC \cong \triangle EDF$

10a. Reflexive

b. ASA

11. $\overline{AC} \perp \overline{BD}$ (Given), so $\angle ACB \cong \angle ACD$ because ⊥ lines form rt. ∠s, and all rt. ∠s are ≅. $\angle BAC \cong \angle DAC$ (Given) and $\overline{AC} \cong \overline{AC}$ (Refl. Prop. of ≅), so $\triangle ABC \cong \triangle ADC$ by ASA.

12. It is given that $\overline{QR} \cong \overline{TS}$ and $\overline{QR} \parallel \overline{TS}$. Then $\angle RQT \cong \angle STQ$ because alt. int. ∠s are ≅. Also, $\overline{QT} \cong \overline{QT}$ by the Refl. Prop. of ≅. So $\triangle QRT \cong \triangle TSQ$ by SAS.

13. Developing Proof Complete the two-column proof by filling in the blanks.

See Problem 3.

Given: $\angle N \cong \angle S$, line ℓ bisects $\overline{TR}$ at Q

Prove: $\triangle NQT \cong \triangle SQR$

Statements	Reasons
1) $\angle N \cong \angle S$	1) Given
2) $\angle NQT \cong \angle SQR$	2) a. ?
3) Line ℓ bisects $\overline{TR}$ at Q.	3) b. ?
4) c. ?	4) Definition of bisect
5) $\triangle NQT \cong \triangle SQR$	5) d. ?

14. Given: $\angle V \cong \angle Y$, $\overline{WZ}$ bisects $\angle VWY$

Proof

Prove: $\triangle VWZ \cong \triangle YWZ$

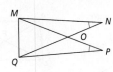

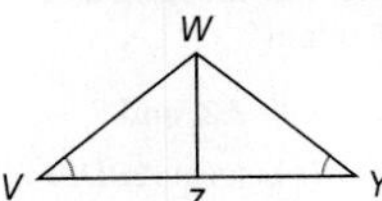

15. Given: $\overline{PQ} \perp \overline{QS}$, $\overline{RS} \perp \overline{SQ}$, T is the midpoint of $\overline{PR}$

Proof

Prove: $\triangle PQT \cong \triangle RST$

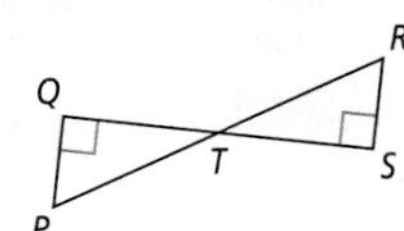

Determine whether the triangles must be congruent. If so, name the postulate or theorem that justifies your answer. If not, explain.

See Problem 4.

16.

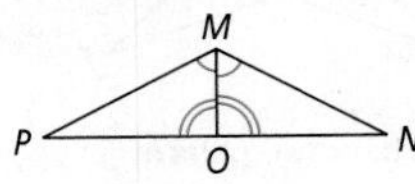

17.

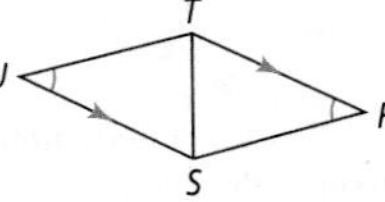

18.

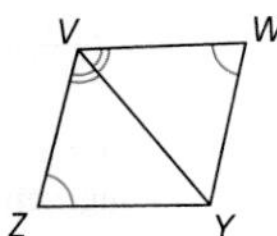

B Apply

19. Given: $\angle N \cong \angle P$, $\overline{MO} \cong \overline{QO}$

Proof

Prove: $\triangle MON \cong \triangle QOP$

20. Given: $\angle FJG \cong \angle HGJ$, $\overline{FG} \parallel \overline{JH}$

Proof

Prove: $\triangle FGJ \cong \triangle HJG$

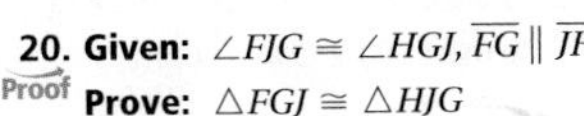

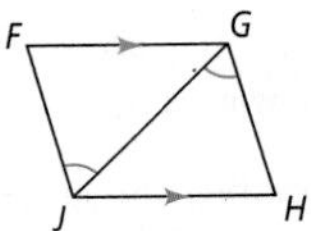

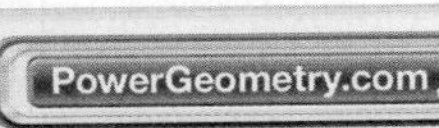

4 Practice

ASSIGNMENT GUIDE

Basic: 8–18 all, 21, 22–28 even
Average: 9–17 odd, 19–28
Advanced: 9–17 odd, 19–31
Standardized Test Prep: 32–35
Mixed Review: 36–39

Reasoning exercises have blue headings.
Applications exercises have red headings.

EXERCISE 28: Use the Think About a Plan worksheet in the **Practice and Problem Solving Workbook** (also available in the Teaching Resources in print and online) to further support students' development in becoming independent learners.

HOMEWORK QUICK CHECK

To check students' understanding of key skills and concepts, go over Exercises 9, 17, 21, 24, and 28.

13a. Vert. ∠s are ≅.
b. Given
c. $\overline{TQ} \cong \overline{RQ}$
d. AAS

14. $\overline{WZ}$ bisects $\angle VWY$ (Given), so $\angle VWZ \cong \angle YWZ$ by the def. of ∠ bisector. $\angle V \cong \angle Y$ (Given) and $\overline{WZ} \cong \overline{WZ}$ (Refl. Prop. of ≅), so $\triangle VWZ \cong \triangle YWZ$ by AAS.

15. Given the ⊥ segments, $\angle Q \cong \angle S$ because ⊥ lines form rt. ∠s, and all rt. ∠s are ≅. It is given that T is the midpt. of $\overline{PR}$, so $\overline{PT} \cong \overline{RT}$ by the def. of midpt. $\angle PTQ \cong \angle RTS$ because vert. ∠s are ≅, so $\triangle PQT \cong \triangle RST$ by AAS.

16. $\triangle PMO \cong \triangle NMO$ by ASA.

17. $\triangle UST \cong \triangle RTS$ by AAS.

18. $\triangle VZY \cong \triangle VWY$ by AAS.

19. It is given that $\angle N \cong \angle P$ and $\overline{MO} \cong \overline{QO}$. Also, $\angle MON \cong \angle QOP$ because vert. ∠s are ≅. So $\triangle MON \cong \triangle QOP$ by AAS.

20. It is given that $\angle FJG \cong \angle HGJ$ and $\overline{FG} \parallel \overline{JH}$. Then $\angle FGJ \cong \angle HJG$ because alt. int. ∠s are ≅. Since $\overline{GJ} \cong \overline{GJ}$ by the Refl. Prop. of ≅, then $\triangle FGJ \cong \triangle HJG$ by ASA.

Answers

Practice and Problem-Solving Exercises (continued)

21. Answers may vary. Sample: Yes; ASA guarantees a unique triangle with vertices at the oak tree, the maple tree, and the time capsule.

22.

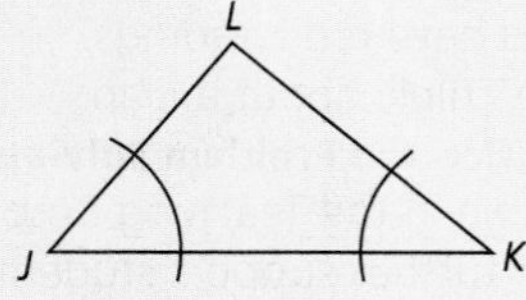

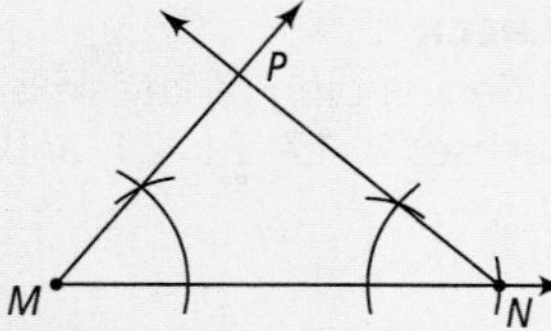

23. No; the common side is included between the two $\cong$ $\angle$s in one $\triangle$, but it is not included between the $\cong$ $\angle$s in the other $\triangle$.

24. Yes; use the Third $\angle$s Thm. Then you have three pairs of $\cong$ $\angle$s and one pair of $\cong$ sides, so you can use the ASA Postulate.

25. $\overline{AE} \parallel \overline{BD}$ (Given), so $\angle A \cong \angle DBC$ (If $\parallel$ lines, corresp. $\angle$s are $\cong$.). Since $\angle E \cong \angle D$ and $\overline{AE} \cong \overline{BD}$ (Given), then $\triangle AEB \cong \triangle BDC$ by ASA.

26. $\overline{DH}$ bisects $\angle BDF$ (Given), so $\angle BDH \cong \angle FDH$ by the def. of $\angle$ bisector. $\angle 1 \cong \angle 2$ (Given) and $\overline{DH} \cong \overline{DH}$ (Refl. Prop. of $\cong$), so $\triangle BDH \cong \triangle FDH$ by ASA.

27. Answers may vary. Sample:

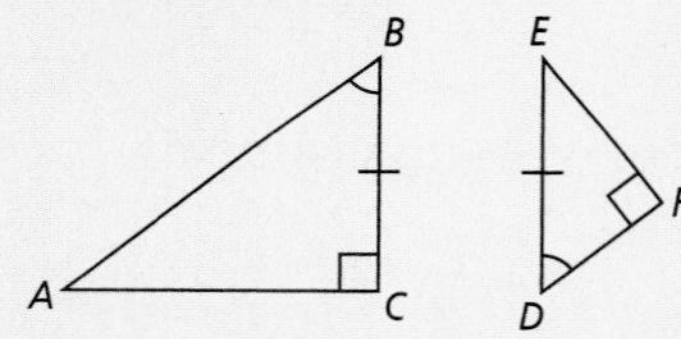

28. Given the parallel lines, $\angle BAC \cong \angle DCA$ and $\angle DAC \cong \angle BCA$ because alt. int. $\angle$s are $\cong$. Also, $\overline{AC} \cong \overline{AC}$ by the Refl. Prop. of $\cong$. So $\triangle ABC \cong \triangle CDA$ by ASA.

29. $\triangle EAB \cong \triangle ECD$, $\triangle EBC \cong \triangle EDA$, $\triangle ABD \cong \triangle CDB$, $\triangle ABC \cong \triangle CDA$

30.

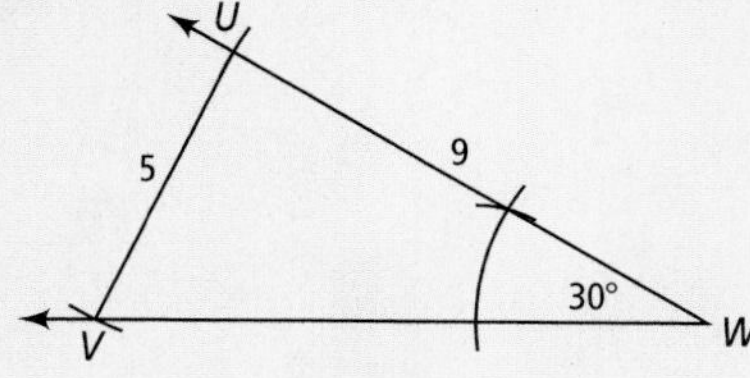

21. Think About a Plan While helping your family clean out the attic, you find the piece of paper shown at the right. The paper contains clues to locate a time capsule buried in your backyard. The maple tree is due east of the oak tree in your backyard. Will the clues always lead you to the correct spot? Explain.

- How can you use a diagram to help you?
- What type of geometric figure do the paths and the marked line form?
- How does the position of the marked line relate to the positions of the angles?

Mark a line on the ground from the oak tree to the maple tree. From the oak tree, walk along a path that forms a 70° angle with the marked line, keeping the maple tree to your right. From the maple tree, walk along a path that forms a 40° angle with the marked line. The time capsule is buried where the paths meet.

22. Constructions Use a straightedge to draw a triangle. Label it $\triangle JKL$. Construct $\triangle MNP \cong \triangle JKL$ so that the triangles are congruent by ASA.

23. Reasoning Can you prove that the triangles at the right are congruent? Justify your answer.

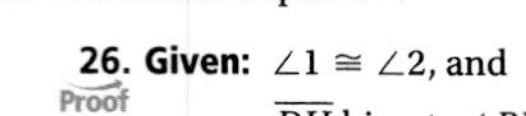

24. Writing Anita says that you can rewrite any proof that uses the AAS Theorem as a proof that uses the ASA Postulate. Do you agree with Anita? Explain.

25. Proof **Given:** $\overline{AE} \parallel \overline{BD}$, $\overline{AE} \cong \overline{BD}$, $\angle E \cong \angle D$

Prove: $\triangle AEB \cong \triangle BDC$

26. Proof **Given:** $\angle 1 \cong \angle 2$, and $\overline{DH}$ bisects $\angle BDF$.

Prove: $\triangle BDH \cong \triangle FDH$

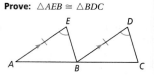

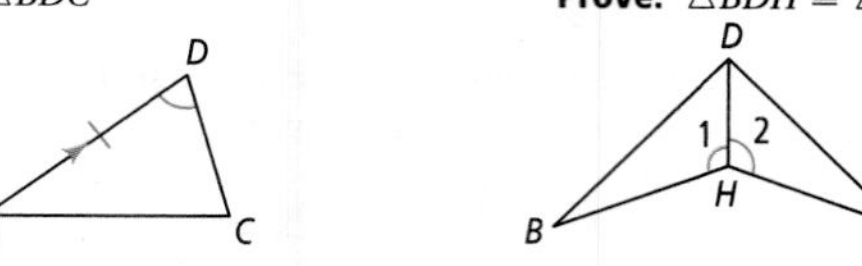

27. Draw a Diagram Draw two noncongruent triangles that have two pairs of congruent angles and one pair of congruent sides.

28. Proof **Given:** $\overline{AB} \parallel \overline{DC}$, $\overline{AD} \parallel \overline{BC}$

Prove: $\triangle ABC \cong \triangle CDA$

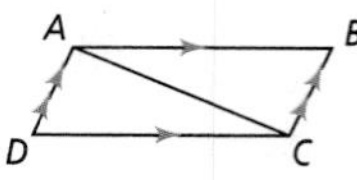

Challenge

29. Given $\overline{AD} \parallel \overline{BC}$ and $\overline{AB} \parallel \overline{DC}$, name as many pairs of congruent triangles as you can.

30. Constructions In $\triangle RST$ at the right, $RS = 5$, $RT = 9$, and $m\angle T = 30$. Show that there is no SSA congruence rule by constructing $\triangle UVW$ with $UV = RS$, $UW = RT$, and $m\angle W = m\angle T$, but with $\triangle UVW \not\cong \triangle RST$.

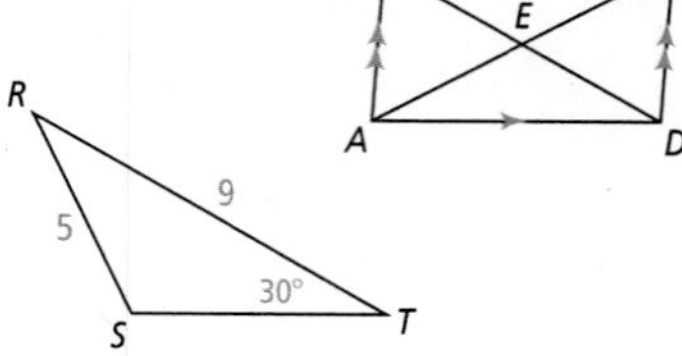

31. **Probability** Below are six statements about the triangles at the right.

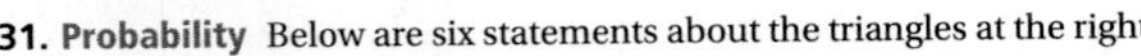

$\angle A \cong \angle X$ $\quad$ $\angle B \cong \angle Y$ $\quad$ $\angle C \cong \angle Z$

$\overline{AB} \cong \overline{XY}$ $\quad$ $\overline{AC} \cong \overline{XZ}$ $\quad$ $\overline{BC} \cong \overline{YZ}$

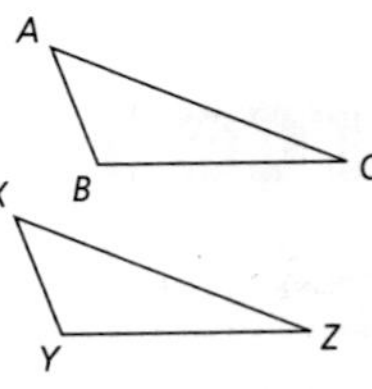

There are 20 ways to choose a group of three statements from these six. What is the probability that three statements chosen at random from the six will guarantee that the triangles are congruent?

Standardized Test Prep

SAT/ACT

32. Suppose $\overline{RT} \cong \overline{ND}$ and $\angle R \cong \angle N$. What additional information do you need to prove that $\triangle RTJ \cong \triangle NDF$ by ASA?

Ⓐ $\angle T \cong \angle D$ $\quad$ Ⓑ $\angle J \cong \angle F$ $\quad$ Ⓒ $\angle J \cong \angle D$ $\quad$ Ⓓ $\angle T \cong \angle F$

33. You plan to make a 2 ft-by-3 ft rectangular poster of class trip photos. Each photo is a 4 in.-by-6 in. rectangle. If the photos do not overlap, what is the greatest number of photos you can fit on your poster?

Ⓕ 4 $\quad$ Ⓖ 24 $\quad$ Ⓗ 32 $\quad$ Ⓘ 36

34. Which of the following figures is a concave polygon?

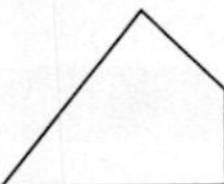
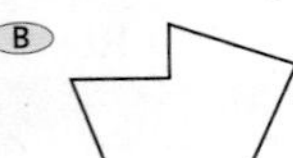

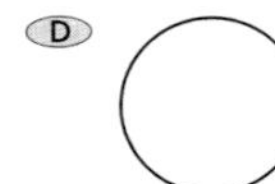

Ⓐ $\quad$ Ⓑ $\quad$ Ⓒ $\quad$ Ⓓ

Short Response

35. Write the converse of the true conditional statement below. Then determine whether the converse is true or false.

If you are less than 18 years old, then you are too young to vote in the United States.

Mixed Review

Would you use SSS or SAS to prove the triangles congruent? Explain.

See Lesson 4-2.

36.

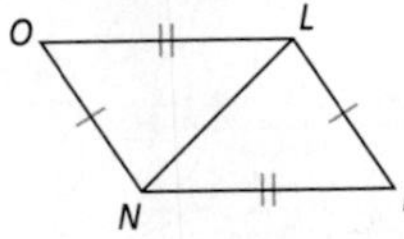

37.

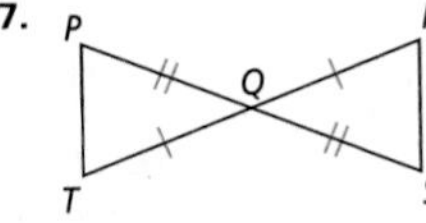

Get Ready! **To prepare for Lesson 4-4, do Exercises 38 and 39.**

For $\triangle TIC \cong \triangle LOK$, list the indicated parts.

See Lesson 4-1.

38. congruent corresponding angles

39. congruent corresponding sides

31. $\frac{13}{20}$ $\quad$ **32.** A

33. I $\quad$ **34.** B

35. [2] Converse: If you are too young to vote in the United States, then you are less than 18 years old; true.

[1] Converse correct, but truth value incorrect *OR* Converse incorrect but truth value correct

36. SSS; you are given two pairs of $\cong$ sides. Another pair of sides are $\cong$ by the Refl. Prop. of $\cong$.

37. SAS; you are given two pairs of $\cong$ sides. The pair of included angles are congruent because they are vertical angles.

38. $\angle T \cong \angle L$, $\angle I \cong \angle O$, $\angle C \cong \angle K$

39. $\overline{TI} \cong \overline{LO}$, $\overline{IC} \cong \overline{OK}$, $\overline{TC} \cong \overline{LK}$

4-3 Lesson Resources

Differentiated Remediation

Instructional Support

Geometry Companion

Students can use the **Geometry Companion** worktext (4 pages) . . .

- New Vocabulary
- Key Concepts
- Got It for each Problem
- Lesson Check

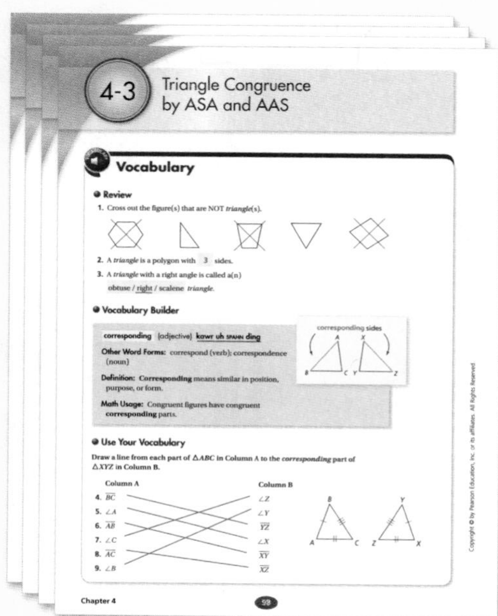

4-3 Triangle Congruence by ASA and AAS

Vocabulary

Review

1. Cross out the figure(s) that are NOT *triangle*(s).
2. A *triangle* is a polygon with 3 sides.
3. A *triangle* with a right angle is called a(n) obtuse / right / scalene *triangle*.

Vocabulary Builder

corresponding (adjective) kawr uh SPAHN ding

Other Word Forms: correspond (verb); correspondence (noun)

Definition: **Corresponding** means similar in position, purpose, or form.

Math Usage: Congruent figures have congruent **corresponding** parts.

corresponding sides

Use Your Vocabulary

Draw a line from each part of $\triangle ABC$ in Column A to the *corresponding* part of $\triangle XYZ$ in Column B.

Column A	Column B
4. $\overline{BC}$	$\angle Z$
5. $\angle A$	$\angle Y$
6. $\overline{AB}$	$\overline{YZ}$
7. $\angle C$	$\angle X$
8. $\overline{AC}$	$\overline{XY}$
9. $\angle B$	$\overline{XZ}$

Copyright © by Pearson Education, Inc. or its affiliates. All Rights Reserved.

Chapter 4 98

ELL Support

Focus on Language Project or write the ASA Postulate on the board. Read the postulate, pointing to each word as you read. Discuss its meaning. Do the same for the AAS Theorem. Ask how these two methods are different and how they are the same.

Focus on Communication Turn off the projector or erase the board and have students write the ASA Postulate and AAS Theorem in their own words. Pair students and ask them to read their sentences to each other. Encourage questions, clarification (What do you mean?), and peer assistance in learning.

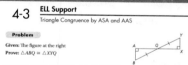

5 Assess & Remediate

Lesson Quiz

1. **Given:** $\angle XWY \cong \angle ZYW$, $\angle X$ and $\angle Z$ are both right angles.
   Prove: $\triangle YXW \cong \triangle WZY$

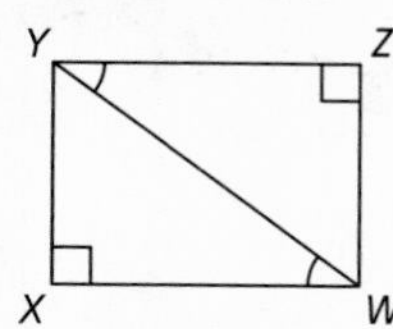

Y
Z
X
W

2. In Exercise 1, how could you prove the triangles congruent using ASA?
3. **Do you UNDERSTAND?** Which of the following best represents the answer and justification to the question: "Are the triangles congruent?"
   A. Yes, by ASA.
   B. Yes, by AAS.
   C. Yes, by SSA.
   D. No, there is not enough information to prove congruence.

A B D C

ANSWERS TO LESSON QUIZ

1. It is given that $\angle XWY \cong \angle ZYW$, and $\angle X$ and $\angle Z$ are both right angles. So, $\angle X \cong \angle Z$ because all rt. $\angle$s are $\cong$. $\overline{WY} \cong \overline{WY}$ by the Reflexive Property of Congruence. So, $\triangle YXW \cong \triangle WZY$ by AAS.
2. Get $\angle XYW \cong \angle ZWY$ by the Third Angles Thm.
3. D

PRESCRIPTION FOR REMEDIATION

Use the student work on the Lesson Quiz to prescribe a differentiated review assignment.

Points	Differentiated Remediation
0	Intervention
1	On-level
2	Extension

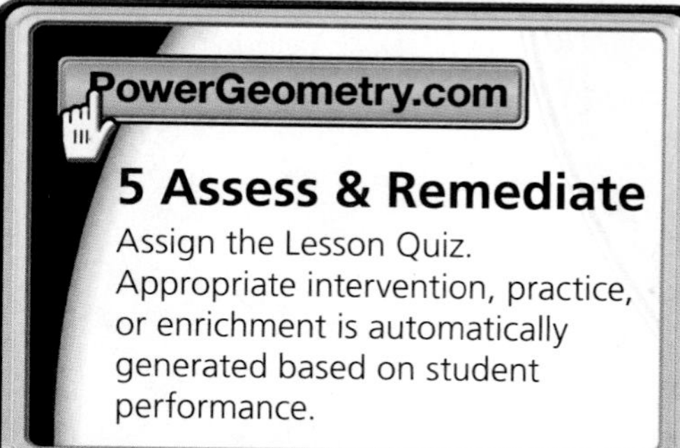

PowerGeometry.com
5 Assess & Remediate
Assign the Lesson Quiz.
Appropriate intervention, practice, or enrichment is automatically generated based on student performance.

Intervention

- **Reteaching** (2 pages) Provides reteaching and practice exercises for the key lesson concepts. Use with struggling students or absent students.
- **English Language Learner Support** Helps students develop and reinforce mathematical vocabulary and key concepts.

All-in-One Resources/Online

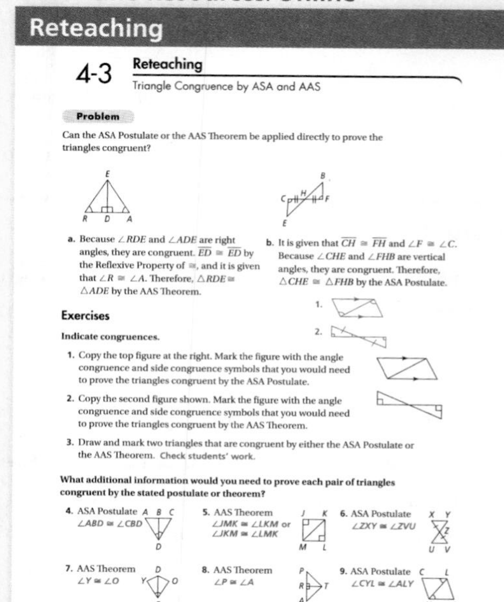

Reteaching

4-3 Reteaching

Triangle Congruence by ASA and AAS

Problem

Can the ASA Postulate or the AAS Theorem be applied directly to prove the triangles congruent?

a. Because $\angle RDE$ and $\angle ADE$ are right angles, they are congruent. $\overline{ED} \cong \overline{ED}$ by the Reflexive Property of $\cong$, and it is given that $\angle R \cong \angle A$. Therefore, $\triangle RDE \cong \triangle ADE$ by the AAS Theorem.

b. It is given that $\overline{CH} \cong \overline{FH}$ and $\angle F \cong \angle C$. Because $\angle CHE$ and $\angle FHB$ are vertical angles, they are congruent. Therefore, $\triangle CHE \cong \triangle FHB$ by the ASA Postulate.

Exercises

Indicate congruences.

1. Copy the top figure at the right. Mark the figure with the angle congruence and side congruence symbols that you would need to prove the triangles congruent by the ASA Postulate.
2. Copy the second figure shown. Mark the figure with the angle congruence and side congruence symbols that you would need to prove the triangles congruent by the AAS Theorem.
3. Draw and mark two triangles that are congruent by either the ASA Postulate or the AAS Theorem. Check students' work.

What additional information would you need to prove each pair of triangles congruent by the stated postulate or theorem?

4. ASA Postulate $\angle ABD \cong \angle CBD$
5. AAS Theorem $\angle JMK \cong \angle LKM$ or $\angle JKM \cong \angle LMK$
6. ASA Postulate $\angle ZXY \cong \angle ZVU$
7. AAS Theorem $\angle Y \cong \angle O$
8. AAS Theorem $\angle P \cong \angle A$
9. ASA Postulate $\angle CYL \cong \angle ALY$

All-in-One Resources/Online

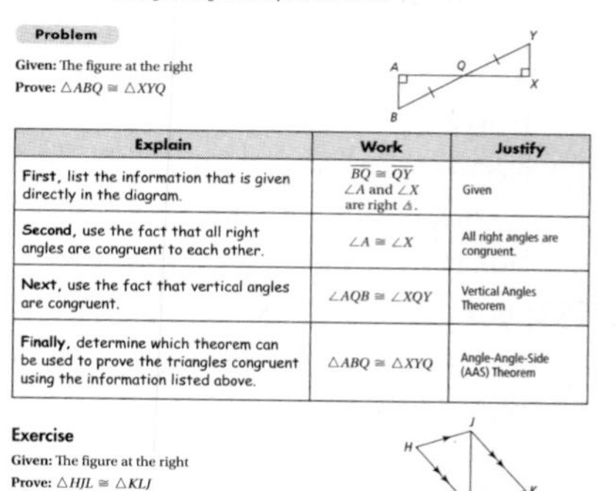

English Language Learner Support

4-3 ELL Support

Triangle Congruence by ASA and AAS

Problem

Given: The figure at the right

Prove: $\triangle ABQ \cong \triangle XYQ$

Explain	Work	Justify
First, list the information that is given directly in the diagram.	$\overline{BQ} \cong \overline{QY}$, $\angle A$ and $\angle X$ are right $\angle$s.	Given
Second, use the fact that all right angles are congruent to each other.	$\angle A \cong \angle X$	All right angles are congruent.
Next, use the fact that vertical angles are congruent.	$\angle AQB \cong \angle XQY$	Vertical Angles Theorem
Finally, determine which theorem can be used to prove the triangles congruent using the information listed above.	$\triangle ABQ \cong \triangle XYQ$	Angle-Angle-Side (AAS) Theorem

Exercise

Given: The figure at the right

Prove: $\triangle HJL \cong \triangle KLJ$

Explain	Work	Justify
First, list the information that is given directly in the diagram.	$\overline{HJ} \parallel \overline{KL}$, $\overline{HL} \parallel \overline{KJ}$	Given
Second, use the fact that alternate interior angles are congruent when parallel lines are cut by a transversal.	$\angle HJL \cong \angle KLJ$, $\angle HLJ \cong \angle KJL$	Alternate Interior Angles Theorem
Next, recall that any line segment is congruent to itself.	$\overline{JL} \cong \overline{LJ}$	Reflexive Property of Congruence
Finally, determine which theorem can be used to prove the triangles congruent using the information listed above.	$\triangle HJL \cong \triangle KLJ$	Angle-Side-Angle (ASA) Postulate

Differentiated Remediation *continued*

On-Level

- **Practice** (2 pages) Provides extra practice for each lesson. For simpler practice exercises, use the Form K Practice pages found in the All-in-One Teaching Resources and online.
- **Think About a Plan** Helps students develop specific problem-solving skills and strategies by providing scaffolded guiding questions.
- **Standardized Test Prep** Focuses on all major exercises, all major question types, and helps students prepare for the high-stakes assessments.

Extension

- **Enrichment** Provides students with interesting problems and activities that extend the concepts of the lesson.
- **Activities, Games, and Puzzles** Worksheets that can be used for concepts development, enrichment, and for fun!

Practice and Problem Solving Wkbk/ All-in-One Resources/Online

Practice page 1

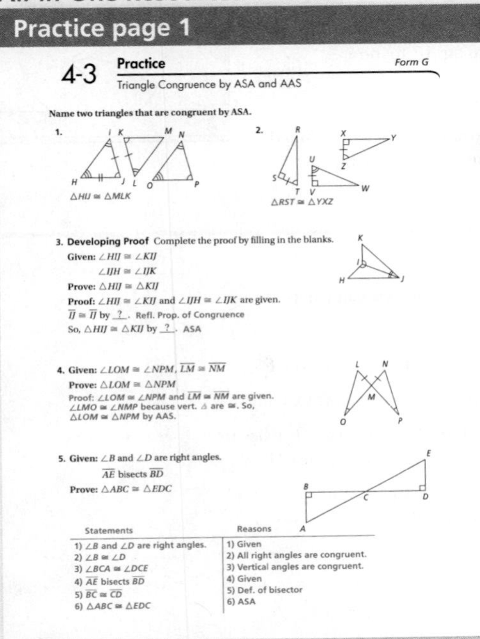

4-3 **Practice** *Form G*
Triangle Congruence by ASA and AAS

Name two triangles that are congruent by ASA.

1. $\triangle HIJ \cong \triangle MLK$
2. $\triangle RST \cong \triangle YXZ$
3. **Developing Proof** Complete the proof by filling in the blanks.
   Given: $\angle HIJ \cong \angle KIJ$, $\angle IJH \cong \angle IJK$
   Prove: $\triangle HIJ \cong \triangle KIJ$
   Proof: $\angle HIJ \cong \angle KIJ$ and $\angle IJH \cong \angle IJK$ are given.
   $\overline{IJ} \cong \overline{IJ}$ by __?__. Refl. Prop. of Congruence
   So, $\triangle HIJ \cong \triangle KIJ$ by __?__. ASA
4. **Given:** $\angle LOM \cong \angle NPM$, $\overline{LM} \cong \overline{NM}$
   Prove: $\triangle LOM \cong \triangle NPM$
   Proof: $\angle LOM \cong \angle NPM$ and $\overline{LM} \cong \overline{NM}$ are given. $\angle LMO \cong \angle NMP$ because vert. ∠s are ≅. So, $\triangle LOM \cong \triangle NPM$ by AAS.
5. **Given:** $\angle B$ and $\angle D$ are right angles. $\overline{AE}$ bisects $\overline{BD}$
   Prove: $\triangle ABC \cong \triangle EDC$

Statements	Reasons
1) $\angle B$ and $\angle D$ are right angles.	1) Given
2) $\angle B \cong \angle D$	2) All right angles are congruent.
3) $\angle BCA \cong \angle DCE$	3) Vertical angles are congruent.
4) $\overline{AE}$ bisects $\overline{BD}$	4) Given
5) $\overline{BC} \cong \overline{CD}$	5) Def. of bisector
6) $\triangle ABC \cong \triangle EDC$	6) ASA

Practice and Problem Solving Wkbk/ All-in-One Resources/Online

Practice page 2

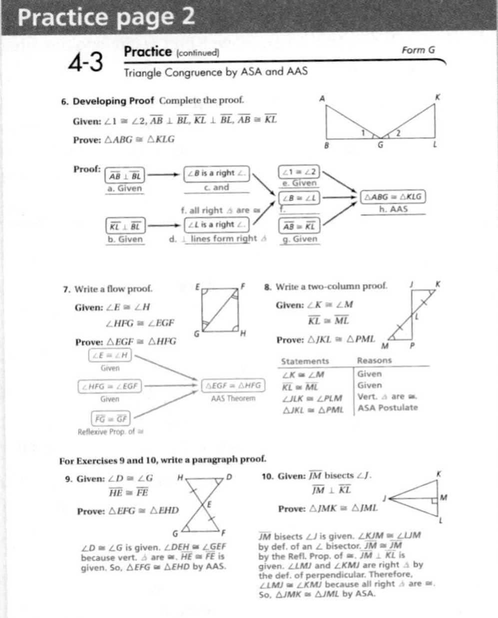

4-3 **Practice** (continued) *Form G*
Triangle Congruence by ASA and AAS

6. **Developing Proof** Complete the proof.
   Given: $\angle 1 \cong \angle 2$, $\overline{AB} \perp \overline{BL}$, $\overline{KL} \perp \overline{BL}$, $\overline{AB} \cong \overline{KL}$
   Prove: $\triangle ABG \cong \triangle KLG$
   Proof: $\overline{AB} \perp \overline{BL}$ (a. Given) → $\angle B$ is a right ∠ (c. and); $\overline{KL} \perp \overline{BL}$ (b. Given) → $\angle L$ is a right ∠ (d. ⊥ lines form right ∠s); $\angle 1 \cong \angle 2$ (e. Given); $\angle B \cong \angle L$ (f. all right ∠s are ≅); $\overline{AB} \cong \overline{KL}$ (g. Given) → $\triangle ABG \cong \triangle KLG$ (h. AAS)
7. Write a flow proof.
   Given: $\angle E \cong \angle H$, $\angle HFG \cong \angle EGF$
   Prove: $\triangle EGF \cong \triangle HFG$
   $\angle E \cong \angle H$ (Given); $\angle HFG \cong \angle EGF$ (Given); $\overline{FG} \cong \overline{GF}$ (Reflexive Prop. of ≅) → $\triangle EGF \cong \triangle HFG$ (AAS Theorem)
8. Write a two-column proof.
   Given: $\angle K \cong \angle M$, $\overline{KL} \cong \overline{ML}$
   Prove: $\triangle JKL \cong \triangle PML$

Statements	Reasons
$\angle K \cong \angle M$	Given
$\overline{KL} \cong \overline{ML}$	Given
$\angle JLK \cong \angle PLM$	Vert. ∠s are ≅.
$\triangle JKL \cong \triangle PML$	ASA Postulate

For Exercises 9 and 10, write a paragraph proof.

9. **Given:** $\angle D \cong \angle G$, $\overline{HE} \cong \overline{FE}$
   Prove: $\triangle EFG \cong \triangle EHD$
   $\angle D \cong \angle G$ is given. $\angle DEH \cong \angle GEF$ because vert. ∠s are ≅. $\overline{HE} \cong \overline{FE}$ is given. So, $\triangle EFG \cong \triangle EHD$ by AAS.
10. **Given:** $\overline{JM}$ bisects $\angle J$. $\overline{JM} \perp \overline{KL}$
    Prove: $\triangle JMK \cong \triangle JML$
    $\overline{JM}$ bisects $\angle J$ is given. $\angle KJM \cong \angle LJM$ by def. of an ∠ bisector. $\overline{JM} \cong \overline{JM}$ by the Refl. Prop. of ≅. $\overline{JM} \perp \overline{KL}$ is given. $\angle LMJ$ and $\angle KMJ$ are right ∠s by the def. of perpendicular. Therefore, $\angle LMJ \cong \angle KMJ$ because all right ∠s are ≅. So, $\triangle JMK \cong \triangle JML$ by ASA.

All-in-One Resources/Online

Enrichment

4-3 **Enrichment**
Triangle Congruence by ASA and AAS

Follow these steps to create a stunt plane from a sheet of $8\frac{1}{2}$-in.-by-11-in. paper.

1. Fold the paper in half vertically. Using the definition of segment bisectors, note the congruent segments. Check students' work.
2. Fold the upper corners to lie on either side of the center line. Using the definitions of angle bisectors and right angles, note the angles that are congruent. **Step 2**
   a. What theorem allows you to conclude that the two triangles you created are congruent? ASA
   b. Identify the congruent angles and sides. Check students' work.
3. Fold the top point down along a line that is 1 in. below the bottom side of the triangles. Again, fold the upper corners to lie on either side of the center line. **Step 3**
   a. What theorem allows you to conclude that the two triangles you created are congruent? ASA
   b. Identify the congruent angles and sides. Check students' work.
4. Fold the small triangle up along the line formed by the bottom sides of the triangles formed in Step 3. This exposes two more congruent triangles. The two triangles are congruent by ASA.
   a. Explain which angles are congruent and why. Check students' work.
   b. Name the congruent sides, and explain how you know the sides are congruent. The included sides are congruent because the fold in Step 1 found the midpoint of the width of the paper, thus creating two equal segments.
5. Fold along the vertical fold line formed in Step 1 so that the triangles formed in Step 4 are on the outside of the airplane. **Step 5**
6. Turn the paper so that the long edge is at the bottom. To complete the paper airplane, fold each top edge down to meet the bottom edge, and crease.

Follow the Steps to create a dart plane from a sheet of $8\frac{1}{2}$-in.-by-11-in. paper.

7. Repeat Steps 1 and 2 above.
8. Fold the upper side corners to lie on either side of the center line. **Step 8**
   a. What theorem allows you to conclude that the two triangles you created are congruent? ASA
   b. Identify the congruent angles and sides. Check students' work.
9. Turn the paper over. Fold the outer edges in so that they lie on either side of the center line.
10. Fold the paper in half along the original fold made in Step 7.
11. Adjust the wing flaps until they are at right angles with the body to complete the dart.

Practice and Problem Solving Wkbk/ All-in-One Resources/Online

Think About a Plan

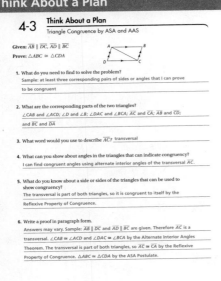

4-3 **Think About a Plan**
Triangle Congruence by ASA and AAS

Given: $\overline{AB} \parallel \overline{DC}$, $\overline{AD} \parallel \overline{BC}$
Prove: $\triangle ABC \cong \triangle CDA$

1. What do you need to find to solve the problem?
   Sample: at least three corresponding pairs of sides or angles that I can prove to be congruent
2. What are the corresponding parts of the two triangles?
   $\angle CAB$ and $\angle ACD$; $\angle D$ and $\angle B$; $\angle DAC$ and $\angle BCA$; $\overline{AC}$ and $\overline{CA}$; $\overline{AB}$ and $\overline{CD}$; and $\overline{BC}$ and $\overline{DA}$
3. What word would you use to describe $\overline{AC}$? transversal
4. What can you show about angles in the triangles that can indicate congruency?
   I can find congruent angles using alternate interior angles of the transversal $\overline{AC}$.
5. What do you know about a side or sides of the triangles that can be used to show congruency?
   The transversal is part of both triangles, so it is congruent to itself by the Reflexive Property of Congruence.
6. Write a proof in paragraph form.
   Answers may vary. Sample: $\overline{AB} \parallel \overline{DC}$ and $\overline{AD} \parallel \overline{BC}$ are given. Therefore $\overline{AC}$ is a transversal. $\angle CAB \cong \angle ACD$ and $\angle DAC \cong \angle BCA$ by the Alternate Interior Angles Theorem. The transversal is part of both triangles, so $\overline{AC} \cong \overline{CA}$ by the Reflexive Property of Congruence. $\triangle ABC \cong \triangle CDA$ by the ASA Postulate.

Practice and Problem Solving Wkbk/ All-in-One Resources/Online

Standardized Test Prep

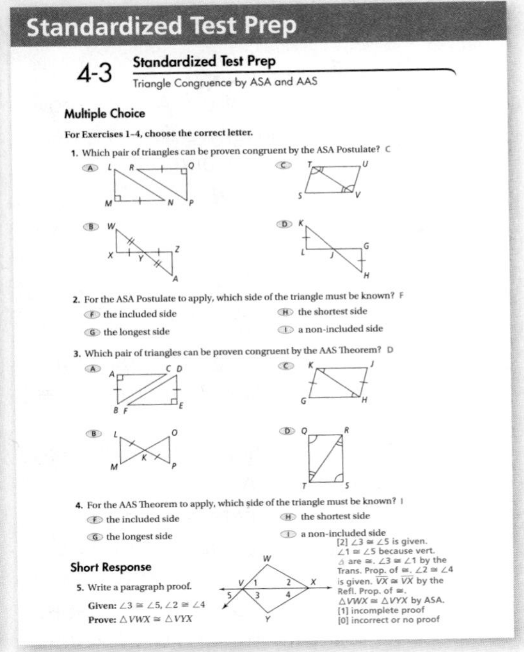

4-3 **Standardized Test Prep**
Triangle Congruence by ASA and AAS

Multiple Choice

For Exercises 1–4, choose the correct letter.

1. Which pair of triangles can be proven congruent by the ASA Postulate? C
   A. B. C. D.
2. For the ASA Postulate to apply, which side of the triangle must be known? F
   F. the included side
   G. the longest side
   H. the shortest side
   I. a non-included side
3. Which pair of triangles can be proven congruent by the AAS Theorem? D
   A. B. C. D.
4. For the AAS Theorem to apply, which side of the triangle must be known? I
   F. the included side
   G. the longest side
   H. the shortest side
   I. a non-included side

Short Response

5. Write a paragraph proof.
   Given: $\angle 3 \cong \angle 5$, $\angle 2 \cong \angle 4$
   Prove: $\triangle VWX \cong \triangle VYX$
   [2] $\angle 3 \cong \angle 5$ is given. $\angle 1 \cong \angle 5$ because vert. ∠s are ≅. $\angle 3 \cong \angle 1$ by the Trans. Prop. of ≅. $\angle 2 \cong \angle 4$ is given. $\overline{VX} \cong \overline{VX}$ by the Refl. Prop. of ≅. $\triangle VWX \cong \triangle VYX$ by ASA.
   [1] incomplete proof
   [0] incorrect or no proof

Online Teacher Resource Center

Activities, Games, and Puzzles

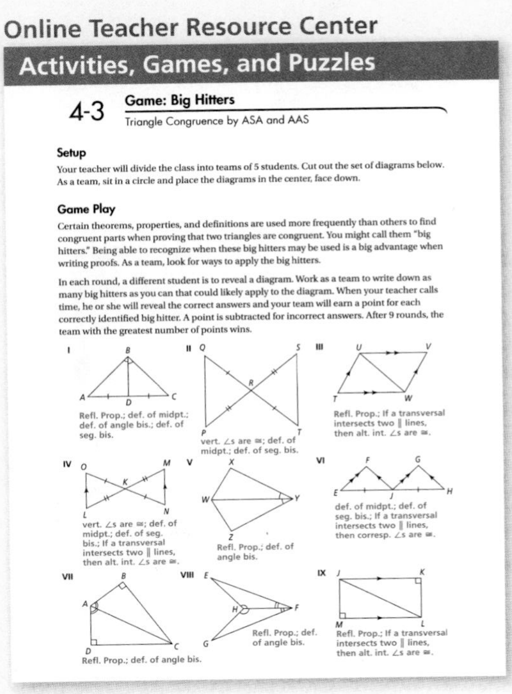

4-3 **Game: Big Hitters**
Triangle Congruence by ASA and AAS

Setup

Your teacher will divide the class into teams of 5 students. Cut out the set of diagrams below. As a team, sit in a circle and place the diagrams in the center, face down.

Game Play

Certain theorems, properties, and definitions are used more frequently than others to find congruent parts when proving that two triangles are congruent. You might call them "big hitters." Being able to recognize when these big hitters may be used is a big advantage when writing proofs. As a team, look for ways to apply the big hitters.

In each round, a different student is to reveal a diagram. Work as a team to write down as many big hitters as you can that could likely apply to the diagram. When your teacher calls time, he or she will reveal the correct answers and your team will earn a point for each correctly identified big hitter. A point is subtracted for incorrect answers. After 9 rounds, the team with the greatest number of points wins.

I. Refl. Prop.; def. of midpt.; def. of angle bis.; def. of seg. bis.
II. vert. ∠s are ≅; def. of midpt.; def. of seg. bis.
III. Refl. Prop.; If a transversal intersects two ∥ lines, then alt. int. ∠s are ≅.
IV. vert. ∠s are ≅; def. of midpt.; def. of seg. bis.; If a transversal intersects two ∥ lines, then alt. int. ∠s are ≅.
V. Refl. Prop.; def. of angle bis.
VI. def. of midpt.; def. of seg. bis.; If a transversal intersects two ∥ lines, then corresp. ∠s are ≅.
VII. Refl. Prop.; def. of angle bis.
VIII. Refl. Prop.; def. of angle bis.
IX. Refl. Prop.; If a transversal intersects two ∥ lines, then alt. int. ∠s are ≅.

Guided Instruction

PURPOSE To use geometry software to explore whether triangles can be proved congruent using AAA or SSA

PROCESS Students will use geometry software to create triangles based on certain criteria and examine the triangles for congruence.

DISCUSS Before students begin their constructions, ask them to make a conjecture about whether it is possible to prove triangles congruent using AAA or SSA.

Activity 1

In this Activity, students explore whether triangles can be proved congruent using AAA.

Q What is the reason $\angle AED \cong \angle ACB$? **[When two parallel lines are cut by a transversal, corresponding angles are congruent.]**

Q Can you make the same argument for $\angle ADE$ and $\angle ABC$? **[Yes]**

Q Why are the triangles not congruent? **[Their side lengths are not equal.]**

Activity 2

In this Activity, students explore whether triangles can be proved congruent using SSA.

Q Does the length of side $\overline{CE}$ of your triangles change as you move point E? Why or why not? **[No, it remains the same because it is the radius of circle C.]**

Q Does the measure of $\angle ACE$ remain the same within your two triangles? **[No]**

Q Does the measure of $\angle AEC$ remain the same within your two triangles? **[No]**

Concept Byte

Use With Lesson 4-3

TECHNOLOGY

Exploring AAA and SSA

So far, you know four ways to conclude that two triangles are congruent—SSS, SAS, ASA, and AAS. It is good mathematics to wonder about the other two possibilities.

Activity 1

Construct Use geometry software to construct $\overrightarrow{AB}$ and $\overrightarrow{AC}$. Construct $\overline{BC}$ to form $\triangle ABC$. Construct a line parallel to $\overline{BC}$ that intersects $\overrightarrow{AB}$ and $\overrightarrow{AC}$ at points D and E to form $\triangle ADE$.

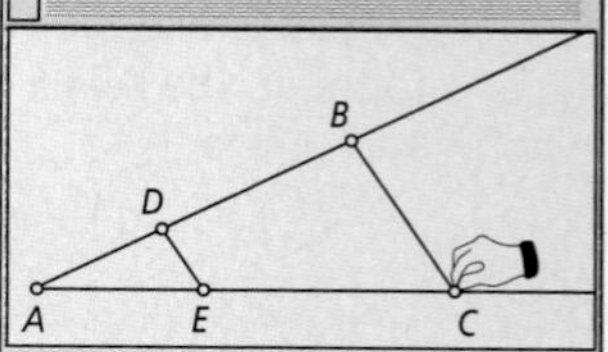

Investigate Are the three angles of $\triangle ABC$ congruent to the three angles of $\triangle ADE$? Manipulate the figure to change the positions of $\overline{DE}$ and $\overline{BC}$. Do the corresponding angles of the triangles remain congruent? Are the two triangles congruent? Can the two triangles be congruent?

Activity 2

Construct Construct $\overrightarrow{AB}$. Draw a circle with center C that intersects $\overrightarrow{AB}$ at two points. Construct $\overline{AC}$. Construct point E on the circle and construct $\overline{CE}$.

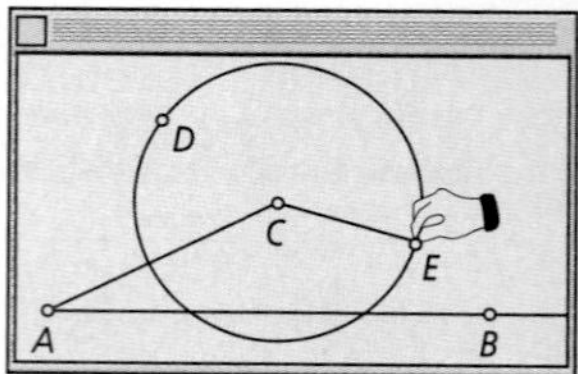

Investigate Move point E around the circle until E is on $\overrightarrow{AB}$ and forms $\triangle ACE$. Then move E on the circle to the other point on $\overrightarrow{AB}$ to form another $\triangle ACE$.

Compare AC, CE, and $m\angle A$ in the two triangles. Are two sides and a nonincluded angle of one triangle congruent to two sides and a nonincluded angle of the other triangle? Are the triangles congruent? If you change the measure of $\angle A$ and the size of the circle, do you get the same results?

Exercises

1. **Make a Conjecture** Based on your first investigation above, can you prove triangles congruent using AAA? Explain.

For Exercises 2–4, use what you learned in your second investigation above.

2. **Make a Conjecture** Can you prove triangles congruent using SSA? Explain.
3. Manipulate the figure so that $\angle A$ is obtuse. Can the circle intersect $\overrightarrow{AB}$ twice to form two triangles? Would SSA work if the congruent angles are obtuse? Explain.
4. Suppose you are given $\overline{CE}$, $\overline{AC}$, and $\angle A$. What must be true about CE, AC, and $m\angle A$ so that you can construct exactly one $\triangle ACE$? (*Hint:* Consider cases.)

Answers

Exercises

1. No, you cannot use AAA to prove ▲s ≅ because two ▲s can have 3 pairs of ≅ ∠s and not be the same size.
2. No, you cannot use SSA to prove ▲s ≅ because two sides of a △ and the nonincluded ∠ can be parts of two noncongruent ▲s.
3. No; the circle intersects $\overrightarrow{AB}$ just once, so only one △ is formed. If the ≅ ∠s are obtuse, then there could be an SSA congruency since a △ can have only one obtuse ∠.
4. If $CE \geq CA$ there is exactly one $\triangle ACE$ for any $m\angle A$. If $CE < CA$ there is exactly one $\triangle ACE$ only when $CE^2 + EA^2 = CA^2$, that is, when $\angle A$ (and $\angle C$) is an acute angle of a right triangle (with right $\angle AEC$).

4 Mid-Chapter Quiz

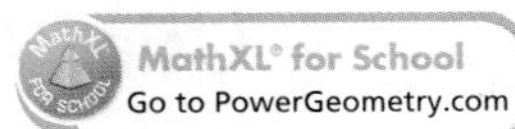

Do you know HOW?

1. $\triangle RST \cong \triangle JKL$. List the three pairs of congruent corresponding sides and the three pairs of congruent corresponding angles.

$LMNO \cong PQRS$. Name the angle or side that corresponds to the given part.

2. $\overline{RS}$
3. $\angle L$
4. $\angle Q$
5. $\overline{MN}$

State the postulate or theorem you can use to prove the triangles congruent. If you do not have enough information to prove the triangles congruent, write *not enough information*.

6.  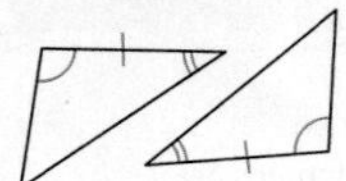 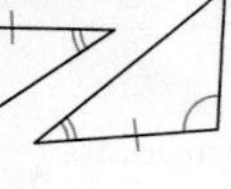

7. 

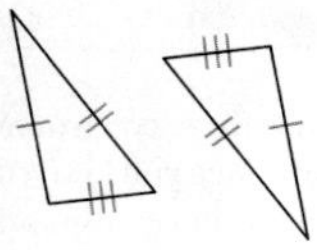

8. 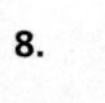 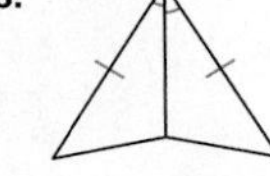

9.

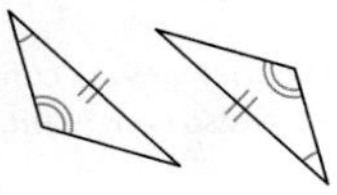

10. 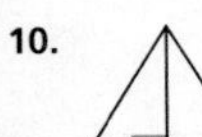 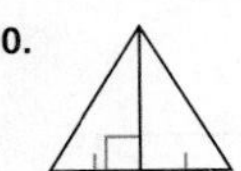

11.  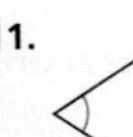

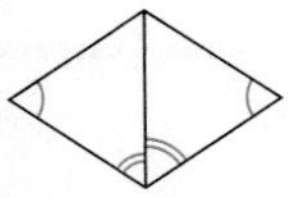

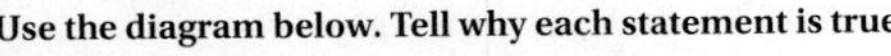

Use the diagram below. Tell why each statement is true.

12. $\angle H \cong \angle K$
13. $\angle HNL \cong \angle KNJ$
14. $\triangle HNL \cong \triangle KNJ$

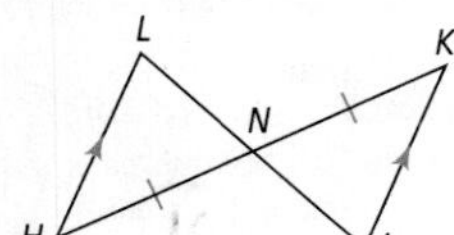

Determine what other information you need to prove the two triangles congruent. Then write the congruence statement and name the postulate or theorem you would use.

15. 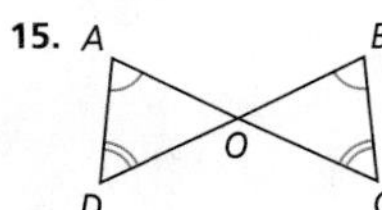

16. 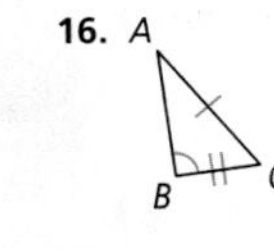

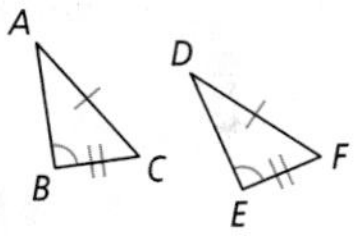

17. **Constructions** Construct $\triangle LMN$ congruent to $\triangle PQR$ using SSS.

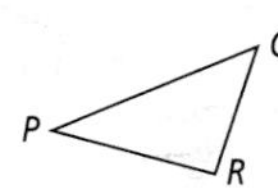

Do you UNDERSTAND?

18. **Given:** $\angle A \cong \angle D$, O is the midpoint of $\overline{AD}$
Prove: $\triangle AOB \cong \triangle DOC$

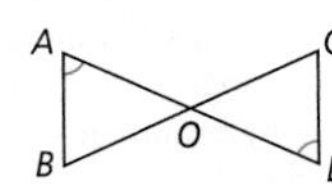

19. **Given:** $\overline{AB} \cong \overline{BC} \cong \overline{CD} \cong \overline{DA}$, $\angle A$, $\angle B$, $\angle C$, and $\angle D$ are right angles
Prove: $\triangle ABC \cong \triangle CDA$

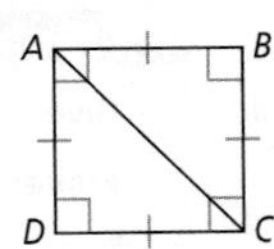

20. **Reasoning** Three segments form a triangle. How many unique triangles can you construct using the same three segments? Using the same three angles? Explain.

21. **Open-Ended** Write a congruency postulate for quadrilaterals. Does your postulate always hold true? Explain.

Answers

Mid-Chapter Quiz

1. $\overline{RS} \cong \overline{JK}$, $\overline{ST} \cong \overline{KL}$, $\overline{RT} \cong \overline{JL}$, $\angle R \cong \angle J$, $\angle S \cong \angle K$, $\angle T \cong \angle L$
2. $\overline{NO}$
3. $\angle P$
4. $\angle M$
5. $\overline{QR}$
6. ASA
7. SSS
8. SAS
9. AAS
10. SAS
11. AAS
12. The ∠s are alt. int. ∠s formed by parallel lines and a transversal.
13. The ∠s are vert. ∠s.
14. ASA
15. Answers may vary. Sample: $\overline{AD} \cong \overline{BC}$; $\triangle OAD \cong \triangle OBC$ by ASA.
16. Answers may vary. Sample: If $\overline{AB} \cong \overline{DE}$, then $\triangle ABC \cong \triangle DEF$ by SSS or SAS; if $\angle C \cong \angle F$, then $\triangle ABC \cong \triangle DEF$ by SAS, ASA, or AAS; if $\angle A \cong \angle D$, then $\triangle ABC \cong \triangle DEF$ by AAS.
17. 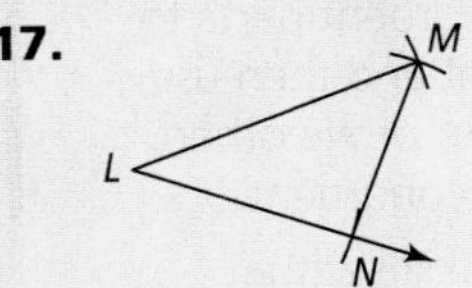

18. Point O is the midpt. of $\overline{AD}$ (Given), so $\overline{AO} \cong \overline{DO}$ by the def. of midpt. $\angle A \cong \angle D$ (Given) and $\angle AOB \cong \angle DOC$ (Vert. ∠s are ≅.), so $\triangle AOB \cong \triangle DOC$ by ASA.
19. Answers may vary. Sample: $\angle B \cong \angle D$ because $\angle B$ and $\angle D$ are given to be rt. ∠s, and all rt. ∠s are ≅. Also given is $\overline{AB} \cong \overline{CD}$ and $\overline{BC} \cong \overline{DA}$. So $\triangle ABC \cong \triangle CDA$ by SAS.
20. 3 segments: 1 △; all the △s are ≅ by SSS. 3 ∠s: an infinite number of △s; they will all have the same shape but they can be different sizes.
21. Answers may vary. Sample: If two quadrilaterals have 4 pairs of ≅ sides and a pair of ≅ corresp. diagonals, then the quadrilaterals must be ≅; yes. (See the discussion of "rigid figures" in Lesson 4-2, Ex. 32 answer.)

1 Interactive Learning

Solve It!

PURPOSE To draw conclusions about triangles based on congruence statements

PROCESS Students must prove $\triangle ABC \cong \triangle DEF$ by SAS or prove $\triangle DEF \cong \triangle GHI$ by AAS or ASA.

FACILITATE

Q What is the measure of $\angle E$? **[80]**

Q Which angle in each triangle measures 62? **[$\angle A$, $\angle D$, $\angle G$]**

Q What theorems can prove $\triangle DEF \cong \triangle GHI$? **[Third Angles Theorem and AAS or ASA.]**

ANSWER See Solve It in Answers on next page.

CONNECT THE MATH Students have learned how to use congruent parts to prove triangles are congruent. In this lesson they will use congruent triangles to prove that parts are congruent.

2 Guided Instruction

Problem 1

Q What is the relationship between the two triangles in the diagram? Explain. **[They are congruent by AAS.]**

Got It?

Q Which angles in the diagram do you know to be congruent? Explain your answer. **[$\angle CAB \cong \angle EAD$; vertical angles are $\cong$.]**

4-4 Using Corresponding Parts of Congruent Triangles

TN State Performance Indicator
SPI 3108.4.12 Solve problems involving congruence, similarity, proportional reasoning and/or scale factor of two similar figures or solids.

Objective To use triangle congruence and corresponding parts of congruent triangles to prove that parts of two triangles are congruent

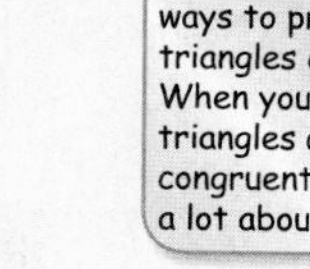

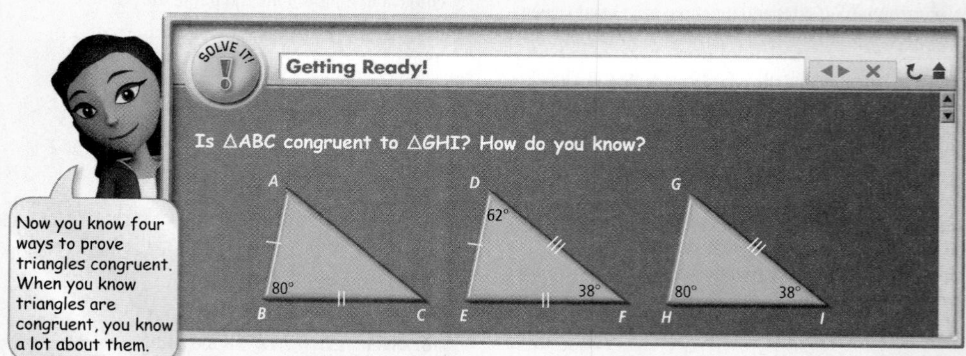

Now you know four ways to prove triangles congruent. When you know triangles are congruent, you know a lot about them.

With SSS, SAS, ASA, and AAS, you know how to use three congruent parts of two triangles to show that the triangles are congruent. Once you know that two triangles are congruent, you can make conclusions about their other corresponding parts because, by definition, corresponding parts of congruent triangles are congruent.

Essential Understanding If you know two triangles are congruent, then you know that every pair of their corresponding parts is also congruent.

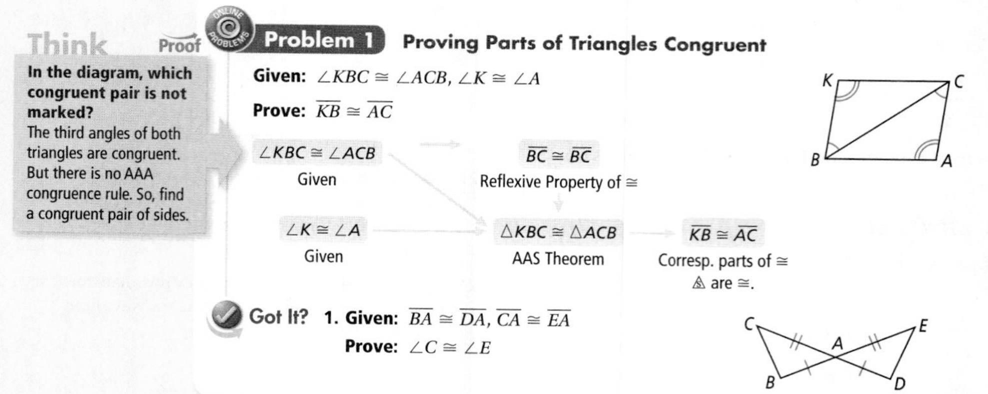

Think Proof

In the diagram, which congruent pair is not marked?
The third angles of both triangles are congruent. But there is no AAA congruence rule. So, find a congruent pair of sides.

Problem 1 Proving Parts of Triangles Congruent

Given: $\angle KBC \cong \angle ACB$, $\angle K \cong \angle A$

Prove: $\overline{KB} \cong \overline{AC}$

$\angle KBC \cong \angle ACB$ — Given

$\overline{BC} \cong \overline{BC}$ — Reflexive Property of $\cong$

$\angle K \cong \angle A$ — Given

$\triangle KBC \cong \triangle ACB$ — AAS Theorem

$\overline{KB} \cong \overline{AC}$ — Corresp. parts of $\cong$ △ are $\cong$.

Got It? **1. Given:** $\overline{BA} \cong \overline{DA}$, $\overline{CA} \cong \overline{EA}$
Prove: $\angle C \cong \angle E$

C A E B D

4-4 Preparing to Teach

BIG idea Reasoning and Proof **UbD**

ESSENTIAL UNDERSTANDING

- If two triangles are congruent, then every pair of their corresponding parts is also congruent.

Math Background

The statement *corresponding parts of congruent triangles are congruent* can be thought of as one half of the biconditional definition of congruent triangles. Two triangles are congruent if and only if their corresponding parts are congruent. In Lesson 4-1 students used the " ← " direction: If two triangles' corresponding parts are congruent, then the triangles are congruent. Here they are using the " → " direction: If two triangles are congruent, then their corresponding parts are congruent. The SSS, SAS, ASA Postulates and AAS Theorem offer a shortcut to the " ← " direction. Now the " → " direction leads to individual congruence statements about the parts.

The statement *corresponding parts of congruent triangles are congruent* is often abbreviated CPCTC. When teaching proofs that culminate in using the CPCTC statement, guide students to think of stages within the proof. One common line of logic is to use congruent parts to prove triangles congruent and then use the congruent triangles to prove other corresponding parts are congruent.

Students will develop a skill set that allows them to determine characteristics of figures based on only a few given statements. Building proofs like these is essential to many career fields. Logical reasoning and drawing conclusions are skills needed in any area of study.

Support Student Learning

Use the **Geometry Companion** to engage and support students during instructions. See Lesson Resources at the end of this lesson for details.

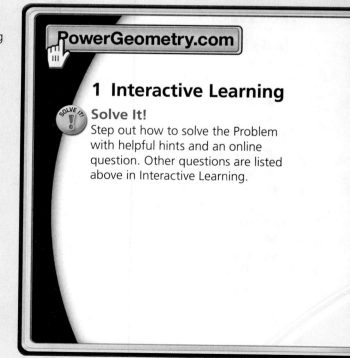

PowerGeometry.com

1 Interactive Learning

Solve It!

Step out how to solve the Problem with helpful hints and an online question. Other questions are listed above in Interactive Learning.

Proof  **Problem 2** **Proving Triangle Parts Congruent to Measure Distance**

Measurement **Thales, a Greek philosopher, is said to have developed a method to measure the distance to a ship at sea. He made a compass by nailing two sticks together. Standing on top of a tower, he would hold one stick vertical and tilt the other until he could see the ship *S* along the line of the tilted stick. With this compass setting, he would find a landmark *L* on the shore along the line of the tilted stick. How far would the ship be from the base of the tower?**

Plan

Which congruency rule can you use? You have information about two pairs of angles. *Guess-and-check* AAS and ASA.

Given: $\angle TRS$ and $\angle TRL$ are right angles, $\angle RTS \cong \angle RTL$

Prove: $\overline{RS} \cong \overline{RL}$

Statements	Reasons
1) $\angle RTS \cong \angle RTL$	1) Given
2) $\overline{TR} \cong \overline{TR}$	2) Reflexive Property of Congruence
3) $\angle TRS$ and $\angle TRL$ are right angles.	3) Given
4) $\angle TRS \cong \angle TRL$	4) All right angles are congruent.
5) $\triangle TRS \cong \triangle TRL$	5) ASA Postulate
6) $\overline{RS} \cong \overline{RL}$	6) Corresponding parts of $\cong$ $\triangle$s are $\cong$.

The distance between the ship and the base of the tower would be the same as the distance between the base of the tower and the landmark.

 **Got It?** **2. a. Given:** $\overline{AB} \cong \overline{AC}$, M is the midpoint of $\overline{BC}$
Prove: $\angle AMB \cong \angle AMC$

b. Reasoning If the landmark were not at sea level, would the method in Problem 2 work? Explain.

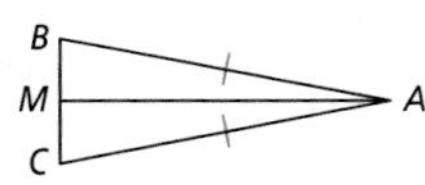

Problem 2

Students may benefit from working backward through this proof. Have students begin with the conclusion and identify information that is needed to reach the desired congruence statement. Then ask students to find a justification of each claim.

Q What congruence statement must be proved before you can state $\overline{RS} \cong \overline{RL}$? **[$\triangle TRS \cong \triangle TRL$]**

Q The compass setting is the same toward the ship as it is toward the landmark. What can you conclude about the triangles? **[The angles *STR* and *LTR* are congruent.]**

Q Which side is shared by the triangles? **[$\overline{TR}$ is shared by both triangles.]**

Q What postulate or theorem proves that the triangles are congruent? **[ASA]**

Got It?

ERROR PREVENTION

Caution students to use only congruence statements that can be justified by theorems, definitions, and properties. They should not allow themselves to be mislead by appearances in a diagram. Point out to students that although $\angle BMA$ and $\angle CMA$ appear to be right angles, it cannot be assumed that they are. Likewise, although $\overline{AM}$ appears to bisect $\angle BAC$, that cannot be assumed from the diagram.

2 Guided Instruction

 Each Problem is worked out and supported online.

Problem 1
Proving Parts of Triangles Congruent
Animated

Problem 2
Proving Triangle Parts Congruent to Measure Distance
Animated

Support in Geometry Companion
- Vocabulary
- Key Concepts
- Got It?

Answers

Solve It!

$m\angle E = 80$ and $m\angle G = 62$ by the Triangle Angle-Sum Theorem. So $\triangle ABC \cong \triangle DEF$ by SAS and $\triangle DEF \cong \triangle GHI$ by AAS or ASA. Since both $\triangle ABC$ and $\triangle GHI$ are $\cong$ to $\triangle DEF$, they are $\cong$ to each other by the Transitive Prop. of $\cong$.

Got It?

1. $\overline{BA} \cong \overline{DA}$ and $\overline{CA} \cong \overline{ED}$ (Given). $\angle CAB \cong \angle EAD$ (Vert. $\angle$s are $\cong$.) So $\triangle ABC \cong \triangle ADE$ by SAS and $\angle C \cong \angle E$ because corresp. parts of $\cong$ $\triangle$s are $\cong$.

2a. M is the midpt. of $\overline{BC}$, so $\overline{BM} \cong \overline{CM}$ by the def. of midpt. $\overline{AB} \cong \overline{AC}$ (Given) and $\overline{AM} \cong \overline{AM}$ (Refl. Prop. of $\cong$), so $\triangle AMB \cong \triangle AMC$ by SSS. Thus $\angle AMB \cong \angle AMC$ because corresp. parts of $\cong$ $\triangle$s are $\cong$.

b. No; while $\overline{TR} \perp \overline{RS}$, if point L is not at sea level, then $\overline{TR}$ would not be $\perp$ to $\overline{RL}$.

3 Lesson Check

Do you know HOW?

- If students have difficulty with Exercise 2, then have them review Problem 2.

Do you UNDERSTAND?

- If students have difficulty with Exercise 4, then have them review Problem 1.

Close

Q What postulates or theorems can be used to show that two triangles are congruent? **[AAS, SAS, SSS, ASA]**

Q How can you use congruent triangles to make statements about their parts? **[Once you know triangles are congruent, you can state that any corresponding parts of the triangles are congruent.]**

Lesson Check

Do you know HOW?

Name the postulate or theorem that you can use to show the triangles are congruent. Then explain why the statement is true.

1. $\overline{EA} \cong \overline{MA}$

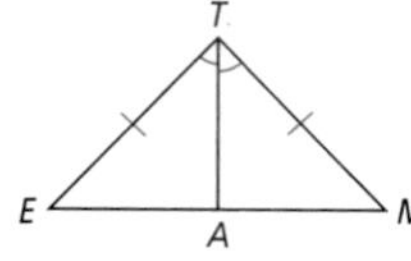

2. $\angle U \cong \angle E$

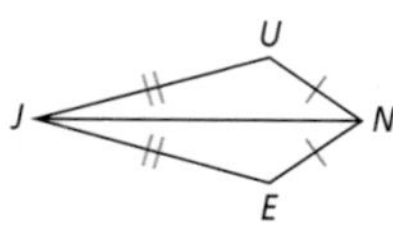

Do you UNDERSTAND?

3. Reasoning How does the fact that corresponding parts of congruent triangles are congruent relate to the definition of congruent triangles?

4. Error Analysis Find and correct the error(s) in the proof.

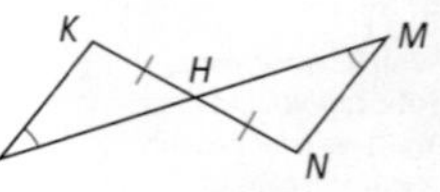

Given: $\overline{KH} \cong \overline{NH}$, $\angle L \cong \angle M$

Prove: H is the midpoint of $\overline{LM}$.

Proof: $\overline{KH} \cong \overline{NH}$ because it is given. $\angle L \cong \angle M$ because it is given. $\angle KHL \cong \angle NHM$ because vertical angles are congruent. So, $\triangle KHL \cong \triangle MHN$ by ASA Postulate. Since corresponding parts of congruent triangles are congruent, $\overline{LH} \cong \overline{MH}$. By the definition of midpoint, H is the midpoint of $\overline{LM}$.

Practice and Problem-Solving Exercises

A Practice

5. Developing Proof Tell why the two triangles are congruent. Give the congruence statement. Then list all the other corresponding parts of the triangles that are congruent.

See Problem 1.

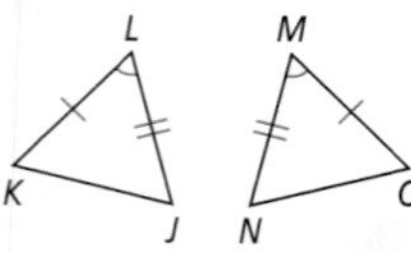

6. Given: $\angle ABD \cong \angle CBD$, $\angle BDA \cong \angle BDC$

Proof

Prove: $\overline{AB} \cong \overline{CB}$

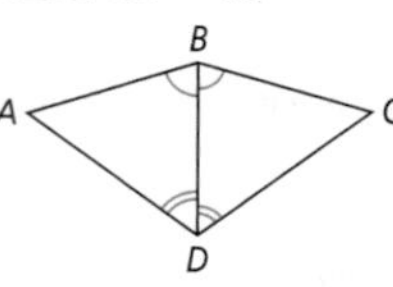

7. Given: $\overline{OM} \cong \overline{ER}$, $\overline{ME} \cong \overline{RO}$

Proof

Prove: $\angle M \cong \angle R$

See Problem 2.

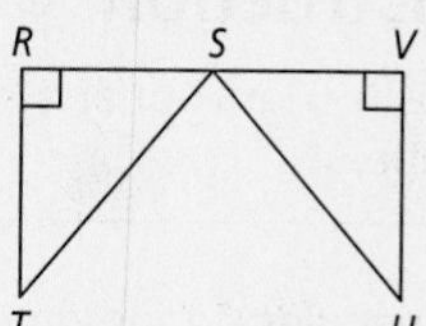

8. Developing Proof A balalaika is a stringed instrument. Prove that the bases of the balalaikas are congruent.

Given: $\overline{RA} \cong \overline{NY}$, $\angle KRA \cong \angle JNY$, $\angle KAR \cong \angle JYN$

Prove: $\overline{KA} \cong \overline{JY}$

Proof: It is given that two angles and the included side of one triangle are congruent to two angles and the included side of the other. So, **a.** ___?___ $\cong \triangle JNY$ by **b.** ___?___. $\overline{KA} \cong \overline{JY}$ because **c.** ___?___.

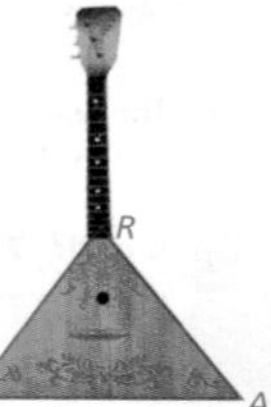

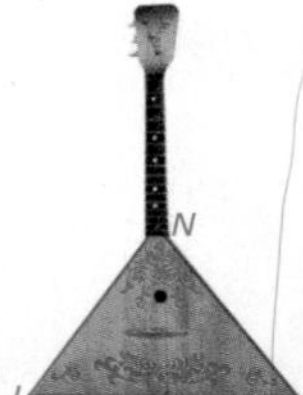

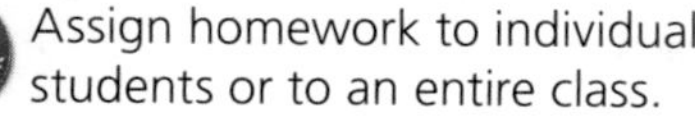

PowerGeometry.com

3 Lesson Check

For a digital lesson check, use the Got It questions.

Support in Geometry Companion

- Lesson Check

4 Practice

Assign homework to individual students or to an entire class.

Additional Problems

1. Given: $\overline{RS} \cong \overline{UT}$, $\overline{RT} \cong \overline{US}$

Prove: $\angle T \cong \angle S$

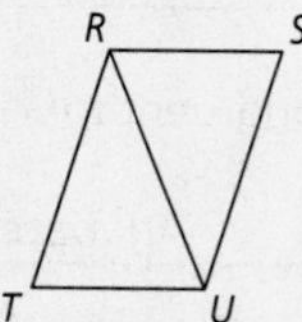

ANSWER It is given that $\overline{RS} \cong \overline{UT}$ and $\overline{RT} \cong \overline{US}$. $\overline{RU} \cong \overline{RU}$ by the Reflexive Property of Congruence. So, $\triangle RSU \cong \triangle UTR$ by SSS Postulate. Therefore, $\angle T \cong \angle S$ because the angles are corresponding parts of congruent triangles.

2. Given: $\overline{RS} \cong \overline{VS}$, $\overline{RT} \cong \overline{VU}$, $\angle R$ and $\angle V$ are both right angles

Prove: $\angle T \cong \angle U$

R S V

T U

ANSWER It is given that $\overline{RS} \cong \overline{VS}$, $\overline{RT} \cong \overline{VU}$, and $\angle R$ and $\angle V$ are both right angles. So, $\angle R \cong \angle V$ because all right angles are congruent. $\triangle RST \cong \triangle VSU$ by SAS. So, $\angle T \cong \angle U$ because the angles are corresponding parts of congruent triangles.

B Apply

9. **Given:** $\angle SPT \cong \angle OPT$, $\overline{SP} \cong \overline{OP}$
Proof
Prove: $\angle S \cong \angle O$

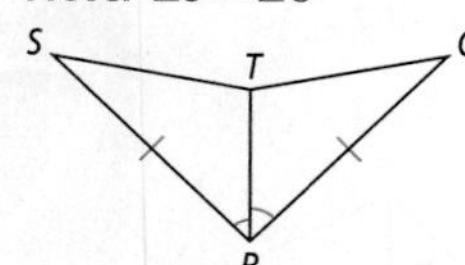

10. **Given:** $\overline{YT} \cong \overline{YP}$, $\angle C \cong \angle R$, $\angle T \cong \angle P$
Proof
Prove: $\overline{CT} \cong \overline{RP}$

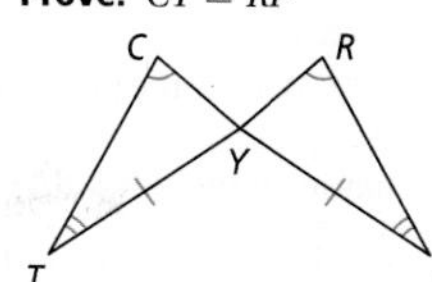

Reasoning Copy and mark the figure to show the given information. Explain how you would prove $\angle P \cong \angle Q$.

11. **Given:** $\overline{PK} \cong \overline{QK}$, $\overline{KL}$ bisects $\angle PKQ$

12. **Given:** $\overline{KL}$ is the perpendicular bisector of $\overline{PQ}$.

13. **Given:** $\overline{KL} \perp \overline{PQ}$, $\overline{KL}$ bisects $\angle PKQ$

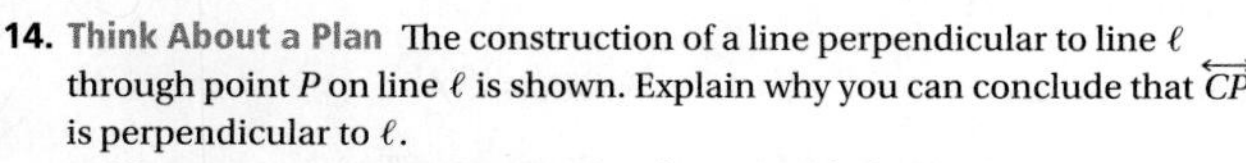

14. **Think About a Plan** The construction of a line perpendicular to line ℓ through point P on line ℓ is shown. Explain why you can conclude that $\overleftrightarrow{CP}$ is perpendicular to ℓ.
- How can you use congruent triangles to justify the construction?
- Which lengths or distances are equal by construction?

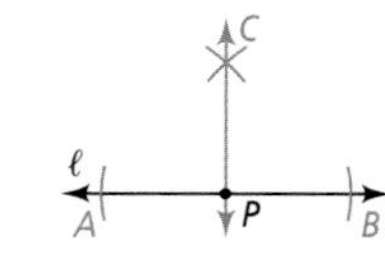

15. **Given:** $\overline{BA} \cong \overline{BC}$, $\overline{BD}$ bisects $\angle ABC$
Proof
Prove: $\overline{BD} \perp \overline{AC}$, $\overline{BD}$ bisects $\overline{AC}$

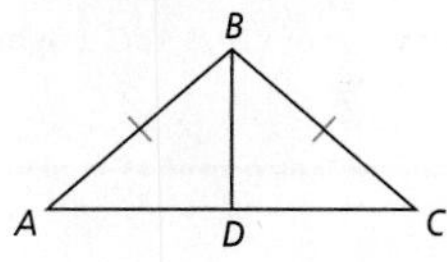

16. **Given:** $\ell \perp \overline{AB}$, ℓ bisects $\overline{AB}$ at C, P is on ℓ
Proof
Prove: $PA = PB$

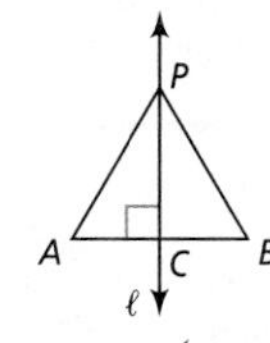

17. **Constructions** The construction of $\angle B$ congruent to given $\angle A$ is shown. $\overline{AD} \cong \overline{BF}$ because they are congruent radii. $\overline{DC} \cong \overline{FE}$ because both arcs have the same compass settings. Explain why you can conclude that $\angle A \cong \angle B$.

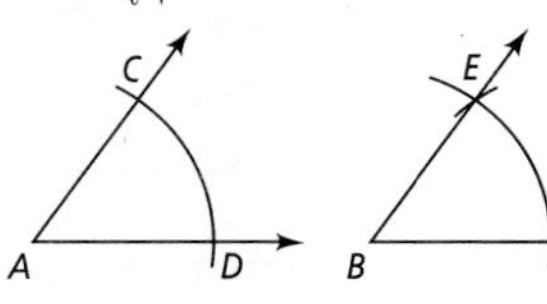

18. **Given:** $\overline{BE} \perp \overline{AC}$, $\overline{DF} \perp \overline{AC}$, $\overline{BE} \cong \overline{DF}$, $\overline{AF} \cong \overline{CE}$
Proof
Prove: $\overline{AB} \cong \overline{CD}$

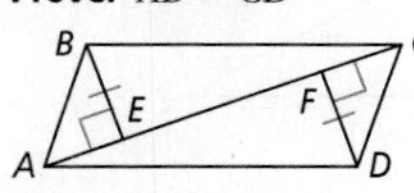

19. **Given:** $\overline{JK} \parallel \overline{QP}$, $\overline{JK} \cong \overline{PQ}$
Proof
Prove: $\overline{KQ}$ bisects $\overline{JP}$.

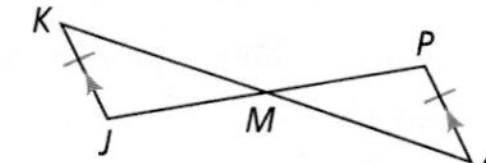

4 Practice

ASSIGNMENT GUIDE
Basic: 5–8 all, 10–16 even, 17, 20
Average: 5, 7, 9–20
Advanced: 5, 7, 9–22
Standardized Test Prep: 23–26
Mixed Review: 27–32
Reasoning exercises have blue headings.
Applications exercises have red headings.
EXERCISE 17: Use the Think About a Plan worksheet in the **Practice and Problem Solving Workbook** (also available in the Teaching Resources in print and online) to further support students' development in becoming independent learners.

HOMEWORK QUICK CHECK
To check students' understanding of key skills and concepts, go over Exercises 5, 7, 14, 17, and 20.

Answers

Lesson Check

1. SAS; so $\overline{EA} \cong \overline{MA}$ because corresp. parts of $\cong$ ▲s are $\cong$.
2. SSS; so $\angle U \cong \angle E$ because corresp. parts of $\cong$ ▲s are $\cong$.
3. "Corresp. parts of $\cong$ ▲s are $\cong$" is a short version of the def. of $\cong$ ▲s.
4. $\triangle KHL \cong \triangle NHM$ by AAS Thm.

Practice and Problem Solving Exercises

5. $\triangle KLJ \cong \triangle OMN$ by SAS; $\overline{KJ} \cong \overline{ON}$, $\angle K \cong \angle O$, $\angle J \cong \angle N$.
6. $\angle ABD \cong \angle CBD$ and $\angle BDA \cong \angle BDC$ (Given). $\overline{BD} \cong \overline{BD}$ by the Refl. Prop. of $\cong$. $\triangle ABD \cong \triangle CBD$ by ASA, so $\overline{AB} \cong \overline{CB}$ because corresp. parts of $\cong$ ▲s are $\cong$.
7. $\overline{OM} \cong \overline{EB}$ and $\overline{ME} \cong \overline{RO}$ (Given). $\overline{OE} \cong \overline{OE}$ by the Refl. Prop. of $\cong$. $\triangle MOE \cong \triangle REO$ by SSS, so $\angle M \cong \angle R$ because corresp. parts of $\cong$ ▲s are $\cong$.

8a. $\triangle KRA$
b. ASA
c. Corresp. parts of $\cong$ ▲s are $\cong$.

9. A pair of $\cong$ sides and a pair of $\cong$ ∠s are given. Since $\overline{PT} \cong \overline{PT}$ (Refl. Prop. of $\cong$), then $\triangle STP \cong \triangle OTP$ by SAS. $\angle S \cong \angle O$ because corresp. parts of $\cong$ ▲s are $\cong$.
10. From the given information, $\triangle YCT \cong \triangle YRP$ by AAS. So $\overline{CT} \cong \overline{RP}$ because corresp. parts of $\cong$ ▲s are $\cong$.

11–13. Check students' diagrams.

11. $\overline{KL}$ bisects $\angle PKQ$, so $\angle PKL \cong \angle QKL$. $\overline{KL} \cong \overline{KL}$ by Refl. Prop. of $\cong$. $\triangle PKL \cong \triangle QKL$ by SAS, so $\angle P \cong \angle Q$ because corresp. parts of $\cong$ ▲s are $\cong$.
12. From the def. of $\perp$ bisector, $\overline{PL} \cong \overline{QL}$ and $\angle PLK \cong \angle QLK$ because all rt. ∠s are $\cong$. Since $\overline{KL} \cong \overline{KL}$, then $\triangle PKL \cong \triangle QKL$ by SAS, and $\angle P \cong \angle Q$ because corresp. parts of $\cong$ ▲s are $\cong$.
13. $\angle PLK \cong \angle QLK$ because $\perp$ lines form rt. ∠s, and all rt. ∠s are $\cong$. From the $\angle$ bisector, $\angle PKL \cong \angle QKL$. So with $\overline{KL} \cong \overline{KL}$ by the Refl. Prop. of $\cong$, $\triangle PKL \cong \triangle QKL$ by ASA and $\angle P \cong \angle Q$ because corresp. parts of $\cong$ ▲s are $\cong$.

14–19. See next page.

Answers

Practice and Problem Solving Exercises (continued)

14. The arcs with center P make $\overline{PA} \cong \overline{PB}$, and the arcs with centers at A and B make $\overline{CA} \cong \overline{CB}$. Since $\overline{CP} \cong \overline{CP}$, $\triangle APC \cong \triangle BPC$ by SSS. $\angle APC \cong \angle BPC$ because corresp. parts of $\cong$ ⧍ are $\cong$. $\angle APC$ and $\angle BPC$ are suppl. because they form a linear pair. So $\angle APC$ is a rt. $\angle$, which means its sides are $\perp$.

15. $\overline{BA} \cong \overline{BC}$ (Given) and $\overline{BD}$ bisects $\angle ABC$ (Given) $\angle ABD \cong \angle CBD$ (Def. of $\angle$ bisector). $\overline{BD} \cong \overline{BD}$ (Refl. Prop. of $\cong$), so $\triangle ABD \cong \triangle CBD$ by SAS. $\angle ADB \cong \angle CDB$ (Corresp. parts of $\cong$ ⧍ are $\cong$.) and $\angle ADB$ and $\angle CDB$ are suppl. so they must be rt. ⦣. By def. of $\perp$ lines, $\overline{BD} \perp \overline{AC}$. $\overline{AD} \cong \overline{CD}$ (Corresp. parts of $\cong$ ⧍ are $\cong$.), so $\overline{BD}$ bisects $\overline{AC}$ (Def. of seg. bisector).

16. $\ell \perp \overline{AB}$ (Given), so $\angle ACP$ and $\angle BCP$ are rt. ⦣ (Def. of $\perp$ lines). $\angle ACP \cong \angle BCP$ (All rt. ⦣ are $\cong$.). ℓ bisects $\overline{AB}$ at C (Given), so $\overline{AC} \cong \overline{BC}$ (Def. of seg. bisector). P is on ℓ (Given), and $\overline{PC} \cong \overline{PC}$ (Refl. Prop. of $\cong$), so $\triangle PAC \cong \triangle PBC$ by SAS. $\overline{PA} \cong \overline{PB}$ because corresp. parts of $\cong$ ⧍ are $\cong$. So $PA = PB$ by def. of $\cong$ segments.

17. The construction makes $\overline{AC} \cong \overline{BE}$, $\overline{AD} \cong \overline{BF}$, and $\overline{CD} \cong \overline{EF}$. So $\triangle ACD \cong \triangle BEF$ by SSS. Thus $\angle A \cong \angle B$ because corresp. parts of $\cong$ ⧍ are $\cong$.

18. $\overline{BE} \perp \overline{AC}$ (Given) and $\overline{DF} \perp \overline{AC}$ (Given). $\angle AEB$ and $\angle CFD$ are rt. ⦣ (Def. of $\perp$ lines). $\angle AEB \cong \angle CFD$ (All rt. ⦣ are $\cong$.). $\overline{BE} \cong \overline{DF}$ (Given) and $\overline{AF} \cong \overline{CE}$ (Given), so $AF = CE$, $AE + EF = CF + FE$ (Segment Addition Post.), $AE = CF$ (Subraction Prop. of =) and $\overline{AE} \cong \overline{CF}$. $\triangle AEB \cong \triangle CFD$ by SAS, so $\overline{AB} \cong \overline{CD}$ because corresp. parts of $\cong$ ⧍ are $\cong$.

19. It is given that $\overline{JK} \parallel \overline{QP}$, so $\angle K \cong \angle Q$ and $\angle J \cong \angle P$ because they are alt. int. ⦣. With $\overline{JK} \cong \overline{PQ}$ (Given), $\triangle KJM \cong \triangle QPM$ by ASA and then $\overline{JM} \cong \overline{PM}$ because corresp. parts of $\cong$ ⧍ are $\cong$. Thus M is the midpt. of $\overline{JP}$ by def. of midpt. So $\overline{KQ}$, which contains point M, bisects $\overline{JP}$ by the def. of segment bisector.

20. 36

21–22. Using the given information and $\overline{AE} \cong \overline{AE}$ (Refl. Prop. of $\cong$), $\triangle AKE \cong \triangle ABE$ by SSS. Thus $\angle KAS \cong \angle BAS$ because corresp. parts of $\cong$ ⧍ are $\cong$. In $\triangle KAS$ and $\triangle BAS$, $\overline{AK} \cong \overline{AB}$ (Given) and $\overline{AS} \cong \overline{AS}$ (Refl. Prop. of $\cong$), so $\triangle KAS \cong \triangle BAS$ by SAS. Thus $\overline{KS} \cong \overline{BS}$ because corresp. parts of $\cong$ ⧍ are $\cong$, and S is the midpt. of $\overline{BK}$ by the def. of midpt. $\angle KSA \cong \angle BSA$ because corresp. parts of $\cong$ ⧍ are $\cong$; the angles are also suppl., so the measure of each is 90. Thus $\overline{BK} \perp \overline{AE}$ by the def. of $\perp$ lines.

20. Designs Rangoli is a colorful design pattern drawn outside houses in India, especially during festivals. Vina plans to use the pattern at the right as the base of her design. In this pattern, $\overline{RU}$, $\overline{SV}$, and $\overline{QT}$ bisect each other at O. $RS = 6$, $RU = 12$, $\overline{RU} \cong \overline{SV}$, $\overline{ST} \parallel \overline{RU}$, and $\overline{RS} \parallel \overline{QT}$. What is the perimeter of the hexagon?

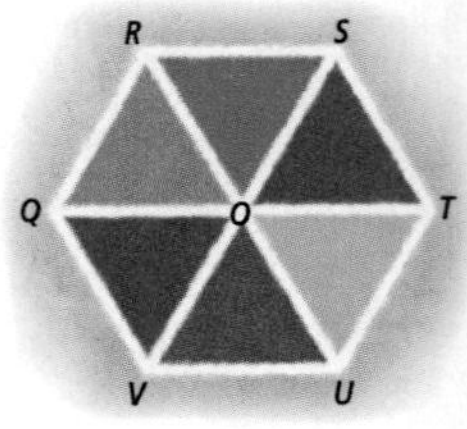

Challenge In the diagram at the right, $\overline{BA} \cong \overline{KA}$ and $\overline{BE} \cong \overline{KE}$.

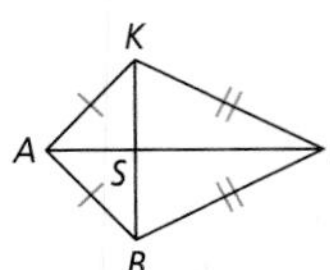

21. Prove: S is the midpoint of $\overline{BK}$.

Proof

22. Prove: $\overline{BK} \perp \overline{AE}$

Proof

Standardized Test Prep

SAT/ACT — GRIDDED RESPONSE

For Exercises 23 and 24, use the diagram at the right. $\overline{TM} \perp \overline{BD}$ and $\overline{TM}$ bisects $\angle BTD$ and $\angle ATC$.

23. Suppose $BD = 17$ and $AM = 5$. What is the length of $\overline{CD}$?

24. Suppose $m\angle ATC = 64$, and $m\angle BTA = 16$. What is $m\angle B$?

25. Two parallel lines q and s are cut by a transversal t. $\angle 1$ and $\angle 2$ are a pair of alternate interior angles and $m\angle 2 = 38$. $\angle 1$ and $\angle 3$ are vertical angles. What is $m\angle 3$?

26. $\triangle ABC$ has vertices $A(1, 9)$, $B(4, 3)$, and $C(x, 6)$. For what value of x is $\triangle ABC$ a right triangle with right $\angle B$?

Mixed Review

For Exercises 27 and 28, tell the postulate or theorem that you can use to prove the triangles congruent.

See Lesson 4-3.

27.

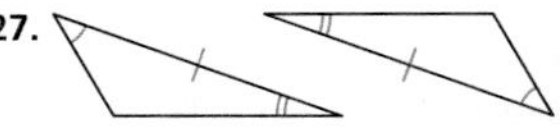

28.

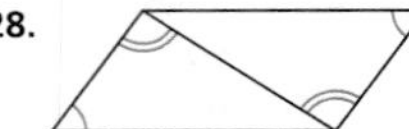

Get Ready! To prepare for Lesson 4-5, do Exercises 29–32.

See Lesson 3-5.

29. What is the side opposite $\angle ABC$?

30. What is the angle opposite side $\overline{AB}$?

31. What is the angle opposite side $\overline{BC}$?

32. Find the value of x.

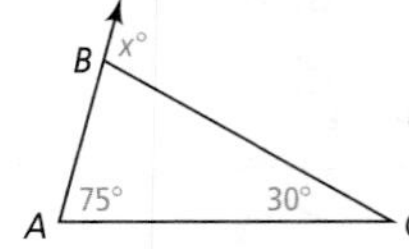

23. 3.5	**24.** 42
25. 38	**26.** 10
27. ASA	**28.** AAS
29. $\overline{AC}$	**30.** $\angle C$
31. $\angle A$	**32.** 105

4-4 Lesson Resources

Instructional Support

Geometry Companion

Students can use the **Geometry Companion** worktext (4 pages) . . .

- New Vocabulary
- Key Concepts
- Got It for each Problem
- Lesson Check

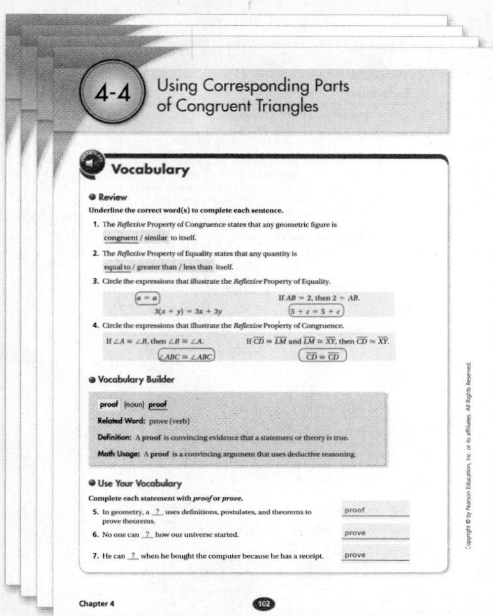

4-4 Using Corresponding Parts of Congruent Triangles

Vocabulary

Review

Underline the correct word(s) to complete each sentence.

1. The *Reflexive* Property of Congruence states that any geometric figure is congruent / similar to itself.
2. The *Reflexive* Property of Equality states that any quantity is equal to / greater than / less than itself.
3. Circle the expressions that illustrate the *Reflexive* Property of Equality.

$a = a$ If $AB = 2$, then $2 = AB$. $3(x + y) = 3x + 3y$ $5 + c = 5 + c$

4. Circle the expressions that illustrate the *Reflexive* Property of Congruence.

If $\angle A \cong \angle B$, then $\angle B \cong \angle A$.   If $\overline{CD} \cong \overline{LM}$ and $\overline{LM} \cong \overline{XY}$, then $\overline{CD} \cong \overline{XY}$. $\angle ABC \cong \angle ABC$ $\overline{CD} \cong \overline{CD}$

Vocabulary Builder

proof (noun) proof

Related Word: prove (verb)

Definition: A **proof** is convincing evidence that a statement or theory is true.

Math Usage: A **proof** is a convincing argument that uses deductive reasoning.

Use Your Vocabulary

Complete each statement with *proof* or *prove*.

5. In geometry, a _?_ uses definitions, postulates, and theorems to prove theorems.   proof
6. No one can _?_ how our universe started.   prove
7. He can _?_ when he bought the computer because he has a receipt.   prove

Copyright © by Pearson Education, Inc. or its affiliates. All Rights Reserved.

Chapter 4   102

ELL Support

Use Graphic Organizers Have students draw a concept wheel.

Label a middle circle:

Congruent triangles postulates/theorems. Add five spokes off the wheel that lead to five more circles. Label four of the circles with the concepts SSS, SAS, ASA, and AAS. Have students write each postulate or theorem in its respective circle, along with an example. Point out that there is another congruence concept to come. Have students discuss what it could be.

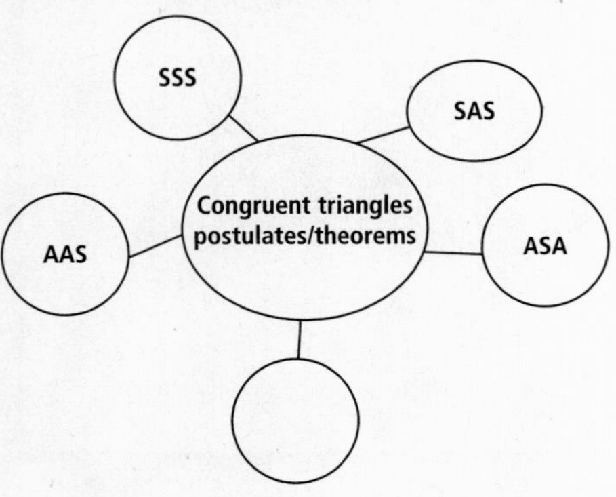

SSS
SAS
Congruent triangles postulates/theorems
AAS
ASA

5 Assess & Remediate

Lesson Quiz

1. **Given:** $\overline{WX} \cong \overline{ZY}$, $\overline{WY} \cong \overline{ZX}$

Prove: $\angle W \cong \angle Z$

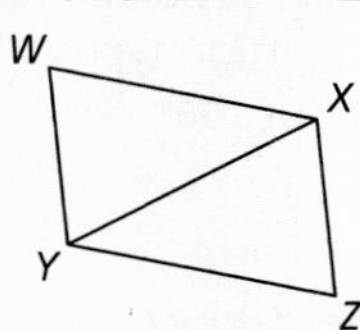

W
X
Y
Z

2. **Do you UNDERSTAND?**

Given: $\angle ONL \cong \angle MLN$, $\angle O$ and $\angle M$ are right angles.

Prove: $\overline{LM} \cong \overline{NO}$

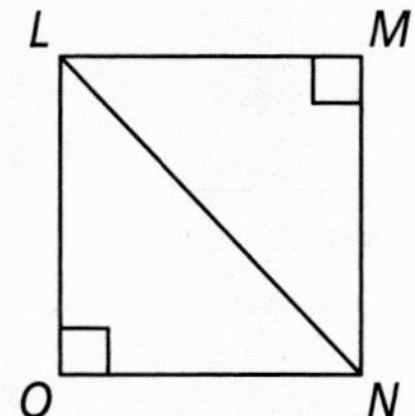

L
M
O
N

ANSWERS TO LESSON QUIZ

1. It is given that $\overline{WX} \cong \overline{ZY}$ and $\overline{WY} \cong \overline{ZX}$. $\overline{XY} \cong \overline{XY}$ by the Reflexive Property of Congruence. So, $\triangle WXY \cong \triangle ZYX$ by the SSS Postulate. So, $\angle W \cong \angle Z$ because they are corresponding parts of congruent triangles.
2. It is given that $\angle ONL \cong \angle MLN$ and $\angle O$ and $\angle M$ are right angles. So, $\angle O \cong \angle M$ because all right angles are congruent. So, $\triangle ONL \cong \triangle MLN$ by AAS. $\overline{LM} \cong \overline{NO}$ because they are corresponding parts of congruent triangles.

PRESCRIPTION FOR REMEDIATION

Use the student work on the Lesson Quiz to prescribe a differentiated review assignment.

Points	Differentiated Remediation
0	Intervention
1	On-level
2	Extension

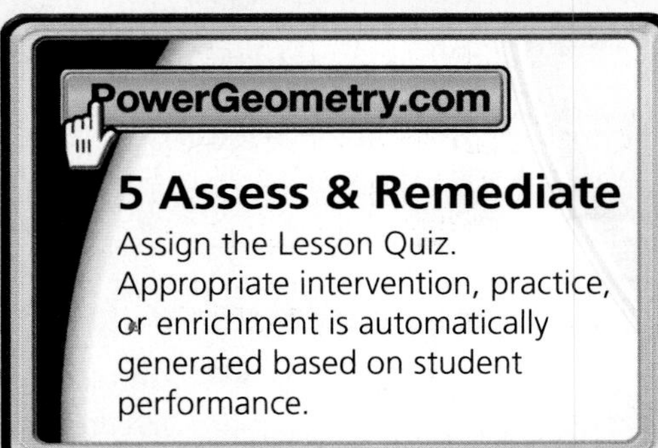

PowerGeometry.com
5 Assess & Remediate
Assign the Lesson Quiz.
Appropriate intervention, practice, or enrichment is automatically generated based on student performance.

Differentiated Remediation

Intervention

- **Reteaching** (2 pages) Provides reteaching and practice exercises for the key lesson concepts. Use with struggling students or absent students.
- **English Language Learner Support** Helps students develop and reinforce mathematical vocabulary and key concepts.

All-in-One Resources/Online

Reteaching

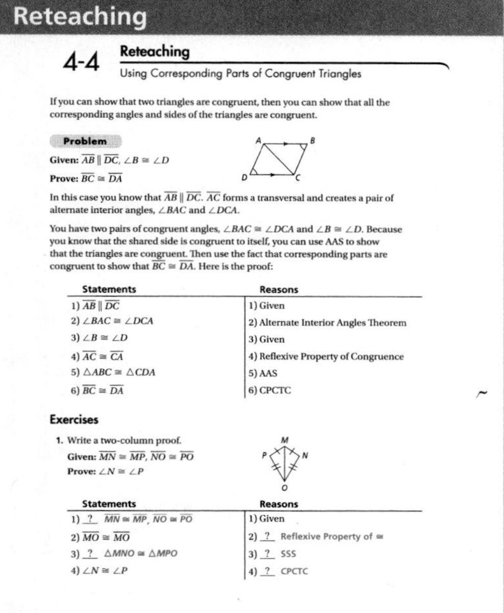

4-4 Reteaching

Using Corresponding Parts of Congruent Triangles

If you can show that two triangles are congruent, then you can show that all the corresponding angles and sides of the triangles are congruent.

Problem

Given: $\overline{AB} \parallel \overline{DC}$, $\angle B \cong \angle D$

Prove: $\overline{BC} \cong \overline{DA}$

In this case you know that $\overline{AB} \parallel \overline{DC}$. $\overline{AC}$ forms a transversal and creates a pair of alternate interior angles, $\angle BAC$ and $\angle DCA$.

You have two pairs of congruent angles, $\angle BAC \cong \angle DCA$ and $\angle B \cong \angle D$. Because you know that the shared side is congruent to itself, you can use AAS to show that the triangles are congruent. Then use the fact that corresponding parts are congruent to show that $\overline{BC} \cong \overline{DA}$. Here is the proof:

Statements	Reasons
1) $\overline{AB} \parallel \overline{DC}$	1) Given
2) $\angle BAC \cong \angle DCA$	2) Alternate Interior Angles Theorem
3) $\angle B \cong \angle D$	3) Given
4) $\overline{AC} \cong \overline{CA}$	4) Reflexive Property of Congruence
5) $\triangle ABC \cong \triangle CDA$	5) AAS
6) $\overline{BC} \cong \overline{DA}$	6) CPCTC

Exercises

1. Write a two-column proof.

Given: $\overline{MN} \cong \overline{MP}$, $\overline{NO} \cong \overline{PO}$

Prove: $\angle N \cong \angle P$

Statements	Reasons
1) _?_ $\overline{MN} \cong \overline{MP}$, $\overline{NO} \cong \overline{PO}$	1) Given
2) $\overline{MO} \cong \overline{MO}$	2) _?_ Reflexive Property of ≅
3) _?_ $\triangle MNO \cong \triangle MPO$	3) _?_ SSS
4) $\angle N \cong \angle P$	4) _?_ CPCTC

All-in-One Resources/Online

English Language Learner Support

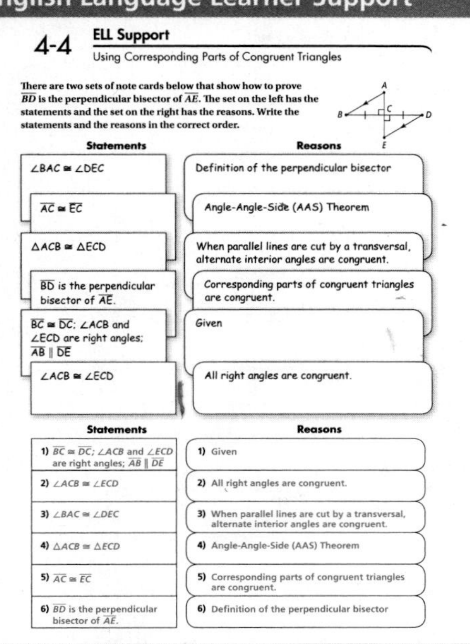

4-4 ELL Support

Using Corresponding Parts of Congruent Triangles

There are two sets of note cards below that show how to prove $\overline{BD}$ is the perpendicular bisector of $\overline{AE}$. The set on the left has the statements and the set on the right has the reasons. Write the statements and the reasons in the correct order.

Statements	Reasons
$\angle BAC \cong \angle DEC$	Definition of the perpendicular bisector
$\overline{AC} \cong \overline{EC}$	Angle-Angle-Side (AAS) Theorem
$\triangle ACB \cong \triangle ECD$	When parallel lines are cut by a transversal, alternate interior angles are congruent.
$\overline{BD}$ is the perpendicular bisector of $\overline{AE}$.	Corresponding parts of congruent triangles are congruent.
$\overline{BC} \cong \overline{DC}$; $\angle ACB$ and $\angle ECD$ are right angles; $\overline{AB} \parallel \overline{DE}$	Given
$\angle ACB \cong \angle ECD$	All right angles are congruent.

Statements	Reasons
1) $\overline{BC} \cong \overline{DC}$; $\angle ACB$ and $\angle ECD$ are right angles; $\overline{AB} \parallel \overline{DE}$	1) Given
2) $\angle ACB \cong \angle ECD$	2) All right angles are congruent.
3) $\angle BAC \cong \angle DEC$	3) When parallel lines are cut by a transversal, alternate interior angles are congruent.
4) $\triangle ACB \cong \triangle ECD$	4) Angle-Angle-Side (AAS) Theorem
5) $\overline{AC} \cong \overline{EC}$	5) Corresponding parts of congruent triangles are congruent.
6) $\overline{BD}$ is the perpendicular bisector of $\overline{AE}$.	6) Definition of the perpendicular bisector

Differentiated Remediation *continued*

On-Level

- **Practice** (2 pages) Provides extra practice for each lesson. For simpler practice exercises, use the Form K Practice pages found in the All-in-One Teaching Resources and online.
- **Think About a Plan** Helps students develop specific problem-solving skills and strategies by providing scaffolded guiding questions.
- **Standardized Test Prep** Focuses on all major exercises, all major question types, and helps students prepare for the high-stakes assessments.

Extension

- **Enrichment** Provides students with interesting problems and activities that extend the concepts of the lesson.
- **Activities, Games, and Puzzles** Worksheets that can be used for concepts development, enrichment, and for fun!

Practice and Problem Solving Wkbk/ All-in-One Resources/Online

Practice page 1

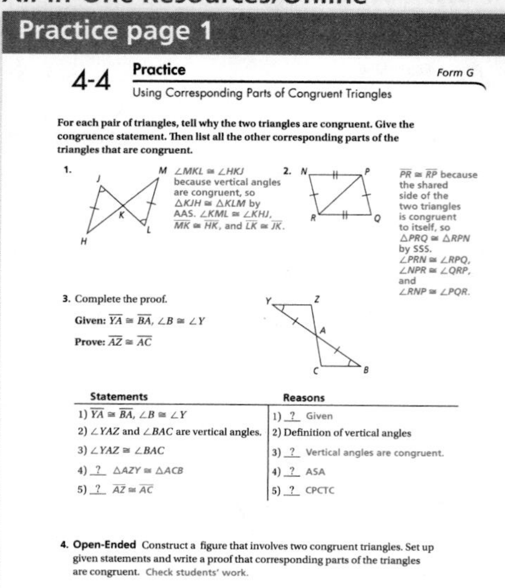

4-4 Practice *Form G*
Using Corresponding Parts of Congruent Triangles

For each pair of triangles, tell why the two triangles are congruent. Give the congruence statement. Then list all the other corresponding parts of the triangles that are congruent.

1. $\angle MKL \cong \angle HKJ$ because vertical angles are congruent, so $\triangle KJH \cong \triangle KLM$ by AAS. $\angle KML \cong \angle KHJ$, $\overline{MK} \cong \overline{HK}$, and $\overline{LK} \cong \overline{JK}$.

2. $\overline{PR} \cong \overline{RP}$ because the shared side of the two triangles is congruent to itself, so $\triangle PRQ \cong \triangle RPN$ by SSS. $\angle PRN \cong \angle RPQ$, $\angle NPR \cong \angle QRP$, and $\angle RNP \cong \angle PQR$.

3. Complete the proof.
Given: $\overline{YA} \cong \overline{BA}$, $\angle B \cong \angle Y$
Prove: $\overline{AZ} \cong \overline{AC}$

Statements	Reasons
1) $\overline{YA} \cong \overline{BA}$, $\angle B \cong \angle Y$	1) ? Given
2) $\angle YAZ$ and $\angle BAC$ are vertical angles.	2) Definition of vertical angles
3) $\angle YAZ \cong \angle BAC$	3) ? Vertical angles are congruent.
4) ? $\triangle AZY \cong \triangle ACB$	4) ? ASA
5) ? $\overline{AZ} \cong \overline{AC}$	5) ? CPCTC

4. **Open-Ended** Construct a figure that involves two congruent triangles. Set up given statements and write a proof that corresponding parts of the triangles are congruent. Check students' work.

Practice and Problem Solving Wkbk/ All-in-One Resources/Online

Practice page 2

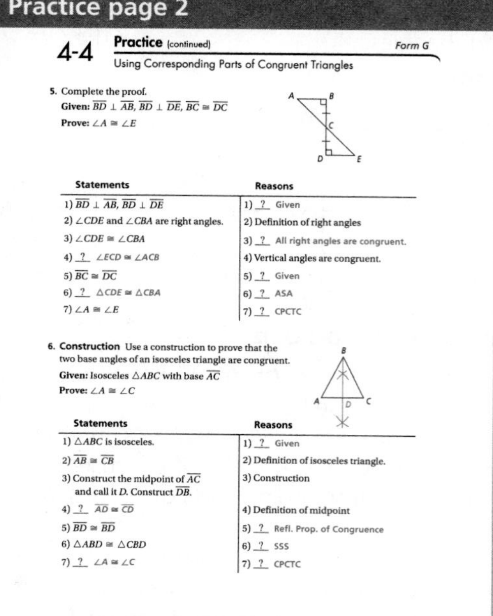

4-4 Practice (continued) *Form G*
Using Corresponding Parts of Congruent Triangles

5. Complete the proof.
Given: $\overline{BD} \perp \overline{AB}$, $\overline{BD} \perp \overline{DE}$, $\overline{BC} \cong \overline{DC}$
Prove: $\angle A \cong \angle E$

Statements	Reasons
1) $\overline{BD} \perp \overline{AB}$, $\overline{BD} \perp \overline{DE}$	1) ? Given
2) $\angle CDE$ and $\angle CBA$ are right angles.	2) Definition of right angles
3) $\angle CDE \cong \angle CBA$	3) ? All right angles are congruent.
4) ? $\angle ECD \cong \angle ACB$	4) Vertical angles are congruent.
5) $\overline{BC} \cong \overline{DC}$	5) ? Given
6) ? $\triangle CDE \cong \triangle CBA$	6) ? ASA
7) $\angle A \cong \angle E$	7) ? CPCTC

6. **Construction** Use a construction to prove that the two base angles of an isosceles triangle are congruent.
Given: Isosceles $\triangle ABC$ with base $\overline{AC}$
Prove: $\angle A \cong \angle C$

Statements	Reasons
1) $\triangle ABC$ is isosceles.	1) ? Given
2) $\overline{AB} \cong \overline{CB}$	2) Definition of isosceles triangle.
3) Construct the midpoint of $\overline{AC}$ and call it D. Construct $\overline{DB}$.	3) Construction
4) ? $\overline{AD} \cong \overline{CD}$	4) Definition of midpoint
5) $\overline{BD} \cong \overline{BD}$	5) ? Refl. Prop. of Congruence
6) $\triangle ABD \cong \triangle CBD$	6) ? SSS
7) ? $\angle A \cong \angle C$	7) ? CPCTC

All-in-One Resources/Online

Enrichment

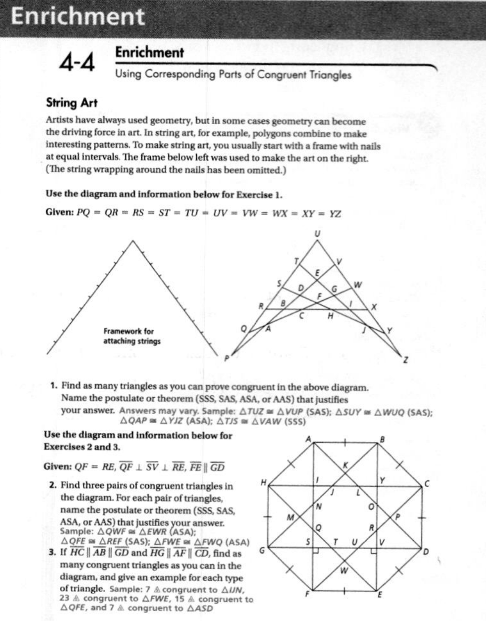

4-4 Enrichment
Using Corresponding Parts of Congruent Triangles

String Art

Artists have always used geometry, but in some cases geometry can become the driving force in art. In string art, for example, polygons combine to make interesting patterns. To make string art, you usually start with a frame with nails at equal intervals. The frame below left was used to make the art on the right. (The string wrapping around the nails has been omitted.)

Use the diagram and information below for Exercise 1.

Given: $PQ = QR = RS = ST = TU = UV = VW = WX = XY = YZ$

1. Find as many triangles as you can prove congruent in the above diagram. Name the postulate or theorem (SSS, SAS, ASA, or AAS) that justifies your answer. Answers may vary. Sample: $\triangle TUZ \cong \triangle VUP$ (SAS); $\triangle SUY \cong \triangle WUQ$ (SAS); $\triangle QAP \cong \triangle YJZ$ (ASA); $\triangle TJS \cong \triangle VAW$ (SSS)

Use the diagram and information below for Exercises 2 and 3.

Given: $QF = RE$, $\overline{QF} \perp \overline{SV} \perp \overline{RE}$, $\overline{FE} \parallel \overline{GD}$

2. Find three pairs of congruent triangles in the diagram. For each pair of triangles, name the postulate or theorem (SSS, SAS, ASA, or AAS) that justifies your answer. Sample: $\triangle QWF \cong \triangle EWR$ (ASA); $\triangle QFE \cong \triangle REF$ (SAS); $\triangle FWE \cong \triangle FWQ$ (ASA)
3. If $\overline{HC} \parallel \overline{AB} \parallel \overline{GD}$ and $\overline{HG} \parallel \overline{AF} \parallel \overline{CD}$, find as many congruent triangles as you can in the diagram, and give an example for each type of triangle. Sample: 7 △ congruent to $\triangle IJN$, 23 △ congruent to $\triangle FWE$, 15 △ congruent to $\triangle QFE$, and 7 △ congruent to $\triangle ASD$

Practice and Problem Solving Wkbk/ All-in-One Resources/Online

Think About a Plan

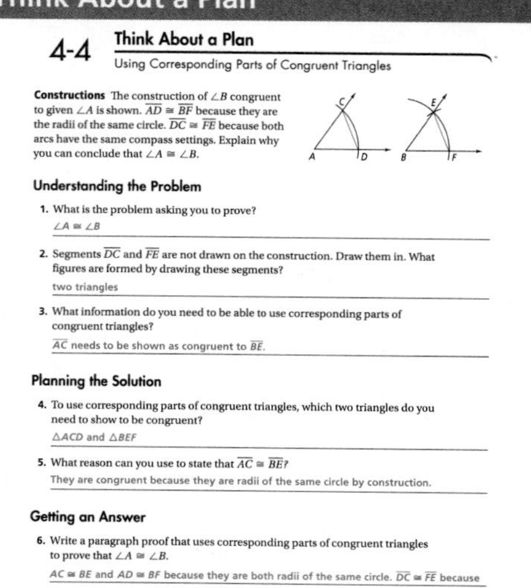

4-4 Think About a Plan
Using Corresponding Parts of Congruent Triangles

Constructions The construction of $\angle B$ congruent to given $\angle A$ is shown. $\overline{AD} \cong \overline{BF}$ because they are the radii of the same circle. $\overline{DC} \cong \overline{FE}$ because both arcs have the same compass settings. Explain why you can conclude that $\angle A \cong \angle B$.

Understanding the Problem

1. What is the problem asking you to prove?
$\angle A \cong \angle B$
2. Segments $\overline{DC}$ and $\overline{FE}$ are not drawn on the construction. Draw them in. What figures are formed by drawing these segments?
two triangles
3. What information do you need to be able to use corresponding parts of congruent triangles?
$\overline{AC}$ needs to be shown as congruent to $\overline{BE}$.

Planning the Solution

4. To use corresponding parts of congruent triangles, which two triangles do you need to show to be congruent?
$\triangle ACD$ and $\triangle BEF$
5. What reason can you use to state that $\overline{AC} \cong \overline{BE}$?
They are congruent because they are radii of the same circle by construction.

Getting an Answer

6. Write a paragraph proof that uses corresponding parts of congruent triangles to prove that $\angle A \cong \angle B$.
$AC \cong BE$ and $AD \cong BF$ because they are both radii of the same circle. $\overline{DC} \cong \overline{FE}$ because they both have the same compass settings. Therefore, $\triangle ACD \cong \triangle BEF$ by SSS and $\angle A \cong \angle B$ by CPCTC.

Practice and Problem Solving Wkbk/ All-in-One Resources/Online

Standardized Test Prep

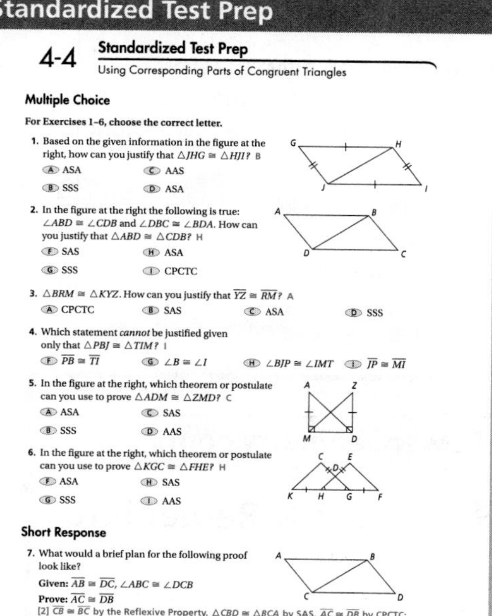

4-4 Standardized Test Prep
Using Corresponding Parts of Congruent Triangles

Multiple Choice

For Exercises 1–6, choose the correct letter.

1. Based on the given information in the figure at the right, how can you justify that $\triangle JHG \cong \triangle HJI$? B
A ASA C AAS B SSS D ASA
2. In the figure at the right the following is true: $\angle ABD \cong \angle CDB$ and $\angle DBC \cong \angle BDA$. How can you justify that $\triangle ABD \cong \triangle CDB$? H
F SAS H ASA G SSS I CPCTC
3. $\triangle BRM \cong \triangle KYZ$. How can you justify that $\overline{YZ} \cong \overline{RM}$? A
A CPCTC B SAS C ASA D SSS
4. Which statement *cannot* be justified given only that $\triangle PBJ \cong \triangle TIM$? I
F $\overline{PB} \cong \overline{TI}$ G $\angle B \cong \angle I$ H $\angle BJP \cong \angle IMT$ I $\overline{JP} \cong \overline{MI}$
5. In the figure at the right, which theorem or postulate can you use to prove $\triangle ADM \cong \triangle ZMD$? C
A ASA C SAS B SSS D AAS
6. In the figure at the right, which theorem or postulate can you use to prove $\triangle KGC \cong \triangle FHE$? H
F ASA H SAS G SSS I AAS

Short Response

7. What would a brief plan for the following proof look like?
Given: $\overline{AB} \cong \overline{DC}$, $\angle ABC \cong \angle DCB$
Prove: $\overline{AC} \cong \overline{DB}$
[2] $\overline{CB} \cong \overline{BC}$ by the Reflexive Property. $\triangle CBD \cong \triangle BCA$ by SAS. $\overline{AC} \cong \overline{DB}$ by CPCTC; [1] one step missing or one reason incorrect [0] incorrect or no response

Online Teacher Resource Center

Activities, Games, and Puzzles

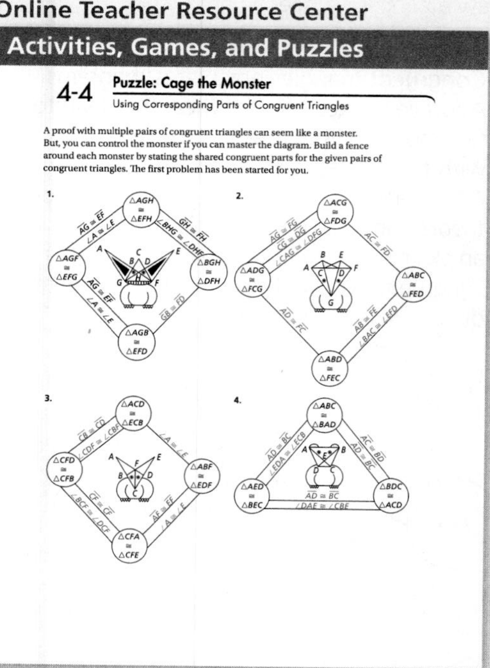

4-4 Puzzle: Cage the Monster
Using Corresponding Parts of Congruent Triangles

A proof with multiple pairs of congruent triangles can seem like a monster. But, you can control the monster if you can master the diagram. Build a fence around each monster by stating the shared congruent parts for the given pairs of congruent triangles. The first problem has been started for you.

Concept Byte

Use With Lesson 4-5

ACTIVITY

Paper-Folding Conjectures

Isosceles triangles have two congruent sides. Folding one of the sides onto the other will suggest another important property of isosceles triangles.

Activity 1

Step 1 Construct an isosceles $\triangle ABC$ on tracing paper, with $\overline{AC} \cong \overline{BC}$.

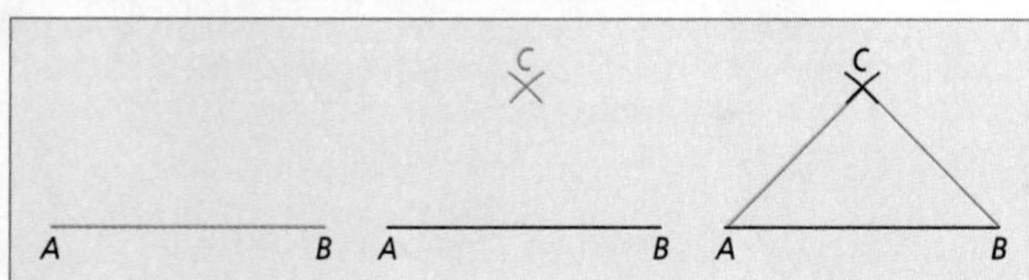

Step 2 Fold the paper so the two congruent sides fit exactly one on top of the other. Crease the paper. Label the intersection of the fold line and $\overline{AB}$ as point D.

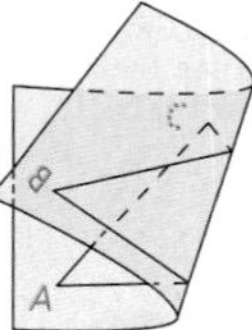

1. What do you notice about $\angle A$ and $\angle B$? Compare your results with others. Make a conjecture about the angles opposite the congruent sides in an isosceles triangle.

2. a. Study the fold line $\overline{CD}$ and the base $\overline{AB}$. What type of angles are $\angle CDA$ and $\angle CDB$? How do $\overline{AD}$ and $\overline{BD}$ seem to be related?

b. Use your answers to part (a) to complete the conjecture: The fold line $\overline{CD}$ is the __?__ of the base $\overline{AB}$ of isosceles $\triangle ABC$.

Activity 2

In Activity 1, you made a conjecture about angles opposite the congruent sides of a triangle. You can also fold paper to study whether the converse is true.

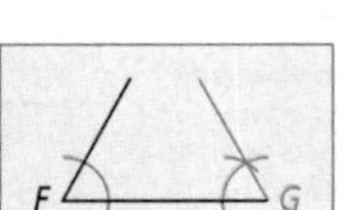

Step 1 On tracing paper, draw acute angle F and one side $\overline{FG}$. Construct $\angle G$ as shown, so that $\angle G \cong \angle F$.

Step 2 Fold the paper so $\angle F$ and $\angle G$ fit exactly one on top of the other.

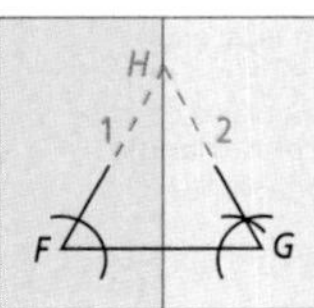

3. Why do sides 1 and 2 meet at point H on the fold line? Make a conjecture about sides $\overline{FH}$ and $\overline{GH}$ opposite congruent angles in a triangle.

4. Write your conjectures from Questions 1 and 3 as a biconditional.

Answers

Activity 1

1. $\angle A \cong \angle B$; in an isosc. △, the ∠s opposite the ≅ sides are ≅ to each other.

2a. Rt. ∠s; they are ≅.

b. ⊥ bisector

Activity 2

3. Answers may vary. Sample: The fold line is the ⊥ bisector of $\overline{FG}$. The two parts of $\overline{FG}$ formed by the fold line are ≅, and the ∠s formed by the fold line and $\overline{FG}$ are ≅ rt. ∠s. Since $\angle F \cong \angle G$, the two △s are ≅ by ASA. Thus the side the two △s share is ≅ to itself, so sides 1 and 2 meet at the fold line. Conjecture: If two ∠s of a △ are ≅, then the sides opposite those ∠s are ≅.

4. Two sides of a △ are ≅ if and only if the ∠s opposite those sides are ≅.

Guided Instruction

PURPOSE To use paper-folding activities to reveal important properties of isosceles triangles

PROCESS Students will

- construct an isosceles triangle and make conjectures about this triangle and its parts.
- draw an acute angle and one segment as a side of a triangle, then construct a second angle (as shown) that is congruent to the first acute angle and make conjectures about this triangle and its parts.

DISCUSS These activities focus primarily on isosceles triangles and some unique properties they have.

Q Are there any other kinds of triangles for which you could use this paper-folding technique and end up with similar results? **[equilateral triangles]**

Activity 1

In this Activity students construct an isosceles triangle, perform some paper-folding with their isosceles triangle, and make conjectures with regards to the base angles of their triangle, the fold line, the angles the fold line makes with the triangle's base, and the two segments into which the fold line divides the base.

Q If you use the "fold line" created, what postulate allows you to prove $\triangle CDA$ and $\triangle CDB$ congruent? **[SAS]**

Activity 2

In this Activity students use the paper-folding technique to study whether the converse of what they discovered in Activity 1 is true.

Q Side 1 intersects the fold line in a point H_1. Side 2 intersects the fold line in a point H_2. How do you that $H_1 = H_2 = H$? **[If the fold line and $\overline{FG}$ intersect in point L, show $\triangle FLH_1 \cong \triangle FLH_2$ by ASA.]**

1 Interactive Learning

Solve It!

PURPOSE To discover that an isosceles triangle has two congruent base angles

PROCESS Students use their knowledge of congruent triangles to complete the puzzle.

FACILITATE

Q Which triangles have sides that could be adjacent sides in the large triangle? **[Any of the congruent triangles could be adjacent at corresponding sides. The orange triangles have a side that could be adjacent to a side of the blue triangles.]**

Q Which triangles have sides that could combine together to equal the side length of another triangle? **[The green triangles have side lengths of 3, which together add up to the blue triangle's side length of 6.]**

ANSWER See Solve It in Answers on next page.

CONNECT THE MATH Students will make several conjectures about the properties of isosceles triangles as they manipulate the pieces of this puzzle. The lesson investigates these conjectures and other special relationships in isosceles triangles.

2 Guided Instruction

Take Note

Discuss the definition of *isosceles triangle.* Ask what is true about the two triangles that you get if you consider, from the vertex, each of the following: the angle bisector, the altitude, the median. Be certain students understand what is meant by an angle being "opposite" a side.

4-5 Isosceles and Equilateral Triangles

TN State Performance Indicators

SPI 3108.4.3 Identify, describe and/or apply the relationships and theorems involving different types of triangles, quadrilaterals and other polygons.

Also SPI 3108.1.1, SPI 3108.4.2, and SPI 3108.4.12

Objective To use and apply properties of isosceles and equilateral triangles

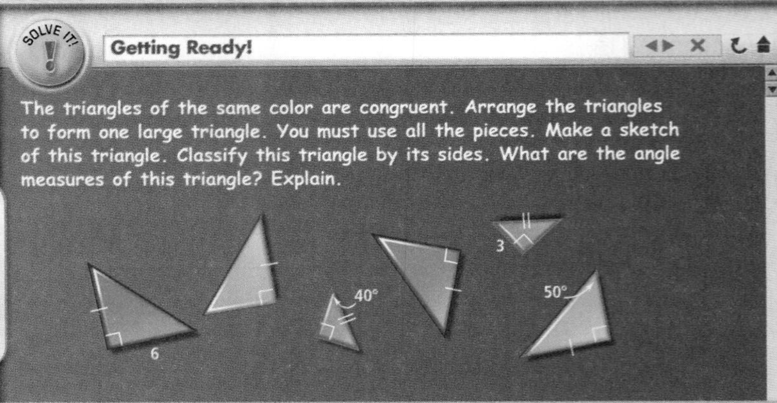

SOLVE IT!
Getting Ready!
The triangles of the same color are congruent. Arrange the triangles to form one large triangle. You must use all the pieces. Make a sketch of this triangle. Classify this triangle by its sides. What are the angle measures of this triangle? Explain.
40°
3
50°
6

You may think identifying isosceles and equilateral triangles is old news! Get ready to see them in a new light.

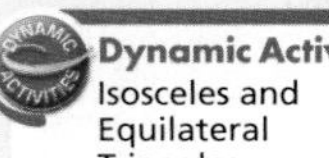

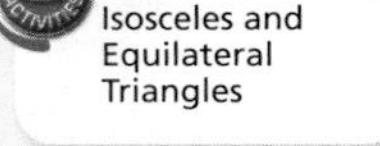

Dynamic Activity
Isosceles and Equilateral Triangles

Lesson Vocabulary
- legs of an isosceles triangle
- base of an isosceles triangle
- vertex angle of an isosceles triangle
- base angles of an isosceles triangle
- corollary

In the Solve It, you classified a triangle based on the lengths of its sides. You can also identify certain triangles based on information about their angles. In this lesson, you will learn how to use and apply properties of isosceles and equilateral triangles.

Essential Understanding The angles and sides of isosceles and equilateral triangles have special relationships.

Isosceles triangles are common in the real world. You can frequently see them in structures such as bridges and buildings, as well as in art and design. The congruent sides of an isosceles triangle are its **legs.** The third side is the **base.** The two congruent legs form the **vertex angle.** The other two angles are the **base angles.**

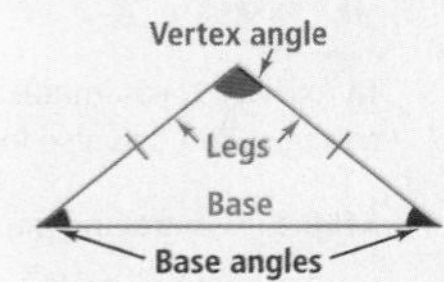

Theorem 4-3 Isosceles Triangle Theorem

Theorem	If . . .	Then . . .
If two sides of a triangle are congruent, then the angles opposite those sides are congruent.	$\overline{AC} \cong \overline{BC}$	$\angle A \cong \angle B$

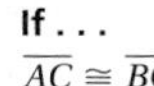

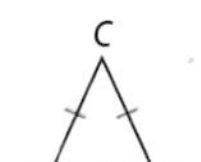

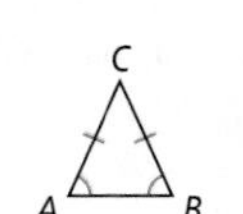

4-5 Preparing to Teach

BIG idea Reasoning and Proof

ESSENTIAL UNDERSTANDING
- The angles and sides of isosceles and equilateral triangles have special relationships.

Math Background

The Venn diagram below illustrates how quadrilaterals, rectangles, and squares are related. All squares are rectangles. All rectangles are quadrilaterals, which means all squares are also quadrilaterals.

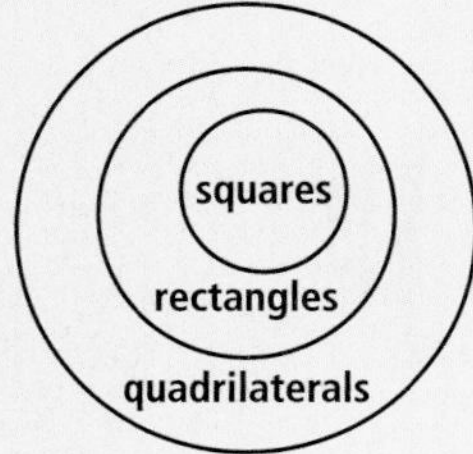

One relationship among triangles can be modeled the same way.

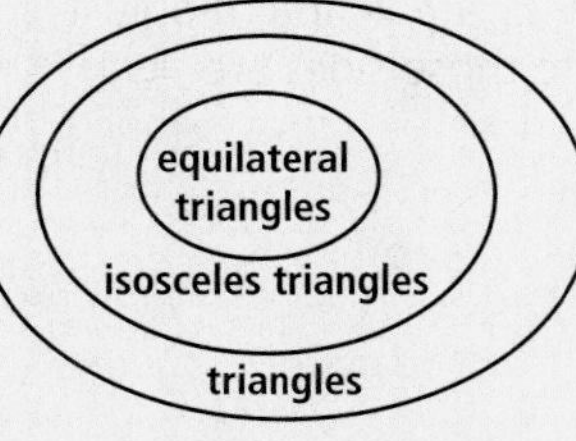

From the diagram, you can state the following relationships.

All equilateral triangles are isosceles triangles and some isosceles triangles are not equilateral triangles. Also, some triangles are not isosceles triangles.

Support Student Learning

Use the **Geometry Companion** to engage and support students during instructions. See Lesson Resources at the end of this lesson for details.

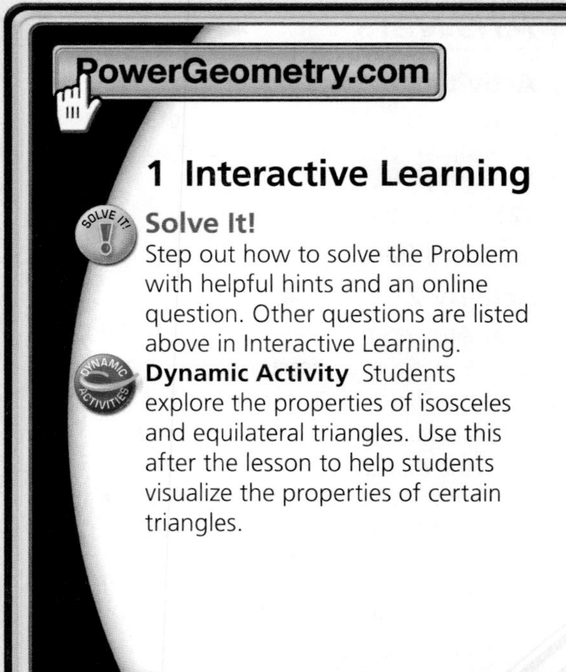

The proof of the Isosceles Triangle Theorem requires an auxiliary line.

Proof of Theorem 4-3: Isosceles Triangle Theorem

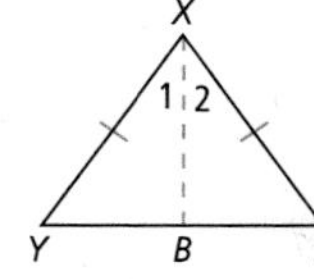

Begin with isosceles $\triangle XYZ$ with $\overline{XY} \cong \overline{XZ}$. Draw $\overline{XB}$, the bisector of the vertex angle $\angle YXZ$.

Given: $\overline{XY} \cong \overline{XZ}$, $\overline{XB}$ bisects $\angle YXZ$

Prove: $\angle Y \cong \angle Z$

Proof: $\overline{XY} \cong \overline{XZ}$ is given. By the definition of angle bisector, $\angle 1 \cong \angle 2$. By the Reflexive Property of Congruence, $\overline{XB} \cong \overline{XB}$. So by the SAS Postulate, $\triangle XYB \cong \triangle XZB$. $\angle Y \cong \angle Z$ since corresponding parts of congruent triangles are congruent.

Theorem 4-4 Converse of the Isosceles Triangle Theorem

Theorem	If . . .	Then . . .
If two angles of a triangle are congruent, then the sides opposite those angles are congruent.	$\angle A \cong \angle B$ 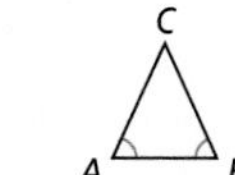	$\overline{AC} \cong \overline{BC}$ 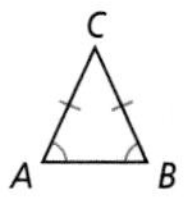

You will prove Theorem 4-4 in Exercise 23.

Problem 1 Using the Isosceles Triangle Theorems

Think

What are you looking for in the diagram?
To use the Isosceles Triangle Theorems, you need a pair of congruent angles or a pair of congruent sides.

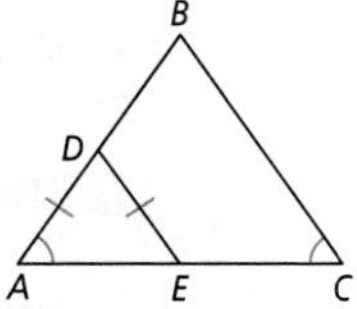

A Is $\overline{AB}$ congruent to $\overline{CB}$? Explain.

Yes. Since $\angle C \cong \angle A$, $\overline{AB} \cong \overline{CB}$ by the Converse of the Isosceles Triangle Theorem.

B Is $\angle A$ congruent to $\angle DEA$? Explain.

Yes. Since $\overline{AD} \cong \overline{ED}$, $\angle A \cong \angle DEA$ by the Isosceles Triangle Theorem.

Got It? **1. a.** Is $\angle WVS$ congruent to $\angle S$? Is $\overline{TR}$ congruent to $\overline{TS}$? Explain.

b. Reasoning Can you conclude that $\triangle RUV$ is isosceles? Explain.

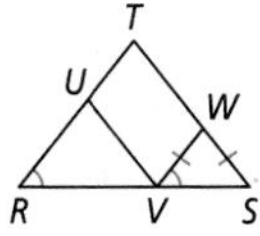

An isosceles triangle has a certain type of symmetry about a line through its vertex angle. The theorems in this lesson suggest this symmetry, which you will study in greater detail in Lesson 9-4.

Remind students of the definition of an auxiliary line. Ask them to identify the type of line that is used as the auxiliary line in this proof.

Take Note

Ask students to identify the relationship between this theorem and the previous one. Have them identify the hypothesis and conclusion of each theorem. Then, have students write the two theorems as one biconditional statement.

Problem 1

Have students draw the triangles separately for both parts.

Q In 1A, what are the base angles of the large triangle? **[$\angle BAC$ and $\angle BCA$]**

Q What conclusion can you draw about $\triangle ABC$ using a congruence statement about the base angles? **[Congruent base angles imply that the opposite sides are congruent, and therefore $\triangle ABC$ is an isosceles triangle.]**

Q In 1B, what is true about the small triangle with the marked sides? **[It is isosceles.]**

Got It? ERROR PREVENTION

To answer 1b, students should draw on their answer to 1a. The reasoning that leads to the conclusion involves several steps.

2 Guided Instruction

Each Problem is worked out and supported online.

Problem 1
Using the Isosceles Triangle Theorems
Animated

Problem 2
Using Algebra
Animated

Problem 3
Finding Angle Measures
Animated

Support in Geometry Companion
- Vocabulary
- Key Concepts
- Got It?

Answers

Solve It!

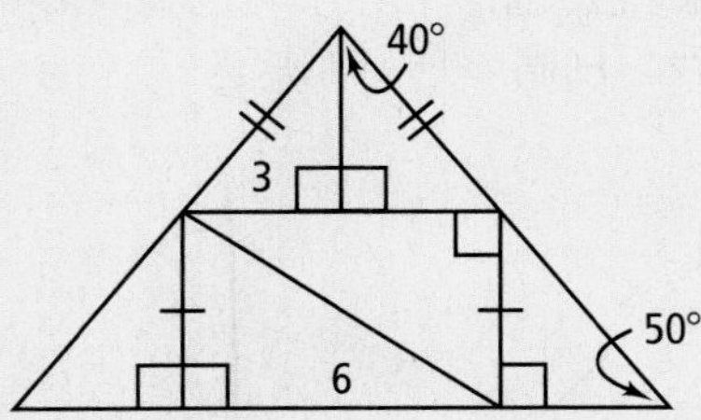

isosc.; 50, 50, 80

Got It?

1a. Yes; since $\overline{WV} \cong \overline{WS}$, $\angle WVS \cong \angle S$ by the Isosc. $\triangle$ Thm.; yes; since $\angle WVS \cong \angle S$, and $\angle R \cong \angle WVS$ (Given), $\angle R \cong \angle S$ (Trans. Prop. of $\cong$). Therefore, $\overline{TR} \cong \overline{TS}$ by the Converse of the Isosc. $\triangle$ Thm.

b. No; there is not enough information about the sides or $\angle$s of $\triangle RUV$.

Take Note

Emphasize to students that Theorem 4-5 can be proven only by using congruent triangles.

Problem 2

Q What type of triangle is in the diagram? **[an isosceles triangle]**

Q Can you determine the measure of $\angle C$? Justify your answer. **[$m\angle C = 54$ because the base angles in an isosceles triangle are congruent.]**

Q The fact that $\angle ABD \cong \angle CBD$ implies that $\overline{BD}$ is what type of segment? **[an angle bisector]**

Q Because $\overline{BD}$ is an angle bisector, what is $m\angle BDC$? Justify your answer. **[$m\angle BDC = 90$ by Theorem 4-5.]**

Got It? VISUAL LEARNERS

Students should redraw the triangle with the new angle measure. Students could also use an equation based on the Triangle Angle-Sum Theorem and substitute the new value for $m\angle C$.

Take Note

Ask students to describe the relationship between the two corollaries presented. They should identify the corollaries as converses of each other. Have students combine the two to form one biconditional statement.

take note **Theorem 4-5**

Theorem	If . . .	Then . . .
If a line bisects the vertex angle of an isosceles triangle, then the line is also the perpendicular bisector of the base.	$\overline{AC} \cong \overline{BC}$ and $\angle ACD \cong \angle BCD$ 	$\overline{CD} \perp \overline{AB}$ and $\overline{AD} \cong \overline{BD}$ 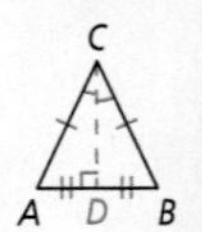

You will prove Theorem 4-5 in Exercise 26.

Problem 2 Using Algebra

GRIDDED RESPONSE

Think
What does the diagram tell you?
Since $\overline{AB} \cong \overline{CB}$, $\triangle ABC$ is isosceles. Since $\angle ABD \cong \angle CBD$, $\overline{BD}$ bisects the vertex angle of the isosceles triangle.

What is the value of x?

Since $\overline{AB} \cong \overline{CB}$, by the Isosceles Triangle Theorem, $\angle A \cong \angle C$. So $m\angle C = 54$.

Since $\overline{BD}$ bisects $\angle ABC$, you know by Theorem 4-5 that $\overline{BD} \perp \overline{AC}$. So $m\angle BDC = 90$.

$m\angle C + m\angle BDC + m\angle DBC = 180$	Triangle Angle-Sum Theorem
$54 + 90 + x = 180$	Substitute.
$x = 36$	Subtract 144 from each side.

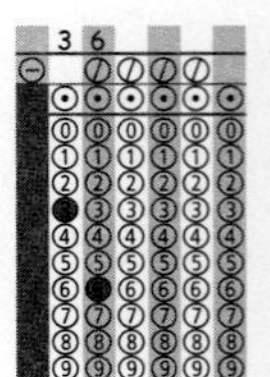

Got It? 2. Suppose $m\angle A = 27$. What is the value of x?

A **corollary** is a theorem that can be proved easily using another theorem. Since a corollary is a theorem, you can use it as a reason in a proof.

take note **Corollary to Theorem 4-3**

Corollary	If . . .	Then . . .
If a triangle is equilateral, then the triangle is equiangular.	$\overline{XY} \cong \overline{YZ} \cong \overline{ZX}$ 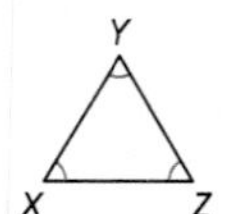	$\angle X \cong \angle Y \cong \angle Z$ 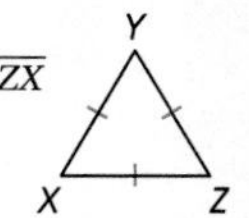

Corollary to Theorem 4-4

Corollary	If . . .	Then . . .
If a triangle is equiangular, then the triangle is equilateral.	$\angle X \cong \angle Y \cong \angle Z$	$\overline{XY} \cong \overline{YZ} \cong \overline{ZX}$

Additional Problems

1. a. Is $\overline{GK} \cong \overline{HK}$? Explain.

b. Is $\overline{HL} \cong \overline{KJ}$? Explain.

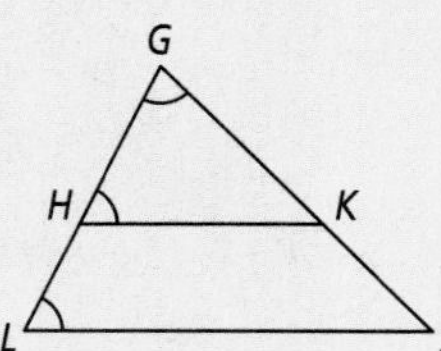

ANSWER a. Yes, by the Converse of the Isosceles Triangle Theorem **b.** Not necessarily; they are not corresponding parts of isosceles triangles.

2. What is the value of x?

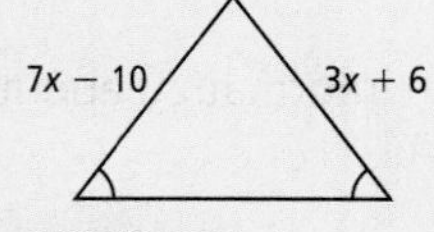

ANSWER 4

3. In the diagram, $\triangle PLN \cong \triangle LNS$. What is the measure of $\angle S$ in the figure below?

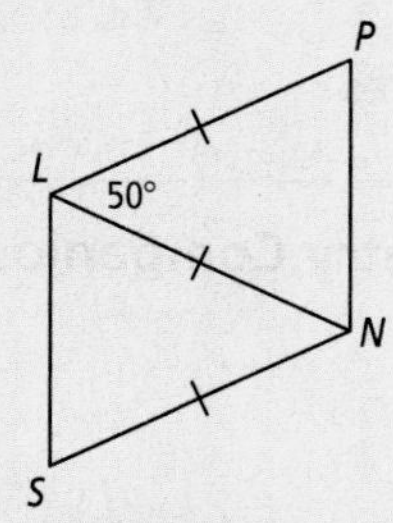

ANSWER 65

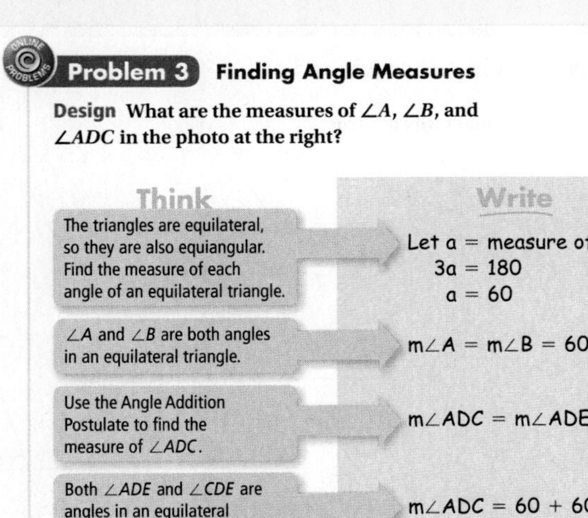

Problem 3 Finding Angle Measures

Design What are the measures of $\angle A$, $\angle B$, and $\angle ADC$ in the photo at the right?

Think	Write
The triangles are equilateral, so they are also equiangular. Find the measure of each angle of an equilateral triangle.	Let a = measure of one angle. $3a = 180$ $a = 60$
$\angle A$ and $\angle B$ are both angles in an equilateral triangle.	$m\angle A = m\angle B = 60$
Use the Angle Addition Postulate to find the measure of $\angle ADC$.	$m\angle ADC = m\angle ADE + m\angle CDE$
Both $\angle ADE$ and $\angle CDE$ are angles in an equilateral triangle. So $m\angle ADE = 60$ and $m\angle CDE = 60$. Substitute into the above equation and simplify.	$m\angle ADC = 60 + 60$ $m\angle ADC = 120$

Got It? 3. Suppose the triangles in Problem 3 are isosceles triangles, where $\angle ADE$, $\angle DEC$, and $\angle ECB$ are vertex angles. If the vertex angles each have a measure of 58, what are $m\angle A$ and $m\angle BCD$?

Lesson Check

Do you know HOW?

1. What is $m\angle A$?

a. 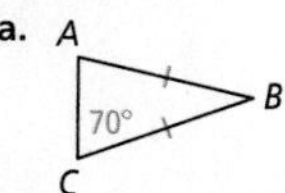

b. 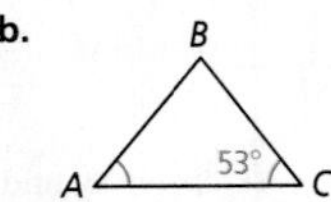

2. What is the value of x?

a. 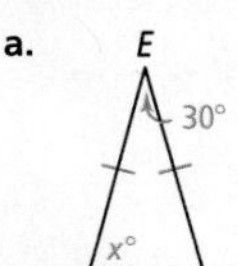

b. 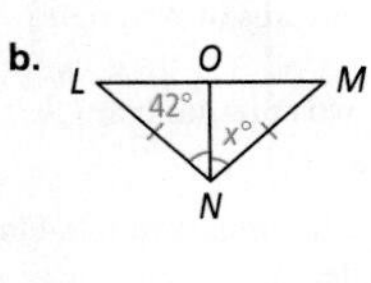

3. The measure of one base angle of an isosceles triangle is 23. What are the measures of the other two angles?

Do you UNDERSTAND?

4. What is the relationship between sides and angles for each type of triangle?
   a. isosceles
   b. equilateral

5. **Error Analysis** Claudia drew an isosceles triangle. She asked Sue to mark it. Explain why the marking of the diagram is incorrect.

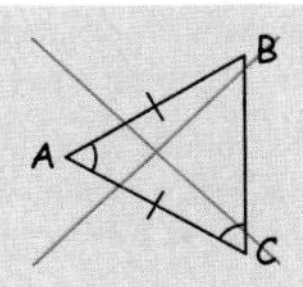

Problem 3

Q What types of triangles are shown in the stained glass window? **[equilateral triangles]**

Q What is the relationship between the angles in an equilateral triangle? **[They are all congruent.]**

Q How can you find the measure of one angle in the equilateral triangle? What theorem will you use? **[Use the Triangle Angle-Sum Theorem to write an equation. Let x = the measure of an angle in the equilateral triangle. $3x = 180$]**

Q Can you write $m\angle ADC$ as the sum of two angle measures? **[Yes; $m\angle ADC = m\angle ADE + m\angle EDC$]**

Got It? VISUAL LEARNERS

Have students draw the isosceles triangles in the problem and label the given measures.

3 Lesson Check

Do you know HOW?

- If students have difficulty with Exercise 1, then have them review Problem 2.

Do you UNDERSTAND?

- If students have difficulty with Exercise 5, then have them review the Isosceles Triangle Theorem.

Close

Q What properties are specific to isosceles triangles? **[The triangles have two congruent sides and two congruent base angles, and the vertex angle bisector is perpendicular to and bisects the opposite side.]**

Q How are the angles of an equilateral triangle related? **[All angles are congruent.]**

Answers

Got It? (continued)

2. 63

3. $m\angle A = 61$, $m\angle BCD = 119$

Lesson Check

1a. 70

b. 53

2a. 75

b. 48

3. 23, 134

4a. The ∡ opposite the ≅ sides are ≅.

b. All three ∡ have measure 60, and all three sides are ≅.

5. The ≅ ∡ should be opposite the ≅ sides.

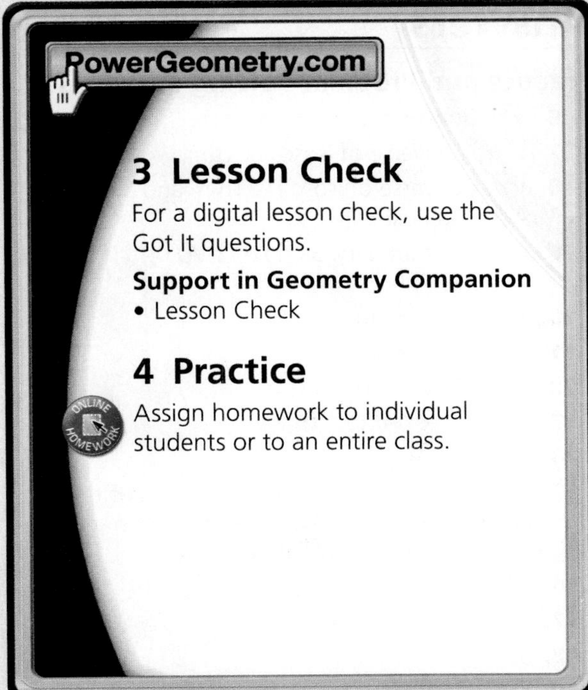

PowerGeometry.com

3 Lesson Check

For a digital lesson check, use the Got It questions.

Support in Geometry Companion

- Lesson Check

4 Practice

Assign homework to individual students or to an entire class.

4 Practice

ASSIGNMENT GUIDE

Basic: 6–13 all, 15, 16–24 even, 28–32 even
Average: 7–13 odd, 14–32
Advanced: 7–13 odd, 14–36
Standardized Test Prep: 37–40
Mixed Review: 41–44

Reasoning exercises have blue headings.
Applications exercises have red headings.
EXERCISE 28: Use the Think About a Plan worksheet in the **Practice and Problem Solving Workbook** (also available in the Teaching Resources in print and online) to further support students' development in becoming independent learners.

HOMEWORK QUICK CHECK

To check students' understanding of key skills and concepts, go over Exercises 7, 11, 15, 20, and 28.

Practice and Problem-Solving Exercises

A Practice

Complete each statement. Explain why it is true. See Problem 1.

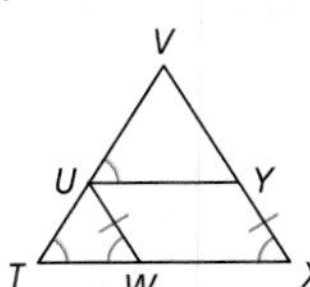

6. $\overline{VT} \cong$?
7. $\overline{UT} \cong$? $\cong \overline{YX}$
8. $\overline{VU} \cong$?
9. $\angle VYU \cong$?

Algebra Find the values of x and y. See Problem 2.

10. 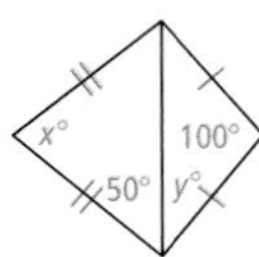

11. 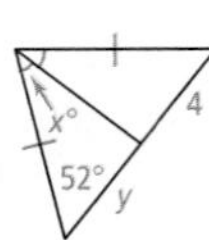

12. 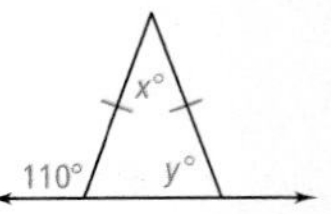

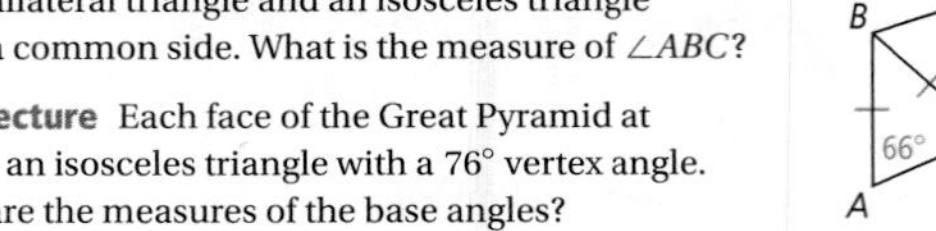

13. An equilateral triangle and an isosceles triangle share a common side. What is the measure of $\angle ABC$? See Problem 3.

B Apply

14. **Architecture** Each face of the Great Pyramid at Giza is an isosceles triangle with a 76° vertex angle. What are the measures of the base angles?
15. **Reasoning** What are the measures of the base angles of a right isosceles triangle? Explain.

Given isosceles $\triangle JKL$ with base $\overline{JL}$, find each value.

16. If $m\angle L = 58$, then $m\angle LKJ =$? .
17. If $JL = 5$, then $ML =$? .
18. If $m\angle JKM = 48$, then $m\angle J =$? .
19. If $m\angle J = 55$, then $m\angle JKM =$? .

K
J M L

20. **Think About a Plan** A triangle has angle measures $x + 15$, $3x - 35$, and $4x$. What type of triangle is it? Be as specific as possible. Justify your answer.
    - What do you know about the sum of the angle measures of a triangle?
    - What do you need to know to classify a triangle?
    - What type of triangle has no congruent angles? Two congruent angles? Three congruent angles?
21. **Reasoning** An exterior angle of an isosceles triangle has measure 100. Find two possible sets of measures for the angles of the triangle.

Answers

Practice and Problem-Solving Exercises

6. $\overline{VX}$; Converse of Isosc. △ Thm.
7. $\overline{UW}$; Converse of Isosc. △ Thm.
8. $\overline{VY}$; Converse of Isosc. △ Thm. and Segment Addition Postulate
9. Answers may vary. Sample: $\angle VUY$; Isosc. △ Thm.
10. $x = 80$, $y = 40$
11. $x = 38$, $y = 4$
12. $x = 40$, $y = 70$
13. 108
14. 52, 52
15. 45 and 45; the sum of the measures of the acute ∠s must be 90, so the measure of each acute ∠ must be half of 90.
16. 64
17. 2.5
18. 42
19. 35
20. The △ is an obtuse isosc. △; $(x + 15) + (3x - 35) + 4x = 180$, so the ∠ measures are 40, 40, and 100.
21. 20, 80, 80 or 50, 50, 80

22. **Developing Proof** Here is another way to prove the Isosceles Triangle Theorem. Supply the missing information.

Begin with isosceles $\triangle HKJ$ with $\overline{KH} \cong \overline{KJ}$.
Draw **a.** __?__, a bisector of the base $\overline{HJ}$.

Given: $\overline{KH} \cong \overline{KJ}$, **b.** __?__ bisects $\overline{HJ}$

Prove: $\angle H \cong \angle J$

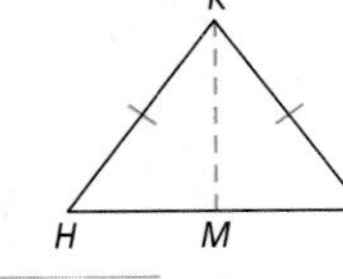

Statements	Reasons
1) $\overline{KM}$ bisects $\overline{HJ}$.	1) **c.** __?__
2) $\overline{HM} \cong \overline{JM}$	2) **d.** __?__
3) $\overline{KH} \cong \overline{KJ}$	3) Given
4) $\overline{KM} \cong \overline{KM}$	4) **e.** __?__
5) $\triangle KHM \cong \triangle KJM$	5) **f.** __?__
6) $\angle H \cong \angle J$	6) **g.** __?__

23. Supply the missing information in this statement of the Converse of the Isosceles Triangle Theorem. Then write a proof.
Proof

Begin with $\triangle PRQ$ with $\angle P \cong \angle Q$.
Draw **a.** __?__, the bisector of $\angle PRQ$.

Given: $\angle P \cong \angle Q$, **b.** __?__ bisects $\angle PRQ$

Prove: $\overline{PR} \cong \overline{QR}$

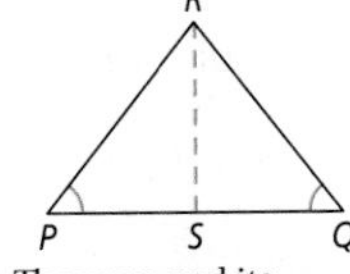

24. **Writing** Explain how the corollaries to the Isosceles Triangle Theorem and its converse follow from the theorems.

25. **Given:** $\overline{AE} \cong \overline{DE}$, $\overline{AB} \cong \overline{DC}$
Proof
Prove: $\triangle ABE \cong \triangle DCE$

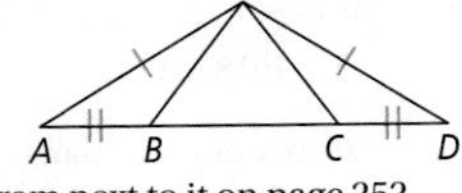

26. Prove Theorem 4-5. Use the diagram next to it on page 252.
Proof

27. a. **Communications** In the diagram at the right, what type of triangle is formed by the cables of the same height and the ground?
   b. What are the two different base lengths of the triangles?
   c. How is the tower related to each of the triangles?

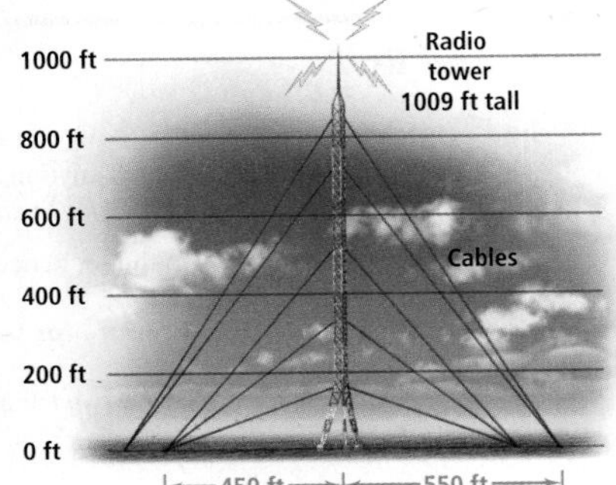

28. **Algebra** The length of the base of an isosceles triangle is x. The length of a leg is $2x - 5$. The perimeter of the triangle is 20. Find x.

29. **Constructions** Construct equiangular triangle ABC. Justify your method.

29.

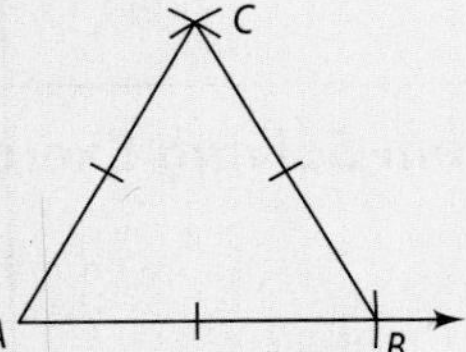

Draw $\overline{AB}$. Using AB as a radius, draw arcs with centers A and B. The intersection of these arcs is C. Since $\triangle ABC$ is equilateral, $\triangle ABC$ is equiangular by the Corollary to Theorem 4-3.

22a. $\overline{KM}$
b. $\overline{KM}$
c. Given
d. Def. of bisector
e. Refl. Prop. of $\cong$
f. SSS
g. Corresp. parts of $\cong$ ⚠ are $\cong$.

23a. $\overline{RS}$
b. $\overline{RS}$
$\overline{RS} \cong \overline{RS}$ (Refl. Prop. of $\cong$) and $\angle PRS \cong \angle QRS$ (def. of $\angle$ bisector). Also, $\angle P \cong \angle Q$ (Given). So $\triangle PRS \cong \triangle QRS$ by AAS. $\overline{PR} \cong \overline{QR}$ because corresp. parts of $\cong$ ⚠ are $\cong$.

24. Answers may vary. Sample: Apply the Isosc. $\triangle$ Thm. (or the Converse of the Isosc. $\triangle$ Thm.) two times to show that each angle (or side) is $\cong$ to each of the other two $\angle$s (or sides), so that all three $\angle$s (or sides) are $\cong$.

25. $\overline{AE} \cong \overline{DE}$ (Given), so $\angle A \cong \angle D$ by the Isosc. $\triangle$ Thm. Since $\overline{AB} \cong \overline{DC}$ (Given), then $\triangle ABE \cong \triangle DCE$ by SAS.

26. $\overline{AC} \cong \overline{BC}$ and $\angle ACD \cong \angle BCD$ (Given). Also, $\overline{CD} \cong \overline{CD}$ by the Refl. Prop. of $\cong$. So $\triangle CAD \cong \triangle CBD$ by SAS. Therefore $\overline{AD} \cong \overline{BD}$ and $\angle ADC \cong \angle BDC$ because corresp. parts of $\cong$ ⚠ are $\cong$. Since $\angle ADC$ and $\angle BDC$ are suppl., each must have measure 90. So $\overline{CD} \perp \overline{AB}$ (Def. of $\perp$).

27a. isosc. ⚠
b. 900 ft; 1100 ft
c. The tower is the $\perp$ bisector of each base.

28. 6

Answers

Practice and Problem-Solving Exercises (continued)

30. $m = 20, n = 45$

31. $m = 36, n = 27$

32. $m = 60, n = 30$

33. (−4, 0), (0, 0), (0, −4), (4, 4), (4, 8), (8, 4)

34. (−5, 5), (0, 5), (0, 10), (5, 0), (5, −5), (10, 0)

35. (−1, 6), (2, 6), (2, 9), (5, 0), (5, 3), (8, 3)

36. any real number greater than 45 and less than 90

37. B

38. F

39. C

40. [2] You need to know $\overline{BC} \cong \overline{EF}$ to prove the △s ≅ by SAS OR you need to know $\angle A \cong \angle D$ to prove the △s ≅ by ASA OR you need to know $\angle C \cong \angle F$ to prove the △s ≅ by AAS.

[1] incomplete OR incorrect answer

41. $RC = GV$; there are three pairs of ≅ ∠s and one pair of ≅ sides, so $\triangle TRC \cong \triangle HGV$ by AAS or ASA, and $\overline{RC} \cong \overline{GV}$ because corresp. parts of ≅ △s are ≅.

42. The letters are the first letters of the days of the week; S, S.

43. Yes; the △s share a common side, so they are ≅ by SAS.

44. Yes; the vertical ∠s are ≅, so the △s are ≅ by SAS.

Algebra Find the values of m and n.

30.

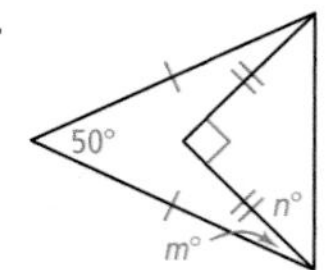

31.

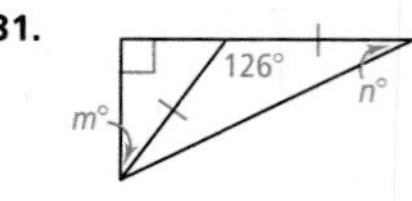

32.

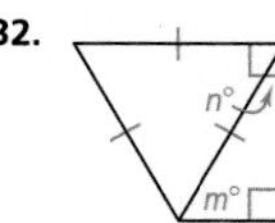

Challenge **Coordinate Geometry** For each pair of points, there are six points that could be the third vertex of an isosceles right triangle. Find the coordinates of each point.

33. (4, 0) and (0, 4) **34.** (0, 0) and (5, 5) **35.** (2, 3) and (5, 6)

36. Reasoning What measures are possible for the base angles of an acute isosceles triangle?

Standardized Test Prep

SAT/ACT

37. In isosceles $\triangle ABC$, the vertex angle is $\angle A$. What can you prove?

A $AB = CB$ B $m\angle B = m\angle C$ C $\angle A \cong \angle B$ D $\overline{BC} \cong \overline{AC}$

38. $\triangle LMN \cong \triangle PQR$. What is LM?

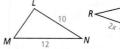

F 3 H 8
G 4 I 10

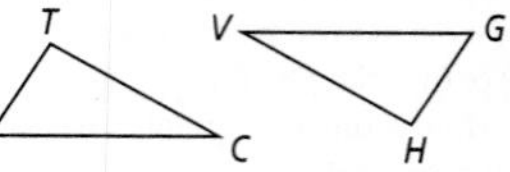

39. What is the exact area of the base of a circular swimming pool with diameter 16 ft?

A 1018.29 ft^2 B 1018.3 ft^2 C 64π ft^2 D 256π ft^2

Short Response

40. Suppose $\triangle ABC$ and $\triangle DEF$ are nonright triangles. If $\angle B \cong \angle E$ and $\overline{AB} \cong \overline{DE}$, what else do you need to know to prove $\triangle ABC \cong \triangle DEF$? Explain.

Mixed Review

41. $m\angle R = 59$, $m\angle T = 93 = m\angle H$, $m\angle V = 28$, and $RT = GH$. What, if anything, can you conclude about RC and GV? Explain.

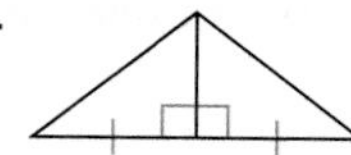

See Lesson 4-4.

42. Find the pattern of the sequence M, T, W, T, F, . . . Then find the next two terms. See Lesson 2-1.

Get Ready! To prepare for Lesson 4-6, do Exercises 43 and 44.

Can you conclude that the two triangles are congruent? Explain. See Lesson 4-2.

43.

44.

4-5 Lesson Resources

Differentiated Remediation

Instructional Support

Geometry Companion

Students can use the **Geometry Companion** worktext (4 pages) . . .

- New Vocabulary
- Key Concepts
- Got It for each Problem
- Lesson Check

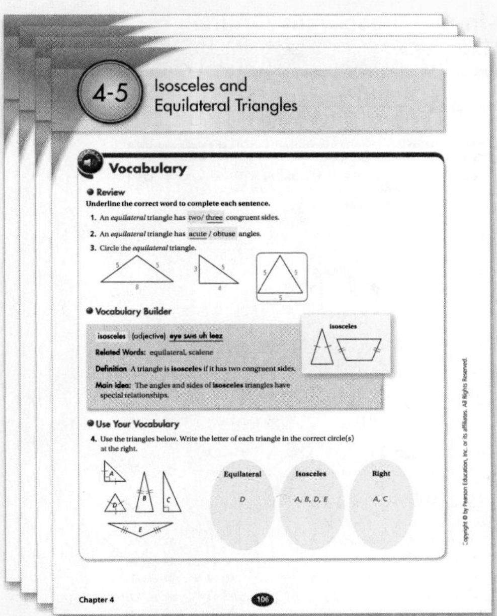

4-5 Isosceles and Equilateral Triangles

Vocabulary

Review

Underline the correct word to complete each sentence.

1. An *equilateral* triangle has two/ three congruent sides.
2. An *equilateral* triangle has acute / obtuse angles.
3. Circle the *equilateral* triangle.

Vocabulary Builder

isosceles (adjective) **eye SAHS uh leez**

Related Words: equilateral, scalene

Definition A triangle is **isosceles** if it has two congruent sides.

Main Idea: The angles and sides of **isosceles** triangles have special relationships.

Use Your Vocabulary

4. Use the triangles below. Write the letter of each triangle in the correct circle(s) at the right.

Equilateral	Isosceles	Right
D	A, B, D, E	A, C

Chapter 4 106

ELL Support

Focus on Language Draw an isosceles triangle on the board. Ask: What type of triangle is this? Trace the base of the triangle. Ask: What is this side of the triangle called? Trace the sides and ask: What are these two sides called? Trace the vertex angle and ask: What is this angle called? How would you define it? What are the other two angles called?

Focus on Communication Place the "Think and Write" presentation from page 253 on the overhead projector. Point to each word as you read. Ask students to come up with their own examples in the "Write" column for each row. Place students in mixed pairs and have them share their four examples with their partner.

5 Assess & Remediate

Lesson Quiz

1. Is $\overline{DE} \cong \overline{DF}$? Explain.

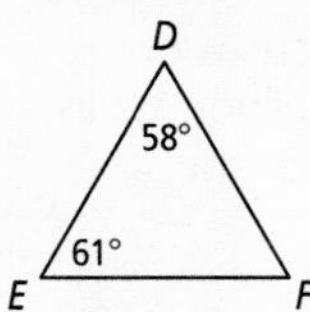

2. Do you UNDERSTAND? What is the value of x?

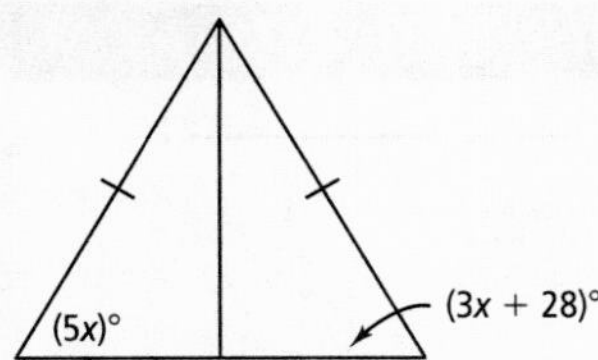

3. Isosceles triangle XYZ has base $\overline{XY}$ and $m\angle Y = 34$. What is $m\angle Z$?

ANSWERS TO LESSON QUIZ

1. Yes; $m\angle F = 61$, so $\overline{DE} \cong \overline{DF}$ by the Converse of the Isosceles Triangle Theorem.

2. 14

3. 112

PRESCRIPTION FOR REMEDIATION

Use the student work on the Lesson Quiz to prescribe a differentiated review assignment.

Points	Differentiated Remediation
0–1	Intervention
2	On-level
3	Extension

PowerGeometry.com

5 Assess & Remediate

Assign the Lesson Quiz. Appropriate intervention, practice, or enrichment is automatically generated based on student performance.

Intervention

- **Reteaching** (2 pages) Provides reteaching and practice exercises for the key lesson concepts. Use with struggling students or absent students.
- **English Language Learner Support** Helps students develop and reinforce mathematical vocabulary and key concepts.

All-in-One Resources/Online

Reteaching

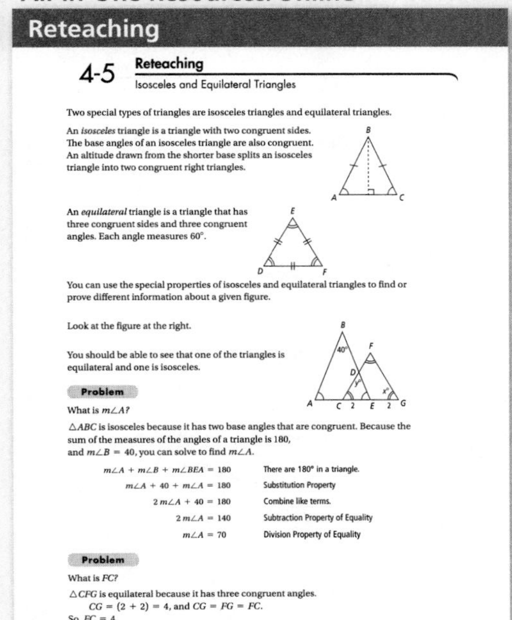

4-5 **Reteaching**

Isosceles and Equilateral Triangles

Two special types of triangles are isosceles triangles and equilateral triangles.

An *isosceles* triangle is a triangle with two congruent sides. The base angles of an isosceles triangle are also congruent. An altitude drawn from the shorter base splits an isosceles triangle into two congruent right triangles.

An *equilateral* triangle is a triangle that has three congruent sides and three congruent angles. Each angle measures 60°.

You can use the special properties of isosceles and equilateral triangles to find or prove different information about a given figure.

Look at the figure at the right.

You should be able to see that one of the triangles is equilateral and one is isosceles.

Problem

What is $m\angle A$?

$\triangle ABC$ is isosceles because it has two base angles that are congruent. Because the sum of the measures of the angles of a triangle is 180, and $m\angle B = 40$, you can solve to find $m\angle A$.

$m\angle A + m\angle B + m\angle BEA = 180$	There are 180° in a triangle.
$m\angle A + 40 + m\angle A = 180$	Substitution Property
$2\,m\angle A + 40 = 180$	Combine like terms.
$2\,m\angle A = 140$	Subtraction Property of Equality
$m\angle A = 70$	Division Property of Equality

Problem

What is FC?

$\triangle CFG$ is equilateral because it has three congruent angles.

$CG = (2 + 2) = 4$, and $CG = FG = FC$.

So, $FC = 4$.

All-in-One Resources/Online

English Language Learner Support

4-5 **ELL Support**

Isosceles and Equilateral Triangles

Complete the vocabulary chart by filling in the missing information.

Word or Word Phrase	Definition	Picture or Example
base	The *base* of an isosceles triangle is the side included between the pair of congruent angles.	
base angles	1. The *base angles* are the two congruent angles of an isosceles triangle.	
corollary	2. A *corollary* is a theorem that can be proved easily by another theorem.	A corollary to the Isosceles Triangle Theorem is: If a triangle is equilateral, then the triangle is equiangular.
equiangular triangle	An *equiangular triangle* is a triangle with three congruent angles. The angles of an equiangular triangle all measure 60.	3.
isosceles triangle	4. An *isosceles triangle* is a triangle with two congruent sides.	
legs	The *legs* are the two congruent sides of an isosceles triangle.	5.
vertex angle	6. The *vertex angle* is the angle formed by the legs of an isosceles triangle.	7.

Differentiated Remediation *continued*

On-Level

- **Practice** (2 pages) Provides extra practice for each lesson. For simpler practice exercises, use the Form K Practice pages found in the All-in-One Teaching Resources and online.
- **Think About a Plan** Helps students develop specific problem-solving skills and strategies by providing scaffolded guiding questions.
- **Standardized Test Prep** Focuses on all major exercises, all major question types, and helps students prepare for the high-stakes assessments.

Extension

- **Enrichment** Provides students with interesting problems and activities that extend the concepts of the lesson.
- **Activities, Games, and Puzzles** Worksheets that can be used for concepts development, enrichment, and for fun!

Practice and Problem Solving Wkbk/ Resources/Online

Practice page 1

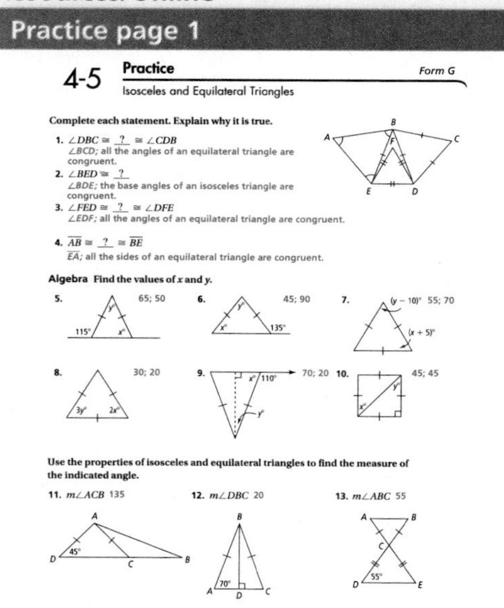

4-5 **Practice** *Form G*

Isosceles and Equilateral Triangles

Complete each statement. Explain why it is true.

1. $\angle DBC \cong$? $\cong \angle CDB$
   $\angle BCD$; all the angles of an equilateral triangle are congruent.
2. $\angle BED \cong$?
   $\angle BDE$; the base angles of an isosceles triangle are congruent.
3. $\angle FED \cong$? $\cong \angle DFE$
   $\angle EDF$; all the angles of an equilateral triangle are congruent.
4. $\overline{AB} \cong$? $\cong \overline{BE}$
   $\overline{EA}$; all the sides of an equilateral triangle are congruent.

Algebra Find the values of x and y.

5. 65; 50
6. 45; 90
7. 55; 70
8. 30; 20
9. 70; 20
10. 45; 45

Use the properties of isosceles and equilateral triangles to find the measure of the indicated angle.

11. $m\angle ACB$ 135
12. $m\angle DBC$ 20
13. $m\angle ABC$ 55

14. Equilateral $\triangle ABC$ and isosceles $\triangle DBC$ share side BC. If $m\angle BDC = 34$ and $BD = BC$, what is the measure of $\angle ABD$? (*Hint:* it may help to draw the figure described.) 172

Practice and Problem Solving Wkbk/ Resources/Online

Practice page 2

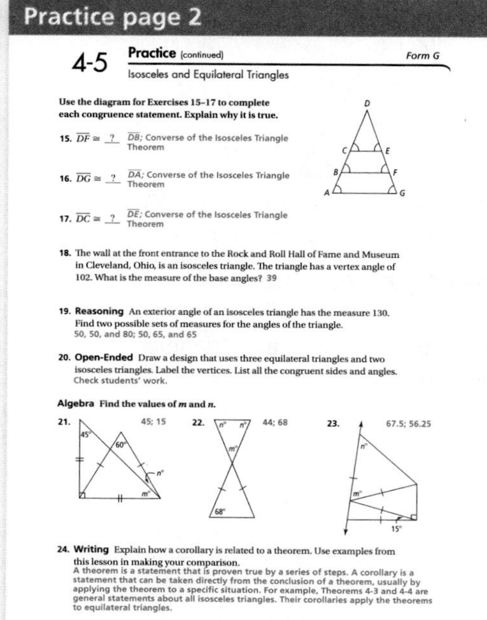

4-5 **Practice** (continued) *Form G*

Isosceles and Equilateral Triangles

Use the diagram for Exercises 15–17 to complete each congruence statement. Explain why it is true.

15. $\overline{DF} \cong$? $\overline{DB}$; Converse of the Isosceles Triangle Theorem
16. $\overline{DG} \cong$? $\overline{DA}$; Converse of the Isosceles Triangle Theorem
17. $\overline{DC} \cong$? $\overline{DE}$; Converse of the Isosceles Triangle Theorem
18. The wall at the front entrance to the Rock and Roll Hall of Fame and Museum in Cleveland, Ohio, is an isosceles triangle. The triangle has a vertex angle of 102. What is the measure of the base angles? 39
19. **Reasoning** An exterior angle of an isosceles triangle has the measure 130. Find two possible sets of measures for the angles of the triangle.
    50, 50, and 80; 50, 65, and 65
20. **Open-Ended** Draw a design that uses three equilateral triangles and two isosceles triangles. Label the vertices. List all the congruent sides and angles.
    Check students' work.

Algebra Find the values of m and n.

21. 45; 15
22. 44; 68
23. 67.5; 56.25

24. **Writing** Explain how a corollary is related to a theorem. Use examples from this lesson in making your comparison.
    A theorem is a statement that is proven true by a series of steps. A corollary is a statement that can be taken directly from the conclusion of a theorem, usually by applying the theorem to a specific situation. For example, Theorems 4-3 and 4-4 are general statements about all isosceles triangles. Their corollaries apply the theorems to equilateral triangles.

All-in-One Resources/Online

Enrichment

4-5 **Enrichment**

Isosceles and Equilateral Triangles

The swan below is composed of several triangles. Use the given information and the figure to find each angle measure. Note: Figure not drawn to scale.

Given: $\triangle ABC$ is equilateral; $\angle BCD \cong \angle BDC$; $\overline{DE} \cong \overline{CE} \cong \overline{EF}$; $\angle CGF \cong \angle CFG$; $\triangle GCF \cong \triangle GKF \cong \triangle JHM$; $\triangle KFH \cong \triangle KLH$; $\overline{KO} \cong \overline{FO}$; $\angle HKN \cong \angle HNK$; $\overline{JN} \cong \overline{JO}$

1. $m\angle ABC$ 60	2. $m\angle BCA$ 60	3. $m\angle CAB$ 60	4. $m\angle BCD$ 70
5. $m\angle BDC$ 70	6. $m\angle CBD$ 40	7. $m\angle EDC$ 72	8. $m\angle ECD$ 72
9. $m\angle CED$ 36	10. $m\angle ECF$ 30	11. $m\angle EFC$ 30	12. $m\angle CEF$ 120
13. $m\angle CGF$ 80	14. $m\angle CFG$ 80	15. $m\angle GCF$ 20	16. $m\angle KGF$ 80
17. $m\angle KFG$ 80	18. $m\angle GKF$ 20	19. $m\angle FKH$ 41	20. $m\angle FHK$ 23
21. $m\angle KFH$ 116	22. $m\angle KHL$ 23	23. $m\angle HKL$ 41	24. $m\angle KLH$ 116
25. $m\angle HJM$ 80	26. $m\angle HMJ$ 80	27. $m\angle JHM$ 20	28. $m\angle OFK$ 82
29. $m\angle OKF$ 82	30. $m\angle KOF$ 16	31. $m\angle HKN$ 78.5	32. $m\angle HNK$ 78.5
33. $m\angle OKN$ 37.5	34. $m\angle JNO$ 40	35. $m\angle JON$ 40	36. $m\angle NJO$ 100

Practice and Problem Solving Wkbk/ Resources/Online

Think About a Plan

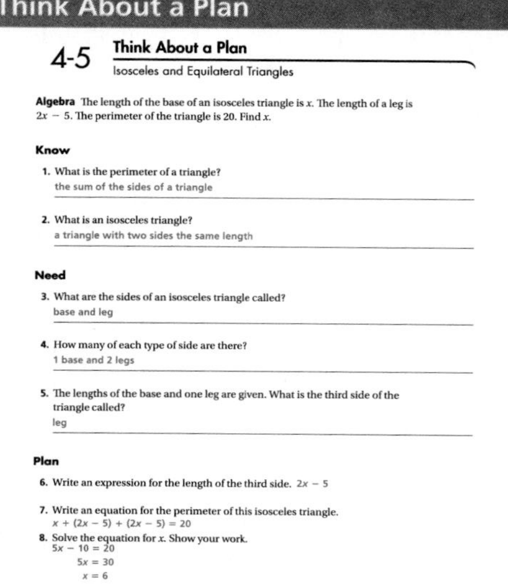

4-5 **Think About a Plan**

Isosceles and Equilateral Triangles

Algebra The length of the base of an isosceles triangle is x. The length of a leg is $2x - 5$. The perimeter of the triangle is 20. Find x.

Know

1. What is the perimeter of a triangle?
   the sum of the sides of a triangle
2. What is an isosceles triangle?
   a triangle with two sides the same length

Need

3. What are the sides of an isosceles triangle called?
   base and leg
4. How many of each type of side are there?
   1 base and 2 legs
5. The lengths of the base and one leg are given. What is the third side of the triangle called?
   leg

Plan

6. Write an expression for the length of the third side. $2x - 5$
7. Write an equation for the perimeter of this isosceles triangle.
   $x + (2x - 5) + (2x - 5) = 20$
8. Solve the equation for x. Show your work.
   $5x - 10 = 20$
   $5x = 30$
   $x = 6$

Practice and Problem Solving Wkbk/ Resources/Online

Standardized Test Prep

4-5 **Standardized Test Prep**

Isosceles and Equilateral Triangles

Gridded Response

Solve each exercise and enter your answer on the grid provided.

Refer to the diagram for Exercises 1–3.

1. What is the value of x?
2. What is the value of y?
3. What is the value of z?
4. The measures of two of the sides of an equilateral triangle are $3x + 15$ in. and $7x - 5$ in. What is the measure of the third side in inches?
5. In $\triangle GHI$, $HI = GH$, $m\angle IHG = 3x + 4$, and $m\angle IGH = 2x - 24$. What is $m\angle HIG$?

Answers

1. 55 2. 70 3. 55 4. 30 5. 40

Online Teacher Resource Center

Activities, Games, and Puzzles

4-5 **Activity: Isosceles Triangles**

Isosceles and Equilateral Triangles

Use geometry software to do this activity.

Construct

Construct isosceles triangle $\triangle ABC$ with base $\overline{BC}$. Construct angle bisectors for $\angle ABC$ and $\angle ACB$ intersecting at D.

Investigate

1. Measure the sides and angles of $\triangle DBC$ and classify the triangle as specifically as possible.
   isosceles
2. Drag the vertices of $\triangle DBC$ to observe the effect on the measures. Explain why this classification holds.
   $\angle DBC$ and $\angle DCB$ are congruent. Therefore $\triangle BCD$ remains isosceles.
3. Construct line $\overleftrightarrow{AD}$. What conclusions can be drawn about the relationship between $\overleftrightarrow{AD}$ and $\overline{BC}$?
   $\overleftrightarrow{AD}$ is the perpendicular bisector of $\overline{BC}$.

Extend

Construct isosceles triangle $\triangle ABC$ with base $\overline{BC}$. Construct the midpoint D of $\overline{AB}$ and midpoint E of $\overline{AC}$. Construct point F on $\overline{BC}$. Construct $\overline{DF}$ and $\overline{EF}$.

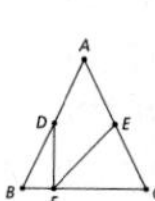

Investigate

Measure the areas of $\triangle ABC$ and quadrilateral $ADFE$. Drag the vertices of the original triangle and observe the effect on those measures.

4. Determine the relationship between the measures of the areas of $\triangle ABC$ and quadrilateral $ADFE$.
   The area of $\triangle ABC$ is twice the area of $ADFE$.
5. Consider dividing quadrilateral $ADFE$ into $\triangle ADE$ and $\triangle FDE$. How does the height of these two triangles compare with the height of $\triangle ABC$?
   The height is half that of $\triangle ABC$.

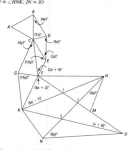

Algebra Review

Use With Lesson 4-6

Systems of Linear Equations

You can solve a system of equations in two variables by using substitution.

Example 1

Algebra Solve the system. $y = 3x + 5$
$y = x + 1$

$y = x + 1$	Start with one equation.
$3x + 5 = x + 1$	Substitute $3x + 5$ for y.
$2x = -4$	Solve for x.
$x = -2$	

Substitute -2 for x in either equation and solve for y.

$y = x + 1 = (-2) + 1 = -1$

Since $x = -2$ and $y = 1$, the solution is $(-2, -1)$. This is the point of intersection of the two lines.

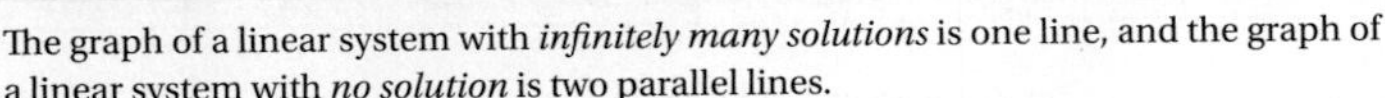

The graph of a linear system with *infinitely many solutions* is one line, and the graph of a linear system with *no solution* is two parallel lines.

Example 2

Algebra Solve the system. $x + y = 3$
$4x + 4y = 8$

$x + y = 3$	Start with one equation.
$x = 3 - y$	Solve the equation for x.
$4(3 - y) + 4y = 8$	Substitute $3 - y$ for x in the second equation.
$12 - 4y + 4y = 8$	Solve for y.
$12 = 8$	False!

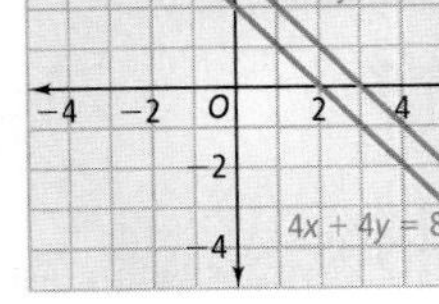

Since $12 = 8$ is a false statement, the system has no solution.

Exercises

Solve each system of equations.

1. $y = x - 4$; $y = 3x + 2$
2. $2x - y = 8$; $x + 2y = 9$
3. $3x + y = 4$; $-6x - 2y = 12$
4. $2x - 3 = y + 3$; $2x + y = -3$
5. $y = x + 1$; $x = y - 1$
6. $x - y = 4$; $3x - 3y = 6$
7. $y = -x + 2$; $2y = 4 - 2x$
8. $y = 2x - 1$; $y = 3x - 7$

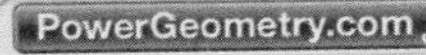

Answers

Exercises

1. $(-3, -7)$
2. $(5, 2)$
3. no solution
4. $(0.75, -4.5)$
5. infinitely many solutions
6. no solution
7. infinitely many solutions
8. $(6, 11)$

Guided Instruction

PURPOSE To review how to solve a system of linear equations in two variables using the substitution method

PROCESS Students will

- isolate a variable in one of the equations.
- substitute the expression equal to the isolated variable and solve the other equation for the other variable.

DISCUSS This set of examples and exercises focuses on the method of solving a system of equations in two variables by substitution.

Q What are some other ways that you can solve a system of equations in two variables? **[graphing and elimination]**

Q If given a choice among all three methods, when would it be best to use substitution? **[When one equation has a variable with a coefficient of 1 or −1.]**

Example 1

This Example focuses on the steps performed to solve a system of equations in two variables by the substitution method when the equations are solved for the same variable.

Q Can you solve this same system of equations by substituting a value for x? Explain. **[Yes; solve the second equation for x ($x = y - 1$) and substitute into the first equation ($y = 3(y - 1) + 5$).]**

Example 2

In this Example students will again see the step-by-step approach to solving a system of equations in two variables by using substitution, but the result is *no solution*.

Q Without the aid of a graph, the end result of this example is $12 = 8$. What about this result is an indication that there is *no solution*? **[the fact that this statement is not true for any values of x and y]**

Q What will be the end result of solving a system of linear equations with *infinitely many solutions*? **[a statement that is always true such as $5 = 5$]**

1 Interactive Learning

Solve It!

PURPOSE To use properties of isosceles triangles to show that right triangles are congruent

PROCESS Students must conclude that $\triangle ABC$ is an isosceles triangle and show that $\triangle ABD \cong \triangle CBD$ using the Isosc. $\triangle$ Thm. and AAS.

FACILITATE

Q What type of triangle is $\triangle ABC$? **[isosceles]**

Q Knowing that the triangle is isosceles leads you to conclude which angles are congruent? **[$\angle A$ and $\angle C$]**

Q What is the relationship between $\angle ADB$ and $\angle CDB$? **[They are congruent.]**

ANSWER See Solve It in Answers on next page.

CONNECT THE MATH Once students realize that the right triangles in the diagram are congruent, they will see a new set of conditions to prove that the two right triangles are congruent.

4-6 Congruence in Right Triangles

TN State Performance Indicators

SPI 3108.4.11 Use basic theorems about similar and congruent triangles to solve problems.

SPI 3108.4.12 Solve problems involving congruence, similarity, proportional reasoning and/or scale factor of two similar figures or solids.

Objective To prove right triangles congruent using the Hypotenuse-Leg Theorem

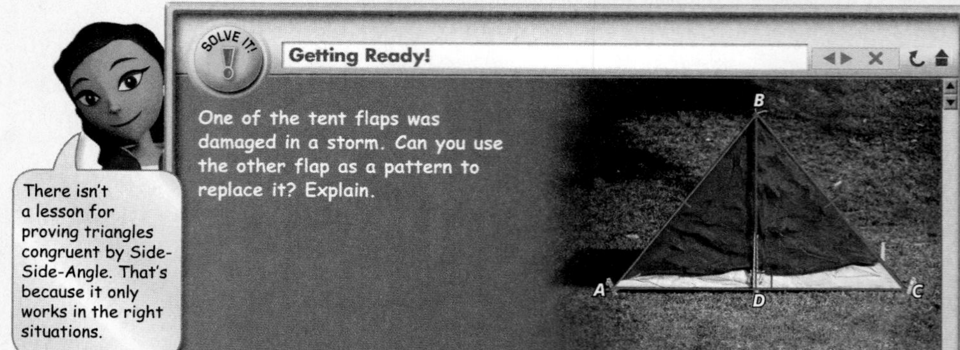

Getting Ready!
One of the tent flaps was damaged in a storm. Can you use the other flap as a pattern to replace it? Explain.
B
A
D
C

There isn't a lesson for proving triangles congruent by Side-Side-Angle. That's because it only works in the right situations.

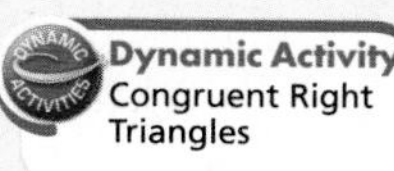

Lesson Vocabulary
- hypotenuse
- legs of a right triangle

In the diagram below, two sides and a nonincluded angle of one triangle are congruent to two sides and the nonincluded angle of another triangle.

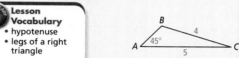

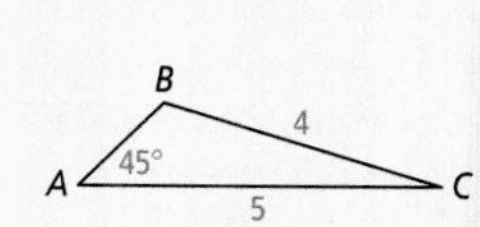

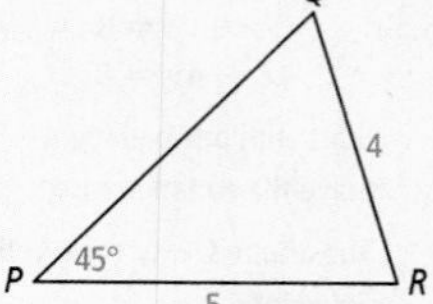

Notice that the triangles are not congruent. So, you can conclude that Side-Side-Angle is *not* a valid method for proving two triangles congruent. This method, however, works in the special case of right triangles, where the right angles are the nonincluded angles.

In a right triangle, the side opposite the right angle is called the **hypotenuse.** It is the longest side in the triangle. The other two sides are called **legs.**

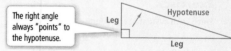

The right angle always "points" to the hypotenuse.

Leg — Hypotenuse — Leg

Essential Understanding You can prove that two triangles are congruent without having to show that *all* corresponding parts are congruent. In this lesson, you will prove right triangles congruent by using one pair of right angles, a pair of hypotenuses, and a pair of legs.

4-6 Preparing to Teach

BIG idea Reasoning and Proof UbD

ESSENTIAL UNDERSTANDINGS
- Two triangles can be proven to be congruent without having to show that all corresponding parts are congruent.
- Another way triangles can be proven to be congruent is by using one pair of right angles, a pair of hypotenuses, and a pair of legs.

Math Background

Before students learned the HL Theorem for proving two right triangles congruent, they could use the Pythagorean Theorem to give enough information to prove the triangles congruent. If you are given two right triangles with congruent hypotenuses and congruent legs, consider the following process to show that the remaining legs are congruent.

In Triangle$_1$, let c = length of the hypotenuse. Because the hypotenuses are congruent, c = length of hypotenuse in Triangle$_2$.

Let b be the length of the congruent legs of each triangle.

In Triangle$_1$, the length of the other leg $a_1 = \sqrt{c^2 - b^2}$. In Triangle$_2$, the length of the other leg $a_2 = \sqrt{c^2 - b^2}$. Therefore, $a_1 = a_2$. The triangles are congruent by SSS.

Once the third sides are confirmed to be congruent, you could also choose to justify the triangle congruence by SAS using the right angles as the included angles.

This line of reasoning leads to the HL Theorem presented in this lesson. With the introduction of the HL Theorem, students can use this shortcut in their proofs.

Support Student Learning

Use the **Geometry Companion** to engage and support students during instructions. See Lesson Resources at the end of this lesson for details.

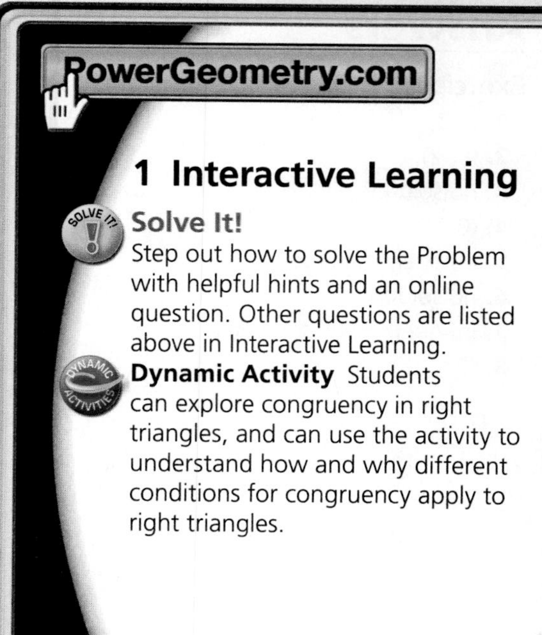

Theorem 4-6 Hypotenuse-Leg (HL) Theorem

Theorem	If . . .	Then . . .
If the hypotenuse and a leg of one right triangle are congruent to the hypotenuse and a leg of another right triangle, then the triangles are congruent.	$\triangle PQR$ and $\triangle XYZ$ are right ⦣s, $\overline{PR} \cong \overline{XZ}$, and $\overline{PQ} \cong \overline{XY}$ 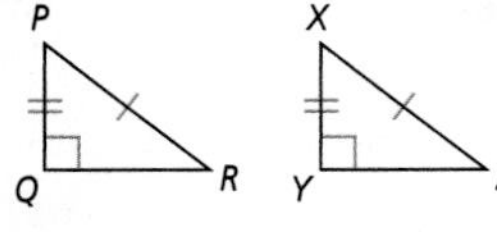	$\triangle PQR \cong \triangle XYZ$

To prove the HL Theorem you will need to draw auxiliary lines to make a third triangle.

Proof of Theorem 4-6: Hypotenuse-Leg Theorem

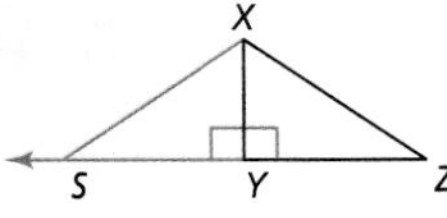

Given: $\triangle PQR$ and $\triangle XYZ$ are right triangles, with right angles Q and Y. $\overline{PR} \cong \overline{XZ}$ and $\overline{PQ} \cong \overline{XY}$.

Prove: $\triangle PQR \cong \triangle XYZ$

Proof: On $\triangle XYZ$, draw $\overrightarrow{ZY}$.

Mark point S so that $YS = QR$. Then, $\triangle PQR \cong \triangle XYS$ by SAS.

Since corresponding parts of congruent triangles are congruent, $\overline{PR} \cong \overline{XS}$. It is given that $\overline{PR} \cong \overline{XZ}$, so $\overline{XS} \cong \overline{XZ}$ by the Transitive Property of Congruence. By the Isosceles Triangle Theorem, $\angle S \cong \angle Z$, so $\triangle XYS \cong \triangle XYZ$ by AAS. Therefore, $\triangle PQR \cong \triangle XYZ$ by the Transitive Property of Congruence.

Key Concept Conditions for HL Theorem

To use the HL Theorem, the triangles must meet three conditions.

Conditions

- There are two right triangles.
- The triangles have congruent hypotenuses.
- There is one pair of congruent legs.

2 Guided Instruction

Take Note

Have students compare and contrast the triangle congruence postulates and theorem with this right triangle congruence theorem. They should notice that though only two conditions are specified in the HL Theorem, there are three conditions met by the theorem: 1) the triangles are right triangles, 2) the hypotenuses are congruent, and 3) one pair of legs is congruent. This theorem is a specific case of SSA.

Challenge students to prove the Hypotenuse-Leg Theorem using the Pythagorean Theorem. Students should be able to write QR and YZ in terms of the lengths of the other two sides. Then they can show that the two quantities are equal by the Substitution Property of Equality.

Take Note

Ask students to draw diagrams that show the three conditions listed for the HL Theorem in Take Note.

2 Guided Instruction

Each Problem is worked out and supported online.

Problem 1
Using the HL Theorem
Animated

Problem 2
Writing a Proof Using the HL Theorem
Animated

Support in Geometry Companion

- Vocabulary
- Key Concepts
- Got It?

Answers

Solve It!

Yes; $\overline{AB} \cong \overline{CB}$ (Given). By the Isosc. △ Thm., $\angle A \cong \angle C$ and $\angle BDC \cong \angle BDA$ (All rt. ⦣ are ≅.), so $\triangle ABD \cong \triangle CBD$ by AAS.

Problem 1

Q Which angles can be marked as right angles in the diagram? **[$\angle ADC$ and $\angle BDC$]**

Q Which segments are legs of $\triangle ACD$? **[$\overline{AD}$ and $\overline{CD}$]**

Q Which segments are legs of $\triangle BCD$? **[$\overline{BD}$ and $\overline{CD}$]**

Q Is there another pair of congruent sides in the triangles? Explain. **[Yes, side $\overline{CD}$ is shared by both triangles; therefore it is congruent to itself by the Reflexive Property of Congruence.]**

Got It? ERROR PREVENTION

For 1a, have students list the given information and identify what other information they need to prove the triangles are congruent. For 1b, your friend is right! By the Pythagorean Theorem, the other two legs are automatically congruent. The only issue is one of correspondence.

Proof **Problem 1** **Using the HL Theorem**

On the basketball backboard brackets shown below, $\angle ADC$ and $\angle BDC$ are right angles and $\overline{AC} \cong \overline{BC}$. Are $\triangle ADC$ and $\triangle BDC$ congruent? Explain.

Plan

How can you visualize the two right triangles? Imagine cutting $\triangle ABC$ along $\overline{DC}$. On either side of the cut, you get triangles with the same leg $\overline{DC}$.

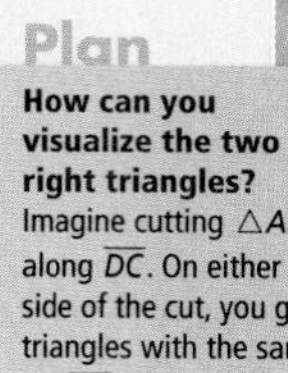

- You are given that $\angle ADC$ and $\angle BDC$ are right angles. So, $\triangle ADC$ and $\triangle BDC$ are right triangles.
- The hypotenuses of the two right triangles are $\overline{AC}$ and $\overline{BC}$. You are given that $\overline{AC} \cong \overline{BC}$.
- $\overline{DC}$ is a common leg of both $\triangle ADC$ and $\triangle BDC$. $\overline{DC} \cong \overline{DC}$ by the Reflexive Property of Congruence.

Yes, $\triangle ADC \cong \triangle BDC$ by the HL Theorem.

Got It? 1. a. Given: $\angle PRS$ and $\angle RPQ$ are right angles, $\overline{SP} \cong \overline{QR}$

Prove: $\triangle PRS \cong \triangle RPQ$

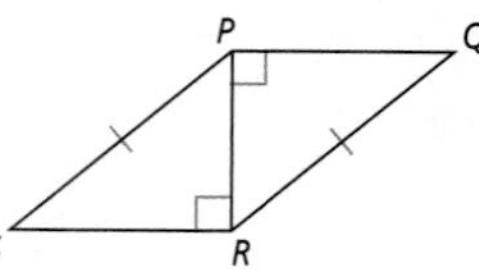

b. Reasoning Your friend says, "Suppose you have two right triangles with congruent hypotenuses and one pair of congruent legs. It does not matter which leg in the first triangle is congruent to which leg in the second triangle. The triangles will be congruent." Is your friend correct? Explain.

Additional Problems

1. Raymond built two triangular supports for a picnic table with the dimensions shown below. Are the supports congruent? Explain.

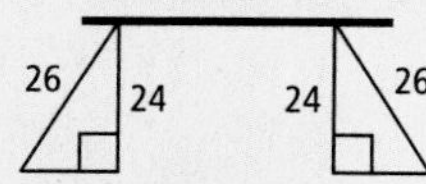

ANSWER Yes, by the HL Theorem

2. Given: $\overline{AD} \cong \overline{CB}$, $\angle B$ and $\angle D$ are right angles

Prove: $\triangle ABC \cong \triangle CDA$

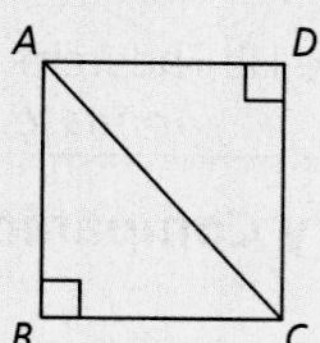

ANSWER It is given that $\overline{AD} \cong \overline{CB}$ and $\angle B$ and $\angle D$ are right angles. Therefore, $\triangle ABC$ and $\triangle CDA$ are right triangles. $\overline{AC} \cong \overline{AC}$ by the Reflexive Property of Congruence. So, $\triangle ABC \cong \triangle CDA$ by the HL Theorem.

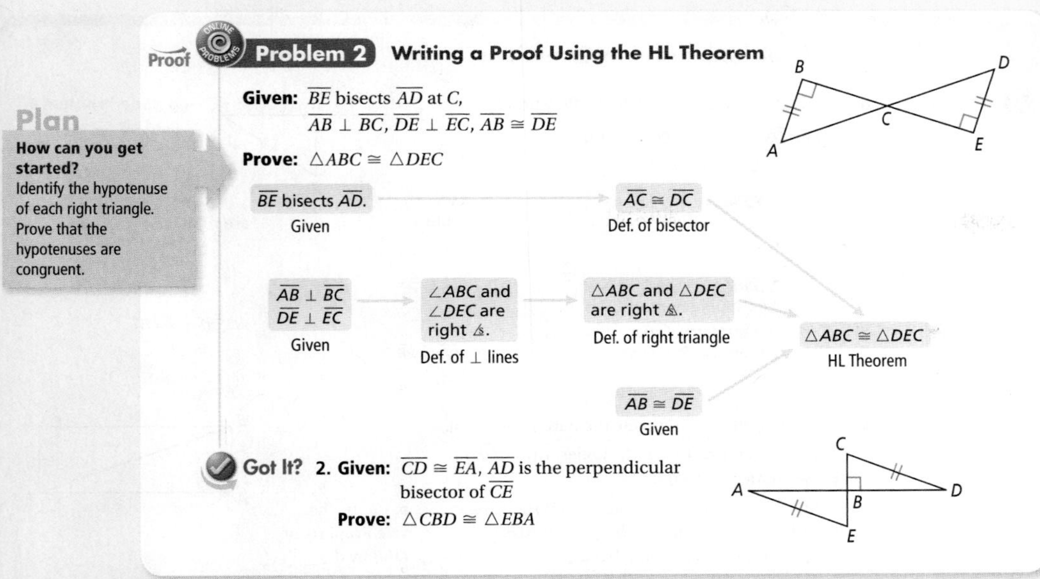

Plan

How can you get started? Identify the hypotenuse of each right triangle. Prove that the hypotenuses are congruent.

Proof **Problem 2** **Writing a Proof Using the HL Theorem**

Given: $\overline{BE}$ bisects $\overline{AD}$ at C, $\overline{AB} \perp \overline{BC}$, $\overline{DE} \perp \overline{EC}$, $\overline{AB} \cong \overline{DE}$

Prove: $\triangle ABC \cong \triangle DEC$

Got It? 2. Given: $\overline{CD} \cong \overline{EA}$, $\overline{AD}$ is the perpendicular bisector of $\overline{CE}$

Prove: $\triangle CBD \cong \triangle EBA$

Lesson Check

Do you know HOW?

Are the two triangles congruent? If so, write the congruence statement.

1.

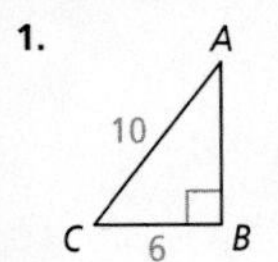

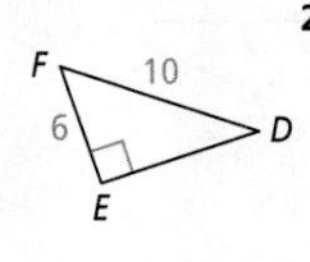

2.

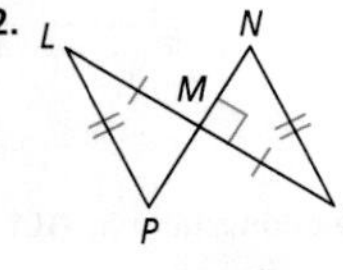

3.

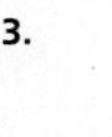

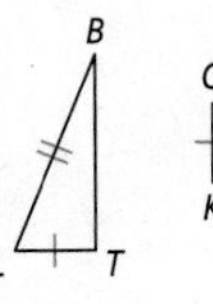

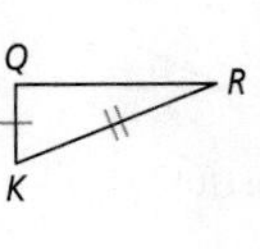

4.

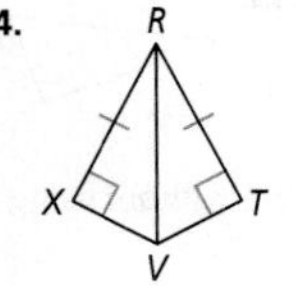

Do you UNDERSTAND?

5. Vocabulary A right triangle has side lengths of 5 cm, 12 cm, and 13 cm. What is the length of the hypotenuse? How do you know?

6. Compare and Contrast How do the HL Theorem and the SAS Postulate compare? How are they different? Explain.

7. Error Analysis Your classmate says that there is not enough information to determine whether the two triangles below are congruent. Is your classmate correct? Explain.

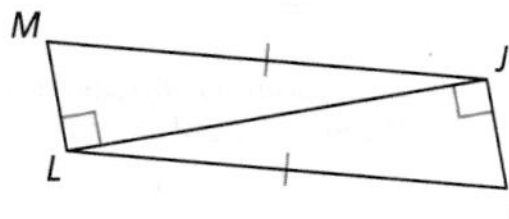

Problem 2

Q What statement results from knowing that $\overline{BE}$ bisects $\overline{AD}$? **[$\overline{AC} \cong \overline{CD}$]**

Q What types of triangles are shown in the diagram? Justify your answer. **[Because $\overline{AB} \perp \overline{BC}$ and $\overline{DE} \perp \overline{EC}$, $\angle B$ and $\angle E$ are right angles. Therefore the triangles are right triangles.]**

Q What information do you need to prove right triangles are congruent? **[The hypotenuses and one pair of legs must be congruent.]**

Got It?

Have students review the definition of *perpendicular bisector*. Ask them to draw the diagram and mark the properties of this line. Students should be able to use the HL Theorem to prove the triangles congruent.

3 Lesson Check

Do you know HOW?

- If students have difficulty with Exercise 3, then have them refer to the Take Note at the bottom of page 259.

Do you UNDERSTAND?

- If students have difficulty with Exercise 7, then have them review Problem 1.

Close

Q What two conditions are necessary to prove two right triangles are congruent? **[The hypotenuses and one pair of sides are congruent.]**

Answers

Got It?

1a. $\triangle PRS$ and $\triangle RPQ$ are rt. $\triangle$s with $\cong$ hypotenuses ($\overline{SP} \cong \overline{QR}$) and $\cong$ legs ($\overline{PR} \cong \overline{PR}$). So $\triangle PRS \cong \triangle RPQ$ by HL.

b. Yes; the two $\triangle$s satisfy the three conditions of the HL Thm., so they are $\cong$.

2. It is given that $\overline{AD}$ is the $\perp$ bisector of $\overline{CE}$, so $\triangle CBD$ and $\triangle EBA$ are rt. $\triangle$s and $\overline{CB} \cong \overline{EB}$ by the def. of $\perp$ bisector. Also, $\overline{CD} \cong \overline{EA}$ (Given), so $\triangle CBD \cong \triangle EBA$ by HL.

Lesson Check

1. yes; $\triangle BCA \cong \triangle EFD$

2. yes; $\triangle MPL \cong \triangle MNO$

3. no

4. yes; $\triangle XVR \cong \triangle TVR$

5. 13 cm; the hypotenuse is the longest side of a rt. $\triangle$.

6. Answers may vary. Sample: Alike: They both require information on two pairs of sides and one pair of $\angle$s. Different: For HL, the rt. $\angle$s are NOT included between the two pairs of $\cong$ sides, while for SAS the $\angle$s ARE included between the two pairs of $\cong$ sides.

7. No; $\triangle LMJ$ and $\triangle JKL$ are rt. $\triangle$s with $\cong$ hypotenuses ($\overline{MJ} \cong \overline{KL}$) and $\cong$ legs ($\overline{LJ} \cong \overline{LJ}$), so $\triangle LMJ \cong \triangle JKL$ by HL.

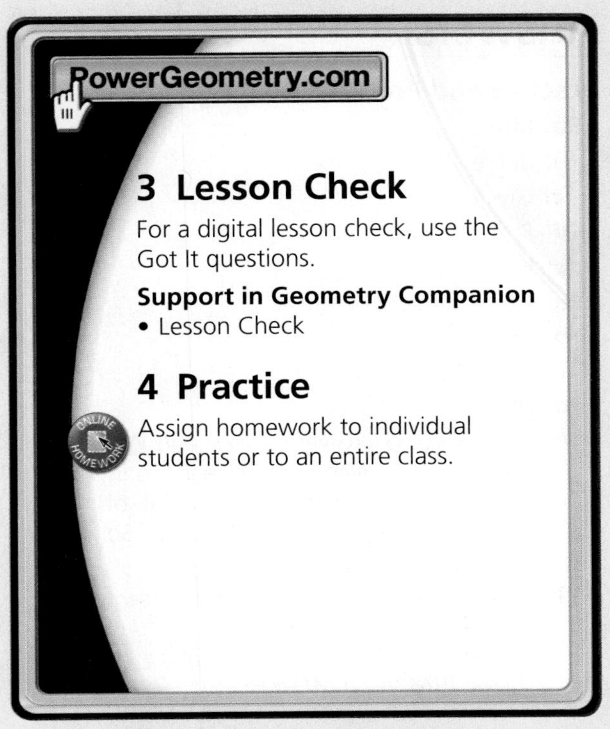

PowerGeometry.com

3 Lesson Check

For a digital lesson check, use the Got It questions.

Support in Geometry Companion

- Lesson Check

4 Practice

Assign homework to individual students or to an entire class.

4 Practice

ASSIGNMENT GUIDE
Basic: 8–16, 20, 22, 25
Average: 9, 11–26
Advanced: 9, 11–28
Standardized Test Prep: 29–31
Mixed Review: 32–36
Reasoning exercises have blue headings.
Applications exercises have red headings.
EXERCISE 13: Use the Think About a Plan worksheet in the **Practice and Problem Solving Workbook** (also available in the Teaching Resources in print and online) to further support students' development in becoming independent learners.

HOMEWORK QUICK CHECK
To check students' understanding of key skills and concepts, go over Exercises 9, 11, 13, 15, and 25.

Practice and Problem-Solving Exercises

A Practice

See Problem 1.

8. **Developing Proof** Complete the flow proof.

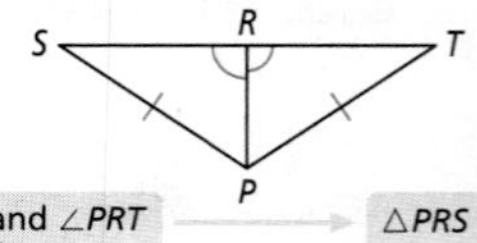

Given: $\overline{PS} \cong \overline{PT}$, $\angle PRS \cong \angle PRT$
Prove: $\triangle PRS \cong \triangle PRT$

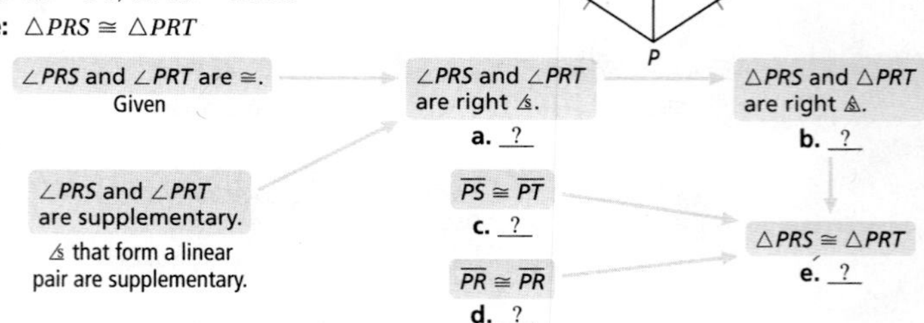

9. **Developing Proof** Complete the paragraph proof.

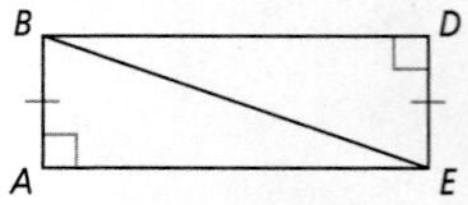

Given: $\angle A$ and $\angle D$ are right angles, $\overline{AB} \cong \overline{DE}$
Prove: $\triangle ABE \cong \triangle DEB$
Proof: It is given that $\angle A$ and $\angle D$ are right angles. So, **a.** __?__ by the definition of right triangles. **b.** __?__, because of the Reflexive Property of Congruence. It is also given that **c.** __?__. So, $\triangle ABE \cong \triangle DEB$ by **d.** __?__.

10. **Given:** $\overline{HV} \perp \overline{GT}$, $\overline{GH} \cong \overline{TV}$, I is the midpoint of $\overline{HV}$
Proof
Prove: $\triangle IGH \cong \triangle ITV$

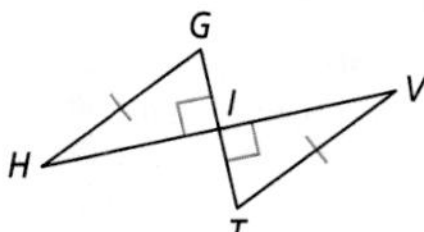

11. **Given:** $\overline{PM} \cong \overline{RJ}$, $\overline{PT} \perp \overline{TJ}$, $\overline{RM} \perp \overline{TJ}$, M is the midpoint of $\overline{TJ}$
Proof
Prove: $\triangle PTM \cong \triangle RMJ$

See Problem 2.

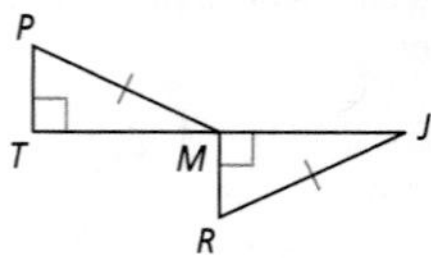

B Apply

Algebra For what values of x and y are the triangles congruent by HL?

12.

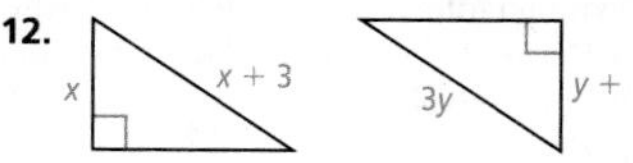

13. (figure labels: $3y + x$, $y - x$, $x + 5$, $y + 5$)

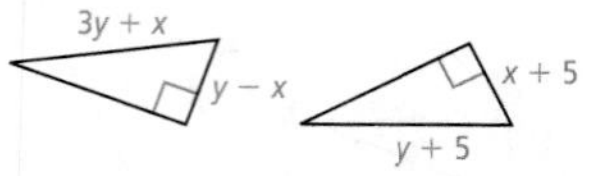

14. Study Exercise 8. Can you prove that $\triangle PRS \cong \triangle PRT$ without using the HL Theorem? Explain.

Answers

Practice and Problem-Solving Exercises

8a. If two ⊿s are ≅ and suppl., they are rt. ⊿s.
b. def. of a rt. △
c. Given
d. Refl. Prop. of ≅
e. HL

9a. $\triangle ABE$ and $\triangle DEB$ are rt. ⊿s.
b. $\overline{BE} \cong \overline{EB}$
c. $\overline{AB} \cong \overline{DE}$
d. HL

10. Since $\overline{HV} \perp \overline{GT}$ (Given), $\triangle IGH$ and $\triangle ITV$ are rt. ⊿s. It is given that $\overline{GH} \cong \overline{TV}$, and it is also given that point I is the midpt. of $\overline{HV}$, so $\overline{HI} \cong \overline{VI}$ by the def. of midpt. So $\triangle IGH \cong \triangle ITV$ by HL.

11. From the given information about ⊥ segments, $\triangle PTM$ and $\triangle RMJ$ are rt. ⊿s. $\overline{PM} \cong \overline{RJ}$ (Given), and since M is the midpt. of $\overline{TJ}$, $\overline{TM} \cong \overline{JM}$. Thus $\triangle PTM \cong \triangle RMJ$ by HL.

12. $x = 3$, $y = 2$

13. $x = -1$, $y = 3$

14. Answers may vary. Sample: $\angle S \cong \angle T$ by the Isosc. △ Thm., so $\triangle PRS \cong \triangle PRT$ by AAS.

15. Think About a Plan $\triangle ABC$ and $\triangle PQR$ are right triangular sections of a fire escape, as shown. Is each story of the building the same height? Explain.

- What can you tell from the diagram?
- How can you use congruent triangles here?

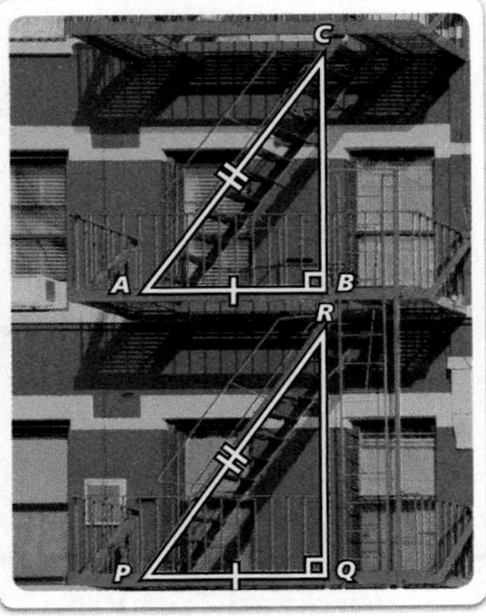

16. Writing "A HA!" exclaims your classmate. "There must be an HA Theorem, sort of like the HL Theorem!" Is your classmate correct? Explain.

17. Given: $\overline{RS} \cong \overline{TU}$, $\overline{RS} \perp \overline{ST}$, $\overline{TU} \perp \overline{UV}$, T is the midpoint of $\overline{RV}$
Proof

Prove: $\triangle RST \cong \triangle TUV$

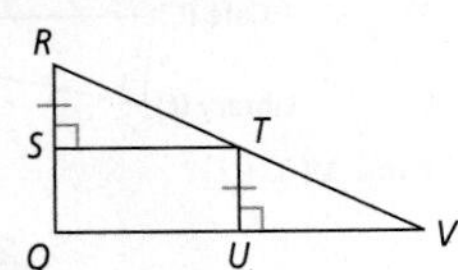

18. Given: $\triangle LNP$ is isosceles with base $\overline{NP}$, $\overline{MN} \perp \overline{NL}$, $\overline{QP} \perp \overline{PL}$, $\overline{ML} \cong \overline{QL}$
Proof

Prove: $\triangle MNL \cong \triangle QPL$

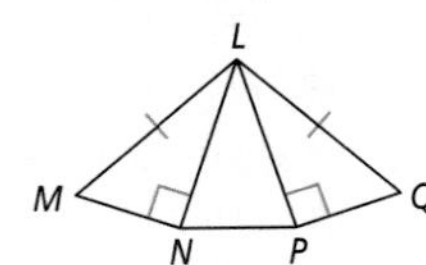

Constructions Copy the triangle and construct a triangle congruent to it using the given method.

19. SAS

20. HL

21. ASA

22. SSS

23. Given: $\triangle GKE$ is isosceles with base $\overline{GE}$, $\angle L$ and $\angle D$ are right angles, and K is the midpoint of $\overline{LD}$.
Proof

Prove: $\overline{LG} \cong \overline{DE}$

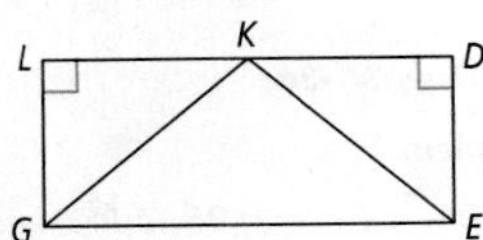

24. Given: $\overline{LO}$ bisects $\angle MLN$, $\overline{OM} \perp \overline{LM}$, $\overline{ON} \perp \overline{LN}$
Proof

Prove: $\triangle LMO \cong \triangle LNO$

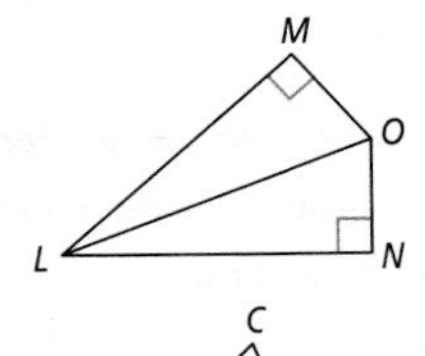

25. Reasoning Are the triangles congruent? Explain.

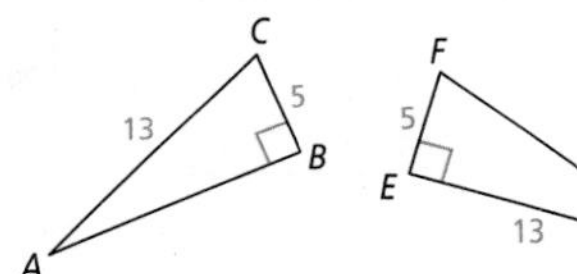

15. Yes; the two ⚠ are rt. ⚠ with ≅ hypotenuses and ≅ legs, so the two ⚠ are ≅ by HL. Then $\overline{RQ} \cong \overline{CB}$ because corresp. parts of ≅ ⚠ are ≅.

16. Yes; two rt. ⚠ with ≅ hypotenuses and a pair of ≅ acute ∠s also have a pair of ≅ rt. ∠s. So the two rt. ⚠ are ≅ by AAS.

17. Using the information about ⊥ segments, $\triangle RST$ and $\triangle TUV$ are rt. ⚠. $\overline{RS} \cong \overline{TU}$ (Given), and T is the midpt. of $\overline{RV}$ (Given), so $\overline{RT} \cong \overline{TV}$ (Def. of midpt.). Thus $\triangle RST \cong \triangle TUV$ by HL.

18. From the information about ⊥ segments, $\triangle MNL$ and $\triangle QPL$ are rt. ⚠. It is given that $\overline{ML} \cong \overline{QL}$, and since $\overline{NP}$ is the base of isosc. $\triangle LNP$ (Given), then $\overline{LN} \cong \overline{LP}$ (Def. of isosc. △). So $\triangle MNL \cong \triangle QPL$ by HL.

19.

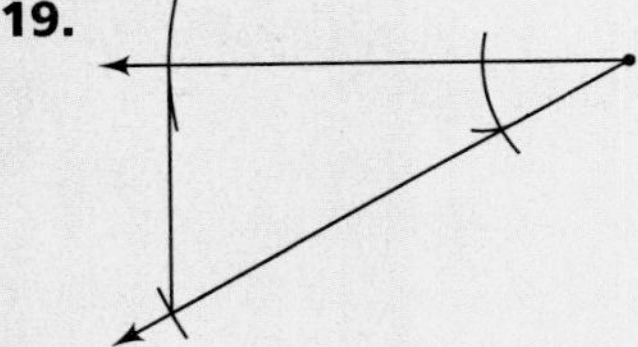

20.

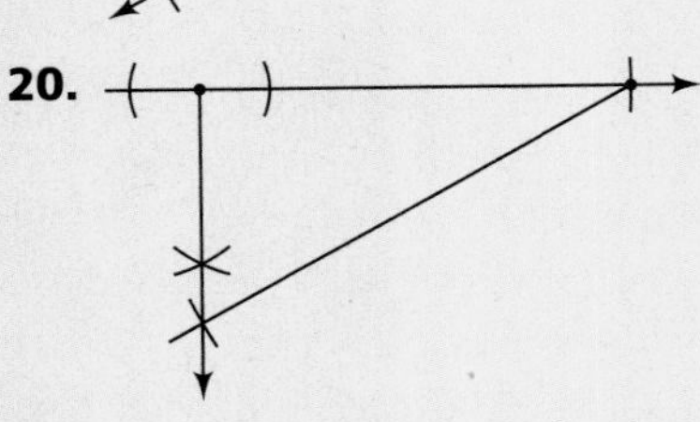

21.

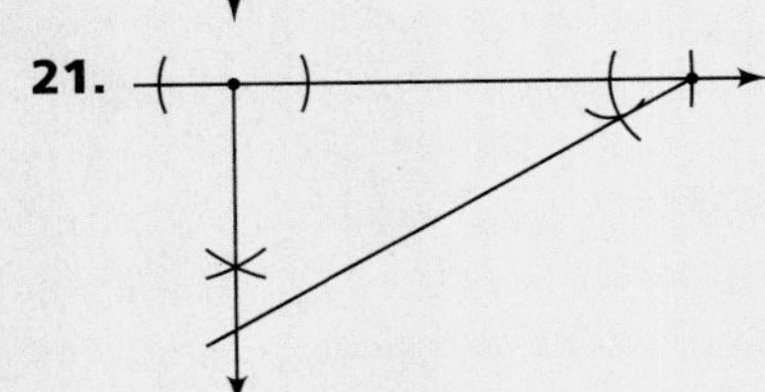

22.

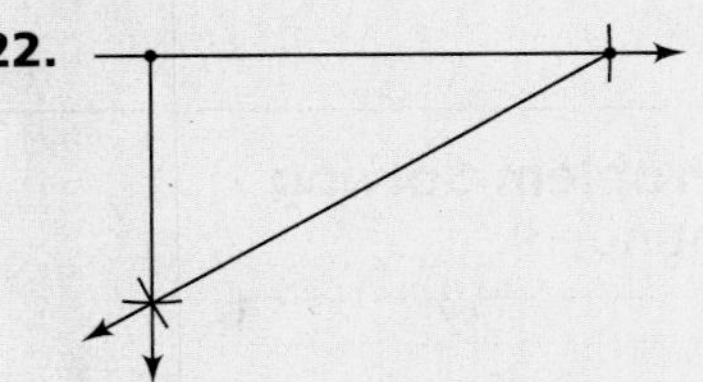

23. From the given information about an isosc. △, rt. ∠s, and midpt., you can conclude that $\overline{KG} \cong \overline{KE}$ (Def. of isosc. △), $\triangle LKG$ and $\triangle DKE$ are rt. ⚠ (Def. of rt. △), and $\overline{LK} \cong \overline{DK}$ (Def. of midpt.). So $\triangle LKG \cong \triangle DKE$ by HL, and $\overline{LG} \cong \overline{DE}$ because corresp. parts of ≅ ⚠ are ≅.

24. From the given ⊥ segments, $\angle M \cong \angle N$ because ⊥ lines form rt. ∠s, which are ≅. $\overline{LO}$ bisects $\angle MLN$ (Given), so $\angle MLO \cong \angle NLO$ by the def. of ∠ bisector. The Refl. Prop. of ≅ gives $\overline{LO} \cong \overline{LO}$, so $\triangle LMO \cong \triangle LNO$ by AAS.

25. No, the triangles are not ≅. Explanations may vary. Sample: $\overline{DF}$ is the hypotenuse of $\triangle DEF$, so it is the longest side of the triangle. Therefore, it is greater than 5 and greater than 13 because it is longer than either of the legs. So $\overline{DF}$ cannot be congruent to $\overline{AC}$, which is the hypotenuse of $\triangle ABC$ and has length 13.

Answers

Practice and Problem-Solving Exercises (continued)

26a.

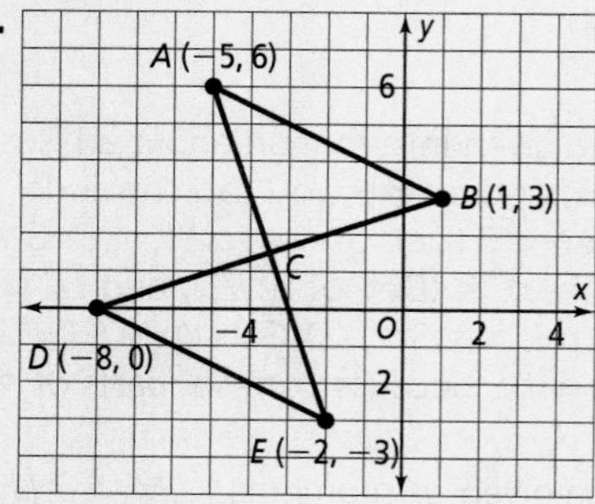

b. Slope of $\overline{AE} = -3$, slope of $\overline{BD} = \frac{1}{3}$; they are rt. ∠s.

c. $\overleftrightarrow{AE}: y - 6 = -3(x + 5)$
$\overleftrightarrow{BD}: y - 3 = \frac{1}{3}(x - 1)$; $C\left(-\frac{7}{2}, \frac{3}{2}\right)$

d. $AB = \sqrt{45}$, $BC = \sqrt{\frac{45}{2}}$, $DC = \sqrt{\frac{45}{2}}$, $DE = \sqrt{45}$

e. Answers may vary. Sample: ∠ACB and ∠ECD are rt. ∠s so △ABC and △EDC are rt. △s. $AB = DE = \sqrt{45}$, so the hypotenuses of the two △s are ≅. $BC = DC = \sqrt{\frac{45}{2}}$, so a pair of legs are congruent. So △ABC ≅ △EDC by HL.

27. △AEB and △CEB are rt. △s because the given information includes $\overline{BE} \perp \overline{EA}$ and $\overline{BE} \perp \overline{EC}$. △ABC is equilateral (Given), so $\overline{AB} \cong \overline{CB}$ by the def. of equilateral. Also, $\overline{BE} \cong \overline{BE}$ by the Refl. Prop. of ≅. So △AEB ≅ △CEB by HL.

28. No; visualize "squeezing" at points A and C. That would change the distance AC but would not change any of the given information. Since you can change the length of $\overline{AC}$, you cannot prove △ABC to be equilateral.

29. C

30. F

31. [2] △XRY ≅ △XRZ by HL, △YQX ≅ △YQZ by HL, △ZPX ≅ △ZPY by HL, and △XPS ≅ △YPS by SAS OR other correct pairs and explanations.
[1] incomplete OR incorrect explanation

32. △STU is isosceles. $\overline{ST} \cong \overline{UT}$ because corresp. parts of ≅ △s are ≅.

33. △STU is equilateral. $\overline{ST} \cong \overline{US}$, $\overline{TU} \cong \overline{ST}$, and $\overline{US} \cong \overline{TU}$ because corresp. parts of ≅ △s are ≅.

34. Yes; △ABC ≅ △LMN by HL.

35. No; △LMN and △HJK have one pair of ≅ sides and one pair of ≅ ∠s, but that is not enough to conclude that they are ≅.

36. No; the hypotenuse of rt. △ABC is ≅ to a leg of rt. △RST, so the △s cannot be ≅.

26. a. Coordinate Geometry Graph the points A(−5, 6), B(1, 3), D(−8, 0), and E(−2, −3). Draw $\overline{AB}$, $\overline{AE}$, $\overline{BD}$, and $\overline{DE}$. Label point C, the intersection of $\overline{AE}$ and $\overline{BD}$.
b. Find the slopes of $\overline{AE}$ and $\overline{BD}$. How would you describe ∠ACB and ∠ECD?
c. Algebra Write equations for $\overleftrightarrow{AE}$ and $\overleftrightarrow{BD}$. What are the coordinates of C?
d. Use the Distance Formula to find AB, BC, DC, and DE.
e. Write a paragraph to prove that △ABC ≅ △EDC.

Challenge **Geometry in 3 Dimensions** **For Exercises 27 and 28, use the figure at the right.**

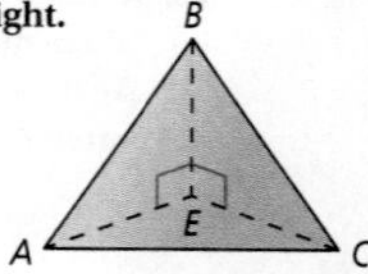

27. Given: $\overline{BE} \perp \overline{EA}$, $\overline{BE} \perp \overline{EC}$, △ABC is equilateral
Proof **Prove:** △AEB ≅ △CEB

28. Given: △AEB ≅ △CEB, $\overline{BE} \perp \overline{EA}$, $\overline{BE} \perp \overline{EC}$
Can you prove that △ABC is equilateral? Explain.

Standardized Test Prep

SAT/ACT

29. You often walk your dog around the neighborhood. Based on the diagram at the right, which of the following statements about distances is true?

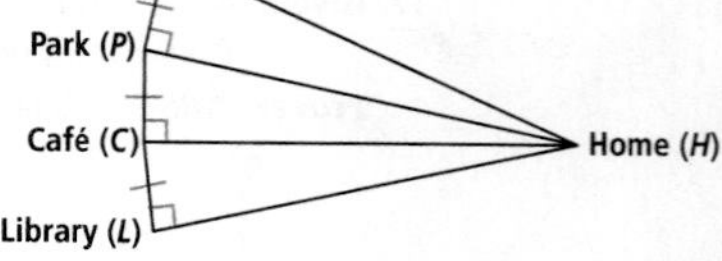

Ⓐ SH = LH
Ⓑ PH = CH
Ⓒ SH > LH
Ⓓ PH < CH

30. What is the midpoint of $\overline{LM}$ with endpoints L(2, 7) and M(5, −1)?

Ⓕ (3.5, 3)
Ⓖ (3.5, 4)
Ⓗ (2, 4.5)
Ⓘ (7, 6)

Short Response

31. In equilateral △XYZ, name four pairs of congruent right triangles. Explain why they are congruent.

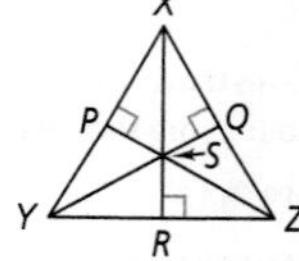

Mixed Review

For Exercises 32 and 33, what type of triangle must △STU be? Explain. See Lesson 4-5.

32. △STU ≅ △UTS

33. △STU ≅ △UST

Get Ready! **To prepare for Lesson 4-7, do Exercises 34–36.**

Can you conclude that the triangles are congruent? Explain. See Lessons 4-3 and 4-6.

34. △ABC and △LMN

35. △LMN and △HJK

36. △RST and △ABC

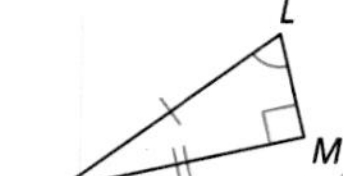

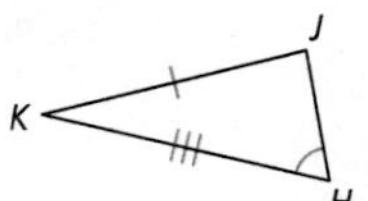

4-6 Lesson Resources

Differentiated Remediation

Instructional Support

Geometry Companion

Students can use the **Geometry Companion** worktext (4 pages) . . .

- New Vocabulary
- Key Concepts
- Got It for each Problem
- Lesson Check

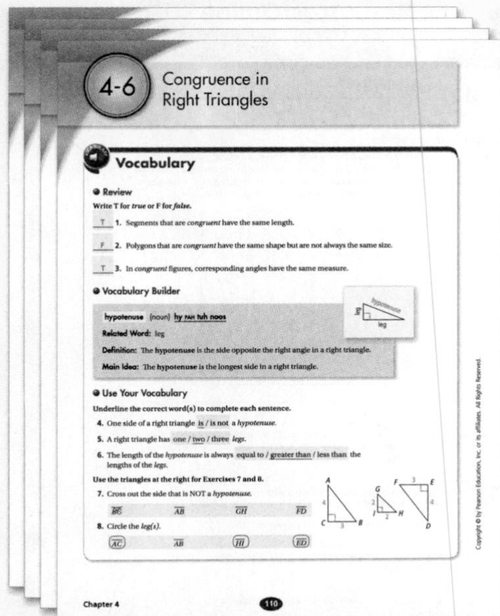

4-6 Congruence in Right Triangles

Vocabulary

Review

Write T for *true* or F for *false*.

T 1. Segments that are *congruent* have the same length.

F 2. Polygons that are *congruent* have the same shape but are not always the same size.

T 3. In *congruent* figures, corresponding angles have the same measure.

Vocabulary Builder

hypotenuse (noun) hy PAH tuh noos

Related Word: leg

Definition: The hypotenuse is the side opposite the right angle in a right triangle.

Main Idea: The **hypotenuse** is the longest side in a right triangle.

Use Your Vocabulary

Underline the correct word(s) to complete each sentence.

4. One side of a right triangle is / is not a *hypotenuse*.
5. A right triangle has one / two / three *legs*.
6. The length of the *hypotenuse* is always equal to / greater than / less than the lengths of the *legs*.

Use the triangles at the right for Exercises 7 and 8.

7. Cross out the side that is NOT a *hypotenuse*.

$\overline{BC}$ $\overline{AB}$ $\overline{GH}$ $\overline{FD}$

8. Circle the *leg(s)*.

$\overline{AC}$ $\overline{AB}$ $\overline{HI}$ $\overline{ED}$

Chapter 4 110

ELL Support

Focus on Language Consider the word *hypotenuse*. The hypotenuse is the side of a right triangle that is opposite the right angle. Possible origins are in 1571, Late Latin, *hypotenusa*, from the Greek *hypoteinousa* "stretching under" (the right angle), formed from *hypo-* "under" + *teinein* "to stretch." The derivation is more understandable if you visualize an inverted right triangle with its base at the top, as shown below.

Focus on Language Place students in groups of mixed proficiency. Have them each make a set of flash cards with a vocabulary word on one side. Then students can discuss the meaning of the term before writing its definition, including sketches, on the other side. Students can quiz one another on the topics learned in this chapter and keep the cards for later individual review.

5 Assess & Remediate

Lesson Quiz

1. Are the triangles shown below congruent? Explain.

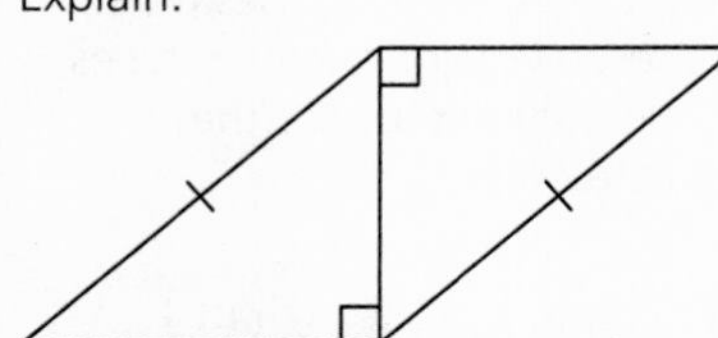

2. **Do you UNDERSTAND?**
Given: $\overline{ON} \cong \overline{ML}$, $\overline{LP} \cong \overline{PN}$, $\angle OPN$ is a right angle.
Prove: $\triangle OPN \cong \triangle MPL$

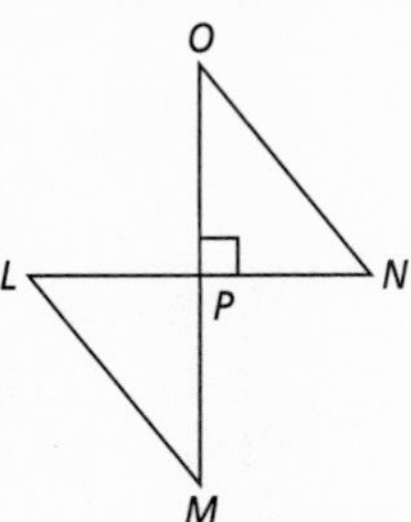

ANSWERS TO LESSON QUIZ

1. yes, by the HL Theorem
2. It is given that $\overline{ON} \cong \overline{ML}$, $\overline{LP} \cong \overline{PN}$, and $\angle OPN$ is a right angle. $\angle OPN \cong \angle LPM$ by Vertical Angles Theorem. $m\angle OPN = m\angle LPM$ by the def. of cong. angles. $m\angle OPN = 90$ by the def. of right angles. $m\angle LPM = 90$ by subst. $\angle LPM$ is a right angle by the def. of right angles. $\triangle OPN$ and $\triangle MPL$ are right triangles. So, $\triangle OPN \cong \triangle MPL$ by HL.

PRESCRIPTION FOR REMEDIATION

Use the student work on the Lesson Quiz to prescribe a differentiated review assignment.

Points	Differentiated Remediation
0	Intervention
1	On-level
2	Extension

PowerGeometry.com

5 Assess & Remediate

Assign the Lesson Quiz. Appropriate intervention, practice, or enrichment is automatically generated based on student performance.

Intervention

- **Reteaching** (2 pages) Provides reteaching and practice exercises for the key lesson concepts. Use with struggling students or absent students.
- **English Language Learner Support** Helps students develop and reinforce mathematical vocabulary and key concepts.

All-in-One Resources/Online

Reteaching

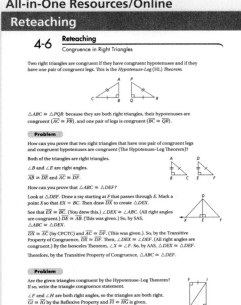

4-6 **Reteaching**
Congruence in Right Triangles

Two right triangles are congruent if they have congruent hypotenuses and if they have one pair of congruent legs. This is the *Hypotenuse-Leg* (HL) *Theorem*.

$\triangle ABC \cong \triangle PQR$ because they are both right triangles, their hypotenuses are congruent ($\overline{AC} \cong \overline{PR}$), and one pair of legs is congruent ($\overline{BC} \cong \overline{QR}$).

Problem

How can you prove that two right triangles that have one pair of congruent legs and congruent hypotenuses are congruent (The Hypotenuse-Leg Theorem)?

Both of the triangles are right triangles.

$\angle B$ and $\angle E$ are right angles.

$\overline{AB} \cong \overline{DE}$ and $\overline{AC} \cong \overline{DF}$.

How can you prove that $\triangle ABC \cong \triangle DEF$?

Look at $\triangle DEF$. Draw a ray starting at F that passes through E. Mark a point X so that $EX = BC$. Then draw $\overline{DX}$ to create $\triangle DEX$.

See that $\overline{EX} \cong \overline{BC}$. (You drew this.) $\angle DEX \cong \angle ABC$. (All right angles are congruent.) $\overline{DE} \cong \overline{AB}$. (This was given.) So, by SAS, $\triangle ABC \cong \triangle DEX$.

$\overline{DX} \cong \overline{AC}$ (by CPCTC) and $\overline{AC} \cong \overline{DF}$. (This was given.). So, by the Transitive Property of Congruence, $\overline{DX} \cong \overline{DF}$. Then, $\angle DEX \cong \angle DEF$. (All right angles are congruent.) By the Isosceles Theorem, $\angle X \cong \angle F$. So, by AAS, $\triangle DEX \cong \triangle DEF$.

Therefore, by the Transitive Property of Congruence, $\triangle ABC \cong \triangle DEF$.

Problem

Are the given triangles congruent by the Hypotenuse-Leg Theorem? If so, write the triangle congruence statement.

$\angle F$ and $\angle H$ are both right angles, so the triangles are both right. $\overline{GI} \cong \overline{IG}$ by the Reflexive Property and $\overline{FI} \cong \overline{HG}$ is given.

So, $\triangle FIG \cong \triangle HGI$.

All-in-One Resources/Online

English Language Learner Support

4-6 **ELL Support**
Congruence in Right Triangles

The column on the left shows the steps used to prove that $\overline{AB} \cong \overline{ED}$. Use the column on the left to answer each question in the column on the right.

Problem $\cong$ in Right Triangles	
Given: C is the midpoint of $\overline{AE}$ and $\overline{BD}$. Prove: $\overline{AB} \cong \overline{ED}$	1. What is the definition of the midpoint of a line segment? The midpoint is halfway between the two endpoints. It divides the line segment into two equal halves.
1) C is the midpoint of $\overline{AE}$ and $\overline{BD}$; $\overline{AB} \parallel \overline{DE}$; $m\angle B = 90$ Given	2. How do you know that $\overline{AB} \parallel \overline{DE}$ and $m\angle B = 90$? by reading the diagram
2) $\overline{AC} \cong \overline{EC}$; $\overline{BC} \cong \overline{DC}$ Definition of midpoint	3. What does the symbol $\cong$ between two line segments mean? The line segments are congruent.
3) $\angle B \cong \angle D$ Alternate Interior Angles Theorem	4. What does the word *interior* mean? Interior means on the inside of.
4) $\angle B$ and $\angle D$ are right angles. Definition of a right angle	5. What is the measure of $\angle D$? 90
5) $\triangle ABC \cong \triangle EDC$ Hypotenuse-Leg (HL) Postulate	6. What information is necessary to apply the HL Postulate? Two right triangles must have congruent hypotenuses and one congruent leg.
6) $\overline{AB} \cong \overline{ED}$ Corresponding parts of congruent triangles are congruent.	7. What are the corresponding angles and sides for $\triangle ABC$ and $\triangle EDC$? $\angle B$ and $\angle D$, $\angle A$ and $\angle E$, $\angle BCA$ and $\angle DCE$, $\overline{AB}$ and $\overline{ED}$, $\overline{AC}$ and $\overline{EC}$, $\overline{BC}$ and $\overline{DC}$

Differentiated Remediation *continued*

On-Level

- **Practice** (2 pages) Provides extra practice for each lesson. For simpler practice exercises, use the Form K Practice pages found in the All-in-One Teaching Resources and online.
- **Think About a Plan** Helps students develop specific problem-solving skills and strategies by providing scaffolded guiding questions.
- **Standardized Test Prep** Focuses on all major exercises, all major question types, and helps students prepare for the high-stakes assessments.

Extension

- **Enrichment** Provides students with interesting problems and activities that extend the concepts of the lesson.
- **Activities, Games, and Puzzles** Worksheets that can be used for concepts development, enrichment, and for fun!

Practice and Problem Solving Wkbk/ All-in-One Resources/Online

Practice page 1

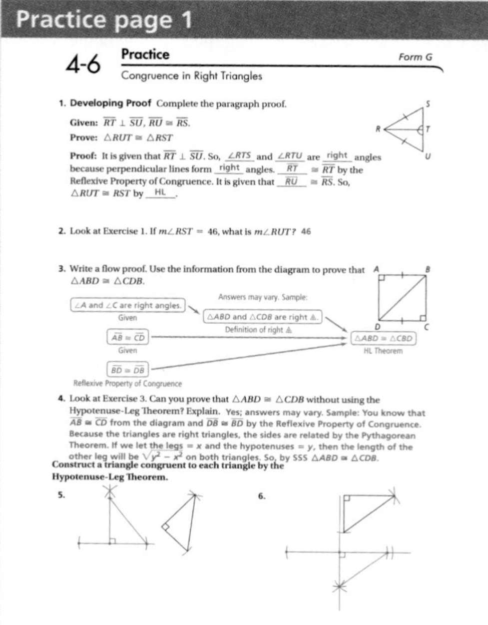

4-6 **Practice** — Congruence in Right Triangles — *Form G*

1. **Developing Proof** Complete the paragraph proof.
   Given: $\overline{RT} \perp \overline{SU}$, $\overline{RU} \cong \overline{RS}$.
   Prove: $\triangle RUT \cong \triangle RST$
   Proof: It is given that $\overline{RT} \perp \overline{SU}$. So, $\angle RTS$ and $\angle RTU$ are right angles because perpendicular lines form right angles. $\overline{RT} \cong \overline{RT}$ by the Reflexive Property of Congruence. It is given that $\overline{RU} \cong \overline{RS}$. So, $\triangle RUT \cong RST$ by HL.
2. Look at Exercise 1. If $m\angle RST = 46$, what is $m\angle RUT$? 46
3. Write a flow proof. Use the information from the diagram to prove that $\triangle ABD \cong \triangle CDB$.
   Answers may vary. Sample:
   $\angle A$ and $\angle C$ are right angles. (Given) → $\triangle ABD$ and $\triangle CDB$ are right △. (Definition of right △)
   $\overline{AB} \cong \overline{CD}$ (Given)
   $\overline{BD} \cong \overline{DB}$ (Reflexive Property of Congruence)
   → $\triangle ABD \cong \triangle CBD$ (HL Theorem)
4. Look at Exercise 3. Can you prove that $\triangle ABD \cong \triangle CDB$ without using the Hypotenuse-Leg Theorem? Explain. Yes; answers may vary. Sample: You know that $\overline{AB} \cong \overline{CD}$ from the diagram and $\overline{DB} \cong \overline{BD}$ by the Reflexive Property of Congruence. Because the triangles are right triangles, the sides are related by the Pythagorean Theorem. If we let the legs $= x$ and the hypotenuses $= y$, then the length of the other leg will be $\sqrt{y^2 - x^2}$ on both triangles. So, by SSS $\triangle ABD \cong \triangle CDB$.

Construct a triangle congruent to each triangle by the Hypotenuse-Leg Theorem.

5.

6.

Practice and Problem Solving Wkbk/ All-in-One Resources/Online

Practice page 2

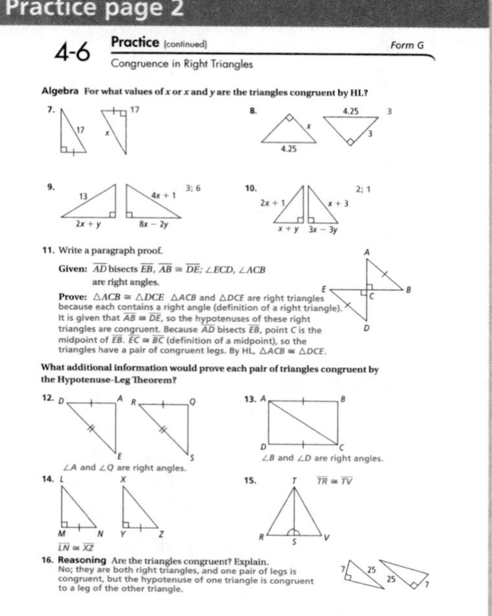

4-6 **Practice** (continued) — Congruence in Right Triangles — *Form G*

Algebra For what values of *x* or *x* and *y* are the triangles congruent by HL?

7. 17
8. 3
9. 3; 6
10. 2; 1

11. Write a paragraph proof.
    Given: $\overline{AD}$ bisects $\overline{EB}$, $\overline{AB} \cong \overline{DE}$; $\angle ECD$, $\angle ACB$ are right angles.
    Prove: $\triangle ACB \cong \triangle DCE$ $\triangle ACB$ and $\triangle DCE$ are right triangles because each contains a right angle (definition of a right triangle). It is given that $\overline{AB} \cong \overline{DE}$, so the hypotenuses of these right triangles are congruent. Because $\overline{AD}$ bisects $\overline{EB}$, point *C* is the midpoint of $\overline{EB}$. $\overline{EC} \cong \overline{BC}$ (definition of a midpoint), so the triangles have a pair of congruent legs. By HL, $\triangle ACB \cong \triangle DCE$.

What additional information would prove each pair of triangles congruent by the Hypotenuse-Leg Theorem?

12. $\angle A$ and $\angle Q$ are right angles.
13. $\angle B$ and $\angle D$ are right angles.
14. $\overline{LN} \cong \overline{XZ}$
15. $\overline{TR} \cong \overline{TV}$
16. **Reasoning** Are the triangles congruent? Explain. No; they are both right triangles, and one pair of legs is congruent, but the hypotenuse of one triangle is congruent to a leg of the other triangle.

All-in-One Resources/Online

Enrichment

4-6 **Enrichment** — Congruence in Right Triangles

Right Triangle Patterns

An art student wants to make a painting with a simple geometric pattern. She starts with a square. She divides this square into two congruent triangles. Then she divides each of these triangles into two smaller congruent triangles. She repeats the process seven more times. What does her pattern look like in the end?

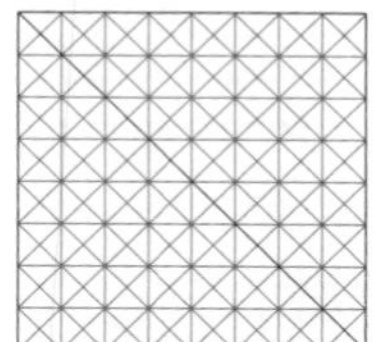

1. Show that the two triangles are congruent using the Hypotenuse-Leg Theorem. Sample: Each is a right triangle. They have at least one pair of congruent legs and they have congruent hypotenuses.
2. Use your knowledge of the Hypotenuse-Leg Theorem to divide each triangle in the figure above into two smaller congruent triangles. Repeat the process six more times. Check students' work.
3. How do you know that the triangles at each step are congruent? Sample: Each is a right triangle, with equal legs and hypotenuses.
4. How many triangles of the smallest size are shown? 256
5. How many triangles are shown if they each contain 64 of the smallest-sized unit? 32
6. How many triangles are shown if they each contain nine of the smallest-sized unit? 168
7. **Challenge** Find the sizes of all 16 different-sized triangles in the diagram. 1, 2, 4, 8, 9, 16, 18, 25, 32, 36, 49, 50, 64, 72, 98, 128

Practice and Problem Solving Wkbk/ All-in-One Resources/Online

Think About a Plan

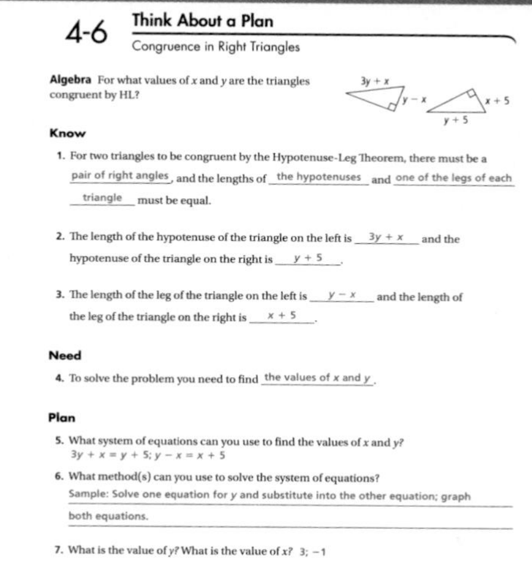

4-6 **Think About a Plan** — Congruence in Right Triangles

Algebra For what values of *x* and *y* are the triangles congruent by HL?

Know

1. For two triangles to be congruent by the Hypotenuse-Leg Theorem, there must be a pair of right angles, and the lengths of the hypotenuses and one of the legs of each triangle must be equal.
2. The length of the hypotenuse of the triangle on the left is $3y + x$ and the hypotenuse of the triangle on the right is $y + 5$.
3. The length of the leg of the triangle on the left is $y - x$ and the length of the leg of the triangle on the right is $x + 5$.

Need

4. To solve the problem you need to find the values of *x* and *y*.

Plan

5. What system of equations can you use to find the values of *x* and *y*? $3y + x = y + 5$; $y - x = x + 5$
6. What method(s) can you use to solve the system of equations? Sample: Solve one equation for *y* and substitute into the other equation; graph both equations.
7. What is the value of *y*? What is the value of *x*? 3; −1

Practice and Problem Solving Wkbk/ All-in-One Resources/Online

Standardized Test Prep

4-6 **Standardized Test Prep** — Congruence in Right Triangles

Multiple Choice

For Exercises 1–4, choose the correct letter.

1. Which additional piece of information would allow you to prove that the triangles are congruent by the HL theorem? C
   A. $m\angle DFE = 40$
   B. $m\angle F = m\angle ABC$
   C. $\overline{AB} \cong \overline{DE}$
   D. $\overline{AC} \cong \overline{DF}$
2. For what values of *x* and *y* are the triangles shown congruent? F
   F. $x = 1, y = 4$
   G. $x = 2, y = 4$
   H. $x = 4, y = 1$
   I. $x = 1, y = 3$
3. Two triangles have two pairs of corresponding sides that are congruent. What else must be true for the triangles to be congruent by the HL Theorem? D
   A. The included angles must be right angles.
   B. They have one pair of congruent angles.
   C. Both triangles must be isosceles.
   D. There are right angles adjacent to just one pair of congruent sides.
4. Which of the following statements is true? H
   F. $\triangle BAC \cong \triangle GHI$ by SAS.
   G. $\triangle DEF \cong \triangle GHI$ by SAS.
   H. $\triangle BAC \cong \triangle DEF$ by HL.
   I. $\triangle DEF \cong \triangle GHI$ by HL.

Extended Response

5. Are the given triangles congruent by the HL Theorem? Explain. [4] No; they are right triangles, and have a pair of congruent legs ($\overline{AB} \cong \overline{BC}$), but the hypotenuses, $\overline{DB}$ and $\overline{DC}$, are not congruent. So, the triangles only meet two of the three conditions for congruence by the HL Theorem. [3] appropriate response plus a discussion of two of the three criteria for congruence [2] recognition only that the hypotenuses are not congruent [1] recognition that the triangles are not congruent [0] incorrect or no response

Online Teacher Resource Center

Activities, Games, and Puzzles

4-6 **Activity: Proof Tangle** — Congruence in Right Triangles

Materials
- Scissors
- Index cards

Setup

Your teacher will divide the class into groups. He or she will give your group an envelope with all the statements and reasons you need for one proof. Write out each step on an index card.

Game Play

Cut out the proof set-ups below (each of the 4 large boxes). Set all but one of the set-ups aside. Make sure to use the set-up that corresponds to the envelope you received. Work as a group to "untangle" the proof. When you are done, place your index cards in the envelope and trade envelopes with another group. Continue until you untangle all four proofs. Answers may vary. Samples are given.

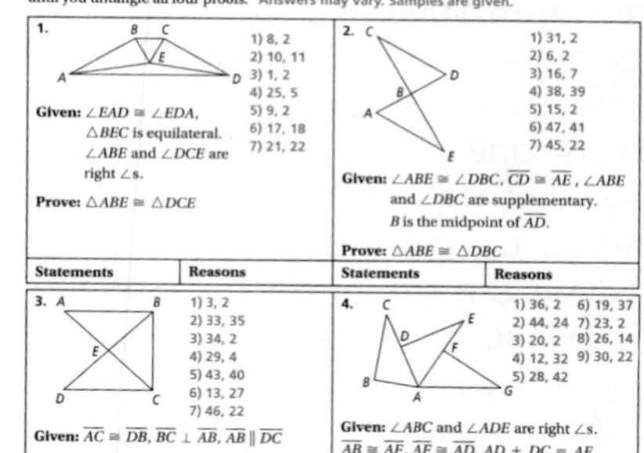

1. 1) 8, 2 2) 10, 11 3) 1, 2 4) 25, 5 5) 9, 2 6) 17, 18 7) 21, 22
   Given: $\angle EAD \cong \angle EDA$, $\triangle BEC$ is equilateral. $\angle ABE$ and $\angle DCE$ are right ∠s.
   Prove: $\triangle ABE \cong \triangle DCE$

Statements	Reasons

2. 1) 31, 2 2) 6, 2 3) 16, 7 4) 38, 39 5) 15, 2 6) 47, 41 7) 45, 22
   Given: $\angle ABE \cong \angle DBC$, $\overline{CD} \cong \overline{AE}$, $\angle ABE$ and $\angle DBC$ are supplementary. *B* is the midpoint of $\overline{AD}$.
   Prove: $\triangle ABE \cong \triangle DBC$

Statements	Reasons

3. 1) 3, 2 2) 33, 35 3) 34, 2 4) 29, 4 5) 43, 40 6) 13, 27 7) 46, 22
   Given: $\overline{AC} \cong \overline{DB}$, $\overline{BC} \perp \overline{AB}$, $\overline{AB} \parallel \overline{DC}$
   Prove: $\triangle ABC \cong \triangle DCB$

Statements	Reasons

4. 1) 36, 2 2) 44, 24 3) 20, 2 4) 12, 32 5) 28, 42 6) 19, 37 7) 23, 2 8) 26, 14 9) 30, 22
   Given: $\angle ABC$ and $\angle ADE$ are right ∠s. $\overline{AB} \cong \overline{AF}$, $\overline{AF} \cong \overline{AD}$, $AD + DC = AE$
   Prove: $\triangle ABC \cong \triangle ADE$

Statements	Reasons

4-7 Congruence in Overlapping Triangles

TN State Performance Indicator
SPI 3108.4.12 Solve problems involving congruence, similarity, proportional reasoning and/or scale factor of two similar figures or solids.

Objectives To identify congruent overlapping triangles
To prove two triangles congruent using other congruent triangles

Do all the triangles make you dizzy? Try to see each one. Then learn some tricks that may help you.

Getting Ready!

An assignment for your graphic design class is to make a colorful design using triangles. How many triangles are in your design? Explain how you count them.

In the Solve It, you located individual triangles among a jumble of triangles. Some triangle relationships are difficult to see because the triangles overlap.

Essential Understanding You can sometimes use the congruent corresponding parts of one pair of congruent triangles to prove another pair of triangles congruent. This often involves overlapping triangles.

Overlapping triangles may have a common side or angle. You can simplify your work with overlapping triangles by separating and redrawing the triangles.

Think
How can you see an individual triangle in order to redraw it? Use your finger to trace along the lines connecting the three vertices. Then cover up any untraced lines.

Problem 1 Identifying Common Parts

What common angle do $\triangle ACD$ and $\triangle ECB$ share?

Separate and redraw $\triangle ACD$ and $\triangle ECB$.

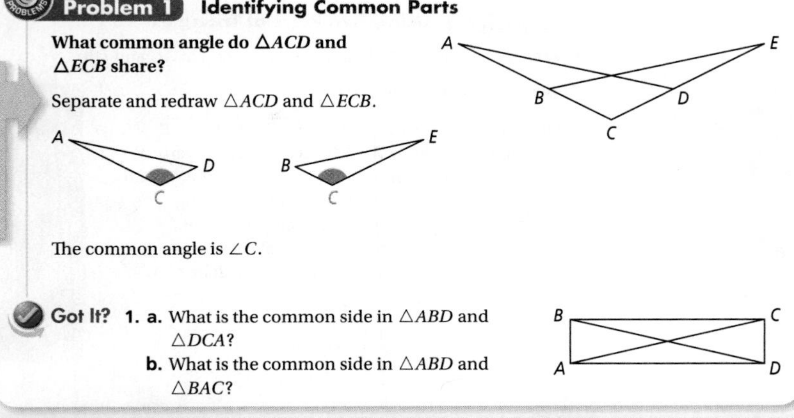

A
E
B
D
C

The common angle is $\angle C$.

Got It? 1. a. What is the common side in $\triangle ABD$ and $\triangle DCA$?
b. What is the common side in $\triangle ABD$ and $\triangle BAC$?

1 Interactive Learning

Solve It!

PURPOSE To discover ways to identify triangles when they overlap
PROCESS Students may redraw the triangles separately or systematically count the number of triangles in the diagram.

FACILITATE
Q Does the diagram have a line of symmetry? If yes, describe the location of that line. **[yes, a vertical line that can be drawn in the middle of the diagram]**
Q Using the line of symmetry, how many triangles do you count on the left side of the design? **[10]**
Q Can you double that number to find the number of triangles in the entire design? Explain. **[No; there are triangles that include sections on both sides of the line of symmetry.]**

ANSWER See Solve It in Answers on next page.
CONNECT THE MATH Students can see that there are many ways two triangles can overlap. In designs such as the one in the Solve It, students need to be able to count triangles systematically to ensure an accurate count.

2 Guided Instruction

Problem 1

Q What segments (or parts of segments) are shared by the two triangles? **[$\overline{BC}$ and $\overline{CD}$]**

Got It? ERROR PREVENTION
Have students redraw the triangles. Have them use their hand or a piece of paper to cover up parts that are not included as they work.

4-7 Preparing to Teach

BIG ideas **Reasoning and Proof**
Visualization

UbD

ESSENTIAL UNDERSTANDING
- Congruent corresponding parts of one pair of congruent triangles can sometimes be used to prove another pair of triangles congruent. This often involves overlapping triangles.

Math Background

The topic of overlapping triangles is a topic rich in both spatial reasoning and logical reasoning. Activities and proofs with overlapping triangles provide opportunities to use definitions, properties, postulates, and theorems.

Overlapping triangles may share angles, sides, or portions of angles or sides.

Visualizing the triangles and their parts is a challenge for many students. Using color can help distinguish the triangles and make their corresponding parts easier to track. Being able to see the separate triangles when they share sides and angles is a skill that students will use throughout geometry. The visual skills students develop, together with the skills of logic and proof, are invaluable in this course and in other studies.

Support Student Learning

Use the **Geometry Companion** to engage and support students during instructions. See Lesson Resources at the end of this lesson for details.

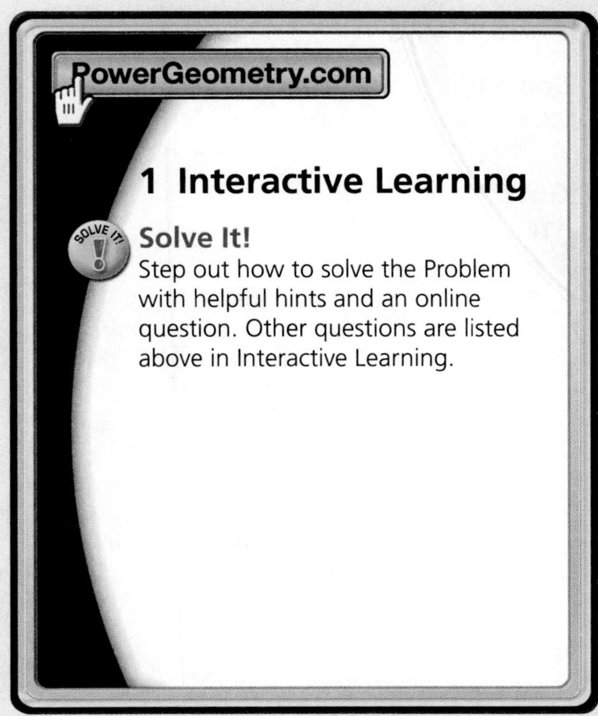

PowerGeometry.com
1 Interactive Learning
Solve It!
Step out how to solve the Problem with helpful hints and an online question. Other questions are listed above in Interactive Learning.

Problem 2

Q Which part of the triangles is common to both? **[$\overline{WX}$]**

Q What theorem or postulate can you use to prove that the two triangles are congruent? **[ASA Postulate]**

Q Once the two triangles are proved congruent, how can you show that $\overline{ZW} \cong \overline{YX}$? Explain. **[They are corresponding sides of congruent triangles. Thus, they are congruent.]**

Got It?

Students can show that $\angle BCD \cong \angle ADC$ since they are corresponding parts of congruent triangles. Then $\overline{CE} \cong \overline{DE}$ by the converse of the Isosceles Triangle Theorem.

Problem 3

Q Are there any special pairs of angles present in the diagram? Explain. **[Yes, there are two pairs of congruent vertical angles.]**

Q For which pair of triangles can you use this information? **[$\triangle AED$ and $\triangle BEC$]**

Q How can you use these triangles to show that two other triangles are congruent? **[Because corresponding parts of congruent triangles are congruent, $\angle D \cong \angle B$. This is the last piece of information you need to conclude that $\triangle GED \cong \triangle JEB$.]**

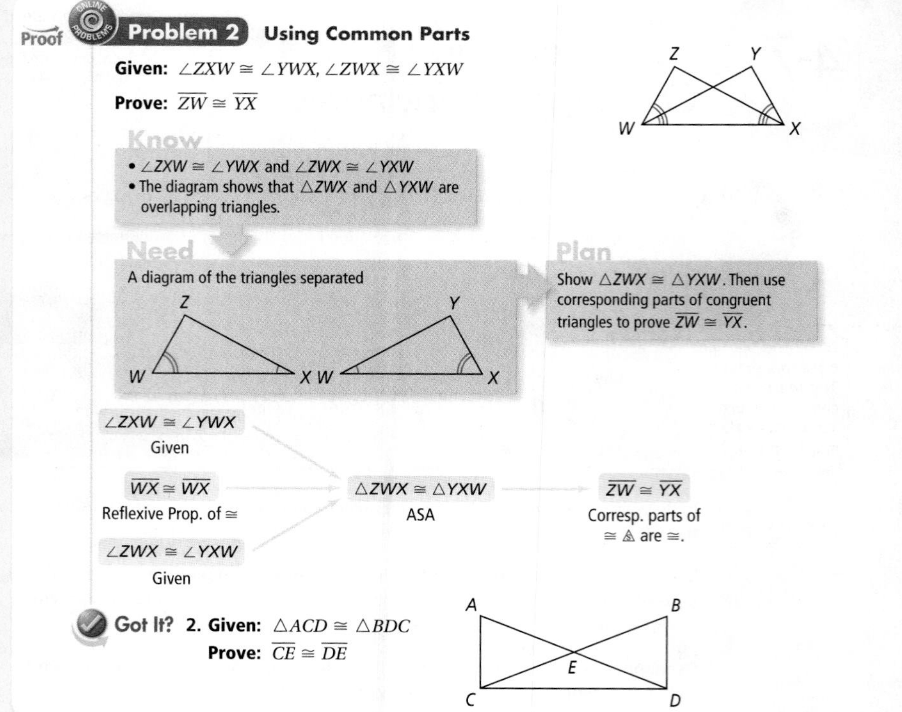

Got It? 2. **Given:** $\triangle ACD \cong \triangle BDC$
Prove: $\overline{CE} \cong \overline{DE}$

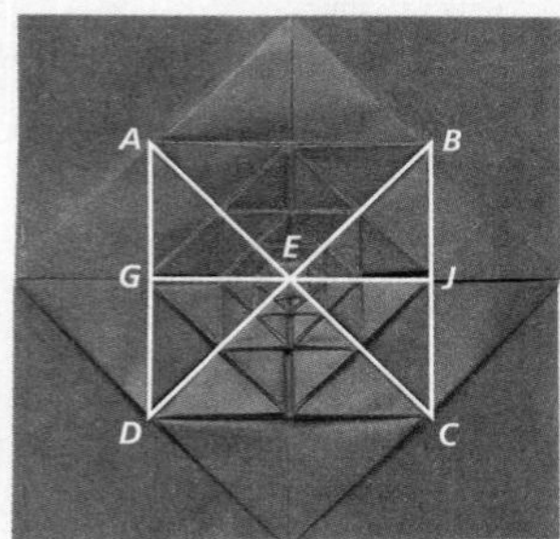

Proof **Problem 3** Using Two Pairs of Triangles

Plan

How do you choose another pair of triangles to help in your proof?
Look for triangles that share parts with $\triangle GED$ and $\triangle JEB$ and that you can prove congruent. In this case, first prove $\triangle AED \cong \triangle CEB$.

Given: In the origami design, E is the midpoint of $\overline{AC}$ and $\overline{DB}$.

Prove: $\triangle GED \cong \triangle JEB$

Proof: E is the midpoint of $\overline{AC}$ and $\overline{DB}$, so $\overline{AE} \cong \overline{CE}$ and $\overline{DE} \cong \overline{BE}$. $\angle AED \cong \angle CEB$ because vertical angles are congruent. Therefore, $\triangle AED \cong \triangle CEB$ by SAS. $\angle D \cong \angle B$ because corresponding parts of congruent triangles are congruent. $\angle GED \cong \angle JEB$ because vertical angles are congruent. Therefore, $\triangle GED \cong \triangle JEB$ by ASA.

Answers

Solve It!

23; Explanations may vary. Sample: Count individual ▲. Then count overlapping ▲ and look for symmetry.

Got It?

1a. $\overline{AD}$

b. $\overline{AB}$

2. It is given that $\triangle ACD \cong \triangle BDC$, so $\angle ADC \cong \angle BCD$ because corresp. parts of ≅ ▲ are ≅. Therefore, $\overline{CE} \cong \overline{DE}$ by the Converse of the Isosc. △ Thm.

3. $\triangle PSQ \cong \triangle RSQ$ by SAS because $\overline{PS} \cong \overline{RS}$ (Given), $\angle PSQ \cong \angle RSQ$ (Given), and $\overline{SQ} \cong \overline{SQ}$ (Refl. Prop. of ≅). So $\overline{PQ} \cong \overline{RQ}$ and $\angle PQT \cong \angle RQT$ (Corresp. parts of ≅ ▲ are ≅.). Also, $\overline{QT} \cong \overline{QT}$ (Refl. Prop. of ≅), so $\triangle QPT \cong \triangle QRT$ by SAS.

4. See back of book.

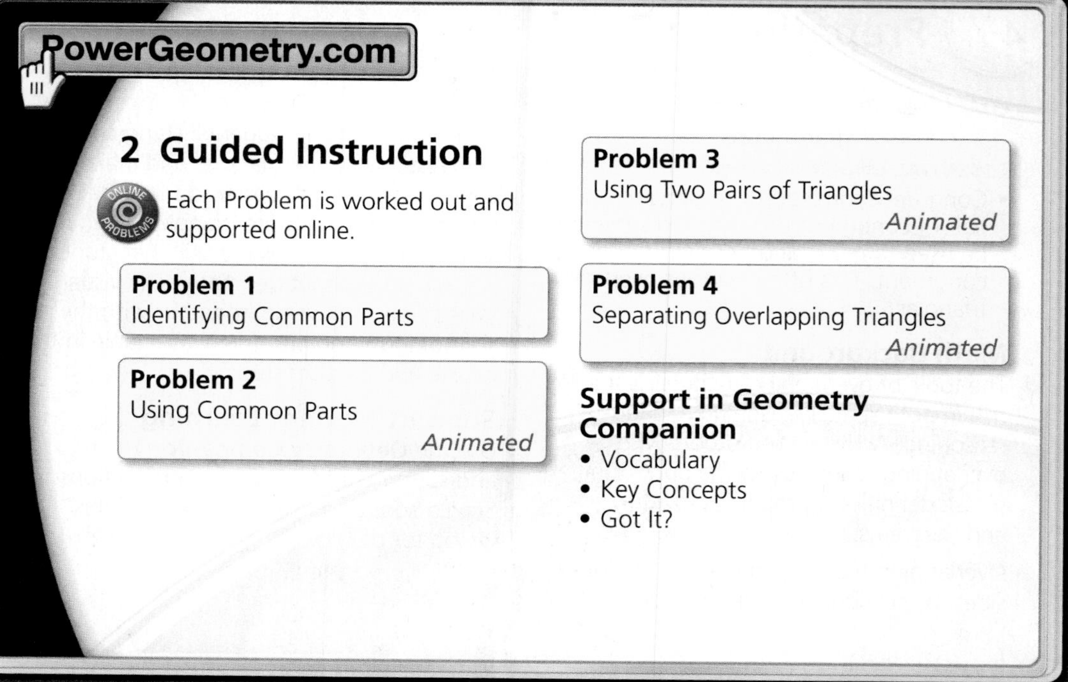

PowerGeometry.com
2 Guided Instruction
Each Problem is worked out and supported online.
Problem 1
Identifying Common Parts
Problem 2
Using Common Parts
Animated
Problem 3
Using Two Pairs of Triangles
Animated
Problem 4
Separating Overlapping Triangles
Animated
Support in Geometry Companion
• Vocabulary
• Key Concepts
• Got It?

Got It? **3. Given:** $\overline{PS} \cong \overline{RS}$, $\angle PSQ \cong \angle RSQ$

Prove: $\triangle QPT \cong \triangle QRT$

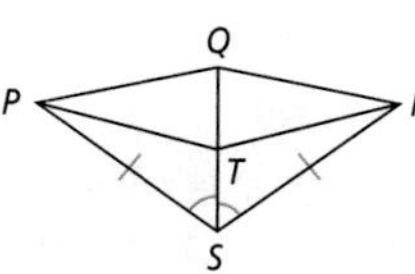

When several triangles overlap and you need to use one pair of congruent triangles to prove another pair congruent, you may find it helpful to draw a diagram of each pair of triangles.

Problem 4 Separating Overlapping Triangles

Proof

Given: $\overline{CA} \cong \overline{CE}$, $\overline{BA} \cong \overline{DE}$

Prove: $\overline{BX} \cong \overline{DX}$

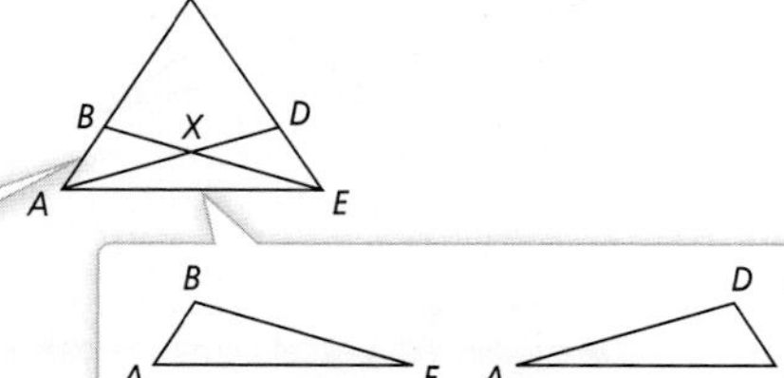

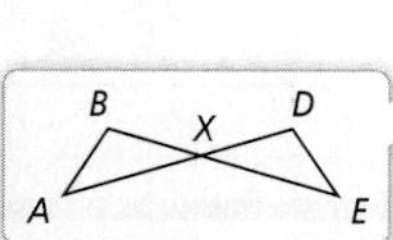

Plan

Which triangles are useful here?

If $\triangle BXA \cong \triangle DXE$, then $\overline{BX} \cong \overline{DX}$ because they are corresponding parts. If $\triangle BAE \cong \triangle DEA$, you will have enough information to show $\triangle BXA \cong \triangle DXE$.

Statements	Reasons
1) $\overline{BA} \cong \overline{DE}$	1) Given
2) $\overline{CA} \cong \overline{CE}$	2) Given
3) $\angle CAE \cong \angle CEA$	3) Base ⦣ of an isosceles △ are ≅.
4) $\overline{AE} \cong \overline{AE}$	4) Reflexive Property of ≅
5) $\triangle BAE \cong \triangle DEA$	5) SAS
6) $\angle ABE \cong \angle EDA$	6) Corresp. parts of ≅ ⧍ are ≅.
7) $\angle BXA \cong \angle DXE$	7) Vertical angles are ≅.
8) $\triangle BXA \cong \triangle DXE$	8) AAS
9) $\overline{BX} \cong \overline{DX}$	9) Corresp. parts of ≅ ⧍ are ≅.

Got It? **4. Given:** $\angle CAD \cong \angle EAD$, $\angle C \cong \angle E$

Prove: $\overline{BD} \cong \overline{FD}$

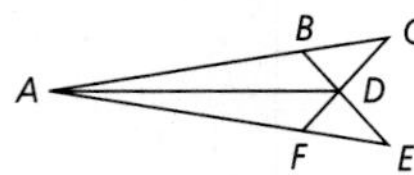

Got It? SYNTHESIZING

Instruct students to think of smaller proofs within the complete proof. Students must first prove that $\triangle PSQ \cong \triangle RSQ$ by the SAS Postulate. Then, $\overline{PQ} \cong \overline{QR}$ and $\angle PQT \cong \angle RQT$ because they are corresponding parts of congruent triangles. Because $\overline{QT} \cong \overline{QT}$, $\triangle QPT \cong \triangle QRT$ by the SAS Postulate.

Problem 4

Q What type of triangle is $\triangle CAE$? **[isosceles]**

Q Which triangles have the sides $\overline{BX}$ and $\overline{DX}$? **[$\triangle BXA$ and $\triangle DXE$]**

Q What parts of these triangles are congruent? **[$\overline{BA} \cong \overline{DE}$ and $\angle BXA \cong \angle DXE$]**

Q What other information do you need to prove $\triangle BXA$ and $\triangle DXE$ are congruent? **[$\angle ABE \cong \angle EDA$]**

Got It?

Students should dissect the diagram similarly to the way the diagram was dissected in Problem 4. They should model the proof to match the proof in Problem 4.

Students will need to prove $\triangle AED \cong \triangle ACD$. Then they should be able to use corresponding parts to prove that $\triangle FED \cong \triangle BCD$ by the ASA Postulate.

Additional Problems

1. What is the common side in $\triangle WXZ$ and $\triangle XWY$?

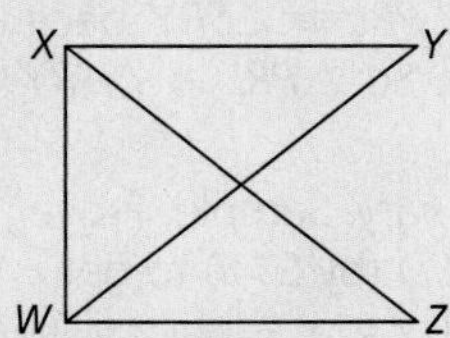

ANSWER $\overline{WX}$

2. Given: $\overline{RT} \cong \overline{US}$, $\angle URS$ and $\angle TSR$ are right angles.

Prove: $\angle T \cong \angle U$

ANSWER It is given that $\overline{RT} \cong \overline{US}$ and $\angle URS$ and $\angle TSR$ are right angles. $\overline{RS} \cong \overline{RS}$ by the Reflexive Property of Congruence. So, $\triangle RSU \cong \triangle SRT$ by HL. Therefore, $\angle T \cong \angle U$ because they are corresponding parts of congruent triangles.

3. Given: $\overline{AR} \cong \overline{LR}$, $\overline{PR} \cong \overline{IR}$

Prove: $\overline{AS} \cong \overline{LS}$

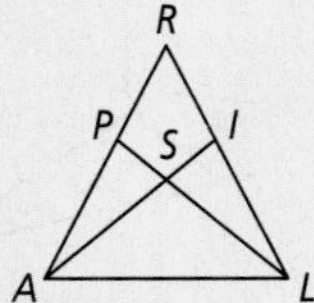

ANSWER It is given that $\overline{AR} \cong \overline{LR}$, and $\overline{PR} \cong \overline{IR}$. $\angle R \cong \angle R$ by the Reflexive Property of Congruence. So, $\triangle ARI \cong \triangle LRP$ by the SAS Postulate. $\angle RAI \cong \angle RLP$ because they are corresponding parts of congruent triangles. $\overline{AP} \cong \overline{LI}$ by the Seg. Add. Post. $\angle PSA \cong \angle ISL$ by the Vertical Angles Thm. Therefore, $\triangle PSA \cong \triangle ISL$ by AAS, and $\overline{AS} \cong \overline{LS}$ because they are corresponding parts of congruent triangles.

4. Given: $\overline{AE} \cong \overline{BE}$, $\angle C \cong \angle D$

Prove: $\overline{BD} \cong \overline{AC}$

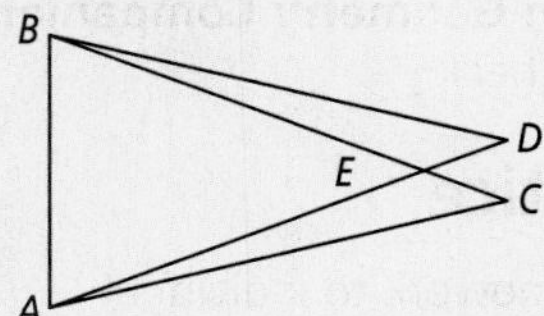

ANSWER It is given that $\overline{AE} \cong \overline{BE}$ and $\angle C \cong \angle D$. $\angle ABE \cong \angle BAE$ by the Isosceles Triangle Theorem. $\overline{AB} \cong \overline{AB}$ by the Reflexive Property of Congruence. $\triangle ABD \cong \triangle BAC$ by the AAS Theorem, and $\overline{BD} \cong \overline{AC}$ because they are corresponding parts of congruent triangles.

3 Lesson Check

Do you know HOW?

- If students have difficulty with Exercise 1, then have them review Problem 1.

Do you UNDERSTAND?

- If students have difficulty with Exercise 6, then have them review Problem 2.

Close

Q When triangles overlap, what parts can you use to show that the triangles are congruent? **[Any parts that are shared in their entirety may be used as congruent parts.]**

Lesson Check

Do you know HOW?

Identify any common angles or sides.

1. $\triangle MKJ$ and $\triangle LJK$

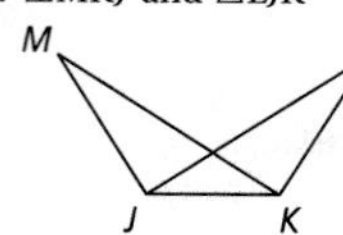

2. $\triangle DEH$ and $\triangle DFG$

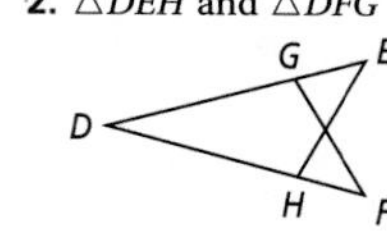

Separate and redraw the overlapping triangles. Label the vertices.

3.

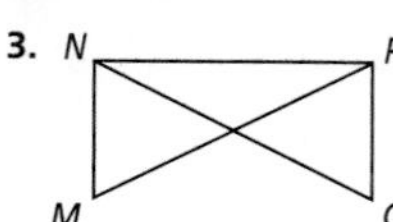

4.

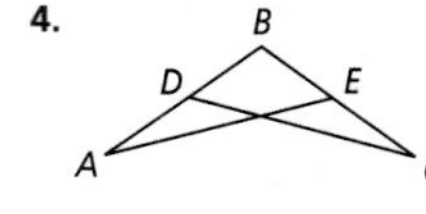

Do you UNDERSTAND?

5. Reasoning In Exercise 1, both triangles have vertices J and K. Are $\angle J$ and $\angle K$ common angles for $\triangle MKJ$ and $\triangle LJK$? Explain.

6. Error Analysis In the diagram, $\triangle PSY \cong \triangle SPL$. Based on that fact, your friend claims that $\triangle PRL \ncong \triangle SRY$. Explain why your friend is incorrect.

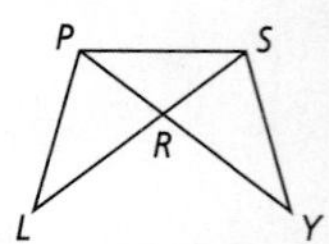

7. In the figure below, which pair of triangles could you prove congruent first in order to prove that $\triangle ACD \cong \triangle CAB$? Explain.

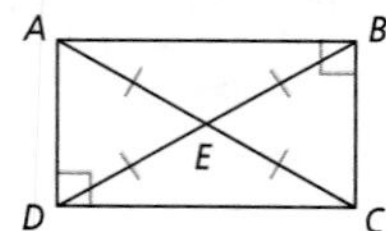

Practice and Problem-Solving Exercises

Practice In each diagram, the red and blue triangles are congruent. Identify their common side or angle.

See Problem 1.

8.

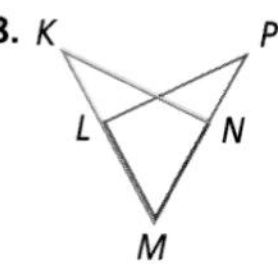

9.

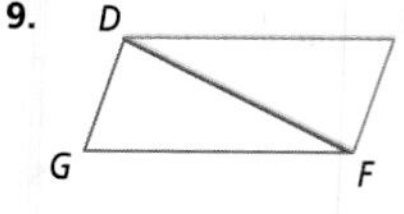

10.

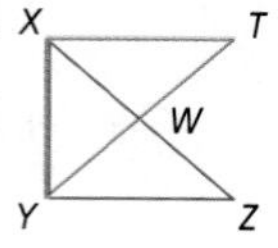

Separate and redraw the indicated triangles. Identify any common angles or sides.

11. $\triangle PQS$ and $\triangle QPR$

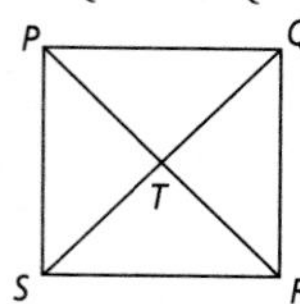

12. $\triangle ACB$ and $\triangle PRB$

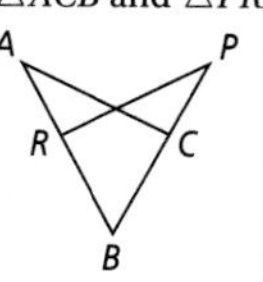

13. $\triangle JKL$ and $\triangle MLK$

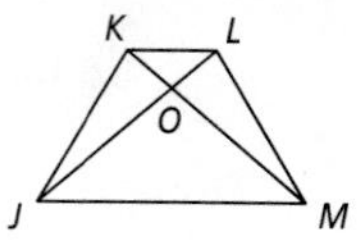

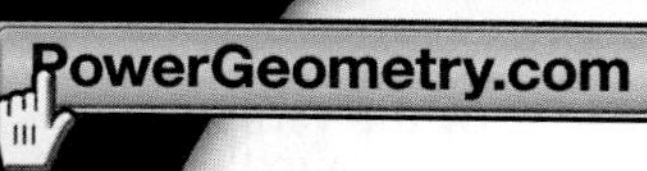

PowerGeometry.com

3 Lesson Check

For a digital lesson check, use the Got It questions.

Support in Geometry Companion

- Lesson Check

4 Practice

Assign homework to individual students or to an entire class.

Answers

Lesson Check

1. $\overline{JK}$

2. $\angle D$

3.

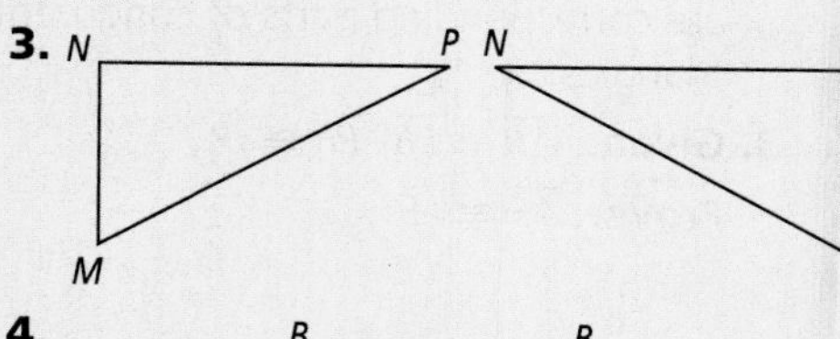

4.

5. No; there are several $\triangle$s with vertex J and several $\triangle$s with vertex K, and a different $\angle$ at each vertex is in each $\triangle$.

6. Answers may vary. Sample: Based on the given statement that $\triangle PSY \cong \triangle SPL$, $\overline{PL} \cong \overline{SY}$, and $\angle L \cong \angle Y$ because corresp. parts of $\cong$ $\triangle$s are $\cong$. $\angle PRL \cong \angle SRY$ because vert. $\angle$s are $\cong$. So $\triangle PRL \cong \triangle SRY$ by AAS.

7. Answers may vary. Sample: Prove $\triangle AEB \cong \triangle CED$ (by SAS) to get $\overline{AB} \cong \overline{CD}$ and $\angle BAE \cong \angle DCE$. Use those $\cong$ segments and $\cong$ angles, along with rt. $\angle$s ADC and ABC, to show $\triangle ACD \cong \triangle CAB$ by ASA.

Practice and Problem-Solving Exercises

8. $\angle M$

9. $\overline{DF}$

10. $\overline{XY}$

14. **Developing Proof** Complete the flow proof. See Problem 2.

Given: $\angle T \cong \angle R$, $\overline{PQ} \cong \overline{PV}$

Prove: $\angle PQT \cong \angle PVR$

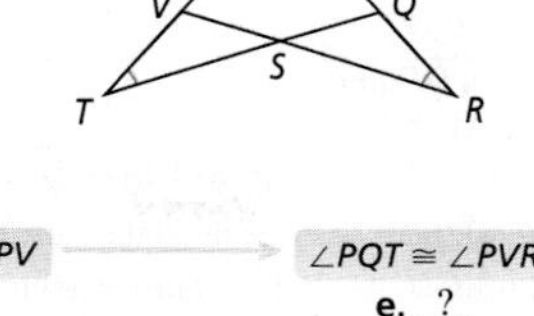

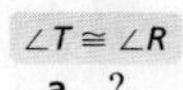

$\angle T \cong \angle R$
a. ?

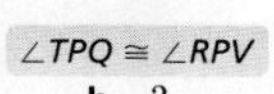

$\angle TPQ \cong \angle RPV$
b. ?

$\overline{PQ} \cong \overline{PV}$
c. ?

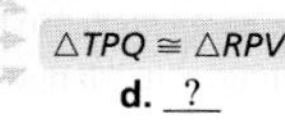

$\triangle TPQ \cong \triangle RPV$
d. ?

$\angle PQT \cong \angle PVR$
e. ?

15. **Given:** $\overline{RS} \cong \overline{UT}$, $\overline{RT} \cong \overline{US}$
Prove: $\triangle RST \cong \triangle UTS$

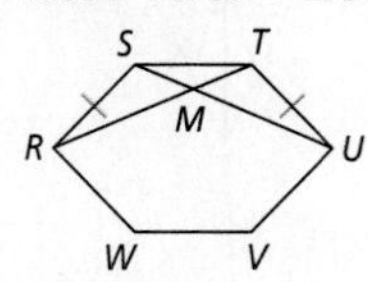

16. **Given:** $\overline{QD} \cong \overline{UA}$, $\angle QDA \cong \angle UAD$
Prove: $\triangle QDA \cong \triangle UAD$

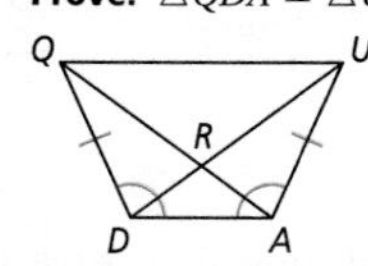

17. **Given:** $\angle 1 \cong \angle 2$, $\angle 3 \cong \angle 4$
Prove: $\triangle QET \cong \triangle QEU$

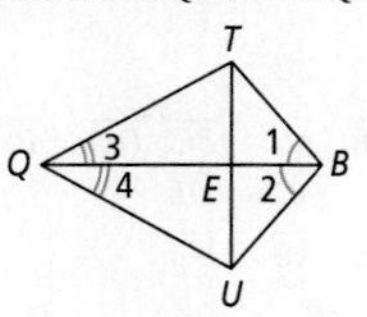

18. **Given:** $\overline{AD} \cong \overline{ED}$, See Problems 3 and 4.
D is the midpoint of $\overline{BF}$
Prove: $\triangle ADC \cong \triangle EDG$

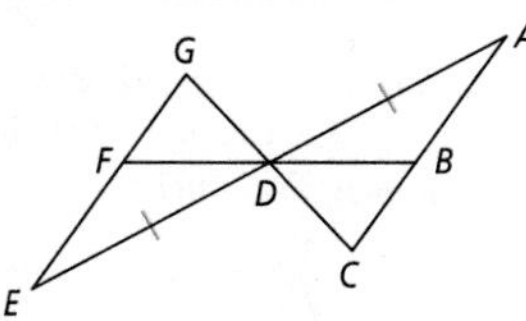

Apply

19. **Think About a Plan** In the diagram at the right, $\angle V \cong \angle S$, $\overline{VU} \cong \overline{ST}$, and $\overline{PS} \cong \overline{QV}$. Which two triangles are congruent by SAS? Explain.
- How can you use a new diagram to help you identify the triangles?
- What do you need to prove triangles congruent by SAS?

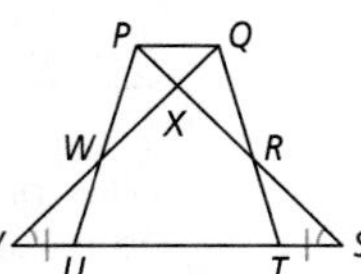

4 Practice

ASSIGNMENT GUIDE

Basic: 8–20 all, 22–26 even
Average: 9–17 odd, 19–26
Advanced: 9–17 odd, 19–28
Standardized Test Prep: 29–32
Mixed Review: 33–37

Reasoning exercises have blue headings.
Applications exercises have red headings.

EXERCISE 22: Use the Think About a Plan worksheet in the **Practice and Problem Solving Workbook** (also available in the Teaching Resources in print and online) to further support students' development in becoming independent learners.

HOMEWORK QUICK CHECK

To check students' understanding of key skills and concepts, go over Exercises 9, 13, 19, 22, and 24.

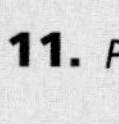

11.

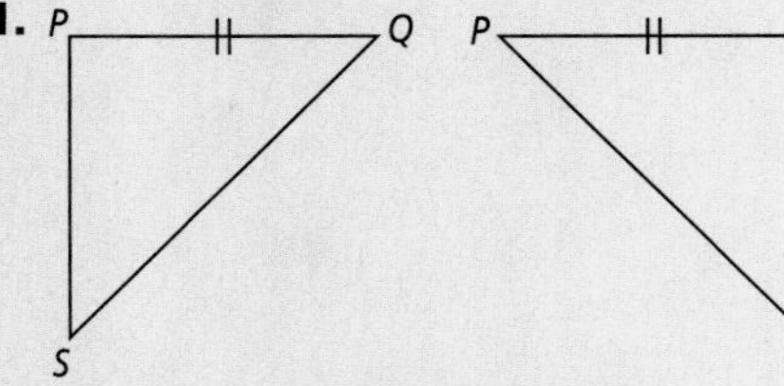

$\overline{PQ}$ is a common side.

12.

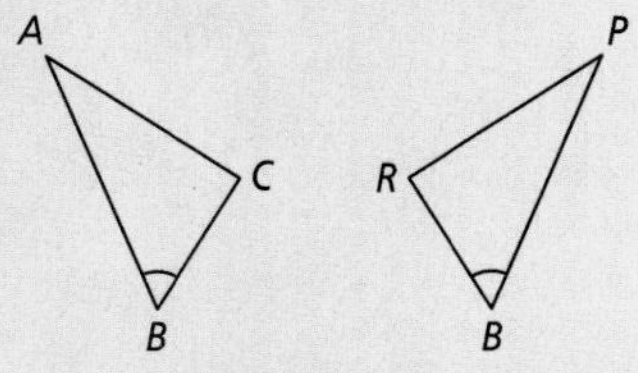

$\angle B$ is a common $\angle$.

13.

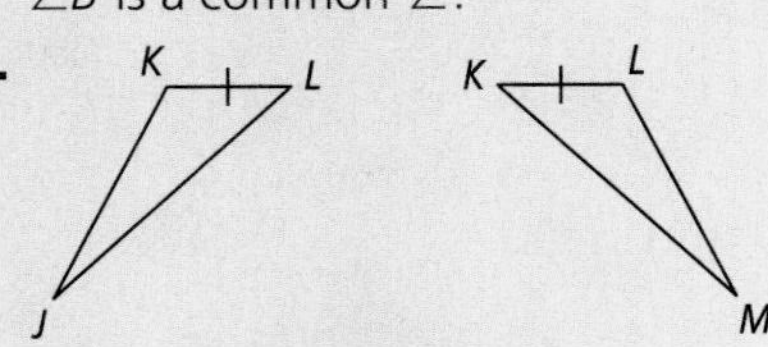

$\overline{KL}$ is a common side.

14a. Given
b. Refl. Prop. of $\cong$
c. Given
d. AAS
e. Corresp. parts of $\cong$ ≜ are $\cong$.

15. $\overline{RS} \cong \overline{UT}$ and $\overline{RT} \cong \overline{US}$ (Given), and $\overline{ST} \cong \overline{ST}$ (Refl. Prop. of $\cong$), so $\triangle RST \cong \triangle UTS$ by SSS.

16. $\overline{QD} \cong \overline{UA}$ and $\angle QDA \cong \angle UAD$ (Given), and $\overline{DA} \cong \overline{DA}$ (Refl. Prop. of $\cong$). So $\triangle QDA \cong \triangle UAD$ by SAS.

17. $\angle 1 \cong \angle 2$ and $\angle 3 \cong \angle 4$ (Given), and $\overline{QB} \cong \overline{QB}$ by the Refl. Prop. of $\cong$. So $\triangle QTB \cong \triangle QUB$ by ASA. Thus $\overline{QT} \cong \overline{QU}$ (Corresp. parts of $\cong$ ≜ are $\cong$.). $\overline{QE} \cong \overline{QE}$ (Refl. Prop. of $\cong$), so $\triangle QET \cong \triangle QEU$ by SAS.

18. Answers may vary. Sample: $\overline{AD} \cong \overline{ED}$ and D is the midpt. of $\overline{BF}$ (Given). $\overline{BD} \cong \overline{FD}$ (Def. of midpt.), and $\angle ADB \cong \angle EDF$ (Vert. ∡ are $\cong$.). So $\triangle ADB \cong \triangle EDF$ by SAS, and $\angle A \cong \angle E$ because corresp. parts of $\cong$ ≜ are $\cong$. $\angle ADC \cong \angle EDG$ because vert. ∡ are $\cong$, so $\triangle ADC \cong \triangle EDG$ by ASA.

19. Since $VT = VU + UT = UT + TS = US$, $\overline{VT} \cong \overline{US}$. Therefore, $\triangle QVT \cong \triangle PSU$ by SAS.

Answers

Practice and Problem-Solving Exercises (continued)

20a. $m\angle 1 = 50$, $m\angle 2 = 50$, $m\angle 3 = 40$, $m\angle 4 = 90$, $m\angle 5 = 10$, $m\angle 6 = 40$, $m\angle 7 = 40$, $m\angle 8 = 80$, $m\angle 9 = 100$

b. $\triangle ABC \cong \triangle FCG$ by ASA because $\angle B \cong \angle FCG$ (All rt. ∠s are ≅.), $\overline{AB} \cong \overline{FC}$ (Given), and $\angle A \cong \angle GFC$ (Their measures are =.).

21. It is given that $\overline{AC} \cong \overline{EC}$ and $\overline{CD} \cong \overline{CB}$, and $\angle C \cong \angle C$ by the Refl. Prop. of ≅. So $\triangle ACD \cong \triangle ECB$ by SAS, and $\angle A \cong \angle E$ because corresp. parts of ≅ △s are ≅.

22. $\triangle PQT \cong \triangle RQT$ by SAS because $\overline{QT} \cong \overline{QT}$ (Refl. Prop. of ≅), $\angle PQT \cong \angle RQT$ (⊥ lines form rt. ∠s, which are ≅.), and $\overline{PQ} \cong \overline{RQ}$ (because $\overline{QT}$ bisects $\overline{PR}$). Then $\angle QTP \cong \angle QTR$ because corresp. parts of ≅ △s are ≅. Also, $\angle VQT \cong \angle SQT$ (because $\overline{QT}$ bisects $\angle VQS$), so $\triangle VQT \cong \triangle SQT$ by ASA. So $\overline{VQ} \cong \overline{SQ}$ because corresp. parts of ≅ △s are ≅.

23. Answers may vary. Sample:

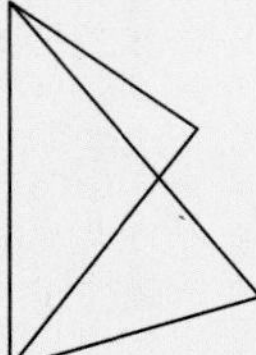

24. Answers may vary. Sample:

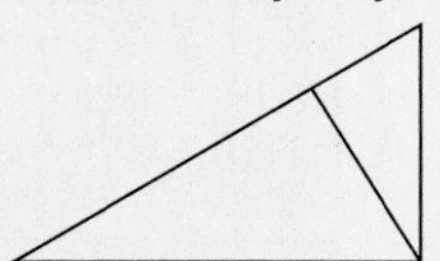

25. $\overline{TE} \cong \overline{RI}$ and $\overline{TI} \cong \overline{RE}$ (Given) and $\overline{EI} \cong \overline{EI}$ (Refl. Prop. of ≅), so $\triangle TEI \cong \triangle RIE$ by SSS. Thus $\angle TIE \cong \angle REI$ because corresp. parts of ≅ △s are ≅. Also, $\angle TDI \cong \angle ROE$ because $\angle TDI$ and $\angle ROE$ are rt. ∠s (Given) and all rt. ∠s are ≅. So $\triangle TDI \cong \triangle ROE$ by AAS and $\overline{TD} \cong \overline{RO}$ because corresp. parts of ≅ △s are ≅.

26. The given ⊥ segments indicate that $\triangle ABC$ and $\triangle DCB$ are rt. △s. Since $\overline{AC} \cong \overline{DB}$ (Given) and $\overline{BC} \cong \overline{BC}$ (Refl. Prop. of ≅), then $\triangle ABC \cong \triangle DCB$ by HL. $\overline{AB} \cong \overline{DC}$, and $\angle A \cong \angle D$ because corresp. parts of ≅ △s are ≅. $\angle AEB \cong \angle DEC$ because rt. ∠s are ≅, so $\triangle AEB \cong \triangle DEC$ by AAS and $\overline{AE} \cong \overline{DE}$ because corresp. parts of ≅ △s are ≅.

27.

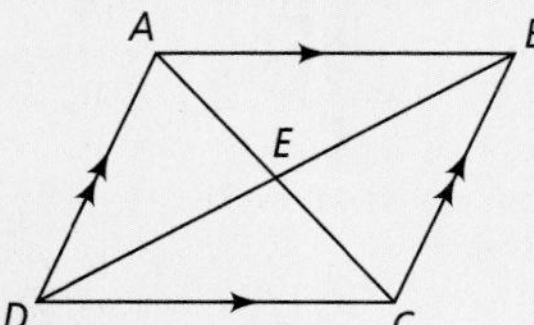

a. $\overline{AB} \cong \overline{DC}$, $\overline{AD} \cong \overline{BC}$, $\overline{AE} \cong \overline{EC}$, $\overline{DE} \cong \overline{EB}$

b. By showing that $\triangle ABC \cong \triangle CDA$ (by ASA), you can then prove that $\triangle AEB \cong \triangle CED$ and $\triangle AED \cong \triangle CEB$ (by ASA or AAS). The segments are ≅ because corresp. parts of ≅ △s are ≅.

20. Clothing Design The figure at the right is part of a clothing design pattern, and it has the following relationships.

- $\overline{GC} \perp \overline{AC}$
- $\overline{AB} \perp \overline{BC}$
- $\overline{AB} \parallel \overline{DE} \parallel \overline{FG}$
- $m\angle A = 50$
- $\triangle DEC$ is isosceles with base $\overline{DC}$.

a. Find the measures of all the numbered angles in the figure.

b. Suppose $\overline{AB} \cong \overline{FC}$. Name two congruent triangles and explain how you can prove them congruent.

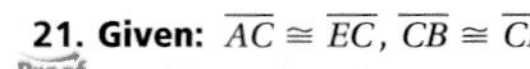

21. Given: $\overline{AC} \cong \overline{EC}$, $\overline{CB} \cong \overline{CD}$
Proof
Prove: $\angle A \cong \angle E$

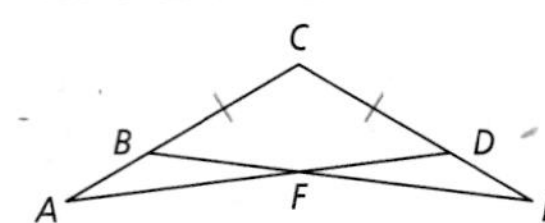

22. Given: $\overline{QT} \perp \overline{PR}$, $\overline{QT}$ bisects $\overline{PR}$,
Proof
$\overline{QT}$ bisects $\angle VQS$
Prove: $\overline{VQ} \cong \overline{SQ}$

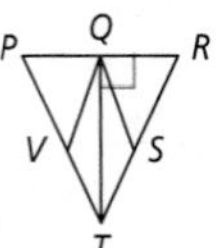

Open-Ended **Draw the diagram described.**

23. Draw a vertical segment on your paper. On the right side of the segment draw two triangles that share the vertical segment as a common side.

24. Draw two triangles that have a common angle.

25. Given: $\overline{TE} \cong \overline{RI}$, $\overline{TI} \cong \overline{RE}$,
Proof
$\angle TDI$ and $\angle ROE$ are right ∠s
Prove: $\overline{TD} \cong \overline{RO}$

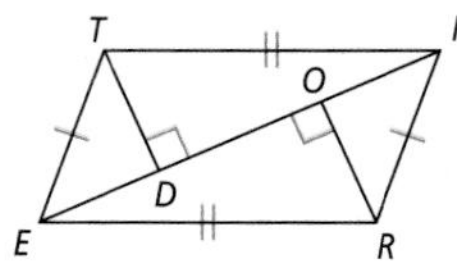

26. Given: $\overline{AB} \perp \overline{BC}$, $\overline{DC} \perp \overline{BC}$,
Proof
$\overline{AC} \cong \overline{DB}$
Prove: $\overline{AE} \cong \overline{DE}$

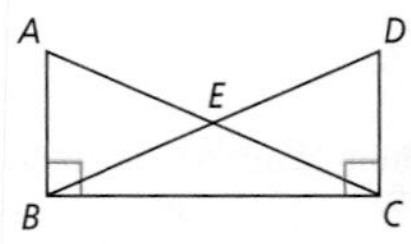

Challenge

27. Reasoning Draw a quadrilateral *ABCD* with $\overline{AB} \parallel \overline{DC}$, $\overline{AD} \parallel \overline{BC}$, and diagonals $\overline{AC}$ and $\overline{DB}$ intersecting at *E*. Label your diagram to indicate the parallel sides.

a. List all the pairs of congruent segments in your diagram.

b. Writing Explain how you know that the segments you listed are congruent.

28. Identify a pair of overlapping congruent triangles in the diagram. Then use the given information to write a proof to show that the triangles are congruent.
Proof

Given: $\overline{AC} \cong \overline{BC}$, $\angle A \cong \angle B$

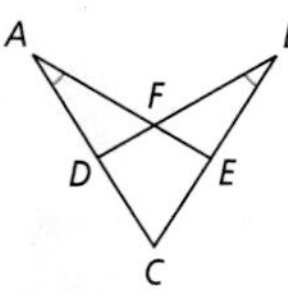

Standardized Test Prep

SAT/ACT

29. According to the diagram at the right, which statement is true?

Ⓐ $\triangle DEH \cong \triangle GFH$ by AAS

Ⓑ $\triangle DEH \cong \triangle GFH$ by SAS

Ⓒ $\triangle DEF \cong \triangle GFE$ by AAS

Ⓓ $\triangle DEF \cong \triangle GFE$ by SAS

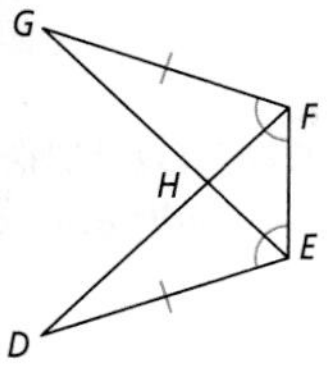

30. $\triangle ABC$ is isosceles with base $\overline{AC}$. If $m\angle C = 37$, what is $m\angle B$?

Ⓕ 37 Ⓖ 74 Ⓗ 106 Ⓘ 143

31. Which word correctly completes the statement "All __?__ angles are congruent"?

Ⓐ adjacent Ⓑ supplementary Ⓒ right Ⓓ corresponding

Extended Response

32. In the figure, $\overline{LJ} \parallel \overline{GK}$ and M is the midpoint of $\overline{LG}$.

a. Copy the diagram. Then mark your diagram with the given information.
b. Prove $\triangle LJM \cong \triangle GKM$.
c. Can you prove that $\triangle LJM \cong \triangle GKM$ another way? Explain.

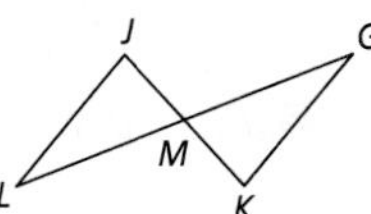

Mixed Review

33. Developing Proof Complete the paragraph proof. See Lesson 4-6.

Given: $\overline{AB} \cong \overline{DB}$, $\angle A$ and $\angle D$ are right angles

Prove: $\triangle ABC \cong \triangle DBC$

Proof: You are given that $\overline{AB} \cong \overline{DB}$ and $\angle A$ and $\angle D$ are right angles. $\triangle ABC$ and $\triangle DBC$ are **a.** __?__ triangles by the definition of **b.** __?__ triangle. $\overline{BC} \cong \overline{BC}$ by the **c.** __?__ Property of Congruence. $\triangle ABC \cong \triangle DBC$ by the **d.** __?__ Theorem.

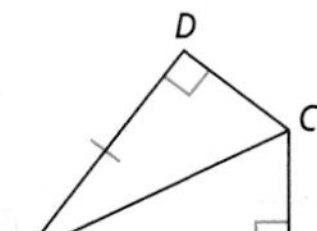

34. Constructions Draw a line p and a point M not on p. Then construct line n through M so that $n \perp p$. See Lesson 3-6.

Get Ready! **To prepare for Lesson 5-1, do Exercises 35–37.**

Find the coordinates of the midpoint of $\overline{AB}$. See Lesson 1-7.

35. $A(-2, 3)$, $B(4, 1)$ **36.** $A(0, 5)$, $B(3, 6)$ **37.** $A(7, 10)$, $B(-5, -8)$

28. The overlapping $\triangle$s are $\triangle CAE$ and $\triangle CBD$. It is given that $\overline{AC} \cong \overline{BC}$ and $\angle A \cong \angle B$. Also, $\angle C \cong \angle C$ by the Refl. Prop. of $\cong$. So $\triangle CAE \cong \triangle CBD$ by ASA.

29. D

30. H

31. C

32. [4] **a.**

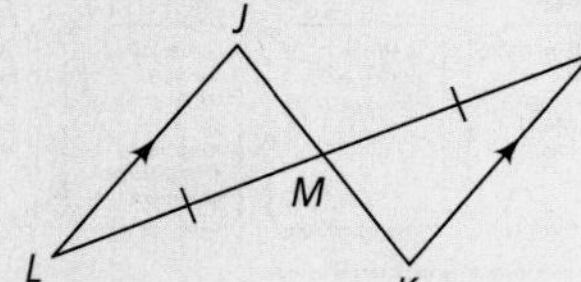

b. It is given that $\overline{LJ} \parallel \overline{GK}$, so $\angle J \cong \angle K$ and $\angle L \cong \angle G$ because if lines are $\parallel$, then alt. int. $\angle$s are $\cong$. Also, $\overline{LM} \cong \overline{GM}$ because M is the midpt. of $\overline{LG}$ (Given) and a midpt. divides a segment into two $\cong$ segments. So $\triangle LJM \cong \triangle GKM$ by AAS.

c. If you use the $\cong$ vertical $\angle$s JML and KMG, you can prove $\triangle LJM \cong \triangle GKM$ by ASA.

[3] part (a) incorrect OR minor error in either part (b) or part (c)

[2] part (a) incorrect and minor error in either part (b) or part (c) OR part (b) incorrect OR part (c) incorrect

[1] only part (a) correct

33a. right
b. right
c. Reflexive
d. HL

34.

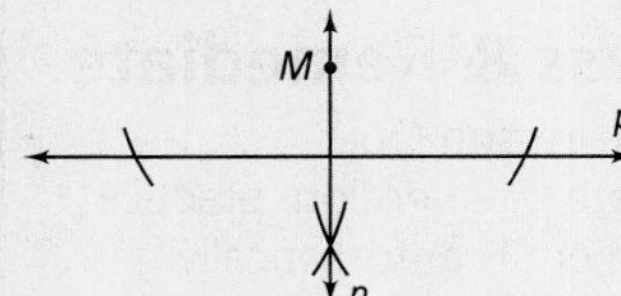

35. (1, 2)
36. (1.5, 5.5)
37. (1, 1)

4-7 Lesson Resources

Instructional Support

Geometry Companion

Students can use the **Geometry Companion** worktext (4 pages) . . .

- New Vocabulary
- Key Concepts
- Got It for each Problem
- Lesson Check

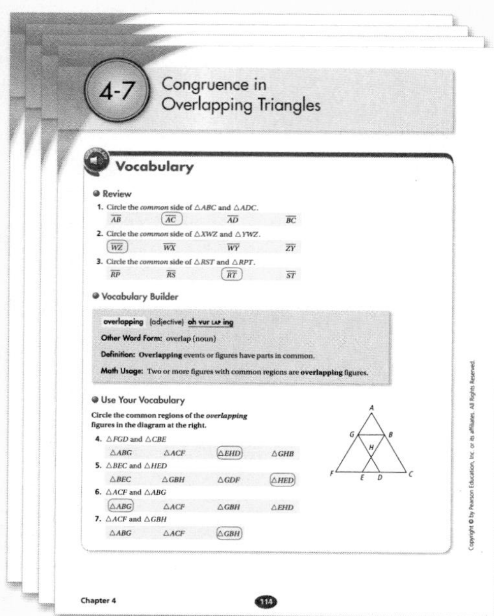

4-7 Congruence in Overlapping Triangles

Vocabulary

Review

1. Circle the *common* side of $\triangle ABC$ and $\triangle ADC$.
   $\overline{AB}$ $\overline{AC}$ $\overline{AD}$ $\overline{BC}$
2. Circle the *common* side of $\triangle XWZ$ and $\triangle YWZ$.
   $\overline{WZ}$ $\overline{WX}$ $\overline{WY}$ $\overline{ZY}$
3. Circle the *common* side of $\triangle RST$ and $\triangle RPT$.
   $\overline{RP}$ $\overline{RS}$ $\overline{RT}$ $\overline{ST}$

Vocabulary Builder

overlapping (adjective) oh vur LAP ing

Other Word Form: overlap (noun)

Definition: **Overlapping** events or figures have parts in common.

Math Usage: Two or more figures with common regions are **overlapping** figures.

Use Your Vocabulary

Circle the common regions of the *overlapping* figures in the diagram at the right.

4. $\triangle FGD$ and $\triangle CBE$
   $\triangle ABG$ $\triangle ACF$ $\triangle EHD$ $\triangle GHB$
5. $\triangle BEC$ and $\triangle HED$
   $\triangle BEC$ $\triangle GBH$ $\triangle GDF$ $\triangle HED$
6. $\triangle ACF$ and $\triangle ABG$
   $\triangle ABG$ $\triangle ACF$ $\triangle GBH$ $\triangle EHD$
7. $\triangle ACF$ and $\triangle GBH$
   $\triangle ABG$ $\triangle ACF$ $\triangle GBH$

Chapter 4 114

ELL Support

Use Graphic Organizers Set up a "word wall" where you post vocabulary words and their definitions from each lesson. Have students draw diagrams and models to represent each concept. Ask students for words that share the same word base (cognates) or use the Internet or a dictionary. These roots can be placed on the word wall in a separate section on different colored paper to differentiate them.

Use Manipulatives Have students draw a pair of congruent, overlapping triangles. Then they can trade with a partner and separate and redraw the triangles.

5 Assess & Remediate

Lesson Quiz

1. **Do you UNDERSTAND?** What is the common angle in $\triangle LMP$ and $\triangle LNO$?

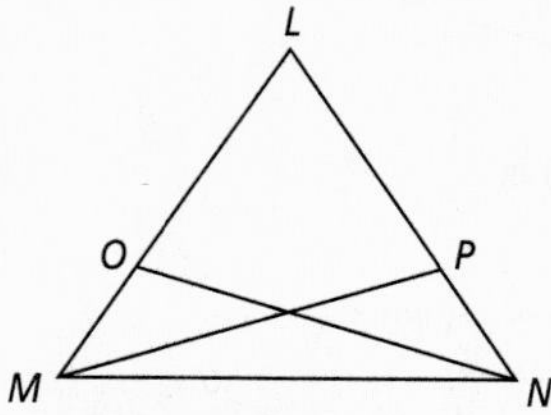

2. **Given:** $\overline{RU} \cong \overline{TS}$, V is the midpoint of $\overline{RT}$ and $\overline{US}$.
   Prove: $\angle RUV \cong \angle TSV$.

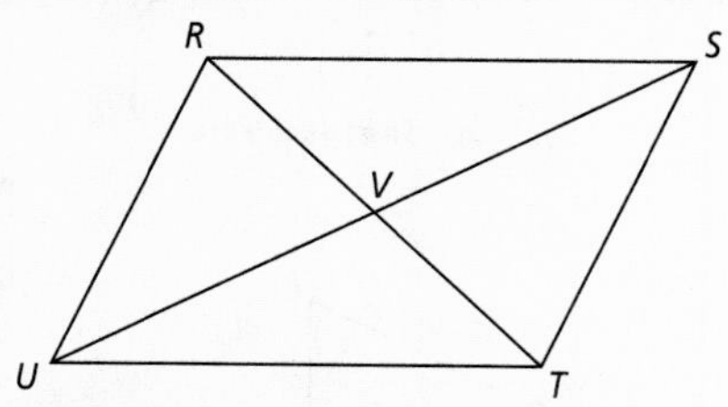

ANSWERS TO LESSON QUIZ

1. $\angle L$
2. It is given that $\overline{RU} \cong \overline{TS}$ and V is the midpoint of $\overline{RT}$ and $\overline{US}$. So, $RV = VT$ and $UV = VS$ by the definition of midpoint. So, $\overline{RV} \cong \overline{VT}$ and $\overline{UV} \cong \overline{VS}$ by the definition of congruent segments. So, $\triangle RVU \cong \triangle TVS$ by SSS. $\angle RUV \cong \angle TSV$ because they are corresponding parts of congruent triangles.

PRESCRIPTION FOR REMEDIATION

Use the student work on the Lesson Quiz to prescribe a differentiated review assignment.

Points	Differentiated Remediation
0	Intervention
1	On-level
2	Extension

PowerGeometry.com

5 Assess & Remediate

Assign the Lesson Quiz. Appropriate intervention, practice, or enrichment is automatically generated based on student performance.

Differentiated Remediation

Intervention

- **Reteaching** (2 pages) Provides reteaching and practice exercises for the key lesson concepts. Use with struggling students or absent students.
- **English Language Learner Support** Helps students develop and reinforce mathematical vocabulary and key concepts.

All-in-One Resources/Online

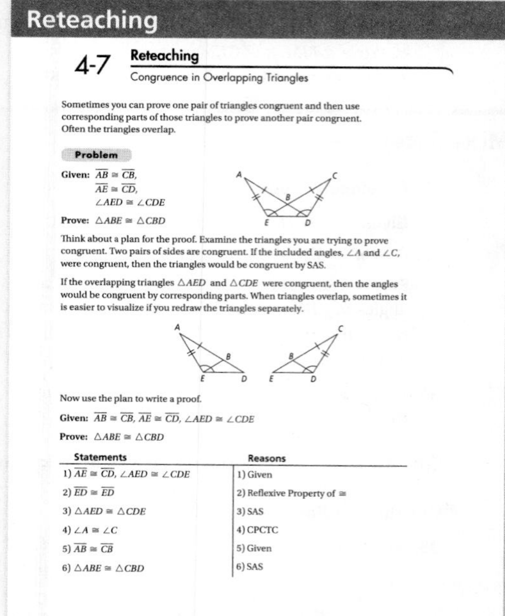

Reteaching

4-7 Reteaching
Congruence in Overlapping Triangles

Sometimes you can prove one pair of triangles congruent and then use corresponding parts of those triangles to prove another pair congruent. Often the triangles overlap.

Problem

Given: $\overline{AB} \cong \overline{CB}$, $\overline{AE} \cong \overline{CD}$, $\angle AED \cong \angle CDE$

Prove: $\triangle ABE \cong \triangle CBD$

Think about a plan for the proof. Examine the triangles you are trying to prove congruent. Two pairs of sides are congruent. If the included angles, $\angle A$ and $\angle C$, were congruent, then the triangles would be congruent by SAS.

If the overlapping triangles $\triangle AED$ and $\triangle CDE$ were congruent, then the angles would be congruent by corresponding parts. When triangles overlap, sometimes it is easier to visualize if you redraw the triangles separately.

Now use the plan to write a proof.

Given: $\overline{AB} \cong \overline{CB}$, $\overline{AE} \cong \overline{CD}$, $\angle AED \cong \angle CDE$

Prove: $\triangle ABE \cong \triangle CBD$

Statements	Reasons
1) $\overline{AE} \cong \overline{CD}$, $\angle AED \cong \angle CDE$	1) Given
2) $\overline{ED} \cong \overline{ED}$	2) Reflexive Property of $\cong$
3) $\triangle AED \cong \triangle CDE$	3) SAS
4) $\angle A \cong \angle C$	4) CPCTC
5) $\overline{AB} \cong \overline{CB}$	5) Given
6) $\triangle ABE \cong \triangle CBD$	6) SAS

All-in-One Resources/Online

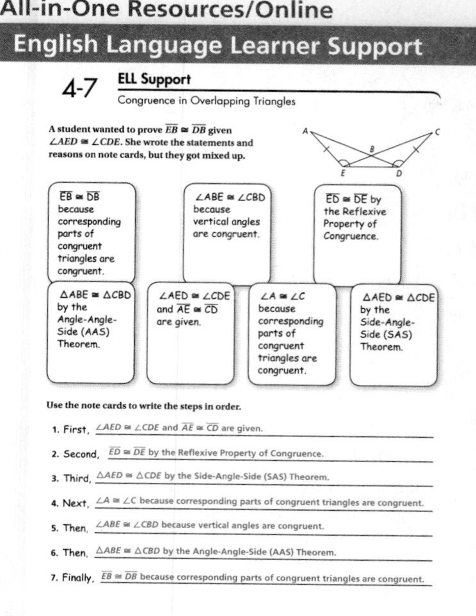

English Language Learner Support

4-7 ELL Support
Congruence in Overlapping Triangles

A student wanted to prove $\overline{EB} \cong \overline{DB}$ given $\angle AED \cong \angle CDE$. She wrote the statements and reasons on note cards, but they got mixed up.

$\overline{EB} \cong \overline{DB}$ because corresponding parts of congruent triangles are congruent.

$\angle ABE \cong \angle CBD$ because vertical angles are congruent.

$\overline{ED} \cong \overline{DE}$ by the Reflexive Property of Congruence.

$\triangle ABE \cong \triangle CBD$ by the Angle-Angle-Side (AAS) Theorem.

$\angle AED \cong \angle CDE$ and $\overline{AE} \cong \overline{CD}$ are given.

$\angle A \cong \angle C$ because corresponding parts of congruent triangles are congruent.

$\triangle AED \cong \triangle CDE$ by the Side-Angle-Side (SAS) Theorem.

Use the note cards to write the steps in order.

1. First, $\angle AED \cong \angle CDE$ and $\overline{AE} \cong \overline{CD}$ are given.
2. Second, $\overline{ED} \cong \overline{DE}$ by the Reflexive Property of Congruence.
3. Third, $\triangle AED \cong \triangle CDE$ by the Side-Angle-Side (SAS) Theorem.
4. Next, $\angle A \cong \angle C$ because corresponding parts of congruent triangles are congruent.
5. Then, $\angle ABE \cong \angle CBD$ because vertical angles are congruent.
6. Then, $\triangle ABE \cong \triangle CBD$ by the Angle-Angle-Side (AAS) Theorem.
7. Finally, $\overline{EB} \cong \overline{DB}$ because corresponding parts of congruent triangles are congruent.

Differentiated Remediation *continued*

On-Level

- **Practice** (2 pages) Provides extra practice for each lesson. For simpler practice exercises, use the Form K Practice pages found in the All-in-One Teaching Resources and online.
- **Think About a Plan** Helps students develop specific problem-solving skills and strategies by providing scaffolded guiding questions.
- **Standardized Test Prep** Focuses on all major exercises, all major question types, and helps students prepare for the high-stakes assessments.

Extension

- **Enrichment** Provides students with interesting problems and activities that extend the concepts of the lesson.
- **Activities, Games, and Puzzles** Worksheets that can be used for concepts development, enrichment, and for fun!

Practice and Problem Solving Wkbk/ All-in-One Resources/Online

Practice page 1

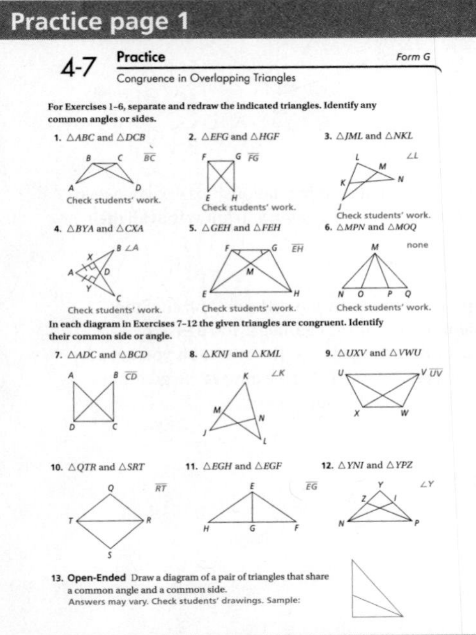

4-7 **Practice** *Form G*

Congruence in Overlapping Triangles

For Exercises 1–6, separate and redraw the indicated triangles. Identify any common angles or sides.

1. $\triangle ABC$ and $\triangle DCB$ — $\overline{BC}$ Check students' work.
2. $\triangle EFG$ and $\triangle HGF$ — $\overline{FG}$ Check students' work.
3. $\triangle JML$ and $\triangle NKL$ — $\angle L$ Check students' work.
4. $\triangle BYA$ and $\triangle CXA$ — $\angle A$ Check students' work.
5. $\triangle GEH$ and $\triangle FEH$ — $\overline{EH}$ Check students' work.
6. $\triangle MPN$ and $\triangle MOQ$ — none Check students' work.

In each diagram in Exercises 7–12 the given triangles are congruent. Identify their common side or angle.

7. $\triangle ADC$ and $\triangle BCD$ — $\overline{CD}$
8. $\triangle KNJ$ and $\triangle KML$ — $\angle K$
9. $\triangle UXV$ and $\triangle VWU$ — $\overline{UV}$
10. $\triangle QTR$ and $\triangle SRT$ — $\overline{RT}$
11. $\triangle EGH$ and $\triangle EGF$ — $\overline{EG}$
12. $\triangle YNI$ and $\triangle YPZ$ — $\angle Y$
13. **Open-Ended** Draw a diagram of a pair of triangles that share a common angle and a common side. Answers may vary. Check students' drawings. Sample:

Practice and Problem Solving Wkbk/ All-in-One Resources/Online

Practice page 2

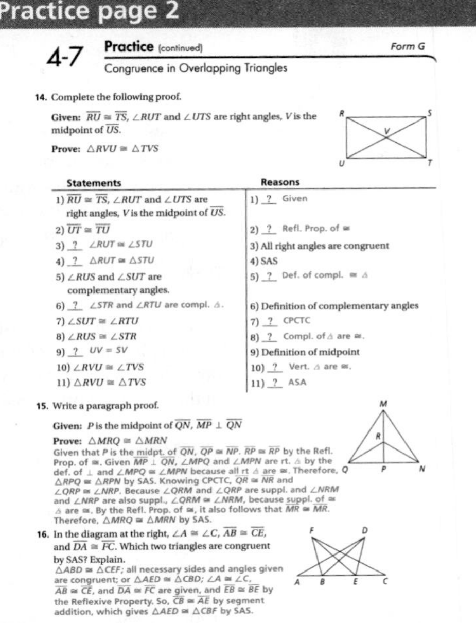

4-7 **Practice** (continued) *Form G*

Congruence in Overlapping Triangles

14. Complete the following proof.

Given: $\overline{RU} \cong \overline{TS}$, $\angle RUT$ and $\angle UTS$ are right angles, V is the midpoint of $\overline{US}$.

Prove: $\triangle RVU \cong \triangle TVS$

Statements	Reasons
1) $\overline{RU} \cong \overline{TS}$, $\angle RUT$ and $\angle UTS$ are right angles, V is the midpoint of $\overline{US}$.	1) _?_ Given
2) $\overline{UT} \cong \overline{TU}$	2) _?_ Refl. Prop. of ≅
3) _?_ $\angle RUT \cong \angle STU$	3) All right angles are congruent
4) _?_ $\triangle RUT \cong \triangle STU$	4) SAS
5) $\angle RUS$ and $\angle SUT$ are complementary angles.	5) _?_ Def. of compl. ≅ △
6) _?_ $\angle STR$ and $\angle RTU$ are compl. △.	6) Definition of complementary angles
7) $\angle SUT \cong \angle RTU$	7) _?_ CPCTC
8) $\angle RUS \cong \angle STR$	8) _?_ Compl. of △ are ≅.
9) _?_ $UV = SV$	9) Definition of midpoint
10) $\angle RVU \cong \angle TVS$	10) _?_ Vert. △ are ≅.
11) $\triangle RVU \cong \triangle TVS$	11) _?_ ASA

15. Write a paragraph proof.

Given: P is the midpoint of $\overline{QN}$, $\overline{MP} \perp \overline{QN}$

Prove: $\triangle MRQ \cong \triangle MRN$

Given that P is the midpt. of $\overline{QN}$, $\overline{QP} \cong \overline{NP}$. $\overline{RP} \cong \overline{RP}$ by the Refl. Prop. of ≅. Given $\overline{MP} \perp \overline{QN}$, $\angle MPQ$ and $\angle MPN$ are rt. △ by the def. of ⊥ and $\angle MPQ \cong \angle MPN$ because all rt △ are ≅. Therefore, $\triangle RPQ \cong \triangle RPN$ by SAS. Knowing CPCTC, $\overline{QR} \cong \overline{NR}$ and $\angle QRP \cong \angle NRP$. Because $\angle QRM$ and $\angle QRP$ are suppl. and $\angle NRM$ and $\angle NRP$ are also suppl., $\angle QRM \cong \angle NRM$, because suppl. of ≅ △ are ≅. By the Refl. Prop. of ≅, it also follows that $\overline{MR} \cong \overline{MR}$. Therefore, $\triangle MRQ \cong \triangle MRN$ by SAS.

16. In the diagram at the right, $\angle A \cong \angle C$, $\overline{AB} \cong \overline{CE}$, and $\overline{DA} \cong \overline{FC}$. Which two triangles are congruent by SAS? Explain.
$\triangle ABD \cong \triangle CEF$; all necessary sides and angles given are congruent; or $\triangle AED \cong \triangle CBD$; $\angle A \cong \angle C$, $\overline{AB} \cong \overline{CE}$, and $\overline{DA} \cong \overline{FC}$ are given, and $\overline{EB} \cong \overline{BE}$ by the Reflexive Property. So, $\overline{CB} \cong \overline{AE}$ by segment addition, which gives $\triangle AED \cong \triangle CBF$ by SAS.

All-in-One Resources/Online

Enrichment

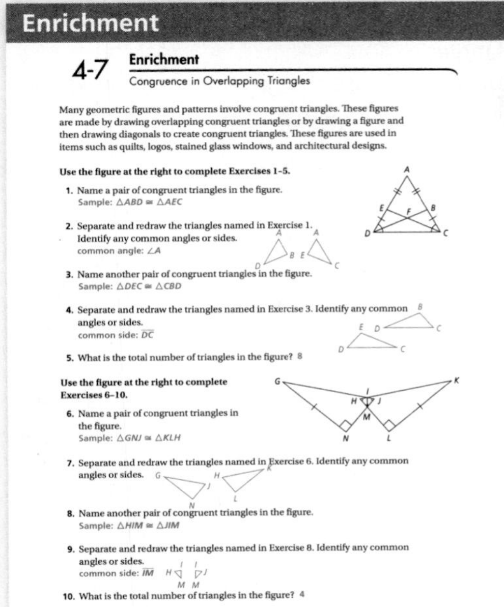

4-7 **Enrichment**

Congruence in Overlapping Triangles

Many geometric figures and patterns involve congruent triangles. These figures are made by drawing overlapping congruent triangles or by drawing a figure and then drawing diagonals to create congruent triangles. These figures are used in items such as quilts, logos, stained glass windows, and architectural designs.

Use the figure at the right to complete Exercises 1–5.

1. Name a pair of congruent triangles in the figure. Sample: $\triangle ABD \cong \triangle AEC$
2. Separate and redraw the triangles named in Exercise 1. Identify any common angles or sides. common angle: $\angle A$
3. Name another pair of congruent triangles in the figure. Sample: $\triangle DEC \cong \triangle CBD$
4. Separate and redraw the triangles named in Exercise 3. Identify any common angles or sides. common side: $\overline{DC}$
5. What is the total number of triangles in the figure? 8

Use the figure at the right to complete Exercises 6–10.

6. Name a pair of congruent triangles in the figure. Sample: $\triangle GNJ \cong \triangle KLH$
7. Separate and redraw the triangles named in Exercise 6. Identify any common angles or sides.
8. Name another pair of congruent triangles in the figure. Sample: $\triangle HIM \cong \triangle JIM$
9. Separate and redraw the triangles named in Exercise 8. Identify any common angles or sides. common side: $\overline{IM}$
10. What is the total number of triangles in the figure? 4

Practice and Problem Solving Wkbk/ All-in-One Resources/Online

Think About a Plan

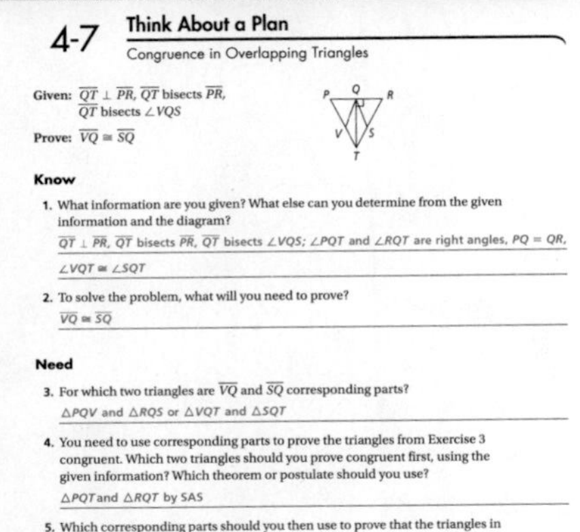

4-7 **Think About a Plan**

Congruence in Overlapping Triangles

Given: $\overline{QT} \perp \overline{PR}$, $\overline{QT}$ bisects $\overline{PR}$, $\overline{QT}$ bisects $\angle VQS$

Prove: $\overline{VQ} \cong \overline{SQ}$

Know

1. What information are you given? What else can you determine from the given information and the diagram?
$\overline{QT} \perp \overline{PR}$, $\overline{QT}$ bisects $\overline{PR}$, $\overline{QT}$ bisects $\angle VQS$; $\angle PQT$ and $\angle RQT$ are right angles, $PQ = QR$, $\angle VQT \cong \angle SQT$
2. To solve the problem, what will you need to prove?
$\overline{VQ} \cong \overline{SQ}$

Need

3. For which two triangles are $\overline{VQ}$ and $\overline{SQ}$ corresponding parts?
$\triangle PQV$ and $\triangle RQS$ or $\triangle VQT$ and $\triangle SQT$
4. You need to use corresponding parts to prove the triangles from Exercise 3 congruent. Which two triangles should you prove congruent first, using the given information? Which theorem or postulate should you use?
$\triangle PQT$ and $\triangle RQT$ by SAS
5. Which corresponding parts should you then use to prove that the triangles in Exercise 3 are congruent?
Answers may vary. Sample: $\angle P$ and $\angle R$

Plan

6. Use the space below to write the proof.
Statements: 1) $\overline{QT} \perp \overline{PR}$; $\overline{QT}$ bisects $\overline{PR}$, $\overline{QT}$ bisects $\angle VQS$; 2) $m\angle PQT = m\angle RQT = 90$; 3) $PQ = QR$; 4) $QT = QT$; 5) $\triangle PQT \cong \triangle RQT$; 6) $\angle P \cong \angle R$; 7) $\angle PQV$ and $\angle VQT$ are compl. $\angle RQS$ and $\angle SQT$ are compl.; 8) $\angle VQT \cong \angle SQT$; 9) $\angle PQV \cong \angle RQS$; 10) $\triangle PQV \cong \triangle RQS$; 11) $\overline{VQ} \cong \overline{SQ}$; Reasons: 1) Given; 2) Definition of perpendicular lines; 3) Definition of bisector; 4) Reflexive Property of Congruence; 5) SAS; 6) CPCTC; 7) Definition of complementary angles; 8) Definition of angle bisector; 9) Complements of ≅ △ are ≅; 10) ASA; 11) CPCTC

Practice and Problem Solving Wkbk/ All-in-One Resources/Online

Standardized Test Prep

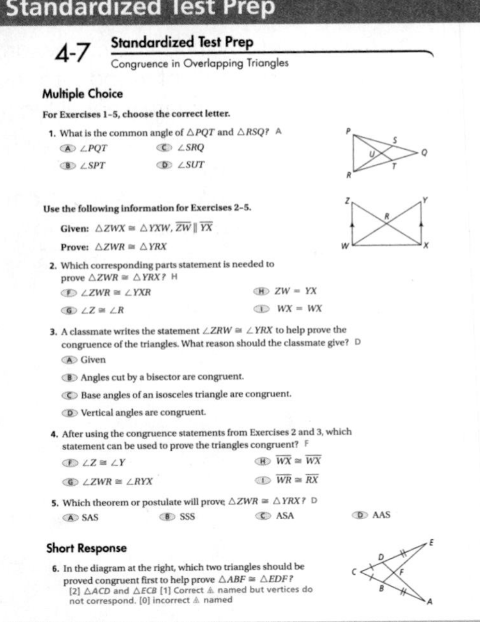

4-7 **Standardized Test Prep**

Congruence in Overlapping Triangles

Multiple Choice

For Exercises 1–5, choose the correct letter.

1. What is the common angle of $\triangle PQT$ and $\triangle RSQ$? A
(A) $\angle PQT$ (B) $\angle SPT$ (C) $\angle SRQ$ (D) $\angle SUT$

Use the following information for Exercises 2–5.

Given: $\triangle ZWX \cong \triangle YXW$, $\overline{ZW} \parallel \overline{YX}$

Prove: $\triangle ZWR \cong \triangle YRX$

2. Which corresponding parts statement is needed to prove $\triangle ZWR \cong \triangle YRX$? H
(F) $\angle ZWR \cong \angle YXR$ (G) $\angle Z \cong \angle R$ (H) $ZW = YX$ (I) $WX = WX$
3. A classmate writes the statement $\angle ZRW \cong \angle YRX$ to help prove the congruence of the triangles. What reason should the classmate give? D
(A) Given
(B) Angles cut by a bisector are congruent.
(C) Base angles of an isosceles triangle are congruent.
(D) Vertical angles are congruent.
4. After using the congruence statements from Exercises 2 and 3, which statement can be used to prove the triangles congruent? F
(F) $\angle Z \cong \angle Y$ (G) $\angle ZWR \cong \angle RYX$ (H) $\overline{WX} \cong \overline{WX}$ (I) $\overline{WR} \cong \overline{RX}$
5. Which theorem or postulate will prove $\triangle ZWR \cong \triangle YRX$? D
(A) SAS (B) SSS (C) ASA (D) AAS

Short Response

6. In the diagram at the right, which two triangles should be proved congruent first to help prove $\triangle ABF \cong \triangle EDF$?
[2] $\triangle ACD$ and $\triangle ECB$ [1] Correct △ named but vertices do not correspond. [0] incorrect △ named

Online Teacher Resource Center

Activities, Games, and Puzzles

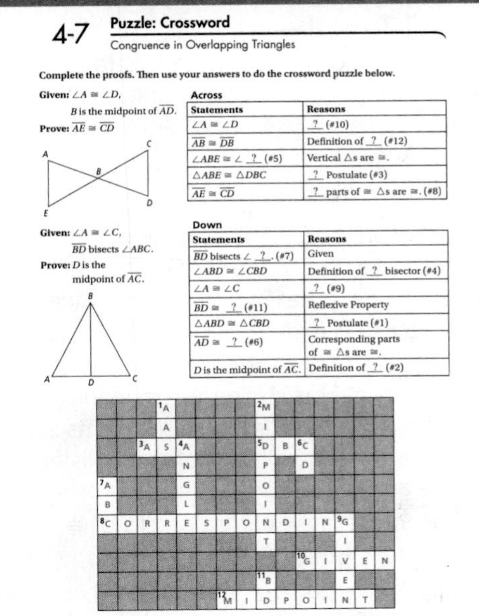

4-7 **Puzzle: Crossword**

Congruence in Overlapping Triangles

Complete the proofs. Then use your answers to do the crossword puzzle below.

Given: $\angle A \cong \angle D$, B is the midpoint of $\overline{AD}$.

Prove: $\overline{AE} \cong \overline{CD}$

Across

Statements	Reasons
$\angle A \cong \angle D$	_?_ (#10)
$\overline{AB} \cong \overline{DB}$	Definition of _?_ (#12)
$\angle ABE \cong \angle$ _?_ (#5)	Vertical △s are ≅.
$\triangle ABE \cong \triangle DBC$	_?_ Postulate (#3)
$\overline{AE} \cong \overline{CD}$	_?_ parts of ≅ △s are ≅. (#8)

Given: $\angle A \cong \angle C$, $\overline{BD}$ bisects $\angle ABC$.

Prove: D is the midpoint of $\overline{AC}$.

Down

Statements	Reasons
$\overline{BD}$ bisects $\angle$ _?_. (#7)	Given
$\angle ABD \cong \angle CBD$	Definition of _?_ bisector (#4)
$\angle A \cong \angle C$	_?_ (#9)
$\overline{BD} \cong$ _?_ (#11)	Reflexive Property
$\triangle ABD \cong \triangle CBD$	_?_ Postulate (#1)
$\overline{AD} \cong$ _?_ (#6)	Corresponding parts of ≅ △s are ≅.
D is the midpoint of $\overline{AC}$.	Definition of _?_ (#2)

Performance Task 

Pull It All Together

The concepts and skills required to solve these problems are from several lessons within this chapter and from the previous chapter. As students solve these problems, they will demonstrate their reasoning strategies and their growth as independent problem solvers.

The following questions are designed to:

- help support students as they do the Tasks.
- gauge the amount of support students need as they become independent problem solvers.

Task 1

- What are the corresponding parts of the triangles?
- Are any of the corresponding parts congruent?

Task 2

- How can you use the given tools to construct the triangles?
- How can you use the given tools to prove that the triangles are congruent?

4 *Pull It* All Together

To solve these problems you will pull together many concepts and skills that you have studied about congruent triangles.

BIG idea Visualization

The corresponding parts of congruent triangles are the parts that match if you place the triangles on top of each other.

Task 1

Copy the diagram below. $\triangle GAB$ is isosceles with vertex angle A and $\triangle BCD$ is isosceles with vertex angle C. Is $\triangle BGH$ congruent to $\triangle BDH$? Justify your reasoning.

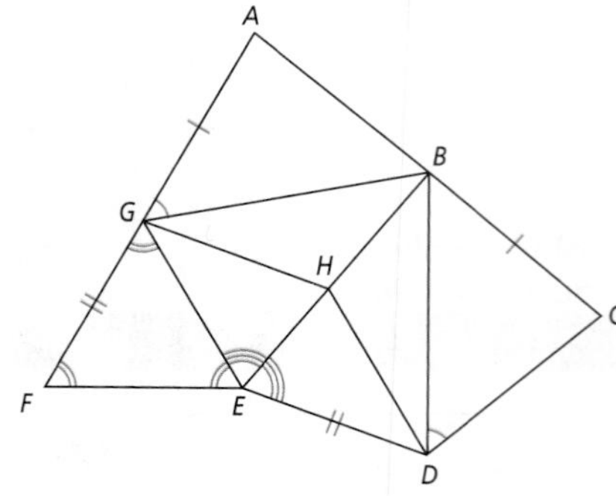

BIG idea Reasoning and Proof

You can prove triangles congruent if you know that certain relationships exist between corresponding parts. If you know that triangles are congruent, you know that all their corresponding parts are congruent.

Task 2

You and some neighbors are landscaping a community park. The organizer of the project selects an area for two congruent triangular rock gardens. You agree to be in charge of placing the pieces of wood to outline the gardens. The only tools you have are a saw, a protractor, and two very long pieces of wood. Describe one way to guarantee that the triangular outlines will be congruent. Justify your answer.

Assess Performance UbD

Pull It All Together

See p. 69 for a holistic scoring rubric to gauge a student's progress on Understanding the Problem, Planning a Solution, Getting an Answer, and Assessing Autonomy.

SOLUTION OUTLINES

1. Yes, $\triangle BGH \cong \triangle BDH$. Possible plan to explain why the △s are ≅: Given that $\angle A$ and $\angle C$ are vertex ∠s of issoc. △s, then $\overline{AG} \cong \overline{AB}$, $\angle AGB \cong \angle ABG$, $\overline{CB} \cong \overline{CD}$, and $\angle CBD \cong \angle CDB$ by the def. of isosc. △ and the Isosc. △ Thm. Using the markings in the diagram, all four of the segments listed above are ≅ and all four of the ∠s listed above are ≅, so $\triangle ABG \cong \triangle CBD$ by AAS and $\overline{BG} \cong \overline{BD}$ because corresp. parts of ≅ △s are ≅. By the Corollary to Theorem 4-4, $\triangle GFE$ is equilateral. Using $\overline{GE} \cong \overline{DE}$, $\angle GEH \cong \angle DEH$, and $\overline{EH} \cong \overline{EH}$, $\triangle GEH \cong \triangle DEH$ by SAS and $\overline{GH} \cong \overline{DH}$. Finally, using $\overline{HB} \cong \overline{HB}$, $\triangle BGH \cong \triangle BDH$ by SSS.
2. Answers may vary. Sample: Saw one of the long pieces of wood into three pieces of approximately equal length. Saw the other long piece of wood into three pieces that are equal in length to the three pieces cut from the first piece of wood. The two triangular outlines are ≅ by SSS.

Chapter Review

Connecting BIG ideas and Answering the Essential Questions

1 Visualization
You can identify corresponding parts of congruent triangles by visualizing the figures placed on top of each other.

Congruent Figures (Lesson 4-1)

$\triangle ABC \cong \triangle DEF$

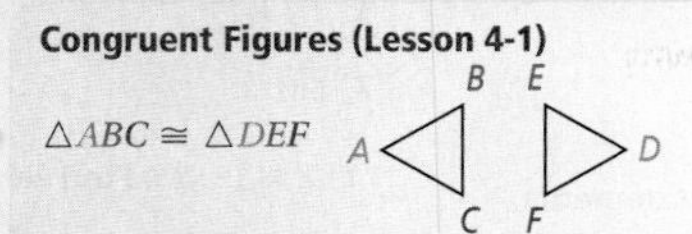

2 Reasoning and Proof
You can show two triangles are congruent by proving that certain relationships exist between three pairs of corresponding parts.

Proving Triangles Congruent (Lessons 4-2, 4-3, and 4-6)
Side-Side-Side (SSS), Side-Angle-Side (SAS), Angle-Side-Angle (ASA), Angle-Angle-Side (AAS), Hypotenuse-Leg (HL)

Using Corresponding Parts of Congruent Triangles (Lessons 4-4 and 4-7)

If $\triangle LMN \cong \triangle QRS$

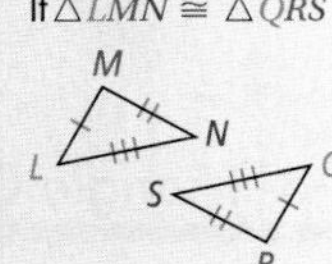

$\overline{LM} \cong \overline{QR}$
$\overline{MN} \cong \overline{RS}$
$\overline{NL} \cong \overline{SQ}$
$\angle L \cong \angle Q$
$\angle M \cong \angle R$
$\angle N \cong \angle S$

3 Reasoning and Proof
You can tell whether a triangle is isosceles or equilateral by looking at the number of congruent angles or sides.

Isosceles and Equilateral Triangles (Lesson 4-5)
- The base angles of an isosceles triangle are congruent.
- All equilateral triangles are equiangular.
- All equiangular triangles are equilateral.

Chapter Vocabulary

- base angles of an isosceles triangle (p. 250)
- base of an isosceles triangle (p. 250)
- congruent polygons (p. 219)
- corollary (p. 252)
- hypotenuse (p. 258)
- legs of an isosceles triangle (p. 250)
- legs of a right triangle (p. 258)
- vertex angle of an isosceles triangle (p. 250)

Choose the correct term to complete each sentence.

1. The two congruent sides of an isosceles triangle are the __?__.

2. The side opposite the right angle of a right triangle is the __?__.

3. A __?__ to a theorem is a statement that follows immediately from the theorem.

4. __?__ have congruent corresponding parts.

Essential Questions 

BIG idea Visualization

ESSENTIAL QUESTION How do you identify corresponding parts of congruent triangles?

ANSWER You can identify corresponding parts of congruent triangles by visualizing the figures placed on top of each other.

BIG idea Reasoning and Proof

ESSENTIAL QUESTION How do you show that two triangles are congruent?

ANSWER You can show two triangles are congruent by proving that certain relationships exist between three pairs of corresponding parts.

BIG idea Reasoning and Proof

ESSENTIAL QUESTION How can you tell whether a triangle is isosceles or equilateral?

ANSWER You can tell whether a triangle is isosceles or equilateral by looking at the number of congruent angles or sides.

Answers

Chapter Review

1. legs
2. hypotenuse
3. corollary
4. congruent polygons

Summative Questions UbD

Use the following prompts as you review this chapter with your students. The prompts are designed to help you assess your students' understanding of the Big Ideas they have studied.
- What are the postulates and theorems used to prove triangles congruent?
- What conditions exist in isosceles triangles?
- is every equilateral triangle isosceles?

Answers

Chapter Review (continued)

5. $\overline{ML}$
6. $\angle U$
7. $\overline{ST}$
8. *ONMLK*
9. 80
10. 3
11. 5
12. 35
13. 100
14. 145
15. $\angle D$
16. $\overline{MR}$
17. not enough information
18. not enough information
19. SAS
20. AAS or ASA

4-1 Congruent Figures

Quick Review

Congruent polygons have congruent corresponding parts. When you name congruent polygons, always list corresponding vertices in the same order.

Example

***HIJK* ≅ *PQRS*. Write all possible congruence statements.**

The order of the parts in the congruence statement tells you which parts correspond.

Sides: $\overline{HI} \cong \overline{PQ}$, $\overline{IJ} \cong \overline{QR}$, $\overline{JK} \cong \overline{RS}$, $\overline{KH} \cong \overline{SP}$

Angles: $\angle H \cong \angle P$, $\angle I \cong \angle Q$, $\angle J \cong \angle R$, $\angle K \cong \angle S$

Exercises

***RSTUV* ≅ *KLMNO*. Complete the congruence statements.**

5. $\overline{TS} \cong$? **6.** $\angle N \cong$?

7. $\overline{LM} \cong$? **8.** $VUTSR \cong$?

***WXYZ* ≅ *PQRS*. Find each measure or length.**

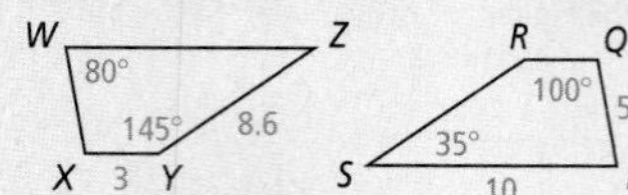

9. $m\angle P$ **10.** QR **11.** WX

12. $m\angle Z$ **13.** $m\angle X$ **14.** $m\angle R$

4-2 and 4-3 Triangle Congruence by SSS, SAS, ASA, and AAS

Quick Review

You can prove triangles congruent with limited information about their congruent sides and angles.

Postulate or Theorem	You need
Side-Side-Side (SSS)	three sides
Side-Angle-Side (SAS)	two sides and an included angle
Angle-Side-Angle (ASA)	two angles and an included side
Angle-Angle-Side (AAS)	two angles and a nonincluded side

Example

What postulate would you use to prove the triangles congruent?

You know that three sides are congruent. Use SSS.

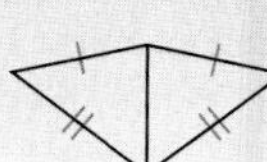

Exercises

15. In $\triangle HFD$, what angle is included between $\overline{DH}$ and $\overline{DF}$?

16. In $\triangle OMR$, what side is included between $\angle M$ and $\angle R$?

Which postulate or theorem, if any, could you use to prove the two triangles congruent? If there is not enough information to prove the triangles congruent, write *not enough information*.

17. 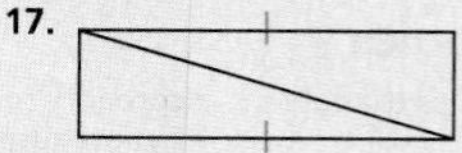

18. 

19. 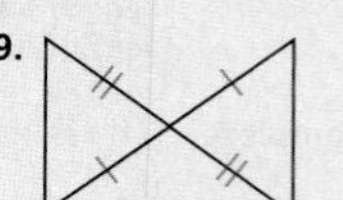

20. 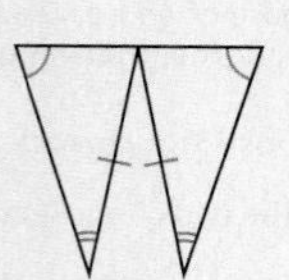

4-4 Using Corresponding Parts of Congruent Triangles

Quick Review

Once you know that triangles are congruent, you can make conclusions about corresponding sides and angles because, by definition, corresponding parts of congruent triangles are congruent. You can use congruent triangles in the proofs of many theorems.

Example

How can you use congruent triangles to prove $\angle Q \cong \angle D$?

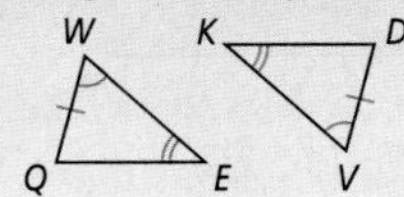

Since $\triangle QWE \cong \triangle DVK$ by AAS, you know that $\angle Q \cong \angle D$ because corresponding parts of congruent triangles are congruent.

Exercises

How can you use congruent triangles to prove the statement true?

21. $\overline{TV} \cong \overline{YW}$

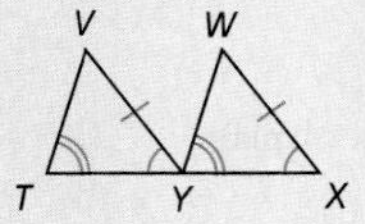

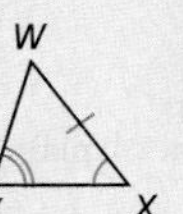

22. $\overline{BE} \cong \overline{DE}$

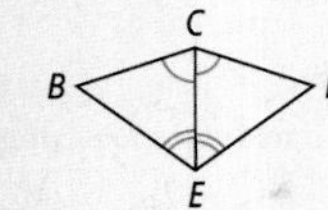

23. $\angle B \cong \angle D$

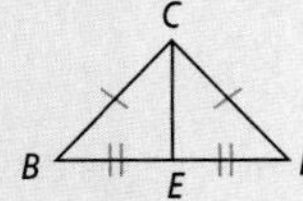

24. $\overline{KN} \cong \overline{ML}$

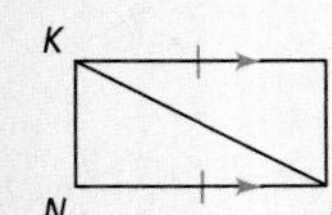

4-5 Isosceles and Equilateral Triangles

Quick Review

If two sides of a triangle are congruent, then the angles opposite those sides are also congruent by the **Isosceles Triangle Theorem.** If two angles of a triangle are congruent, then the sides opposite the angle are congruent by the **Converse of the Isosceles Triangle Theorem.**

Equilateral triangles are also equiangular.

Example

What is $m\angle G$?

Since $\overline{EF} \cong \overline{EG}$, $\angle F \cong \angle G$ by the Isosceles Triangle Theorem. So $m\angle G = 30$.

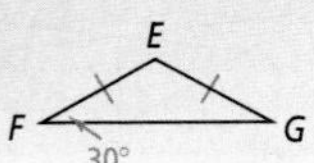

Exercises

Algebra Find the values of *x* and *y*.

25.

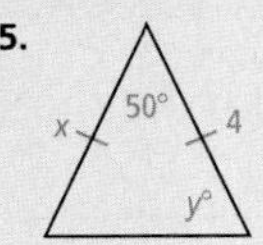

26.

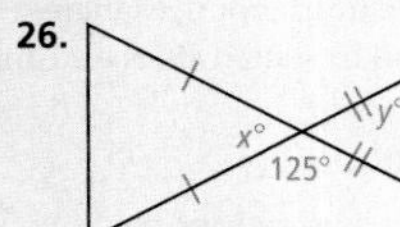

27.

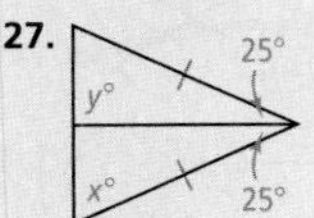

28.

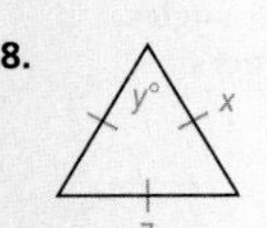

21. $\triangle TVY \cong \triangle YWX$ by AAS, so $\overline{TV} \cong \overline{YW}$ because corresp. parts of $\cong$ ▲s are $\cong$.

22. $\triangle BEC \cong \triangle DEC$ by ASA, so $\overline{BE} \cong \overline{DE}$ because corresp. parts of $\cong$ ▲s are $\cong$.

23. $\triangle BEC \cong \triangle DEC$ by SSS, so $\angle B \cong \angle D$ because corresp. parts of $\cong$ ▲s are $\cong$.

24. If $\parallel$ lines, alt. int. ∠s are $\cong$, so $\angle LKM \cong \angle NMK$. Then $\triangle LKM \cong \triangle NMK$ by SAS, and $\overline{KN} \cong \overline{ML}$ because corresp. parts of $\cong$ ▲s are $\cong$.

25. $x = 4$, $y = 65$

26. $x = 55$, $y = 62.5$

27. $x = 65$, $y = 90$

28. $x = 7$, $y = 60$

Answers

Chapter Review (continued)

29. $\overline{LN} \perp \overline{KM}$ (Given), so $\triangle KLN$ and $\triangle MLN$ are rt. ⚠s. $\overline{KL} \cong \overline{ML}$ (Given) and $\overline{LN} \cong \overline{LN}$ (Refl. Prop. of $\cong$), so $\triangle KLN \cong \triangle MLN$ by HL.

30. The given information on $\perp$ segments means $\triangle PSQ$ and $\triangle RQS$ are rt. ⚠s. You know $\overline{PQ} \cong \overline{RS}$ (Given) and $\overline{QS} \cong \overline{QS}$ (Refl. Prop. of $\cong$). So $\triangle PSQ \cong \triangle RQS$ by HL.

31. $\triangle AEC \cong \triangle ABD$ by SAS, ASA, or AAS.

32. $\triangle FIH \cong \triangle GHI$ by SAS.

33. $\triangle TAR \cong \triangle TSP$ by ASA.

4-6 Congruence in Right Triangles

Quick Review

If the hypotenuse and a leg of one right triangle are congruent to the hypotenuse and a leg of another right triangle, then the triangles are congruent by the **Hypotenuse-Leg (HL) Theorem.**

Example

Which two triangles are congruent? Explain.

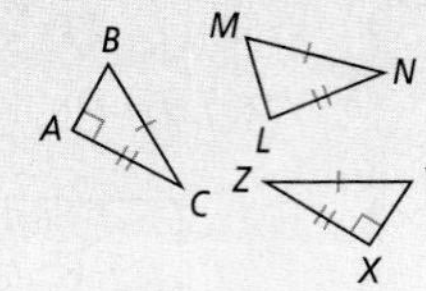

Since $\triangle ABC$ and $\triangle XYZ$ are right triangles with congruent legs, and $\overline{BC} \cong \overline{YZ}$, $\triangle ABC \cong \triangle XYZ$ by HL.

Exercises

Write a proof for each of the following.

29. Given: $\overline{LN} \perp \overline{KM}$, $\overline{KL} \cong \overline{ML}$

Prove: $\triangle KLN \cong \triangle MLN$

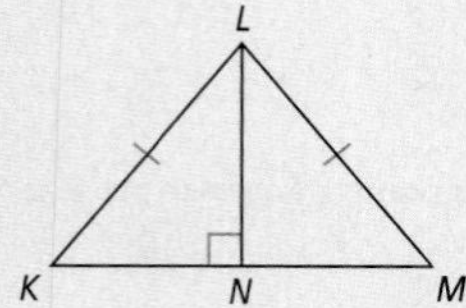

30. Given: $\overline{PS} \perp \overline{SQ}$, $\overline{RQ} \perp \overline{QS}$, $\overline{PQ} \cong \overline{RS}$

Prove: $\triangle PSQ \cong \triangle RQS$

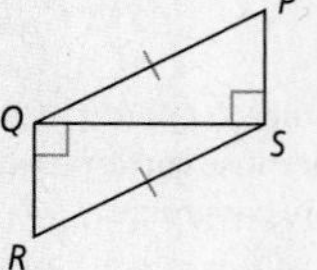

4-7 Congruence in Overlapping Triangles

Quick Review

To prove overlapping triangles congruent, you look for the common or shared sides and angles.

Example

Separate and redraw the overlapping triangles. Label the vertices.

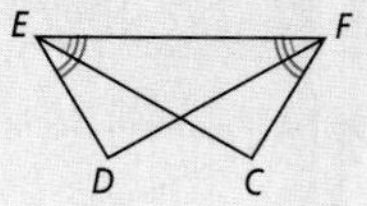

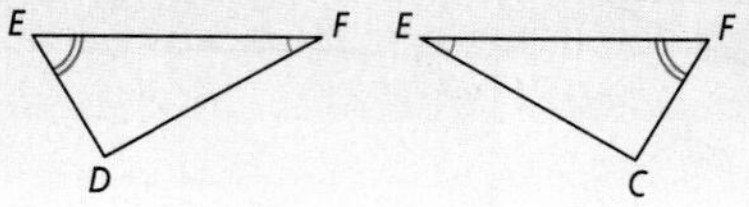

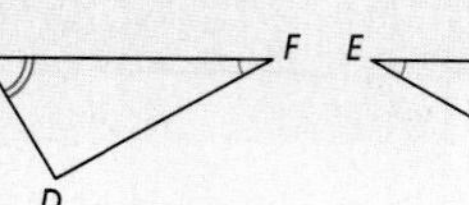

Exercises

Name a pair of overlapping congruent triangles in each diagram. State whether the triangles are congruent by SSS, SAS, ASA, AAS, or HL.

31.

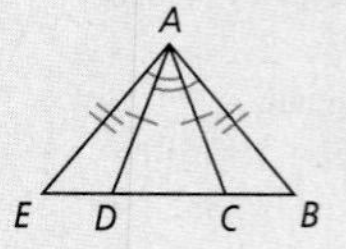

32.

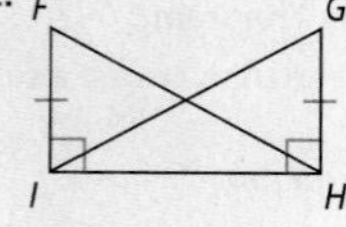

33.

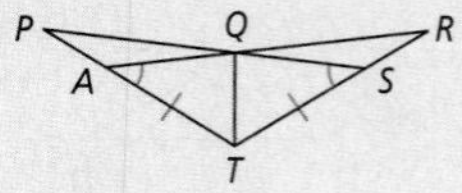

Chapter Test

MathXL® for School
Go to PowerGeometry.com

Do you know HOW?

Write a congruence statement for each pair of triangles.

1.

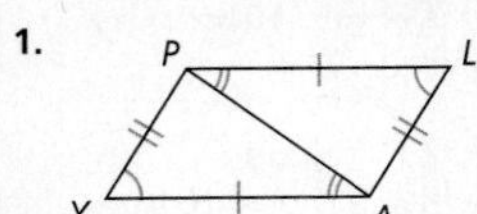

2.

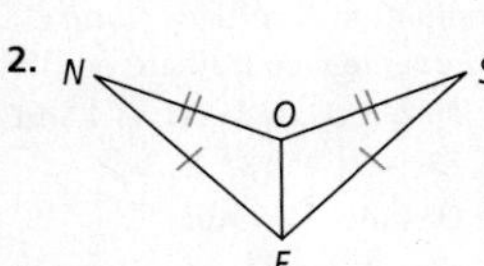

Which postulate or theorem, if any, could you use to prove the two triangles congruent? If not enough information is given, write *not enough information*.

3.

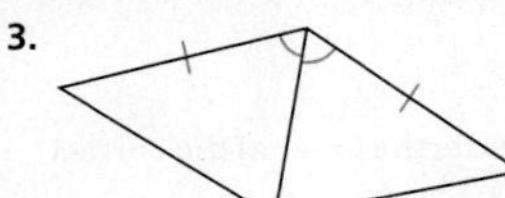

4.

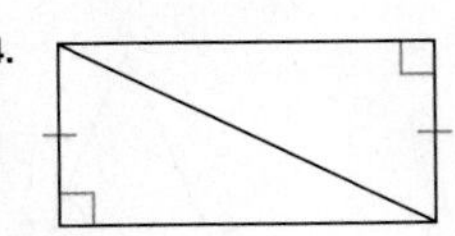

5.

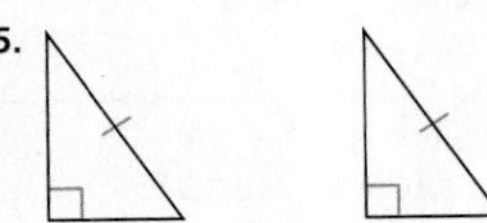

6.

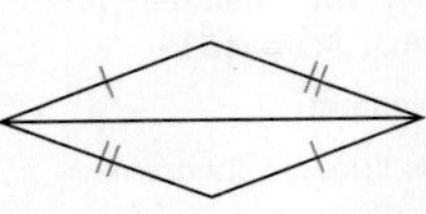

7.

8. $\triangle CEO \cong \triangle HDF$. Name all of the pairs of corresponding congruent parts.

9. Algebra Find the value of x.

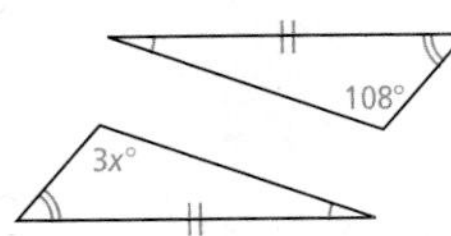

Name a pair of overlapping congruent triangles in each diagram. State whether the triangles are congruent by SSS, SAS, ASA, AAS, or HL.

10. Given: $\overline{CE} \cong \overline{DF}$, $\overline{CF} \cong \overline{DE}$

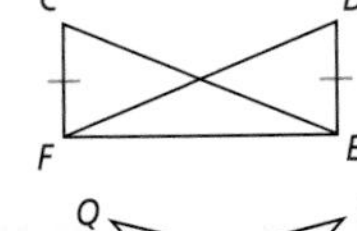

11. Given: $\overline{RT} \cong \overline{QT}$, $\overline{AT} \cong \overline{ST}$

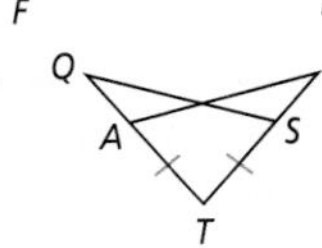

Do you UNDERSTAND?

12. Reasoning Isosceles $\triangle ABC$, with right $\angle B$, has a point D on $\overline{AC}$ such that $\overline{BD} \perp \overline{AC}$. What is the relationship between $\triangle ABD$ and $\triangle CBD$? Explain.

Write a proof for each of the following.

13. Given: $\overline{AT} \cong \overline{GS}$, $\overline{AT} \parallel \overline{GS}$
Prove: $\triangle GAT \cong \triangle TSG$

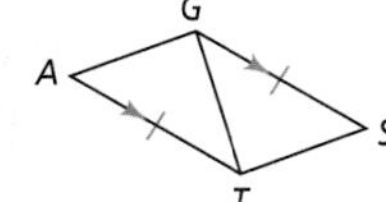

14. Given: $\overline{LN}$ bisects $\angle OLM$ and $\angle ONM$.
Prove: $\overline{ON} \cong \overline{MN}$

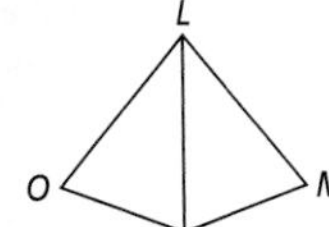

Answers

Chapter Test

1. Answers may vary. Sample: $\triangle PYA \cong \triangle ALP$
2. Answers may vary. Sample: $\triangle OEN \cong \triangle OES$
3. SAS
4. HL
5. not enough information
6. SSS
7. ASA
8. $\angle C \cong \angle H$, $\angle E \cong \angle D$, $\angle O \cong \angle F$, $\overline{CE} \cong \overline{HD}$, $\overline{EO} \cong \overline{DF}$, $\overline{CO} \cong \overline{HF}$
9. 36
10. $\triangle CFE \cong \triangle DEF$ by SSS.
11. $\triangle ATR \cong \triangle STQ$ by SAS.
12. Answers may vary. Sample: $\triangle ABD \cong \triangle CBD$ by AAS because $\angle A \cong \angle C$ (Isosc. △ Thm.), $\overline{BD} \cong \overline{BD}$ (Refl. Prop. of ≅), and the two △ have rt. ∠, which are ≅.
13. $\overline{AT} \parallel \overline{GS}$ (Given), so $\angle ATG \cong \angle SGT$ (Alt. int. ∠ are ≅.). $\overline{AT} \cong \overline{GS}$ (Given) and $\overline{GT} \cong \overline{GT}$ (Refl. Prop. of ≅), so $\triangle GAT \cong \triangle TSG$ by SAS.
14. $\overline{LN}$ bisects $\angle OLM$ and $\angle ONM$ (Given), so $\angle OLN \cong \angle MLN$ and $\angle ONL \cong \angle MNL$ (Def. of ∠ bisector). Also, $\overline{LN} \cong \overline{LN}$ (Refl. Prop. of ≅). So $\triangle OLN \cong \triangle MLN$ by ASA, and $\overline{ON} \cong \overline{MN}$ because corresp. parts of ≅ △ are ≅.

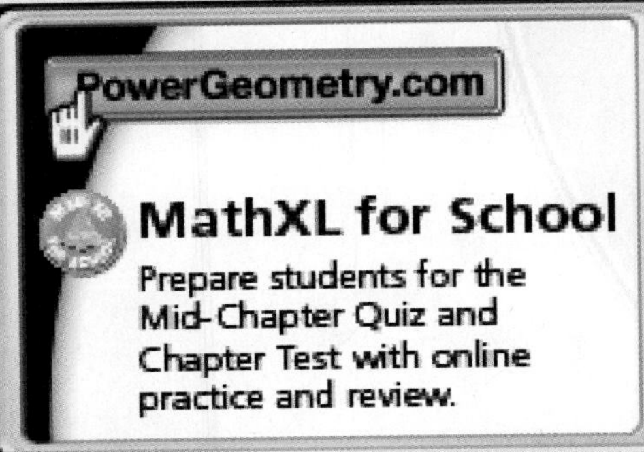

Item Number	Lesson
Example	4-2
1	4-5
2	4-1
3	4-4
4	4-3
5	2-6
6	3-3
7	3-7
8	4-4
9	3-8
10	1-8
11	3-5
12	1-8
13	3-2
14	4-1
15	3-7
16	1-4
17	4-2
18	2-1
19	1-8

4 Cumulative Test Prep

TIPS FOR SUCCESS

Some test questions ask you to compare geometric figures. Read the sample question at the right. Then follow the tips to answer it.

In the coordinate plane, the vertices of $\triangle ABC$ are $A(-2, 5)$, $B(2, 5)$, and $C(-2, 2)$. Which of the following are the side lengths for $\triangle DEF$, such that $\triangle ABC \cong \triangle DEF$?

Ⓐ $DE = 3, DF = 4, EF = 4$

Ⓑ $DE = 3, DF = 4, EF = 5$

Ⓒ $DE = 4, DF = 3, EF = 5$

Ⓓ $DE = 4, DF = 5, EF = 5$

TIP 1

Find the lengths of the sides of $\triangle ABC$.

TIP 2

You can use SSS to show triangles are congruent. Find the corresponding side lengths of $\triangle DEF$.

Think It Through

Vertices A and B have the same y-coordinate and vertices A and C have the same x-coordinate, so $AB = |-2 - 2| = |-4| = 4$ and $AC = |5 - 2| = |3| = 3$.
By the Distance Formula, $BC = \sqrt{(4)^2 + (3)^2} = \sqrt{25} = 5$. So $DE = AB = 4$, $DF = AC = 3$, and $EF = BC = 5$. The correct answer is C.

Vocabulary Builder

As you solve test items, you must understand the meanings of mathematical terms. Match each term with its mathematical meaning.

A. slope

B. perpendicular lines

C. polygon

D. conjecture

E. congruent

I. lines that intersect to form right angles

II. having the same size and shape

III. a conclusion reached by inductive reasoning

IV. a closed plane figure with at least three sides that are segments

V. the ratio of the vertical change (rise) to the horizontal change (run)

Multiple Choice

Read each question. Then write the letter of the correct answer on your paper.

1. Given: $\overline{DE} \parallel \overline{CB}$, $\angle ADE \cong \angle AED$

Prove: $\overline{AC} \cong \overline{AB}$

Proof: Since $\overline{DE} \parallel \overline{CB}$, $\angle ACB \cong \angle ADE$ and $\angle AED \cong \angle ABC$ by the Corresponding Angles Postulate. Since $\angle ADE \cong \angle AED$, $\angle ACB \cong \angle ABC$ by the Transitive Property. Which theorem or definition proves that $\overline{AC} \cong \overline{AB}$?

Ⓐ Isosceles Triangle Theorem

Ⓑ Converse of Isosceles Triangle Theorem

Ⓒ Alternate Interior Angles Theorem

Ⓓ Definition of congruent segments

Answers

Cumulative Test Prep

A. V
B. I
C. IV
D. III
E. II
1. B

2. Which statement must be true for two polygons to be congruent?

Ⓕ All the corresponding sides should be congruent.

Ⓖ All the corresponding sides and angles should be congruent.

Ⓗ All the corresponding angles should be congruent.

Ⓘ All sides in each polygon should be congruent.

3. If $\triangle ABC \cong \triangle CDA$, which of the following must be true?

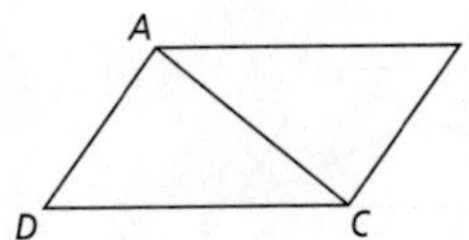

Ⓐ $\overline{AB} \cong \overline{CA}$

Ⓑ $\overline{BC} \cong \overline{DC}$

Ⓒ $\angle CAB \cong \angle ACD$

Ⓓ $\angle ABC \cong \angle CAD$

4. **Given:** $\angle 1 \cong \angle 2$, $\overline{AB} \cong \overline{AC}$

What additional information do you need to prove $\triangle ABD \cong \triangle ACE$ by AAS?

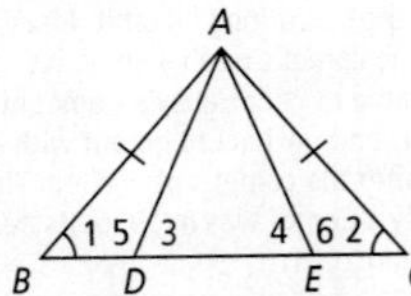

Ⓕ $\overline{AD} \cong \overline{AE}$

Ⓖ $\overline{BD} \cong \overline{EC}$

Ⓗ $\angle 5 \cong \angle 6$

Ⓘ $\overline{BE} \cong \overline{DC}$

5. Which of the following statements is true?

Ⓐ *Point*, *line*, and *plane* are undefined terms.

Ⓑ A theorem is an accepted statement of fact.

Ⓒ "Vertical angles are congruent" is a definition.

Ⓓ A postulate is a conjecture that is proven.

6. Which condition allows you to prove that $\ell \parallel m$?

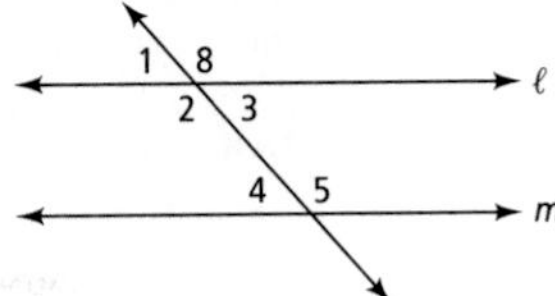

Ⓕ $\angle 1 \cong \angle 8$

Ⓖ $\angle 2 \cong \angle 8$

Ⓗ $\angle 3 \cong \angle 4$

Ⓘ $\angle 3 \cong \angle 5$

7. A line passes through $(3, -4)$ and has a slope of -5. How can you find the y-intercept of the graph?

Ⓐ Substitute -5 for b, -4 for x, and 3 for y in $y = mx + b$. Then solve for m, the y-intercept.

Ⓑ Substitute -5 for b, 3 for x, and -4 for y in $y = mx + b$. Then solve for m, the y-intercept.

Ⓒ Substitute -5 for m, -4 for x, and 3 for y in $y = mx + b$. Then solve for b, the y-intercept.

Ⓓ Substitute -5 for m, 3 for x, and -4 for y in $y = mx + b$. Then solve for b, the y-intercept.

8. **Given:** $\triangle RST \cong \triangle LMN$

Which reason could you use to prove that $\angle R \cong \angle L$?

Ⓕ SAS

Ⓖ SSS

Ⓗ ASA

Ⓘ Corresponding parts of congruent triangles are congruent.

9. Which equation represents the perpendicular bisector of the segment shown?

Ⓐ $y = x - 3$

Ⓑ $3x + 3y = 3$

Ⓒ $y = 3x$

Ⓓ $x + y = 3$

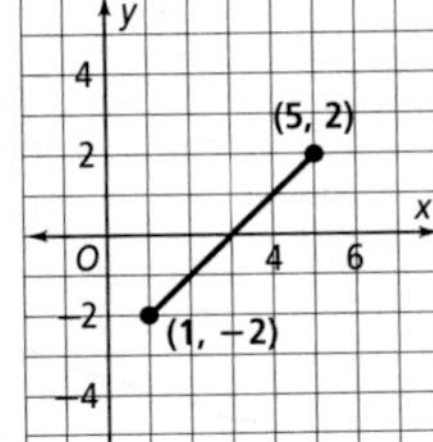

2. G
3. C
4. H
5. A
6. H
7. D
8. I
9. D

Answers

Cumulative Test Prep (continued)

10. H

11. 25

12. 48

13. 70

14. 3

15. 48

16. [2] Since an acute angle has a measure less than 90, the rays that form the angle form a "sharp point." Since an obtuse angle has a measure greater than 90, the rays that form the angle do not form a "sharp point."

[1] incomplete OR incorrect explanation

17. [2] $\overline{AE} \cong \overline{DE}$ and $\overline{EB} \cong \overline{EC}$ (Given), and $\angle AEB \cong \angle DEC$ (Vert. ∠s are ≅.). So $\triangle AEB \cong \triangle DEC$ by SAS.

[1] incomplete answer OR incorrect steps

18. [4] **a.** The comet should appear in 2137. Here is the information from the passage: 1835 to 1910: 75 years; 1910 to 1986: 76 years; 1986 to 2061: 75 years. The time between appearances seems to alternate between 75 and 76 years. The period after 2061 would be a 76-year period, so it should appear in $2061 + 76 = 2137$.

b. Answers may vary. Sample: Fairly confident; to be more confident, you would need to know the exact dates of appearances and a greater number of appearance dates.

[3] minor computational error in presenting the years for Halley's Comet

[2] incomplete answer for either part (a) or part (b)

[1] explanation missing for part (a) or part (b)

19. [4] For *LMNK*, $LM = KN = 4$ and $MN = LK = 2$, while for *PQRS*, $PQ = SR = 3$ and $PS = RQ = 2$. The length of rectangle *LMNK* is 4 units, while the length of rectangle *PQRS* is 3 units, so the rectangles are not ≅. Answers may vary. Sample: To make the rectangles ≅, you could change the vertices of *LMNK* so that *M* has coordinates (1, 5) and *N* has coordinates (1, 3). OR you could change the vertices of *PQRS* so that *R* has coordinates (1, −4) and *Q* has coordinates (3, −4).

[3] minor computational error

[2] incomplete explanation OR incorrect vertices

[1] incorrect or no explanation and incorrect vertices

10. One bag of garden soil covers approximately 16 ft^2. If it takes 16π ft of fencing to enclose a circular garden, how many bags of soil do you need to cover the garden?

(F) 4 bags (H) 13 bags

(G) 7 bags (I) 16 bags

GRIDDED RESPONSE

11. What is the value of *x* in the figure below?

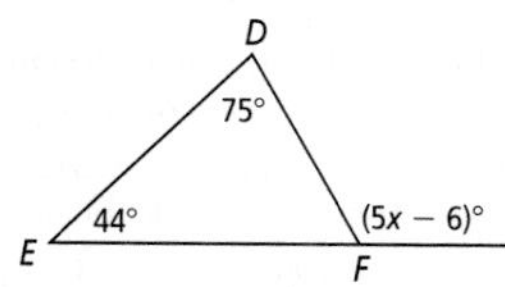

12. The length of a rectangle is seven more than three times its width. If the perimeter is 38 cm, what is the area, in square centimeters, of the rectangle?

13. What is the value of *x* in the figure below?

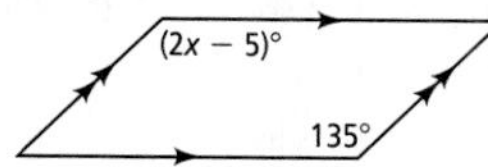

14. $ABCD \cong WXYZ$. What is *WX*?

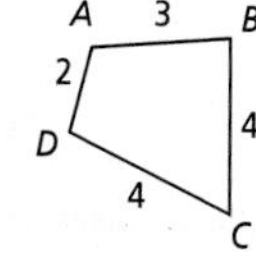

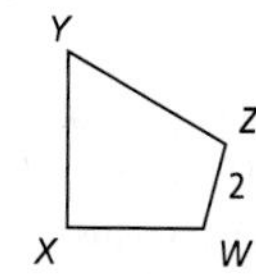

15. Amy is designing a ramp up to a 16-in.-high skateboarding platform, as shown on the graph below. If she wants the slope of the ramp to be $\frac{1}{3}$, what value should she choose for the *x*-coordinate at the top of the ramp?

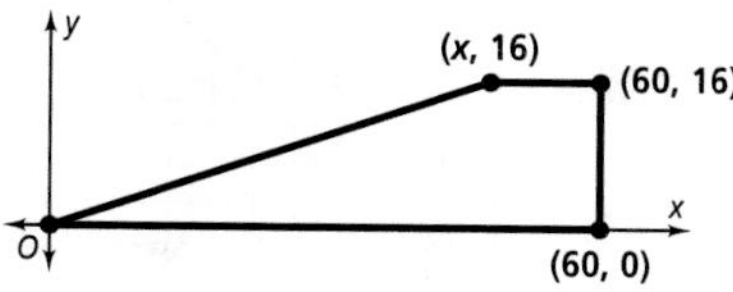

Short Response

16. Describe how the following everyday meanings of *acute* and *obtuse* help you to remember their mathematical meanings.

acute *adj.* Having a sharp point

obtuse *adj.* Not sharp or pointed; blunt

17. Write a proof for the following.

Given: $\overline{AE} \cong \overline{DE}$, $\overline{EB} \cong \overline{EC}$

Prove: $\triangle AEB \cong \triangle DEC$

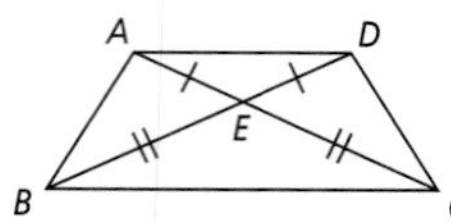

Extended Response

18. Read this excerpt from an online news article.

http://www.

Halley's Comet can be seen periodically at its *perihelion*, the shortest distance from the sun during its orbit. Mark Twain was born two weeks after the comet's perihelion. In his biography he said, "I came in with Halley's Comet in 1835. It is coming again next year, and I expect to go out with it." Twain died in 1910, the day after the comet's perihelion. The most recent sighting of Halley's Comet was in 1986. Its next appearance is expected in 2061.

a. Make a conjecture about the year in which Halley's Comet will appear after 2061. Explain your reasoning.

b. How confident are you about your conjecture? Explain.

19. The coordinates of the vertices of rectangle *LMNK* are *L*(−2, 5), *M*(2, 5), *N*(2, 3), and *K*(−2, 3). The coordinates of the vertices of rectangle *PQRS* are *P*(3, 0), *Q*(3, −3), *R*(1, −3), and *S*(1, 0). Are these two rectangles congruent? Explain why or why not. If not, how could you change the vertices of one of the rectangles to make them congruent?

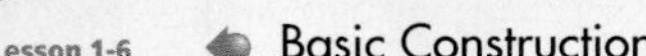

CHAPTER 5

Get Ready!

Lesson 1-6 **Basic Constructions**

Use a compass and straightedge for each construction.

1. Construct the perpendicular bisector of a segment.

2. Construct the bisector of an angle.

Lesson 1-7 **The Midpoint Formula and Distance Formula**

Find the coordinates of the midpoints of the sides of $\triangle ABC$. Then find the lengths of the three sides of the triangle.

3. $A(5, 1)$, $B(-3, 3)$, $C(1, -7)$

4. $A(-1, 2)$, $B(9, 2)$, $C(-1, 8)$

5. $A(-2, -3)$, $B(2, -3)$, $C(0, 3)$

Lesson 2-2 **Finding the Negation**

Write the negation of each statement.

6. The team won. **7.** It is not too late. **8.** $m\angle R > 60$

Lesson 3-7 **Slope**

Find the slope of the line passing through the given points.

9. $A(9, 6)$, $B(8, 12)$ **10.** $C(3, -2)$, $D(0, 6)$ **11.** $E(-3, 7)$, $F(-3, 12)$

Looking Ahead Vocabulary

12. The *altitude* of an airplane is the height of the airplane above ground. What do you think an *altitude of a triangle* is?

13. The *distance* between your home and your school is the length of the shortest path connecting them. How might you define the *distance between a point and a line* in geometry?

14. In Chapter 1, you learned the definition of a *midpoint* of a segment. What do you think a *midsegment* of a triangle is?

15. If two parties are happening at the same time, they are *concurrent*. What would it mean for three lines to be *concurrent*?

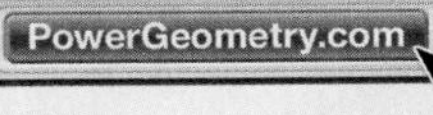

Answers

Get Ready!

1.

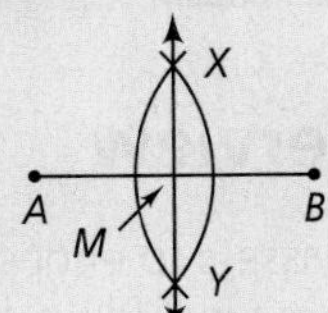

2.

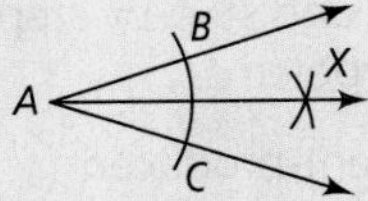

3. midpt. of $\overline{AB}$: (1, 2); midpt. of $\overline{BC}$: (−1, −2); midpt. of $\overline{AC}$: (3, −3); $AB = 2\sqrt{17}$; $BC = 2\sqrt{29}$; $AC = 4\sqrt{5}$

4. midpt. of $\overline{AB}$: (4, 2); midpt. of $\overline{BC}$: (4, 5); midpt. of $\overline{AC}$: (−1, 5); $AB = 10$; $BC = 2\sqrt{34}$; $AC = 6$

5. midpt. of $\overline{AB}$: (0, −3); midpt. of $\overline{BC}$: (1, 0); midpt. of $\overline{AC}$: (−1, 0); $AB = 4$; $BC = 2\sqrt{10}$; $AC = 2\sqrt{10}$

6. The team did not win.

7. It is too late.

8. $m\angle R \leq 60$

9. −6

10. $-\frac{8}{3}$

11. undefined

12. the length of a segment from a vertex to the opposite side *(Note: students will not know that this is the ⊥ segment yet, but encourage them to think about which is the shortest segment.)*

13. the length of a ⊥ segment from the point to the line

14. a segment that connects the midpts. of 2 sides of the △

15. The lines intersect at one point, or the lines have exactly one point in common.

Get Ready!

Assign this diagnostic assessment to determine if students have the prerequisite skills for Chapter 5.

Lesson	Skill
1-6	Basic Constructions
1-7	The Midpoint Formula and Distance Formula
2-2	Finding the Negation
3-7	Slope

To remediate students, select from these resources (available for every lesson).

- Online Problems (PowerGeometry.com)
- Reteaching (All-in-One Teaching Resources)
- Practice (All-in-One Teaching Resources)

Why Students Need These Skills

BASIC CONSTRUCTIONS Students will use construction techniques for generating perpendicular and angle bisectors.

THE MIDPOINT FORMULA AND DISTANCE FORMULA For triangles on the coordinate plane, these formulas are used to identify special segments in triangles.

FINDING THE NEGATION Negations are used to begin indirect proofs.

SLOPE Students will use slope to find relationships within triangles on the coordinate plane.

Looking Ahead Vocabulary

ALTITUDE OF A TRIANGLE Have students identify other objects that may involve altitude, such as a hot-air balloon.

DISTANCE BETWEEN A POINT AND A LINE Have students identify the shortest path between their location and a wall in the classroom.

MIDSEGMENT Have students identify other words that use the prefix *mid-*.

CONCURRENT Have students name events that may occur concurrently.

Chapter 5 Overview

UbD Understanding by Design

In Chapter 5 students expand on the skills learned in the previous chapter. In this chapter, students will develop the answers to the Essential Questions posed on the opposite page as they learn the concepts and skills listed below.

BIG idea Coordinate Geometry

ESSENTIAL QUESTION How do you use coordinate geometry to find relationships within triangles?

- Students will use the Midpoint Formula to find midsegments of triangles.
- Students will use the Distance Formula to examine relationships in triangles.

BIG idea Measurement

ESSENTIAL QUESTION How do you solve problems that involve measurements of triangles?

- Students will examine inequalities in one triangle.
- Students will examine inequalities in two triangles.

BIG idea Reasoning and Proof

ESSENTIAL QUESTION How do you write indirect proofs?

- Students will begin with the negation of the statement to be proved and will show a counterexample.

TN Checks for Understanding

3108.1.5 Use technology, hands-on activities, and manipulatives to develop the language and the concepts of geometry, including specialized vocabulary.
3108.1.10 Use visualization, spatial reasoning, and geometric modeling to solve problems.
3108.1.13 Use proofs to further develop and deepen the understanding of the study of geometry.
3108.4.11 Use the triangle inequality theorems to solve problems.
3108.4.14 Identify and use medians, midsegments, altitudes, angle bisectors, and perpendicular bisectors of triangles to solve problems.
3108.4.20 Prove key basic theorems in geometry.

CHAPTER 5

Relationships Within Triangles

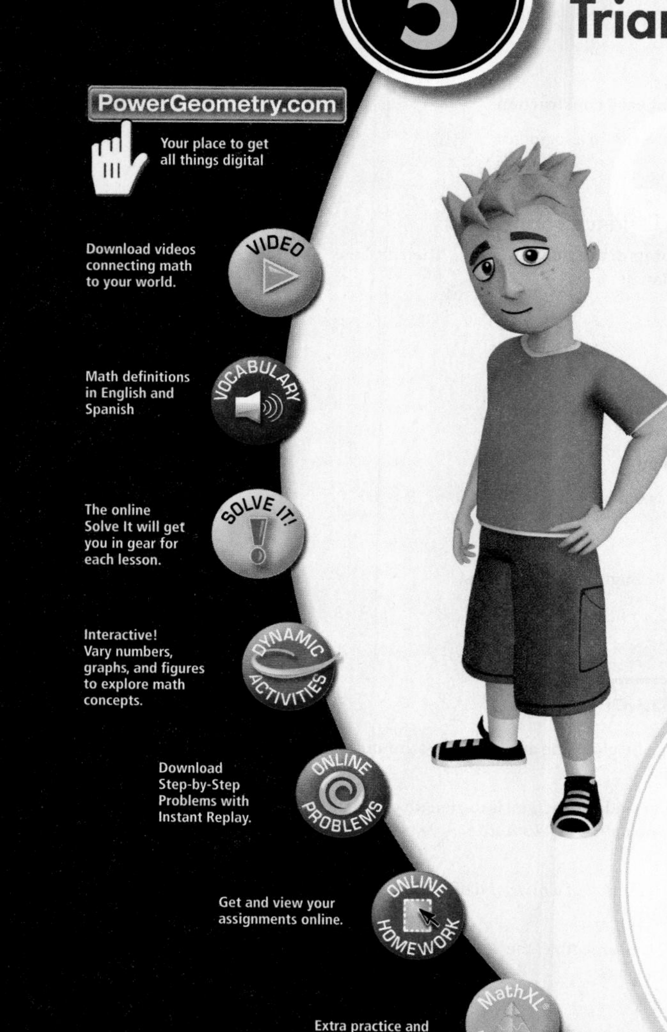

PowerGeometry.com
Your place to get all things digital
Download videos connecting math to your world.
VIDEO
Math definitions in English and Spanish
VOCABULARY
The online Solve It will get you in gear for each lesson.
SOLVE IT!
Interactive! Vary numbers, graphs, and figures to explore math concepts.
DYNAMIC ACTIVITIES
Download Step-by-Step Problems with Instant Replay.
ONLINE PROBLEMS
Get and view your assignments online.
ONLINE HOMEWORK
Extra practice and review online
MathXL FOR SCHOOL

Look at that roof of triangles! It's interesting how the support beams in each triangle meet at one point.

In this chapter, you will learn how special lines and segments in triangles relate.

Vocabulary

English/Spanish Vocabulary Audio Online:

English	Spanish
altitude of a triangle, *p. 310*	altura de un triángulo
centroid, *p. 309*	centroide
circumcenter, *p. 301*	circuncentro
concurrent, *p. 301*	concurrente
equidistant, *p. 292*	equidistante
incenter, *p. 303*	incentro
indirect proof, *p. 317*	prueba indirecta
median, *p. 309*	mediana
midsegment of a triangle, *p. 285*	segmento medio de un triángulo
orthocenter, *p. 311*	ortocentro

PowerGeometry.com

Chapter 5 Overview

Use these online assets to engage your students. These include support for the Solve It and step-by step solutions for Problems.

Show the student-produced video demonstrating relevant and engaging applications of the new concepts in this chapter.

Find online definitions for new terms in English and Spanish.

Start each lesson with an attention-getting Problem. View the Problem online with helpful hints.

BIG ideas

1 **Coordinate Geometry**
Essential Question How do you use coordinate geometry to find relationships within triangles?

2 **Measurement**
Essential Question How do you solve problems that involve measurements of triangles?

3 **Reasoning and Proof**
Essential Question How do you write indirect proofs?

Chapter Preview

 Increase students' depth of knowledge with interactive online activities.

 Show Problems from each lesson solved step by step. Instant replay allows students to go at their own pace when studying online.

 Assign homework to individual students or to an entire class.

 Prepare students for the Mid-Chapter Quiz and Chapter Test with online practice and review.

My Math Video

FACILITATE Use this photo to discuss the concept of special segments in triangles. In the photo, the triangles in the roof are supported by segments that join the vertices to the opposite side and meet at a single point in the interior of the triangle. In this chapter, students will learn about special segments in triangles that are concurrent at a single point.

Q How would you describe a single support beam in the photo? **[The beams appear to connect a vertex of the triangle to a point on the opposite side from the vertex.]**

Q Based on what you know about segments and angles from previous chapters, how can you classify the beams in the photo? **[The beams appear to be angle bisectors.]**

Q What do you notice about all three beams in the photo? **[The beams all meet at a single point in the interior of the triangle.]**

EXTENSION

To confirm the observations students make about the photos, have each student draw a large triangle (encourage different shapes). Have students construct the bisectors of the angles. Ask students to describe what they notice about the segments they construct.

CHAPTER 5

RELATIONSHIPS WITHIN TRIANGLES

Math Background

UbD

Coordinate Geometry

BIG idea A coordinate system in a plane is formed by two perpendicular number lines, called the *x*- and *y*-axes, and the quadrants they form. It is possible to verify some complex truths using deductive reasoning in combination with Distance, Midpoint, and Slope formulas.

ESSENTIAL UNDERSTANDING

5-1 The midsegment of a triangle can be used to uncover relationships within a triangle.

Reasoning and Proof

BIG idea Definitions establish meanings and remove possible misunderstanding. Other truths are more complex and difficult to see. It is often possible to verify complex truths by reasoning from simpler ones by using deductive reasoning.

ESSENTIAL UNDERSTANDINGS

5-2 Triangles play a key role in relationships involving perpendicular bisectors and angle bisectors.

5-3 to 5-4 There are special parts of a triangle that are always concurrent. A triangle's three perpendicular bisectors are always concurrent, as are a triangle's three angle bisectors, its three medians, and its three altitudes.

5-5 In indirect reasoning, all possibilities are considered and then all but one are proved false. The remaining possibility must be true.

5-6 The measures of the angles of a triangle are related to the lengths of the opposite sides.

5-7 In triangles that have two pairs of congruent sides, there is a relationship between the included angles and the third pair of sides.

Measurement

BIG idea Some attributes of geometric figures, such as length, area, volume, and angle measure, are measurable. Units are used to describe these attributes.

ESSENTIAL UNDERSTANDINGS

5-2 Geometric figures such as angle bisectors and perpendicular bisectors can be used to cut the measure of an angle or segment in half.

5-3 Angle bisectors and segment bisectors can be used in triangles to determine various angle and segment measures.

5-4 The length of medians and altitudes in a triangle can be determined given the measures of other triangle segments.

Special Segments in Triangles

Five special segments are defined in this chapter.

Midsegment is a segment that connects the midpoints of two sides.

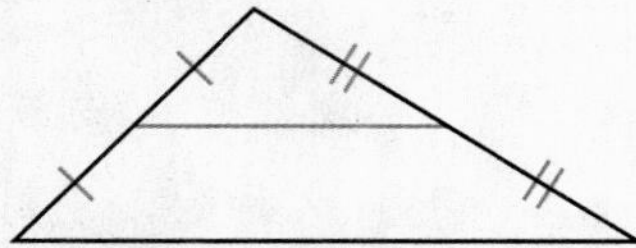

Perpendicular Bisector is a segment that bisects a side and is perpendicular to that side.

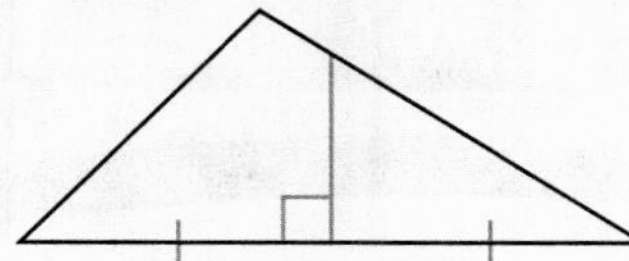

Angle Bisector is a segment that bisects an angle.

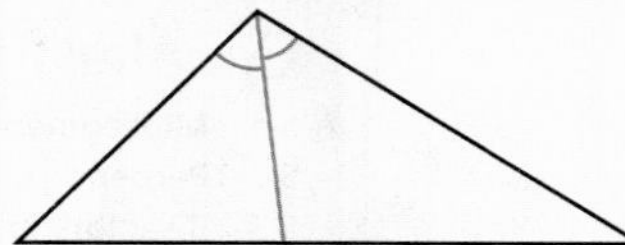

Median is a segment that connects a vertex to the midpoint of the opposite side.

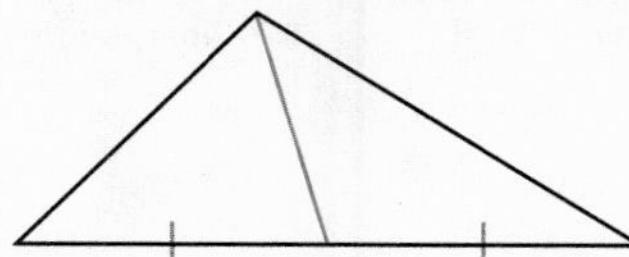

Altitude is a segment from a vertex, perpendicular to the opposite side.

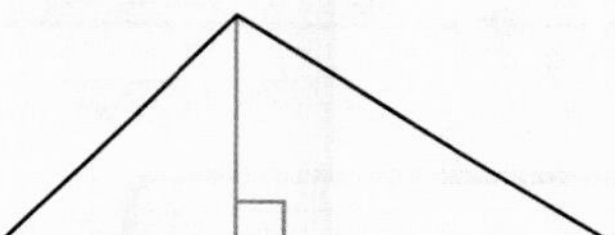

Common Errors With Special Segments in Triangles

Special segments can often be difficult to distinguish from each other. Students should use angle and segment congruency marks and right angle marks (as above) to help make clear the purpose of a given segment.

Indirect Proof

Indirect proof involves assuming the opposite of a statement you wish to prove, then showing a contradiction of the given information. Indirect proof is usually used in situations where there are only two possibilities: the given is true or the given is false. If there are more possibilities, each must be contradicted in order to use an indirect proof.

For example:

Given: Two distinct lines in a plane do not intersect.

Prove: The two lines are parallel.

Two distinct lines in a plane are either parallel, or they are not parallel. Since only two possibilites exist, an indirect proof can be used.

1. Assume the opposite of what you want to prove:

   The two lines are *not* parallel.

2. Show that this assumption leads to a contradiction:

   If they are *not* parallel, then they intersect.

   This contradicts the given information that they do not intersect.

3. Conclude the assumption is false.

   It is false that the two lines are not parallel.

   There is only one other possibility: the lines are parallel.

Common Errors With Indirect Proof

Sometimes it is not safe to assume that there are only two possibilities. To demonstrate this, consider the example above. Notice that it was given that the two lines were in a plane. If the two lines were in three-dimensional space, there would be a third possibility: the two lines might be skew. In this case, to prove that the two lines are parallel by indirect proof, students would also need to have sufficient given information to show that the lines being skew leads to a contradiction, otherwise they could not prove the lines parallel from the given information.

The Triangle Inequality Theorem

It is possible to have three line segments but not be able to use those segments to form a triangle. Consider the following three segments:

One segment is longer than the other two combined and therefore cannot be used to form a triangle. The Triangle Inequality Theorem states: the sum of the lengths of any two sides of a triangle must be greater than the length of the third side.

The best way to check this is to see if the sum of the shorter two segments is greater than the longest segment.

Can the side lengths 6, 8, and 9 form a triangle?

Check that the sum of the lengths of the two shorter sides is greater than the length of the longest side.

$6 + 8 > 9$

The side lengths 6, 8, and 9 can form a triangle.

Can the side lengths 12, 15, and 32 form a triangle?

Check that the sum of the lengths of the two shorter sides is greater than the length of the longest side.

$12 + 15 < 32$

Because the sum of the lengths of the two shorter sides is not greater than the length of the longest side, the side lengths 12, 15, and 32 cannot form a triangle.

Common Errors With The Triangle Inequality Theorem

Sometimes students have trouble accepting the fact that any three given sides may not form a triangle. Giving them experiences in trying to form triangles using pieces of spaghetti before studying the inequality theorems will help them go from the concrete to the abstract.

When checking to see if three segments can be combined to form a triangle, students must make sure they are comparing the sums of the lengths of the two shorter sides to the length of the longest side.

RELATIONSHIPS WITHIN TRIANGLES

Pacing and Assignment Guide

		TRADITIONAL			BLOCK
Lesson	**Teaching Day(s)**	**Basic**	**Average**	**Advanced**	**Block**
5-1	**1**	Problems 1–3 Exs. 7–26 all, 28–30 all, 32–42 even, 49–57	Problems 1–3 Exs. 7–25 odd, 26–45, 49–57	Problems 1–3 Exs. 7–25 odd, 26–57	**Day 1** Problems 1–3 Exs. 7–25 odd, 26–45, 49–57
5-2	**1**	Problems 1–3 Exs. 6–17 all, 18–22 even, 23, 25, 28–32 even, 39–47	Problems 1–3 Exs. 7–17 odd, 18–36, 39–47	Problems 1–3 Exs. 7–17 odd, 18–47	Problems 1–3 Exs. 7–17 odd, 18–36, 39–47
5-3	**1**	Problems 1–3 Exs. 7–20, 23, 26–29, 33–40	Problems 1–3 Exs. 7–17 odd, 18–29, 33–40	Problems 1–3 Exs. 7–17 odd, 18–40	**Day 2** Problems 1–3 Exs. 7–17 odd, 18–29, 33–40
5-4	**1**	Problems 1–3 Exs. 8–16 all, 18, 20–22 all, 24–34 even, 40–47	Problems 1–3 Exs. 9–15 odd, 17–34, 40–47	Problems 1–3 Exs. 9–15 odd, 17–47	Problems 1–3 Exs. 9–15 odd, 17–34, 40–47
5-5	**1**	Problems 1–2 Exs. 4–13 all, 31–40	Problems 1–2 Exs. 5–13 odd, 31–40	Problems 1–2 Exs. 5–13 odd, 31–40	**Day 3** Problems 1–3 Exs. 5–13 odd, 15–28, 31–40
	2	Problem 3 Exs. 14–18 all, 20, 23, 24–28 even	Problem 3 Exs. 15–28	Problem 3 Exs. 15–30	
5-6	**1**	Problems 1–3 Exs. 6–20 all, 46–55	Problems 1–3 Exs. 7–19 odd, 46–55	Problems 1–3 Exs. 7–19 odd, 46–55	**Day 4** Problems 1–3 Exs. 7–31 odd, 33–41, 46–55
	2	Problems 4–5 Exs. 21–34 all, 36–40 even, 41	Problems 4–5 Exs. 21–31 odd, 33–41	Problems 4–5 Exs. 21–31 odd, 33–45	
5-7	**1**	Problems 1–2 Exs. 6–10, 26–39	Problems 1–2 Exs. 7–9 odd, 26–39	Problems 1–2 Exs. 7–9 odd, 26–39	**Day 1** Problems 1–4 Exs. 7–15 odd, 16–23, 26–39
	2	Problems 3–4 Exs. 11–20, 22	Problems 3–4 Exs. 11–15 odd, 16–23	Problems 3–4 Exs. 11–15 odd, 16–25	
Review	**1**	Chapter 5 Review	Chapter 5 Review	Chapter 5 Review	**Day 1** Chapter 5 Review Chapter 5 Test
Assess	**1**	Chapter 5 Test	Chapter 5 Test	Chapter 5 Test	
Total		**12 Days**	**12 Days**	**12 Days**	**6 Days**

Note: Pacing does not include Concept Bytes and other feature pages. Please see individual feature pages for pacing.

Resources

KEY

I = Interactive asset at PowerGeometry.com
E = Editable master at PowerGeometry.com
P = Available in Print
T = Available as a Transparency
M = Master at PowerGeometry.com
✓ = CD-ROM

	For the Chapter	5-1	5-2	5-3	5-4	5-5	5-6	5-7
Planning								
Teacher Center Online Planner & Grade Book	I	I	I	I	I	I	I	I
Interactive Learning & Guided Instruction								
My Math Video	I							
Solve It!		I TM	I TM	I TM	I TM	I TM	I TM	I TM
Student Companion (SP)*		P M	P M	P M	P M	P M	P M	
Vocabulary Support		I P M	I P M	I P M	I P M	I P M	I P M	I P M
Got It? Support		I P	I P	I P	I P	I P	I P	I P
Dynamic Activity			I	I	I		I	
Online Problems		I	I	I	I	I	I	I
Additional Problems		M	M	M	M	M	M	M
English Language Learner Support (TR)		E P M	E P M	E P M	E P M	E P M	E P M	E P M
Activities, Games, and Puzzles		E M	E M	E M	E M	E M	E M	E M
Teaching With TI Technology With CD-ROM		✓ P		✓ P			✓ P	
TI-Nspire™ Support CD-ROM		✓	✓	✓	✓	✓	✓	✓
Lesson Check & Practice								
Student Companion (SP)*		P M	P M	P M	P M	P M	P M	P M
Lesson Check Support		I P	I P	I P	I P	I P	I P	I P
Practice and Problem Solving Workbook (SP)		P	P	P	P	P	P	P
Think About a Plan (TR)*		E P M	E P M	E P M	E P M	E P M	E P M	E P M
Practice Form G (TR)*		E P M	E P M	E P M	E P M	E P M	E P M	E P M
Standardized Test Prep (TR)*		P M	P M	P M	P M	P M	P M	P M
Practice *Form K* (TR)*		E P M	E P M	E P M	E P M	E P M	E P M	E P M
Extra Practice	E M							
Find the Errors!	M							
Enrichment (TR)		E P M	E P M	E P M	E P M	E P M	E P M	E P M
Answers and Solutions CD-ROM	✓	✓	✓	✓	✓	✓	✓	✓
Assess & Remediate								
ExamView CD-ROM	✓	✓	✓	✓	✓	✓	✓	✓
Lesson Quiz		I TM	I TM	I TM	I TM	I TM	I TM	I TM
Quizzes and Tests *Form G* (TR)*	E P M				E P M			E P M
Quizzes and Tests *Form K* (TR)*	E P M				E P M			E P M
Reteaching (TR)*		E P M	E P M	E P M	E P M	E P M	E P M	E P M
Performance Tasks (TR)*	P M							
Cumulative Review (TR)*	P M							
Progress Monitoring Assessments	I P M							

(TR) Available in All-In-One Teaching Resources *Spanish available

Guided Instruction

PURPOSE To use geometry software to investigate properties of triangle midsegments

PROCESS Students will

- use geometry software to construct a triangle and its midsegment.
- measure the midsegment and the sides of triangles.
- make conjectures about the properties of midsegments of triangles.

DISCUSS The Exercises allow students to further examine midsegment properties by constructing all three midsegments of a triangle and studying the four smaller triangles that are formed from the three midsegments.

Activity

In this Activity students relate the midsegment of a triangle to the third side of the triangle.

Q How do you know that the midsegment and the third side of the triangle are parallel? **[Their slopes are equal.]**

SYNTHESIZING

For early finishers, have students work with a partner or in small groups to verify their conjectures using grid paper.

Concept Byte: Investigating Midsegments

Use With Lesson 5-1

TECHNOLOGY

Activity

Step 1 Use geometry software to draw and label $\triangle ABC$. Construct the midpoints D and E of $\overline{AB}$ and $\overline{AC}$. Connect the midpoints with a *midsegment*.

Step 2 Measure $\overline{DE}$ and $\overline{BC}$. Calculate $\frac{DE}{BC}$.

Step 3 Measure the slopes of $\overline{DE}$ and $\overline{BC}$.

Step 4 Manipulate the triangle and observe the lengths and slopes of $\overline{DE}$ and $\overline{BC}$.

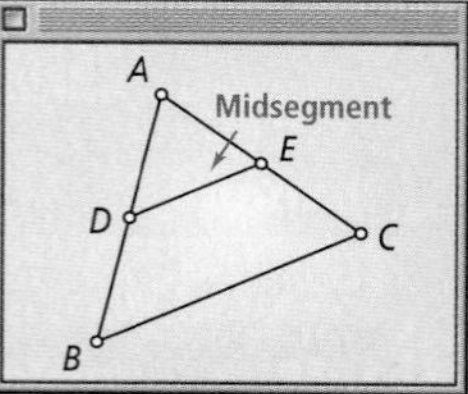

Exercises

1. **Make a Conjecture** Make conjectures about the lengths and slopes of midsegments.
2. Construct the midpoint F of $\overline{BC}$. Then construct the other two midsegments of $\triangle ABC$. Test whether these midsegments support your conjectures in Exercise 1.
3. $\triangle ABC$ and the three midsegments form four small triangles.
   a. Measure the sides of the four small triangles and list those that you find are congruent.
   b. **Make a Conjecture** Make a conjecture about the four small triangles formed by a triangle and its three midsegments.

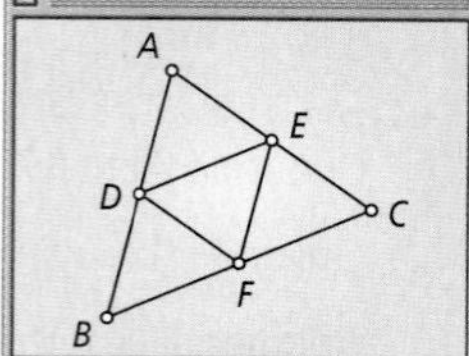

For the remaining exercises, assume your conjectures in Exercises 1 and 3 are true.

4. What can you say about the areas of the four small triangles in the window above?
5. a. How does $\triangle ABC$ compare to each small triangle in area?
   b. How does $\triangle ABC$ compare to each small triangle in perimeter?
6. Construct the three midsegments of $\triangle DEF$. Label this triangle $\triangle GHI$.
   a. How does $\triangle ABC$ compare to $\triangle GHI$ in area?
   b. How does $\triangle ABC$ compare to $\triangle GHI$ in perimeter?
   c. Suppose you construct the midsegment triangle inside $\triangle GHI$. How would $\triangle ABC$ compare to this third midsegment triangle in area and perimeter?

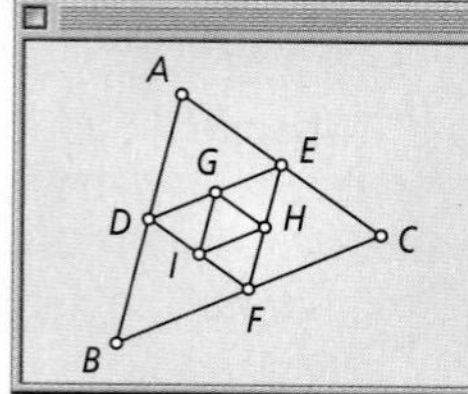

Answers

Exercises

1. The length of a midsegment of a △ is half the length of the third side of the △ and its slope is the same as the slope of the third side.
2. yes

3a. $\overline{DE} \cong \overline{BF} \cong \overline{FC}$, $\overline{EF} \cong \overline{AD} \cong \overline{DB}$, $\overline{DF} \cong \overline{AE} \cong \overline{EC}$

b. A triangle's three midsegments divide the △ into four ≅ △s.

4. The areas are equal.

5a. The area of $\triangle ABC$ is 4 times the area of each small △.

b. The perimeter of $\triangle ABC$ is 2 times the perimeter of each small △.

6a. The area of $\triangle ABC$ is 16 times the area of $\triangle GHI$.

b. The perimeter of $\triangle ABC$ is 4 times the perimeter of $\triangle GHI$.

c. The area of $\triangle ABC$ will be 64 times the area of the new △, and its perimeter will be 8 times the perimeter of the new △.

5-1 Midsegments of Triangles

TN State Performance Indicator
SPI 3108.4.12 Solve problems involving congruence, similarity, proportional reasoning and/or scale factor of two similar figures or solids.

Objective To use properties of midsegments to solve problems

You know about midpoints, and you know about segments. This problem combines the two.

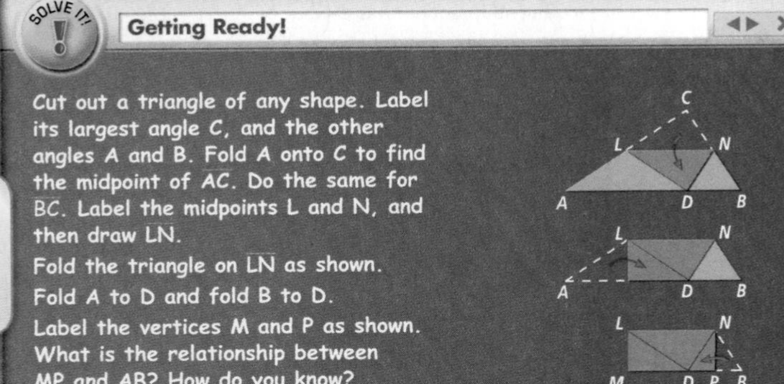

Getting Ready!

Cut out a triangle of any shape. Label its largest angle C, and the other angles A and B. Fold A onto C to find the midpoint of AC. Do the same for BC. Label the midpoints L and N, and then draw LN.
Fold the triangle on $\overline{LN}$ as shown.
Fold A to D and fold B to D.
Label the vertices M and P as shown.
What is the relationship between MP and AB? How do you know?
What conjecture can you make about the relationship between LN and AB?

C
L
N
A
D
B
M
P

Lesson Vocabulary
- midsegment of a triangle

In the Solve It, $\overline{LN}$ is a midsegment of $\triangle ABC$. A **midsegment of a triangle** is a segment connecting the midpoints of two sides of the triangle.

Essential Understanding There are two special relationships between a midsegment of a triangle and the third side of the triangle.

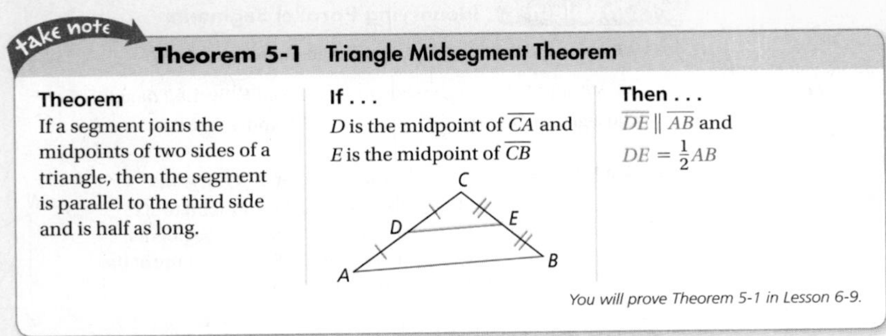

Take note — Theorem 5-1 Triangle Midsegment Theorem

Theorem	If . . .	Then . . .
If a segment joins the midpoints of two sides of a triangle, then the segment is parallel to the third side and is half as long.	D is the midpoint of $\overline{CA}$ and E is the midpoint of $\overline{CB}$	$\overline{DE} \parallel \overline{AB}$ and $DE = \frac{1}{2}AB$

C
D
E
A
B

You will prove Theorem 5-1 in Lesson 6-9.

1 Interactive Learning

Solve It!

PURPOSE To identify characteristics of midsegments

PROCESS Students may cut out and fold the triangle as instructed or use properties of isosceles triangles using $\triangle ALD$ and $\triangle BND$ to discover the relationship of LN and AB.

FACILITATE

Q What kind of triangles are $\triangle ALD$ and $\triangle BND$ **[Isosceles; $\overline{AL} \cong \overline{LD}$ and $\overline{BN} \cong \overline{ND}$]**

Q After both A and B are folded to D, what is the relationship between MP and AB? **[$MP = \frac{1}{2}AD + \frac{1}{2}BD = \frac{1}{2}AB$]**

Q What is the apparent relationship between $\overline{LN}$ and $\overline{AB}$? **[$LN = \frac{1}{2}AB$]**

ANSWER See Solve It in Answers on next page.

CONNECT THE MATH Students should begin to see that the midsegment is related to the third side of the triangle. In the lesson, students learn that the midsegment is half the length of the third side and is parallel to the third side.

2 Guided Instruction

Take Note

Have students draw the other two midsegments of the triangle. Then they can use the Triangle Midsegment Theorem to practice writing statements about the relationships between the midsegments they drew and the sides of the triangle.

5-1 Preparing to Teach

BIG idea Coordinate Geometry

ESSENTIAL UNDERSTANDINGS
- To draw a midsegment, students must find the midpoint of two sides of a triangle and draw the segment joining the midpoints.
- The midsegment of a triangle is related to the third side in two ways.

Math Background

The midsegment is one of a number of special segments in a triangle. Because of the relationship to the side lengths of the triangle, midsegments create a second triangle within the original triangle that is similar to the original triangle. Midsegments are used to create a type of fractal because they represent an iterative process of shortening side lengths. The Midsegment Theorem is proved using coordinate geometry. There are different proofs of this theorem, and a few appear later in the book. Later in this text, a midsegment is also presented in the discussion of trapezoids.

Support Student Learning

Use the **Geometry Companion** to engage and support students during instructions. See Lesson Resources at the end of this lesson for details.

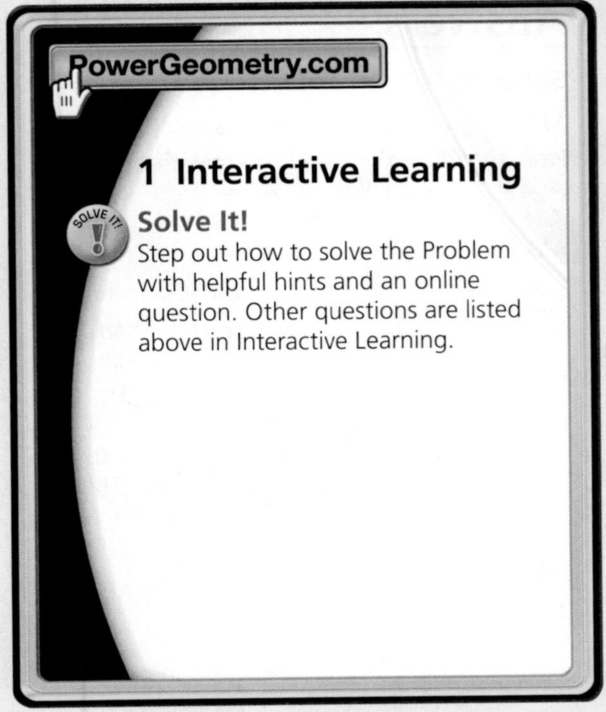

PowerGeometry.com
1 Interactive Learning
Solve It!
Step out how to solve the Problem with helpful hints and an online question. Other questions are listed above in Interactive Learning.

Here's Why It Works

The problem given in the Here's Why It Works is a specific problem that demonstrates the Triangle Midsegment Theorem. Students can be challenged by having them draw a triangle in a coordinate plane with general coordinates $A(0, 0)$, $B(a, b)$, and $C(c, 0)$. Students will be able to recreate the proof of the Triangle Midsegment Theorem using these general coordinates. They will be able to show that the same two properties are always true. This proof is in Chapter 6.

Q What will having the coordinates of the points D and E allow you to verify? **[Sample: I will be able to find the length of $\overline{DE}$, which I will need to compare to the length of $\overline{AB}$.]**

Q What will having the slopes of $\overline{DE}$ and $\overline{AB}$ allow you to verify? **[Sample: I can verify that the lines are parallel because I will know if their slopes are the same.]**

Problem 1

Q The midsegment $\overline{RS}$ is parallel to which side of $\triangle DEF$? **[$\overline{DF}$]**

Q The midsegment $\overline{TS}$ is parallel to which side of $\triangle DEF$? **[$\overline{DE}$]**

Got It?

ERROR PREVENTION

Have students draw the triangle and label each point as given in the instructions. Have them look for the side not connected to the midsegment.

Here's Why It Works You can verify that the Triangle Midsegment Theorem works for a particular triangle. Use the following steps to show that $\overline{DE} \parallel \overline{AB}$ and that $DE = \frac{1}{2}AB$ for a triangle with vertices at $A(4, 6)$, $B(6, 0)$, and $C(0, 0)$, where D and E are the midpoints of $\overline{CA}$ and $\overline{CB}$.

Step 1 Use the Midpoint Formula, $M = \left(\frac{x_1 + x_2}{2}, \frac{y_1 + y_2}{2}\right)$, to find the coordinates of D and E.

The midpoint of $\overline{CA}$ is $D\left(\frac{0+4}{2}, \frac{0+6}{2}\right) = D(2, 3)$.

The midpoint of $\overline{CB}$ is $E\left(\frac{0+6}{2}, \frac{0+0}{2}\right) = E(3, 0)$.

Step 2 To show that the midsegment $\overline{DE}$ is parallel to the side $\overline{AB}$, find the slope, $m = \frac{y_2 - y_1}{x_2 - x_1}$, of each segment.

slope of $\overline{DE} = \frac{0-3}{3-2} = \frac{-3}{1} = -3$ slope of $AB = \frac{0-6}{6-4} = \frac{-6}{2} = -3$

Step 3 To show $DE = \frac{1}{2}AB$, use the Distance Formula, $d = \sqrt{(x_2 - x_1)^2 + (y_2 - y_1)^2}$ to find DE and AB.

$DE = \sqrt{(3-2)^2 + (0-3)^2} = \sqrt{1+9} = \sqrt{10}$ $AB = \sqrt{(6-4)^2 + (0-6)^2} = \sqrt{4+36} = \sqrt{40} = 2\sqrt{10}$

Since $\sqrt{10} = \frac{1}{2}(2\sqrt{10})$, you know that $DE = \frac{1}{2}AB$.

Problem 1 **Identifying Parallel Segments**

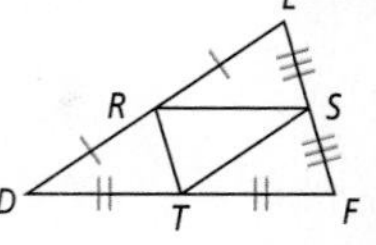

Think

How do you identify a midsegment?
Look for indications that the endpoints of a segment are the midpoints of a side of the triangle.

What are the three pairs of parallel segments in $\triangle DEF$?

$\overline{RS}$, $\overline{ST}$, and $\overline{TR}$ are the midsegments of $\triangle DEF$. By the Triangle Midsegment Theorem, $\overline{RS} \parallel \overline{DF}$, $\overline{ST} \parallel \overline{ED}$, and $\overline{TR} \parallel \overline{FE}$.

Got It? **1. a.** In $\triangle XYZ$, A is the midpoint of $\overline{XY}$, B is the midpoint of $\overline{YZ}$, and C is the midpoint of $\overline{ZX}$. What are the three pairs of parallel segments?

b. Reasoning What is $m\angle VUO$ in the figure at the right? Explain your reasoning.

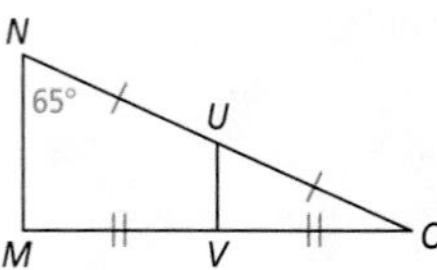

Answers

Solve It!

$MP = \frac{1}{2}AB$; answers may vary. Sample: From the folding process you know that $AM = MD$ and $DP = PB$. $AB = AM + MD + DP + PB$, so $AB = MD + MD + DP + DP$ or $AB = 2(MD + DP) = 2MP$. Then $\frac{1}{2}AB = \frac{1}{2}(2MP) = MP$. Conjecture: LN is the same length as MP, so $LN = \frac{1}{2}AB$.

Got It?

1a. $\overline{AC} \parallel \overline{YZ}$, $\overline{CB} \parallel \overline{XY}$, $\overline{AB} \parallel \overline{XZ}$

b. 65; $\overline{UV}$ is a midsegment of $\triangle NOM$, so by the $\triangle$ Midseg. Thm., $\overline{UV} \parallel \overline{NM}$. Then $m\angle VUO = m\angle N = 65$ because corresp. ∠s of ∥ lines are ≅.

PowerGeometry.com

2 Guided Instruction

Each Problem is worked out and supported online.

Problem 1
Identifying Parallel Segments
Animated

Problem 2
Finding Lengths
Animated

Problem 3
Using a Midsegment of a Triangle
Animated

Support in Geometry Companion
- Vocabulary
- Key Concepts
- Got It?

Problem 2 Finding Lengths

Plan

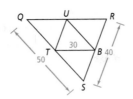

Which relationship stated in the Triangle Midsegment Theorem should you use?
You are asked to find lengths, so use the relationship that refers to the lengths of a midsegment and the third side.

In $\triangle QRS$, T, U, and B are midpoints. What are the lengths of $\overline{TU}$, $\overline{UB}$, and $\overline{QR}$?

Use the relationship

length of a midsegment $= \frac{1}{2}$(length of the third side)

to write an equation about the length of each midsegment.

$TU = \frac{1}{2}SR$	$UB = \frac{1}{2}QS$	$TB = \frac{1}{2}QR$
$= \frac{1}{2}(40)$	$= \frac{1}{2}(50)$	$30 = \frac{1}{2}QR$
$= 20$	$= 25$	$60 = QR$

Got It? 2. In the figure at the right, $AD = 6$ and $DE = 7.5$. What are the lengths of $\overline{DC}$, $\overline{AC}$, $\overline{EF}$, and $\overline{AB}$?

You can use the Triangle Midsegment Theorem to find lengths of segments that might be difficult to measure directly.

Problem 3 Using a Midsegment of a Triangle

Think

Why does the geologist find the length of $\overline{CD}$?
$\overline{CD}$ is a midsegment of $\triangle AEB$, so the geologist can use its length to find AB, the distance across the sinkhole.

Environmental Science **A geologist wants to determine the distance, AB, across a sinkhole. Choosing a point E outside the sinkhole, she finds the distances AE and BE. She locates the midpoints C and D of $\overline{AE}$ and $\overline{BE}$ and then measures $\overline{CD}$. What is the distance across the sinkhole?**

CD is a midsegment of $\triangle AEB$.

$CD = \frac{1}{2}AB$	$\triangle$ Midsegment Thm.
$46 = \frac{1}{2}AB$	Substitute 46 for CD.
$92 = AB$	Multiply each side by 2.

The distance across the sinkhole is 92 ft.

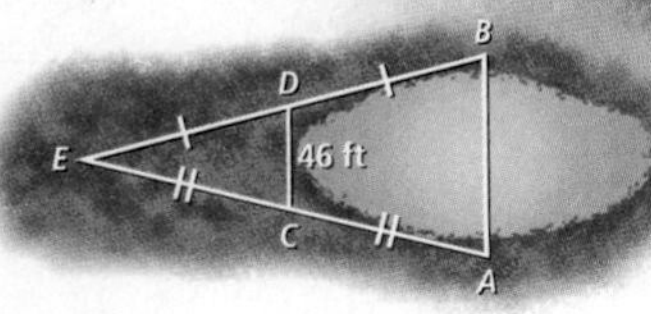

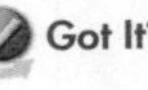

Got It? 3. $\overline{CD}$ is a bridge being built over a lake, as shown in the figure at the right. What is the length of the bridge?

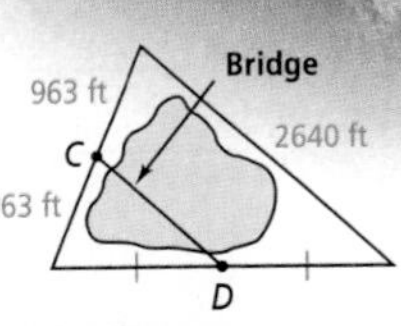

Problem 2

Q What is the relationship between the length of a midsegment and the length of the side to which it is parallel? **[The midsegment is half the length of the third side.]**

Q How can you find the length of a side given the length of the midsegment parallel to it? **[Multiply the length of the midsegment by 2.]**

Got It?

Have students describe the relationship between each of the segments in the question and the segment with the given length.

Problem 3

Q What type of segment is $\overline{CD}$? Justify your answer. **[$\overline{CD}$ is a midsegment because it connects the midpoints of two sides of the triangle.]**

Q What is the relationship between CD and AB? **[$CD = \frac{1}{2}AB$]**

Got It?

Have students classify the segment which represents the new bridge. Ask them to state the relationship between the length of the new bridge and the side of the triangle to which the bridge will be parallel.

Additional Problems

1. What are the three pairs of parallel segments in $\triangle DEF$?

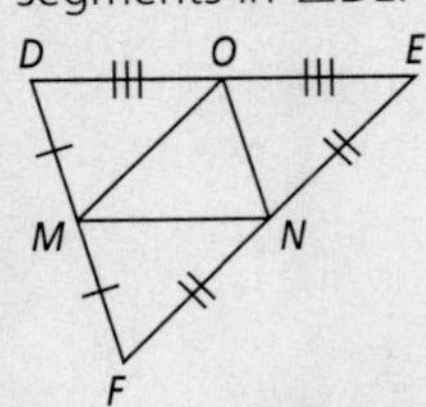

ANSWER $\overline{DE} \parallel \overline{MN}$, $\overline{DF} \parallel \overline{ON}$, $\overline{EF} \parallel \overline{OM}$

2. In $\triangle RST$, G, H, and K are midpoints. If $RS = 28$, $GH = 20$, and $RH = 22$, what is the length of KH, ST, and GK?

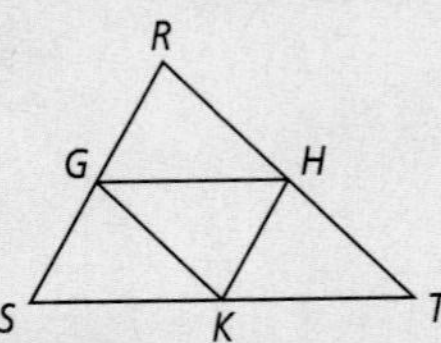

ANSWER $KH = 14$, $ST = 40$, $GK = 22$

3. What is the distance across the river?

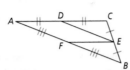

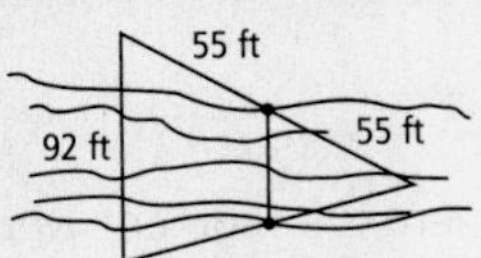

ANSWER 46 feet

Answers

Got It? (continued)

2. $DC = 6$; $AC = 12$; $EF = 6$; $AB = 15$

3. 1320 ft

3 Lesson Check

Do you know HOW?

- If students have difficulty with Exercise 1, then have them review Problem 1.

Do you UNDERSTAND?

- If students have difficulty with Exercise 5, then have them review the Solve It.

Close

Q How is the length of a midsegment of a triangle related to the length of the third side? **[The length of the midsegment is half the length of the third side.]**

Q In the coordinate plane, how are the slopes of a midsegment and the third side of the triangle related? Explain. **[They are the same because the two segments are parallel.]**

Lesson Check

Do you know HOW?

Use the figure at the right for Exercises 1–3.

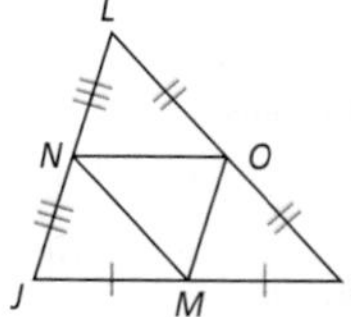

1. Which segment is parallel to $\overline{JK}$?
2. If $LK = 46$, what is NM?
3. If $JK = 5x + 20$ and $NO = 20$, what is the value of x?

Do you UNDERSTAND?

4. **Vocabulary** How does the term *midsegment* describe the segments discussed in this lesson?
5. **Reasoning** If two noncollinear segments in the coordinate plane have slope 3, what can you conclude?
6. **Error Analysis** A student sees this figure and concludes that $\overline{PL} \parallel \overline{NO}$. What is the error in the student's reasoning?

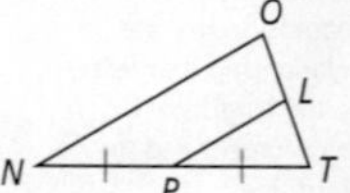

Practice and Problem-Solving Exercises

A Practice

Identify three pairs of parallel segments in each diagram. See Problem 1.

7.

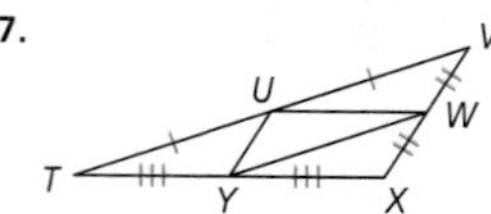

8.

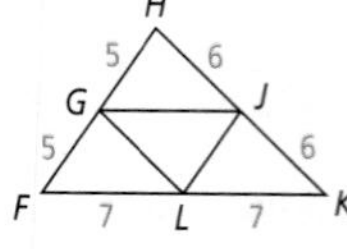

Name the segment that is parallel to the given segment.

9. $\overline{AB}$
10. $\overline{BC}$
11. $\overline{EF}$
12. $\overline{CA}$
13. $\overline{GE}$
14. $\overline{FG}$

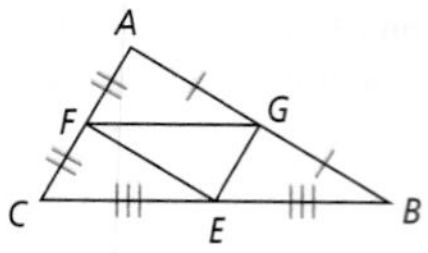

Points E, D, and H are the midpoints of the sides of $\triangle TUV$. $UV = 80$, $TV = 100$, and $HD = 80$. See Problem 2.

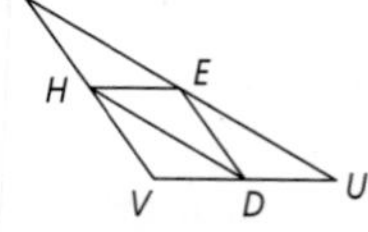

15. Find HE.
16. Find ED.
17. Find TU.
18. Find TE.

Algebra **Find the value of x.**

19.

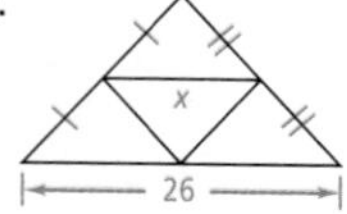

20.

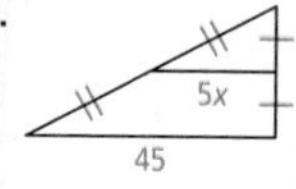

21.

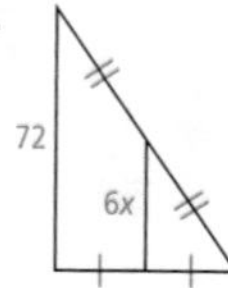

PowerGeometry.com

3 Lesson Check

For a digital lesson check, use the Got It questions.

Support in Geometry Companion

- Lesson Check

4 Practice

Assign homework to individual students or to an entire class.

Answers

Lesson Check

1. $\overline{NO}$
2. 23
3. 4
4. A midsegment is a segment whose endpoints are the midpts. of two sides of a triangle.
5. The segments are $\parallel$.
6. The student is assuming that L is the midpt. of $\overline{OT}$, which is not given.

Practice and Problem-Solving Exercises

7. $\overline{UY} \parallel \overline{XV}$, $\overline{UW} \parallel \overline{TX}$, $\overline{YW} \parallel \overline{TV}$
8. $\overline{GJ} \parallel \overline{FK}$, $\overline{JL} \parallel \overline{FH}$, $\overline{GL} \parallel \overline{HK}$
9. $\overline{FE}$
10. $\overline{FG}$
11. $\overline{AB}$
12. $\overline{EG}$
13. $\overline{AC}$
14. $\overline{BC}$
15. 40
16. 50
17. 160
18. 80
19. 13
20. 4.5
21. 6

Algebra Find the value of x.

22. 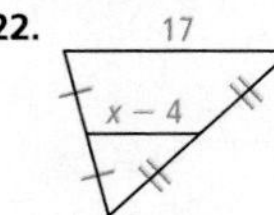

23.

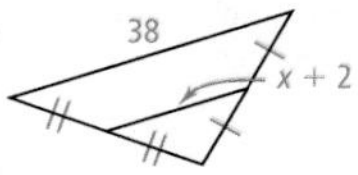

24. 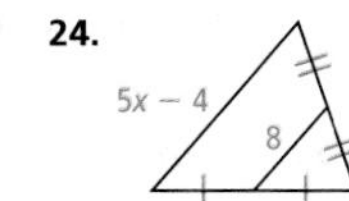

25. Surveying A surveyor needs to measure the distance PQ across the lake. Beginning at point S, she locates the midpoints of $\overline{SQ}$ and $\overline{SP}$ at M and N. She then measures $\overline{NM}$. What is PQ?

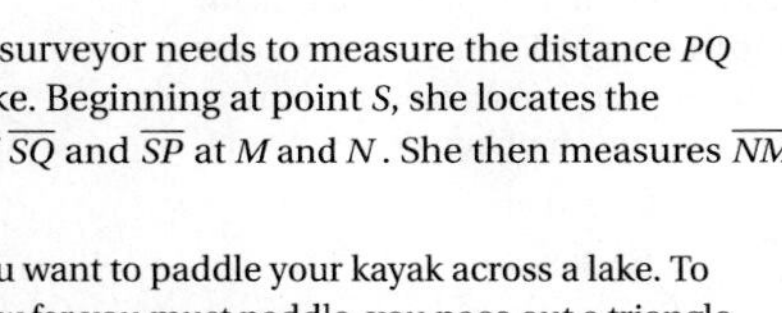

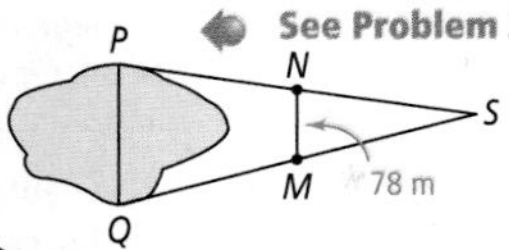

See Problem 3.

26. Kayaking You want to paddle your kayak across a lake. To determine how far you must paddle, you pace out a triangle, counting the number of strides, as shown.

a. If your strides average 3.5 ft, what is the length of the longest side of the triangle?

b. What distance must you paddle across the lake?

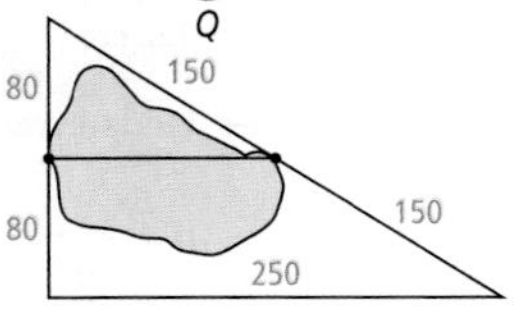

27. Architecture The triangular face of the Rock and Roll Hall of Fame in Cleveland, Ohio, is isosceles. The length of the base is 229 ft 6 in. Each leg is divided into four congruents parts by the red segments. What is the length of the white segment? Explain your reasoning.

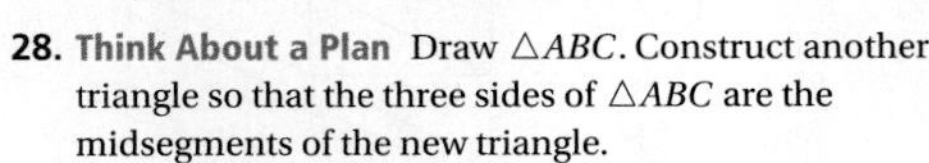

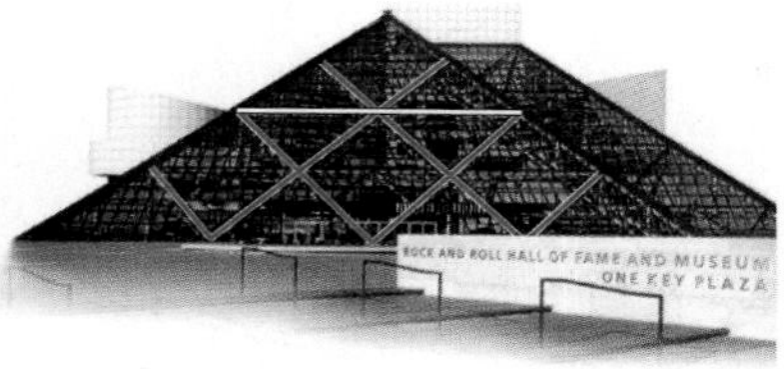

28. Think About a Plan Draw $\triangle ABC$. Construct another triangle so that the three sides of $\triangle ABC$ are the midsegments of the new triangle.

- Can you visualize or sketch the final figure?
- Which segments in your final construction will be parallel?

29. Writing In the figure at the right, $m\angle QST = 40$. What is $m\angle QPR$? Explain how you know.

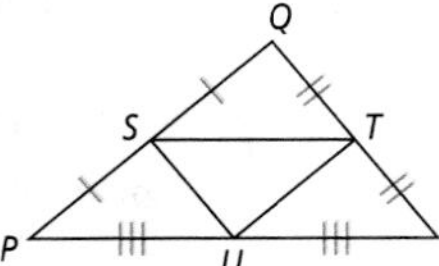

30. Coordinate Geometry The coordinates of the vertices of a triangle are $E(1, 2)$, $F(5, 6)$, and $G(3, -2)$.

a. Find the coordinates of H, the midpoint of $\overline{EG}$, and J, the midpoint of $\overline{FG}$.

b. Show that $\overline{HJ} \parallel \overline{EF}$.

c. Show that $HJ = \frac{1}{2}EF$.

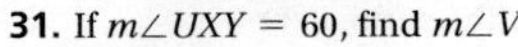

***X* is the midpoint of $\overline{UV}$. *Y* is the midpoint of $\overline{UW}$.**

31. If $m\angle UXY = 60$, find $m\angle V$.

32. If $m\angle W = 45$, find $m\angle UYX$.

33. If $XY = 50$, find VW.

34. If $VW = 110$, find XY.

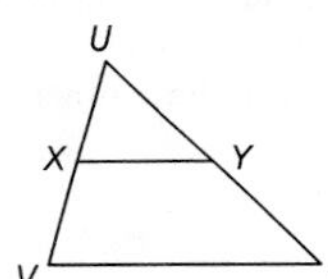

4 Practice

ASSIGNMENT GUIDE

Basic: 7–26 all, 28–30 all, 32–42 even

Average: 7–25 odd, 26–45

Advanced: 7–25 odd, 26–48

Standardized Test Prep: 49–52

Mixed Review: 53–57

Reasoning exercises have blue headings.

Applications exercises have red headings.

EXERCISE 30: Use the Think About a Plan worksheet in the **Practice and Problem Solving Workbook** (also available in the Teaching Resources in print and online) to further support students' development in becoming independent learners.

HOMEWORK QUICK CHECK

To check students' understanding of key skills and concepts, go over Exercises 11, 23, 28, 29, and 30.

22. 12.5

23. 17

24. 4

25. 156 m

26a. 1050 ft

b. 437.5 ft

27. 114 ft 9 in.; because the red segments divide the legs into four ≅ parts, the white segment divides each leg into two ≅ parts. The white segment is a midsegment of the triangular face of the building, so its length is one half the length of the base.

28. 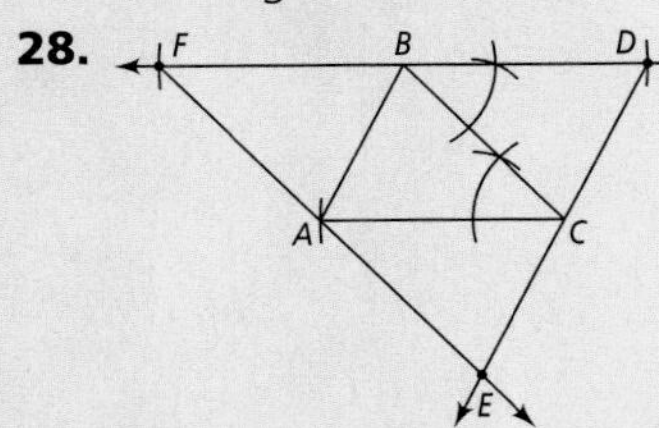

$FD \parallel AC$, $DE \parallel AB$, $FE \parallel BC$

29. 40; $\overline{ST}$ is a midsegment of $\triangle PQR$, so by the △ Midseg. Thm., $\overline{ST} \parallel \overline{PR}$. Then $m\angle QPR = m\angle QST$ because corresp. ⦞ of ∥ lines are ≅.

30a. $H(2, 0)$; $J(4, 2)$

b. Slope of $\overline{HJ} = \frac{2-0}{4-2} = 1$; slope of $\overline{EF} = \frac{6-2}{5-1} = 1$; the slopes are =, so $\overline{HJ} \parallel \overline{EF}$.

c. $HJ = \sqrt{(2-4)^2 + (0-2)^2} = \sqrt{8} = 2\sqrt{2}$ and $EF = \sqrt{(1-5)^2 + (2-6)^2} = \sqrt{32} = 4\sqrt{2}$, so $HJ = \frac{1}{2}EF$.

31. 60

32. 45

33. 100

34. 55

Answers

Practice and Problem-Solving Exercises (continued)

35. 18.5
36. 37
37. C
38. 60
39. 50
40. 10
41. $x = 6$; $y = 6.5$
42. 52
43. 24
44. 26
45. Draw $\overrightarrow{CA}$. Find P on $\overrightarrow{CA}$ such that $CA = AP$. Draw $\overline{PD}$. Construct the ⊥ bisector of $\overline{PD}$. Label the intersection point B. Draw $\overline{AB}$. This is a midsegment of $\triangle CPD$. According to the △ Midsegment Thm., $\overline{AB} \parallel \overline{CD}$ and $AB = \frac{1}{2}CD$.
46. 30 cm

$\overline{IJ}$ is a midsegment of $\triangle FGH$. $IJ = 7$, $FH = 10$, and $GH = 13$. Find the perimeter of each triangle.

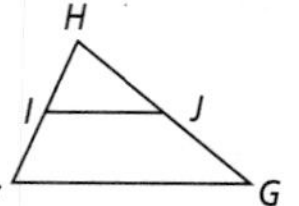

35. $\triangle IJH$

36. $\triangle FGH$

37. Kite Design You design a kite to look like the one at the right. Its diagonals measure 64 cm and 90 cm. You plan to use ribbon, represented by the purple rectangle, to connect the midpoints of its sides. How much ribbon do you need?

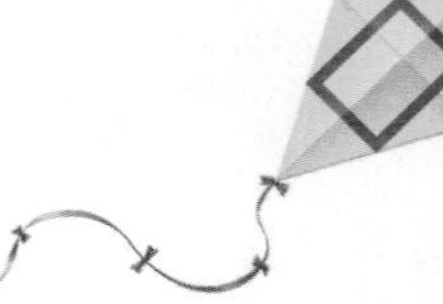

Ⓐ 77 cm　　Ⓒ 154 cm
Ⓑ 122 cm　　Ⓓ 308 cm

Algebra **Find the value of each variable.**

38.

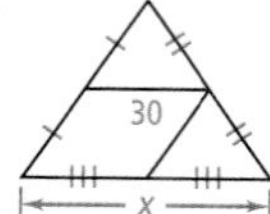

39.

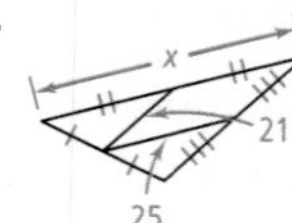

40.

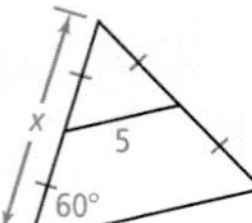

41.

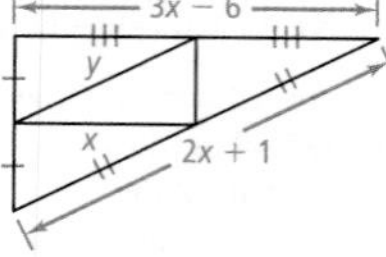

Use the figure at the right for Exercises 42–44.

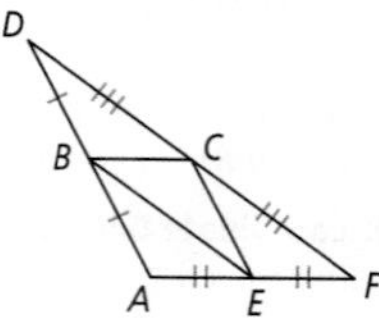

42. $DF = 24$, $BC = 6$, and $DB = 8$. Find the perimeter of $\triangle ADF$.

43. Algebra If $BE = 2x + 6$ and $DF = 5x + 9$, find DF.

44. Algebra If $EC = 3x - 1$ and $AD = 5x + 7$, find EC.

45. Open-Ended Explain how you could use the Triangle Midsegment Theorem as the basis for this construction: Draw $\overline{CD}$. Draw point A not on $\overline{CD}$. Construct $\overline{AB}$ so that $\overline{AB} \parallel \overline{CD}$ and $AB = \frac{1}{2}CD$.

Challenge

46. Reasoning In the diagram at the right, K, L, and M are the midpoints of the sides of $\triangle ABC$. The vertices of the three small purple triangles are the midpoints of the sides of $\triangle KBL$, $\triangle AKM$, and $\triangle MLC$. The perimeter of $\triangle ABC$ is 24 cm. What is the perimeter of the shaded region?

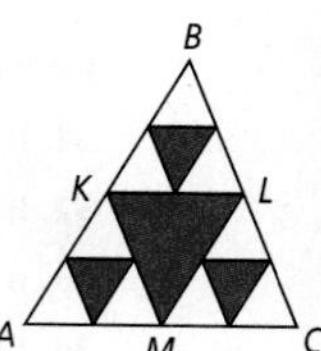

47. **Coordinate Geometry** In $\triangle GHJ$, $K(2, 3)$ is the midpoint of $\overline{GH}$, $L(4, 1)$ is the midpoint of $\overline{HJ}$, and $M(6, 2)$ is the midpoint of $\overline{GJ}$. Find the coordinates of G, H, and J.

48. Complete the Prove statement and then write a proof.
Proof **Given:** In $\triangle VYZ$, S, T, and U are midpoints.
Prove: $\triangle YST \cong \triangle TUZ \cong \triangle SVU \cong$ __?__

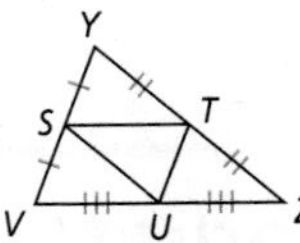

Standardized Test Prep

GRIDDED RESPONSE

SAT/ACT

Use the figure at the right for Exercises 49 and 50. Your home is at point *H*. Your friend lives at point *F*, the midpoint of Elm Street. Elm Street intersects Beech Street and Maple Street at their midpoints.

49. Your friend walks to school by going east on Elm and then turning right on Maple. How far in miles does she walk?

50. You walk your dog along this route: Walk from home to Elm along Maple. Walk west on Elm to Beech, south on Beech to the library, and east on Oak to school. Then walk back home along Maple. How far in miles do you walk?

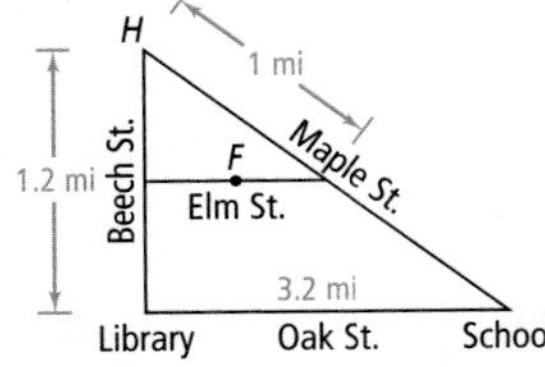

For Exercises 51 and 52, $\triangle ABC$ is a triangle in which $m\angle A = 30$ and $m\angle B = 70$. P, Q, and R are the midpoints of $\overline{AB}$, $\overline{BC}$, and $\overline{CA}$, respectively.

51. What is the measure, in degrees, of $\angle RPQ$?

52. If $QP = 2x + 17$ and $CA = x + 97$, what is CA?

Mixed Review

Use the figure at the right for Exercises 53 and 54.

See Lesson 4-7.

53. List all the pairs of congruent triangles that you can find in the figure.

54. **Given:** $\overline{FD} \cong \overline{FE}$, $\overline{BF} \cong \overline{CF}$, $\angle 1 \cong \angle 2$
Prove: $\overline{AB} \cong \overline{AC}$

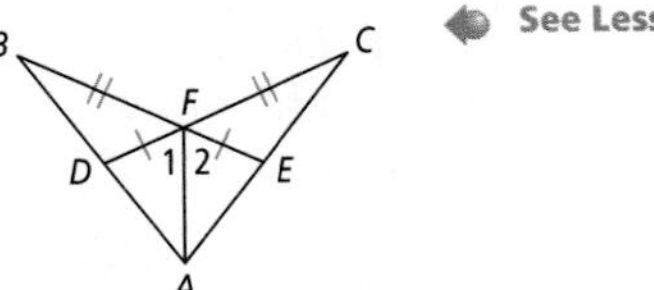

Get Ready! To prepare for Lesson 5-2, do Exercises 55–57.

$\overrightarrow{TM}$ **bisects $\angle STU$ so that $m\angle STM = 5x + 4$ and $m\angle MTU = 6x - 2$.**

See Lesson 1-5.

55. Find the value of x.

56. Find $m\angle STU$.

57. Draw acute $\angle E$. Construct the bisector of $\angle E$.

See Lesson 1-6.

47. $G(4, 4)$; $H(0, 2)$; $J(8, 0)$

48. $\triangle UTS$; answers may vary. Sample: $VS = SY = \frac{1}{2}VY$, $VU = UZ = \frac{1}{2}VZ$, and $YT = TZ = \frac{1}{2}YZ$ by the def. of midpt. Also $ST = \frac{1}{2}VZ$, $SU = \frac{1}{2}YZ$, and $TU = \frac{1}{2}VY$ by the $\triangle$ Midsegment Theorem. So $\triangle YST \cong \triangle TUZ \cong \triangle SVU \cong \triangle UTS$ by SSS.

49. 1.8

50. 8.4

51. 80

52. 118

53. $\triangle FBD \cong \triangle FCE$, $\triangle BAE \cong \triangle CAD$, $\triangle DAF \cong \triangle EAF$, $\triangle ABF \cong \triangle ACF$

54. Answers may vary. Sample: $\angle BFD \cong \angle CFE$ because they are vertical ∡. $\angle 1 \cong \angle 2$ is given. By the $\angle$ Addition Post., it follows that $\angle BFA \cong \angle CFA$. $\overline{BF} \cong \overline{CF}$ is given, and $\overline{FA} \cong \overline{FA}$ by the Refl. Prop. Therefore, $\triangle BFA \cong \triangle CFA$ by SAS. $\overline{AB} \cong \overline{AC}$ because corresp. parts of $\cong$ ≙ are $\cong$.

55. 6

56. 68

57.

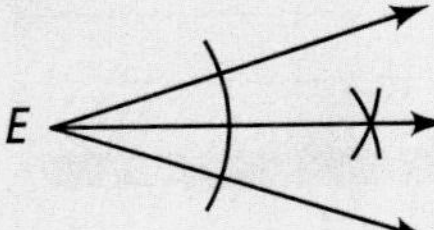

5-1 Lesson Resources

Differentiated Remediation

Instructional Support

Geometry Companion

Students can use the **Geometry Companion** worktext (4 pages) . . .

- New Vocabulary
- Key Concepts
- Got It for each Problem
- Lesson Check

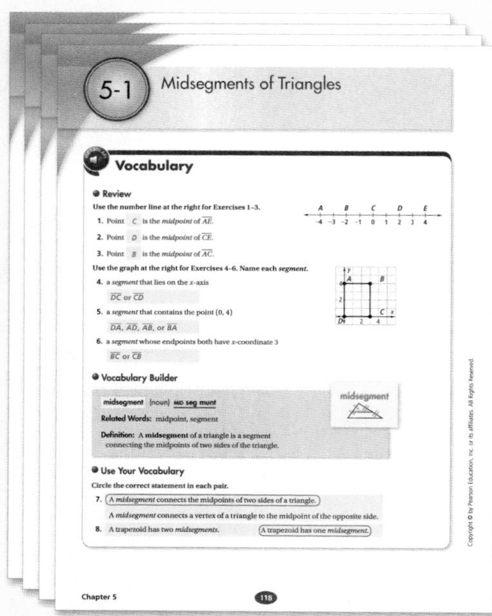

5-1 Midsegments of Triangles

Vocabulary

Review

Use the number line at the right for Exercises 1–3.

1. Point C is the *midpoint* of $\overline{AE}$.
2. Point D is the *midpoint* of $\overline{CE}$.
3. Point B is the *midpoint* of $\overline{AC}$.

Use the graph at the right for Exercises 4–6. Name each *segment*.

4. a *segment* that lies on the *x*-axis
   $\overline{DC}$ or $\overline{CD}$
5. a *segment* that contains the point (0, 4)
   $\overline{DA}$, $\overline{AD}$, $\overline{AB}$, or $\overline{BA}$
6. a *segment* whose endpoints both have *x*-coordinate 3
   $\overline{BC}$ or $\overline{CB}$

Vocabulary Builder

midsegment (noun) MID seg munt

Related Words: midpoint, segment

Definition: A **midsegment** of a triangle is a segment connecting the midpoints of two sides of the triangle.

Use Your Vocabulary

Circle the correct statement in each pair.

7. A *midsegment* connects the midpoints of two sides of a triangle.
   A *midsegment* connects a vertex of a triangle to the midpoint of the opposite side.
8. A trapezoid has two *midsegments*. A trapezoid has one *midsegment*.

Chapter 5 118

ELL Supports

Use Manipulatives Pair a more proficient student with a less proficient student. Have one student give the directions and the other student implement them with a compass and straightedge.

The students should:

- Draw a triangle with a straightedge.
- Label the vertices.
- Bisect each side of the triangle.
- Label the midpoints.
- Connect the midpoints to form an inscribed triangle.
- Measure and list the lengths of each side of the triangles.
- Discuss what they have learned through the activity.

Encourage students to use full sentences and proper mathematical language in their conversation as they complete this project.

5 Assess & Remediate

Lesson Quiz

Use the triangle below for Questions 1–3.

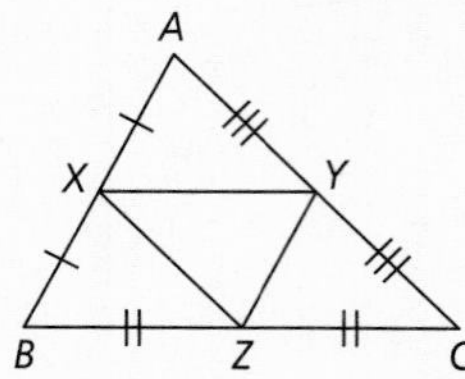

1. What are the three pairs of parallel segments in $\triangle ABC$?
2. If the length of $\overline{XZ}$ is known, what other segment can you assign a length?
3. If it is given that $AX = 3.5$, what is the length of YZ?
4. **Do you UNDERSTAND?** In $\triangle MON$, J, K, and L are midpoints. If $JL = 11$, $LK = 13$, and $ON = 20$, and $JL \parallel MN$, $LK \parallel MO$, and $JK \parallel ON$, what is the length of MN, MO, and JK?

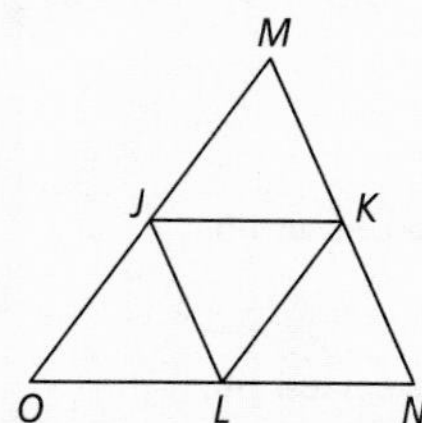

ANSWERS TO LESSON QUIZ

1. $\overline{AB} \parallel \overline{YZ}$, $\overline{BC} \parallel \overline{XY}$, $\overline{AC} \parallel \overline{XZ}$
2. $\overline{AC}$
3. 3.5
4. $MN = 22$, $MO = 26$, $JK = 10$

PRESCRIPTION FOR REMEDIATION

Use the student work on the Lesson Quiz to prescribe a differentiated review assignment.

Points	Differentiated Remediation
0–2	Intervention
3	On-level
4	Extension

PowerGeometry.com

5 Assess & Remediate

Assign the Lesson Quiz. Appropriate intervention, practice, or enrichment is automatically generated based on student performance.

Intervention

- **Reteaching** (2 pages) Provides reteaching and practice exercises for the key lesson concepts. Use with struggling students or absent students.
- **English Language Learner Support** Helps students develop and reinforce mathematical vocabulary and key concepts.

All-in-One Resources/Online

Reteaching

5-1 **Reteaching**

Midsegments of Triangles

Connecting the midpoints of two sides of a triangle creates a segment called a *midsegment* of the triangle.

Point X is the midpoint of $\overline{AB}$.

Point Y is the midpoint of $\overline{BC}$.

So, $\overline{XY}$ is a midsegment of $\triangle ABC$.

There is a special relationship between a midsegment and the side of the triangle that is not connected to the midsegment.

Triangle Midsegment Theorem

- The midsegment is parallel to the third side of the triangle.
- The length of the midsegment is half the length of the third side.

$\overline{XY} \parallel \overline{AC}$ and $XY = \frac{1}{2}AC$.

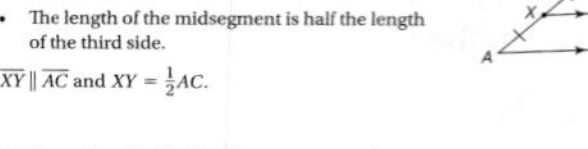

Connecting each pair of midpoints, you can see that a triangle has three midsegments.

$\overline{XY}$, $\overline{YZ}$, and $\overline{ZX}$ are all midsegments of $\triangle ABC$.

Because Z is the midpoint of $\overline{AC}$, $XY = AZ = ZC = \frac{1}{2}AC$.

Problem

$\overline{QR}$ is a midsegment of $\triangle MNO$.

What is the length of $\overline{MO}$?

Start by writing an equation using the Triangle Midsegment Theorem.

$$\frac{1}{2}MO = QR$$
$$MO = 2QR$$
$$= 2(20)$$
$$= 40$$

So, $MO = 40$.

All-in-One Resources/Online

English Language Learner Support

5-1 **ELL Support**

Midsegments of Triangles

There are two sets of note cards below that show how to find *AB* and *CD* for the triangle at the right. The set on the left explains the thinking. The set on the right shows the steps. Write the thinking and the steps in the correct order.

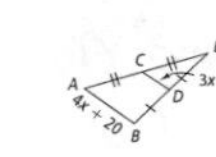

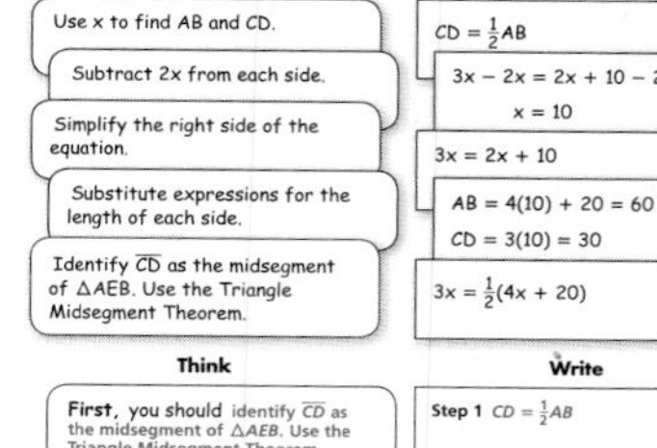

Think Cards

- Use x to find AB and CD.
- Subtract 2x from each side.
- Simplify the right side of the equation.
- Substitute expressions for the length of each side.
- Identify $\overline{CD}$ as the midsegment of $\triangle AEB$. Use the Triangle Midsegment Theorem.

Write Cards

- $CD = \frac{1}{2}AB$
- $3x - 2x = 2x + 10 - 2x$, $x = 10$
- $3x = 2x + 10$
- $AB = 4(10) + 20 = 60$, $CD = 3(10) = 30$
- $3x = \frac{1}{2}(4x + 20)$

Think	Write
First, you should identify $\overline{CD}$ as the midsegment of $\triangle AEB$. Use the Triangle Midsegment Theorem.	**Step 1** $CD = \frac{1}{2}AB$
Second, you should substitute expressions for the length of each side.	**Step 2** $3x = \frac{1}{2}(4x + 20)$
Third, you should simplify the right side of the equation.	**Step 3** $3x = 2x + 10$
Next, you should subtract 2x from each side.	**Step 4** $3x - 2x = 2x + 10 - 2x$ $x = 10$
Finally, you should use x to find AB and CD.	**Step 5** $AB = 4(10) + 20 = 60$ $CD = 3(10) = 30$

Differentiated Remediation *continued*

On-Level

- **Practice** (2 pages) Provides extra practice for each lesson. For simpler practice exercises, use the Form K Practice pages found in the All-in-One Teaching Resources and online.
- **Think About a Plan** Helps students develop specific problem-solving skills and strategies by providing scaffolded guiding questions.
- **Standardized Test Prep** Focuses on all major exercises, all major question types, and helps students prepare for the high-stakes assessments.

Extension

- **Enrichment** Provides students with interesting problems and activities that extend the concepts of the lesson.
- **Activities, Games, and Puzzles** Worksheets that can be used for concepts development, enrichment, and for fun!

Practice and Problem Solving Wkbk/ All-in-One Resources/Online

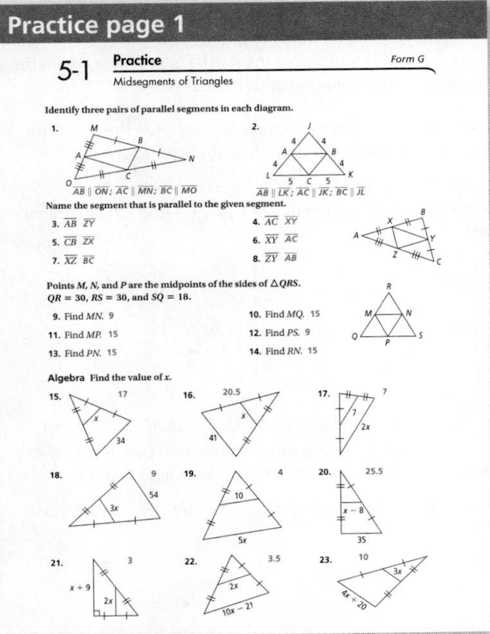

Practice page 1

5-1 **Practice** — Midsegments of Triangles — *Form G*

Identify three pairs of parallel segments in each diagram.

1. $\overline{AB} \parallel \overline{ON}$; $\overline{AC} \parallel \overline{MN}$; $\overline{BC} \parallel \overline{MO}$
2. $\overline{AB} \parallel \overline{LK}$; $\overline{AC} \parallel \overline{JK}$; $\overline{BC} \parallel \overline{JL}$

Name the segment that is parallel to the given segment.

3. $\overline{AB}$ $\overline{ZY}$
4. $\overline{AC}$ $\overline{XY}$
5. $\overline{CB}$ $\overline{ZX}$
6. $\overline{XY}$ $\overline{AC}$
7. $\overline{XZ}$ $\overline{BC}$
8. $\overline{ZY}$ $\overline{AB}$

Points *M*, *N*, and *P* are the midpoints of the sides of $\triangle QRS$. $QR = 30$, $RS = 30$, and $SQ = 18$.

9. Find *MN*. 9
10. Find *MQ*. 15
11. Find *MP*. 15
12. Find *PS*. 9
13. Find *PN*. 15
14. Find *RN*. 15

Algebra Find the value of *x*.

15. 17
16. 20.5
17. 7
18. 9
19. 4
20. 25.5
21. 3
22. 3.5
23. 10

Practice and Problem Solving Wkbk/ All-in-One Resources/Online

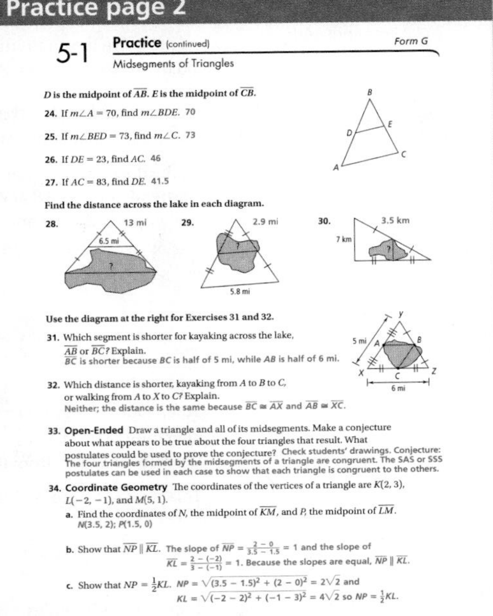

Practice page 2

5-1 **Practice** (continued) — Midsegments of Triangles — *Form G*

***D* is the midpoint of $\overline{AB}$. *E* is the midpoint of $\overline{CB}$.**

24. If $m\angle A = 70$, find $m\angle BDE$. 70
25. If $m\angle BED = 73$, find $m\angle C$. 73
26. If $DE = 23$, find *AC*. 46
27. If $AC = 83$, find *DE*. 41.5

Find the distance across the lake in each diagram.

28. 13 mi
29. 2.9 mi
30. 3.5 km

Use the diagram at the right for Exercises 31 and 32.

31. Which segment is shorter for kayaking across the lake, $\overline{AB}$ or $\overline{BC}$? Explain.
$\overline{BC}$ is shorter because *BC* is half of 5 mi, while *AB* is half of 6 mi.
32. Which distance is shorter, kayaking from *A* to *B* to *C*, or walking from *A* to *X* to *C*? Explain.
Neither; the distance is the same because $\overline{BC} \cong \overline{AX}$ and $\overline{AB} \cong \overline{XC}$.
33. **Open-Ended** Draw a triangle and all of its midsegments. Make a conjecture about what appears to be true about the four triangles that result. What postulates could be used to prove the conjecture? Check students' drawings. Conjecture: The four triangles formed by the midsegments of a triangle are congruent. The SAS or SSS postulates can be used in each case to show that each triangle is congruent to the others.
34. **Coordinate Geometry** The coordinates of the vertices of a triangle are *K*(2, 3), *L*(−2, −1), and *M*(5, 1).
   a. Find the coordinates of *N*, the midpoint of $\overline{KM}$, and *P*, the midpoint of $\overline{LM}$. *N*(3.5, 2); *P*(1.5, 0)
   b. Show that $\overline{NP} \parallel \overline{KL}$. The slope of $\overline{NP} = \frac{2-0}{3.5-1.5} = 1$ and the slope of $\overline{KL} = \frac{2-(-2)}{3-(-1)} = 1$. Because the slopes are equal, $\overline{NP} \parallel \overline{KL}$.
   c. Show that $NP = \frac{1}{2}KL$. $NP = \sqrt{(3.5-1.5)^2 + (2-0)^2} = 2\sqrt{2}$ and $KL = \sqrt{(-2-2)^2 + (-1-3)^2} = 4\sqrt{2}$ so $NP = \frac{1}{2}KL$.

All-in-One Resources/Online

Enrichment

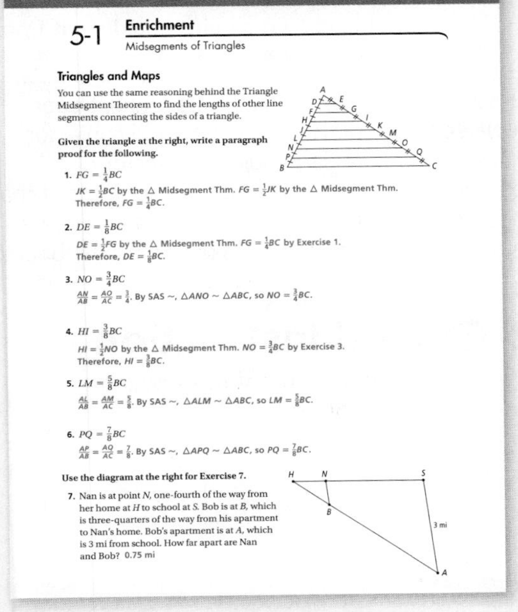

5-1 **Enrichment** — Midsegments of Triangles

Triangles and Maps

You can use the same reasoning behind the Triangle Midsegment Theorem to find the lengths of other line segments connecting the sides of a triangle.

Given the triangle at the right, write a paragraph proof for the following.

1. $FG = \frac{1}{4}BC$
$JK = \frac{1}{2}BC$ by the △ Midsegment Thm. $FG = \frac{1}{2}JK$ by the △ Midsegment Thm. Therefore, $FG = \frac{1}{4}BC$.
2. $DE = \frac{1}{8}BC$
$DE = \frac{1}{2}FG$ by the △ Midsegment Thm. $FG = \frac{1}{4}BC$ by Exercise 1. Therefore, $DE = \frac{1}{8}BC$.
3. $NO = \frac{3}{4}BC$
$\frac{AN}{AB} = \frac{AO}{AC} = \frac{3}{4}$. By SAS ~, $\triangle ANO \sim \triangle ABC$, so $NO = \frac{3}{4}BC$.
4. $HI = \frac{3}{8}BC$
$HI = \frac{1}{2}NO$ by the △ Midsegment Thm. $NO = \frac{3}{4}BC$ by Exercise 3. Therefore, $HI = \frac{3}{8}BC$.
5. $LM = \frac{5}{8}BC$
$\frac{AL}{AB} = \frac{AM}{AC} = \frac{5}{8}$. By SAS ~, $\triangle ALM \sim \triangle ABC$, so $LM = \frac{5}{8}BC$.
6. $PQ = \frac{7}{8}BC$
$\frac{AP}{AB} = \frac{AQ}{AC} = \frac{7}{8}$. By SAS ~, $\triangle APQ \sim \triangle ABC$, so $PQ = \frac{7}{8}BC$.

Use the diagram at the right for Exercise 7.

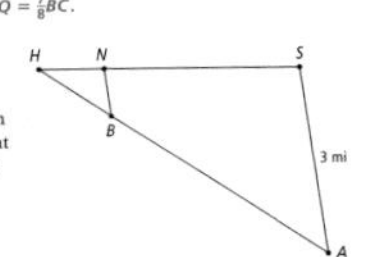

7. Nan is at point *N*, one-fourth of the way from her home at *H* to school at *S*. Bob is at *B*, which is three-quarters of the way from his apartment to Nan's home. Bob's apartment is at *A*, which is 3 mi from school. How far apart are Nan and Bob? 0.75 mi

Practice and Problem Solving Wkbk/ All-in-One Resources/Online

Think About a Plan

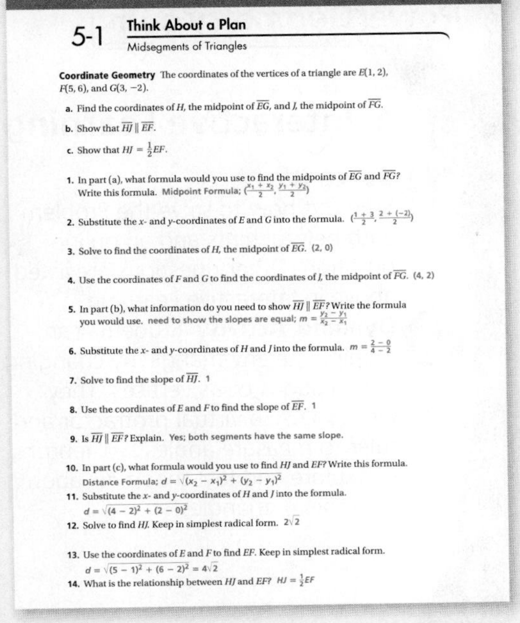

5-1 **Think About a Plan** — Midsegments of Triangles

Coordinate Geometry The coordinates of the vertices of a triangle are *E*(1, 2), *F*(5, 6), and *G*(3, −2).

a. Find the coordinates of *H*, the midpoint of $\overline{EG}$, and *J*, the midpoint of $\overline{FG}$.
b. Show that $\overline{HJ} \parallel \overline{EF}$.
c. Show that $HJ = \frac{1}{2}EF$.

1. In part (a), what formula would you use to find the midpoints of $\overline{EG}$ and $\overline{FG}$? Write this formula. Midpoint Formula; $\left(\frac{x_1 + x_2}{2}, \frac{y_1 + y_2}{2}\right)$
2. Substitute the *x*- and *y*-coordinates of *E* and *G* into the formula. $\left(\frac{1+3}{2}, \frac{2+(-2)}{2}\right)$
3. Solve to find the coordinates of *H*, the midpoint of $\overline{EG}$. (2, 0)
4. Use the coordinates of *F* and *G* to find the coordinates of *J*, the midpoint of $\overline{FG}$. (4, 2)
5. In part (b), what information do you need to show $\overline{HJ} \parallel \overline{EF}$? Write the formula you would use. need to show the slopes are equal; $m = \frac{y_2 - y_1}{x_2 - x_1}$
6. Substitute the *x*- and *y*-coordinates of *H* and *J* into the formula. $m = \frac{2-0}{4-2}$
7. Solve to find the slope of $\overline{HJ}$. 1
8. Use the coordinates of *E* and *F* to find the slope of $\overline{EF}$. 1
9. Is $\overline{HJ} \parallel \overline{EF}$? Explain. Yes; both segments have the same slope.
10. In part (c), what formula would you use to find *HJ* and *EF*? Write this formula. Distance Formula; $d = \sqrt{(x_2 - x_1)^2 + (y_2 - y_1)^2}$
11. Substitute the *x*- and *y*-coordinates of *H* and *J* into the formula. $d = \sqrt{(4-2)^2 + (2-0)^2}$
12. Solve to find *HJ*. Keep in simplest radical form. $2\sqrt{2}$
13. Use the coordinates of *E* and *F* to find *EF*. Keep in simplest radical form. $d = \sqrt{(5-1)^2 + (6-2)^2} = 4\sqrt{2}$
14. What is the relationship between *HJ* and *EF*? $HJ = \frac{1}{2}EF$

Practice and Problem Solving Wkbk/ All-in-One Resources/Online

Standardized Test Prep

5-1 **Standardized Test Prep** — Midsegments of Triangles

Gridded Response

Solve each exercise and enter your answer on the grid provided.

In $\triangle RST$, *U* is the midpoint of $\overline{RS}$, *V* is the midpoint of $\overline{ST}$, and *W* is the midpoint of $\overline{TR}$.

1. What is the length of $\overline{RS}$?
2. What is the value of *x*?
3. What is the value of *y*?
4. What is the length of $\overline{UW}$?
5. What is the length of $\overline{UV}$?

Answers

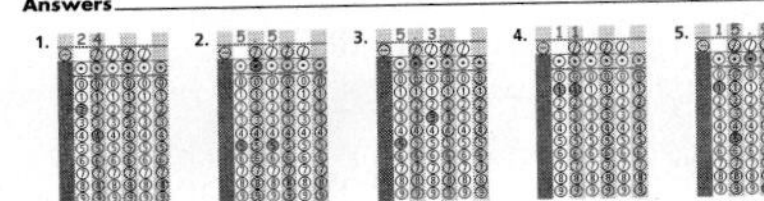

Online Teacher Resource Center

Activities, Games, and Puzzles

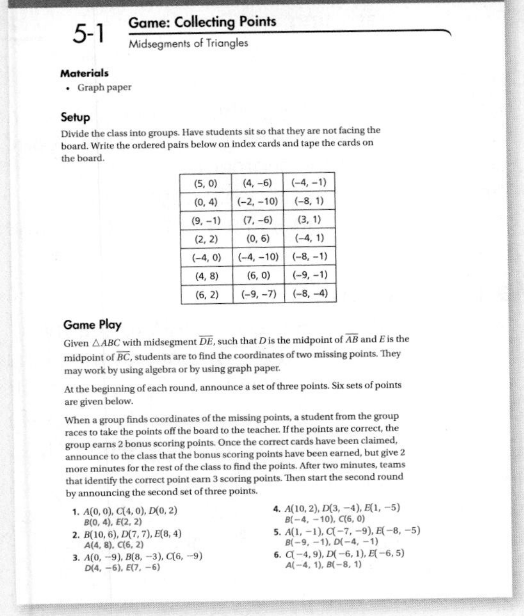

5-1 **Game: Collecting Points** — Midsegments of Triangles

Materials

- Graph paper

Setup

Divide the class into groups. Have students sit so that they are not facing the board. Write the ordered pairs below on index cards and tape the cards on the board.

(5, 0)	(4, −6)	(−4, −1)
(0, 4)	(−2, −10)	(−8, 1)
(9, −1)	(7, −6)	(3, 1)
(2, 2)	(0, 6)	(−4, 1)
(−4, 0)	(−4, −10)	(−8, −1)
(4, 8)	(6, 0)	(−9, −1)
(6, 2)	(−9, −7)	(−8, −4)

Game Play

Given $\triangle ABC$ with midsegment $\overline{DE}$, such that *D* is the midpoint of $\overline{AB}$ and *E* is the midpoint of $\overline{BC}$, students are to find the coordinates of two missing points. They may work by using algebra or by using graph paper.

At the beginning of each round, announce a set of three points. Six sets of points are given below.

When a group finds coordinates of the missing points, a student from the group races to take the points off the board to the teacher. If the points are correct, the group earns 2 bonus scoring points. Once the correct cards have been claimed, announce to the class that the bonus scoring points have been earned, but give 2 more minutes for the rest of the class to find the points. After two minutes, teams that identify the correct point earn 3 scoring points. Then start the second round by announcing the second set of three points.

1. *A*(0, 0), *C*(4, 0), *D*(0, 2)
B(0, 4), *E*(2, 2)
2. *B*(10, 6), *D*(7, 7), *E*(8, 4)
A(4, 8), *C*(6, 2)
3. *A*(0, −9), *B*(8, −3), *C*(6, −9)
D(4, −6), *E*(7, −6)
4. *A*(10, 2), *D*(3, −4), *E*(1, −5)
B(−4, −10), *C*(6, 0)
5. *A*(1, −1), *C*(−7, −9), *E*(−8, −5)
B(−9, −1), *D*(−4, −1)
6. *C*(−4, 9), *D*(−6, 1), *E*(−6, 5)
A(−4, 1), *B*(−8, 1)

1 Interactive Learning

Solve It!

PURPOSE To discover properties of the perpendicular bisector of a segment

PROCESS Students may

- use concepts of triangle properties to make a conjecture.
- use logical reasoning to determine the best location to hang the bulletin board.

FACILITATE

Q Why is the bulletin board crooked? **[The string is longer on the right side of the nail than it is on the left side of the nail.]**

Q What relationship must exist for the lengths of the string on each side of the nail for the bulletin board to hang straight? **[The lengths of the string must be equal.]**

Q If a line is drawn from the nail directly below to the top of a level bulletin board, where will it touch the bulletin board? **[at a point equidistant from the top corners of the bulletin board]**

ANSWER See Solve It in Answers on next page.

CONNECT THE MATH Students should conjecture that points on the perpendicular bisector of a segment are equidistant from the endpoints of that segment. In the lesson, students learn a theorem that relates a segment and its perpendicular bisector.

2 Guided Instruction

Have students write a proof to show that $\triangle CAD \cong \triangle CBD$ using the SAS Theorem.

5-2 Perpendicular and Angle Bisectors

TN State Performance Indicator

SPI 3108.4.12 Solve problems involving congruence, similarity, proportional reasoning and/or scale factor of two similar figures or solids.

Objective To use properties of perpendicular bisectors and angle bisectors

Confused? Try drawing a diagram to "straighten" yourself out.

SOLVE IT! Getting Ready!

You hang a bulletin board over your desk using string. The bulletin board is crooked. When you straighten the bulletin board, what type of triangle does the string form with the top of the board? How do you know? Visualize the vertical line along the wall that passes through the nail. What relationships exist between this line and the top edge of the straightened bulletin board? Explain.

Dynamic Activity Perpendicular and Angle Bisectors

Lesson Vocabulary
- equidistant
- distance from a point to a line

In the Solve It, you thought about the relationships that must exist in order for a bulletin board to hang straight. You will explore these relationships in this lesson.

Essential Understanding There is a special relationship between the points on the perpendicular bisector of a segment and the endpoints of the segment.

In the diagram below on the left, $\overleftrightarrow{CD}$ is the perpendicular bisector of $\overline{AB}$. $\overleftrightarrow{CD}$ is perpendicular to $\overline{AB}$ at its midpoint. In the diagram on the right, $\overline{CA}$ and $\overline{CB}$ are drawn to complete $\triangle CAD$ and $\triangle CBD$.

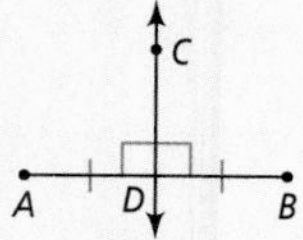

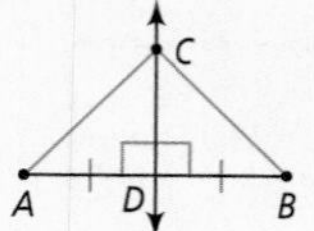

You should recognize from your work in Chapter 4 that $\triangle CAD \cong \triangle CBD$. So you can conclude that $\overline{CA} \cong \overline{CB}$, or that $CA = CB$. A point is **equidistant** from two objects if it is the same distance from the objects. So point C is equidistant from points A and B.

This suggests a proof of Theorem 5-2, the Perpendicular Bisector Theorem. Its converse is also true and is stated as Theorem 5-3.

5-2 Preparing to Teach

BIG ideas **Reasoning and Proof**
Measurement

ESSENTIAL UNDERSTANDINGS

- There is a special relationship between the points on the perpendicular bisector of a segment and the endpoints of the segment.
- There is a special relationship between the points on the bisector of an angle and the sides of the angle.

Math Background

In this lesson, students should begin to see the perpendicular bisector of a segment and the bisector of an angle as a locus of points. The perpendicular bisector of a segment contains all points which are equidistant from the endpoints of the segment.

The bisector of an angle represents all points which are equidistant from the sides of the angle. Loci of points are useful in many real-world applications. They aid surveyors, architects, and designers in locating points central to segments and angles. Loci will be discussed later in this book.

Support Student Learning

Use the **Geometry Companion** to engage and support students during instructions. See Lesson Resources at the end of this lesson for details.

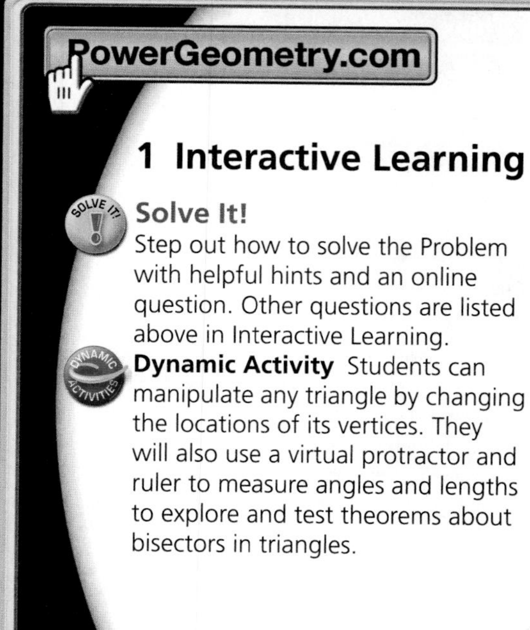

PowerGeometry.com

1 Interactive Learning

Solve It! Step out how to solve the Problem with helpful hints and an online question. Other questions are listed above in Interactive Learning.

Dynamic Activity Students can manipulate any triangle by changing the locations of its vertices. They will also use a virtual protractor and ruler to measure angles and lengths to explore and test theorems about bisectors in triangles.

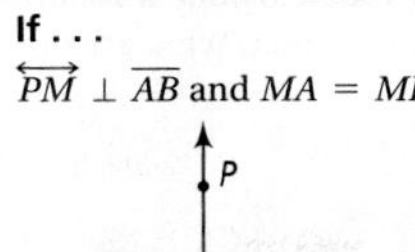

Take Note: Theorem 5-2 Perpendicular Bisector Theorem

Theorem	If . . .	Then . . .
If a point is on the perpendicular bisector of a segment, then it is equidistant from the endpoints of the segment.	$\overleftrightarrow{PM} \perp \overline{AB}$ and $MA = MB$	$PA = PB$

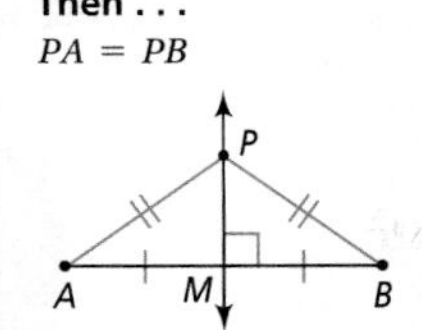

You will prove Theorem 5-2 in Exercise 32.

Theorem 5-3 Converse of the Perpendicular Bisector Theorem

Theorem	If . . .	Then . . .
If a point is equidistant from the endpoints of a segment, then it is on the perpendicular bisector of the segment.	$PA = PB$	$\overleftrightarrow{PM} \perp \overline{AB}$ and $MA = MB$

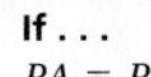

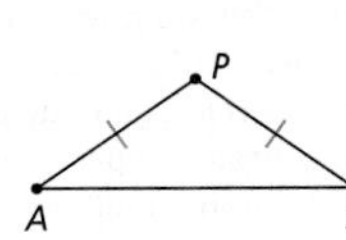

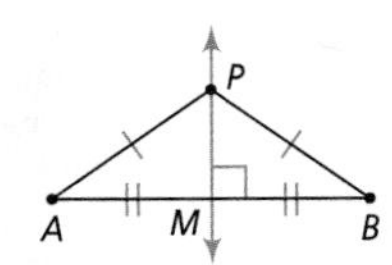

You will prove Theorem 5-3 in Exercise 33.

Problem 1 Using the Perpendicular Bisector Theorem

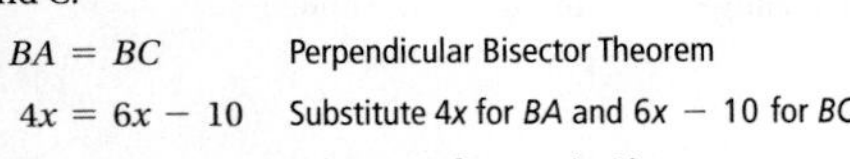

Think

How do you know $\overline{BD}$ is the perpendicular bisector of $\overline{AC}$?
The markings in the diagram show that $\overline{BD}$ is perpendicular to $\overline{AC}$ at the midpoint of $\overline{AC}$.

Algebra What is the length of $\overline{AB}$?

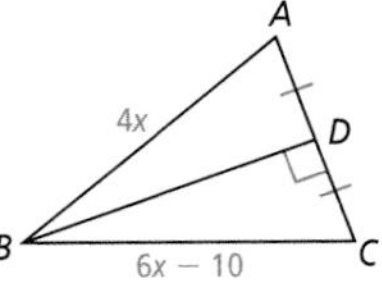

$\overline{BD}$ is the perpendicular bisector of $\overline{AC}$, so B is equidistant from A and C.

$BA = BC$	Perpendicular Bisector Theorem
$4x = 6x - 10$	Substitute $4x$ for BA and $6x - 10$ for BC.
$-2x = -10$	Subtract $6x$ from each side.
$x = 5$	Divide each side by -2.

Now find AB.

$AB = 4x$

$AB = 4(5) = 20$ Substitute 5 for x.

Got It? 1. What is the length of $\overline{QR}$?

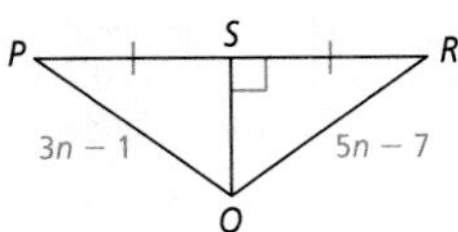

Take Note

Have students compare and contrast the theorems presented in the Take Note section. Ask them to explain why Theorem 5-3 is called the converse of Theorem 5-2. Have them combine the two statements to form one biconditional statement.

Problem 1

Q What information is given in the diagram? **[$\overline{AD} = \overline{DC}$ and $\overline{BD} \perp \overline{DC}$]**

Q Which theorem can you apply? **[Theorem 5-2, The Perpendicular Bisector Theorem]**

Got It?

Have students classify $\overline{QS}$. Emphasize that $PQ = RQ$ by Theorem 5-2.

2 Guided Instruction

Each Problem is worked out and supported online.

Problem 1
Using the Perpendicular Bisector Theorem
Animated

Problem 2
Using a Perpendicular Bisector
Animated

Problem 3
Using the Angle Bisector Theorem
Animated

Support in Geometry Companion

- Vocabulary
- Key Concepts
- Got It?

Answers

Solve It!

Isosceles; the board will be straight when its weight is evenly balanced on either side of the nail, so the string will need to be touching the nail at the point that divides the length of the string in half. The line is perpendicular to and bisects the top edge of the straightened bulletin board; label the top corners of the bulletin board A and B, the nail N, and the point where the vertical line through N intersects the straightened bulletin board M. When the bulletin board is straight, $\overline{AB}$ is horizontal, so $\overleftrightarrow{NM} \perp \overline{AB}$ because a vertical line is perpendicular to a horizontal line. $\overline{AN} \cong \overline{BN}$ because $\triangle ABC$ is isosceles and $\overline{NM} \cong \overline{NM}$ (Refl. Prop. of Eq.), so $\triangle ANM \cong \triangle BNM$ (HL) and $\overline{MA} \cong \overline{MB}$ (Corresp. parts of $\cong$ ≜ are $\cong$.). So, $\overleftrightarrow{NM}$ bisects $\overline{AB}$.

Got It?

1. 8

Problem 2

Have students sketch the triangle created by the locations of the Rollin' Coaster, the Spaceship Shoot, and each of the possible locations for the T-shirt stand.

Q How many possibilities are there for the location of the T-shirt stand? **[Infinite; any point along the perpendicular of $\overline{RS}$ is a possibility.]**

Got It?

Have students sketch the triangle created by the locations of the paddle boats, the Spaceship Shoot, and the Rollin' Coaster. Then have them construct the perpendicular bisector of each side of the triangle.

Q What do you know about the point of intersection of three perpendicular bisectors and the three attractions? **[The point of intersection is the same distance from each of three attractions.]**

Q Does your drawing model Theorem 5-2 or Theorem 5-3? Explain. **[Theorem 5-2; the theorem states that if you know the point is on the perpendicular bisector then it is equidistant from the endpoints. The perpendicular bisectors were constructed to find the point equidistant from endpoints of three segments.]**

Have a student stand at a point in the classroom where the students can model the distance between a point and a line on a wall in the classroom. Have another student describe how to find the student's distance from the wall. Guide the class to conclude that the distance must be measured on a segment that is perpendicular to the wall.

Problem 2 Using a Perpendicular Bisector

Plan

How do you find points that are equidistant from two given points?
By the Converse of the Perpendicular Bisector Theorem, points equidistant from two given points are on the perpendicular bisector of the segment that joins the two points.

A park director wants to build a T-shirt stand equidistant from the Rollin' Coaster and the Spaceship Shoot. What are the possible locations of the stand? Explain.

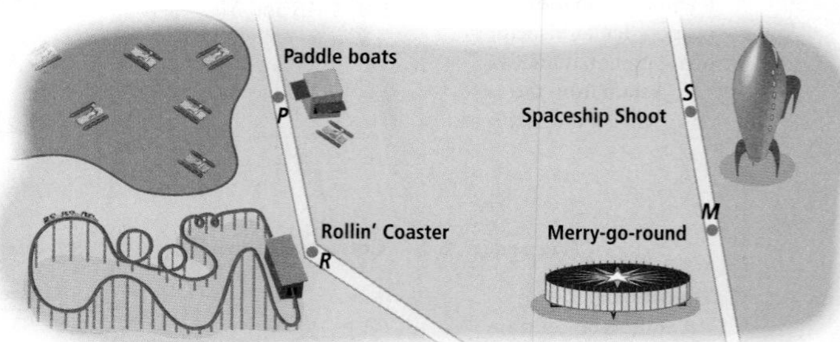

To be equidistant from the two rides, the stand should be on the perpendicular bisector of the segment connecting the rides. Find the midpoint A of $\overline{RS}$ and draw line ℓ through A perpendicular to $\overline{RS}$. The possible locations of the stand are all the points on line ℓ.

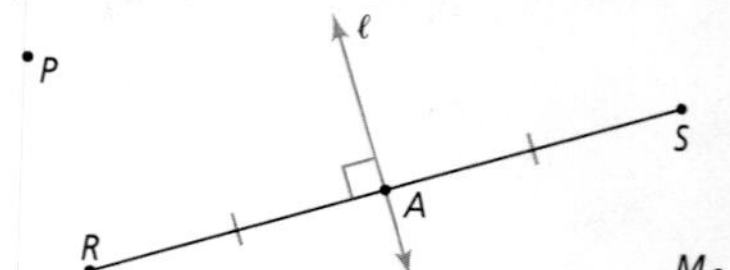

Got It? 2. a. Suppose the director wants the T-shirt stand to be equidistant from the paddle boats and the Spaceship Shoot. What are the possible locations?

b. Reasoning Can you place the T-shirt stand so that it is equidistant from the paddle boats, the Spaceship Shoot, and the Rollin' Coaster? Explain.

Essential Understanding There is a special relationship between the points on the bisector of an angle and the sides of the angle.

The **distance from a point to a line** is the length of the perpendicular segment from the point to the line. This distance is also the length of the shortest segment from the point to the line. You will prove this in Lesson 5-6. In the figure at the right, the distances from A to ℓ and from B to ℓ are represented by the red segments.

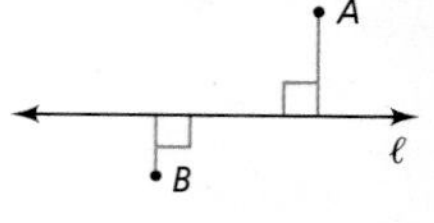

In the diagram, $\overrightarrow{AD}$ is the bisector of $\angle CAB$. If you measure the lengths of the perpendicular segments from D to the two sides of the angle, you will find that the lengths are equal. Point D is equidistant from the sides of the angle.

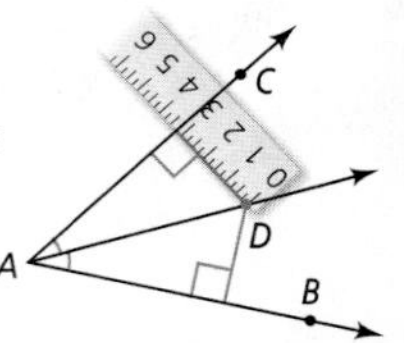

Additional Problems

1. What is MN?

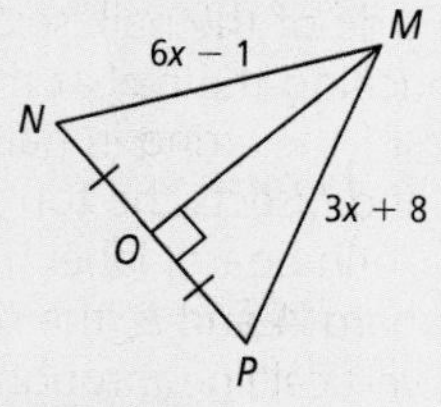

ANSWER 17

2. The monkey bars are located midway between the slide and the tether ball. Which of the following are about equidistant from the slide and the tether ball?

4-Square
Monkey Bars
Slide
Tether Ball
Kick Ball
Hop Scotch

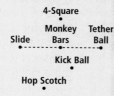

ANSWER 4-Square

3. What is the length of $\overline{OP}$?

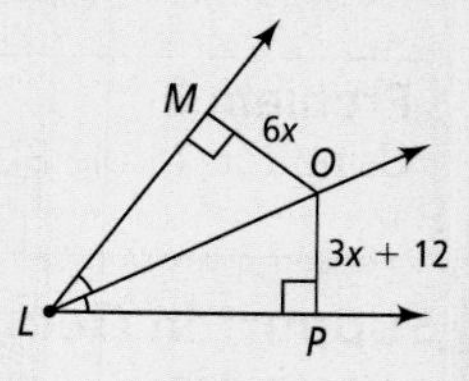

ANSWER 24

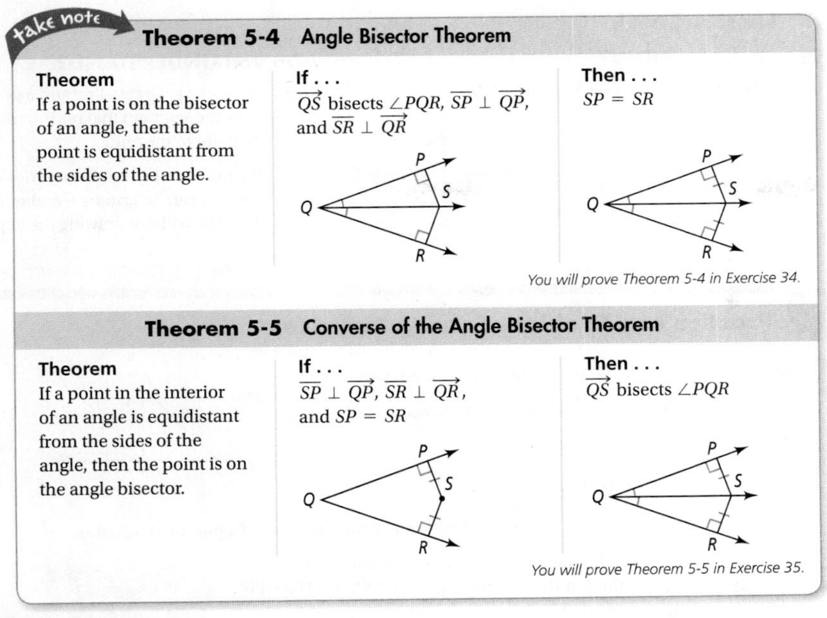

take note

Theorem 5-4 Angle Bisector Theorem

Theorem	If . . .	Then . . .
If a point is on the bisector of an angle, then the point is equidistant from the sides of the angle.	$\overrightarrow{QS}$ bisects $\angle PQR$, $\overline{SP} \perp \overrightarrow{QP}$, and $\overline{SR} \perp \overrightarrow{QR}$	$SP = SR$

You will prove Theorem 5-4 in Exercise 34.

Theorem 5-5 Converse of the Angle Bisector Theorem

Theorem	If . . .	Then . . .
If a point in the interior of an angle is equidistant from the sides of the angle, then the point is on the angle bisector.	$\overline{SP} \perp \overrightarrow{QP}$, $\overline{SR} \perp \overrightarrow{QR}$, and $SP = SR$	$\overrightarrow{QS}$ bisects $\angle PQR$

You will prove Theorem 5-5 in Exercise 35.

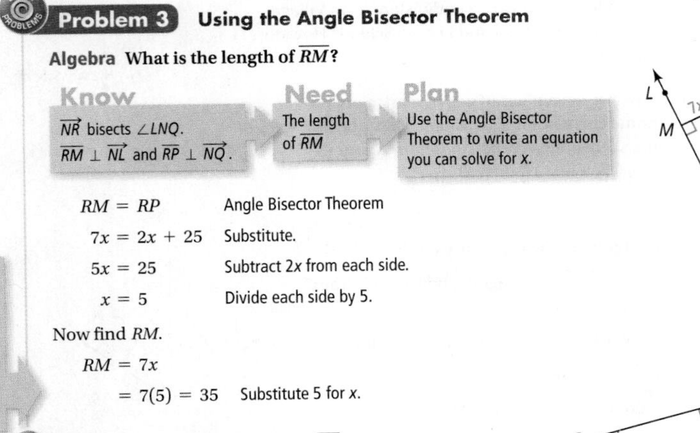

Problem 3 Using the Angle Bisector Theorem

Algebra What is the length of $\overline{RM}$?

Know
- $\overrightarrow{NR}$ bisects $\angle LNQ$.
- $\overline{RM} \perp \overrightarrow{NL}$ and $\overline{RP} \perp \overrightarrow{NQ}$.

Need
The length of $\overline{RM}$

Plan
Use the Angle Bisector Theorem to write an equation you can solve for x.

$RM = RP$	Angle Bisector Theorem
$7x = 2x + 25$	Substitute.
$5x = 25$	Subtract $2x$ from each side.
$x = 5$	Divide each side by 5.

Now find RM.

$RM = 7x$

$= 7(5) = 35$ Substitute 5 for x.

Think
How can you use the expression given for *RP* to check your answer?
Substitute 5 for x in the expression $2x + 25$ and verify that the result is 35.

Got It? 3. What is the length of $\overline{FB}$?

Take Note

Have students compare and contrast the theorems presented in the Take Note section. Ask them to explain why Theorem 5-5 is called the converse of Theorem 5-4. Have them combine the two statements to form one biconditional statement.

Emphasize to students that because $\overline{SP}$ and $\overline{SR}$ are perpendicular to the sides of the angles, SP and SR are the distance from point S to the sides of the angles. Guide students to see that the points on an angle bisector are equidistant from the sides of the angle.

Problem 3

Q How can you classify $\overrightarrow{RN}$? Justify your answer. **[$\overrightarrow{RN}$ is the bisector of $\angle MNP$ because $\angle MNR \cong \angle PNR$.]**

Q What do $\overline{MR}$ and $\overline{PR}$ represent? **[They represent the distance between point *R* and the sides of the angle.]**

Got It?

Have students redraw the diagram and label the lengths of the segments as given. Ask students to classify $\overline{CF}$ as the angle bisector. Remind them to use the value they find for x to find FB.

Answers

Got it! (continued)

2a. any point on the $\perp$ bis of $\overline{PS}$

b. At the intersection point of ℓ and the perpendicular bisector of $\overline{PS}$; let X be the intersection point of ℓ and the perpendicular bisector of $\overline{PS}$. By the $\perp$ Bis. Thm., $XR = XS$ and $XS = XP$, so $XR = XS = XP$. Thus, X is equidistant from R, S, and P.

3. 21

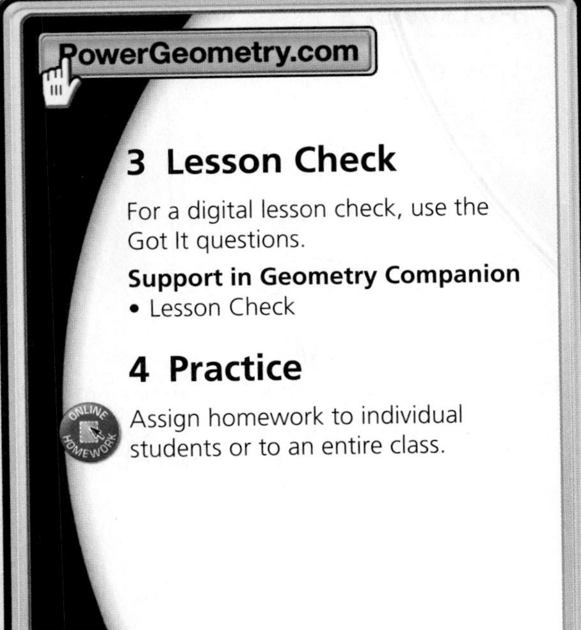

PowerGeometry.com

3 Lesson Check

For a digital lesson check, use the Got It questions.

Support in Geometry Companion
- Lesson Check

4 Practice

Assign homework to individual students or to an entire class.

3 Lesson Check

Do you know HOW?

- If students have difficulty with Exercises 1–3, then have them review Problem 1 to understand the relationship of a point on a perpendicular bisector to the endpoints of the bisected segment.

Do you UNDERSTAND?

- If students have difficulty with Exercise 5, then have them review Theorem 5-4 and the diagram at the bottom of page 294.

Close

Q What statement describes the points on the perpendicular bisector of a segment? **[They are equidistant from the endpoints of the segment.]**

Q What statement can be made about a point on the bisector of an angle? **[It is equidistant from the sides of the angle.]**

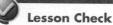

Lesson Check

Do you know HOW?

Use the figure at the right for Exercises 1–3.

1. What is the relationship between $\overline{AC}$ and $\overline{BD}$?

2. What is the length of $\overline{AB}$?

3. What is the length of $\overline{DC}$?

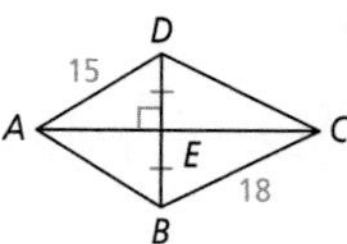

Do you UNDERSTAND?

4. Vocabulary Draw a line and a point not on the line. Draw the segment that represents the distance from the point to the line.

5. Writing Point P is in the interior of $\angle LOX$. Describe how you can determine whether P is on the bisector of $\angle LOX$ without drawing the angle bisector.

Practice and Problem-Solving Exercises

A Practice

Use the figure at the right for Exercises 6–8. See Problem 1.

6. What is the relationship between $\overline{MB}$ and $\overline{JK}$?

7. What is value of x?

8. Find JM.

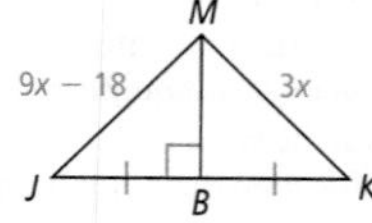

Reading Maps For Exercises 9 and 10, use the map of a part of Manhattan. See Problem 2.

9. Which school is equidistant from the subway stations at Union Square and 14th Street? How do you know?

10. Is St. Vincent's Hospital equidistant from Village Kids Nursery School and Legacy School? How do you know?

11. Writing On a piece of paper, mark a point H for home and a point S for school. Describe how to find the set of points equidistant from H and S.

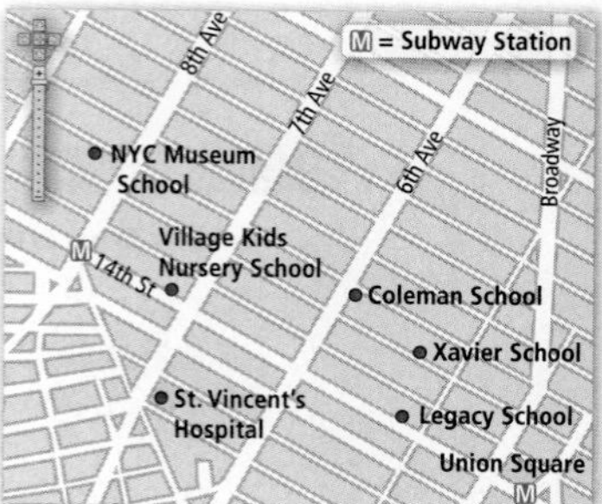

Use the figure at the right for Exercises 12–15. See Problem 3.

12. According to the diagram, how far is L from $\overrightarrow{HK}$? From $\overrightarrow{HF}$?

13. How is $\overrightarrow{HL}$ related to $\angle KHF$? Explain.

14. Find the value of y.

15. Find $m\angle KHL$ and $m\angle FHL$.

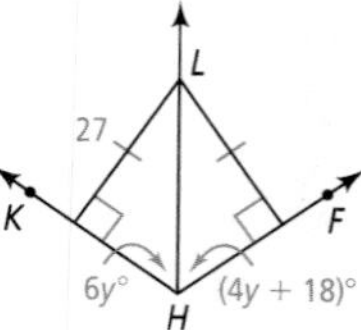

Answers

Lesson Check

1. $\overline{AC}$ is the ⊥ bisector of $\overline{DB}$.

2. 15

3. 18

4. Answers may vary. Sample:

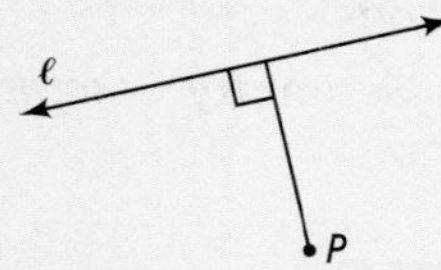

5. Draw the ⊥ segments that join P to $\overrightarrow{OL}$ and $\overrightarrow{OX}$. Use a ruler to determine if $OL = OX$. If $OL = OX$, then P is on the bisector of $\angle LOX$.

Practice and Problem-Solving Exercises

6. $\overline{MB}$ is the ⊥ bisector of $\overline{JK}$.

7. 3

8. 9

9. Coleman School; it is on 6th Ave., which is (approximately) the ⊥ bisector of 14th St. between 8th Ave. and Union Square.

10. No; it is not on the ⊥ bis. of the street connecting the two schools.

11. Draw $\overline{HS}$ and find its midpt., M. Through M, construct the line ⊥ to $\overline{HS}$. Any point on this line will be equidistant from H and S.

12. 27; 27

13. $\overrightarrow{HL}$ bisects $\angle KHF$; point L is equidistant from the sides of the ∠, so L is on the bisector of $\angle KHF$ by the Converse of the ∠ Bisector Thm.

14. 9

15. 54; 54

16. Algebra Find x, JK, and JM.

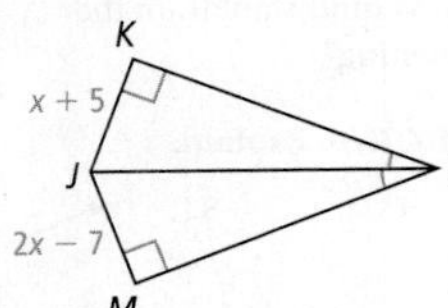

17. Algebra Find y, ST, and TU.

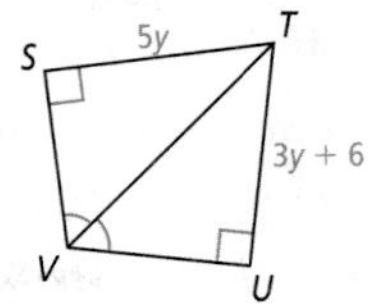

B Apply

Algebra Use the figure at the right for Exercises 18–22.

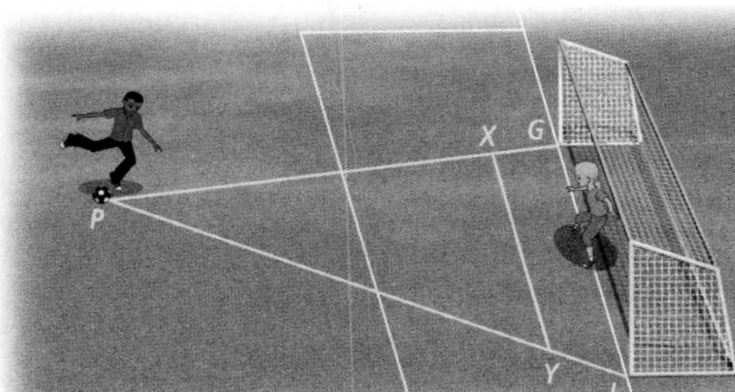

18. Find the value of x.

19. Find TW.

20. Find WZ.

21. What kind of triangle is $\triangle TWZ$? Explain.

22. If R is on the perpendicular bisector of $\overline{TZ}$, then R is _?_ from T and Z, or _?_ = _?_.

23. Think About a Plan In the diagram at the right, the soccer goalie will prepare for a shot from the player at point P by moving out to a point on $\overline{XY}$. To have the best chance of stopping the ball, should the goalie stand at the point on $\overline{XY}$ that lies on the perpendicular bisector of $\overline{GL}$ or at the point on $\overline{XY}$ that lies on the bisector of $\angle GPL$? Explain your reasoning.

- How can you draw a diagram to help?
- Would the goalie want to be the same distance from G and L or from $\overline{PG}$ and $\overline{PL}$?

24. a. Constructions Draw a large triangle, $\triangle CDE$. Construct the angle bisectors of each angle.

b. Make a Conjecture What appears to be true about the angle bisectors?

c. Test your conjecture with another triangle.

25. a. Constructions Draw a large acute scalene triangle, $\triangle PQR$. Construct the perpendicular bisectors of each side.

b. Make a Conjecture What appears to be true about the perpendicular bisectors?

c. Test your conjecture with another triangle.

26. Write Theorems 5-2 and 5-3 as a single biconditional statement.

27. Write Theorems 5-4 and 5-5 as a single biconditional statement.

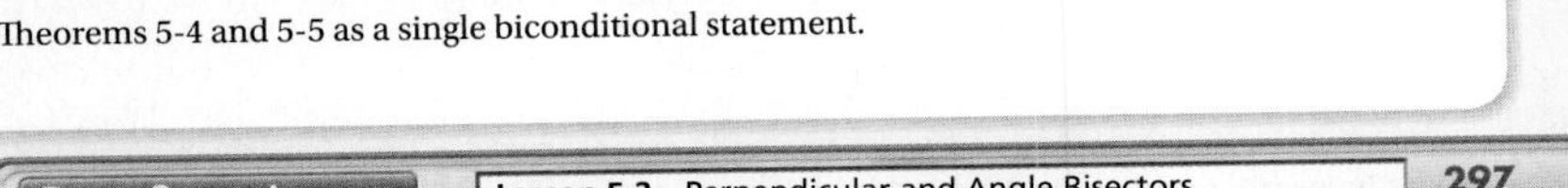

4 Practice

ASSIGNMENT GUIDE

Basic: 6–17 all, 18–22 even, 23, 25, 28–32 even
Average: 7–17 odd, 18–36
Advanced: 7–17 odd, 18–38
Standardized Test Prep: 39–42
Mixed Review: 43–47

Reasoning exercises have blue headings.
Applications exercises have red headings.

EXERCISE 25: Use the Think About a Plan worksheet in the **Practice and Problem Solving Workbook** (also available in the Teaching Resources in print and online) to further support students' development in becoming independent learners.

HOMEWORK QUICK CHECK

To check students' understanding of key skills and concepts, go over Exercises 7, 17, 23, 25, and 28.

16. $x = 12$, $JK = 17$, $JM = 17$
17. $y = 3$, $ST = 15$, $TU = 15$
18. 5
19. 10
20. 10
21. isosc., because $TW = ZW$
22. equidistant; RT; RZ
23. At the point on $\overline{XY}$ that lies on the bisector of $\angle GPL$; the goalie does not know to which side of her the player will aim his shot, so she should keep herself equidistant from the sides of $\angle GPL$. Points on the bisector of $\angle GPL$ are equidistant from $\overline{PG}$ and $\overline{PL}$. If she moves to a point on the ⊥ bisector of $\overline{GL}$, she will be closer to $\overline{PL}$ than to $\overline{PG}$.

24a.

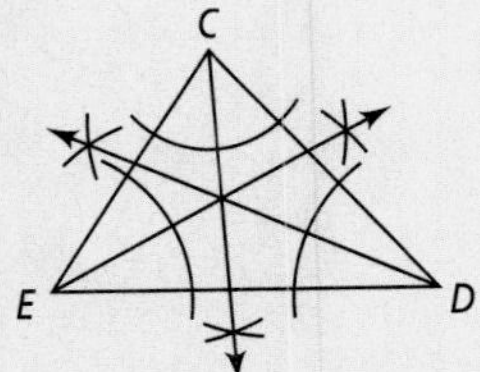

b. Answers may vary. Sample: They meet at a single point.
c. Check students' work.

25a.

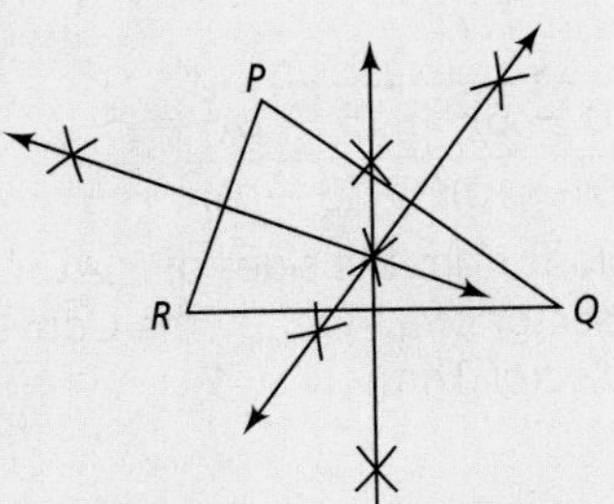

b. Answers may vary. Sample: They meet at a single point.
c. Check students' work.
26. A pt. is on the ⊥ bisector of a seg. if and only if it is equidistant from the endpoints of the seg.
27. A pt. is on the bisector of an ∠ if and only if it is equidistant from the sides of the ∠.

Answers

Practice and Problem-Solving Exercises (continued)

28. To conclude that Q is equidistant from P and R, you must know that $\overline{QS} \perp \overline{PR}$ and that $\overline{QS}$ bisects $\overline{PR}$. The diagram does not show that $PS = SR$.

29. No; A is not equidistant from the sides of $\angle TXR$.

30. Yes; the markings show that $\angle TXA \cong \angle RXA$, so $\overrightarrow{XA}$ is the bisector of $\angle TXR$.

31. Yes; A is equidistant from the sides of $\angle TXR$.

32. $\overline{AM} \cong \overline{BM}$ by definition of bisector. $\overleftrightarrow{PM} \perp \overline{AB}$, so $\angle PMA$ and $\angle PMB$ are rt. $\triangle$s. Therefore, $\angle PMA \cong \angle PMB$ because all rt. $\angle$s are $\cong$. $\overline{PM} \cong \overline{PM}$ by the Refl. Prop. of $\cong$. So $\triangle PMA \cong \triangle PMB$ by SAS, and $\overline{AP} \cong \overline{BP}$ (or $AP = BP$) because corresp. parts of $\cong$ $\triangle$s are $\cong$.

33. $\overline{PA} \cong \overline{PB}$ (Given) and $\angle AMP \cong \angle BMP$ because all rt. $\angle$s are $\cong$. Also, $\overline{PM} \cong \overline{PM}$ by the Refl. Prop. of $\cong$. So rt. $\triangle PMA \cong$ rt. $\triangle PAB$ by HL and $\overline{AM} \cong \overline{BM}$ because corresp. parts of $\cong$ $\triangle$s are $\cong$. Therefore $\overleftrightarrow{PM}$ is the $\perp$ bisector of $\overline{AB}$, by the def. of $\perp$ bisector.

34. In rt. $\triangle SPQ$ and rt. $\triangle SRQ$, $\angle PQS \cong \angle RQS$ (Given), $\angle QPS \cong \angle QRS$ (All rt. $\angle$s are $\cong$.), and $\overline{QS} \cong \overline{QS}$ (Refl. Prop. of $\cong$). So $\triangle SPQ \cong \triangle SRQ$ by AAS, and $\overline{SP} \cong \overline{SR}$ (or $SP = SR$) because corresp. parts of $\cong$ $\triangle$s are $\cong$.

35. In rt. $\triangle SPQ$ and rt. $\triangle SRQ$, $\overline{SP} \cong \overline{SR}$ (Given) and $\overline{QS} \cong \overline{QS}$ (Refl. Prop. of $\cong$), so $\triangle SPQ \cong \triangle SRQ$ by HL. Thus $\angle PQS \cong \angle RQS$ because corresp. parts of $\cong$ $\triangle$s are $\cong$, and $\overrightarrow{QS}$ bisects $\angle PQR$ by the def. of $\angle$ bisector.

36a. $\ell: y = -\frac{3}{4}x + \frac{25}{2}$; $m: x = 10$

b. $C(10, 5)$

c. $CA = \sqrt{(10-6)^2 + (5-8)^2} = 5$;
$CB = \sqrt{(10-10)^2 + (5-0)^2} = 5$

d. C is equidistant from the sides of $\angle AOB$, so C is on the bisector of $\angle AOB$ by the Converse of the $\angle$ Bisector Thm.

28. Error Analysis To prove that $\triangle PQR$ is isosceles, a student began by stating that since Q is on the segment perpendicular to $\overline{PR}$, Q is equidistant from the endpoints of $\overline{PR}$. What is the error in the student's reasoning?

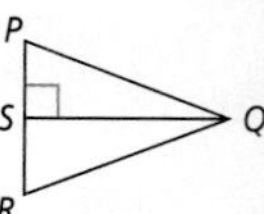

Writing Determine whether A must be on the bisector of $\angle TXR$. Explain.

29.

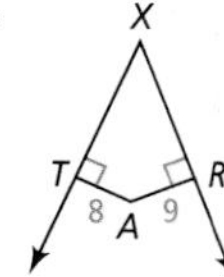

30.

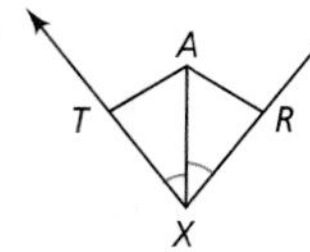

31.

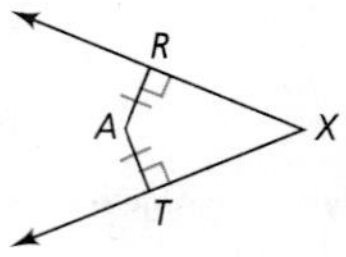

32. Proof Prove the Perpendicular Bisector Theorem.

Given: $\overleftrightarrow{PM} \perp \overline{AB}$, $\overleftrightarrow{PM}$ bisects $\overline{AB}$

Prove: $AP = BP$

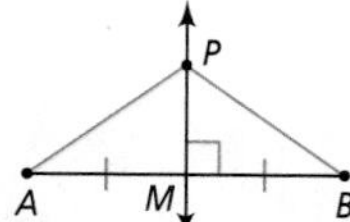

33. Proof Prove the Converse of the Perpendicular Bisector Theorem.

Given: $PA = PB$ with $\overline{PM} \perp \overline{AB}$ at M.

Prove: P is on the perpendicular bisector of $\overline{AB}$.

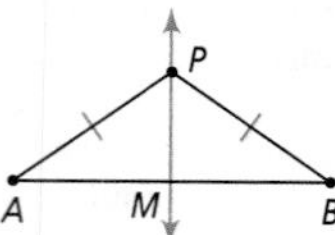

34. Proof Prove the Angle Bisector Theorem.

Given: $\overrightarrow{QS}$ bisects $\angle PQR$, $\overline{SP} \perp \overrightarrow{QP}$, $\overline{SR} \perp \overrightarrow{QR}$

Prove: $SP = SR$

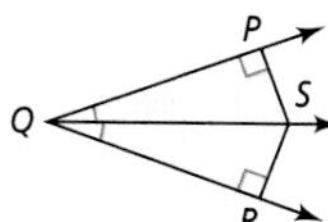

35. Proof Prove the Converse of the Angle Bisector Theorem.

Given: $\overline{SP} \perp \overrightarrow{QP}$, $\overline{SR} \perp \overrightarrow{QR}$, $SP = SR$

Prove: $\overrightarrow{QS}$ bisects $\angle PQR$.

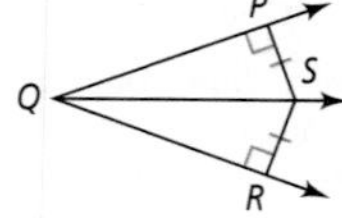

36. Coordinate Geometry Use points $A(6, 8)$, $O(0, 0)$, and $B(10, 0)$.

a. Write equations of lines ℓ and m such that $\ell \perp \overrightarrow{OA}$ at A and $m \perp \overrightarrow{OB}$ at B.

b. Find the intersection C of lines ℓ and m.

c. Show that $CA = CB$.

d. Explain why C is on the bisector of $\angle AOB$.

Challenge

37. A, B, and C are three noncollinear points. Describe and sketch a line in plane ABC such that points A, B, and C are equidistant from the line. Justify your response.

38. **Reasoning** M is the intersection of the perpendicular bisectors of two sides of $\triangle ABC$. Line ℓ is perpendicular to plane ABC at M. Explain why a point E on ℓ is equidistant from A, B, and C. (*Hint:* See page 48, Exercise 33. Explain why $\triangle EAM \cong \triangle EBM \cong \triangle ECM$.)

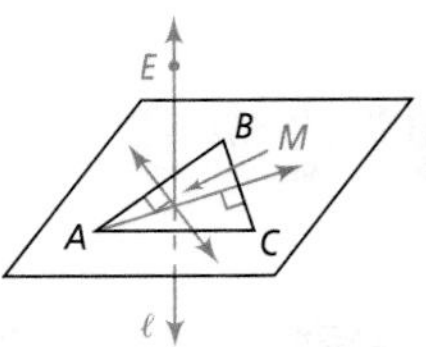

Standardized Test Prep

SAT/ACT

39. For $A(1, 3)$ and $B(1, 9)$, which point lies on the perpendicular bisector of $\overline{AB}$?

Ⓐ (3, 3) Ⓑ (1, 5) Ⓒ (6, 6) Ⓓ (3, 12)

40. What is the converse of the following conditional statement?
If a triangle is isosceles, then it has two congruent angles.

Ⓕ If a triangle is isosceles, then it has two congruent sides.
Ⓖ If a triangle has congruent sides, then it is equilateral.
Ⓗ If a triangle has two congruent angles, then it is isosceles.
Ⓘ If a triangle is not isosceles, then it does not have two congruent angles.

41. Which figure represents the statement $\overline{BD}$ bisects $\angle ABC$?

Ⓐ 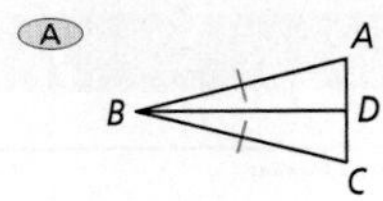

Ⓑ 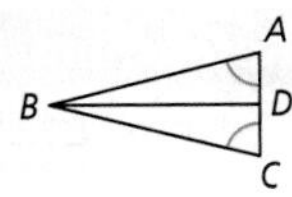

Ⓒ 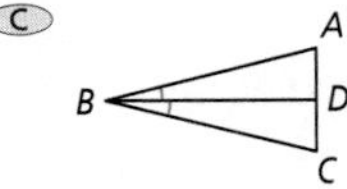

Ⓓ 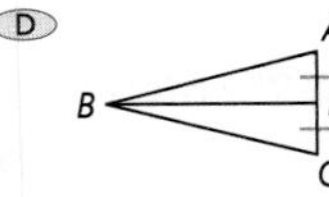

Short Response

42. The line $y = 7$ is the perpendicular bisector of the segment with endpoints $A(2, 10)$ and $B(2, k)$. What is the value of k? Explain your reasoning.

Mixed Review

43. Find the value of x in the figure at the right.

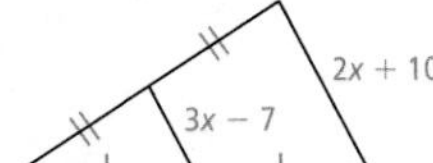

See Lesson 5-1.

44. $\angle 1$ and $\angle 2$ are complementary and $\angle 1$ and $\angle 3$ are supplementary. If $m\angle 2 = 30$, what is $m\angle 3$?

See Lesson 1-5.

Get Ready! **To prepare for Lesson 5-3, do Exercises 45–47.**

45. What is the slope of a line that is perpendicular to the line $y = -3x + 4$?

See Lesson 3-8.

46. Line ℓ is a horizontal line. What is the slope of a line perpendicular to ℓ?

47. Describe the line $x = 5$.

39. C
40. H
41. C
42. [2] Point $A(2, 10)$ is 3 units above the line $y = 7$. Therefore point B must be 3 units below $y = 7$, so the y-coordinate of B must be 4. Since the coordinates of B are $(2, k)$, $k = 4$.
[1] incomplete OR incorrect explanation
43. 6
44. 120
45. $\frac{1}{3}$
46. undefined
47. Answers may vary. Sample: It is a vertical line that contains the point (5, 0).

37. Line ℓ through the midpts. of two sides of $\triangle ABC$ is equidistant from A, B, and C. This is because $\triangle 1 \cong \triangle 2$ and $\triangle 3 \cong \triangle 4$ by ASA. $\overline{AD} \cong \overline{BE}$ and $\overline{BE} \cong \overline{CF}$ because corresp. parts of $\cong$ ⚠ are $\cong$. By the Trans. Prop. of $\cong$, $\overline{AD} \cong \overline{BE} \cong \overline{CF}$. By the def. of $\cong$, $AD = BE = CF$, so points A, B, and C are equidistant from line ℓ.

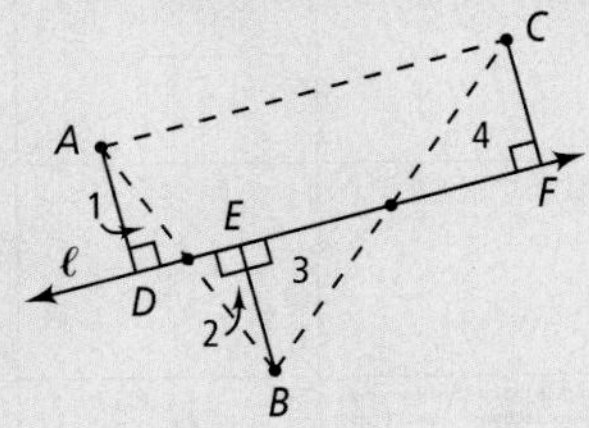

38. M is on the ⊥ bisectors of $\overline{AB}$ and $\overline{BC}$, so $MA = MB$ and $MB = MC$ by the ⊥ Bis. Thm. So $MA = MB = MC$ by the Transitive Prop. of Eq. $\angle AME \cong \angle BME \cong \angle CME$ because if a line is ⊥ to a plane then it is ⊥ to every line in the plane that contains the intersection of the plane and the line (and all rt. ∠s are $\cong$). $\overline{EM} \cong \overline{EM}$ by the Refl. Prop. of $\cong$. So $\triangle EAM \cong \triangle EBM \cong \triangle ECM$ by SAS. Therefore, $\overline{EA} \cong \overline{EB} \cong \overline{EC}$, since corresp. parts of $\cong$ ⚠ are $\cong$. So $EA = EB = EC$.

5-2 Lesson Resources

Differentiated Remediation

Instructional Support

Geometry Companion

Students can use the **Geometry Companion** worktext (4 pages) . . .

- New Vocabulary
- Key Concepts
- Got It for each Problem
- Lesson Check

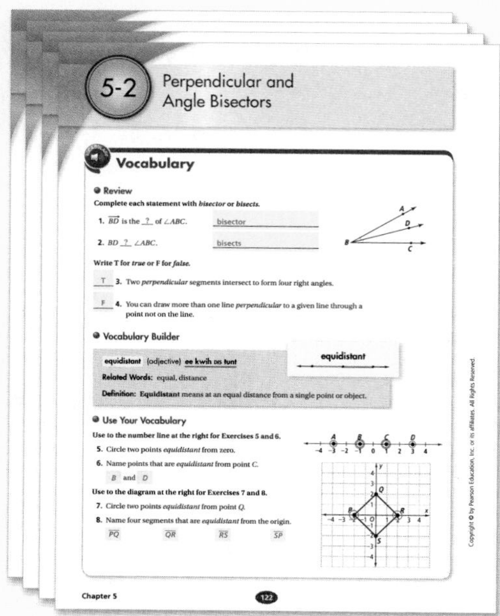

5-2 Perpendicular and Angle Bisectors

Vocabulary

Review

Complete each statement with *bisector* or *bisects*.

1. $\overrightarrow{BD}$ is the _?_ of $\angle ABC$. bisector
2. BD _?_ $\angle ABC$. bisects

Write T for *true* or F for *false*.

T 3. Two *perpendicular* segments intersect to form four right angles.

F 4. You can draw more than one line *perpendicular* to a given line through a point not on the line.

Vocabulary Builder

equidistant (adjective) **ee kwih DIS tunt**

Related Words: equal, distance

Definition: Equidistant means at an equal distance from a single point or object.

Use Your Vocabulary

Use to the number line at the right for Exercises 5 and 6.

5. Circle two points *equidistant* from zero.
6. Name points that are *equidistant* from point C.
   B and D

Use to the diagram at the right for Exercises 7 and 8.

7. Circle two points *equidistant* from point Q.
8. Name four segments that are *equidistant* from the origin.
   $\overline{PQ}$ $\overline{QR}$ $\overline{RS}$ $\overline{SP}$

Chapter 5 122

ELL Support

Use Graphic Organizers Have students verbalize their knowledge of triangles as they work with peers. Have students work in groups of four or five to make graphic organizers showing facts they have learned about triangles. Students should include:

- different kinds of triangles.
- facts about right triangles.
- theorems about triangle congruence.
- facts about triangle midsegments.

Encourage students to use illustrations and familiar language to make formal mathematical terms more understandable. Have each group show their completed graphic organizer to another group. Allow students to add to their graphic organizers as they learn more about triangles.

5 Assess & Remediate

Lesson Quiz

1. What is *RU*?

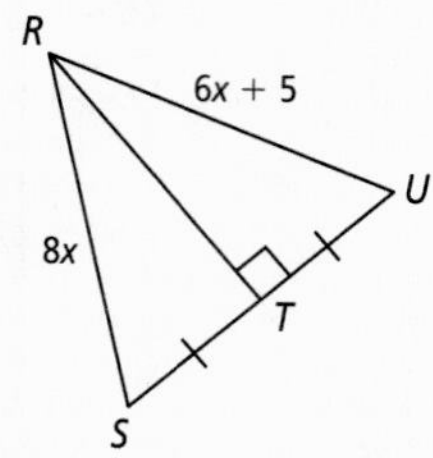

2. **Do you UNDERSTAND?** In the diagram above, if $\overline{RT}$ is extended to contain a point *W* so the *UW* has a length of 8, what is the length of *SW*?
3. What is *CD*?

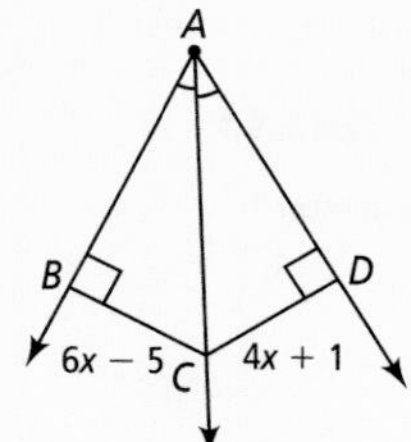

ANSWERS TO LESSON QUIZ

1. 20
2. 8
3. 13

PRESCRIPTION FOR REMEDIATION

Use the student work on the Lesson Quiz to prescribe a differentiated review assignment.

Points	Differentiated Remediation
0–1	Intervention
2	On-level
3	Extension

PowerGeometry.com

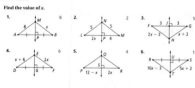

5 Assess & Remediate

Assign the Lesson Quiz. Appropriate intervention, practice, or enrichment is automatically generated based on student performance.

Intervention

- **Reteaching** (2 pages) Provides reteaching and practice exercises for the key lesson concepts. Use with struggling students or absent students.
- **English Language Learner Support** Helps students develop and reinforce mathematical vocabulary and key concepts.

All-in-One Resources/Online

Reteaching

5-2 **Reteaching**

Perpendicular and Angle Bisectors

Perpendicular Bisectors

There are two useful theorems to remember about perpendicular bisectors.

Perpendicular Bisector Theorem

If a point is on the perpendicular bisector of a segment, then it is equidistant from the endpoints of the segment.

X is on the perpendicular bisector, so it is equidistant from the endpoints *A* and *B*.

Converse of the Perpendicular Bisector Theorem

If a point is equidistant from the endpoints of a segment, then it is on the perpendicular bisector of the segment.

Because *X* is equidistant from the endpoints *C* and *D*, it is on the perpendicular bisector of the segment.

Problem

What is the value of *x*?

Since *A* is equidistant from the endpoints of the segment, it is on the perpendicular bisector of $\overline{EG}$. So, $EF = GF$ and $x = 4$.

Exercises

Find the value of *x*.

1. 8
2. 2
3. 5
4. 6
5. 4
6. 1

All-in-One Resources/Online

English Language Learner Support

5-2 **ELL Support**

Perpendicular and Angle Bisectors

Complete the vocabulary chart by filling in the missing information.

Word or Word Phrase	Statement of Theorem	Picture or Example
Perpendicular Bisector Theorem	If a point is on the perpendicular bisector of a segment, then it is equidistant from the endpoints of the segment.	
Converse of Perpendicular Bisector Theorem	1. If a point is equidistant from the endpoints of a segment, then it is on the perpendicular bisector of the segment.	
Angle Bisector Theorem	2. If a point is on the bisector of an angle, then the point is equidistant from the sides of the angle.	
Converse of Angle Bisector Theorem	If a point in the interior of an angle is equidistant from the sides of the angle, then the point is on the angle bisector.	3.

Differentiated Remediation *continued*

On-Level

- **Practice** (2 pages) Provides extra practice for each lesson. For simpler practice exercises, use the Form K Practice pages found in the All-in-One Teaching Resources and online.
- **Think About a Plan** Helps students develop specific problem-solving skills and strategies by providing scaffolded guiding questions.
- **Standardized Test Prep** Focuses on all major exercises, all major question types, and helps students prepare for the high-stakes assessments.

Extension

- **Enrichment** Provides students with interesting problems and activities that extend the concepts of the lesson.
- **Activities, Games, and Puzzles** Worksheets that can be used for concepts development, enrichment, and for fun!

Practice and Problem Solving Wkbk/ All-in-One Resources/Online

Practice page 1

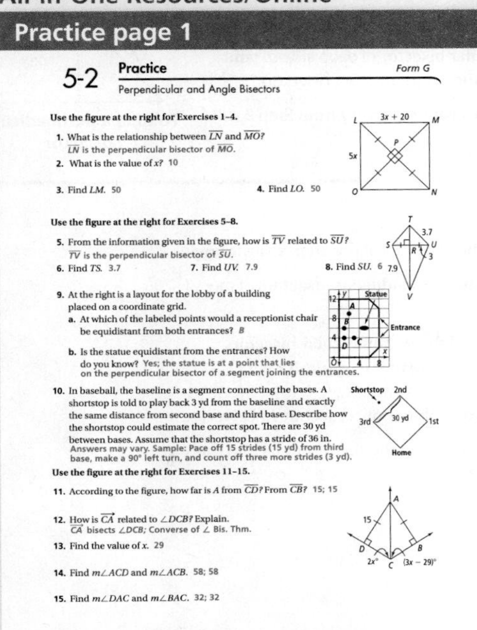

5-2 Practice — Form G
Perpendicular and Angle Bisectors

Use the figure at the right for Exercises 1–4.

1. What is the relationship between $\overline{LN}$ and $\overline{MO}$? $\overline{LN}$ is the perpendicular bisector of $\overline{MO}$.
2. What is the value of x? 10
3. Find LM. 50
4. Find LO. 50

Use the figure at the right for Exercises 5–8.

5. From the information given in the figure, how is $\overline{TV}$ related to $\overline{SU}$? $\overline{TV}$ is the perpendicular bisector of $\overline{SU}$.
6. Find TS. 3.7
7. Find UV. 7.9
8. Find SU. 6
9. At the right is a layout for the lobby of a building placed on a coordinate grid.
   a. At which of the labeled points would a receptionist chair be equidistant from both entrances? B
   b. Is the statue equidistant from the entrances? How do you know? Yes; the statue is at a point that lies on the perpendicular bisector of a segment joining the entrances.
10. In baseball, the baseline is a segment connecting the bases. A shortstop is told to play back 3 yd from the baseline and exactly the same distance from second base and third base. Describe how the shortstop could estimate the correct spot. There are 30 yd between bases. Assume that the shortstop has a stride of 36 in. Answers may vary. Sample: Pace off 15 strides (15 yd) from third base, make a 90° left turn, and count off three more strides (3 yd).

Use the figure at the right for Exercises 11–15.

11. According to the figure, how far is A from $\overleftrightarrow{CD}$? From $\overleftrightarrow{CB}$? 15; 15
12. How is $\overrightarrow{CA}$ related to $\angle DCB$? Explain. $\overrightarrow{CA}$ bisects $\angle DCB$; Converse of $\angle$ Bis. Thm.
13. Find the value of x. 29
14. Find $m\angle ACD$ and $m\angle ACB$. 58; 58
15. Find $m\angle DAC$ and $m\angle BAC$. 32; 32

Practice and Problem Solving Wkbk/ All-in-One Resources/Online

Practice page 2

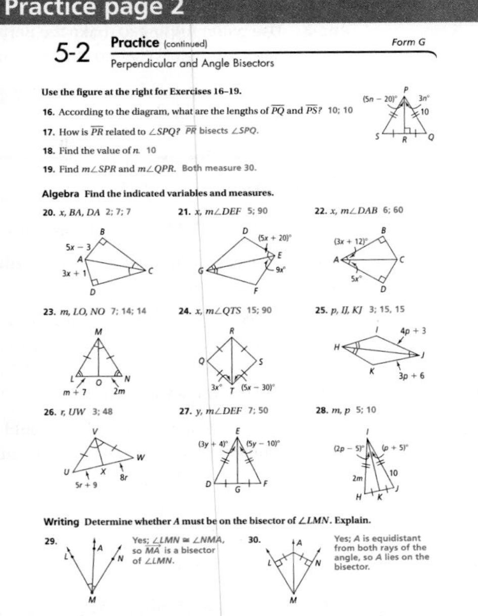

5-2 Practice (continued) — Form G
Perpendicular and Angle Bisectors

Use the figure at the right for Exercises 16–19.

16. According to the diagram, what are the lengths of $\overline{PQ}$ and $\overline{PS}$? 10; 10
17. How is $\overline{PR}$ related to $\angle SPQ$? $\overline{PR}$ bisects $\angle SPQ$.
18. Find the value of n. 10
19. Find $m\angle SPR$ and $m\angle QPR$. Both measure 30.

Algebra Find the indicated variables and measures.

20. x, BA, DA 2; 7; 7
21. x, $m\angle DEF$ 5; 90
22. x, $m\angle DAB$ 6; 60
23. m, LO, NO 7; 14; 14
24. x, $m\angle QTS$ 15; 90
25. p, IJ, KJ 3; 15, 15
26. r, UW 3; 48
27. y, $m\angle DEF$ 7; 50
28. m, p 5; 10

Writing Determine whether A must be on the bisector of $\angle LMN$. Explain.

29. Yes; $\angle LMN \cong \angle NMA$, so $\overrightarrow{MA}$ is a bisector of $\angle LMN$.
30. Yes; A is equidistant from both rays of the angle, so A lies on the bisector.

All-in-One Resources/Online

Enrichment

5-2 Enrichment
Perpendicular and Angle Bisectors

Angle Bisectors and Daisy Designs

Materials
- Compass
- Straightedge

Follow the directions to replicate the daisy design.

1. Use a compass to construct a circle.
2. Pick a point on the circle, keeping the radius the same, and mark a full arc that intersects the circle.
3. From the intersection point of the arc and circle, make another full arc and continue around the circle.
4. Create a point at each intersection.
5. Using two consecutive points on the circle and the center of the circle, draw an angle with the vertex at the center of the circle.
6. Bisect that angle.
7. Mark the point of intersection with the circle.
8. Using this point and the original radius of the circle, make an arc and continue around the circle. Create a point at each intersection.
9. Starting from any point, draw full arcs to connect two points on the circle.
10. Continue around the circle. When the figure is complete, erase any unnecessary marks. Check students' work. Sample:

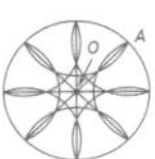

Use your knowledge of straightedge and compass constructions to create the daisy design below.

11. Check students' work. Give hint: $m\angle AOB = 45°$. Sample:

Practice and Problem Solving Wkbk/ All-in-One Resources/Online

Think About a Plan

5-2 Think About a Plan
Perpendicular and Angle Bisectors

a. **Constructions** Draw a large acute scalene triangle, $\triangle PQR$. Construct the perpendicular bisectors of each side.
b. **Make a Conjecture** What appears to be true about the perpendicular bisectors?
c. Test your conjecture with another triangle.

1. For part (a), what is an acute scalene triangle? a triangle in which all angles are acute and no side lengths are equal
2. Sketch a large acute scalene triangle. Use a protractor to make sure each angle is less than 90°. Label the vertices P, Q, and R. Check to make sure the triangle is scalene by comparing the side lengths.
3. To construct the perpendicular bisector for $\overline{PQ}$, set the compass to greater than $\frac{1}{2}QP$. Draw two arcs, one from P and one from R. The arcs intersect at two points. Draw a segment connecting the points. This segment is the perpendicular bisector.
4. Construct the perpendicular bisectors of $\overline{QR}$ and $\overline{RP}$.
5. For part (b), examine the three perpendicular bisectors. Write a conjecture about the perpendicular bisectors in all triangles. Answers may vary. Sample: The perpendicular bisectors of any triangle intersect at one point inside the triangle.
6. For part (c), repeat Steps 1–4 for an obtuse, equilateral, or isosceles triangle. Does the conjecture appear to be true for this triangle? Answers may vary. Sample: No; for an obtuse triangle, the intersection of the perpendicular bisectors lies outside the triangle.

Practice and Problem Solving Wkbk/ All-in-One Resources/Online

Standardized Test Prep

5-2 Standardized Test Prep
Perpendicular and Angle Bisectors

Multiple Choice

For Exercises 1–6, choose the correct letter. Use the figure at the right.

1. Which ray is a bisector of $\angle ABC$? B
   A. $\overrightarrow{BC}$ B. $\overrightarrow{BD}$ C. $\overrightarrow{BA}$ D. $\overrightarrow{BF}$
2. What is GH? H
   F. 5 G. 10 H. 15 I. 25
3. What is the value of y? A
   A. 2 B. 4 C. 16 D. 20
4. What is $m\angle DBE$? H
   F. 20 G. 30 H. 40 I. 50
5. What is $m\angle ABE$? D
   A. 20 B. 30 C. 40 D. 60
6. If $m\angle FBA = 7x + 6y$, what is $m\angle FBA$? H
   F. 40 G. 44 H. 47 I. 60

Short Response

7. Construct the bisector of $\angle ABC$. Answers may vary. Sample:
   [2] Student construction is accurate and complete, including three arcs and a bisector labeled with two points. [1] The construction is incorrect or there are key elements, such as one of the arcs, missing. [0] There is no ray added to the diagram.

Online Teacher Resource Center

Activities, Games, and Puzzles

5-2 Game: Quick Draw for Special Angles
Perpendicular and Angle Bisectors

Materials
- A set of Quick Draw cards
- Board, overhead, or large piece of paper mounted on a wall
- Timer

Setup

Cut out the cards below. Place them into a hat or container and mix them up.

acute angle	180° straight angle	120° angle
congruent angles	45° angle	complementary angles
vertical angles	supplementary angles	perpendicular bisector
60° angle	alternate exterior angles	ray
angle bisector	right angle	alternate interior angles

Divide students into two teams. Each team selects a Sketcher—someone who will draw. This duty rotates to all players in turn. The remaining team members try to guess the word or phrase. A teacher or student not on a team should monitor the time and the rules.

Game Play and Scoring

Determine which team will go first. The Sketcher picks a card and—without revealing it to his or her team members—has only 5 seconds to study the word he or she will sketch. After 5 seconds the teacher or an impartial student should start the time.

The Sketcher has 60 seconds to draw clues for his or her teammates, as long as he or she remains silent; draws no words, letters, or numbers; and uses no body gestures. The team shouts guesses. If teammates shout part of the word or phrase, the sketcher can record it on the board.

If the team guesses the correct word in the allotted time, they receive a point. If the team does not guess in the allotted time or if the Sketcher speaks, writes letters or numbers, or makes any gestures, then the team does not score a point. The person drawing for the opposing team can then take the card and draw. If that team guesses correctly, they score the point for that card.

The other team then picks a new card and draws.

Ending the Game

The game continues until either all cards have been selected and drawn or class time runs out. The team scoring the most points wins!

Guided Instruction

PURPOSE To use paper-folding activities to investigate angle bisectors of a triangle
PROCESS Students will
- use paper folding to make the angle bisectors of each angle of an acute triangle, a right triangle, and an obtuse triangle, and make conjectures about them.
- use paper folding to make the perpendicular bisectors of each side of an acute triangle and a right triangle, and make discoveries about them.

DISCUSS In Chapter 1, students constructed angle bisectors and perpendicular bisectors using a compass and straightedge. Review this process with students to gain context for the activities.

Activity 1
In this Activity students use paper folding to make all three angle bisectors of a triangle.

Q From the point where the angle bisectors intersect each side of your triangle, what do you notice about the distance to the sides? **[The point where the angle bisectors intersect is equidistant to each side of the triangle.]**

Activity 2
In this Activity students use paper folding to make all three perpendicular bisectors of a triangle.

Q From the point where the perpendicular bisectors intersect, what do you notice about the distance to the vertices? **[The point where the perpendicullar bisectors intersect is equidistant to the vertices.]**

Concept Byte: Paper Folding Bisectors
Use With Lesson 5-3
ACTIVITY

In Activity 1, you will use paper folding to investigate the bisectors of the angles of a triangle.

Activity 1

Step 1 Draw and cut out three different triangles: one acute, one right, and one obtuse.

Step 2 Use paper folding to make the angle bisectors of each angle of your acute triangle. What do you notice about the angle bisectors?

Step 3 Repeat Step 2 with your right triangle and your obtuse triangle. Does your discovery from Step 2 still hold true?

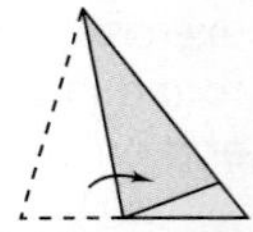
Folding an angle bisector

In Activity 2, you will use paper folding to investigate the perpendicular bisectors of the sides of a triangle.

Activity 2

Step 1 Draw and cut out two different triangles: one acute and one right.

Step 2 Use paper folding to make the perpendicular bisector of each side of your acute triangle. What do you notice about the perpendicular bisectors?

Step 3 Repeat Step 1 with your right triangle. Does your discovery from Step 2 still hold true?

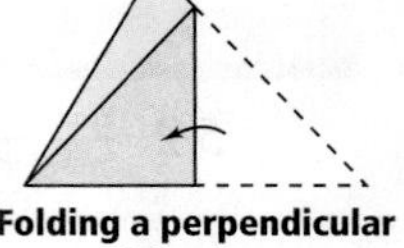
Folding a perpendicular bisector

Exercises

1. **Make a Conjecture** Make a conjecture about the bisectors of the angles of a triangle.
2. **Make a Conjecture** Make a conjecture about the perpendicular bisectors of the sides of a triangle.
3. **Extend** Draw and cut out an obtuse triangle. Fold the perpendicular bisectors.
   a. How do the results for your obtuse triangle compare to the results for your acute and right triangles from Activity 2?
   b. Based on your answer to part (a), how would you revise your conjecture in Exercise 2?
4. **Extend** For what type of triangle would the three perpendicular bisectors and the three angle bisectors intersect at the same point?

Answers

Exercises

1. The bisectors of the $\angle$s of a $\triangle$ meet at a single point.

2. The $\perp$ bisectors of the sides of a $\triangle$ meet at a single point.

3a. The $\perp$ bisectors meet at a single point, but that point is outside the $\triangle$.

b. Answers may vary. Check students' work.

4. an equilateral $\triangle$

5-3 Bisectors in Triangles

TN State Performance Indicator
SPI 3108.4.12 Solve problems involving congruence, similarity, proportional reasoning and/or scale factor of two similar figures or solids.

Objective To identify properties of perpendicular bisectors and angle bisectors

The lines you drew to each side of the triangle aren't just regular perpendicular lines!

Getting Ready!

Construct a circle and label its center C. Choose any three points on the circle and connect them to form a triangle. Draw three lines from C such that each line is perpendicular to one side of the triangle. What conjecture can you make about the two segments into which each side of the triangle is divided? Justify your reasoning.

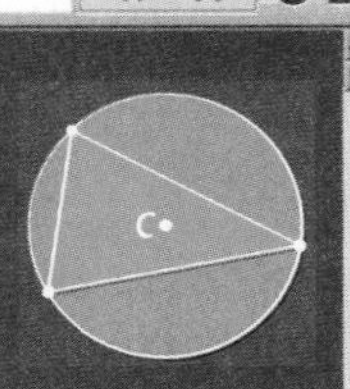

Dynamic Activity Bisectors in Triangles

Lesson Vocabulary
- concurrent
- point of concurrency
- circumcenter of a triangle
- circumscribed about
- incenter of a triangle
- inscribed in

In the Solve It, the three lines you drew intersect at one point, the center of the circle. When three or more lines intersect at one point, they are **concurrent.** The point at which they intersect is the **point of concurrency.**

Essential Understanding For any triangle, certain sets of lines are always concurrent. Two of these sets of lines are the perpendicular bisectors of the triangle's three sides and the bisectors of the triangle's three angles.

take note

Theorem 5-6 Concurrency of Perpendicular Bisectors Theorem

Theorem	Diagram	Symbols
The perpendicular bisectors of the sides of a triangle are concurrent at a point equidistant from the vertices.	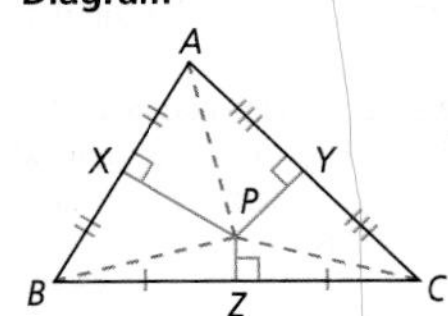	Perpendicular bisectors $\overline{PX}$, $\overline{PY}$, and $\overline{PZ}$ are concurrent at P. $PA = PB = PC$

The point of concurrency of the perpendicular bisectors of a triangle is called the **circumcenter of the triangle.**

Since the circumcenter is equidistant from the vertices, you can use the circumcenter as the center of the circle that contains each vertex of the triangle. You say the circle is **circumscribed about** the triangle.

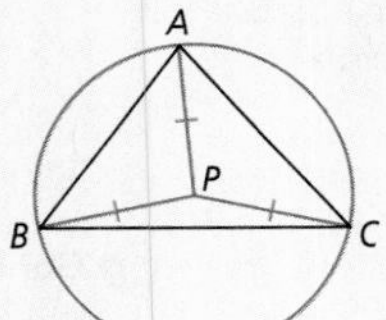

1 Interactive Learning

Solve It!

PURPOSE To discover the relationship between the center of a circle and the perpendicular bisectors of an inscribed triangle

PROCESS Students may
- sketch the diagram as described.
- measure the segments created by the perpendicular segments.

FACILITATE

Q What is true about the distance from C to the vertices? Explain. **[C is equidistant from each vertex because each vertex is on ⊙C.]**

Q How are the perpendicular segments through C related to the sides of the triangle? Explain. **[By Theorem 5-3, the segments are the perpendicular bisectors of the sides.]**

ANSWER See Solve It in Answers on next page.

CONNECT THE MATH In the Solve It, students should realize that the perpendicular bisectors of a triangle are concurrent at a point which is the center of a circumscribed circle. In the lesson, theorems are presented to prove this.

2 Guided Instruction

Take Note

Ask students to relate the conclusion of the theorem to the diagram they drew in the Solve It. Encourage them to connect the phrase "equidistant from the vertices" to the circumscribed circle. The distance from the center of the circle to each vertex is the same because it represents the radius of the circle.

5-3 Preparing to Teach

BIG ideas **Reasoning and Proof**
Measurement

ESSENTIAL UNDERSTANDINGS
- A triangle's three perpendicular bisectors are always concurrent.
- A triangle's three angle bisectors are always concurrent.

Math Background

The points of concurrency in a triangle have special properties based on the segments that create them. Students must apply their knowledge of perpendicular bisectors and angle bisectors to understand the properties of the points of concurrency.

A circumcenter is so named because it is the center of a circumscribed circle.

Similarly, an incenter is so named because it is the center of an inscribed circle.

Points of concurrency are useful in locating a point that is equidistant from three points or three segments. Architects, landscapers, and city planners can use these points to determine the location of key points. Lesson 5-4 will present the points of concurrency of the medians and altitudes of a triangle.

Make sure students understand that the point of concurrency for angle bisectors is equidistant from the sides and that the point of concurrency for perpendicular bisectors of sides is equidistant from the vertices. This is often a point of confusion for students.

Support Student Learning

Use the **Geometry Companion** to engage and support students during instructions. See Lesson Resources at the end of this lesson for details.

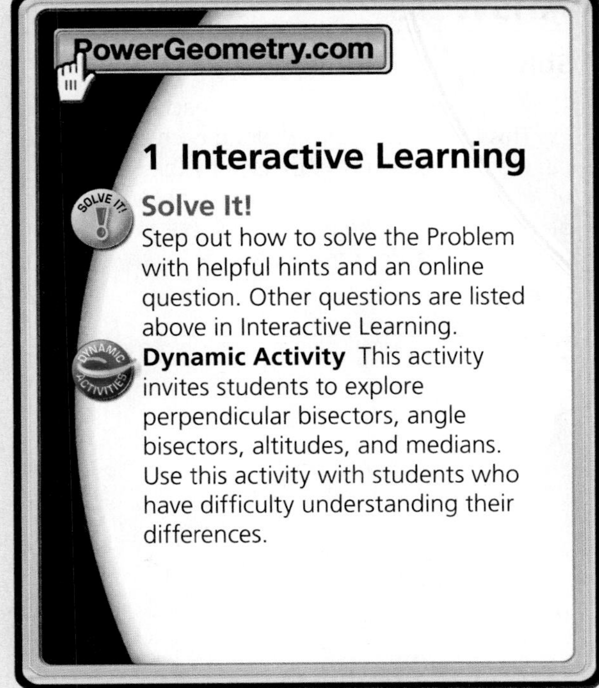

PowerGeometry.com

1 Interactive Learning

Solve It! Step out how to solve the Problem with helpful hints and an online question. Other questions are listed above in Interactive Learning.

Dynamic Activity This activity invites students to explore perpendicular bisectors, angle bisectors, altitudes, and medians. Use this activity with students who have difficulty understanding their differences.

Have students sketch each segment and its perpendicular bisector separately. Students should use information from the previous lesson to identify congruent segments in their diagram. Then, they can transfer these congruent marks to the larger diagram associated with the proof.

Problem 1

Q Why is it sufficient to find the intersection of two of the three perpendicular bisectors? **[The third perpendicular bisector will intersect at the same point.]**

Q Why is the perpendicular bisector of $\overline{PO}$ a horizontal line? **[$\overline{PO}$ is a vertical line, so a line perpendicular to $\overline{PO}$ must be horizontal.]**

Q What is the equation of a horizontal line? **[$y = a$ where a is the y-coordinate of every point on the line.]**

Q What segment represents the radius of the circle that could circumscribe $\triangle POS$? **[the segment from the center of the hypotenuse to any vertex]**

Q What is the length of the radius? **[$\sqrt{13}$]**

Got It?

Have students sketch the triangle in the coordinate plane. Ask students to identify the equations of the perpendicular bisectors of the horizontal and vertical sides of the triangle, and then use these equations to identify the point of concurrency.

Proof **Proof of Theorem 5-6**

Given: Lines ℓ, m, and n are the perpendicular bisectors of the sides of $\triangle ABC$. P is the intersection of lines ℓ and m.

Prove: Line n contains point P, and $PA = PB = PC$.

Proof: A point on the perpendicular bisector of a segment is equidistant from the endpoints of the segment. Point P is on ℓ, which is the perpendicular bisector of $\overline{AB}$, so $PA = PB$. Using the same reasoning, since P is on m, and m is the perpendicular bisector of $\overline{BC}$, $PB = PC$. Thus, $PA = PC$ by the Transitive Property. Since $PA = PC$, P is equidistant from the endpoints of $\overline{AC}$. Then, by the converse of the Perpendicular Bisector Theorem, P is on line n, the perpendicular bisector of $\overline{AC}$.

The circumcenter of a triangle can be inside, on, or outside a triangle.

Acute triangle	Right triangle	Obtuse triangle
	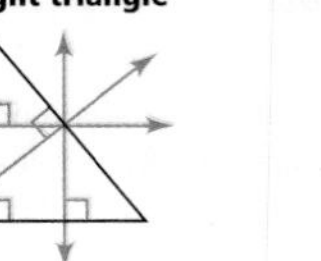	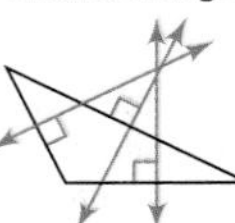

Problem 1 Finding the Circumcenter of a Triangle

What are the coordinates of the circumcenter of the triangle with vertices $P(0, 6)$, $O(0, 0)$, and $S(4, 0)$?

Find the intersection point of two of the triangle's perpendicular bisectors. Here, it is easiest to find the perpendicular bisectors of $\overline{PO}$ and $\overline{OS}$.

Think
Does the location of the circumcenter make sense?
Yes, $\triangle POS$ is a right triangle, so its circumcenter should lie on its hypotenuse.

Step 1 (0, 3) is the midpoint of $\overline{PO}$. The line through (0, 3) that is perpendicular to $\overline{PO}$ is $y = 3$.

Step 2 (2, 0) is the midpoint of $\overline{OS}$. The line through (2, 0) that is perpendicular to $\overline{OS}$ is $x = 2$.

Step 3 Find the point where the two perpendicular bisectors intersect. $x = 2$ and $y = 3$ intersect at (2, 3).

The coordinates of the circumcenter of the triangle are (2, 3).

Got It? 1. What are the coordinates of the circumcenter of the triangle with vertices $A(2, 7)$, $B(10, 7)$, and $C(10, 3)$?

Answers

Solve It!

They are ≅. Draw radii from C to each vertex of the △. This forms two right ▲ along each side. In any pair, the shared leg is ≅ to itself by the Refl. Prop. of ≅. The two hypotenuses are ≅, because all radii of a ⊙ are ≅. So the two right ▲ are ≅ by HL. The two segments are corresp. parts of ≅ ▲.

Got It?

1. (6, 5)

PowerGeometry.com

2 Guided Instruction

Each Problem is worked out and supported online.

Problem 1
Finding the Circumcenter of a Triangle
Animated

Problem 2
Using a Circumcenter
Animated

Problem 3
Identifying and Using the Incenter of a Triangle
Animated

Support in Geometry Companion
- Vocabulary
- Key Concepts
- Got It?

Think

How do you find a point equidistant from three points?
As long as the three points are noncollinear, they are vertices of a triangle. Find the circumcenter of the triangle.

Problem 2 Using a Circumcenter

A town planner wants to locate a new fire station equidistant from the elementary, middle, and high schools. Where should he locate the station?

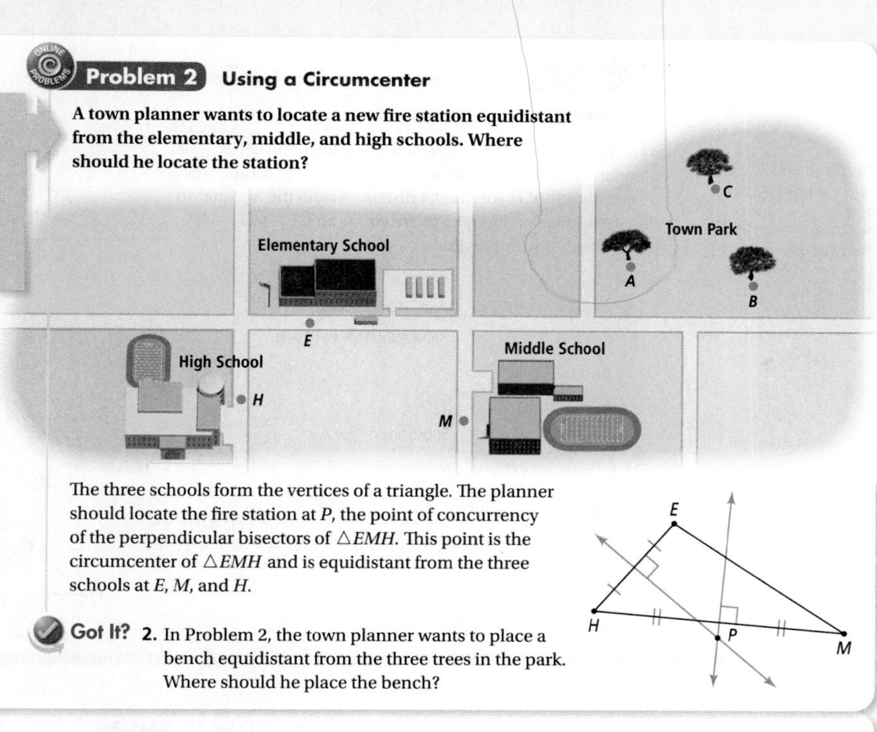

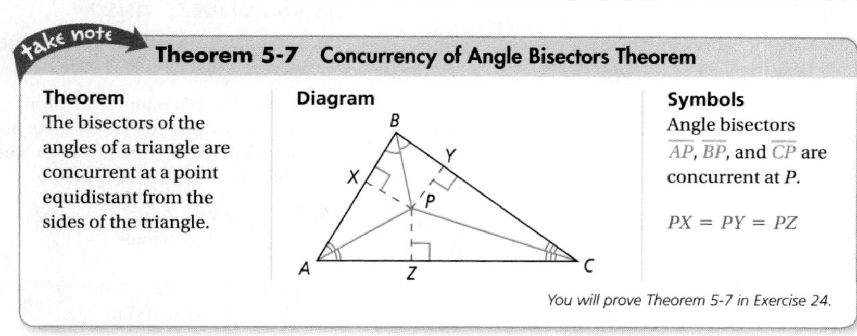

The three schools form the vertices of a triangle. The planner should locate the fire station at P, the point of concurrency of the perpendicular bisectors of $\triangle EMH$. This point is the circumcenter of $\triangle EMH$ and is equidistant from the three schools at E, M, and H.

Got It? **2.** In Problem 2, the town planner wants to place a bench equidistant from the three trees in the park. Where should he place the bench?

take note

Theorem 5-7 Concurrency of Angle Bisectors Theorem

Theorem
The bisectors of the angles of a triangle are concurrent at a point equidistant from the sides of the triangle.

Diagram

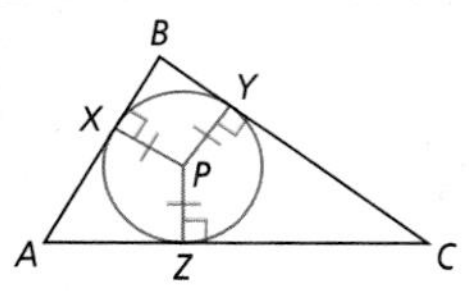

Symbols
Angle bisectors $\overline{AP}$, $\overline{BP}$, and $\overline{CP}$ are concurrent at P.

$PX = PY = PZ$

You will prove Theorem 5-7 in Exercise 24.

The point of concurrency of the angle bisectors of a triangle is called the **incenter of the triangle.** For any triangle, the incenter is always inside the triangle. In the diagram, points X, Y, and Z are equidistant from P, the incenter of $\triangle ABC$. P is the center of the circle that is **inscribed in** the triangle.

Problem 2

Q Why is the point of concurrency of the perpendicular bisectors equidistant from the three buildings? **[The circumcenter is equidistant from the vertices of the triangle. In this problem, the buildings represent the vertices of the triangle.]**

Got It?

Have students make a statement about the location of the bench in relation to the triangle formed by the three trees. Be sure that students can explain how to choose the location.

Take Note

Ask students to use the Angle Bisector Theorem to justify the conclusion of Theorem 5-7. They may need to redraw the triangle and focus on one angle bisector at a time. Emphasize the relationship between the point of concurrency of the angle bisectors and the sides of the triangle. Relate this to the radius of an inscribed circle.

Have students draw three triangles: one that is acute, one that is obtuse, and one that is right. Have them sketch the incenter of each triangle and describe its location. Compare and contrast the possible locations of the circumcenter of a triangle and the incenter of a triangle. Be sure students can explain why the incenter cannot fall outside the triangle. Students should know an inscribed circle is contained within the triangle. Therefore, the center of the circle must also be inside the triangle.

Additional Problems

1. What is the center of the circle that you can circumscribe about a triangle with vertices $A(0, 4)$, $B(0, 0)$, and $C(8, 0)$?

ANSWER (4, 2)

2. A civil engineer wants to install a cell phone tower that is equidistant from the mall, the airport, and the subway. How should the civil engineer determine where to build the tower?

Mall
Airport
Subway

ANSWER The civil engineer should position the cell phone tower at the point of concurrency of the triangle's perpendicular bisectors.

3. $GB = 8x - 7$ and $GD = 5x + 8$. What is GF?

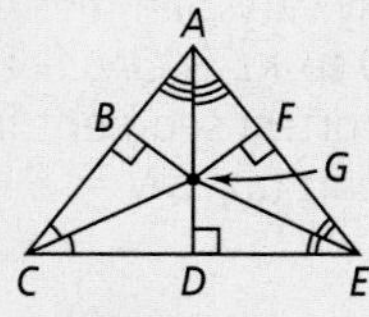

ANSWER 33

Answers

Got It? (continued)

2. at the circumcenter of the $\triangle$ whose vertices are the three trees

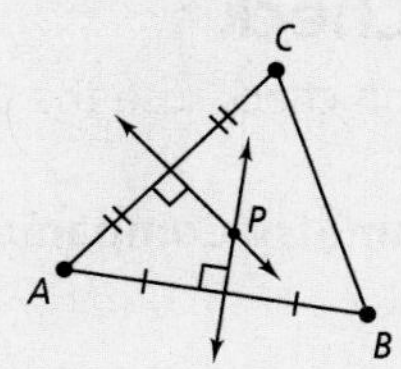

Problem 3

Q How can you justify the statement that G is the point of concurrency of the angle bisectors? **[Each angle of the triangle is bisected.]**

Q Which segments in the diagram are congruent? **[$\overline{GF} \cong \overline{GD} \cong \overline{GE}$]**

Got It?

Q What type of triangle is formed by the segments $\overline{QN}$ and $\overline{QP}$? Explain. **[A right triangle is formed because $\overline{QN} \perp \overline{KL}$.]**

Problem 3 Identifying and Using the Incenter of a Triangle

Think

What is the distance from a point to a line?
The distance from a point to a line is the length of the perpendicular segment that joins the point to the line.

Algebra $GE = 2x - 7$ and $GF = x + 4$. What is GD?

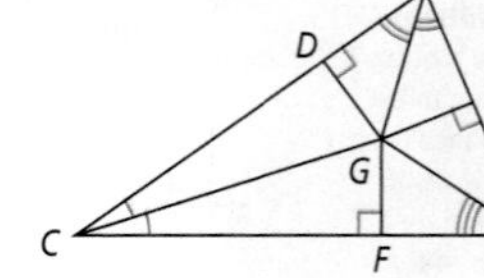

G is the incenter of $\triangle ABC$ because it is the point of concurrency of the angle bisectors. By the Concurrency of Angle Bisectors Theorem, the distances from the incenter to the three sides of the triangle are equal, so $GE = GF = GD$. Use this relationship to find x.

$2x - 7 = x + 4$ — $GE = GF$

$2x = x + 11$ — Add 7 to each side.

$x = 11$ — Subtract x from each side.

Now find GF.

$GF = x + 4$

$= 11 + 4 = 15$ — Substitute 11 for x.

Since $GF = GD$, $GD = 15$.

Got It? 3. a. $QN = 5x + 36$ and $QM = 2x + 51$. What is QO?

b. **Reasoning** Is it possible for QP to equal 50? Explain.

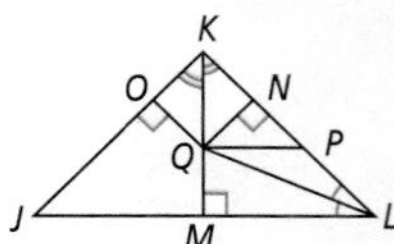

Lesson Check

Do you know HOW?

1. What are the coordinates of the circumcenter of the following triangle?

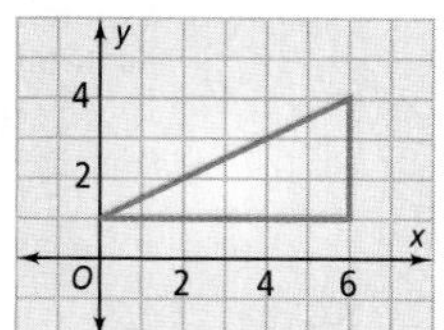

2. In the figure at the right, $TV = 3x - 12$ and $TU = 5x - 24$. What is the value of x?

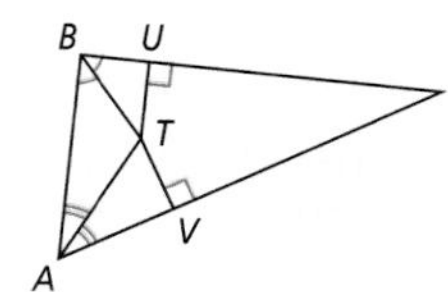

Do you UNDERSTAND?

3. **Vocabulary** A triangle's circumcenter is outside the triangle. What type of triangle is it?

4. **Reasoning** You want to find the circumcenter of a triangle. Why do you only need to find the intersection of two of the triangle's perpendicular bisectors, instead of all three?

5. **Error Analysis** Your friend sees the triangle at the right and concludes that $CT = CP$. What is the error in your friend's reasoning?

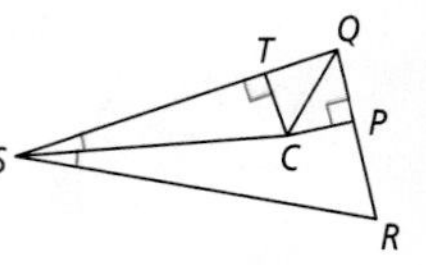

6. **Compare and Contrast** How are the circumcenter and incenter of a triangle alike? How are they different?

3 Lesson Check

Do you know HOW?

- If students have difficulty with Exercise 1, then have them review Problem 1 to see that they must find the center of the circle that circumscribes the triangle.

Do you UNDERSTAND?

- If students have difficulty with Exercise 5, then have them review Problem 3.

Close

Q What are the properties of the circumcenter of a triangle? **[It is equidistant from the vertices of the triangle and contained in the perpendicular bisectors of the sides of the triangle.]**

Q What are the properties of the incenter of a triangle? **[It is equidistant from the sides of the triangle and contained in the bisectors of the angles of the triangle.]**

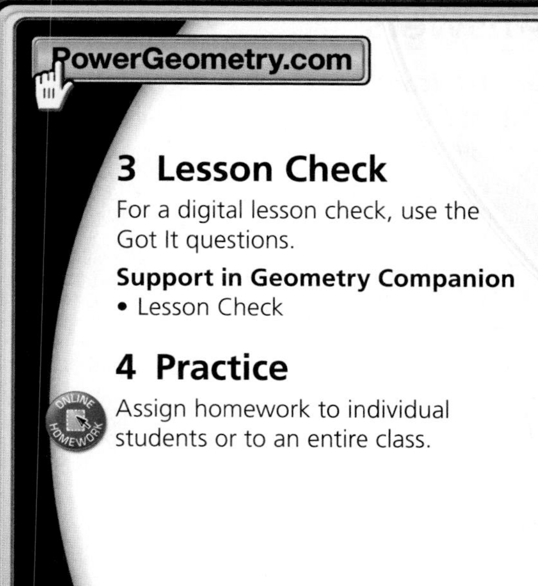

PowerGeometry.com

3 Lesson Check

For a digital lesson check, use the Got It questions.

Support in Geometry Companion
- Lesson Check

4 Practice

Assign homework to individual students or to an entire class.

Answers

Got It? (continued)

3a. 61

b. No; answers may vary. Sample: The distance from Q to $\overline{KL}$ is QN, the length of the shortest segment from Q to $\overline{KL}$. From part (a), $QN = 61$, so $QP > 61$.

Lesson Check

1. (3, 2.5)
2. 6
3. obtuse △
4. Since the three ⊥ bisectors of a △ are concurrent, the third ⊥ bisector goes through the pt. of intersection of the other two ⊥ bisectors.
5. Answers may vary. Sample: The diagram does not show that $\overline{QC}$ bisects $\angle SQR$, so you cannot conclude that point C is equidistant from the sides of $\angle SQR$.
6. Each one is a point of concurrency of bisectors of parts of a △, each is equidistant from three parts of the △, and each is the center of a ⊙ that contains three points of the △. The circumcenter is equidistant from three points, while the incenter is equidistant from three segments. The △ is inside the ⊙ centered at the circumcenter and outside the ⊙ centered at the incenter.

Practice and Problem-Solving Exercises

A Practice

Coordinate Geometry Find the coordinates of the circumcenter of each triangle.

See Problem 1.

7.

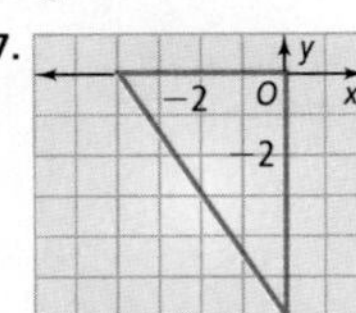

8.

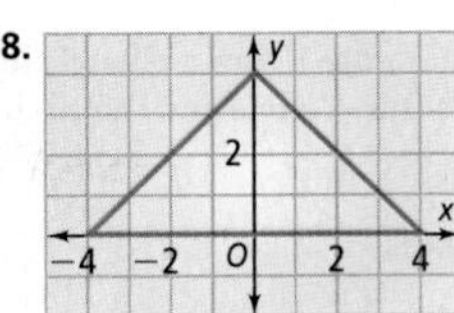

Coordinate Geometry Find the coordinates of the circumcenter of $\triangle ABC$.

9. $A(0, 0)$ $B(3, 0)$ $C(3, 2)$

10. $A(0, 0)$ $B(4, 0)$ $C(4, -3)$

11. $A(-4, 5)$ $B(-2, 5)$ $C(-2, -2)$

12. $A(-1, -2)$ $B(-5, -2)$ $C(-1, -7)$

13. $A(1, 4)$ $B(1, 2)$ $C(6, 2)$

14. City Planning Copy the diagram of the beach. Show where town officials should place a recycling barrel so that it is equidistant from the lifeguard chair, the snack bar, and the volleyball court. Explain.

See Problem 2.

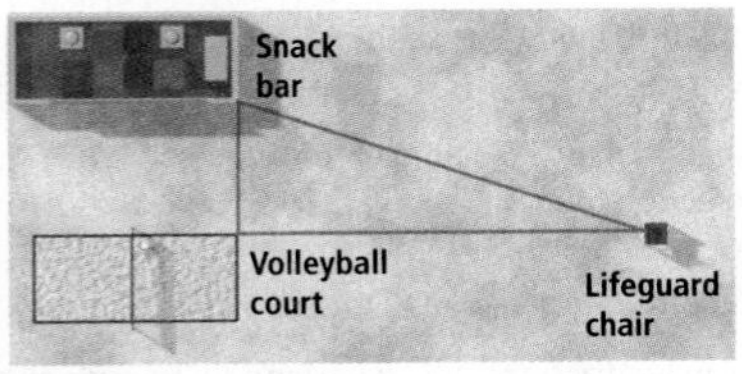

Snack bar

Volleyball court

Lifeguard chair

Name the point of concurrency of the angle bisectors.

See Problem 3.

15.

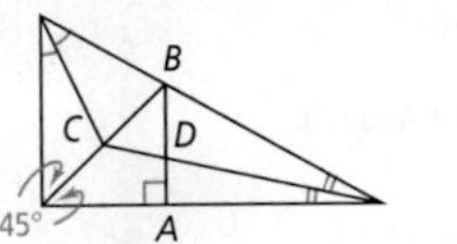

16.

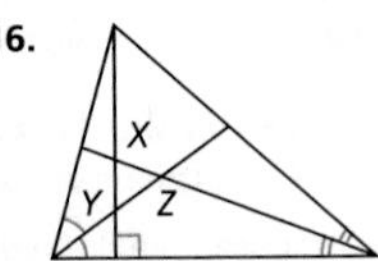

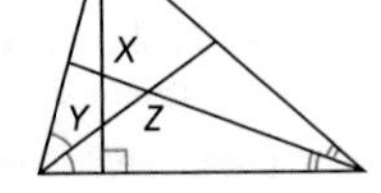

Find the value of x.

17.

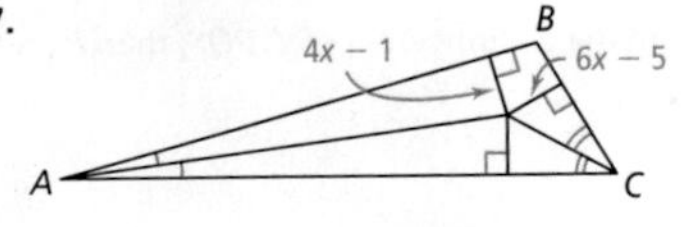

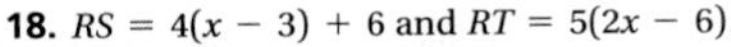

18. $RS = 4(x - 3) + 6$ and $RT = 5(2x - 6)$.

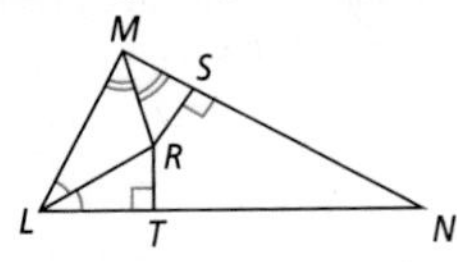

4 Practice

ASSIGNMENT GUIDE

Basic: 7–20 all, 23, 26–29

Average: 7–17 odd, 18–29

Advanced: 7–17 odd, 18–32

Standardized Test Prep: 33–36

Mixed Review: 37–40

Reasoning exercises have blue headings.

Applications exercises have red headings.

EXERCISE 23: Use the Think About a Plan worksheet in the **Practice and Problem Solving Workbook** (also available in the Teaching Resources in print and online) to further support students' development in becoming independent learners.

HOMEWORK QUICK CHECK

To check students' understanding of key skills and concepts, go over Excercises 11, 17, 19, 23, and 26.

Practice and Problem-Solving Exercises

7. (−2, −3)

8. (0, 0)

9. (1.5, 1)

10. (2, −1.5)

11. (−3, 1.5)

12. (−3, −4.5)

13. (3.5, 3)

14. The circumcenter of the △ formed by the lifeguard chair, snack bar, and volleyball court is equidistant from the vertices of the △. Place the recycling barrel at the intersection pt. of two of the triangle's ⊥ bisectors.

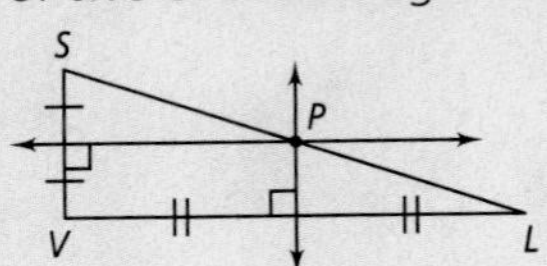

15. C

16. Z

17. 2

18. 4

Answers

Practice and Problem-Solving Exercises (continued)

19. Isosceles; $SR = ST$, so $\angle SRT \cong \angle STR$ (Isosc. △ Thm.). Since P is the incenter of $\triangle RST$, $\overline{PR}$ and $\overline{PT}$ are ∠ bisectors. So $m\angle PRT = \frac{1}{2}m\angle SRT = \frac{1}{2}m\angle STR = m\angle PTR$. Thus $PR = PT$ by the Converse of the Isosc. △ Thm.

20. Inscribed circle: Construct two ∠ bisectors. Their intersection is the center of the circle. Construct a ⊥ to any side from the center. The distance to the side is the radius. Construct a circle with this center and radius. Circumscribed circle: Construct two ⊥ bisectors. Their intersection is the center of the circle. Draw a circle from that center passing through the vertices.

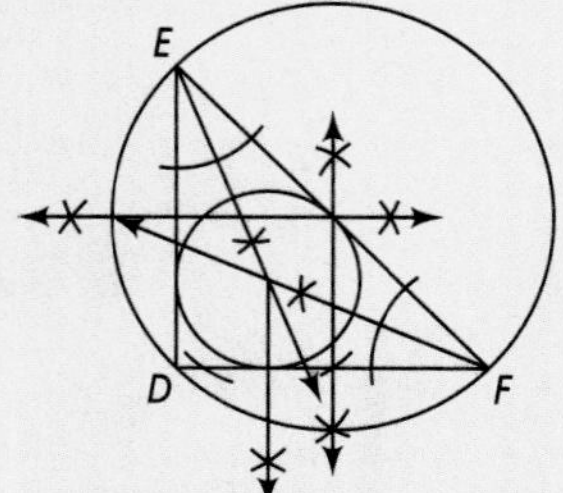

21. Same method as for Exercise 20.

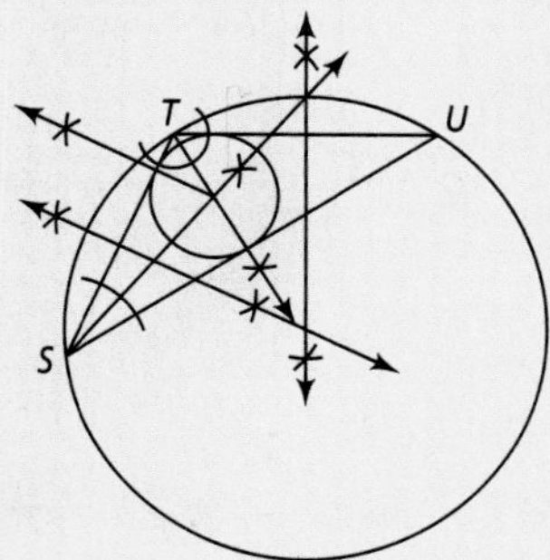

22. $m\angle DGE = 130$, $m\angle DGF = 120$, $m\angle EGF = 110$

23. An interpretation of the passage is that the treasure is equidistant from three Norway pines. To find the treasure, Karl can find the circumcenter of the △ whose vertices are the three pines.

24. From the given information, $\angle XBF \cong \angle XBE$ and $\angle XAE \cong \angle XAD$; also, $\angle XFB \cong \angle XEB \cong \angle XEA \cong \angle XDA$ because ⊥ lines form rt. ∠s, which are ≅. $\overline{XB} \cong \overline{XB}$ and $\overline{XA} \cong \overline{XA}$ by the Reflexive Prop. of ≅, so $\triangle XFB \cong \triangle XEB$ and $\triangle XEA \cong \triangle XDA$ by AAS. Thus $XF = XE$ and $XE = XD$ because corresp. parts of ≅ △s are ≅, and $XF = XD$ by the Transitive Prop. of Equality. Thus X is on the bisector of $\angle BCA$ by the Converse of the ∠ Bisector Thm. Since n is the bisector of $\angle BCA$ (Given), then n contains X.

19. Think About a Plan In the figure at the right, P is the incenter of isosceles $\triangle RST$. What type of triangle is $\triangle RPT$? Explain.
- What segments determine the incenter of a triangle?
- What do you know about the base angles of an isosceles triangle?

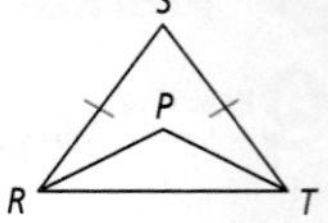

Constructions Draw a triangle that fits the given description. Then construct the inscribed circle and the circumscribed circle. Describe your method.

20. right triangle, $\triangle DEF$

21. obtuse triangle, $\triangle STU$

22. Algebra In the diagram at the right, G is the incenter of $\triangle DEF$, $m\angle DEF = 60$, and $m\angle EFD = 2 \cdot m\angle EDF$. What are $m\angle DGE$, $m\angle DGF$, and $m\angle EGF$?

23. Writing Ivars found an old piece of paper inside an antique book. It read,

From the spot I buried Olaf's treasure, equal sets of paces did I measure; each of three directions in a line, there to plant a seedling Norway pine. I could not return for failing health; now the hounds of Haiti guard my wealth. —Karl

After searching Caribbean islands for five years, Ivars found an island with three tall Norway pines. How might Ivars find where Karl buried Olaf's treasure?

24. Use the diagram at the right to prove the Concurrrency of Angle Bisectors Theorem.
Proof

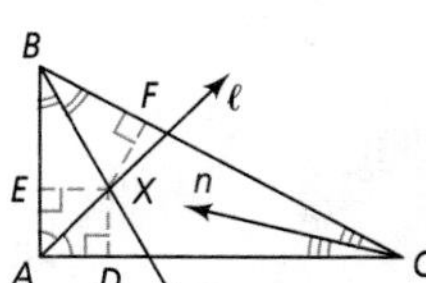

Given: Rays ℓ, m, and n are bisectors of the angles of $\triangle ABC$. X is the intersection of rays ℓ and m, $\overline{XD} \perp \overline{AC}$, $\overline{XE} \perp \overline{AB}$, and $\overline{XF} \perp \overline{BC}$.

Prove: Ray n contains point X, and $XD = XE = XF$.

25. Noise Control You are trying to talk to a friend on the phone in a busy bus station. The buses are so loud that you can hardly hear. Referring to the figure at the right, should you stand at P or C to be as far as possible from all the buses? Explain.

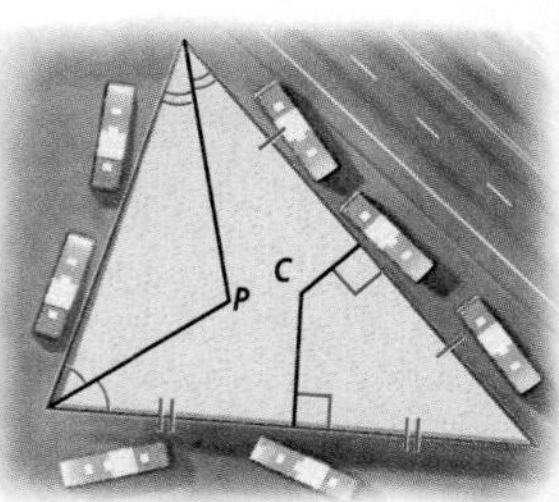

Reasoning Determine whether each statement is *true* or *false*. If the statement is false, give a counterexample.

26. The incenter of a triangle is equidistant from all three vertices.

27. The incenter of a triangle always lies inside the triangle.

28. You can circumscribe a circle about any three points in a plane.

29. If point C is the circumcenter of $\triangle PQR$ and the circumcenter of $\triangle PQS$, then R and S must be the same point.

25. P; the markings in the diagram show that P is the incenter of the triangular station and C is the circumcenter. If you stand at P, you will be equidistant from the three sides along which the buses are parked. If you move away from P, you will move closer to some of the buses.

26. False; the circumcenter is equidistant from the vertices, and the incenter and circumcenter are different (unless the △ is an equilateral △).

27. true

28. False; if the points are collinear, then the ⊥ bisectors of the segments determined by the points will be ∥. Since the ⊥ bisectors are ∥, they will not intersect, so there is no point that is equidistant from all 3 points.

29.

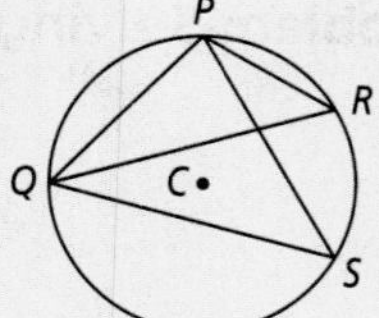

As the diagram shows, circle C is circumscribed about both $\triangle PQR$ and $\triangle PQS$, so points R and S do not have to coincide.

Challenge

30. **Reasoning** Explain why the circumcenter of a right triangle is on one of the triangle's sides.

Determine whether each statement is *always, sometimes,* or *never* true. Explain.

31. It is possible to find a point equidistant from three parallel lines in a plane.

32. The circles inscribed in and circumscribed about an isosceles triangle have the same center.

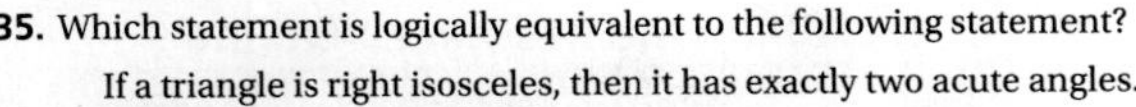

Standardized Test Prep

SAT/ACT

33. Which of the following statements is *false*?

(A) The bisectors of the angles of a triangle are concurrent.
(B) The midsegments of a triangle are concurrent.
(C) The perpendicular bisectors of the sides of a triangle are concurrent.
(D) Four lines intersecting in one point are concurrent.

34. What type of triangle is $\triangle PUT$?

(F) right isosceles (H) obtuse scalene
(G) acute isosceles (I) acute scalene

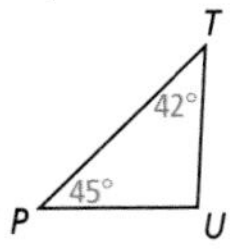

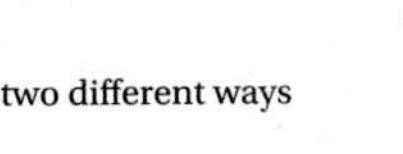

35. Which statement is logically equivalent to the following statement?

If a triangle is right isosceles, then it has exactly two acute angles.

(A) If a triangle is right isosceles, then it has one right angle.
(B) If a triangle has exactly two acute angles, then it is right isosceles.
(C) If a triangle does not have exactly two acute angles, then it is not right isosceles.
(D) If a triangle is not right isosceles, then it does not have a right angle.

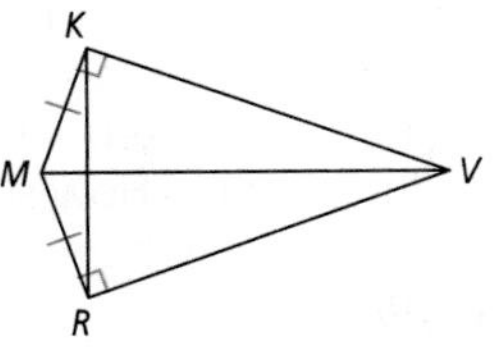

Short Response

36. Refer to the figure at the right above. Explain in two different ways why $\overline{MV}$ is the angle bisector of $\angle KVR$.

Mixed Review

Use the figure at the right for Exercises 37 and 38.

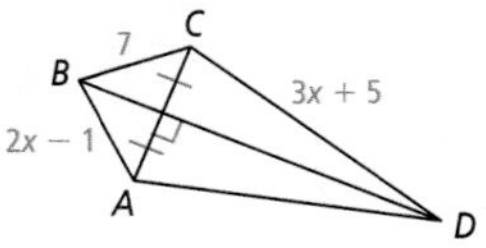

See Lesson 5-2.

37. Find the value of x.

38. Find the length of $\overline{AD}$.

B, C, A, D; 7; 3x + 5; 2x − 1

Get Ready! **To prepare for Lesson 5-4, do Exercises 39 and 40.**

Find the coordinates of the midpoint of $\overline{AB}$ with the given endpoints.

See Lesson 1-7.

39. $A(3, 0)$, $B(3, 16)$

40. $A(6, 8)$, $B(4, -1)$

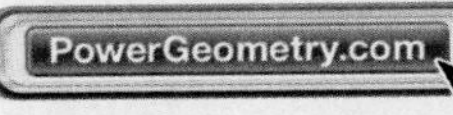

30. Answers may vary. Sample: The two midsegments that extend from the midpt. of the hypotenuse are ∥ to the two legs by the △ Midsegment Thm. Since the two legs form a right ∠, the midsegments therefore form right ∠s with the legs (Corresp. ∠s Post.). Hence, they are the ⊥ bisectors of the legs (Def. of ⊥ bis). Their meeting point—the midpt. of the hypotenuse—is the circumcenter (Def.).

31. Never; if you have three ∥ lines ℓ, m, and n, with m in between ℓ and n, then a point equidistant from ℓ and m would be (midway) between them. A point equidistant from m and n would be (midway) between those two lines. A point equidistant from all three would therefore have to be on both sides of m! This is impossible.

32. Sometimes; the circumcenter and the incenter of a △ are the same if the △ is an equilateral △.

33. B

34. H

35. C

36. [2] Method 1: $\overline{MK} \cong \overline{MR}$ and $\angle MKV$ and $\angle MRV$ are rt. ∠s. So M is equidistant from the sides of $\angle KVR$. It follows that M is on the angle bisector. Thus $\overline{VM}$ is the bisector of $\angle KVR$. Method 2: $\angle MKV$ and $\angle MRV$ are rt. ∠s, so $\triangle MKV$ and $\triangle MRV$ are rt. △s. $\overline{MK} \cong \overline{MR}$ (Given) and $\overline{MV} \cong \overline{MV}$ (Refl. Prop. of ≅), so $\triangle MKV \cong \triangle MRV$ (HL). Then $\angle KVM \cong \angle RVM$ since they are corresp. parts of ≅ △s, so $\overline{VM}$ bisects $\angle KVR$.

[1] only one method shown OR incorrect explanation

37. 4

38. 17

39. (3, 8)

40. (5, 3.5)

5-3 Lesson Resources

Differentiated Remediation

Instructional Support

Geometry Companion

Students can use the **Geometry Companion** worktext (4 pages) . . .

- New Vocabulary
- Key Concepts
- Got It for each Problem
- Lesson Check

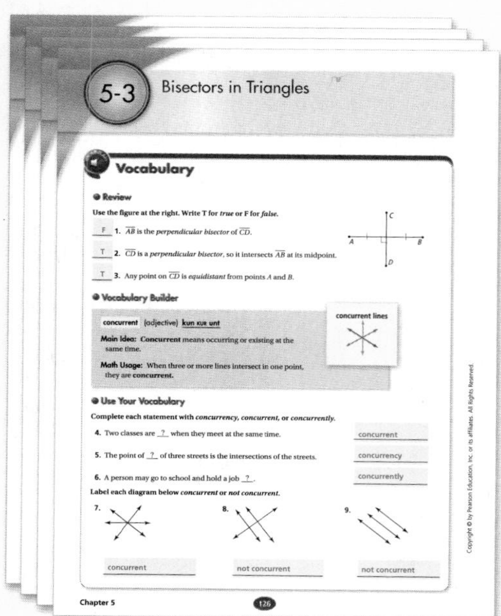

5-3 Bisectors in Triangles

Vocabulary

Review

Use the figure at the right. Write T for *true* or F for *false*.

F 1. $\overline{AB}$ is the *perpendicular bisector* of $\overline{CD}$.

T 2. $\overline{CD}$ is a *perpendicular bisector*, so it intersects $\overline{AB}$ at its midpoint.

T 3. Any point on $\overline{CD}$ is *equidistant* from points A and B.

Vocabulary Builder

concurrent (adjective) kun KUR unt

Main Idea: **Concurrent** means occurring or existing at the same time.

Math Usage: When three or more lines intersect in one point, they are **concurrent.**

concurrent lines

Use Your Vocabulary

Complete each statement with *concurrency, concurrent,* or *concurrently.*

4. Two classes are _?_ when they meet at the same time. concurrent

5. The point of _?_ of three streets is the intersections of the streets. concurrency

6. A person may go to school and hold a job _?_. concurrently

Label each diagram below *concurrent* or *not concurrent*.

7. concurrent 8. not concurrent 9. not concurrent

Copyright © by Pearson Education, Inc. or its affiliates. All Rights Reserved.

Chapter 5 126

ELL Support

Assess Understanding Assign groups of three students to draw acute, right, or obtuse triangles. Next, have each group find and label the circumcenter and incenter of the triangles that they have drawn.

Have groups exchange triangles. Each group should

- verify the other group's work
- compare and contrast the triangle that they drew and the triangle the other group gave to them
- discuss what might be true about the circumcenter and incenter of every triangle

Have each group write and illustrate a short report on what they have learned about triangles.

5 Assess & Remediate

Lesson Quiz

1. What congruence statements can you write for the inscribed triangle below?

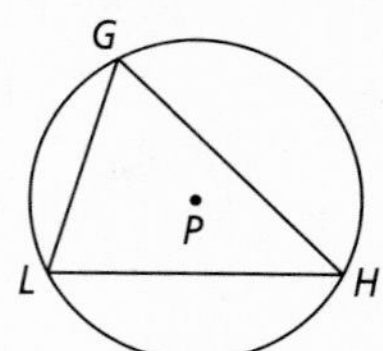
G
P
L
H

2. What is the center of the circle that you can circumscribe about a triangle with vertices $A(2, 6)$, $B(2, 0)$, and $C(10, 0)$?

3. **Do you UNDERSTAND?** A landscaper wants to build a goldfish pond that is equidistant from the gazebo, the rose garden, and the bench. How should the landscaper determine where to build the goldfish pond?

Bench Gazebo

Rose Garden

ANSWERS TO LESSON QUIZ

1. $\overline{GP} \cong \overline{LP}$; $\overline{GP} \cong \overline{HP}$; $\overline{HP} \cong \overline{LP}$
2. (6, 3)
3. The landscaper should locate the goldfish pond at the point of concurrency of the triangle's perpendicular bisectors.

PRESCRIPTION FOR REMEDIATION

Use the student work on the Lesson Quiz to prescribe a differentiated review assignment.

Points	Differentiated Remediation
0–1	Intervention
2	On-level
3	Extension

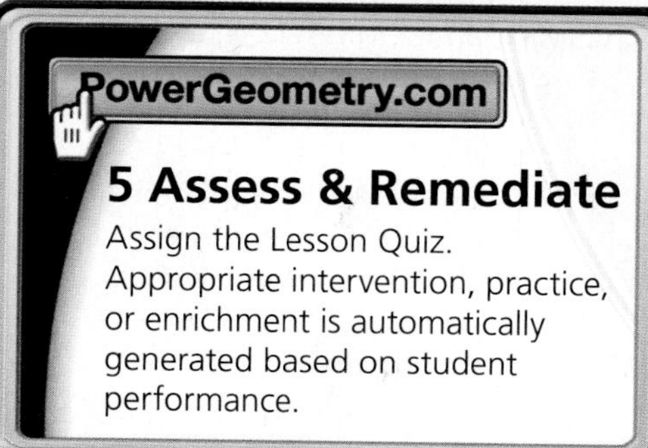
PowerGeometry.com
5 Assess & Remediate
Assign the Lesson Quiz.
Appropriate intervention, practice, or enrichment is automatically generated based on student performance.

Intervention

- **Reteaching** (2 pages) Provides reteaching and practice exercises for the key lesson concepts. Use with struggling students or absent students.
- **English Language Learner Support** Helps students develop and reinforce mathematical vocabulary and key concepts.

All-in-One Resources/Online

Reteaching

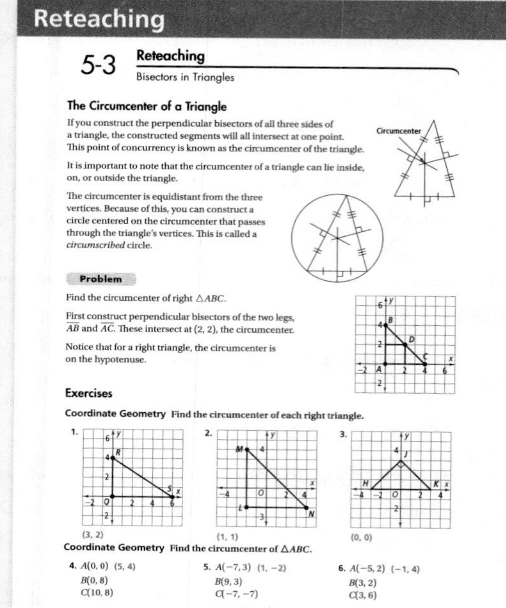

5-3 Reteaching

Bisectors in Triangles

The Circumcenter of a Triangle

If you construct the perpendicular bisectors of all three sides of a triangle, the constructed segments will all intersect at one point. This point of concurrency is known as the circumcenter of the triangle.

It is important to note that the circumcenter of a triangle can lie inside, on, or outside the triangle.

The circumcenter is equidistant from the three vertices. Because of this, you can construct a circle centered on the circumcenter that passes through the triangle's vertices. This is called a *circumscribed* circle.

Circumcenter

Problem

Find the circumcenter of right $\triangle ABC$.

First construct perpendicular bisectors of the two legs, $\overline{AB}$ and $\overline{AC}$. These intersect at (2, 2), the circumcenter.

Notice that for a right triangle, the circumcenter is on the hypotenuse.

Exercises

Coordinate Geometry Find the circumcenter of each right triangle.

1. (3, 2) 2. (1, 1) 3. (0, 0)

Coordinate Geometry Find the circumcenter of $\triangle ABC$.

4. $A(0, 0)$ (5, 4) $B(0, 8)$ $C(10, 8)$

5. $A(-7, 3)$ (1, −2) $B(9, 3)$ $C(-7, -7)$

6. $A(-5, 2)$ (−1, 4) $B(3, 2)$ $C(3, 6)$

All-in-One Resources/Online

English Language Learner Support

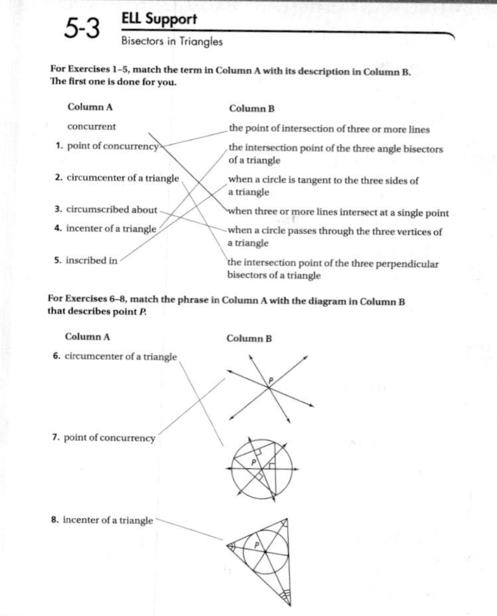

5-3 ELL Support

Bisectors in Triangles

For Exercises 1–5, match the term in Column A with its description in Column B. The first one is done for you.

Column A	Column B
concurrent	the point of intersection of three or more lines
1. point of concurrency	the intersection point of the three angle bisectors of a triangle
2. circumcenter of a triangle	when a circle is tangent to the three sides of a triangle
3. circumscribed about	when three or more lines intersect at a single point
4. incenter of a triangle	when a circle passes through the three vertices of a triangle
5. inscribed in	the intersection point of the three perpendicular bisectors of a triangle

For Exercises 6–8, match the phrase in Column A with the diagram in Column B that describes point *P*.

Column A Column B

6. circumcenter of a triangle

7. point of concurrency

8. incenter of a triangle

Differentiated Remediation *continued*

On-Level

- **Practice** (2 pages) Provides extra practice for each lesson. For simpler practice exercises, use the Form K Practice pages found in the All-in-One Teaching Resources and online.
- **Think About a Plan** Helps students develop specific problem-solving skills and strategies by providing scaffolded guiding questions.
- **Standardized Test Prep** Focuses on all major exercises, all major question types, and helps students prepare for the high-stakes assessments.

Practice and Problem Solving Wkbk/ All-in-One Resources/Online

Practice page 1

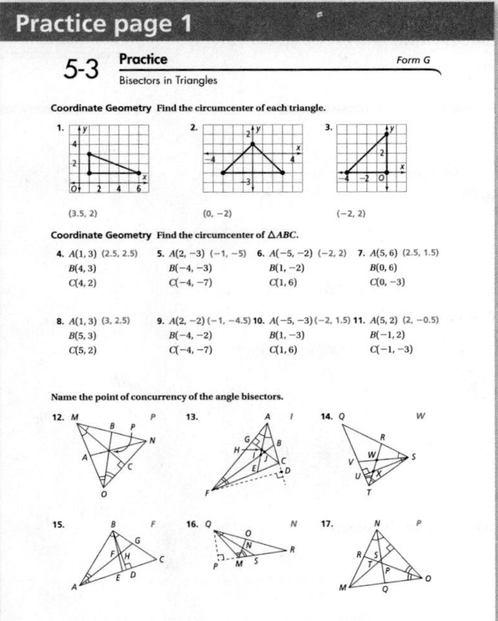

5-3 **Practice** *Form G*

Bisectors in Triangles

Coordinate Geometry Find the circumcenter of each triangle.

1\. (3.5, 2) 2. (0, −2) 3. (−2, 2)

Coordinate Geometry Find the circumcenter of $\triangle ABC$.

4\. $A(1, 3)$, $B(4, 3)$, $C(4, 2)$ (2.5, 2.5)
5\. $A(2, -3)$, $B(-4, -3)$, $C(-4, -7)$ (−1, −5)
6\. $A(-5, -2)$, $B(1, -2)$, $C(1, 6)$ (−2, 2)
7\. $A(5, 6)$, $B(0, 6)$, $C(0, -3)$ (2.5, 1.5)
8\. $A(1, 3)$, $B(5, 3)$, $C(5, 2)$ (3, 2.5)
9\. $A(2, -2)$, $B(-4, -2)$, $C(-4, -7)$ (−1, −4.5)
10\. $A(-5, -3)$, $B(1, -3)$, $C(1, 6)$ (−2, 1.5)
11\. $A(5, 2)$, $B(-1, 2)$, $C(-1, -3)$ (2, −0.5)

Name the point of concurrency of the angle bisectors.

12\. P 13. I 14. W 15. F 16. N 17. P

Practice and Problem Solving Wkbk/ All-in-One Resources/Online

Practice page 2

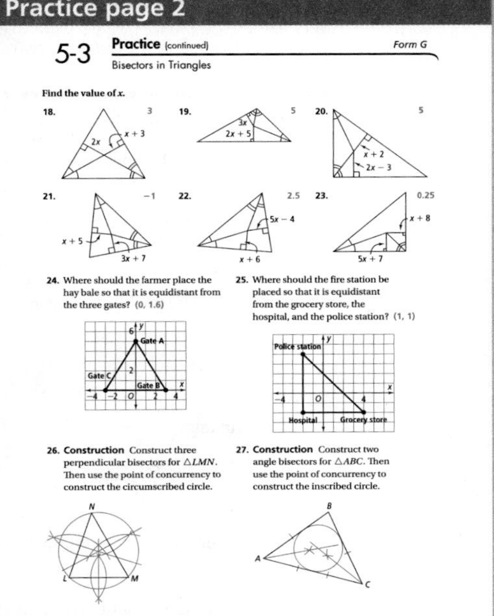

5-3 **Practice** (continued) *Form G*

Bisectors in Triangles

Find the value of x.

18\. 3 19. 5 20. 5 21. −1 22. 2.5 23. 0.25

24\. Where should the farmer place the hay bale so that it is equidistant from the three gates? (0, 1.6)

25\. Where should the fire station be placed so that it is equidistant from the grocery store, the hospital, and the police station? (1, 1)

26\. **Construction** Construct three perpendicular bisectors for $\triangle LMN$. Then use the point of concurrency to construct the circumscribed circle.

27\. **Construction** Construct two angle bisectors for $\triangle ABC$. Then use the point of concurrency to construct the inscribed circle.

Practice and Problem Solving Wkbk/ All-in-One Resources/Online

Think About a Plan

5-3 **Think About a Plan**

Bisectors in Triangles

Writing Ivars found an old piece of paper inside an antique book. It read:

From the spot I buried Olaf's treasure, equal sets of paces did I measure; each of three directions in a line, there to plant a seedling Norway pine. I could not return for failing health; now the hounds of Haiti guard my wealth. —Karl

After searching Caribbean islands for five years, Ivars found an island with three tall Norway pines. How might Ivars find where Karl buried Olaf's treasure?

Know

1. Make a sketch as you answer the questions. Check students' drawings.
2. "*From the spot I buried Olaf's treasure ...*" Mark a point X on your paper.
3. "*... equal sets of paces I did measure; each of the three directions in a line ...*" This tells you to draw segments that have an endpoint at X.
   a. Explain how you know these are segments. the words "in a line"
   b. How many segments should you draw? 3
   c. What do you know about the length of the segments? They are equal.
   d. What do you know about the endpoints of the segments? Each segment has an endpoint at X and an endpoint at a Norway pine.
4. You do not know in which direction to draw each segment, but you can choose three directions for your sketch. Mark the locations of the trees. Draw a triangle with the trees at its vertices. What is the name of the point where X is located? circumcenter

Need

5\. Look at your sketch. What do you need to find? point X, the location of the circumcenter

Plan

6\. Describe how to find the treasure. The first step is done for you.

Step 1 Find the midpoints of each side of the triangle.
Step 2 Use the midpoints to draw perpendicular bisectors for each side.
Step 3 Find the point of concurrency of the perpendicular bisectors. This is the circumcenter, where point X is located.

Practice and Problem Solving Wkbk/ All-in-One Resources/Online

Standardized Test Prep

5-3 **Standardized Test Prep**

Bisectors in Triangles

Multiple Choice

For Exercises 1–5, choose the correct letter. Use the figure below.

1\. Which point is the incenter of $\triangle ABC$? B
A. X B. T C. R D. Y

2\. Which point is the circumcenter of $\triangle ABC$? H
F. X G. T H. R I. Y

3\. Which segment is an angle bisector of $\triangle ABC$? A
A. $\overline{BX}$ B. $\overline{SX}$ C. $\overline{AS}$ D. $\overline{RZ}$

4\. Which segment is a perpendicular bisector of $\triangle ABC$? I
F. $\overline{BW}$ G. $\overline{SB}$ H. $\overline{AS}$ I. $\overline{RZ}$

5\. If $RC = x + 3$ and $RA = 3x - 3$, what is the value of x? A
A. 3 B. 6 C. 7 D. 9

Extended Response

6\. Draw $\triangle ABC$. Construct three angle bisectors. Use the point of concurrency to construct the inscribed circle.
[4] Student draws $\triangle ABC$, constructs three angle bisectors, and constructs the inscribed circle. [3] Student draws $\triangle ABC$, constructs two angle bisectors and the inscribed circle. [2] Student submits an incomplete but accurate drawing. [1] Student drawing is inaccurate. [0] Student fails to submit a drawing or constructs no angle bisectors.

Extension

- **Enrichment** Provides students with interesting problems and activities that extend the concepts of the lesson.
- **Activities, Games, and Puzzles** Worksheets that can be used for concepts development, enrichment, and for fun!

All-in-One Resources/Online

Enrichment

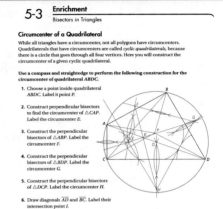

5-3 **Enrichment**

Bisectors in Triangles

Circumcenter of a Quadrilateral

While all triangles have a circumcenter, not all polygons have circumcenters. Quadrilaterals that have circumcenters are called *cyclic quadrilaterals,* because there is a circle that goes through all four vertices. Here you will construct the circumcenter of a given cyclic quadrilateral.

Use a compass and straightedge to perform the following construction for the circumcenter of quadrilateral $ABDC$.

1. Choose a point inside quadrilateral $ABDC$. Label it point P.
2. Construct perpendicular bisectors to find the circumcenter of $\triangle CAP$. Label the circumcenter E.
3. Construct the perpendicular bisectors of $\triangle ABP$. Label the circumcenter F.
4. Construct the perpendicular bisectors of $\triangle BDP$. Label the circumcenter G.
5. Construct the perpendicular bisectors of $\triangle DCP$. Label the circumcenter H.
6. Draw diagonals $\overline{AD}$ and $\overline{BC}$. Label their intersection point I.
7. Draw $\overleftrightarrow{EG}$ and $\overleftrightarrow{FH}$. Label their intersection point K.
8. Draw $\overleftrightarrow{KI}$.
9. Mark a point on $\overleftrightarrow{KI}$ that is the same distance from K as is I, but on the other side of K. Label this O. This is the circumcenter.
10. To draw a circle that circumscribes quadrilateral $ABDC$, put your compass point at O and your pencil on one of the vertices and draw a circle through the vertices of the quadrilateral.

Online Teacher Resource Center

Activities, Games, and Puzzles

5-3 **Puzzle: Crossword**

Bisectors in Triangles

Each clue below involves a vocabulary word you have used or will use soon. Find the missing word or words to complete each sentence. Then place your answers in the crossword puzzle.

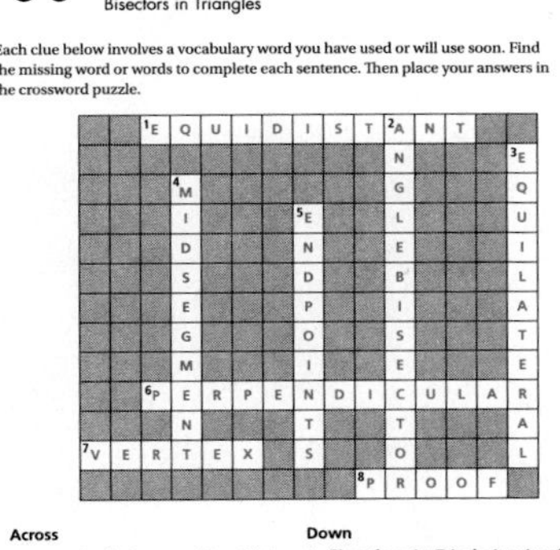

Across

1. A point is _?_ from two objects if it is the same distance from the objects.
6. The distance from a point to a line is the length of the _?_ segment from the point to the line.
7. The point where two or more sides of a figure meet is called a(n) _?_.
8. A convincing argument that logically shows why a conjecture is true is called a(n) _?_.

Down

2. Given the point D in the interior of $\angle ABC$, if $m\angle ABC = 40°$ and $m\angle DBC = 20°$, then $\overrightarrow{BD}$ is called a(n) _?_ (two words).
3. A(n) _?_ triangle has all congruent sides.
4. A segment that connects the midpoints of two sides of a triangle is called a(n) _?_.
5. If a point is on the perpendicular bisector of a segment, then it is equidistant from the _?_ of the segment.

Guided Instruction

PURPOSE To use geometry software to explore special segments in triangles

PROCESS Students will

- use geometry software to construct a triangle and the three perpendicular bisectors of its sides.
- use geometry software to construct a triangle and its three angle bisectors.
- use geometry software to construct a triangle and all three altitudes.
- use geometry software to construct a triangle and all three medians.

DISCUSS Review the term concurrent. Examine triangles in which the altitude is not within the triangle. Ensure students that this case is feasible.

Activity

In this Activity students construct special segments in triangles.

Q What appears to be true for the possible points of intersection for the altitudes for each type of triangle: acute, right, and obtuse? **[They are concurrent at a point that is inside a triangle for acute triangles, on the vertex of the right angle for right triangles and outside the triangle for obtuse triangles.]**

Q If you measure the distance from the point at which your medians meet to each vertex, then to the respective midpoint of the opposite side, what do you notice? **[The point of intersection for the medians is two-thirds of the total distance from each vertex to the midpoint of the opposite side.]**

Concept Byte

Use With Lesson 5-4

TECHNOLOGY

Special Segments in Triangles

You already know about two sets of lines that are concurrent for any triangle. In the following activity, you will use geometry software to confirm what you know about the concurrency of a triangle's perpendicular bisectors and angle bisectors. Then you will explore two more sets of special segments in triangles.

Activity

Use geometry software.

- Construct a triangle and the three perpendicular bisectors of its sides. Use your result to confirm Theorem 5-6, the Concurrency of Perpendicular Bisectors Theorem.
- Construct a triangle and its three angle bisectors. Use your result to confirm Theorem 5-7, the Concurrency of Angle Bisectors Theorem.
- An *altitude* of a triangle is the perpendicular segment from a vertex to the line containing the opposite side. Construct a triangle. Through a vertex of the triangle construct a segment that is perpendicular to the line containing the side opposite that vertex. Next construct the altitudes from the other two vertices.
- A *median* of a triangle is the segment joining the midpoint of a side and the opposite vertex. Construct a triangle. Construct the midpoint of one side. Draw the median. Then construct the other two medians.

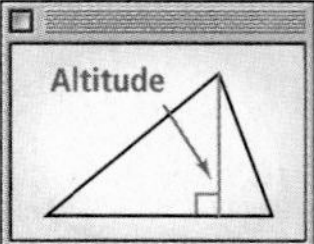

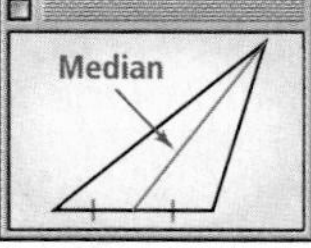

Exercises

1. What property do the lines containing altitudes and the medians seem to have? Does the property still hold as you manipulate the triangles?
2. State your conjectures about the lines containing altitudes and about the medians of a triangle.
3. Copy the table. Think about acute, right, and obtuse triangles. Use *inside*, *on*, or *outside* to describe the location of each point of concurrency.

	Perpendicular Bisectors	Angle Bisectors	Lines Containing the Altitudes	Medians
Acute Triangle	■	■	■	■
Right Triangle	■	■	■	■
Obtuse Triangle	■	■	■	■

4. **Extend** What observations, if any, can you make about these special segments for isosceles triangles? For equilateral triangles?

Answers

Exercises

1. They appear to be concurrent; yes.
2. Answers may vary. Sample: The three lines containing the altitudes of a △ are concurrent. The three medians of a △ are concurrent.
3. acute △: inside, inside, inside, inside; rt. △: on, inside, on, inside; obtuse △: outside, inside, outside, inside
4. Answers may vary. Sample: For isosc. ⚠, these lines are the same: the ⊥ bisector of, altitude to, and median to the base, and the bisector of the vertex ∠. For equilateral ⚠, the ∠ bisector, median, altitude, and ⊥ bisector to each side are all the same line.

5-4 Medians and Altitudes

TN State Performance Indicator
SPI 3108.4.12 Solve problems involving congruence, similarity, proportional reasoning and/or scale factor of two similar figures or solids.

Objective To identify properties of medians and altitudes of a triangle

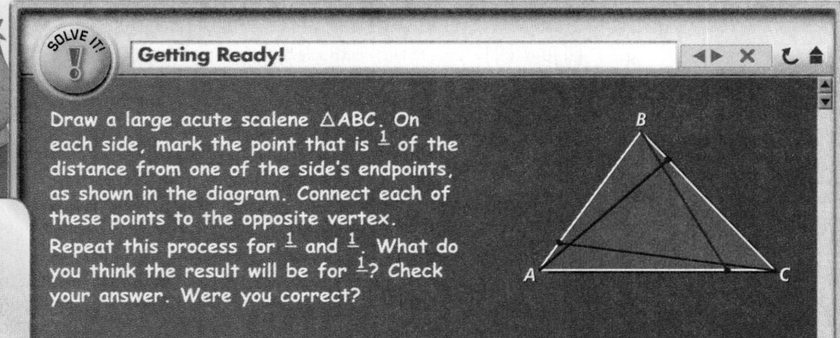

SOLVE IT!
Getting Ready!
Draw a large acute scalene △ABC. On each side, mark the point that is $\frac{1}{}$ of the distance from one of the side's endpoints, as shown in the diagram. Connect each of these points to the opposite vertex. Repeat this process for $\frac{1}{}$ and $\frac{1}{}$. What do you think the result will be for $\frac{1}{}$? Check your answer. Were you correct?
B
A
C

You can use different colors for the sets of segments so you can see the pattern more easily.

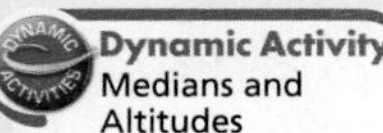

Dynamic Activity
Medians and Altitudes

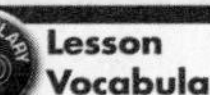

Lesson Vocabulary
- median of a triangle
- centroid of a triangle
- altitude of a triangle
- orthocenter of a triangle

In the Solve It, the last set of segments you drew are the triangle's medians. A **median of a triangle** is a segment whose endpoints are a vertex and the midpoint of the opposite side.

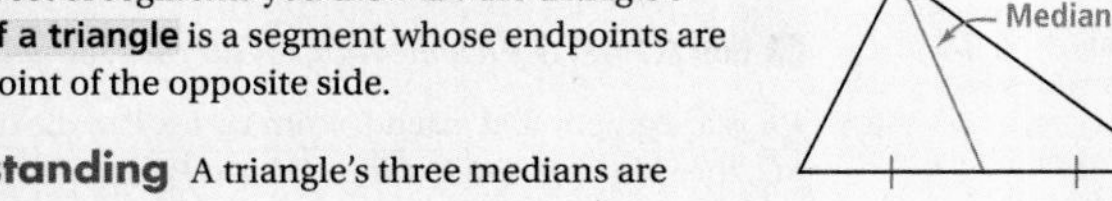

Essential Understanding A triangle's three medians are always concurrent.

Theorem 5-8 Concurrency of Medians Theorem

The medians of a triangle are concurrent at a point that is two thirds the distance from each vertex to the midpoint of the opposite side.

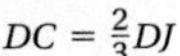 $DC = \frac{2}{3}DJ$ 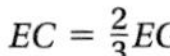 $EC = \frac{2}{3}EG$ $FC = \frac{2}{3}FH$

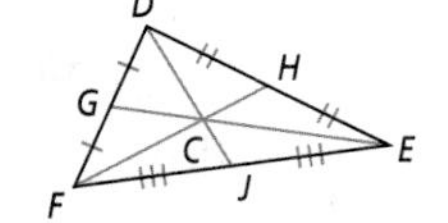

You will prove Theorem 5-8 in Lesson 6-9.

In a triangle, the point of concurrency of the medians is the **centroid of the triangle.** The point is also called the *center of gravity* of a triangle because it is the point where a triangular shape will balance. For any triangle, the centroid is always inside the triangle.

1 Interactive Learning

Solve It!

PURPOSE To find the point of concurrency of the medians of a triangle

PROCESS Students investigate the intersection of segments drawn from the vertices to the sides of a triangle as the point on the side gets closer and closer to the midpoint.

FACILITATE

Q What would be a logical first step for this Solve It? **[Measure the length of each side of the triangle.]**

Q What unit of measure makes the most sense to use? Explain. **[Answers will vary. Sample answer: millimeters because it is a precise measure and the measurements will be whole numbers.]**

Q What do you notice as the segments drawn from the vertices to opposite sides get closer to the midpoint of the opposite sides? **[The triangles formed get smaller and smaller.]**

ANSWER See Solve It in Answers on next page.

CONNECT THE MATH In the Solve It, students made a conjecture about the concurrency of the medians of a triangle. In this lesson their conjecture will be confirmed. They will also study the point of concurrency for altitudes of a triangle.

2 Guided Instruction

Take Note

Have students label the lengths of each segment of the medians. If the median lengths are x, y, and z, then the longest sections should be labeled $\frac{2}{3}x$, $\frac{2}{3}y$, and $\frac{2}{3}z$ respectively.

5-4 Preparing to Teach

BIG ideas **Reasoning and Proof**
Measurement

ESSENTIAL UNDERSTANDINGS
- A triangle's three medians are always concurrent.
- A triangle's three altitudes are always concurrent.

Math Background

Students can use inductive reasoning to hypothesize that particular segments in a triangle such as altitudes, medians, angle bisectors, or perpendicular bisectors are always concurrent.

The point of concurrency of the medians of a triangle is the centroid. This point represents the center of gravity of the triangle. The median of a triangle occurs on the segment $\frac{2}{3}$ from the vertex to the midpoint opposite it. The altitudes of a triangle are concurrent at a point called the orthocenter of the triangle. The orthocenter of a triangle can be located using coordinate geometry. Students will learn that all four types of special segments in triangles have a point of concurrency.

Support Student Learning

Use the **Geometry Companion** to engage and support students during instructions. See Lesson Resources at the end of this lesson for details.

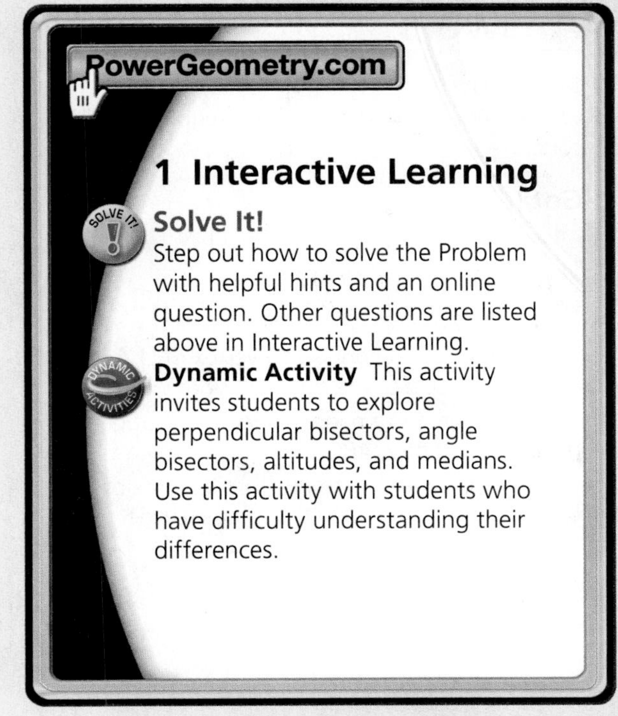

PowerGeometry.com
1 Interactive Learning
Solve It!
Step out how to solve the Problem with helpful hints and an online question. Other questions are listed above in Interactive Learning.
Dynamic Activity This activity invites students to explore perpendicular bisectors, angle bisectors, altitudes, and medians. Use this activity with students who have difficulty understanding their differences.

Problem 1

Q How do you know that the segments $\overline{XB}$ and $\overline{ZC}$ are medians? **[Points *B* and *C* are the bisectors of the sides.]**

Got It?

ERROR PREVENTION

For 1b, let $ZC = x$. Write a ratio that relates the lengths of the two segments. Have students simplify the ratio and then explain the result. Because $ZA = \frac{2}{3}ZC$, it is twice AC.

Problem 2

Q What is the relationship between $\overline{PR}$ and $\overline{QR}$? **[They are perpendicular.]**

Q What type of segment is perpendicular to a side of a triangle? **[an altitude]**

Q What is the relationship between $\overline{PT}$ and $\overline{ST}$? **[They are congruent.]**

Q What type of segment joins a vertex and the midpoint of the opposite side? **[a median]**

Got It?

Have students redraw the triangle so that it contains only the segment they are examining. Ask them to list the facts that help them to classify the segment.

Plan

How do you use the centroid?

Write an equation relating the length of the whole median to the length of the segment from the vertex to the centroid.

Problem 1 Finding the Length of a Median

GRIDDED RESPONSE

In the diagram at the right, $XA = 8$. What is the length of $\overline{XB}$?

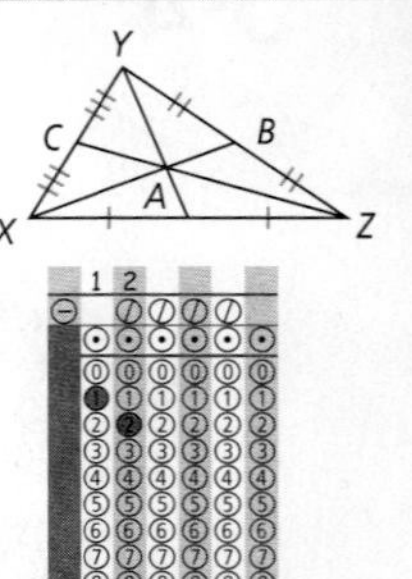

A is the centroid of $\triangle XYZ$ because it is the point of concurrency of the triangle's medians.

$XA = \frac{2}{3}XB$	Concurrency of Medians Theorem
$8 = \frac{2}{3}XB$	Substitute 8 for *XA*.
$\left(\frac{3}{2}\right)8 = \left(\frac{3}{2}\right)\frac{2}{3}XB$	Multiply each side by $\frac{3}{2}$.
$12 = XB$	Simplify.

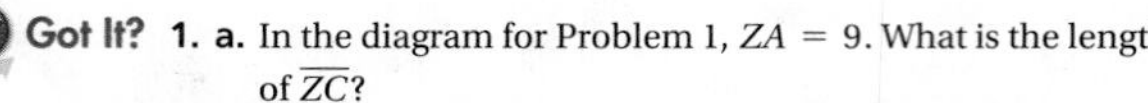

Got It? 1. a. In the diagram for Problem 1, $ZA = 9$. What is the length of $\overline{ZC}$?

b. Reasoning What is the ratio of *ZA* to *AC*? Explain.

An **altitude of a triangle** is the perpendicular segment from a vertex of the triangle to the line containing the opposite side. An altitude of a triangle can be inside or outside the triangle, or it can be a side of the triangle.

Plan

How do you determine whether a segment is an altitude or a median? Look at whether the segment is perpendicular to a side (altitude) and/or bisects a side (median).

Problem 2 Identifying Medians and Altitudes

A For $\triangle PQS$, is $\overline{PR}$ a *median*, an *altitude*, or *neither*? Explain.

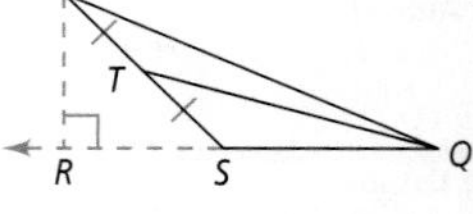

$\overline{PR}$ is a segment that extends from vertex *P* to the line containing $\overline{SQ}$, the side opposite *P*. $\overline{PR} \perp \overrightarrow{QR}$, so $\overline{PR}$ is an altitude of $\triangle PQS$.

B For $\triangle PQS$, is $\overline{QT}$ a *median*, an *altitude*, or *neither*? Explain.

$\overline{QT}$ is a segment that extends from vertex *Q* to the side opposite *Q*. Since $\overline{PT} \cong \overline{TS}$, *T* is the midpoint of $\overline{PS}$. So $\overline{QT}$ is a median of $\triangle PQS$.

Got It? 2. For $\triangle ABC$, is each segment a *median*, an *altitude*, or *neither*? Explain.

a. $\overline{AD}$ **b.** $\overline{EG}$ **c.** $\overline{CF}$

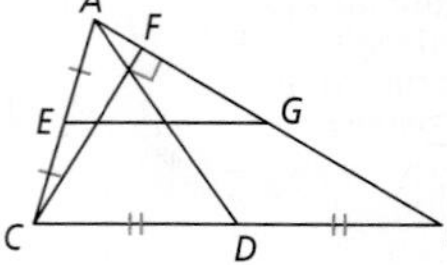

Theorem 5-9 Concurrency of Altitudes Theorem

The lines that contain the altitudes of a triangle are concurrent.

You will prove Theorem 5-9 in Lesson 6-9.

Answers

Solve It!

Check students' work; the three segments will be concurrent.

Got It?

1a. 13.5

b. 2 : 1; $ZA = \frac{2}{3}CZ$ and $AC = \frac{1}{3}CZ$, so $ZA : AC = \frac{2}{3} : \frac{1}{3} = 2 : 1$.

2a. A median; it connects a vertex of $\triangle ABC$ and the midpt. of the opposite side.

b. Neither; *E* is a midpt. of $\triangle ABC$, but *G* is not a vertex of $\triangle ABC$.

c. An altitude; it extends from a vertex of $\triangle ABC$ and is $\perp$ to the opposite side.

PowerGeometry.com

2 Guided Instruction

Each Problem is worked out and supported online.

Problem 1
Finding the Length of a Median
Animated

Problem 2
Identifying Medians and Altitudes
Animated

Problem 3
Finding the Orthocenter
Animated

Support in Geometry Companion
- Vocabulary
- Key Concepts
- Got It?

The lines that contain the altitudes of a triangle are concurrent at the **orthocenter of the triangle.** The orthocenter of a triangle can be inside, on, or outside the triangle.

Acute triangle

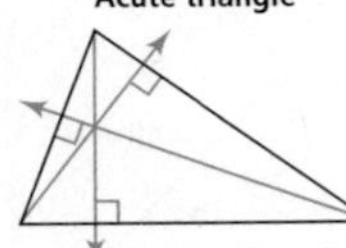

Right triangle

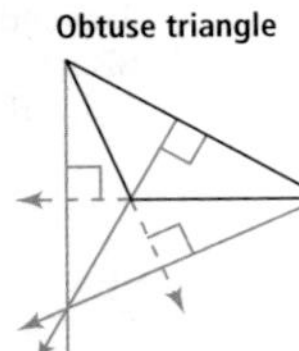

Obtuse triangle

Problem 3 Finding the Orthocenter

$\triangle ABC$ has vertices $A(1, 3)$, $B(2, 7)$, and $C(6, 3)$. What are the coordinates of the orthocenter of $\triangle ABC$?

Know	Need	Plan
The coordinates of the three vertices	The intersection point of the triangle's altitudes	Write the equations of the lines that contain two of the altitudes. Then solve the system of equations.

Think

Which two altitudes should you choose? It does not matter, but the altitude to $\overline{AC}$ is a vertical line, so its equation will be easy to find.

Step 1 Find the equation of the line containing the altitude to $\overline{AC}$. Since $\overline{AC}$ is horizontal, the line containing the altitude to $\overline{AC}$ is vertical. The line passes through the vertex $B(2, 7)$. The equation of the line is $x = 2$.

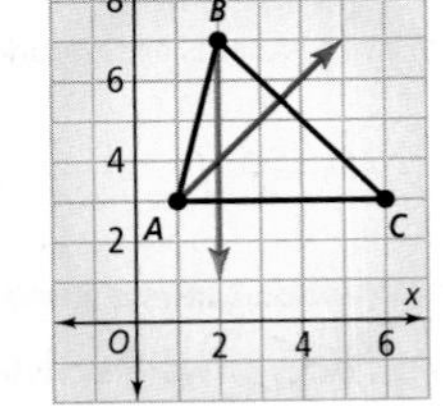

Step 2 Find the equation of the line containing the altitude to $\overline{BC}$. The slope of the line containing $\overline{BC}$ is $\frac{3-7}{6-2} = -1$. Since the product of the slopes of two perpendicular lines is -1, the line containing the altitude to $\overline{BC}$ has slope 1.

The line passes through the vertex $A(1, 3)$. The equation of the line is $y - 3 = 1(x - 1)$, which simplifies to $y = x + 2$.

Step 3 Find the orthocenter by solving this system of equations: $x = 2$, $y = x + 2$

$y = 2 + 2$ Substitute 2 for x in the second equation.

$y = 4$ Simplify.

The coordinates of the orthocenter are (2, 4).

Got It? 3. $\triangle DEF$ has vertices $D(1, 2)$, $E(1, 6)$, and $F(4, 2)$. What are the coordinates of the orthocenter of $\triangle DEF$?

Ask students to compare and contrast an altitude with a perpendicular bisector. Both segments are perpendicular to one side of the triangle. A perpendicular bisector does not necessarily pass through the vertex of the opposite side. An altitude must pass through the opposite vertex. Challenge students to identify a triangle in which an altitude and a perpendicular bisector are the same segment.

Problem 3

Q What linear equations do you need to find the coordinates of the orthocenter? **[the equations that represent at least two altitudes of the triangle]**

Q How are the slopes of the altitudes related to the slope of the sides to which they are perpendicular? **[The slopes are opposite reciprocals. Their product equals –1.]**

Q How can you identify the point where two lines intersect? **[Solve the system of equations using substitution, elimination, or graphing.]**

Got It?

Because the triangle is a right triangle, the legs are also the altitudes. Consequently, the orthocenter is the vertex of the right angle.

Additional Problems

1. $SP = 16$. What is SM?

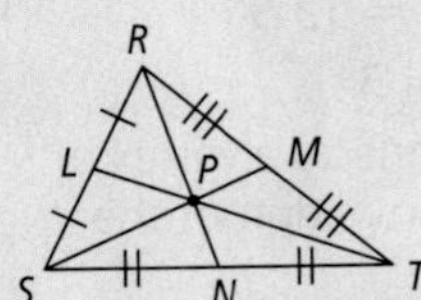

ANSWER 24

2. a. Is $\overline{AC}$ a median, an altitude, or neither?

b. Is $\overline{AE}$ a median, an altitude, or neither?

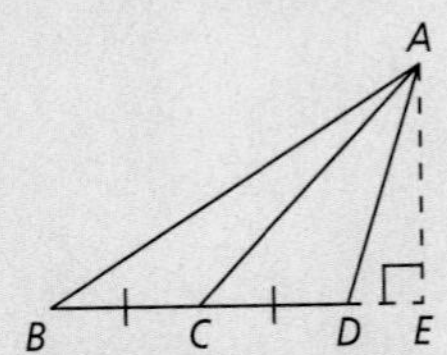

ANSWER a. median **b.** altitude

3. What are the coordinates of the orthocenter of $\triangle DEF$?

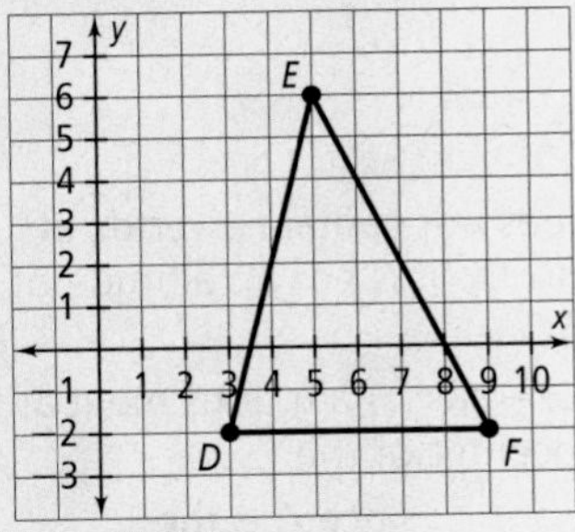

ANSWER (5, −1)

Answers

Got It? (continued)

3. (1, 2)

Take Note

Ask students to define each of the special segments in triangles. They should be able to identify their characteristics, their points of concurrency, and list any special characteristics of these points.

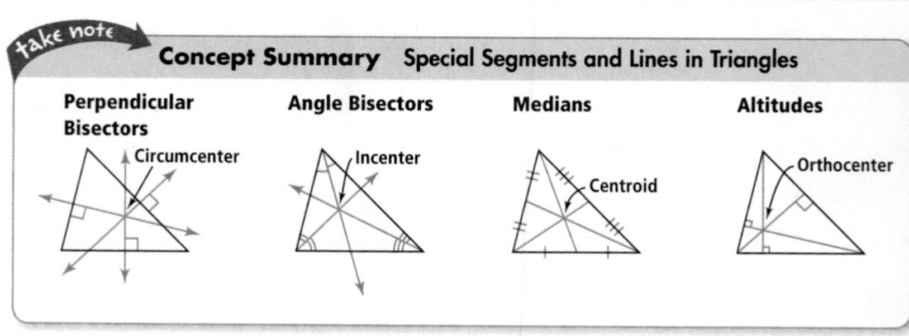

take note
Concept Summary Special Segments and Lines in Triangles
Perpendicular Bisectors
Circumcenter
Angle Bisectors
Incenter
Medians
Centroid
Altitudes
Orthocenter

3 Lesson Check

Do you know HOW?

- If students have difficulty with Exercise 1, then have them review Problem 2 to make of a list of the needed information.

Do you UNDERSTAND?

- If students have difficulty with Exercise 7, then have them review the Got It after Problem 3. Compare the triangles and their characteristics.

Close

Q Where do the medians of a triangle intersect? Does the point have any special characteristics? **[The medians intersect at a point called the centroid. It is located $\frac{2}{3}$ of the way from a vertex to its opposite side.]**

Q Where do the altitudes of a triangle intersect? **[The altitudes intersect at a point called the orthocenter.]**

Lesson Check

Do you know HOW?

Use $\triangle ABC$ for Exercises 1–4.

1. Is $\overline{AP}$ a *median* or an *altitude*?

2. If $AP = 18$, what is KP?

3. If $BK = 15$, what is KQ?

4. Which two segments are altitudes?

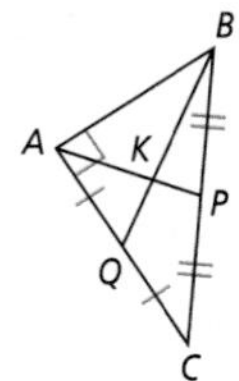

Do you UNDERSTAND?

5. Error Analysis Your classmate says she drew $\overline{HJ}$ as an altitude of $\triangle ABC$. What error did she make?

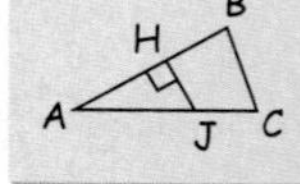

6. Reasoning Does it matter which two altitudes you use to locate the orthocenter of a triangle? Explain.

7. Reasoning The orthocenter of $\triangle ABC$ lies at vertex A. What can you conclude about $\overline{BA}$ and $\overline{AC}$? Explain.

Practice and Problem-Solving Exercises

A Practice

In $\triangle TUV$, Y is the centroid. See Problem 1.

8. If $YW = 9$, find TY and TW.

9. If $YU = 9$, find ZY and ZU.

10. If $VX = 9$, find VY and YX.

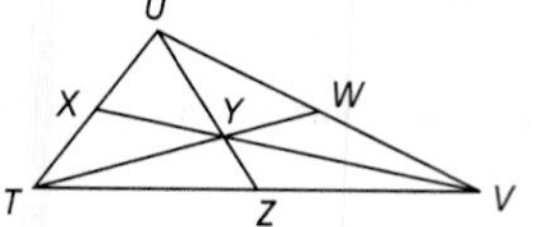

For $\triangle ABC$, is the red segment a *median*, an *altitude*, or *neither*? Explain. See Problem 2.

11. A B C

12.

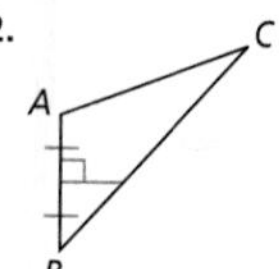

13.

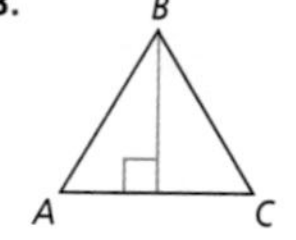

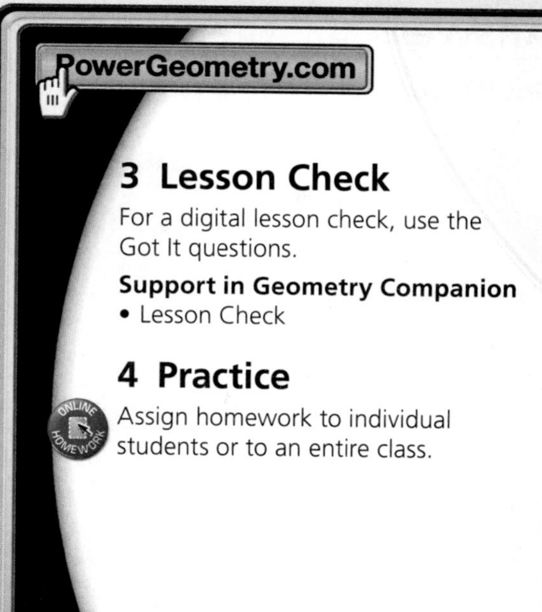

Answers

Lesson Check

1. median

2. 6

3. 7.5

4. $\overline{AB}$, $\overline{AC}$

5. $\overline{HJ}$ does not contain a vertex of $\triangle ABC$, so it is not an altitude of $\triangle ABC$.

6. No; any pair of altitudes meet at the orthocenter of the $\triangle$.

7. They are $\perp$; since A is the orthocenter of $\triangle ABC$, A lies on the altitude from B to $\overline{AC}$. B also lies on this altitude, so the altitude from B to $\overline{AC}$ must be $\overline{BA}$. Therefore, $\overline{BC} \perp \overline{AC}$.

Practice and Problem-Solving Exercises

8. $TY = 18$, $TW = 27$

9. $ZY = 4.5$, $ZU = 13.5$

10. $VY = 6$, $YX = 3$

11. Median; it connects a vertex of $\triangle ABC$ and the midpt. of the opposite side.

12. Neither; it does not have a vertex of $\triangle ABC$ as an endpoint.

13. Altitude; it extends from a vertex of $\triangle ABC$ and is $\perp$ to the opposite side.

Coordinate Geometry **Find the coordinates of the orthocenter of $\triangle ABC$.** See Problem 3.

14. $A(0, 0)$, $B(4, 0)$, $C(4, 2)$

15. $A(2, 6)$, $B(8, 6)$, $C(6, 2)$

16. $A(0, -2)$, $B(4, -2)$, $C(-2, -8)$

B Apply

Name the centroid.

17.

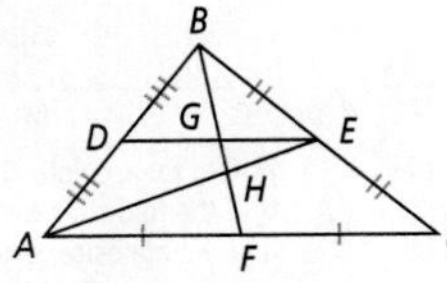

18.

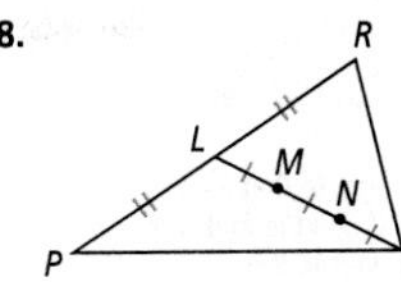

Name the orthocenter of $\triangle XYZ$.

19.

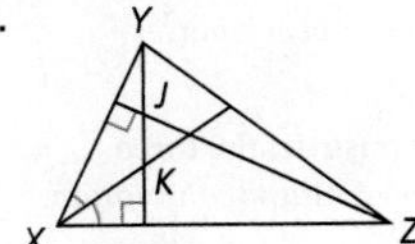

20.

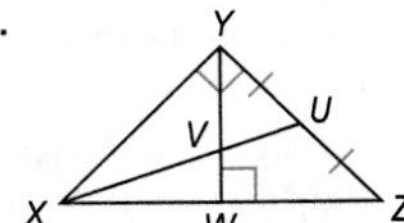

21. Think About a Plan In the diagram at the right, $\overline{QS}$ and $\overline{PT}$ are altitudes and $m\angle R = 55$. What is $m\angle POQ$?

- What does it mean for a segment to be an altitude?
- What do you know about the sum of the angle measures in a triangle?
- How do you sketch overlapping triangles separately?

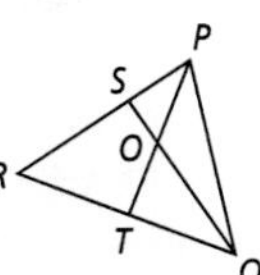

Constructions **Draw a triangle that fits the given description. Then construct the centroid and the orthocenter.**

22. acute scalene triangle, $\triangle LMN$

23. obtuse isosceles triangle, $\triangle RST$

In Exercises 24–27, name each segment.

24. a median in $\triangle ABC$

25. an altitude in $\triangle ABC$

26. a median in $\triangle BDC$

27. an altitude in $\triangle AOC$

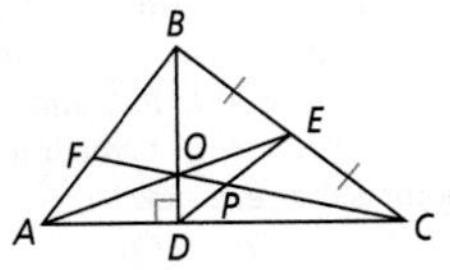

28. Reasoning A centroid separates a median into two segments. What is the ratio of the length of the shorter segment to the length of the longer segment?

4 Practice

ASSIGNMENT GUIDE

Basic: 8–16 all, 18, 20–22, 24–34 even

Average: 9–15 odd, 17–34

Advanced: 9–15 odd, 17–39

Standardized Test Prep: 40–42

Mixed Review: 43–47

Reasoning exercises have blue headings.

Applications exercises have red headings.

EXERCISE 34: Use the Think About a Plan worksheet in the **Practice and Problem Solving Workbook** (also available in the Teaching Resources in print and online) to further support students' development in becoming independent learners.

HOMEWORK QUICK CHECK

To check students' understanding of key skills and concepts, go over Exercises 9, 15, 21, 28, and 34.

14. (4, 0)
15. (6, 4)
16. (−2, 0)
17. *H*
18. *M*
19. *J*
20. *Y*
21. 125
22.

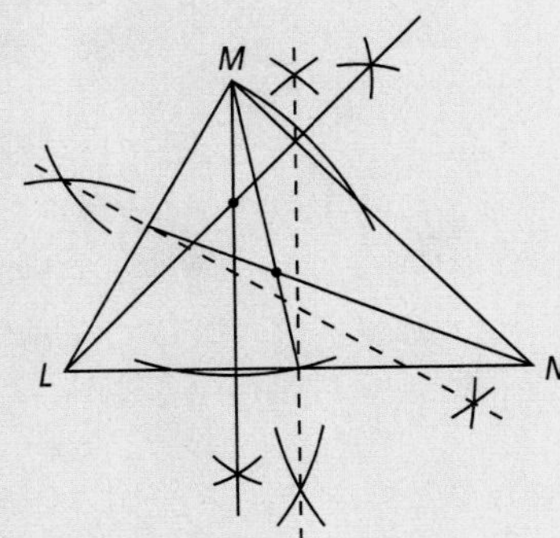

23.

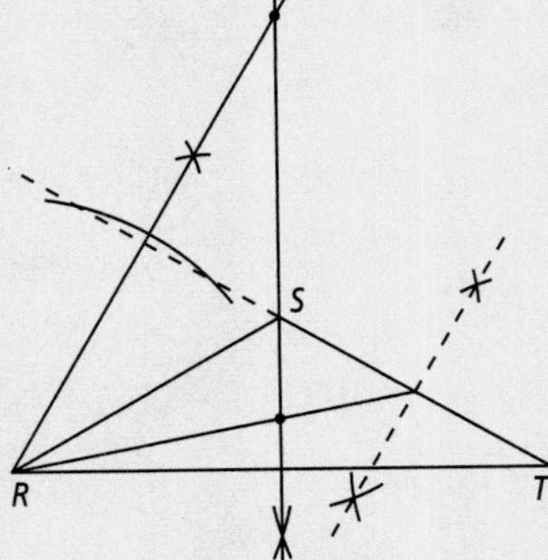

24. $\overline{AE}$
25. $\overline{BD}$
26. $\overline{DE}$
27. $\overline{OD}$
28. 1 : 2

Answers

Practice and Problem-Solving Exercises (continued)

29. Check students' work. The folds should show the $\perp$ bisectors of the sides to identify the midpt. of each side, and also show the fold through each vertex and the midpt. of the opposite side.

30. Check students' work. The folds should show three lines where each contains a vertex and is $\perp$ to the opposite side.

31. C

32. an obtuse $\triangle$

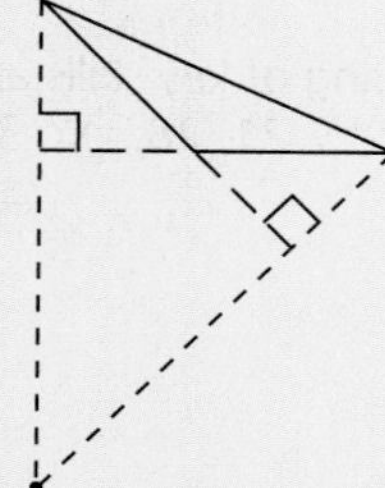

33. Answers may vary. Sample: The $\angle$ bisector of the vertex $\angle$ forms two $\triangle$s that are $\cong$ by SAS. Therefore the 2 segments formed on the base are $\cong$ (so the $\angle$ bisector contains a median), and the two $\triangle$s formed by the $\angle$ bisector and the base are rt. $\triangle$s (so the $\angle$ bisector contains an altitude). Thus the median and the altitude are the same.

34a. $L(1, 3)$; $M(5, 3)$; $N(4, 0)$

b. $\overleftrightarrow{AM} : y = \frac{3}{5}x$; $\overleftrightarrow{BN} : y = -3x + 12$; $\overleftrightarrow{CL} : y = -\frac{3}{7}x + \frac{24}{7}$

c. $\left(\frac{10}{3}, 2\right)$

d. $-\frac{3}{7}\left(\frac{10}{3}\right) + \frac{24}{7} = -\frac{10}{7} + \frac{24}{7} = \frac{14}{7} = 2$

e. $AM = \sqrt{34}$, $AP = \sqrt{\frac{136}{9}} = \frac{2}{3}\sqrt{34}$;

$CL = \sqrt{58}$, $CP = \sqrt{\frac{232}{9}} = \frac{2}{3}\sqrt{58}$;

$BN = \sqrt{40} = 2\sqrt{10}$, $BP = \sqrt{\frac{160}{9}} = \frac{4}{3}\sqrt{10}$

35.

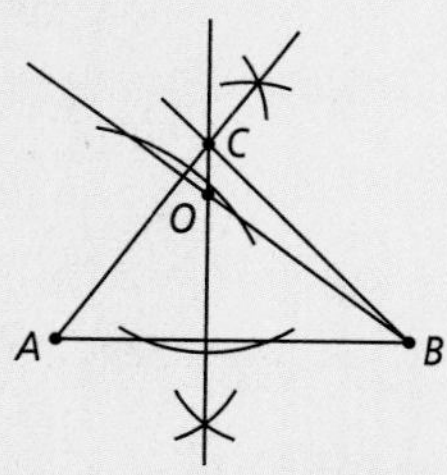

Draw $\overleftrightarrow{AB}$. Construct the $\perp$ to $\overleftrightarrow{AB}$ through O. Draw $\overleftrightarrow{BO}$. Construct the $\perp$ to $\overleftrightarrow{BO}$ through A. The two $\perp$s intersect at C. Draw $\overline{BC}$.

36. Answers may vary. Sample: The answer to Ex. 33 shows that if line ℓ is the $\angle$ bisector of the vertex $\angle$ of an isosc. $\triangle$, then ℓ contains the median and the altitude. That same line ℓ is the $\perp$ bisector of the base because it bisects the base (it contains the median) and it is $\perp$ to the base (it contains the altitude to the base). Since the circumcenter, incenter, centroid, and orthocenter must all be on line ℓ, the four points must be collinear.

Paper Folding The figures below show how to construct altitudes and medians by paper folding. Refer to them for Exercises 29 and 30.

Folding an Altitude

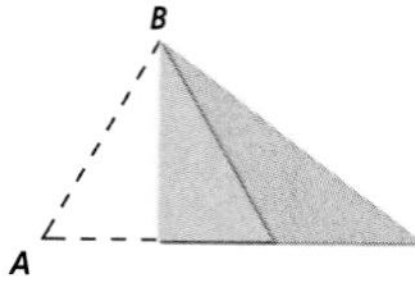

Fold the triangle so that a side $\overline{AC}$ overlaps itself and the fold contains the opposite vertex B.

Folding a Median

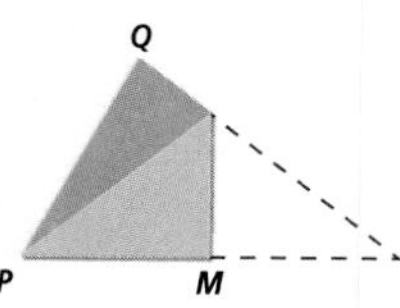

Fold one vertex R to another vertex P. This locates the midpoint M of a side.

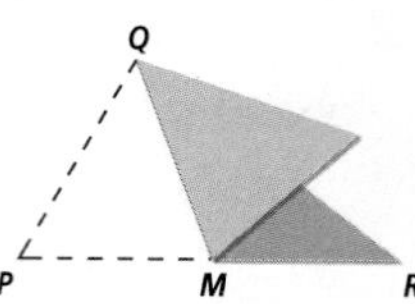

Unfold the triangle. Then fold it so that the fold contains the midpoint M and the opposite vertex Q.

29. Cut out a large triangle. Fold the paper carefully to construct the three medians of the triangle and demonstrate the Concurrency of Medians Theorem. Use a ruler to measure the length of each median and the distance of each vertex from the centroid.

30. Cut out a large acute triangle. Fold the paper carefully to construct the three altitudes of the triangle and demonstrate the Concurrency of Altitudes Theorem.

31. In the figure at the right, C is the centroid of $\triangle DEF$. If $GF = 12x^2 + 6y$, which expression represents CF?

Ⓐ $6x^2 + 3y$ Ⓒ $8x^2 + 4y$

Ⓑ $4x^2 + 2y$ Ⓓ $8x^2 + 3y$

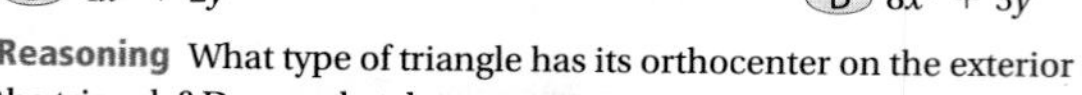

32. Reasoning What type of triangle has its orthocenter on the exterior of the triangle? Draw a sketch to support your answer.

33. Writing Explain why the median to the base of an isosceles triangle is also an altitude.

34. Coordinate Geometry $\triangle ABC$ has vertices $A(0, 0)$, $B(2, 6)$, and $C(8, 0)$. Complete the following steps to verify the Concurrency of Medians Theorem for $\triangle ABC$.

a. Find the coordinates of midpoints L, M, and N.

b. Find equations of $\overleftrightarrow{AM}$, $\overleftrightarrow{BN}$, and $\overleftrightarrow{CL}$.

c. Find the coordinates of P, the intersection of $\overleftrightarrow{AM}$ and $\overleftrightarrow{BN}$. This point is the centroid.

d. Show that point P is on $\overleftrightarrow{CL}$.

e. Use the Distance Formula to show that point P is two-thirds of the distance from each vertex to the midpoint of the opposite side.

Challenge

35. Constructions A, B, and O are three noncollinear points. Construct point C such that O is the orthocenter of $\triangle ABC$. Describe your method.

36. Reasoning In an isosceles triangle, show that the circumcenter, incenter, centroid, and orthocenter can be four different points, but all four must be collinear.

A, *B*, *C*, and *D* are points of concurrency for the triangle. Determine whether each point is a *circumcenter*, *incenter*, *centroid*, or *orthocenter*. Explain.

37. 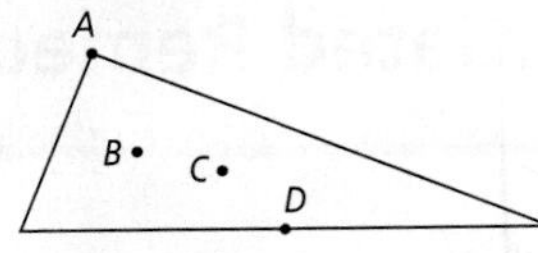

38. 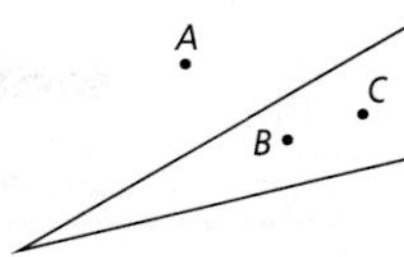

39. History In 1765, Leonhard Euler proved that, for any triangle, three of the four points of concurrency are collinear. The line that contains these three points is known as Euler's Line. Use Exercises 37 and 38 to determine which point of concurrency does not necessarily lie on Euler's Line.

Standardized Test Prep

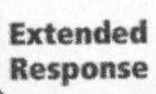

For Exercises 40 and 41, use the figure at the right.

40. If $CR = 24$, what is KR?

(A) 6 (B) 8 (C) 12 (D) 16

41. If $TR = 12$ what is CP?

(F) 16 (G) 18 (H) 24 (I) 36

Extended Response

42. The orthocenter of a triangle lies outside the triangle. Where are its circumcenter, incenter, and centroid located in relation to the triangle? Draw and label diagrams to support your answers.

Mixed Review

Is $\overline{XY}$ a *perpendicular bisector*, an *angle bisector*, or *neither*? Explain.

See Lesson 5-3.

43. 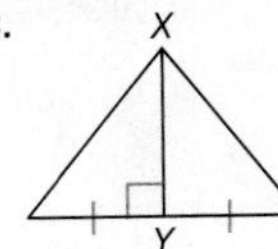

44. 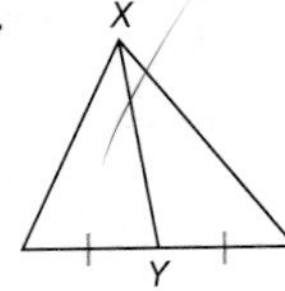

Get Ready! To prepare for Lesson 5-5, do Exercises 45–47.

Write the negation of each statement.

See Lesson 2-2.

45. Two angles are congruent. **46.** You are not 16 years old. **47.** $m\angle A < 90$

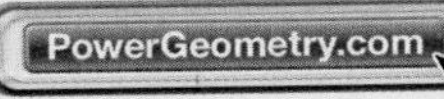

Lesson 5-4 Medians and Altitudes 315

37. *A* is the intersection of the altitudes, so it is the orthocenter; *B* is the intersection of the ∠ bisectors, so it is the incenter; *C* is the intersection of the medians, so it is the centroid; *D* is the intersection of the ⊥ bisectors of the sides, so it is the circumcenter.

38. *A* is the intersection of the ⊥ bisectors of the sides, so it is the circumcenter; *B* is the intersection of the medians, so it is the centroid; *C* is the intersection of the ∠ bisectors, so it is the incenter; *D* is the intersection of the altitudes, so it is the orthocenter.

39. incenter

40. B

41. H

42. [4]

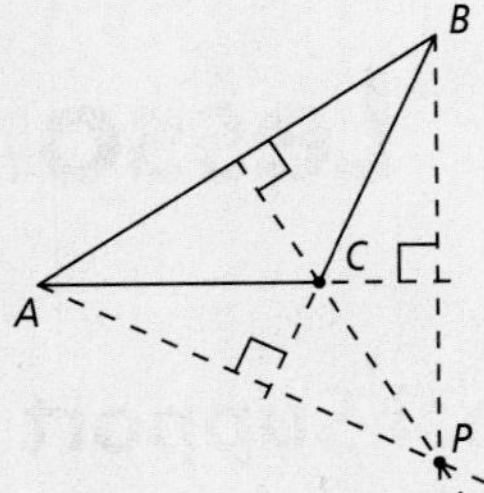

Circumcenter-outside

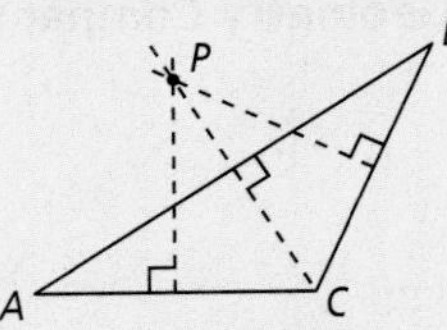

Incenter-inside

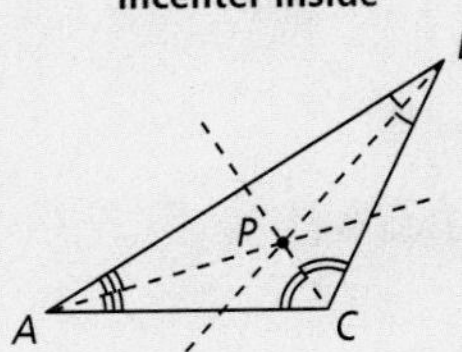

Centroid-inside

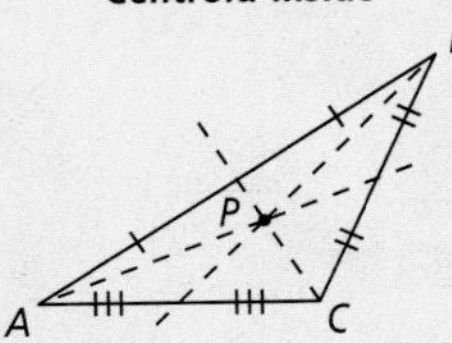

[3] one diagram partially or completely incorrect

[2] two diagrams partially or completely incorrect

[1] three diagrams partially or completely incorrect

43. Both; the markings show directly that $\overline{XY}$ is a ⊥ bisector. The two ⊿ formed are congruent by SAS, so the two ⊿ at top are ≅. Therefore, $\overline{XY}$ is also an ∠ bisector.

44. Neither; $\overline{XY}$ connects vertex *X* and the midpt., *Y*, of the opposite side, so $\overline{XY}$ is a median.

45. Two angles are not congruent.

46. You are 16 years old.

47. $m\angle A \geq 90$

5-4 Lesson Resources

Differentiated Remediation

Instructional Support

Geometry Companion

Students can use the **Geometry Companion** worktext (4 pages) . . .

- New Vocabulary
- Key Concepts
- Got It for each Problem
- Lesson Check

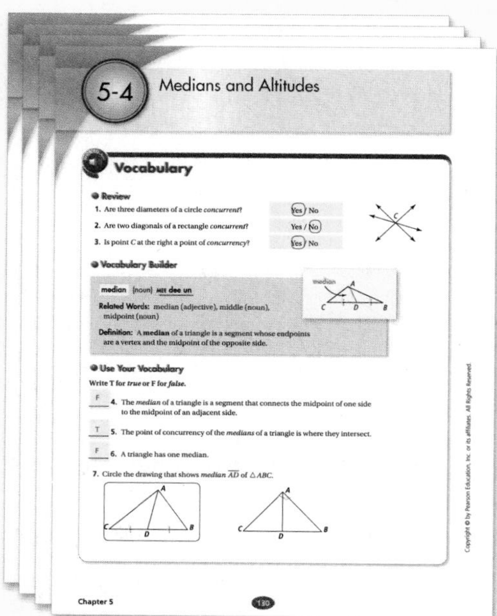

5-4 Medians and Altitudes

Vocabulary

Review

1. Are three diameters of a circle *concurrent*? Yes / No (Yes circled)
2. Are two diagonals of a rectangle *concurrent*? Yes / No (No circled)
3. Is point *C* at the right a point of *concurrency*? Yes / No (Yes circled)

Vocabulary Builder

median (noun) MEE dee un

Related Words: median (adjective), middle (noun), midpoint (noun)

Definition: A **median** of a triangle is a segment whose endpoints are a vertex and the midpoint of the opposite side.

Use Your Vocabulary

Write T for *true* or F for *false*.

F 4. The *median* of a triangle is a segment that connects the midpoint of one side to the midpoint of an adjacent side.

T 5. The point of concurrency of the *medians* of a triangle is where they intersect.

F 6. A triangle has one median.

7. Circle the drawing that shows *median* $\overline{AD}$ of $\triangle ABC$.

Chapter 5 130

ELL Support

Focus on Language Have pairs of students work together to make word cards for the chapter vocabulary. Remind students to include the words: incenter, circumcenter, orthocenter, concurrency, centroid, altitude, median, midsegment, and equidistant.

Students should write the vocabulary word on one side of the card. On the other side they should write a formal definition and illustrations and familiar words which will help them understand the word's meaning.

Each pair of students should compare their vocabulary cards with those of another group. Students can change their cards to include ideas suggested by the other group.

5 Assess & Remediate

Lesson Quiz

1. Is $\overline{AC}$ a median, an altitude, or neither?

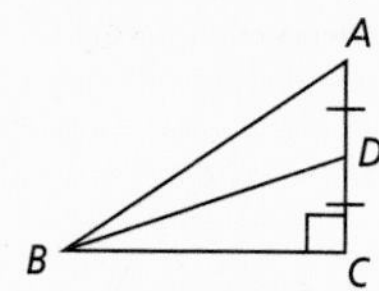

2. **Do you UNDERSTAND?** What are the coordinates of the orthocenter of $\triangle LMN$?

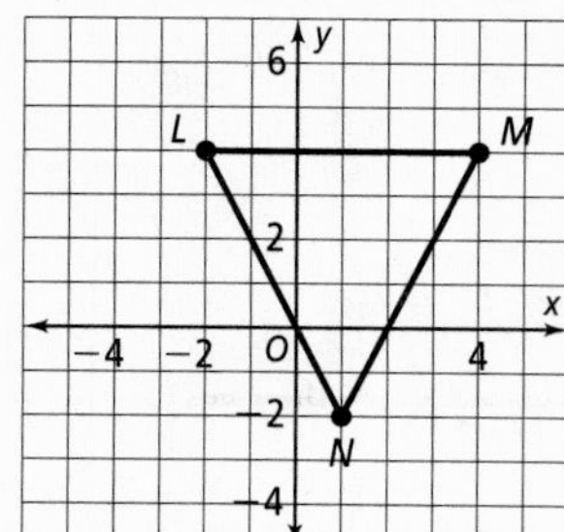

3. In the triangle shown in Question 2, which altitude length can be found without using the Distance Formula? What is the length?

ANSWERS TO LESSON QUIZ

1. altitude
2. (1, 2.5)
3. the altitude from *N* to $\overline{LM}$; 6 units

PRESCRIPTION FOR REMEDIATION

Use the student work on the Lesson Quiz to prescribe a differentiated review assignment.

Points	Differentiated Remediation
0–1	Intervention
2	On-level
3	Extension

PowerGeometry.com

5 Assess & Remediate

Assign the Lesson Quiz. Appropriate intervention, practice, or enrichment is automatically generated based on student performance.

Intervention

- **Reteaching** (2 pages) Provides reteaching and practice exercises for the key lesson concepts. Use with struggling students or absent students.
- **English Language Learner Support** Helps students develop and reinforce mathematical vocabulary and key concepts.

All-in-One Resources/Online

Reteaching

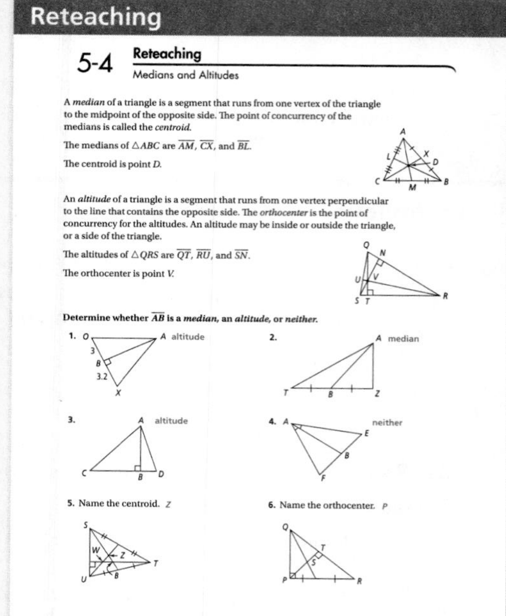

5-4 Reteaching
Medians and Altitudes

A *median* of a triangle is a segment that runs from one vertex of the triangle to the midpoint of the opposite side. The point of concurrency of the medians is called the *centroid*.

The medians of $\triangle ABC$ are $\overline{AM}$, $\overline{CX}$, and $\overline{BL}$.

The centroid is point *D*.

An *altitude* of a triangle is a segment that runs from one vertex perpendicular to the line that contains the opposite side. The *orthocenter* is the point of concurrency for the altitudes. An altitude may be inside or outside the triangle, or a side of the triangle.

The altitudes of $\triangle QRS$ are $\overline{QT}$, $\overline{RU}$, and $\overline{SN}$.

The orthocenter is point *V*.

Determine whether $\overline{AB}$ is a *median*, an *altitude*, or *neither*.

1. altitude
2. median
3. altitude
4. neither
5. Name the centroid. *Z*
6. Name the orthocenter. *P*

All-in-One Resources/Online

English Language Learner Support

5-4 ELL Support
Medians and Altitudes

Concept List

altitude	centroid	circumcenter
concurrent lines	incenter	median
orthocenter	point of concurrency	vertex

Choose the concept from the list above that best represents the item in each box.

1. median	2. Point *Z* point of concurrency	3. Point *Q* centroid
4. Point *W* incenter	5. Three or more lines that meet at a single point concurrent lines	6. Point *K* circumcenter
7. altitude	8. Point *P* orthocenter	9. Point *A*, *B*, or *C* vertex

Differentiated Remediation *continued*

On-Level

- **Practice** (2 pages) Provides extra practice for each lesson. For simpler practice exercises, use the Form K Practice pages found in the All-in-One Teaching Resources and online.
- **Think About a Plan** Helps students develop specific problem-solving skills and strategies by providing scaffolded guiding questions.
- **Standardized Test Prep** Focuses on all major exercises, all major question types, and helps students prepare for the high-stakes assessments.

Extension

- **Enrichment** Provides students with interesting problems and activities that extend the concepts of the lesson.
- **Activities, Games, and Puzzles** Worksheets that can be used for concepts development, enrichment, and for fun!

Practice and Problem Solving Wkbk/ All-in-One Resources/Online

Practice page 1

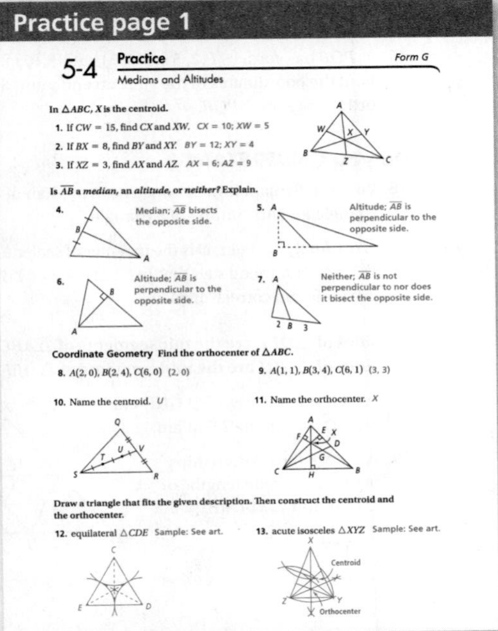

5-4 Practice — Medians and Altitudes — Form G

In $\triangle ABC$, X is the centroid.

1. If $CW = 15$, find CX and XW. $CX = 10$; $XW = 5$
2. If $BX = 8$, find BY and XY. $BY = 12$; $XY = 4$
3. If $XZ = 3$, find AX and AZ. $AX = 6$; $AZ = 9$

Is $\overline{AB}$ a *median*, an *altitude*, or *neither*? Explain.

4. Median; $\overline{AB}$ bisects the opposite side.
5. Altitude; $\overline{AB}$ is perpendicular to the opposite side.
6. Altitude; $\overline{AB}$ is perpendicular to the opposite side.
7. Neither; $\overline{AB}$ is not perpendicular to nor does it bisect the opposite side.

Coordinate Geometry Find the orthocenter of $\triangle ABC$.

8. $A(2, 0)$, $B(2, 4)$, $C(6, 0)$ (2, 0)
9. $A(1, 1)$, $B(3, 4)$, $C(6, 1)$ (3, 3)
10. Name the centroid. U
11. Name the orthocenter. X

Draw a triangle that fits the given description. Then construct the centroid and the orthocenter.

12. equilateral $\triangle CDE$ Sample: See art.
13. acute isosceles $\triangle XYZ$ Sample: See art.

Practice and Problem Solving Wkbk/ All-in-One Resources/Online

Practice page 2

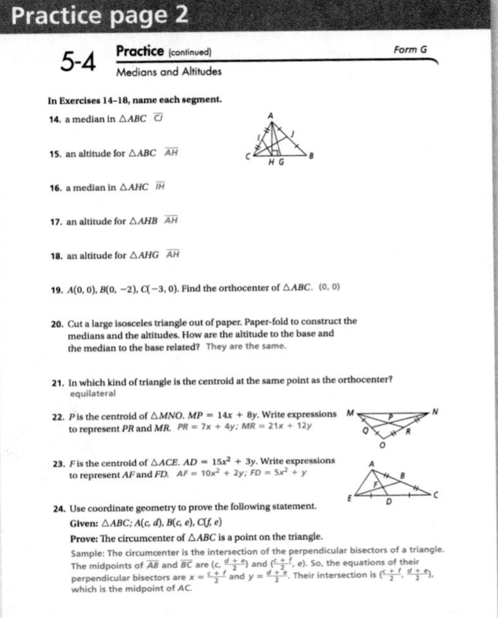

5-4 Practice (continued) — Medians and Altitudes — Form G

In Exercises 14–18, name each segment.

14. a median in $\triangle ABC$ $\overline{CI}$
15. an altitude for $\triangle ABC$ $\overline{AH}$
16. a median in $\triangle AHC$ $\overline{IH}$
17. an altitude for $\triangle AHB$ $\overline{AH}$
18. an altitude for $\triangle AHG$ $\overline{AH}$
19. $A(0, 0)$, $B(0, -2)$, $C(-3, 0)$. Find the orthocenter of $\triangle ABC$. (0, 0)
20. Cut a large isosceles triangle out of paper. Paper-fold to construct the medians and the altitudes. How are the altitude to the base and the median to the base related? They are the same.
21. In which kind of triangle is the centroid at the same point as the orthocenter? equilateral
22. P is the centroid of $\triangle MNO$. $MP = 14x + 8y$. Write expressions to represent PR and MR. $PR = 7x + 4y$; $MR = 21x + 12y$
23. F is the centroid of $\triangle ACE$. $AD = 15x^2 + 3y$. Write expressions to represent AF and FD. $AF = 10x^2 + 2y$; $FD = 5x^2 + y$
24. Use coordinate geometry to prove the following statement.
Given: $\triangle ABC$; $A(c, d)$, $B(c, e)$, $C(f, e)$
Prove: The circumcenter of $\triangle ABC$ is a point on the triangle.
Sample: The circumcenter is the intersection of the perpendicular bisectors of a triangle. The midpoints of $\overline{AB}$ and $\overline{BC}$ are $(c, \frac{d+e}{2})$ and $(\frac{c+f}{2}, e)$. So, the equations of their perpendicular bisectors are $x = \frac{c+f}{2}$ and $y = \frac{d+e}{2}$. Their intersection is $(\frac{c+f}{2}, \frac{d+e}{2})$, which is the midpoint of $\overline{AC}$.

All-in-One Resources/Online

Enrichment

5-4 Enrichment — Medians and Altitudes

Constructions—Centroid and Orthocenter

Materials
- Compass
- Straightedge
- Card stock

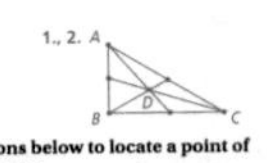

Follow the directions below to locate a point of concurrency of $\triangle ABC$.

1. Using a construction or folding, find the midpoint of each side of the triangle.
2. Draw all three medians of the triangle.
3. What word names the point of intersection of three medians? Label this point D. centroid
4. Is this point in the interior or the exterior of $\triangle ABC$? interior
5. Is it possible for this point to lie outside a triangle? Explain. It is not possible for the centroid to be on the exterior because all the medians are in the interior of the triangle.

Trace $\triangle XYZ$ on a piece of card stock or cardboard, and cut it out.

6. Find the balancing point of the triangle using constructions.
7. Test your answer by placing the point on the tip of a pencil and observing whether the triangle is balanced. Check students' work.
8. Did you find the circumcenter, incenter, centroid, or orthocenter of the triangle? centroid

Follow the directions below to locate a point of concurrency of $\triangle EFH$.

9. Construct all three altitudes of $\triangle EFH$. (*Hint:* Remember that some altitudes may lie outside the triangle.)
10. What word names the point of intersection of the altitudes? Label this point I. orthocenter
11. Repeat steps 9 and 10 for $\triangle ABC$ and $\triangle XYZ$. Check students' work.
12. Where do the orthocenters for obtuse, right, and acute triangles lie? for an obtuse triangle, exterior to the triangle; for a right triangle, on the vertex of the right angle; for an acute triangle, on the triangle interior

Practice and Problem Solving Wkbk/ All-in-One Resources/Online

Think About a Plan

5-4 Think About a Plan — Medians and Altitudes

Coordinate Geometry $\triangle ABC$ has vertices $A(0, 0)$, $B(2, 6)$, and $C(8, 0)$. Complete the following steps to verify the Concurrency of Medians Theorem for $\triangle ABC$.

a. Find the coordinates of midpoints L, M, and N.
b. Find equations of $\overleftrightarrow{AM}$, $\overleftrightarrow{BN}$, and $\overleftrightarrow{CL}$.
c. Find the coordinates of P, the intersection of $\overleftrightarrow{AM}$ and $\overleftrightarrow{BN}$. This is the centroid.
d. Show that point P is on $\overleftrightarrow{CL}$.
e. Use the Distance Formula to show that point P is two-thirds of the distance from each vertex to the midpoint of the opposite side.

1. Write the midpoint formula. $(\frac{x_1 + x_2}{2}, \frac{y_1 + y_2}{2})$
2. Use the formula to find the coordinates L, M, and N. (1, 3); (5, 3); (4, 0)
3. Solve to find the slope of $\overleftrightarrow{AM}$, $\overleftrightarrow{BN}$, and $\overleftrightarrow{CL}$. $\frac{3}{5}$; -3; $-\frac{3}{7}$
4. Write the general point-slope form of an equation. $y - y_1 = m(x - x_1)$
5. Write the point-slope form equation of $\overleftrightarrow{AM}$, $\overleftrightarrow{BN}$, and $\overleftrightarrow{CL}$. $y = \frac{3}{5}x$; $y = -3x + 12$; $y = -\frac{3}{7}(x - 8)$
6. Solve the system of equations for $\overleftrightarrow{AM}$ and $\overleftrightarrow{BN}$ to find the intersection. $(3\frac{1}{3}, 2)$
7. Show that point P is a solution to the equation of $\overleftrightarrow{CL}$. $2 = -\frac{3}{7}(3\frac{1}{3} - 8)$
8. Use the distance formula to find AM, BN, and CL. Use a calculator and round to the nearest hundredth. 5.83; 6.32; 7.62
9. Use the distance formula to find AP, BP, and CP. 3.89; 4.22; 5.08
10. Check to see that $AP = \frac{2}{3}AM$, $BP = \frac{2}{3}BN$, and $CP = \frac{2}{3}CL$. $5.83 \times \frac{2}{3} = 3.89$; $6.32 \times \frac{2}{3} = 4.21$; $7.62 \times \frac{2}{3} = 5.08$

Practice and Problem Solving Wkbk/ All-in-One Resources/Online

Standardized Test Prep

5-4 Standardized Test Prep — Medians and Altitudes

Multiple Choice

For Exercises 1–5, choose the correct letter.

1. Z is the centroid of $\triangle ABC$. If $AZ = 12$, what is ZY? A
   A. 6 C. 12
   B. 9 D. 18
2. What is the best description of $\overline{AB}$? F
   F. altitude
   G. perpendicular bisector
   H. median
   I. angle bisector
3. What is the best description of $\overline{PI}$? D
   A. incenter
   B. centroid
   C. circumcenter
   D. orthocenter

Use $\triangle XYZ$ for Exercises 4 and 5.

4. Which is an altitude of $\triangle XYZ$? F
   F. $\overline{AZ}$ H. $\overline{XB}$
   G. $\overline{XY}$ I. $\overline{ZY}$
5. Which is a median of $\triangle XYZ$? B
   A. $\overline{AZ}$ C. $\overline{XY}$
   B. $\overline{BX}$ D. $\overline{YZ}$

Short Response

6. M is the centroid of $\triangle QRS$, and $QM = 22x + 10y$. What expressions can you write for MV and QV?
   [2] $MV = 11x + 5y$ AND $QV = 33x + 15y$
   [1] $MV = 11x + 5y$ OR $QV = 33x + 15y$
   [0] No correct response is given.

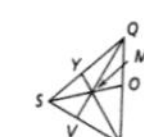

Online Teacher Resource Center

Activities, Games, and Puzzles

5-4 Activity: Exploring Orthocenters — Medians and Altitudes

Extend

Step 1
Use 'Point at Midpoint' and 'Perpendicular Line' to construct the three perpendicular bisectors of $\triangle ABC$. Construct point H, the point of intersection of these lines.

Step 2
Hide the perpendicular bisectors and midpoints, then use 'Circle by Center + Point' to create a circle that circumscribes $\triangle ABC$.

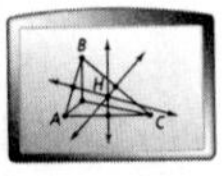

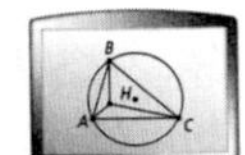

Repeat this process to construct the three circles that circumscribe the smaller triangles.

Investigate

Measure the circumference and the area of each of the four circumscribed circles. Drag $\triangle ABC$ and observe the effect on the circles and on the circumferences and areas.

3. Make a conjecture about the relationships between the circle circumscribed about $\triangle ABC$ and those circumscribed about the triangles created by two of its vertices together with its orthocenter.
The circumferences and areas of all four circles are equal.

Answers

Mid-Chapter Quiz

1. 6
2. 3
3. 104
4. 228
5. $\angle Z$; $\overline{AB}$ is a midseg. of $\triangle XYZ$, so by the $\triangle$ Midseg. Thm., $\overline{AB} \parallel \overline{YZ}$. Then $\angle Z \cong \angle XBA$ because corresp. ⦞ of $\parallel$ lines are $\cong$.
6. $\angle CDB$ is a rt. $\angle$; it is suppl. to $\angle ADB$.
7. They are $\cong$ by HL.
8. They are $\cong$; they are corresp. parts in $\cong$ ⦻.
9. $AP = 12$, $AR = 18$
10. $QP = 3$, $QB = 9$
11. $CP = 4$, $PS = 2$
12. $\angle$ bisector; the diagram indicates that the red line forms two $\cong$ ⦞ with vertex C.
13. $\perp$ bisector, $\angle$ bisector, median, and altitude; for any isosc. $\triangle$, those four segments from the vertex $\angle$ coincide.
14. $\perp$ bisector; the two small rt. ⦻ that have the red line as a leg are $\cong$ by HL, so $\overline{AB}$ is split into two equal pieces by the red line.
15. circumcenter: (5, 3); orthocenter: (8, 5)
16. Answers may vary. Sample: Median: Construct the $\perp$ bisector of one side of the $\triangle$ to find the midpt. of that side. Then draw a segment from that point to the opposite vertex. Altitude: From one vertex, construct a line that is $\perp$ to the side of the $\triangle$ opposite that vertex; you may have to extend the opposite side beyond the endpoints of the side.
17. No; the incenter is the intersection of the $\angle$ bisectors, so $m\angle YXO = m\angle ZXO$ and $m\angle YZO = m\angle XZO$.
18. By the Midsegment Thm., $\overline{AB} \parallel \overline{ED}$ and $\overline{ED} \parallel \overline{GH}$, $\overline{AC} \parallel \overline{FD}$ and $\overline{FD} \parallel \overline{GI}$, and $\overline{BC} \parallel \overline{FE}$ and $\overline{FE} \parallel \overline{HI}$. Therefore $\overline{GH} \parallel \overline{AB}$, $\overline{GI} \parallel \overline{AC}$, and $\overline{HI} \parallel \overline{BC}$, because if two segments are $\parallel$ to the same segment, they are $\parallel$ to each other.
19. Each side of $\triangle GHI$ is half as long as its corresp. ($\parallel$) side in $\triangle DEF$, and each side in $\triangle DEF$ is half as long as its corresp. ($\parallel$) side in $\triangle ABC$. So the side lengths of $\triangle GHI$ are one quarter the side lengths of $\triangle ABC$.

PowerGeometry.com

MathXL for School

Prepare students for the Mid-Chapter Quiz and Chapter Test with online practice and review.

5 Mid-Chapter Quiz

Do you know HOW?

Algebra Find the value of x.

1.

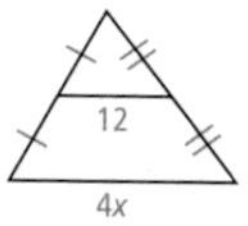

2.

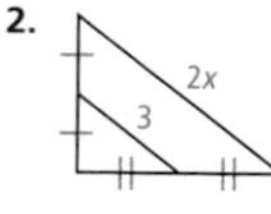

Use the figure below for Exercises 3–5.

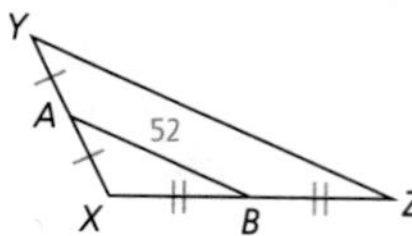

3. Find YZ.
4. $AX = 26$ and $BZ = 36$. Find the perimeter of $\triangle XYZ$.
5. Which angle is congruent to $\angle XBA$? How do you know?

For the figure below, what can you conclude about each of the following? Explain.

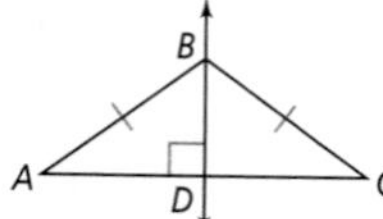

6. $\angle CDB$
7. $\triangle ABD$ and $\triangle CBD$
8. $\overline{AD}$ and $\overline{DC}$

In the figure at the right, P is the centroid of $\triangle ABC$.

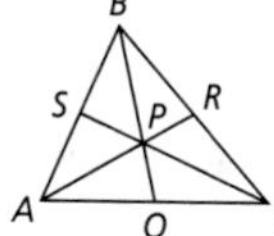

9. If $PR = 6$, find AP and AR.
10. If $PB = 6$, find QP and QB.
11. If $SC = 6$, find CP and PS.

For $\triangle ABC$, is the red line a *perpendicular bisector*, an *angle bisector*, a *median*, an *altitude*, or *none of these*? Explain.

12.

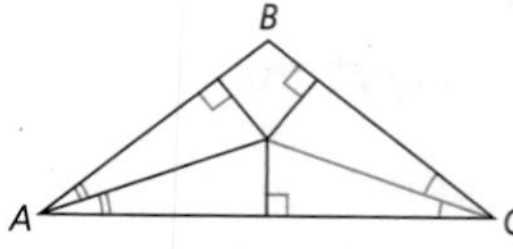

13.

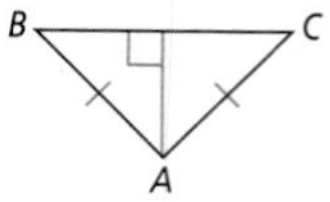

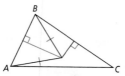

14.

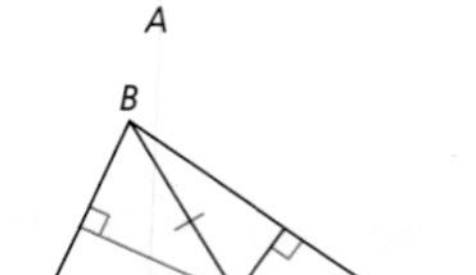

15. $\triangle PQR$ has vertices $P(2, 5)$, $Q(8, 5)$, and $R(8, 1)$. Find the coordinates of the circumcenter and the orthocenter of $\triangle PQR$.

Do you UNDERSTAND?

16. **Writing** Explain how to construct a median of a triangle and an altitude of a triangle.
17. **Error Analysis** Point O is the incenter of scalene $\triangle XYZ$. Your friend says that $m\angle YXO = m\angle YZO$. Is your friend correct? Explain.

The sides of $\triangle DEF$ are the midsegments of $\triangle ABC$. The sides of $\triangle GHI$ are the midsegments of $\triangle DEF$.

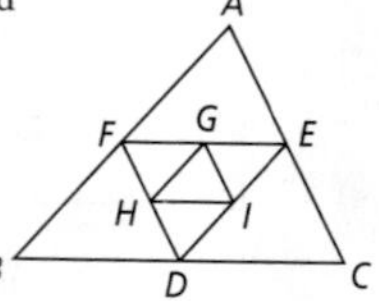

18. Which sides, if any, of $\triangle GHI$ and $\triangle ABC$ are parallel? Explain.
19. What are the relationships between the side lengths of $\triangle GHI$ and $\triangle ABC$? Explain.

5-5 Indirect Proof

TN State Performance Indicators
SPI 3108.4.4 Analyze different types and formats of proofs.
Also SPI 3108.4.12

Objective To use indirect reasoning to write proofs

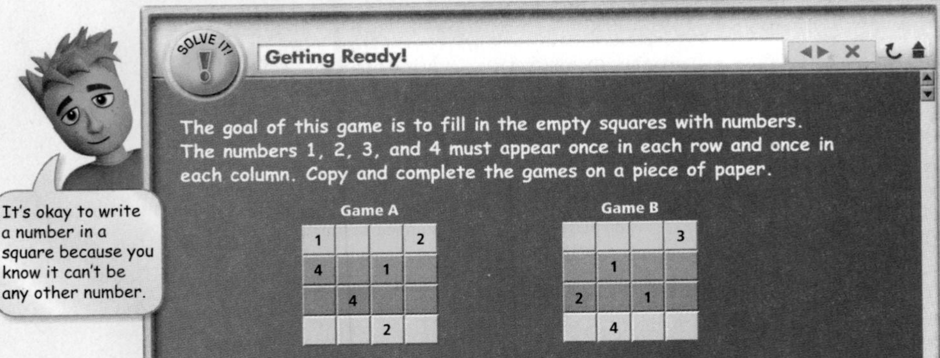

Getting Ready!
The goal of this game is to fill in the empty squares with numbers. The numbers 1, 2, 3, and 4 must appear once in each row and once in each column. Copy and complete the games on a piece of paper.
Game A
Game B
It's okay to write a number in a square because you know it can't be any other number.

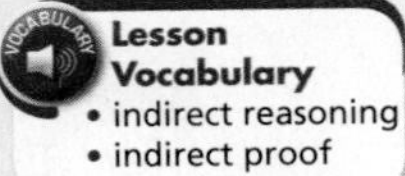

Lesson Vocabulary
- indirect reasoning
- indirect proof

In the Solve It, you can conclude that a square must contain a certain number if you can eliminate the other three numbers as possibilities. This type of reasoning is called indirect reasoning. In **indirect reasoning,** all possibilities are considered and then all but one are proved false. The remaining possibility must be true.

Essential Understanding You can use indirect reasoning as another method of proof.

A proof involving indirect reasoning is an **indirect proof.** Often in an indirect proof, a statement and its negation are the only possibilities. When you see that one of these possibilities leads to a conclusion that contradicts a fact you know to be true, you can eliminate that possibility. For this reason, indirect proof is sometimes called *proof by contradiction.*

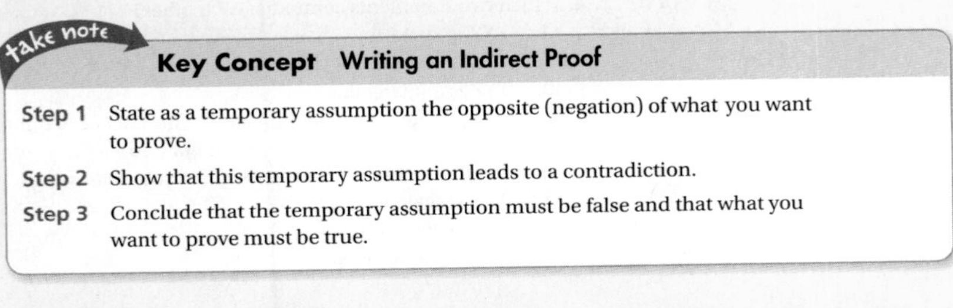

Key Concept Writing an Indirect Proof

Step 1 State as a temporary assumption the opposite (negation) of what you want to prove.

Step 2 Show that this temporary assumption leads to a contradiction.

Step 3 Conclude that the temporary assumption must be false and that what you want to prove must be true.

1 Interactive Learning

Solve It!

PURPOSE To use indirect reasoning to complete the number squares

PROCESS Students may use a process of elimination to fill in the squares.

FACILITATE

Q What number must go in the second square of the first row? Justify your reasoning. **[3; The numbers 3 and 4 are the numbers left for that row. 4 already appears in the column, so it must be 3.]**

Q How can you determine which number goes in each square? **[Compare the numbers that already exist in that column and row and write the remaining number.]**

ANSWER See Solve It in Answers on next page.

CONNECT THE MATH Students should realize that they are indirectly proving which number must go in each box by eliminating other possibilities. In this lesson, students study indirect proofs.

2 Guided Instruction

Take Note

Practice identifying negations of statements with students. Give them a statement and have them identify the opposite. Discuss the concept that if the negation of a statement is false, then the statement itself is true.

5-5 Preparing to Teach

BIG idea Reasoning and Proof UbD

ESSENTIAL UNDERSTANDINGS
- In indirect reasoning, all possibilities are considered and then all but one are proved false. The remaining possibility must be true.
- An essential element of an indirect proof is showing a contradiction.

Math Background

Indirect Proof is another method of proof that students can add to their repertoire of logic skills. Also called Proof by Contradiction, the negation of the desired conclusion is assumed to be true and then it is shown that the negation of the premise is false. Thus, the contrapositive of the original statement is proven true, so the original statement must be true (because they have the same truth value).

Indirect proofs can be very challenging for students who find it confusing to argue validly by beginning with a negation. In this lesson the emphasis is on writing portions of indirect proofs, such as the first sentence of the proof (the negation of the Prove statement). Generally, negations are easier for students to write than contrapositives because a contrapositive requires students to negate both phrases of a conditional and then to form converses of the resulting negations. It may help to review Lesson 2-2.

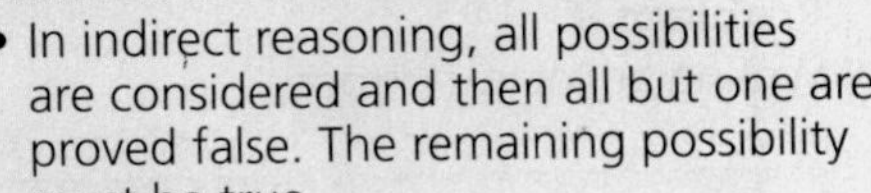

Support Student Learning

Use the **Geometry Companion** to engage and support students during instructions. See Lesson Resources at the end of this lesson for details.

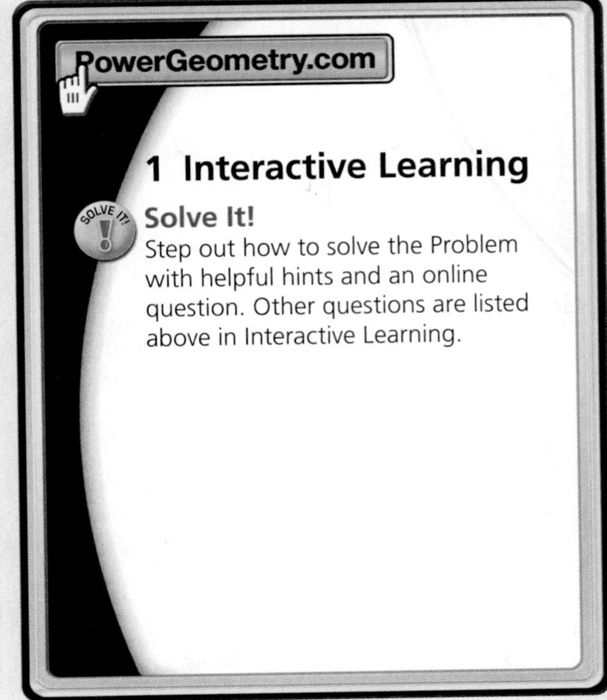

Problem 1

Q What is the opposite of "divisible by 5?" **[not divisible by 5]**

Q What is the opposite of "do not have?" **[do have]**

Got It? ERROR PREVENTION

In 1b, some students may write the negation as "At least one pair of shoes you bought did not cost more than $25." Point out that this is not the negation because both it and the original statement can be true.

Problem 2

Have students sketch a diagram of each statement. Then, they can try to combine the sketches. If it is not possible to combine two sketches, those two statements are contradictions.

Q Which two statements are mutually exclusive? Explain. **[Two segments cannot be both parallel and perpendicular because perpendicular lines intersect and parallel lines do not intersect.]**

Got It?

Have students sketch a diagram that combines two of the three statements.

Q Can they draw an acute triangle that is scalene? **[yes]**

Q Can they draw a scalene triangle that is equiangular? **[no]**

Q Can they draw an acute triangle that is equiangular? **[yes]**

In 2b, students should realize that contradicting statements are not necessarily negations of each other.

In the first step of an indirect proof you assume as true the opposite of what you want to prove.

Problem 1 Writing the First Step of an Indirect Proof

Think
How do you find the opposite of a statement?
Write the negation of the statement. This often involves adding or removing the word *not*.

Suppose you want to write an indirect proof of each statement. As the first step of the proof, what would you assume?

A An integer n is divisible by 5.

The opposite of "is divisible by" is "is not divisible by."
Assume temporarily that n is not divisible by 5.

B You do not have soccer practice today.

The opposite of "do not have" is "do have."
Assume temporarily that you do have soccer practice today.

Got It? 1. Suppose you want to write an indirect proof of each statement. As the first step of the proof, what would you assume?

a. $\triangle BOX$ is not acute.

b. At least one pair of shoes you bought cost more than $25.

To write an indirect proof, you have to be able to identify a contradiction.

Problem 2 Identifying Contradictions

Think
How do you know that two statements contradict each other?
A statement contradicts another statement if it is impossible for both to be true at the same time.

Which two statements contradict each other?

I. $\overline{FG} \parallel \overline{KL}$ **II.** $\overline{FG} \cong \overline{KL}$ **III.** $\overline{FG} \perp \overline{KL}$

Segments can be parallel and congruent. Statements I and II do not contradict each other.

Segments can be congruent and perpendicular. Statements II and III do not contradict each other.

Parallel segments do not intersect, so they cannot be perpendicular. Statements I and III contradict each other.

Got It? 2. a. Which two statements contradict each other?

I. $\triangle XYZ$ is acute.
II. $\triangle XYZ$ is scalene.
III. $\triangle XYZ$ is equiangular.

b. Reasoning Statements I and II below contradict each other. Statement III is the negation of Statement I. Are Statements II and III equivalent? Explain your reasoning.

I. $\triangle ABC$ is scalene.
II. $\triangle ABC$ is equilateral.
III. $\triangle ABC$ is not scalene.

Answers

Solve It!

Game A

1	3	4	2
4	2	1	3
2	4	3	1
3	1	2	4

Game B

1	2	4	3
4	1	3	2
2	3	1	4
3	4	2	1

Got It?

1a. Assume temporarily that $\triangle BOX$ is acute.

b. Assume temporarily that no pair of shoes you bought cost more than $25.

2a. II and III

b. No; if $\triangle ABC$ is an isosc., nonequilateral $\triangle$, then Statement III is true but Statement II is not true. Therefore, Statements II and III are not equivalent.

2 Guided Instruction

Each Problem is worked out and supported online.

Problem 1
Writing the First Step of an Indirect Proof
Animated

Problem 2
Identifying Contradictions
Animated

Problem 3
Writing an Indirect Proof
Animated

Support in Geometry Companion
- Vocabulary
- Key Concepts
- Got It?

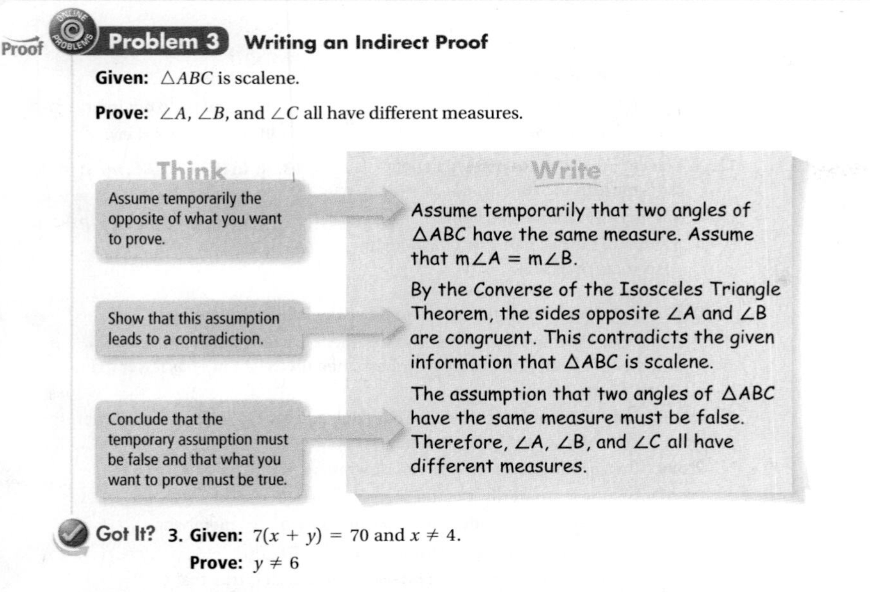

Proof
Problem 3 Writing an Indirect Proof
Given: △ABC is scalene.
Prove: ∠A, ∠B, and ∠C all have different measures.
Think
Write
Assume temporarily the opposite of what you want to prove.
Assume temporarily that two angles of △ABC have the same measure. Assume that m∠A = m∠B.
Show that this assumption leads to a contradiction.
By the Converse of the Isosceles Triangle Theorem, the sides opposite ∠A and ∠B are congruent. This contradicts the given information that △ABC is scalene.
Conclude that the temporary assumption must be false and that what you want to prove must be true.
The assumption that two angles of △ABC have the same measure must be false. Therefore, ∠A, ∠B, and ∠C all have different measures.

Got It? 3. **Given:** $7(x + y) = 70$ and $x \neq 4$.
Prove: $y \neq 6$

Lesson Check

Do you know HOW?

1. Suppose you want to write an indirect proof of the following statement. As the first step of the proof, what would you assume?
   Quadrilateral *ABCD* has four right angles.
2. Write a statement that contradicts the following statement. Draw a diagram to support your answer.
   Lines *a* and *b* are parallel.

Do you UNDERSTAND?

3. **Error Analysis** A classmate began an indirect proof as shown below. Explain and correct your classmate's error.

Given: △ABC
Prove: ∠A is obtuse.
Assume temporarily that ∠A is acute.

Practice and Problem-Solving Exercises

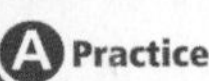

A Practice Write the first step of an indirect proof of the given statement.

See Problem 1.

4. It is raining outside.
5. $\angle J$ is not a right angle.
6. $\triangle PEN$ is isosceles.
7. At least one angle is obtuse.
8. $\overline{XY} \cong \overline{AB}$
9. $m\angle 2 > 90$

Problem 3

Q What is the opposite of "have different measures?" **[have the same measures]**

Q Where is the contradiction in the proof? **[If a triangle has congruent angles, then it cannot be a scalene triangle.]**

Got It?

Q What statement should be negated to begin the proof? **[$y \neq 6$ should be $y = 6$]**

Q Where is the contradiction in the proof? **[If $y = 6$, then $x = 4$.]**

3 Lesson Check

Do you know HOW?

- If students have difficulty with Exercise 1, then have them review Problem 1.

Do you UNDERSTAND?

- If students have difficulty with Exercise 3, then have them review Problem 2 Got It, 2b to review the different types of triangles.

Close

Q How does an indirect proof lead to the desired conclusion? **[The assumption of the opposite statement leads to a contradiction with some of the given information.]**

Answers

Got It? (continued)

3. Assume temporarily that $y = 6$. Then $7(x + 6) = 70$; divide each side by 7 to get $x + 6 = 10$ and so $x = 4$. But this contradicts the given statement that $x \neq 4$. The temporary assumption that $y = 6$ led to a contradiction, so we can conclude that $y \neq 6$.

Lesson Check

1. Assume temporarily that at least one ∠ in quadrilateral *ABCD* is not a rt. ∠.
2. Lines *a* and *b* meet at *P*.

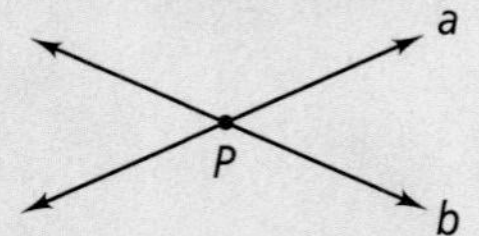

3. The negation of "∠*A* is obtuse" is "∠*A* is not obtuse."

Practice and Problem-Solving Exercises

4. Assume temporarily that it is not raining outside.
5. Assume temporarily that ∠*J* is a rt. ∠.
6. Assume temporarily that △*PEN* is not isosc.
7. Assume temporarily that no ∠ is obtuse.
8. Assume temporarily that $\overline{XY}$ and $\overline{AB}$ are not ≅.
9. Assume temporarily that $m\angle 2 \leq 90$.

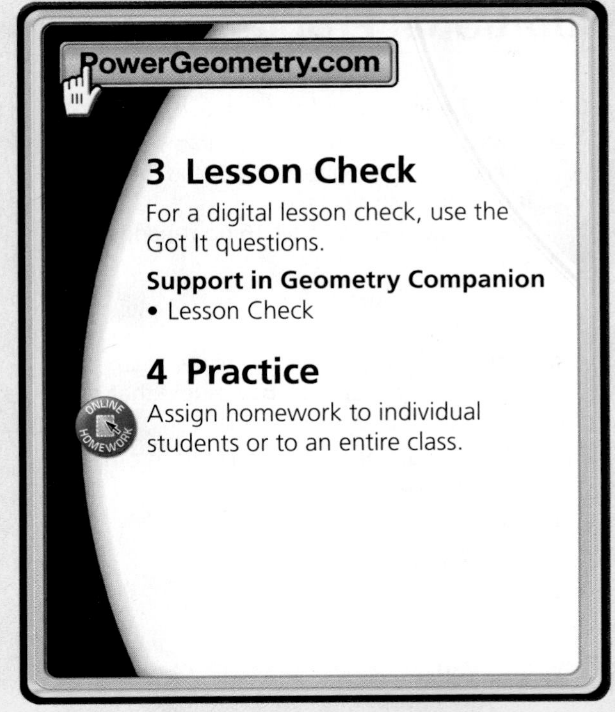

4 Practice

ASSIGNMENT GUIDE

Basic: 4–18 all, 20, 23, 24–28 even
Average: 5–15 odd, 16–28
Advanced: 5–15 odd, 16–30
Standardized Test Prep: 31–34
Mixed Review: 35–40
Reasoning exercises have blue headings.
Applications exercises have red headings.
EXERCISE 23: Use the Think About a Plan worksheet in the **Practice and Problem Solving Workbook** (also available in the Teaching Resources in print and online) to further support students' development in becoming independent learners.

HOMEWORK QUICK CHECK

To check students' understanding of key skills and concepts, go over Exercises 7, 15, 17, 23, and 26.

Identify the two statements that contradict each other. See Problem 2.

10. **I.** $\triangle PQR$ is equilateral.
II. $\triangle PQR$ is a right triangle.
III. $\triangle PQR$ is isosceles.

11. **I.** $\ell \parallel m$
II. ℓ and m do not intersect.
III. ℓ and m are skew.

12. **I.** Each of the two items that Val bought costs more than \$10.
II. Val spent \$34 for the two items.
III. Neither of the two items that Val bought costs more than \$15.

13. **I.** In right $\triangle ABC$, $m\angle A = 60$.
II. In right $\triangle ABC$, $\angle A \cong \angle C$.
III. In right $\triangle ABC$, $m\angle B = 90$.

14. Developing Proof Fill in the blanks to prove the following statement. See Problem 3.
If the Yoga Club and Go Green Club together have fewer than 20 members and the Go Green Club has 10 members, then the Yoga Club has fewer than 10 members.
Given: The total membership of the Yoga Club and the Go Green Club is fewer than 20. The Go Green Club has 10 members.
Prove: The Yoga Club has fewer than 10 members.
Proof: Assume temporarily that the Yoga Club has 10 or more members.
This means that together the two clubs have **a.** _?_ members.
This contradicts the given information that **b.** _?_.
The temporary assumption is false. Therefore, it is true that **c.** _?_.

15. Developing Proof Fill in the blanks to prove the following statement.
In a given triangle, $\triangle LMN$, there is at most one right angle.
Given: $\triangle LMN$
Prove: $\triangle LMN$ has at most one right angle.
Proof: Assume temporarily that $\triangle LMN$ has more than one **a.** _?_. That is, assume that both $\angle M$ and $\angle N$ are **b.** _?_. If $\angle M$ and $\angle N$ are both right angles, then $m\angle M = m\angle N =$ **c.** _?_. By the Triangle Angle-Sum Theorem, $m\angle L + m\angle M + m\angle N =$ **d.** _?_. Use substitution to write the equation $m\angle L +$ **e.** _?_ + **f.** _?_ = 180. When you solve for $m\angle L$, you find that $m\angle L =$ **g.** _?_. This means that there is no $\triangle LMN$, which contradicts the given statement. So the temporary assumption that $\triangle LMN$ has **h.** _?_ must be false. Therefore, $\triangle LMN$ has **i.** _?_.

Apply

16. History Use indirect reasoning to eliminate all but one of the following answers. In what year was George Washington born?

(A) 1492 (B) 1732 (C) 1902 (D) 2002

17. Think About a Plan Write an indirect proof.
Proof
Given: $\angle 1 \not\cong \angle 2$
Prove: $\ell \nparallel p$
- What assumption should be the first step of your proof?
- In the figure, what type of angle pair do $\angle 1$ and $\angle 2$ form?

Additional Problems

1. What is the first step of the indirect proof?
a. Given: There are 30 students in a classroom. There are more right-handed students than left-handed students.
Prove: There are at least 16 right-handed students.
b. Given: an integer n
Prove: n is divisible by 2.
ANSWER **a.** Assume there are fewer than 16 right-handed students. **b.** Assume that n is not divisible by 2.

2. Which two statements contradict each other?
I. $\triangle URT$ is acute
II. $\triangle URT$ is scalene
III. $\triangle URT$ is obtuse
ANSWER I and III

3. Given: $5(x + y) = 50$ and $x \neq 3$
Prove: $y \neq 7$
ANSWER Assume that $y = 7$. Then substitute 7 for y in the equation and solve for x. The result is $x = 3$ which is a contradiction, so $y \neq 7$.

Answers

Practice and Problem-Solving Exercises (continued)

10. I and II
11. I and III
12. II and III
13. I and II
14a. 20 or more
b. The total membership is fewer than 20.
c. The Yoga Club has fewer than 10 members.
15a. rt. ∠
b. rt. ∠s
c. 90
d. 180
e. 90
f. 90
g. 0
h. more than one rt. ∠
i. at most one rt. ∠

Write the first step of an indirect proof of the given statement.

18. If a number n ends in 5, then it is not divisible by 2.

19. If point X is on the perpendicular bisector of $\overline{AB}$, then $\overline{XB} \cong \overline{XA}$.

20. If a transversal intersects two parallel lines, then alternate exterior angles are congruent.

21. Reasoning Identify the two statements that contradict each other.

I. The orthocenter of $\triangle JRK$ is on the triangle.
II. The centroid of $\triangle JRK$ is inside the triangle.
III. $\triangle JRK$ is an obtuse triangle.

Write an indirect proof.

22. Use the figure at the right.
Proof **Given:** $\triangle ABC$ with $BC > AC$
Prove: $\angle A \not\cong \angle B$

23. Given: $\triangle XYZ$ is isosceles.
Proof **Prove:** Neither base angle is a right angle.

Writing For Exercises 24 and 25, write a convincing argument that uses indirect reasoning.

24. Chemistry Ice is forming on the sidewalk in front of Toni's house. Show that the temperature of the sidewalk surface must be 32°F or lower.

25. Show that an obtuse triangle cannot contain a right angle.

26. Error Analysis Your friend wants to prove indirectly that $\triangle ABC$ is equilateral. For a first step, he writes, "Assume temporarily that $\triangle ABC$ is scalene." What is wrong with your friend's statement? How can he correct himself?

27. Literature In Arthur Conan Doyle's story "The Sign of the Four," Sherlock Holmes talks to his friend Watson about how a culprit enters a room that has only four entrances: a door, a window, a chimney, and a hole in the roof.

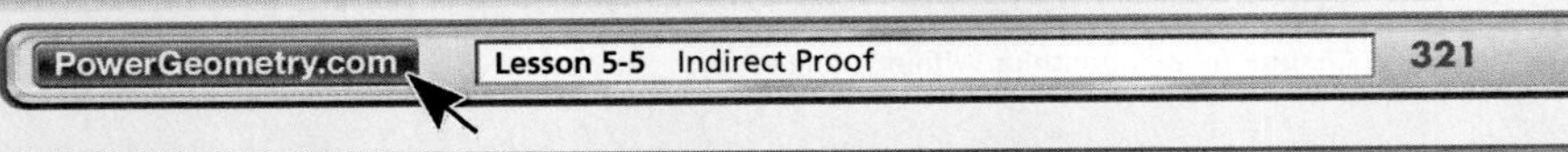
"You will not apply my precept," he said, shaking his head. "How often have I said to you that when you have eliminated the impossible, whatever remains, however improbable, must be the truth? We know that he did not come through the door, the window, or the chimney. We also know that he could not have been concealed in the room, as there is no concealment possible. Whence, then, did he come?"

How did the culprit enter the room? Explain.

28. Open-Ended Describe a real-life situation in which you used an indirect argument to convince someone of your point of view. Outline your argument.

16. B

17. Assume temporarily $\ell \parallel p$. Then $\angle 1 \cong \angle 2$ because if lines are $\parallel$ then corresp. ∠s are $\cong$. But this contradicts the given statement that $\angle 1 \not\cong \angle 2$. Therefore the temporary assumption is false, and we can conclude that $\ell \nparallel p$.

18. Assume temporarily that the number is divisible by 2.

19. Assume temporarily that $\overline{XB} \not\cong \overline{XA}$.

20. Assume temporarily that two alt. ext. ∠s are not $\cong$.

21. I and III

22. Assume temporarily that $\angle A \cong \angle B$. Then $BC = AC$ by the Converse of the Isosc. △ Thm. But this contradicts the given statement that $BC > AC$. Therefore the temporary assumption is false, and we can conclude that $\angle A$ is not $\cong$ to $\angle B$.

23. Assume temporarily that at least one base ∠ is a rt. ∠. Then both base ∠s must be rt. ∠s, by the Isosc. △ Thm. But this contradicts the fact that a △ is formed, because in a plane, two lines ⊥ to the same line are $\parallel$. Therefore the temporary assumption is false that at least one base ∠ is a rt. ∠, and we can conclude that neither base ∠ is a rt. ∠.

24. Answers may vary. Sample: Assume temporarily that the temperature is greater than 32°F. This is above the freezing pt. of water. Thus, ice cannot form at that temperature, which contradicts the given statement that ice is forming. Therefore the temporary assumption that the temperature is greater than 32°F is incorrect, and we can conclude that the temperature is 32°F or lower.

25. Assume temporarily that an obtuse △ can contain a rt. ∠. Then the measure of the obtuse ∠ plus the measure of the rt. ∠ must be greater than $90 + 90 = 180$. This contradicts the △ Angle-Sum Thm., so the temporary assumption that an obtuse △ can contain a rt. ∠ is incorrect. We can conclude that an obtuse △ cannot contain a rt. ∠.

26. He is omitting the possibility of the △ being isosceles. He could instead write, "Assume temporarily that $\triangle ABC$ has two sides that are not congruent."

27. The culprit entered the room through a hole in the roof; all the other possibilities were ruled out.

28. Check students' work.

Answers

Practice and Problem-Solving Exercises (continued)

29. Assume temporarily $\overline{XB} \perp \overline{AC}$. Then $\angle BXA \cong \angle BXC$ (All rt. ∠s are ≅.), $\angle ABX \cong \angle CBX$ (Given), and $\overline{BX} \cong \overline{BX}$ (Reflexive Prop. of ≅), so $\triangle BXA \cong \triangle BXC$ by ASA and $BA = BC$ because corresp. parts of ≅ △s are ≅. But this contradicts the given statement that $\triangle ABC$ is scalene. Therefore the temporary assumption that $\overline{XB} \perp \overline{AC}$ is wrong, and we can conclude that $\overline{XB}$ is not ⊥ to $\overline{AC}$.

30.

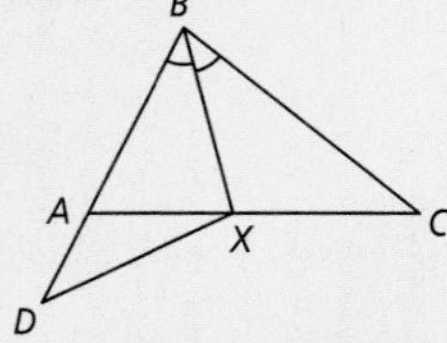

Assume temporarily that $\overline{AX} \cong \overline{XC}$. Since the △ is scalene, we may suppose that $BA < BC$. Find D on $\overrightarrow{BA}$ so that $BD = BC$. We have $\angle DBX \cong \angle CBX$ (Given) and $\overline{BX} \cong \overline{BX}$ (Refl. Prop. of ≅). So $\triangle DBX \cong \triangle CBX$ by SAS. Then $\overline{DX} \cong \overline{CX}$ (Corresp. parts of ≅ △s are ≅.) so $\overline{DX} \cong \overline{AX}$ (Trans. Prop. of ≅). Let $m\angle BDX = q$. Then $m\angle BCX = q$ (Corresp. parts of ≅ △s are ≅.) and $m\angle XAD = q$ (Isosc. △ Thm.). Therefore, $m\angle BAX = 180 - q$. Now the sum of the ∠ measures in $\triangle ABC$ is $180 - q + 72 + q = 252$. This contradicts the △ Angle-Sum Thm. Therefore, the temporary assumption that $\overline{AX} \cong \overline{XC}$ is incorrect. So $\overline{AX} \not\cong \overline{XC}$.

31. D

32. G

33. C

34. [2] All acute △s; the centroid and incenter are always inside. The circumcenter and orthocenter are on the △ if it is a rt. △; they are outside the △ if it is obtuse.
[1] correct answer with no explanation

35. 24 cm

36. 30 and 120

37. Law of Syllogism

38. $\overline{AC}$, $\overline{BC}$, $\overline{AB}$

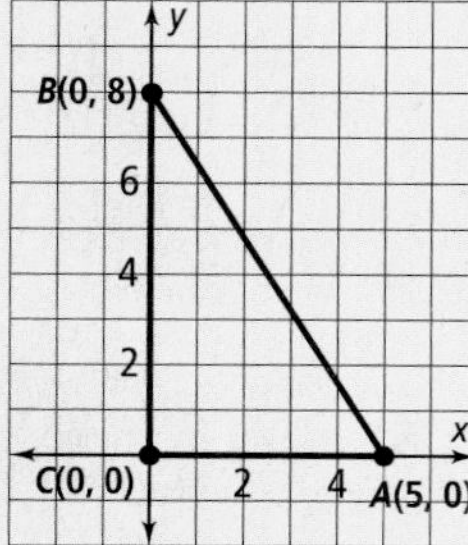

C Challenge Use the figure at the right for Exercises 29 and 30.

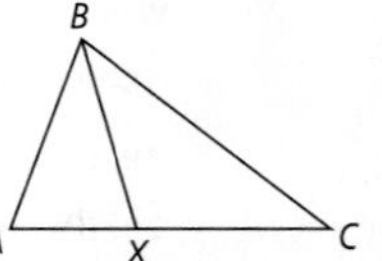

29. Given: $\triangle ABC$ is scalene, $m\angle ABX = 36$, $m\angle CBX = 36$
Proof **Prove:** $\overline{XB}$ is not perpendicular to $\overline{AC}$.

30. Given: $\triangle ABC$ is scalene, $m\angle ABX = 36$, $m\angle CBX = 36$
Proof **Prove:** $\overline{AX} \not\cong \overline{XC}$

Standardized Test Prep

SAT/ACT

31. What temporary assumption is the first step of the following indirect proof?
Given: The sides of $\triangle SFK$ measure 3 cm, 4 cm, and 5 cm.
Prove: The orthocenter of $\triangle SFK$ is on the triangle.

- (A) The incenter of $\triangle SFK$ is inside the triangle.
- (B) The orthocenter of $\triangle SFK$ is inside the triangle.
- (C) The centroid of $\triangle SFK$ is outside the triangle.
- (D) The orthocenter of $\triangle SFK$ is inside or outside the triangle.

32. $\triangle LMN \cong \triangle OPQ$, $m\angle L = 39$, and $m\angle P = 61$. What is $m\angle Q$?

(F) 39 (G) 80 (H) 100 (I) 141

33. In the diagram, what are the coordinates of the circumcenter of $\triangle KMF$?

(A) (1.5, 1.5) (C) (3, 1.5)
(B) (6, 0) (D) (0, 0)

Short Response

34. For what types of triangles are the centroid, circumcenter, incenter, and orthocenter all inside the triangle? Explain.

Mixed Review

35. The distances from the centroid of a triangle to its vertices are 16 cm, 17 cm, and 18 cm. What is the length of the shortest median? See Lesson 5-4.

36. The orthocenter of isosceles $\triangle ABC$ lies outside the triangle and $m\angle A = 30$. What are the measures of the two other angles?

37. You think, "If I leave home at 7:10, I'll catch the 7:25 bus. If I catch the 7:25 bus, I'll get to school before class starts. I am leaving and it's 7:10, so I'll get to school on time." Which law of deductive reasoning are you using? See Lesson 2-4.

Get Ready! **To prepare for Lesson 5-6, do Exercises 38–40.**

Graph $\triangle ABC$. List the sides in order from shortest to longest. See Lesson 1-7.

38. $A(5, 0)$, $B(0, 8)$, $C(0, 0)$ **39.** $A(2, 4)$, $B(-5, 1)$, $C(0, 0)$ **40.** $A(3, 0)$, $B(4, 3)$, $C(8, 0)$

39. $\overline{CA}$, $\overline{BC}$, $\overline{BA}$

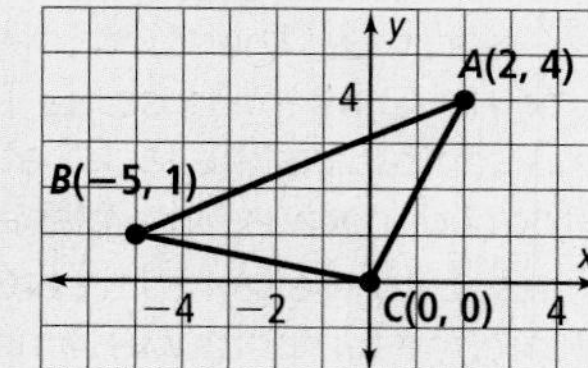

40. $\overline{AB}$, $\overline{AC} \cong \overline{BC}$

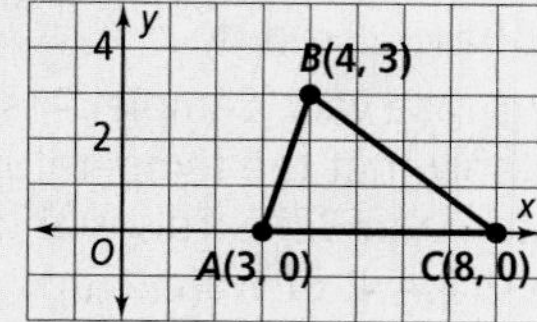

5-5 Lesson Resources

Instructional Support

Geometry Companion

Students can use the **Geometry Companion** worktext (4 pages) . . .

- New Vocabulary
- Key Concepts
- Got It for each Problem
- Lesson Check

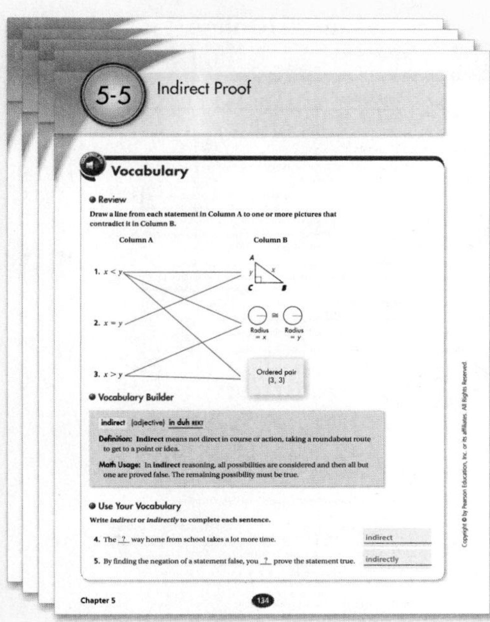

5-5 Indirect Proof

Vocabulary

Review

Draw a line from each statement in Column A to one or more pictures that contradict it in Column B.

Column A | Column B

1. $x < y$
2. $x = y$
3. $x > y$

Vocabulary Builder

indirect (adjective) in duh REKT

Definition: **Indirect** means not direct in course or action, taking a roundabout route to get to a point or idea.

Math Usage: In **indirect** reasoning, all possibilities are considered and then all but one are proved false. The remaining possibility must be true.

Use Your Vocabulary

Write *indirect* or *indirectly* to complete each sentence.

4. The _?_ way home from school takes a lot more time. indirect
5. By finding the negation of a statement false, you _?_ prove the statement true. indirectly

Chapter 5 134

ELL Support

Use Role Playing Have students write the names of different plants, different animals, and different machines on pieces of paper. Demonstrate the game *20 Questions*, attaching one of the pieces of paper behind a student and having the student ask Yes/No questions such as: Am I an animal? Write the information learned from each question on the board and point out how indirect reasoning can be used when a "No" answer eliminates some possibility, e.g: I am a plant, animal, or a machine. I am not a plant or an animal, so I must be a machine.

Now have the students play the game in groups of four or five. Have each group report examples of indirect reasoning that came up as they played.

5 Assess & Remediate

Lesson Quiz

1. What is the first step of the indirect proof?
   a. Given: There are 12 dogs and cats at a veterinarian's office. There are more dogs than cats.
   Prove: There are at least 7 dogs.
   b. Given: an integer n
   Prove: n is odd.
2. Which two statements contradict each other?
   I. $\overline{RS}$ is an altitude.
   II. $\overline{RS}$ is a median.
   III. $\overline{RS}$ is a side of $\triangle RST$.
3. **Do you UNDERSTAND?** Given: $8(x + y) = 48$ and $y \neq 2$
   Prove: $x \neq 4$

ANSWERS TO LESSON QUIZ

1. a. Assume that there are fewer than 7 dogs. b. Assume that n is even.
2. II and III
3. Assume that $x = 4$. Then substitute 4 for x in the equation and solve for y. This results in $y = 2$ which is a contradiction. So, $x \neq 4$.

PRESCRIPTION FOR REMEDIATION

Use the student work on the Lesson Quiz to prescribe a differentiated review assignment.

Points	Differentiated Remediation
0–1	Intervention
2	On-level
3	Extension

PowerGeometry.com

5 Assess & Remediate

Assign the Lesson Quiz. Appropriate intervention, practice, or enrichment is automatically generated based on student performance.

Differentiated Remediation

Intervention

- **Reteaching** (2 pages) Provides reteaching and practice exercises for the key lesson concepts. Use with struggling students or absent students.
- **English Language Learner Support** Helps students develop and reinforce mathematical vocabulary and key concepts.

All-in-One Resources/Online

Reteaching

5-5 **Reteaching**
Indirect Proof

In an *indirect proof*, you prove a statement or conclusion to be true by proving the opposite of the statement to be false.

There are three steps to writing an indirect proof.

Step 1: State as a temporary assumption the opposite (negation) of what you want to prove.

Step 2: Show that this temporary assumption leads to a contradiction.

Step 3: Conclude that the temporary assumption is false and that what you want to prove must be true.

Problem

Given: There are 13 dogs in a show; some are long-haired and the rest are short-haired. There are more long-haired than short-haired dogs.

Prove: There are at least seven long-haired dogs in the show.

Step 1: Assume that fewer than seven long-haired dogs are in the show.

Step 2: Let ℓ be the number of long-haired dogs and s be the number of short-haired dogs. Because $\ell + s = 13$, $s = 13 - \ell$. If ℓ is less than 7, s is greater than or equal to 7. Therefore, s is greater than ℓ. This *contradicts* the statement that there are more long-haired than short-haired dogs.

Step 3: Therefore, there are at least seven long-haired dogs.

Exercises

Write the temporary assumption you would make as a first step in writing an indirect proof.

1. **Given:** an integer q; **Prove:** q is a factor of 34. Assume q is not a factor of 34.
2. **Given:** $\triangle XYZ$; **Prove:** $XY + XZ > YZ$. Assume $XY + XZ \leq YZ$.
3. **Given:** rectangle $GHIJ$; **Prove:** $m\angle G = 90$ Assume $m\angle G \neq 90$.
4. **Given:** $\overline{XY}$ and $\overline{XM}$; **Prove:** $XY = XM$ Assume $XY \neq XM$.

Write a statement that contradicts the given statement.

5. Whitney lives in an apartment. Whitney does not live in an apartment.
6. Marc does not have three sisters. Marc has three sisters.
7. $\angle 1$ is a right angle. $\angle 1$ is an acute angle.
8. Lines m and h intersect. Lines m and h do not intersect.

All-in-One Resources/Online

English Language Learner Support

5-5 **ELL Support**
Indirect Proof

Use the chart below to review vocabulary. These vocabulary words will help you complete this page.

Related Words	Explanations	Examples
Assume uh SOOM	to say or believe something to be true	The weather has been cold every day this week. I *assume* it will be cold today, too.
Assumption uh SUMP shun	something taken to be true, or believed to be true	My *assumption* is that the weather in Canada is cold.
Reason (noun) REE zun	a basis for a belief or an action	My *reason* for believing that the sun will rise tomorrow is that it has always risen before.
Reason (verb) REE zun	to think or argue logically; to form conclusions	Dirk *reasons* with his sister to get her to eat her vegetables.
Reasoning REE zun ing	way of thinking, analysis	inductive *reasoning*, deductive *reasoning*
Reasonable REE zuh nuh bul	to be logical, to make sense	After solving a problem, Maria checks to see if her answer is *reasonable*.

Circle the correct answer. The first one is done for you.

I [reason/assume] that people use umbrellas when it rains.

1. A student multiplies 21×43 to get 903. She checks to see if her answer is [reasonable/assumption] by comparing it to the product of 20 and 40.
2. A dad could not find his children's sandals. He made the [reason/assumption] that his children wore the sandals to the beach.

Use the vocabulary above to fill in the blanks.

3. Before he jumped into the pool, a swimmer made the assumption that the water would be warm.
4. A girl's reason for believing that all cats purr is that every cat she knows purrs.
5. Everybody likes the chef's cooking. A diner concludes using inductive reasoning that she will enjoy the dinner the chef is cooking tonight.

Differentiated Remediation *continued*

On-Level

- **Practice** (2 pages) Provides extra practice for each lesson. For simpler practice exercises, use the Form K Practice pages found in the All-in-One Teaching Resources and online.
- **Think About a Plan** Helps students develop specific problem-solving skills and strategies by providing scaffolded guiding questions.
- **Standardized Test Prep** Focuses on all major exercises, all major question types, and helps students prepare for the high-stakes assessments.

Practice and Problem Solving Wkbk/ All-in-One Resources/Online

Practice page 1

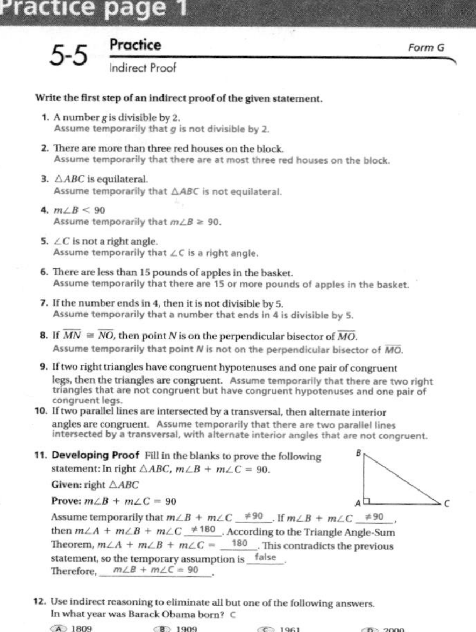

5-5 **Practice** — Indirect Proof — *Form G*

Write the first step of an indirect proof of the given statement.

1. A number g is divisible by 2.
Assume temporarily that g is not divisible by 2.
2. There are more than three red houses on the block.
Assume temporarily that there are at most three red houses on the block.
3. $\triangle ABC$ is equilateral.
Assume temporarily that $\triangle ABC$ is not equilateral.
4. $m\angle B < 90$
Assume temporarily that $m\angle B \geq 90$.
5. $\angle C$ is not a right angle.
Assume temporarily that $\angle C$ is a right angle.
6. There are less than 15 pounds of apples in the basket.
Assume temporarily that there are 15 or more pounds of apples in the basket.
7. If the number ends in 4, then it is not divisible by 5.
Assume temporarily that a number that ends in 4 is divisible by 5.
8. If $\overline{MN} \cong \overline{NO}$, then point N is on the perpendicular bisector of $\overline{MO}$.
Assume temporarily that point N is not on the perpendicular bisector of $\overline{MO}$.
9. If two right triangles have congruent hypotenuses and one pair of congruent legs, then the triangles are congruent. Assume temporarily that there are two right triangles that are not congruent but have congruent hypotenuses and one pair of congruent legs.
10. If two parallel lines are intersected by a transversal, then alternate interior angles are congruent. Assume temporarily that there are two parallel lines intersected by a transversal, with alternate interior angles that are not congruent.
11. **Developing Proof** Fill in the blanks to prove the following statement: In right $\triangle ABC$, $m\angle B + m\angle C = 90$.
Given: right $\triangle ABC$
Prove: $m\angle B + m\angle C = 90$
Assume temporarily that $m\angle B + m\angle C$ <u>$\neq 90$</u>. If $m\angle B + m\angle C$ <u>$\neq 90$</u>, then $m\angle A + m\angle B + m\angle C$ <u>$\neq 180$</u>. According to the Triangle Angle-Sum Theorem, $m\angle A + m\angle B + m\angle C =$ <u>180</u>. This contradicts the previous statement, so the temporary assumption is <u>false</u>.
Therefore, <u>$m\angle B + m\angle C = 90$</u>.
12. Use indirect reasoning to eliminate all but one of the following answers.
In what year was Barack Obama born? C
A 1809 B 1909 C 1961 D 2000

Practice and Problem Solving Wkbk/ All-in-One Resources/Online

Practice page 2

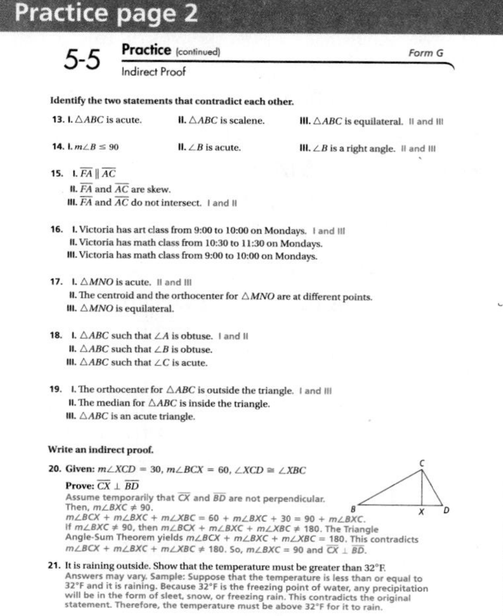

5-5 **Practice** (continued) — Indirect Proof — *Form G*

Identify the two statements that contradict each other.

13. I. $\triangle ABC$ is acute. II. $\triangle ABC$ is scalene. III. $\triangle ABC$ is equilateral. II and III
14. I. $m\angle B \leq 90$ II. $\angle B$ is acute. III. $\angle B$ is a right angle. II and III
15. I. $\overline{FA} \parallel \overline{AC}$
II. $\overline{FA}$ and $\overline{AC}$ are skew.
III. $\overline{FA}$ and $\overline{AC}$ do not intersect. I and II
16. I. Victoria has art class from 9:00 to 10:00 on Mondays. I and III
II. Victoria has math class from 10:30 to 11:30 on Mondays.
III. Victoria has math class from 9:00 to 10:00 on Mondays.
17. I. $\triangle MNO$ is acute. II and III
II. The centroid and the orthocenter for $\triangle MNO$ are at different points.
III. $\triangle MNO$ is equilateral.
18. I. $\triangle ABC$ such that $\angle A$ is obtuse. I and II
II. $\triangle ABC$ such that $\angle B$ is obtuse.
III. $\triangle ABC$ such that $\angle C$ is acute.
19. I. The orthocenter for $\triangle ABC$ is outside the triangle. I and III
II. The median for $\triangle ABC$ is inside the triangle.
III. $\triangle ABC$ is an acute triangle.

Write an indirect proof.

20. **Given:** $m\angle XCD = 30$, $m\angle BCX = 60$, $\angle XCD \cong \angle XBC$
Prove: $\overline{CX} \perp \overline{BD}$
Assume temporarily that $\overline{CX}$ and $\overline{BD}$ are not perpendicular. Then, $m\angle BXC \neq 90$.
$m\angle BCX + m\angle BXC + m\angle XBC = 60 + m\angle BXC + 30 = 90 + m\angle BXC$.
If $m\angle BXC \neq 90$, then $m\angle BCX + m\angle BXC + m\angle XBC \neq 180$. The Triangle Angle-Sum Theorem yields $m\angle BCX + m\angle BXC + m\angle XBC = 180$. This contradicts $m\angle BCX + m\angle BXC + m\angle XBC \neq 180$. So, $m\angle BXC = 90$ and $\overline{CX} \perp \overline{BD}$.
21. It is raining outside. Show that the temperature must be greater than 32°F.
Answers may vary. Sample: Suppose that the temperature is less than or equal to 32°F and it is raining. Because 32°F is the freezing point of water, any precipitation will be in the form of sleet, snow, or freezing rain. This contradicts the original statement. Therefore, the temperature must be above 32°F for it to rain.

Practice and Problem Solving Wkbk/ All-in-One Resources/Online

Think About a Plan

5-5 **Think About a Plan** — Indirect Proof

Write an indirect proof.

Given: $\triangle XYZ$ is isosceles.

Prove: Neither base angle is a right angle.

1. What is the first step in writing an indirect proof?
State the opposite of what you want to prove as a temporary assumption.
2. Write the first step for this indirect proof.
Assume temporarily that at least one of the base angles is a right angle.
3. What is the second step in writing an indirect proof?
Show that the temporary assumption leads to a contradiction.
4. Find the contradiction:
   a. How are the base angle measures of an isosceles triangle related?
   The base angles have equal measures.
   b. What must be the measure of each base angle?
   90; 90
   c. What is the sum of the angle measures in a triangle? <u>180</u>
   d. If both base angles of $\triangle XYZ$ are right angles, and the non-base angle has a measure greater than 0, what must be true of the sum of the angle measures?
   The sum of the angle measures must be greater than 180.
   e. What does your assumption contradict?
   the Triangle Angle-Sum Theorem
5. What is your conclusion?
The assumption is false. Therefore, neither base angle in an isosceles triangle is a right angle.

Practice and Problem Solving Wkbk/ All-in-One Resources/Online

Standardized Test Prep

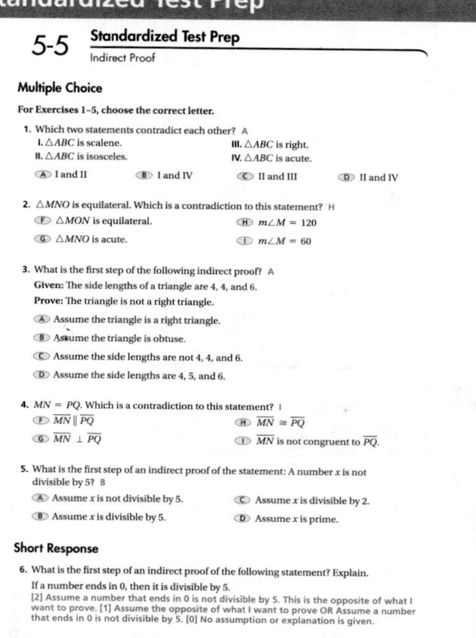

5-5 **Standardized Test Prep** — Indirect Proof

Multiple Choice

For Exercises 1–5, choose the correct letter.

1. Which two statements contradict each other? A
I. $\triangle ABC$ is scalene. III. $\triangle ABC$ is right.
II. $\triangle ABC$ is isosceles. IV. $\triangle ABC$ is acute.
A I and II B I and IV C II and III D II and IV
2. $\triangle MNO$ is equilateral. Which is a contradiction to this statement? H
F $\triangle MON$ is equilateral. H $m\angle M = 120$
G $\triangle MNO$ is acute. I $m\angle M = 60$
3. What is the first step of the following indirect proof? A
Given: The side lengths of a triangle are 4, 4, and 6.
Prove: The triangle is not a right triangle.
A Assume the triangle is a right triangle.
B Assume the triangle is obtuse.
C Assume the side lengths are not 4, 4, and 6.
D Assume the side lengths are 4, 5, and 6.
4. $MN = PQ$. Which is a contradiction to this statement? I
F $\overline{MN} \parallel \overline{PQ}$ H $\overline{MN} \cong \overline{PQ}$
G $\overline{MN} \perp \overline{PQ}$ I $\overline{MN}$ is not congruent to $\overline{PQ}$.
5. What is the first step of an indirect proof of the statement: A number x is not divisible by 5? B
A Assume x is not divisible by 5. C Assume x is divisible by 2.
B Assume x is divisible by 5. D Assume x is prime.

Short Response

6. What is the first step of an indirect proof of the following statement? Explain.
If a number ends in 0, then it is divisible by 5.
[2] Assume a number that ends in 0 is not divisible by 5. This is the opposite of what I want to prove. [1] Assume the opposite of what I want to prove OR Assume a number that ends in 0 is not divisible by 5. [0] No assumption or explanation is given.

Extension

- **Enrichment** Provides students with interesting problems and activities that extend the concepts of the lesson.
- **Activities, Games, and Puzzles** Worksheets that can be used for concepts development, enrichment, and for fun!

All-in-One Resources/Online

Enrichment

5-5 **Enrichment** — Indirect Proof

Proofs About Triangles

Indirect reasoning is a useful way to prove things. Everyone uses indirect reasoning, sometimes without realizing it.

For instance, on the way to play baseball you feel a drop of water land on you, even though you had thought it was not raining. Now, however, you decide that it must be raining, even though the daylight seems too bright for such weather. You look up at the sky and see that there are no clouds, leading you to reason that it is not raining after all, and you will be able to play baseball.

You have just used the three steps of indirect reasoning. First you assume the opposite of what you want to prove. Next, you show that your assumption leads to a contradiction. Last of all, you conclude that your assumption must have been false and what you wanted to prove is true.

Use indirect reasoning to complete the following proofs of statements that have been proven using direct reasoning earlier in the chapter.

1. **Given:** $\triangle ABC$, with perpendicular bisectors meeting at point D
Prove: $AD = BD = CD$
Answers may vary. Sample: Assume $AD \neq BD$. Therefore, $\overline{DE}$ is not a perpendicular bisector, because by the Perpendicular Bisector Theorem, all points on the bisector are equidistant from the endpoints of the segment. But it is given that D is the intersection of the perpendicular bisectors, so $\overline{DE}$ must be a perpendicular bisector because it is perpendicular to $\overline{AB}$ and passes through D. Therefore, $AD = BD = CD$.
2. **Given:** The incenter and circumcenter of $\triangle JKL$ are different points.
Prove: $\triangle JKL$ is not equilateral.
Answers may vary. Sample: Assume $\triangle JKL$ is equilateral. The incenter of a triangle is the intersection of the angle bisectors of a triangle. The circumcenter of a triangle is the intersection of the perpendicular bisectors of a triangle. If $\triangle JKL$ is equilateral, then the perpendicular bisector $\overline{JM}$ makes two triangles, $\triangle JKM$ and $\triangle JLM$. $\overline{JM} \cong \overline{JM}$ by the Reflexive Property of $\cong$. $\overline{JK} \cong \overline{JL}$ because $\triangle JKL$ is equilateral. $\overline{MK} \cong \overline{ML}$ by the Perpendicular Bisector Theorem. So $\triangle JKM \cong \triangle JLM$ by SSS. So by CPCTC, $\angle KJM \cong \angle LJM$. Thus, $\overline{JM}$ is an angle bisector, as are the other perpendicular bisectors. So the incenter and the circumcenter are the same point. But it is given that they are different points. Therefore, $\triangle JKL$ is not equilateral.

Online Teacher Resource Center

Activities, Games, and Puzzles

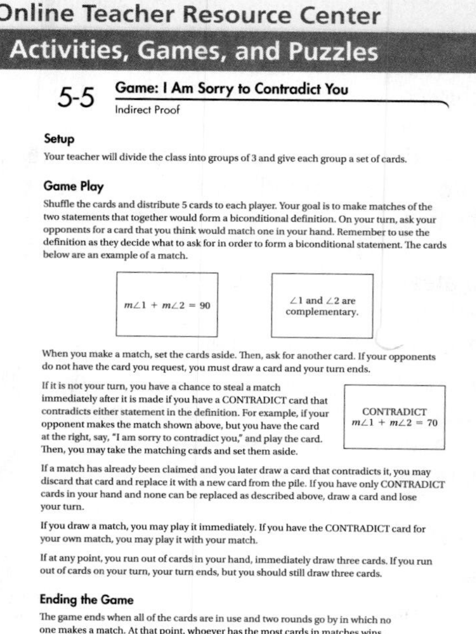

5-5 **Game: I Am Sorry to Contradict You** — Indirect Proof

Setup

Your teacher will divide the class into groups of 3 and give each group a set of cards.

Game Play

Shuffle the cards and distribute 5 cards to each player. Your goal is to make matches of the two statements that together would form a biconditional definition. On your turn, ask your opponents for a card that you think would match one in your hand. Remember to use the definition as they decide what to ask for in order to form a biconditional statement. The cards below are an example of a match.

$m\angle 1 + m\angle 2 = 90$	$\angle 1$ and $\angle 2$ are complementary.

When you make a match, set the cards aside. Then, ask for another card. If your opponents do not have the card you request, you must draw a card and your turn ends.

If it is not your turn, you have a chance to steal a match immediately after it is made if you have a CONTRADICT card that contradicts either statement in the definition. For example, if your opponent makes the match shown above, but you have the card at the right, say, "I am sorry to contradict you," and play the card. Then, you may take the matching cards and set them aside.

CONTRADICT $m\angle 1 + m\angle 2 = 70$

If a match has already been claimed and you later draw a card that contradicts it, you may discard that card and replace it with a new card from the pile. If you have only CONTRADICT cards in your hand and none can be replaced as described above, draw a card and lose your turn.

If you draw a match, you may play it immediately. If you have the CONTRADICT card for your own match, you may play it with your match.

If at any point, you run out of cards in your hand, immediately draw three cards. If you run out of cards on your turn, your turn ends, but you should still draw three cards.

Ending the Game

The game ends when all of the cards are in use and two rounds go by in which no one makes a match. At that point, whoever has the most cards in matches wins.

Algebra Review
Use With Lesson 5-6

Solving Inequalities

The solutions of an inequality are all the numbers that make the inequality true. The following chart reviews the Properties of Inequality.

take note

Key Concept Properties of Inequality

	For all real numbers a, b, c, and d:
Addition Property	If $a > b$ and $c \geq d$, then $a + c > b + d$.
Multiplication Property	If $a > b$ and $c > 0$, then $ac > bc$. If $a > b$ and $c < 0$, then $ac < bc$.
Transitive Property	If $a > b$ and $b > c$, then $a > c$.

You can use the Addition and Multiplication Properties of Inequality to solve inequalities.

Example

Algebra Solve $-6x + 7 > 25$.

$-6x + 7 > 25$

$-6x > 18$ Subtract 7 from each side.

$\frac{-6x}{-6} < \frac{18}{-6}$ Divide each side by -6. Remember to reverse the inequality symbol.

$x < -3$ Simplify.

Exercises

Algebra Solve each inequality.

1. $7x - 13 \leq -20$ **2.** $3x + 8 > 16$ **3.** $-2x - 5 < 16$

4. $8y + 2 \geq 14$ **5.** $a + 1 \leq 91$ **6.** $-x - 2 > 17$

7. $-4z - 10 < -12$ **8.** $9x - 8 \geq 82$ **9.** $6n + 3 \leq -18$

10. $c + 13 > 34$ **11.** $3x - 5x + 2 < 12$ **12.** $2(y - 5) > -24$

13. $-3(4x - 1) \geq 15$ **14.** $-n - 27 \leq 92$ **15.** $8x - 4 + x > -76$

16. $8y - 4y + 11 \leq -33$ **17.** $x + 78 \geq -284$ **18.** $4(5a + 3) < -8$

Answers

Exercises

1. $x \leq -1$
2. $x > \frac{8}{3}$
3. $x > -10.5$
4. $y \geq 1.5$
5. $a \leq 90$
6. $x < -19$
7. $z > 0.5$
8. $x \geq 10$
9. $n \leq -\frac{7}{2}$
10. $c > 21$
11. $x > -5$
12. $y > -7$
13. $x \leq -1$
14. $n \geq -119$
15. $x > -8$
16. $y \leq -11$
17. $x \geq -362$
18. $a < -1$

Guided Instruction

PURPOSE To review what the solution to an inequality represents, and to review the steps to solving inequalities

PROCESS Students will solve inequalities by using Properties of Inequality to isolate the variable.

DISCUSS Caution students to pay careful attention as to whether they have to multiply or divide by a negative number in order to isolate the variable. If they do, remind them to reverse the inequality symbol.

Example

In this Example students solve a two-step inequality.

Q Why is subtracting 7 the first step you would take towards isolating the variable? **[If a value of x is known, it is the last thing done in simplifying the left side of the inequality.]**

Q Why is the inequality symbol reversed? **[because both sides are divided by a negative number]**

VISUAL LEARNERS

It may be a good idea to show the graph of this inequality. Ask students to name a point that is in the solution region of the graph and "test" its coordinates in the original inequality.

1 Interactive Learning

Solve It!

PURPOSE To recognize that only certain side lengths will form a triangle

PROCESS Students may cut out or sketch segments with the given lengths and determine which of the lengths will form a triangle.

FACILITATE

Q Which side lengths cannot be used to make a triangle? **[2 ft and 15 ft]**

Q Why do you think the lengths will not work to create a triangle? **[2 ft is too short and 15 ft is too long.]**

ANSWER See Solve It in Answers on next page.

CONNECT THE MATH In Solve It, students realize that there is a relationship between the lengths of the sides in a triangle. In the lesson, students learn a definition, a corollary, and theorems to support this finding.

2 Guided Instruction

Take Note

Students may benefit from substituting numbers for the variables in the property. Be sure that the numbers they choose satisfy all the conditions given.

Q What happens when $c \leq 0$? **[When $c = 0$, $a = b$. When $c \leq 0$, $b > a$.]**

5-6 Inequalities in One Triangle

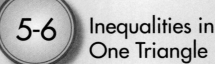

TN State Performance Indicator
SPI 3108.4.4 Analyze different types and formats of proofs.

Objective To use inequalities involving angles and sides of triangles

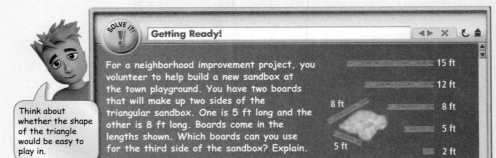

Think about whether the shape of the triangle would be easy to play in.

Getting Ready!

For a neighborhood improvement project, you volunteer to help build a new sandbox at the town playground. You have two boards that will make up two sides of the triangular sandbox. One is 5 ft long and the other is 8 ft long. Boards come in the lengths shown. Which boards can you use for the third side of the sandbox? Explain.

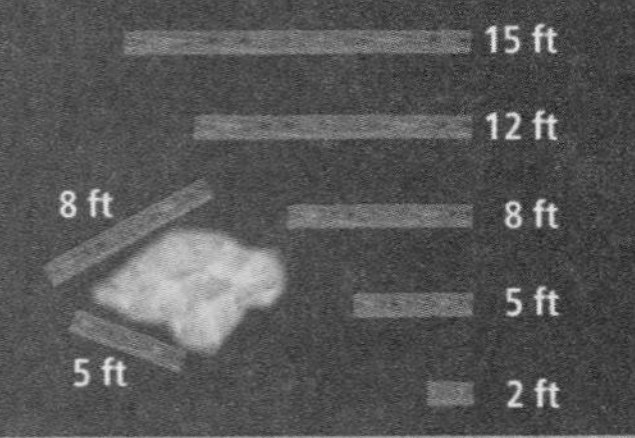

In the Solve It, you explored triangles formed by various lengths of board. You may have noticed that changing the angle formed by two sides of the sandbox changes the length of the third side.

Essential Understanding The angles and sides of a triangle have special relationships that involve inequalities.

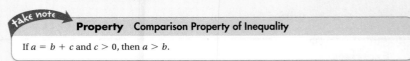

Property Comparison Property of Inequality

If $a = b + c$ and $c > 0$, then $a > b$.

Proof **Proof of the Comparison Property of Inequality**

Given: $a = b + c, c > 0$

Prove: $a > b$

Statements	Reasons
1) $c > 0$	**1)** Given
2) $b + c > b + 0$	**2)** Addition Property of Inequality
3) $b + c > b$	**3)** Identity Property of Addition
4) $a = b + c$	**4)** Given
5) $a > b$	**5)** Substitution

5-6 Preparing to Teach

BIG idea Reasoning and Proof UbD

ESSENTIAL UNDERSTANDINGS

- The measures of the angles of a triangle are related to the lengths of the opposite sides.
- The sum of the lengths of two sides of a triangle is related to the length of the third side.

Math Background

In this lesson, students will learn about the relationships between the lengths of sides and the measures of angles in triangles. The Triangle Inequality places restrictions on the length of the longest side of a triangle given the lengths of the two shortest sides. In addition to an upper bound, students can use the theorem to find lower bounds. You can challenge students to write formulas for the upper and lower bounds of the third side of a triangle.

Many of the theorems presented here could be introduced by asking students for an intuitive description of the relationship. For example, the Triangle Inequality Theorem formalizes the concept of the distance between two points. Students intuitively know that the shortest distance between two points is a straight line. It stands to reason that the distance from A to C is longer if you have to go through another point, B, first.

Support Student Learning

Use the **Geometry Companion** to engage and support students during instructions. See Lesson Resources at the end of this lesson for details.

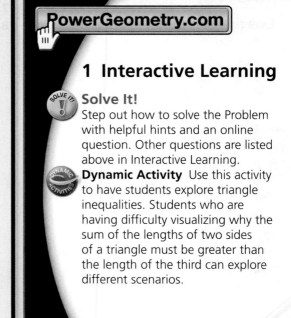

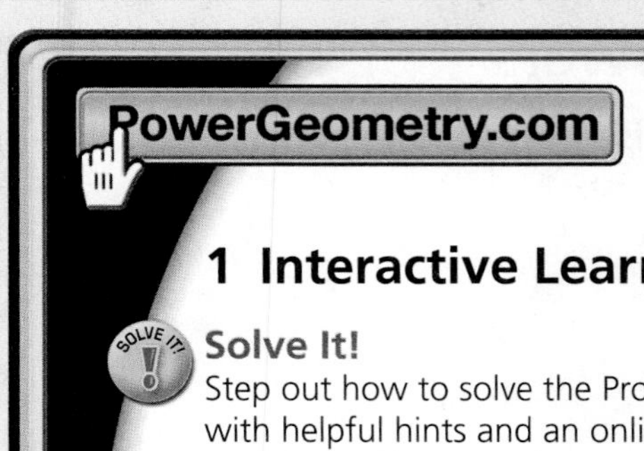

1 Interactive Learning

Solve It!

Step out how to solve the Problem with helpful hints and an online question. Other questions are listed above in Interactive Learning.

Dynamic Activity Use this activity to have students explore triangle inequalities. Students who are having difficulty visualizing why the sum of the lengths of two sides of a triangle must be greater than the length of the third can explore different scenarios.

The Comparison Property of Inequality allows you to prove the following corollary to the Triangle Exterior Angle Theorem (Theorem 3-11).

take note

Corollary — Corollary to the Triangle Exterior Angle Theorem

Corollary	If . . .	Then . . .
The measure of an exterior angle of a triangle is greater than the measure of each of its remote interior angles.	$\angle 1$ is an exterior angle 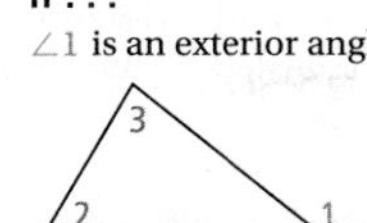	$m\angle 1 > m\angle 2$ and $m\angle 1 > m\angle 3$

Proof **Proof of the Corollary**

Given: $\angle 1$ is an exterior angle of the triangle.

Prove: $m\angle 1 > m\angle 2$ and $m\angle 1 > m\angle 3$.

Proof: By the Triangle Exterior Angle Theorem, $m\angle 1 = m\angle 2 + m\angle 3$. Since $m\angle 2 > 0$ and $m\angle 3 > 0$, you can apply the Comparison Property of Inequality and conclude that $m\angle 1 > m\angle 2$ and $m\angle 1 > m\angle 3$.

Think

How do you identify an exterior angle?
An exterior angle must be formed by the extension of a side of the triangle. Here, $\angle 1$ is an exterior angle of $\triangle ABD$, but $\angle 2$ is not.

Problem 1 Applying the Corollary

Use the figure at the right. Why is $m\angle 2 > m\angle 3$?

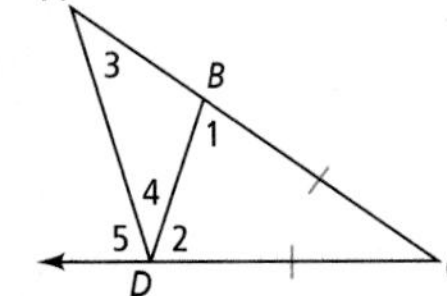

In $\triangle ACD$, $\overline{CB} \cong \overline{CD}$, so by the Isosceles Triangle Theorem, $m\angle 1 = m\angle 2$. $\angle 1$ is an exterior angle of $\triangle ABD$, so by the Corollary to the Triangle Exterior Angle Theorem, $m\angle 1 > m\angle 3$. Then $m\angle 2 > m\angle 3$ by substitution.

Got It? **1.** Why is $m\angle 5 > m\angle C$?

You can use the corollary to Theorem 3-11 to prove the following theorem.

Theorem 5-10

Theorem	If . . .	Then . . .
If two sides of a triangle are not congruent, then the larger angle lies opposite the longer side.	$XZ > XY$ 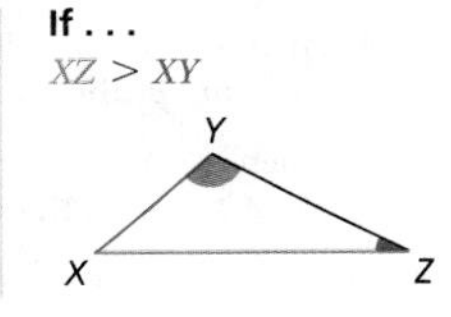	$m\angle Y > m\angle Z$

You will prove Theorem 5-10 in Exercise 40.

2 Guided Instruction

Each Problem is worked out and supported online.

Problem 1
Applying the Corollary
Animated

Problem 2
Using Theorem 5-10

Problem 3
Using Theorem 5-11
Animated

Problem 4
Using the Triangle Inequality Theorem

Problem 5
Finding Possible Side Lengths
Animated

Support in Geometry Companion

- Vocabulary
- Key Concepts
- Got It?

Take Note

Have students state the Triangle Exterior Angle Theorem. Invite them to describe how the Comparison Property of Inequality will help prove the Corollary to the Triangle Exterior Angle Theorem. Have them compare their statements with the proof.

Problem 1

Q What type of triangle is $\triangle CBD$? **[isosceles]**

Q What congruency statement can you write about angles in $\triangle CBD$? **Explain. [$\angle 1 \approx \angle 2$; base angles of an isosceles triangle are congruent.]**

Q Because $\angle 1$ is an exterior angle of $\triangle ABD$, what two inequality statements can you write? **[$m\angle 1 > m\angle 3$ and $m\angle 1 > m\angle 4$]**

Got It? ERROR PREVENTION

Have students write an angle addition statement about $m\angle 5$. Since $m\angle 5 = m\angle C + m\angle 3$, $m\angle 5$ must be greater than $m\angle C$.

Take Note

Draw several examples of triangles on the board. Have students practice identifying the longest side of the triangle and the largest angle.

Answers

Solve It!

5-ft, 8-ft, or 12-ft; the 2-ft board is too short to form a $\triangle$ with the 5-ft board and the 8-ft board, and the 15-ft board is too long.

Got It?

1. $\angle 5$ is an ext. $\angle$ of $\triangle ACD$, so by the Corollary to the $\triangle$ Ext. $\angle$ Thm., $m\angle 5 > m\angle C$.

Problem 2

Q Which road represents the longest side of the triangle? **[Hollingsworth Rd.]**

Got It?

Ask students to write an inequality statement that includes all three sides of the triangle. They can use this to write an inequality statement with the opposite angles.

VISUALIZATION

Before discussing the rest of this page, have students close their books. Distribute rulers and lengths of straws or uncooked spaghetti. Ask students to choose three lengths and record whether the lengths will form a triangle. Repeat until students see a pattern. Have them write a conjecture about the lengths of the sides that will form a triangle. Share conjectures.

Take Note

Have students write the Converse of Theorem 5-10.

Q What is a problem where you would use the Converse. **[Answers will vary. Sample: Any situation in which you know the angle measures in a triangle and want to compare the side lengths.]**

Q What is the premise and conclusion? **[premise: An angle is the largest angle in the triangle; conclusion: The side opposite it is the longest side.]**

Remind students that an indirect proof involves assuming the result is not true and looking for a contradiction. Have students identify the assumption and the contradiction in the proof of Theorem 5-11.

Think

How do you find the side opposite an angle?
Choose an angle of a triangle. The side opposite it is the only side that does not have an endpoint at the vertex of the angle.

Problem 2 Using Theorem 5-10

A town park is triangular. A landscape architect wants to place a bench at the corner with the largest angle. Which two streets form the corner with the largest angle?

Hollingsworth Road is the longest street, so it is opposite the largest angle. MLK Boulevard and Valley Road form the largest angle.

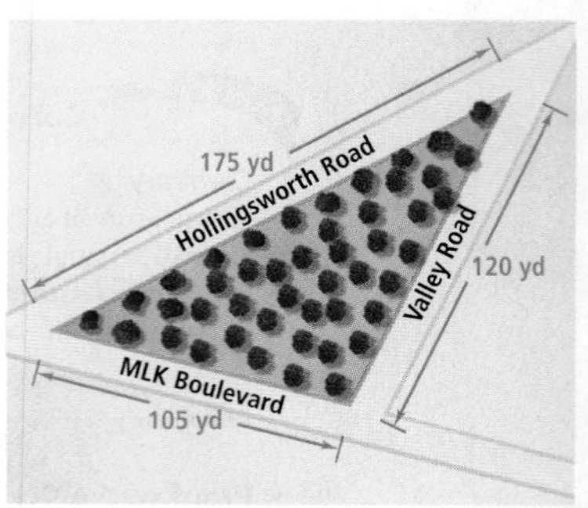

Got It? 2. Suppose the landscape architect wants to place a drinking fountain at the corner with the second largest angle. Which two streets form the corner with the second-largest angle?

Theorem 5-11 below is the converse of Theorem 5-10. The proof of Theorem 5-11 relies on indirect reasoning.

take note **Theorem 5-11**

Theorem	If . . .	Then . . .
If two angles of a triangle are not congruent, then the longer side lies opposite the larger angle.	$m\angle A > m\angle B$	$BC > AC$

Proof Indirect Proof of Theorem 5-11

Given: $m\angle A > m\angle B$

Prove: $BC > AC$

Step 1 Assume temporarily that $BC \ngtr AC$. That is, assume temporarily that either $BC < AC$ or $BC = AC$.

Step 2 If $BC < AC$, then $m\angle A < m\angle B$ (Theorem 5-10). This contradicts the given fact that $m\angle A > m\angle B$. Therefore, $BC < AC$ must be false.

If $BC = AC$, then $m\angle A = m\angle B$ (Isosceles Triangle Theorem). This also contradicts $m\angle A > m\angle B$. Therefore, $BC = AC$ must be false.

Step 3 The temporary assumption $BC \ngtr AC$ is false, so $BC > AC$.

326 Chapter 5 Relationships Within Triangles

Additional Problems

1. Explain why $m\angle 1 > m\angle 4$.

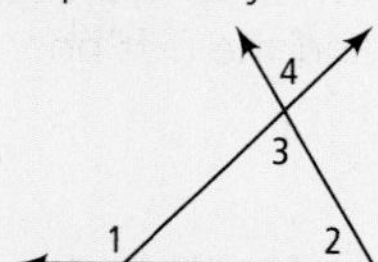

ANSWER By the corollary to the Exterior Angle Theorem, $m\angle 1 > m\angle 3$. Because $\angle 3$ and $\angle 4$ are vertical angles, they are congruent. So, by substitution, $m\angle 1 > m\angle 4$.

2. Which corner of the triangular plot of land forms the largest angle?

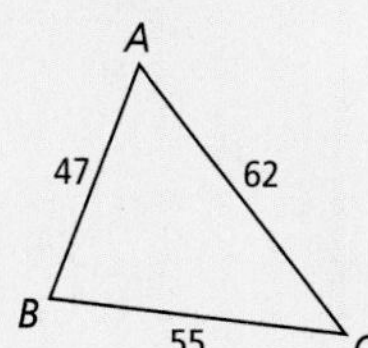

ANSWER corner B

3. Which choice shows the sides of $\triangle LMN$ in order from shortest to longest?

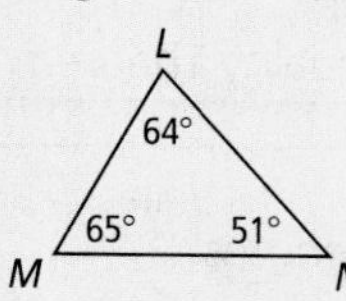

A. $\overline{LM}, \overline{LN}, \overline{MN}$
B. $\overline{LN}, \overline{MN}, \overline{LM}$
C. $\overline{LM}, \overline{MN}, \overline{LN}$
D. $\overline{MN}, \overline{LN}, \overline{LM}$

ANSWER C

4. Can a triangle have sides with the given lengths? Explain.

a. 6, 8, 13
b. 3, 9, 12

ANSWER a. yes; $6 + 8 > 13$ **b.** no; $3 + 9 = 12$. The two shorter sides of a $\triangle$ must be greater than the longest side.

5. Two sides of a triangle are 7 inches and 9 inches. What is the range of possible lengths for the third side?

ANSWER $2 < x < 16$

Problem 3 Using Theorem 5-11

Plan

How do you use the angle measures to order the side lengths?
List the angle measures in order from smallest to largest. Then replace the measure of each angle with the length of the side opposite.

Multiple Choice **Which choice shows the sides of $\triangle TUV$ in order from shortest to longest?**

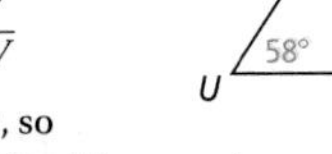

Ⓐ $\overline{TV}, \overline{UV}, \overline{UT}$

Ⓑ $\overline{UT}, \overline{UV}, \overline{TV}$

Ⓒ $\overline{UV}, \overline{UT}, \overline{TV}$

Ⓓ $\overline{TV}, \overline{UT}, \overline{UV}$

By the Triangle Angle-Sum Theorem, $m\angle T = 60$. $58 < 60 < 62$, so $m\angle U < m\angle T < m\angle V$. By Theorem 5-11, $TV < UV < UT$. Choice A is correct.

Got It? 3. Reasoning In the figure at the right, $m\angle S = 24$ and $m\angle O = 130$. Which side of $\triangle SOX$ is the shortest side? Explain your reasoning.

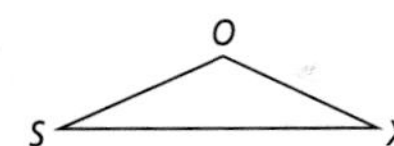

For three segments to form a triangle, their lengths must be related in a certain way. Notice that only one of the sets of segments below can form a triangle. The sum of the smallest two lengths must be greater than the greatest length.

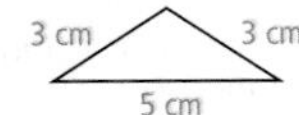

take note — Theorem 5-12 Triangle Inequality Theorem

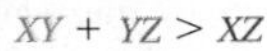

The sum of the lengths of any two sides of a triangle is greater than the length of the third side.

$XY + YZ > XZ \quad YZ + XZ > XY \quad XZ + XY > YZ$

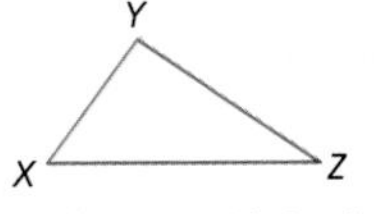

You will prove Theorem 5-12 in Exercise 45.

Problem 4 Using the Triangle Inequality Theorem

Think

How do you use the Triangle Inequality Theorem?
Test each pair of side lengths. The sum of each pair must be greater than the third length.

Can a triangle have sides with the given lengths? Explain.

A 3 ft, 7 ft, 8 ft

$3 + 7 > 8 \qquad 7 + 8 > 3 \qquad 8 + 3 > 7$

$10 > 8 \qquad 15 > 3 \qquad 11 > 7$

Yes. The sum of the lengths of any two sides is greater than the length of the third side.

B 5 ft, 10 ft, 15 ft

$5 + 10 \not> 15$

$15 \not> 15$

No. The sum of 5 and 10 is not greater than 15. This contradicts Theorem 5-12.

Got It? 4. Can a triangle have sides with the given lengths? Explain.

a. 2 m, 6 m, and 9 m

b. 4 yd, 6 yd, and 9 yd

Problem 3

Q What is the measure of the unmarked angle in the triangle? Justify your answer. **[By the Triangle Angle-Sum Theorem, $m\angle T = 180 - (m\angle U + m\angle V) = 180 - (58 + 62) = 60$.]**

Q What inequality can be written using the measures of the angles? **[$m\angle V > m\angle T > m\angle U$]**

Got It?

Have students find the missing angle measure. They can write an inequality with the three angle measures to use when listing the sides.

Take Note

Ask students to choose side lengths which would satisfy the Triangle Inequality Theorem. Invite volunteers to give their lengths and check them as a class.

Problem 4

Q What must be true about the side lengths of a triangle? **[The sum of any two sides must be greater than the length of the third side.]**

Q How can you determine if the lengths can form a triangle? **[Find the sum of each pair of sides and verify that the sum is greater than the third side.]**

Got It?

Point out to students that they only need to check that the sum of the two shorter sides is greater than the length of the longest side.

Answers

Got It? (continued)

2. Holingsworth Rd. and MLK Blvd.

3. $\overline{OX}$; $m\angle X = 180 - (130 + 24) = 26$ so $m\angle O > m\angle X > m\angle S$. By Theorem 5-11, $SX > OS > OX$.

4a. No; $2 + 6 \not> 9$.

b. Yes; the sum of the lengths of any two sides is greater than the length of the third side.

Problem 5

Q What do you notice about the lower bound for the third side length? **[It is the difference between the two given side lengths.]**

Q What do you notice about the upper bound? **[It is the sum of the two given side lengths.]**

Got It?

It may help some students to sketch a diagram of the triangle. Have students write and solve equations to find the range of lengths.

3 Lesson Check

Do you know HOW?

- If students have difficulty with Exercise 3, remind them that they must make comparisons using each pair of the three sides.

Do you UNDERSTAND?

- If students have difficulty with Exercise 4, then have them sketch a diagram of the triangle.

Close

Q What is the relationship between the lengths of the sides and the measures of the angles in a triangle? **[The longest side is across from the largest angle.]**

Q How can you find the range of values for the third side of a triangle when you are given the lengths of the other two sides? **[Find the sum and the difference of the two side lengths.]**

Problem 5 **Finding Possible Side Lengths**

Algebra In the Solve It, you explored the possible dimensions of a triangular sandbox. Two of the sides are 5 ft and 8 ft long. What is the range of possible lengths for the third side?

Know	Need	Plan
The lengths of two sides of the triangle are 5 ft and 8 ft.	The range of possible lengths of the third side	Use the Triangle Inequality Theorem to write three inequalities. Use the solutions of the inequalities to determine the greatest and least possible lengths.

Let x represent the length of the third side. Use the Triangle Inequality Theorem to write three inequalities. Then solve each inequality for x.

$x + 5 > 8$ $\quad$ $x + 8 > 5$ $\quad$ $5 + 8 > x$

$x > 3$ $\quad$ $x > -3$ $\quad$ $x < 13$

Numbers that satisfy $x > 3$ and $x > -3$ must be greater than 3. So, the third side must be greater than 3 ft and less than 13 ft.

Got It? 5. A triangle has side lengths of 4 in. and 7 in. What is the range of possible lengths for the third side?

Lesson Check

Do you know HOW?

Use $\triangle ABC$ for Exercises 1 and 2.

1. Which side is the longest?
2. Which angle is the smallest?
3. Can a triangle have sides of lengths 4, 5, and 10? Explain.

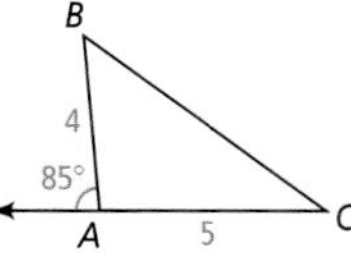

Do you UNDERSTAND?

4. **Error Analysis** A friend tells you that she drew a triangle with perimeter 16 and one side of length 8. How do you know she made an error in her drawing?
5. **Reasoning** Is it possible to draw a right triangle with an exterior angle measuring 88? Explain your reasoning.

Practice and Problem-Solving Exercises

A Practice **Explain why $m\angle 1 > m\angle 2$.** See Problem 1.

6.

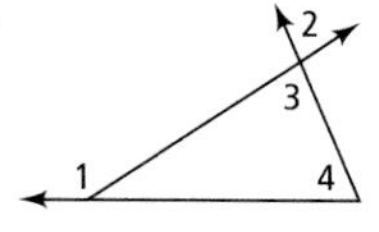

7.

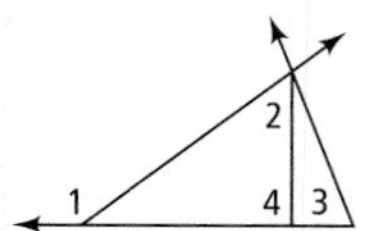

8.

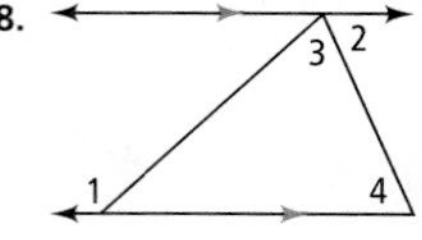

PowerGeometry.com

3 Lesson Check

For a digital lesson check, use the Got It questions.

Support in Geometry Companion

- Lesson Check

4 Practice

Assign homework to individual students or to an entire class.

Answers

Lesson Check

1. $\overline{BC}$
2. $\angle C$
3. No; $5 + 4 \ngtr 10$.
4. If the perimeter is 16 and the length of one side is 8, then the sum of the lengths of the other two sides is $16 - 8 = 8$. However, the $\triangle$ Inequality Thm. tells you that if the length of one side is 8, then the sum of the lengths of the other two sides is greater than 8. So the friend is incorrect.
5. No; the adjacent interior $\angle$ would measure 92. Then, because a second $\angle$ of the $\triangle$ measures 90, the sum of the $\angle$ measures would exceed 180, which contradicts the $\triangle$ Angle-Sum Thm.

Practice and Problem-Solving Exercises

6. $m\angle 1 > m\angle 3$ by the Corollary to the $\triangle$ Ext. $\angle$ Thm. $m\angle 3 = m\angle 2$, because they are vertical $\angle$s. Thus, $m\angle 1 > m\angle 2$ by substitution.
7. This is true by the Corollary to the $\triangle$ Ext. $\angle$ Thm.
8. $m\angle 2 = m\angle 4$ because $\parallel$ lines form alt. int. $\angle$s that are $\cong$, and $m\angle 1 > m\angle 4$ by the Corollary to the $\triangle$ Ext. $\angle$ Thm. So $m\angle 1 > m\angle 2$ by substitution.

For Exercises 9–14, list the angles of each triangle in order from smallest to largest. See Problem 2.

9.

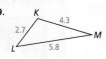

10.

11. 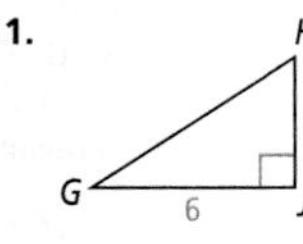

12. $\triangle ABC$, where $AB = 8$, $BC = 5$, and $CA = 7$

13. $\triangle DEF$, where $DE = 15$, $EF = 18$, and $DF = 5$

14. $\triangle XYZ$, where $XY = 12$, $YZ = 24$, and $ZX = 30$

For Exercises 15–20, list the sides of each triangle in order from shortest to longest. See Problem 3.

15. 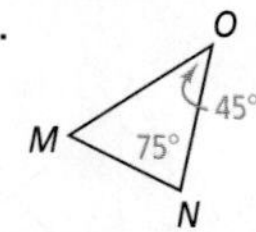

16. 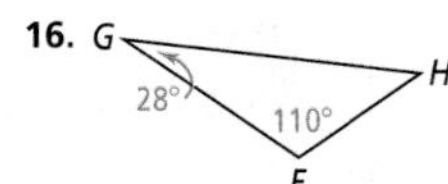

17. 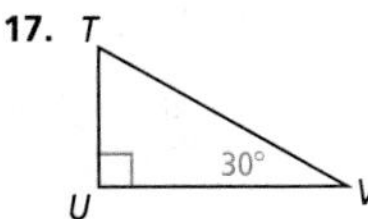

18. $\triangle ABC$, with $m\angle A = 90$, $m\angle B = 40$, and $m\angle C = 50$

19. $\triangle DEF$, with $m\angle D = 20$, $m\angle E = 120$, and $m\angle F = 40$

20. $\triangle XYZ$, with $m\angle X = 51$, $m\angle Y = 59$, and $m\angle Z = 70$

Can a triangle have sides with the given lengths? Explain. See Problem 4.

21. 2 in., 3 in., 6 in.
22. 11 cm, 12 cm, 15 cm
23. 8 m, 10 m, 19 m
24. 1 cm, 15 cm, 15 cm
25. 2 yd, 9 yd, 10 yd
26. 4 m, 5 m, 9 m

Algebra The lengths of two sides of a triangle are given. Find the range of possible lengths for the third side. See Problem 5.

27. 8 ft, 12 ft
28. 5 in., 16 in.
29. 6 cm, 6 cm
30. 18 m, 23 m
31. 4 yd, 7 yd
32. 20 km, 35 km

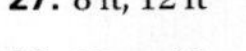

B Apply

33. **Think About a Plan** You are setting up a study area where you will do your homework each evening. It is triangular with an entrance on one side. You want to put your computer in the corner with the largest angle and a bookshelf on the longest side. Where should you place your computer? On which side should you place the bookshelf? Explain.
- What type of triangle is shown in the figure?
- Once you find the largest angle of a triangle, how do you find the longest side?

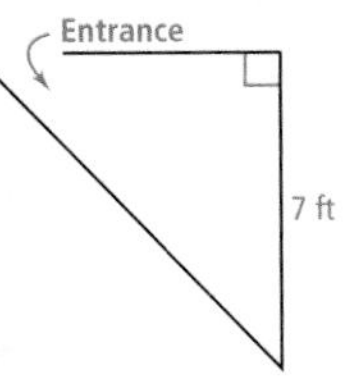

34. **Algebra** Find the longest side of $\triangle ABC$, with $m\angle A = 70$, $m\angle B = 2x - 10$, and $m\angle C = 3x + 20$.

4 Practice

ASSIGNMENT GUIDE
Basic: 6–34 all, 36–40 even, 41
Average: 7–31 odd, 33–41
Advanced: 7–31 odd, 33–45
Standardized Test Prep: 46–49
Mixed Review: 50–55
Reasoning exercises have blue headings.
Applications exercises have red headings.
EXERCISE 41: Use the Think About a Plan worksheet in the **Practice and Problem Solving Workbook** (also available in the Teaching Resources in print and online) to further support students' development in becoming independent learners.

HOMEWORK QUICK CHECK
To check students' understanding of key skills and concepts, go over Exercises 7, 15, 33, 36, and 41.

9. $\angle M, \angle L, \angle K$
10. $\angle D, \angle C, \angle E$
11. $\angle G, \angle H, \angle J$
12. $\angle A, \angle B, \angle C$
13. $\angle E, \angle F, \angle D$
14. $\angle Z, \angle X, \angle Y$
15. $\overline{MN}, \overline{NO}, \overline{MO}$
16. $\overline{FH}, \overline{GF}, \overline{GH}$
17. $\overline{TU}, \overline{UV}, \overline{TV}$
18. $\overline{AC}, \overline{AB}, \overline{BC}$
19. $\overline{EF}, \overline{DE}, \overline{DF}$
20. $\overline{YZ}, \overline{XZ}, \overline{XY}$
21. No; $2 + 3 \not> 6$.
22. Yes; $11 + 12 > 15$, $11 + 15 > 12$, and $12 + 15 > 11$.
23. No; $8 + 10 \not> 19$.
24. Yes; $1 + 15 > 15$ and $15 + 15 > 1$.
25. Yes; $2 + 9 > 10$, $9 + 10 > 2$, and $2 + 10 > 9$.
26. No; $4 + 5 \not> 9$.
27. 4 ft $< x <$ 20 ft
28. 11 in. $< x <$ 21 in.
29. $0 < x <$ 12 cm
30. 5 m $< x <$ 41 m
31. 3 yd $< x <$ 11 yd
32. 15 km $< x <$ 55 km
33. Place the computer at the corner that forms a rt. ∠; place the bookshelf along the wall opposite the rt. ∠. In a rt. △ the rt. ∠ is the largest ∠, and the longest side of a △ is opposite the largest ∠.
34. $\overline{AB}$

Answers

Practice and Problem-Solving Exercises (continued)

35. The dashed red line and the courtyard walkway determine three sides of a △, so by the △ Inequality Thm., the path that follows the dashed red line is longer than the courtyard walkway.

36. The sign, Topeka, and Wichita are either collinear or they determine the vertices of a triangle. If D is the distance between Topeka and Witchita, then $20 \le D \le 200$.

37. $\overline{RS}$

38. $\overline{CD}$

39. $\overline{XY}$

40a. $m\angle OTY$

b. $m\angle 3$

c. Isosc. △ Thm.

d. ∠ Addition Post.

e. Comparison Prop. of Inequality

f. Substitution

g. Corollary to △ Ext. ∠ Thm.

h. Transitive Prop. of Inequality

41. Answers may vary. Sample: The sum of the ∠ measures of a △ is 180, so $m\angle T + m\angle P + m\angle A = 180$. Since $m\angle T = 90$, $m\angle P + m\angle A = 90$ and so $m\angle T > m\angle A$ (Comparison Prop. of Inequality). Therefore $PA > PT$ by Thm. 5-11.

42. 0.5; the lengths of two sides of the △ are 6 cm and 9 cm, so the length of the third side of the △ must be greater than 3 cm and less than 15 cm, by the △ Inequality Thm. Since 2 of the 4 straws satisfy that condition, the probability that she can form a △ is $\frac{2}{4}$ or $\frac{1}{2}$.

35. Writing You and a friend compete in a scavenger hunt at a museum. The two of you walk from the Picasso exhibit to the Native American gallery along the dashed red line. When he sees that another team is ahead of you, your friend says, "They must have cut through the courtyard." Explain what your friend means.

36. Error Analysis Your family drives across Kansas on Interstate 70. A sign reads, "Wichita 90 mi, Topeka 110 mi." Your little brother says, "I didn't know that it was only 20 miles from Wichita to Topeka." Explain why the distance between the two cities does not have to be 20 mi.

Reasoning **Determine which segment is shortest in each diagram.**

37. 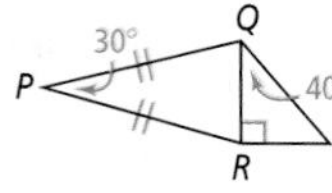

38. 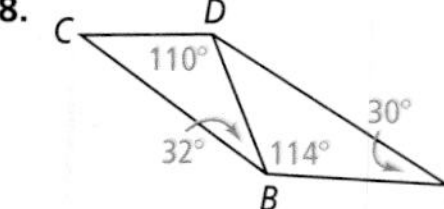

39. 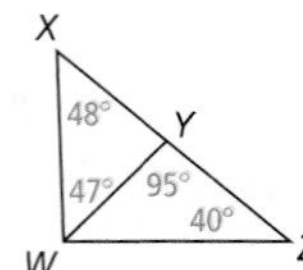

40. Developing Proof Fill in the blanks for a proof of Theorem 5-10: If two sides of a triangle are not congruent, then the larger angle lies opposite the longer side.

Given: $\triangle TOY$, with $YO > YT$

Prove: **a.** ___?___ > **b.** ___?___

Mark P on $\overline{YO}$ so that $\overline{YP} \cong \overline{YT}$. Draw $\overline{TP}$.

Statements	Reasons
1) $\overline{YP} \cong \overline{YT}$	1) Ruler Postulate
2) $m\angle 1 = m\angle 2$	2) **c.** ___?___
3) $m\angle OTY = m\angle 4 + m\angle 2$	3) **d.** ___?___
4) $m\angle OTY > m\angle 2$	4) **e.** ___?___
5) $m\angle OTY > m\angle 1$	5) **f.** ___?___
6) $m\angle 1 > m\angle 3$	6) **g.** ___?___
7) $m\angle OTY > m\angle 3$	7) **h.** ___?___

41. Proof Prove this corollary to Theorem 5-11: The perpendicular segment from a point to a line is the shortest segment from the point to the line.

Given: $\overline{PT} \perp \overline{TA}$

Prove: $PA > PT$

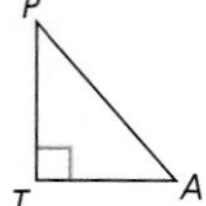

42. Probability A student has two straws. One is 6 cm long and the other is 9 cm long. She picks a third straw at random from a group of four straws whose lengths are 3 cm, 5 cm, 11 cm, and 15 cm. What is the probability that the straw she picks will allow her to form a triangle? Justify your answer.

For Exercises 43 and 44, x and y are integers such that $1 < x < 5$ and $2 < y < 9$.

43. The sides of a triangle are 5 cm, x cm, and y cm. List all possible (x, y) pairs.

44. Probability What is the probability that you can draw an isosceles triangle that has sides 5 cm, x cm, and y cm, with x and y chosen at random?

45. Prove the Triangle Inequality Theorem: The sum of the lengths of any two sides of a triangle is greater than the length of the third side.

Proof

Given: $\triangle ABC$

Prove: $AC + CB > AB$

(*Hint:* On $\overrightarrow{BC}$, mark a point D not on $\overline{BC}$, so that $DC = AC$. Draw $\overline{DA}$ and use Theorem 5-11 with $\triangle ABD$.)

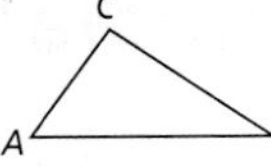

Standardized Test Prep

GRIDDED RESPONSE

SAT/ACT

46. The figure shows the walkways connecting four dormitories on a college campus. What is the greatest possible whole-number length, in yards, for the walkway between South dorm and East dorm?

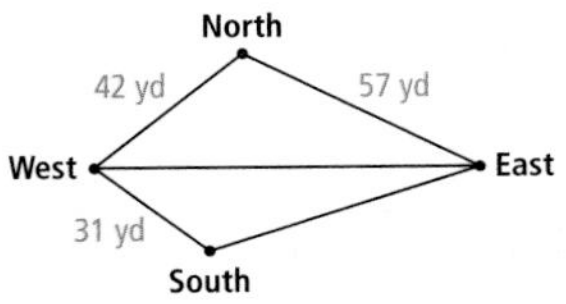

North
42 yd
57 yd
West
East
31 yd
South

47. What is the length of a segment with endpoints $A(-13, -16)$ and $B(-9, -13)$?

48. How many sides does a convex quadrilateral have?

49. $\angle 1$ and $\angle 2$ are corresponding angles formed by two parallel lines and a transversal. If $m\angle 1 = 33x + 2$ and $m\angle 2 = 68$, what is the value of x?

Mixed Review

Write the first step of an indirect proof of the given statement.

See Lesson 5-5.

50. The side is at least 2 ft long.

51. $\triangle PQR$ has two congruent angles.

52. You know that $\overline{AB} \cong \overline{XY}$, $\overline{BC} \cong \overline{YZ}$, and $\overline{CA} \cong \overline{ZX}$. By what theorem or postulate can you conclude that $\triangle ABC \cong \triangle XYZ$?

See Lesson 4-2.

Get Ready! **To prepare for Lesson 5-7, do Exercises 53–55.**

See Lesson 3-5.

Use the figure at the right.

53. What is $m\angle P$?

54. What is $m\angle D$?

55. Is it possible for AW to equal OG?

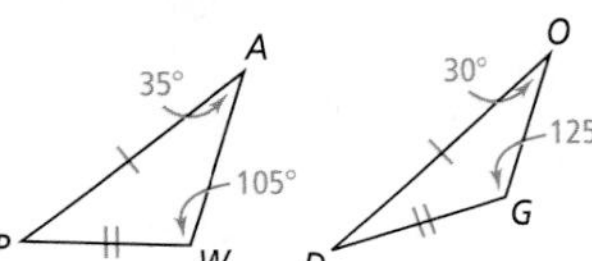

43. (2, 4), (2, 5), (2, 6), (3, 3), (3, 4), (3, 5), (3, 6), (3, 7), (4, 3), (4, 4), (4, 5), (4, 6), (4, 7), (4, 8)

44. $\frac{5}{18}$

45. Answers may vary. Sample:

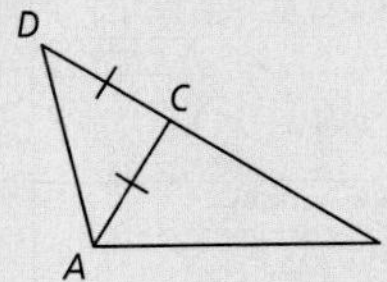

Find point D on $\overrightarrow{BC}$ such that $DC = AC$. $m\angle D = m\angle CAD$ by the Isosc. $\triangle$ Thm. Now $m\angle DAB > m\angle DAC$ by the Comparison Prop. of Inequality, and so $m\angle DAB > m\angle D$ by substitution. Thus $DB > AB$ by Thm. 5-11. We know $DC + CB = DB$ by the Segment Add. Post., so $DC + CB > AB$ (Substitution) and $AC + CB > AB$ (Substitution).

46. 129

47. 5

48. 4

49. 2

50. Assume temporarily that the side is less than 2 ft long.

51. Assume temporarily that no two $\angle$s of $\triangle PQR$ are $\cong$.

52. SSS

53. 40

54. 25

55. no

5-6 Lesson Resources

Differentiated Remediation

Instructional Support

Geometry Companion

Students can use the **Geometry Companion** worktext (4 pages) . . .

- New Vocabulary
- Key Concepts
- Got It for each Problem
- Lesson Check

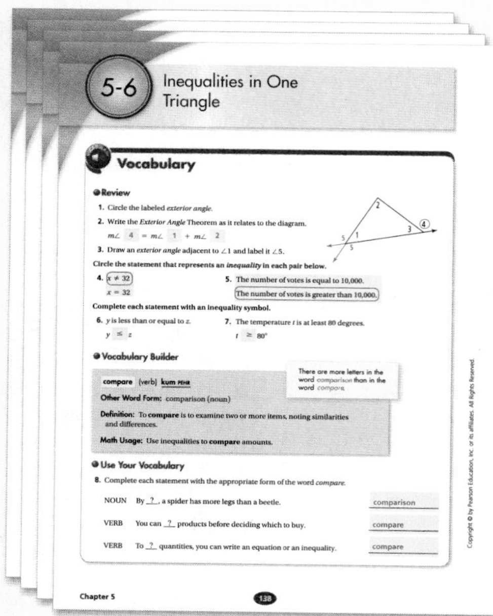

5-6 Inequalities in One Triangle

Vocabulary

Review

1. Circle the labeled *exterior angle*.
2. Write the *Exterior Angle* Theorem as it relates to the diagram.
3. Draw an *exterior angle* adjacent to ∠1 and label it ∠5.

Circle the statement that represents an *inequality* in each pair below.

4. $x \neq 32$ / $x = 32$
5. The number of votes is equal to 10,000. / The number of votes is greater than 10,000.

Complete each statement with an inequality symbol.

6. *y* is less than or equal to *z*. $y \le z$
7. The temperature *t* is at least 80 degrees. $t \ge 80°$

Vocabulary Builder

compare (verb) kum PEHR

Other Word Form: comparison (noun)

Definition: To **compare** is to examine two or more items, noting similarities and differences.

Math Usage: Use inequalities to **compare** amounts.

There are more letters in the word *comparison* than in the word *compare*.

Use Your Vocabulary

8. Complete each statement with the appropriate form of the word *compare*.

NOUN By __?__, a spider has more legs than a beetle. comparison

VERB You can __?__ products before deciding which to buy. compare

VERB To __?__ quantities, you can write an equation or an inequality. compare

Chapter 5 138

ELL Support

Use Role Playing Help students to internalize their understanding of the inequality relationships in a triangle. Assign students in groups of six to play the roles of the following parts of a triangle: longest side, medium side, shortest side, largest angle, medium angle, smallest angle. Have the students form a circle so that they are in the correct relationship. The largest angle should be opposite the longest side, and so forth.

Next have each group think of their own way to illustrate that the longer side of a triangle is opposite the larger angle. Allow the groups to demonstrate their way to other students.

5 Assess & Remediate

Lesson Quiz

1. Which is the smallest angle in $\triangle MNO$?

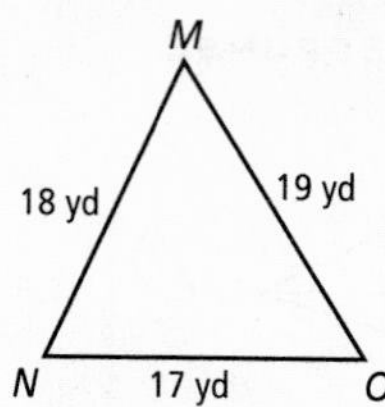

2. Order the sides of $\triangle DEF$ from shortest to longest.

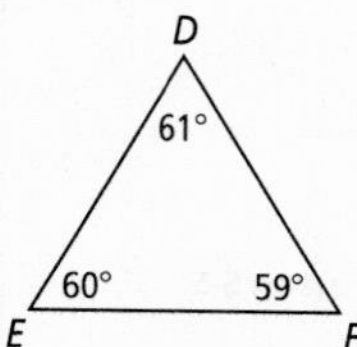

3. Do you UNDERSTAND? Two sides of a triangle are 5 inches and 10 inches. What is the range of possible lengths for the third side?

ANSWERS TO LESSON QUIZ

1. *M*

2. $\overline{DE}$, $\overline{DF}$, $\overline{EF}$

3. $5 < x < 15$

PRESCRIPTION FOR REMEDIATION

Use the student work on the Lesson Quiz to prescribe a differentiated review assignment.

Points	Differentiated Remediation
0–1	Intervention
2	On-level
3	Extension

PowerGeometry.com

5 Assess & Remediate

Assign the Lesson Quiz. Appropriate intervention, practice, or enrichment is automatically generated based on student performance.

Intervention

- **Reteaching** (2 pages) Provides reteaching and practice exercises for the key lesson concepts. Use with struggling students or absent students.
- **English Language Learner Support** Helps students develop and reinforce mathematical vocabulary and key concepts.

All-in-One Resources/Online

Reteaching

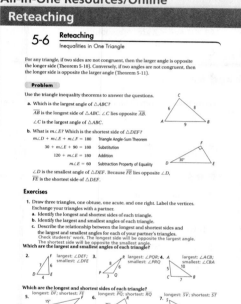

5-6 **Reteaching**
Inequalities in One Triangle

For any triangle, if two sides are not congruent, then the larger angle is opposite the longer side (Theorem 5-10). Conversely, if two angles are not congruent, then the longer side is opposite the larger angle (Theorem 5-11).

Problem

Use the triangle inequality theorems to answer the questions.

a. Which is the largest angle of $\triangle ABC$?

$\overline{AB}$ is the longest side of $\triangle ABC$. $\angle C$ lies opposite $\overline{AB}$.

$\angle C$ is the largest angle of $\triangle ABC$.

b. What is $m\angle E$? Which is the shortest side of $\triangle DEF$?

$m\angle D + m\angle E + m\angle F = 180$	Triangle Angle-Sum Theorem
$30 + m\angle E + 90 = 180$	Substitution
$120 + m\angle E = 180$	Addition
$m\angle E = 60$	Subtraction Property of Equality

$\angle D$ is the smallest angle of $\triangle DEF$. Because $\overline{FE}$ lies opposite $\angle D$, $\overline{FE}$ is the shortest side of $\triangle DEF$.

Exercises

1. Draw three triangles, one obtuse, one acute, and one right. Label the vertices. Exchange your triangles with a partner.
   a. Identify the longest and shortest sides of each triangle.
   b. Identify the largest and smallest angles of each triangle.
   c. Describe the relationship between the longest and shortest sides and the largest and smallest angles for each of your partner's triangles.
   Check students' work. The longest side will be opposite the largest angle. The shortest side will be opposite the smallest angle.

Which are the largest and smallest angles of each triangle?

2. largest: $\angle DEF$; smallest: $\angle DFE$
3. largest: $\angle PQR$; smallest: $\angle PRQ$
4. largest: $\angle ACB$; smallest: $\angle CBA$

Which are the longest and shortest sides of each triangle?

5. longest: $\overline{DF}$; shortest: $\overline{FE}$
6. longest: $\overline{PQ}$; shortest: $\overline{RQ}$
7. longest: $\overline{SV}$; shortest: $\overline{ST}$

All-in-One Resources/Online

English Language Learner Support

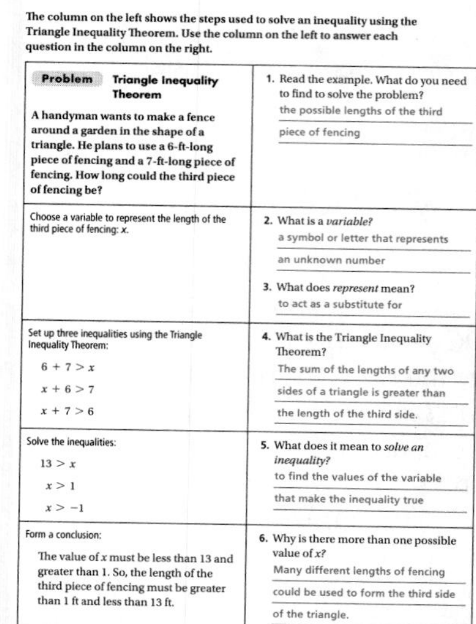

5-6 **ELL Support**
Inequalities in One Triangle

The column on the left shows the steps used to solve an inequality using the Triangle Inequality Theorem. Use the column on the left to answer each question in the column on the right.

Problem **Triangle Inequality Theorem** A handyman wants to make a fence around a garden in the shape of a triangle. He plans to use a 6-ft-long piece of fencing and a 7-ft-long piece of fencing. How long could the third piece of fencing be?	1. Read the example. What do you need to find to solve the problem? the possible lengths of the third piece of fencing
Choose a variable to represent the length of the third piece of fencing: *x*.	2. What is a *variable?* a symbol or letter that represents an unknown number 3. What does *represent* mean? to act as a substitute for
Set up three inequalities using the Triangle Inequality Theorem: $6 + 7 > x$ $x + 6 > 7$ $x + 7 > 6$	4. What is the Triangle Inequality Theorem? The sum of the lengths of any two sides of a triangle is greater than the length of the third side.
Solve the inequalities: $13 > x$ $x > 1$ $x > -1$	5. What does it mean to *solve an inequality?* to find the values of the variable that make the inequality true
Form a conclusion: The value of *x* must be less than 13 and greater than 1. So, the length of the third piece of fencing must be greater than 1 ft and less than 13 ft.	6. Why is there more than one possible value of *x?* Many different lengths of fencing could be used to form the third side of the triangle.

Differentiated Remediation *continued*

On-Level

- **Practice** (2 pages) Provides extra practice for each lesson. For simpler practice exercises, use the Form K Practice pages found in the All-in-One Teaching Resources and online.
- **Think About a Plan** Helps students develop specific problem-solving skills and strategies by providing scaffolded guiding questions.
- **Standardized Test Prep** Focuses on all major exercises, all major question types, and helps students prepare for the high-stakes assessments.

Extension

- **Enrichment** Provides students with interesting problems and activities that extend the concepts of the lesson.
- **Activities, Games, and Puzzles** Worksheets that can be used for concepts development, enrichment, and for fun!

Practice and Problem Solving Wkbk/ All-in-One Resources/Online

Practice page 1

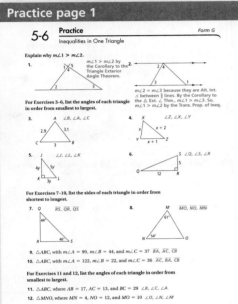

5-6 Practice — Form G
Inequalities in One Triangle

Explain why $m\angle 1 > m\angle 2$.

1. $m\angle 1 > m\angle 2$ by the Corollary to the Triangle Exterior Angle Theorem.
2. $m\angle 2 = m\angle 3$ because they are Alt. Int. $\angle$ between $\parallel$ lines. By the Corollary to the $\triangle$ Ext. $\angle$ Thm., $m\angle 1 > m\angle 3$. So, $m\angle 1 > m\angle 2$ by the Trans. Prop. of Ineq.

For Exercises 3–6, list the angles of each triangle in order from smallest to largest.

3. $\angle B, \angle A, \angle C$
4. $\angle Z, \angle X, \angle Y$
5. $\angle J, \angle L, \angle K$
6. $\angle O, \angle S, \angle R$

For Exercises 7–10, list the sides of each triangle in order from shortest to longest.

7. $\overline{RS}, \overline{QR}, \overline{QS}$
8. $\overline{MO}, \overline{NO}, \overline{MN}$
9. $\triangle ABC$, with $m\angle A = 99$, $m\angle B = 44$, and $m\angle C = 37$ $\overline{BA}, \overline{AC}, \overline{CB}$
10. $\triangle ABC$, with $m\angle A = 122$, $m\angle B = 22$, and $m\angle C = 36$ $\overline{AC}, \overline{BA}, \overline{CB}$

For Exercises 11 and 12, list the angles of each triangle in order from smallest to largest.

11. $\triangle ABC$, where $AB = 17$, $AC = 13$, and $BC = 29$ $\angle B, \angle C, \angle A$
12. $\triangle MNO$, where $MN = 4$, $NO = 12$, and $MO = 10$ $\angle O, \angle N, \angle M$

Practice and Problem Solving Wkbk/ All-in-One Resources/Online

Practice page 2

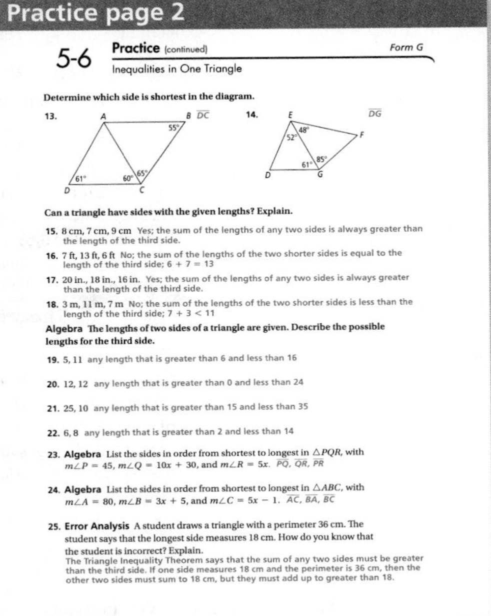

5-6 Practice (continued) — Form G
Inequalities in One Triangle

Determine which side is shortest in the diagram.

13. $\overline{DC}$
14. $\overline{DG}$

Can a triangle have sides with the given lengths? Explain.

15. 8 cm, 7 cm, 9 cm Yes; the sum of the lengths of any two sides is always greater than the length of the third side.
16. 7 ft, 13 ft, 6 ft No; the sum of the lengths of the two shorter sides is equal to the length of the third side; 6 + 7 = 13
17. 20 in., 18 in., 16 in. Yes; the sum of the lengths of any two sides is always greater than the length of the third side.
18. 3 m, 11 m, 7 m No; the sum of the lengths of the two shorter sides is less than the length of the third side; 7 + 3 < 11

Algebra The lengths of two sides of a triangle are given. Describe the possible lengths for the third side.

19. 5, 11 any length that is greater than 6 and less than 16
20. 12, 12 any length that is greater than 0 and less than 24
21. 25, 10 any length that is greater than 15 and less than 35
22. 6, 8 any length that is greater than 2 and less than 14
23. Algebra List the sides in order from shortest to longest in $\triangle PQR$, with $m\angle P = 45$, $m\angle Q = 10x + 30$, and $m\angle R = 5x$. $\overline{PQ}, \overline{QR}, \overline{PR}$
24. Algebra List the sides in order from shortest to longest in $\triangle ABC$, with $m\angle A = 80$, $m\angle B = 3x + 5$, and $m\angle C = 5x - 1$. $\overline{AC}, \overline{BA}, \overline{BC}$
25. Error Analysis A student draws a triangle with a perimeter 36 cm. The student says that the longest side measures 18 cm. How do you know that the student is incorrect? Explain. The Triangle Inequality Theorem says that the sum of any two sides must be greater than the third side. If one side measures 18 cm and the perimeter is 36 cm, then the other two sides must sum to 18 cm, but they must add up to greater than 18.

All-in-One Resources/Online

Enrichment

5-6 Enrichment
Inequalities in One Triangle

The First of the Greek Geometers

Euclid organized the known geometry of his day into one of history's all-time best sellers, *The Elements*. However, Euclid was not the father of Greek geometry. That honor belongs to a philosopher known as one of the Seven Wise Men of ancient Greece, who first introduced geometry to Greece. He founded the geometry of lines and was probably the first great mathematician in history.

To discover the identity of this great mathematician and philosopher, consider this diagram in which every angle that appears to be acute is acute, and every angle that appears to be obtuse is obtuse. Answer each question individually, and without the use of a ruler or a protractor.

Each statement below is true (T), false (F), or undecidable (U). The answers to Exercises 1–3 will supply the hint to decode the first letter of the name, the answers to Exercises 4–6 to the second letter, and so on.

A - TTT	B - TTF	C - TTU	D - TFT	E - TFF	F - TFU	G - TUT
H - TUF	I - TUU	J - FTT	K - FTF	L - FTU	M - FFT	N - FFF
O - FFU	P - FUT	Q - FUF	R - FUU	S - UTT	T - UTF	U - UTU
V - UFT	W - UFF	X - UFU	Y - UUT	Z - UUF		

Relation	T, U, or F	Relation	T, U, or F
1. $BG > DF$	U	10. $m\angle AGB > m\angle AGD$	F
2. $CF > DF$	T	11. $m\angle CBG > m\angle BAG$	T
3. $m\angle CEF > m\angle CFE$	F	12. $AG > CH$	U
4. $m\angle BHC > m\angle CDH$	T	13. $CF > HI$	T
5. $DG > DE$	U	14. $m\angle CFD > m\angle AFD$	F
6. $m\angle DGF > m\angle DFE$	F	15. $BH > BD$	F
7. $DG > IG$	T	16. $BH > EF$	U
8. $m\angle AFD > m\angle AEC$	T	17. $CE > CF$	T
9. $m\angle CDF > m\angle GBD$	T	18. $m\angle ACE > m\angle ACF$	T

The name of the mathematician is T H A L E S (thā' lēz).

19. List at least five reasons that you used to determine whether the statements above were true, false, or undecidable. Answers may vary. Sample: Theorem 5-10, Theorem 5-11, Angle Addition Postulate, Segment Addition Postulate, Comparison Property of Inequality, Transitive Property of Inequality, and an exterior angle of a triangle is greater than either remote interior angle.

Practice and Problem Solving Wkbk/ All-in-One Resources/Online

Think About a Plan

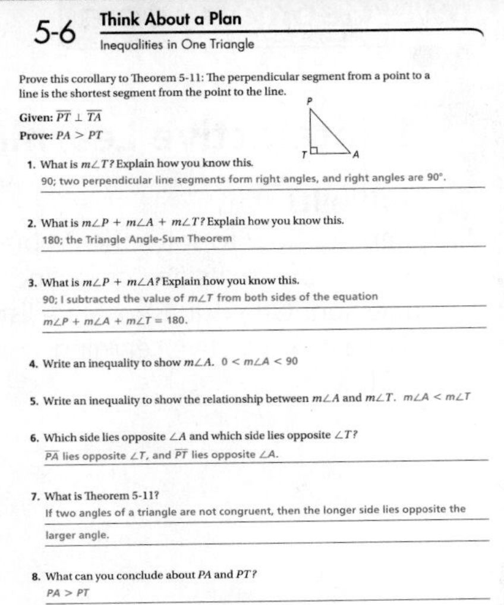

5-6 Think About a Plan
Inequalities in One Triangle

Prove this corollary to Theorem 5-11: The perpendicular segment from a point to a line is the shortest segment from the point to the line.

Given: $\overline{PT} \perp \overline{TA}$
Prove: $PA > PT$

1. What is $m\angle T$? Explain how you know this. 90; two perpendicular line segments form right angles, and right angles are 90°.
2. What is $m\angle P + m\angle A + m\angle T$? Explain how you know this. 180; the Triangle Angle-Sum Theorem
3. What is $m\angle P + m\angle A$? Explain how you know this. 90; I subtracted the value of $m\angle T$ from both sides of the equation $m\angle P + m\angle A + m\angle T = 180$.
4. Write an inequality to show $m\angle A$. $0 < m\angle A < 90$
5. Write an inequality to show the relationship between $m\angle A$ and $m\angle T$. $m\angle A < m\angle T$
6. Which side lies opposite $\angle A$ and which side lies opposite $\angle T$? $\overline{PA}$ lies opposite $\angle T$, and $\overline{PT}$ lies opposite $\angle A$.
7. What is Theorem 5-11? If two angles of a triangle are not congruent, then the longer side lies opposite the larger angle.
8. What can you conclude about PA and PT? $PA > PT$

Practice and Problem Solving Wkbk/ All-in-One Resources/Online

Standardized Test Prep

5-6 Standardized Test Prep
Inequalities in One Triangle

Multiple Choice

For Exercises 1–6, choose the correct letter.

1. Which of the following could be lengths of sides of a triangle? C
   A 11, 15, 27 B 13, 14, 32 C 16, 19, 34 D 33, 22, 55
2. $\triangle ABC$ has the following angle measures: $m\angle A = 120$, $m\angle B = 40$, and $m\angle C = 20$. Which lists the sides in order from shortest to longest? G
   F $\overline{CB}, \overline{BA}, \overline{AC}$ G $\overline{BA}, \overline{AC}, \overline{CB}$ H $\overline{AC}, \overline{BA}, \overline{CB}$ I $\overline{CB}, \overline{AC}, \overline{BA}$
3. $\triangle RST$ has the following side lengths: $RS = 7$, $ST = 13$, and $RT = 19$. Which lists the angles in order from smallest to largest? D
   A $\angle R, \angle S, \angle T$ B $\angle T, \angle S, \angle R$ C $\angle S, \angle T, \angle R$ D $\angle T, \angle R, \angle S$
4. A triangle has side lengths 21 and 17. Which is a possible length for the third side? H
   F 2 G 4 H 25 I 39
5. Look at $\triangle LMN$. Which lists the angles in order from the smallest to the largest? D
   A $\angle L, \angle M, \angle N$ B $\angle M, \angle N, \angle L$ C $\angle N, \angle M, \angle L$ D $\angle M, \angle L, \angle N$
6. Algebra What are the possible lengths for x, the third side of a triangle, if two sides are 13 and 7? F
   F $6 < x < 20$ G $7 < x < 13$ H $6 \le x \le 20$ I $7 \le x \le 13$

Short Response

7. What is the relationship between a and y? Explain.
   [2] $a > y$; the measure of an exterior angle of a triangle is greater than the measure of a remote interior angle (Corollary to the Triangle Exterior Angle Theorem).
   [1] $a > y$ OR the measure of an exterior angle of a triangle is greater than the measure of a remote interior angle (Corollary to the Triangle Exterior Angle Theorem).
   [0] No relationship is stated nor explanation given.

Online Teacher Resource Center

Activities, Games, and Puzzles

5-6 Activity: The Last Straw
Inequalities in One Triangle

Materials
- Drinking straws (pre-cut to various lengths), two for each pair of students — Make the lengths easy to measure.
- Pipe cleaner (3-inch piece), one for each pair of students
- Centimeter rulers

Your teacher will divide the class into pairs and will give you and your partner two straws. Complete the table below with the data from Trials 1 and 2.

Trial 1

1. Measure the length of each straw in centimeters. Each straw represents the side of a triangle.
2. Put the pipe cleaner halfway into the end of one straw. Then, put the other straw on the other half of the pipe cleaner so that the straws are just touching. Bend the pipe cleaner to make an angle.
3. Open and close the angle along the ruler to determine two possible lengths for a third straw that could be the third side of a triangle.
4. Open and close the angle along the ruler to determine two lengths for a third straw that would *not* work for the third side of a triangle.
5. Let the length of the third side of the triangle be x. Write an inequality to show the longest and shortest possible lengths for the third side.

Trial 2

Trade straws with another pair of students and repeat the steps in Trial 1.

Summary

Work as a class with your teacher to determine the possible lengths for the third side of a triangle whose first two sides measure a and b. Check students' work.

	Trial 1		Trial 2		Summary	
Straw lengths					a	b
Possible lengths for a third side						
Impossible lengths for a third side						
Inequality for third side of length x					$\lvert a - b\rvert < x < a + b$	

1 Interactive Learning

Solve It!

PURPOSE To discover the Hinge Theorem
PROCESS Students may
- draw each time on the clock and measure x
- use algebra to find the measures of the angles at each time

FACILITATE

Q Is x greater at 1:00 or 3:00? Explain. **[x is greater at 3:00 because the hands are farther apart.]**

Q What part of the clock affects the length of x? **[On a clock, the angle between the hour and minute hands changes the length of x.]**

ANSWER See Solve It in Answers on next page.
CONNECT THE MATH In the Solve It, students use a clock face to investigate properties of angles in a triangle. In the lesson, students learn a theorem that relates angle measures and side lengths in triangles.

2 Guided Instruction

Take Note

Have students review the definition of an included angle. Then, have them sketch a triangle with side lengths 3 cm and 4 cm. Have students compare the third side lengths with those around them. They should be able to make a statement about the sizes of the angles.

5-7 Inequalities in Two Triangles

TN State Performance Indicator
SPI 3108.4.4 Analyze different types and formats of proofs.

Objective To apply inequalities in two triangles

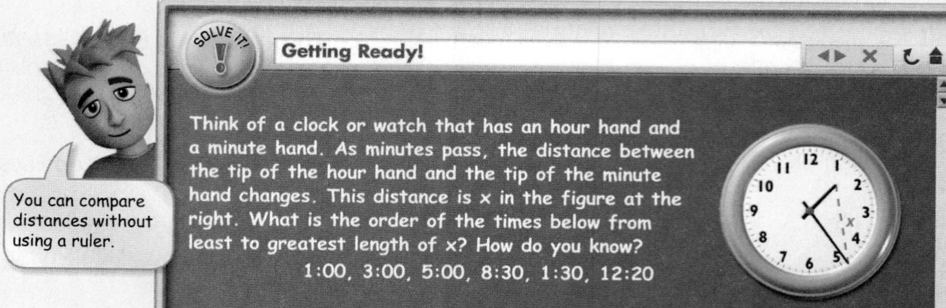

Getting Ready!
You can compare distances without using a ruler.
Think of a clock or watch that has an hour hand and a minute hand. As minutes pass, the distance between the tip of the hour hand and the tip of the minute hand changes. This distance is x in the figure at the right. What is the order of the times below from least to greatest length of x? How do you know?
1:00, 3:00, 5:00, 8:30, 1:30, 12:20

In the Solve It, the hands of the clock and the segment labeled x form a triangle. As the time changes, the shape of the triangle changes, but the lengths of two of its sides do not change.

Essential Understanding In triangles that have two pairs of congruent sides, there is a relationship between the included angles and the third pair of sides.

When you close a door, the angle between the door and the frame (at the hinge) gets smaller. The relationship between the measure of the hinge angle and the length of the opposite side is the basis for the SAS Inequality Theorem, also known as the Hinge Theorem.

take note **Theorem 5-13 The Hinge Theorem (SAS Inequality Theorem)**

Theorem	If . . .	Then . . .
If two sides of one triangle are congruent to two sides of another triangle, and the included angles are not congruent, then the longer third side is opposite the larger included angle.	$m\angle A > m\angle X$	$BC > YZ$

You will prove Theorem 5-13 in Exercise 25.

5-7 Preparing to Teach

BIG ideas Reasoning and Proof, Visualization — UbD

ESSENTIAL UNDERSTANDING
- In triangles that have two pairs of congruent sides, there is a relationship between the included angles and the third pair of sides.

Math Background

Relationships between angles and sides in triangles follow several rules. Students have already learned that the side lengths are related by inequalities. They know that the largest angle of a triangle is located across from the longest side. In this lesson, they will see that they can compare two triangles with two pairs of congruent sides. The triangle with the longest non-congruent side will also contain the largest included angle. Properties of triangles will be used to examine properties of other geometric figures.

Illustrate the Hinge Theorem with the hands of two students. Show that as one hand opens wider (the angle), the side opposite the hands must get longer.

Support Student Learning

Use the **Geometry Companion** to engage and support students during instructions. See Lesson Resources at the end of this lesson for details.

PowerGeometry.com

1 Interactive Learning

Solve It!

Step out how to solve the Problem with helpful hints and an online question. Other questions are listed above in Interactive Learning.

Problem 1 Using the Hinge Theorem

Multiple Choice **Which of the following statements must be true?**

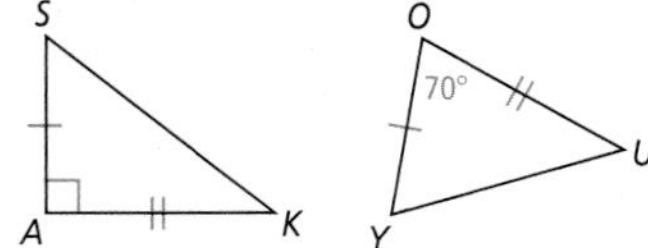

Ⓐ $AS < YU$ Ⓒ $SK < YU$

Ⓑ $SK > YU$ Ⓓ $AK = YU$

Plan

How do you apply the Hinge Theorem? After you identify the angles included between the pairs of congruent sides, locate the sides opposite those angles.

$\overline{SA} \cong \overline{YO}$ and $\overline{AK} \cong \overline{OU}$, so the triangles have two pairs of congruent sides. The included angles, $\angle A$ and $\angle O$, are not congruent. Since $m\angle A > m\angle O$, $SK > YU$ by the Hinge Theorem. The correct answer is B.

Got It? **1. a.** What inequality relates LN and OQ in the figure at the right?

b. Reasoning In $\triangle ABC$, $AB = 3$, $BC = 4$, and $CA = 6$. In $\triangle PQR$, $PQ = 3$, $QR = 5$, and $RP = 6$. How can you use indirect reasoning to explain why $m\angle P > m\angle A$?

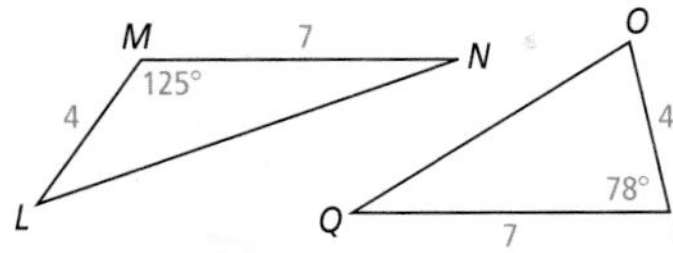

Problem 2 Applying the Hinge Theorem

Swing Ride **The diagram below shows the position of a swing at two different times. As the speed of the swing ride increases, the angle between the chain and $\overline{AB}$ increases. Is the rider farther from point A at Time 1 or Time 2? Explain how the Hinge Theorem justifies your answer.**

Think

For $\triangle ABC$, which side lengths are the same at Time 1 and Time 2? The lengths of the chain and $\overline{AB}$ do not change. So, AB and BC are the same at Time 1 and Time 2.

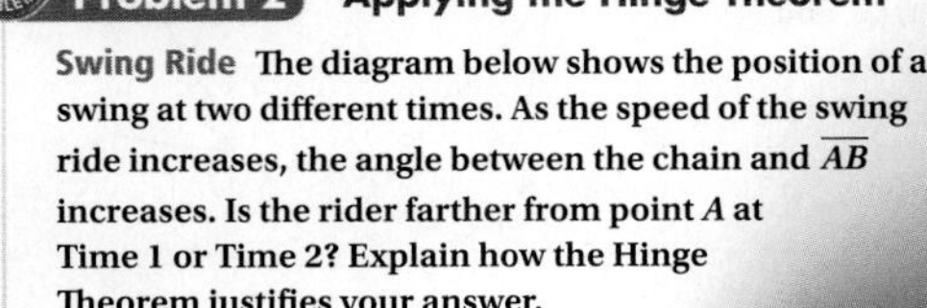

The rider is farther from point A at Time 2. The lengths of $\overline{AB}$ and $\overline{BC}$ stay the same throughout the ride. Since the angle formed at Time 2 ($\angle 2$) is greater than the angle formed at Time 1 ($\angle 1$), you can use the Hinge Theorem to conclude that $\overline{AC}$ at Time 2 is longer than $\overline{AC}$ at Time 1.

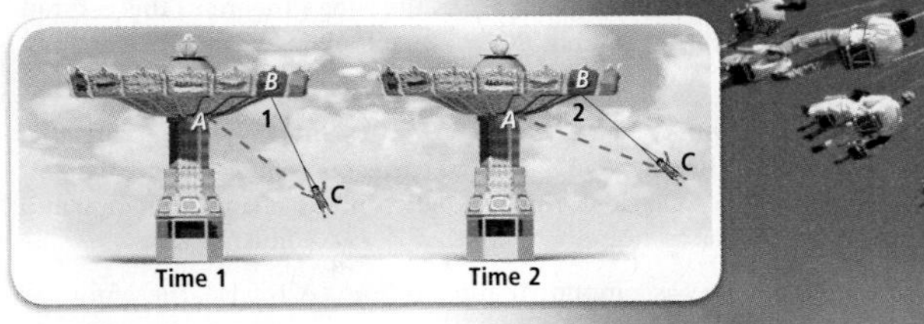

Problem 1

Q Which two pairs of sides are marked congruent? **[$\overline{SA} \cong \overline{OY}$ and $\overline{AK} \cong \overline{OU}$]**

Q Which angles are included between these pairs of sides? **[$\angle A$ and $\angle O$]**

Q Which angle is larger? **[$\angle A$]**

Got It? ERROR PREVENTION

Have students identify the congruent pairs of sides and their included angles. Then, have students identify the largest angle.

Problem 2

Q Which segments remain the same throughout the ride? **[$\overline{AB}$ and the length of the swing's chain $\overline{BC}$]**

Q What changes throughout the ride? **[The angle between $\overline{AB}$ and the swing gets larger.]**

2 Guided Instruction

Each Problem is worked out and supported online.

Problem 1
Using the Hinge Theorem
Animated

Problem 2
Applying the Hinge Theorem

Problem 3
Using the Converse of the Hinge Theorem
Animated

Problem 4
Proving Relationships in Triangles
Animated

Support in Geometry Companion

- Vocabulary
- Key Concepts
- Got It?

Answers

Solve It!

The order of the times is 1:00, 8:30, 3:00, 12:20, 1:30, 5:00; the measures of the ⦣s between the clock hands for these times are 30, 75, 90, 110, 135, 150. The larger the $\angle$ between the clock hands, the greater the length of *x*.

Got It?

1a. $LN > OQ$

b. Assume temporarily that $m\angle P \ngtr m\angle A$. If $m\angle P = m\angle A$, then $\triangle ABC \cong \triangle PQR$ (SAS), but this contradicts the fact that $BC \neq QR$. If $m\angle P < m\angle A$, then by the Hinge Thm., $QR < BC$. This contradicts the fact that $QR > BC$. Therefore, $m\angle P > m\angle A$.

Got It?

Q What does not change about both pairs of scissors in the diagram? **[the length of the blade parts of the scissors]**

Q Why can you use the Hinge Theorem to answer this question? **[The diagram shows the same scissors twice, so the "sides" of two triangles are congruent. The diagram also shows that the included angles are not congruent.]**

Take Note

Have students state the converse of the Hinge Theorem. Ask them to identify the hypothesis and conclusion to the statement. Challenge students to create a biconditional statement from the theorem and its converse.

Remind students how an indirect proof is constructed. Ask them to identify the assumption. Be sure that they understand the negation of an inequality is the reverse inequality OR the equality. Ask them to identify both contradictions in the proof of the Converse of the Hinge Theorem.

Got It? 2. The diagram below shows a pair of scissors in two different positions. In which position is the distance between the tips of the two blades greater? Use the Hinge Theorem to justify your answer.

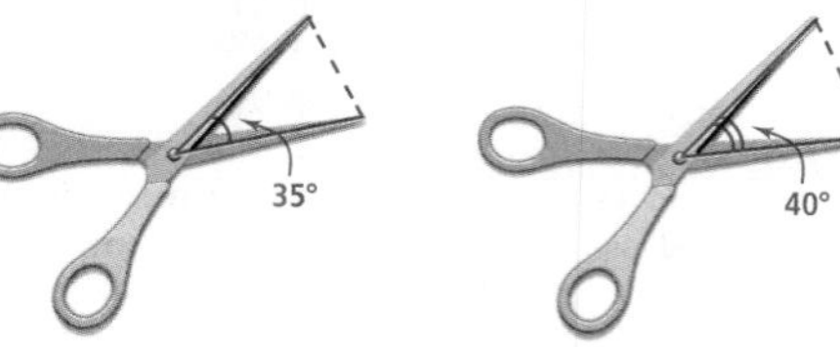

The Converse of the Hinge Theorem is also true. The proof of the converse is an indirect proof.

Theorem 5-14 Converse of the Hinge Theorem (SSS Inequality)

Theorem	If . . .	Then . . .
If two sides of one triangle are congruent to two sides of another triangle, and the third sides are not congruent, then the larger included angle is opposite the longer third side.	$BC > YZ$	$m\angle A > m\angle X$

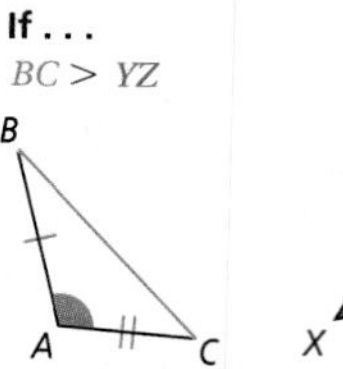

Proof Indirect Proof of the Converse of the Hinge Theorem (SSS Inequality)

Given: $\overline{AB} \cong \overline{XY}$, $\overline{AC} \cong \overline{XZ}$, $BC > YZ$

Prove: $m\angle A > m\angle X$

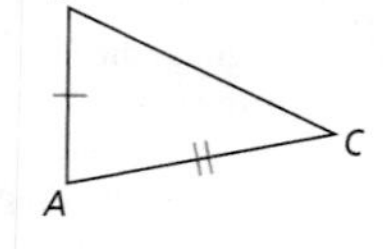

Step 1 Assume temporarily that $m\angle A \ngtr m\angle X$. This means either $m\angle A < m\angle X$ or $m\angle A = m\angle X$.

Step 2 If $m\angle A < m\angle X$, then $BC < YZ$ by the Hinge Theorem. This contradicts the given information that $BC > YZ$. Therefore, the assumption that $m\angle A < m\angle X$ must be false.

If $m\angle A = m\angle X$, then $\triangle ABC \cong \triangle XYZ$ by SAS. If the two triangles are congruent, then $BC = YZ$ because corresponding parts of congruent triangles are congruent. This contradicts the given information that $BC > YZ$. Therefore, the assumption that $m\angle A = m\angle X$ must be false.

Step 3 The temporary assumption that $m\angle A \ngtr m\angle X$ is false. Therefore, $m\angle A > m\angle X$.

Additional Problems

1. Which of the following statements must be true?

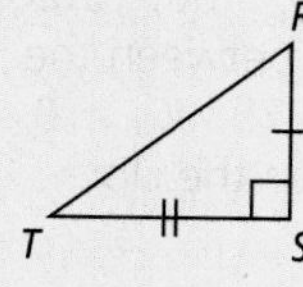

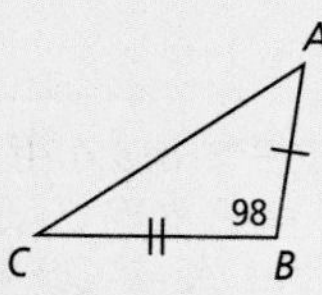

A. $AC = ST$

B. $RS > AC$

C. $AC < RT$

D. $AC > RT$

ANSWER D

2. Which cheerleader's hands are farther apart?

ANSWER cheerleader B

3. What is the range of possible values for x?

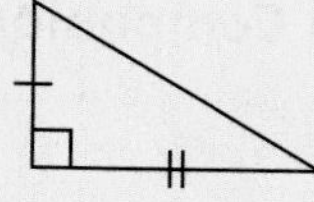

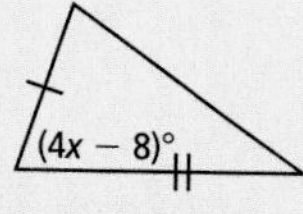

ANSWER $2 < x < 24.5$

4. Given: $m\angle RUS = 100°$, $SU = UT$
Prove: $RT < RS$

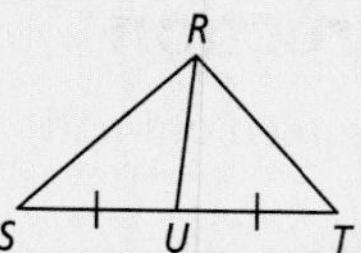

ANSWER It is given that $m\angle RUS = 100°$. So, $m\angle RUT = 80°$ by the definition of a straight angle. It is also given that $SU = UT$. By the Reflexive Property of Congruence, $\overline{RU} \cong \overline{RU}$. So, $RU = RU$. So, by the Converse of the Hinge Theorem, $RT < RS$.

Problem 3 Using the Converse of the Hinge Theorem

Plan

How do you put upper and lower limits on the value of x?
Use the largest possible value of $m\angle TUS$ as the upper limit for $5x - 20$ and the smallest possible value of $m\angle TUS$ as the lower limit for $5x - 20$.

Algebra **What is the range of possible values for x?**

Step 1 Find an upper limit for the value of x. $\overline{UT} \cong \overline{UR}$ and $\overline{US} \cong \overline{US}$, so $\triangle TUS$ and $\triangle RUS$ have two pairs of congruent sides. $RS > TS$, so you can use the Converse of the Hinge Theorem to write an inequality.

$m\angle RUS > m\angle TUS$	Converse of the Hinge Theorem
$60 > 5x - 20$	Substitute.
$80 > 5x$	Add 20 to each side.
$16 > x$	Divide each side by 5.

Step 2 Find a lower limit for the value of x.

$m\angle TUS > 0$	The measure of an angle of a triangle is greater than 0.
$5x - 20 > 0$	Substitute.
$5x > 20$	Add 20 to each side.
$x > 4$	Divide each side by 5.

Rewrite $16 > x$ and $x > 4$ as $4 < x < 16$.

Got It? 3. What is the range of possible values for x in the figure at the right?

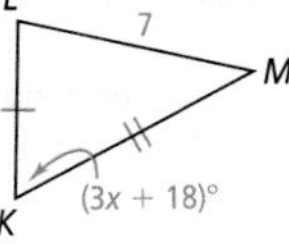

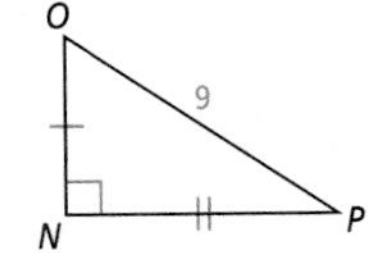

Problem 4 Proving Relationships in Triangles

Proof

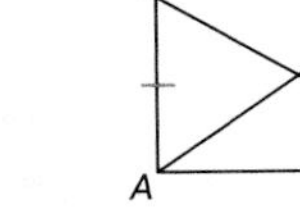

Given: $BA = DE$, $BE > DA$

Prove: $m\angle BAE > m\angle BEA$

Statement	Reasons
1) $BA = DE$	1) Given
2) $AE = AE$	2) Reflexive Property of Equality
3) $BE > DA$	3) Given
4) $m\angle BAE > m\angle DEA$	4) Converse of the Hinge Theorem
5) $m\angle DEA = m\angle DEB + m\angle BEA$	5) Angle Addition Postulate
6) $m\angle DEA > m\angle BEA$	6) Comparison Property of Inequality
7) $m\angle BAE > m\angle BEA$	7) Transitive Property of Inequality

Think

How do you know $m\angle BAE > m\angle BEA$?
Use the Transitive Property of Inequality on the inequalities in Statements 4 and 6.

Got It? 4. **Given:** $m\angle MON = 80$, O is the midpoint of $\overline{LN}$
Prove: $LM > MN$

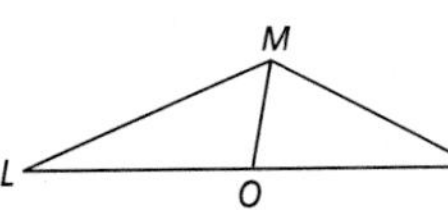

Problem 3

Q Which pairs of sides are congruent in the two triangles? **[$\overline{RU} \cong \overline{TU}$ and $\overline{US} \cong \overline{US}$]**

Q What is the relationship between the included angles for these pairs of sides? Justify your answer. **[By the Converse of the Hinge Theorem, $\angle RUS > \angle TUS$.]**

Got It?

Have students identify the pairs of congruent sides in the diagram. Then, ask them to write an inequality that relates the included angles. Finally, remind students that an angle in a triangle must have a measure greater than 0°.

Problem 4

Q Which pairs of sides are congruent in the two triangles? **[$\overline{BA} \cong \overline{DE}$ and $\overline{AE} \cong \overline{AE}$]**

Q Which angles are across from the unequal sides in the triangles? **[$\angle BAE$ and $\angle DEA$]**

Q Which of these angles appears to be smaller? **[$\angle DEA$]**

Q What theorem can you use to prove this fact? **[Converse of the Hinge Theorem]**

Got It?

Q Which segments are congruent in the diagram? Justify your answer. **[$\overline{MO} \cong \overline{MO}$ by the Reflexive Property. $\overline{LO} \cong \overline{NO}$ because O is the midpoint of the segment.]**

Answers

Got It? (continued)

2. The 40° opening; the lengths of the blades do not change as the scissors open. The included angle between the blades of the 40° opening is greater than the included angle of the 35° opening, so by the Hinge Thm., the distance between the blades is greater for the 40° opening.
3. $-6 < x < 24$
4. From the given information, $LO = ON$ (Def. of midpt.) and $m\angle MOL = 100$ (Suppl. $\angle$ to $\angle MON$). Since $\overline{MO} \cong \overline{MO}$, and $m\angle MOL > m\angle MON$, the Hinge Thm. yields $LM > MN$.

3 Lesson Check

Do you know HOW?

- If students have difficulty with Exercise 1, then have them review Problem 1 and list everything they know from the markings on the diagram.

Do you UNDERSTAND?

- If students have difficulty with Exercise 4, then have them draw several triangles with two congruent sides and compare them.

Close

Q If each of two triangles has two congruent sides, how are their included angles related? **[The largest included angle is located in the triangle with the longest non-congruent side.]**

Lesson Check

Do you know HOW?

Write an inequality relating the given side lengths or angle measures.

1. FD and BC

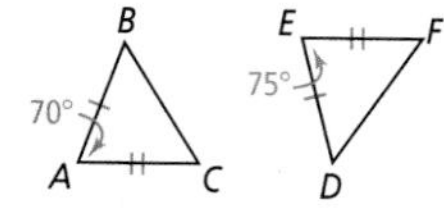

2. $m\angle UST$ and $m\angle VST$

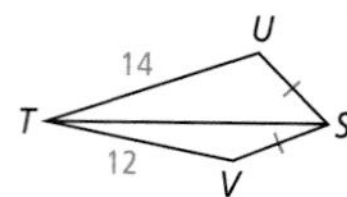

Do you UNDERSTAND?

3. Vocabulary Explain why *Hinge Theorem* is an appropriate name for Theorem 5-13.

4. Error Analysis From the figure at the right, your friend concludes that $m\angle BAD > m\angle BCD$. How would you correct your friend's mistake?

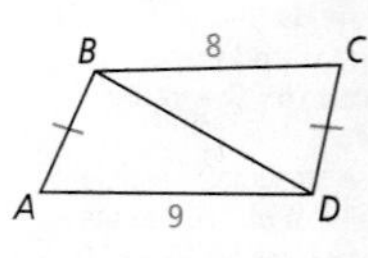

5. Compare and Contrast How are the Hinge Theorem and the SAS Congruence Postulate similar?

Practice and Problem-Solving Exercises

A Practice

Write an inequality relating the given side lengths. If there is not enough information to reach a conclusion, write *no conclusion*.

See Problem 1.

6. AB and AD

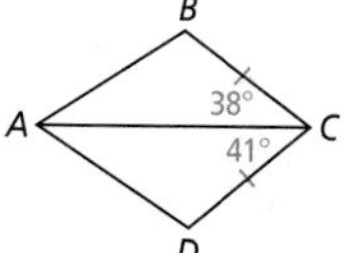

7. PR and RT

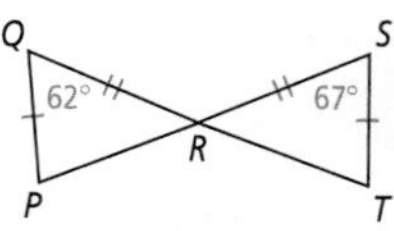

8. LM and KL

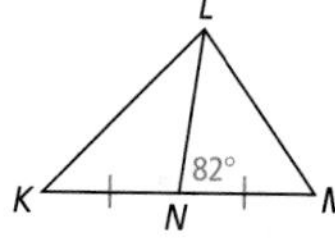

9. YZ and UV

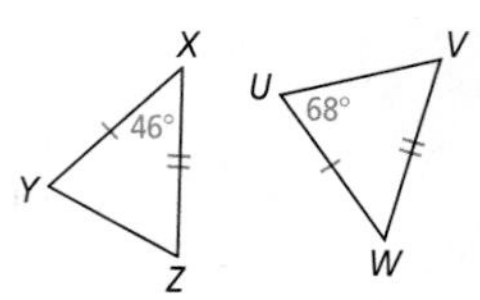

10. The diagram below shows a robotic arm in two different positions. In which position is the tip of the robotic arm closer to the base? Use the Hinge Theorem to justify your answer.

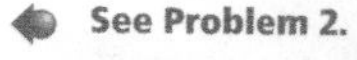

See Problem 2.

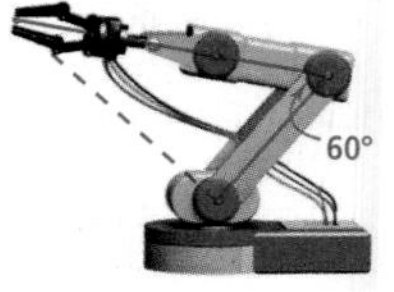

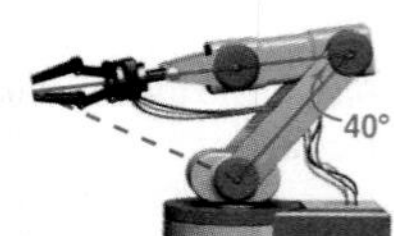

3 Lesson Check

For a digital lesson check, use the Got It questions.

Support in Geometry Companion

- Lesson Check

4 Practice

Assign homework to individual students or to an entire class.

Answers

Lesson Check

1. $FD > BC$

2. $m\angle UST > m\angle VST$

3. Answers may vary. Sample: As a door opens, and the angle between the door and doorway increases, the distance between the door jamb and the nonhinge vertical edge of the door increases.

4. The two △ that are formed by ≅ sides are $\angle ABD$ and $\angle CDB$. Since the side opposite $\angle ABD$ is longer than the side opposite $\angle CDB$, the correct conclusion is $m\angle ABD > m\angle CDB$.

5. Answers may vary. Sample: Both deal with a pair of △ that have two pairs of ≅ corresponding sides along with a relationship between the △ formed by those sides.

Practice and Problem-Solving Exercises

6. $AB < AD$

7. $PR < RT$

8. $LM < KL$

9. no conclusion

10. The 40° opening; the lengths of the two sections of the robotic arm do not change as the arm moves. The included angle between the arm sections of the 60° opening is greater than the included angle of the 40° opening, so by the Hinge Thm., the tip of the arm is closer to the base for the 40° opening.

Algebra Find the range of possible values for each variable.

See Problem 3.

11.

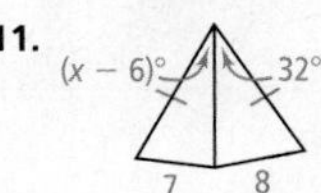

12.

13.

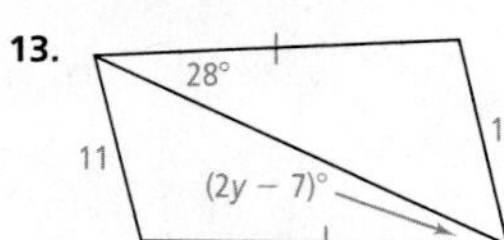

14.

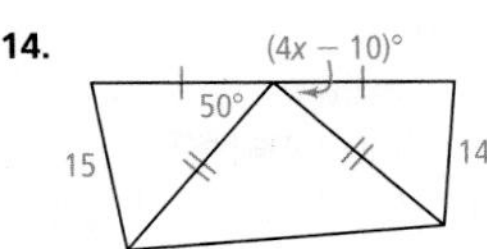

15. **Developing Proof** Complete the following proof.

See Problem 4.

Given: C is the midpoint of $\overline{BD}$,
$m\angle EAC = m\angle AEC$,
$m\angle BCA > m\angle DCE$

Prove: $AB > ED$

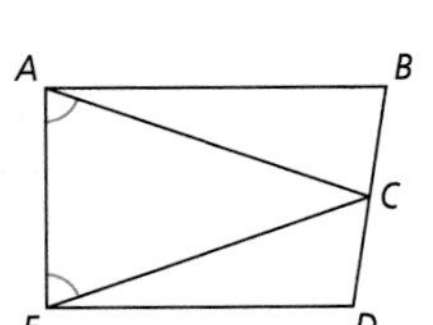

Statements	Reasons
1) $m\angle EAC = m\angle AEC$	1) Given
2) $AC = EC$	2) a. ?
3) C is the midpoint of $\overline{BD}$.	3) b. ?
4) $\overline{BC} \cong \overline{CD}$	4) c. ?
5) d. ?	5) $\cong$ segments have = length.
6) $m\angle BCA > m\angle DCE$	6) e. ?
7) $AB > ED$	7) f. ?

B Apply

Copy and complete with $>$ or $<$. Explain your reasoning.

16. PT ■ QR

17. $m\angle QTR$ ■ $m\angle RTS$

18. PT ■ RS

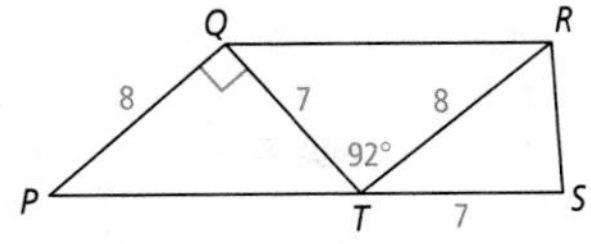

19. a. **Error Analysis** Your classmate draws the figure at the right. Explain why the figure cannot have the labeled dimensions.

b. **Open-Ended** Describe a way you could change the dimensions to make the figure possible.

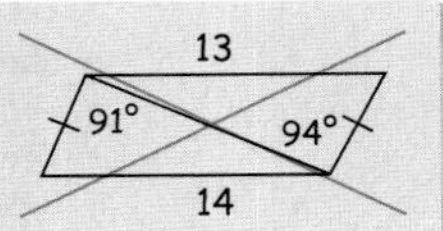

4 Practice

ASSIGNMENT GUIDE

Basic: 6–20, 22
Average: 7–15 odd, 16–23
Advanced: 7–15 odd, 16–25
Standardized Test Prep: 26–30
Mixed Review: 31–39

Reasoning exercises have blue headings.
Applications exercises have red headings.
EXERCISE 22: Use the Think About a Plan worksheet in the **Practice and Problem Solving Workbook** (also available in the Teaching Resources in print and online) to further support students' development in becoming independent learners.

HOMEWORK QUICK CHECK

To check students' understanding of key skills and concepts, go over Exercises 9, 15, 19, 20, and 22.

11. $6 < x < 38$
12. $6 < x < 24$
13. $3.5 < y < 17.5$
14. $2.5 < x < 15$
15a. Converse of Isosc. △ Thm.
b. Given
c. Def. of midpt.
d. $BC = CD$
e. Given
f. Hinge Theorem
16. $PT < QR$; $QP = TR$, $QT = TQ$, and $m\angle PQT < m\angle RTQ$, so $PT < QR$ by the Hinge Thm.
17. $m\angle QTR > m\angle RTS$; $m\angle PTQ + m\angle QTR + m\angle RTS = 180$, so $m\angle PTQ + m\angle RTS = 88$. Thus $m\angle RTS < 88$ by the Comparison Prop. of Inequality, so $m\angle QTR > m\angle RTS$ by the Transitive Prop. of Inequality.
18. $PT > RS$; $QP = TR$, $QT = TS$, and $m\angle PQT > m\angle RTS$ (from Ex. 17), so $PT > RS$ by the Hinge Thm.
19a. The two labeled ∡ are formed by ≅ corresp. sides of the two ▲, so the side opposite the 94° ∠ should be longer than the side opposite the 91° ∠, by the Hinge Thm. Thus the side labeled "13" must be longer than the side labeled "14."
b. Answers may vary. Sample: Switch the angle labels 91° and 94°.

Answers

Practice and Problem-Solving Exercises (continued)

20. Ship A; the two $\triangle$s in the diagram have two pairs of $\cong$ corresp. sides. The included $\angle$ for Ship A measures $180 - 65 = 115$ and the included $\angle$ for Ship B measures $180 - 70 = 110$. Since $115 > 110$, the side opposite 115 is longer than the side opposite 110, by the Hinge Thm.

21. A

22. The rt. isosc. $\triangle$; two pairs of legs are $\cong$, and the hypotenuse of the rt. $\triangle$ is longer than the third side of the other $\triangle$, by the Hinge Thm.

23. $\triangle ABE \cong \triangle CBD$ (Given) so $\triangle ABE$ and $\triangle CBD$ are isosc. with $AB = EB = DB = CB$. Since $m\angle EBD > m\angle ABE$ (Given), $ED > AE$ by the Hinge Thm.

24. In $\triangle AOB$ and $\triangle AOC$, $AO = AO = 7$, $OB = OC = \sqrt{5}$, $AB = \sqrt{82}$, and $AC = \sqrt{68}$. Since $AB > AC$, then $m\angle AOB > m\angle AOC$ by the Converse of the Hinge Thm.

25. Using the diagram in the Plan for Proof, $BC = YZ$, $BD = YX$, and $m\angle ZYX = m\angle CBD$, so $\triangle DBC \cong \triangle XYZ$ by SAS. $\angle FBA \cong \angle FBD$ (Def. of $\angle$ bisector), $\overline{BD} \cong \overline{BA}$ (because each is $\cong$ to $\overline{XY}$), and $\overline{BF} \cong \overline{BF}$, so $\triangle ABF \cong \triangle DBF$ by SAS. $\overline{AF} \cong \overline{DF}$, because corresp. parts of $\cong$ $\triangle$s are $\cong$. $AF + FC = AC$ (Segment Addition Post.), so $DF + FC = AC$. Using the $\triangle$ Inequality Thm. in $\triangle FDC$, $DF + FC > DC$. Now $AC > DC$ by substitution. Since $DC = XZ$ (Corresp. parts of $\cong$ $\triangle$s are $\cong$.), it follows that $AC > XZ$ by substitution.

20. Think About a Plan Ship A and Ship B leave from the same point in the ocean. Ship A travels 150 mi due west, turns 65° toward north, and then travels another 100 mi. Ship B travels 150 mi due east, turns 70° toward south, and then travels another 100 mi. Which ship is farther from the starting point? Explain.
- How can you use the given angle measures?
- How does the Hinge Theorem help you to solve this problem?

21. Which of the following lists the segment lengths in order from least to greatest?

(A) CD, AB, DE, BC, EF
(B) EF, DE, AB, BC, CD
(C) BC, DE, EF, AB, CD
(D) EF, BC, DE, AB, CD

22. Reasoning The legs of a right isosceles triangle are congruent to the legs of an isosceles triangle with an 80° vertex angle. Which triangle has a greater perimeter? How do you know?

23. Use the figure at the right.
Proof
Given: $\triangle ABE$ is isosceles with vertex $\angle B$,
$\triangle ABE \cong \triangle CBD$,
$m\angle EBD > m\angle ABE$
Prove: $ED > AE$

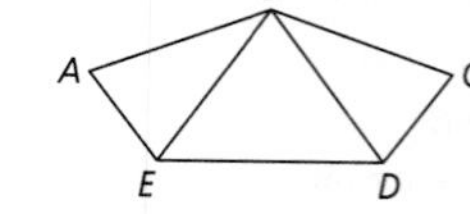

Challenge

24. Coordinate Geometry $\triangle ABC$ has vertices $A(0, 7)$, $B(-1, -2)$, $C(2, -1)$, and $O(0, 0)$. Show that $m\angle AOB > m\angle AOC$.

25. Use the plan below to complete a proof of the Hinge Theorem: If two sides of one triangle are congruent to two sides of another triangle and the included angles are not congruent, then the longer third side is opposite the larger included angle.
Proof
Given: $\overline{AB} \cong \overline{XY}$, $\overline{BC} \cong \overline{YZ}$, $m\angle B > m\angle Y$
Prove: $AC > XZ$

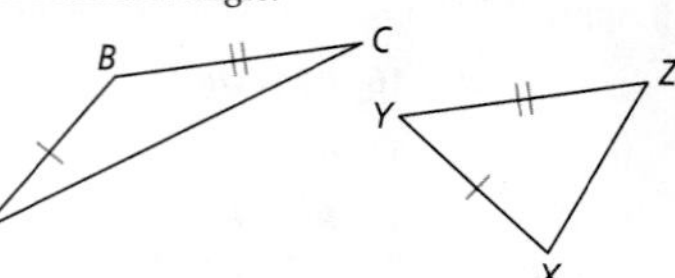

Plan for proof:
- Copy $\triangle ABC$. Locate point D outside $\triangle ABC$ so that $m\angle CBD = m\angle ZYX$ and $BD = YX$. Show that $\triangle DBC \cong \triangle XYZ$.
- Locate point F on $\overline{AC}$, so that $\overline{BF}$ bisects $\angle ABD$.
- Show that $\triangle ABF \cong \triangle DBF$ and that $\overline{AF} \cong \overline{DF}$.
- Show that $AC = FC + DF$.
- Use the Triangle Inequality Theorem to write an inequality that relates DC to the lengths of the other sides of $\triangle FCD$.
- Relate DC and XZ.

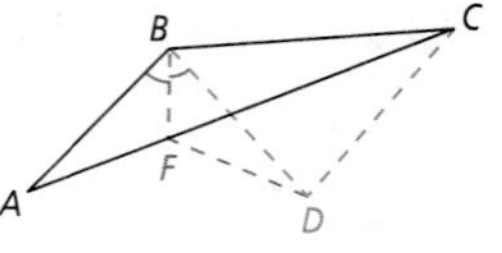

Standardized Test Prep

SAT/ACT

26. Which is a possible value for x in the figure at the right?

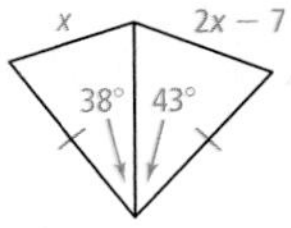

Ⓐ 2 Ⓒ 6

Ⓑ 4 Ⓓ 8

27. A quilter cuts out and sews together two triangles, as shown in the figure. She tries to make $\triangle ABD$ and $\triangle BDC$ equilateral triangles, but the angle measures are as shown. Assuming that the side $\overline{BD}$ is actually the same length in both triangles, which segment is the longest side in the figure?

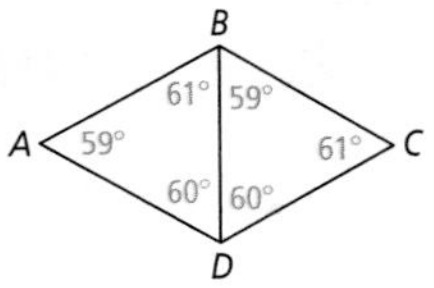

Ⓕ $\overline{AB}$ Ⓗ $\overline{CD}$

Ⓖ $\overline{BC}$ Ⓘ $\overline{AD}$

28. What is the equation of the perpendicular bisector of $\overline{MN}$ with endpoints $M(8, 0)$ and $N(0, 0)$?

Ⓐ $y = x - 8$ Ⓒ $x = 4$

Ⓑ $x = 8$ Ⓓ $y = 4$

29. The orthocenter of a triangle lies outside the triangle. Which of the following statements cannot be true?

Ⓕ The triangle has a 120° angle. Ⓗ The incenter is inside the triangle.

Ⓖ The triangle is isosceles. Ⓘ The triangle is acute.

Short Response

30. Use indirect reasoning to write a convincing argument that a triangle has at most one obtuse angle.

Mixed Review

List the angles of each triangle in order from smallest to largest. See Lesson 5-6.

31.

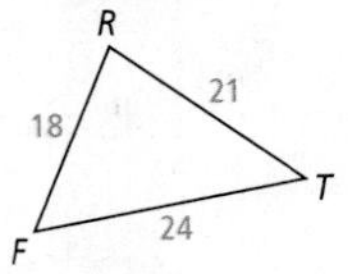

32.

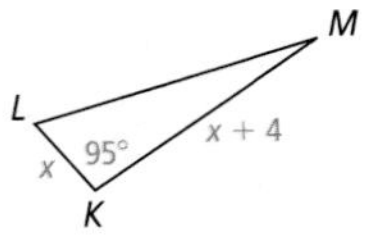

Algebra **The lengths of two sides of a triangle are given. Find the range of possible lengths for the third side.**

33. 15 cm, 19 cm **34.** 6 ft, 11 ft **35.** 3 in., 3 in.

36. In $\triangle GHI$, which side is included between $\angle G$ and $\angle H$? See Lesson 4-2.

Get Ready! **To prepare for Lesson 6-1, do Exercises 37–39.**

Find the slope of the line through each pair of points. See Lesson 3-7.

37. $X(0, 6)$, $Y(4, 9)$ **38.** $R(3, 8)$, $S(6, 0)$ **39.** $A(4, 3)$, $B(2, 1)$

26. D
27. I
28. C
29. I
30. [2] Assume temporarily that there is a △ with at least 2 obtuse ∠s. Then the sum of the measures of those two ∠s is > 180. This is impossible because the sum of the measures of all 3 ∠s is 180. Therefore the temporary assumption that the △ could have at least 2 obtuse ∠s is false, and thus any △ has at most one obtuse ∠.
[1] incomplete OR incorrect explanation
31. $\angle T$, $\angle F$, $\angle R$
32. $\angle M$, $\angle L$, $\angle K$
33. 4 cm $< x <$ 34 cm
34. 5 ft $< x <$ 17 ft
35. 0 in. $< x <$ 6 in.
36. $\overline{GH}$
37. $\frac{3}{4}$
38. $-\frac{8}{3}$
39. 1

5-7 Lesson Resources

Instructional Support

Geometry Companion

Students can use the **Geometry Companion** worktext (4 pages) . . .

- New Vocabulary
- Key Concepts
- Got It for each Problem
- Lesson Check

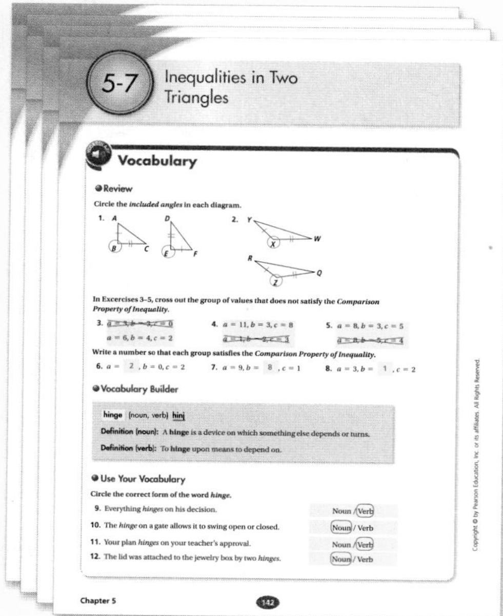

5-7 Inequalities in Two Triangles

Vocabulary

Review

Circle the *included angles* in each diagram.

1. 2.

In Excercises 3–5, cross out the group of values that does not satisfy the *Comparison Property of Inequality.*

3. ~~[illegible]~~ $a = 6, b = 4, c = 2$
4. $a = 11, b = 3, c = 8$ ~~[illegible]~~
5. $a = 8, b = 3, c = 5$ ~~[illegible]~~

Write a number so that each group satisfies the *Comparison Property of Inequality.*

6. $a =$ 2 $, b = 0, c = 2$
7. $a = 9, b =$ 8 $, c = 1$
8. $a = 3, b =$ 1 $, c = 2$

Vocabulary Builder

hinge (noun, verb) hinj

Definition (noun): A **hinge** is a device on which something else depends or turns.

Definition (verb): To **hinge** upon means to depend on.

Use Your Vocabulary

Circle the correct form of the word *hinge.*

9. Everything *hinges* on his decision. Noun / Verb
10. The *hinge* on a gate allows it to swing open or closed. Noun / Verb
11. Your plan *hinges* on your teacher's approval. Noun / Verb
12. The lid was attached to the jewelry box by two *hinges.* Noun / Verb

Chapter 5 142

ELL Support

Focus on Language Arrange students into groups of 2-5. Assign each group a lesson to list its vocabulary words and then define them. A student from each of these groups will then form new groups so there is one student in each of the second groups that has worked on a different lesson. Students combine their definitions to make their own flashcards which can be used to quiz each other and for review later.

Use Multiple Representation There are two identical cabinet doors, one that opens to the right and the other opens to the left. The right door is opened half way and the left door is open all the way. Draw a picture to show which has the largest angle at the cabinet door's hinge.

5 Assess & Remediate

Lesson Quiz

1. Which of the following statements must be true?

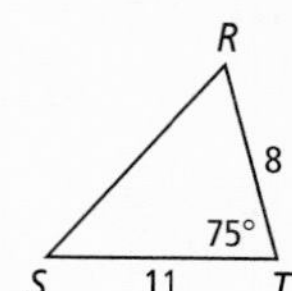

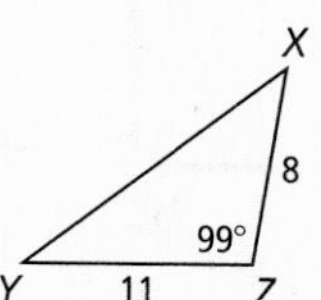

A. $XZ > ST$
B. $XY = RS$
C. $XY > RS$
D. $RS > XY$

2. **Do you UNDERSTAND?** What is the range of possible values for x?

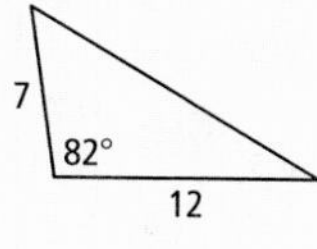

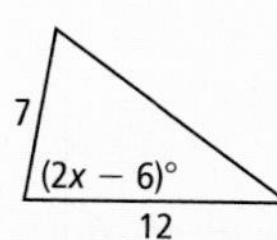

ANSWERS TO LESSON QUIZ

1. C
2. $3 < x < 44$

PRESCRIPTION FOR REMEDIATION

Use the student work on the Lesson Quiz to prescribe a differentiated review assignment.

Points	Differentiated Remediation
0	Intervention
1	On-level
2	Extension

PowerGeometry.com

5 Assess & Remediate

Assign the Lesson Quiz. Appropriate intervention, practice, or enrichment is automatically generated based on student performance.

Differentiated Remediation

Intervention

- **Reteaching** (2 pages) Provides reteaching and practice exercises for the key lesson concepts. Use with struggling students or absent students.
- **English Language Learner Support** Helps students develop and reinforce mathematical vocabulary and key concepts.

All-in-One Resources/Online

Reteaching

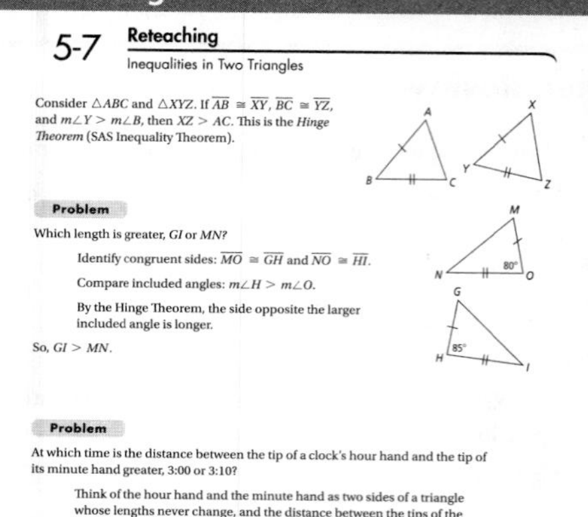

5-7 **Reteaching**

Inequalities in Two Triangles

Consider $\triangle ABC$ and $\triangle XYZ$. If $\overline{AB} \cong \overline{XY}$, $\overline{BC} \cong \overline{YZ}$, and $m\angle Y > m\angle B$, then $XZ > AC$. This is the *Hinge Theorem* (SAS Inequality Theorem).

Problem

Which length is greater, GI or MN?

Identify congruent sides: $\overline{MO} \cong \overline{GH}$ and $\overline{NO} \cong \overline{HI}$.

Compare included angles: $m\angle H > m\angle O$.

By the Hinge Theorem, the side opposite the larger included angle is longer.

So, $GI > MN$.

Problem

At which time is the distance between the tip of a clock's hour hand and the tip of its minute hand greater, 3:00 or 3:10?

Think of the hour hand and the minute hand as two sides of a triangle whose lengths never change, and the distance between the tips of the hands as the third side. 3:00 and 3:10 can then be represented as triangles with two pairs of congruent sides. The distance between the tips of the hands is the side of the triangle opposite the included angle.

At 3:00, the measure of the angle formed by the bases of the hour hand and minute hand is 90°. At 3:10, the measure of the angle is less than 90°.

So, the distance between the tip of the hour hand and the tip of the minute hand is greater at 3:00.

Exercises

1. What is the inequality relationship between LP and XA in the figure at the right? $XA > LP$
2. At which time is the distance between the tip of a clock's hour hand and the tip of its minute hand greater, 5:00 or 5:15? 5:00

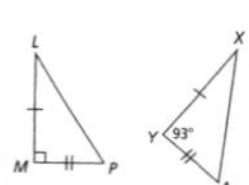

All-in-One Resources/Online

English Language Learner Support

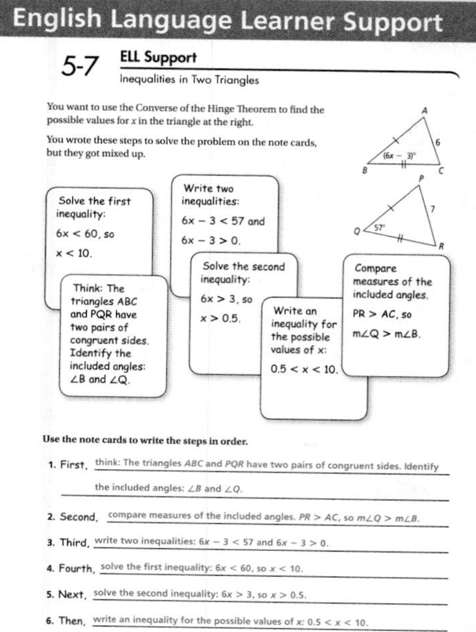

5-7 **ELL Support**

Inequalities in Two Triangles

You want to use the Converse of the Hinge Theorem to find the possible values for x in the triangle at the right.

You wrote these steps to solve the problem on the note cards, but they got mixed up.

Solve the first inequality: $6x < 60$, so $x < 10$.

Write two inequalities: $6x - 3 < 57$ and $6x - 3 > 0$.

Solve the second inequality: $6x > 3$, so $x > 0.5$.

Think: The triangles ABC and PQR have two pairs of congruent sides. Identify the included angles: $\angle B$ and $\angle Q$.

Write an inequality for the possible values of x: $0.5 < x < 10$.

Compare measures of the included angles. $PR > AC$, so $m\angle Q > m\angle B$.

Use the note cards to write the steps in order.

1. First, think: The triangles ABC and PQR have two pairs of congruent sides. Identify the included angles: $\angle B$ and $\angle Q$.
2. Second, compare measures of the included angles. $PR > AC$, so $m\angle Q > m\angle B$.
3. Third, write two inequalities: $6x - 3 < 57$ and $6x - 3 > 0$.
4. Fourth, solve the first inequality: $6x < 60$, so $x < 10$.
5. Next, solve the second inequality: $6x > 3$, so $x > 0.5$.
6. Then, write an inequality for the possible values of x: $0.5 < x < 10$.

Differentiated Remediation *continued*

On-Level

- **Practice** (2 pages) Provides extra practice for each lesson. For simpler practice exercises, use the Form K Practice pages found in the All-in-One Teaching Resources and online.
- **Think About a Plan** Helps students develop specific problem-solving skills and strategies by providing scaffolded guiding questions.
- **Standardized Test Prep** Focuses on all major exercises, all major question types, and helps students prepare for the high-stakes assessments.

Practice and Problem Solving Wkbk/ All-in-One Resources/Online

Practice page 1

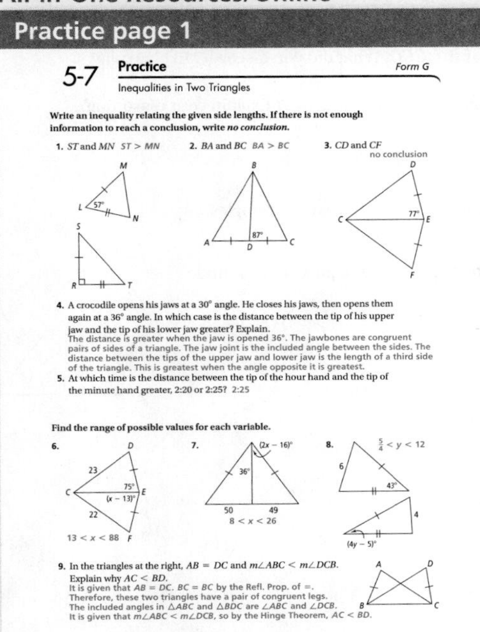

5-7 **Practice** *Form G*
Inequalities in Two Triangles

Write an inequality relating the given side lengths. If there is not enough information to reach a conclusion, write *no conclusion*.

1. ST and MN $ST > MN$
2. BA and BC $BA > BC$
3. CD and CF no conclusion
4. A crocodile opens his jaws at a 30° angle. He closes his jaws, then opens them again at a 36° angle. In which case is the distance between the tip of his upper jaw and the tip of his lower jaw greater? Explain.
   The distance is greater when the jaw is opened 36°. The jawbones are congruent pairs of sides of a triangle. The jaw joint is the included angle between the sides. The distance between the tips of the upper jaw and lower jaw is the length of a third side of the triangle. This is greatest when the angle opposite it is greatest.
5. At which time is the distance between the tip of the hour hand and the tip of the minute hand greater, 2:20 or 2:25? 2:25

Find the range of possible values for each variable.

6. $13 < x < 88$
7. $8 < x < 26$
8. $\frac{5}{4} < y < 12$
9. In the triangles at the right, $AB = DC$ and $m\angle ABC < m\angle DCB$. Explain why $AC < BD$.
   It is given that $AB = DC$. $BC = BC$ by the Refl. Prop. of =. Therefore, these two triangles have a pair of congruent legs. The included angles in $\triangle ABC$ and $\triangle BDC$ are $\angle ABC$ and $\angle DCB$. It is given that $m\angle ABC < m\angle DCB$, so by the Hinge Theorem, $AC < BD$.

Practice and Problem Solving Wkbk/ All-in-One Resources/Online

Practice page 2

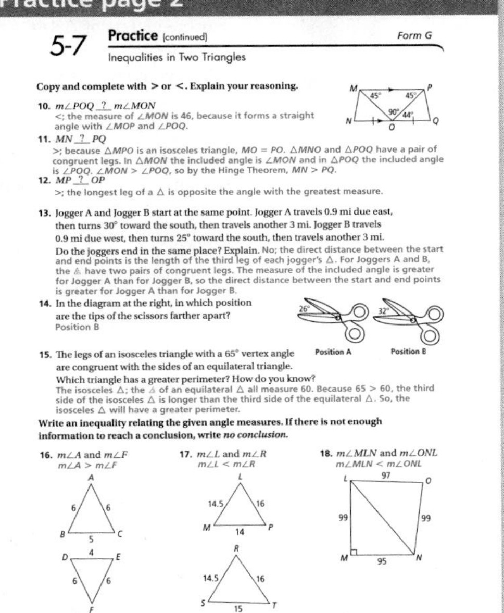

5-7 **Practice** (continued) *Form G*
Inequalities in Two Triangles

Copy and complete with > or <. Explain your reasoning.

10. $m\angle POQ$ _?_ $m\angle MON$
    <; the measure of $\angle MON$ is 46, because it forms a straight angle with $\angle MOP$ and $\angle POQ$.
11. MN _?_ PQ
    >; because $\triangle MPO$ is an isosceles triangle, $MO = PO$. $\triangle MNO$ and $\triangle POQ$ have a pair of congruent legs. In $\triangle MON$ the included angle is $\angle MON$ and in $\triangle POQ$ the included angle is $\angle POQ$. $\angle MON > \angle POQ$, so by the Hinge Theorem, $MN > PQ$.
12. MP _?_ OP
    >; the longest leg of a △ is opposite the angle with the greatest measure.
13. Jogger A and Jogger B start at the same point. Jogger A travels 0.9 mi due east, then turns 30° toward the south, then travels another 3 mi. Jogger B travels 0.9 mi due west, then turns 25° toward the south, then travels another 3 mi. Do the joggers end in the same place? Explain. No; the direct distance between the start and end points is the length of the third leg of each jogger's △. For Joggers A and B, the △ have two pairs of congruent legs. The measure of the included angle is greater for Jogger A than for Jogger B, so the direct distance between the start and end points is greater for Jogger A than for Jogger B.
14. In the diagram at the right, in which position are the tips of the scissors farther apart? Position B
15. The legs of an isosceles triangle with a 65° vertex angle are congruent with the sides of an equilateral triangle. Which triangle has a greater perimeter? How do you know?
    The isosceles △; the △ of an equilateral △ all measure 60. Because 65 > 60, the third side of the isosceles △ is longer than the third side of the equilateral △. So, the isosceles △ will have a greater perimeter.

Write an inequality relating the given angle measures. If there is not enough information to reach a conclusion, write *no conclusion*.

16. $m\angle A$ and $m\angle F$ $m\angle A > m\angle F$
17. $m\angle L$ and $m\angle R$ $m\angle L < m\angle R$
18. $m\angle MLN$ and $m\angle ONL$ $m\angle MLN < m\angle ONL$

Practice and Problem Solving Wkbk/ All-in-One Resources/Online

Think About a Plan

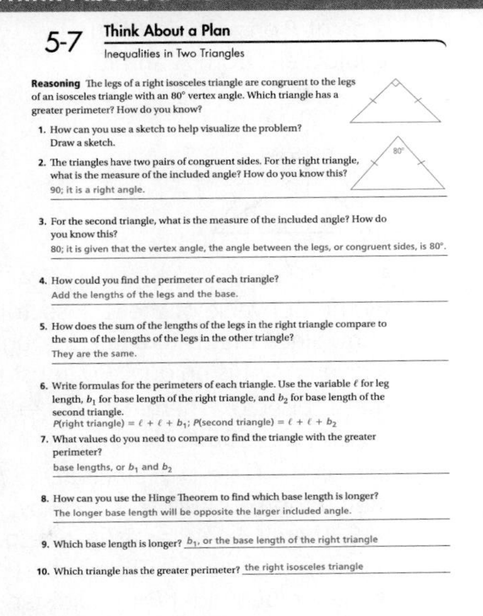

5-7 **Think About a Plan**
Inequalities in Two Triangles

Reasoning The legs of a right isosceles triangle are congruent to the legs of an isosceles triangle with an 80° vertex angle. Which triangle has a greater perimeter? How do you know?

1. How can you use a sketch to help visualize the problem? Draw a sketch.
2. The triangles have two pairs of congruent sides. For the right triangle, what is the measure of the included angle? How do you know this?
   90; it is a right angle.
3. For the second triangle, what is the measure of the included angle? How do you know this?
   80; it is given that the vertex angle, the angle between the legs, or congruent sides, is 80°.
4. How could you find the perimeter of each triangle?
   Add the lengths of the legs and the base.
5. How does the sum of the lengths of the legs in the right triangle compare to the sum of the lengths of the legs in the other triangle?
   They are the same.
6. Write formulas for the perimeters of each triangle. Use the variable ℓ for leg length, b_1 for base length of the right triangle, and b_2 for base length of the second triangle.
   $P(\text{right triangle}) = \ell + \ell + b_1$; $P(\text{second triangle}) = \ell + \ell + b_2$
7. What values do you need to compare to find the triangle with the greater perimeter?
   base lengths, or b_1 and b_2
8. How can you use the Hinge Theorem to find which base length is longer?
   The longer base length will be opposite the larger included angle.
9. Which base length is longer? b_1, or the base length of the right triangle
10. Which triangle has the greater perimeter? the right isosceles triangle

Practice and Problem Solving Wkbk/ All-in-One Resources/Online

Standardized Test Prep

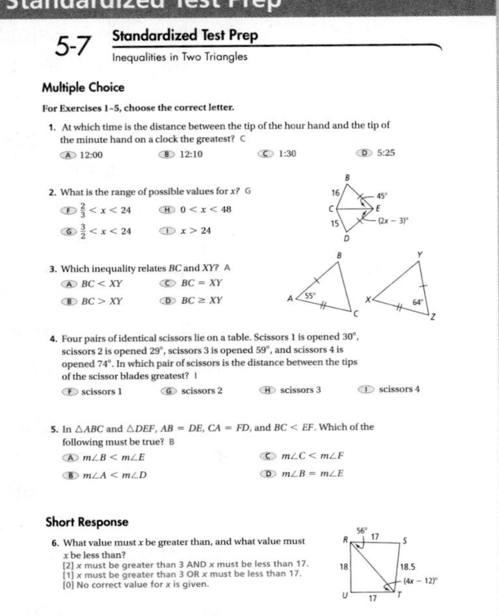

5-7 **Standardized Test Prep**
Inequalities in Two Triangles

Multiple Choice

For Exercises 1–5, choose the correct letter.

1. At which time is the distance between the tip of the hour hand and the tip of the minute hand on a clock the greatest? C
   (A) 12:00 (B) 12:10 (C) 1:30 (D) 5:25
2. What is the range of possible values for x? G
   (F) $\frac{2}{3} < x < 24$ (H) $0 < x < 48$
   (G) $\frac{3}{2} < x < 24$ (I) $x > 24$
3. Which inequality relates BC and XY? A
   (A) $BC < XY$ (C) $BC = XY$
   (B) $BC > XY$ (D) $BC \geq XY$
4. Four pairs of identical scissors lie on a table. Scissors 1 is opened 30°, scissors 2 is opened 29°, scissors 3 is opened 59°, and scissors 4 is opened 74°. In which pair of scissors is the distance between the tips of the scissor blades greatest? I
   (F) scissors 1 (G) scissors 2 (H) scissors 3 (I) scissors 4
5. In $\triangle ABC$ and $\triangle DEF$, $AB = DE$, $CA = FD$, and $BC < EF$. Which of the following must be true? B
   (A) $m\angle B < m\angle E$ (C) $m\angle C < m\angle F$
   (B) $m\angle A < m\angle D$ (D) $m\angle B = m\angle E$

Short Response

6. What value must x be greater than, and what value must x be less than?
   [2] x must be greater than 3 AND x must be less than 17.
   [1] x must be greater than 3 OR x must be less than 17.
   [0] No correct value for x is given.

Extension

- **Enrichment** Provides students with interesting problems and activities that extend the concepts of the lesson.
- **Activities, Games, and Puzzles** Worksheets that can be used for concepts development, enrichment, and for fun!

All-in-One Resources/Online

Enrichment

5-7 **Enrichment**
Inequalities in Two Triangles

Comparing Distances

Triangle inequalities can be used to solve real-world problems like the following: Samantha works at a bakery, and delivers pastries to local businesses.

On Tuesdays and Thursdays, she walks due west out of the bakery and travels 150 ft to the Sewing Shop. From there, she turns 45° toward the south, and travels another 150 ft to the gas station. From the gas station she travels 107 ft due east to Howard's Flowers. Howard's Flowers is due south of the Sewing Shop.

On Mondays and Wednesdays, Samantha travels 150 ft due south of the bakery to Richard's Records. From there, she makes a 40° turn toward the west and travels 107 ft to Dualla's Hardware.

On Fridays, Samantha makes the Monday-Wednesday route, but also goes to Melki's Meats. From the hardware store, she turns 133° to her right and travels 150 ft northeast to Melki's.

1. Make a drawing of Samantha's delivery routes. Label all angles and all distances between buildings.

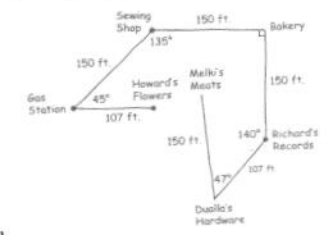

2. Use your drawing to answer the following questions. Assume a straight path between each set of points.
   a. Which is greater, the distance between the Sewing Shop and Howard's Flowers, or the distance between Richard's Records and Melki's Meats?
      the distance between Richard's Records and Melki's Meats
   b. Which is greater, the distance between the bakery and Howard's Flowers, or the distance between Howard's Flowers and the gas station?
      the distance between the bakery and Howard's Flowers
3. One day Samantha has to make a delivery from the bakery to Richard's Records, then to Melki's Meats. What is the minimum distance she must walk to get to Melki's via Richard's? Explain.
   At least 257 ft; the distance between Richard's and Melki's is more than the distance between Richard's and Dualla's Hardware, which is 107 ft. The distance between the bakery and Richard's is 150 ft. So, she must walk *at least* 150 + 107 = 257 ft.

Online Teacher Resource Center

Activities, Games, and Puzzles

5-7 **Game: Cows vs. Hens**
Inequalities in Two Triangles

Materials

- Paper
- COW and HEN cards

Setup

Your teacher will divide the class into pairs and give you and your partner a set of COW cards and a set of HEN cards. You and your partner should determine who will take the COW cards and who will take the HEN cards. Separate your cards into two piles: ANGLE and SIDE.

Round 1

You and your partner should follow the steps below using your own pile of SIDE cards. Set the ANGLE cards aside for Round 2.

1. Shuffle your cards and place them in a pile in front of you.
2. Draw a card from your pile.
3. Sketch a triangle using the descriptions on the card. Label the given measures.
4. Place your sketch next to your partner's sketch. Write an inequality that compares the missing side length of your triangle to the missing side length of your partner's triangle, if possible. The player with the greater segment length takes both cards.

Suppose you and your partner draw these cards.

SIDE 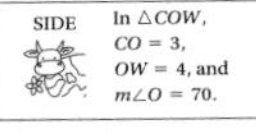 In $\triangle COW$, $CO = 3$, $OW = 4$, and $m\angle O = 70$.

SIDE 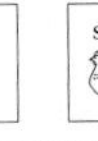 In $\triangle HEN$, $HE = 3$, $EN = 4$, and $m\angle E = 110$.

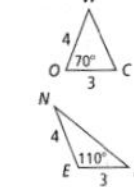

The figures at the right might be your sketches. From the sketches you may conclude that $HN > CW$ by the Hinge Theorem. In this case the player with the HEN cards would take both cards. Those cards are now out of play and will count as points for that player at the end of the game.

If you and your partner sketch congruent triangles, each player should flip a new card and repeat Steps 3 and 4 above. Then the player with the greater side length takes all four cards.

Round 2

Follow Steps 1–4 above using your ANGLE cards except, write an inequality that compares the missing angle measures, if possible.

Ending the Game

After 2 rounds, the player with the most cards wins.

Performance Task 

Pull It All Together

The concepts and skills required to solve these problems are from several lessons within this chapter and from the previous chapter. As students solve these problems, they will demonstrate their reasoning strategies and their growth as independent problem solvers.

The following questions are designed to:
- Help support students as they do the Tasks.
- Gauge the amount of support students need as they become independent problem solvers.

Task 1
- What formula is used to find the midpoint?
- Which point of concurrency in a triangle is equidistant from each vertex?

Task 2
- What is an orthocenter?
- How can you test your conjecture?

Task 3
- What is the first step in an indirect proof?
- What is the goal of an indirect proof?
- What information do you know?

5 Pull It All Together

To solve these problems you will pull together many concepts and skills that you have studied about relationships within triangles.

BIG idea Coordinate Geometry

You can use the Midpoint Formula, the slope formula, and the relationship between perpendicular lines to find points of concurrency.

Task 1

Your math teacher manages a campground during summer vacation. He loves math so much that he has mapped the campground on a coordinate grid. The campsites have the following coordinates: Brighton Bluff at $B(2, 2)$, Ponaganset Peak at $P(4, 10)$, and Harmony Hill at $H(12, 2)$. He wants to build showers that are equidistant from all three campsites. Find the coordinates of the point where the showers should be placed.

BIG idea Reasoning and Proof

You can use proven theorems to explore relationships among sides, angles, and special lines and segments in triangles.

Task 2

a. Draw $\triangle ABC$ with obtuse $\angle C$ and construct its orthocenter O. Then find the orthocenters of $\triangle ABO$, $\triangle ACO$, and $\triangle BCO$. What did you discover? Explain why you get this result.

b. Will your conjecture be true for any acute or right $\triangle ABC$? Explain your reasoning.

BIG idea Reasoning and Proof

You can use indirect reasoning to prove relationships within triangles.

Task 3

In $\triangle ABC$, $AB \neq BC$. Show that there does not exist a point P on altitude $\overline{BD}$ that is equidistant from A and C.

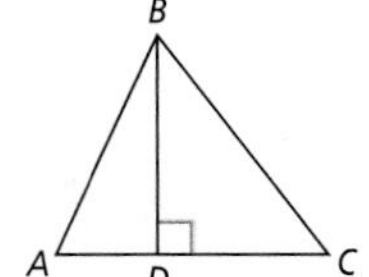

Assess Performance UbD

Pull It All Together

See p. 69 for a holistic scoring rubric to gauge a student's progress on Understanding the Problem, Planning a Solution, Getting an Answer, and Assessing Autonomy.

SOLUTION OUTLINES

1. Possible plan: On a coordinate grid, draw the triangle with vertices $B(2, 2)$, $P(4, 10)$, and $H(12, 2)$. Find the circumcenter of $\triangle BPH$ by finding the point of intersection of the $\perp$ bisectors of two sides of $\triangle BPH$. (Answer: (7, 5))

2a. First step: Draw $\triangle ABC$ with obtuse $\angle C$ and find its orthocenter O by constructing the altitudes to the extensions of sides $\overline{AC}$ and $\overline{CB}$. (Answer:

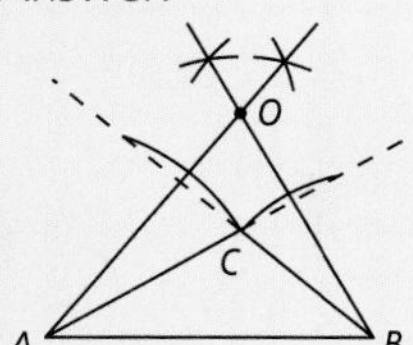

For $\triangle ABO$, the orthocenter is C; for $\triangle ACO$, the orthocenter is B; for $\triangle BCO$, the orthocenter is A. Sample explanation: In $\triangle ABO$, the sides $\overline{BO}$ and $\overline{AO}$ are $\perp$ to the extended sides $\overleftrightarrow{AC}$ and $\overleftrightarrow{BC}$ (they are altitudes). Reversing the perspective, the extended sides $\overleftrightarrow{AC}$ and $\overleftrightarrow{BC}$ are $\perp$ to $\overline{BO}$ and $\overline{AO}$, so they contain altitudes of $\triangle ABO$. Hence their intersection (point C) is the orthocenter of $\triangle ABO$.)

b. Possible plan: Draw $\triangle ABC$ with right $\angle C$ and $\triangle ABC$ with acute $\angle C$. Construct the orthocenter of each triangle and compare the result to the result in part (a).

(Answer: If C is a rt. $\angle$, then points O and C coincide, so $\triangle BCO$ and $\triangle ACO$ do not exist, and the orthocenter of $\triangle ABO$ is C. For an acute $\triangle$, the results are the same as for an obtuse $\triangle$, except the orthocenter of $\triangle ABC$ is inside the $\triangle$.)

3. Possible plan: Use indirect reasoning. Assume temporarily that there is a point P on altitude $\overline{BD}$ that is equidistant from A and C.

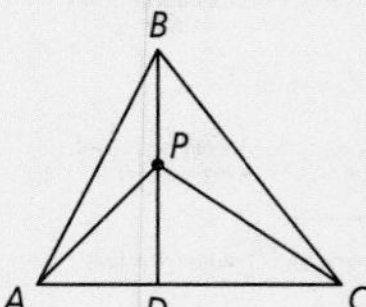

Then P is on the $\perp$ bisector of $\overline{AC}$ by the Converse of the $\perp$ Bisector Thm. Since the $\perp$ to a line through a given point is unique, $\overleftrightarrow{BD}$ must be the $\perp$ bisector. Therefore, $\overline{AD} \cong \overline{DC}$. $\angle ADB \cong \angle CDB$ ($\perp$ lines form rt. $\angle$s and all rt. $\angle$s are $\cong$.). Since $\overline{BD} \cong \overline{BD}$ (Refl. Prop.), $\triangle ABD \cong \triangle CBD$ by SAS. Therefore, $AB = BC$ (Corresp. parts of $\cong$ $\triangle$s are $\cong$.) This contradicts the assumption that P is equidistant from A and C. Hence, there is no point P on $\overline{BD}$ that is equidistant from A and C.)

5 Chapter Review

Connecting BIG ideas and Answering the Essential Questions

1 Coordinate Geometry
Use parallel and perpendicular lines, and the slope, midpoint, and distance formulas to find intersection points and unknown lengths.

2 Measurement
Use theorems about perpendicular bisectors, angle bisectors, medians, and altitudes to find points of concurrency, angle measures, and segment lengths.

3 Reasoning and Proof
You can write an indirect proof by showing that a temporary assumption is false.

Midsegments of Triangles (Lesson 5-1)
If $\overline{DE}$ is a midsegment, then $\overline{AC} \parallel \overline{DE}$ and $DE = \frac{1}{2}AC$.

Concurrent Lines and Segments in Triangles (Lessons 5-2, 5-3, and 5-4)

Concurrent Lines and Segments	Intersection
• perpendicular bisectors	• circumcenter
• angle bisectors	• incenter
• medians	• centroid
• lines containing altitudes	• orthocenter

Indirect Proof (Lesson 5-5)
1) Assume temporarily the opposite of what you want to prove.
2) Show that this temporary assumption leads to a contradiction.
3) Conclude that what you want to prove is true.

Inequalities in Triangles (Lessons 5-6 and 5-7)
Use indirect reasoning to prove that the longer of two sides of a triangle lies opposite the larger angle, and to prove the Converse of the Hinge Theorem.

Chapter Vocabulary

- altitude of a triangle (p. 310)
- centroid of a triangle (p. 309)
- circumcenter of a triangle (p. 301)
- circumscribed about (p. 301)
- concurrent (p. 301)
- distance from a point to a line (p. 294)
- equidistant (p. 292)
- incenter of a triangle (p. 303)
- indirect proof (p. 317)
- indirect reasoning (p. 317)
- inscribed in (p. 303)
- median of a triangle (p. 309)
- midsegment of a triangle (p. 285)
- orthocenter of a triangle (p. 311)
- point of concurrency (p. 301)

Choose the correct vocabulary term to complete each sentence.

1. A *(centroid, median)* of a triangle is a segment from a vertex of the triangle to the midpoint of the side opposite the vertex.
2. The length of the perpendicular segment from a point to a line is the *(midsegment, distance from a point to the line)*.
3. The *(circumcenter, incenter)* of a triangle is the point of concurrency of the angle bisectors of the triangle.

Essential Questions 

BIG idea Coordinate Geometry
ESSENTIAL QUESTION How do you use coordinate geometry to find relationships within triangles?
ANSWER Use parallel and perpendicular lines, and the slope, midpoint, and distance formulas to find intersection points and unknown lengths.

BIG idea Measurement
ESSENTIAL QUESTION How do you solve problems that involve measurements of triangles?
ANSWER Use theorems about perpendicular bisectors, angle bisectors, medians, and altitudes to find points of concurrency, angle measures, and segment lengths.

BIG idea Reasoning and Proof
ESSENTIAL QUESTION How do you write indirect proofs?
ANSWER You can write an indirect proof by showing that a temporary assumption is false.

Answers

Chapter Review

1. median
2. distance from a point to a line
3. incenter

Summative Questions UbD

Use the following prompts as you review this chapter with your students. The prompts are designed to help you assess your students' understanding of the Big Ideas they have studied.

- What is a midsegment of a triangle?
- What relationship does the midsegment make in a triangle?
- What are the concurrent lines in triangles?
- How do you write an indirect proof?

Answers

Chapter Review (continued)

4. 15

5. 11

6. $L\left(\frac{5}{2}, -\frac{1}{2}\right)$; $M\left(\frac{7}{2}, \frac{1}{2}\right)$; slope of $\overline{AB} = 1$ and slope of $\overline{LM} = 1$, so $\overline{LM} \parallel \overline{AB}$; $AB = 2\sqrt{2}$ and $LM = \sqrt{2}$, so $LM = \frac{1}{2}AB$.

7. Let point S be second base and point T be third base. Find the midpt. M of $\overline{ST}$ and then through M construct the line $\ell \perp$ to $\overline{ST}$. Points of the baseball field that are on line ℓ are equidistant from second and third base.

8. 40

9. 40

10. 6

11. 11

12. 33

13. 33

5-1 Midsegments of Triangles

Quick Review

A **midsegment of a triangle** is a segment that connects the midpoints of two sides. A midsegment is parallel to the third side and is half as long.

Example

Algebra **Find the value of x.**

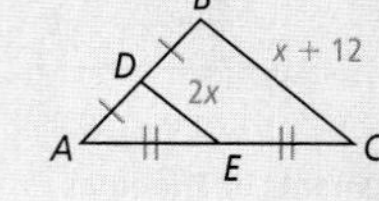

$\overline{DE}$ is a midsegment because D and E are midpoints.

$DE = \frac{1}{2}BC$	△ Midsegment Theorem
$2x = \frac{1}{2}(x + 12)$	Substitute.
$4x = x + 12$	Simplify.
$3x = 12$	Subtract x from each side.
$x = 4$	Divide each side by 3.

Exercises

Algebra **Find the value of x.**

4.

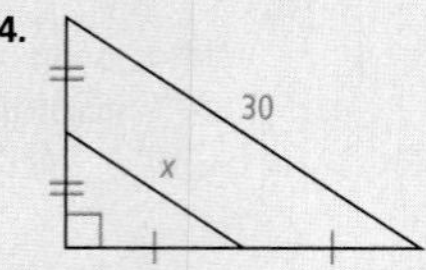

5.

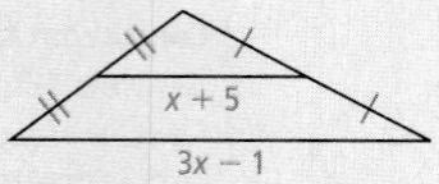

x + 5

3x − 1

6. $\triangle ABC$ has vertices $A(0, 0)$, $B(2, 2)$, and $C(5, -1)$. Find the coordinates of L, the midpoint of $\overline{AC}$, and M, the midpoint of $\overline{BC}$. Verify that $\overline{LM} \parallel \overline{AB}$ and $LM = \frac{1}{2}AB$.

5-2 Perpendicular and Angle Bisectors

Quick Review

The **Perpendicular Bisector Theorem** together with its converse states that P is equidistant from A and B if and only if P is on the perpendicular bisector of $\overline{AB}$.

The **distance from a point to a line** is the length of the perpendicular segment from the point to the line.

The **Angle Bisector Theorem** together with its converse states that P is equidistant from the sides of an angle if and only if P is on the angle bisector.

Example

In the figure, $QP = 4$ and $AB = 8$. Find QR and CB.

Q is on the bisector of $\angle ABC$, so $QR = QP = 4$.

B is on the perpendicular bisector of $\overline{AC}$, so $CB = AB = 8$.

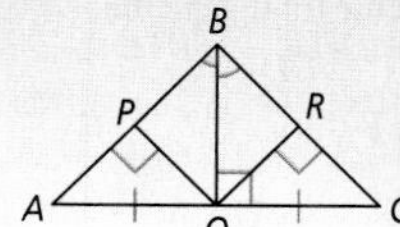

Exercises

7. Writing Describe how to find all the points on a baseball field that are equidistant from second base and third base.

In the figure, $m\angle DBE = 50$. Find each of the following.

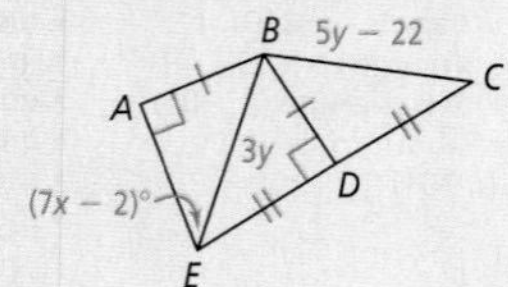

8. $m\angle BED$

9. $m\angle BEA$

10. x

11. y

12. BE

13. BC

5-3 Bisectors in Triangles

Quick Review

When three or more lines intersect in one point, they are **concurrent.**

- The point of concurrency of the perpendicular bisectors of a triangle is the **circumcenter of the triangle.**
- The point of concurrency of the angle bisectors of a triangle is the **incenter of the triangle.**

Example

Identify the incenter of the triangle.

The incenter of a triangle is the point of concurrency of the angle bisectors. $\overline{MR}$ and $\overline{LQ}$ are angle bisectors that intersect at Z. So, Z is the incenter.

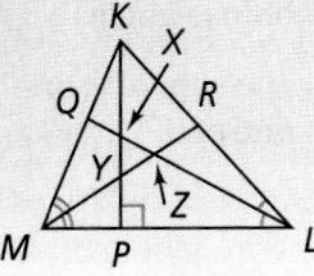

Exercises

Find the coordinates of the circumcenter of $\triangle DEF$.

14. $D(6, 0)$, $E(0, 6)$, $F(-6, 0)$

15. $D(0, 0)$, $E(6, 0)$, $F(0, 4)$

16. $D(5, -1)$, $E(-1, 3)$, $F(3, -1)$

17. $D(2, 3)$, $E(8, 3)$, $F(8, -1)$

P is the incenter of $\triangle XYZ$. Find the indicated angle measure.

18. $m\angle PXY$

19. $m\angle XYZ$

20. $m\angle PZX$

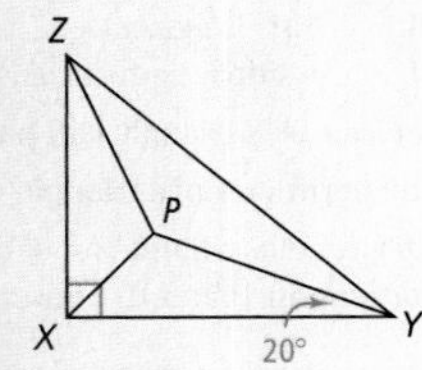

5-4 Medians and Altitudes

Quick Review

A **median of a triangle** is a segment from a vertex to the midpoint of the opposite side. An **altitude of a triangle** is a perpendicular segment from a vertex to the line containing the opposite side.

- The point of concurrency of the medians of a triangle is the **centroid of the triangle.** The centroid is two thirds the distance from each vertex to the midpoint of the opposite side.
- The point of concurrency of the altitudes of a triangle is the **orthocenter of the triangle.**

Example

If $PB = 6$, what is SB?

S is the centroid because $\overline{AQ}$ and $\overline{CR}$ are medians. So, $SB = \frac{2}{3}PB = \frac{2}{3}(6) = 4$.

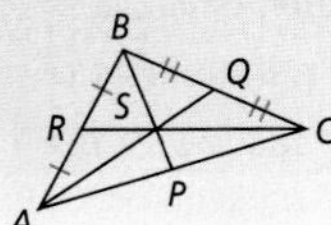

Exercises

Determine whether $\overline{AB}$ is a *median*, an *altitude*, or *neither*. Explain.

21.

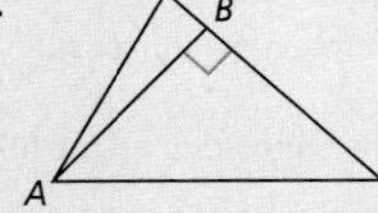

22.

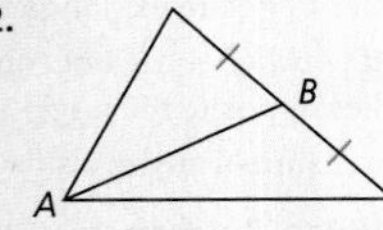

23. $\triangle PQR$ has medians $\overline{QM}$ and $\overline{PN}$ that intersect at Z. If $ZM = 4$, find QZ and QM.

$\triangle ABC$ has vertices $A(2, 3)$, $B(-4, -3)$, and $C(2, -3)$. Find the coordinates of each point of concurrency.

24. centroid

25. orthocenter

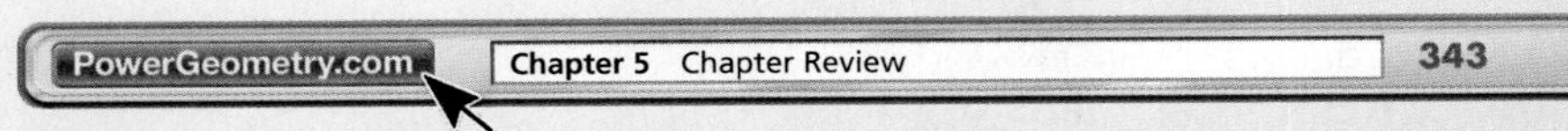

14. (0, 0)
15. (3, 2)
16. (4, 4)
17. (5, 1)
18. 45
19. 40
20. 25
21. $\overline{AB}$ is an altitude; it is a segment from a vertex that is ⊥ to the opposite side.
22. $\overline{AB}$ is a median; it is a segment from a vertex to the midpt. of the opposite side.
23. $QZ = 8$, $QM = 12$
24. (0, −1)
25. (2, −3)

Answers

Chapter Review (continued)

26. Assume temporarily that neither of the two numbers is even. That means each number is odd, so the product of the two numbers must be odd. That contradicts the statement that the product of the two numbers is even. Thus the temporary assumption is false, and we can conclude that at least one of the numbers must be even.

27. Assume temporarily that the third line intersects neither of the first two. Then it is ∥ to both of them. Since the first two lines are ∥ to the same line, they are ∥ to each other. This contradicts the given information. Therefore the temporary assumption is false, and the third line must intersect at least one of the two others.

28. Assume temporarily that there is a △ with two obtuse ∠s. Then the sum of the measures of those two ∠s is greater than 180, which contradicts the △ Angle-Sum Thm. Therefore the temporary assumption is false, and a △ can have at most one obtuse ∠.

29. Assume temporarily that an equilateral △ has an obtuse ∠. Since all the ∠s are ≅ in an equilateral △, then all three ∠s must be obtuse. But we showed in Ex. 28 that a △ can have at most one obtuse ∠. Therefore the temporary assumption is false, and an equilateral △ cannot have an obtuse ∠.

30. Assume temporarily that each of the three integers is less than or equal to 3. Then the sum of the three integers must be less than or equal to $3 \cdot 3$, or 9. This contradicts the given statement that the sum of the three integers is greater than 9. Therefore the temporary assumption is false, and you can conclude that one of the integers must be greater than 3.

31. $\overline{RS}$, $\overline{ST}$, $\overline{RT}$

32. No; $5 + 8 \not> 15$.

33. Yes; $10 + 12 > 20$, $10 + 20 > 12$, and $12 + 20 > 10$.

34. $1 \text{ ft} < x < 25 \text{ ft}$

35. $<$

36. $>$

37. $<$

5-5 Indirect Proof

Quick Review

In an **indirect proof,** you first assume temporarily the opposite of what you want to prove. Then you show that this temporary assumption leads to a contradiction.

Example

Which two statements contradict each other?

I. The perimeter of $\triangle ABC$ is 14.
II. $\triangle ABC$ is isosceles.
III. The side lengths of $\triangle ABC$ are 3, 5, and 6.

An isosceles triangle can have a perimeter of 14.

The perimeter of a triangle with side lengths 3, 5, and 6 is 14.

An isosceles triangle must have two sides of equal length. Statements II and III contradict each other.

Exercises

Write a convincing argument that uses indirect reasoning.

26. The product of two numbers is even. Show that at least one of the numbers must be even.

27. Two lines in the same plane are not parallel. Show that a third line in the plane must intersect at least one of the two lines.

28. Show that a triangle can have at most one obtuse angle.

29. Show that an equilateral triangle cannot have an obtuse angle.

30. The sum of three integers is greater than 9. Show that one of the integers must be greater than 3.

5-6 and 5-7 Inequalities in Triangles

Quick Review

For any triangle,

- the measure of an exterior angle is greater than the measure of each of its remote interior angles
- if two sides are not congruent, then the larger angle lies opposite the longer side
- if two angles are not congruent, then the longer side lies opposite the larger angle
- the sum of any two side lengths is greater than the third

The **Hinge Theorem** states that if two sides of one triangle are congruent to two sides of another triangle, and the included angles are not congruent, then the longer third side is opposite the larger included angle.

Example

Which is greater, *BC* or *AD*?

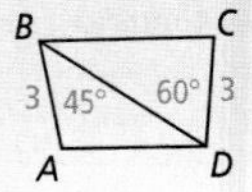

$\overline{BA} \cong \overline{CD}$ and $\overline{BD} \cong \overline{DB}$, so $\triangle ABD$ and $\triangle CDB$ have two pairs of congruent corresponding sides. Since $60 > 45$, you know $BC > AD$ by the Hinge Theorem.

Exercises

31. In $\triangle RST$, $m\angle R = 70$ and $m\angle S = 80$. List the sides of $\triangle RST$ in order from shortest to longest.

Is it possible for a triangle to have sides with the given lengths? Explain.

32. 5 in., 8 in., 15 in.

33. 10 cm, 12 cm, 20 cm

34. The lengths of two sides of a triangle are 12 ft and 13 ft. Find the range of possible lengths for the third side.

Use the figure below. Complete each statement with >, <, or =.

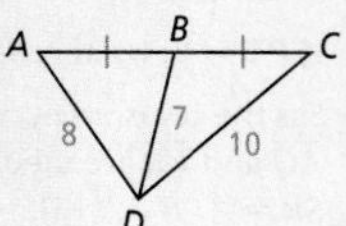

35. $m\angle BAD$ ■ $m\angle ABD$

36. $m\angle CBD$ ■ $m\angle BCD$

37. $m\angle ABD$ ■ $m\angle CBD$

5 Chapter Test

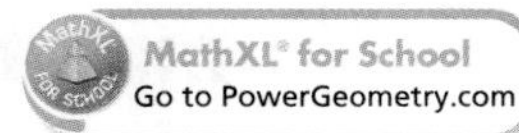

Do you know HOW?

Find the coordinates of the circumcenter of $\triangle ABC$.

1. $A(3, -1)$, $B(-2, -1)$, $C(3, -8)$

2. $A(0, 5)$, $B(-4, 5)$, $C(-4, -3)$

Find the coordinates of the orthocenter of $\triangle ABC$.

3. $A(-1, -1)$, $B(-1, 5)$, $C(-4, -1)$

4. $A(0, 0)$, $B(5, 0)$, $C(5, 3)$

Identify the two statements that contradict each other.

5. **I.** $\triangle PQR$ is a right triangle.
II. $\triangle PQR$ is an obtuse triangle.
III. $\triangle PQR$ is scalene.

6. **I.** $\angle DOS \cong \angle CAT$
II. $\angle DOS$ and $\angle CAT$ are vertical.
III. $\angle DOS$ and $\angle CAT$ are adjacent.

7. If $AB = 9$, $BC = 4\frac{1}{2}$, and $AC = 12$, list the angles of $\triangle ABC$ from smallest to largest.

8. Point P is inside $\triangle ABC$ and equidistant from all three sides. If $m\angle ABC = 60$, what is $m\angle PBC$?

List the sides from shortest to longest.

9.

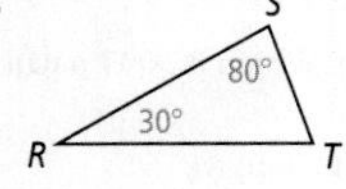

10.

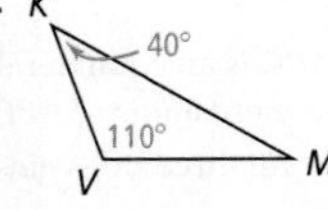

11. In $\triangle ABC$, $EP = 4$. What is PC?

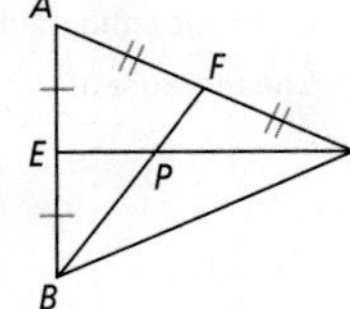

12. Which is greater, AD or DC? Explain.

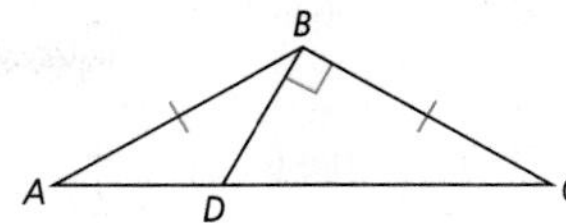

Algebra Find the value of x.

13.

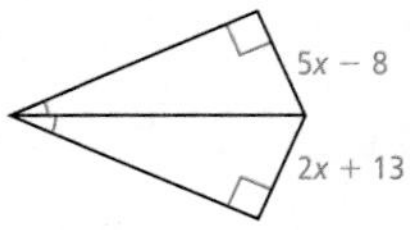

5x − 8
2x + 13

14.

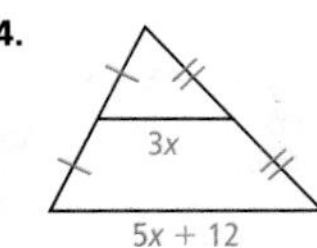

Do you UNDERSTAND?

15. What can you conclude from the diagram at the right? Justify your answer.

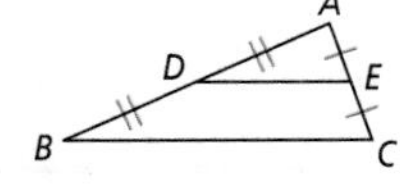

16. Reasoning In $\triangle ABC$, $BC > BA$. Draw $\triangle ABC$ and the median $\overline{BD}$. Use the Converse of the Hinge Theorem to explain why $\angle BDC$ is obtuse.

17. Given: $\overleftrightarrow{PQ}$ is the perpendicular bisector of $\overline{AB}$. $\overleftrightarrow{QT}$ is the perpendicular bisector of $\overline{AC}$.

Prove: $QC = QB$

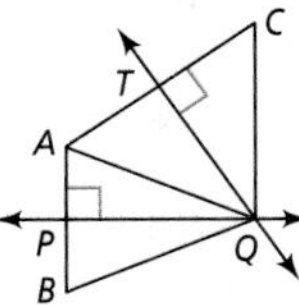

18. Writing Use indirect reasoning to explain why the following statement is true: If an isosceles triangle is obtuse, then the obtuse angle is the vertex angle.

19. In the figure, $WK = KR$. What can you conclude about point A? Explain.

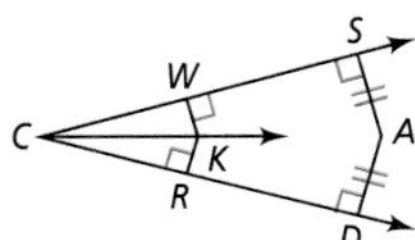

Chapter Test

1. (0.5, −4.5)

2. (−2, 1)

3. (−1, −1)

4. (5, 0)

5. I and II

6. II and III

7. $\angle A$, $\angle C$, $\angle B$

8. 30

9. $\overline{ST}$, $\overline{SR}$, $\overline{RT}$

10. $\overline{KV}$, $\overline{VM}$, $\overline{KM}$

11. 8

12. DC; since $m\angle ABC < 180$, $m\angle ABC = m\angle ABD + m\angle DBC$, and $m\angle DBC = 90$, we have $m\angle ABD + 90 < 180$ (Substitution). So $m\angle ABD < 90$. Also $\overline{AB} \cong \overline{CB}$ and $\overline{BD} \cong \overline{BD}$, so the Hinge Thm. applies. Hence $AD < DC$.

13. 7

14. 12

15. D and E are midpts. of $\overline{AB}$ and $\overline{AC}$, so $\overline{DE} \parallel \overline{BC}$ and $DE = \frac{1}{2}BC$ by the $\triangle$ Midsegment Thm. (You can also conclude that $\angle B \cong \angle ADE$ and $\angle C \cong \angle AED$.)

16.

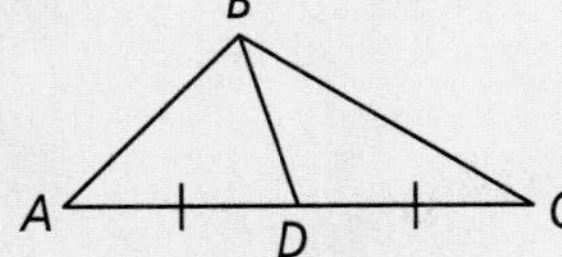

In $\triangle BDA$ and $\triangle BDC$, $BC > BA$ (Given), $BD = BD$ (Refl. Prop. of Eq.), and $DA = DC$ (Def. of midpt.). So $m\angle BDC > m\angle BDA$ by the Converse of the Hinge Thm. Since these two ∠s are suppl., the larger one is obtuse.

17. $\overleftrightarrow{PQ}$ is the ⊥ bis. of $\overline{AB}$, and $\overleftrightarrow{QT}$ is the ⊥ bis. of $\overline{AC}$ (Given). So $\overline{QB} \cong \overline{QA}$ and $\overline{QA} \cong \overline{QC}$ (⊥ Bis. Thm.). Now $\overline{QB} \cong \overline{QC}$ (Trans. Prop. of ≅), so $QB = QC$ (≅ segments have = length.).

18. Assume temporarily that an obtuse ∠ in an isosc. △ is not the vertex ∠. Then the obtuse ∠ must be a base ∠. In an isosc. △ the base ∠s are ≅, so each base ∠ would have measure > 90 and their sum would be greater than 180. This contradicts the △ Angle-Sum Thm. Therefore the temporary assumption is false, and you can conclude that if an isosc. △ is obtuse, then the obtuse ∠ is the vertex ∠.

19. A is on $\overrightarrow{CK}$; points K and A are equidistant from the sides of $\angle SCD$, so points K and A are on the bisector of $\angle SCD$ by the Converse of the △ ∠ Bisector Thm. Since $\overrightarrow{CK}$ is the bisector of $\angle SCD$, you can conclude that A is on $\overrightarrow{CK}$.

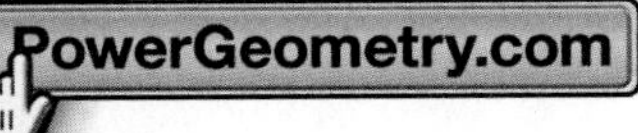

MathXL for School

Prepare students for the Mid-Chapter Quiz and Chapter Test with online practice and review.

Item Number	Lesson
1	5-6
2	4-5
3	5-1
4	1-8
5	4-7
6	5-2
7	2-2
8	5-6
9	3-8
10	4-6
11	4-2
12	2-1
13	5-4
14	4-5
15	5-1
16	1-8
17	5-3
18	2-4
19	4-2
20	5-5
21	5-3

5 Cumulative Test Prep

TIPS FOR SUCCESS

Some test questions ask you to find missing measurements. Read the sample question at the right. Then follow the tips to answer it.

TIP 2

From the dimensions given in the diagram, you can conclude that S and T are midpoints of sides of $\triangle XYZ$. So you can use the Triangle Midsegment Theorem to find ST.

The diagram below shows the walkways in a triangular park. What is the distance from point S to point Z using the walkways $\overline{ST}$ and $\overline{TZ}$?

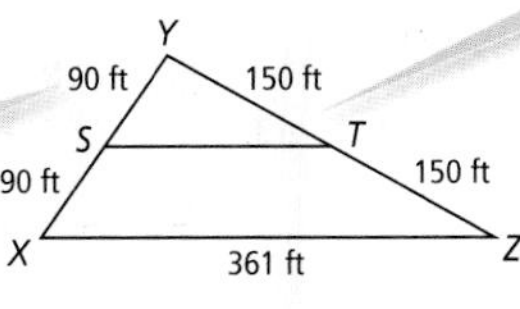

A 180.5 ft
B 330.5 ft
C 390 ft
D 451 ft

TIP 1

You need to find the length of $\overline{ST}$ and add it to 150 ft, the length of $\overline{TZ}$.

Think It Through

$\overline{ST}$ is a midsegment of $\triangle XYZ$. By the Triangle Midsegment Theorem, you know $ST = \frac{1}{2}(XZ) = \frac{1}{2}(361)$, or 180.5 ft. The distance from point S to point Z using walkways $\overline{ST}$ and $\overline{TZ}$ is $ST + TZ = 180.5 + 150$, or 330.5 ft. The correct answer is B.

Vocabulary Builder

As you solve test items, you must understand the meanings of mathematical terms. Choose the correct term to complete each sentence.

I. The (*inverse, converse*) of a conditional statement negates both the hypothesis and the conclusion.

II. The lines containing the altitudes of a triangle are concurrent at the (*orthocenter, centroid*) of the triangle.

III. The side opposite the vertex angle of an isosceles triangle is the (*hypotenuse, base*).

IV. The linear equation $y = mx + b$ is in (*slope-intercept form, point-slope form*).

Multiple Choice

Read each question. Then write the letter of the correct answer on your paper.

1. One side of a triangle has length 6 in. and another side has length 3 in. Which is the greatest possible value for the length of the third side?

A 3 in.
B 6 in.
C 8 in.
D 9 in.

2. $\triangle ABC$ is an equilateral triangle. Which is NOT a true statement about $\triangle ABC$?

F All three sides have the same length.
G $\triangle ABC$ is isosceles.
H $\triangle ABC$ is equiangular.
I The measure of $\angle A$ is 50.

Answers

Cumulative Test Prep

I. inverse
II. orthocenter
III. base
IV. slope-intercept form
1. C
2. I

3. In the figure below, $\triangle ABC$ has vertices $A(-2, -4)$, $B(-3, 2)$, and $C(3, 0)$. D is the midpoint of $\overline{AB}$, E is the midpoint of $\overline{BC}$, and F is the midpoint of $\overline{AC}$. What are the coordinates of the vertices of $\triangle DEF$?

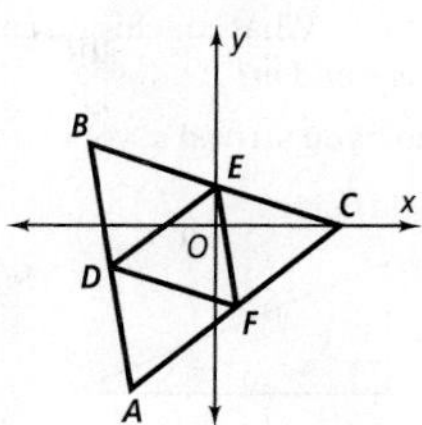

A $D(-2.5, -1), E(0, 1), F(0.5, -2)$

B $D(-2, -1), E(0, 0.5), F(0.5, -1)$

C $D(-2, -1.5), E(0, 1.5), F(0.8, -2)$

D $D(-2.2, -0.8), E(0, 1.5), F(0.5, -2)$

4. A square and a rectangle have the same area. The square has side length 8 in. The length of the rectangle is four times its width. What is the length of the rectangle?

F 4 in. H 32 in.

G 16 in. I 64 in.

5. In the figure below, $\angle A \cong \angle DBE$ and $\overline{AB} \cong \overline{BE}$. What additional information do you need in order to prove a pair of triangles congruent by AAS?

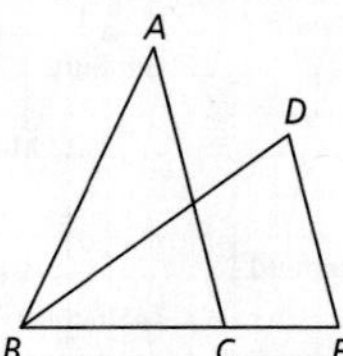

A $\angle ABC \cong \angle BED$

B C is the midpoint of $\overline{BE}$.

C $\angle ACB \cong \angle BDE$

D $\angle ABC \cong \angle BDE$

6. What is the value of y in the figure below?

F $\frac{3}{7}$

G 1

H $\frac{7}{3}$

I 3

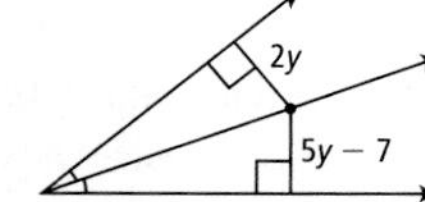

7. Which statement is the inverse of the following statement?

If $\overline{PQ}$ is a midsegment of $\triangle ABC$, then $\overline{PQ}$ is parallel to a side of $\triangle ABC$.

A If $\overline{PQ}$ is a midsegment of $\triangle ABC$, then $\overline{PQ}$ is not parallel to a side of $\triangle ABC$.

B If $\overline{PQ}$ is not a midsegment of $\triangle ABC$, then $\overline{PQ}$ is not parallel to a side of $\triangle ABC$.

C If $\overline{PQ}$ is not parallel to a side of $\triangle ABC$, then $\overline{PQ}$ is not a midsegment of $\triangle ABC$.

D If $\overline{PQ}$ is parallel to a side of $\triangle ABC$, then $\overline{PQ}$ is a midsegment of $\triangle ABC$.

8. Which statement is true for the figure below?

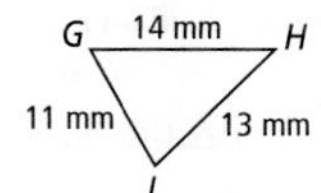

F $m\angle J < m\angle G < m\angle H$

G $m\angle H < m\angle G < m\angle J$

H $m\angle J < m\angle H < m\angle G$

I $m\angle H < m\angle J < m\angle G$

9. $\overline{AB}$ has endpoints $A(0, -4)$ and $B(8, -2)$. What is the slope-intercept form of the equation of the perpendicular bisector of $\overline{AB}$?

A $y = -4x + 13$ C $y + 3 = -4(x - 4)$

B $y = 4x - 19$ D $y + 3 = 4(x - 4)$

10. How can you prove that the two triangles at the right are congruent?

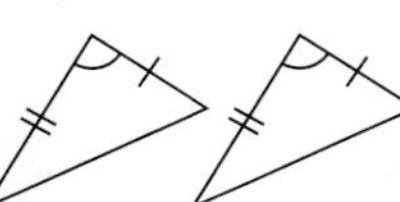

F ASA H SAS

G SSS I HL

3. A
4. G
5. C
6. H
7. B
8. G
9. A
10. H

Answers

Cumulative Test Prep (continued)

11. C

12. 20

13. 3.5

14. 70

15. 11.5

16. 30

17. 1.5

18. [2] **a.** ℓ and m do not have any points in common.

b. Answers may vary. Sample: Use the Law of Detachment to conclude that ℓ and m do not intersect. Then use the Law of Detachment again to conclude that ℓ and m do not have any points in common.

[1] one part correct

19. [2] **a.**

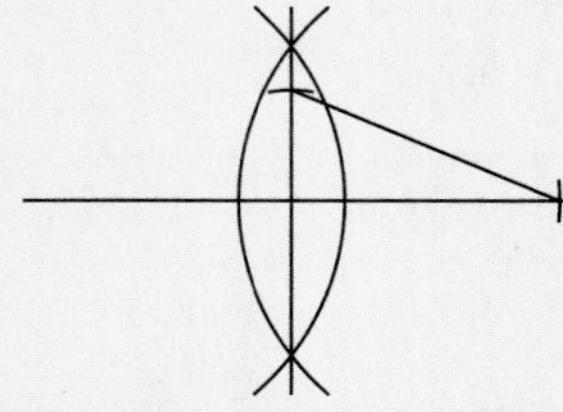

b. Answers may vary. Sample: Draw a line. Use a compass to mark off a segment that is twice the length of the original base. Construct the ⊥ bis. of this segment. Use a compass to mark off a segment on the bisector equal in length to the original altitude. Draw a segment connecting the endpoints of the two legs.

[1] one part correct

20. [4] Assume temporarily that $\triangle ABC$ is a rt. △, as well as obtuse (Given). Then one ∠ measure is 90 (Def. of rt. △), and one ∠ measure is $>$ 90 (Def of obtuse △). The sum of these two measures is $>$ 180. This contradicts the △ Angle-Sum Thm., so the temporary assumption is false. Hence $\triangle ABC$ is not a rt. △.

[3] a minor error or a missing step in the proof

[2] 2 or 3 missing steps in the proof

[1] more than 3 missing steps in the proof

21. [4] **a.** (7, 6); the circumcenter of a △ is equidistant from the 3 vertices of the △, so the new tower should be located at the circumcenter of the △ whose vertices are (3, 3) (for Westfield), (3, 9) (for Bayville), and (11, 3) (for Oxboro). Those three vertices determine a rt. △; the circumcenter of a rt. △ is the midpt. of the hypotenuse, so this will be $\left(\frac{3+11}{2}, \frac{9+3}{2}\right)$ or (7, 6).

b. Using the Distance Formula, it is 5 mi to Westfield. It is the same to the other two towns, since it is located at the circumcenter.

c. Yes, Seabury and Medfield; using the Distance Formula, Seabury is $\sqrt{5}$ mi from the tower and Medfield is 5 mi away. Eastham is farther than 5 mi away.

[3] correct methods with minor calculation error

[2] two parts correct

[1] correct answers without explanations

---

11. Which statement contradicts the statement $\triangle ABC \cong \triangle JMK$ by SAS?

(A) $\angle A$ and $\angle J$ are vertical angles.

(B) $\overline{BC}$ is the hypotenuse of $\triangle ABC$.

(C) $\triangle ABC$ is isosceles and $\triangle JMK$ is scalene.

(D) $\overline{AB}$ is not congruent to $\overline{MK}$.

GRIDDED RESPONSE

12. What is the next term in the pattern below?

5, 6, 8, 11, 15, . . .

13. $\triangle ABC$ is a right triangle with area 14 in.^{2}. $\overline{BM}$ and $\overline{CN}$ are medians and $BN = 2$ in. What is the area of $\triangle CNM$ in square inches?

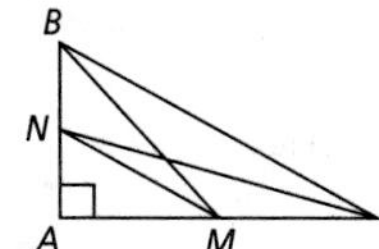

14. The measure of one angle of an isosceles triangle is 70. What is the measure of the largest angle?

15. $\overline{DE}$ is a midsegment of $\triangle ABC$. In millimeters, what is DE?

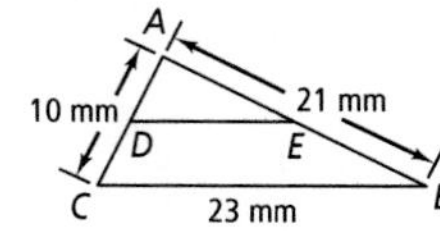

16. What is the area in square units of a rectangle with vertices (−2, 5), (3, 5), (3, −1), and (−2, −1)?

17. In the figure below, the area of $\triangle ADB$ is 4.5 cm^2. In centimeters, what is DF?

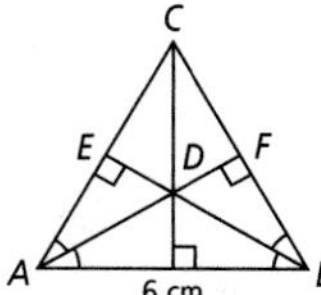

Short Response

18. If two lines are parallel, then they do not intersect. If two lines do not intersect, then they do not have any points in common.

a. Suppose $\ell \parallel m$. What conclusion can you make about lines ℓ and m?

b. Explain how you arrived at your conclusion.

19. Copy the triangle below.

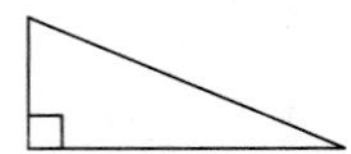

a. Construct a congruent triangle.

b. Describe your method.

Extended Response

20. Write an indirect proof.

Given: $\triangle ABC$ is obtuse.

Prove: $\triangle ABC$ is not a right triangle.

21. The towns of Westfield, Bayville, and Oxboro need a cell phone tower. The strength of the signal from the tower should be the same for each of the three towns. The map below shows the location of each town, with each grid square representing 1 square mile.

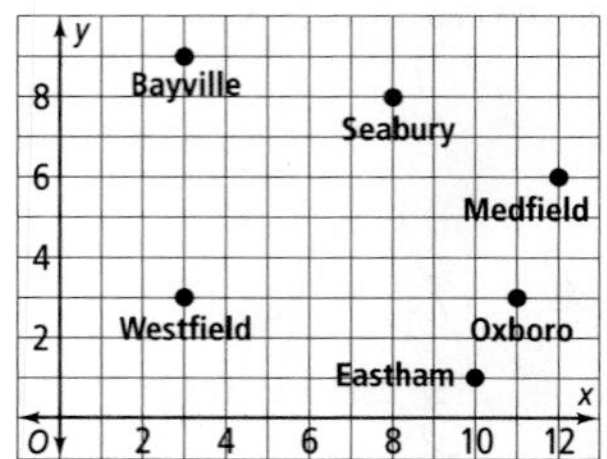

a. At what coordinates should the new cell phone tower be located? Explain.

b. What is the distance from the new tower to Westfield? To Bayville? To Oxboro?

c. Can any of the other towns shown on the map benefit from the new cell phone tower? Explain.

CHAPTER 6

Get Ready!

Lesson 3-2

Properties of Parallel Lines

Algebra **Use properties of parallel lines to find the value of x.**

1.
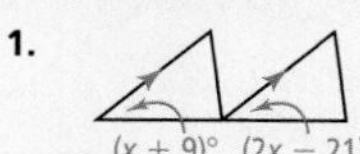

2.
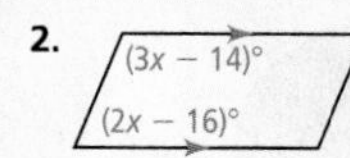

3.
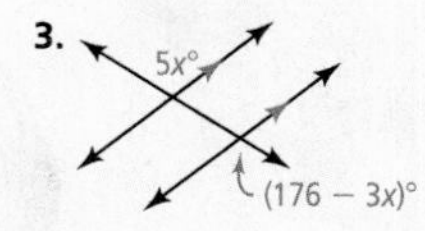

Lesson 3-3

Proving Lines Parallel

Algebra **Determine whether $\overline{AB}$ is parallel to $\overline{CD}$.**

4.
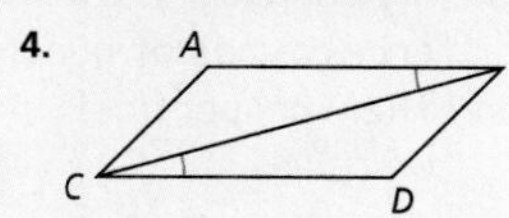

5.
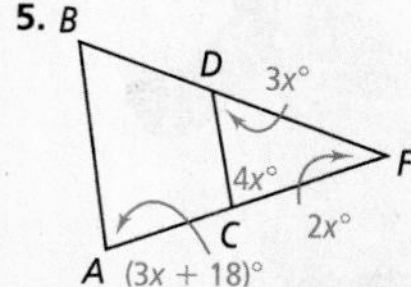

6.
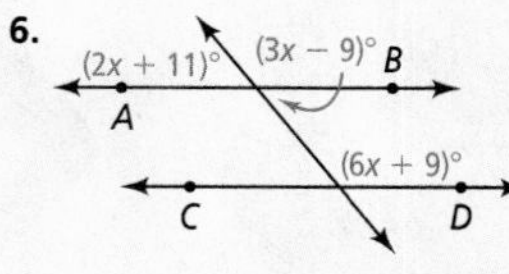

Lesson 3-8

Using Slope to Determine Parallel and Perpendicular Lines

Algebra **Determine whether each pair of lines is *parallel, perpendicular,* or *neither*.**

7. $y = -2x;\ y = -2x + 4$

8. $y = -\frac{3}{5}x + 1;\ y = \frac{5}{3}x - 3$

9. $2x - 3y = 1;\ 3x - 2y = 8$

Lessons 4-2 and 4-3

Proving Triangles Congruent

Determine the postulate or theorem that makes each pair of triangles congruent.

10.
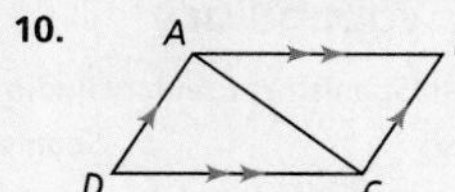

11.
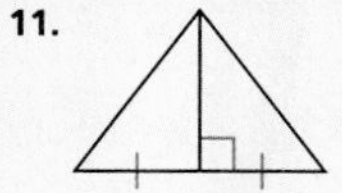

12.
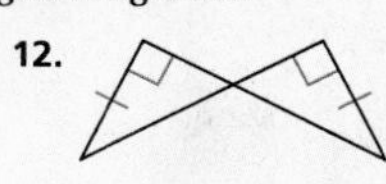

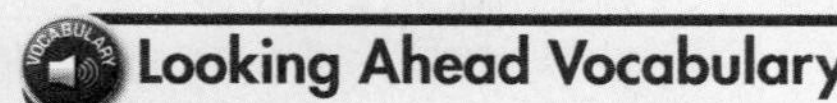

Looking Ahead Vocabulary

13. You know the meaning of *equilateral*. What do you think an *equiangular* polygon is?

14. Think about what a *kite* looks like. What characteristics might a *kite* in geometry have?

15. When a team wins two *consecutive* gold medals, it means they have won two gold medals in a row. What do you think two *consecutive* angles in a quadrilateral means?

Answers

Get Ready!

1. 30
2. 42
3. 22
4. yes
5. no
6. yes
7. ∥
8. ⊥
9. neither
10. ASA
11. SAS
12. AAS
13. Answers may vary. Sample: polygon in which all the ∠s are ≅
14. Answers may vary. Sample: four-sided figure formed by joining two isosc. △s
15. Answers may vary. Sample: angles that follow one right after the other

Get Ready!

Assign this diagnostic assessment to determine if students have the prerequisite skills for Chapter 6.

Lesson	Skill
3-2	Properties of Parallel Lines
3-3	Proving Lines Parallel
3-8	Using Slope to Determine Parallel and Perpendicular Lines
4-2 and 4-3	Proving Triangles Congruent

To remediate students, select from these resources (available for every lesson).

- Online Problems (PowerGeometry.com)
- Reteaching (All-in-One Teaching Resources)
- Practice (All-in-One Teaching Resources)

Why Students Need These Skills

PROPERTIES OF PARALLEL LINES Students will use properties of parallel lines to find missing angle measures in quadrilaterals.

PROVING LINES PARALLEL Students will use parallel lines to prove that a given quadrilateral is a specific type of parallelogram.

USING SLOPE TO DETERMINE PARALLEL AND PERPENDICULAR LINES Students will use slope in proofs involving coordinate geometry.

PROVING TRIANGLES CONGRUENT When a diagonal of a quadrilateral is drawn, two triangles are formed. Students will generate congruence statements to prove parts of the triangles congruent, which in turn will reveal information about the original quadrilateral.

Looking Ahead Vocabulary

EQUILATERAL Ask students to give examples of other words that use the prefix *equi-*.

KITE Show drawings of kites. Point out how the diagonals relate to one another.

CONSECUTIVE Have students name consecutive numbers.

Chapter 6 Overview

UbD Understanding by Design

In Chapter 6 students examine properties of quadrilaterals and use the properties to prove special types of quadrilaterals. In this chapter, students will develop the answers to the Essential Questions posed on the opposite page as they learn the concepts and skills bulleted below.

BIG idea Measurement

ESSENTIAL QUESTION How can you find the sum of the measures of polygon angles?

- The formula for angle measures of a polygon will be derived using diagonals.

BIG idea Reasoning and Proof

ESSENTIAL QUESTION How can you classify quadrilaterals?

- Students will use the properties of parallel and perpendicular lines and diagonals to classify quadrilaterals.
- Students will use coordinate geometry to classify special parallelograms.

BIG idea Coordinate Geometry

ESSENTIAL QUESTION How can you use coordinate geometry to prove general relationships?

- Students will examine slope and segment length in the coordinate plane.
- Students will use the Distance Formula in the coordinate plane.

TN Checks for Understanding

3108.1.2 Determine position using spatial sense with two and three-dimensional coordinate systems.
3108.1.13 Use proofs to further develop and deepen the understanding of the study of geometry.
3108.3.1 Prove two lines are parallel, perpendicular, or oblique using coordinate geometry.
3108.3.2 Connect coordinate geometry to geometric figures in the plane.
3108.3.4 Apply the midpoint and distance formulas to points and segments to find midpoints, distances, and missing information in two and three dimensions.
3108.4.4 Describe and recognize minimal conditions necessary to define geometric objects.
3108.4.9 Classify triangles, quadrilaterals, and polygons (regular, non-regular, convex and concave) using their properties.
3108.4.10 Identify and apply properties and relationships of special figures.
3108.4.12 Apply the Angle Sum Theorem for polygons to find interior and exterior angle measures given the number of sides, to find the number of sides given angle measures, and to solve contextual problems.
3108.4.1 Use coordinate geometry to prove properties of plane figures.
3108.4.20 Prove key basic theorems in geometry.

CHAPTER 6
PowerGeometry.com
Your place to get all things digital
Download videos connecting math to your world.
VIDEO
Math definitions in English and Spanish
VOCABULARY
The online Solve It will get you in gear for each lesson.
SOLVE IT!
Interactive! Vary numbers, graphs, and figures to explore math concepts.
DYNAMIC ACTIVITIES
Download Step-by-Step Problems with Instant Replay.
ONLINE PROBLEMS
Get and view your assignments online.
ONLINE HOMEWORK
Extra practice and review online
MathXL FOR SCHOOL

Polygons and Quadrilaterals

That is one cool building! The side of the building has the shape of a quadrilateral that is not a rectangle.

In this chapter, you'll learn about different types of quadrilaterals and their properties.

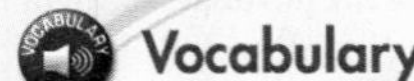

Vocabulary

English/Spanish Vocabulary Audio Online:

English	Spanish
coordinate proof, *p. 408*	prueba de coordenadas
equiangular polygon, *p. 354*	polígono equiángulo
equilateral polygon, *p. 354*	polígono equilátero
isosceles trapezoid, *p. 389*	trapecio isósceles
kite, *p. 392*	cometa
midsegment of a trapezoid, *p. 391*	segmento medio de un trapecio
parallelogram, *p. 359*	paralelogramo
rectangle, *p. 375*	rectángulo
regular polygon, *p. 354*	polígono regular
rhombus, *p. 375*	rombo
trapezoid, *p. 389*	trapecio

PowerGeometry.com

Chapter 6 Overview

Use these online assets to engage your students. These include support for the Solve It and step-by step solutions for Problems.

Show the student-produced video demonstrating relevant and engaging applications of the new concepts in this chapter.

Find online definitions for new terms in English and Spanish.

Start each lesson with an attention-getting Problem. View the Problem online with helpful hints.

BIG ideas

1 **Measuring**
Essential Question How can you find the sum of the measures of polygon angles?

2 **Reasoning and Proof**
Essential Question How can you classify quadrilaterals?

3 **Coordinate Geometry**
Essential Question How can you use coordinate geometry to prove general relationships?

Chapter Preview

- **6-1** **The Polygon Angle-Sum Theorems**
- **6-2** **Properties of Parallelograms**
- **6-3** **Proving That a Quadrilateral Is a Parallelogram**
- **6-4** **Properties of Rhombuses, Rectangles, and Squares**
- **6-5** **Conditions for Rhombuses, Rectangles, and Squares**
- **6-6** **Trapezoids and Kites**
- **6-7** **Polygons in the Coordinate Plane**
- **6-8** **Applying Coordinate Geometry**
- **6-9** **Proofs Using Coordinate Geometry**

My Math Video

FACILITATE Use this photo to discuss types of quadrilaterals. In the photo, the building is shaped like a parallelogram. In the chapter, students will learn to classify quadrilaterals by their sides and angle measures.

Q How does the building in the photo compare to typical buildings you have seen? **[It has four sides, but the sides do not appear to form right angles with the ground.]**

Q What shape is the side of the building in the picture? **[The side of the building is a quadrilateral.]**

Q What is the relationship between opposite sides of the building? **[The opposite sides are parallel.]**

Q What do you notice about opposite angles in the building? **[They appear to be congruent.]**

Q The side of the building in the photo forms a parallelogram. Based on your observations, what properties do parallelograms have? **[They have opposite sides that are parallel and opposite angles that are congruent.]**

EXTENSION

Have students research unique buildings in their local communities. They should describe the shape of the building and the properties of that shape. Students can make a presentation to the class about the challenges faced by architects in creating the building.

Increase students' depth of knowledge with interactive online activities.

Show Problems from each lesson solved step by step. Instant replay allows students to go at their own pace when studying online.

Assign homework to individual students or to an entire class.

Prepare students for the Mid-Chapter Quiz and Chapter Test with online practice and review.

CHAPTER 6

POLYGONS AND QUADRILATERALS
Math Background

UbD

Measurement

BIG idea Some attributes of geometric figures, such as length, area, volume, and angle measure, are measurable. Units are used to describe these attributes.

ESSENTIAL UNDERSTANDING

6–1 The sum of the angle measures of a polygon depends on the number of sides the polygon has.

Reasoning and Proof

BIG idea Definitions establish meanings and remove possible misunderstandings. Other truths are more complex and difficult to see. It is often possible to verify complex truths by reasoning from simpler ones using deductive reasoning.

ESSENTIAL UNDERSTANDINGS

6–2 Parallelograms have special properties regarding their sides, angles, and diagonals.

6–3 If a quadrilateral's sides, angles, and diagonals have certain properties, it can be shown that the quadrilateral is a parallelogram.

6–4 to 6–5 The special parallelograms, rhombus, rectangle, and square, have basic properties of their sides, angles, and diagonals that help identify them.

6–6 The angles, sides, and diagonals of a trapezoid have certain properties.

6–8 to 6–9 Variables can be used to name the coordinates of a figure in the coordinate plane. This allows relationships to be shown to be true for a general case.

Coordinate Geometry

BIG idea A coordinate system in a plane is formed by two perpendicular lines, called the *x*- and *y*-axes. It is possible to verify some complex truths using deductive reasoning in combination with the Distance, Midpoint, and Slope formulas.

ESSENTIAL UNDERSTANDINGS

6–7 to 6–9 The formulas for slope, distance and midpoint can be used to classify and to prove geometric relationships for figures in the coordinate plane. Using variables to name the coordinates of a figure allow relationships to be shown to be true for a general case.

Properties of Parallelograms

If you know that this quadrilateral is a parallelogram, then you can use properties of parallelograms to find the missing measurements.

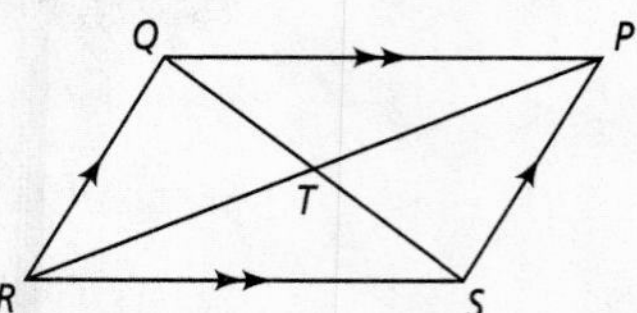

Property: Opposite sides are congruent.

$\overline{QR} \cong \overline{PS}$ and $\overline{SR} \cong \overline{PQ}$

Property: Consecutive angles are supplementary.

$m\angle P + m\angle Q = 180°$, $m\angle Q + m\angle R = 180°$, $m\angle R + m\angle S = 180°$, $m\angle S + m\angle P = 180°$

Property: Opposite angles are congruent.

$\angle P \cong \angle R$ and $\angle Q \cong \angle S$

Property: Diagonals bisect each other.

$\overline{QT} \cong \overline{TS}$ and $\overline{RT} \cong \overline{TP}$

Common Errors With Properties of Parallelograms

If it is known that two sides of a quadrilateral are parallel, but it is not known if they are congruent, then it cannot be determined from that information alone whether the quadrilateral is a parallelogram.

For example, if it is given that $\overline{PQ} \parallel \overline{SR}$, but it is not known if $\overline{PQ} \cong \overline{SR}$, it would be incorrect to assume that the quadrilateral is a parallelogram.

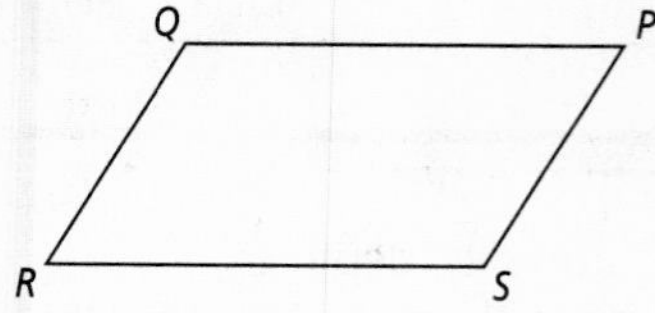

PROGRAM ORGANIZATION BIG IDEA ESSENTIAL UNDERSTANDING PROGRAM ORGANIZATION

Special Parallelograms

There are three special parallelograms: rhombus, rectangle and square. One way to classify rhombuses, rectangles and squares is by their diagonals.

Rhombus

A rhombus is a parallelogram with all four sides congruent.

The diagonals of a rhombus are perpendicular.

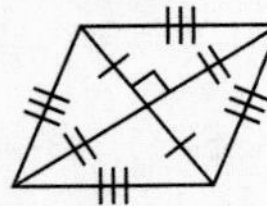

Rectangle

A rectangle is a parallelogram whose angles are right angles.

The diagonals are congruent.

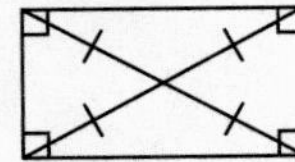

Square

A square is a parallelogram with all four sides congruent and its angles are right angles.

The diagonals are perpendicular and congruent.

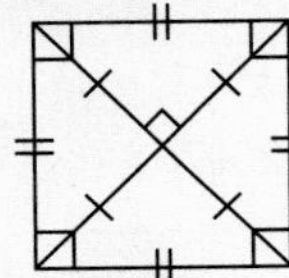

Common Errors With Special Parallelograms

Students may get confused about all the properties of special parallelograms. One way to help them see the relationship between the figures is with a Venn diagram.

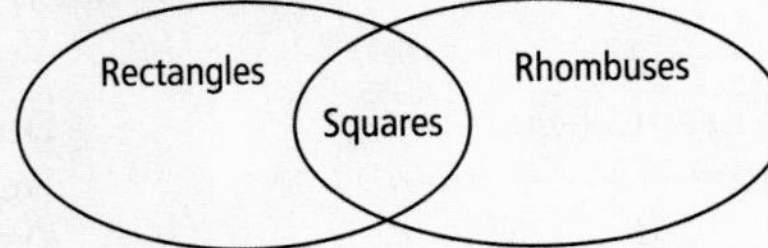

Coordinate Geometry

A coordinate plane can be used to classify quadrilaterals. Students can verify properties of special quadrilaterals using the Midpoint, Slope, and Distance Formulas in the coordinate plane.

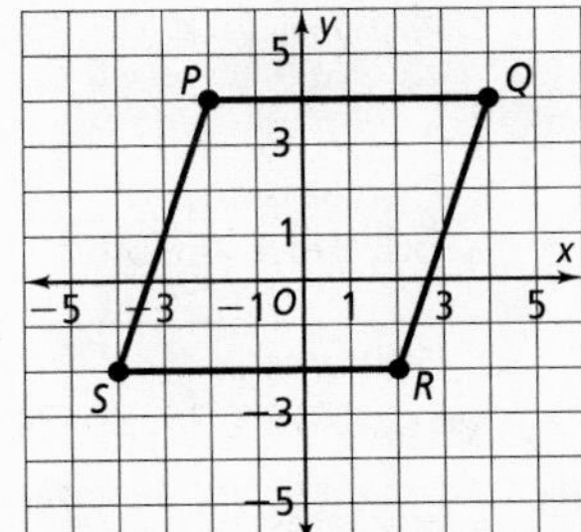

Figure *PQRS* appears to be a parallelogram. If one pair of opposite sides is parallel and congruent, then the quadrilateral is a parallelogram.

Find and compare the slopes of $\overline{SP}$ and $\overline{RQ}$.

$\overline{SP} : m = \frac{4 - (-2)}{-2 - (-4)} = \frac{6}{2} = 3$

$\overline{RQ} : m = \frac{4 - (-2)}{4 - 2} = \frac{6}{2} = 3$

Their slopes are equal so they are parallel.

Find and compare the lengths of $\overline{SP}$ and $\overline{RQ}$.

$\overline{SP} : d = \sqrt{(-2 - (-4))^2 + (4 - (-2))^2} = \sqrt{40}$

$\overline{RQ} : d = \sqrt{(4 - 2)^2 + (4 - (-2))^2} = \sqrt{40}$

Their lengths are equal so they are congruent. Figure *PQRS* is a parallelogram.

Common Errors With Coordinate Geometry

Figure *PQRS* is a parallelogram. Students might make the mistake of classifying it as a rhombus, either because its shape is close to that of a rhombus or because it has been shown that one pair of sides is parallel and congruent. However, proving one pair of sides is congruent and parallel is not sufficient to classify the figure as a rhombus. The other two sides need to be proved congruent.

POLYGONS AND QUADRILATERALS

Pacing and Assignment Guide

		TRADITIONAL			BLOCK
Lesson	**Teaching Day(s)**	**Basic**	**Average**	**Advanced**	**Block**
6-1	**1**	Problems 1–2 Exs. 7–14, 45–54	Problems 1–2 Exs. 7–21 odd, 22–25, 45–54	Problems 1–4 Exs. 7–21 odd, 22–54	**Day 1** Problems 1–4 Exs. 7–21 odd, 22–41, 45–54
	2	Problems 3–4 Exs. 15–21, 26, 28, 33, 35, 40	Problems 3-4 Exs. 1–21 odd, 26–41		
6-2	**1**	Problems 1–2 Exs. 9–13, 45–54	Problems 1–2 Exs. 9–13 odd, 32, 45–54	Problems 1–2 Exs. 9–13 odd, 32, 45–54	**Day 2** Problems 1–4 Exs. 9–23 odd, 25–41, 45–54
	2	Problems 3–4 Exs. 14–24, 28, 30–31, 38–41	Problems 3–4 Exs. 15–23 odd, 25–31, 33–41	Problems 3–4 Exs. 15–23 odd, 25–31, 33–44	
6-3	**1**	Problems 1–3 Exs. 7–16, 18–20, 22–23, 29–44	Problems 1–3 Exs. 7–15 odd, 17–26, 29–44	Problems 1–3 Exs. 7–15 odd, 17–44	**Day 3** Problems 1–3 Exs. 7–15 odd, 17–26, 29–44
6-4	**1**	Problems 1–3 Exs. 7–23 all, 24–40 even, 41, 43, 46, 47, 55–69	Problems 1–3 Exs. 7–23 odd, 24–52, 55–69	Problems 1–3 Exs. 7–23 odd, 24–69	Problems 1–3 Exs. 7–23 odd, 24–52, 55–69
6-5	**1**	Problems 1–2 Exs. 8–13, 32–43	Problems 1–3 Exs. 9–13 odd, 15–27, 32–43	Problems 1–3 Exs. 9–13 odd, 15–43	**Day 4** Problems 1–3 Exs. 9–13 odd, 15–27, 32–43
	2	Problem 3 Exs. 14–16, 18, 24–27			
6-6	**1**	Problems 1–3 Exs. 7–15 all, 67–76	Problems 1–3 Exs. 7–15 odd, 67–76	Problems 1–4 Exs. 7–23 odd, 25–76	Problems 1–3 Exs. 7–15 odd, 67–76 **Day 5** Problem 4 Exs. 17–23 odd, 25–62
	2	Problem 4 Exs. 16–24 all, 26–34 even, 46–49	Problem 4 Exs. 17–23 odd, 25–62		
6-7	**1**	Problems 1–3 Exs. 5–18, 21–24, 31, 35–36, 45–54	Problems 1–3 Exs. 5–15 odd, 17–38, 45–54	Problems 1–3 Exs. 5–15 odd, 17–54	Problems 1–3 Exs. 5–15 odd, 17–38, 45–54
6-8	**1**	Problems 1–2 Exs. 7–13, 38–49	Problems 1–2 Exs. 7–13 odd, 38–49	Problems 1–3 Exs. 7–13 odd, 14–49	**Day 6** Problems 1–3 Exs. 7–13 odd, 14–31, 38–49
	2	Problem 3 Exs. 14, 17, 19, 23, 24, 28	Problem 3 Exs. 14–31		
6-9	**1**	Problem 1 Exs. 4, 6–14 even, 29–40	Problem 1 Exs. 4–14, 29–40	Problems 1–2 Exs. 4–40	**Day 7** Problems 1–2 Exs. 4–26, 29–40
	2	Problem 2 Exs. 5, 16–20 even, 21, 23	Problem 2 Exs. 15–26		
Review	**1**	Chapter 6 Review	Chapter 6 Review	Chapter 6 Review	**Day 8** Chapter 6 Review
Assess	**1**	Chapter 6 Test	Chapter 6 Test	Chapter 6 Test	Chapter 6 Test
Total		**16 Days**	**16 Days**	**12 Days**	**8 Days**

Note: Pacing does not include Concept Bytes and other feature pages.

Resources

KEY
I = Interactive asset at PowerGeometry.com
E = Editable master at PowerGeometry.com
P = Available in Print
T = Available as a Transparency
M = Master at PowerGeometry.com
✓ = CD-ROM

	For the Chapter	6-1	6-2	6-3	6-4	6-5	6-6	6-7	6-8	6-9
Planning										
Teacher Center Online Planner & Grade Book	I	I	I	I	I	I	I	I	I	I
Interactive Learning & Guided Instruction										
My Math Video	I									
Solve It!		I TM	I TM	I TM	I TM	I TM	I TM	I TM	I TM	I TM
Student Companion (SP)*		P M	P M	P M	P M	P M	P M	P M	P M	P M
Vocabulary Support		I P M	I P M	I P M	I P M	I P M	I P M	I P M	I P M	I P M
Got It? Support		I P	I P	I P	I P	I P	I P	I P	I P	I P
Dynamic Activity		I		I		I	I			
Online Problems		I	I	I	I	I	I	I	I	I
Additional Problems		M	M	M	M	M	M	M	M	M
English Language Learner Support (TR)		E P M	E P M	E P M	E P M	E P M	E P M	E P M	E P M	E P M
Activities, Games, and Puzzles		E M	E M	E M	E M	E M	E M	E M	E M	E M
Teaching With TI Technology With CD-ROM										
TI-Nspire™ Support CD-ROM		✓	✓	✓	✓	✓	✓	✓	✓	✓
Lesson Check & Practice										
Student Companion (SP)*		P M	P M	P M	P M	P M	P M	P M	P M	P M
Lesson Check Support		I P	I P	I P	I P	I P	I P	I P	I P	I P
Practice and Problem Solving Workbook (SP)		P	P	P	P	P	P	P	P	P
Think About a Plan (TR)*		E P M	E P M	E P M	E P M	E P M	E P M	E P M	E P M	E P M
Practice Form G (TR)*		E P M	E P M	E P M	E P M	E P M	E P M	E P M	E P M	E P M
Standardized Test Prep (TR)*		P M	P M	P M	P M	P M	P M	P M	P M	P M
Practice *Form K* (TR)*		E P M	E P M	E P M	E P M	E P M	E P M	E P M	E P M	E P M
Extra Practice	E M									
Find the Errors!	M									
Enrichment (TR)		E P M	E P M	E P M	E P M	E P M	E P M	E P M	E P M	E P M
Answers and Solutions CD-ROM	✓	✓	✓	✓	✓	✓	✓	✓	✓	✓
Assess & Remediate										
ExamView CD-ROM	✓	✓	✓	✓	✓	✓	✓	✓	✓	✓
Lesson Quiz		I TM	I TM	I TM	I TM	I TM	I TM	I TM	I TM	I TM
Quizzes and Tests *Form G* (TR)*	E P M						E P M			E P M
Quizzes and Tests *Form K* (TR)*	E P M						E P M			E P M
Reteaching (TR)*		E P M	E P M	E P M	E P M	E P M	E P M	E P M	E P M	E P M
Performance Tasks (TR)*	P M									
Cumulative Review (TR)*	P M									
Progress Monitoring Assessments	I P M									

(TR) Available in All-In-One Teaching Resources   * Spanish available

Guided Instruction

PURPOSE To use geometry software to create, measure, explore, and make conjectures about the sum of the exterior angles of polygons

PROCESS Students will

- use geometry software to construct a specific polygon and calculate the sum of the measures of the exterior angles of the polygon they construct.
- manipulate a polygon, observing the sum of the measures of the exterior angles of the new polygon created.
- make conjectures about the sum of the measures of the exterior angles of polygons.

DISCUSS Exercise 3 refers to "tiling" a plane with regular polygons. This is a time when tessellations could be mentioned. It might also be a good idea to tell the students to start taking note of different patterns on floors and/or walls (carpet patterns, bricks, tile patterns, etc.).

Activity

In this Activity students focus on exterior angles of polygons. It is important for students to know first the definition of an exterior angle and how exterior angles are formed.

Q What is the sum of the exterior angles of a polygon? **[360°]**

Q What conclusion can be made about the interior and exterior angles of a polygon at each of its vertices? **[They are supplementary; their sum is 180°.]**

Q When is a polygon convex? **[Every diagonal of the polygon is in the interior of the polygon.]**

Q When is a polygon concave? **[At least one diagonal is in the exterior of the polygon.]**

Concept Byte: Exterior Angles of Polygons

Use With Lesson 6-1

TECHNOLOGY

Activity

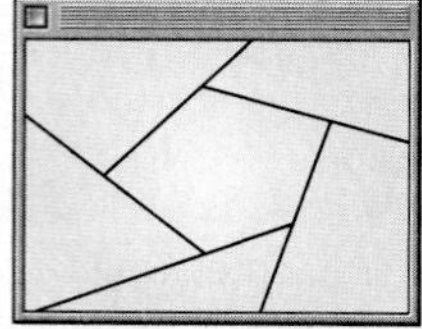

Construct Use geometry software. Construct a polygon similar to the one at the right. Extend each side as shown. Mark a point on each ray so that you can measure the exterior angles.

Investigate **Use your figure to explore properties of a polygon.**

- Measure each exterior angle.
- Calculate the sum of the measures of the exterior angles.
- Manipulate the polygon. Observe the sum of the measures of the exterior angles of the new polygon.

Exercises

1. Write a conjecture about the sum of the measures of the exterior angles (one at each vertex) of a convex polygon. Test your conjecture with another polygon.
2. **Extend** The figures below show a polygon that is decreasing in size until it finally becomes a point. Describe how you could use this to justify your conjecture in Exercise 1.

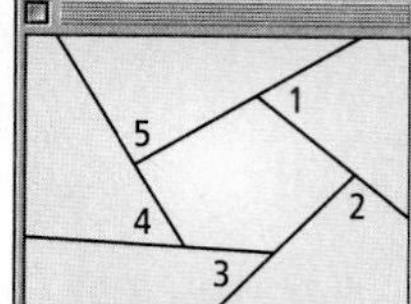

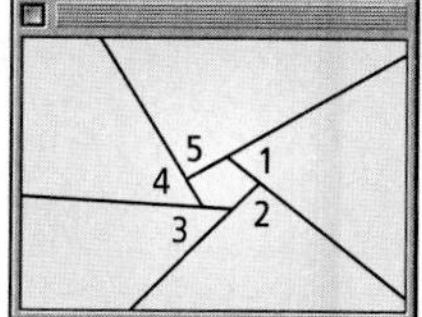

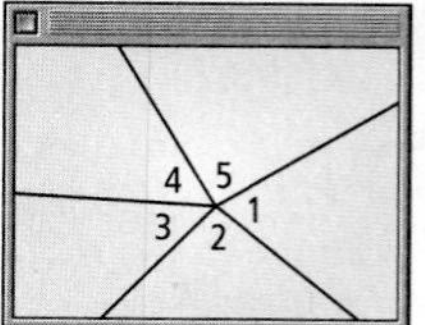

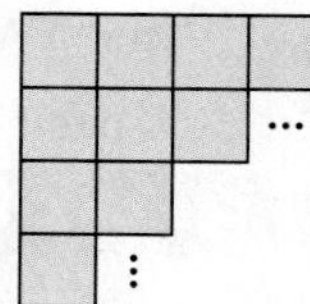

3. The figure at the right shows a square that has been copied several times. Notice that you can use the square to completely cover, or tile, a plane, without gaps or overlaps.
   a. Using geometry software, make several copies of other regular polygons with 3, 5, 6, and 8 sides. Regular polygons have sides of equal length and angles of equal measure.
   b. Which of the polygons you made can tile a plane?
   c. Measure *one* exterior angle of each polygon (including the square).
   d. Write a conjecture about the relationship between the measure of an exterior angle and your ability to tile a plane with the polygon. Test your conjecture with another regular polygon.

Answers

Exercises

1. Answers may vary. Sample: ∠s form a circle, which has 360 degrees.
2. Answers may vary. Sample: The sum of the measures of all the ∠s around a point is 360.

3a. Check students' work.

b. regular △, regular hexagon

c. 3 sides: 120; 4 sides: 90; 5 sides: 72; 6 sides: 60; 8 sides: 45

d. Answers may vary. Sample: To tile a plane, the measure of ext. ∠ must be a factor of 360. Check students' work.

6-1 The Polygon Angle-Sum Theorems

TN State Performance Indicators
SPI 3108.4.2 Define, identify, describe, and/or model plane figures using appropriate mathematical symbols (including collinear and non-collinear points, lines, segments, rays, angles, triangles, quadrilaterals, and other polygons).
Also SPI 3108.1.1

Objectives To find the sum of the measures of the interior angles of a polygon
To find the sum of the measures of the exterior angles of a polygon

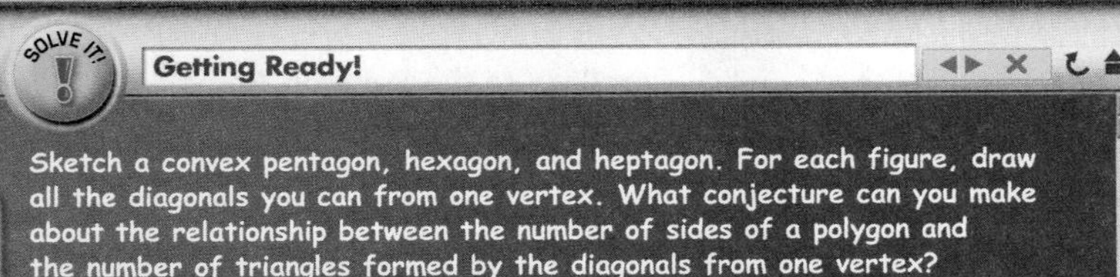

Sketch a convex pentagon, hexagon, and heptagon. For each figure, draw all the diagonals you can from one vertex. What conjecture can you make about the relationship between the number of sides of a polygon and the number of triangles formed by the diagonals from one vertex?

You don't need to draw all the diagonals from every vertex.

Dynamic Activity Polygon Angle-Sum Theorem

Lesson Vocabulary
- equilateral polygon
- equiangular polygon
- regular polygon

The Solve It is related to a formula for the sum of the interior angle measures of a polygon. (In this textbook, a polygon is convex unless otherwise stated.)

Essential Understanding The sum of the interior angle measures of a polygon depends on the number of sides the polygon has.

By dividing a polygon with n sides into $(n - 2)$ triangles, you can show that the sum of the interior angle measures of any polygon is a multiple of 180.

Theorem 6-1 Polygon Angle-Sum Theorem

The sum of the measures of the interior angles of an n-gon is $(n - 2)180$.

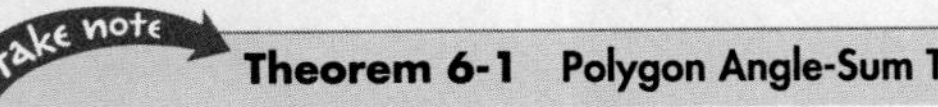

Problem 1 Finding a Polygon Angle Sum

Think
How many sides does a heptagon have?
A heptagon has 7 sides.

What is the sum of the interior angle measures of a heptagon?

Sum	$= (n - 2)180$	Polygon Angle-Sum Theorem
	$= (7 - 2)180$	Substitute 7 for n.
	$= 5 \cdot 180$	Simplify.
	$= 900$	

The sum of the interior angle measures of a heptagon is 900.

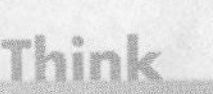

Got It? 1. a. What is the sum of the interior angle measures of a 17-gon?
b. **Reasoning** The sum of the interior angle measures of a polygon is 1980. How can you find the number of sides in the polygon?

1 Interactive Learning

Solve It!

PURPOSE To familiarize students with the process of dividing the interior of any polygon into non-overlapping triangles

PROCESS Students may use inductive reasoning to make conjectures after drawing the diagonals to collect data.

FACILITATE

Q What is a diagonal of a polygon? **[a segment that connects two nonconsecutive vertices]**

Q What is a convex pentagon? **[a five-sided figure that has no diagonal with points outside the polygon]**

ANSWER See Solve It in Answers on next page.

CONNECT THE MATH In the Solve It students investigate a convex polygon and the number of triangles that it contains. In the lesson, students use this relationship to understand the Polygon Angle-Sum Theorem.

2 Guided Instruction

Problem 1

Q How many non-overlapping triangles can a nonagon be divided into? Explain. **[7, because the number of triangles is always 2 less than the number of sides.]**

Got It?

Students may attempt to use trial and error to answer 1b. Help students to write the equation $1980 = (n - 2)180$.

6-1 Preparing to Teach

BIG idea Measurement UbD

ESSENTIAL UNDERSTANDING

- The sum of the angle measures of a polygon depends on the number of sides the polygon has.

Math Background

The hierarchy of quadrilaterals can help students who are troubled by questions such as "Is a square always a rectangle?" or "Is a rectangle always a square?" Students may gain insight by making a Venn diagram. Practice in learning definitions and theorems will help students classify quadrilaterals.

The Polygon Angle-Sum Theorems are extensions of the Triangle Angle-Sum Theorems. These theorems can be developed through inductive reasoning by examining examples or proved using deductive reasoning. The rest of this chapter will focus on polygons with four sides, or quadrilaterals. Quadrilaterals have the property that the sum of the interior angles as well as the sum of the exterior angles is 360.

Support Student Learning

Use the **Geometry Companion** to engage and support students during instructions. See Lesson Resources at the end of this lesson for details.

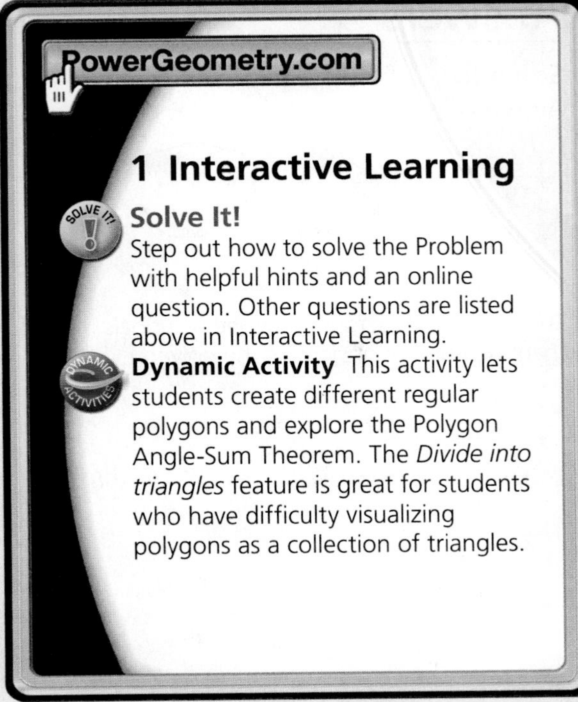

PowerGeometry.com
1 Interactive Learning
Solve It!
Step out how to solve the Problem with helpful hints and an online question. Other questions are listed above in Interactive Learning.
Dynamic Activity This activity lets students create different regular polygons and explore the Polygon Angle-Sum Theorem. The Divide into triangles feature is great for students who have difficulty visualizing polygons as a collection of triangles.

Ask students to create a Venn diagram to show the relationships among polygons, equilateral polygons, equiangular polygons, and regular polygons.

Take Note

Point out that the corollary is derived by starting with the formula given in the Theorem, and dividing the sum of the measures by the number of sides (which is the same as the number of angles).

Problem 2

Q Is the sum of the measures of the interior angles of a hexagon different from the sum of the measures of the interior angles of a regular hexagon? Explain. **[No, the sum of the measures of the interior angles of any hexagon is the same.]**

Q How many interior angles does a hexagon have? **[six]**

Q Could you solve this problem if you were told that the hexagons are NOT regular? Explain. **[No, you must know that all angles are equal to be able to divide by 6 to determine the measure of each individual angle.]**

Got It?

Q What is the sum of the measures of the interior angles of a regular nonagon? Explain. **[The sum is 1260 because (9 − 2)180 = 1260.]**

An **equilateral polygon** is a polygon with all sides congruent.

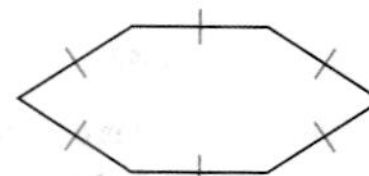

An **equiangular polygon** is a polygon with all angles congruent.

A **regular polygon** is a polygon that is both equilateral and equiangular.

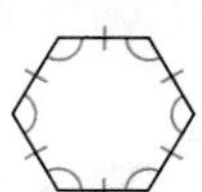

take note **Corollary to the Polygon Angle-Sum Theorem**

The measure of each interior angle of a regular n-gon is $\frac{(n-2)180}{n}$.

You will prove the Corollary to the Polygon Angle-Sum Theorem in Exercise 43.

Problem 2 Using the Polygon Angle-Sum Theorem

Think
How does the word *regular* help you answer the question?
The word *regular* tells you that each angle has the same measure.

Biology The common housefly, *Musca domestica*, has eyes that consist of approximately 4000 facets. Each facet is a regular hexagon. What is the measure of each interior angle in one hexagonal facet?

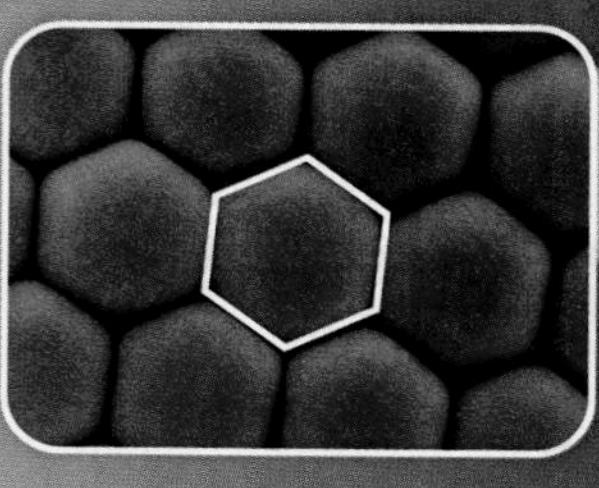

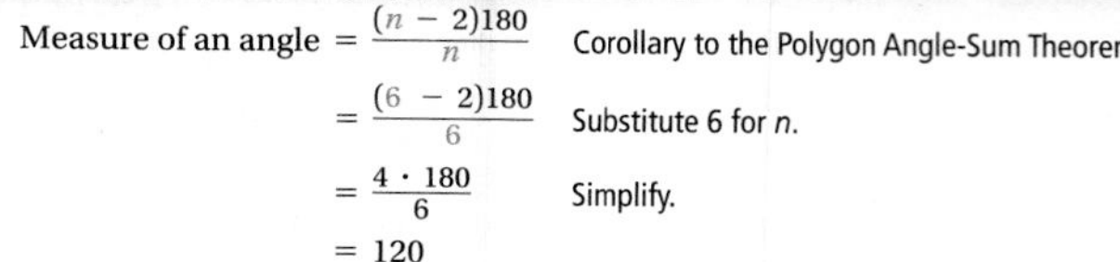

$$\text{Measure of an angle} = \frac{(n-2)180}{n} \quad \text{Corollary to the Polygon Angle-Sum Theorem}$$
$$= \frac{(6-2)180}{6} \quad \text{Substitute 6 for } n.$$
$$= \frac{4 \cdot 180}{6} \quad \text{Simplify.}$$
$$= 120$$

The measure of each interior angle in one hexagonal facet is 120.

Got It? 2. What is the measure of each interior angle in a regular nonagon?

Answers

Solve It!

Answers may vary. Sample:

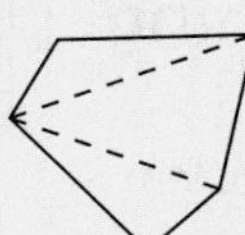

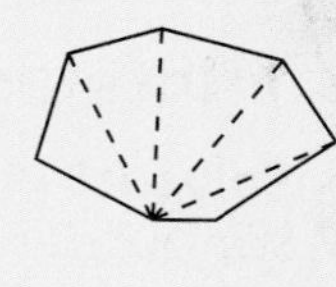

The number of △s formed by the diagonals is 2 less than the number of sides of the polygon.

Got It?

1a. 2700

b. Answers may vary. Sample: Divide 1980 by 180, and then add 2.

2. 140

PowerGeometry.com

2 Guided Instruction

Each Problem is worked out and supported online.

Problem 1
Finding a Polygon Angle-Sum
Animated

Problem 2
Using the Polygon Angle-Sum Theorem
Animated

Problem 3
Using the Polygon Angle-Sum Theorem
Animated

Problem 4
Finding an Exterior Angle Measure

Support in Geometry Companion
- Vocabulary
- Key Concepts
- Got It?

Problem 3 Using the Polygon Angle-Sum Theorem

Think

How does the diagram help you?
You know the number of sides and four of the five angle measures.

What is $m\angle Y$ in pentagon *TODAY*?

Use the Polygon Angle-Sum Theorem for $n = 5$.

$$m\angle T + m\angle O + m\angle D + m\angle A + m\angle Y = (5 - 2)180$$

$$110 + 90 + 120 + 150 + m\angle Y = 3 \cdot 180 \quad \text{Substitute.}$$

$$470 + m\angle Y = 540 \quad \text{Simplify.}$$

$$m\angle Y = 70 \quad \text{Subtract 470 from each side.}$$

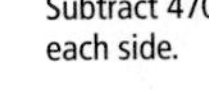

Got It? 3. What is $m\angle G$ in quadrilateral *EFGH*?

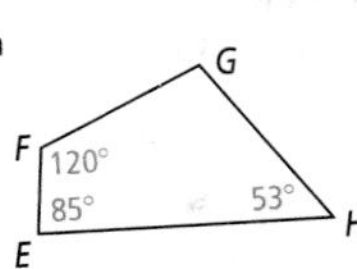

You can draw exterior angles at any vertex of a polygon. The figures below show that the sum of the measures of the exterior angles, one at each vertex, is 360.

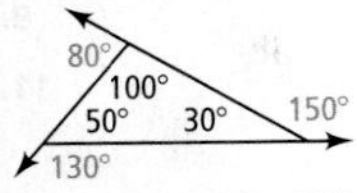

$80 + 150 + 130 = 360$

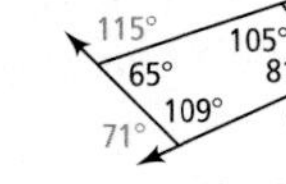

$115 + 75 + 99 + 71 = 360$

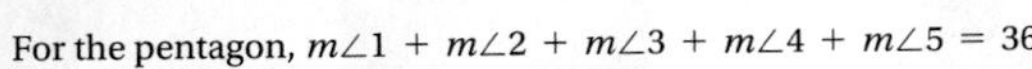

take note

Theorem 6-2 Polygon Exterior Angle-Sum Theorem

The sum of the measures of the exterior angles of a polygon, one at each vertex, is 360.

For the pentagon, $m\angle 1 + m\angle 2 + m\angle 3 + m\angle 4 + m\angle 5 = 360$.

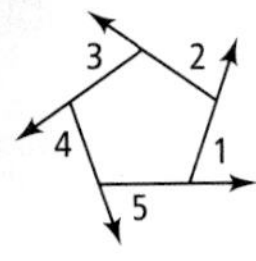

You will prove Theorem 6-2 in Exercise 39.

Problem 4 Finding an Exterior Angle Measure

Think

What kind of angle is $\angle 1$?
Looking at the diagram, you know that $\angle 1$ is an exterior angle.

What is $m\angle 1$ in the regular octagon at the right?

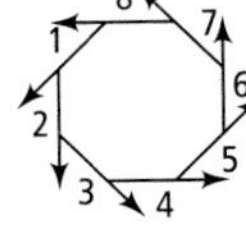

By the Polygon Exterior Angle-Sum Theorem, the sum of the exterior angle measures is 360. Since the octagon is regular, the interior angles are congruent. So their supplements, the exterior angles, are also congruent.

$$m\angle 1 = \frac{360}{8} \quad \text{Divide 360 by 8, the number of sides in an octagon.}$$

$$= 45 \quad \text{Simplify.}$$

Got It? 4. What is the measure of an exterior angle of a regular nonagon?

Problem 3

Q What is the sum of the labeled angles in the pentagon *TODAY*? **[The sum of the measures is 470.]**

Q What is the sum of the measures of all five of the interior angles of a pentagon? **[540°]**

Q How can you determine the measure of the unlabeled angle? **[You can subtract 470 from 540.]**

Got It?

Remind students that the sum of the measures of the angles of any quadrilateral is the same. Ask them the sum of the angles in a square.

Take Note

Students may be confused with the phrase "one at each vertex." Draw a polygon on the board and remind students that at each vertex there are two ways to draw an exterior angle.

Problem 4

Students may wish to solve this problem using the following alternate method: First, determine that the measure of each interior angle is 135 using the Polygon Angle-Sum Theorem. Second, determine the measure of $\angle 1$ by considering that it is supplementary to an angle that measures 135.

Got It?

Q What is the sum of the exterior angles for a regular nonagon? **[360]**

Additional Problems

1. What is the sum of the angle measures of a 10-gon?

ANSWER 1440

2. Marcy creates a floor tile pattern using squares, regular hexagons, and regular dodecagons (12-sided polygons). What is the measure of each angle in one regular dodecagon?

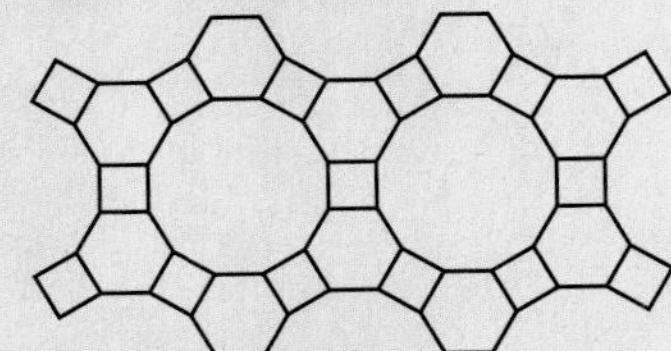

ANSWER 150

3. What is $m\angle D$ in quadrilateral *ABCD*?

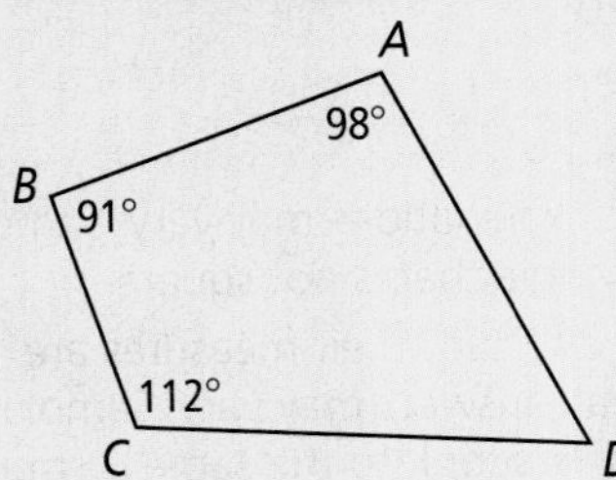

ANSWER 59

4. What is the measure of an exterior angle of a regular hexagon?

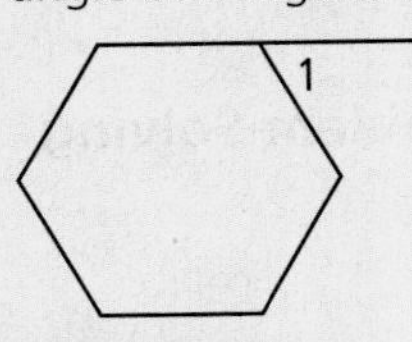

ANSWER 60

Answers

Got It? (continued)

3. 102

4. 40

3 Lesson Check

Do you know HOW?

- If students have difficulty with Exercise 1, then remind them how to use the Polygon Angle-Sum Theorem.

Do you UNDERSTAND?

- If students have difficulty with Exercise 4, then provide them with the familiar examples of a square and a rectangle.

Close

Q For what n-gon is the sum of the measures of the interior angles equal to the sum of the measures of the exterior angles? Explain. **[The sum of the exterior angles is always 360, so find an n-gon such that $(n - 2)180 = 360$. Solving this equation gives $n = 4$. A quadrilateral has the same sum for the measures of the interior angles and the measures of the exterior angles.]**

Lesson Check

Do you know HOW?

1. What is the sum of the interior angle measures of an 11-gon?
2. What is the sum of the measures of the exterior angles of a 15-gon?
3. Find the measures of an interior angle and an exterior angle of a regular decagon.

Do you UNDERSTAND?

4. **Vocabulary** Can you draw an equiangular polygon that is not equilateral? Explain.
5. **Reasoning** Which angles are the exterior angles for $\angle 1$? What do you know about their measures? Explain.

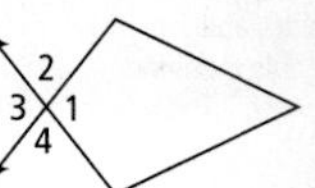

6. **Error Analysis** Your friend says that she measured an interior angle of a regular polygon as 130. Explain why this result is impossible.

Practice and Problem-Solving Exercises

A Practice

Find the sum of the interior angle measures of each polygon. See Problem 1.

7. (hexagon)
8. 35-gon
9. 14-gon
10. 20-gon
11. 1002-gon

Find the measure of one interior angle in each regular polygon. See Problem 2.

12.

13.

14.

Algebra Find the missing angle measures. See Problem 3.

15.
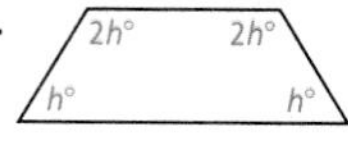

16.
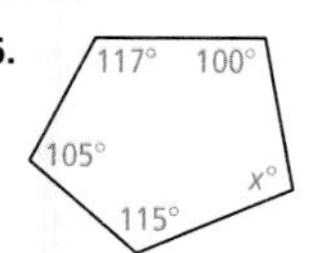

17. 129°, 116°, 120°, 130°, y°, 135°, 125°

Find the measure of an exterior angle of each regular polygon. See Problem 4.

18. pentagon
19. 36-gon
20. 18-gon
21. 100-gon

B Apply

The sum of the interior angle measures of a polygon with n sides is given. Find n.

22. 180
23. 1080
24. 1980
25. 2880

PowerGeometry.com

3 Lesson Check

For a digital lesson check, use the Got It questions.

Support in Geometry Companion

- Lesson Check

4 Practice

Assign homework to individual students or to an entire class.

Answers

Lesson Check

1. 1620
2. 360
3. 144, 36
4. Yes; explanations may vary. Sample: rectangle that is not square
5. $\angle 2$ and $\angle 4$; their measures are equal; answers may vary. Sample: Two $\angle$s suppl. to the same $\angle$ must be $\cong$.
6. Answers may vary. Sample: ext. $\angle$ would measure 50, which is not a factor of 360.

Practice and Problem-Solving Exercises

7. 900
8. 5940
9. 2160
10. 3240
11. 180,000
12. 135
13. 150
14. 108
15. 60, 120, 120, 60
16. 103
17. 145
18. 72
19. 10
20. 20
21. 3.6
22. 3
23. 8
24. 13
25. 18

26. **Open-Ended** Sketch an equilateral polygon that is not equiangular.

27. **Stage Design** A theater-in-the-round allows for a play to have an audience on all sides. The diagram at the right shows a platform constructed for a theater-in-the-round stage. What type of regular polygon is the largest platform? Find the measure of each numbered angle.

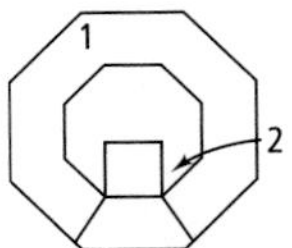

28. **Think About a Plan** A triangle has two congruent interior angles and an exterior angle that measures 100. Find two possible sets of interior angle measures for the triangle.
- How can a diagram help you?
- What is the sum of the angle measures in a triangle?

Algebra **Find the value of each variable.**

29.

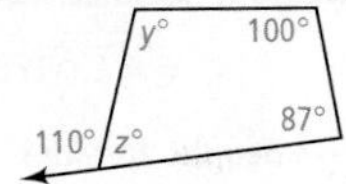

30.

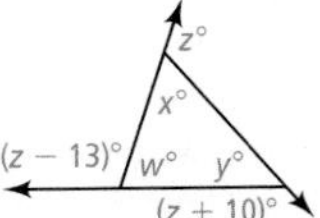

31.

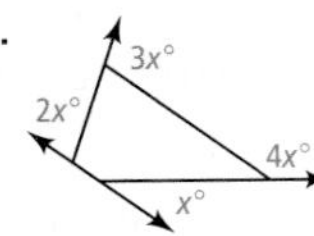

The measure of an exterior angle of a regular polygon is given. Find the measure of an interior angle. Then find the number of sides.

32. 72 33. 36 34. 18 35. 30 36. x

Packaging **The gift package at the right contains fruit and cheese. The fruit is in a container that has the shape of a regular octagon. The fruit container fits in a square box. A triangular cheese wedge fills each corner of the box.**

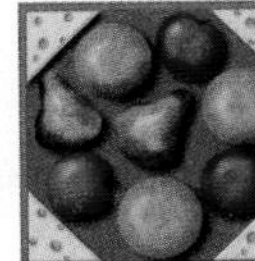

37. Find the measure of each interior angle of a cheese wedge.

38. **Reasoning** Show how to rearrange the four pieces of cheese to make a regular polygon. What is the measure of each interior angle of the polygon?

39. **Algebra** A polygon has n sides. An interior angle of the polygon and an adjacent exterior angle form a straight angle.
   a. What is the sum of the measures of the n straight angles?
   b. What is the sum of the measures of the n interior angles?
   c. Using your answers above, what is the sum of the measures of the n exterior angles?
   d. What theorem do the steps above prove?

40. **Reasoning** Your friend says she has another way to find the sum of the interior angle measures of a polygon. She picks a point inside the polygon, draws a segment to each vertex, and counts the number of triangles. She multiplies the total by 180, and then subtracts 360 from the product. Does her method work? Explain.

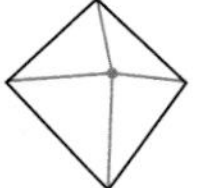

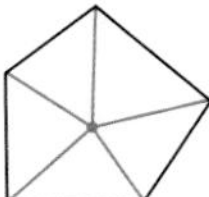

41. **Algebra** The measure of an interior angle of a regular polygon is three times the measure of an exterior angle of the same polygon. What is the name of the polygon?

4 Practice

ASSIGNMENT GUIDE

Basic: 7–21, 26, 28, 33, 35, 40
Average: 7–21 odd, 22–41
Advanced: 7–21 odd, 22–44
Standardized Test Prep: 45–48
Mixed Review: 49–54

Reasoning exercises have blue headings.
Applications exercises have red headings.

EXERCISE 40: Use the Think About a Plan worksheet in the **Practice and Problem Solving Workbook** (also available in the Teaching Resources in print and online) to further support students' development in becoming independent learners.

HOMEWORK QUICK CHECK

To check students' understanding of key skills and concepts, go over Exercises 13, 19, 26, 28, and 40.

26. Answers may vary. Sample:

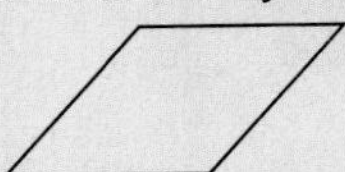

27. octagon; $m\angle 1 = 135$, $m\angle 2 = 45$
28. 20, 80, 80; 80, 50, 50
29. $y = 103$, $z = 70$
30. $w = 72$, $x = 59$, $y = 49$, $z = 121$
31. 36
32. 108; 5
33. 144; 10
34. 162; 20
35. 150; 12
36. $180 - x$; $\frac{360}{x}$
37. 45, 45, 90
38. 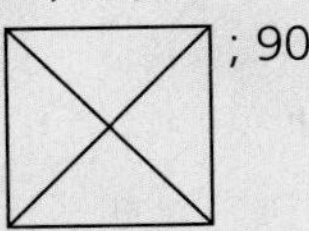 ; 90

39a. $180n$
b. $(n - 2) \cdot 180$
c. $180n - [(n - 2) \cdot 180] = 360$
d. Polygon Ext. ∠ Sum Theorem
40. Yes; answers may vary. Sample: Sum of the measures of interior ∠s $= (n - 2) \cdot 180$.
41. octagon

Answers

Practice and Problem-Solving Exercises

42. 0.8

43a. Answers may vary. Sample: The sum of the interior ∠ measures = $(n - 2)180$. All ∡ of a regular n-gon are ≅. So each interior ∠ measure = $\frac{180(n-2)}{n}$, and $\frac{180(n-2)}{n} = \frac{180n - 360}{n} = 180 - \frac{360}{n}$.

b. As n gets larger, $\frac{360}{n}$ gets smaller. The interior angle measure gets closer to 180. The polygon becomes more like a circle.

44. 36

45. 225

46. 24

47. 79

48. 81

49. $\overline{CD}$; the longer side is opposite the larger ∠.

50. Distr. Prop.

51. Refl. Prop. of ≅

52. Sym. Prop. of ≅

53. ASA

54a. ∠HGE

b. ∠GHE

c. ∠HEG

d. $\overline{GH}$

e. $\overline{HE}$

f. $\overline{EG}$

Challenge

42. Probability Find the probability that the measure of an interior angle of a regular n-gon is a positive integer when n is an integer and $3 \le n \le 12$.

43. a. In the Corollary to the Polygon Angle-Sum Theorem, explain why the measure of an interior angle of a regular n-gon is given by the formulas $\frac{180(n-2)}{n}$ and $180 - \frac{360}{n}$.

b. Use the second formula to explain what happens to the measures of the interior angles of regular n-gons as n becomes a large number. Explain also what happens to the polygons.

44. $ABCDEFGHJK$ is a regular decagon. A ray bisects ∠C, and another ray bisects ∠D. The two rays intersect in the decagon's interior. Find the measure of the acute angles formed by the intersecting rays.

Standardized Test Prep

GRIDDED RESPONSE

SAT/ACT

45. The car at each vertex of a Ferris wheel holds a maximum of five people. The sum of the interior angle measures of the Ferris wheel is 7740. What is the maximum number of people the Ferris wheel can hold?

46. A rectangle and a square have equal areas. The rectangle has length 9 cm and width 4 cm. What is the perimeter of the square, in centimeters?

47. The Public Garden is located between two parallel streets: Maple Street and Oak Street. The garden faces Maple Street and is bordered by rows of shrubs that intersect Oak Street at point B. What is $m\angle ABC$, the angle formed by the shrubs?

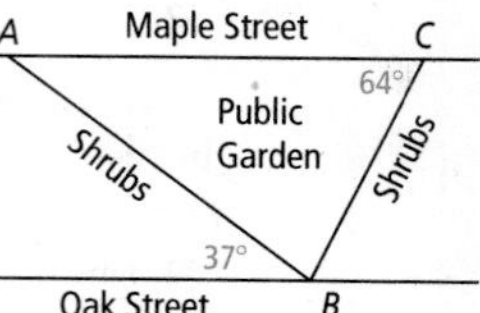

48. $\triangle ABC \cong \triangle DEF$. If $m\angle A = 3x + 4$, $m\angle C = 2x$, and $m\angle E = 4x + 5$, what is $m\angle B$?

Mixed Review

49. If $\overline{AB} \cong \overline{CB}$ and $m\angle ABD < m\angle CBD$, which is longer, $\overline{AD}$ or $\overline{CD}$? Explain.

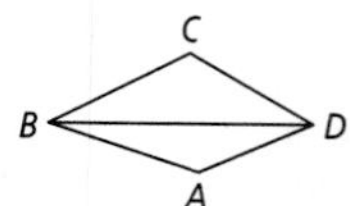

See Lesson 5-7.

Name the property that justifies each statement.

See Lesson 2-5.

50. $4(2a - 3) = 8a - 12$

51. $\overline{RS} \cong \overline{RS}$

52. If ∠1 ≅ ∠4, then ∠4 ≅ ∠1.

Get Ready! **To prepare for Lesson 6-2, do Exercises 53 and 54.**

Use the figure below.

See Lessons 4-1 and 4-3.

53. Name the postulate or theorem that justifies $\triangle EFG \cong \triangle GHE$.

54. Complete each statement.

a. ∠FEG ≅ ■ **b.** ∠EFG ≅ ■ **c.** ∠FGE ≅ ■

d. $\overline{EF}$ ≅ ■ **e.** $\overline{FG}$ ≅ ■ **f.** $\overline{GE}$ ≅ ■

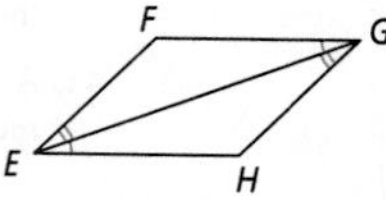

6-1 Lesson Resources

Differentiated Remediation

Instructional Support

Geometry Companion

Students can use the **Geometry Companion** worktext (4 pages) . . .

- New Vocabulary
- Key Concepts
- Got It for each Problem
- Lesson Check

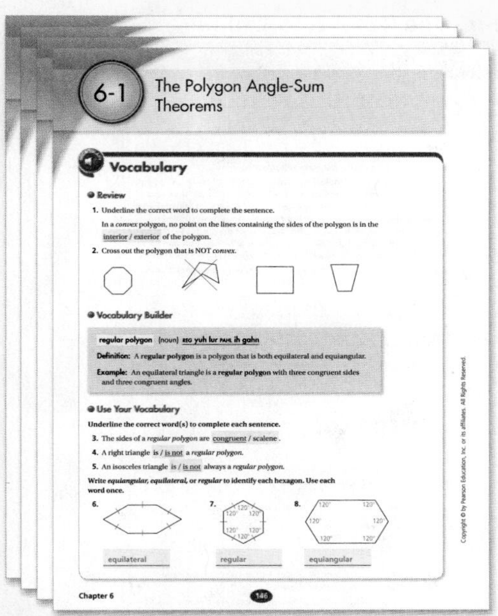
6-1 The Polygon Angle-Sum Theorems

Vocabulary

Review

1. Underline the correct word to complete the sentence.
   In a *convex* polygon, no point on the lines containing the sides of the polygon is in the interior / exterior of the polygon.
2. Cross out the polygon that is NOT *convex*.

Vocabulary Builder

regular polygon (noun) REG yuh lur PAHL ih gahn

Definition: A **regular polygon** is a polygon that is both equilateral and equiangular.

Example: An equilateral triangle is a **regular polygon** with three congruent sides and three congruent angles.

Use Your Vocabulary

Underline the correct word(s) to complete each sentence.

3. The sides of a *regular polygon* are congruent / scalene.
4. A right triangle is / is not a *regular polygon*.
5. An isosceles triangle is / is not always a *regular polygon*.

Write *equiangular*, *equilateral*, or *regular* to identify each hexagon. Use each word once.

6. equilateral
7. regular
8. equiangular

Chapter 6 146

Copyright © by Pearson Education, Inc. or its affiliates. All Rights Reserved.

ELL Support

Assess Understanding Draw a triangle on the board. Trace the interior angles of the triangle and ask: How many interior angles are in a triangle? What is the sum of the measures of those angle measures? How do you know? Then draw a rectangle on the board. Ask: How many interior angles are in a rectangle? What is the sum of those angle measures? Draw a diagonal and trace it with your finger. Ask: What do you notice about the rectangle with a diagonal?

Use Manipulatives Arrange students in mixed pairs. Have them draw polygons with 5, 6, 7, 8, 9, and 10 sides. Model how to draw a diagonal from one vertex to each of the other vertices. Ask them to do the same. Tell them to discuss their results and make a conjecture about the sum of the angle measures in a polygon.

5 Assess & Remediate

Lesson Quiz

1. What is the sum of the angle measures of a 14-gon?
2. What is the measure of each angle of a regular pentagon?
3. What is $m\angle C$ in pentagon *ABCDE*?

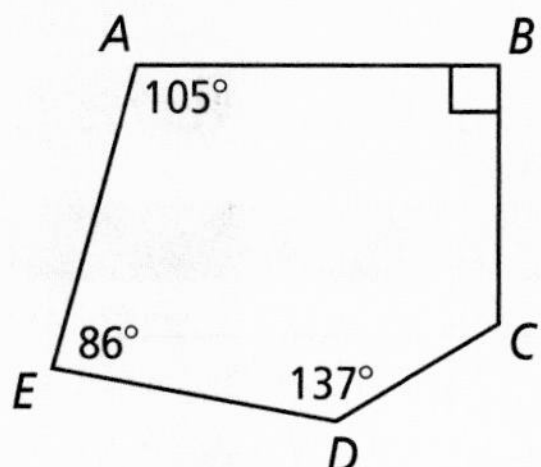
A
B
105°
86°
137°
C
E
D

4. What is the measure of an exterior angle of a regular pentagon?

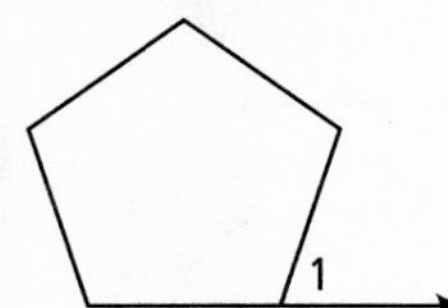
1

5. **Do you UNDERSTAND?** How many sides does a regular polygon have if each exterior angle is 24°? How do you know?

ANSWERS TO LESSON QUIZ

1. 2160
2. 108
3. 122
4. 72
5. The sum of the exterior angles of any polygon is 360°, so the number of sides is $\frac{360}{24}$ or 15.

PRESCRIPTION FOR REMEDIATION

Use the student work on the Lesson Quiz to prescribe a differentiated review assignment.

Points	Differentiated Remediation
0–2	Intervention
3–4	On-level
5	Extension

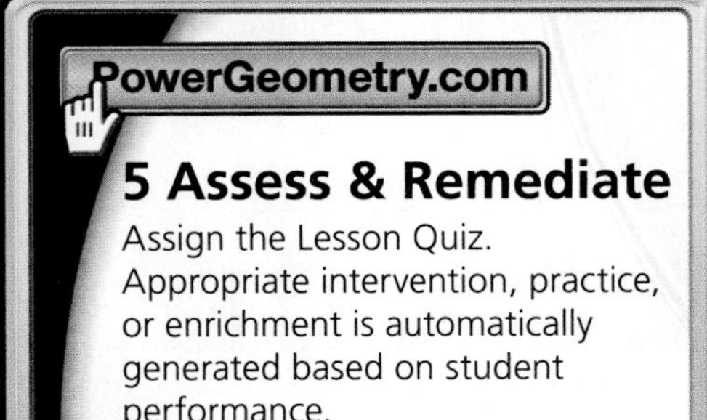
PowerGeometry.com
5 Assess & Remediate
Assign the Lesson Quiz.
Appropriate intervention, practice, or enrichment is automatically generated based on student performance.

Intervention

- **Reteaching** (2 pages) Provides reteaching and practice exercises for the key lesson concepts. Use with struggling students or absent students.
- **English Language Learner Support** Helps students develop and reinforce mathematical vocabulary and key concepts.

All-in-One Resources/Online

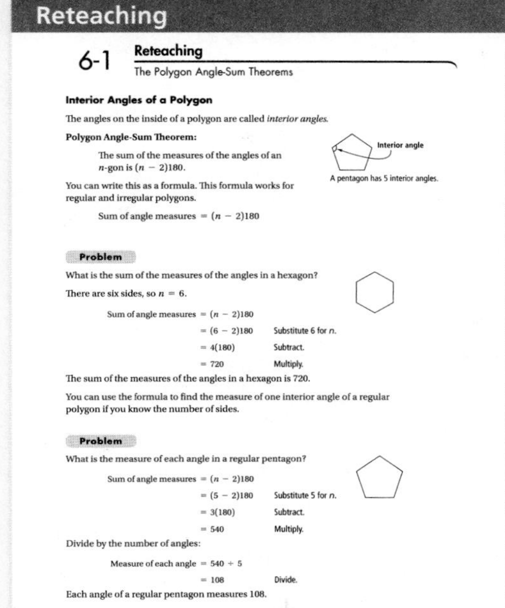
Reteaching

6-1 **Reteaching**
The Polygon Angle-Sum Theorems

Interior Angles of a Polygon

The angles on the inside of a polygon are called *interior angles.*

Polygon Angle-Sum Theorem:

The sum of the measures of the angles of an n-gon is $(n - 2)180$.

You can write this as a formula. This formula works for regular and irregular polygons.

Sum of angle measures $= (n - 2)180$

Interior angle

A pentagon has 5 interior angles.

Problem

What is the sum of the measures of the angles in a hexagon?

There are six sides, so $n = 6$.

Sum of angle measures	$= (n - 2)180$	
	$= (6 - 2)180$	Substitute 6 for *n*.
	$= 4(180)$	Subtract.
	$= 720$	Multiply.

The sum of the measures of the angles in a hexagon is 720.

You can use the formula to find the measure of one interior angle of a regular polygon if you know the number of sides.

Problem

What is the measure of each angle in a regular pentagon?

Sum of angle measures	$= (n - 2)180$	
	$= (5 - 2)180$	Substitute 5 for *n*.
	$= 3(180)$	Subtract.
	$= 540$	Multiply.

Divide by the number of angles:

Measure of each angle	$= 540 \div 5$	
	$= 108$	Divide.

Each angle of a regular pentagon measures 108.

All-in-One Resources/Online

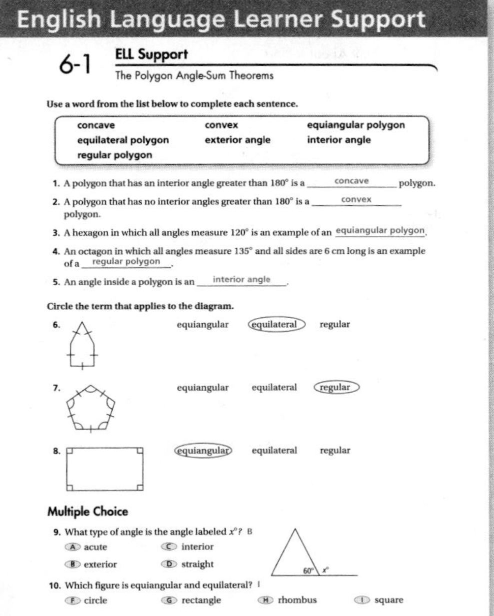
English Language Learner Support

6-1 **ELL Support**
The Polygon Angle-Sum Theorems

Use a word from the list below to complete each sentence.

concave	convex	equiangular polygon
equilateral polygon	exterior angle	interior angle
regular polygon		

1. A polygon that has an interior angle greater than 180° is a __concave__ polygon.
2. A polygon that has no interior angles greater than 180° is a __convex__ polygon.
3. A hexagon in which all angles measure 120° is an example of an __equiangular polygon__.
4. An octagon in which all angles measure 135° and all sides are 6 cm long is an example of a __regular polygon__.
5. An angle inside a polygon is an __interior angle__.

Circle the term that applies to the diagram.

6. equiangular (equilateral) regular
7. equiangular equilateral (regular)
8. (equiangular) equilateral regular

Multiple Choice

9. What type of angle is the angle labeled $x°$? B
   A acute C interior
   B exterior D straight
   60° $x°$
10. Which figure is equiangular and equilateral? I
    F circle G rectangle H rhombus I square

Differentiated Remediation *continued*

On-Level

- **Practice** (2 pages) Provides extra practice for each lesson. For simpler practice exercises, use the Form K Practice pages found in the All-in-One Teaching Resources and online.
- **Think About a Plan** Helps students develop specific problem-solving skills and strategies by providing scaffolded guiding questions.
- **Standardized Test Prep** Focuses on all major exercises, all major question types, and helps students prepare for the high-stakes assessments.

Practice and Problem Solving Wkbk/ All-in-One Resources/Online

Practice page 1

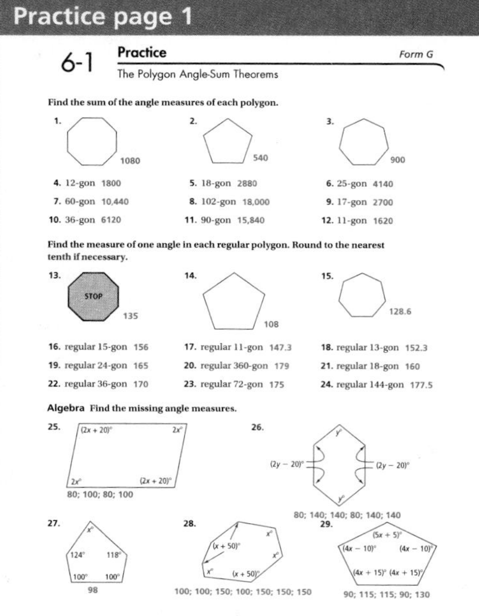

6-1 Practice — Form G

The Polygon Angle-Sum Theorems

Find the sum of the angle measures of each polygon.

1. 1080 2. 540 3. 900

4. 12-gon 1800 5. 18-gon 2880 6. 25-gon 4140

7. 60-gon 10,440 8. 102-gon 18,000 9. 17-gon 2700

10. 36-gon 6120 11. 90-gon 15,840 12. 11-gon 1620

Find the measure of one angle in each regular polygon. Round to the nearest tenth if necessary.

13. 135 14. 108 15. 128.6

16. regular 15-gon 156 17. regular 11-gon 147.3 18. regular 13-gon 152.3

19. regular 24-gon 165 20. regular 360-gon 179 21. regular 18-gon 160

22. regular 36-gon 170 23. regular 72-gon 175 24. regular 144-gon 177.5

Algebra Find the missing angle measures.

25. 80; 100; 80; 100 26. 80; 140; 140; 80; 140; 140

27. 98 28. 100; 100; 150; 100; 150; 150; 150 29. 90; 115; 115; 90; 130

Practice and Problem Solving Wkbk/ All-in-One Resources/Online

Practice page 2

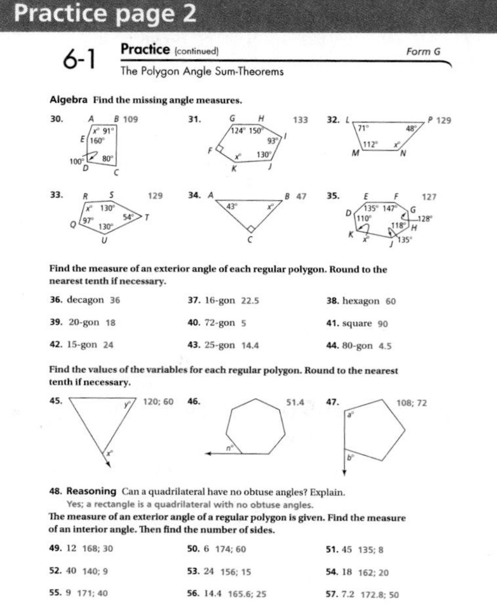

6-1 Practice (continued) — Form G

The Polygon Angle-Sum Theorems

Algebra Find the missing angle measures.

30. 109 31. 133 32. 129

33. 129 34. 47 35. 127

Find the measure of an exterior angle of each regular polygon. Round to the nearest tenth if necessary.

36. decagon 36 37. 16-gon 22.5 38. hexagon 60

39. 20-gon 18 40. 72-gon 5 41. square 90

42. 15-gon 24 43. 25-gon 14.4 44. 80-gon 4.5

Find the values of the variables for each regular polygon. Round to the nearest tenth if necessary.

45. 120; 60 46. 51.4 47. 108; 72

48. Reasoning Can a quadrilateral have no obtuse angles? Explain.
Yes; a rectangle is a quadrilateral with no obtuse angles.

The measure of an exterior angle of a regular polygon is given. Find the measure of an interior angle. Then find the number of sides.

49. 12 168; 30 50. 6 174; 60 51. 45 135; 8

52. 40 140; 9 53. 24 156; 15 54. 18 162; 20

55. 9 171; 40 56. 14.4 165.6; 25 57. 7.2 172.8; 50

Extension

- **Enrichment** Provides students with interesting problems and activities that extend the concepts of the lesson.
- **Activities, Games, and Puzzles** Worksheets that can be used for concepts development, enrichment, and for fun!

All-in-One Resources/Online

Enrichment

6-1 Enrichment

The Polygon Angle-Sum Theorems

Detective

1. A suspect in a case gives the following information:
"I started at point A, then I walked forward 10 paces to B. I made a 60° right turn and walked forward 10 more paces to C. Then I made a 60° right turn and walked forward yet again 10 more paces to D. I stopped to think for a few minutes and decided to make a 120° right turn and walk forward 10 more paces to E. I was a bit confused, so I decided to turn right again 110° and walk 10 more paces to F. Finally, I made one more right turn of 60° and walked forward 10 paces, and guess what? I was exactly where I started from—A!"
Is the suspect telling the truth? Explain how you know. Draw a sketch of the path of the suspect based on the description.
No; with her first two turns the suspect begins to walk a path that would create a regular hexagon and get her back to her original spot in 5 turns. Each 60° right turn is like turning through the *exterior angle* of the hexagon, creating a 120° interior angle. But when she changes her turns to angles other than 60°, she loses her chance of getting back to A as her turns create a sort of spiral.
2. Describe a path that would involve eight turns and would result in returning to the same place as the beginning. Draw a sketch and explain how you know the plan works.
Answers may vary. Sample: The angles of a regular octagon are each 135°. If you walk a path with segments of equal length, that exclusively uses 45° turns in the same direction, you will end up back at the starting point.
3. Describe a path that would involve ten turns and would result in returning to the same place as the beginning. Draw a sketch and explain how you know the plan works.
Answers may vary. Sample: The angles of a regular decagon are each 144°. If you walk a path with segments of equal length, that exclusively uses 36° turns in the same direction, you will eventually end up back at the starting point.
4. An equilateral triangle has three 60° angles. Explain why making three 60° left turns does not produce an equilateral triangle.
Turning left 60° is turning through an exterior angle, which results in a 120° interior angle, not the 60° interior angle needed for an equilateral triangle.

Practice and Problem Solving Wkbk/ All-in-One Resources/Online

Think About a Plan

6-1 Think About a Plan

The Polygon Angle-Sum Theorems

Reasoning Your friend says she has another way to find the sum of the angle measures of a polygon. She picks a point inside the polygon, draws a segment to each vertex, and counts the number of triangles. She multiplies the total by 180, and then subtracts 360 from the product. Does her method work? Explain.

Understanding the Problem

1. According to the Polygon Angle-Sum Theorem, what is the relationship between the number of sides of a polygon and the sum of the measures of the interior angles of a polygon?
The sum is always 180 times two less than the number of sides.
2. How can you write this relationship as an expression in which *n* is the number of sides? $(n - 2)180$

Planning the Solution

3. Mark a point near the center of each figure. Then draw a segment from that point to each vertex as described in the problem.
4. What is the relationship between the number of sides in a polygon and the number of triangles in that polygon?
The number of triangles is the same as the number of sides.
5. What expression can you write to represent multiplying the number of triangles by 180 and then subtracting 360? Let *n* represent the number of sides. Explain how this expression relates to the picture you drew.
$180n - 360$; the sum of the angles in the triangles is 180 times *n*, and this is always 360 (the degrees around the point in the center) more than the sum of the angles in the polygon.

Getting an Answer

6. Can you show that the two expressions you wrote are equal? Explain.
Yes; if you apply the Distributive Property, the expressions become the same.

Practice and Problem Solving Wkbk/ All-in-One Resources/Online

Standardized Test Prep

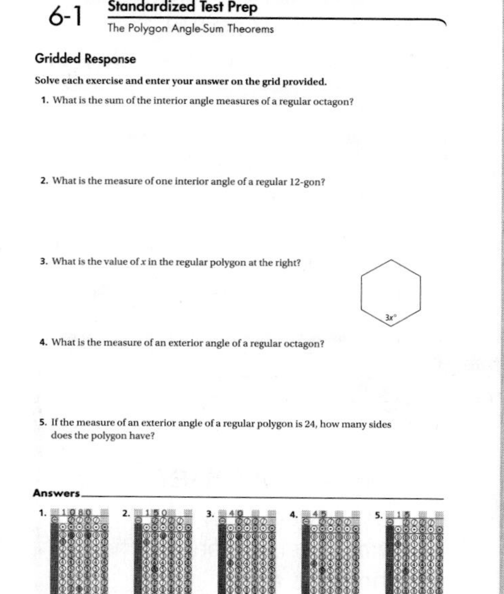

6-1 Standardized Test Prep

The Polygon Angle-Sum Theorems

Gridded Response

Solve each exercise and enter your answer on the grid provided.

1. What is the sum of the interior angle measures of a regular octagon?
2. What is the measure of one interior angle of a regular 12-gon?
3. What is the value of *x* in the regular polygon at the right?
4. What is the measure of an exterior angle of a regular octagon?
5. If the measure of an exterior angle of a regular polygon is 24, how many sides does the polygon have?

Answers

1. 1080 2. 150 3. 40 4. 45 5. 15

Online Teacher Resource Center

Activities, Games, and Puzzles

6-1 Game: I Have . . . Who Has?

The Polygon Angle Sum Theorems

In this game, one student begins the chain by reading his or her "Who Has" question aloud and then waiting for the next participant to read the only "I Have" answer that correctly answers that question. Play continues until the first student reads his or her "I Have."

Materials

- Game strips (one set per group, one strip per student or pair)

Setup

Your teacher will divide the class into two groups. You may be playing alone or with a partner. You will receive a strip of paper that has an "I Have" statement paired with a "Who Has" question at its right.

Game Play

Your teacher will determine the student in each group who has the strip of paper with "**Who Has . . .** the sum of the interior angles of a hexagon?" This student begins the game in his or her group by reading this "Who Has" question. Whoever has the strip with the answer to that "Who Has" replies by announcing their "I Have" to the group. After the correct "I Have" is given, the student reads the "Who Has" from that strip.

Ending the Game

The process repeats until the student who started the game reads the "I Have" on his or her strip. Since the strips are linked, each "Who Has" has exactly one correct answer, and therefore the game will loop back to the first student. Your teacher will collect the strips and save them for future use.

Variations

- Your teacher may choose to time the speed with which you complete the loop, so you can compete with the other group.
- Your teacher may choose to make the game a class challenge by keeping everyone in one large group and having you play several rounds to race against yourselves.
- As a group, make a set of "I Have . . . Who Has" strips with questions similar to the ones in the game you just played. Exchange cards with another group and play the game using that group's cards.

6-2 Properties of Parallelograms

TN State Performance Indicators
SPI 3108.4.3 Identify, describe and/or apply the relationships and theorems involving different types of triangles, quadrilaterals and other polygons.
Also SPI 3108.1.1 and SPI 3108.4.2

Objectives To use relationships among sides and angles of parallelograms
To use relationships among diagonals of parallelograms

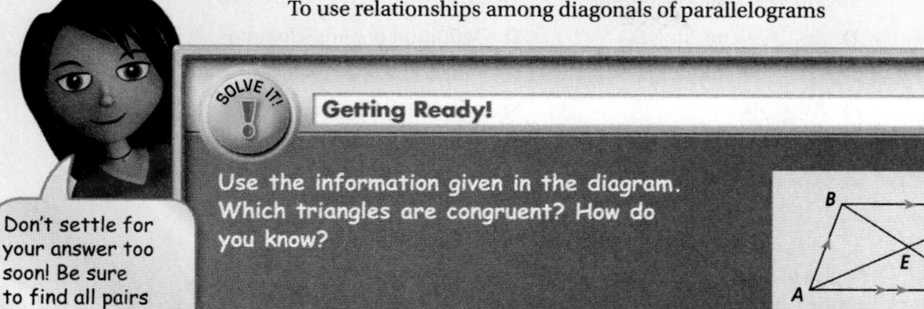

Don't settle for your answer too soon! Be sure to find all pairs of congruent triangles.

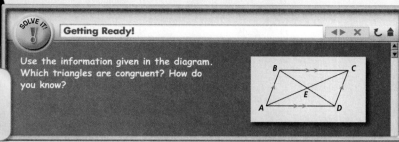

Getting Ready!

Use the information given in the diagram. Which triangles are congruent? How do you know?

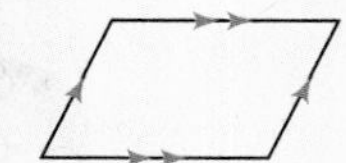

Lesson Vocabulary
- parallelogram
- opposite sides
- opposite angles
- consecutive angles

A **parallelogram** is a quadrilateral with both pairs of opposite sides parallel. In the Solve It, you made some conjectures about the characteristics of a parallelogram. In this lesson, you will verify whether your conjectures are correct.

Essential Understanding Parallelograms have special properties regarding their sides, angles, and diagonals.

In a quadrilateral, **opposite sides** do not share a vertex and **opposite angles** do not share a side.

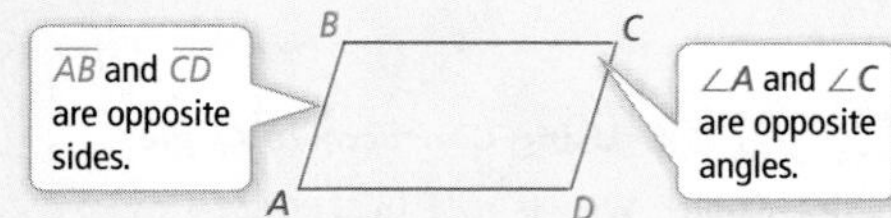

$\overline{AB}$ and $\overline{CD}$ are opposite sides.
$\angle A$ and $\angle C$ are opposite angles.

You can abbreviate *parallelogram* with the symbol ▱ and *parallelograms* with the symbol ▱s. You can use what you know about parallel lines and transversals to prove some theorems about parallelograms.

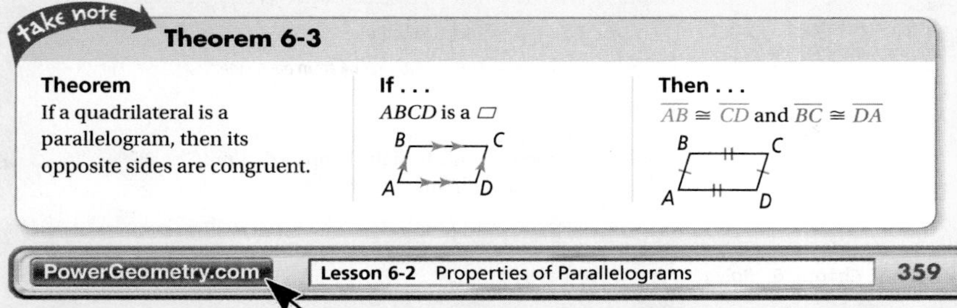

Take note — Theorem 6-3

Theorem	If . . .	Then . . .
If a quadrilateral is a parallelogram, then its opposite sides are congruent.	$ABCD$ is a ▱	$\overline{AB} \cong \overline{CD}$ and $\overline{BC} \cong \overline{DA}$

1 Interactive Learning

Solve It!

PURPOSE To familiarize students with the characteristics of a parallelogram

PROCESS Students may use previous knowledge of congruent triangle theorems and properties of parallel lines.

FACILITATE

Q Are there any angles in the diagram that you know are congruent? Explain. **[Yes, vertical angles and alternate interior angles are congruent.]**

Q Can you make a conjecture about the congruence of any segments? Explain. **[Yes, The opposite sides appear congruent and the diagonals appear to bisect each other.]**

Q Based on your conjectures, what triangle congruence theorems might you use to determine congruent triangles? **[ASA and AAS]**

ANSWER See Solve It in Answers on next page.

CONNECT THE MATH In the Solve It, students identify congruent angles and make conjectures about congruent segments. In the lesson, students learn properties of parallelograms and theorems related to quadrilaterals.

2 Guided Instruction

Take Note

Some students may ask if a quadrilateral in which all sides are congruent rather than just opposite sides being congruent is also considered a parallelogram. This special case will be considered in subsequent lessons.

6-2 Preparing to Teach

BIG idea Reasoning and Proof UbD

ESSENTIAL UNDERSTANDINGS
- Parallelograms have special properties regarding their sides, angles, and diagonals.
- Parallelograms can be used to prove theorems about parallel lines and their transversals.

Math Background

The study of polygons is a study of hierarchy. Quadrilaterals are a subset of polygons and parallelograms are a subset of quadrilaterals. Thus parallelograms have all properties of polygons and quadrilaterals as well as special properties of their own. Parallelograms themselves contain several subsets. Each of these subsets will have all properties of polygons, quadrilaterals, and parallelograms.

Remind students that they have seen properties similar to those in this lesson in Chapter 4 when studying congruent triangles. Exploring such properties can be made easier by using geometry software.

Support Student Learning

Use the **Geometry Companion** to engage and support students during instructions. See Lesson Resources at the end of this lesson for details.

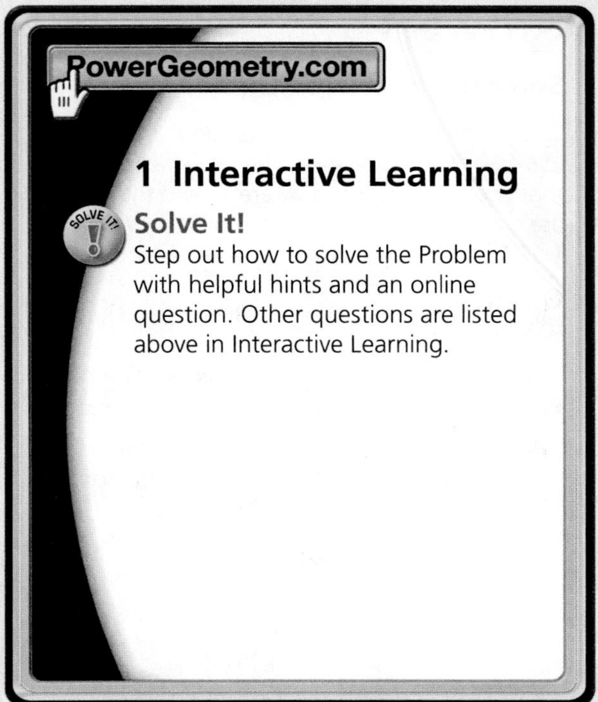

PowerGeometry.com
1 Interactive Learning
Solve It!
Step out how to solve the Problem with helpful hints and an online question. Other questions are listed above in Interactive Learning.

Because you are given that *ABCD* is a parallelogram, you know that 2 pairs of segments are parallel. Therefore, the diagonal of the parallelogram can serve as a transversal.

Proof of Theorem 6-3

Given: $\square ABCD$

Prove: $\overline{AB} \cong \overline{CD}$ and $\overline{BC} \cong \overline{DA}$

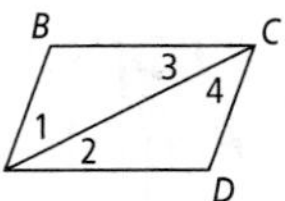

Statements	Reasons
1) *ABCD* is a parallelogram.	1) Given
2) $\overline{AB} \parallel \overline{CD}$ and $\overline{BC} \parallel \overline{DA}$	2) Definition of parallelogram
3) $\angle 1 \cong \angle 4$ and $\angle 3 \cong \angle 2$	3) If lines are $\parallel$, then alt. int. $\angle$s are $\cong$.
4) $\overline{AC} \cong \overline{AC}$	4) Reflexive Property of $\cong$
5) $\triangle ABC \cong \triangle CDA$	5) ASA
6) $\overline{AB} \cong \overline{CD}$ and $\overline{BC} \cong \overline{DA}$	6) Corresp. parts of $\cong$ $\triangle$s are $\cong$.

Angles of a polygon that share a side are **consecutive angles.** In the diagram, $\angle A$ and $\angle B$ are consecutive angles because they share side $\overline{AB}$.

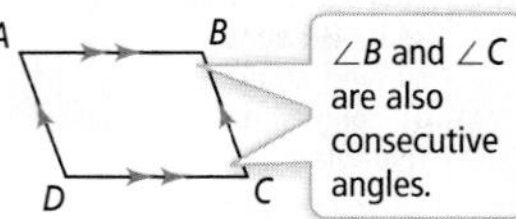

The theorem below uses the fact that consecutive angles of a parallelogram are same-side interior angles of parallel lines.

Take Note TACTILE LEARNERS

Have students cut out two identical parallelograms. Students can use the parallelograms to "test" the supplementary relationship of the consecutive angles.

take note: Theorem 6-4

Theorem	If . . .	Then . . .
If a quadrilateral is a parallelogram, then its consecutive angles are supplementary.	*ABCD* is a $\square$ 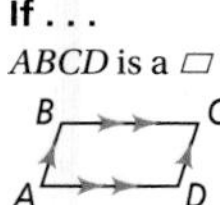	$m\angle A + m\angle B = 180$ $m\angle B + m\angle C = 180$ $m\angle C + m\angle D = 180$ $m\angle D + m\angle A = 180$

You will prove Theorem 6-4 in Exercise 32.

Problem 1

Q How are $\angle S$ and $\angle P$ related? **[They are consecutive angles of a parallelogram. They are supplementary.]**

Q What other angle in the diagram is also supplementary to $\angle S$ and is therefore congruent to $\angle P$? **[$\angle R$]**

Got It?

Q What is the relationship of $\angle S$ and $\angle R$? Explain. **[The angles are consecutive angles and therefore are supplementary.]**

Problem 1 Using Consecutive Angles

Plan

What information from the diagram helps you get started? From the diagram, you know $m\angle PSR$ and that $\angle P$ and $\angle PSR$ are consecutive angles. So, you can *write an equation* and solve for $m\angle P$.

Multiple Choice What is $m\angle P$ in $\square PQRS$?

Ⓐ 26 Ⓑ 64 Ⓒ 116 Ⓓ 126

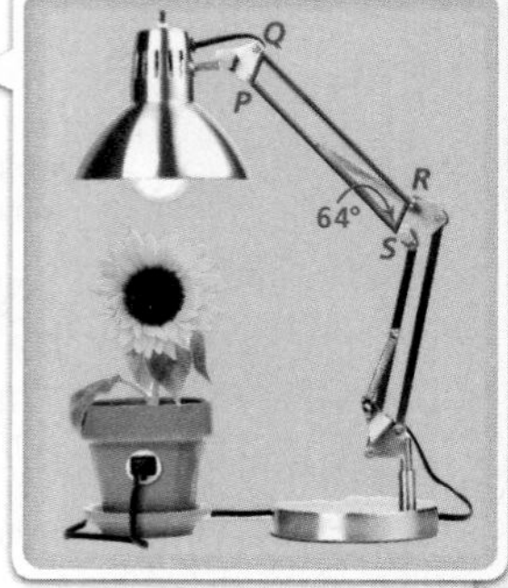

$m\angle P + m\angle S = 180$ Consecutive angles of a $\square$ are suppl.

$m\angle P + 64 = 180$ Substitute.

$m\angle P = 116$ Subtract 64 from each side.

The correct answer is C.

Got It? 1. Suppose you adjust the lamp so that $m\angle S = 86$. What is $m\angle R$ in $\square PQRS$?

Answers

Solve It!

You can show $\triangle BAD \cong \triangle DCB$ and $\triangle BAC \cong \triangle DCA$ by ASA. Then you can use the fact that corresp. parts of $\cong$ $\triangle$s are $\cong$ and that vert. $\angle$s are $\cong$ to show that $\triangle ABE \cong \triangle CDE$ by ASA or AAS, and $\triangle BCE \cong \triangle DAE$ by ASA, AAS, or SAS.

Got It?

1. 94

2. 1. *ABCD* is a $\square$ and $\overline{AK} \cong \overline{MK}$. (Given)
2. $\angle A \cong \angle BCD$ (Opp. $\angle$s of a $\square$ are $\cong$.)
3. $\angle A \cong \angle CMD$ (Isosc. $\triangle$ Theorem)
4. $\angle BCD \cong \angle CMD$ (Transitive Prop. of $\cong$)

PowerGeometry.com

2 Guided Instruction

Each Problem is worked out and supported online.

Problem 1
Using Consecutive Angles

Problem 2
Using Properties of Parallelograms in a Proof
Animated

Problem 3
Using Algebra to Find Lengths
Animated

Problem 4
Using Parallel Lines and Transversals
Animated

Support in Geometry Companion
- Vocabulary
- Key Concepts
- Got It?

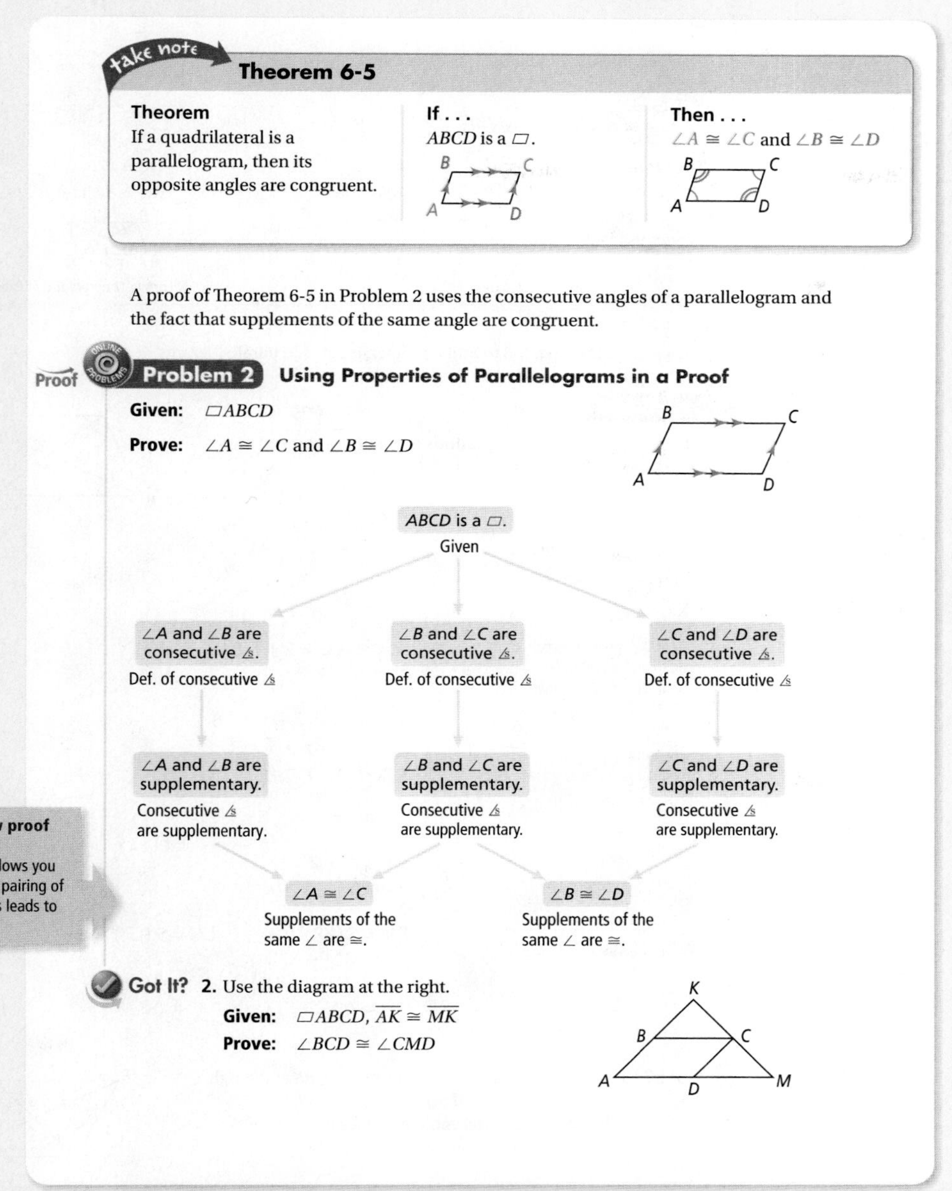

take note

Theorem 6-5

Theorem	If . . .	Then . . .
If a quadrilateral is a parallelogram, then its opposite angles are congruent.	$ABCD$ is a ▱.	$\angle A \cong \angle C$ and $\angle B \cong \angle D$

A proof of Theorem 6-5 in Problem 2 uses the consecutive angles of a parallelogram and the fact that supplements of the same angle are congruent.

Proof **Problem 2** **Using Properties of Parallelograms in a Proof**

Given: ▱$ABCD$

Prove: $\angle A \cong \angle C$ and $\angle B \cong \angle D$

$ABCD$ is a ▱.
Given

$\angle A$ and $\angle B$ are consecutive ∠s.
Def. of consecutive ∠s

$\angle B$ and $\angle C$ are consecutive ∠s.
Def. of consecutive ∠s

$\angle C$ and $\angle D$ are consecutive ∠s.
Def. of consecutive ∠s

$\angle A$ and $\angle B$ are supplementary.
Consecutive ∠s are supplementary.

$\angle B$ and $\angle C$ are supplementary.
Consecutive ∠s are supplementary.

$\angle C$ and $\angle D$ are supplementary.
Consecutive ∠s are supplementary.

$\angle A \cong \angle C$
Supplements of the same ∠ are ≅.

$\angle B \cong \angle D$
Supplements of the same ∠ are ≅.

Think
Why is a flow proof useful here?
A flow proof allows you to see how the pairing of two statements leads to a conclusion.

Got It? **2.** Use the diagram at the right.

Given: ▱$ABCD$, $\overline{AK} \cong \overline{MK}$

Prove: $\angle BCD \cong \angle CMD$

Take Note

Make sure that students understand that consecutive angles are angles that share a side, while opposite angles are angles that do not share a side.

Problem 2

Show students that Theorem 6-5 could also be proved similarly to the way Theorem 6-3 was proved using congruent triangles.

Q Does the order of the boxes in the second row of the flow proof matter? Can they be interchanged? **[no; yes]**

Q If the order of these boxes is changed, what must change accordingly? Explain. **[The order of the boxes in the third row; the box stating the angles are consecutive must connect to the box stating the same angles are supplementary.]**

Got It?

ERROR PREVENTION

If students have trouble constructing the proof, tell them to make sure that they identify the isosceles triangle in the diagram.

Additional Problems

1. What is $m\angle R$ in ▱$RSTU$?

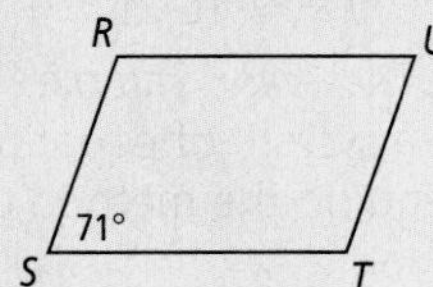

A. 109

B. 99

C. 81

D. 71

ANSWER A

2. Given: ▱$ABCD$ and ▱$NMLB$

Prove: $\angle M \cong \angle D$

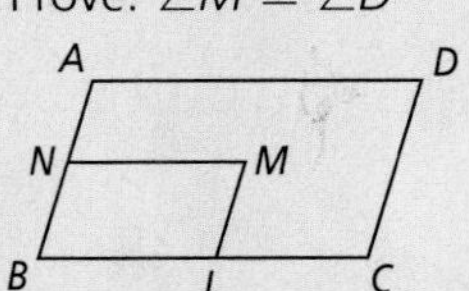

ANSWER It is given that $ABCD$ and $NMLB$ are parallelograms. So their opposite angles are congruent. That is, $\angle B \cong \angle M$ and $\angle B \cong \angle D$. So, by the Transitive Property of Congruence, $\angle M \cong \angle D$.

3. Solve a system of linear equations to find the values of a and b in ▱$HIJK$. What are HJ and IK?

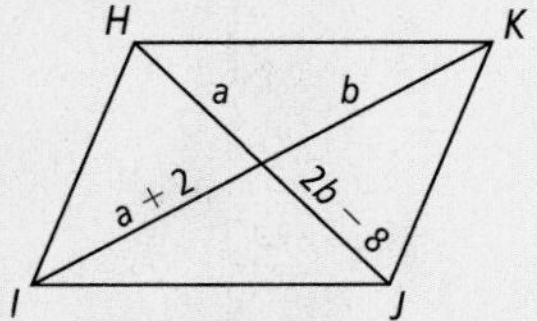

ANSWER $HJ = 8$, $IK = 12$

4. In the figure below, $\overline{RW} \parallel \overline{SV}$ and $\overline{SV} \parallel \overline{TU}$. If $RS = ST = 5$ and $WV = 7$, what is WU?

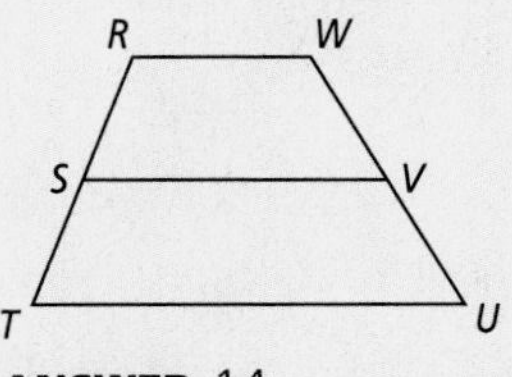

ANSWER 14

Take Note

Make certain that students realize what relationships this theorem describes and does not describe. While the segments created by the intersection of the diagonals are congruent, the diagonals themselves are not congruent.

Problem 3

Q What theorem allows you to write $KP = MP$ and $LP = NP$? **[Theorem 6-6]**

Q Can you substitute 14 for y in equation 2 to determine the value of x? Explain. **[Yes, the solution is the common ordered pair of both equations.]**

Q What other methods are available for solving the system of equations? **[graphing method or elimination method]**

Q What are three algebraic expressions that represent KM? LN? **[KM: $2(y + 10)$, $y + 2x + 2$, $2(2x - 8)$; LN: $2x$, $2(y + 2)$, $x + y + 2$]**

Got It?

ERROR PREVENTION

In 3a, if students give answers of 4 and 5, then they likely thought they had finished the problem once they had solved the system of equations. Tell students to make sure that they use the values of x and y to determine PR and SQ.

The diagonals of parallelograms have a special property.

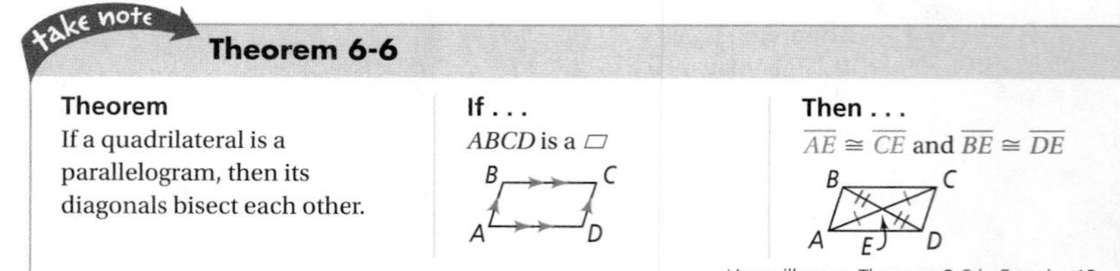

Take note — Theorem 6-6

Theorem	If . . .	Then . . .
If a quadrilateral is a parallelogram, then its diagonals bisect each other.	$ABCD$ is a ▱	$\overline{AE} \cong \overline{CE}$ and $\overline{BE} \cong \overline{DE}$

You will prove Theorem 6-6 in Exercise 13.

You can use Theorem 6-6 to find unknown lengths in parallelograms.

Problem 3 Using Algebra to Find Lengths

Solve a system of linear equations to find the values of x and y in ▱$KLMN$. What are KM and LN?

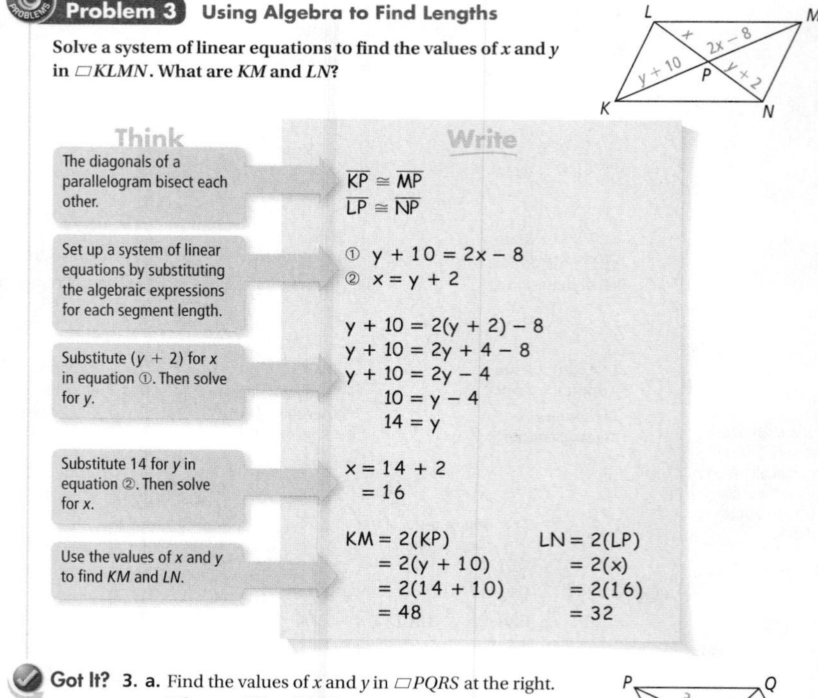

Think	Write
The diagonals of a parallelogram bisect each other.	$\overline{KP} \cong \overline{MP}$ $\overline{LP} \cong \overline{NP}$
Set up a system of linear equations by substituting the algebraic expressions for each segment length.	① $y + 10 = 2x - 8$ ② $x = y + 2$
Substitute $(y + 2)$ for x in equation ①. Then solve for y.	$y + 10 = 2(y + 2) - 8$ $y + 10 = 2y + 4 - 8$ $y + 10 = 2y - 4$ $10 = y - 4$ $14 = y$
Substitute 14 for y in equation ②. Then solve for x.	$x = 14 + 2$ $= 16$
Use the values of x and y to find KM and LN.	$KM = 2(KP) = 2(y + 10) = 2(14 + 10) = 48$ $LN = 2(LP) = 2(x) = 2(16) = 32$

Got It? 3. a. Find the values of x and y in ▱$PQRS$ at the right. What are PR and SQ?

b. Reasoning In Problem 3, does it matter which variable you solve for first? Explain.

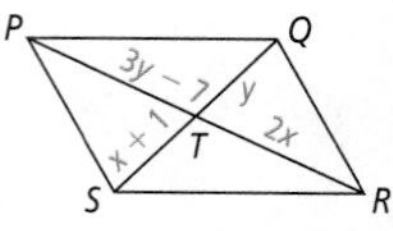

Answers

Got It? (continued)

3a. $x = 4$, $y = 5$, $PR = 16$, $SQ = 10$

b. No; answers may vary. Sample: Solutions to a system of equations do not depend on the method used to solve it.

4. 5

You will use parallelograms to prove the following theorem.

take note

Theorem 6-7

Theorem	If ...	Then ...
If three (or more) parallel lines cut off congruent segments on one transversal, then they cut off congruent segments on every transversal.	$\overleftrightarrow{AB} \parallel \overleftrightarrow{CD} \parallel \overleftrightarrow{EF}$ and $\overline{AC} \cong \overline{CE}$ 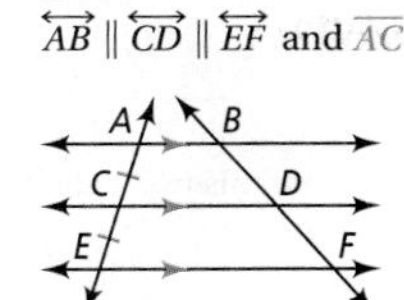	$\overline{BD} \cong \overline{DF}$ 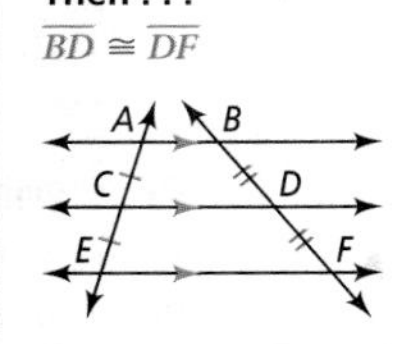

You will prove Theorem 6-7 in Exercise 43.

Problem 4 Using Parallel Lines and Transversals

Plan

What information do you need?
You know the length of $\overline{EF}$. To find EH, you need the lengths of $\overline{FG}$ and $\overline{GH}$.

In the figure, $\overleftrightarrow{AE} \parallel \overleftrightarrow{BF} \parallel \overleftrightarrow{CG} \parallel \overleftrightarrow{DH}$, $AB = BC = CD = 2$, and $EF = 2.25$. What is EH?

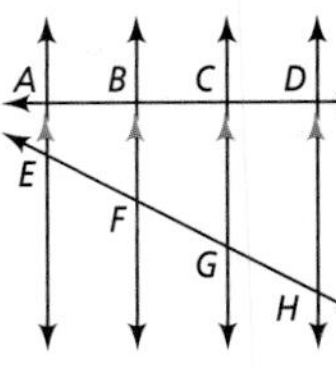

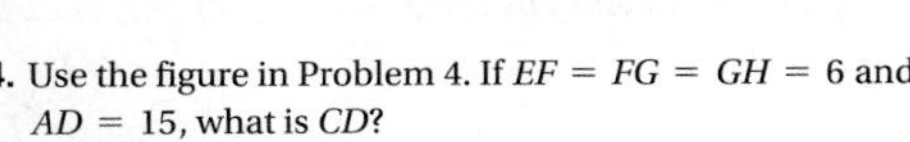

$EF = FG = GH$ — Since $\parallel$ lines divide $\overline{AD}$ into equal parts, they also divide $\overline{EH}$ into equal parts.

$EH = EF + FG + GH$ — Segment Addition Postulate

$EH = 2.25 + 2.25 + 2.25 = 6.75$ — Substitute.

Got It? 4. Use the figure in Problem 4. If $EF = FG = GH = 6$ and $AD = 15$, what is CD?

Lesson Check

Do you know HOW?

Use the diagram of $\square ABCD$ to find each value.

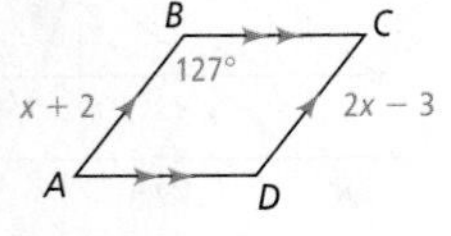

1. $m\angle A$
2. $m\angle D$
3. x
4. AB
5. What are ED and FD in the figure at the right?

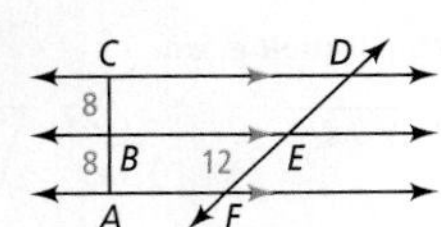

Do you UNDERSTAND?

6. **Reasoning** If you know one angle measure of a parallelogram, how do you find the other three angle measures? Explain.
7. **Compare and Contrast** What is the difference between a quadrilateral and a parallelogram?
8. **Error Analysis** Your classmate says that $QV = 10$. Explain why the statement may not be correct.

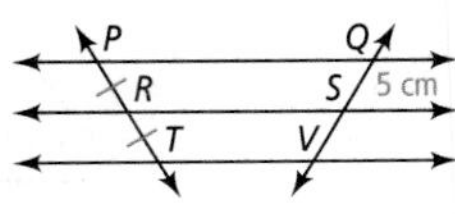

Take Note

The Theorem states that if $\overline{AC} \cong \overline{CE}$, then $\overline{BD} \cong \overline{DF}$, not that $\overline{AC} \cong \overline{BD}$ or $\overline{CE} \cong \overline{DF}$.

Problem 4

Q What does the Segment Addition Postulate state? **[The sum of all lengths of the parts of a segment equals the length of the segment.]**

Q What segment addition equation can be used to find AD? **[$AD = AB + BC + CD$]**

Got It?

Q Does $AB = BC = CD$? Explain. **[Yes, if the segments cut from the transversal $\overleftrightarrow{EH}$ are congruent, the segments cut from the transversal $\overleftrightarrow{AD}$ are also congruent.]**

3 Lesson Check

Do you know HOW?

- If students have difficulty with Exercises 1-2, then have them review Problem 1 to learn which angles are consecutive and what that means in terms of writing an equation.

Do you UNDERSTAND?

- If students have difficulty with Exercise 7, then have them make sketches of both shapes.

Close

Q What are the distinguishing properties of a parallelogram? **[In a parallelogram, opposite sides are congruent and parallel, opposite angles are congruent, consecutive angles are supplementary, and diagonals bisect each other.]**

Lesson Check

1. 53
2. 127
3. 5
4. 7
5. $ED = 12$, $FD = 24$
6. Answers may vary. Sample: The ∠ opposite the given ∠ is congruent to it. The other two ∠s and the given ∠ are consecutive ∠s, so they are supplements of the given ∠.
7. A quad. and a ▱ both have four sides, but if both pairs of opp. sides are ∥, then the figure is a ▱.
8. It is not given that $\overleftrightarrow{PQ}$, $\overleftrightarrow{RS}$, and $\overleftrightarrow{TV}$ are ∥.

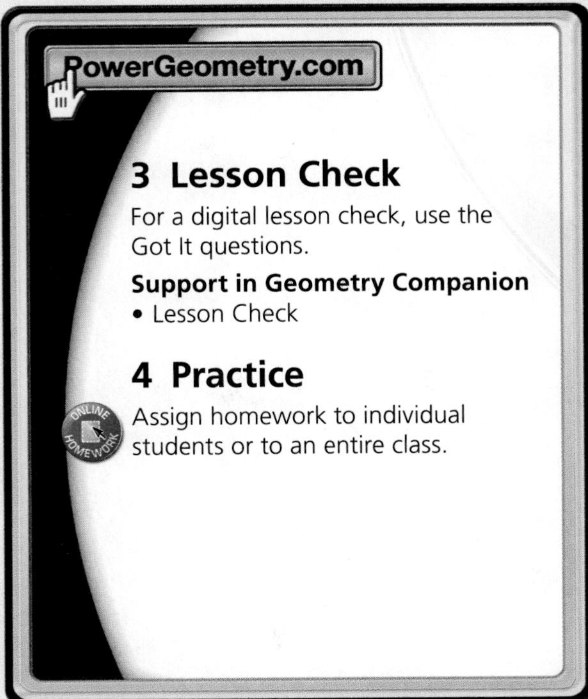

4 Practice

ASSIGNMENT GUIDE

Basic: 9–24, 28, 30–31, 38–41
Average: 9–23 odd, 25–41
Advanced: 9–23 odd, 25–44
Standardized Test Prep: 45–48
Mixed Review: 49–54

Reasoning exercises have blue headings.
Applications exercises have red headings.

EXERCISE 41: Use the Think About a Plan worksheet in the **Practice and Problem Solving Workbook** (also available in the Teaching Resources in print and online) to further support students' development in becoming independent learners.

HOMEWORK QUICK CHECK

To check students' understanding of key skills and concepts, go over Exercises 13, 15, 28, 30, and 41.

Practice and Problem-Solving Exercises

A Practice

Algebra Find the value of x in each parallelogram.

See Problem 1.

9.

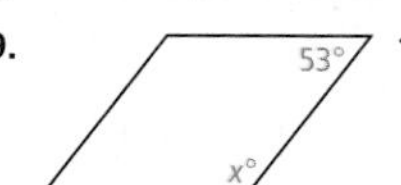

10.

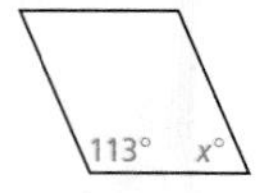

11.

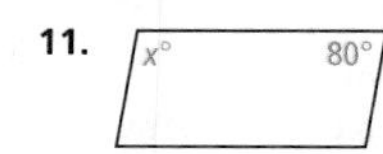

12.

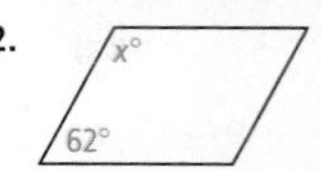

13. Developing Proof Complete this two-column proof of Theorem 6-6.

See Problem 2.

Given: ▱$ABCD$

Prove: $\overline{AC}$ and $\overline{BD}$ bisect each other at E.

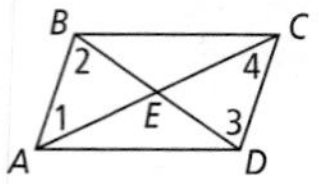

Statements	Reasons
1) $ABCD$ is a parallelogram.	1) Given
2) $\overline{AB} \parallel \overline{DC}$	2) a. ?
3) $\angle 1 \cong \angle 4$; $\angle 2 \cong \angle 3$	3) b. ?
4) $\overline{AB} \cong \overline{DC}$	4) c. ?
5) d. ?	5) ASA
6) $\overline{AE} \cong \overline{CE}$; $\overline{BE} \cong \overline{DE}$	6) e. ?
7) f. ?	7) Definition of bisector

Algebra Find the values of x and y in ▱$PQRS$.

See Problem 3.

14. $PT = 2x$, $TR = y + 4$, $QT = x + 2$, $TS = y$

15. $PT = x + 2$, $TR = y$, $QT = 2x$, $TS = y + 3$

16. $PT = y$, $TR = x + 3$, $QT = 2y$, $TS = 3x - 1$

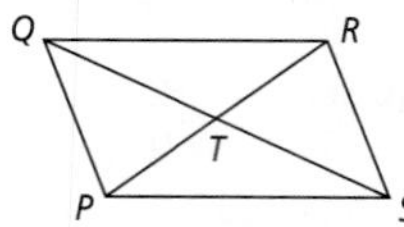

In the figure, $PQ = QR = RS$. Find each length.

See Problem 4.

17. ZU	**18.** XZ
19. TU	**20.** XV
21. YX	**22.** YV
23. WX	**24.** WV

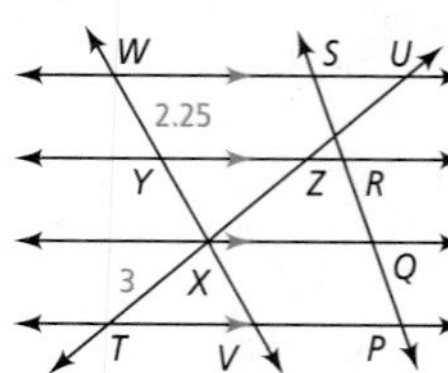

B Apply

Algebra Find the value(s) of the variable(s) in each parallelogram.

25.

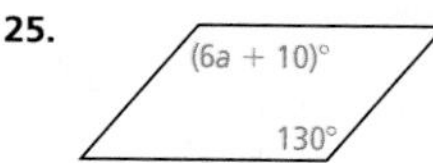

26.

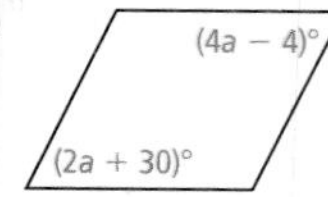

27.

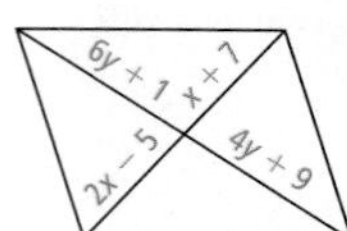

Answers

Practice and Problem-Solving Exercises

9. 127
10. 67
11. 100
12. 118
13a. Def. of ▱
b. If lines are ∥, then alt. int. ∠s are ≅.
c. Opp. sides of a ▱ are ≅.
d. $\triangle ABE \cong \triangle CDE$
e. Corresp. parts of ≅ △s are ≅.
f. $\overline{AC}$ and $\overline{BD}$ bisect each other at E.
14. $x = 6$, $y = 8$
15. $x = 5$, $y = 7$
16. $x = 7$, $y = 10$
17. 3
18. 3
19. 9
20. 2.25
21. 2.25
22. 4.5
23. 4.5
24. 6.75
25. 20
26. 17
27. $x = 12$, $y = 4$

28. Think About a Plan What are the values of x and y in the parallelogram?
- How are the angles related?
- Which variable should you solve for first?

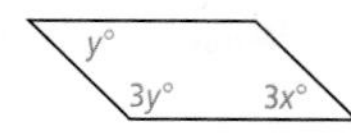

Algebra **Find the value of a. Then find each side length or angle measure.**

29.

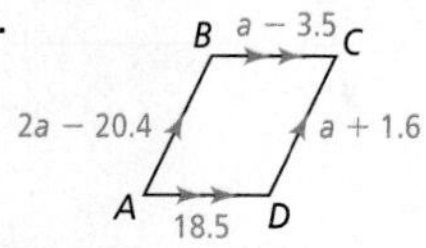

30.

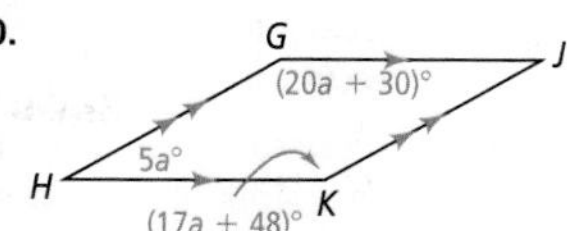

31. Studio Lighting A pantograph is an expandable device shown at the right. Pantographs are used in the television industry in positioning lighting and other equipment. In the photo, points D, E, F, and G are the vertices of a parallelogram. $\square DEFG$ is one of many parallelograms that change shape as the pantograph extends and retracts.

a. If $DE = 2.5$ ft, what is FG? b. If $m\angle E = 129$, what is $m\angle G$?

c. What happens to $m\angle D$ as $m\angle E$ increases or decreases? Explain.

32. Prove Theorem 6-4.

Proof

Given: $\square ABCD$

Prove: $\angle A$ is supplementary to $\angle B$.
$\angle A$ is supplementary to $\angle D$.

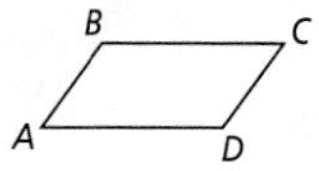

Use the diagram at the right for each proof.

Proof

33. Given: $\square LENS$ and $\square NGTH$
Prove: $\angle L \cong \angle T$

34. Given: $\square LENS$ and $\square NGTH$
Prove: $\overline{LS} \parallel \overline{GT}$

35. Given: $\square LENS$ and $\square NGTH$
Prove: $\angle E$ is supplementary to $\angle T$.

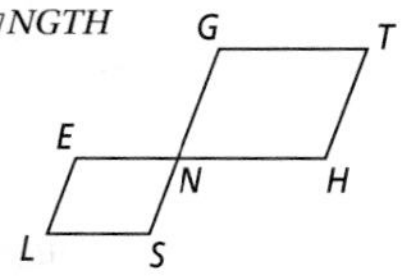

Use the diagram at the right for each proof.

Proof

36. Given: $\square RSTW$ and $\square XYTZ$
Prove: $\angle R \cong \angle X$

37. Given: $\square RSTW$ and $\square XYTZ$
Prove: $\overline{XY} \parallel \overline{RS}$

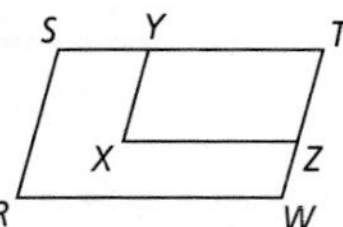

Find the measures of the numbered angles for each parallelogram.

38.

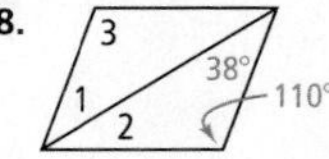

39.

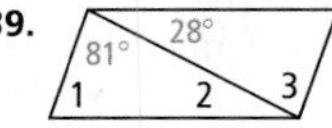

40.

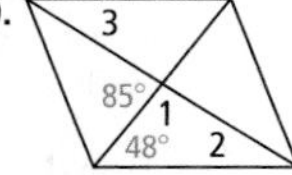

41. Algebra The perimeter of $\square ABCD$ is 92 cm. AD is 7 cm more than twice AB. Find the lengths of all four sides of $\square ABCD$.

28. $x = 15$, $y = 45$

29. 22, $AB = 23.6$, $BC = 18.5$, $CD = 23.6$, $AD = 18.5$

30. 6, $m\angle H = 30$, $m\angle G = 150$, $m\angle J = 30$, $m\angle K = 150$

31a. 2.5 ft

b. 129

c. Answers may vary. Sample: As $m\angle E$ increases, $m\angle D$ decreases. $\angle E$ and $\angle D$ are suppl.

32. 1. $\square ABCD$ (Given)
2. $\overline{AB} \parallel \overline{CD}$ and $\overline{BC} \parallel \overline{DA}$. (Def. of a $\square$)
3. $\angle A$ is suppl. to $\angle B$ and $\angle A$ is suppl. to $\angle D$. (Same-side int. $\angle$s are suppl.)

33. Answers may vary. Sample:
1. $\square$ $LENS$ and $NGTH$ (Given)
2. $\angle L \cong \angle ENS$ and $\angle GNH \cong \angle T$. (Opp. $\angle$s of a $\square$ are $\cong$.)
3. $\angle ENS \cong \angle GNH$ (Vert. $\angle$s are $\cong$.)
4. $\angle L \cong \angle T$ (Transitive Prop. of $\cong$)

34. Answers may vary. Sample:
1. $\square$ $LENS$ and $NGTH$ (Given)
2. $\overline{LS} \parallel \overline{EN}$ and $\overline{NH} \parallel \overline{GT}$. (Def. of $\square$)
3. $\overline{LS} \parallel \overline{GT}$ (If two lines are $\parallel$ to the same line, then they are $\parallel$ to each other.)

35. Answers may vary. Sample:
1. $\square$ $LENS$ and $NGTH$ (Given)
2. $\angle E$ is suppl. to $\angle ENS$. (Consecutive $\angle$s in a $\square$ are suppl.)
3. $\angle GNH \cong \angle ENS$ (Vert. $\angle$s are $\cong$.)
4. $\angle GNH \cong \angle T$ (Opp. $\angle$s of a $\square$ are $\cong$.)
5. $\angle ENS \cong \angle T$ (Transitive Prop. of $\cong$)
6. $\angle E$ is suppl. to $\angle T$. (Substitution Prop.)

36. Answers may vary. Sample:
1. $\square$ $RSTW$ and $XYTZ$ (Given)
2. $\angle R \cong \angle T$ and $\angle T \cong \angle X$. (Opp. $\angle$s of a $\square$ are $\cong$.)
3. $\angle R \cong \angle X$ (Transitive Prop. of $\cong$)

37. 1. $\square$ $RSTW$ and $XYTZ$ (Given)
2. $\overline{XY} \parallel \overline{TZ}$ and $\overline{TZ} \parallel \overline{RS}$. (Def. of $\square$)
3. $\overline{XY} \parallel \overline{RS}$ (If two lines are $\parallel$ to the same line, then they are $\parallel$ to each other.)

38. $m\angle 1 = 38$, $m\angle 2 = 32$, $m\angle 3 = 110$

39. $m\angle 1 = 71$, $m\angle 2 = 28$, $m\angle 3 = 81$

40. $m\angle 1 = 95$, $m\angle 2 = 37$, $m\angle 3 = 37$

41. $AB = CD = 13$, $BC = AD = 33$

Answers

Practice and Problem-Solving Exercises (continued)

42. No; answers may vary. Sample: Corresponding sides ≅ does not prove ▱s ≅.

43. Answers may vary. Sample:

1. $\overline{AB} \parallel \overline{CD}$, $\overline{CD} \parallel \overline{EF}$ (Given)
2. $\overline{BG} \parallel \overline{AC}$, $\overline{DH} \parallel \overline{CE}$ (Construction)
3. *ABGC* and *CDHE* are ▱s. (Def. of ▱)
4. $\overline{AC} \cong \overline{BG}$, $\overline{CE} \cong \overline{DH}$ (Opp. sides of a ▱ are ≅.)
5. $\overline{AC} \cong \overline{CE}$ (Given)
6. $\overline{BG} \cong \overline{DH}$ (Trans. Prop. of ≅)
7. $\overline{BG} \parallel \overline{DH}$ (If two lines are ∥ to the same line, then they are ∥ to each other.)
8. $\angle 3 \cong \angle 6$ and $\angle GBD \cong \angle HDF$. (If lines are ∥, corresp. ∠s are ≅.)
9. $\triangle GBD \cong \triangle HDF$ (AAS)
10. $\overline{BD} \cong \overline{DF}$ (Corresp. parts of ≅ ▵s are ≅.)

44. Answers may vary. Sample: The lines of the paper are ∥ and equally spaced. Place the right corner of the top edge of the card on the first line of the paper. Place the right corner of the bottom edge on the fourth line. Mark the points where the second and third lines intersect the card. The marks will be equally spaced because the edge of the card is a transversal for the equally spaced ∥ lines of the paper. Repeat for the left side of the card. Connect the marks using a straightedge.

45. D

46. G

47. C

48. [2] 60; sample explanation: A hexagon has 6 sides, so exterior ∠ measure $= \frac{360}{6} = 60$.

[1] correct answer, without work shown

49. 1440

50. 2520

51. 4140

52. 6840

53. $\overline{AC} \perp \overline{DB}$ (or ∠*ACD* and ∠*ACB* are rt. ∠s)

54. 42

Challenge

42. Writing Is there an SSSS congruence theorem for parallelograms? Explain.

43. Prove Theorem 6-7. Use the diagram at the right.

Proof

Given: $\overleftrightarrow{AB} \parallel \overleftrightarrow{CD} \parallel \overleftrightarrow{EF}$, $\overline{AC} \cong \overline{CE}$

Prove: $\overline{BD} \cong \overline{DF}$

(*Hint:* Draw lines through *B* and *D* parallel to $\overleftrightarrow{AE}$ and intersecting $\overleftrightarrow{CD}$ at *G* and $\overleftrightarrow{EF}$ at *H*.)

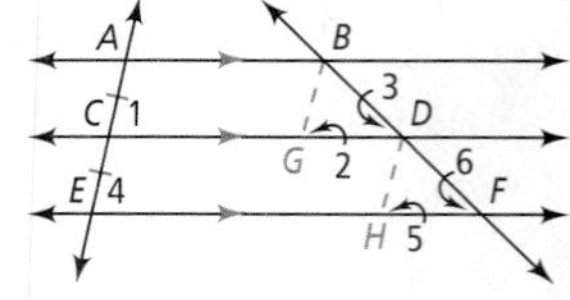

44. Measurement Explain how to separate a blank card into three strips that are the same height by using lined paper, a straightedge, and Theorem 6-7.

Standardized Test Prep

SAT/ACT

45. *PQRS* is a parallelogram with $m\angle Q = 4x$ and $m\angle R = x + 10$. Which statement explains why you can use the equation $4x + (x + 10) = 180$ to solve for *x*?

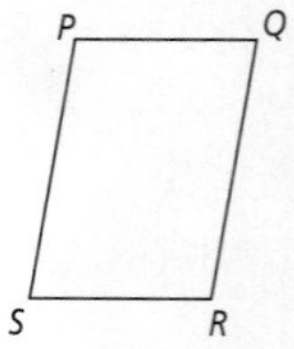

- (A) The measures of the interior angles of a quadrilateral have a sum of 360.
- (B) Opposite sides of a parallelogram are congruent.
- (C) Opposite angles of a parallelogram are congruent.
- (D) Consecutive angles of a parallelogram are supplementary.

46. In the figure of *DEFG* at the right, $\overline{DE} \parallel \overline{GF}$. Which statement must be true?

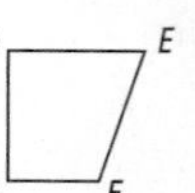

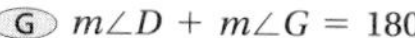

- (F) $m\angle D + m\angle E = 180$
- (H) $\overline{DE} \cong \overline{GF}$
- (G) $m\angle D + m\angle G = 180$
- (I) $\overline{DG} \cong \overline{EF}$

47. An obtuse triangle has side lengths of 5 cm, 9 cm, and 12 cm. What is the length of the side opposite the obtuse angle?

- (A) 5 cm
- (B) 9 cm
- (C) 12 cm
- (D) not enough information

Short Response

48. Find the measure of one exterior angle of a regular hexagon. Explain your method.

Mixed Review

Find the sum of the measures of the interior angles of each polygon. See Lesson 6-1.

49. decagon **50.** 16-gon **51.** 25-gon **52.** 40-gon

53. What additional information do you need to prove $\triangle ADC \cong \triangle ABC$ by the HL Theorem? See Lesson 4-6.

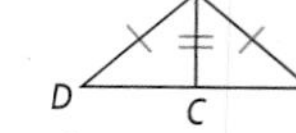

Get Ready! **To prepare for Lesson 6-3, do Exercise 54.**

54. Two consecutive angles in a parallelogram have measures $x + 5$ and $4x - 10$. Find the measure of the smaller angle. See Lesson 6-2.

6-2 Lesson Resources

Differentiated Remediation

Instructional Support

Geometry Companion

Students can use the **Geometry Companion** worktext (4 pages) . . .

- New Vocabulary
- Key Concepts
- Got It for each Problem
- Lesson Check

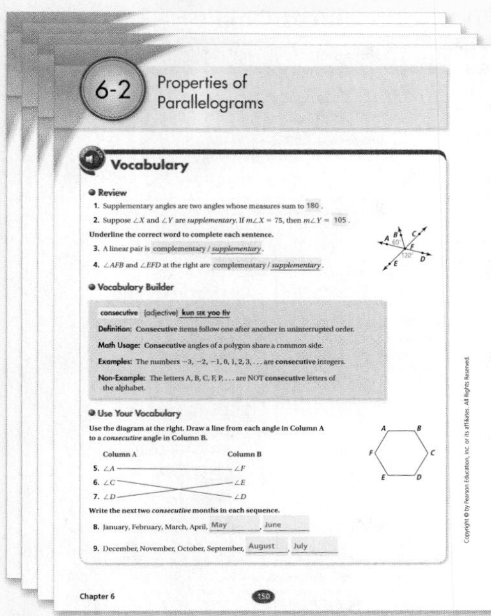

6-2 Properties of Parallelograms

Vocabulary

Review

1. Supplementary angles are two angles whose measures sum to 180.
2. Suppose $\angle X$ and $\angle Y$ are *supplementary*. If $m\angle X = 75$, then $m\angle Y = 105$.

Underline the correct word to complete each sentence.

3. A linear pair is complementary / *supplementary*.
4. $\angle AFB$ and $\angle EFD$ at the right are complementary / *supplementary*.

Vocabulary Builder

consecutive (adjective) kun SEK yoo tiv

Definition: **Consecutive** items follow one after another in uninterrupted order.

Math Usage: **Consecutive** angles of a polygon share a common side.

Examples: The numbers −3, −2, −1, 0, 1, 2, 3, . . . are **consecutive** integers.

Non-Example: The letters A, B, C, F, P, . . . are NOT **consecutive** letters of the alphabet.

Use Your Vocabulary

Use the diagram at the right. Draw a line from each angle in Column A to a *consecutive* angle in Column B.

Column A	Column B
5. $\angle A$	$\angle F$
6. $\angle C$	$\angle E$
7. $\angle D$	$\angle D$

Write the next two *consecutive* months in each sequence.

8. January, February, March, April, May, June
9. December, November, October, September, August, July

Chapter 6 150

Copyright © by Pearson Education, Inc. or its affiliates. All Rights Reserved.

ELL Support

Focus on Language Explore the word *opposite*. Ask: What other words sound like *opposite*? (*opposing*, *oppositional*) As a noun, *opposite* means a person or thing that is contrary. As an adjective, *opposite* means the other of two related or corresponding things. The word *opposite* is from the Latin *oppositus*, meaning "placed across from."

Use Multiple Representations Have other materials available of varied instructional levels. This text should describe the properties of parallelograms using the relationships between sides and angles, and the diagonals of a parallelogram.

5 Assess & Remediate

Lesson Quiz

1. What is $m\angle O$ in $\square LMNO$?

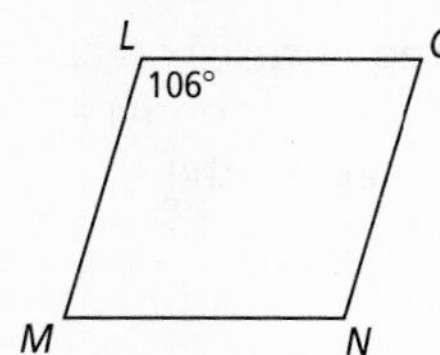

2. Solve a system of linear equations to find the values of a and b in $\square EFGH$. What are EG and FH?

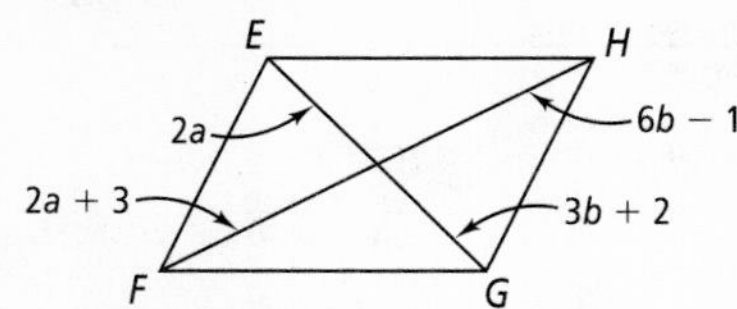

3. Do you UNDERSTAND? If $MQ = 29.5$, what is MN?

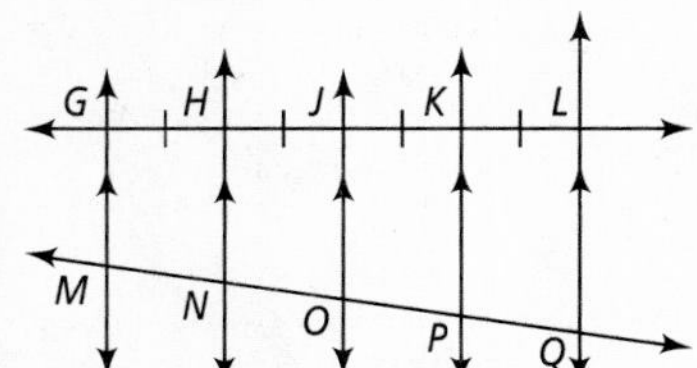

ANSWERS TO LESSON QUIZ

1. 74

2. $EG = 16$, $FH = 22$

3. 7.375

PRESCRIPTION FOR REMEDIATION

Use the student work on the Lesson Quiz to prescribe a differentiated review assignment.

Points	Differentiated Remediation
0–1	Intervention
2	On-level
3	Extension

PowerGeometry.com

5 Assess & Remediate

Assign the Lesson Quiz. Appropriate intervention, practice, or enrichment is automatically generated based on student performance.

Intervention

- **Reteaching** (2 pages) Provides reteaching and practice exercises for the key lesson concepts. Use with struggling students or absent students.
- **English Language Learner Support** Helps students develop and reinforce mathematical vocabulary and key concepts.

All-in-One Resources/Online

Reteaching

6-2 **Reteaching**
Properties of Parallelograms

Parallelograms

Remember, a *parallelogram* is a quadrilateral with both pairs of opposite sides parallel. Here are some attributes of a parallelogram:

The opposite sides are congruent.
The consecutive angles are supplementary.
The opposite angles are congruent.
The diagonals bisect each other.

You can use these attributes to solve problems about parallelograms.

Problem

Find the value of x.

Because the consecutive angles are supplementary,

$$x + 60 = 180$$
$$x = 120$$

Problem

Find the value of x.

Because opposite sides are congruent,

$$x + 7 = 15$$
$$x = 8$$

Problem

Find the value of x and y.

Because the diagonals bisect each other, $y = 3x$ and $4x = y + 3$.

$4x = y + 3$	
$4x = 3x + 3$	Substitute for y.
$x = 3$	Subtraction Property of =
$y = 3x$	Given
$y = 3(3)$	Substitute for x.
$y = 9$	Simplify.

All-in-One Resources/Online

English Language Learner Support

6-2 **ELL Support**
Properties of Parallelograms

Concept List

congruent angles	congruent segments	consecutive angles
diagonal	is parallel to	opposite angles
opposite sides	parallelogram	transversal

Choose the concept from the list above that best represents the item in each box.

1. $\angle A$ and $\angle B$ — consecutive angles	2. $\parallel$ — is parallel to	3. diagonal
4. $\overline{EF}$ and $\overline{HG}$ — opposite sides	5. $\angle H$ and $\angle F$ — opposite angles	6. $m\angle X = m\angle Y$ — congruent angles
7. $WX = YZ$ — congruent segments	8. $\square EFGH$ — parallelogram	9. transversal

Differentiated Remediation *continued*

On-Level

- **Practice** (2 pages) Provides extra practice for each lesson. For simpler practice exercises, use the Form K Practice pages found in the All-in-One Teaching Resources and online.
- **Think About a Plan** Helps students develop specific problem-solving skills and strategies by providing scaffolded guiding questions.
- **Standardized Test Prep** Focuses on all major exercises, all major question types, and helps students prepare for the high-stakes assessments.

Extension

- **Enrichment** Provides students with interesting problems and activities that extend the concepts of the lesson.
- **Activities, Games, and Puzzles** Worksheets that can be used for concepts development, enrichment, and for fun!

Practice and Problem Solving Wkbk/ All-in-One Resources/Online

Practice page 1

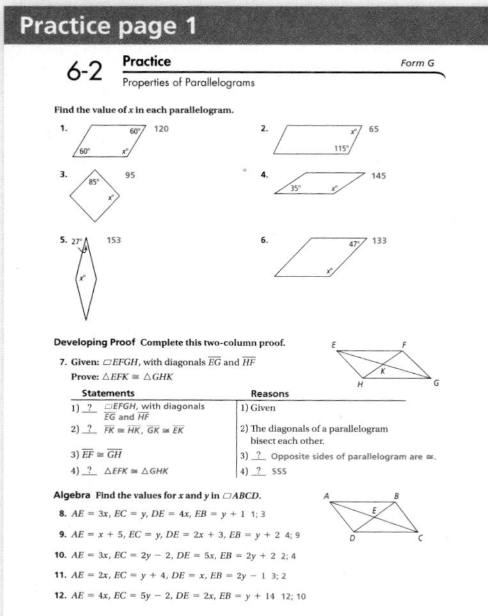

6-2 Practice — Form G
Properties of Parallelograms

Find the value of x in each parallelogram.

1. 120
2. 65
3. 95
4. 145
5. 153
6. 133

Developing Proof Complete this two-column proof.

7. Given: ▱EFGH, with diagonals $\overline{EG}$ and $\overline{HF}$
Prove: $\triangle EFK \cong \triangle GHK$

Statements	Reasons
1) ? ▱EFGH, with diagonals $\overline{EG}$ and $\overline{HF}$	1) Given
2) ? $\overline{FK} \cong \overline{HK}$, $\overline{GK} \cong \overline{EK}$	2) The diagonals of a parallelogram bisect each other.
3) $\overline{EF} \cong \overline{GH}$	3) ? Opposite sides of parallelogram are ≅.
4) ? $\triangle EFK \cong \triangle GHK$	4) ? SSS

Algebra Find the values for x and y in ▱ABCD.

8. $AE = 3x$, $EC = y$, $DE = 4x$, $EB = y + 1$ 1; 3
9. $AE = x + 5$, $EC = y$, $DE = 2x + 3$, $EB = y + 2$ 4; 9
10. $AE = 3x$, $EC = 2y - 2$, $DE = 5x$, $EB = 2y + 2$ 2; 4
11. $AE = 2x$, $EC = y + 4$, $DE = x$, $EB = 2y - 1$ 3; 2
12. $AE = 4x$, $EC = 5y - 2$, $DE = 2x$, $EB = y + 14$ 12; 10

Practice and Problem Solving Wkbk/ All-in-One Resources/Online

Practice page 2

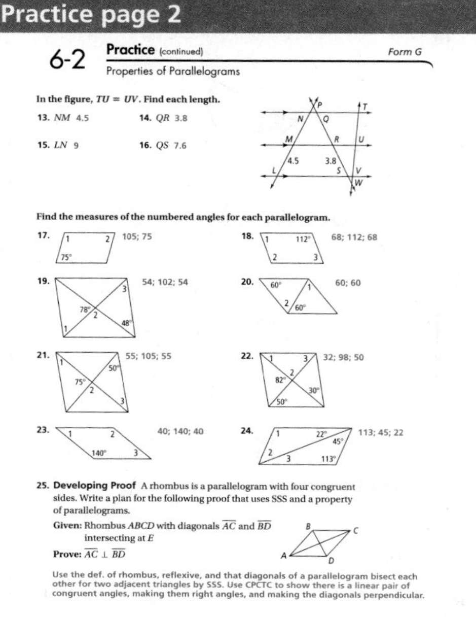

6-2 Practice (continued) — Form G
Properties of Parallelograms

In the figure, $TU = UV$. Find each length.

13. NM 4.5
14. QR 3.8
15. LN 9
16. QS 7.6

Find the measures of the numbered angles for each parallelogram.

17. 105; 75
18. 68; 112; 68
19. 54; 102; 54
20. 60; 60
21. 55; 105; 55
22. 32; 98; 50
23. 40; 140; 40
24. 113; 45; 22

25. Developing Proof A rhombus is a parallelogram with four congruent sides. Write a plan for the following proof that uses SSS and a property of parallelograms.
Given: Rhombus $ABCD$ with diagonals $\overline{AC}$ and $\overline{BD}$ intersecting at E
Prove: $\overline{AC} \perp \overline{BD}$
Use the def. of rhombus, reflexive, and that diagonals of a parallelogram bisect each other for two adjacent triangles by SSS. Use CPCTC to show there is a linear pair of congruent angles, making them right angles, and making the diagonals perpendicular.

All-in-One Resources/Online

Enrichment

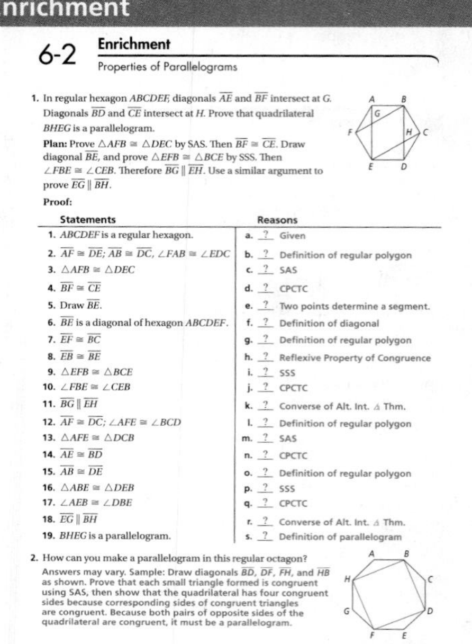

6-2 Enrichment
Properties of Parallelograms

1. In regular hexagon $ABCDEF$, diagonals $\overline{AE}$ and $\overline{BF}$ intersect at G. Diagonals $\overline{BD}$ and $\overline{CE}$ intersect at H. Prove that quadrilateral $BHEG$ is a parallelogram.
Plan: Prove $\triangle AFB \cong \triangle DEC$ by SAS. Then $\overline{BF} \cong \overline{CE}$. Draw diagonal $\overline{BE}$, and prove $\triangle EFB \cong \triangle BCE$ by SSS. Then $\angle FBE \cong \angle CEB$. Therefore $\overline{BG} \parallel \overline{EH}$. Use a similar argument to prove $\overline{EG} \parallel \overline{BH}$.
Proof:

Statements	Reasons
1. $ABCDEF$ is a regular hexagon.	a. ? Given
2. $\overline{AF} \cong \overline{DE}$; $\overline{AB} \cong \overline{DC}$, $\angle FAB \cong \angle EDC$	b. ? Definition of regular polygon
3. $\triangle AFB \cong \triangle DEC$	c. ? SAS
4. $\overline{BF} \cong \overline{CE}$	d. ? CPCTC
5. Draw $\overline{BE}$.	e. ? Two points determine a segment.
6. $\overline{BE}$ is a diagonal of hexagon $ABCDEF$.	f. ? Definition of diagonal
7. $\overline{EF} \cong \overline{BC}$	g. ? Definition of regular polygon
8. $\overline{EB} \cong \overline{BE}$	h. ? Reflexive Property of Congruence
9. $\triangle EFB \cong \triangle BCE$	i. ? SSS
10. $\angle FBE \cong \angle CEB$	j. ? CPCTC
11. $\overline{BG} \parallel \overline{EH}$	k. ? Converse of Alt. Int. ∠s Thm.
12. $\overline{AF} \cong \overline{DC}$; $\angle AFE \cong \angle BCD$	l. ? Definition of regular polygon
13. $\triangle AFE \cong \triangle DCB$	m. ? SAS
14. $\overline{AE} \cong \overline{BD}$	n. ? CPCTC
15. $\overline{AB} \cong \overline{DE}$	o. ? Definition of regular polygon
16. $\triangle ABE \cong \triangle DEB$	p. ? SSS
17. $\angle AEB \cong \angle DBE$	q. ? CPCTC
18. $\overline{EG} \parallel \overline{BH}$	r. ? Converse of Alt. Int. ∠s Thm.
19. $BHEG$ is a parallelogram.	s. ? Definition of parallelogram

2. How can you make a parallelogram in this regular octagon?
Answers may vary. Sample: Draw diagonals $\overline{BD}$, $\overline{DF}$, $\overline{FH}$, and $\overline{HB}$ as shown. Prove that each small triangle formed is congruent using SAS, then show that the quadrilateral has four congruent sides because corresponding sides of congruent triangles are congruent. Because both pairs of opposite sides of the quadrilateral are congruent, it must be a parallelogram.

Practice and Problem Solving Wkbk/ All-in-One Resources/Online

Think About a Plan

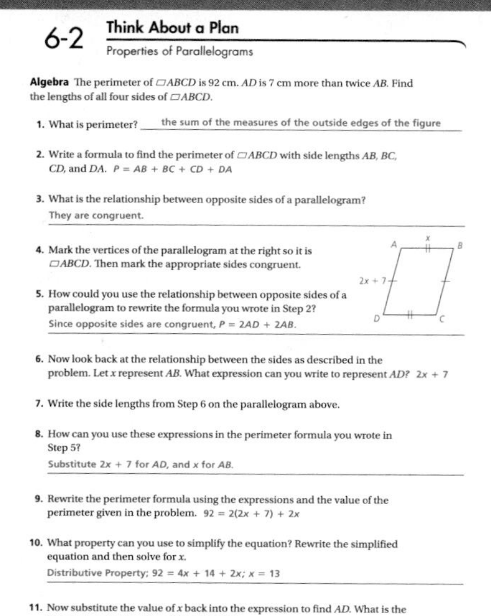

6-2 Think About a Plan
Properties of Parallelograms

Algebra The perimeter of ▱ABCD is 92 cm. AD is 7 cm more than twice AB. Find the lengths of all four sides of ▱ABCD.

1. What is perimeter? the sum of the measures of the outside edges of the figure
2. Write a formula to find the perimeter of ▱ABCD with side lengths AB, BC, CD, and DA. $P = AB + BC + CD + DA$
3. What is the relationship between opposite sides of a parallelogram? They are congruent.
4. Mark the vertices of the parallelogram at the right so it is ▱ABCD. Then mark the appropriate sides congruent.
5. How could you use the relationship between opposite sides of a parallelogram to rewrite the formula you wrote in Step 2? Since opposite sides are congruent, $P = 2AD + 2AB$.
6. Now look back at the relationship between the sides as described in the problem. Let x represent AB. What expression can you write to represent AD? $2x + 7$
7. Write the side lengths from Step 6 on the parallelogram above.
8. How can you use these expressions in the perimeter formula you wrote in Step 5? Substitute $2x + 7$ for AD, and x for AB.
9. Rewrite the perimeter formula using the expressions and the value of the perimeter given in the problem. $92 = 2(2x + 7) + 2x$
10. What property can you use to simplify the equation? Rewrite the simplified equation and then solve for x. Distributive Property; $92 = 4x + 14 + 2x$; $x = 13$
11. Now substitute the value of x back into the expression to find AD. What is the length of each of the four sides of $ABCD$? $AB = 13$ cm; $BC = 33$ cm; $CD = 13$ cm; $AD = 33$ cm

Practice and Problem Solving Wkbk/ All-in-One Resources/Online

Standardized Test Prep

6-2 Standardized Test Prep
Properties of Parallelograms

Multiple Choice

For Exercises 1–5, choose the correct letter.

1. In ▱ABCD, $m\angle A = 53$. What is $m\angle C$? B
 A 37 B 53 C 127 D 307
2. What is the value of x in ▱QRST? I
 F 16 H 8 G 12 I 4
3. What is the value of y in ▱LMNO? C
 A 4 C 12 B 6 D 24
4. What is $m\angle 1$ in this parallelogram? H
 F 20 H 80 G 60 I 100
5. What is $m\angle 2$ in this parallelogram? C
 A 115 C 15 B 50 D 2

Extended Response

6. Figure $ABCD$ is a parallelogram. What are four geometric attributes you know because $ABCD$ is a parallelogram?
[4] Student lists four attributes from the following list of seven attributes: $\overline{AB} \cong \overline{CD}$, $\overline{BC} \cong \overline{DA}$, $\angle A \cong \angle C$, $\angle B \cong \angle D$, $\overline{AB} \parallel \overline{CD}$, $\overline{BC} \parallel \overline{DA}$, and diagonals bisect each other. [3] Student lists three attributes. [2] Student lists two attributes. [1] Student lists one attribute. [0] Student gives no answer or wrong answer based on an inappropriate plan.

Online Teacher Resource Center

Activities, Games, and Puzzles

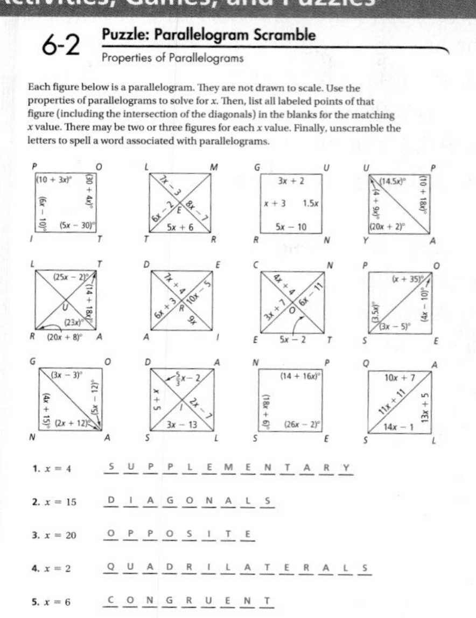

6-2 Puzzle: Parallelogram Scramble
Properties of Parallelograms

Each figure below is a parallelogram. They are not drawn to scale. Use the properties of parallelograms to solve for x. Then, list all labeled points of that figure (including the intersection of the diagonals) in the blanks for the matching x value. There may be two or three figures for each x value. Finally, unscramble the letters to spell a word associated with parallelograms.

1. $x = 4$ S U P P L E M E N T A R Y
2. $x = 15$ D I A G O N A L S
3. $x = 20$ O P P O S I T E
4. $x = 2$ Q U A D R I L A T E R A L S
5. $x = 6$ C O N G R U E N T

6-3 Proving That a Quadrilateral Is a Parallelogram

TN State Performance Indicator
SPI 3108.4.3 Identify, describe and/or apply the relationships and theorems involving different types of triangles, quadrilaterals and other polygons.

Objective To determine whether a quadrilateral is a parallelogram

Solve It! Getting Ready!

Each section of glass in the exterior of a building in Macau, China, forms an equilateral triangle. Do you think the window washer's feet stay parallel to the ground as he lands at each level of windows? Explain. (Assume that the bases of the lowest triangles are parallel to the ground.)

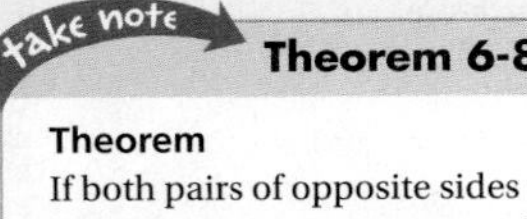

In the Solve It, you used angle properties to show that lines are parallel. In this lesson, you will apply the same properties to show that a quadrilateral is a parallelogram.

Essential Understanding You can decide whether a quadrilateral is a parallelogram if its sides, angles, and diagonals have certain properties.

In Lesson 6-2, you learned theorems about the properties of parallelograms. In this lesson, you will learn the converses of those theorems. That is, if a quadrilateral has certain properties, then it must be a parallelogram. Theorem 6-8 is the converse of Theorem 6-3.

take note **Theorem 6-8**

Theorem	If . . .	Then . . .
If both pairs of opposite sides of a quadrilateral are congruent, then the quadrilateral is a parallelogram.	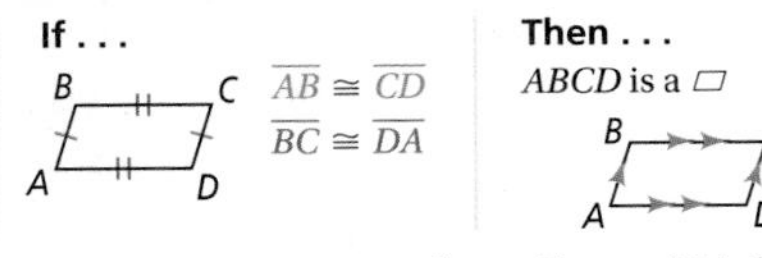 $\overline{AB} \cong \overline{CD}$, $\overline{BC} \cong \overline{DA}$	*ABCD* is a ▱

You will prove Theorem 6-8 in Exercise 20.

Theorems 6-9 and 6-10 are the converses of Theorems 6-4 and 6-5, respectively. They use angle relationships to conclude that a quadrilateral is a parallelogram.

1 Interactive Learning

Solve It!

PURPOSE To use properties of geometric figures to show that lines are parallel

PROCESS Students may use previous knowledge of congruent triangle theorems and properties of parallel lines and equilateral triangles.

FACILITATE

Q What are the properties of an equilateral triangle? **[All angles are congruent and all sides are congruent. Each angle has a measure of 60.]**

Q Are all of the equilateral triangles in the diagram congruent? Explain. **[Yes, the triangles share one side and have congruent angles, so they are congruent by ASA.]**

Q Can you identify parallel lines cut by a transversal in the diagram? Explain. **[Yes, the angles of the triangles are congruent. They form congruent alternate interior angles.]**

ANSWER See Solve It in Answers on next page.

CONNECT THE MATH In the Solve It equilateral triangles and their properties are used to prove lines parallel. In the lesson, similar approaches will be used to prove a quadrilateral is a parallelogram.

2 Guided Instruction

Take Note

Students may recognize that Theorem 6-8 is the converse of Theorem 6-3.

6-3 Preparing to Teach

BIG idea **Reasoning and Proof** UbD

ESSENTIAL UNDERSTANDINGS

- If a quadrilateral's sides, angles, and diagonals have certain properties, it can be shown that the quadrilateral is a parallelogram.
- The properties of parallelograms and algebra can be used to find the lengths of some sides and the measures of some angles of some parallelograms.

Math Background

A definition in geometry is a biconditional statement. Thus, the definition of a parallelogram given in Lesson 6-2 could be read as "A quadrilateral is a parallelogram if and only if both pairs of opposite sides are parallel." The theorems presented in Lesson 6-2 concerning the properties of parallelograms were only stated as conditional statements and thus could not be interpreted as biconditional statements. However, the theorems presented and proven in Lesson 6-3 are their converses, so now many properties of parallelograms can be written as biconditional statements.

Students need to distinguish between the properties and their converses in writing proofs as they examine more complex diagrams.

Support Student Learning

Use the **Geometry Companion** to engage and support students during instructions. See Lesson Resources at the end of this lesson for details.

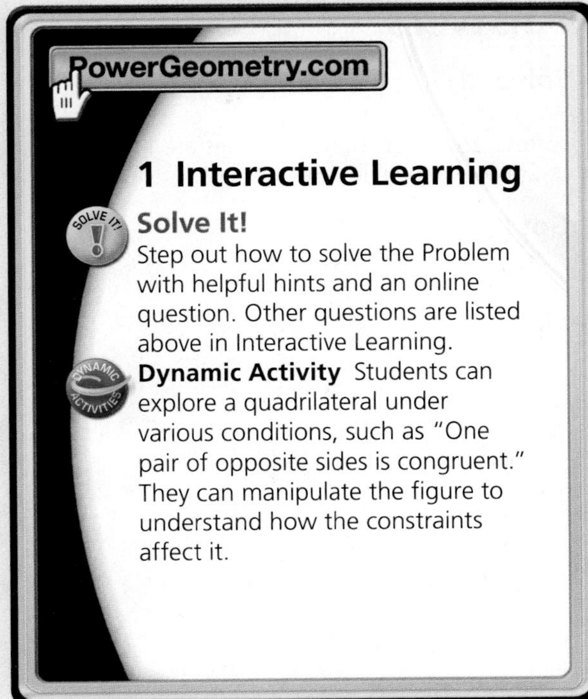

PowerGeometry.com
1 Interactive Learning
Solve It!
Step out how to solve the Problem with helpful hints and an online question. Other questions are listed above in Interactive Learning.
Dynamic Activity Students can explore a quadrilateral under various conditions, such as "One pair of opposite sides is congruent." They can manipulate the figure to understand how the constraints affect it.

Take Note
Emphasize the importance of the word "both" in this theorem. Ask students to sketch a counterexample to the conclusion of this theorem if the word "both" is not included.

Q The diagram shows two sets of congruent angles. What relationship do you know about all four angles of the quadrilateral? **[The sum of the measures of the angles is 360.]**

take note

Theorem 6-9

Theorem	If . . .	Then . . .
If an angle of a quadrilateral is supplementary to both of its consecutive angles, then the quadrilateral is a parallelogram.	$m\angle A + m\angle B = 180$ $m\angle A + m\angle D = 180$	$ABCD$ is a ▱

You will prove Theorem 6-9 in Exercise 21.

Theorem 6-10

Theorem	If . . .	Then . . .
If both pairs of opposite angles of a quadrilateral are congruent, then the quadrilateral is a parallelogram.	$\angle A \cong \angle C$ $\angle B \cong \angle D$	$ABCD$ is a ▱

You will prove Theorem 6-10 in Exercise 18.

Problem 1

Q For quadrilateral $PQRS$ to be a parallelogram, what relationship must exist between the opposite sides of the quadrilateral? **[Pairs of opposite sides must be congruent.]**

Q What equations represent that the opposite sides are congruent? **[$3x - 5 = 2x + 1$ and $y = x + 2$]**

Q How can you find the value of x? **[Solve the equation $3x - 5 = 2x + 1$.]**

Q How can you find the value of y in the diagram? **[Substitute the value for x into the equation $y = x + 2$.]**

Got It?

Q Which theorem should you use? Explain. **[The diagram gives you information about the angles, so you should use Theorem 6-10.]**

You can use algebra together with Theorems 6-8, 6-9, and 6-10 to find segment lengths and angle measures that assume that a quadrilateral is a parallelogram.

Plan

Which theorem should you use?
The diagram gives you information about sides. Use Theorem 6-8 because it uses sides to conclude that a quadrilateral is a parallelogram.

Problem 1 **Finding Values for Parallelograms** GRIDDED RESPONSE

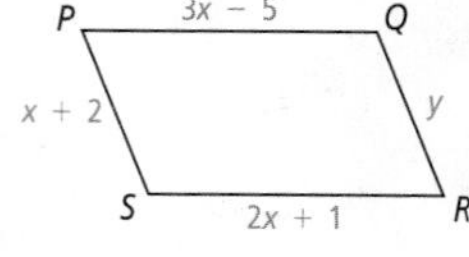

For what value of y must $PQRS$ be a parallelogram?

Step 1 Find x.

$3x - 5 = 2x + 1$ If opp. sides are ≅, then the quad. is a ▱.

$x - 5 = 1$ Subtract $2x$ from each side.

$x = 6$ Add 5 to each side.

Step 2 Find y.

$y = x + 2$ If opp. sides are ≅, then the quad. is a ▱.

$= 6 + 2$ Substitute 6 for x.

$= 8$ Simplify.

For $PQRS$ to be a parallelogram, the value of y must be 8.

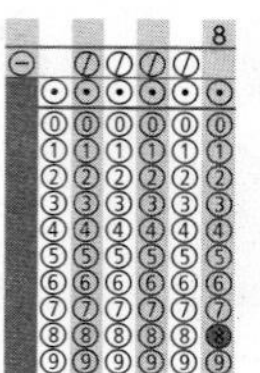

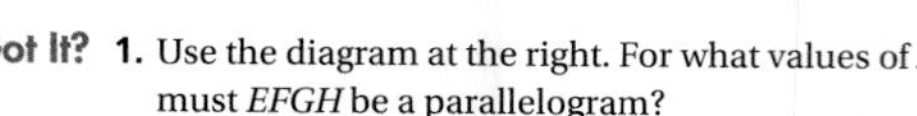

Got It? 1. Use the diagram at the right. For what values of x and y must $EFGH$ be a parallelogram?

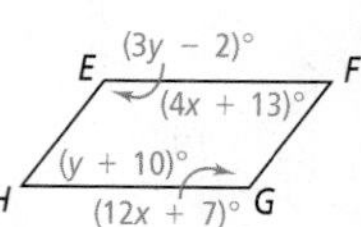

Answers

Solve It!
Yes; explanations may vary. Sample: ≰ are ≅ corresp. ≰, so the horizontal lines are ∥, or alt. int. ≰ are ≅, so the lines are ∥.

Got It?
1. $x = 10$, $y = 43$

PowerGeometry.com

2 Guided Instruction

Each Problem is worked out and supported online.

Problem 1
Finding Values for Parallelograms
Animated

Problem 2
Deciding Whether a Quadrilateral is a Parallelogram
Animated

Problem 3
Identifying Parallelograms
Animated

Support in Geometry Companion
- Vocabulary
- Key Concepts
- Got It?

You know that the converses of Theorems 6-3, 6-4, and 6-5 are true. Using what you have learned, you can show that the converse of Theorem 6-6 is also true.

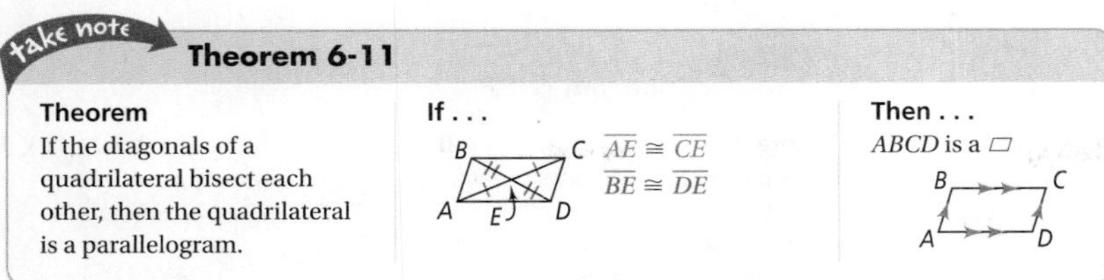

Take note — Theorem 6-11

Theorem	If . . .	Then . . .
If the diagonals of a quadrilateral bisect each other, then the quadrilateral is a parallelogram.	$\overline{AE} \cong \overline{CE}$, $\overline{BE} \cong \overline{DE}$	$ABCD$ is a ▱

Proof of Theorem 6-11

Given: $\overline{AC}$ and $\overline{BD}$ bisect each other at E.

Prove: $ABCD$ is a parallelogram.

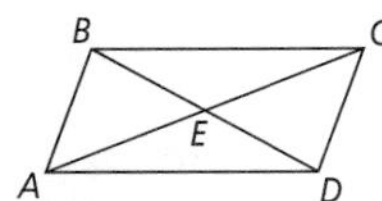

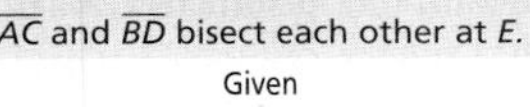

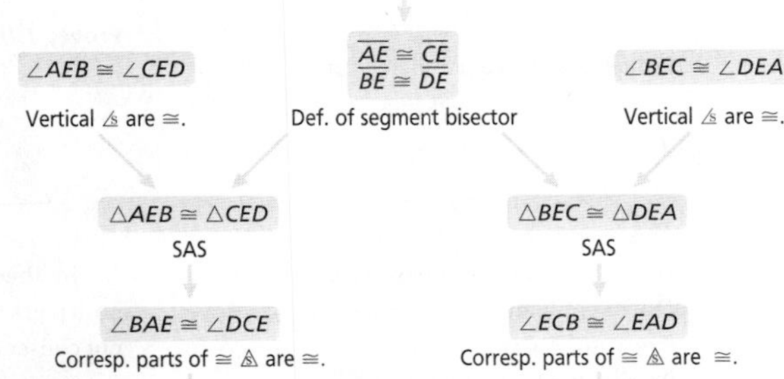

$\angle AEB \cong \angle CED$
Vertical ∠s are ≅.
$\overline{AE} \cong \overline{CE}$
$\overline{BE} \cong \overline{DE}$
Def. of segment bisector
$\angle BEC \cong \angle DEA$
Vertical ∠s are ≅.
$\triangle AEB \cong \triangle CED$
SAS
$\triangle BEC \cong \triangle DEA$
SAS
$\angle BAE \cong \angle DCE$
Corresp. parts of ≅ △s are ≅.
$\angle ECB \cong \angle EAD$
Corresp. parts of ≅ △s are ≅.

$\overline{AB} \parallel \overline{CD}$
If alternate interior ∠s ≅, then lines are ∥.

$\overline{BC} \parallel \overline{AD}$
If alternate interior ∠s ≅, then lines are ∥.

$ABCD$ is a parallelogram.
Def. of parallelogram

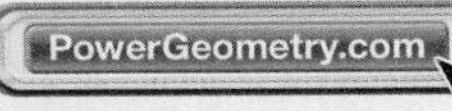

Take Note

Ask students the following questions to prepare them for the logical reasoning presented in the proof for this theorem.

Q Which angles in the diagram do you know are congruent? **[The pairs of vertical angles formed by the intersection of the diagonals are congruent.]**

Q Can you determine by visual inspection that the opposite sides of the quadrilateral *BCDA* are congruent? Explain. **[No, it is not known if the quadrilateral is a parallelogram.]**

Q Do any triangles in the diagram appear to be congruent? How can you prove them to be congruent? Explain. **[Yes, $\triangle BEC$ appears congruent to $\triangle DEA$ and $\triangle BEA$ appears congruent to $\triangle DEC$. You can prove them congruent using SAS.]**

Additional Problems

1. For what value of x must $RSTU$ be a parallelogram?

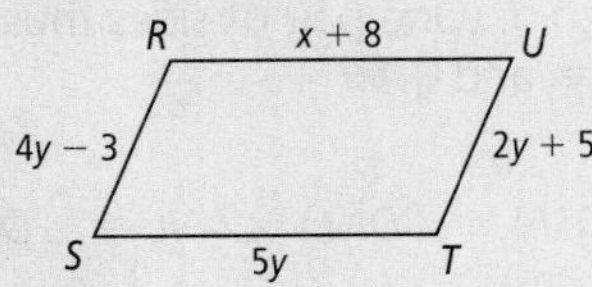

ANSWER 12

2. Can you prove the quadrilateral is a parallelogram based on the given information? What theorem can you use?

a. Given: $AE = CE = 14$, $DB = 2DE$
Prove: $ABCD$ is a parallelogram

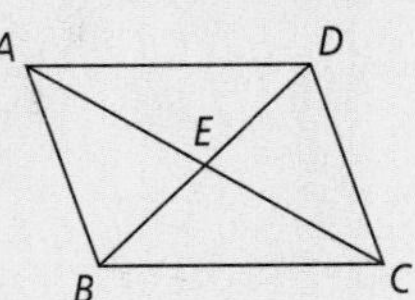

b. Given: $m\angle Y = 49$, $m\angle Z = 131$, $m\angle W = 49$
Prove: $WXYZ$ is a parallelogram

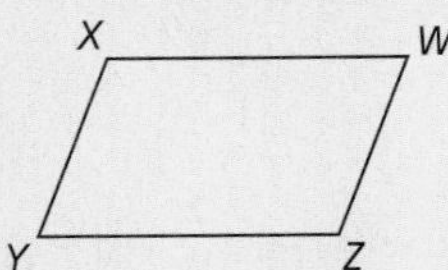

ANSWER a. Yes, by Theorem 6-11
b. Yes, by Theorem 6-9

3. A table tray can be adjusted up or down by raising or lowering the table on its hinged legs as shown. Will the table always remain parallel to the surface that it sits on? Explain.

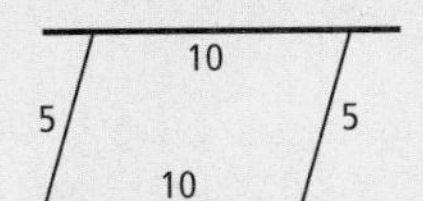

ANSWER Yes, both pairs of opposite sides are congruent, so the table will form a parallelogram.

Take Note

Point out to students that unlike all of the other theorems presented in this lesson, Theorem 6-12 is not the converse of a previous theorem.

Problem 2

Q Can you use the information given in the diagram in 2A to conclude that $\angle B \cong \angle D$ and $\angle A \cong \angle C$? Explain. **[No, you can conclude that $\angle B$ and $\angle C$ are supplementary, but you cannot conclude congruence.]**

Ask students to create a quadrilateral with given information that would allow a classmate to determine that the quadrilateral is a parallelogram using Theorem 6-8.

Got It?

ERROR PREVENTION

Q Can you prove that $\triangle ALN \cong \triangle DNL$ in the diagram given for 2b? Explain. **[Yes, by using ASA.]**

Q Can you prove that $\triangle ALD \cong \triangle DNA$? Explain. **[Yes, by using the Angle Addition Postulate.]**

Theorem 6-12 suggests that if you keep two objects of the same length parallel, such as cross-country skis, then the quadrilateral formed by connecting their endpoints is always a parallelogram.

take note

Theorem 6-12

Theorem	If . . .	Then . . .
If one pair of opposite sides of a quadrilateral is both congruent and parallel, then the quadrilateral is a parallelogram.	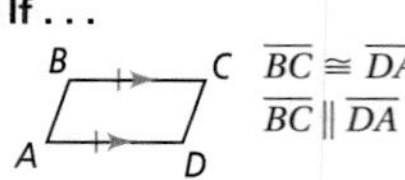 $\overline{BC} \cong \overline{DA}$ $\overline{BC} \parallel \overline{DA}$	$ABCD$ is a ▱

You will prove Theorem 6-12 in Exercise 19.

Think

How do you decide if you have enough information?
If you can satisfy every condition of a theorem about parallelograms, then you have enough information.

Problem 2 Deciding Whether a Quadrilateral Is a Parallelogram

Can you prove that the quadrilateral is a parallelogram based on the given information? Explain.

A Given: $AB = 5$, $CD = 5$, $m\angle A = 50$, $m\angle D = 130$

Prove: $ABCD$ is a parallelogram.

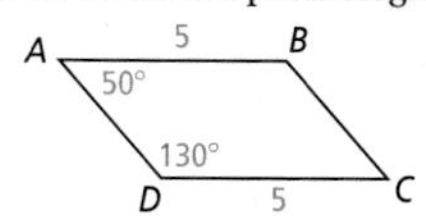

Yes. Same-side interior angles A and D are supplementary, so $\overline{AB} \parallel \overline{CD}$. Since $\overline{AB} \cong \overline{CD}$, $ABCD$ is a parallelogram by Theorem 6-12.

B Given: $\overline{HI} \cong \overline{HK}$, $\overline{JI} \cong \overline{JK}$

Prove: $HIJK$ is a parallelogram.

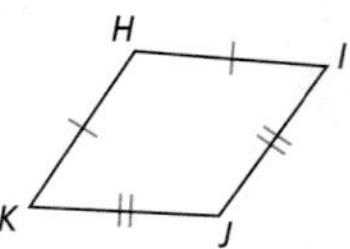

No. By Theorem 6-8, you need to show that both pairs of *opposite* sides are congruent, not consecutive sides.

Got It? 2. Can you prove that the quadrilateral is a parallelogram based on the given information? Explain.

a. Given: $\overline{EF} \cong \overline{GD}$, $\overline{DE} \parallel \overline{FG}$
Prove: $DEFG$ is a parallelogram.

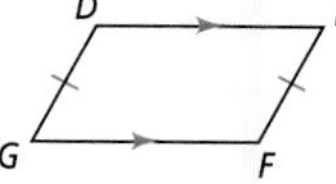

b. Given: $\angle ALN \cong \angle DNL$, $\angle ANL \cong \angle DLN$
Prove: $LAND$ is a parallelogram.

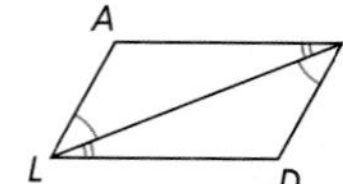

Answers

Got It? (continued)

2a. No; $DEFG$ could be an isosc. trapezoid. (One pair of sides must be both $\cong$ and $\parallel$.)

b. yes

1. $\angle ALN \cong \angle DNL$; $\angle ANL \cong \angle DLN$ (Given)
2. $\overline{AN} \parallel \overline{LD}$ and $\overline{AL} \parallel \overline{ND}$. (If alt. int. ∠s are $\cong$, then lines are $\parallel$.)
3. $LAND$ is a ▱. (Def. of ▱)

Think

As the arms of the lift move, what changes and what stays the same?

The angles the arms form with the ground and the platform change, but the lengths of the arms and the platform stay the same.

Problem 3 Identifying Parallelograms

Vehicle Lifts **A truck sits on the platform of a vehicle lift. Two moving arms raise the platform until a mechanic can fit underneath. Why will the truck always remain parallel to the ground as it is lifted? Explain.**

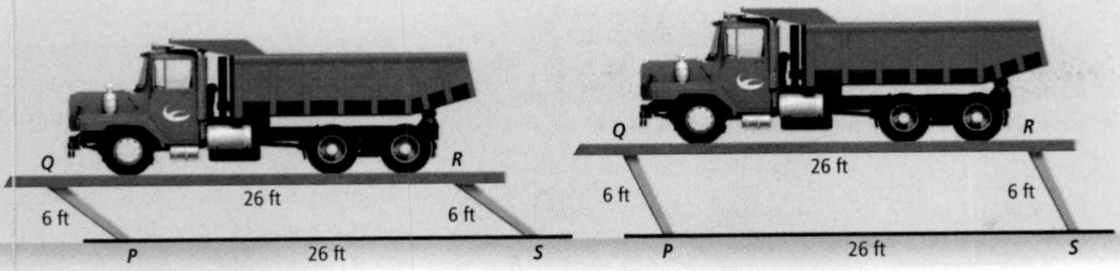

The angles of $PQRS$ change as platform $\overline{QR}$ rises, but its side lengths remain the same. Both pairs of opposite sides are congruent, so $PQRS$ is a parallelogram by Theorem 6-8. By the definition of a parallelogram, $\overline{PS} \parallel \overline{QR}$. Since the base of the lift $\overline{PS}$ lies along the ground, platform $\overline{QR}$, and therefore the truck, will always be parallel to the ground.

Got It? 3. **Reasoning** What is the maximum height that the vehicle lift can elevate the truck? Explain.

take note — Concept Summary: Proving That a Quadrilateral Is a Parallelogram

Method	Source	Diagram
Prove that both pairs of opposite sides are parallel.	Definition of parallelogram	
Prove that both pairs of opposite sides are congruent.	Theorem 6-8	
Prove that an angle is supplementary to both of its consecutive angles.	Theorem 6-9	75° 75° 105°
Prove that both pairs of opposite angles are congruent.	Theorem 6-10	
Prove that the diagonals bisect each other.	Theorem 6-11	
Prove that one pair of opposite sides is congruent and parallel.	Theorem 6-12	

Problem 3 — TACTILE LEARNERS

Cut the bottom out of a shoebox to use as a model for exploring this problem. Students will be able to manipulate the angles of the quadrilateral while still maintaining the parallel and congruent relationships of the sides.

Got It? — TACTILE LEARNERS

Remind students that while the lengths of $\overline{QP}$ and $\overline{RS}$ remain constant as the lift raises, the length of a segment perpendicular to both $\overline{QR}$ and $\overline{PS}$ does not remain constant as the lift raises.

Take Note

Remind students that all but one of the sources presented in this table was already presented in the form of its converse in Lesson 6-2. For example, in Lesson 6-2, if you knew a quadrilateral was a parallelogram, then you could conclude that both pairs of opposite angles were congruent. In this lesson, if you know that both pairs of opposite angles in a quadrilateral are congruent, then you can conclude that the quadrilateral is a parallelogram.

3. 6 ft; explanations may vary. Sample: The maximum height occurs when $\overline{QP}$ is vertical.

3 Lesson Check

Do you know HOW?

- If students have difficulty with Exercises 2-3, then have them revise the diagrams as necessary so that the given information is sufficient.

Do you UNDERSTAND?

- If students have difficulty with Exercise 6, then tell them to make a sketch of a diagram that meets only the conditions of the classmate's statement in order to visually show the error in the statement.

Close

Q What biconditional can you write concerning a parallelogram and its opposite angles? **[A quadrilateral is a parallelogram if and only if both pairs of opposite angles are congruent.]**

Lesson Check

Do you know HOW?

1. For what value of y must *LMNP* be a parallelogram?

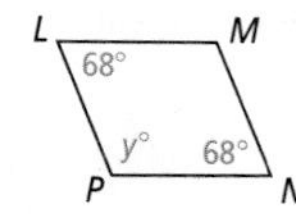

For Exercises 2 and 3, is the given information enough to prove that *ABCD* is a parallelogram? Explain.

2.

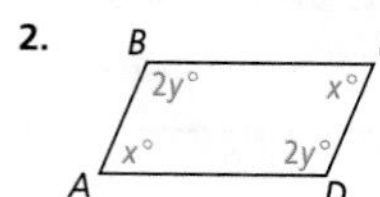

3.

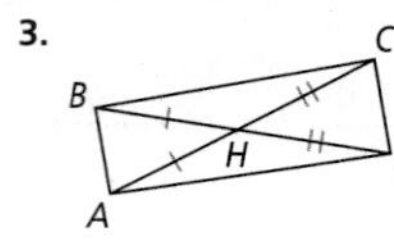

Do you UNDERSTAND?

4. **Vocabulary** Explain why you can now write a biconditional statement regarding opposite sides of a parallelogram.
5. **Compare and Contrast** How is Theorem 6-11 in this lesson different from Theorem 6-6 in the previous lesson? In what situations should you use each theorem? Explain.
6. **Error Analysis** Your friend says, "If a quadrilateral has a pair of opposite sides that are congruent and a pair of opposite sides that are parallel, then it is a parallelogram." What is your friend's error? Explain.

Practice and Problem-Solving Exercises

A Practice

Algebra For what values of x and y must *ABCD* be a parallelogram?

See Problems 1 and 2.

7. (B, $4x - 5$, C, $3x$, A, D)

8.

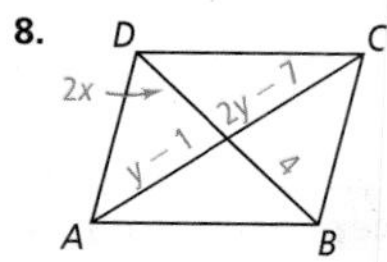

9. (B, C, $3x°$, $(y + 78)°$, $3y°$, $(4x - 21)°$, A, D)

10. (D, C, $6x - 4$, $3x + 1$, A, B)

11.

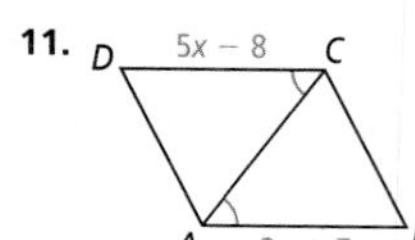

12.

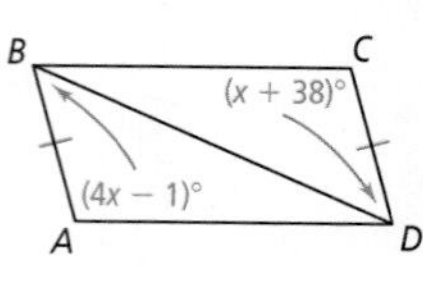

Can you prove that the quadrilateral is a parallelogram based on the given information? Explain.

13.

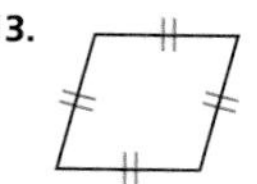

14.

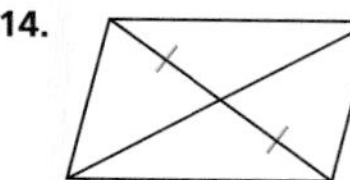

15.

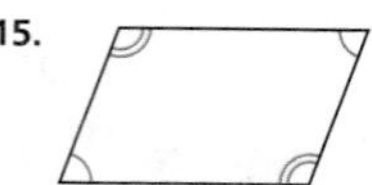

16. **Fishing** Quadrilaterals are formed on the side of this fishing tackle box by the adjustable shelves and connecting pieces. Explain why the shelves are always parallel to each other no matter what their position is.

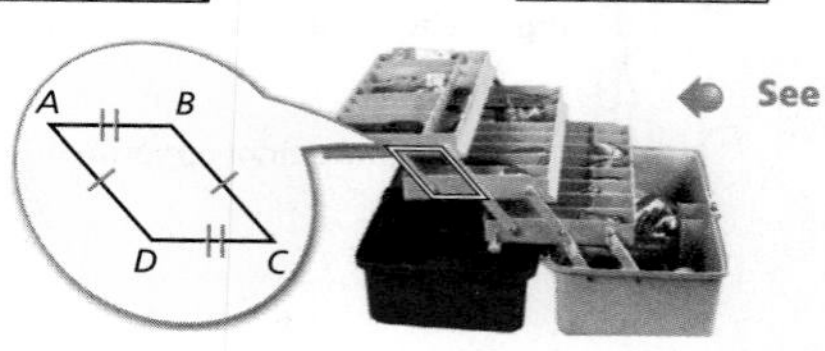

See Problem 3.

PowerGeometry.com

3 Lesson Check

For a digital lesson check, use the Got It questions.

Support in Geometry Companion

- Lesson Check

4 Practice

Assign homework to individual students or to an entire class.

Answers

Lesson Check

1. 112
2. Yes; opp. ∠s are ≅.
3. No; the diagonals may not bisect each other.
4. because Thm. 6-3 and its converse are both true
5. Thm. 6-11 and Thm. 6-6 are converses of each other. Use Thm. 6-11 if you need to show the figure is a ▱. Use Thm. 6-6 if it is given that the figure is a ▱.
6. It is a ▱ only if the same pair of opp. sides are ≅ and ∥.

Practice and Problem-Solving Exercises

7. 5
8. $x = 2$, $y = 6$
9. $x = 21$, $y = 39$
10. $\frac{5}{3}$
11. 5
12. 13
13. Yes; both pairs of opp. sides are ≅.
14. No; only one diagonal is bisected.
15. Yes; both pairs of opp. ∠s are ≅.
16. The connecting pieces $\overline{AD}$ and $\overline{BC}$ are ≅, and the distances AB and CD between where the two pieces attach are =. The side lengths of *ABCD* do not change as the tackle box opens and closes. Since both pairs of opp. sides are ≅, *ABCD* is always a ▱. By def. of ▱, $\overline{AB} \parallel \overline{CD}$, so the shelves are always ∥ to each other.

B Apply

17. **Writing** Combine each of Theorems 6-3, 6-4, 6-5, and 6-6 with its converse from this lesson into biconditional statements.

18. **Developing Proof** Complete this two-column proof of Theorem 6-10.

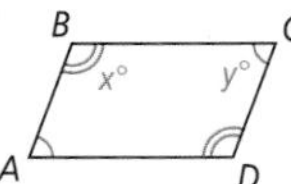

Given: $\angle A \cong \angle C$, $\angle B \cong \angle D$

Prove: *ABCD* is a parallelogram.

Statements	Reasons
1) $x + y + x + y = 360$	1) The sum of the measures of the angles of a quadrilateral is 360.
2) $2(x + y) = 360$	2) a. ?
3) $x + y = 180$	3) b. ?
4) $\angle A$ and $\angle B$ are supplementary. $\angle A$ and $\angle D$ are supplementary.	4) Definition of supplementary
5) c. ? ∥ ? , ? ∥ ?	5) d. ?
6) *ABCD* is a parallelogram.	6) e. ?

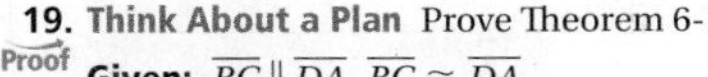

19. **Think About a Plan** Prove Theorem 6-12.
Proof

Given: $\overline{BC} \parallel \overline{DA}$, $\overline{BC} \cong \overline{DA}$

Prove: *ABCD* is a parallelogram.

- How can drawing diagonals help you?
- How can you use triangles in this proof?

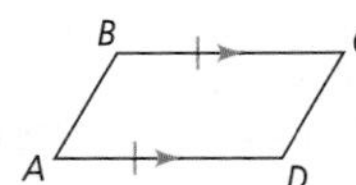

20. Prove Theorem 6-8.
Proof

Given: $\overline{AB} \cong \overline{CD}$, $\overline{BC} \cong \overline{DA}$

Prove: *ABCD* is a parallelogram.

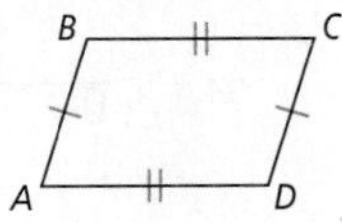

21. Prove Theorem 6-9.
Proof

Given: $\angle A$ is supplementary to $\angle B$. $\angle A$ is supplementary to $\angle D$.

Prove: *ABCD* is a parallelogram.

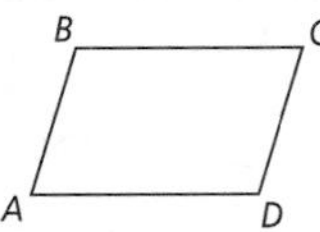

Algebra **For what values of the variables must *ABCD* be a parallelogram?**

22.

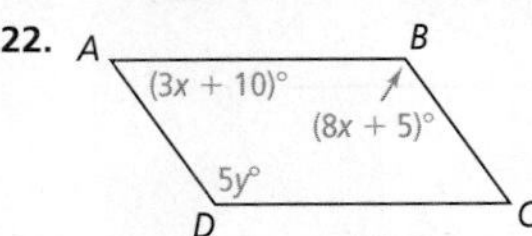

23.

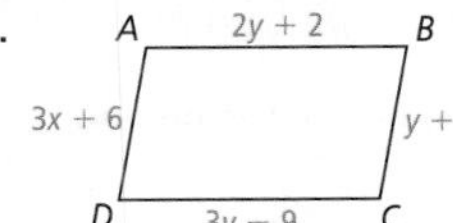

24.

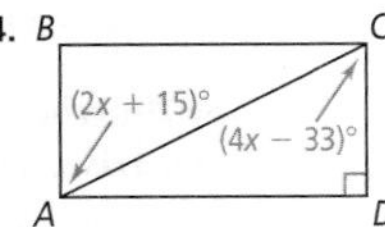

25. **Given:** $\triangle TRS \cong \triangle RTW$
Proof

Prove: *RSTW* is a parallelogram.

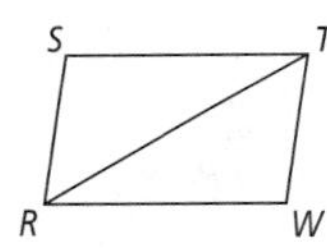

26. **Open-Ended** Sketch two noncongruent parallelograms *ABCD* and *EFGH* such that $\overline{AC} \cong \overline{EG}$ and $\overline{BD} \cong \overline{FH}$.

4 Practice

ASSIGNMENT GUIDE

Basic: 7–16, 18–20, 22–23
Average: 7–15 odd, 17–26
Advanced: 7–15 odd, 17–28
Standardized Test Prep: 29–31
Mixed Review: 32–44

Reasoning exercises have blue headings.
Applications exercises have red headings.

EXERCISE 20: Use the Think About a Plan worksheet in the **Practice and Problem Solving Workbook** (also available in the Teaching Resources in print and online) to further support students' development in becoming independent learners.

HOMEWORK QUICK CHECK

To check students' understanding of key skills and concepts, go over Exercises 9, 11, 18, 19, and 20.

17. A quad. is a ▱ if and only if its opp. sides are ≅; a quad. is a ▱ if and only if its consecutive ∠s are suppl.; a quad. is a ▱ if and only if its opp. ∠s are ≅; a quad. is a ▱ if and only if its diagonals bisect each other.

18a. Distr. Prop.
b. Div. Prop. of Eq.
c. $\overline{AD} \parallel \overline{BC}$, $\overline{AB} \parallel \overline{DC}$
d. If same-side int. ∠s are suppl., then lines are ∥.
e. Def. of ▱

19. Answers may vary. Sample:
1. Draw $\overline{BD}$. (Construction)
2. $\angle CBD \cong \angle ADB$ (Alt. int. ∠s are ≅.)
3. $\overline{BC} \cong \overline{DA}$ (Given)
4. $\overline{BD} \cong \overline{BD}$ (Refl. Prop. of ≅)
5. $\triangle BCD \cong \triangle DAB$ (SAS)
6. $\angle BDC \cong \angle DBA$ (Corresp. parts of ≅ ▵s are ≅.)
7. $\overline{AB} \parallel \overline{CD}$ (If alt. int. ∠s are ≅, then lines are ∥.)
8. *ABCD* is a ▱. (Def. of ▱)

20. Answers may vary. Sample:
1. Draw $\overline{BD}$. (Construction)
2. $\overline{AB} \cong \overline{CD}$ and $\overline{BC} \cong \overline{DA}$. (Given)
3. $\overline{BD} \cong \overline{BD}$ (Refl. Prop. of ≅)
4. $\triangle ABD \cong \triangle CDB$ (SSS)
5. $\angle ADB \cong \angle CBD$ and $\angle CDB \cong \angle ABD$. (Corresp. parts of ≅ ▵s are ≅.)
6. $\overline{AB} \parallel \overline{DC}$ and $\overline{BC} \parallel \overline{AD}$. (Converse of Corresp. ∠s Postulate)
7. *ABCD* is a ▱. (Def. of ▱)

21. Answers may vary. Sample:
1. $\angle A$ is suppl. to $\angle B$. (Given)
2. $\overline{BC} \parallel \overline{AD}$ (Converse of Corresp. ∠s Postulate)
3. $\angle A$ is suppl. to $\angle D$. (Given)
4. $\overline{AB} \parallel \overline{DC}$ (Converse of Corresp. ∠s Postulate)
5. *ABCD* is a ▱. (Def. of ▱)

22. $x = 15$, $y = 25$
23. $x = 3$, $y = 11$
24. 24
25. Answers may vary. Sample:
1. $\triangle TRS \cong \triangle RTW$ (Given)
2. $\overline{SR} \cong \overline{WT}$ and $\overline{ST} \cong \overline{WR}$. (Corresp. parts of ≅ ▵s are ≅.)
3. *RSTW* is a ▱. (If both pairs of opp. sides of a quad. are ≅, then the quad. is a ▱.)

26. Check students' work.

Answers

Practice and Problem-Solving Exercises (continued)

27. Answers may vary. Sample:

1. $\overline{AB} \cong \overline{CD}$, $\overline{AC} \cong \overline{BD}$ (Construction)
2. ▱$ABCD$ (Opp. sides of a ▱ are ≅.)
3. M is the midpt. of $\overline{BC}$. (Diagonals of a ▱ bisect each other.)
4. $\overline{AM}$ is a median. (Def. of median)

28. $\frac{1}{6}$

29. D

30. Answers may vary. Sample:

[2] 1. $\triangle NRJ \cong \triangle CPT$ (Given)
2. $\overline{NJ} \cong \overline{CT}$ (Corresp. parts of ≅ ▲s are ≅.)
3. $\overline{JN} \parallel \overline{CT}$ (Given)
4. $JNTC$ is a ▱. (If one pair of opp. sides of a quad. is both ≅ and ∥, then the quad. is a ▱.)

[1] one error OR missing step

31. [4] **a.** $7x - 11 = 6x$, $x = 11$

b. Yes; $m\angle F = 66$ and $m\angle FED = 114$. So $m\angle F + m\angle FED = 66 + 114 = 180$, and $\overline{AF} \parallel \overline{DE}$. (Converse of Corresp. ∠s Postulate)

c. Yes; $\overline{BD} \parallel \overline{FE}$ (Given) and $\overline{BF} \parallel \overline{DE}$ from part (b). So $BDEF$ is a ▱. (Def. of ▱)

[3] one error OR missing step

[2] two or three missing OR incorrect steps

[1] correct answers, with no work shown

32. $a = 8$, $h = 30$, $k = 120$

33. $m = 9.5$, $x = 15$

34. $c = 204$, $e = 13$, $f = 11$

35. 1. $\overline{AD} \cong \overline{BC}$, $\angle DAB \cong \angle CBA$ (Given)
2. $\overline{AB} \cong \overline{AB}$ (Refl. Prop. of ≅)
3. $\triangle ACB \cong \triangle BDA$ (SAS)
4. $\overline{AC} \cong \overline{BD}$ (Corresp. parts of ≅ ▲s are ≅.)

36. 7.47

37. 7.47

38. 7.47

39. 3.5

40. 13.2

41. 124

42. 56

43. 56

44. 28

27. Construction (Proof) In the figure at the right, point D is constructed by drawing two arcs. One has center C and radius AB. The other has center B and radius AC. Prove that $\overline{AM}$ is a median of $\triangle ABC$.

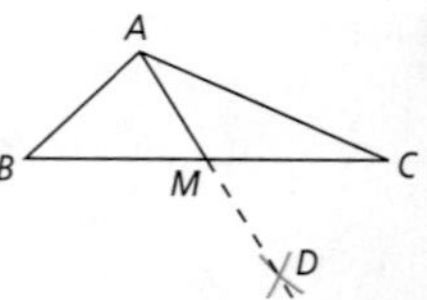

28. Probability If two opposite angles of a quadrilateral measure 120 and the measures of the other angles are multiples of 10, what is the probability that the quadrilateral is a parallelogram?

Standardized Test Prep

SAT/ACT

29. From which set of information can you conclude that $RSTW$ is a parallelogram?

Ⓐ $\overline{RS} \parallel \overline{WT}$, $\overline{RS} \cong \overline{ST}$

Ⓑ $\overline{RS} \parallel \overline{WT}$, $\overline{ST} \cong \overline{RW}$

Ⓒ $\overline{RS} \cong \overline{ST}$, $\overline{RW} \cong \overline{WT}$

Ⓓ $\overline{RZ} \cong \overline{TZ}$, $\overline{SZ} \cong \overline{WZ}$

Short Response

30. Write a proof using the diagram.

Given: $\triangle NRJ \cong \triangle CPT$, $\overline{JN} \parallel \overline{CT}$

Prove: $JNTC$ is a parallelogram.

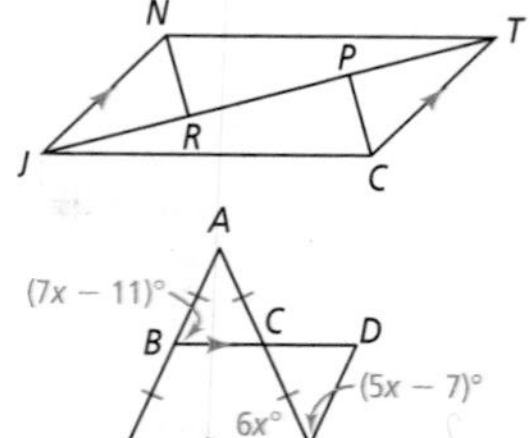

Extended Response

31. Use the figure at the right.

a. Write an equation and solve for x.

b. Is $\overline{AF} \parallel \overline{DE}$? Explain.

c. Is $BDEF$ a parallelogram? Explain.

Mixed Review

Algebra Find the value of each variable in each parallelogram.

See Lesson 6-2.

32.

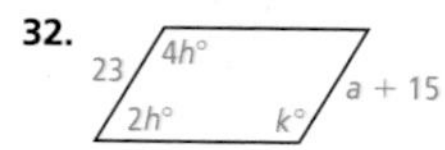

33.

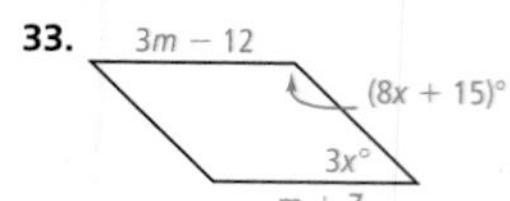

34.

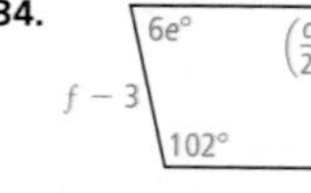

35. Explain how you can use overlapping congruent triangles to prove $\overline{AC} \cong \overline{BD}$.

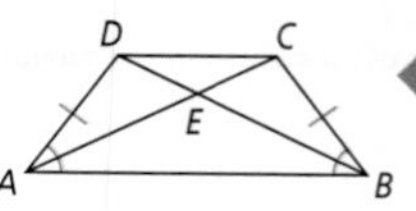

See Lessons 4-4 and 4-7.

Get Ready! To prepare for Lesson 6-4, do Exercises 36–44.

***PACE* is a parallelogram and $m\angle PAC = 124$. Complete the following.**

See Lessons 5-2 and 6-2.

36. AC = ■ **37.** CE = ■ **38.** PA = ■

39. RE = ■ **40.** CP = ■ **41.** $m\angle CEP$ = ■

42. $m\angle EPA$ = ■ **43.** $m\angle ECA$ = ■ **44.** $m\angle ACR$ = ■

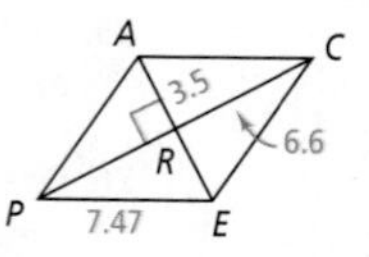

6-3 Lesson Resources

Differentiated Remediation

Instructional Support

Geometry Companion

Students can use the **Geometry Companion** worktext (4 pages) . . .

- New Vocabulary
- Key Concepts
- Got It for each Problem
- Lesson Check

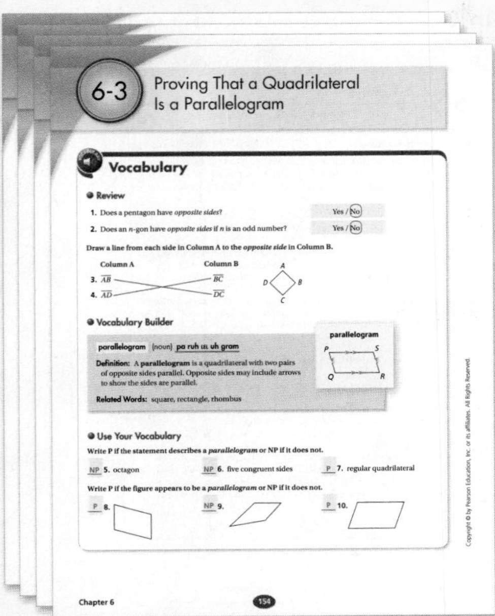

6-3 Proving That a Quadrilateral Is a Parallelogram

Vocabulary

Review

1. Does a pentagon have *opposite sides*? Yes / No
2. Does an n-gon have *opposite sides* if n is an odd number? Yes / No

Draw a line from each side in Column A to the *opposite side* in Column B.

Column A	Column B
3. $\overline{AB}$	$\overline{BC}$
4. $\overline{AD}$	$\overline{DC}$

Vocabulary Builder

parallelogram (noun) pa ruh LEL uh gram

Definition: A **parallelogram** is a quadrilateral with two pairs of opposite sides parallel. Opposite sides may include arrows to show the sides are parallel.

Related Words: square, rectangle, rhombus

Use Your Vocabulary

Write P if the statement describes a *parallelogram* or NP if it does not.

NP 5. octagon NP 6. five congruent sides P 7. regular quadrilateral

Write P if the figure appears to be a *parallelogram* or NP if it does not.

P 8. NP 9. P 10.

Chapter 6 154

ELL Support

Use Graphic Organizers Have students fold a sheet of paper in half widthwise and then lengthwise so there are 4 equal sections. Ask students to write Theorems 6-3 through 6-6 in their own words in each of the sections. Throughout this lesson, have them fill in the appropriate section with the converse of that theorem. Students can use different colored pencils to visually differentiate the theorems.

For example, in the first section, students would rephrase Theorem 6-3, and then write Theorem 6-7. Use the strategy of Compare and Contrast by asking what is similar and different about the two theorems.

5 Assess & Remediate

Lesson Quiz

1. For what value of a must $LMNO$ be a parallelogram?

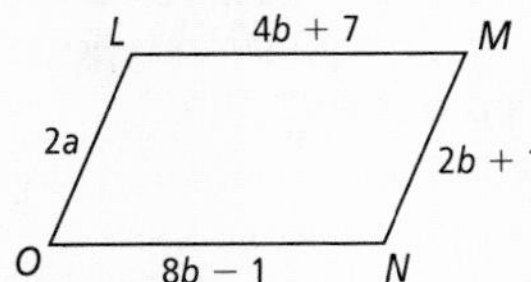

2. Can you prove $ABCD$ is a parallelogram based on the given information? Explain.
   Given: $x = 5$, $y = 4$
   Prove: $ABCD$ is a parallelogram

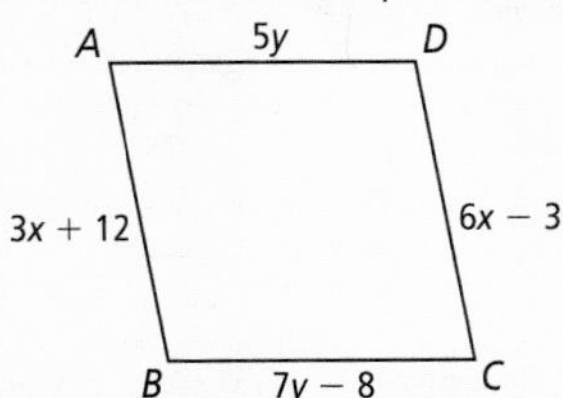

3. **Do you UNDERSTAND?** Quadrilateral $QRST$ has two pairs of congruent sides. Is it a parallelogram? If not, what additional information do you need to conclude that it is a parallelogram?

ANSWERS TO LESSON QUIZ

1. 2.5
2. Yes, by Theorem 6-8
3. No. To be a parallelogram, $QRST$ must have two pairs of opposite sides congruent.

PRESCRIPTION FOR REMEDIATION

Use the student work on the Lesson Quiz to prescribe a differentiated review assignment.

Points	Differentiated Remediation
0–1	Intervention
2	On-level
3	Extension

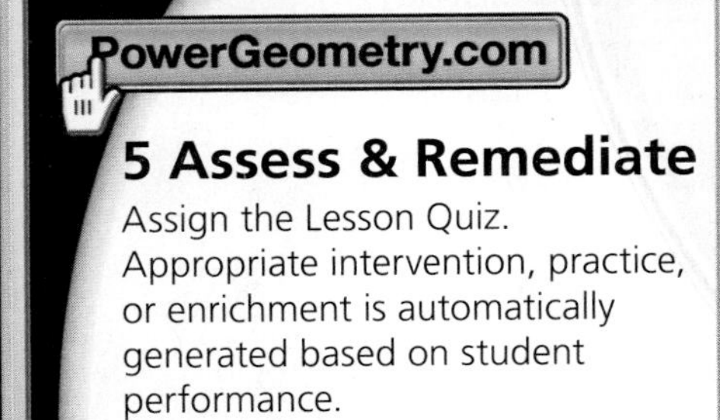

Intervention

- **Reteaching** (2 pages) Provides reteaching and practice exercises for the key lesson concepts. Use with struggling students or absent students.
- **English Language Learner Support** Helps students develop and reinforce mathematical vocabulary and key concepts.

All-in-One Resources/Online

Reteaching

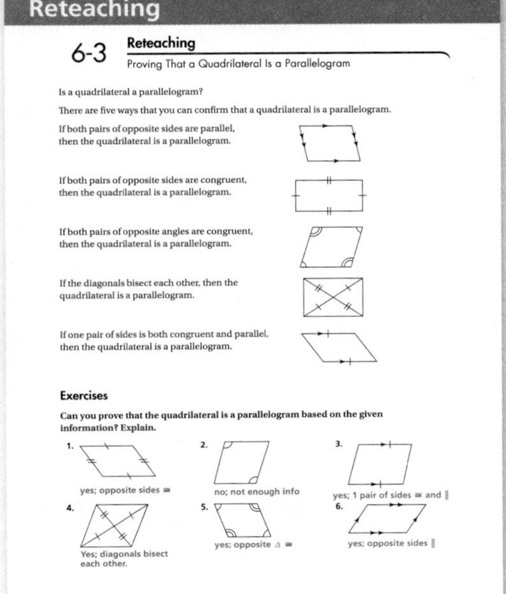

6-3 **Reteaching**
Proving That a Quadrilateral Is a Parallelogram

Is a quadrilateral a parallelogram?

There are five ways that you can confirm that a quadrilateral is a parallelogram.

If both pairs of opposite sides are parallel, then the quadrilateral is a parallelogram.

If both pairs of opposite sides are congruent, then the quadrilateral is a parallelogram.

If both pairs of opposite angles are congruent, then the quadrilateral is a parallelogram.

If the diagonals bisect each other, then the quadrilateral is a parallelogram.

If one pair of sides is both congruent and parallel, then the quadrilateral is a parallelogram.

Exercises

Can you prove that the quadrilateral is a parallelogram based on the given information? Explain.

1. yes; opposite sides ≅
2. no; not enough info
3. yes; 1 pair of sides ≅ and ∥
4. Yes; diagonals bisect each other.
5. yes; opposite ∠s ≅
6. yes; opposite sides ∥

All-in-One Resources/Online

English Language Learner Support

6-3 **ELL Support**
Proving That a Quadrilateral Is a Parallelogram

The **converse** of a statement reverses the conclusion and the hypothesis.	
Example: If A is true, then B is true.	**Converse:** If B is true, then A is true.
Hypothesis: A is true.	Hypothesis: B is true.
Conclusion: B is true.	Conclusion: A is true.
Sample	
Example: If a number is 5 more than 7, then the number is 12.	**Converse:** If a number is 12, then the number is 5 more than 7.

For each statement below, circle the hypothesis and underline the conclusion. Then write the converse.

1. If an apple is red, then the apple is ripe. If an apple is ripe, then it is red.
2. If the tree has leaves, then the season is summer.
   If the season is summer, then the tree has leaves.
3. Complete the converse of this statement: If water is solid, then it is frozen.
   Converse: If water is frozen, then it is solid.

The **converse** of a theorem reverses the conclusion and the hypothesis.	
Sample	
Theorem: If a transversal intersects two parallel lines, then corresponding angles are congruent.	**Converse:** If two lines and a transversal form alternate interior angles that are congruent, then the two lines are parallel.

Match each theorem from Section A with its converse in Section B.

Section A:	Section B:
4. If a quadrilateral is a parallelogram, then both pairs of opposite sides are congruent.	If the diagonals of a quadrilateral bisect each other, then the quadrilateral is a parallelogram.
5. If a quadrilateral is a parallelogram, then its diagonals bisect each other.	If both pairs of opposite angles of a quadrilateral are congruent, then the quadrilateral is a parallelogram.
6. If a quadrilateral is a parallelogram, then both pairs of opposite angles are congruent.	If both pairs of opposite sides of a quadrilateral are congruent, then the quadrilateral is a parallelogram.

Differentiated Remediation *continued*

On-Level

- **Practice** (2 pages) Provides extra practice for each lesson. For simpler practice exercises, use the Form K Practice pages found in the All-in-One Teaching Resources and online.
- **Think About a Plan** Helps students develop specific problem-solving skills and strategies by providing scaffolded guiding questions.
- **Standardized Test Prep** Focuses on all major exercises, all major question types, and helps students prepare for the high-stakes assessments.

Extension

- **Enrichment** Provides students with interesting problems and activities that extend the concepts of the lesson.
- **Activities, Games, and Puzzles** Worksheets that can be used for concepts development, enrichment, and for fun!

Practice and Problem Solving Wkbk/ All-in-One Resources/Online

Practice page 1

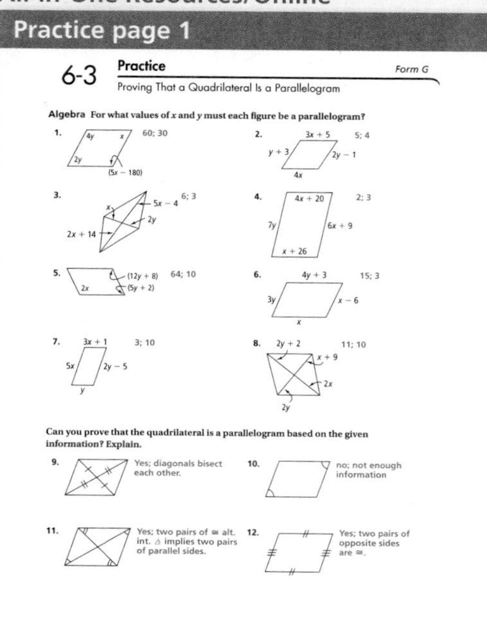

6-3 **Practice** *Form G*
Proving That a Quadrilateral Is a Parallelogram

Algebra For what values of x and y must each figure be a parallelogram?

1. 60; 30
2. 5; 4
3. 6; 3
4. 2; 3
5. 64; 10
6. 15; 3
7. 3; 10
8. 11; 10

Can you prove that the quadrilateral is a parallelogram based on the given information? Explain.

9. Yes; diagonals bisect each other.
10. no; not enough information
11. Yes; two pairs of ≅ alt. int. ∠s implies two pairs of parallel sides.
12. Yes; two pairs of opposite sides are ≅.

Practice and Problem Solving Wkbk/ All-in-One Resources/Online

Practice page 2

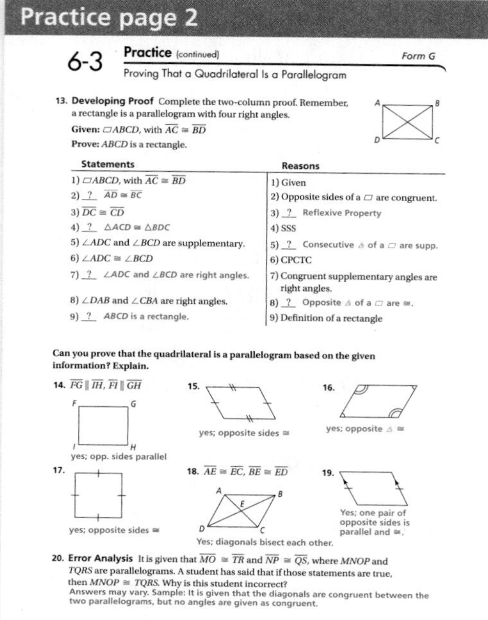

6-3 **Practice** (continued) *Form G*
Proving That a Quadrilateral Is a Parallelogram

13. **Developing Proof** Complete the two-column proof. Remember, a rectangle is a parallelogram with four right angles.
Given: ▱$ABCD$, with $\overline{AC} \cong \overline{BD}$
Prove: $ABCD$ is a rectangle.

Statements	Reasons
1) ▱$ABCD$, with $\overline{AC} \cong \overline{BD}$	1) Given
2) _?_ $\overline{AD} \cong \overline{BC}$	2) Opposite sides of a ▱ are congruent.
3) $\overline{DC} \cong \overline{CD}$	3) _?_ Reflexive Property
4) _?_ $\triangle ACD \cong \triangle BDC$	4) SSS
5) $\angle ADC$ and $\angle BCD$ are supplementary.	5) _?_ Consecutive ∠s of a ▱ are supp.
6) $\angle ADC \cong \angle BCD$	6) CPCTC
7) _?_ $\angle ADC$ and $\angle BCD$ are right angles.	7) Congruent supplementary angles are right angles.
8) $\angle DAB$ and $\angle CBA$ are right angles.	8) _?_ Opposite ∠s of a ▱ are ≅.
9) _?_ $ABCD$ is a rectangle.	9) Definition of a rectangle

Can you prove that the quadrilateral is a parallelogram based on the given information? Explain.

14. $\overline{FG} \parallel \overline{IH}$, $\overline{FI} \parallel \overline{GH}$ yes; opp. sides parallel
15. yes; opposite sides ≅
16. yes; opposite ∠s ≅
17. yes; opposite sides ≅
18. $\overline{AE} \cong \overline{EC}$, $\overline{BE} \cong \overline{ED}$ Yes; diagonals bisect each other.
19. Yes; one pair of opposite sides is parallel and ≅.
20. **Error Analysis** It is given that $\overline{MO} \cong \overline{TR}$ and $\overline{NP} \cong \overline{QS}$, where $MNOP$ and $TQRS$ are parallelograms. A student has said that if those statements are true, then $MNOP \cong TQRS$. Why is this student incorrect?
Answers may vary. Sample: It is given that the diagonals are congruent between the two parallelograms, but no angles are given as congruent.

All-in-One Resources/Online

Enrichment

6-3 **Enrichment**
Proving That a Quadrilateral Is a Parallelogram

Parallelogram Features

The figures below are diagonals of a parallelogram. Each has one diagonal longer than the other. The pair of diagonals have the same length across all four figures. The diagonals for each figure differ only in the number of degrees between them.

1. Connect the sides on each set of diagonals to form parallelograms. Write any observations you have about the set of parallelograms.
Answers may vary. Sample: They have different heights and bases.
2. The parallelograms are arranged so that their bases all sit on the same line. Draw this line. Also, extend the lines for the side opposite the bases of all the parallelograms that you completed. What do you notice?
Answers may vary. Sample: All these lines are parallel to each other.
3. Extend the lines for all the left and right sides of the parallelograms. What do you notice?
Answers may vary. Sample: The left and right sides of each parallelogram are parallel, but not all sides are parallel to each other.
4. Each of these parallelograms has the same set of diagonals. Name some real-world objects that utilize this feature of parallelograms.
Answers may vary. Sample: lifts, lamp extensions, accordions, jewelry box shelves, clothes drying racks

The parallelograms above have congruent diagonals. The parallelograms below have congruent side lengths. They are like a scissor jack that you would use to lift your car when changing a tire. The horizontal diagonal of a scissor jack is a long screw that, as you turn it, changes the degrees of the angles that it intersects.

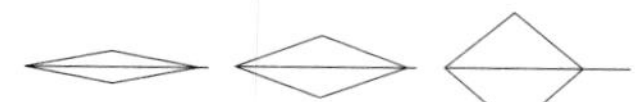

5. What is true about the diagonals of the quadrilaterals above?
The diagonals bisect each other, and they are perpendicular.
6. What makes these parallelograms safer for use in a jack design than the shapes at the top of the page? The perpendicular diagonals would cause a collapsing jack to go straight down instead of to the side.

Practice and Problem Solving Wkbk/ All-in-One Resources/Online

Think About a Plan

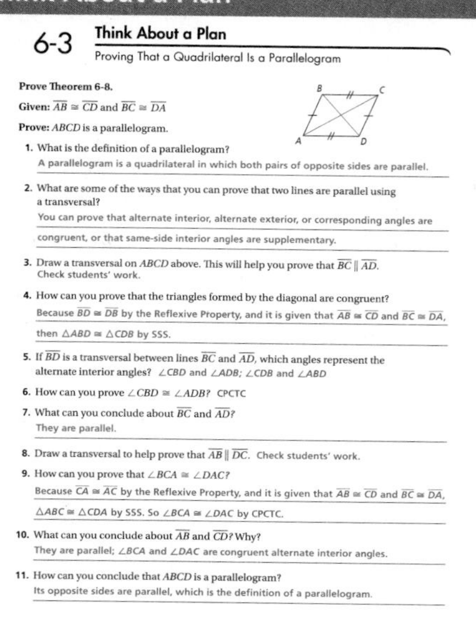

6-3 **Think About a Plan**
Proving That a Quadrilateral Is a Parallelogram

Prove Theorem 6-8.
Given: $\overline{AB} \cong \overline{CD}$ and $\overline{BC} \cong \overline{DA}$
Prove: $ABCD$ is a parallelogram.

1. What is the definition of a parallelogram?
A parallelogram is a quadrilateral in which both pairs of opposite sides are parallel.
2. What are some of the ways that you can prove that two lines are parallel using a transversal?
You can prove that alternate interior, alternate exterior, or corresponding angles are congruent, or that same-side interior angles are supplementary.
3. Draw a transversal on $ABCD$ above. This will help you prove that $\overline{BC} \parallel \overline{AD}$.
Check students' work.
4. How can you prove that the triangles formed by the diagonal are congruent?
Because $\overline{BD} \cong \overline{DB}$ by the Reflexive Property, and it is given that $\overline{AB} \cong \overline{CD}$ and $\overline{BC} \cong \overline{DA}$, then $\triangle ABD \cong \triangle CDB$ by SSS.
5. If $\overline{BD}$ is a transversal between lines $\overline{BC}$ and $\overline{AD}$, which angles represent the alternate interior angles? $\angle CBD$ and $\angle ADB$; $\angle CDB$ and $\angle ABD$
6. How can you prove $\angle CBD \cong \angle ADB$? CPCTC
7. What can you conclude about $\overline{BC}$ and $\overline{AD}$?
They are parallel.
8. Draw a transversal to help prove that $\overline{AB} \parallel \overline{DC}$. Check students' work.
9. How can you prove that $\angle BCA \cong \angle DAC$?
Because $\overline{CA} \cong \overline{AC}$ by the Reflexive Property, and it is given that $\overline{AB} \cong \overline{CD}$ and $\overline{BC} \cong \overline{DA}$, $\triangle ABC \cong \triangle CDA$ by SSS. So $\angle BCA \cong \angle DAC$ by CPCTC.
10. What can you conclude about $\overline{AB}$ and $\overline{CD}$? Why?
They are parallel; $\angle BCA$ and $\angle DAC$ are congruent alternate interior angles.
11. How can you conclude that $ABCD$ is a parallelogram?
Its opposite sides are parallel, which is the definition of a parallelogram.

Practice and Problem Solving Wkbk/ All-in-One Resources/Online

Standardized Test Prep

6-3 **Standardized Test Prep**
Proving That a Quadrilateral Is a Parallelogram

Multiple Choice

For Exercises 1–4, choose the correct letter.

1. For what value of x must $ABCD$ be a parallelogram? A
   A. 5 C. 15
   B. 10 D. 20
2. For what value of y must $QRST$ be a parallelogram? G
   F. 0.5 H. 2
   G. 1 I. 3
3. Which reason can be used to conclude that $DFGH$ is a parallelogram? C
   A. There are two pairs of congruent opposite angles.
   B. The diagonals bisect each other.
   C. There are two pairs of congruent opposite sides.
   D. There are two pairs of opposite parallel sides.
4. Which reason can be used to conclude that $LMNO$ is a parallelogram? I
   F. There are two pairs of congruent opposite angles.
   G. There are two pairs of congruent opposite sides.
   H. There are two pairs of opposite parallel sides.
   I. There is one pair of congruent and parallel sides.

Short Response

5. What additional pieces of information could be supplied to make $ABCD$ a parallelogram?
[2] Answers may vary. Sample: $\overline{AD} \parallel \overline{BC}$ or $\overline{AB} \cong \overline{DC}$
[1] Only one piece of information is listed. [0] no answer or wrong answer based on an inappropriate plan

Online Teacher Resource Center

Activities, Games, and Puzzles

6-3 **Activity: Geo-Models**
Proving That a Quadrilateral Is a Parallelogram

By definition, a quadrilateral is a parallelogram if both pairs of opposite sides are parallel. You can use a geoboard or geopaper to explore other conditions that seem to force a quadrilateral to be a parallelogram.

1. On geopaper or a geoboard, make pairs of segments that are congruent and parallel.
   a. The figure at the right shows one pair. Imagine the endpoints connected to form a quadrilateral. Does the quadrilateral appear to be a parallelogram? yes
   b. The photo at the left shows other pairs of congruent parallel segments. A large elastic band wraps around each pair to form a quadrilateral. Does each quadrilateral appear to be a parallelogram? yes
   c. Make a conjecture about a quadrilateral that has one pair of opposite sides congruent and parallel. A quadrilateral with 1 pair of congruent and parallel sides is a parallelogram.
2. Make pairs of segments that bisect each other.
   a. For the pair shown at the right, imagine a quadrilateral wrapped around them. Does the quadrilateral appear to be a parallelogram? yes

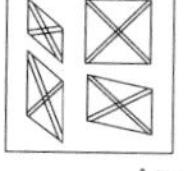

   b. The photo at the left shows four more quadrilaterals wrapped around diagonals that bisect each other. Does each quadrilateral appear to be a parallelogram? yes
   c. Make a conjecture about a quadrilateral whose diagonals bisect each other.
A quadrilateral whose diagonals bisect each other is a parallelogram.
3. The chart at the right shows a 2-by-2 geoboard and a 3-by-3 geoboard at the top. Copy and complete the chart, listing in each cell the number of different quadrilaterals of the indicated type that you can find on each size geoboard. Two quadrilaterals are different if they are not congruent. One cell has been completed for you.
4. How many different squares can you find on a 4-by-4 geoboard? 5

	2-by-2	3-by-3
parallelogram	1	5
rhombus	1	3
rectangle	1	4
square	1	3
kite	0	1
trapezoid	0	3

6-4 Properties of Rhombuses, Rectangles, and Squares

TN State Performance Indicators
SPI 3108.4.3 Identify, describe and/or apply the relationships and theorems involving different types of triangles, quadrilaterals and other polygons.
Also SPI 3108.1.1 and SPI 3108.4.2

Objectives To define and classify special types of parallelograms
To use properties of diagonals of rhombuses and rectangles

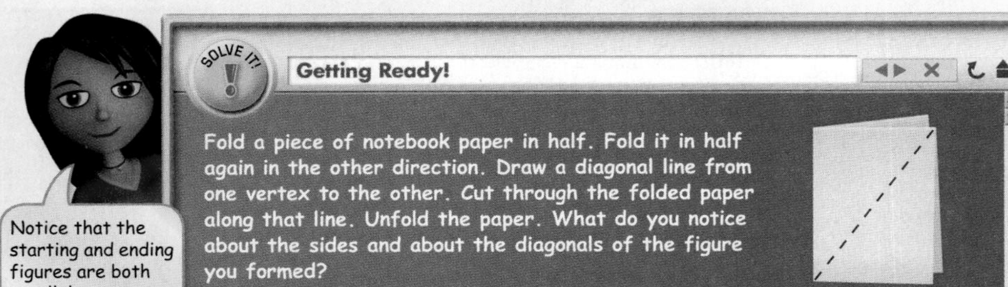

Getting Ready!
Fold a piece of notebook paper in half. Fold it in half again in the other direction. Draw a diagonal line from one vertex to the other. Cut through the folded paper along that line. Unfold the paper. What do you notice about the sides and about the diagonals of the figure you formed?
Notice that the starting and ending figures are both parallelograms.

In the Solve It, you formed a special type of parallelogram with characteristics that you will study in this lesson.

Lesson Vocabulary
- rhombus
- rectangle
- square

Essential Understanding The parallelograms in the Take Note box below have basic properties about their sides and angles that help identify them. The diagonals of these parallelograms also have certain properties.

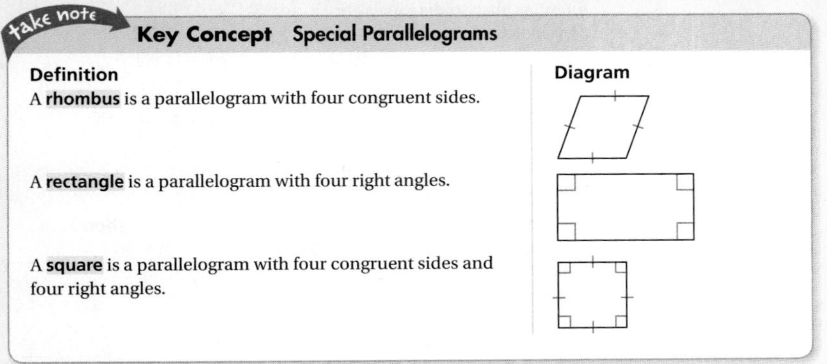

Key Concept Special Parallelograms

Definition	Diagram
A **rhombus** is a parallelogram with four congruent sides.	
A **rectangle** is a parallelogram with four right angles.	
A **square** is a parallelogram with four congruent sides and four right angles.	

1 Interactive Learning

Solve It!

PURPOSE To explore the properties of a rhombus
PROCESS Students may use previous knowledge of the properties of parallelograms as well as visual inspection.

FACILITATE

Q How can you tell that all four sides are congruent? **[When the quadrilateral is folded along both diagonals, all four sides overlap entirely.]**

Q How can you tell that the resulting figure is a parallelogram? **[When both pairs of opposite sides are congruent, the quadrilateral is a parallelogram.]**

Q Are consecutive angles congruent? How can you tell? **[No, when you fold the figure such that one angle is lying on top of another, the angles are not congruent.]**

ANSWER See Solve It in Answers on next page.
CONNECT THE MATH In the Solve It, you manipulated a paper figure to learn its special characteristics. In this lesson, students will learn the names of special parallelograms that have these characteristics.

2 Guided Instruction

Take Note

Have students create a hierarchical chart showing the relationships between the special parallelograms listed and the classifications: parallelogram, quadrilateral, and polygon. Make sure that students realize that in a hierarchical chart any figure listed must be a special case of all figures listed above it.

6-4 Preparing to Teach

BIG idea Reasoning and Proof

ESSENTIAL UNDERSTANDING
- The special parallelograms, rhombus, rectangle, and square, have basic properties about their sides, angles, and diagonals that help identify them.

Math Background

In Chapter 5, students were introduced to the hierarchical classification of triangles. Equilateral and isosceles triangles had all of the properties of any triangle as well as their own special properties. Likewise, the special parallelograms introduced in this lesson have all of the properties of parallelograms as well as their own special properties.

It is important to treat proofs as a means to an end and not as the goal of this lesson. Remind students that, for example, because a square is a special rhombus, it has all the properties of a rhombus. This relationship holds true for all special quadrilaterals in the hierarchy of quadrilaterals.

Support Student Learning

Use the **Geometry Companion** to engage and support students during instructions. See Lesson Resources at the end of this lesson for details.

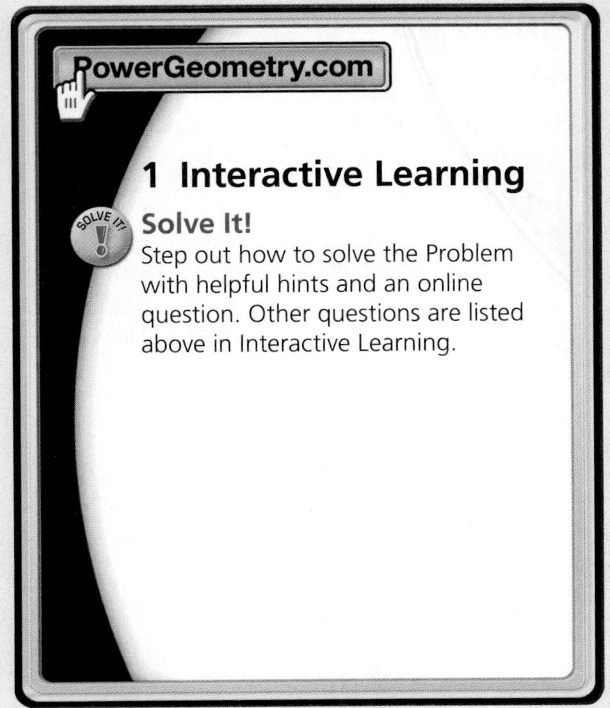

Problem 1

Q What conclusions can you draw regarding the angles of ▱*ABCD*? **[All angles are congruent and measure 90°.]**

Q What conclusions can you draw regarding the sides of ▱*ABCD*? **[Opposite sides are congruent and parallel.]**

Got It?

Q Can the parallelogram be classified as more than one of the quadrilaterals listed? Explain. **[Yes; every square is both a rhombus and a rectangle.]**

Take Note

Ask students the following questions in preparation for the proof of the theorem.

Q What does the Perpendicular Bisector Theorem state? **[If a point is on the perpendicular bisector of a segment, then it is equidistant from the endpoints of the segment.]**

Q Which labeled points are equidistant from the endpoints of segment *BD*? Explain. **[Since *ABCD* is a rhombus and all sides are congruent, points *A* and *C* are equidistant from the endpoints of *BD*.]**

Ask students the following question in preparation for the proof of the theorem.

Q What are the properties of an isosceles triangle? **[Isosceles triangles have two congruent sides and two congruent base angles that are opposite those sides by the Isosceles Triangle Theorem.]**

The Venn diagram at the right shows the relationships among special parallelograms.

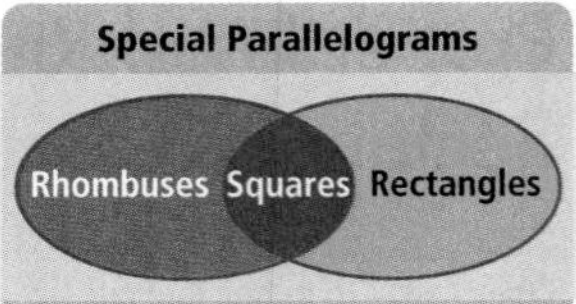

Think

How do you decide whether *ABCD* is a rhombus, rectangle, or square?
Use the definitions of *rhombus*, *rectangle*, and *square* along with the markings on the figure.

Problem 1 Classifying Special Parallelograms

Is ▱*ABCD* a rhombus, a rectangle, or a square? Explain.

▱*ABCD* is a rectangle. Opposite angles of a parallelogram are congruent so $m\angle D$ is 90. By the Same-Side Interior Angles Theorem, $m\angle A = 90$ and $m\angle C = 90$. Since ▱*ABCD* has four right angles, it is a rectangle. You cannot conclude that *ABCD* is a square because you do not know its side lengths.

Got It? 1. Is ▱*EFGH* a rhombus, a rectangle, or a square? Explain.

Take note

Theorem 6-13

Theorem	If . . .	Then . . .
If a parallelogram is a rhombus, then its diagonals are perpendicular.	*ABCD* is a rhombus	$\overline{AC} \perp \overline{BD}$

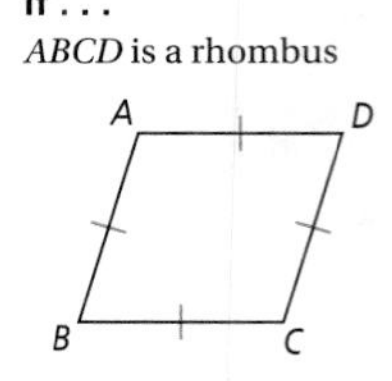

Theorem 6-14

Theorem	If . . .	Then . . .
If a parallelogram is a rhombus, then each diagonal bisects a pair of opposite angles.	*ABCD* is a rhombus	$\angle 1 \cong \angle 2$ $\angle 3 \cong \angle 4$ $\angle 5 \cong \angle 6$ $\angle 7 \cong \angle 8$

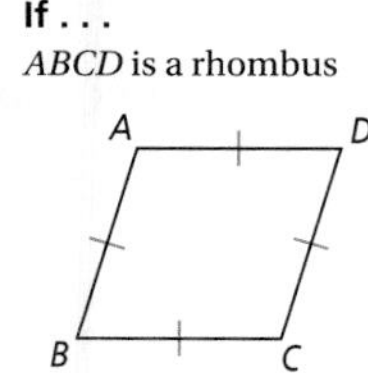

You will prove Theorem 6-14 in Exercise 45.

Answers

Solve It!

The quadrilateral has ≅ sides. Diagonals are ⊥ bis. of each other, and each diagonal bisects two ∠s.

Got It?

1. Rhombus; opp. sides of a ▱ are ≅, so all sides of *EFGH* are ≅, and there are no rt. ∠s.

PowerGeometry.com

2 Guided Instruction

Each Problem is worked out and supported online.

Problem 1
Classifying Special Parallelograms
Animated

Problem 2
Finding Angle Measures
Animated

Problem 3
Finding Diagonal Length
Animated

Support in Geometry Companion
- Vocabulary
- Key Concepts
- Got It?

Proof **Proof of Theorem 6-13**

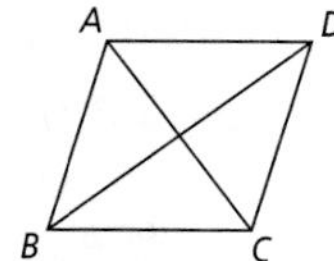

Given: *ABCD* is a rhombus.

Prove: The diagonals of *ABCD* are perpendicular.

Statements	Reasons
1) *A* and *C* are equidistant from *B* and *D*; *B* and *D* are equidistant from *A* and *C*.	**1)** All sides of a rhombus are $\cong$.
2) *A* and *C* are on the perpendicular bisector of $\overline{BD}$; *B* and *D* are on the perpendicular bisector of $\overline{AC}$.	**2)** Converse of the Perpendicular Bisector Theorem
3) $\overline{AC} \perp \overline{BD}$	**3)** Through two points, there is one unique line perpendicular to a given line.

You can use Theorems 6-13 and 6-14 to find angle measures in a rhombus.

Think

How are the numbered angles formed?
The angles are formed by diagonals. Use what you know about the diagonals of a rhombus to find the angle measures.

Problem 2 Finding Angle Measures

What are the measures of the numbered angles in rhombus *ABCD*?

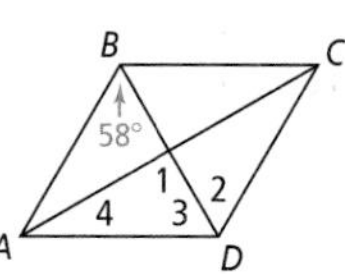

$m\angle 1 = 90$	The diagonals of a rhombus are $\perp$.
$m\angle 2 = 58$	Alternate Interior Angles Theorem
$m\angle 3 = 58$	Each diagonal of a rhombus bisects a pair of opposite angles.
$m\angle 1 + m\angle 3 + m\angle 4 = 180$	Triangle Angle-Sum Theorem
$90 + 58 + m\angle 4 = 180$	Substitute.
$148 + m\angle 4 = 180$	Simplify.
$m\angle 4 = 32$	Subtract 148 from each side.

Got It? **2.** What are the measures of the numbered angles in rhombus *PQRS*?

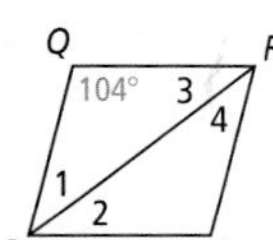

Have students make all the geometric markings that identify special characteristics, given that *ABCD* is a rhombus. Then have them identify what information might be useful in the proof. The following marks can be added to the diagram.

- Parallel line indicators on $\overline{AD}$ and $\overline{BC}$, and $\overline{BA}$ and $\overline{CD}$
- Congruence marks on $\overline{AD}$, $\overline{CD}$, $\overline{BC}$, $\overline{AB}$
- Congruence marks on $\angle ADB$ and $\angle DBC$, $\angle BDC$ and $\angle DBA$, $\angle DAC$ and $\angle BCA$, $\angle CAB$ and $\angle ACD$

Problem 2

Q What is the measure of $\angle DBC$? Explain. **[58, $\overline{BD}$ is a diagonal of rhombus *ABCD*.]**

Q What is the sum of the measures of $\angle 4$ and $\angle 3$? Explain. **[90, $\angle 4$ and $\angle 3$ form a triangle along with a right angle.]**

Got It? ERROR PREVENTION

Remind students that the sum of all four angles in rhombus *PQRS* is 360 because the figure is a quadrilateral. Hence, the sum of the measures of angles 3 and 4 must be 76. Diagonals bisect the opposite angles of a rhombus, so the measures of angles 3 and 4 are both 38.

Alternatively, point out that $\triangle PQR$ is an isosceles triangle with a vertex angle of 104°, so the two base angles, $\angle 1$ and $\angle 3$ would each have a measure of $\frac{180 - 104}{2} = 38$.

Additional Problems

1. Is parallelogram *FGHJ* a rhombus, a rectangle, or a square? Explain.

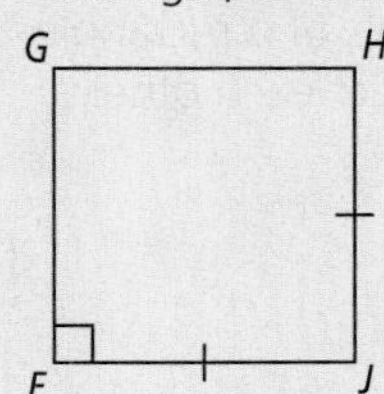

ANSWER Square; the parallelogram has 4 right angles by the Same-Side Interior Angles Theorem. It also has 4 congruent sides since opposite sides are congruent. Because it is a square, it is also a rhombus and a rectangle.

2. What are the measures of the numbered angles in rhombus *ABCD*?

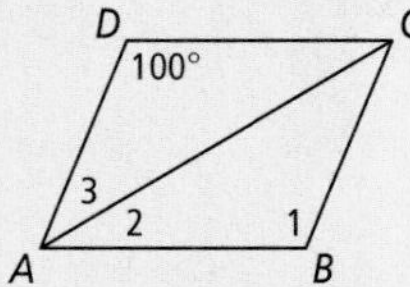

ANSWER $m\angle 1 = 100$, $m\angle 2 = 40$, $m\angle 3 = 40$

3. In rectangle *MNOP*, $PN = 7x - 8$ and $MO = 4x + 10$. What is the length of $\overline{PN}$?

ANSWER 34

Answers

Got It? (continued)

2. $m\angle 1 = m\angle 2 = m\angle 3 = m\angle 4 = 38$

Take Note

Ask students the following question in preparation for the proof of the theorem.

Q What congruence theorem can you use to prove that $\triangle ABC \cong \triangle DCB$? Explain. **[SAS, you know that $\overline{AB} \cong \overline{DC}$, $\overline{BC} \cong \overline{BC}$, and $\angle ABC \cong \angle DCB$.]**

Problem 3

TACTILE LEARNERS

Q If a student selects answer choice B, what mistake is he or she likely making? **[The student is likely indicating the value of *x* rather than the length of $\overline{RB}$.]**

Q Could you also substitute the value of *x* into the expression $2x + 15$ to find *RB*? Explain. **[Yes, $RB = SF$, so you can use either expression.]**

Got It?

Q What is the length of *PM*? of *PN*? Explain. **[The length of both segments is 21.5. $\overline{MO}$ and $\overline{LN}$ are bisectors of each other and $MO = LN = 43$.]**

The diagonals of a rectangle also have a special property.

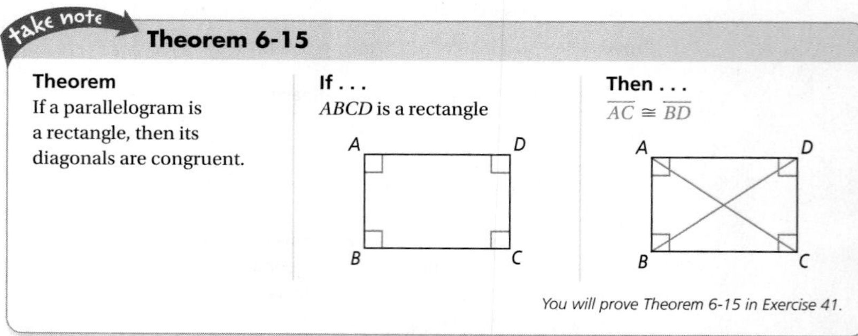

take note — Theorem 6-15

Theorem	If . . .	Then . . .
If a parallelogram is a rectangle, then its diagonals are congruent.	*ABCD* is a rectangle	$\overline{AC} \cong \overline{BD}$

You will prove Theorem 6-15 in Exercise 41.

Problem 3 Finding Diagonal Length

Plan

How can you find the length of a diagonal? Since *RSBF* is a rectangle and its diagonals are congruent, use the expressions to *write an equation.*

Multiple Choice **In rectangle *RSBF*, $SF = 2x + 15$ and $RB = 5x - 12$. What is the length of a diagonal?**

Ⓐ 1 Ⓑ 9 Ⓒ 18 Ⓓ 33

Think	Write
You know that the diagonals of a rectangle are congruent, so their lengths are equal.	$SF = RB$
Set the algebraic expressions for *SF* and *RB* equal to each other and find the value of *x*.	$2x + 15 = 5x - 12$ $15 = 3x - 12$ $27 = 3x$ $9 = x$
Substitute 9 for *x* in the expression for *RB*.	$RB = 5x - 12$ $= 5(9) - 12$ $= 33$ The correct answer is D.

Got It? **3. a.** If $LN = 4x - 17$ and $MO = 2x + 13$, what are the lengths of the diagonals of rectangle *LMNO*?

b. Reasoning What type of triangle is $\triangle PMN$? Explain.

Answers

Got It? (continued)

3a. 43

b. Isosc.; diagonals of a rectangle are ≅ and bisect each other.

Lesson Check

Do you know HOW?

Is each parallelogram a rhombus, rectangle, or square? Explain.

1. 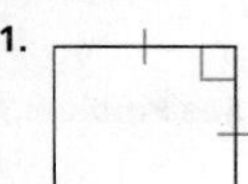

2. 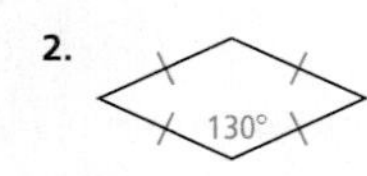

3. What are the measures of the numbered angles in the rhombus?

2, 1, 3, 50°

4. Algebra $JKLM$ is a rectangle. If $JL = 4x - 12$ and $MK = x$, what is the value of x? What is the length of each diagonal?

Do you UNDERSTAND?

5. Vocabulary Which special parallelograms are equiangular? Which special parallelograms are equilateral?

6. Error Analysis Your class needs to find the value of x for which $\square DEFG$ is a rectangle. A classmate's work is shown below. What is the error? Explain.

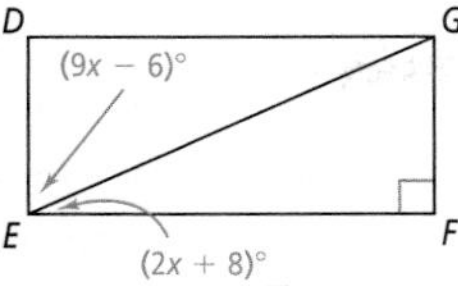

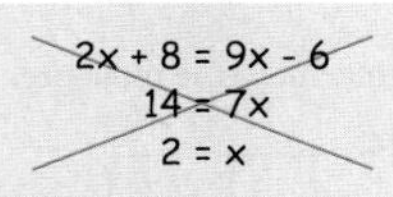

Practice and Problem-Solving Exercises

A Practice

Decide whether the parallelogram is a rhombus, a rectangle, or a square. Explain.

7. 

8. 

Find the measures of the numbered angles in each rhombus.

9. 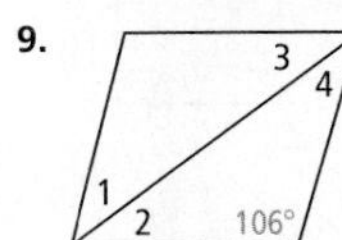

10. 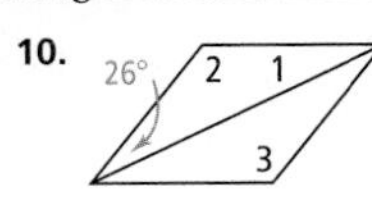

11. 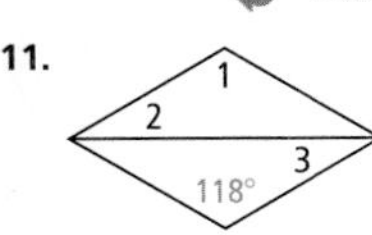

12. 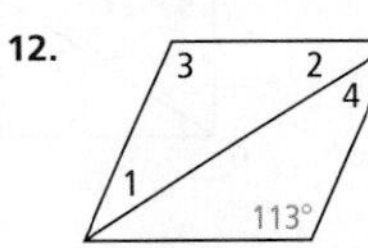

13. 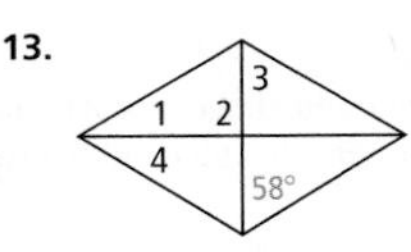

14. 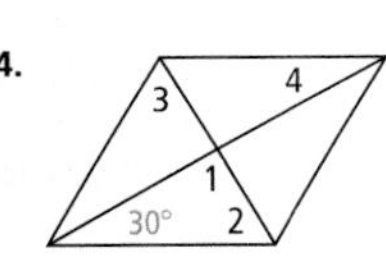

3 Lesson Check

Do you know HOW?

- If students have difficulty with Exercise 3, then have them identify which angles are congruent and which angles are supplementary.

Do you UNDERSTAND?

- If students have difficulty with Exercise 6, then have them identify the special parallelogram that the classmate was likely thinking of when he wrote the equation $2x + 8 = 9x - 6$.

Close

Q Why can quadrilaterals that are squares be considered the intersection of parallelograms, rhombuses, and rectangles? **[A quadrilateral that is a square must have all properties of parallelograms, rhombuses, and rectangles.]**

Lesson Check

1. Square; it is a rectangle because of the rt. ∠, and a rhombus because it has 4 ≅ sides.
2. Rhombus; it has 4 ≅ sides, and no rt. ∠s.
3. $m\angle 1 = 40$, $m\angle 2 = 90$, $m\angle 3 = 50$
4. 4, 4
5. rectangle and square; rhombus and square
6. The first step should be $2x + 8 + 9x - 6 = 90$.

Practice and Problem-Solving Exercises

7. Rectangle; the ▱ has 4 rt. ∠s and does not have 4 ≅ sides.
8. Rhombus; the ▱ has 4 ≅ sides and no rt. ∠s.
9. $m\angle 1 = m\angle 2 = m\angle 3 = m\angle 4 = 37$
10. $m\angle 1 = 26$, $m\angle 2 = m\angle 3 = 128$
11. $m\angle 1 = 118$, $m\angle 2 = m\angle 3 = 31$
12. $m\angle 1 = m\angle 2 = 33.5$, $m\angle 3 = 113$, $m\angle 4 = 33.5$
13. $m\angle 1 = 32$, $m\angle 2 = 90$, $m\angle 3 = 58$, $m\angle 4 = 32$
14. $m\angle 1 = 90$, $m\angle 2 = m\angle 3 = 60$, $m\angle 4 = 30$

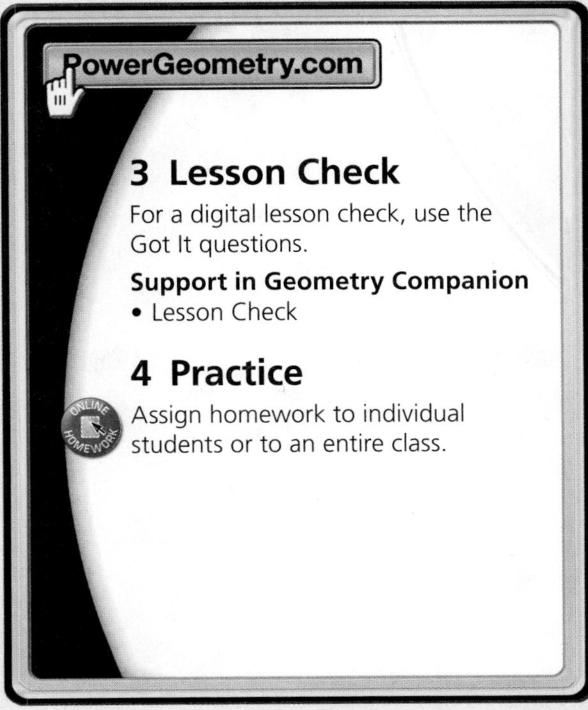

4 Practice

ASSIGNMENT GUIDE

Basic: 7–23 all, 24–40 even, 41, 43, 46, 47
Average: 7–23 odd, 24–52
Advanced: 7–23 odd, 24–54
Standardized Test Prep: 55–58
Mixed Review: 59–69

Reasoning exercises have blue headings.
Applications exercises have red headings.

EXERCISE 47: Use the Think About a Plan worksheet in the **Practice and Problem Solving Workbook** (also available in the Teaching Resources in print and online) to further support students' development in becoming independent learners.

HOMEWORK QUICK CHECK

To check students' understanding of key skills and concepts, go over Exercises 13, 19, 34, 46, and 47.

Find the measures of the numbered angles in each rhombus.

15.

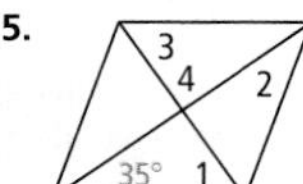

16.

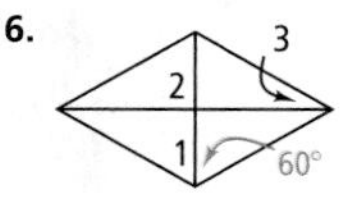

17.

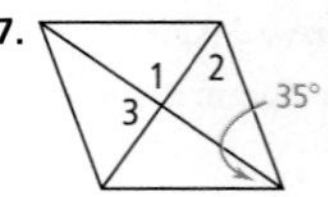

Algebra ***LMNP* is a rectangle. Find the value of *x* and the length of each diagonal.**

See Problem 3.

18. $LN = x$ and $MP = 2x - 4$

19. $LN = 5x - 8$ and $MP = 2x + 1$

20. $LN = 3x + 1$ and $MP = 8x - 4$

21. $LN = 9x - 14$ and $MP = 7x + 4$

22. $LN = 7x - 2$ and $MP = 4x + 3$

23. $LN = 3x + 5$ and $MP = 9x - 10$

Determine the most precise name for each quadrilateral.

24.

25.

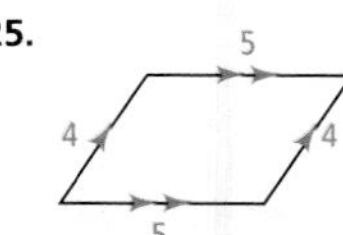

26.

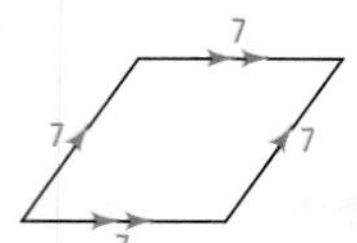

27.

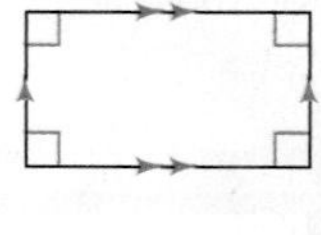

List the quadrilaterals that have the given property. Choose among *parallelogram, rhombus, rectangle,* and *square.*

28. All sides are ≅.

29. Opposite sides are ≅.

30. Opposite sides are ∥.

31. Opposite ∠s are ≅.

32. All ∠s are right ∠s.

33. Consecutive ∠s are supplementary.

34. Diagonals bisect each other.

35. Diagonals are ≅.

36. Diagonals are ⊥.

37. Each diagonal bisects opposite ∠s.

Algebra **Find the values of the variables. Then find the side lengths.**

38. rhombus

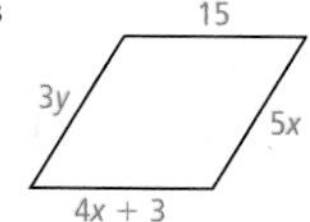

39. square

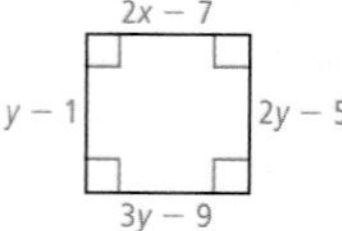

40. **Think About a Plan** Write a proof.

Proof

Given: Rectangle *PLAN*

Prove: $\triangle LTP \cong \triangle NTA$

- What do you know about the diagonals of rectangles?
- Which triangle congruence postulate or theorem can you use?

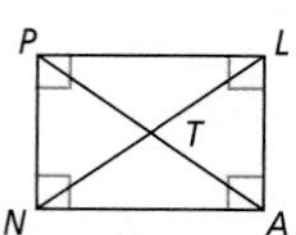

Answers

Practice and Problem-Solving Exercises (continued)

15. $m\angle 1 = 55$, $m\angle 2 = 35$, $m\angle 3 = 55$, $m\angle 4 = 90$

16. $m\angle 1 = 60$, $m\angle 2 = 90$, $m\angle 3 = 30$

17. $m\angle 1 = 90$, $m\angle 2 = 55$, $m\angle 3 = 90$

18. $x = 4$; $LN = MP = 4$

19. $x = 3$; $LN = MP = 7$

20. $x = 1$; $LN = MP = 4$

21. $x = 9$; $LN = MP = 67$

22. $x = \frac{5}{3}$; $LN = MP = \frac{29}{3}$

23. $x = 2.5$; $LN = MP = 12.5$

24. rhombus

25. ▱

26. rhombus

27. rectangle

28. rhombus, square

29. ▱, rhombus, rectangle, square

30. ▱, rhombus, rectangle, square

31. ▱, rhombus, rectangle, square

32. rectangle, square

33. ▱, rhombus, rectangle, square

34. ▱, rhombus, rectangle, square

35. rectangle, square

36. rhombus, square

37. rhombus, square

38. $x = 3$, $y = 5$; all sides are 15

39. $x = 5$, $y = 4$; all sides are 3

40. Answers may vary. Sample:

1. *PLAN* is a rectangle. (Given)
2. $\overline{PA} \cong \overline{LN}$ (Diagonals of a rectangle are ≅.)
3. $TP = TL = TN = TA$ (Diagonals of a ▱ bisect each other.)
4. $\angle LTP \cong \angle ATN$ (Vert. ∠s are ≅.)
5. $\triangle LTP \cong \triangle ATN$ (SAS)

41. Developing Proof Complete the flow proof of Theorem 6-15.

Given: *ABCD* is a rectangle.

Prove: $\overline{AC} \cong \overline{BD}$

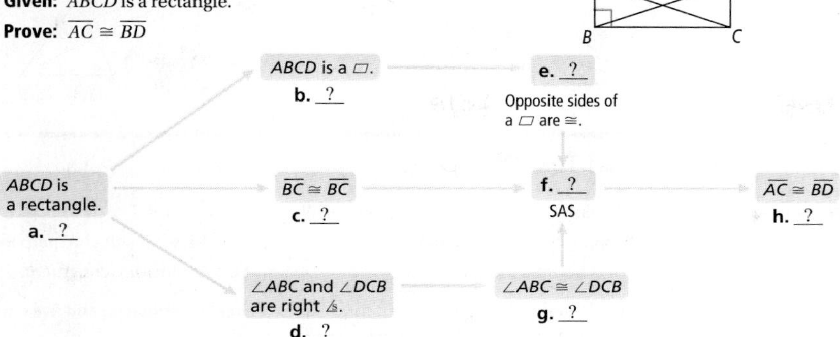

Algebra **Find the value(s) of the variable(s) for each parallelogram.**

42. $RZ = 2x + 5$, $SW = 5x - 20$

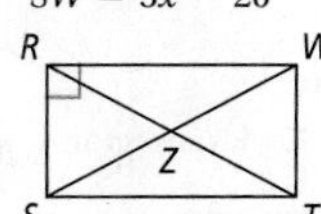

43. $m\angle 1 = 3y - 6$

44. $BD = 4x - y + 1$

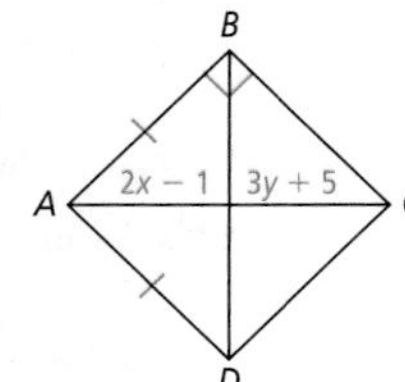

45. Prove Theorem 6-14.

Proof **Given:** *ABCD* is a rhombus.

Prove: $\overline{AC}$ bisects $\angle BAD$ and $\angle BCD$.

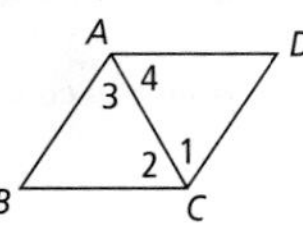

46. Writing Summarize the properties of squares that follow from a square being (a) a parallelogram, (b) a rhombus, and (c) a rectangle.

47. Algebra Find the angle measures and the side lengths of the rhombus at the right.

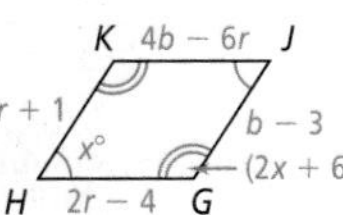

48. Open-Ended On graph paper, draw a parallelogram that is neither a rectangle nor a rhombus.

Algebra ***ABCD*** **is a rectangle. Find the length of each diagonal.**

49. $AC = 2(x - 3)$ and $BD = x + 5$

50. $AC = 2(5a + 1)$ and $BD = 2(a + 1)$

51. $AC = \frac{3y}{5}$ and $BD = 3y - 4$

52. $AC = \frac{3c}{9}$ and $BD = 4 - c$

41a. Given
b. Def. of rectangle
c. Refl. Prop. of ≅
d. Def. of rectangle
e. $\overline{AB} \cong \overline{DC}$
f. $\triangle ABC \cong \triangle DCB$
g. All rt. ∠s are ≅.
h. Corresp. parts of ≅ △s are ≅.
42. 30
43. $x = 5$, $y = 32$, $z = 7.5$
44. $x = 7.5$, $y = 3$
45. Answers may vary. Sample:
1. *ABCD* is a rhombus. (Given)
2. $\overline{AB} \cong \overline{AD}$ and $\overline{CB} \cong \overline{CD}$. (Def. of rhombus)
3. $\overline{AC} \cong \overline{AC}$ (Refl. Prop. of ≅)
4. $\triangle ABC \cong \triangle ADC$ (SSS)
5. $\angle 3 \cong \angle 4$ and $\angle 2 \cong \angle 1$. (Corresp. parts of ≅ △s are ≅.)
6. $\overline{AC}$ bisects $\angle BAD$ and $\angle BCD$. (Def. of ∠ bisector)

46a. Opp. sides are ≅ and ∥; consecutive ∠s are suppl.; opp. ∠s are ≅; diagonals bisect each other.
b. All 4 sides are ≅; diagonals are ⊥ and bisect opp. ∠s.
c. All 4 ∠s are rt. ∠s; diagonals are ≅.
47. $m\angle H = m\angle J = 58$, $m\angle K = m\angle G = 122$, $HK = KJ = JG = GH = 6$
48. Answers may vary. Sample:

49. $AC = BD = 16$
50. $AC = BD = 2$
51. $AC = BD = 1$
52. $AC = BD = 1$

Answers

Practice and Problem-Solving Exercises (continued)

53. 2
54. −1
55. D
56. G
57. A
58. [2] Assume that $\triangle PQR$ is a rt. $\triangle$.
[1] incomplete OR incorrect statement
59. Yes; both pairs of opp. sides of the quad. are $\cong$.
60. No; two opp. sides are $\cong$ and two opp. sides are $\parallel$, but not the same pair of opp. sides.
61. Yes; diagonals of the quad. bisect each other.
62. 6
63. 16
64. 5
65. $\overline{RQ}$
66. $\overline{PR}$
67. $\overline{ST}$
68. Answers may vary. Sample:

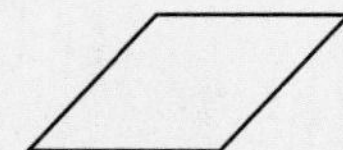

69. Answers may vary. Sample:

Challenge **Algebra** **Find the value of x in the rhombus.**

53.

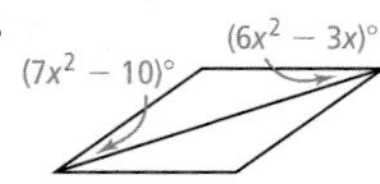

54.

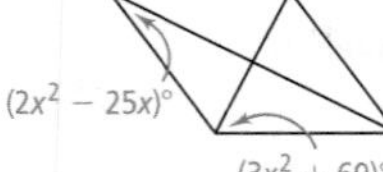

Standardized Test Prep

SAT/ACT

55. Which statement is true for some, but not all, rectangles?
- (A) Opposite sides are parallel.
- (B) It is a parallelogram.
- (C) Adjacent sides are perpendicular.
- (D) All sides are congruent.

56. A part of a design for a quilting pattern consists of a regular pentagon and five isosceles triangles, as shown. What is $m\angle 1$?

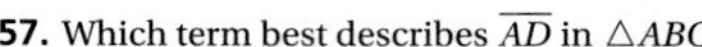
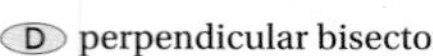

- (F) 18
- (G) 36
- (H) 72
- (I) 108

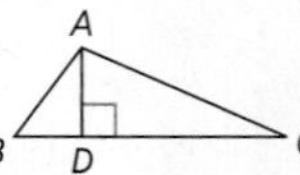

57. Which term best describes $\overline{AD}$ in $\triangle ABC$?
- (A) altitude
- (B) angle bisector
- (C) median
- (D) perpendicular bisector

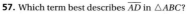

Short Response

58. Write the first step of an indirect proof that $\triangle PQR$ is not a right triangle.

Mixed Review

Can you conclude that the quadrilateral is a parallelogram? Explain. See Lesson 6-3.

59.

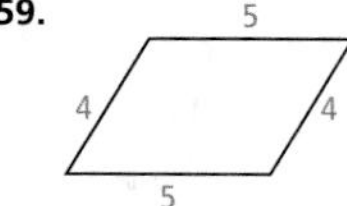

60.

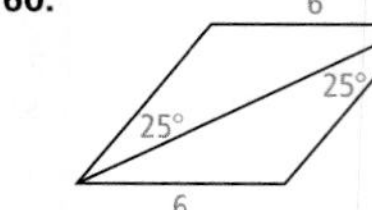

61.

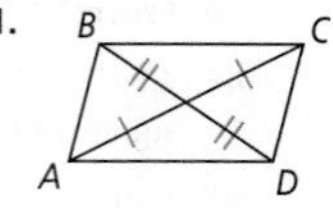

In $\triangle PQR$, points S, T, and U are midpoints. Complete each statement. See Lesson 5-1.

62. $TQ = \underline{\ ?\ }$ **63.** $PQ = \underline{\ ?\ }$ **64.** $TU = \underline{\ ?\ }$

65. $\overline{SU} \parallel \underline{\ ?\ }$ **66.** $\overline{TU} \parallel \underline{\ ?\ }$ **67.** $\overline{PQ} \parallel \underline{\ ?\ }$

Get Ready! **To prepare for Lesson 6-5, do Exercises 68 and 69.**

68. Draw a rhombus that is not a square. See Lesson 6-4.

69. Draw a rectangle that is not a square.

6-4 Lesson Resources

Differentiated Remediation

Instructional Support

Geometry Companion

Students can use the **Geometry Companion** worktext (4 pages) . . .

- New Vocabulary
- Key Concepts
- Got It for each Problem
- Lesson Check

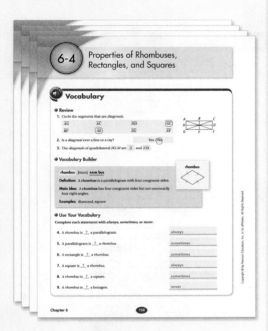

ELL Support

Focus on Language Place the lesson on an overhead and read the essential portions, including the direction lines. Use your finger to point at each word as students follow along. Ask students to analyze the key words and phrases such as "characteristics," "properties," and "congruent." Ask students to clarify the meaning of these words in their own words.

Use Manipulatives Cut out a variety of rhombuses, rectangles, and squares from construction paper. Divide students into pairs of mixed abilities. Give each student pair several quadrilaterals. Ask them to classify each of the shapes they receive as a rhombus, a rectangle, or a square. Invite students to share their reasoning. Use the sharing as an instructional opportunity as well as peer teaching.

5 Assess & Remediate

Lesson Quiz

1. Is parallelogram *KLMN* a rhombus, a rectangle, or a square? Explain.

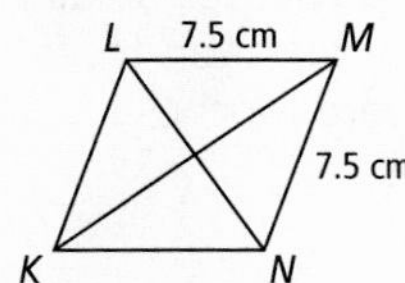

2. In the parallelogram above, if $m\angle KLN = 63$, what is $m\angle MNL$?
3. In square *ABCD*, $AE = 3x + 5$ and $BD = 10x + 2$. What is the length of $\overline{AC}$?

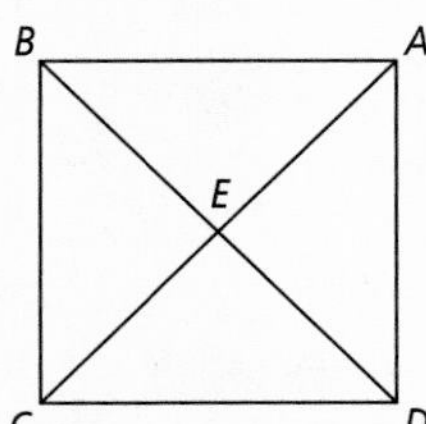

4. **Do you UNDERSTAND?** You are asked to draw an equiangular rhombus, an equilateral rectangle, and a parallelogram with four right angles. Will all three figures be squares?

ANSWERS TO LESSON QUIZ

1. rhombus; The opposite sides of a parallelogram are congruent, so the figure has 4 congruent sides.
2. 63
3. 22
4. A parallelogram with four right angles is a rectangle but not necessarily a square.

PRESCRIPTION FOR REMEDIATION

Use the student work on the Lesson Quiz to prescribe a differentiated review assignment.

Points	Differentiated Remediation
0–2	Intervention
3	On-level
4	Extension

PowerGeometry.com

5 Assess & Remediate

Assign the Lesson Quiz. Appropriate intervention, practice, or enrichment is automatically generated based on student performance.

Intervention

- **Reteaching** (2 pages) Provides reteaching and practice exercises for the key lesson concepts. Use with struggling students or absent students.
- **English Language Learner Support** Helps students develop and reinforce mathematical vocabulary and key concepts.

All-in-One Resources/Online

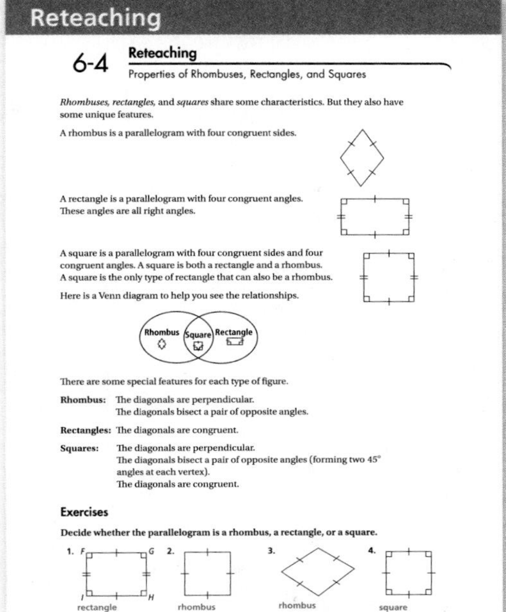

Reteaching

6-4 **Reteaching**

Properties of Rhombuses, Rectangles, and Squares

Rhombuses, rectangles, and *squares* share some characteristics. But they also have some unique features.

A rhombus is a parallelogram with four congruent sides.

A rectangle is a parallelogram with four congruent angles. These angles are all right angles.

A square is a parallelogram with four congruent sides and four congruent angles. A square is both a rectangle and a rhombus. A square is the only type of rectangle that can also be a rhombus.

Here is a Venn diagram to help you see the relationships.

Rhombus Square Rectangle

There are some special features for each type of figure.

Rhombus: The diagonals are perpendicular. The diagonals bisect a pair of opposite angles.

Rectangles: The diagonals are congruent.

Squares: The diagonals are perpendicular. The diagonals bisect a pair of opposite angles (forming two 45° angles at each vertex). The diagonals are congruent.

Exercises

Decide whether the parallelogram is a rhombus, a rectangle, or a square.

1. F G I H rectangle
2. rhombus
3. rhombus
4. square

All-in-One Resources/Online

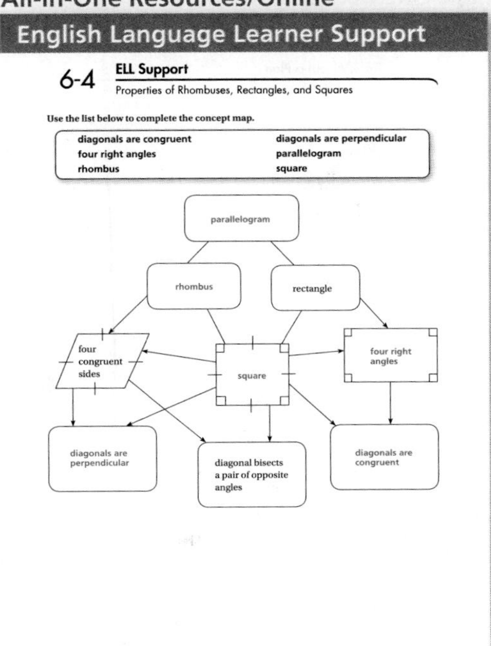

English Language Learner Support

6-4 **ELL Support**

Properties of Rhombuses, Rectangles, and Squares

Use the list below to complete the concept map.

diagonals are congruent	diagonals are perpendicular
four right angles	parallelogram
rhombus	square

Differentiated Remediation *continued*

On-Level

- **Practice** (2 pages) Provides extra practice for each lesson. For simpler practice exercises, use the Form K Practice pages found in the All-in-One Teaching Resources and online.
- **Think About a Plan** Helps students develop specific problem-solving skills and strategies by providing scaffolded guiding questions.
- **Standardized Test Prep** Focuses on all major exercises, all major question types, and helps students prepare for the high-stakes assessments.

Practice and Problem Solving Wkbk/ All-in-One Resources/Online

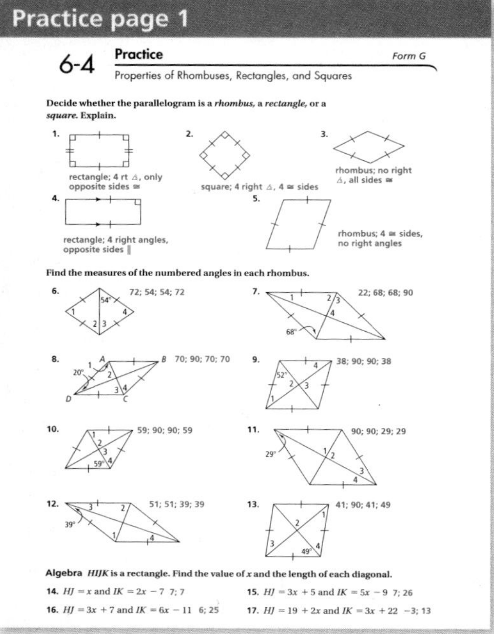

Practice page 1

6-4 Practice *Form G*

Properties of Rhombuses, Rectangles, and Squares

Decide whether the parallelogram is a *rhombus*, a *rectangle*, or a *square*. Explain.

1. rectangle; 4 rt ∠s, only opposite sides ≅
2. square; 4 right ∠s, 4 ≅ sides
3. rhombus; no right ∠s, all sides ≅
4. rectangle; 4 right angles, opposite sides ∥
5. rhombus; 4 ≅ sides, no right angles

Find the measures of the numbered angles in each rhombus.

6. 72; 54; 54; 72
7. 22; 68; 68; 90
8. 70; 90; 70; 70
9. 38; 90; 90; 38
10. 59; 90; 90; 59
11. 90; 90; 29; 29
12. 51; 51; 39; 39
13. 41; 90; 41; 49

Algebra ***HIJK* is a rectangle. Find the value of *x* and the length of each diagonal.**

14. $HJ = x$ and $IK = 2x - 7$ 7; 7
15. $HJ = 3x + 5$ and $IK = 5x - 9$ 7; 26
16. $HJ = 3x + 7$ and $IK = 6x - 11$ 6; 25
17. $HJ = 19 + 2x$ and $IK = 3x + 22$ −3; 13

Practice and Problem Solving Wkbk/ All-in-One Resources/Online

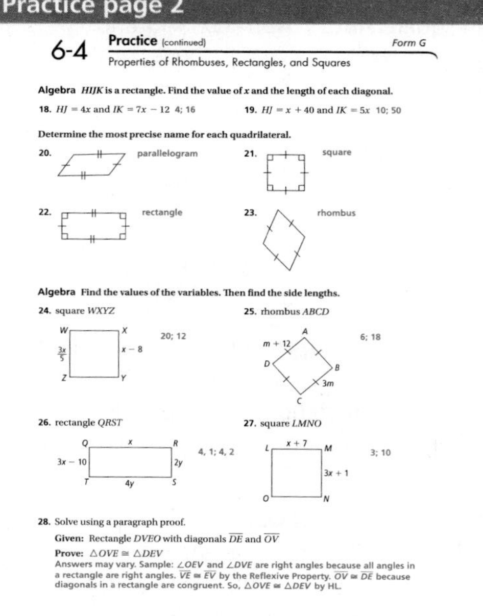

Practice page 2

6-4 Practice (continued) *Form G*

Properties of Rhombuses, Rectangles, and Squares

Algebra ***HIJK* is a rectangle. Find the value of *x* and the length of each diagonal.**

18. $HJ = 4x$ and $IK = 7x - 12$ 4; 16
19. $HJ = x + 40$ and $IK = 5x$ 10; 50

Determine the most precise name for each quadrilateral.

20. parallelogram
21. square
22. rectangle
23. rhombus

Algebra Find the values of the variables. Then find the side lengths.

24. square *WXYZ* 20; 12
25. rhombus *ABCD* 6; 18
26. rectangle *QRST* 4, 1; 4, 2
27. square *LMNO* 3; 10

28. Solve using a paragraph proof.

Given: Rectangle *DVEO* with diagonals $\overline{DE}$ and $\overline{OV}$

Prove: $\triangle OVE \cong \triangle DEV$

Answers may vary. Sample: ∠*OEV* and ∠*DVE* are right angles because all angles in a rectangle are right angles. $\overline{VE} \cong \overline{EV}$ by the Reflexive Property. $\overline{OV} \cong \overline{DE}$ because diagonals in a rectangle are congruent. So, $\triangle OVE \cong \triangle DEV$ by HL.

Practice and Problem Solving Wkbk/ All-in-One Resources/Online

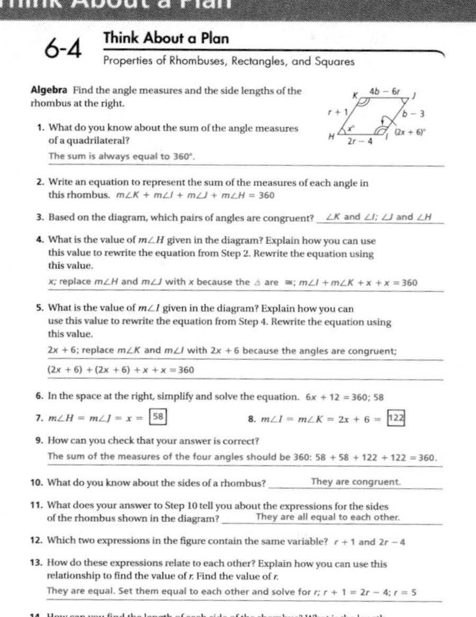

Think About a Plan

6-4 Think About a Plan

Properties of Rhombuses, Rectangles, and Squares

Algebra Find the angle measures and the side lengths of the rhombus at the right.

1. What do you know about the sum of the angle measures of a quadrilateral? The sum is always equal to 360°.
2. Write an equation to represent the sum of the measures of each angle in this rhombus. $m\angle K + m\angle I + m\angle J + m\angle H = 360$
3. Based on the diagram, which pairs of angles are congruent? ∠*K* and ∠*I*; ∠*J* and ∠*H*
4. What is the value of $m\angle H$ given in the diagram? Explain how you can use this value to rewrite the equation from Step 2. Rewrite the equation using this value. *x*; replace $m\angle H$ and $m\angle J$ with *x* because the ∠s are ≅; $m\angle I + m\angle K + x + x = 360$
5. What is the value of $m\angle I$ given in the diagram? Explain how you can use this value to rewrite the equation from Step 4. Rewrite the equation using this value. $2x + 6$; replace $m\angle K$ and $m\angle I$ with $2x + 6$ because the angles are congruent; $(2x + 6) + (2x + 6) + x + x = 360$
6. In the space at the right, simplify and solve the equation. $6x + 12 = 360$; 58
7. $m\angle H = m\angle J = x =$ 58
8. $m\angle I = m\angle K = 2x + 6 =$ 122
9. How can you check that your answer is correct? The sum of the measures of the four angles should be 360: $58 + 58 + 122 + 122 = 360$.
10. What do you know about the sides of a rhombus? They are congruent.
11. What does your answer to Step 10 tell you about the expressions for the sides of the rhombus shown in the diagram? They are all equal to each other.
12. Which two expressions in the figure contain the same variable? $r + 1$ and $2r - 4$
13. How do these expressions relate to each other? Explain how you can use this relationship to find the value of *r*. Find the value of *r*. They are equal. Set them equal to each other and solve for *r*; $r + 1 = 2r - 4$; $r = 5$
14. How can you find the length of each side of the rhombus? What is the length of each side? Substitute 5 into an expression and simplify; 6

Practice and Problem Solving Wkbk/ All-in-One Resources/Online

Standardized Test Prep

6-4 Standardized Test Prep

Properties of Rhombuses, Rectangles, and Squares

Multiple Choice

For Exercises 1–6, choose the correct letter.

Use rhombus *TQRS* for Exercises 1–4.

1. What is the measure of ∠1? D
   - A 47
   - B 37
   - C 74
   - D 53
2. What is the measure of ∠2? H
   - F 47
   - G 74
   - H 37
   - I 53
3. What is the value of *x*? B
   - A 2
   - B 1
   - C 5
   - D 4
4. What is the value of *y*? F
   - F 4
   - G 3
   - H 2
   - I 1
5. What statement would be sufficient to prove that a quadrilateral is a rhombus? C
   - A The quadrilateral has four congruent angles.
   - B The quadrilateral has two pairs of parallel sides.
   - C The quadrilateral has four congruent sides.
   - D The quadrilateral has two pairs of congruent angles.
6. *EFGH* is a kite. To prove that the diagonals of a kite are perpendicular, which pair of angles must you prove congruent using CPCTC? H
   - F ∠*EFI* and ∠*EHI*
   - G ∠*GFI* and ∠*GHI*
   - H ∠*EIF* and ∠*EIH*
   - I ∠*FIE* and ∠*HIG*

Short Response

7. Why is it that the statement "all rhombuses are squares" is false, but the statement "all squares are rhombuses" is true? Explain.
   [2] A square has all the properties of a rhombus, plus the additional property of four congruent angles. Not all rhombuses have four congruent angles, so they cannot all be categorized as squares. [1] Student only provides a description of the properties of a square or a rhombus but does not compare the properties of squares and rhombuses. [0] Student does not describe squares and rhombuses or compare their properties.

Extension

- **Enrichment** Provides students with interesting problems and activities that extend the concepts of the lesson.
- **Activities, Games, and Puzzles** Worksheets that can be used for concepts development, enrichment, and for fun!

All-in-One Resources/Online

Enrichment

6-4 Enrichment

Properties of Rhombuses, Rectangles, and Squares

For Exercises 1–15, write *All*, *Some*, or *No*. Explain.

1. __?__ rectangles are squares.
   Some; only rectangles with all sides congruent are squares.
2. __?__ isosceles trapezoids are parallelograms.
   No; only one pair of sides is parallel in any trapezoid.
3. __?__ rhombuses are quadrilaterals.
   All; all rhombuses have four sides.
4. __?__ kites are parallelograms.
   No; opposite sides of kites are never congruent.
5. __?__ squares are triangles.
   No; all squares have four sides and all triangles have three sides.
6. __?__ rectangles are regular quadrilaterals.
   Some; squares have four sides of equal length, four right angles, and opposite sides parallel.
7. __?__ quadrilaterals have four congruent angles.
   Some; rectangles are quadrilaterals with four congruent angles.
8. __?__ rectangles are rhombuses.
   Some; only rectangles that have all sides congruent are rhombuses.
9. __?__ trapezoids have one pair of opposite sides parallel.
   All; all trapezoids have only one pair of parallel sides.
10. __?__ trapezoids have two pairs of congruent sides.
    No; if a quadrilateral has two pairs of congruent sides, it is a parallelogram.
11. __?__ kites have two pairs of congruent sides.
    All; all kites have two pairs of adjacent sides congruent.
12. __?__ squares are regular quadrilaterals.
    All; squares are regular quadrilaterals because all their sides and angles are congruent.
13. __?__ kites have congruent diagonals.
    No; only rectangles and isosceles trapezoids have congruent diagonals.
14. __?__ trapezoids have four congruent sides.
    No; trapezoids can have a maximum of three congruent sides.
15. __?__ parallelograms have four congruent angles.
    Some; parallelograms that are rectangles have four congruent angles.

Make up five exercises of your own. Each should be a statement about quadrilaterals starting with a fill-in blank for *All*, *Some*, or *No*. Write your answers and explanations on a separate sheet of paper. Answers may vary. Sample:

16. __?__ rhombuses are squares.
    Some; rhombuses with four congruent angles are squares.
17. __?__ squares have congruent diagonals.
    All; squares are special rectangles, and all rectangles have congruent diagonals.
18. __?__ trapezoids are isosceles trapezoids.
    Some; trapezoids with one pair of congruent sides are isosceles.
19. __?__ squares are parallelograms.
    All; squares have opposite sides parallel.
20. __?__ trapezoids have both pairs of opposite sides parallel.
    No; all trapezoids have only one pair of parallel sides.

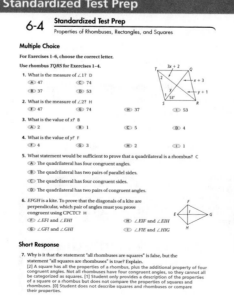

Online Teacher Resource Center

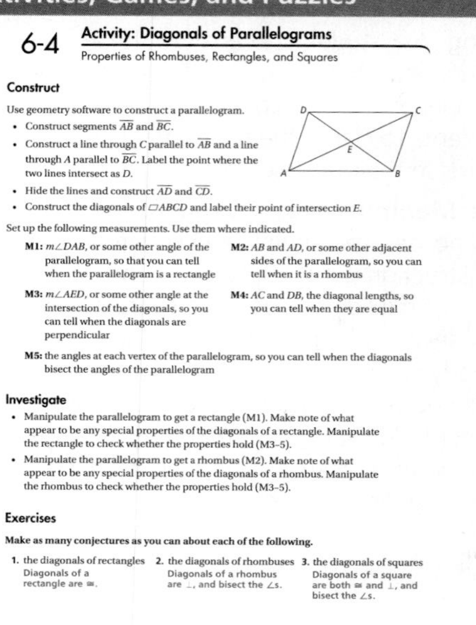

Activities, Games, and Puzzles

6-4 Activity: Diagonals of Parallelograms

Properties of Rhombuses, Rectangles, and Squares

Construct

Use geometry software to construct a parallelogram.

- Construct segments $\overline{AB}$ and $\overline{BC}$.
- Construct a line through *C* parallel to $\overline{AB}$ and a line through *A* parallel to $\overline{BC}$. Label the point where the two lines intersect as *D*.
- Hide the lines and construct $\overline{AD}$ and $\overline{CD}$.
- Construct the diagonals of ▱*ABCD* and label their point of intersection *E*.

Set up the following measurements. Use them where indicated.

M1: $m\angle DAB$, or some other angle of the parallelogram, so that you can tell when the parallelogram is a rectangle

M2: *AB* and *AD*, or some other adjacent sides of the parallelogram, so you can tell when it is a rhombus

M3: $m\angle AED$, or some other angle at the intersection of the diagonals, so you can tell when the diagonals are perpendicular

M4: *AC* and *DB*, the diagonal lengths, so you can tell when they are equal

M5: the angles at each vertex of the parallelogram, so you can tell when the diagonals bisect the angles of the parallelogram

Investigate

- Manipulate the parallelogram to get a rectangle (M1). Make note of what appear to be any special properties of the diagonals of a rectangle. Manipulate the rectangle to check whether the properties hold (M3–5).
- Manipulate the parallelogram to get a rhombus (M2). Make note of what appear to be any special properties of the diagonals of a rhombus. Manipulate the rhombus to check whether the properties hold (M3–5).

Exercises

Make as many conjectures as you can about each of the following.

1. the diagonals of rectangles
   Diagonals of a rectangle are ≅.
2. the diagonals of rhombuses
   Diagonals of a rhombus are ⊥, and bisect the ∠s.
3. the diagonals of squares
   Diagonals of a square are both ≅ and ⊥, and bisect the ∠s.

Conditions for Rhombuses, Rectangles, and Squares

TN State Performance Indicators
SPI 3108.4.3 Identify, describe and/or apply the relationships and theorems involving different types of triangles, quadrilaterals and other polygons.
Also SPI 3108.4.2

Objective To determine whether a parallelogram is a rhombus or rectangle

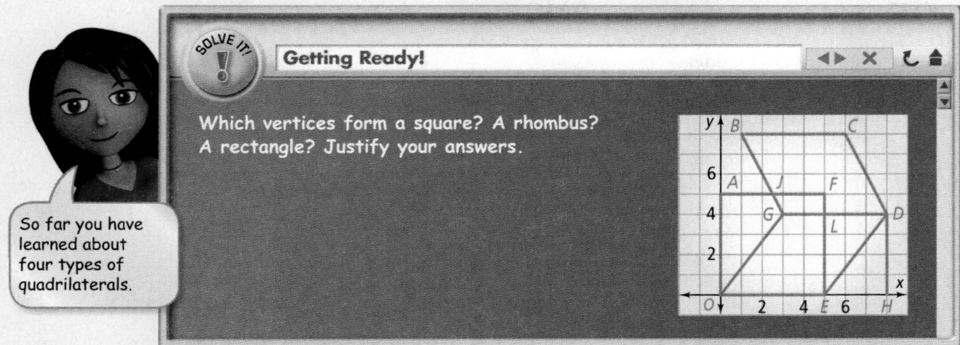

Getting Ready!
Which vertices form a square? A rhombus? A rectangle? Justify your answers.
So far you have learned about four types of quadrilaterals.

Essential Understanding You can determine whether a parallelogram is a rhombus or a rectangle based on the properties of its diagonals.

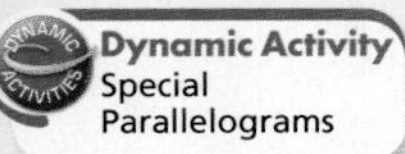

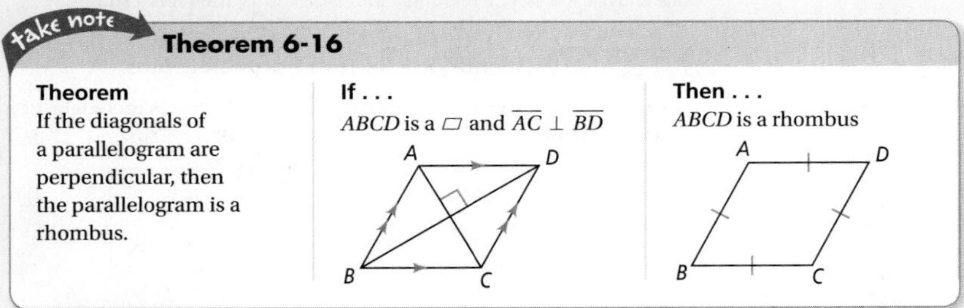

Theorem	If . . .	Then . . .
If the diagonals of a parallelogram are perpendicular, then the parallelogram is a rhombus.	$ABCD$ is a ▱ and $\overline{AC} \perp \overline{BD}$	$ABCD$ is a rhombus

Proof of Theorem 6-16

Given: $ABCD$ is a parallelogram, $\overline{AC} \perp \overline{BD}$

Prove: $ABCD$ is a rhombus.

Since $ABCD$ is a parallelogram, $\overline{AC}$ and $\overline{BD}$ bisect each other, so $\overline{BE} \cong \overline{DE}$. Since $\overline{AC} \perp \overline{BD}$, $\angle AED$ and $\angle AEB$ are congruent right angles. By the Reflexive Property of Congruence, $\overline{AE} \cong \overline{AE}$. So $\triangle AEB \cong \triangle AED$ by SAS. Corresponding parts of congruent triangles are congruent, so $\overline{AB} \cong \overline{AD}$. Since opposite sides of a parallelogram are congruent, $\overline{AB} \cong \overline{DC} \cong \overline{BC} \cong \overline{AD}$. By definition, $ABCD$ is a rhombus.

1 Interactive Learning

Solve It!

PURPOSE To explore how to determine if a given figure is a rhombus

PROCESS Students may use previous knowledge of the properties of rhombuses and parallelograms and visual inspection.

FACILITATE

Q What formula can you use to examine whether points form a rhombus? **[the Distance Formula]**

Q What formula can you use to examine whether points form a rectangle? **[the Slope Formula]**

ANSWER See Solve It in Answers on next page.

CONNECT THE MATH In the Solve It, students identify figures that satisfy the definitions of rhombuses and rectangles. In the lesson, students learn that figures can also be identified as rhombuses or rectangles.

2 Guided Instruction

Take Note

Point out to students that although the theorem states the parallelogram is a rhombus, that rhombus could be a square if the necessary conditions are met.

6-5 Preparing to Teach

BIG idea Reasoning and Proof UbD

ESSENTIAL UNDERSTANDING

- A parallelogram can be shown to be a rhombus, rectangle, or square based on the properties of its diagonals.

Math Background

In this lesson, students expand their understanding of special quadrilaterals to include rhombuses, rectangles, and squares. They explore the relationship between side lengths and diagonals of these figures. If students were to draw a Venn diagram to demonstrate the relationship between rhombuses, rectangles, and squares, they would see that rhombuses and rectangles have different characteristics. However, squares are both rectangles and rhombuses, thus the intersection of the two figures is the set of all squares.

Support Student Learning

Use the **Geometry Companion** to engage and support students during instructions. See Lesson Resources at the end of this lesson for details.

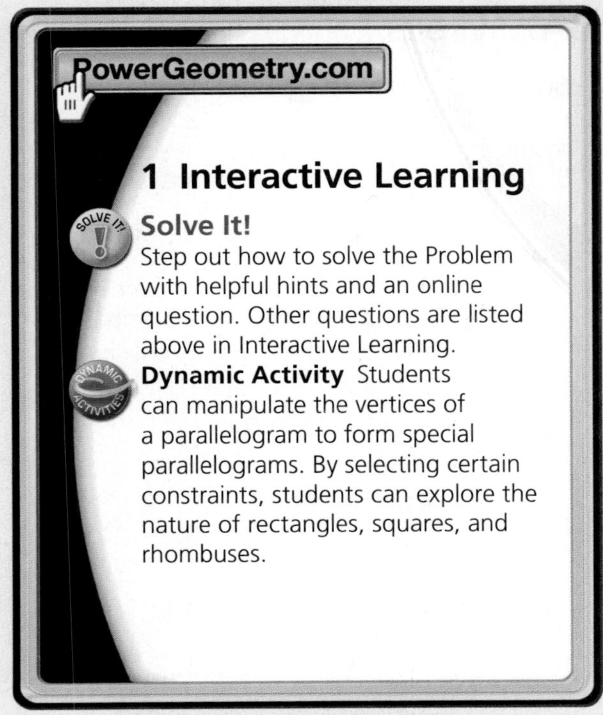

Take Note

Q Is $\angle 1$ congruent to any other angles in the diagram? Explain. **[$\angle ABC$ and $\angle CDA$ are congruent; $\angle 1$ is congruent to $\angle 3$ because $m\angle 1 = \frac{1}{2} m\angle ABC$ and $m\angle 3 = \frac{1}{2} m\angle CDA$. Also, $\angle 4 \cong \angle 1$ by the Alternate Interior Angles Theorem.]**

Q Are the two triangles formed by the diagonal congruent? Explain. **[Yes, they are congruent by ASA.]**

Point out to students that this theorem is the converse of Theorem 6-15 from Lesson 6-4. Remind students that these two theorems can be stated as the biconditional "A parallelogram is a rectangle if and only if its diagonals are congruent."

Problem 1

Q What two conditions concerning the diagonals of a parallelogram indicate that the figure is also a rhombus? **[You can conclude that the parallelogram is a rhombus if a diagonal bisects the opposite angles or if the diagonals are shown to be perpendicular.]**

Q What conditions concerning the diagonals of a parallelogram indicate that the figure is also a rectangle? **[You can conclude that the parallelogram is a rectangle if the diagonals are congruent.]**

Got It?

Students may have difficulty answering 1b if they think that they must choose one of the three quadrilaterals given as their answer. Use a sketch to remind students that all parallelograms have diagonals that bisect each other.

take note

Theorem 6-17

Theorem
If one diagonal of a parallelogram bisects a pair of opposite angles, then the parallelogram is a rhombus.

If . . .
$ABCD$ is a ▱, $\angle 1 \cong \angle 2$, and $\angle 3 \cong \angle 4$

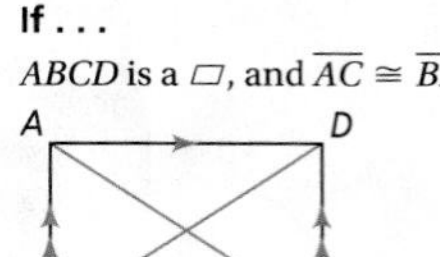

Then . . .
$ABCD$ is a rhombus

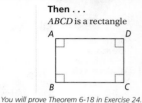

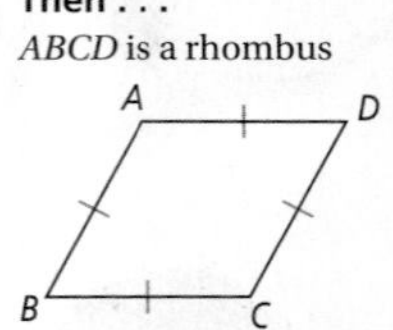

You will prove Theorem 6-17 in Exercise 23.

Theorem 6-18

Theorem
If the diagonals of a parallelogram are congruent, then the parallelogram is a rectangle.

If . . .
$ABCD$ is a ▱, and $\overline{AC} \cong \overline{BD}$

Then . . .
$ABCD$ is a rectangle

You will prove Theorem 6-18 in Exercise 24.

You can use Theorems 6-16, 6-17, and 6-18 to classify parallelograms. Notice that if a parallelogram is both a rectangle and a rhombus, then it is a square.

Think
How can you determine whether a figure is a special parallelogram?
See if you can satisfy every condition of a definition or theorem about rhombuses, rectangles, or squares.

Problem 1 Identifying Special Parallelograms

Can you conclude that the parallelogram is a rhombus, a rectangle, or a square? Explain.

A

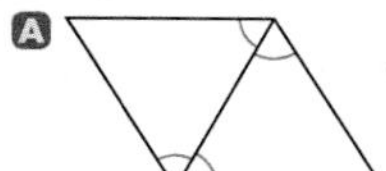

Yes. A diagonal bisects two angles. By Theorem 6-17, this parallelogram is a rhombus.

B

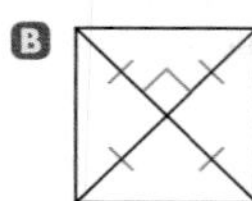

Yes. The diagonals are congruent, so by Theorem 6-18, this parallelogram is a rectangle. The diagonals are perpendicular, so by Theorem 6-16, it is a rhombus. Therefore, this parallelogram is a square.

Got It? **1. a.** A parallelogram has angle measures of 20, 160, 20, and 160. Can you conclude that it is a rhombus, a rectangle, or a square? Explain.

b. Reasoning Suppose the diagonals of a quadrilateral bisect each other. Can you conclude that it is a rhombus, a rectangle, or a square? Explain.

Answers

Solve It!

square: *OEFA*, because it has 4 rt. ∡ and 4 ≅ sides; rhombus: *OEDG*, because it has 4 ≅ sides of length 5; rectangle: *EHDL*, because it has 4 rt. ∡ and opp. sides ≅

Got It?

1a. The ▱ is not a rectangle or a square because ∡ are not rt. ∡. It might be a rhombus.

b. No; the fact that the diagonals bisect each other is true of all ▱.

PowerGeometry.com

2 Guided Instruction

Each Problem is worked out and supported online.

Problem 1
Identifying Special Parallelograms
Animated

Problem 2
Using Properties of Special Parallelograms
Animated

Problem 3
Using Properties of Parallelograms
Animated

Support in Geometry Companion
- Vocabulary
- Key Concepts
- Got It?

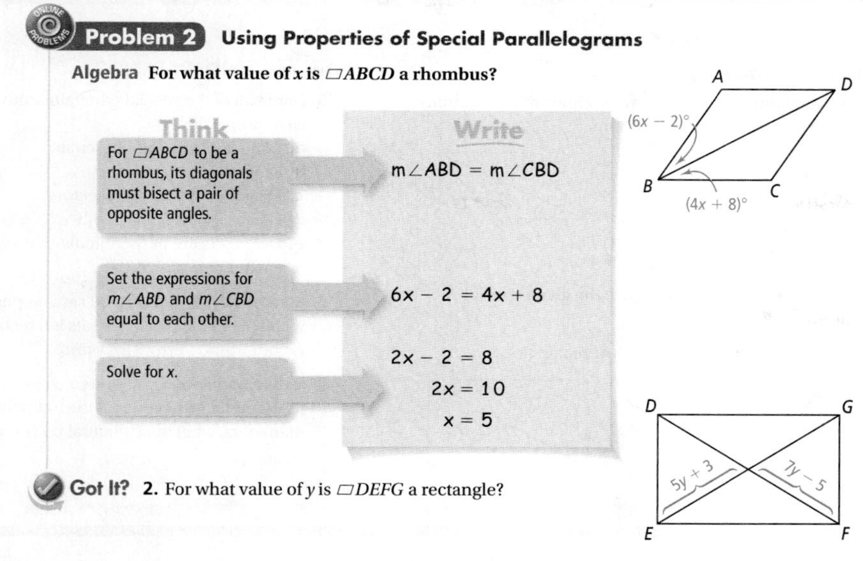

Problem 2 Using Properties of Special Parallelograms

Algebra **For what value of x is $\square ABCD$ a rhombus?**

Think	Write
For $\square ABCD$ to be a rhombus, its diagonals must bisect a pair of opposite angles.	$m\angle ABD = m\angle CBD$
Set the expressions for $m\angle ABD$ and $m\angle CBD$ equal to each other.	$6x - 2 = 4x + 8$
Solve for x.	$2x - 2 = 8$ $2x = 10$ $x = 5$

Got It? 2. For what value of y is $\square DEFG$ a rectangle?

Problem 3 Using Properties of Parallelograms

Community Service **Builders use properties of diagonals to "square up" rectangular shapes like building frames and playing-field boundaries. Suppose you are on the volunteer building team at the right. You are helping to lay out a rectangular patio for a youth center. How can you use properties of diagonals to locate the four corners?**

You can use two theorems.

- Theorem 6-11: If the diagonals of a quadrilateral bisect each other, then the quadrilateral is a parallelogram.
- Theorem 6-18: If the diagonals of a parallelogram are congruent, then the parallelogram is a rectangle.

Think
Is there only one rectangle that can be formed by pulling the ropes taut?
No, you can change the shape of the rectangle. Have two of the people move closer together. Then the other two people move until the ropes are taut again.

Step 1 Cut two pieces of rope that will be the diagonals of the foundation rectangle. Cut them the same length because of Theorem 6-18.

Step 2 Join the two pieces of rope at their midpoints because of Theorem 6-11.

Step 3 Pull the ropes straight and taut. The ends of the ropes will be the corners of a rectangle.

Got It? 3. Can you adapt this method slightly to stake off a square play area? Explain.

Problem 2

Q Is $\square ABCD$ also a square? Explain. **[No, the measure of $\angle B$ is 56 degrees given that $x = 5$.]**

Q What equation can you use to determine for what value of x $\square ABCD$ is a rectangle? **[$6x - 2 + 4x + 8 = 90$]**

Got It?

Q What statements are true about the diagonals of a rectangle? **[The diagonals bisect each other and are congruent.]**

Q What equation can you use to determine for what value of y $\square DEFG$ is a rectangle? **[$5y + 3 = 7y - 5$]**

Problem 3

Q What kind of shape(s) can be formed if the ropes are made to bisect each other but are not congruent? **[Only rhombuses or other parallelograms can be formed.]**

Q What kind of shape(s) can be formed if the ropes are congruent but do not bisect each other? **[Only quadrilaterals can be formed.]**

Got It? TACTILE LEARNERS

Ask students to use strands of spaghetti to form a square as in Problem 3. State all conditions the diagonals must meet in order to make the square.

Additional Problems

1. Can you conclude that the parallelogram is a rhombus, a rectangle, or a square? Explain.

a.

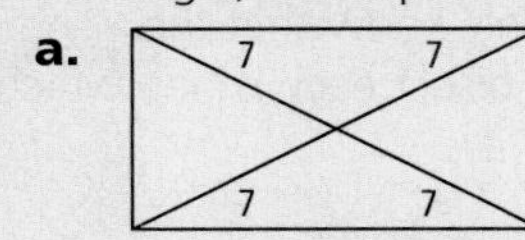

b.

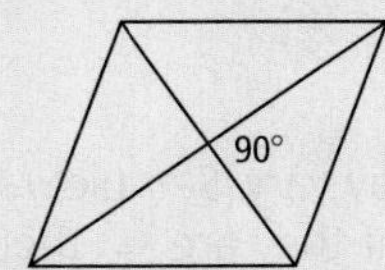

ANSWER **a.** rectangle; The diagonals are congruent, so the figure is a rectangle by Theorem 6-18.
b. rhombus; The diagonals are perpendicular, so the figure is a rhombus by Theorem 6-16.

2. For what value of x is parallelogram $ABCD$ a square?

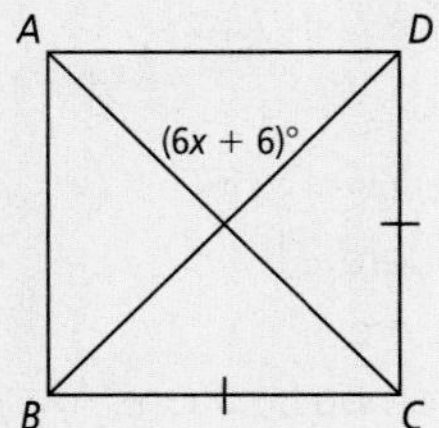

ANSWER 14

3. Describe how you can use two strings to mark the four corners of a rectangle.

ANSWER Cut the strings to be the same length and connect them at their midpoints. Pull the strings tight to locate the corners of the rectangle.

Answers

Got It? (continued)

2. 4

3. Yes; make diagonals $\perp$. The result will be a rectangle and a rhombus, so it is square.

3 Lesson Check

Do you know HOW?

- If students have difficulty with Exercises 3–4, then have them review the definitions of *rhombus* and *rectangle* from Problem 1.

Do you UNDERSTAND?

- If students have difficulty with Exercise 5, then remind them that there may be more than one special parallelogram for each property. For example, both squares and rectangles have diagonals that are congruent.

Close

Q If you conclude that quadrilateral *ABCD* is a square, what other names can be used to describe *ABCD*? **[If *ABCD* is a square, then it is also a parallelogram, a rhombus, and a rectangle.]**

Lesson Check

Do you know HOW?

Can you conclude that the parallelogram is a rhombus, a rectangle, or a square? Explain.

1.

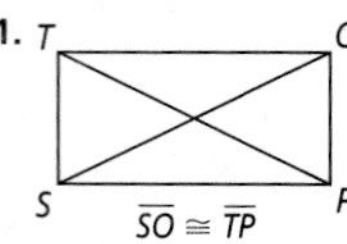

2.

For what value of *x* is the figure the given special parallelogram?

3. rhombus

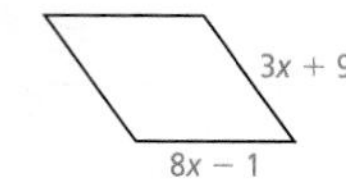

4. rectangle

3x − 5
x + 1

Do you UNDERSTAND?

5. Name all of the special parallelograms that have each property.
- **a.** Diagonals are perpendicular.
- **b.** Diagonals are congruent.
- **c.** Diagonals are angle bisectors.
- **d.** Diagonals bisect each other.
- **e.** Diagonals are perpendicular bisectors of each other.

6. Error Analysis Your friend says, "A parallelogram with perpendicular diagonals is a rectangle." What is your friend's error? Explain.

7. Reasoning When you draw a circle and two of its diameters and connect the endpoints of the diameters, what quadrilateral do you get? Explain.

Practice and Problem-Solving Exercises

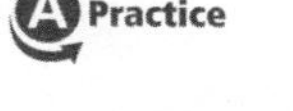

A Practice

Can you conclude that the parallelogram is a rhombus, a rectangle, or a square? Explain.

See Problem 1.

8.

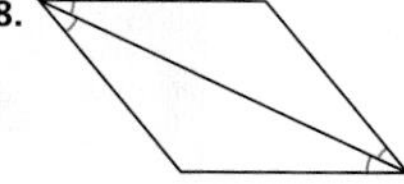

9.

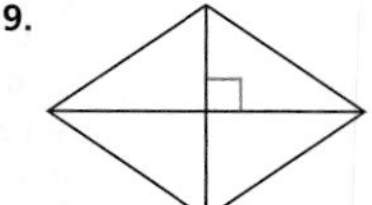

10.

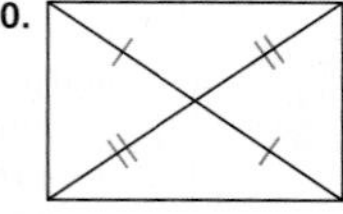

For what value of *x* is the figure the given special parallelogram?

See Problem 2.

11. rhombus

(6x − 9)°
(2x + 39)°

12. rectangle

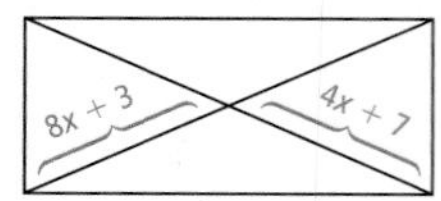

13. rectangle

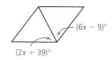

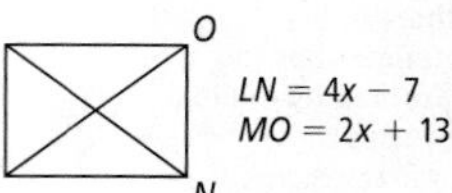

14. Carpentry A carpenter is building a bookcase. How can the carpenter use a tape measure to check that the bookshelf is rectangular? Justify your answer and name any theorems used.

See Problem 3.

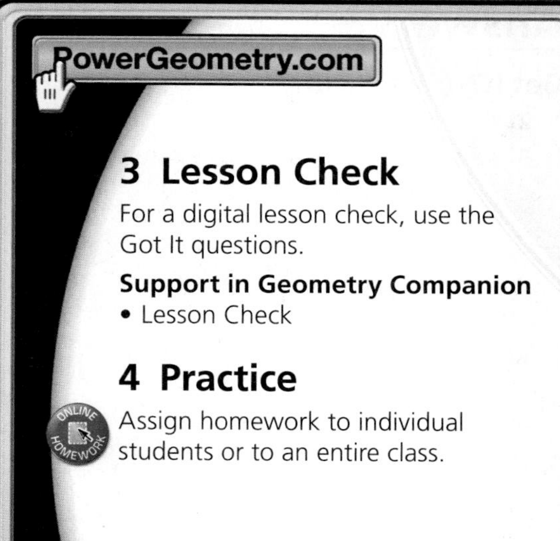

Answers

Lesson Check

1. Rectangle; diagonals are ≅.
2. Rhombus; diagonals are ⊥.
3. 2
4. 3
5a. rhombus, square
b. rectangle, square
c. rhombus, square
d. rectangle, rhombus, square
e. rhombus, square
6. The only ▱s with ⊥ diagonals are rhombuses and squares.
7. Rectangle; diagonals are ≅.

Practice and Problem-Solving Exercises

8. Rhombus; one diagonal bisects a pair of opp. ∠s.
9. Rhombus; diagonals are ⊥.
10. No; you only know that the diagonals bisect each other, which is true of all ▱s.
11. 12
12. 1
13. 10
14. Answers may vary. Sample: Measure opp. sides; if they are ≅, then it is a ▱. Then measure the diagonals; if they are ≅, then the bookshelf is a rectangle.

15. **Hardware** You can use a simple device called a turnbuckle to "square up" structures that are parallelograms. For the gate pictured at the right, you tighten or loosen the turnbuckle on the diagonal cable so that the rectangular frame will keep the shape of a parallelogram when it sags. What are two ways you can make sure that the turnbuckle works? Explain.

16. **Reasoning** Suppose the diagonals of a parallelogram are both perpendicular and congruent. What type of special quadrilateral is it? Explain your reasoning.

Algebra **For what value of x is the figure the given special parallelogram?**

17. rectangle

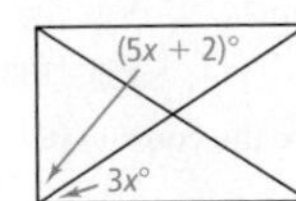

18. rhombus

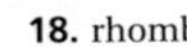

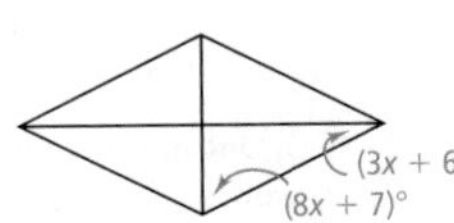

19. rectangle

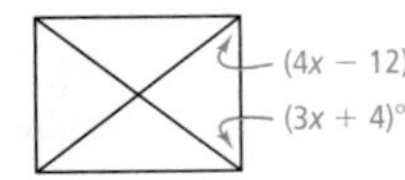

Open-Ended **Given two segments with lengths a and b ($a \neq b$), what special parallelograms meet the given conditions? Show each sketch.**

20. Both diagonals have length a.

21. The two diagonals have lengths a and b.

22. One diagonal has length a, and one side of the quadrilateral has length b.

23. Prove Theorem 6-17.
Proof
Given: $ABCD$ is a parallelogram.
$\overline{AC}$ bisects $\angle BAD$ and $\angle BCD$.
Prove: $ABCD$ is a rhombus.

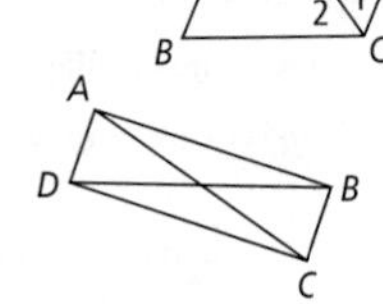

24. Prove Theorem 6-18.
Proof
Given: $\square ABCD$, $\overline{AC} \cong \overline{BD}$
Prove: $ABCD$ is a rectangle.

A D B C

Think About a Plan **Explain how to construct each figure given its diagonals.**
- What do you know about the diagonals of each figure?
- How can you apply constructions to what you know about the diagonals?

25. parallelogram
26. rectangle
27. rhombus

Determine whether the quadrilateral can be a parallelogram. Explain.

28. The diagonals are congruent, but the quadrilateral has no right angles.

29. Each diagonal is 3 cm long and two opposite sides are 2 cm long.

30. Two opposite angles are right angles, but the quadrilateral is not a rectangle.

4 Practice

ASSIGNMENT GUIDE
Basic: 8–16, 18, 24–27
Average: 9–13 odd, 15–27
Advanced: 9–13 odd, 15–31
Standardized Test Prep: 32–35
Mixed Review: 36–43
Reasoning exercises have blue headings.
Applications exercises have red headings.
EXERCISE 24: Use the Think About a Plan worksheet in the **Practice and Problem Solving Workbook** (also available in the Teaching Resources in print and online) to further support students' development in becoming independent learners.

HOMEWORK QUICK CHECK
To check students' understanding of key skills and concepts, go over Exercises 9, 13, 16, 18, and 24.

15. Answers may vary. Sample: Measure the lengths of the frame's diagonals. If they are ≅, then the frame has the shape of a rectangle, and therefore a parallelogram; measure the two pairs of alt. int. ∠s formed by the turnbuckle (the transversal). If both pairs of ∠s are ≅, then both pairs of opposite sides of the frame are ∥.
16. Square; since it is a rhombus and a rectangle, it must be a square.
17. 11
18. 7
19. 16

20. Rectangle, square; answers may vary. Sample:

a

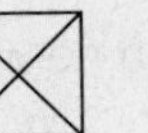
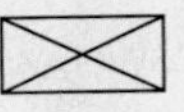

21. Rhombus; answers may vary. Sample:

a b

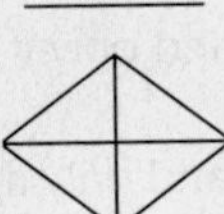

22. Rectangle, rhombus, square; answers may vary. Sample:

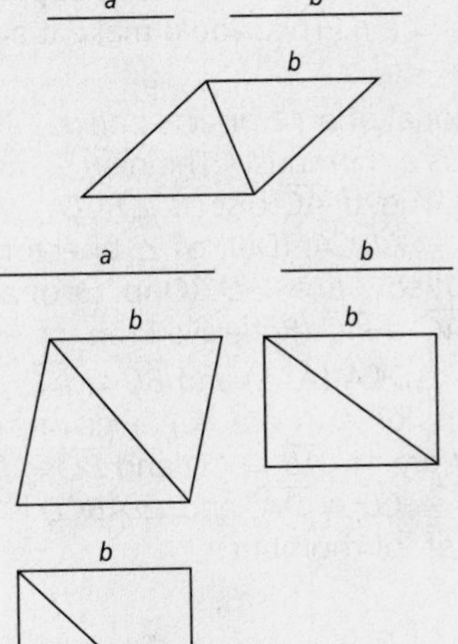

23–30. See next page.

Answers

Practice and Problem-Solving Exercises (continued)

23. Answers may vary. Sample:

1. $\overline{AB}$ bisects $\angle BAD$ and $\angle BCD$. (Given)
2. $\angle 1 \cong \angle 2$ and $\angle 3 \cong \angle 4$. (Def. of bisect)
3. $\overline{AC} \cong \overline{AC}$ (Refl. Prop. of ≅)
4. $\triangle ABC \cong \triangle ADC$ (ASA)
5. $\overline{AB} \cong \overline{AD}$ and $\overline{BC} \cong \overline{DC}$. (Corresp. parts of ≅ △s are ≅.)
6. $\overline{AB} \cong \overline{CD}$ and $\overline{BC} \cong \overline{AD}$. (Opp. sides of a ▱ are ≅.)
7. $\overline{AB} \cong \overline{AD} \cong \overline{BC} \cong \overline{CD}$ (Trans. Prop. of ≅)
8. $ABCD$ is a rhombus. (Def. of rhombus)

24. Answers may vary. Sample:

1. $\overline{AC} \cong \overline{BD}$, ▱$ABCD$ (Given)
2. $\overline{AD} \cong \overline{BC}$ (Opposite sides of a ▱ are ≅.)
3. $\overline{DC} \cong \overline{DC}$ (Refl. Prop. of ≅)
4. $\triangle ADC \cong \triangle BCD$ (SSS)
5. $\angle ADC \cong \angle BCD$ (Corresp. parts of ≅ △s are ≅.)
6. $m\angle ADC + m\angle BCD = 180$ (Same-side int. ∠s are suppl.)
7. $\angle ADC$ and $\angle BCD$ are rt. ∠s. (Def. of rt. ∠)
8. $ABCD$ is a rectangle. (Def. of rectangle)

25. Construct the midpt. of each diagonal. Copy the diagonals so the two midpts. coincide. Connect the endpoints of the diagonals.

26. Construct the midpt. of ≅ diagonals. Copy the diagonals so the two midpts. coincide. Connect the endpoints of the diagonals.

27. Construct the midpts. of each diagonal. Construct two ⊥ lines, and mark off diagonal lengths on the ⊥ lines. Connect the endpoints of the diagonals.

28. No; if the diagonals of a ▱ are ≅, then it would have to be a rectangle and have rt. ∠s.

29. Yes; ≅ diagonals in a ▱ mean it can be a rectangle with 2 opp. sides 2 cm long.

30. No; in a ▱, consecutive ∠s must be suppl., so all ∠s must be rt. This would make it a rectangle.

31. "If one diagonal of a ▱ bisects one ∠, then the ▱ is a rhombus." The new statement is true. If $\overline{AC}$ bisects $\angle BCD$, then $\angle BCA \cong \angle DCA$. (Def. of ∠ bisector) $ABCD$ is a ▱, so $\angle B \cong \angle D$. (Opp. ∠s of a ▱ are ≅.) $\overline{AC} \cong \overline{AC}$ (Reflexive Prop. of ≅), so $\triangle BCA \cong \triangle DCA$ (AAS) and $\overline{BC} \cong \overline{DC}$. (Corresp. parts of ≅ △s are ≅.) Since opp. sides of a ▱ are ≅, $\overline{AB} \cong \overline{CD}$ and $\overline{BC} \cong \overline{DA}$. So $\overline{AB} \cong \overline{BC} \cong \overline{CD} \cong \overline{DA}$, and ▱$ABCD$ is a rhombus. (Def. of rhombus)

32. B

33. I

34. B

31. Proof In Theorem 6-17, replace "a pair of opposite angles" with "one angle." Write a paragraph that proves this new statement to be true, or give a counterexample to prove it to be false.

Standardized Test Prep

SAT/ACT

32. Each diagonal of a quadrilateral bisects a pair of opposite angles of the quadrilateral. What is the most precise name for the quadrilateral?

(A) parallelogram (B) rhombus (C) rectangle (D) not enough information

33. Given a triangle with side lengths 7 and 11, which value could NOT be the length of the third side of the triangle?

(F) 13 (G) 7 (H) 5 (I) 2

34. What is the sum of the measures of the exterior angles in a pentagon?

(A) 180 (B) 360 (C) 540 (D) 108

Short Response

35. The midpoint of $\overline{PQ}$ is $(-1, 4)$. One endpoint is $P(-7, 10)$. What are the coordinates of endpoint Q? Explain your work.

Mixed Review

Find the measures of the numbered angles in each rhombus. See Lesson 6-4.

36. 128°, 1, 2, 3

37. 57°, 1, 2, 3

38.

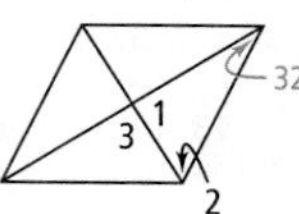

Write the two conditionals as a biconditional. See Lesson 2-3.

39. If a parallelogram is a rhombus, then its diagonals are perpendicular.

If the diagonals of a parallelogram are perpendicular, then the parallelogram is a rhombus.

40. If a parallelogram is a rectangle, then its diagonals are congruent.

If the diagonals of a parallelogram are congruent, then the parallelogram is a rectangle.

Get Ready! To prepare for Lesson 6-6, do Exercises 41–43.

Algebra Find the values of the variables. Then find the lengths of the sides. See Lesson 1-3.

41.

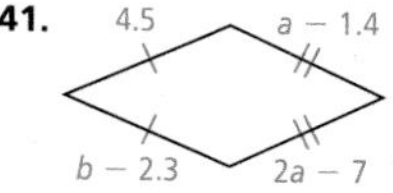

42.

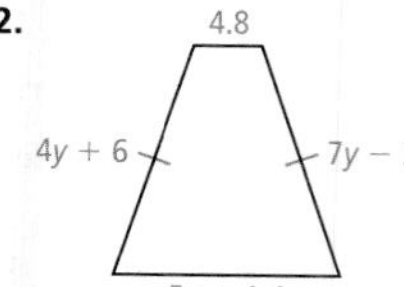

43.

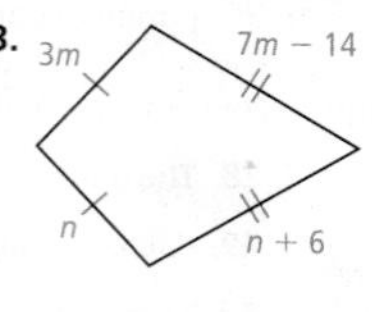

35. [2] $\left(\frac{-7+x}{2}, \frac{10+y}{2}\right) = (-1, 4)$. $-7 + x = -2$, $x = 5$, and $10 + y = 8$, $y = -2$, so $Q(5, -2)$.

[1] correct answer, with no work shown

36. $m\angle 1 = 128$, $m\angle 2 = 26$, $m\angle 3 = 26$

37. $m\angle 1 = 57$, $m\angle 2 = 57$, $m\angle 3 = 66$

38. $m\angle 1 = 90$, $m\angle 2 = 58$, $m\angle 3 = 90$

39. A ▱ is a rhombus if and only if its diagonals are ⊥.

40. A ▱ is a rectangle if and only if its diagonals are ≅.

41. $a = 5.6$, $b = 6.8$; 4.5, 4.5, 4.2, 4.2

42. 3; 18, 4.8, 18, 16.4

43. $m = 5$, $n = 15$; 15, 15, 21, 21

6-5 Lesson Resources

Differentiated Remediation

Instructional Support

Geometry Companion

Students can use the **Geometry Companion** worktext (4 pages) . . .

- New Vocabulary
- Key Concepts
- Got It for each Problem
- Lesson Check

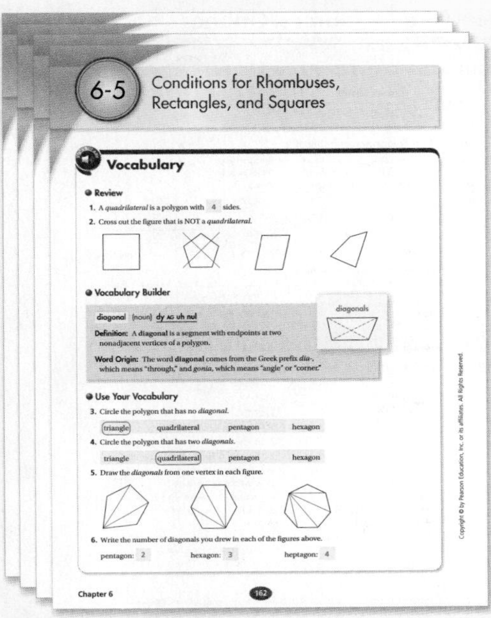

6-5 Conditions for Rhombuses, Rectangles, and Squares

Vocabulary

Review

1. A *quadrilateral* is a polygon with 4 sides.
2. Cross out the figure that is NOT a *quadrilateral*.

Vocabulary Builder

diagonal (noun) dy AG uh nul

Definition: A **diagonal** is a segment with endpoints at two nonadjacent vertices of a polygon.

Word Origin: The word **diagonal** comes from the Greek prefix *dia-*, which means "through," and *gonia*, which means "angle" or "corner."

diagonals

Use Your Vocabulary

3. Circle the polygon that has no *diagonal*.
   triangle quadrilateral pentagon hexagon
4. Circle the polygon that has two *diagonals*.
   triangle quadrilateral pentagon hexagon
5. Draw the *diagonals* from one vertex in each figure.
6. Write the number of diagonals you drew in each of the figures above.
   pentagon: 2 hexagon: 3 heptagon: 4

Chapter 6 162

ELL Support

Focus on Communication Summarize the most important concepts. Because Theorems 6-15, 6-16, and 6-17 are important for students to know, either tell students repeatedly of their importance, or have a place on the board labeled "Important" and write the concepts, theorems, or key words that are the most important for students to learn.

Assess Understanding Have students draw a diagram for the following word problem.

Mr. Brown is building a shed with a square floor. If one wall of the shed is 8 ft, how can Mr. Brown make sure the shed is a square?

5 Assess & Remediate

Lesson Quiz

1. Can you conclude that the parallelogram is a rhombus, a rectangle, or a square? Explain.

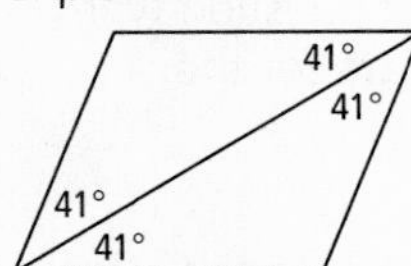
41°
41°
41°
41°

2. For what value of x is parallelogram $ABCD$ a rectangle?

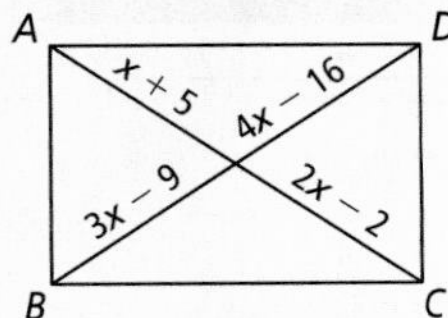
A
D
B
C
x + 5
4x − 16
3x − 9
2x − 2

3. **Do you UNDERSTAND?** Given $WRST$ is a parallelogram and $\overline{WS} \cong \overline{RT}$, how can you classify $WRST$? Explain.

ANSWERS TO LESSON QUIZ

1. rhombus; The diagonal bisects a pair of opposite angles, so the figure is a rhombus by Theorem 6-17. Also, by ASA and the converse of the Isosceles Triangle Theorem, all four sides are congruent.
2. 7
3. Rectangle; $\overline{WS}$ and $\overline{RT}$ are congruent diagonals, and by Theorem 6-18, $WRST$ is a rectangle.

PRESCRIPTION FOR REMEDIATION

Use the student work on the Lesson Quiz to prescribe a differentiated review assignment.

Points	Differentiated Remediation
0–1	Intervention
2	On-level
3	Extension

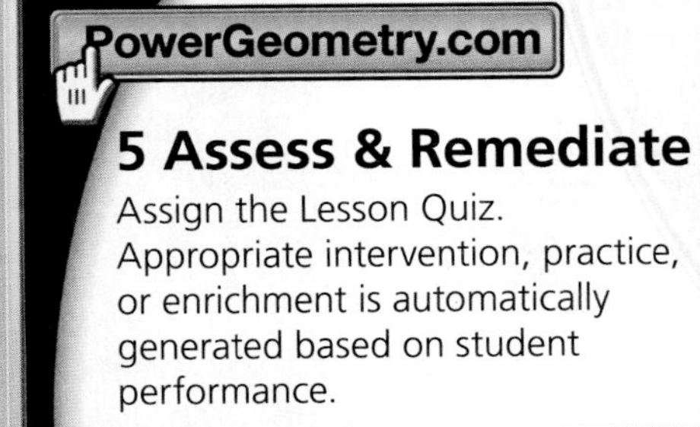
PowerGeometry.com
5 Assess & Remediate
Assign the Lesson Quiz.
Appropriate intervention, practice, or enrichment is automatically generated based on student performance.

Intervention

- **Reteaching** (2 pages) Provides reteaching and practice exercises for the key lesson concepts. Use with struggling students or absent students.
- **English Language Learner Support** Helps students develop and reinforce mathematical vocabulary and key concepts.

All-in-One Resources/Online

Reteaching

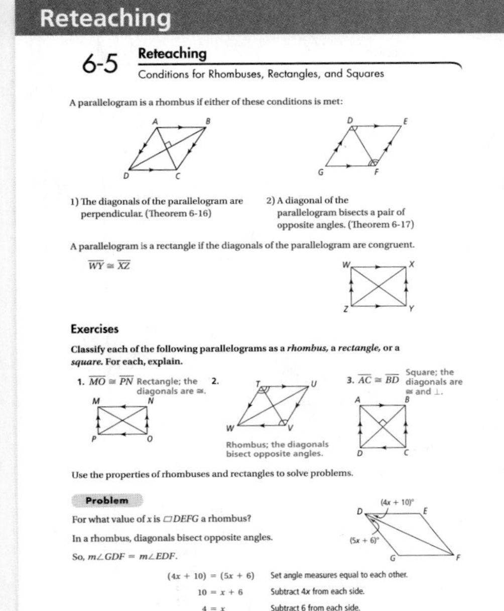

6-5 Reteaching
Conditions for Rhombuses, Rectangles, and Squares

A parallelogram is a rhombus if either of these conditions is met:

1) The diagonals of the parallelogram are perpendicular. (Theorem 6-16)

2) A diagonal of the parallelogram bisects a pair of opposite angles. (Theorem 6-17)

A parallelogram is a rectangle if the diagonals of the parallelogram are congruent.

$\overline{WY} \cong \overline{XZ}$

Exercises

Classify each of the following parallelograms as a *rhombus*, a *rectangle*, or a *square*. For each, explain.

1. $\overline{MO} \cong \overline{PN}$ Rectangle; the diagonals are ≅.
2. Rhombus; the diagonals bisect opposite angles.
3. $\overline{AC} \cong \overline{BD}$ Square; the diagonals are ≅ and ⊥.

Use the properties of rhombuses and rectangles to solve problems.

Problem

For what value of x is ▱$DEFG$ a rhombus?

In a rhombus, diagonals bisect opposite angles.

So, $m\angle GDF = m\angle EDF$.

$(4x + 10) = (5x + 6)$ Set angle measures equal to each other.
$10 = x + 6$ Subtract $4x$ from each side.
$4 = x$ Subtract 6 from each side.

All-in-One Resources/Online

English Language Learner Support

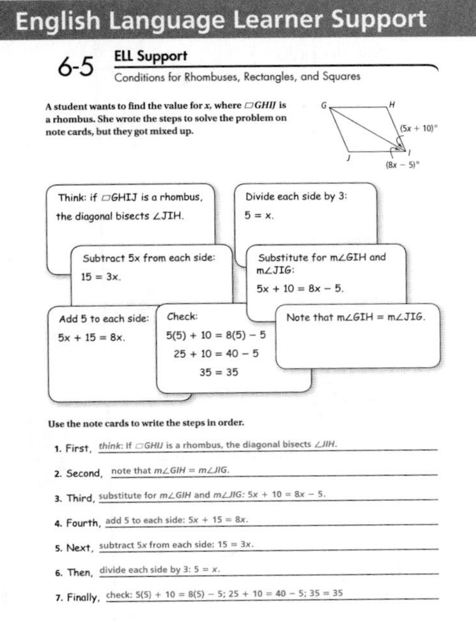

6-5 ELL Support
Conditions for Rhombuses, Rectangles, and Squares

A student wants to find the value for x, where ▱$GHIJ$ is a rhombus. She wrote the steps to solve the problem on note cards, but they got mixed up.

Think: if ▱GHIJ is a rhombus, the diagonal bisects ∠JIH.

Divide each side by 3: 5 = x.

Subtract 5x from each side: 15 = 3x.

Substitute for m∠GIH and m∠JIG: 5x + 10 = 8x − 5.

Add 5 to each side: 5x + 15 = 8x.

Check: 5(5) + 10 = 8(5) − 5; 25 + 10 = 40 − 5; 35 = 35

Note that m∠GIH = m∠JIG.

Use the note cards to write the steps in order.

1. First, *think*: If ▱GHIJ is a rhombus, the diagonal bisects ∠JIH.
2. Second, note that m∠GIH = m∠JIG.
3. Third, substitute for m∠GIH and m∠JIG: 5x + 10 = 8x − 5.
4. Fourth, add 5 to each side: 5x + 15 = 8x.
5. Next, subtract 5x from each side: 15 = 3x.
6. Then, divide each side by 3: 5 = x.
7. Finally, check: 5(5) + 10 = 8(5) − 5; 25 + 10 = 40 − 5; 35 = 35

Differentiated Remediation *continued*

On-Level

- **Practice** (2 pages) Provides extra practice for each lesson. For simpler practice exercises, use the Form K Practice pages found in the All-in-One Teaching Resources and online.
- **Think About a Plan** Helps students develop specific problem-solving skills and strategies by providing scaffolded guiding questions.
- **Standardized Test Prep** Focuses on all major exercises, all major question types, and helps students prepare for the high-stakes assessments.

Extension

- **Enrichment** Provides students with interesting problems and activities that extend the concepts of the lesson.
- **Activities, Games, and Puzzles** Worksheets that can be used for concepts development, enrichment, and for fun!

Practice and Problem Solving Wkbk/ All-in-One Resources/Online

Practice page 1

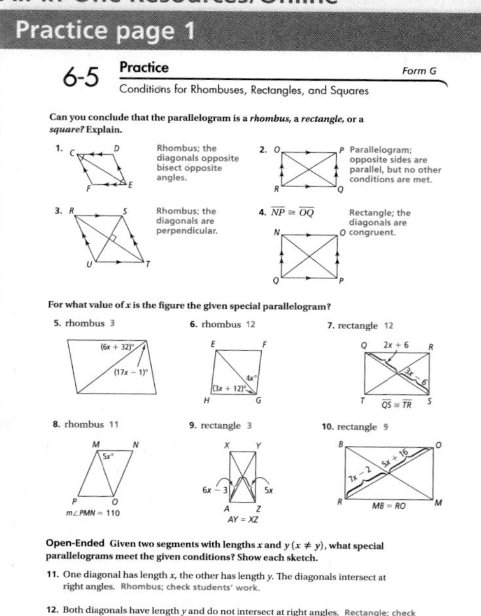

6-5 **Practice** *Form G*

Conditions for Rhombuses, Rectangles, and Squares

Can you conclude that the parallelogram is a *rhombus,* a *rectangle,* or a *square?* Explain.

1. Rhombus; the diagonals opposite bisect opposite angles.
2. Parallelogram; opposite sides are parallel, but no other conditions are met.
3. Rhombus; the diagonals are perpendicular.
4. $\overline{NP} \cong \overline{OQ}$ Rectangle; the diagonals are congruent.

For what value of *x* is the figure the given special parallelogram?

5. rhombus 3
6. rhombus 12
7. rectangle 12 ($\overline{QS} \cong \overline{TR}$)
8. rhombus 11 ($m\angle PMN = 110$)
9. rectangle 3 ($AY = XZ$)
10. rectangle 9 ($MB = RO$)

Open-Ended Given two segments with lengths *x* and *y* ($x \neq y$), what special parallelograms meet the given conditions? Show each sketch.

11. One diagonal has length *x*, the other has length *y*. The diagonals intersect at right angles. Rhombus; check students' work.
12. Both diagonals have length *y* and do not intersect at right angles. Rectangle; check students' work.

Practice and Problem Solving Wkbk/ All-in-One Resources/Online

Practice page 2

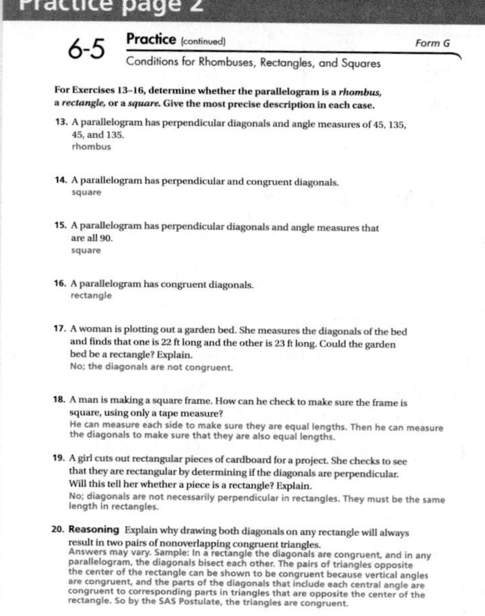

6-5 **Practice** (continued) *Form G*

Conditions for Rhombuses, Rectangles, and Squares

For Exercises 13–16, determine whether the parallelogram is a *rhombus,* a *rectangle,* or a *square.* Give the most precise description in each case.

13. A parallelogram has perpendicular diagonals and angle measures of 45, 135, 45, and 135. rhombus
14. A parallelogram has perpendicular and congruent diagonals. square
15. A parallelogram has perpendicular diagonals and angle measures that are all 90. square
16. A parallelogram has congruent diagonals. rectangle
17. A woman is plotting out a garden bed. She measures the diagonals of the bed and finds that one is 22 ft long and the other is 23 ft long. Could the garden bed be a rectangle? Explain. No; the diagonals are not congruent.
18. A man is making a square frame. How can he check to make sure the frame is square, using only a tape measure? He can measure each side to make sure they are equal lengths. Then he can measure the diagonals to make sure that they are also equal lengths.
19. A girl cuts out rectangular pieces of cardboard for a project. She checks to see that they are rectangular by determining if the diagonals are perpendicular. Will this tell her whether a piece is a rectangle? Explain. No; diagonals are not necessarily perpendicular in rectangles. They must be the same length in rectangles.
20. **Reasoning** Explain why drawing both diagonals on any rectangle will always result in two pairs of nonoverlapping congruent triangles. Answers may vary. Sample: In a rectangle the diagonals are congruent, and in any parallelogram, the diagonals bisect each other. The pairs of triangles opposite the center of the rectangle can be shown to be congruent because vertical angles are congruent, and the parts of the diagonals that include each central angle are congruent to corresponding parts in triangles that are opposite the center of the rectangle. So by the SAS Postulate, the triangles are congruent.

All-in-One Resources/Online

Enrichment

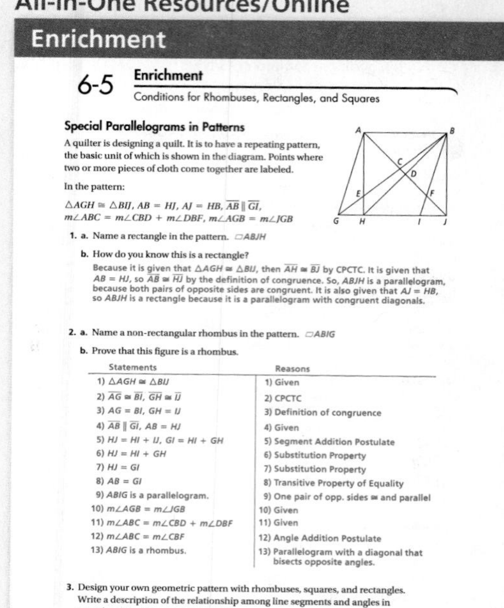

6-5 **Enrichment**

Conditions for Rhombuses, Rectangles, and Squares

Special Parallelograms in Patterns

A quilter is designing a quilt. It is to have a repeating pattern, the basic unit of which is shown in the diagram. Points where two or more pieces of cloth come together are labeled.

In the pattern:

$\triangle AGH \cong \triangle BIJ$, $AB = HJ$, $AJ = HB$, $\overline{AB} \parallel \overline{GI}$, $m\angle ABC = m\angle CBD + m\angle DBF$, $m\angle AGB = m\angle JGB$

1. a. Name a rectangle in the pattern. ▱ABJH

   b. How do you know this is a rectangle? Because it is given that $\triangle AGH \cong \triangle BIJ$, then $\overline{AH} \cong \overline{BJ}$ by CPCTC. It is given that $AB = HJ$, so $\overline{AB} \cong \overline{HJ}$ by the definition of congruence. So, *ABJH* is a parallelogram, because both pairs of opposite sides are congruent. It is also given that $AJ = HB$, so *ABJH* is a rectangle because it is a parallelogram with congruent diagonals.

2. a. Name a non-rectangular rhombus in the pattern. ▱ABIG

   b. Prove that this figure is a rhombus.

Statements	Reasons
1) $\triangle AGH \cong \triangle BIJ$	1) Given
2) $\overline{AG} \cong \overline{BI}$, $\overline{GH} \cong \overline{IJ}$	2) CPCTC
3) $AG = BI$, $GH = IJ$	3) Definition of congruence
4) $\overline{AB} \parallel \overline{GI}$, $AB = HJ$	4) Given
5) $HJ = HI + IJ$, $GI = HI + GH$	5) Segment Addition Postulate
6) $HJ = HI + GH$	6) Substitution Property
7) $HJ = GI$	7) Substitution Property
8) $AB = GI$	8) Transitive Property of Equality
9) *ABIG* is a parallelogram.	9) One pair of opp. sides ≅ and parallel
10) $m\angle AGB = m\angle JGB$	10) Given
11) $m\angle ABC = m\angle CBD + m\angle DBF$	11) Given
12) $m\angle ABC = m\angle CBF$	12) Angle Addition Postulate
13) *ABIG* is a rhombus.	13) Parallelogram with a diagonal that bisects opposite angles.

3. Design your own geometric pattern with rhombuses, squares, and rectangles. Write a description of the relationship among line segments and angles in your drawing. Check students' work.

Practice and Problem Solving Wkbk/ All-in-One Resources/Online

Think About a Plan

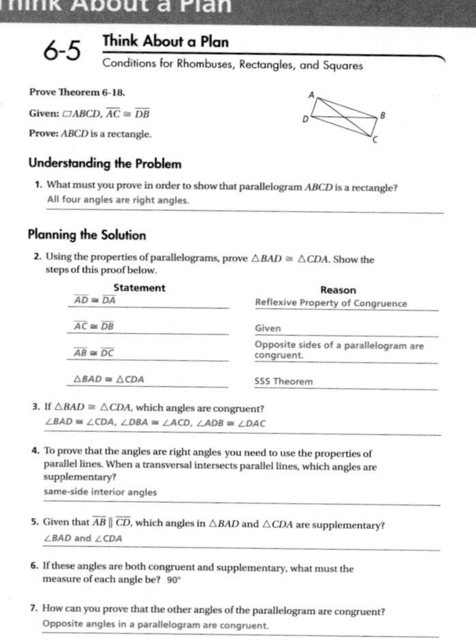

6-5 **Think About a Plan**

Conditions for Rhombuses, Rectangles, and Squares

Prove Theorem 6-18.

Given: ▱*ABCD*, $\overline{AC} \cong \overline{DB}$

Prove: *ABCD* is a rectangle.

Understanding the Problem

1. What must you prove in order to show that parallelogram *ABCD* is a rectangle? All four angles are right angles.

Planning the Solution

2. Using the properties of parallelograms, prove $\triangle BAD \cong \triangle CDA$. Show the steps of this proof below.

Statement	Reason
$\overline{AD} \cong \overline{DA}$	Reflexive Property of Congruence
$\overline{AC} \cong \overline{DB}$	Given
$\overline{AB} \cong \overline{DC}$	Opposite sides of a parallelogram are congruent.
$\triangle BAD \cong \triangle CDA$	SSS Theorem

3. If $\triangle BAD \cong \triangle CDA$, which angles are congruent? $\angle BAD \cong \angle CDA$, $\angle DBA \cong \angle ACD$, $\angle ADB \cong \angle DAC$
4. To prove that the angles are right angles you need to use the properties of parallel lines. When a transversal intersects parallel lines, which angles are supplementary? same-side interior angles
5. Given that $\overline{AB} \parallel \overline{CD}$, which angles in $\triangle BAD$ and $\triangle CDA$ are supplementary? $\angle BAD$ and $\angle CDA$
6. If these angles are both congruent and supplementary, what must the measure of each angle be? 90°
7. How can you prove that the other angles of the parallelogram are congruent? Opposite angles in a parallelogram are congruent.

Practice and Problem Solving Wkbk/ All-in-One Resources/Online

Standardized Test Prep

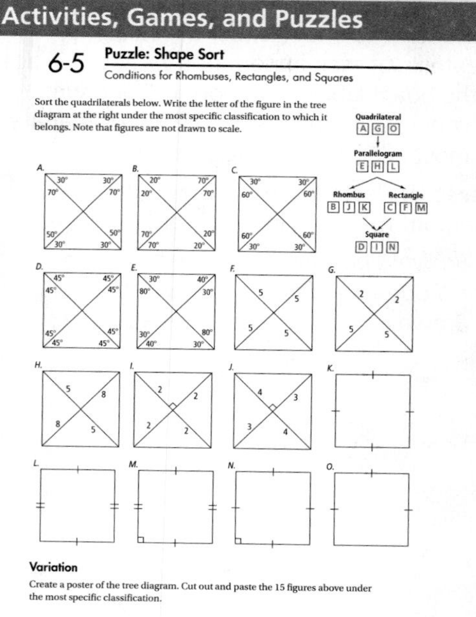

6-5 **Standardized Test Prep**

Conditions for Rhombuses, Rectangles, and Squares

Multiple Choice

For Exercises 1–4, choose the correct letter.

1. Which is the most precise name of this figure? B
   A parallelogram C rectangle
   B rhombus D square
2. Which of the following conditions or set of conditions must be met for a parallelogram to be a rectangle? G
   F Diagonals are perpendicular.
   G Diagonals are congruent.
   H All sides are congruent.
   I The length of a diagonal is equal to the length of a side.
3. Which of the following conditions or set of conditions is sufficient for a parallelogram to be a square? A
   A Diagonals are perpendicular and diagonals are congruent.
   B Diagonals are congruent.
   C All sides are congruent.
   D The length of a diagonal is equal to the length of a side.
4. For what value of *x* is ▱*XYZA* a rectangle? H
   F 2 H 4
   G 3 I 5

Short Response

5. The diagonals of a parallelogram are 2.3 cm and 3.2 cm long. Can you tell if the parallelogram is a rhombus? Explain. [2] No; no information is given to indicate the diagonals are perpendicular, and no information is given to indicate that a diagonal bisects opposite angles. [1] Student offers half the explanation. [0] no answer or wrong answer based on an inappropriate plan

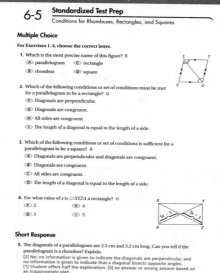

Online Teacher Resource Center

Activities, Games, and Puzzles

6-5 **Puzzle: Shape Sort**

Conditions for Rhombuses, Rectangles, and Squares

Sort the quadrilaterals below. Write the letter of the figure in the tree diagram at the right under the most specific classification to which it belongs. Note that figures are not drawn to scale.

Variation

Create a poster of the tree diagram. Cut out and paste the 15 figures above under the most specific classification.

6-6 Trapezoids and Kites

TN State Performance Indicators
SPI 3108.4.3 Identify, describe and/or apply the relationships and theorems involving different types of triangles, quadrilaterals and other polygons.
Also SPI 3108.1.1 and SPI 3108.4.2

Objective To verify and use properties of trapezoids and kites

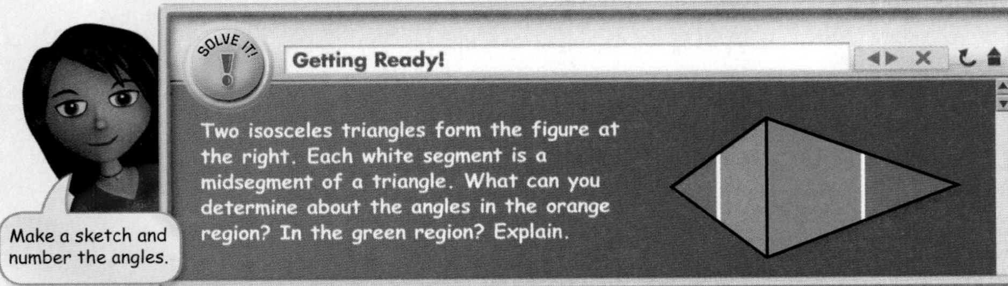

Getting Ready!
Two isosceles triangles form the figure at the right. Each white segment is a midsegment of a triangle. What can you determine about the angles in the orange region? In the green region? Explain.
Make a sketch and number the angles.

Dynamic Activity Classifying Quadrilaterals

Lesson Vocabulary
- trapezoid
- base
- leg
- base angle
- isosceles trapezoid
- midsegment of a trapezoid
- kite

In the Solve It, the orange and green regions are trapezoids. The entire figure is a kite. In this lesson, you will learn about these special quadrilaterals that are not parallelograms.

Essential Understanding The angles, sides, and diagonals of a trapezoid have certain properties.

A **trapezoid** is a quadrilateral with exactly one pair of parallel sides. The parallel sides of a trapezoid are called **bases.** The nonparallel sides are called **legs.** The two angles that share a base of a trapezoid are called **base angles.** A trapezoid has two pairs of base angles.

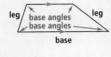

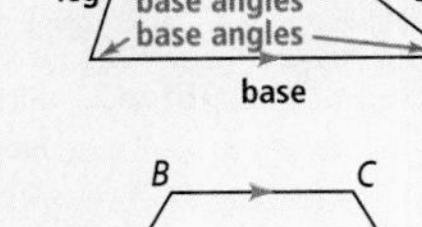

An **isosceles trapezoid** is a trapezoid with legs that are congruent. *ABCD* at the right is an isosceles trapezoid. The angles of an isosceles trapezoid have some unique properties.

A B C D

Theorem 6-19

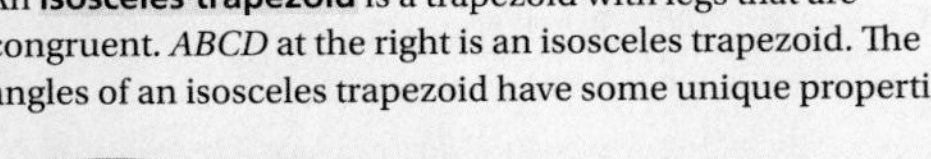

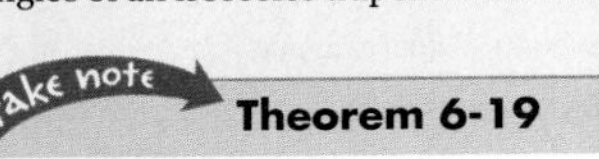

Theorem	If . . .	Then . . .
If a quadrilateral is an isosceles trapezoid, then each pair of base angles is congruent.	*TRAP* is an isosceles trapezoid with bases $\overline{RA}$ and $\overline{TP}$	$\angle T \cong \angle P$, $\angle R \cong \angle A$

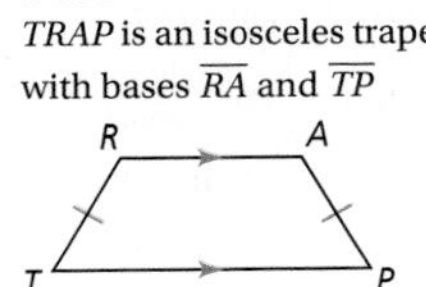

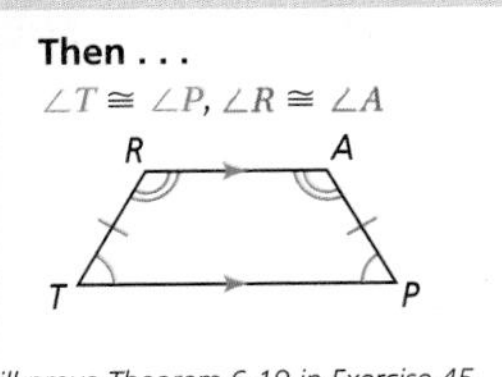

You will prove Theorem 6-19 in Exercise 45.

1 Interactive Learning

Solve It!

PURPOSE To explore the properties of isosceles trapezoids

PROCESS Students may use previous knowledge of isosceles triangles, midsegments of triangles, and angle pairs formed when parallel lines are cut by a transversal.

FACILITATE

Q How are the midsegments related to the base of each isosceles triangle? Explain. **[The midsegments are parallel to the base of each isosceles triangle by the Triangle Midsegment Theorem.]**

Q What are same side interior angles? What property do they have? **[Same side interior angles are the angles formed along one side of the transversal when a transversal cuts two parallel lines. They are supplementary.]**

ANSWER See Solve It in Answers on next page.

CONNECT THE MATH In the Solve It, students explore the figures of trapezoids. In the lesson, students learn the characteristics of trapezoids and kites.

2 Guided Instruction

Take Note

Drawing and labeling isosceles trapezoids in many different orientations can help students identify base angles of trapezoids.

6-6 Preparing to Teach

BIG idea Reasoning and Proof UbD

ESSENTIAL UNDERSTANDING
- The angles, sides, and diagonals of a trapezoid have certain properties.

Math Background

A kite is introduced in this lesson as the union of two isosceles triangles that share a common base. Construction methods for kites depend on a kite's relationship to circles. A kite can be formed by constructing two noncongruent intersecting circles. The sides of the kite are the radii connecting the centers of the two circles to the two intersection points of the circles.

Having studied all properties of all special quadrilaterals, students can now make a list of figures with common properties (congruent diagonals, perpendicular diagonals, mutually bisecting diagonals, reflectional symmetries).

Support Student Learning

Use the **Geometry Companion** to engage and support students during instructions. See Lesson Resources at the end of this lesson for details.

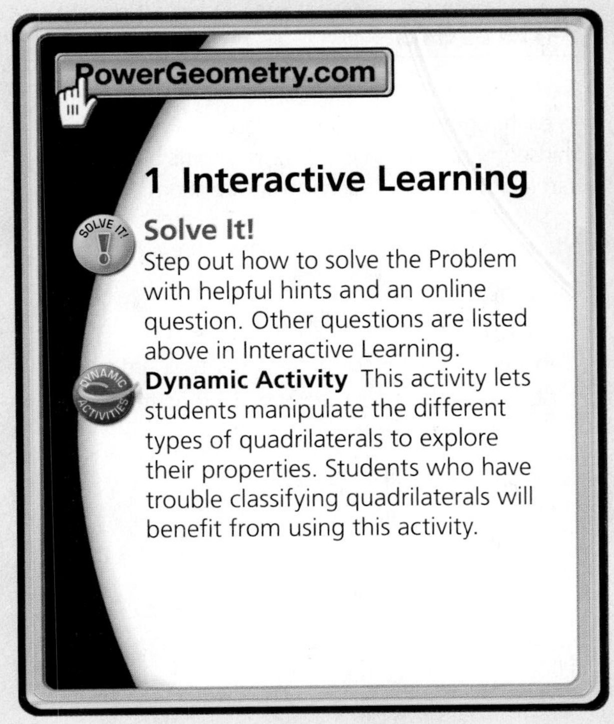

Problem 1

Q How are the opposite angles in an isosceles trapezoid related? Explain. **[They are supplementary. Each pair of base angles is congruent and each pair of base angles is supplementary to the other same-side interior angle formed along the same leg.]**

Q What is the sum of the measures of all of the angles of an isosceles trapezoid? Explain. **[360, because it is a quadrilateral.]**

Got It?

Q What are the pairs of base angles in the diagram? **[$\angle Q$ and $\angle P$ are a pair of base angles and $\angle R$ and $\angle S$ are a pair of base angles.]**

Q What is the sum of $m\angle Q$ and $m\angle R$? Explain. **[The sum is 180, because these are same-side interior angles.]**

Problem 2

Q What figures are formed in the first ring of the paper fan? How many are formed? **[Twenty isosceles triangles are formed.]**

Q How are the base angles of the isosceles triangles related to the adjacent base angles of the isosceles trapezoids created in the second ring? Explain. **[The base angles are supplementary because they form a straight angle.]**

Q How are the obtuse base angles of the isosceles trapezoids related to the acute base angles of the isosceles trapezoids? Explain. **[They are supplementary. They form same-side interior angles.]**

Think

What do you know about the angles of an isosceles trapezoid?
You know that each pair of base angles is congruent. Because the bases of a trapezoid are parallel, you also know that two angles that share a leg are supplementary.

Problem 1 Finding Angle Measures in Trapezoids

***CDEF* is an isosceles trapezoid and $m\angle C = 65$. What are $m\angle D$, $m\angle E$, and $m\angle F$?**

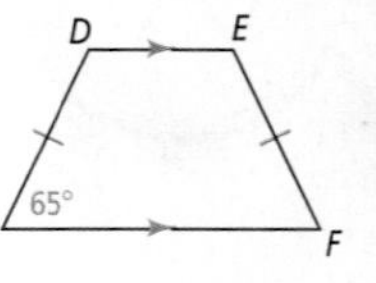

$m\angle C + m\angle D = 180$	Two angles that form same-side interior angles along one leg are supplementary.
$65 + m\angle D = 180$	Substitute.
$m\angle D = 115$	Subtract 65 from each side.

Since each pair of base angles of an isosceles trapezoid is congruent, $m\angle C = m\angle F = 65$ and $m\angle D = m\angle E = 115$.

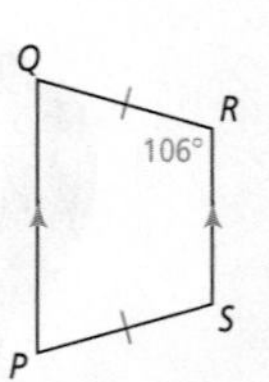

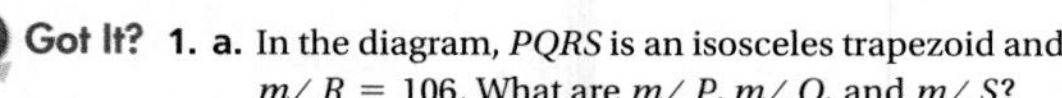

Got It? 1. a. In the diagram, *PQRS* is an isosceles trapezoid and $m\angle R = 106$. What are $m\angle P$, $m\angle Q$, and $m\angle S$?

b. Reasoning In Problem 1, if *CDEF* were not an isosceles trapezoid, would $\angle C$ and $\angle D$ still be supplementary? Explain.

Problem 2 Finding Angle Measures in Isosceles Trapezoids

Think

What do you notice about the diagram?
Each trapezoid is part of an isosceles triangle with base angles that are the acute base angles of the trapezoid.

Paper Fans The second ring of the paper fan shown at the right consists of 20 congruent isosceles trapezoids that appear to form circles. What are the measures of the base angles of these trapezoids?

Step 1 Find the measure of each angle at the center of the fan. This is the measure of the vertex angle of an isosceles triangle.

$$m\angle 1 = \frac{360}{20} = 18$$

Step 2 Find the measure of each acute base angle of an isosceles triangle.

$18 + x + x = 180$	Triangle Angle-Sum Theorem
$18 + 2x = 180$	Combine like terms.
$2x = 162$	Subtract 18 from each side.
$x = 81$	Divide each side by 2.

Step 3 Find the measure of each obtuse base angle of the isosceles trapezoid.

$81 + y = 180$	Two angles that form same-side interior angles along one leg are supplementary.
$y = 99$	Subtract 81 from each side.

Each acute base angle measures 81. Each obtuse base angle measures 99.

Got It? 2. A fan like the one in Problem 2 has 15 angles meeting at the center. What are the measures of the base angles of the trapezoids in its second ring?

Answers

Solve It!

In each region, ∡ are either suppl. or ≅; the midsegment of each isosc. △ is ∥ to its base, so same-side int. ∡ in each region are suppl. Since the ∡ sharing the base of each isosc. △ are ≅, the ∡ sharing the midsegment of each △ are also ≅.

Got It?

1a. $m\angle P = m\angle Q = 74$, $m\angle S = 106$

b. Yes; $\overline{DE} \parallel \overline{CF}$ so same-side int. ∡ are suppl.

2. obtuse base ∡ measure: 102; acute base ∡ measure: 78

PowerGeometry.com

2 Guided Instruction

Each Problem is worked out and supported online.

Problem 1
Finding Angle Measures in Trapezoids

Problem 2
Finding Angle Measures in Isosceles Trapezoids
Animated

Problem 3
Using the Midsegment of a Trapezoid
Animated

Problem 4
Finding Angle Measures in Kites
Animated

Support in Geometry Companion
- Vocabulary
- Key Concepts
- Got It?

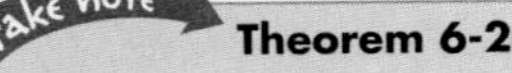

Theorem 6-20

Theorem	If . . .	Then . . .
If a quadrilateral is an isosceles trapezoid, then its diagonals are congruent.	*ABCD* is an isosceles trapezoid	$\overline{AC} \cong \overline{BD}$

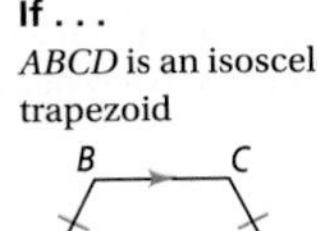

You will prove Theorem 6-20 in Exercise 54.

In Lesson 5-1, you learned about midsegments of triangles. Trapezoids also have midsegments. The **midsegment of a trapezoid** is the segment that joins the midpoints of its legs. The midsegment has two unique properties.

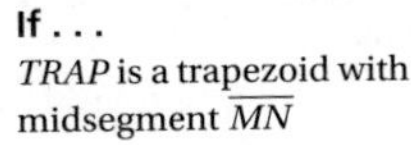

Theorem 6-21 Trapezoid Midsegment Theorem

Theorem	If . . .	Then . . .
If a quadrilateral is a trapezoid, then (1) the midsegment is parallel to the bases, and (2) the length of the midsegment is half the sum of the lengths of the bases.	*TRAP* is a trapezoid with midsegment $\overline{MN}$	(1) $\overline{MN} \parallel \overline{TP}$, $\overline{MN} \parallel \overline{RA}$, and (2) $MN = \frac{1}{2}(TP + RA)$

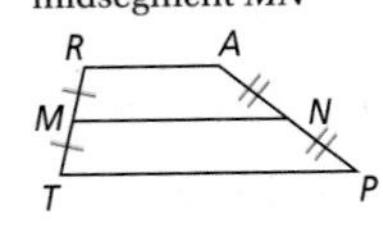

You will prove Theorem 6-21 in Lesson 6-9.

Problem 3 Using the Midsegment of a Trapezoid

Algebra $\overline{QR}$ **is the midsegment of trapezoid *LMNP*. What is *x*?**

$QR = \frac{1}{2}(LM + PN)$	Trapezoid Midsegment Theorem
$x + 2 = \frac{1}{2}[(4x - 10) + 8]$	Substitute.
$x + 2 = \frac{1}{2}(4x - 2)$	Simplify.
$x + 2 = 2x - 1$	Distributive Property
$3 = x$	Subtract *x* and add 1 to each side.

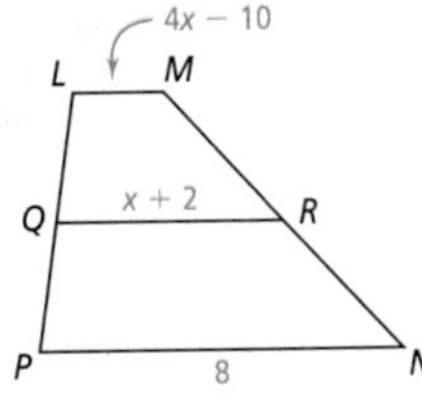

Think

How can you check your answer?
Find *LM* and *QR*. Then see if *QR* equals half of the sum of the base lengths.

Got It?

Direct students to verify that the total measure of the interior angles of a 15-sided polygon is the same as the sum of the measures of the base angles of the isosceles triangles and the same as the sum of the measures of the acute base angles of the isosceles trapezoids.

Take Note

Ask students the following questions in preparation for proving the theorem.

Q Do $\triangle ABD$ and $\triangle DCA$ have any congruent angles? Explain. **[Yes, $\angle BAD \cong \angle CDA$, Base angles of an isosceles trapezoid are congruent.]**

Q Do $\triangle ABD$ and $\triangle DCA$ have any congruent sides? Explain. **[Yes, the side they share, $\overline{AD}$, is congruent to itself and $\overline{AB}$: $\overline{CD}$ by def. of Isosc. Trap.]**

Take Note

Ask students to compare and contrast this theorem with the Triangle Midsegment Theorem. This comparison will aid students in understanding and retaining the theorem.

Problem 3

Q What is another way to describe the relationship of the midsegment and the bases? **[The length of the midsegment is equal to the mean of the lengths of the two bases.]**

Q How can you use the value of *x* to verify Theorem 6-21? **[Substitute 3 into the expressions and verify the relationship. $LM = 2$, $QR = 5$, so $(LM + PN) \div 2 = (2 + 8) \div 2 = 5$, which is the length of *QR*.]**

Additional Problems

1. *RSTU* is an isosceles trapezoid and $m\angle S = 75$. What are $m\angle R$, $m\angle T$, and $m\angle U$?

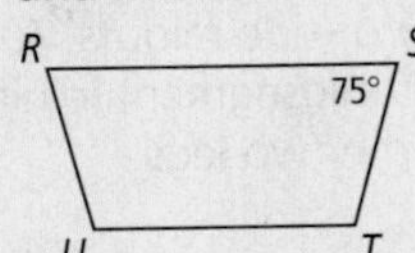

ANSWER $m\angle R = 75$, $m\angle U = 105$, $m\angle T = 105$

2. What are the values of *x* and *y* in the isosceles triangle below if $\overline{DE} \parallel \overline{BC}$?

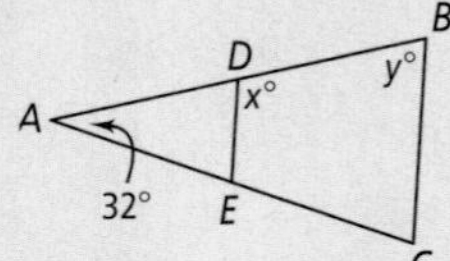

ANSWER $x = 106$, $y = 74$

3. $\overline{TU}$ is the midsegment of trapezoid *WXYZ*. What is *x*?

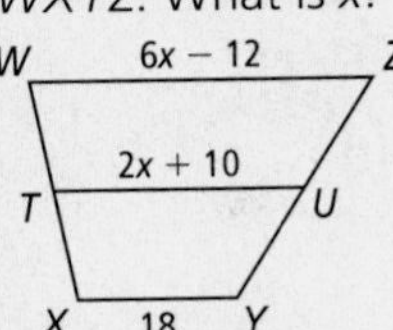

ANSWER 7

4. Quadrilateral *ABCD* is a kite. What are $m\angle 1$ and $m\angle 2$?

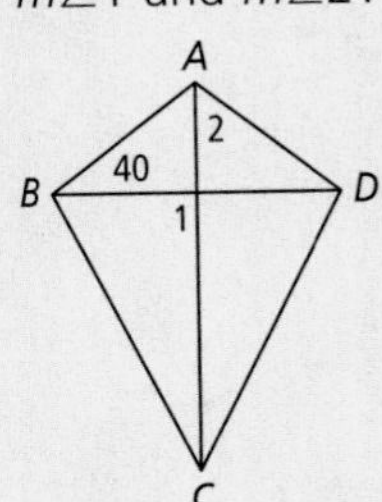

ANSWER $m\angle 1 = 90$, $m\angle 2 = 50$

Got It?

Q Is $\overline{MN} \parallel \overline{PS}$? Explain. **[Yes, The midsegment of an isosceles trapezoid is parallel to the bases of an isosceles trapezoid.]**

Q How is $\angle QMN$ related to $\angle MPS$? Explain. **[The angles are congruent because they are corresponding angles.]**

Take Note

Ask students to identify other quadrilaterals whose diagonals are perpendicular bisectors. Ask students to compare and contrast the other properties of those quadrilaterals.

Got It? 3. a. Algebra $\overline{MN}$ is the midsegment of trapezoid $PQRS$. What is x? What is MN?

b. Reasoning How many midsegments can a triangle have? How many midsegments can a trapezoid have? Explain.

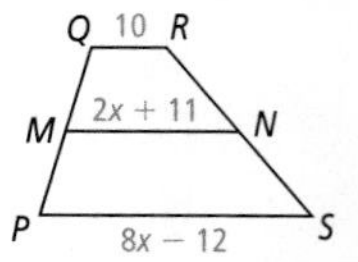

A **kite** is a quadrilateral with two pairs of consecutive sides congruent and no opposite sides congruent.

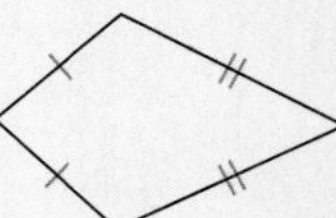

Essential Understanding The angles, sides, and diagonals of a kite have certain properties.

take note **Theorem 6-22**

Theorem	If . . .	Then . . .
If a quadrilateral is a kite, then its diagonals are perpendicular.	$ABCD$ is a kite 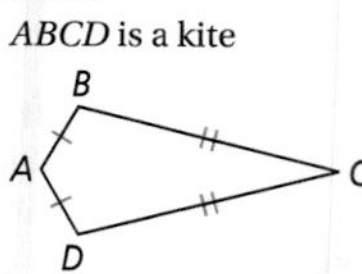	$\overline{AC} \perp \overline{BD}$ 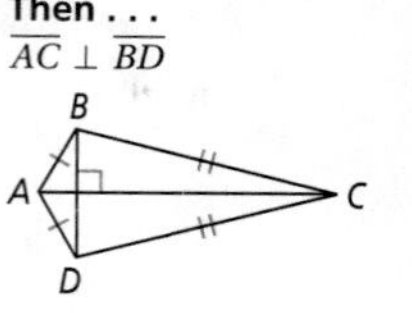

Proof **Proof of Theorem 6-22**

Given: Kite $ABCD$ with $\overline{AB} \cong \overline{AD}$ and $\overline{CB} \cong \overline{CD}$

Prove: $\overline{AC} \perp \overline{BD}$

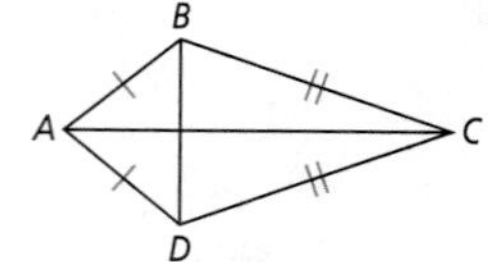

Statements	Reasons
1) Kite $ABCD$ with $\overline{AB} \cong \overline{AD}$ and $\overline{CB} \cong \overline{CD}$	1) Given
2) A and C lie on the perpendicular bisector of $\overline{BD}$.	2) Converse of Perpendicular Bisector Theorem
3) $\overline{AC}$ is the perpendicular bisector of $\overline{BD}$.	3) Two points determine a line.
4) $\overline{AC} \perp \overline{BD}$	4) Definition of perpendicular bisector

Answers

Got It? (continued)

3a. 6; 23

b. 3; 1; A △ has 3 midsegments joining any pair of side midpts. A trapezoid has 1 midsegment joining the midpts. of the two legs.

Problem 4 Finding Angle Measures in Kites

Quadrilateral $DEFG$ is a kite. What are $m\angle 1$, $m\angle 2$, and $m\angle 3$?

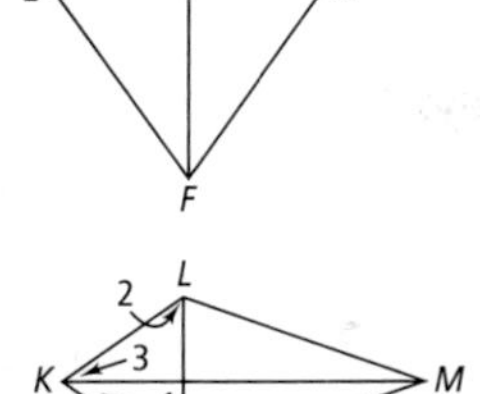

$m\angle 1 = 90$	Diagonals of a kite are $\perp$.
$90 + m\angle 2 + 52 = 180$	Triangle Angle-Sum Theorem
$142 + m\angle 2 = 180$	Simplify.
$m\angle 2 = 38$	Subtract 142 from each side.

Think
How are the triangles congruent by SSS?
$\overline{DE} \cong \overline{DG}$ and $\overline{FE} \cong \overline{FG}$ because a kite has congruent consecutive sides. $\overline{DF} \cong \overline{DF}$ by the Reflexive Property of Congruence.

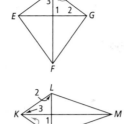

$\triangle DEF \cong \triangle DGF$ by SSS. Since corresponding parts of congruent triangles are congruent, $m\angle 3 = m\angle GDF = 52$.

Got It? 4. Quadrilateral $KLMN$ is a kite. What are $m\angle 1$, $m\angle 2$, and $m\angle 3$?

L, 2, K, 3, 1, M, 36°, N

take note

Concept Summary Relationships Among Quadrilaterals

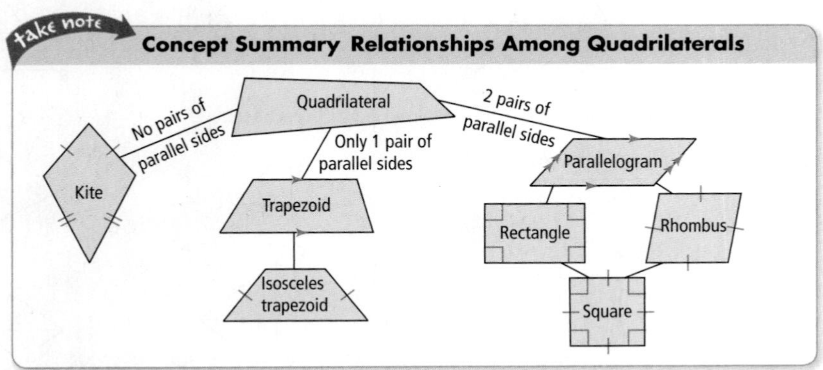

Lesson Check

Do you know HOW?

What are the measures of the numbered angles?

1. 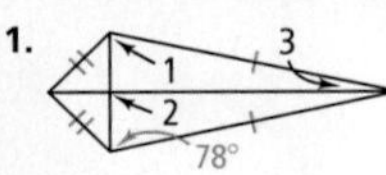

2. 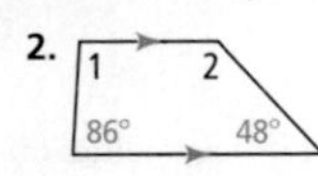

3. What is the length of the midsegment of a trapezoid with bases of length 14 and 26?

Do you UNDERSTAND?

4. **Vocabulary** Is a kite a parallelogram? Explain.
5. **Compare and Contrast** How is a kite similar to a rhombus? How is it different? Explain.
6. **Error Analysis** Since a parallelogram has two pairs of parallel sides, it certainly has one pair of parallel sides. Therefore, a parallelogram must also be a trapezoid. What is the error in this reasoning? Explain.

Problem 4

Q Is $\angle DEF \cong \angle DGF$? Explain. **[Yes, $\triangle DEF \cong DGF$ by SSS, and the angles are corresponding parts.]**

Q What is the sum of $\angle EGF$ and $\angle GFD$? Explain. **[The sum of the angles is 90 because the third angle of the triangle is a right angle.]**

Got It?

Q What theorems can you use to find the value of each of the angles? **[$\angle 1$ by Theorem 6-22, $\angle 3$ by CPCTC from SSS; $\angle 2$ by the Triangle-Angle Sum Theorem.]**

3 Lesson Check

Do you know HOW?

- If students have difficulty with Exercise 2, then tell them that the trapezoid is not an isosceles trapezoid, and thus the base angles will not be congruent.

Do you UNDERSTAND?

- If students have difficulty with Exercise 6, then have them review the definition of a trapezoid given on page 389. Students need to make note of the word "exactly."

Close

Q Are either kites or trapezoids a subset of parallelograms? Explain. **[No, neither figure meets the conditions for being a parallelogram.]**

Got It? (continued)

4. $m\angle 1 = 90$, $m\angle 2 = 54$, $m\angle 3 = 36$

Lesson Check

1. $m\angle 1 = 78$, $m\angle 2 = 90$, $m\angle 3 = 12$
2. $m\angle 1 = 94$, $m\angle 2 = 132$
3. 20
4. No; a kite's opp. sides are not $\cong$ or $\parallel$.
5. Answers may vary. Sample: Similar: diagonals are $\perp$, consecutive sides $\cong$. Different: one diagonal of a kite bisects opp. ⦞ but the other diagonal does not; all sides of a rhombus are $\cong$.
6. Def. of trapezoid is a quad. with exactly one pair of $\parallel$ sides. A ▱ has two pairs of $\parallel$ sides, so a ▱ is not a trapezoid.

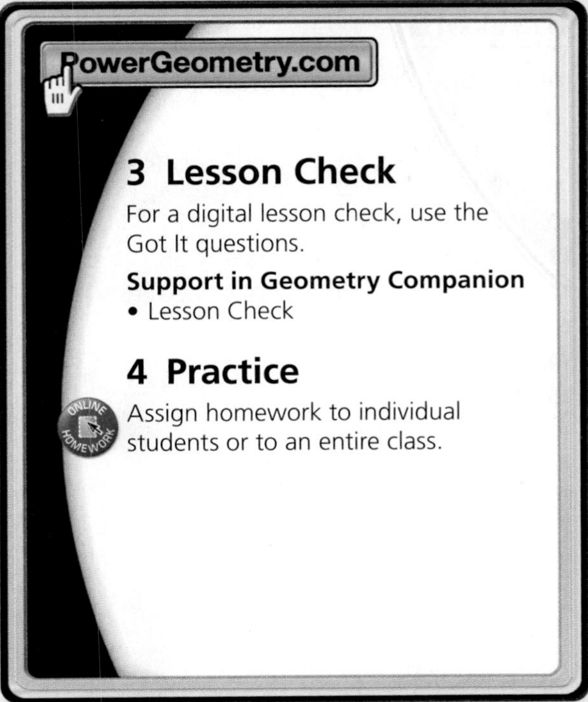

4 Practice

ASSIGNMENT GUIDE
Basic: 7–24 all, 26–34 even, 46–49
Average: 7–23 odd, 25–62
Advanced: 7–23 odd, 25–66
Standardized Test Prep: 67–70
Mixed Review: 71–76
Reasoning exercises have blue headings.
Applications exercises have red headings.
EXERCISE 46: Use the Think About a Plan worksheet in the **Practice and Problem Solving Workbook** (also available in the Teaching Resources in print and online) to further support students' development in becoming independent learners.

HOMEWORK QUICK CHECK
To check students' understanding of key skills and concepts, go over Exercises 13, 21, 26, 32, and 46.

Practice and Problem-Solving Exercises

Find the measures of the numbered angles in each isosceles trapezoid. See Problems 1 and 2.

7. 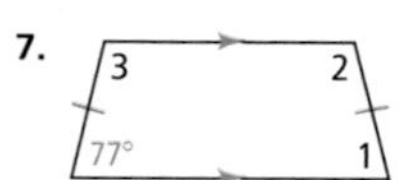

8. 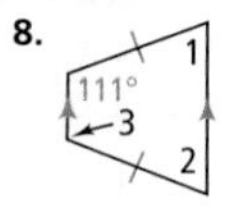

9. 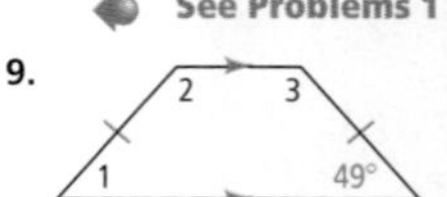

10. Y, Z, X, W; 1, 2, 105°, 3

11. 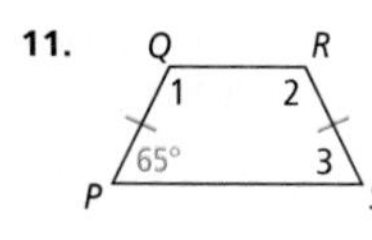

12. 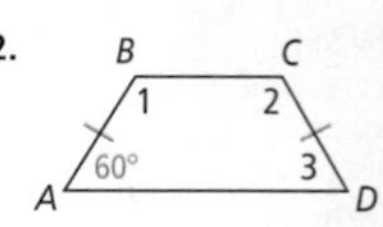

Find EF in each trapezoid. See Problem 3.

13. 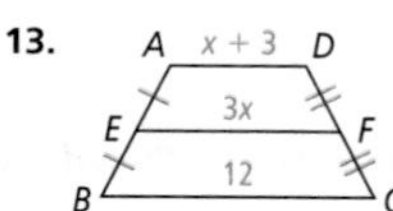

14. 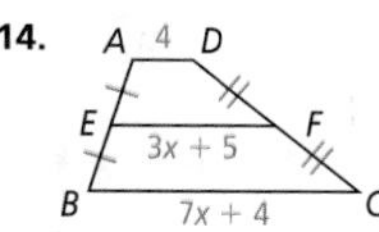

15. 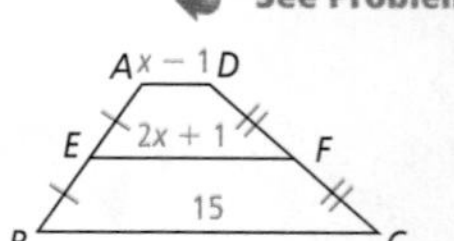

Find the measures of the numbered angles in each kite. See Problem 4.

16. 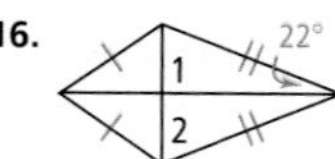

17. 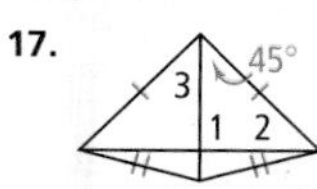

18. 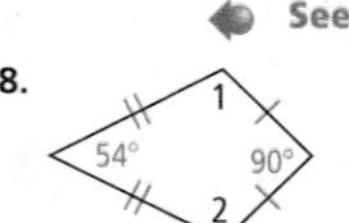

19. 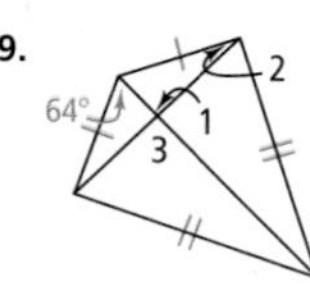

20. 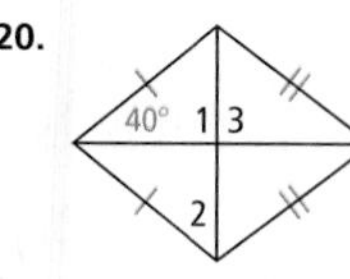

21. 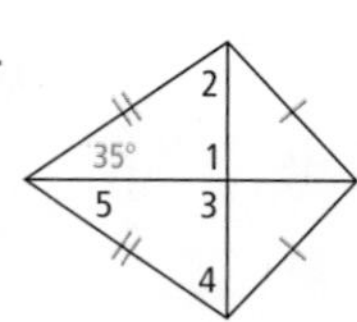

22. 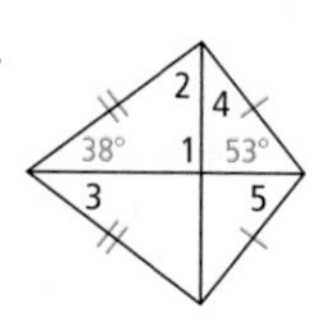

23. 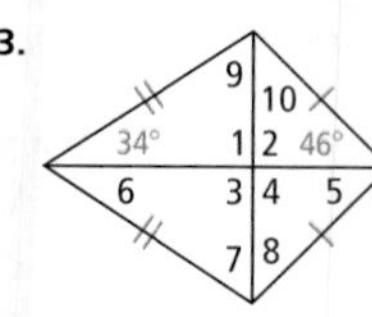

24. 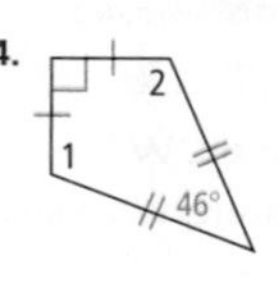

25. **Open-Ended** Sketch two noncongruent kites such that the diagonals of one are congruent to the diagonals of the other.

Answers

Practice and Problem-Solving Exercises

7. $m\angle 1 = 77$, $m\angle 2 = 103$, $m\angle 3 = 103$
8. $m\angle 1 = 69$, $m\angle 2 = 69$, $m\angle 13 = 111$
9. $m\angle 1 = 49$, $m\angle 2 = 131$, $m\angle 3 = 131$
10. $m\angle 1 = 105$, $m\angle 2 = m\angle 3 = 75$
11. $m\angle 1 = m\angle 2 = 115$, $m\angle 3 = 65$
12. $m\angle 1 = m\angle 2 = 120$, $m\angle 3 = 60$
13. 9
14. 11
15. 9
16. $m\angle 1 = 90$, $m\angle 2 = 68$
17. $m\angle 1 = 90$, $m\angle 2 = 45$, $m\angle 3 = 45$
18. $m\angle 1 = 108$, $m\angle 2 = 108$
19. $m\angle 1 = 90$, $m\angle 2 = 26$, $m\angle 3 = 90$
20. $m\angle 1 = 90$, $m\angle 2 = 50$, $m\angle 3 = 90$
21. $m\angle 1 = 90$, $m\angle 2 = 55$, $m\angle 3 = 90$, $m\angle 4 = 55$, $m\angle 5 = 35$
22. $m\angle 1 = 90$, $m\angle 2 = 52$, $m\angle 3 = 38$, $m\angle 4 = 37$, $m\angle 5 = 53$
23. $m\angle 1 = 90$, $m\angle 2 = 90$, $m\angle 3 = 90$, $m\angle 4 = 90$, $m\angle 5 = 46$, $m\angle 6 = 34$, $m\angle 7 = 56$, $m\angle 8 = 44$, $m\angle 9 = 56$, $m\angle 10 = 44$
24. $m\angle 1 = 112$, $m\angle 2 = 112$
25. Answers may vary. Sample:

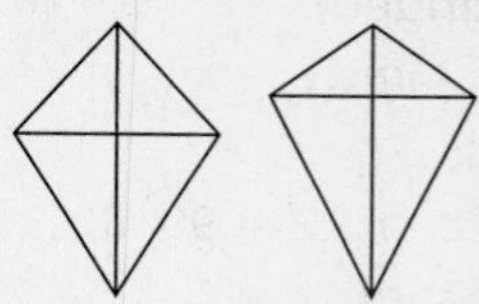

26. **Think About a Plan** The perimeter of a kite is 66 cm. The length of one of its sides is 3 cm less than twice the length of another. Find the length of each side of the kite.
- Can you draw a diagram?
- How can you write algebraic expressions for the lengths of the sides?

27. **Reasoning** If $KLMN$ is an isosceles trapezoid, is it possible for $\overline{KM}$ to bisect $\angle LMN$ and $\angle LKN$? Explain.

Algebra **Find the value of the variable in each isosceles trapezoid.**

28. 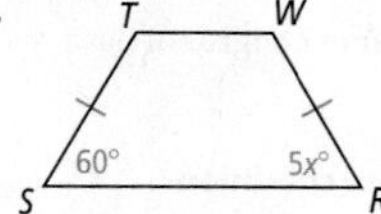

29. 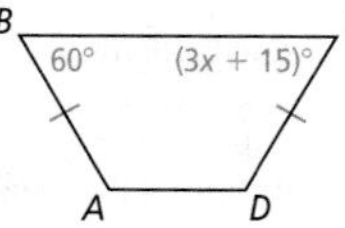

30. 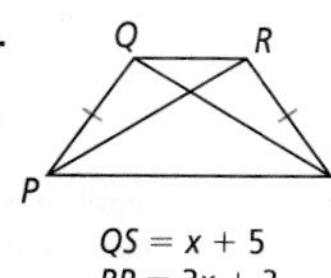

Algebra **Find the lengths of the segments with variable expressions.**

31. 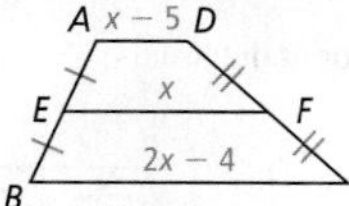

32. 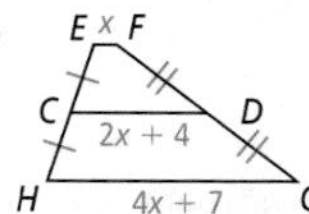

33. 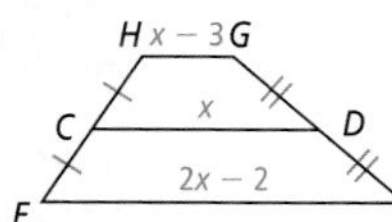

Algebra **Find the value(s) of the variable(s) in each kite.**

34. 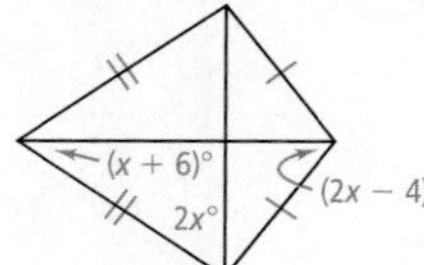

35. 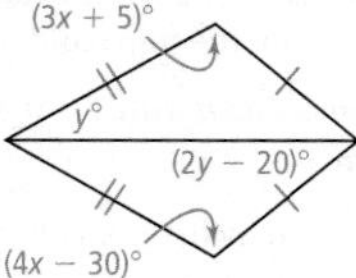

36. 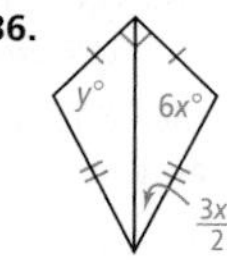

Bridge Design **The beams of the bridge at the right form quadrilateral $ABCD$. $\triangle AED \cong \triangle CDE \cong \triangle BEC$ and $m\angle DCB = 120$.**

37. Classify the quadrilateral. Explain your reasoning.

38. Find the measures of the other interior angles of the quadrilateral.

Reasoning **Can two angles of a kite be as follows? Explain.**

39. opposite and acute

40. consecutive and obtuse

41. opposite and supplementary

42. consecutive and supplementary

43. opposite and complementary

44. consecutive and complementary

26. 12 cm, 12 cm, 21 cm, 21 cm

27. No; explanations may vary. Sample: Assume $\overline{KM}$ bisects both ∠s. Then $\angle MKL \cong \angle MKN \cong \angle KML \cong \angle KMN$. Both pairs of sides of $KLMN$ would be ∥, and $KLMN$ would be a ▱. It is impossible for an isosc. trap. to also be a ▱, so $\overline{KM}$ cannot bis. $\angle LMN$ and $\angle LKN$.

28. 12

29. 15

30. 1

31. $AD = 4$, $EF = 9$, $BC = 14$

32. $EF = 1$, $CD = 6$, $HG = 11$

33. $HG = 2$, $CD = 5$, $EF = 8$

34. 28

35. $x = 35$, $y = 30$

36. $x = 18$, $y = 108$

37. Isosc. trapezoid; $\overline{AB} \parallel \overline{DC}$ (If alt. int. ∠s are ≅, then lines are ∥.) and $\overline{AD} \cong \overline{BC}$. (Corresp. parts of ≅ △s are ≅.)

38. $m\angle A = m\angle B = 60$, $m\angle CDA = 120$

39. Yes; the ≅ ∠s can be obtuse.

40. Yes; the ≅ ∠s and one other ∠ can be obtuse.

41. Yes; if two ≅ ∠s are rt. ∠s, they are suppl. The other two ∠s are also suppl.

42. No; if two consecutive ∠s are suppl., then another pair must also be suppl. because one pair of opp. ∠s is ≅. Therefore, the opp. ∠s would be ≅, which means the figure would be a ▱ and not a kite.

43. Yes; the ≅ ∠s each have measure 45.

44. No; if consecutive ∠s are compl., the figure is concave, so not a kite.

Answers

Practice and Problem-Solving Exercises (continued)

45. Answers may vary. Sample:
1. Draw $\overline{AE} \parallel \overline{DC}$. (Construction)
2. $AECD$ is a ▱. (Def. of ▱)
3. $\overline{AE} \cong \overline{DC}$ (Opp. sides of a ▱ are $\cong$.)
4. $\angle 1 \cong \angle C$ (If $\parallel$ lines, corresp. $\angle$s are $\cong$.)
5. $\angle B \cong \angle 1$ (Isosc. $\triangle$ Thm.)
6. $\angle B \cong \angle C$ (Transitive Prop. of $\cong$)
7. $\angle D$ and $\angle C$ are suppl. (If $\parallel$ lines, same-side int. $\angle$s are suppl.)
8. $\angle BAD$ and $\angle B$ are suppl. (If $\parallel$ lines, same-side int. $\angle$s are suppl.)
9. $\angle BAD \cong \angle D$ ($\angle$s suppl. to $\cong$ $\angle$s are $\cong$.)

46. Answers may vary. Sample:
Given: Trapezoid $ABCD$ with $\overline{BC} \parallel \overline{AD}$, $\angle A \cong \angle D$
Prove: $ABCD$ is an isosc. trapezoid.
1. $\overleftrightarrow{AB}$ is not $\parallel$ to $\overleftrightarrow{DC}$. (Def. of trapezoid)
2. Extend $\overleftrightarrow{AB}$ and $\overleftrightarrow{DC}$ to meet at point T. (Construction)
3. $\angle A \cong \angle D$ (Given)
4. $\overline{AT} \cong \overline{DT}$ (Converse of Isosc. $\triangle$ Thm.)
5. $\angle TBC \cong \angle A$ and $\angle TCB \cong \angle D$ (If $\parallel$ lines, then corresp. $\angle$s are $\cong$.)
6. $\angle TBC \cong \angle TCB$ (Transitive Prop. of $\cong$)
7. $\overline{TB} \cong \overline{TC}$ (Converse of Isosc. $\triangle$ Thm.)
8. $TA + AB = TB$, $TD + DC = TC$ (Seg. Add. Post.)
9. $AB = TB - TA$, $DC = TC - TD$ (Subtr. Prop. of Eq.)
10. $AB = DC$ (Subst. Prop. of Eq.)
11. $ABCD$ is an isosc. trapezoid. (Def. of isosc. trapezoid)

47. Isosc. trapezoid; answers may vary. Sample:

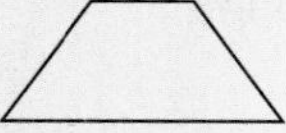

48. ▱, rhombus, rectangle, square; answers may vary. Sample:

49. Rectangle, square; answers may vary. Sample:

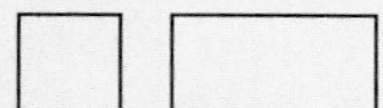

50. Kite, isosc. trapezoid, rhombus, square; answers may vary. Sample:

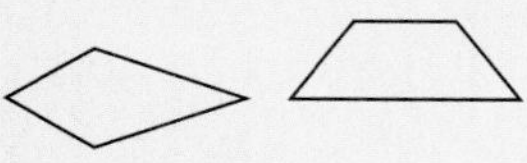

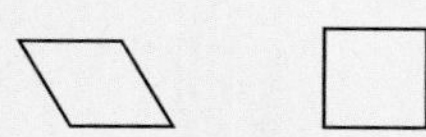

51. Kite, rhombus, square; answers may vary. Sample:

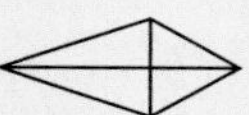 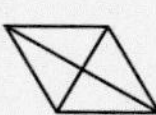 

45. Developing Proof The plan suggests a proof of Theorem 6-19. Write a proof that follows the plan.

Given: Isosceles trapezoid $ABCD$ with $\overline{AB} \cong \overline{DC}$

Prove: $\angle B \cong \angle C$ and $\angle BAD \cong \angle D$

Plan: Begin by drawing $\overline{AE} \parallel \overline{DC}$ to form parallelogram $AECD$ so that $\overline{AE} \cong \overline{DC} \cong \overline{AB}$. $\angle B \cong \angle C$ because $\angle B \cong \angle 1$ and $\angle 1 \cong \angle C$. Also, $\angle BAD \cong \angle D$ because they are supplements of the congruent angles, $\angle B$ and $\angle C$.

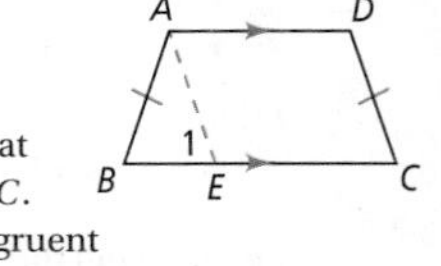

46. Proof Prove the converse of Theorem 6-19: If a trapezoid has a pair of congruent base angles, then the trapezoid is isosceles.

Name each type of special quadrilateral that can meet the given condition. Make sketches to support your answers.

47. exactly one pair of congruent sides
48. two pairs of parallel sides
49. four right angles
50. adjacent sides that are congruent
51. perpendicular diagonals
52. congruent diagonals

53. Proof Prove Theorem 6-20.
Given: Isosceles trapezoid $ABCD$ with $\overline{AB} \cong \overline{DC}$
Prove: $\overline{AC} \cong \overline{DB}$

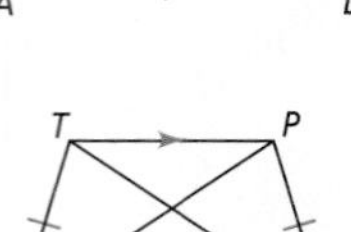

54. Proof Prove the converse of Theorem 6-20: If the diagonals of a trapezoid are congruent, then the trapezoid is isosceles.

55. Proof **Given:** Isosceles trapezoid $TRAP$ with $\overline{TR} \cong \overline{PA}$
Prove: $\angle RTA \cong \angle APR$

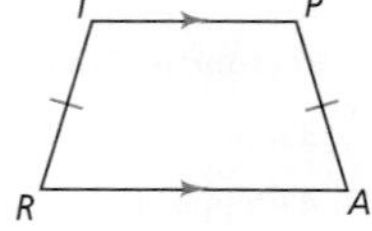

56. Proof Prove that the angles formed by the noncongruent sides of a kite are congruent. (*Hint:* Draw a diagonal of the kite.)

Determine whether each statement is *true* or *false*. Justify your response.

57. All squares are rectangles.
58. A trapezoid is a parallelogram.
59. A rhombus can be a kite.
60. Some parallelograms are squares.
61. Every quadrilateral is a parallelogram.
62. All rhombuses are squares.

Challenge

63. Proof **Given:** Isosceles trapezoid $TRAP$ with $\overline{TR} \cong \overline{PA}$; $\overline{BI}$ is the perpendicular bisector of $\overline{RA}$, intersecting $\overline{RA}$ at B and $\overline{TP}$ at I.
Prove: $\overline{BI}$ is the perpendicular bisector of $\overline{TP}$.

T P R A

52. Rectangle, isosc. trapezoid, kite; answers may vary. Sample:

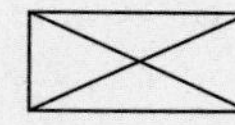  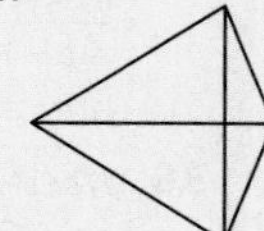

53. Answers may vary. Sample:
1. $\overline{AB} \cong \overline{DC}$ (Given)
2. $\angle BAD \cong \angle CDA$ (Base $\angle$s of an isosc. trapezoid are $\cong$.)
3. $\overline{AD} \cong \overline{AD}$ (Refl. Prop. of $\cong$)
4. $\triangle BAD \cong \triangle CDA$ (SAS)
5. $\overline{BD} \cong \overline{CA}$ (Corresp. parts of $\cong$ $\triangle$s are $\cong$.)

54. Given: Trapezoid $ABCD$ with $\overline{BC} \parallel \overline{AD}$, $\overline{BD} \cong \overline{AC}$
Prove: $\overline{AB} \cong \overline{DC}$
1. Draw $\overline{BP} \perp \overline{AD}$ and $\overline{CQ} \perp \overline{AD}$. (Construction)
2. $\overline{BP} \cong \overline{CQ}$ (Opp. sides of a rectangle are $\cong$.)
3. $\overline{BD} \cong \overline{AC}$ (Given)
4. $\triangle BPD \cong \triangle CQA$ (HL)
5. $\angle BDP \cong \angle CAQ$ (Corresp. parts of $\cong$ $\triangle$s are $\cong$.)
6. $\overline{AD} \cong \overline{DA}$ (Refl. Prop. of $\cong$)
7. $\triangle BAD \cong \triangle CDA$ (SAS)
8. $\overline{AB} \cong \overline{DC}$ (Corresp. parts of $\cong$ $\triangle$s are $\cong$.)

55. Answers may vary. Sample:
1. Draw $\overline{TA}$ and $\overline{PR}$. (Construction)
2. $\overline{TR} \cong \overline{PA}$ (Given)
3. $\angle TRA \cong \angle PAR$ (Base $\angle$s of an isosc. trapezoid are $\cong$.)
4. $\overline{RA} \cong \overline{RA}$ (Refl. Prop. of $\cong$)
5. $\triangle TRA \cong \triangle PAR$ (SAS)
6. $\angle RTA \cong \angle APR$ (Corresp. parts of $\cong$ $\triangle$s are $\cong$.)

For a trapezoid, consider the segment joining the midpoints of the two given segments. How are its length and the lengths of the two parallel sides of the trapezoid related? Justify your answer.

64. the two nonparallel sides

65. the diagonals

66. $\overleftrightarrow{BN}$ is the perpendicular bisector of $\overline{AC}$ at N. Describe the set of points, D, for which $ABCD$ is a kite.

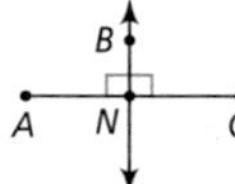

Standardized Test Prep

SAT/ACT

67. Which statement is never true?

Ⓐ Square $ABCD$ is a rhombus.

Ⓑ Trapezoid $GHJK$ is a parallelogram.

Ⓒ Parallelogram $PQRS$ is a square.

Ⓓ Square $WXYZ$ is a parallelogram.

68. A quadrilateral has four congruent sides. Which name best describes the figure?

Ⓕ trapezoid Ⓖ parallelogram Ⓗ rhombus Ⓘ kite

69. How would you classify triangle LMN?

Ⓐ acute isosceles

Ⓑ right isosceles

Ⓒ obtuse scalene

Ⓓ acute scalene

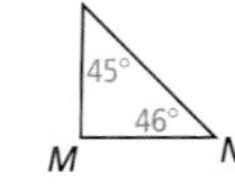

Extended Response

70. Given $\overline{DE}$ is congruent to $\overline{FG}$ and $\overline{EF}$ is congruent to $\overline{GD}$, prove $\angle E \cong \angle G$.

Mixed Review

Find the value of x for which the figure is the given special parallelogram.

See Lesson 6-5.

71. Rhombus

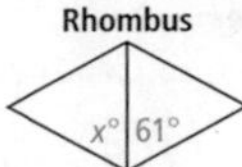

72. Rectangle

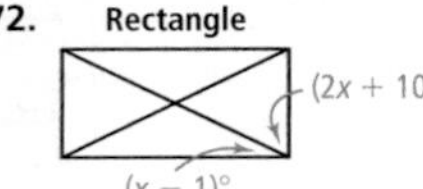

73. Rhombus

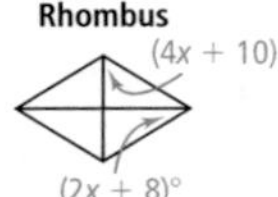

74. Algebra Find the value of c.

See Lesson 6-1.

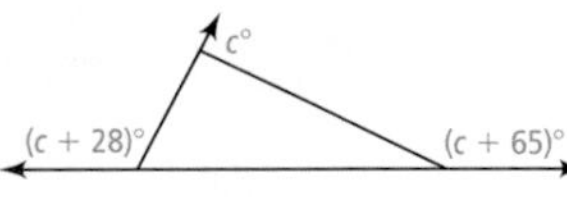

Get Ready! **To prepare for Lesson 6-7, do Exercises 75 and 76.**

75. Given $A(6, -2)$ and $B(-4, 8)$, find the midpoint and the length of $\overline{AB}$. See Lesson 1-7.

76. Find the slope of the line containing the points $C(-1, 5)$ and $D(7, 3)$. See Lesson 3-7.

56. 1. kite $ABCD$ with $\overline{AB} \cong \overline{AD}$, $\overline{BC} \cong \overline{CD}$ (Given)
2. Draw $\overline{AC}$. (Construction)
3. $\triangle ABC \cong \triangle ADC$ (SSS)
4. $\angle B \cong \angle D$ (Corresp. parts of $\cong$ ▲s are $\cong$.)

57. True; a square is a ▱ with 4 rt. ∠s.

58. False; a trapezoid has exactly one pair of ∥ sides.

59. False; a rhombus has 4 $\cong$ sides, and a kite does not.

60. True; a square is a ▱ that has four $\cong$ sides and four rt. ∠s.

61. False; counterexample: kites and trapezoids are not ▱s.

62. False; a rhombus without 4 rt. ∠s is not a square.

63. Answers may vary. Sample:
1. $\overline{RT}$ and $\overline{PA}$ are not ∥. (Def. of trapezoid)
2. Extend $\overline{RT}$ and $\overline{PA}$ to meet at M. (Construction)
3. $\angle MTP \cong \angle R$ and $\angle MPT \cong \angle A$. (If ∥ lines, then corresp. ∠s are $\cong$.)
4. $\angle MTP \cong \angle MPT$ (Trans. Prop. of $\cong$)
5. $\overline{MT} \cong \overline{MP}$ (Converse of Isosc. △ Thm.)
6. $\angle MIT$ and $\angle MIP$ are rt. ∠s. (A line ⊥ to one of two ∥ lines is also ⊥ to the other line.)
7. $\overline{MI} \cong \overline{MI}$ (Refl. Prop. of $\cong$)
8. $\triangle MIT \cong \triangle MIP$ (HL)
9. $\overline{TI} \cong \overline{PI}$ (Corresp. parts of $\cong$ ▲s are $\cong$.)
10. $\overline{BI}$ is the ⊥ bis. of $\overline{TP}$. (Def. of ⊥ bis.)

64. half the sum of the bases; Trapezoid Midsegment Thm.

65. half the difference of the bases; △ Midsegment Thm.

66. D is a point on $\overleftrightarrow{BN}$ such that $ND \neq BN$, and B and D are on opp. sides of N.

67. B

68. H

69. D

70. [4] 1. $\overline{DE} \cong \overline{FG}$ and $\overline{EF} \cong \overline{GD}$ (Given)
2. $\overline{DF} \cong \overline{FD}$ (Refl. Prop. of $\cong$)
3. $\triangle EDF \cong \triangle GFD$ (SSS)
4. $\angle E \cong \angle G$ (Corresp. parts of $\cong$ ▲s are $\cong$.)

[3] one missing OR incorrect step in the proof

[2] two or three missing OR incorrect steps in the proof

[1] more than three missing OR incorrect steps in the proof

71. 61

72. 27

73. 12

74. 89

75. (1, 3); $\sqrt{200}$ or $10\sqrt{2}$

76. $-\frac{1}{4}$

6-6 Lesson Resources

Differentiated Remediation

Instructional Support

Geometry Companion

Students can use the **Geometry Companion** worktext (4 pages) . . .

- New Vocabulary
- Key Concepts
- Got It for each Problem
- Lesson Check

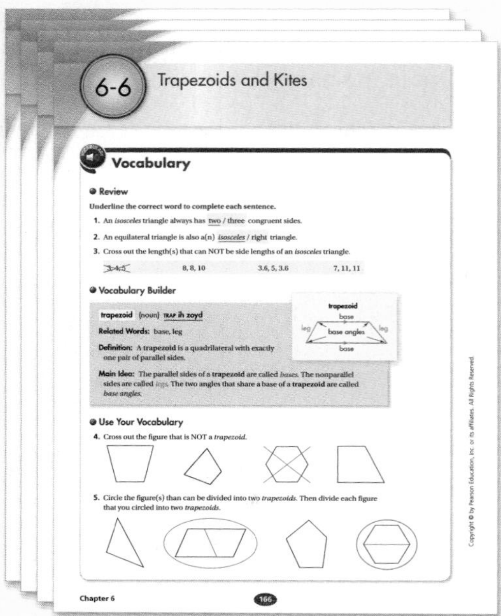

6-6 Trapezoids and Kites

Vocabulary

Review

Underline the correct word to complete each sentence.

1. An isosceles triangle always has two / three congruent sides.
2. An equilateral triangle is also a(n) isosceles / right triangle.
3. Cross out the length(s) that can NOT be side lengths of an isosceles triangle.

Vocabulary Builder

trapezoid (noun) TRAP ih zoyd

Related Words: base, leg

Definition: A trapezoid is a quadrilateral with exactly one pair of parallel sides.

Main Idea: The parallel sides of a trapezoid are called bases. The nonparallel sides are called legs. The two angles that share a base of a trapezoid are called base angles.

Use Your Vocabulary

4. Cross out the figure that is NOT a trapezoid.

5. Circle the figure(s) than can be divided into two trapezoids. Then divide each figure that you circled into two trapezoids.

Chapter 6 166

ELL Support

Focus on Language Project the Essential Understanding paragraph on the board and point to each word as you read the text, as students follow. Point out that vocabulary words are in boldface. Model how to underline or highlight the key words. Ask students to name cognates (same base word) of any key words.

As you encounter the vocabulary words in the text, ask: What is a *trapezoid*? Invite volunteers to draw the figure on the board and point out as you trace the base, legs, and base angles. Do the same with an isosceles trapezoid. Invite students to compare and contrast an isosceles trapezoid with other trapezoids.

5 Assess & Remediate

Lesson Quiz

1. $QRST$ is an isosceles trapezoid and $m\angle R = 116$. What are $m\angle Q$, $m\angle T$, and $m\angle S$?

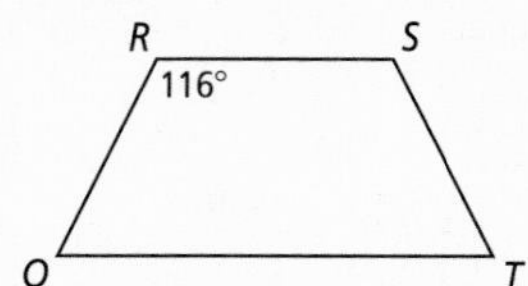

2. $\overline{AB}$ is the midsegment of trapezoid $DEFG$. What is x?

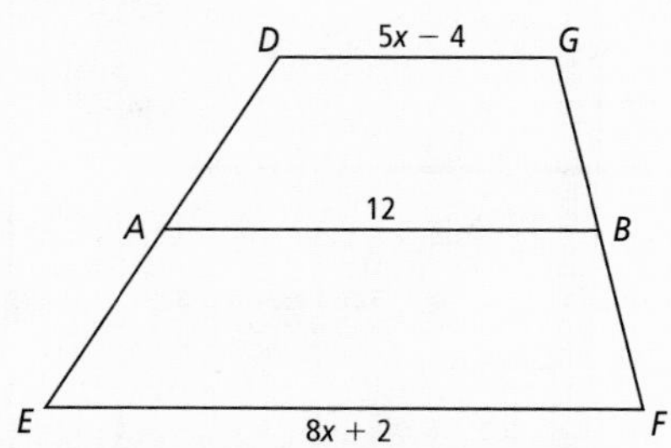

3. **Do you UNDERSTAND?** In kite $NPRQ$, what is $m\angle RPT$?

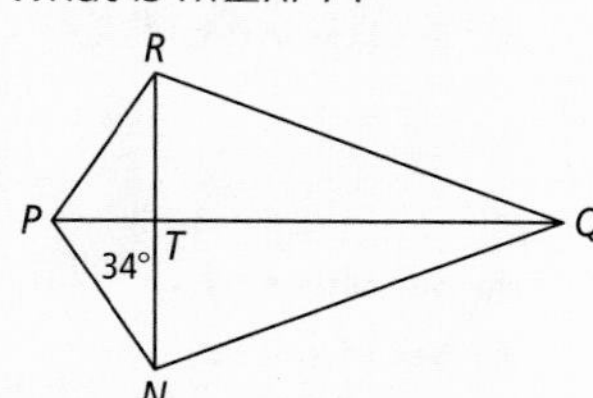

ANSWERS TO LESSON QUIZ

1. $m\angle S = 116$, $m\angle Q = 64$, $m\angle T = 64$
2. 2
3. 56

PRESCRIPTION FOR REMEDIATION

Use the student work on the Lesson Quiz to prescribe a differentiated review assignment.

Points	Differentiated Remediation
0–1	Intervention
2	On-level
3	Extension

PowerGeometry.com

5 Assess & Remediate

Assign the Lesson Quiz. Appropriate intervention, practice, or enrichment is automatically generated based on student performance.

Intervention

- **Reteaching** (2 pages) Provides reteaching and practice exercises for the key lesson concepts. Use with struggling students or absent students.
- **English Language Learner Support** Helps students develop and reinforce mathematical vocabulary and key concepts.

All-in-One Resources/Online

Reteaching

6-6 Reteaching

Trapezoids and Kites

A *trapezoid* is a quadrilateral with exactly one pair of parallel sides. The two parallel sides are called *bases*. The two nonparallel sides are called *legs*.

A pair of base angles share a common base.

$\angle 1$ and $\angle 2$ are one pair of base angles.

$\angle 3$ and $\angle 4$ are a second pair of base angles.

In any trapezoid, the *midsegment* is parallel to the bases. The length of the midsegment is half the sum of the lengths of the bases.

$MN = \frac{1}{2}(QR + ZX)$

An *isosceles trapezoid* is a trapezoid in which the legs are congruent. An isosceles trapezoid has some special properties:

Each pair of base angles is congruent. The diagonals are congruent.

$AC = BD$

Exercises

1. In trapezoid $LMNO$, what is the measure of $\angle OLM$? 70 What is the measure of $\angle LMN$? 110
2. $WXYZ$ is an isosceles trapezoid and $WY = 12$. What is XZ? 12
3. $\overline{XZ}$ is the midsegment of trapezoid $EFGH$. If $FG = 8$ and $EH = 12$, what is XZ? 10

All-in-One Resources/Online

English Language Learner Support

6-6 ELL Support

Trapezoids and Kites

Complete the vocabulary chart by filling in the missing information.

Word or Word Phrase	Definition	Picture or Example
trapezoid	A *trapezoid* is a quadrilateral with one pair of parallel sides.	
legs of a trapezoid	1. The *legs of a trapezoid* are the non-parallel sides.	$\overline{TP}$ and $\overline{RA}$
bases of a trapezoid	2. The *bases of a trapezoid* are the parallel sides.	$\overline{TR}$ and $\overline{PA}$
isosceles trapezoid	An *isosceles trapezoid* is a trapezoid with legs that are congruent.	3.
base angles	4. The *base angles* are the angles that share the base of a trapezoid.	$\angle A$ and $\angle B$ or $\angle C$ and $\angle D$
kite	A *kite* is a quadrilateral with two pairs of consecutive, congruent sides. In a kite, no opposite sides are congruent.	5.
midsegment of a trapezoid	6. The *midsegment of a trapezoid* is the segment that joins the midpoints of the legs.	

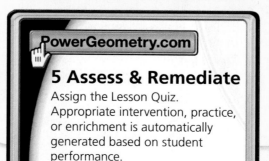

Differentiated Remediation *continued*

On-Level

- **Practice** (2 pages) Provides extra practice for each lesson. For simpler practice exercises, use the Form K Practice pages found in the All-in-One Teaching Resources and online.
- **Think About a Plan** Helps students develop specific problem-solving skills and strategies by providing scaffolded guiding questions.
- **Standardized Test Prep** Focuses on all major exercises, all major question types, and helps students prepare for the high-stakes assessments.

Extension

- **Enrichment** Provides students with interesting problems and activities that extend the concepts of the lesson.
- **Activities, Games, and Puzzles** Worksheets that can be used for concepts development, enrichment, and for fun!

Practice and Problem Solving Wkbk/ All-in-One Resources/Online

Practice page 1

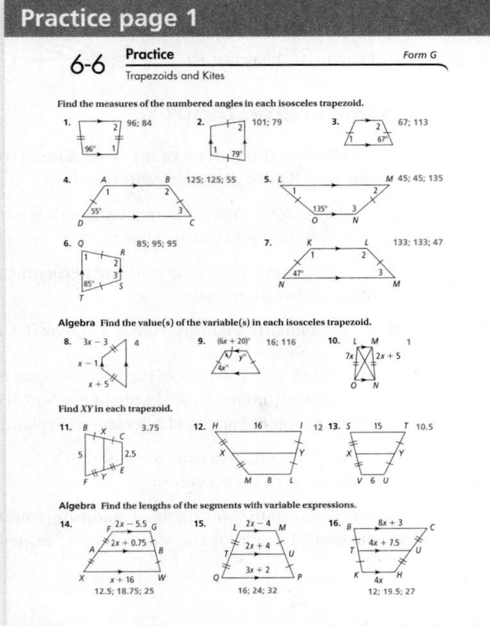

6-6 Practice — Form G
Trapezoids and Kites

Find the measures of the numbered angles in each isosceles trapezoid.

1. 96; 84
2. 101; 79
3. 67; 113
4. 125; 125; 55
5. 45; 45; 135
6. 85; 95; 95
7. 133; 133; 47

Algebra Find the value(s) of the variable(s) in each isosceles trapezoid.

8. 4
9. 16; 116
10. 1

Find XY in each trapezoid.

11. 3.75
12. 12
13. 10.5

Algebra Find the lengths of the segments with variable expressions.

14. 12.5; 18.75; 25
15. 16; 24; 32
16. 12; 19.5; 27

Practice and Problem Solving Wkbk/ All-in-One Resources/Online

Practice page 2

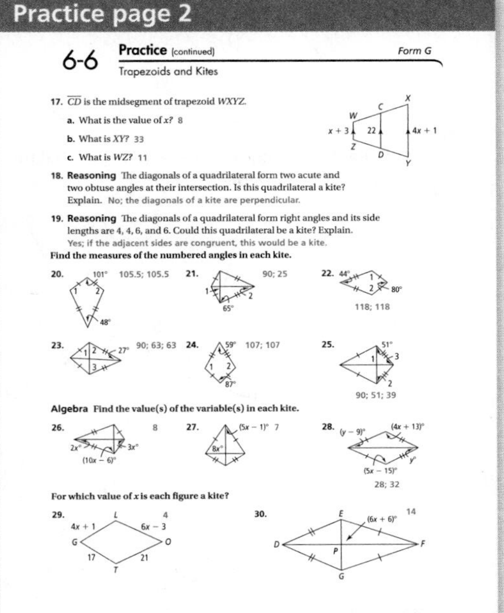

6-6 Practice (continued) — Form G
Trapezoids and Kites

17. $\overline{CD}$ is the midsegment of trapezoid $WXYZ$.
a. What is the value of x? 8
b. What is XY? 33
c. What is WZ? 11

18. **Reasoning** The diagonals of a quadrilateral form two acute and two obtuse angles at their intersection. Is this quadrilateral a kite? Explain. No; the diagonals of a kite are perpendicular.

19. **Reasoning** The diagonals of a quadrilateral form right angles and its side lengths are 4, 4, 6, and 6. Could this quadrilateral be a kite? Explain. Yes; if the adjacent sides are congruent, this would be a kite.

Find the measures of the numbered angles in each kite.

20. 105.5; 105.5
21. 90; 25
22. 118; 118
23. 90; 63; 63
24. 107; 107
25. 90; 51; 39

Algebra Find the value(s) of the variable(s) in each kite.

26. 8
27. 7
28. 28; 32

For which value of x is each figure a kite?

29. 4
30. 14

All-in-One Resources/Online

Enrichment

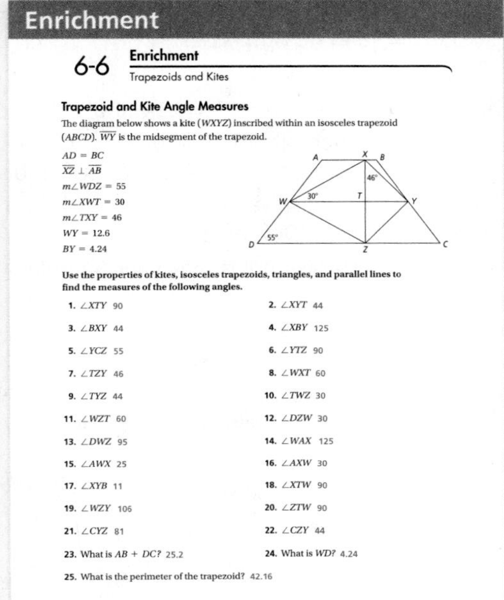

6-6 Enrichment
Trapezoids and Kites

Trapezoid and Kite Angle Measures

The diagram below shows a kite ($WXYZ$) inscribed within an isosceles trapezoid ($ABCD$). $\overline{WY}$ is the midsegment of the trapezoid.

$AD = BC$
$\overline{XZ} \perp \overline{AB}$
$m\angle WDZ = 55$
$m\angle XWT = 30$
$m\angle TXY = 46$
$WY = 12.6$
$BY = 4.24$

Use the properties of kites, isosceles trapezoids, triangles, and parallel lines to find the measures of the following angles.

1. $\angle XTY$ 90
2. $\angle XYT$ 44
3. $\angle BXY$ 44
4. $\angle XBY$ 125
5. $\angle YCZ$ 55
6. $\angle YTZ$ 90
7. $\angle TZY$ 46
8. $\angle WXT$ 60
9. $\angle TYZ$ 44
10. $\angle TWZ$ 30
11. $\angle WZT$ 60
12. $\angle DZW$ 30
13. $\angle DWZ$ 95
14. $\angle WAX$ 125
15. $\angle AWX$ 25
16. $\angle AXW$ 30
17. $\angle XYB$ 11
18. $\angle XTW$ 90
19. $\angle WZY$ 106
20. $\angle ZTW$ 90
21. $\angle CYZ$ 81
22. $\angle CZY$ 44
23. What is $AB + DC$? 25.2
24. What is WD? 4.24
25. What is the perimeter of the trapezoid? 42.16

Practice and Problem Solving Wkbk/ All-in-One Resources/Online

Think About a Plan

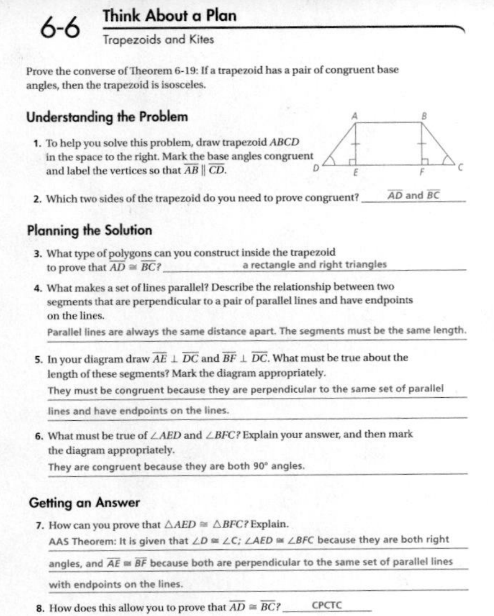

6-6 Think About a Plan
Trapezoids and Kites

Prove the converse of Theorem 6-19: If a trapezoid has a pair of congruent base angles, then the trapezoid is isosceles.

Understanding the Problem

1. To help you solve this problem, draw trapezoid $ABCD$ in the space to the right. Mark the base angles congruent and label the vertices so that $\overline{AB} \parallel \overline{CD}$.
2. Which two sides of the trapezoid do you need to prove congruent? $\overline{AD}$ and $\overline{BC}$

Planning the Solution

3. What type of polygons can you construct inside the trapezoid to prove that $\overline{AD} \cong \overline{BC}$? a rectangle and right triangles
4. What makes a set of lines parallel? Describe the relationship between two segments that are perpendicular to a pair of parallel lines and have endpoints on the lines. Parallel lines are always the same distance apart. The segments must be the same length.
5. In your diagram draw $\overline{AE} \perp \overline{DC}$ and $\overline{BF} \perp \overline{DC}$. What must be true about the length of these segments? Mark the diagram appropriately. They must be congruent because they are perpendicular to the same set of parallel lines and have endpoints on the lines.
6. What must be true of $\angle AED$ and $\angle BFC$? Explain your answer, and then mark the diagram appropriately. They are congruent because they are both 90° angles.

Getting an Answer

7. How can you prove that $\triangle AED \cong \triangle BFC$? Explain. AAS Theorem: It is given that $\angle D \cong \angle C$; $\angle AED \cong \angle BFC$ because they are both right angles, and $\overline{AE} \cong \overline{BF}$ because both are perpendicular to the same set of parallel lines with endpoints on the lines.
8. How does this allow you to prove that $\overline{AD} \cong \overline{BC}$? CPCTC

Practice and Problem Solving Wkbk/ All-in-One Resources/Online

Standardized Test Prep

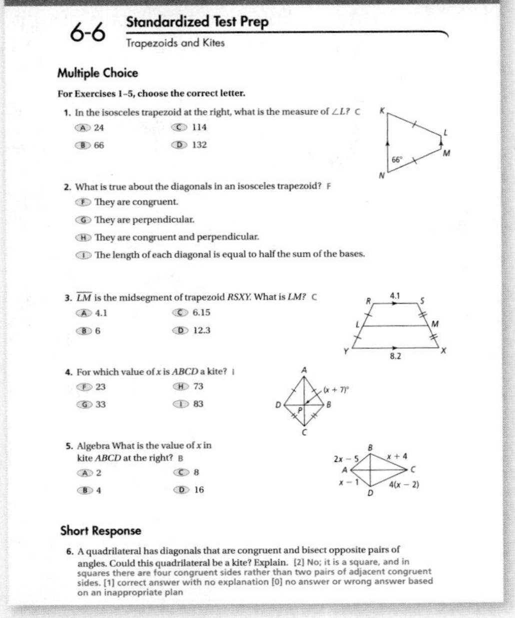

6-6 Standardized Test Prep
Trapezoids and Kites

Multiple Choice

For Exercises 1–5, choose the correct letter.

1. In the isosceles trapezoid at the right, what is the measure of $\angle L$? C
A 24 B 66 C 114 D 132
2. What is true about the diagonals in an isosceles trapezoid? F
F They are congruent.
G They are perpendicular.
H They are congruent and perpendicular.
I The length of each diagonal is equal to half the sum of the bases.
3. $\overline{LM}$ is the midsegment of trapezoid $RSXY$. What is LM? C
A 4.1 B 6 C 6.15 D 12.3
4. For which value of x is $ABCD$ a kite? I
F 23 G 33 H 73 I 83
5. Algebra What is the value of x in kite $ABCD$ at the right? B
A 2 B 4 C 8 D 16

Short Response

6. A quadrilateral has diagonals that are congruent and bisect opposite pairs of angles. Could this quadrilateral be a kite? Explain. [2] No; it is a square, and in squares there are four congruent sides rather than two pairs of adjacent congruent sides. [1] correct answer with no explanation [0] no answer or wrong answer based on an inappropriate plan

Online Teacher Resource Center

Activities, Games, and Puzzles

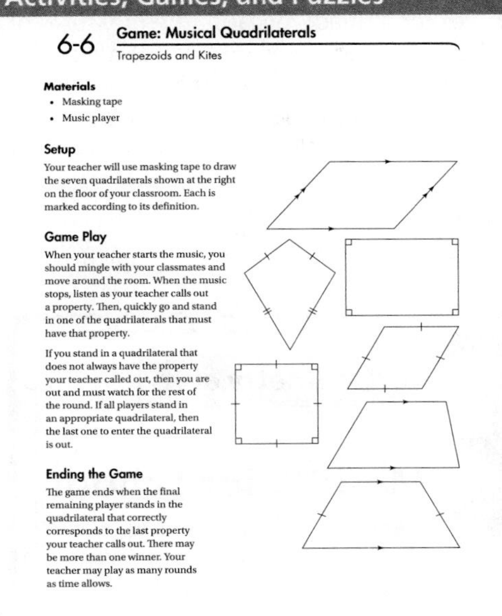

6-6 Game: Musical Quadrilaterals
Trapezoids and Kites

Materials
- Masking tape
- Music player

Setup
Your teacher will use masking tape to draw the seven quadrilaterals shown at the right on the floor of your classroom. Each is marked according to its definition.

Game Play
When your teacher starts the music, you should mingle with your classmates and move around the room. When the music stops, listen as your teacher calls out a property. Then, quickly go and stand in one of the quadrilaterals that must have that property.

If you stand in a quadrilateral that does not always have the property your teacher called out, then you are out and must watch for the rest of the round. If all players stand in an appropriate quadrilateral, then the last one to enter the quadrilateral is out.

Ending the Game
The game ends when the final remaining player stands in the quadrilateral that correctly corresponds to the last property your teacher calls out. There may be more than one winner. Your teacher may play as many rounds as time allows.

Answers

Mid-Chapter Quiz

1. $w = 90$, $x = 122$
2. $a = 105$, $m = 116$
3. $x = 45$, $y = 60$
4. $x = 1$, $y = 2$
5. isosc. trapezoid; $x = 3$
6. rhombus; $x = 58$, $y = 32$
7. kite; $x = \frac{5}{3}$, $y = 4.5$
8. ▱; $x = 2$, $y = 4$
9. $AB = 6$, $CD = 10$, $EF = 8$
10. Isosc. trapezoid; the quad. has one pair of ∥ sides and another pair of ≅ sides.
11. Rectangle; the quad. is a ▱ with a rt. ∠.
12. Rectangle; the quad. has 4 rt. ∠s.
13. Kite; the quad. has two pairs of consecutive sides ≅, and no opp. sides ≅.
14. 20.6
15. ▱$ABCD$ (Given), so ∠1 ≅ ∠4 and ∠2 ≅ ∠3 (If ∥ lines, then alt. int. ∠s are ≅.). $\overline{AC}$ bisects ∠DAB (Given), so ∠1 ≅ ∠2. (Def. of ∠ bis.) ∠3 ≅ ∠4 (Transitive Prop. of ≅), and $\overline{AC}$ bisects ∠DCE. (Def. of ∠ bis.)
16. False; counterexamples may vary. Sample:

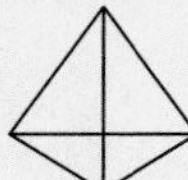

17. False; counterexamples may vary. Sample:

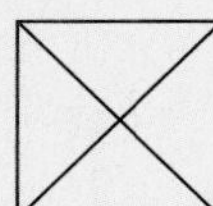

18. False; counterexamples may vary. Sample:

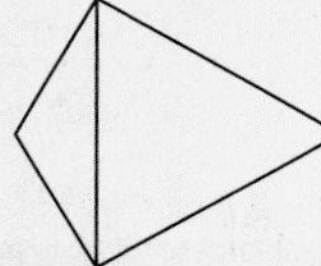

19. yes for a quad., because the measures of int. ∠s of a quad. total 360; no for a pentagon, because the measures of int. ∠s of a pentagon total 540 (more than a circle)

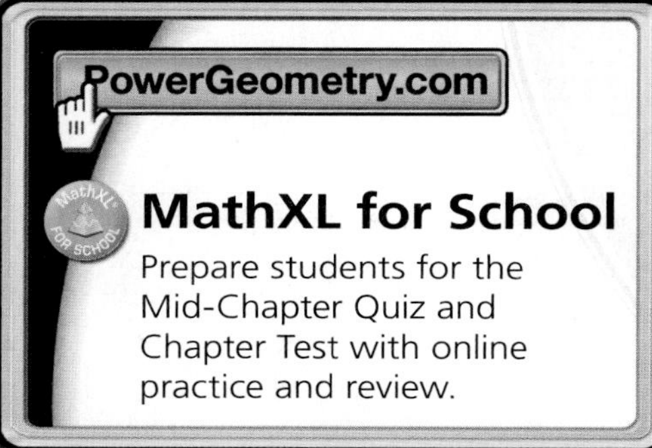

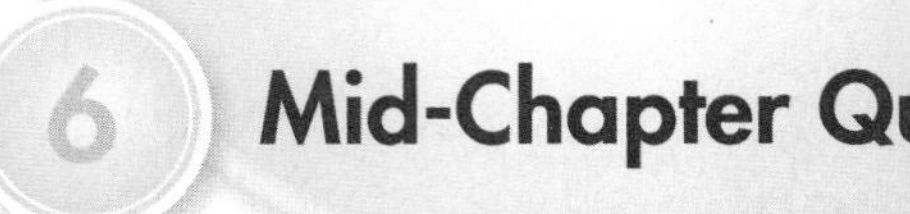

6 Mid-Chapter Quiz

Do you know HOW?

Find the value of each variable.

1. 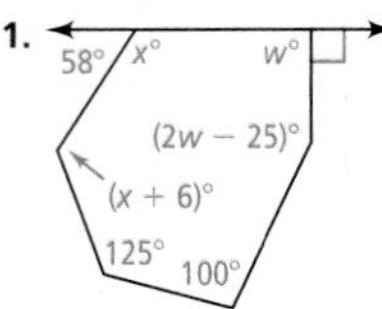

2. 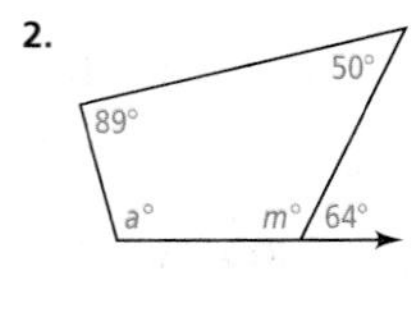

Algebra Find the values of the variables for which $ABCD$ is a parallelogram.

3. 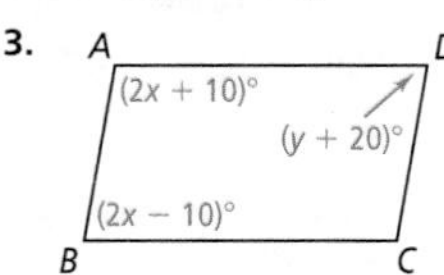

4. 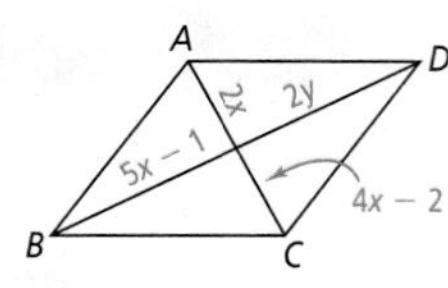

Algebra Classify the quadrilateral. Then find the value(s) of the variable(s).

5. 

6. 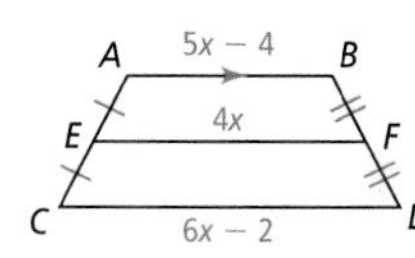

7. 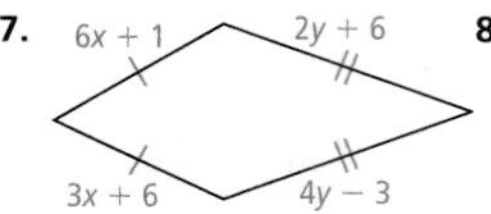

8. 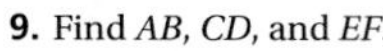

9. Find AB, CD, and EF.

Classify the quadrilateral as precisely as possible. Explain your reasoning.

10. 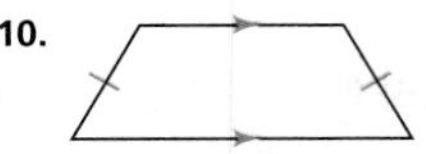

11. 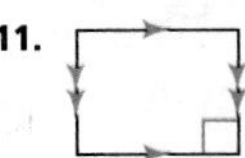

12. 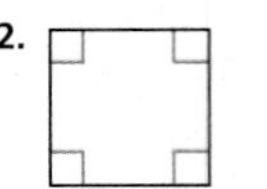

13. 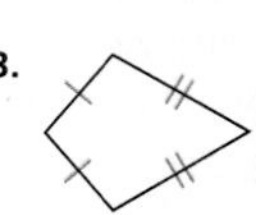

14. In the figure at the right, $\overleftrightarrow{AB} \parallel \overleftrightarrow{CD} \parallel \overleftrightarrow{EF}$. Find AE.

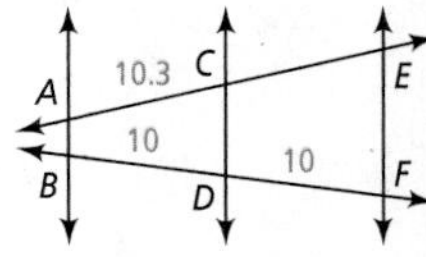

15. **Given:** ▱$ABCD$, $\overline{AC}$ bisects ∠DAB
Prove: $\overline{AC}$ bisects ∠DCB.

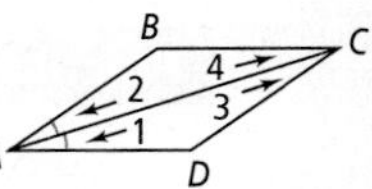

Do you UNDERSTAND?

Decide whether the statement is *true* or *false*. If true, explain why. If false, show a counterexample.

16. A quadrilateral with congruent diagonals is either an isosceles trapezoid or a rectangle.
17. A quadrilateral with congruent and perpendicular diagonals must be a kite.
18. Each diagonal of a kite bisects two angles of the kite.
19. **Reasoning** Can you fit all of the interior angles of a quadrilateral around a point without overlap? What about the interior angles of a pentagon? Explain.
20. **Writing** Explain two ways to show that a parallelogram is a rhombus.
21. Draw a diagram showing the relationships among the special quadrilaterals that you have learned.

20. Answers may vary. Sample: A ▱ is a rhombus if its diagonals are ⊥, if one diagonal bisects a pair of opp. ∠s, or if 4 sides are ≅.

21. 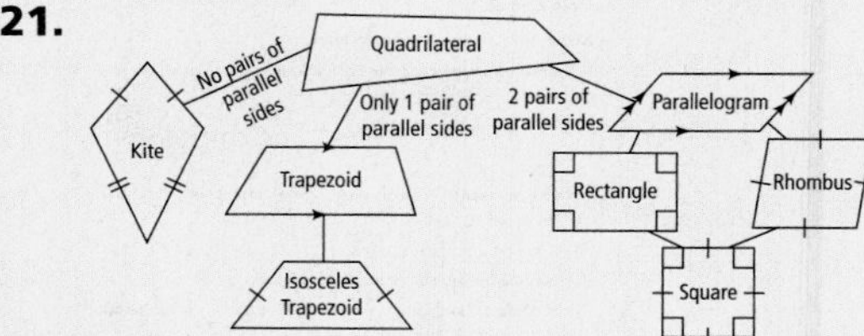

Algebra Review

Use With Lesson 6-7

Simplifying Radicals

A radical expression is in simplest form when all of the following are true.

- The radicand has no perfect square factors other than 1.
- The radicand does not contain a fraction.
- A denominator does not contain a radical expression.

radical symbol ↓ $\sqrt{a}$ ← radicand

Example 1

Simplify the expressions $\sqrt{2} \cdot \sqrt{8}$ and $\sqrt{294} \div \sqrt{3}$.

$\sqrt{2} \cdot \sqrt{8} = \sqrt{2 \cdot 8}$ Write both numbers under one radical.

$= \sqrt{16}$ Simplify the expression under the radical.

$= 4$ Factor out perfect squares and simplify.

$\sqrt{294} \div \sqrt{3} = \sqrt{\frac{294}{3}}$

$= \sqrt{98}$

$= \sqrt{49 \cdot 2}$

$= 7\sqrt{2}$

Example 2

Write $\sqrt{\frac{4}{3}}$ in simplest form.

$\sqrt{\frac{4}{3}} = \frac{\sqrt{4}}{\sqrt{3}}$ Rewrite the single radical as a quotient.

$= \frac{2}{\sqrt{3}}$ Simplify the numerator.

$= \frac{2}{\sqrt{3}} \cdot \frac{\sqrt{3}}{\sqrt{3}}$ Multiply by $\frac{\sqrt{3}}{\sqrt{3}}$ (a form of 1) to remove the radical from the denominator. This is called *rationalizing the denominator*.

$= \frac{2\sqrt{3}}{3}$

Exercises

Simplify each expression.

1. $\sqrt{5} \cdot \sqrt{10}$
2. $\sqrt{243}$
3. $\sqrt{128} \div \sqrt{2}$
4. $\sqrt{\frac{125}{4}}$
5. $\sqrt{6} \cdot \sqrt{8}$
6. $\frac{\sqrt{36}}{\sqrt{3}}$
7. $\frac{\sqrt{144}}{\sqrt{2}}$
8. $\sqrt{3} \cdot \sqrt{12}$
9. $\sqrt{72} \div \sqrt{2}$
10. $\sqrt{169}$
11. $28 \div \sqrt{8}$
12. $\sqrt{300} \div \sqrt{5}$
13. $\sqrt{12} \cdot \sqrt{2}$
14. $\frac{\sqrt{6} \cdot \sqrt{3}}{\sqrt{9}}$
15. $\frac{\sqrt{3} \cdot \sqrt{15}}{\sqrt{2}}$

Answers

Exercises

1. $5\sqrt{2}$
2. $9\sqrt{3}$
3. 8
4. $\frac{5\sqrt{5}}{2}$
5. $4\sqrt{3}$
6. $2\sqrt{3}$
7. $6\sqrt{2}$
8. 6
9. 6
10. 13
11. $7\sqrt{2}$
12. $2\sqrt{15}$
13. $2\sqrt{6}$
14. $\sqrt{2}$
15. $\frac{3\sqrt{10}}{2}$

Guided Instruction

PURPOSE To recognize when a radical expression is in simplest form and to simplify radical expressions

PROCESS Students will simplify radical expressions.

DISCUSS Emphasize to students that for a radical expression to be in simplest form, all three of the conditions presented must be true.

Example 1

In this Example students simplify one radical expression that involves a product and one that involves a quotient.

Q Is there another way the expression $\sqrt{2} \cdot \sqrt{8}$ could have been simplified? Explain. **[Yes, $\sqrt{2} \cdot \sqrt{8} = \sqrt{2} \cdot \sqrt{2} \cdot \sqrt{4} = \sqrt{4} \cdot \sqrt{4} = 4$]**

ERROR PREVENTION

Let the students know that one of the best strategies for simplifying radicals is to identify perfect square factors in the radicand and rewrite the expression.

Example 2

In this Example students simplify a radical expression by rationalizing the denominator.

Q What is the first step when rationalizing a denominator? **[Multiply by the least number that will make the denominator a perfect square.]**

ERROR PREVENTION

Remind students that when they are rationalizing the denominator, they are multiplying by a form of the number 1. Multiplying by 1 does not change the value of the original expression.

1 Interactive Learning

Solve It!

PURPOSE To explore the relationship between the slopes of perpendicular lines in a coordinate plane
PROCESS Students may use knowledge of right triangles, slope, and perpendicular lines.

FACILITATE

Q What is the relationship between two perpendicular lines drawn in the coordinate plane? **[Answers may vary. Sample: The slopes of the lines are opposite reciprocals.]**

Q How would you describe the slope of the rubber band shown in the diagram? **[It has a rise of 3 for a run of 1.]**

Q How would you describe the slope of a rubber band that is perpendicular to the one shown? **[It would have a fall of 1 for a run of 3.]**

ANSWER See Solve It in Answers on next page.
CONNECT THE MATH Students can share their triangles with the class to show that there is more than one correct answer. However, point out that each right triangle contains two lines whose slopes are opposite reciprocals, a topic which is discussed in the lesson.

2 Guided Instruction

Take Note

Students were introduced to each of these formulas at the beginning of their study of coordinate geometry. Ask students to share any memory techniques they have used for remembering these formulas.

6-7 Polygons in the Coordinate Plane

TN State Performance Indicators
SPI 3108.3.1 Use algebra and coordinate geometry to analyze and solve problems about geometric figures (including circles).
SPI 3108.3.2 Use coordinate geometry to prove characteristics of polygonal figures.

Objective To classify polygons in the coordinate plane

Apply what you learned "B-4" about classifying polygons.

Getting Ready!

You and a friend are playing a board game. Players place rubber bands on their own square grid to form different shapes. The object of the game is to guess the vertices of your opponent's shape. How would you place pieces on the grid shown to complete a right isosceles triangle? Sketch the triangle and justify the placement of each piece.

In the Solve It, you formed a polygon on a grid. In this lesson, you will classify polygons in the coordinate plane.

Essential Understanding You can classify figures in the coordinate plane using the formulas for slope, distance, and midpoint.

The chart below reviews these formulas and tells when to use them.

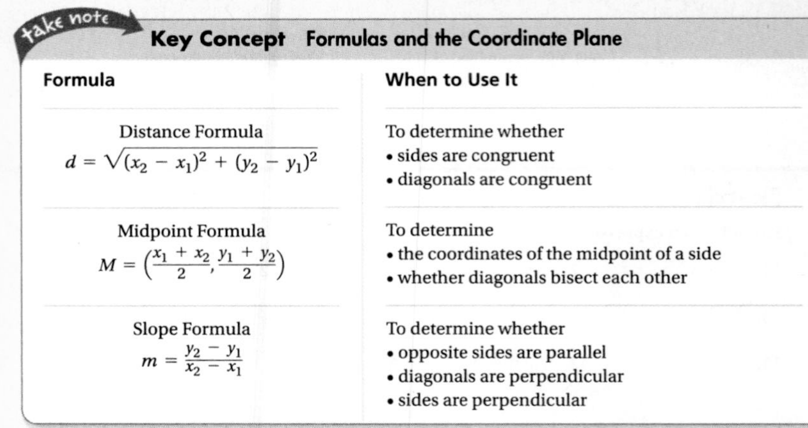

Key Concept Formulas and the Coordinate Plane

Formula	When to Use It
Distance Formula $d = \sqrt{(x_2 - x_1)^2 + (y_2 - y_1)^2}$	To determine whether • sides are congruent • diagonals are congruent
Midpoint Formula $M = \left(\frac{x_1 + x_2}{2}, \frac{y_1 + y_2}{2}\right)$	To determine • the coordinates of the midpoint of a side • whether diagonals bisect each other
Slope Formula $m = \frac{y_2 - y_1}{x_2 - x_1}$	To determine whether • opposite sides are parallel • diagonals are perpendicular • sides are perpendicular

6-7 Preparing to Teach

BIG idea Coordinate Geometry 

ESSENTIAL UNDERSTANDING
- The formulas for slope, distance and midpoint can be used to classify and to prove geometric relationships for figures in the coordinate plane.

Math Background

An introduction to coordinate geometry is provided earlier in this textbook and in the study of algebra. Students learned how to navigate a coordinate plane, represent lines and segments, determine the slopes of lines and segments, and determine the length and midpoint of segments. Now students combine these skills in coordinate geometry with their knowledge of properties of polygons in order to classify polygons drawn in the coordinate plane.

Support Student Learning

Use the **Geometry Companion** to engage and support students during instructions. See Lesson Resources at the end of this lesson for details.

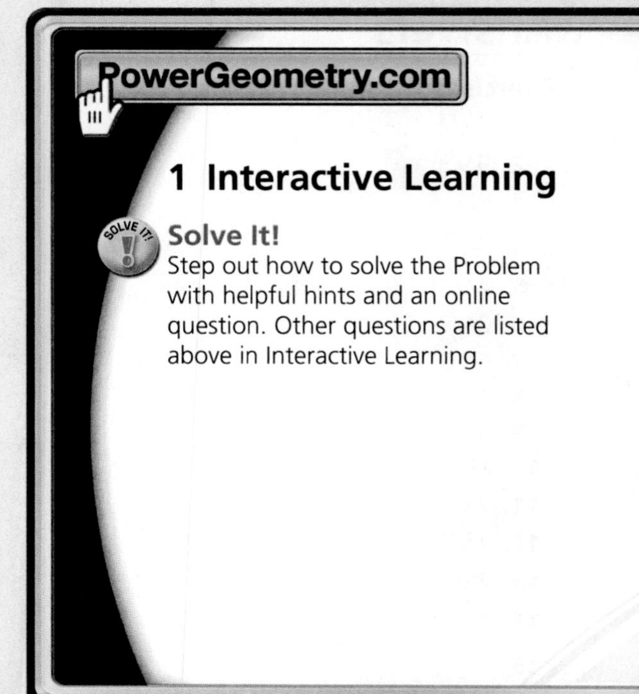

Problem 1 Classifying a Triangle

Think

What formulas do you use?
The terms *scalene*, *isosceles*, and *equilateral* have to do with the side lengths of a triangle. Use the Distance Formula.

Is $\triangle ABC$ *scalene, isosceles,* or *equilateral*?

The vertices of the triangle are $A(0, 1)$, $B(4, 4)$, and $C(7, 0)$.

Find the lengths of the sides using the Distance Formula.

$AB = \sqrt{(4-0)^2 + (4-1)^2}$

$= \sqrt{16 + 9}$ — Simplify within parentheses. Then simplify the powers.

$= \sqrt{25}$ — Simplify the radicand.

$= 5$ — Simplify.

$BC = \sqrt{(7-4)^2 + (0-4)^2} = \sqrt{9 + 16} = \sqrt{25} = 5$

$CA = \sqrt{(0-7)^2 + (1-0)^2} = \sqrt{49 + 1} = \sqrt{50} = 5\sqrt{2}$

Since $AB = BC = 5$, $\triangle ABC$ is isosceles.

Got It? **1.** $\triangle DEF$ has vertices $D(0, 0)$, $E(1, 4)$, and $F(5, 2)$. Is $\triangle DEF$ *scalene, isosceles,* or *equilateral*?

Problem 2 Classifying a Parallelogram

Plan

How can you determine whether *ABCD* is a rhombus?
You can find the length of each side using the Distance Formula, or you can determine whether the diagonals are perpendicular. The second way requires fewer steps.

Is $\square ABCD$ a rhombus? Explain.

Step 1 Use the Slope Formula to find the slopes of the diagonals.

slope of $\overline{AC} = \frac{5-0}{4-(-2)} = \frac{5}{6}$

slope of $\overline{BD} = \frac{1-4}{2-0} = -\frac{3}{2}$

Step 2 Find the product of the slopes.

$\frac{5}{6} \cdot \left(-\frac{3}{2}\right) = -\frac{15}{12}$

Since the product of the slopes is not -1, the diagonals are not perpendicular. So *ABCD* is not a rhombus.

Got It? **2.** $\square MNPQ$ has vertices $M(0, 1)$, $N(-1, 4)$, $P(2, 5)$, and $Q(3, 2)$.
a. Is $\square MNPQ$ a rectangle? Explain.
b. Is $\square MNPQ$ a square? Explain.
c. Reasoning Is the triangle in Problem 1 a right triangle? Explain.

Problem 1

Q What are the characteristics of scalene, isosceles, and equilateral triangles? **[Scalene triangles have no congruent sides; isosceles triangles have at least two congruent sides; equilateral triangles have 3 congruent sides.]**

Q Does the order of the points matter when substituting them into the Distance Formula? Explain. **[No, the difference of the points is squared, so the order of the points does not change the final answer.]**

Q Which of the angles in $\angle ABC$ are congruent? Explain. **[$\angle A \cong \angle C$ because they are the base angles.]**

Got It?

Q If you discover that a triangle is isosceles by determining the lengths of the first two sides, do you need to compute the length of the third side to classify the triangle? Explain. **[Yes, you need to determine the length of the third side to see if the triangle is also equilateral.]**

Problem 2

Ask students to adjust two of the four vertices of $\square ABCD$ so that it is also a rhombus, but not a square. Ask students to justify their figure by showing that the product of the slopes of the diagonals is -1, while the product of the slopes of adjacent sides is not -1.

Got It?

Discuss with students how they could verify that $\square MNPQ$ is a parallelogram by verifying that the opposite sides of the parallelogram have equal slopes.

2 Guided Instruction

Each Problem is worked out and supported online.

Problem 1
Classifying a Triangle
Animated

Problem 2
Classifying a Parallelogram
Animated

Problem 3
Classifying a Quadrilateral
Animated

Support in Geometry Companion

- Vocabulary
- Key Concepts
- Got It?

Answers

Solve It!

Answers may vary. Sample:

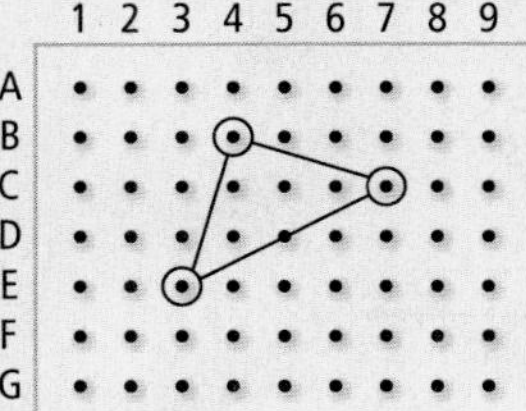

Using the square grid to count units, the slope of Leg 1 (E3 to B4) is 3. The slope of Leg 2 (B4 to C7) is $-\frac{1}{3}$. $3 \cdot \left(-\frac{1}{3}\right) = -1$, so the legs are $\perp$ and form a rt. $\angle$. Using the Distance Formula, both legs have a measure of $\sqrt{1^2 + 3^2}$ or $\sqrt{10}$. Since the legs are congruent and perpendicular to each other, the $\triangle$ is a rt. isosc. $\triangle$.

Got It?

1–2. See back of book.

Problem 3

Q How could you use the Distance Formula to verify that *KITE* is a kite? **[You could determine the length of each side and check to see that it has two pairs of congruent adjacent sides and no opposite congruent sides.]**

Q How could you use the diagonals of ▱*ABCD* to show that it is a rectangle? **[You could determine the length of each diagonal and show that they are equal and find the midpoint of each diagonal to show that they bisect each other (otherwise it could be an isosceles trapezoid).]**

Q At what point would the diagonals of the rectangle intersect? Explain. **[The diagonals bisect each other, so they would intersect at the midpoint of either diagonal. The midpoint of $\overline{AC}$ is (1, 0).]**

Q What is the most precise classification of the quadrilateral formed by connecting the midpoints of the sides of the rectangle? Explain. **[It is a rhombus. It has four congruent sides and two pairs of a parallel opposite sides and two pairs of opposite congruent angles.]**

Got It?

Q Which segments form the parallel sides of the isosceles trapezoid? **[$\overline{AD}$ and $\overline{BC}$]**

Q What are the midpoints of the legs of the isosceles trapezoid? **[(1, 2) and (7, 2)]**

Q What is the length of the midsegment of the trapezoid? **[The length is 6.]**

Problem 3 Classifying a Quadrilateral

A kite is shown at the right. What is the most precise classification of the quadrilateral formed by connecting the midpoints of the sides of the kite?

Know
$K(-4, 0)$, $I(0, 4)$, $T(8, 0)$, and $E(0, -4)$

Need
The midpoints of the sides of the kite

Plan
Use the Midpoint Formula to find the coordinates of the vertices of the inner quadrilateral. *Draw a diagram* to see it. Then classify the figure.

Step 1 Find the midpoint of each side of the kite.

$A = \text{midpoint of } \overline{KI} = \left(\frac{-4+0}{2}, \frac{0+4}{2}\right) = (-2, 2)$

$B = \text{midpoint of } \overline{IT} = \left(\frac{0+8}{2}, \frac{4+0}{2}\right) = (4, 2)$

$C = \text{midpoint of } \overline{TE} = \left(\frac{8+0}{2}, \frac{0+(-4)}{2}\right) = (4, -2)$

$D = \text{midpoint of } \overline{EK} = \left(\frac{0+(-4)}{2}, \frac{-4+0}{2}\right) = (-2, -2)$

Step 2 Draw a diagram of *ABCD*.

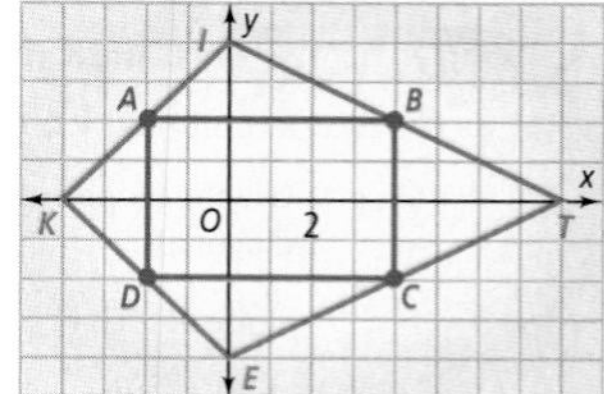

Step 3 Classify *ABCD*.

$AB = |4 - (-2)| = 6$ $CD = |-2 - 4| = 6$ Use the definition of distance on a number line. $BC = |-2 - 2| = 4$ $DA = |2 - (-2)| = 4$

Since opposite sides are congruent, *ABCD* is a parallelogram.

Since $\overline{AB}$ and $\overline{CD}$ are both horizontal, and $\overline{BC}$ and $\overline{DA}$ are both vertical, the segments form right angles. So, *ABCD* is a rectangle.

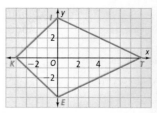

Got It? 3. An isosceles trapezoid has vertices $A(0, 0)$, $B(2, 4)$, $C(6, 4)$, and $D(8, 0)$. What special quadrilateral is formed by connecting the midpoints of the sides of *ABCD*?

Additional Problems

1. Is △*RST scalene*, *isosceles*, or *equilateral*?

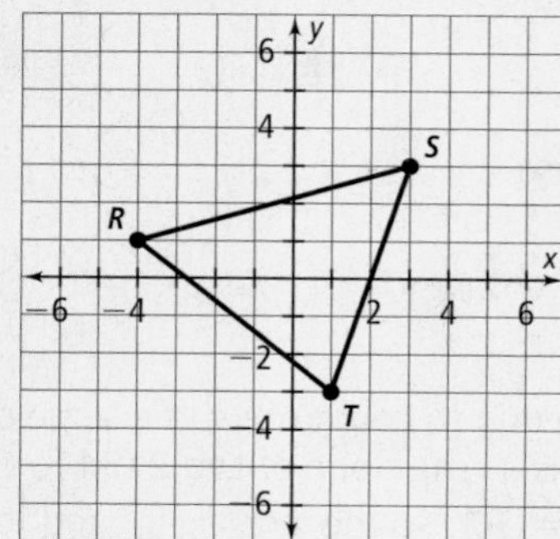

ANSWER scalene

2. Is parallelogram *ABCD* a rhombus? Explain.

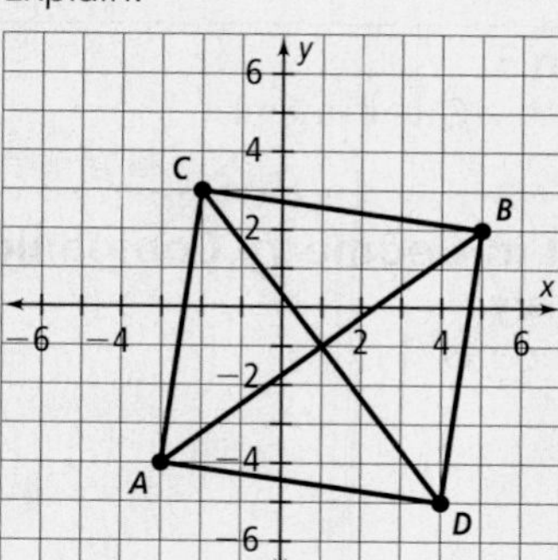

ANSWER Yes, the diagonals are perpendicular. In fact, *ABCD* is a square.

3. What is the most precise classification of the quadrilateral formed by connecting the midpoints of the sides of the isosceles trapezoid?

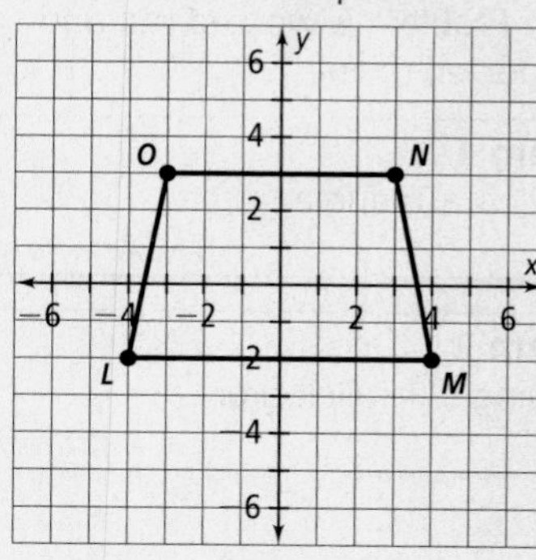

ANSWER rhombus

Lesson Check

Do you know HOW?

1. $\triangle TRI$ has vertices $T(-3, 4)$, $R(3, 4)$, and $I(0, 0)$. Is $\triangle TRI$ *scalene, isosceles,* or *equilateral*?
2. Is *QRST* below a rectangle? Explain.

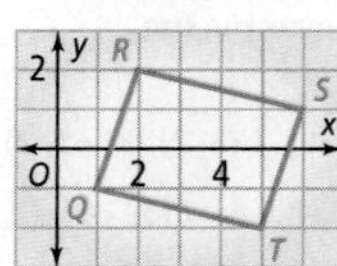

Do you UNDERSTAND?

3. **Writing** Describe how you would determine whether the lengths of the medians from base angles *D* and *F* are congruent.
4. **Error Analysis** A student says that the quadrilateral with vertices $D(1, 2)$, $E(0, 7)$, $F(5, 6)$, and $G(7, 0)$ is a rhombus because its diagonals are perpendicular. What is the student's error?

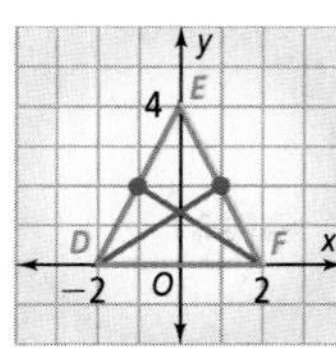

Practice and Problem-Solving Exercises

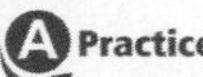

Practice Determine whether $\triangle ABC$ is *scalene, isosceles,* or *equilateral.* Explain.

See Problem 1.

5. 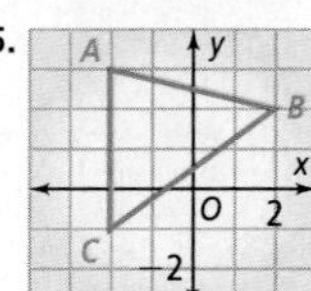
6. 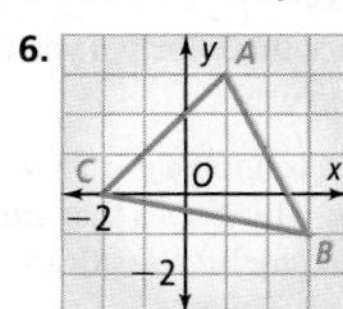
7. 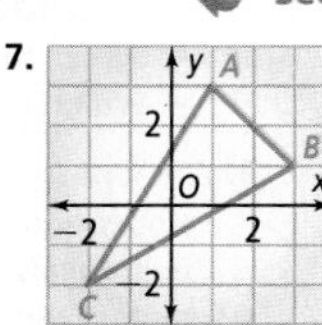

Determine whether the parallelogram is a *rhombus, rectangle, square,* or *none.* Explain.

See Problem 2.

8. $P(-1, 2)$, $O(0, 0)$, $S(4, 0)$, $T(3, 2)$
9. $L(1, 2)$, $M(3, 3)$, $N(5, 2)$, $P(3, 1)$
10. $R(-2, -3)$, $S(4, 0)$, $T(3, 2)$, $V(-3, -1)$
11. $G(0, 0)$, $H(6, 0)$, $I(9, 1)$, $J(3, 1)$
12. $W(-3, 0)$, $I(0, 3)$, $N(3, 0)$, $D(0, -3)$
13. $S(1, 3)$, $P(4, 4)$, $A(3, 1)$, $T(0, 0)$

What is the most precise classification of the quadrilateral formed by connecting in order the midpoints of each figure below?

See Problem 3.

14. parallelogram *PART*

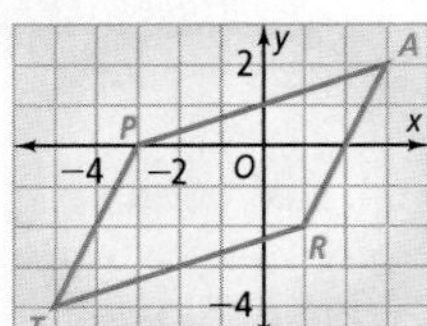

15. rectangle *EFGH*

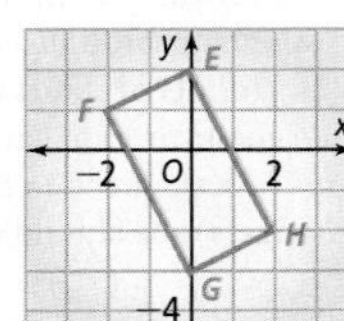

16. isosceles trapezoid *JKLM*

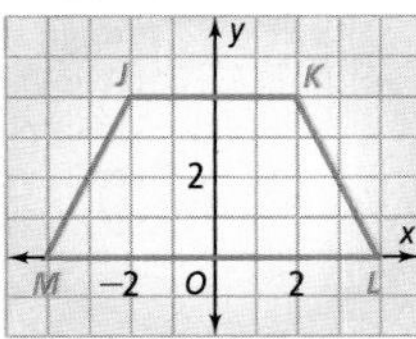

3 Lesson Check

Do you know HOW?

- If students have difficulty with Exercise 1, then have them use coordinate grid paper. They should also write the Distance Formula as the first step to finding the length of each side.

Do you UNDERSTAND?

- If students have difficulty with Exercise 4, then tell them that in order to prove a quadrilateral is a rhombus, it is first necessary to prove that it is a parallelogram.

Close

Q If the product of the slopes of the diagonals of a quadrilateral is -1, what classifications could be given to the quadrilateral? Explain. **[The quadrilateral might be a kite, a rhombus, or a square.]**

Answers

Got It? (continued)

3. rhombus (The length of each side is $\sqrt{13}$.)

Lesson Check

1. isosceles
2. No; explanations may vary. Sample: The diagonal lengths ($\sqrt{29}$ and 5) are not equal.
3. Find the coordinates and use the Distance Formula to compare lengths.
4. Answers may vary. Sample: *DEFG* is not a ▱.

Practice and Problem-Solving Exercises

5. Scalene; side lengths are 4, 5, and $\sqrt{17}$.
6. Scalene; side lengths are $2\sqrt{5}$, $\sqrt{26}$, and $3\sqrt{2}$.
7. Isosceles; side lengths are $2\sqrt{2}$, $\sqrt{34}$, and $\sqrt{34}$.
8. None; explanations may vary. Sample: It has no right angles or consecutive sides $\cong$.
9. Rhombus; explanations may vary. Sample: All four sides are $\cong$ (with length $\sqrt{5}$), and diagonals are not $\cong$ (with lengths 2 and 4).
10. Rectangle; explanations may vary. Sample: Consecutive sides are $\perp$ and not $\cong$.
11. None; explanations may vary. Sample: Consecutive sides are not $\cong$ or $\perp$.
12. Square; explanations may vary. Sample: All sides are $\cong$ and consecutive sides are $\perp$.
13. Rhombus; explanations may vary. Sample: All sides are $\cong$ and consecutive sides are not $\perp$.

14–16. See next page.

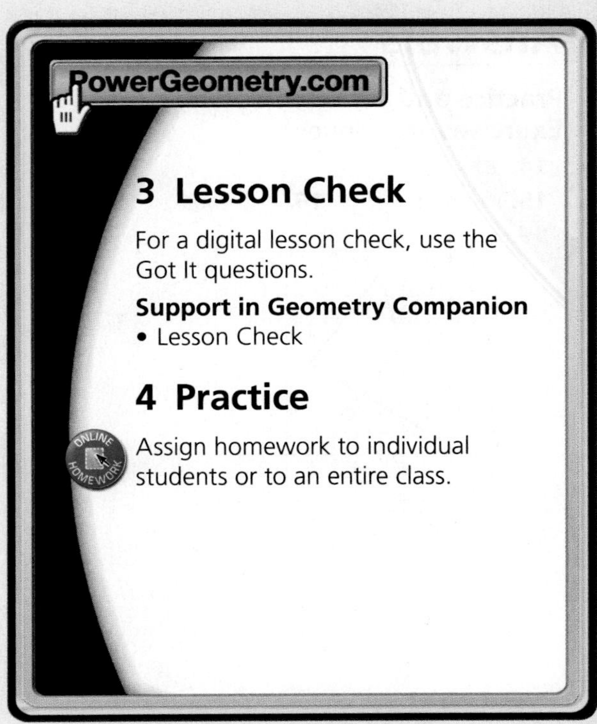

PowerGeometry.com

3 Lesson Check

For a digital lesson check, use the Got It questions.

Support in Geometry Companion

- Lesson Check

4 Practice

Assign homework to individual students or to an entire class.

4 Practice

ASSIGNMENT GUIDE
Basic: 5–18, 21–24, 31, 35–36
Average: 5–15 odd, 17–38
Advanced: 5–15 odd, 17–44
Standardized Test Prep: 45–48
Mixed Review: 49–54
Reasoning exercises have blue headings.
Applications exercises have red headings.
EXERCISE 35: Use the Think About a Plan worksheet in the **Practice and Problem Solving Workbook** (also available in the Teaching Resources in print and online) to further support students' development in becoming independent learners.

HOMEWORK QUICK CHECK
To check students' understanding of key skills and concepts, go over Exercises 11, 15, 31, 35, and 36.

Graph and label each triangle with the given vertices. Determine whether each triangle is *scalene, isosceles,* or *equilateral.* Then tell whether each triangle is a right triangle.

17. $T(1, 1), R(3, 8), I(6, 4)$
18. $J(-5, 0), K(5, 8), L(4, -1)$
19. $A(3, 2), B(-10, 4), C(-5, -8)$
20. $H(1, -2), B(-1, 4), F(5, 6)$

Graph and label each quadrilateral with the given vertices. Then determine the most precise name for each quadrilateral.

21. $P(-5, 0), Q(-3, 2), R(3, 2), S(5, 0)$
22. $S(0, 0), T(4, 0), U(3, 2), V(-1, 2)$
23. $F(0, 0), G(5, 5), H(8, 4), I(7, 1)$
24. $M(-14, 4), N(1, 6), P(3, -9), Q(-12, -11)$
25. $A(3, 5), B(7, 6), C(6, 2), D(2, 1)$
26. $N(-6, 4), P(-3, 1), Q(0, 2), R(-3, 5)$
27. $J(2, 1), K(5, 4), L(8, 1), M(2, -3)$
28. $H(-2, -3), I(4, 0), J(3, 2), K(-3, -1)$
29. $W(-1, 1), X(0, 2), Y(1, 1), Z(0, -2)$
30. $D(-3, 1), E(-7, -3), F(6, -3), G(2, 1)$

31. Think About a Plan Are the triangles at the right congruent? How do you know?
- Which triangle congruence theorem can you use?
- Which formula should you use?

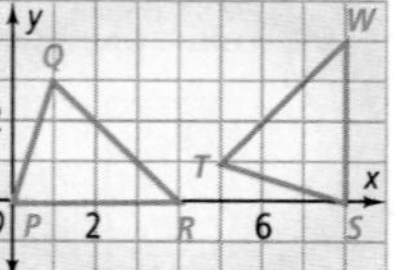

32. Reasoning A quadrilateral has opposite sides with equal slopes and consecutive sides with slopes that are negative reciprocals. What is the most precise classification of the quadrilateral? Explain.

Determine the most precise name for each quadrilateral. Then find its area.

33. $A(0, 2), B(4, 2), C(-3, -4), D(-7, -4)$
34. $J(1, -3), K(3, 1), L(7, -1), M(5, -5)$

35. $\overline{DE}$ is a midsegment of $\triangle ABC$ at the right. Show that the Triangle Midsegment Theorem holds true for $\triangle ABC$.

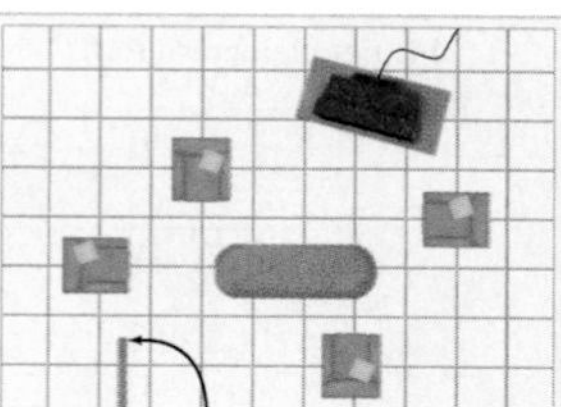

36. a. Writing Describe two ways you can show whether a quadrilateral in the coordinate plane is a square.
b. Reasoning Which method is more efficient? Explain.

37. Interior Design Interior designers often use grids to plan the placement of furniture in a room. The design at the right shows four chairs around a coffee table. The designer plans for cutouts of chairs on lattice points. She wants the chairs oriented at the vertices of a parallelogram. Does she need to fix her plan? If so, describe the change(s) she should make.

Answers

Practice and Problem-Solving Exercises (continued)

14. ▱

15. rhombus **16.** rhombus

17.

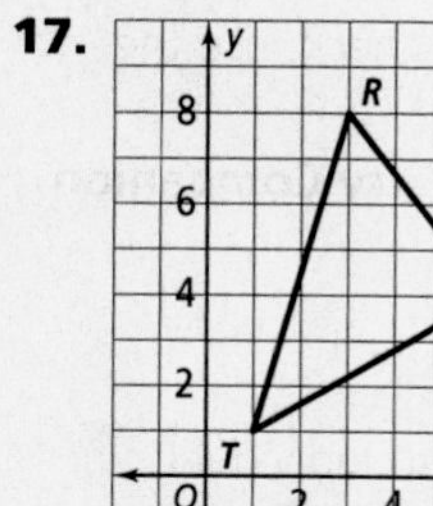

scalene; not rt. △

18.

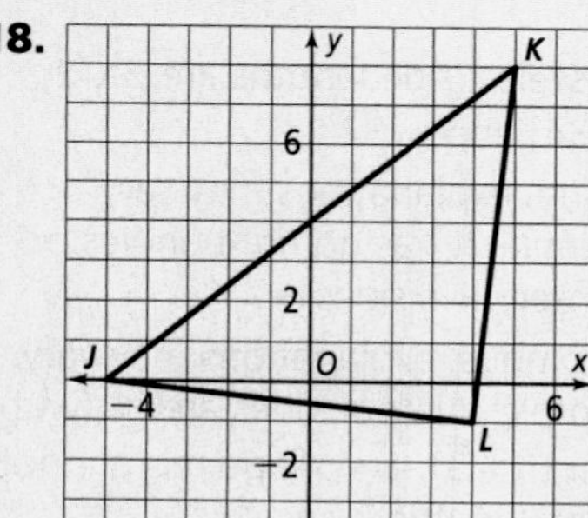

isosc.; rt. △

19.

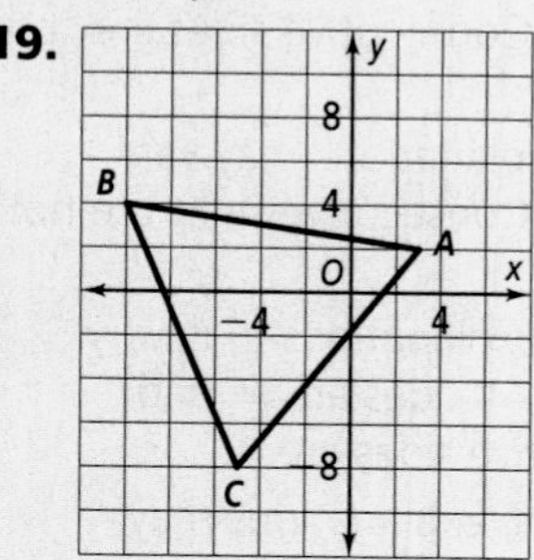

scalene; not a rt. △

20.

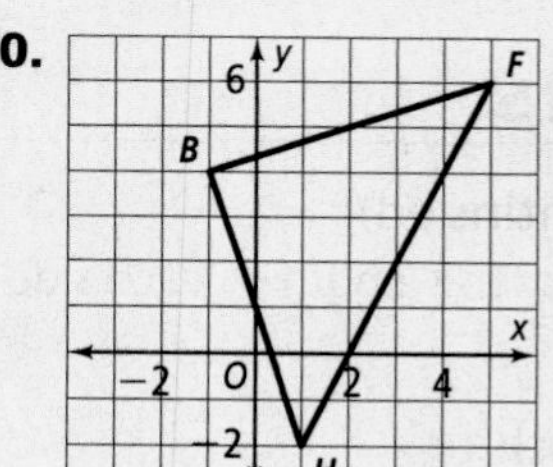

isosc.; rt. △

21.

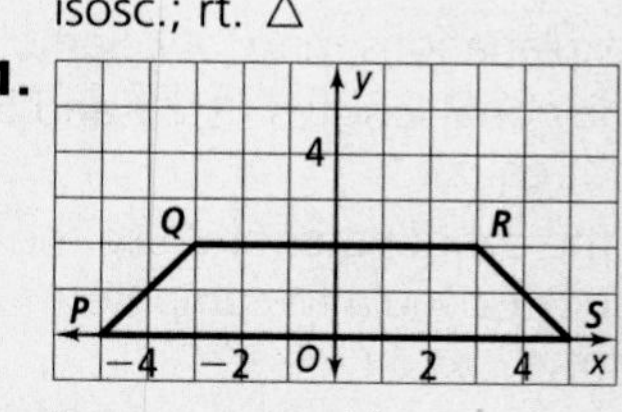

isosc. trapezoid

38. Use the diagram at the right.
a. What is the most precise classification of *ABCD*?
b. What is the most precise classification of *EFGH*?
c. Are *ABCD* and *EFGH* congruent? Explain.

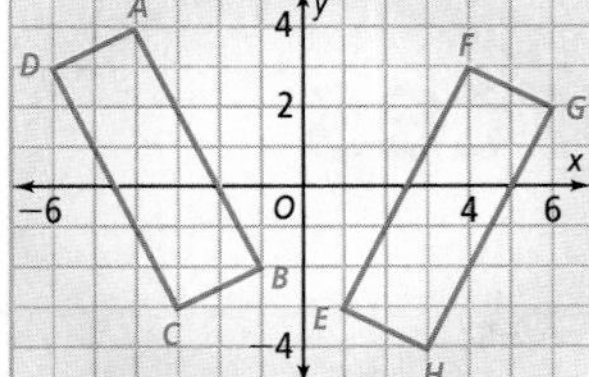

Challenge

39. **Coordinate Geometry** The diagonals of quadrilateral *EFGH* intersect at *D*(−1, 4). *EFGH* has vertices at *E*(2, 7) and *F*(−3, 5). What must be the coordinates of *G* and *H* to ensure that *EFGH* is a parallelogram?

The endpoints of $\overline{AB}$ are *A*(−3, 5) and *B*(9, 15). Find the coordinates of the points that divide $\overline{AB}$ into the given number of congruent segments.

40. 4
41. 6
42. 10
43. 50
44. *n*

Standardized Test Prep

SAT/ACT

45. *K*(−3, 0), *I*(0, 2), and *T*(3, 0) are three vertices of a kite. Which point could be the fourth vertex?

Ⓐ *E*(0, 5) Ⓑ *E*(0, 0) Ⓒ *E*(0, −2) Ⓓ *E*(0, −10)

46. In the diagram, lines ℓ and *m* are parallel. What is the value of *x*?

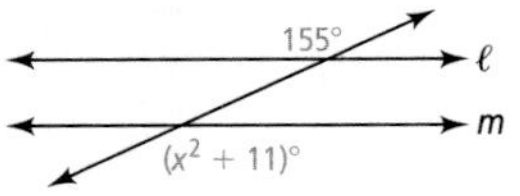

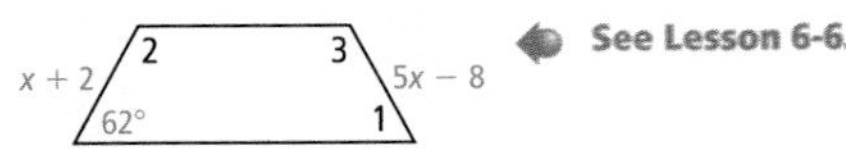

Ⓕ 5 Ⓗ 13
Ⓖ 12 Ⓘ 25

47. In the diagram, which segment is shortest?

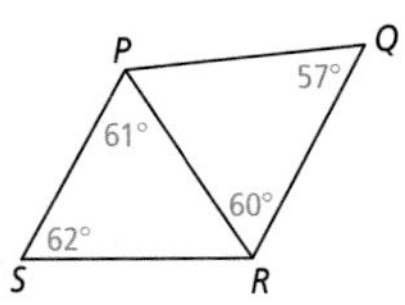

Ⓐ $\overline{PS}$ Ⓒ $\overline{PQ}$
Ⓑ $\overline{PR}$ Ⓓ $\overline{QR}$

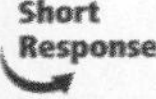
Short Response

48. *A*(−3, 1), *B*(−1, −2), and *C*(2, 1) are three vertices of quadrilateral *ABCD*. Could *ABCD* be a rectangle? Explain.

Mixed Review

49. **Algebra** Find the measure of each angle and the value of *x* in the isosceles trapezoid.

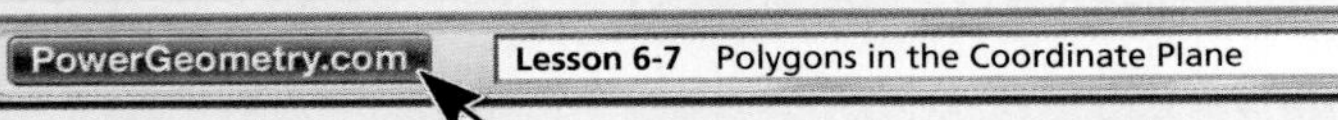

See Lesson 6-6.

Find the circumcenter of △*ABC*. See Lesson 5-3.

50. *A*(1, 1), *B*(5, 3), *C*(5, 1)
51. *A*(−5, 0), *B*(−1, −8), *C*(−1, 0)

Get Ready! **To prepare for Lesson 6-8, do Exercises 52–54.**

Find the slope of $\overline{XY}$. See Lesson 3-7.

52. *X*(0, *a*), *Y*(−*a*, 2*a*)
53. *X*(−*a*, *b*), *Y*(*a*, *b*)
54. *X*(*a*, 0), *Y*(*c* + *d*, *b*)

22. 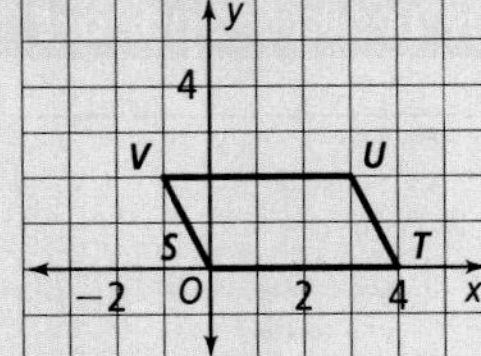

23. 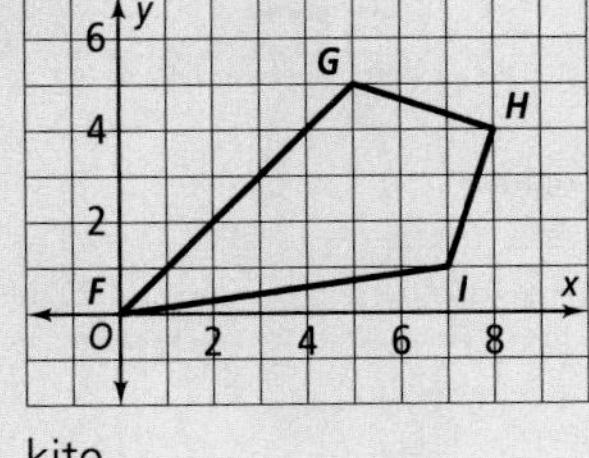

kite

24. 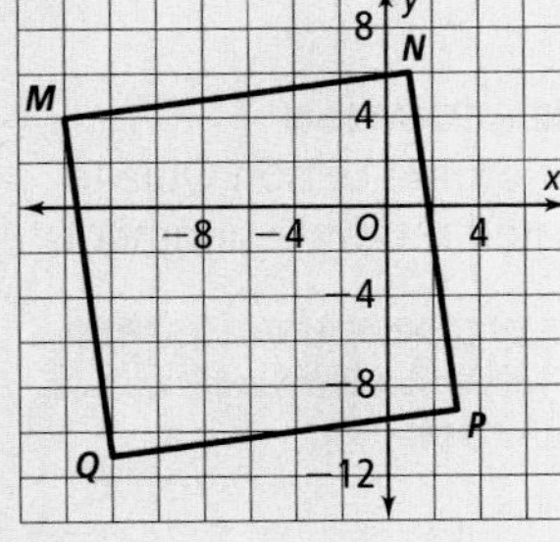

square

25. 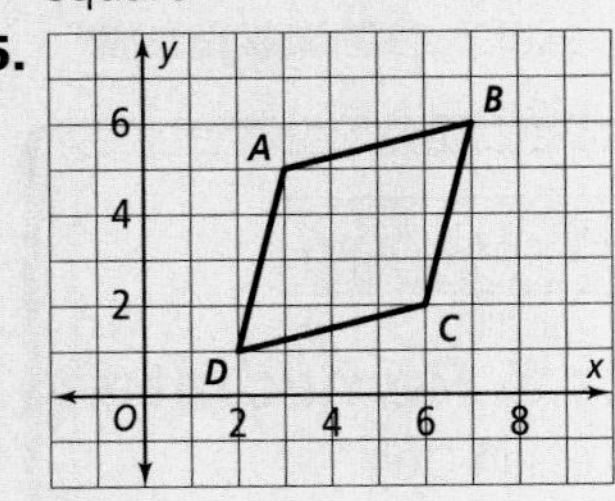

rhombus

26. 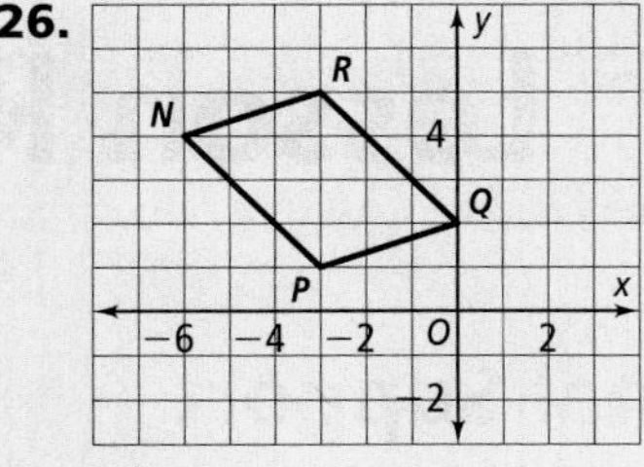

27. 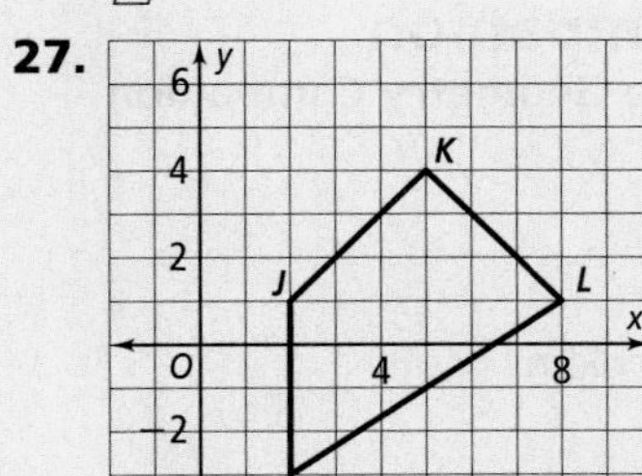

quadrilateral

28. 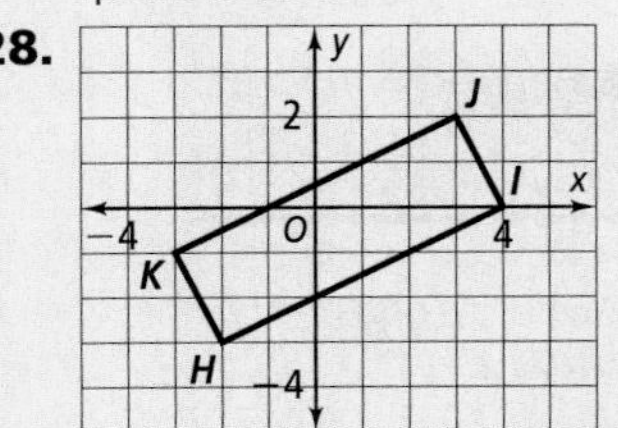

rectangle

29. 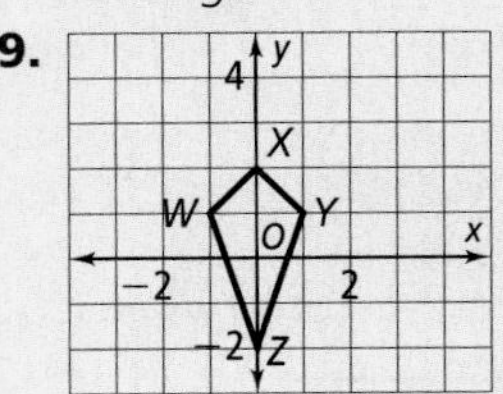

kite

30. 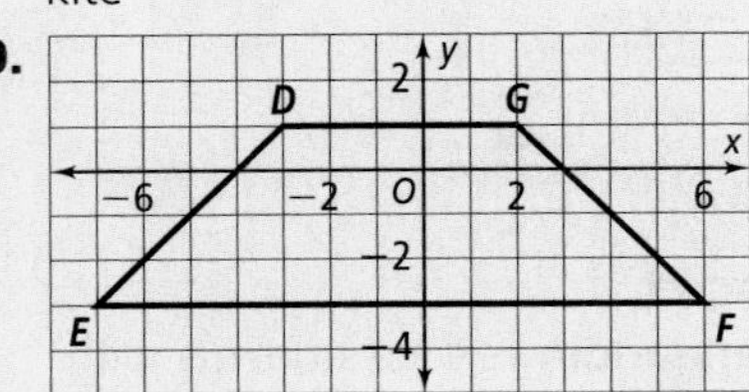

isosc. trapezoid

31. Yes; *PR* = *SW* = 4, *PQ* = *ST* = $\sqrt{10}$, *QR* = *TW* = $3\sqrt{2}$, so △*PQR* ≅ △*STW* by SSS.

32. Rectangle; opp. sides with = slopes makes it a ▱, and consecutive sides with slopes that are negative reciprocals are ⊥.

33. ▱; 24 units^2

34. square; 20 units^2

35. slope of $\overline{DE}$ = 2; slope of $\overline{AB}$ = 2; $DE = \frac{1}{2}\sqrt{5}$; $AB = \sqrt{5}$. So $\overline{DE} \parallel \overline{AB}$ and $DE = \frac{1}{2}AB$.

36a. To show a quadrilateral is a square, show consecutive sides are ⊥ and ≅, or that diagonals bisect each other, and are ⊥ and ≅.

b. Answers may vary. Sample: showing the diagonals bisect each other and are ≅ and ⊥ uses only two pairs of coordinates.

37–54. See back of book.

6-7 Lesson Resources

Differentiated Remediation

Instructional Support

Geometry Companion

Students can use the **Geometry Companion** worktext (4 pages) . . .

- New Vocabulary
- Key Concepts
- Got It for each Problem
- Lesson Check

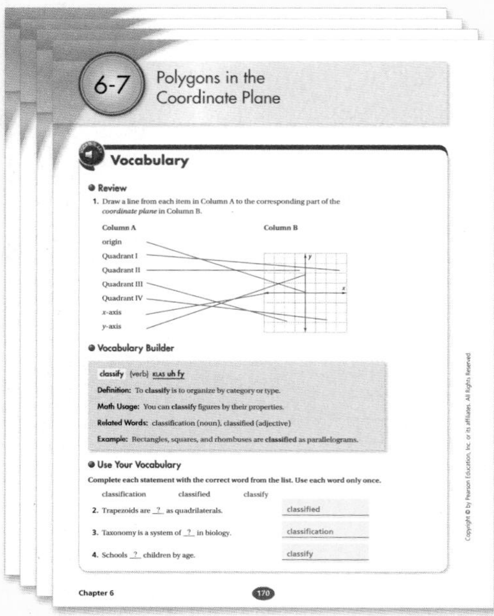

6-7 Polygons in the Coordinate Plane

Vocabulary

Review

1. Draw a line from each item in Column A to the corresponding part of the *coordinate plane* in Column B.

Column A	Column B
origin	
Quadrant I	
Quadrant II	
Quadrant III	
Quadrant IV	
x-axis	
y-axis	

Vocabulary Builder

classify (verb) KLAS uh fy

Definition: To **classify** is to organize by category or type.

Math Usage: You can **classify** figures by their properties.

Related Words: classification (noun), classified (adjective)

Example: Rectangles, squares, and rhombuses are **classified** as parallelograms.

Use Your Vocabulary

Complete each statement with the correct word from the list. Use each word only once.

classification classified classify

2. Trapezoids are _?_ as quadrilaterals. classified
3. Taxonomy is a system of _?_ in biology. classification
4. Schools _?_ children by age. classify

Chapter 6 170

ELL Support

Assess Understanding Place students with mixed abilities in groups of four. Hand out graph paper in page protectors with dry eraser markers. One student will draw a line and label two points on the line. The other students will use the three formulas in the lesson to find the length, midpoint, and slope of the line. Students will trade roles so each has opportunities for practice with each formula.

Assess Understanding Draw a scalene triangle on the board. Think aloud as you show how to use the Distance Formula to classify the triangle. Repeat with other types of triangles, and then model how to classify a quadrilateral, thinking aloud as you work. Draw a quadrilateral on the board and ask students to classify the figure as you monitor their progress.

5 Assess & Remediate

Lesson Quiz

1. Is $\triangle ABC$ scalene, isosceles, or equilateral?

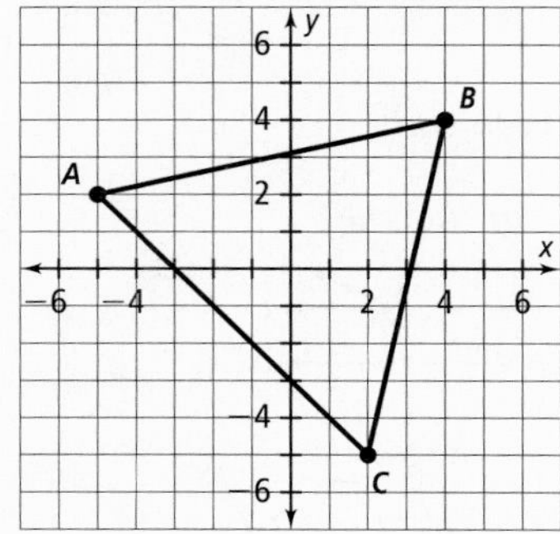

2. Do you UNDERSTAND? What is the most precise classification of the quadrilateral formed by the four segments connecting the midpoints of the sides of the square?

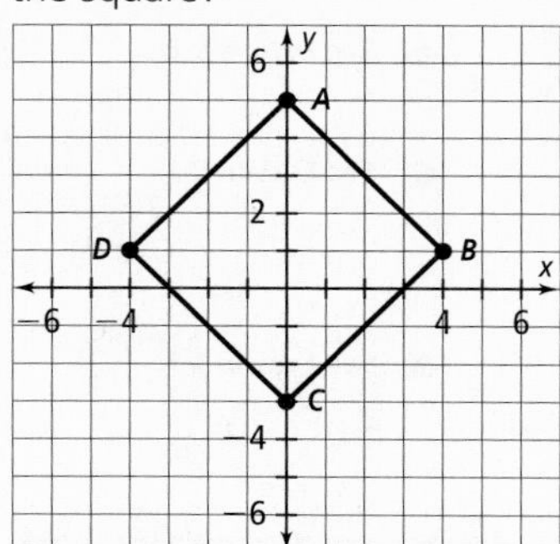

ANSWERS TO LESSON QUIZ

1. isosceles

2. square

PRESCRIPTION FOR REMEDIATION

Use the student work on the Lesson Quiz to prescribe a differentiated review assignment.

Points	Differentiated Remediation
0	Intervention
1	On-level
2	Extension

PowerGeometry.com

5 Assess & Remediate

Assign the Lesson Quiz. Appropriate intervention, practice, or enrichment is automatically generated based on student performance.

Intervention

- **Reteaching** (2 pages) Provides reteaching and practice exercises for the key lesson concepts. Use with struggling students or absent students.
- **English Language Learner Support** Helps students develop and reinforce mathematical vocabulary and key concepts.

All-in-One Resources/Online

Reteaching

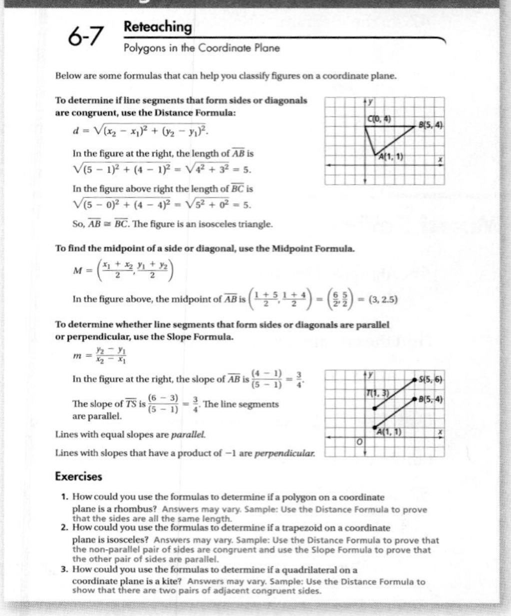

6-7 Reteaching
Polygons in the Coordinate Plane

Below are some formulas that can help you classify figures on a coordinate plane.

To determine if line segments that form sides or diagonals are congruent, use the Distance Formula:

$d = \sqrt{(x_2 - x_1)^2 + (y_2 - y_1)^2}$.

In the figure at the right, the length of $\overline{AB}$ is $\sqrt{(5-1)^2 + (4-1)^2} = \sqrt{4^2 + 3^2} = 5$.

In the figure above right the length of $\overline{BC}$ is $\sqrt{(5-0)^2 + (4-4)^2} = \sqrt{5^2 + 0^2} = 5$.

So, $\overline{AB} \cong \overline{BC}$. The figure is an isosceles triangle.

C(0, 4) B(5, 4) A(1, 1)

To find the midpoint of a side or diagonal, use the Midpoint Formula.

$M = \left(\frac{x_1 + x_2}{2}, \frac{y_1 + y_2}{2}\right)$

In the figure above, the midpoint of $\overline{AB}$ is $\left(\frac{1+5}{2}, \frac{1+4}{2}\right) = \left(\frac{6}{2}, \frac{5}{2}\right) = (3, 2.5)$

To determine whether line segments that form sides or diagonals are parallel or perpendicular, use the Slope Formula.

$m = \frac{y_2 - y_1}{x_2 - x_1}$

In the figure at the right, the slope of $\overline{AB}$ is $\frac{(4-1)}{(5-1)} = \frac{3}{4}$.

The slope of $\overline{TS}$ is $\frac{(6-3)}{(5-1)} = \frac{3}{4}$. The line segments are parallel.

S(5, 6) T(1, 3) B(5, 4) A(1, 1) O

Lines with equal slopes are *parallel*.

Lines with slopes that have a product of −1 are *perpendicular*.

Exercises

1. How could you use the formulas to determine if a polygon on a coordinate plane is a rhombus? Answers may vary. Sample: Use the Distance Formula to prove that the sides are all the same length.
2. How could you use the formulas to determine if a trapezoid on a coordinate plane is isosceles? Answers may vary. Sample: Use the Distance Formula to prove that the non-parallel pair of sides are congruent and use the Slope Formula to prove that the other pair of sides are parallel.
3. How could you use the formulas to determine if a quadrilateral on a coordinate plane is a kite? Answers may vary. Sample: Use the Distance Formula to show that there are two pairs of adjacent congruent sides.

All-in-One Resources/Online

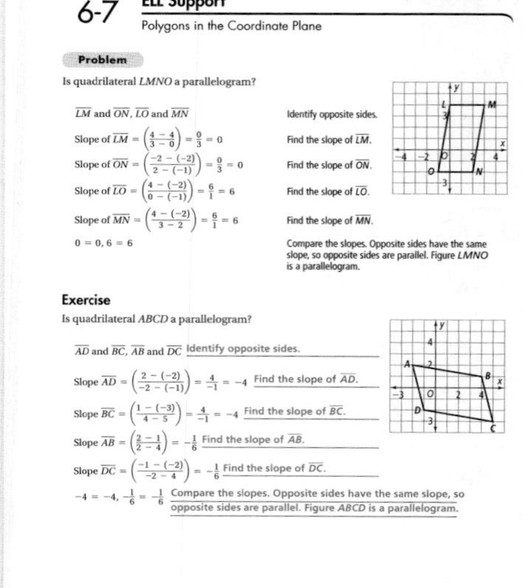

English Language Learner Support

6-7 ELL Support
Polygons in the Coordinate Plane

Problem

Is quadrilateral *LMNO* a parallelogram?

$\overline{LM}$ and $\overline{ON}$, $\overline{LO}$ and $\overline{MN}$	Identify opposite sides.
Slope of $\overline{LM} = \left(\frac{4-4}{3-0}\right) = \frac{0}{3} = 0$	Find the slope of $\overline{LM}$.
Slope of $\overline{ON} = \left(\frac{-2-(-2)}{2-(-1)}\right) = \frac{0}{3} = 0$	Find the slope of $\overline{ON}$.
Slope of $\overline{LO} = \left(\frac{4-(-2)}{0-(-1)}\right) = \frac{6}{1} = 6$	Find the slope of $\overline{LO}$.
Slope of $\overline{MN} = \left(\frac{4-(-2)}{3-2}\right) = \frac{6}{1} = 6$	Find the slope of $\overline{MN}$.
$0 = 0, 6 = 6$	Compare the slopes. Opposite sides have the same slope, so opposite sides are parallel. Figure *LMNO* is a parallelogram.

Exercise

Is quadrilateral *ABCD* a parallelogram?

$\overline{AD}$ and $\overline{BC}$, $\overline{AB}$ and $\overline{DC}$	Identify opposite sides.
Slope $\overline{AD} = \left(\frac{2-(-2)}{-2-(-1)}\right) = \frac{4}{-1} = -4$	Find the slope of $\overline{AD}$.
Slope $\overline{BC} = \left(\frac{1-(-3)}{4-5}\right) = \frac{4}{-1} = -4$	Find the slope of $\overline{BC}$.
Slope $\overline{AB} = \left(\frac{2-1}{2-4}\right) = -\frac{1}{6}$	Find the slope of $\overline{AB}$.
Slope $\overline{DC} = \left(\frac{-1-(-2)}{-2-4}\right) = -\frac{1}{6}$	Find the slope of $\overline{DC}$.
$-4 = -4, -\frac{1}{6} = -\frac{1}{6}$	Compare the slopes. Opposite sides have the same slope, so opposite sides are parallel. Figure *ABCD* is a parallelogram.

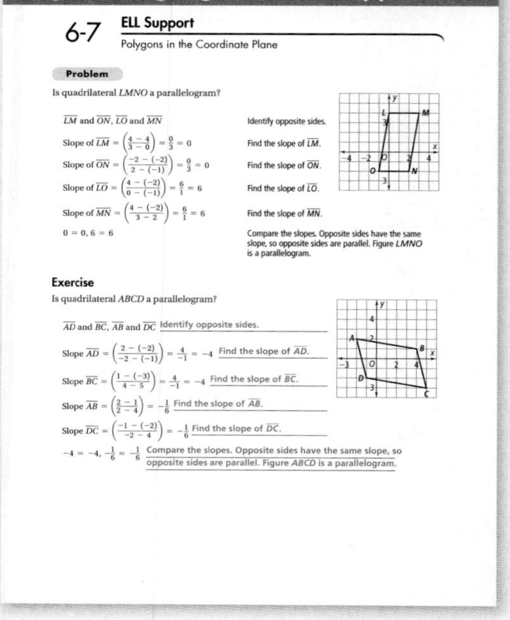

Differentiated Remediation *continued*

On-Level

- **Practice** (2 pages) Provides extra practice for each lesson. For simpler practice exercises, use the Form K Practice pages found in the All-in-One Teaching Resources and online.
- **Think About a Plan** Helps students develop specific problem-solving skills and strategies by providing scaffolded guiding questions.
- **Standardized Test Prep** Focuses on all major exercises, all major question types, and helps students prepare for the high-stakes assessments.

Practice and Problem Solving Wkbk/ All-in-One Resources/Online

Practice page 1

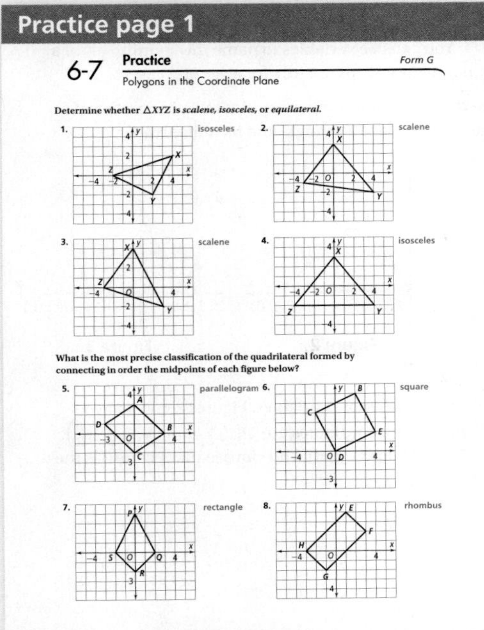

6-7 **Practice** *Form G*

Polygons in the Coordinate Plane

Determine whether $\triangle XYZ$ is *scalene, isosceles,* or *equilateral.*

1. isosceles
2. scalene
3. scalene
4. isosceles

What is the most precise classification of the quadrilateral formed by connecting in order the midpoints of each figure below?

5. parallelogram
6. square
7. rectangle
8. rhombus

Practice and Problem Solving Wkbk/ All-in-One Resources/Online

Practice page 2

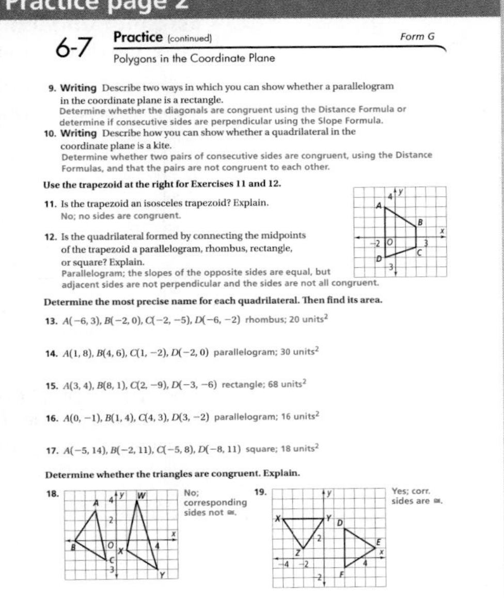

6-7 **Practice** (continued) *Form G*

Polygons in the Coordinate Plane

9. **Writing** Describe two ways in which you can show whether a parallelogram in the coordinate plane is a rectangle.
Determine whether the diagonals are congruent using the Distance Formula or determine if consecutive sides are perpendicular using the Slope Formula.
10. **Writing** Describe how you can show whether a quadrilateral in the coordinate plane is a kite.
Determine whether two pairs of consecutive sides are congruent, using the Distance Formulas, and that the pairs are not congruent to each other.

Use the trapezoid at the right for Exercises 11 and 12.

11. Is the trapezoid an isosceles trapezoid? Explain.
No; no sides are congruent.
12. Is the quadrilateral formed by connecting the midpoints of the trapezoid a parallelogram, rhombus, rectangle, or square? Explain.
Parallelogram; the slopes of the opposite sides are equal, but adjacent sides are not perpendicular and the sides are not all congruent.

Determine the most precise name for each quadrilateral. Then find its area.

13. $A(-6, 3), B(-2, 0), C(-2, -5), D(-6, -2)$ rhombus; 20 units^2
14. $A(1, 8), B(4, 6), C(1, -2), D(-2, 0)$ parallelogram; 30 units^2
15. $A(3, 4), B(8, 1), C(2, -9), D(-3, -6)$ rectangle; 68 units^2
16. $A(0, -1), B(1, 4), C(4, 3), D(3, -2)$ parallelogram; 16 units^2
17. $A(-5, 14), B(-2, 11), C(-5, 8), D(-8, 11)$ square; 18 units^2

Determine whether the triangles are congruent. Explain.

18. No; corresponding sides not ≅.
19. Yes; corr. sides are ≅.

Practice and Problem Solving Wkbk/ All-in-One Resources/Online

Think About a Plan

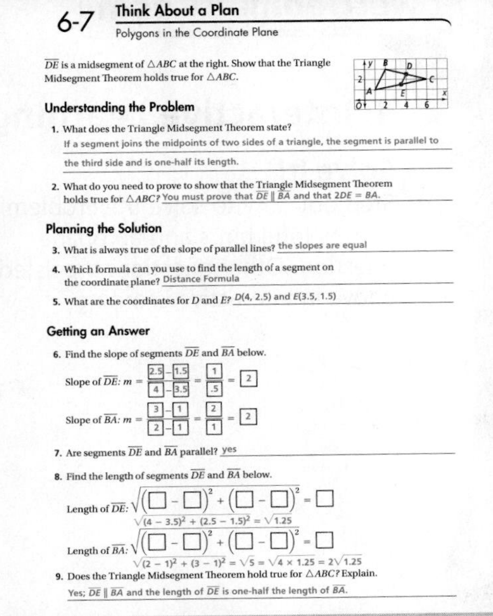

6-7 **Think About a Plan**

Polygons in the Coordinate Plane

$\overline{DE}$ is a midsegment of $\triangle ABC$ at the right. Show that the Triangle Midsegment Theorem holds true for $\triangle ABC$.

Understanding the Problem

1. What does the Triangle Midsegment Theorem state?
If a segment joins the midpoints of two sides of a triangle, the segment is parallel to the third side and is one-half its length.
2. What do you need to prove to show that the Triangle Midsegment Theorem holds true for $\triangle ABC$? You must prove that $\overline{DE} \parallel \overline{BA}$ and that $2DE = BA$.

Planning the Solution

3. What is always true of the slope of parallel lines? the slopes are equal
4. Which formula can you use to find the length of a segment on the coordinate plane? Distance Formula
5. What are the coordinates for D and E? $D(4, 2.5)$ and $E(3.5, 1.5)$

Getting an Answer

6. Find the slope of segments $\overline{DE}$ and $\overline{BA}$ below.
Slope of $\overline{DE}$: $m = \frac{2.5 - 1.5}{4 - 3.5} = \frac{1}{.5} = 2$
Slope of $\overline{BA}$: $m = \frac{3 - 1}{2 - 1} = \frac{2}{1} = 2$
7. Are segments $\overline{DE}$ and $\overline{BA}$ parallel? yes
8. Find the length of segments $\overline{DE}$ and $\overline{BA}$ below.
Length of $\overline{DE}$: $\sqrt{(\square - \square)^2 + (\square - \square)^2} = \square$
$\sqrt{(4 - 3.5)^2 + (2.5 - 1.5)^2} = \sqrt{1.25}$
Length of $\overline{BA}$: $\sqrt{(\square - \square)^2 + (\square - \square)^2} = \square$
$\sqrt{(2 - 1)^2 + (3 - 1)^2} = \sqrt{5} = \sqrt{4 \times 1.25} = 2\sqrt{1.25}$
9. Does the Triangle Midsegment Theorem hold true for $\triangle ABC$? Explain.
Yes; $\overline{DE} \parallel \overline{BA}$ and the length of $\overline{DE}$ is one-half the length of $\overline{BA}$.

Practice and Problem Solving Wkbk/ All-in-One Resources/Online

Standardized Test Prep

6-7 **Standardized Test Prep**

Polygons in the Coordinate Plane

Multiple Choice

For Exercises 1–4, choose the correct letter.

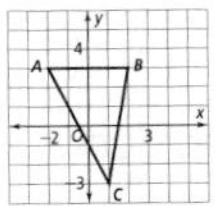

1. What kind of triangle is this? D
   - A right
   - B equilateral
   - C isosceles
   - D scalene
2. What is the most accurate description of the polygon at the right? F 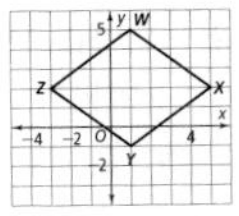
   - F rhombus
   - G square
   - H rectangle
   - I parallelogram
3. What is the most accurate description of the polygon at the right? D 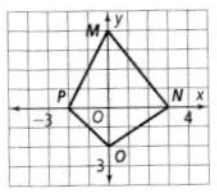
   - A rhombus
   - B trapezoid
   - C kite
   - D quadrilateral
4. What kind of triangle is made by connecting the points $A(0, -6)$, $B(3, -6)$, and $C(3, -2)$? G
   - F equilateral
   - G right
   - H isosceles
   - I right and isosceles

Short Response

5. What type of quadrilateral is formed by connecting the points (0, 9), (3, 6), (0, 1), and (−3, 6)? Explain. [2] Kite; two pairs of consecutive sides are congruent and the diagonals are perpendicular. [1] Kite; student explains that two pairs of consecutive sides are congruent or that the diagonals are perpendicular. [0] no answer or wrong answer based on an inappropriate plan

Extension

- **Enrichment** Provides students with interesting problems and activities that extend the concepts of the lesson.
- **Activities, Games, and Puzzles** Worksheets that can be used for concepts development, enrichment, and for fun!

All-in-One Resources/Online

Enrichment

6-7 **Enrichment**

Polygons in the Coordinate Plane

Mapping a Course

The library is 0.6 mi due east from Geoffrey's house. The post office is 0.8 mi due north of the library. The park is north of the post office, and its southern boundary runs east-west. The school is due east of the post office. Geoffrey jogs along the same route each day through his town.

Geoffrey runs from his house directly to the post office. He turns left, and runs 0.5 mi north to the corner of the park. There he turns right, and runs 1.2 mi to the end of the park. From there he returns along a straight line southwest back to the post office. There he turns left and runs 0.6 mi due east to the school. At the school, he turns right and returns on a straight path southwest to the library. From the library, he runs straight home.

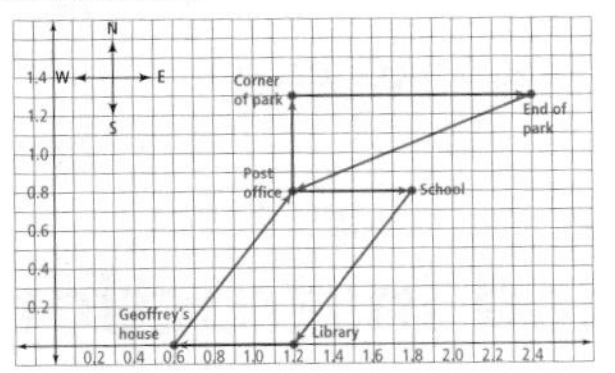

1. Use the coordinate grid above. Set every linear unit equal to 0.1 mi. For example, the distance between 0 and 2 on the x-axis is 0.2 mi. Plot out Geoffrey's running route. Mark each turn with a point and label, and use arrow marks to show Geoffrey's direction.
2. Geoffrey's path makes two polygons. What are these polygons? Give the most precise description of each. Explain. Right scalene triangle and parallelogram; the triangle has a right angle and no ≅ sides; the parallelogram has parallel sides but no right angles and no adjacent sides ≅.
3. How far does Geoffrey run every day? Round your answer to the nearest 0.1 mi. 6.2 mi

Online Teacher Resource Center

Activities, Games, and Puzzles

6-7 **Puzzle: Crossword**

Polygons in the Coordinate Plane

Each clue below describes a figure in the coordinate plane. Use graph paper to determine your answers. Some clues will refer you to another clue. So show your work and make sure to number your graphs!

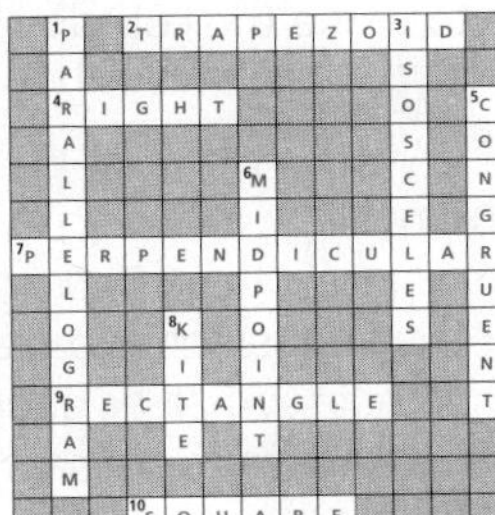

Across

2. The vertices of a quadrilateral are (−1,1), (1, 2), (3, 1), and (−1, −1). What is the most specific name of this figure?
4. What is the angle classification of the triangle in 3 Down?
7. The consecutive sides in the figure in 9 Across are __?__.
9. A quadrilateral has vertices (0, 3), (2, 4), (4, −5), and (6, −4). What is the most specific name of this figure?
10. A parallelogram has vertices (−3, 4), (0, 3), (−1, 0), and (−4, 1). What is the most specific name of this figure?

Down

1. A quadrilateral has vertices (0, 2), (2, 5), (4, 3), and (6, 6). What is the most specific name of this figure?
3. A triangle has vertices (−3, −2), (−1, 1), and (2, −1). Classify the triangle by side lengths.
5. In order for the figure in 2 Across to be isosceles, its diagonals would have to be __?__.
6. A rectangle's vertices are $A(-1, 2)$, $B(4, 2)$, $C(4, -2)$, and $D(-1, -2)$. The point (1.5, 0) is the __?__ of $\overline{AC}$ and $\overline{BD}$.
8. A quadrilateral has the vertices (0, 1), (−5, 3), (−2, 6), and (−5, 6). What is the most specific name of this figure?

1 Interactive Learning

Solve It!

PURPOSE To apply knowledge of the properties of parallelograms to determine the unknown vertex of the parallelogram

PROCESS Students may use previous knowledge of slope, Distance Formula, parallelograms, and visual discretion.

FACILITATE

Q How many sides of the parallelogram can be formed using points *A*, *B*, and *C*? Explain. **[Two, A third segment would form a triangle.]**

Q How many ways are there to form two sides of the parallelogram using points *A*, *B*, and *C*? **[Three: $\overline{AB}$ and $\overline{BC}$; $\overline{AB}$ and $\overline{AC}$; $\overline{AC}$ and $\overline{BC}$.]**

Q Given that $\overline{AB}$ and $\overline{BC}$ are adjacent sides of the parallelogram, what requirements must be met for placing point *D*? **[$\overline{AD}$ must be parallel and congruent to $\overline{BC}$. $\overline{AB}$ must be parallel and congruent to $\overline{CD}$.]**

ANSWER See Solve It in Answers on next page.

CONNECT THE MATH In the Solve It, students look at a diagram showing all three parallelograms on the same coordinate plane. The original points *A*, *B*, and *C* form a triangle. The three placements of point *D* form three additional congruent triangles that share a side with $\triangle ABC$.

2 Guided Instruction

Ask students to use the variables for Figure 1 to write the coordinates of *M* and *N*.

6-8 Applying Coordinate Geometry

TN State Performance Indicators

SPI 3108.3.1 Use algebra and coordinate geometry to analyze and solve problems about geometric figures (including circles).

SPI 3108.3.2 Use coordinate geometry to prove characteristics of polygonal figures.

Objective To name coordinates of special figures by using their properties

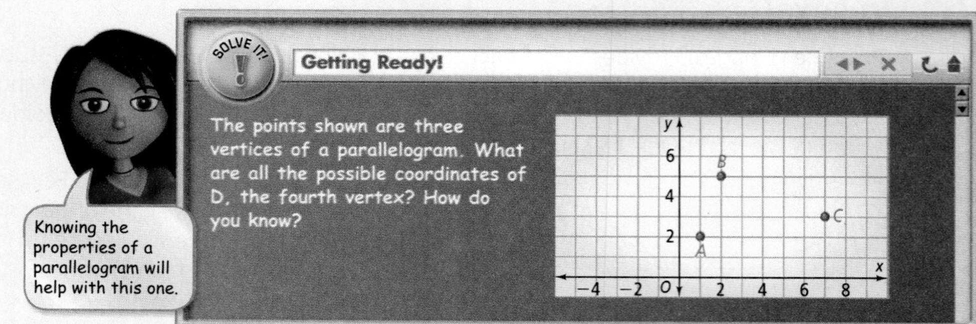

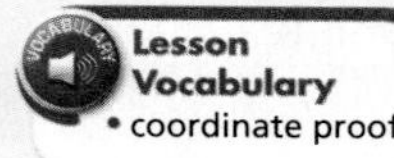

In the Solve It, you found coordinates of a point and named it using numbers for the *x*- and *y*-coordinates. In this lesson, you will learn to use variables for the coordinates.

Essential Understanding You can use variables to name the coordinates of a figure. This allows you to show that relationships are true for a general case.

In Chapter 5, you learned about the segment joining the midpoints of two sides of a triangle. Here are three possible ways to place a triangle and its midsegment.

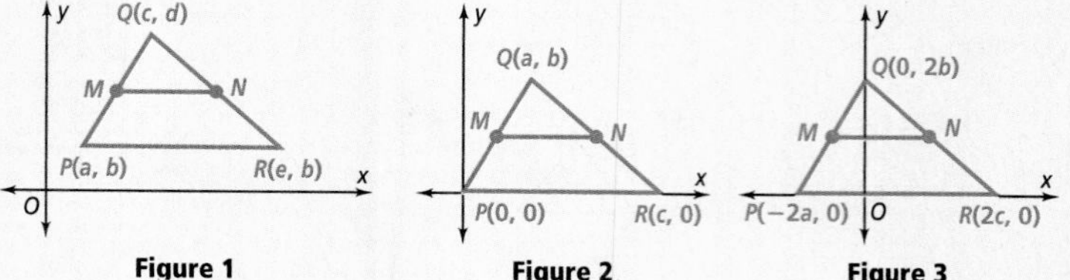

Figure 1 does not use the axes, so it requires more variables. Figures 2 and 3 have good placement. In Figure 2, the midpoint coordinates are $M\left(\frac{a}{2}, \frac{b}{2}\right)$ and $N\left(\frac{a+c}{2}, \frac{b}{2}\right)$. In Figure 3, the coordinates are $M(-a, b)$ and $N(c, b)$. You can see that Figure 3 is the easiest to work with.

6-8 Preparing to Teach

BIG ideas Coordinate Geometry
Reasoning and Proof

ESSENTIAL UNDERSTANDING

- Using variables to name the coordinates of a figure allows relationships to be shown to be true for a general case.

Math Background

In the seventeenth century, René Descartes blended algebraic principles with geometry to create what is called analytic geometry. Analytic geometry is also commonly referred to as coordinate geometry since geometric figures are placed in the coordinate plane. Learning to use variables to represent a figure in the coordinate plane is an important first step in completing proofs using coordinate geometry.

Students will need assistance in the logical placement of quadrilaterals. Show students when it makes sense to place a segment on an axis. Encourage students to think about why it is not practical to place one side of a rhombus or one diagonal of a parallelogram on the *x*-axis. Have them list advantages of a square or rectangle model in the first quadrant versus one symmetrically placed in all four quadrants.

Coordinate geometry can be used to prove some results more easily than a standard deductive proof. For example, coordinate geometry can be used to prove that the midpoint of the hypotenuse of a right triangle is equidistant from its vertices, or that the centroid of a triangle is $\frac{2}{3}$ of the distance from any vertex to the midpoint of the opposite side.

Support Student Learning

Use the **Geometry Companion** to engage and support students during instructions. See Lesson Resources at the end of this lesson for details.

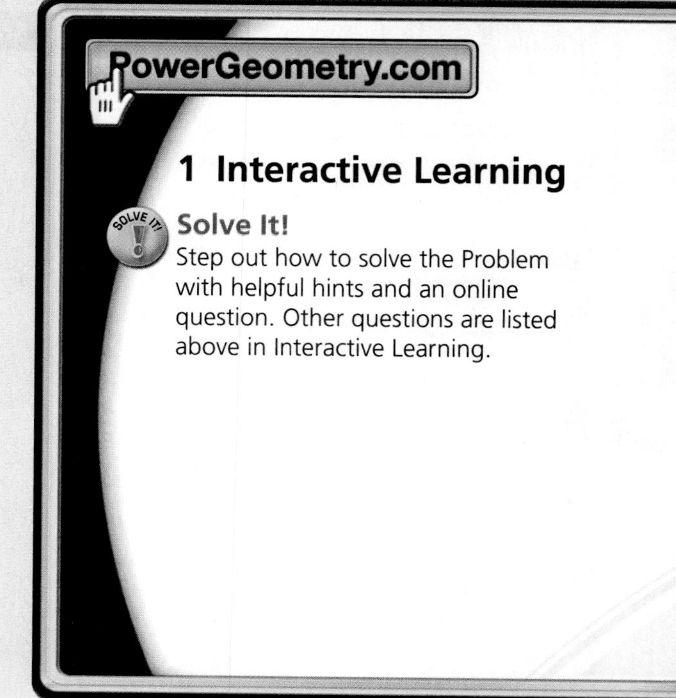

To summarize, to place a figure in the coordinate plane, it is usually helpful to place at least one side on an axis or to center the figure at the origin. For the coordinates, try to anticipate what you will need to do in the problem. Then multiply the coordinates by the appropriate number to make your work easier.

Plan

How do you start the problem?
Look at the position of the figure. Use the given information to determine how far each vertex is from the x- and y-axes.

Problem 1 Naming Coordinates

What are the coordinates of the vertices of each figure?

A ***SQRE* is a square where $SQ = 2a$. The axes bisect each side.**

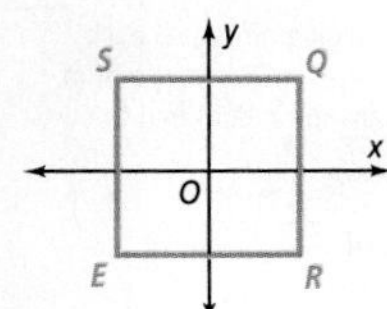

Since *SQRE* is a square centered at the origin and $SQ = 2a$, S and Q are each a units from each axis. The same is true for the other vertices.

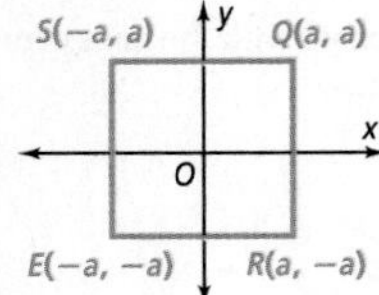

B ***TRI* is an isosceles triangle where $TI = 2a$. The y-axis is a median.**

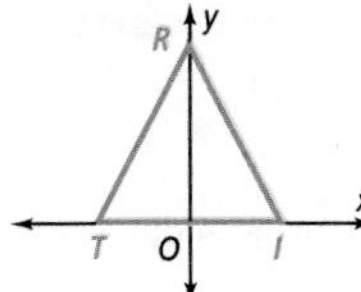

The y-axis is a median, so it bisects $\overline{TI}$. $TI = 2a$, so T and I are both a units from the y-axis. The height of *TRI* does not depend on a, so use a different variable for R.

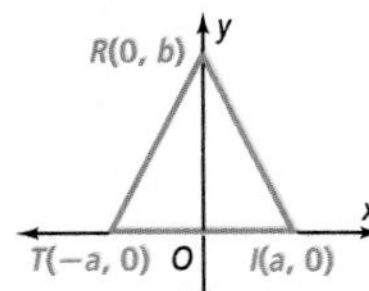

Got It? 1. What are the coordinates of the vertices of each figure?

a. *RECT* is a rectangle with height a and length $2b$. The y-axis bisects $\overline{EC}$ and $\overline{RT}$.

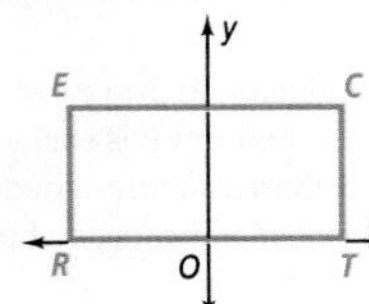

b. *KITE* is a kite where $IE = 2a$, $KO = b$, and $OT = c$. The x-axis bisects $\overline{IE}$.

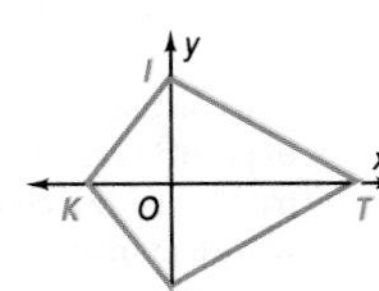
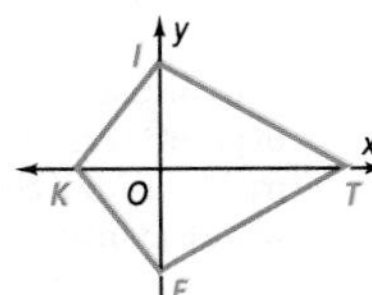

Problem 1

Q In 1A, if $SQ = 2a$, what are QR, RE, and SE? Explain. **[They are all $2a$, because all four sides of a square are congruent.]**

Q Can you use the Distance Formula for a number line to show that $SQ = 2a$? Explain. **[Yes, $|a - (-a)| = |a + a| = 2a$.]**

Q Can you use the Distance Formula to show that $SQ = 2a$? Explain. **[Yes, $\sqrt{(-a - a)^2 + (a - a)^2} = \sqrt{(-2a)^2 + (0)^2} = \sqrt{4a^2} = 2a$]**

Q In 1B, what is a median of a triangle? **[A median is a segment whose endpoints are a vertex and the midpoint of the opposite side.]**

Q If given that the length of the median is c, then what point represents vertex R? **[(0, c)]**

Got It?

Students may be confused when determining the coordinates for points K and T in 1b. Remind students that the length of $\overline{KT}$ is not dependent on the length of $\overline{IE}$ and therefore new variables must be used. Also, remind students that by definition, a kite must have two pairs of congruent adjacent sides and no opposite congruent sides.

2 Guided Instruction

Each Problem is worked out and supported online.

Problem 1
Naming Coordinates
Animated

Problem 2
Using Variable Coordinates
Animated

Problem 3
Planning a Coordinate Proof
Animated

Support in Geometry Companion
- Vocabulary
- Key Concepts
- Got It?

Answers

Solve It!

(8, 6), (6, 0), (−4, 4); each forms ∥ and ≅ sides.

Got It?

1a. $R(-b, 0)$, $E(-b, a)$, $C(b, a)$, $T(b, 0)$

b. $K(-b, 0)$, $I(0, a)$, $T(c, 0)$, $E(0, -a)$

Problem 2

Q What do you know about the diagonals of a parallelogram? **[The diagonals of a parallelogram bisect each other.]**

Q How do you simplify the expression $\frac{2a + 2b}{2}$? **[You must factor the numerator and rewrite it as 2(a + b), then cancel the common factor of 2 in the numerator and denominator.]**

Q If you were to determine the midpoint of $\overline{OB}$, would you arrive at the same answer? Explain. **[Yes, because the diagonals bisect each other, the point of intersection is the midpoint of each diagonal.]**

Got It?

Q Given that the figure is a trapezoid, what must be true about the diagonals in order for it to be an isosceles trapezoid? **[The diagonals must be congruent.]**

Q What is the length of $\overline{RP}$ and $\overline{TA}$? Explain. **[Using the Distance Formula, $RP = \sqrt{(-b - a)^2 + (c - 0)^2} = \sqrt{b^2 + 2ab + a^2 + c^2}$ and $TA = \sqrt{(-b - (-a))^2 + (c - 0)^2} = \sqrt{b^2 + 2ab + a^2 + c^2}$.]**

Problem 2 Using Variable Coordinates

The diagram shows a general parallelogram with a vertex at the origin and one side along the x-axis. What are the coordinates of D, the point of intersection of the diagonals of ▱ABCO? How do you know?

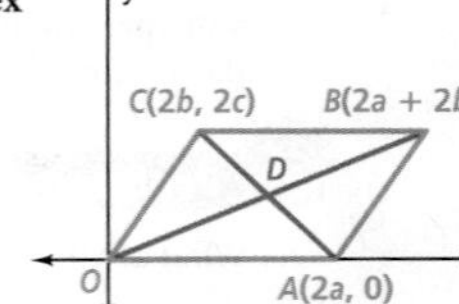

Know
- The coordinates of the vertices of ▱ABCO
- $\overline{OB}$ bisects $\overline{AC}$ and $\overline{AC}$ bisects $\overline{OB}$

Need
The coordinates of D

Plan
Since the diagonals of a parallelogram bisect each other, the midpoint of each segment is their point of intersection. Use the Midpoint Formula to find the midpoint of one diagonal.

Use the Midpoint Formula to find the midpoint of $\overline{AC}$.

$$D = \text{midpoint of } \overline{AC} = \left(\frac{2a + 2b}{2}, \frac{0 + 2c}{2}\right) = (a + b, c)$$

The coordinates of the point of intersection of the diagonals of ▱ABCO are $(a + b, c)$.

Got It? 2. a. Reasoning In Problem 2, explain why the x-coordinate of B is the sum of 2a and 2b.

b. The diagram below shows a trapezoid with the base centered at the origin. Is the trapezoid isosceles? Explain.

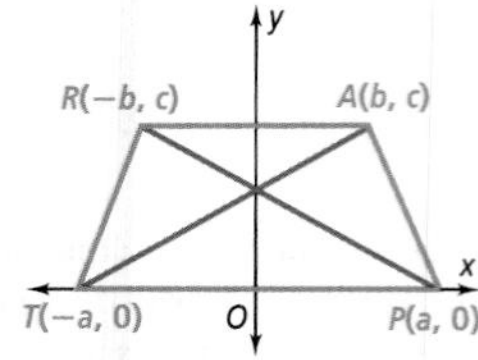

You can use coordinate geometry and algebra to prove theorems in geometry. This kind of proof is called a **coordinate proof.** Sometimes it is easier to show that a theorem is true by using a coordinate proof rather than a standard deductive proof. It is useful to write a plan for a coordinate proof. Problem 3 shows you how.

Additional Problems

1. What are the coordinates of the vertices of the figure below? ABCD is a rectangle with height b and width 2a. The x-axis bisects $\overline{AD}$ and $\overline{BC}$, and the y-axis bisects $\overline{AB}$ and $\overline{DC}$.

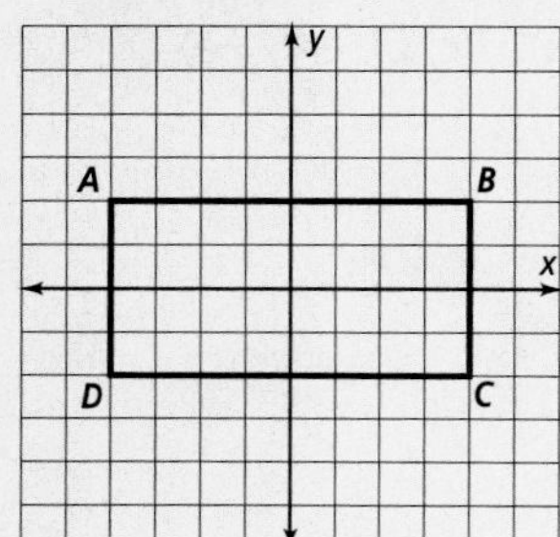

ANSWER $A\left(-a, \frac{b}{2}\right)$, $B\left(a, \frac{b}{2}\right)$, $C\left(a, -\frac{b}{2}\right)$, $D\left(-a, -\frac{b}{2}\right)$

2. The diagram shows a general parallelogram with a vertex at the origin and one side along the x-axis. What are the coordinates of the point of intersection of the diagonals of the parallelogram?

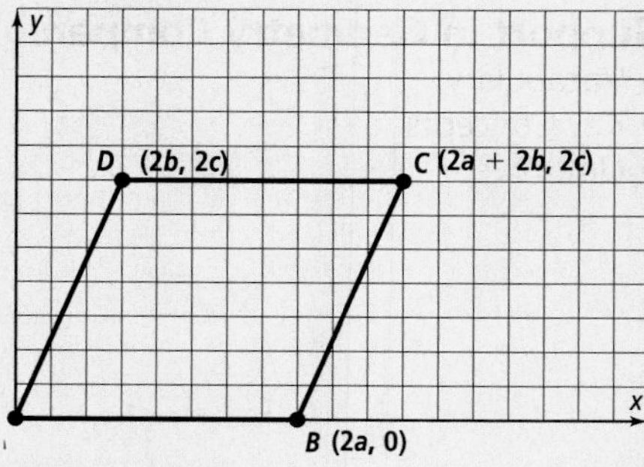

ANSWER $(a + b, c)$

3. Plan a coordinate proof to show that the midpoints of the sides of a kite form a rectangle.

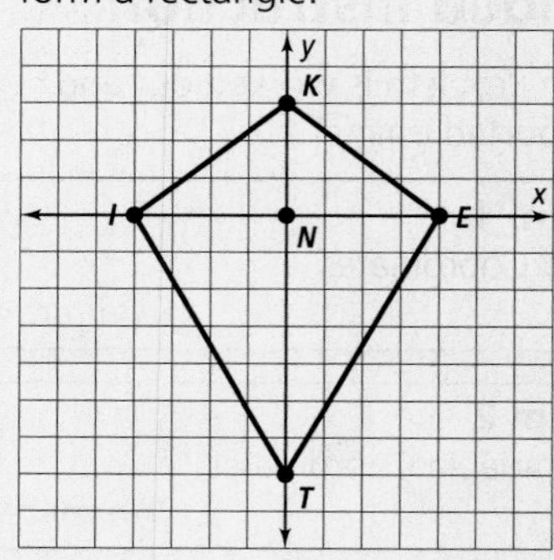

a. Name the coordinates of kite KITE with $IE = 2a$ along the x-axis, and $KN = 2b$ along the y-axis, and $NT = 2c$ along the y-axis.

Plan

How do you start? Start by *drawing a diagram.* Think about how you want to place the figure in the coordinate plane.

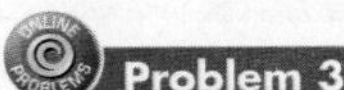

Problem 3 Planning a Coordinate Proof

Plan a coordinate proof of the Trapezoid Midsegment Theorem (Theorem 6-21).
(1) The midsegment of a trapezoid is parallel to the bases.
(2) The length of the midsegment of a trapezoid is half the sum of the lengths of the bases.

Step 1 Draw and label a figure.

Midpoints will be involved, so use multiples of 2 to name coordinates.

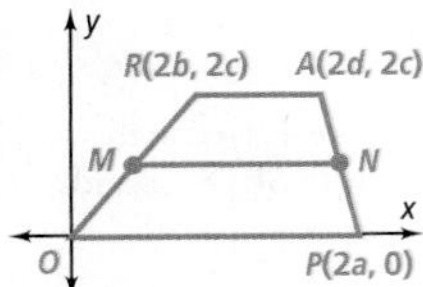
y
R(2b, 2c)
A(2d, 2c)
M
N
x
O
P(2a, 0)

Step 2 Write the *Given* and *Prove* statements.

Use the information on the diagram to write the statements.

Given: $\overline{MN}$ is the midsegment of trapezoid *ORAP*.

Prove: $\overline{MN} \parallel \overline{OP}$, $\overline{MN} \parallel \overline{RA}$, $MN = \frac{1}{2}(OP + RA)$

Step 3 Determine the formulas you will need. Then write the plan.

- First, use the Midpoint Formula to find the coordinates of *M* and *N*.
- Then, use the Slope Formula to determine whether the slopes of $\overline{MN}$, $\overline{OP}$, and $\overline{RA}$ are equal. If they are, $\overline{MN}$, $\overline{OP}$, and $\overline{RA}$ are parallel.
- Finally, use the Distance Formula to find and compare the lengths of $\overline{MN}$, $\overline{OP}$, and $\overline{RA}$.

Got It? 3. Plan a coordinate proof of the Triangle Midsegment Theorem (Theorem 5-1).

Lesson Check

Do you know HOW?

Use the diagram at the right.

1. In ▱*KLMO*, $OM = 2a$. What are the coordinates of *K* and *M*?

2. What are the slopes of the diagonals of *KLMN*?

3. What are the coordinates of the point of intersection of $\overline{KM}$ and $\overline{OL}$?

y
K
L(2a + 2b, c)
x
O
M

Do you UNDERSTAND?

4. Reasoning How do variable coordinates generalize figures in the coordinate plane?

5. Reasoning A vertex of a quadrilateral has coordinates (a, b). The *x*-coordinates of the other three vertices are a or $-a$, and the *y*-coordinates are b or $-b$. What kind of quadrilateral is the figure?

6. Error Analysis A classmate says the endpoints of the midsegment of the trapezoid in Problem 3 are $\left(\frac{b}{2}, \frac{c}{2}\right)$ and $\left(\frac{d+a}{2}, \frac{c}{2}\right)$. What is your classmate's error? Explain.

Problem 3

Q What are the coordinates of *M*? **[(*b*, *c*)]**

Q Considering how the figure is placed in the coordinate plane, what is the slope of both bases and the midsegment? **[The slope for each is zero, since they are all horizontal.]**

Got It?

Q What conditions must be proved for the Triangle Midsegment Theorem? **[The midsegment is parallel to one of the sides of the triangle, and the midsegment is half the length of that side.]**

3 Lesson Check

Do you know HOW?

- If students have difficulty with Exercise 2, then make sure they realize that the slopes of the diagonals of a parallelogram are never parallel and are perpendicular only when the parallelogram is a rhombus.

Do you UNDERSTAND?

- If students have difficulty with Exercise 5, then have them choose sample values for the variables and then sketch the quadrilateral described.

Close

Q How many variables are needed to name the coordinates of a rectangle drawn with one vertex at the origin in a coordinate plane? Explain. **[two, one to represent the length and one to represent the height]**

b. State the *Given* and *Prove*.

c. How will you find the coordinates of the midpoints of each side?

d. How will you determine whether the figure formed is a rectangle?

ANSWER a. *K*(0, 2*b*), *I*(−*a*, 0), *T*(0, −2*c*), *E*(*a*, 0)
b. Given: *KITE* is a kite with vertices *K*(0, 2*b*), *I*(−*a*, 0), *T*(0, −2*c*), *E*(*a*, 0), Prove: The midpoints of the sides of *KITE* form the vertices of a rectangle.
c. Use the Midpoint Formula to find the midpoints of each side **d.** Show that the opposite sides have the same length and are parallel to each other.

Answers

Got It? (continued)

2a. Answers may vary. Sample: *x*-coordinate of *B* is 2*a* more than *x*-coordinate of *C*.

b. yes; $TR = AP = \sqrt{a^2 - 2ab + b^2 + c^2}$

3. See back of book.

Lesson Check

1. *K*(2*b*, *c*), *M*(2*a*, 0)

2. The slope of $\overline{KM}$ is $\frac{c}{2b - 2a}$, and the slope of $\overline{OL}$ is $\frac{c}{2a + 2b}$.

3. $\left(a + b, \frac{c}{2}\right)$

4–6. See next page.

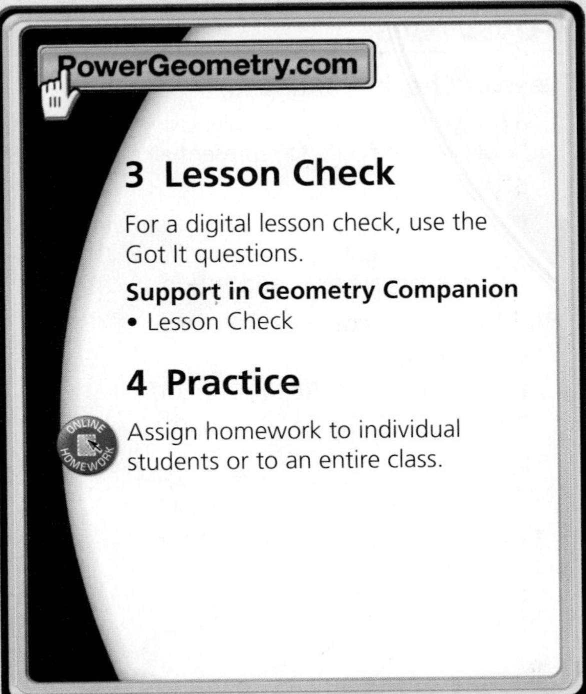
PowerGeometry.com
3 Lesson Check
For a digital lesson check, use the Got It questions.
Support in Geometry Companion
• Lesson Check
4 Practice
Assign homework to individual students or to an entire class.

4 Practice

ASSIGNMENT GUIDE
Basic: 7–14, 17, 19, 23, 24, 28
Average: 7–13 odd, 14–31
Advanced: 7–13 odd, 14–37
Standardized Test Prep: 38–41
Mixed Review: 42–49
Reasoning exercises have blue headings.
Applications exercises have red headings.
EXERCISE 24: Use the Think About a Plan worksheet in the **Practice and Problem Solving Workbook** (also available in the Teaching Resources in print and online) to further support students' development in becoming independent learners.

HOMEWORK QUICK CHECK
To check students' understanding of key skills and concepts, go over Exercises 7, 11, 17, 23, and 24.

Practice and Problem-Solving Exercises

A Practice

Algebra What are the coordinates of the vertices of each figure? See Problem 1.

7. rectangle with base b and height h

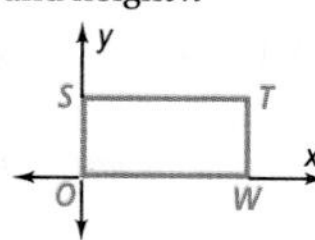

8. square with sides of length a

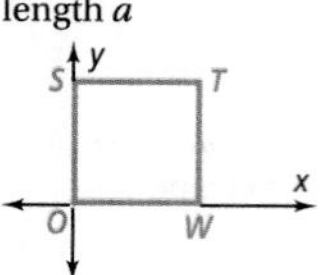

9. square centered at the origin, with side length b

10. parallelogram where S is a units from the origin and Z is b units from the origin

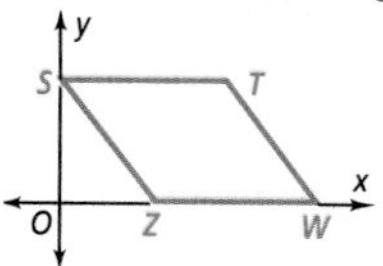

11. rhombus centered at the origin, with $SW = 2r$ and $TZ = 2t$

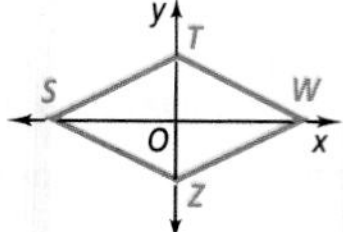

12. isosceles trapezoid with base centered at the origin, with base $2a$ and $OR = c$

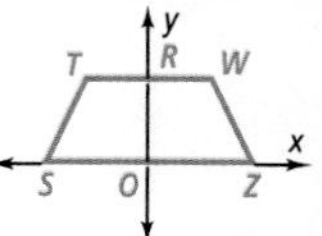

13. The diagram below shows a parallelogram. Without using the Distance Formula, determine whether the parallelogram is a rhombus. How do you know? See Problem 2.

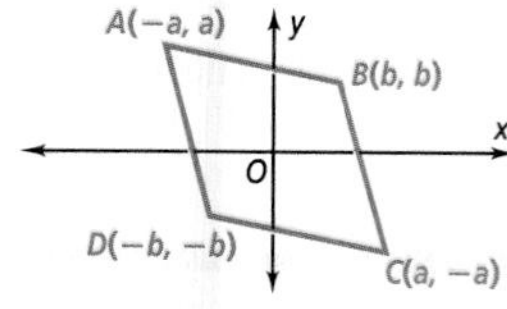

14. Plan a coordinate proof to show that the midpoints of the sides of an isosceles trapezoid form a rhombus. See Problem 3.
   a. Name the coordinates of isosceles trapezoid $TRAP$ at the right, with bottom base length $4a$, top base length $4b$, and $EG = 2c$. The y-axis bisects the bases.
   b. Write the *Given* and *Prove* statements.
   c. How will you find the coordinates of the midpoints of each side?
   d. How will you determine whether $DEFG$ is a rhombus?

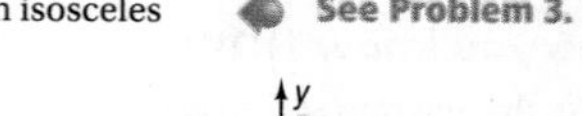

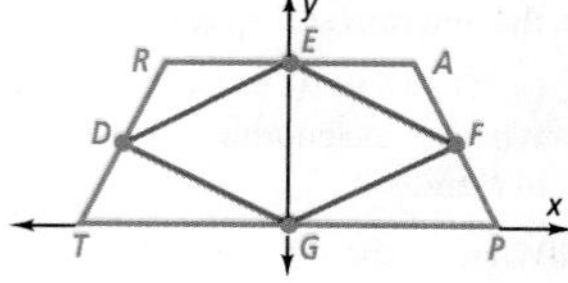

B Apply

15. **Open-Ended** Place a general quadrilateral in the coordinate plane.

16. **Reasoning** A rectangle $LMNP$ is centered at the origin with $M(r, -s)$. What are the coordinates of P?

Answers

Lesson Check (continued)

4. Answers may vary. Sample: Using variables allows the figure to represent all possibilities.
5. rectangle
6. Answers may vary. Sample: Classmate ignored the coefficient 2 in the coordinates. The endpoints are (b, c) and $(a + d, c)$.

Practice and Problem-Solving Exercises

7. $O(0, 0)$, $S(0, h)$, $T(b, h)$, $W(b, 0)$
8. $O(0, 0)$, $S(0, a)$, $T(a, a)$, $W(a, 0)$
9. $S\left(-\frac{b}{2}, -\frac{b}{2}\right)$, $T\left(-\frac{b}{2}, \frac{b}{2}\right)$, $W\left(\frac{b}{2}, \frac{b}{2}\right)$, $Z\left(\frac{b}{2}, -\frac{b}{2}\right)$
10. $Z(b, 0)$, $W(b + c, 0)$, $T(c, a)$, $S(0, a)$
11. $W(r, 0)$, $T(0, t)$, $S(-r, 0)$, $Z(0, -t)$
12. $S(-a, 0)$, $Z(a, 0)$, $W(b, c)$, $T(-b, c)$. Another variable for b is acceptable.
13. Yes, $ABCD$ is a rhombus. The slope of $\overline{AC} = -1$, and the slope of $\overline{BD} = 1$, so the diagonals are $\perp$.

14a. $T(-2a, 0)$, $R(-2b, 2c)$, $A(2b, 2c)$, $P(2a, 0)$
b. Given: $TRAP$ is an isosc. trapezoid, $\overline{TR} \cong \overline{PA}$, D, E, F, and G are midpts. of sides
Prove: $DEFG$ is a rhombus.
c. Use the Midpoint Formula.
d. Answers may vary. Sample: Use the Distance Formula to show $DEFG$ is equilateral.

15. Answers may vary. Sample:

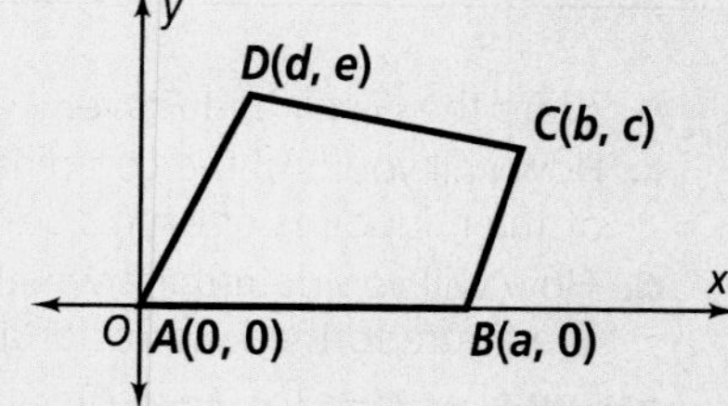

16. $P(-r, s)$

Give the coordinates for point *P* without using any new variables.

17. isosceles trapezoid

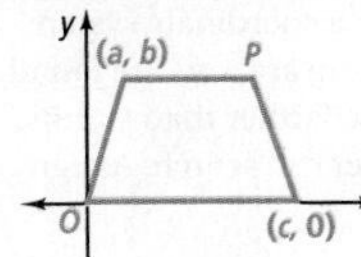

18. trapezoid with a right ∠

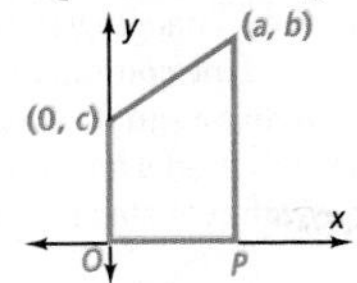

19. kite

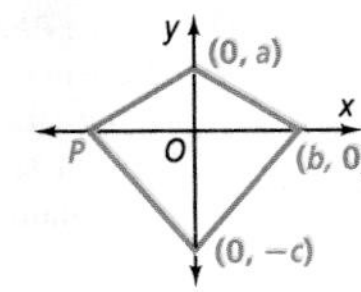

20. a. Draw a square whose diagonals of length $2b$ lie on the x- and y-axes.
   b. Give the coordinates of the vertices of the square.
   c. Compute the length of a side of the square.
   d. Find the slopes of two adjacent sides of the square.
   e. **Writing** Do the slopes show that the sides are perpendicular? Explain.

21. Make two drawings of an isosceles triangle with base length $2b$ and height $2c$.
   a. In one drawing, place the base on the x-axis with a vertex at the origin.
   b. In the second, place the base on the x-axis with its midpoint at the origin.
   c. Find the lengths of the legs of the triangle as placed in part (a).
   d. Find the lengths of the legs of the triangle as placed in part (b).
   e. How do the results of parts (c) and (d) compare?

22. W and Z are the midpoints of $\overline{OR}$ and $\overline{ST}$, respectively. In parts (a)–(c), find the coordinates of W and Z.

a.

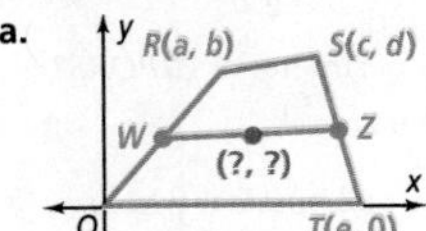

b.

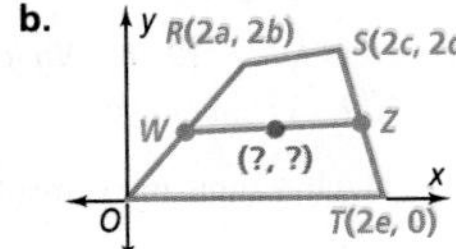

c.

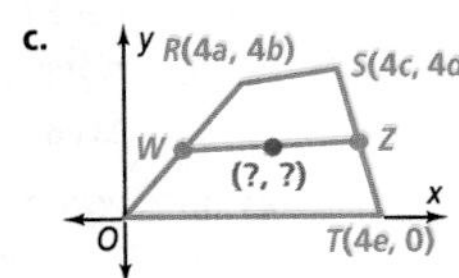

   d. You are to plan a coordinate proof involving the midpoint of $\overline{WZ}$. Which of the figures (a)–(c) would you prefer to use? Explain.

Plan the coordinate proof of each statement.

23. **Think About a Plan** The opposite sides of a parallelogram are congruent (Theorem 6-3).
   - How will you place the parallelogram in a coordinate plane?
   - What formulas will you need to use?

24. The diagonals of a rectangle bisect each other.

25. The consecutive sides of a square are perpendicular.

Classify each quadrilateral as precisely as possible.

26. $A(b, 2c)$, $B(4b, 3c)$, $C(5b, c)$, $D(2b, 0)$

27. $O(0, 0)$, $P(t, 2s)$, $Q(3t, 2s)$, $R(4t, 0)$

28. $E(a, b)$, $F(2a, 2b)$, $G(3a, b)$, $H(2a, -b)$

29. $O(0, 0)$, $L(-e, f)$, $M(f - e, f + e)$, $N(f, e)$

17. $P(c - a, b)$
18. $P(a, 0)$
19. $P(-b, 0)$
20a. Answers may vary. Sample:

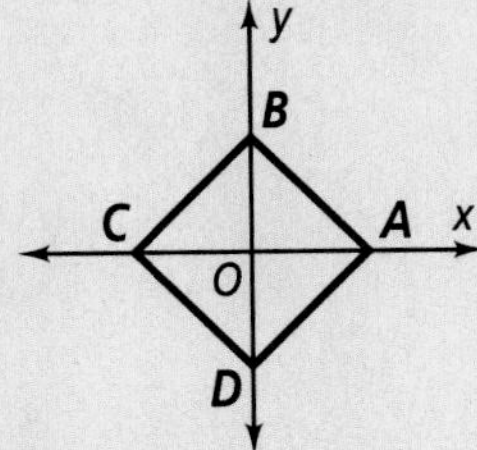

b. Answers may vary. Sample: $(-b, 0)$, $(0, -b)$, $(b, 0)$, $(0, b)$
c. $b\sqrt{2}$
d. 1, −1
e. Yes; product of the slopes is −1.
21a. Answers may vary. Sample:

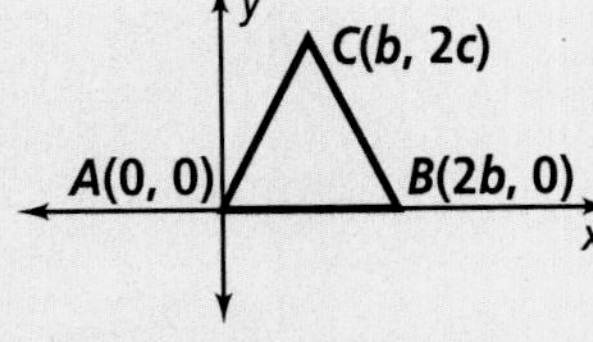

b. Answers may vary. Sample:

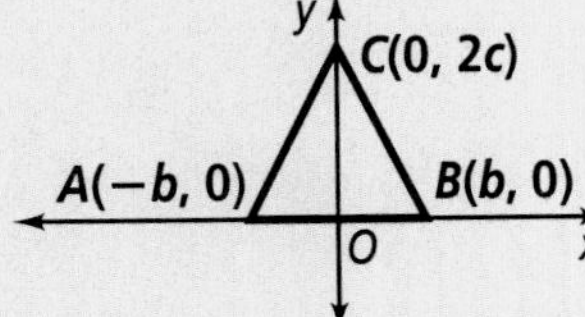

c. $\sqrt{b^2 + 4c^2}$, $\sqrt{b^2 + 4c^2}$
d. $\sqrt{b^2 + 4c^2}$, $\sqrt{b^2 + 4c^2}$
e. The results are the same.

22a. $W\left(\frac{a}{2}, \frac{b}{2}\right)$, $Z\left(\frac{c + e}{2}, \frac{d}{2}\right)$
b. $W(a, b)$, $Z(c + e, d)$
c. $W(2a, 2b)$, $Z(2c + 2e, 2d)$
d. Answers may vary. Sample: Figure (c) avoids fractions.
23. Answers may vary. Sample: Place vertices at $A(0, 0)$, $B(a, 0)$, $C(a + b, 0)$, and $D(b, c)$. Use the Distance Formula to find the lengths of opp. sides.
24. Answers may vary. Sample: Place vertices at $A(-a, -b)$, $B(-a, b)$, $C(a, b)$, and $D(a, -b)$. Show each diagonal has (0, 0) as its midpt.
25. Answers may vary. Sample: Place vertices at $A(0, 0)$, $B(0, a)$, $C(a, a)$, and $D(a, 0)$. Use the fact that a horizontal line is ⊥ to a vertical line.
26. ▱
27. isosc. trapezoid
28. kite
29. square

Answers

Practice and Problem-Solving Exercises (continued)

30. The diagonals of a rhombus are ⊥.

31. Answers may vary. Sample:

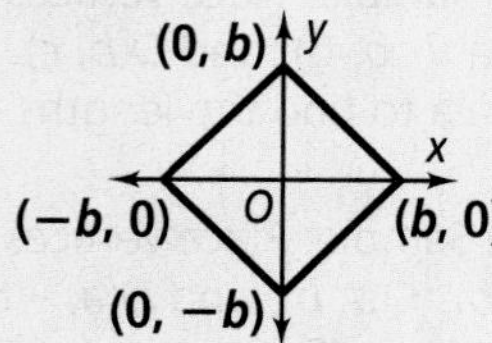

32. Answers may vary. Sample: *A, C, H, F*

33. Answers may vary. Sample: *B, D, H, F*

34. Answers may vary. Sample: *A, B, F, E*

35. Answers may vary. Sample: *A, C, G, E*

36. Answers may vary. Sample: *A, C, F, E*

37. Answers may vary. Sample: *A, D, G, F*

38. C

39. G

40. C

41. [2] 1, 2, 3, 4
[1] extra OR missing value

42. No; product of slopes is not −1, so there are no rt. ⩓.

43a. If $x \neq 51$, then $2x \neq 102$.
b. If $2x \neq 102$, then $x \neq 51$.

44a. If $a \neq 5$, then $a^2 \neq 25$.
b. If $a^2 \neq 25$, then $a \neq 5$.

45a. If *b* not less than −4, then *b* is not negative.
b. If *b* is not negative, then *b* is not less than −4.

46a. If *c* is not greater than 0, then *c* is not positive.
b. If *c* is not positive, then *c* is not greater than 0.

47a. If the sum of the measures of the interior ⩓ of a polygon is 360, then the polygon is a quadrilateral.
b. If a polygon is a quadrilateral, then the sum of the measures of the interior ⩓ of the polygon is 360.

48. $y = \frac{5}{4}x$

49. $y - q = \frac{a}{b}(x - p)$

30. What property of a rhombus makes it convenient to place its diagonals on the *x*- and *y*-axes?

31. Marine Archaeology Marine archaeologists sometimes use a coordinate system on the ocean floor. They record the coordinates of points where artifacts are found. Assume that each diver searches a square area and can go no farther than *b* units from the starting point. Draw a model for the region one diver can search. Assign coordinates to the vertices without using any new variables.

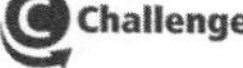

Here are coordinates for eight points in the coordinate plane ($q > p > 0$). $A(0, 0)$, $B(p, 0)$, $C(q, 0)$, $D(p + q, 0)$, $E(0, q)$, $F(p, q)$, $G(q, q)$, $H(p + q, q)$. Which four points, if any, are the vertices for each type of figure?

32. parallelogram **33.** rhombus **34.** rectangle
35. square **36.** trapezoid **37.** isosceles trapezoid

Standardized Test Prep

SAT/ACT

38. Which number of right angles is NOT possible for a quadrilateral to have?

Ⓐ exactly one Ⓑ exactly two Ⓒ exactly three Ⓓ exactly four

39. The vertices of a rhombus are located at $(a, 0)$, $(0, b)$, $(-a, 0)$, and $(0, -b)$, where $a > 0$ and $b > 0$. What is the midpoint of the side that is in Quadrant II?

Ⓕ $\left(\frac{a}{2}, \frac{b}{2}\right)$ Ⓖ $\left(-\frac{a}{2}, \frac{b}{2}\right)$ Ⓗ $\left(-\frac{a}{2}, -\frac{b}{2}\right)$ Ⓘ $\left(\frac{a}{2}, -\frac{b}{2}\right)$

40. In ▱*PQRS*, $PQ = 35$ cm and $QR = 12$ cm. What is the perimeter of ▱*PQRS*?

Ⓐ 23 cm Ⓑ 47 cm Ⓒ 94 cm Ⓓ 420 cm

Short Response

41. In △*PQR*, $PQ > PR > QR$. One angle measures 170. List all possible whole number values for $m\angle P$.

Mixed Review

42. Let $X(-2, 3)$, $Y(5, 5)$, and $Z(4, 10)$. Is △*XYZ* a right triangle? Explain. See Lesson 6-7.

Write (a) the inverse and (b) the contrapositive of each statement. See Lesson 2-2.

43. If $x = 51$, then $2x = 102$. **44.** If $a = 5$, then $a^2 = 25$.

45. If $b < -4$, then *b* is negative. **46.** If $c > 0$, then *c* is positive.

47. If the sum of the interior angle measures of a polygon is not 360, then the polygon is not a quadrilateral.

Get Ready! **To prepare for Lesson 6-9, do Exercises 48 and 49.** See Lesson 3-7.

48. Find the equation for the line that contains the origin and (4, 5).

49. Find the equation for the line that contains (p, q) and has slope $\frac{a}{b}$.

6-8 Lesson Resources

Differentiated Remediation

Instructional Support

Geometry Companion

Students can use the **Geometry Companion** worktext (4 pages) . . .

- New Vocabulary
- Key Concepts
- Got It for each Problem
- Lesson Check

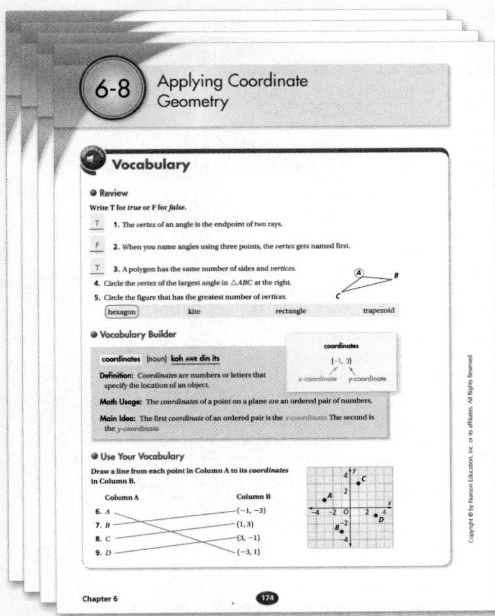

6-8 Applying Coordinate Geometry

Vocabulary

Review

Write T for *true* or F for *false*.

T 1. The *vertex* of an angle is the endpoint of two rays.

F 2. When you name angles using three points, the *vertex* gets named first.

T 3. A polygon has the same number of sides and *vertices*.

4. Circle the *vertex* of the largest angle in $\triangle ABC$ at the right.

5. Circle the figure that has the greatest number of *vertices*.

hexagon kite rectangle trapezoid

Vocabulary Builder

coordinates (noun) **koh AWR din its**

Definition: *Coordinates* are numbers or letters that specify the location of an object.

Math Usage: The *coordinates* of a point on a plane are an ordered pair of numbers.

Main Idea: The first *coordinate* of an ordered pair is the *x-coordinate*. The second is the *y-coordinate*.

Use Your Vocabulary

Draw a line from each point in Column A to its *coordinates* in Column B.

Column A	Column B
6. *A*	(−1, −3)
7. *B*	(1, 3)
8. *C*	(3, −1)
9. *D*	(−3, 1)

Chapter 6 174

ELL Support

Assess Understanding Place students in pairs of mixed abilities. Write Theorem 6-20 on the board. Students will plan a coordinate proof of the theorem. Invite students to draw their isosceles trapezoid on the board, including the axes and coordinates, to explain their work.

Focus on Language After this lesson, have students write why it is better for a figure to be on an axis when on the coordinate plane. Ask them to include examples and sketches to show their thinking.

5 Assess & Remediate

Lesson Quiz

Plan a coordinate proof to show that the midpoints of the sides of an equilateral triangle form another equilateral triangle.

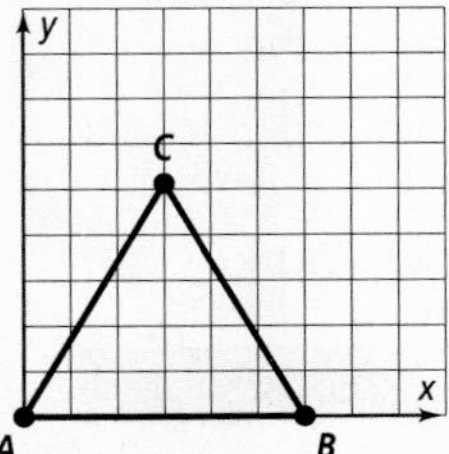

1. Name the coordinates of equilateral triangle *ABC* with base $AB = 2a$ along the *x*-axis and height $\sqrt{3}a$.
2. State the *Given* and *Prove*.
3. How will you find the coordinates of the midpoints of each side?
4. **Do you UNDERSTAND?** How will you determine whether the figure formed is an equilateral triangle?

ANSWERS TO LESSON QUIZ

1. $A(0, 0)$, $B(2a, 0)$, $C(a, \sqrt{3}a)$;
2. Given: $\triangle ABC$ is equilateral with vertices $A(0, 0)$, $B(2a, 0)$, $C(a, \sqrt{3}a)$ Prove: The midpoints of the sides of *ABC* form the vertices of another equilateral triangle.
3. Use the Midpoint Formula.
4. Use the Distance Formula to show that the sides of the resulting triangle are all the same length.

PRESCRIPTION FOR REMEDIATION

Use the student work on the Lesson Quiz to prescribe a differentiated review assignment.

Points	Differentiated Remediation
0–2	Intervention
3	On-level
4	Extension

PowerGeometry.com

5 Assess & Remediate

Assign the Lesson Quiz. Appropriate intervention, practice, or enrichment is automatically generated based on student performance.

Intervention

- **Reteaching** (2 pages) Provides reteaching and practice exercises for the key lesson concepts. Use with struggling students or absent students.
- **English Language Learner Support** Helps students develop and reinforce mathematical vocabulary and key concepts.

All-in-One Resources/Online

Reteaching

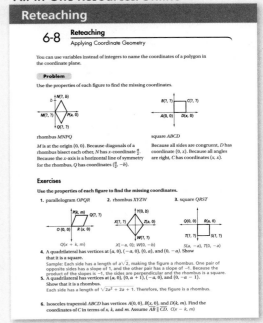

6-8 **Reteaching**

Applying Coordinate Geometry

You can use variables instead of integers to name the coordinates of a polygon in the coordinate plane.

Problem

Use the properties of each figure to find the missing coordinates.

N(?, b), b, M(?, ?), P(a, 0), Q(?, ?)

B(?, ?), C(?, ?), A(0, 0), D(x, 0)

rhombus *MNPQ*

M is at the origin (0, 0). Because diagonals of a rhombus bisect each other, *N* has *x*-coordinate $\frac{a}{2}$. Because the *x*-axis is a horizontal line of symmetry for the rhombus, *Q* has coordinates $(\frac{a}{2}, -b)$.

square *ABCD*

Because all sides are congruent, *D* has coordinate $(0, x)$. Because all angles are right, *C* has coordinates (x, x).

Exercises

Use the properties of each figure to find the missing coordinates.

1. parallelogram *OPQR* — P(k, m), Q(?, ?), O (0, 0), R (x, 0) — $Q(x + k, m)$
2. rhombus *XYZW* — Y(0, b), X(?, ?), Z(a, 0), W(?, ?) — $X(-a, 0)$; $W(0, -b)$
3. square *QRST* — Q(0, 0), R(a, 0), T(?, ?), S(?, ?) — $S(a, -a)$, $T(0, -a)$
4. A quadrilateral has vertices at $(a, 0)$, $(-a, 0)$, $(0, a)$, and $(0, -a)$. Show that it is a square. Sample: Each side has a length of $a\sqrt{2}$, making the figure a rhombus. One pair of opposite sides has a slope of 1, and the other pair has a slope of −1. Because the product of the slopes is −1, the sides are perpendicular and the rhombus is a square.
5. A quadrilateral has vertices at $(a, 0)$, $(0, a + 1)$, $(-a, 0)$, and $(0, -a - 1)$. Show that it is a rhombus. Each side has a length of $\sqrt{2a^2 + 2a + 1}$. Therefore, the figure is a rhombus.
6. Isosceles trapezoid *ABCD* has vertices $A(0, 0)$, $B(x, 0)$, and $D(k, m)$. Find the coordinates of *C* in terms of *x*, *k*, and *m*. Assume $\overline{AB} \parallel \overline{CD}$. $C(x - k, m)$

All-in-One Resources/Online

English Language Learner Support

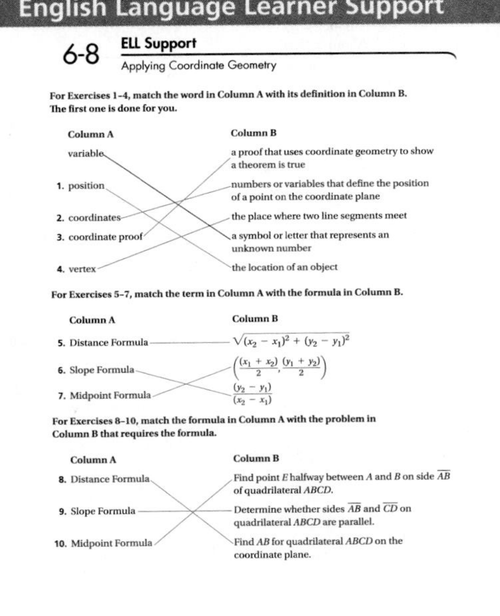

6-8 **ELL Support**

Applying Coordinate Geometry

For Exercises 1–4, match the word in Column A with its definition in Column B. The first one is done for you.

Column A	Column B
variable	a proof that uses coordinate geometry to show a theorem is true
1. position	numbers or variables that define the position of a point on the coordinate plane
2. coordinates	the place where two line segments meet
3. coordinate proof	a symbol or letter that represents an unknown number
4. vertex	the location of an object

For Exercises 5–7, match the term in Column A with the formula in Column B.

Column A	Column B
5. Distance Formula	$\sqrt{(x_2 - x_1)^2 + (y_2 - y_1)^2}$
6. Slope Formula	$\left(\frac{(x_1 + x_2)}{2}, \frac{(y_1 + y_2)}{2}\right)$
7. Midpoint Formula	$\frac{(y_2 - y_1)}{(x_2 - x_1)}$

For Exercises 8–10, match the formula in Column A with the problem in Column B that requires the formula.

Column A	Column B
8. Distance Formula	Find point *E* halfway between *A* and *B* on side $\overline{AB}$ of quadrilateral *ABCD*.
9. Slope Formula	Determine whether sides $\overline{AB}$ and $\overline{CD}$ on quadrilateral *ABCD* are parallel.
10. Midpoint Formula	Find *AB* for quadrilateral *ABCD* on the coordinate plane.

Differentiated Remediation *continued*

On-Level

- **Practice** (2 pages) Provides extra practice for each lesson. For simpler practice exercises, use the Form K Practice pages found in the All-in-One Teaching Resources and online.
- **Think About a Plan** Helps students develop specific problem-solving skills and strategies by providing scaffolded guiding questions.
- **Standardized Test Prep** Focuses on all major exercises, all major question types, and helps students prepare for the high-stakes assessments.

Extension

- **Enrichment** Provides students with interesting problems and activities that extend the concepts of the lesson.
- **Activities, Games, and Puzzles** Worksheets that can be used for concepts development, enrichment, and for fun!

Practice and Problem Solving Wkbk/ All-in-One Resources/Online

Practice page 1

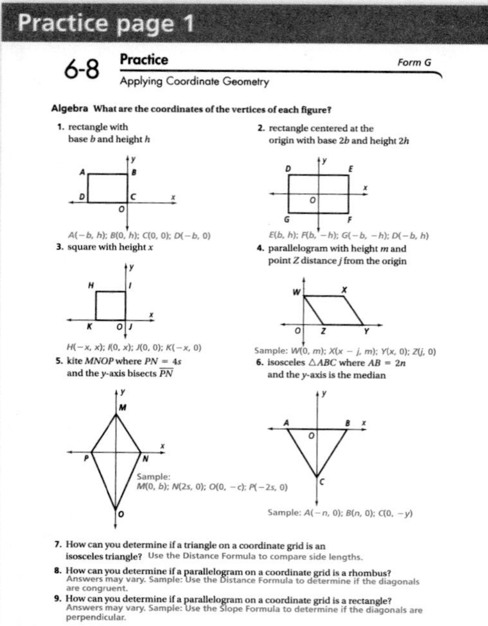

6-8 **Practice** *Form G*

Applying Coordinate Geometry

Algebra What are the coordinates of the vertices of each figure?

1. rectangle with base b and height h
   $A(-b, h)$; $B(0, h)$; $C(0, 0)$; $D(-b, 0)$
2. rectangle centered at the origin with base $2b$ and height $2h$
   $E(b, h)$; $F(b, -h)$; $G(-b, -h)$; $D(-b, h)$
3. square with height x
   $H(-x, x)$; $I(0, x)$; $J(0, 0)$; $K(-x, 0)$
4. parallelogram with height m and point Z distance j from the origin
   Sample: $W(0, m)$; $X(x - j, m)$; $Y(x, 0)$; $Z(j, 0)$
5. kite $MNOP$ where $PN = 4s$ and the y-axis bisects $\overline{PN}$
   Sample: $M(0, b)$; $N(2s, 0)$; $O(0, -c)$; $P(-2s, 0)$
6. isosceles $\triangle ABC$ where $AB = 2n$ and the y-axis is the median
   Sample: $A(-n, 0)$; $B(n, 0)$; $C(0, -y)$
7. How can you determine if a triangle on a coordinate grid is an isosceles triangle? Use the Distance Formula to compare side lengths.
8. How can you determine if a parallelogram on a coordinate grid is a rhombus? Answers may vary. Sample: Use the Distance Formula to determine if the diagonals are congruent.
9. How can you determine if a parallelogram on a coordinate grid is a rectangle? Answers may vary. Sample: Use the Slope Formula to determine if the diagonals are perpendicular.

Practice and Problem Solving Wkbk/ All-in-One Resources/Online

Practice page 2

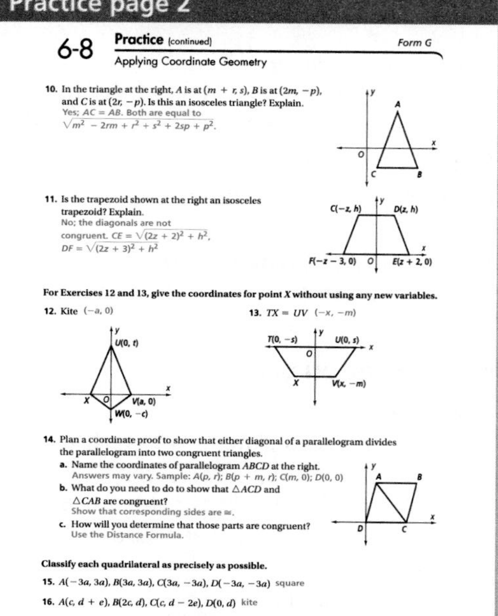

6-8 **Practice** (continued) *Form G*

Applying Coordinate Geometry

10. In the triangle at the right, A is at $(m + r, s)$, B is at $(2m, -p)$, and C is at $(2r, -p)$. Is this an isosceles triangle? Explain.
    Yes; $AC = AB$. Both are equal to $\sqrt{m^2 - 2rm + r^2 + s^2 + 2sp + p^2}$.
11. Is the trapezoid shown at the right an isosceles trapezoid? Explain.
    No; the diagonals are not congruent. $CE = \sqrt{(2z + 2)^2 + h^2}$, $DF = \sqrt{(2z + 3)^2 + h^2}$

For Exercises 12 and 13, give the coordinates for point X without using any new variables.

12. Kite $(-a, 0)$
13. $TX = UV$ $(-x, -m)$
14. Plan a coordinate proof to show that either diagonal of a parallelogram divides the parallelogram into two congruent triangles.
    a. Name the coordinates of parallelogram $ABCD$ at the right. Answers may vary. Sample: $A(p, r)$; $B(p + m, r)$; $C(m, 0)$; $D(0, 0)$
    b. What do you need to do to show that $\triangle ACD$ and $\triangle CAB$ are congruent? Show that corresponding sides are ≅.
    c. How will you determine that those parts are congruent? Use the Distance Formula.

Classify each quadrilateral as precisely as possible.

15. $A(-3a, 3a)$, $B(3a, 3a)$, $C(3a, -3a)$, $D(-3a, -3a)$ square
16. $A(c, d + e)$, $B(2c, d)$, $C(c, d - 2e)$, $D(0, d)$ kite

All-in-One Resources/Online

Enrichment

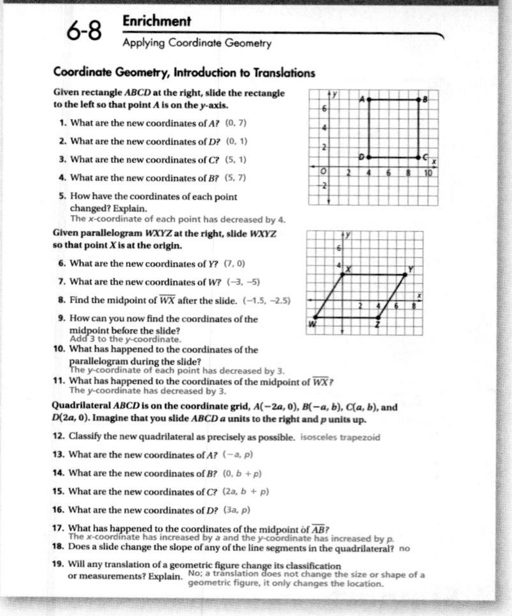

6-8 **Enrichment**

Applying Coordinate Geometry

Coordinate Geometry, Introduction to Translations

Given rectangle $ABCD$ at the right, slide the rectangle to the left so that point A is on the y-axis.

1. What are the new coordinates of A? (0, 7)
2. What are the new coordinates of D? (0, 1)
3. What are the new coordinates of C? (5, 1)
4. What are the new coordinates of B? (5, 7)
5. How have the coordinates of each point changed? Explain.
   The x-coordinate of each point has decreased by 4.

Given parallelogram $WXYZ$ at the right, slide $WXYZ$ so that point X is at the origin.

6. What are the new coordinates of Y? (7, 0)
7. What are the new coordinates of W? (–3, –5)
8. Find the midpoint of $\overline{WX}$ after the slide. (–1.5, –2.5)
9. How can you now find the coordinates of the midpoint before the slide?
   Add 3 to the y-coordinate.
10. What has happened to the coordinates of the parallelogram during the slide?
    The y-coordinate of each point has decreased by 3.
11. What has happened to the coordinates of the midpoint of $\overline{WX}$?
    The y-coordinate has decreased by 3.

Quadrilateral $ABCD$ is on the coordinate grid, $A(-2a, 0)$, $B(-a, b)$, $C(a, b)$, and $D(2a, 0)$. Imagine that you slide $ABCD$ a units to the right and p units up.

12. Classify the new quadrilateral as precisely as possible. isosceles trapezoid
13. What are the new coordinates of A? $(-a, p)$
14. What are the new coordinates of B? $(0, b + p)$
15. What are the new coordinates of C? $(2a, b + p)$
16. What are the new coordinates of D? $(3a, p)$
17. What has happened to the coordinates of the midpoint of $\overline{AB}$?
    The x-coordinate has increased by a and the y-coordinate has increased by p.
18. Does a slide change the slope of any of the line segments in the quadrilateral? no
19. Will any translation of a geometric figure change its classification or measurements? Explain. No; a translation does not change the size or shape of a geometric figure, it only changes the location.

Practice and Problem Solving Wkbk/ All-in-One Resources/Online

Think About a Plan

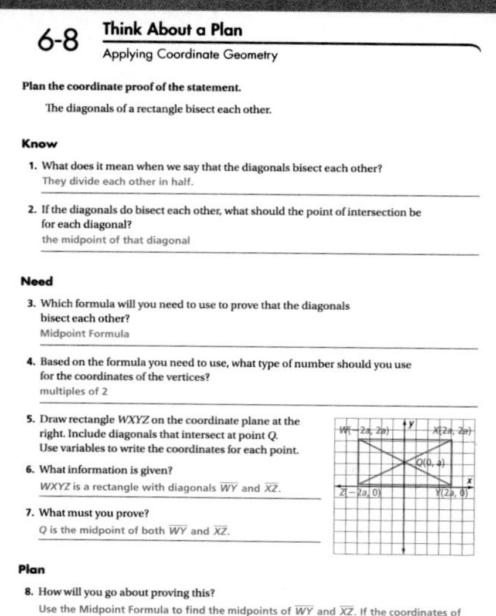

6-8 **Think About a Plan**

Applying Coordinate Geometry

Plan the coordinate proof of the statement.

The diagonals of a rectangle bisect each other.

Know

1. What does it mean when we say that the diagonals bisect each other?
   They divide each other in half.
2. If the diagonals do bisect each other, what should the point of intersection be for each diagonal?
   the midpoint of that diagonal

Need

3. Which formula will you need to use to prove that the diagonals bisect each other?
   Midpoint Formula
4. Based on the formula you need to use, what type of number should you use for the coordinates of the vertices?
   multiples of 2
5. Draw rectangle $WXYZ$ on the coordinate plane at the right. Include diagonals that intersect at point Q. Use variables to write the coordinates for each point.
6. What information is given?
   $WXYZ$ is a rectangle with diagonals $\overline{WY}$ and $\overline{XZ}$.
7. What must you prove?
   Q is the midpoint of both $\overline{WY}$ and $\overline{XZ}$.

Plan

8. How will you go about proving this?
   Use the Midpoint Formula to find the midpoints of $\overline{WY}$ and $\overline{XZ}$. If the coordinates of the midpoint of both lines are the coordinates of Point Q, the statement is proven.

Practice and Problem Solving Wkbk/ All-in-One Resources/Online

Standardized Test Prep

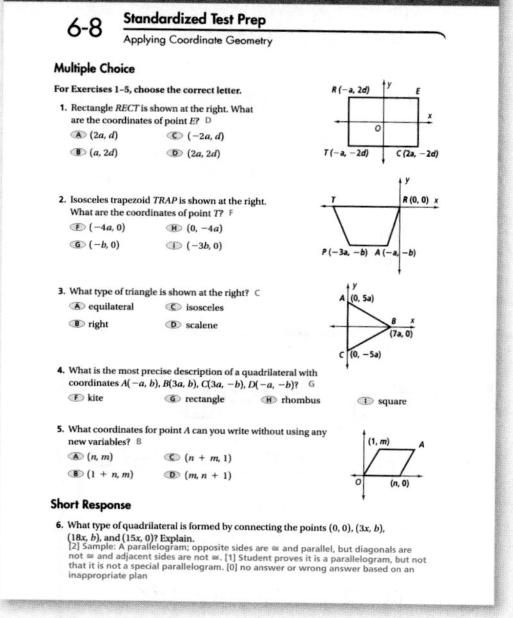

6-8 **Standardized Test Prep**

Applying Coordinate Geometry

Multiple Choice

For Exercises 1–5, choose the correct letter.

1. Rectangle $RECT$ is shown at the right. What are the coordinates of point E? D
   A. $(2a, d)$ C. $(-2a, d)$
   B. $(a, 2d)$ D. $(2a, 2d)$
2. Isosceles trapezoid $TRAP$ is shown at the right. What are the coordinates of point T? F
   F. $(-4a, 0)$ H. $(0, -4a)$
   G. $(-b, 0)$ I. $(-3b, 0)$
3. What type of triangle is shown at the right? C
   A. equilateral C. isosceles
   B. right D. scalene
4. What is the most precise description of a quadrilateral with coordinates $A(-a, b)$, $B(3a, b)$, $C(3a, -b)$, $D(-a, -b)$? G
   F. kite G. rectangle H. rhombus I. square
5. What coordinates for point A can you write without using any new variables? B
   A. (n, m) C. $(n + m, 1)$
   B. $(1 + n, m)$ D. $(m, n + 1)$

Short Response

6. What type of quadrilateral is formed by connecting the points $(0, 0)$, $(3x, b)$, $(18x, b)$, and $(15x, 0)$? Explain.
   [2] Sample: A parallelogram; opposite sides are ≅ and parallel, but diagonals are not ≅ and adjacent sides are not ≅. [1] Student proves it is a parallelogram, but not that it is not a special parallelogram. [0] no answer or wrong answer based on an inappropriate plan

Online Teacher Resource Center

Activities, Games, and Puzzles

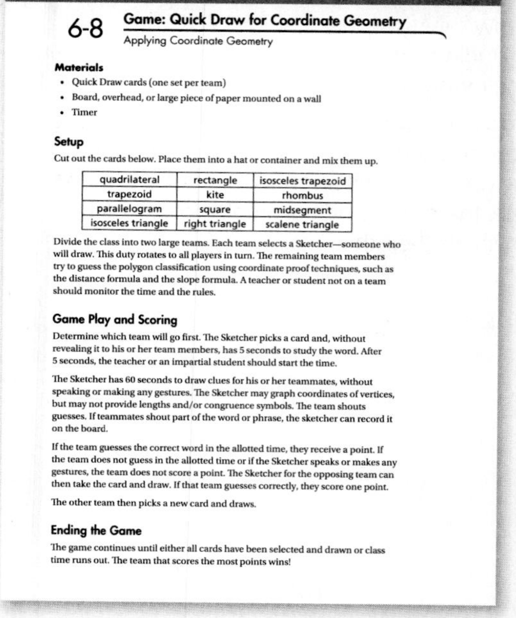

6-8 **Game: Quick Draw for Coordinate Geometry**

Applying Coordinate Geometry

Materials

- Quick Draw cards (one set per team)
- Board, overhead, or large piece of paper mounted on a wall
- Timer

Setup

Cut out the cards below. Place them into a hat or container and mix them up.

quadrilateral	rectangle	isosceles trapezoid
trapezoid	kite	rhombus
parallelogram	square	midsegment
isosceles triangle	right triangle	scalene triangle

Divide the class into two large teams. Each team selects a Sketcher—someone who will draw. This duty rotates to all players in turn. The remaining team members try to guess the polygon classification using coordinate proof techniques, such as the distance formula and the slope formula. A teacher or student not on a team should monitor the time and the rules.

Game Play and Scoring

Determine which team will go first. The Sketcher picks a card and, without revealing it to his or her team members, has 5 seconds to study the word. After 5 seconds, the teacher or an impartial student should start the time.

The Sketcher has 60 seconds to draw clues for his or her teammates, without speaking or making any gestures. The Sketcher may graph coordinates of vertices, but may not provide lengths and/or congruence symbols. The team shouts guesses. If teammates shout part of the word or phrase, the sketcher can record it on the board.

If the team guesses the correct word in the allotted time, they receive a point. If the team does not guess in the allotted time or if the Sketcher speaks or makes any gestures, the team does not score a point. The Sketcher for the opposing team can then take the card and draw. If that team guesses correctly, they score one point.

The other team then picks a new card and draws.

Ending the Game

The game continues until either all cards have been selected and drawn or class time runs out. The team that scores the most points wins!

Concept Byte
Use With Lesson 6-9
TECHNOLOGY

Quadrilaterals in Quadrilaterals

Activity

Construct

- Use geometry software to construct a quadrilateral *ABCD*.
- Construct the midpoint of each side of *ABCD*.
- Construct segments joining the midpoints, in order, to form quadrilateral *EFGH*.

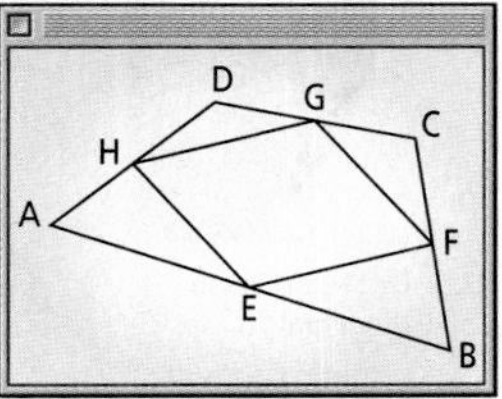

Investigate

- Measure the lengths of the sides of *EFGH* and their slopes.
- Measure the angles of *EFGH*.

What kind of quadrilateral does *EFGH* appear to be?

Exercises

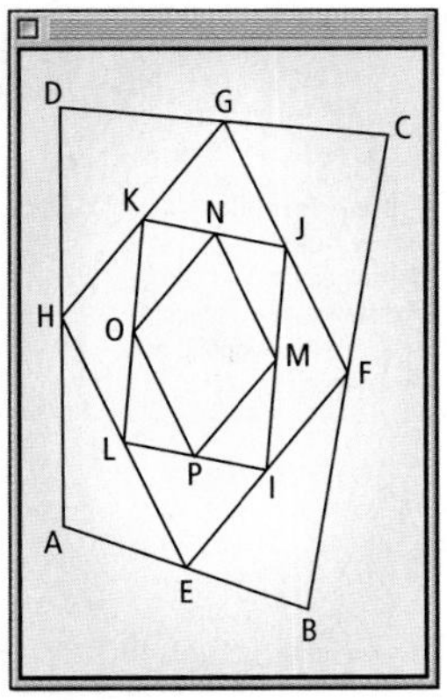

1. Manipulate quadrilateral *ABCD*.
   a. Make a conjecture about the quadrilateral with vertices that are the midpoints of the sides of a quadrilateral.
   b. Does your conjecture hold when *ABCD* is concave?
   c. Can you manipulate *ABCD* so that your conjecture doesn't hold?
2. **Extend** Draw the diagonals of *ABCD*.
   a. Describe *EFGH* when the diagonals are perpendicular.
   b. Describe *EFGH* when the diagonals are congruent.
   c. Describe *EFGH* when the diagonals are both perpendicular and congruent.
3. Construct the midpoints of *EFGH* and use them to construct quadrilateral *IJKL*. Construct the midpoints of *IJKL* and use them to construct quadrilateral *MNOP*. For *MNOP* and *EFGH*, compare the ratios of the lengths of the sides, perimeters, and areas. How are the sides of *MNOP* and *EFGH* related?
4. **Writing** In Exercise 1, you made a conjecture as to the type of quadrilateral *EFGH* appears to be. Prove your conjecture. Include in your proof the Triangle Midsegment Theorem, "If a segment joins the midpoints of two sides of a triangle, then the segment is parallel to the third side and half its length."
5. Describe the quadrilateral formed by joining the midpoints, in order, of the sides of each of the following. Justify each response.
   a. parallelogram
   b. rectangle
   c. rhombus
   d. square
   e. trapezoid
   f. isosceles trapezoid
   g. kite

Guided Instruction

PURPOSE To use geometry software to explore quadrilaterals formed when the segments connecting the midpoints of a quadrilateral are joined

PROCESS Students will

- construct a quadrilateral.
- find the midpoints of each side of the quadrilateral and connect the midpoints with segments.
- measure and make conjectures about the quadrilateral formed by connecting the midpoints.

DISCUSS Review the hierarchy of quadrilaterals, including the differences between rectangles and squares and squares and rhombuses.

Activity

In this Activity students form quadrilaterals within other quadrilaterals by joining the midpoints of the sides of the original quadrilateral.

Q How can you test whether your conjecture is true for any quadrilateral? **[Answers will vary. Sample: To be sure that your conjecture is true for any quadrilateral, you must formulate a geometric proof.]**

Answers

Exercises

1a. The quad. is a ▱.
b. yes
c. no
2a. rhombus
b. rectangle
c. square
3. Ratios of lengths of sides = ratios of lengths of perimeters = 1 : 2; ratio of areas = 1 : 4. The sides are ∥.
4. Answers may vary. Sample:

1. $\overline{HG}$ is midsegment of △*ACD* and $\overline{EF}$ is midsegment of △*ACB*. (Construction)
2. $\overline{HG} \parallel \overline{AC}$, $\overline{EF} \parallel \overline{AC}$, $HG = \frac{1}{2}AC$, and $EF = \frac{1}{2}AC$. (△ Midsegment Thm.)
3. $\overline{HG} \parallel \overline{EF}$ (If two lines are ∥ to the same line, then they are ∥ to each other.)
4. $HG = EF$ (Transitive Prop. of Eq.)
5. *EFGH* is a ▱. (If one pair of opp. sides of a quad. is both ≅ and ∥, the quad. is a ▱.)

5a. ▱; opp. sides are ∥ and ≅.
b. Rhombus; joining midpts. produces 4 ≅ rt. ▵, so hypotenuses are ≅.
c. Rectangle; diagonals of a rhombus are ⊥, so the sides of new figure are ⊥.
d. Square; sides are ≅ and ⊥.
e. ▱; opp. sides are ∥.
f. Rhombus; all sides are ≅.
g. Rectangle; sides are ⊥.

1 Interactive Learning

Solve It!

PURPOSE To use knowledge of the properties of a rectangle that is represented by variables in the coordinate plane

PROCESS Students may use previous knowledge of the properties of rectangles and the Midpoint Formula.

FACILITATE

Q What is the coordinate of the fourth vertex of the rectangle? Explain. **[$(-2a, 2b)$, since it must create sides that are congruent and parallel to the existing sides.]**

Q What are the endpoints of the diagonal for which we need to determine the midpoint? **[$(-2a, 2b)$ and $(2a, 0)$]**

ANSWER See Solve It in Answers on next page.

CONNECT THE MATH In the Solve It, students use coordinate geometry and facts about rectangles to find a midpoint. In the lesson, students will gain more experience with coordinate proofs.

2 Guided Instruction

Problem 1

Q Why should you place the legs of the right triangle on the *x*- and *y*-axes? **[Placing the legs on the axes will make calculations involving the Midpoint Formula and the Distance Formula easier.]**

Got It?

To check understanding of the answer to this question, ask students to list another advantageous set of three points to use as the vertices for the right triangle.

6-9 Proofs Using Coordinate Geometry

TN State Performance Indicators

SPI 3108.3.1 Use algebra and coordinate geometry to analyze and solve problems about geometric figures (including circles).

SPI 3108.3.2 Use coordinate geometry to prove characteristics of polygonal figures.

Objective To prove theorems using figures in the coordinate plane

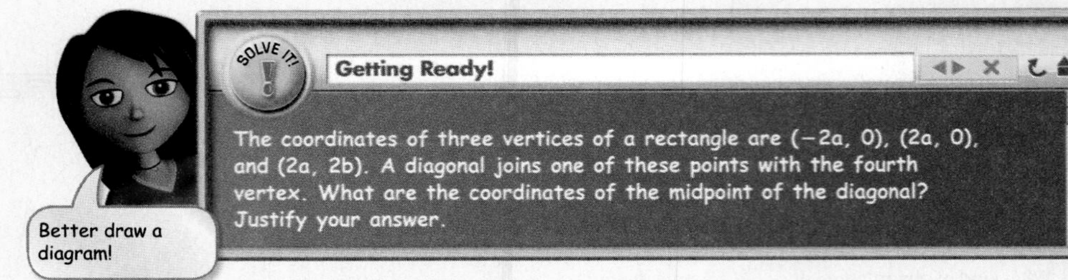

Getting Ready!
The coordinates of three vertices of a rectangle are (−2a, 0), (2a, 0), and (2a, 2b). A diagonal joins one of these points with the fourth vertex. What are the coordinates of the midpoint of the diagonal? Justify your answer.

Better draw a diagram!

In the Solve It, the coordinates of the point include variables. In this lesson, you will use coordinates with variables to write a coordinate proof.

Essential Understanding You can prove geometric relationships using variable coordinates for figures in the coordinate plane.

Plan

What formulas do you need?
You need to find the distance to a midpoint, so use the midpoint and distance formulas.

Proof **Problem 1** **Writing a Coordinate Proof**

Use coordinate geometry to prove that the midpoint of the hypotenuse of a right triangle is equidistant from the three vertices.

Given: $\triangle OEF$ is a right triangle.

M is the midpoint of $\overline{EF}$.

Prove: $EM = FM = OM$

y, E(0, 2b), M, x, O, F(2a, 0)

Coordinate Proof:

By the Midpoint Formula, $M = \left(\frac{2a + 0}{2}, \frac{0 + 2b}{2}\right) = (a, b)$.

By the Distance Formula,

$OM = \sqrt{a^2 + b^2}$

$FM = \sqrt{(2a - a)^2 + (0 - b)^2} = \sqrt{a^2 + b^2}$

$EM = \sqrt{(0 - a)^2 + (2b - b)^2} = \sqrt{a^2 + b^2}$

Since $EM = FM = OM$, the midpoint of the hypotenuse is equidistant from the vertices of the right triangle.

Got It? **1. Reasoning** What is the advantage of using coordinates $O(0, 0)$, $E(0, 2b)$, and $F(2a, 0)$ rather than $O(0, 0)$, $E(0, b)$, and $F(a, 0)$?

6-9 Preparing to Teach

BIG ideas **Coordinate Geometry**
Reasoning and Proof UbD

ESSENTIAL UNDERSTANDING

- Geometric relationships can be proven using variable coordinates for figures in the coordinate plane.

Math Background

Synthetic geometry is the branch of geometry which makes use of observations, postulates and theorems. Euclid's geometry, which is the basis for this textbook, is a synthetic geometry. Proofs for some theorems in synthetic geometry can be very difficult to construct and understand. Using coordinate geometry provides a powerful and sometimes more understandable alternative to proving theorems in synthetic geometry.

Keys to effective coordinate proofs lie in confidently using the Distance Formula, the Midpoint Formula, and the Slope Formula.

Note to students that theorems about angles are generally not provable by coordinate geometry unless the angle is a right angle or a straight angle.

Support Student Learning

Use the **Geometry Companion** to engage and support students during instructions. See Lesson Resources at the end of this lesson for details.

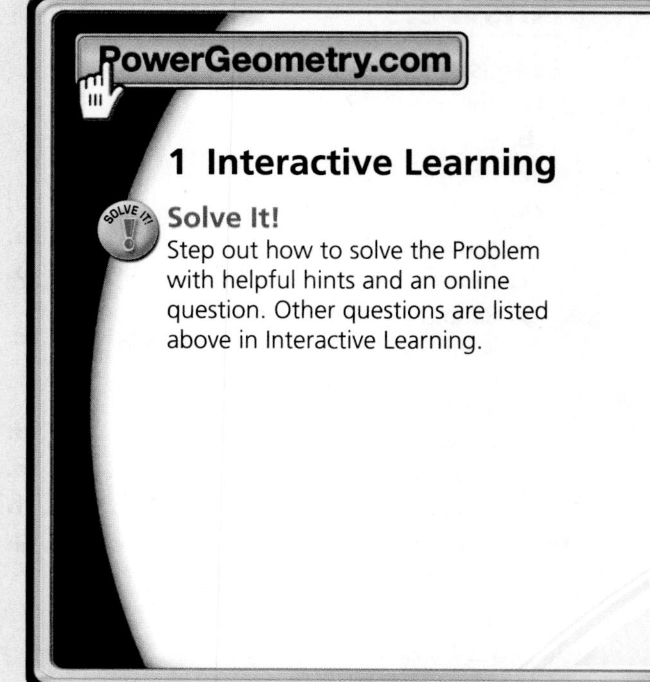

In Lesson 6-8, you wrote a plan for the proof of the Trapezoid Midsegment Theorem. Now you will write the full coordinate proof.

Plan

Refer to the plan from Lesson 6-8. Find the coordinates of M and N. Determine whether $\overline{MN}$ is parallel to $\overline{OP}$ and $\overline{RA}$. Then find and compare the lengths of $\overline{MN}$, $\overline{OP}$, and $\overline{RA}$.

Proof

Problem 2 Writing a Coordinate Proof

Write a coordinate proof of the Trapezoid Midsegment Theorem.

Given: $\overline{MN}$ is the midsegment of trapezoid $ORAP$.

Prove: $\overline{MN} \parallel \overline{OP}$, $\overline{MN} \parallel \overline{RA}$, $MN = \frac{1}{2}(OP + RA)$

y
R(2b, 2c)
A(2d, 2c)
M
N
x
O
P(2a, 0)

Coordinate Proof:

Use the Midpoint Formula to find the coordinates of M and N.

$$M = \left(\frac{2b + 0}{2}, \frac{2c + 0}{2}\right) = (b, c)$$

$$N = \left(\frac{2a + 2d}{2}, \frac{0 + 2c}{2}\right) = (a + d, c)$$

Use the Slope Formula to determine whether $\overline{MN}$ is parallel to $\overline{OP}$ and $\overline{RA}$.

$$\text{slope of } \overline{MN} = \frac{c - c}{(a + d) - b} = 0$$

$$\text{slope of } \overline{RA} = \frac{2c - 2c}{2d - 2b} = 0$$

$$\text{slope of } \overline{OP} = \frac{0 - 0}{2a - 0} = 0$$

The three slopes are equal, so $\overline{MN} \parallel \overline{OP}$ and $\overline{MN} \parallel \overline{RA}$.

Use the Distance Formula to find and compare MN, OP, and RA.

$$MN = \sqrt{[(a + d) - b)]^2 + (c - c)^2} = a + d - b$$

$$OP = \sqrt{(2a - 0)^2 + (0 - 0)^2} = 2a$$

$$RA = \sqrt{(2d - 2b)^2 + (2c - 2c)^2} = 2d - 2b$$

$MN \stackrel{?}{=} \frac{1}{2}(OP + RA)$	Check that $MN = \frac{1}{2}(OP + RA)$ is true.
$a + d - b \stackrel{?}{=} \frac{1}{2}[2a + (2d - 2b)]$	Substitute.
$a + d - b = a + d - b$ ✓	Simplify.

So, (1) the midsegment of a trapezoid is parallel to its bases, and
(2) the length of the midsegment of a trapezoid is half the sum of the lengths of the bases.

Got It? **2.** Write a coordinate proof of the Triangle Midsegment Theorem (Theorem 5-1).

Problem 2

Q How will the Slope Formula be used in this proof? **[The Slope Formula will be used to determine the slopes of the two bases and the midsegment. The slopes must be the same if the segments are parallel.]**

Q How will the Midpoint Formula be used in this proof? **[The Midpoint Formula will be used to determine the endpoints of the midsegment.]**

Q How will the Distance Formula be used in this proof? **[The Distance Formula will be used to determine the length of each base and the midsegment.]**

Q Should you remove the parentheses from the expression $(2d - 2b)^2$ prior to simplifying the expression $\sqrt{(2d - 2b)^2}$? Explain. **[No, the square root and the square are inverses.]**

Q Is it possible to use the distance formula for a number line instead of the distance formula for points on a coordinate plane? Explain. **[Yes; the segments are all horizontal.]**

Q What property do you use to simplify the expression $\frac{1}{2}[2a + (2d - 2b)]$. **[Distributive Property]**

Got It?

Students can use the proof of the Trapezoid Midsegment Theorem as a template for the proof of the Triangle Midsegment Theorem.

2 Guided Instruction

Each Problem is worked out and supported online.

Problem 1
Writing a Coordinate Proof
Animated

Problem 2
Writing a Coordinate Proof
Animated

Support in Geometry Companion

- Vocabulary
- Key Concepts
- Got It?

Answers

Solve It!

(0, b); diagonals have the same midpoint. The midpoint of the diagonal joining $(-2a, 0)$ and $(2a, 2b)$ is $(0, b)$.

Got It?

1. The factor 2 avoids fractions.

2. See back of book.

3 Lesson Check

Do you know HOW?

- If students have difficulty with Exercise 1, then have them review Problem 1 to write a plan for the proof.

Do you UNDERSTAND?

- If students have difficulty with Exercise 3, then have them choose sample values for the variables and try to draw a diagram that fits all the specifications of the given diagram.

Close

Q What three formulas are important for completing coordinate proofs? Explain the importance of each. **[The Slope Formula is important for proving segments parallel and perpendicular. The Distance Formula is important for determining and comparing the lengths of segments. The Midpoint Formula is important for constructing special points and segments on the given figure.]**

Lesson Check

Do you know HOW?

1. Use coordinate geometry to prove that the diagonals of a rectangle are congruent.
   a. Place rectangle $PQRS$ in the coordinate plane with P at (0, 0).
   b. What are the coordinates of Q, R, and S?
   c. Write the *Given* and *Prove* statements.
   d. Write a coordinate proof.

Do you UNDERSTAND?

2. **Reasoning** Describe a good strategy for placing the vertices of a rhombus for a coordinate proof.
3. **Error Analysis** Your classmate places a trapezoid on the coordinate plane. What is the error?

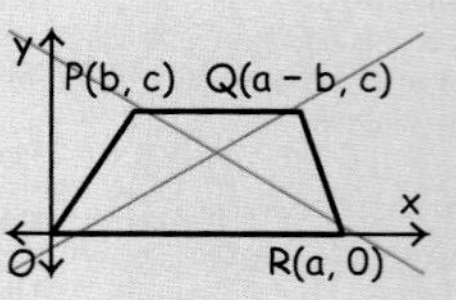

Practice and Problem-Solving Exercises

A Practice

Developing Proof **Complete the following coordinate proofs.**

See Problems 1 and 2.

4. The diagonals of an isosceles trapezoid are congruent.
   Given: Trapezoid $EFGH$ with $\overline{EF} \cong \overline{GH}$
   Prove: $\overline{EG} \cong \overline{FH}$
   a. Find EG.
   b. Find FH.
   c. Explain why $\overline{EG} \cong \overline{FH}$.

5. The medians drawn to the congruent sides of an isosceles triangle are congruent.
   Given: $\triangle PQR$ with $\overline{PQ} \cong \overline{RQ}$, M is the midpoint of $\overline{PQ}$, N is the midpoint of $\overline{RQ}$
   Prove: $\overline{PN} \cong \overline{RM}$
   a. What are the coordinates of M and N?
   b. What are PN and RM?
   c. Explain why $\overline{PN} \cong \overline{RM}$.

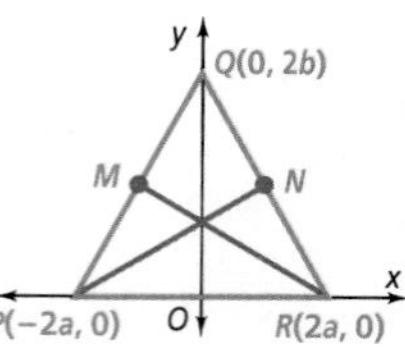

B Apply

Tell whether you can reach each type of conclusion below using coordinate methods. Give a reason for each answer.

6. $\overline{AB} \cong \overline{CD}$
7. $\overline{AB} \parallel \overline{CD}$
8. $\overline{AB} \perp \overline{CD}$
9. $\overline{AB}$ bisects $\overline{CD}$.
10. $\overline{AB}$ bisects $\angle CAD$.
11. $\angle A \cong \angle B$
12. $\angle A$ is a right angle.
13. $AB + BC = AC$
14. $\triangle ABC$ is isosceles.
15. Quadrilateral $ABCD$ is a rhombus.
16. $\overline{AB}$ and $\overline{CD}$ bisect each other.
17. $\angle A$ is the supplement of $\angle B$.
18. $\overline{AB}$, $\overline{CD}$, and $\overline{EF}$ are concurrent.

PowerGeometry.com

3 Lesson Check

For a digital lesson check, use the Got It questions.

Support in Geometry Companion

- Lesson Check

4 Practice

Assign homework to individual students or to an entire class.

Additional Problems

1. Use coordinate geometry to prove that the diagonals of a rhombus with vertices $R(0, b)$, $H(a, 0)$, $M(0, -b)$, and $B(-a, 0)$ are perpendicular.
   Given: $RHMB$ is a rhombus with vertices $R(0, b)$, $H(a, 0)$, $M(0, -b)$, and $B(-a, 0)$.
   Prove: $\overline{RM} \perp \overline{BH}$

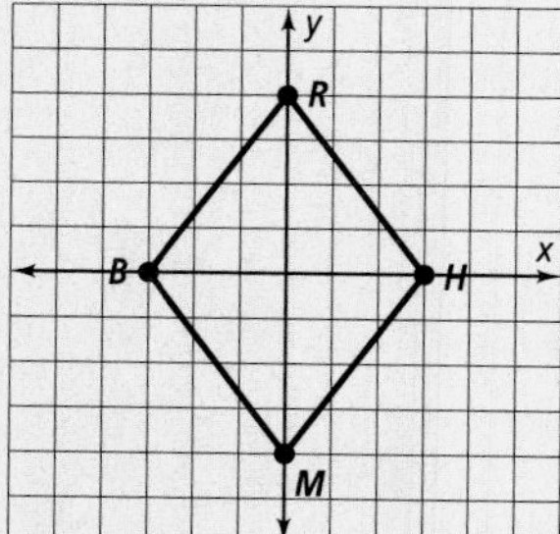

ANSWER The slope of $\overline{RM}$ is $\frac{b-(-b)}{0-0}$ which is undefined. $\overline{RM}$ is a vertical line. The slope of $\overline{BH}$ is $\frac{0-0}{a-(-a)} = 0$. $\overline{BH}$ is a horizontal line. The diagonals are perpendicular.

2. Write a coordinate proof to show that the midpoints of the sides of an equilateral triangle form another equilateral triangle.
   Given: ABC is an equilateral triangle with coordinates $A(0, 0)$, $B(4a, 0)$, and $C(2a, 2\sqrt{3a})$.
   Prove: DEF is an equilateral triangle.

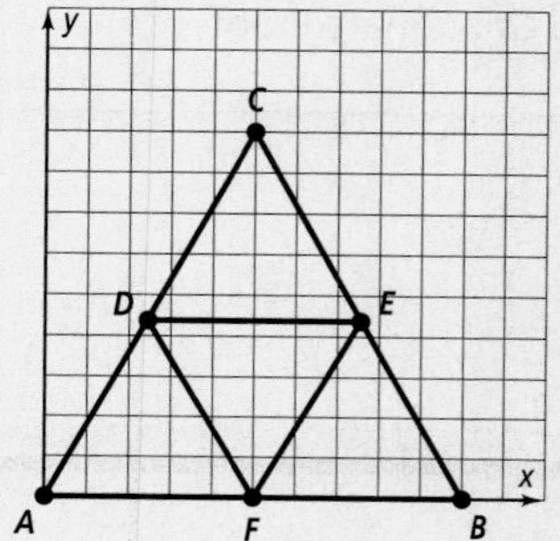

19. **Flag Design** The flag design at the right is made by connecting the midpoints of the sides of a rectangle. Use coordinate geometry to prove that the quadrilateral formed is a rhombus.

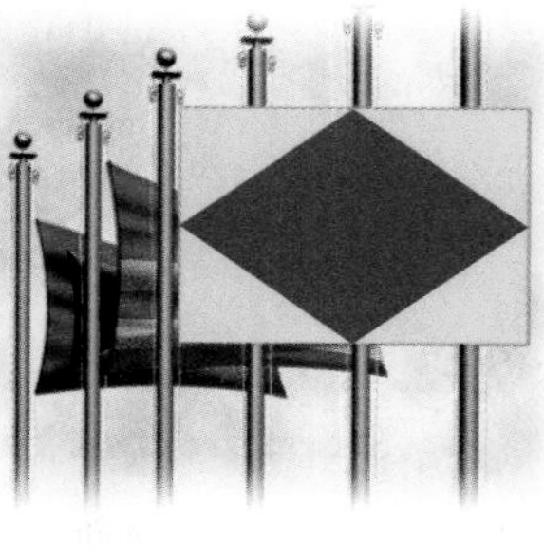

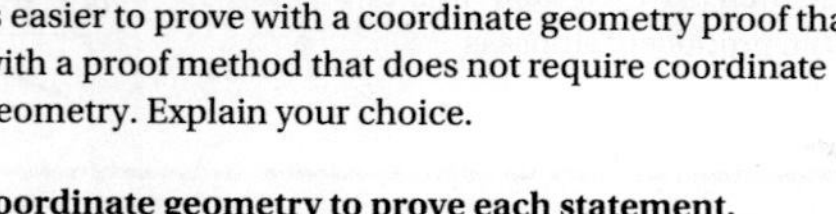

20. **Open-Ended** Give an example of a statement that you think is easier to prove with a coordinate geometry proof than with a proof method that does not require coordinate geometry. Explain your choice.

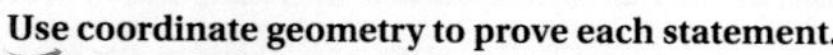

Use coordinate geometry to prove each statement.

21. **Think About a Plan** If a parallelogram is a rhombus, its diagonals are perpendicular (Theorem 6-13).
    - How will you place the rhombus in a coordinate plane?
    - What formulas will you need to use?

22. The altitude to the base of an isosceles triangle bisects the base.

23. If the midpoints of a trapezoid are joined to form a quadrilateral, then the quadrilateral is a parallelogram.

24. One diagonal of a kite divides the kite into two congruent triangles.

25. You learned in Theorem 5-8 that the centroid of a triangle is two thirds the distance from each vertex to the midpoint of the opposite side. Complete the steps to prove this theorem.
    a. Find the coordinates of points L, M, and N, the midpoints of the sides of $\triangle ABC$.
    b. Find equations of $\overleftrightarrow{AM}$, $\overleftrightarrow{BN}$, and $\overleftrightarrow{CL}$.
    c. Find the coordinates of point P, the intersection of $\overleftrightarrow{AM}$ and $\overleftrightarrow{BN}$.
    d. Show that point P is on $\overleftrightarrow{CL}$.
    e. Use the Distance Formula to show that point P is two thirds the distance from each vertex to the midpoint of the opposite side.

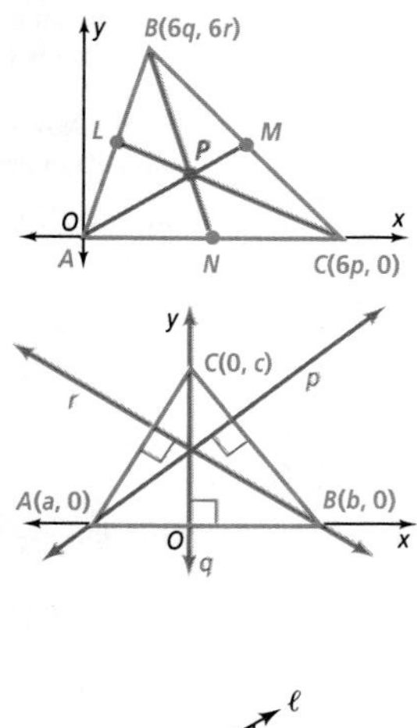

26. Complete the steps to prove Theorem 5-9. You are given $\triangle ABC$ with altitudes p, q, and r. Show that p, q, and r intersect at a point (called the orthocenter of the triangle).
    a. The slope of $\overline{BC}$ is $\frac{c}{-b}$. What is the slope of line p?
    b. Show that the equation of line p is $y = \frac{b}{c}(x - a)$.
    c. What is the equation of line q?
    d. Show that lines p and q intersect at $\left(0, \frac{-ab}{c}\right)$.
    e. The slope of $\overline{AC}$ is $\frac{c}{-a}$. What is the slope of line r?
    f. Show that the equation of line r is $y = \frac{a}{c}(x - b)$.
    g. Show that lines r and q intersect at $\left(0, \frac{-ab}{c}\right)$.
    h. What are the coordinates of the orthocenter of $\triangle ABC$?

Challenge

27. **Multiple Representations** Use the diagram at the right.
    a. Explain using area why $\frac{1}{2}ad = \frac{1}{2}bc$ and therefore $ad = bc$.
    b. Find two ratios for the slope of ℓ. Use these two ratios to show that $ad = bc$.

4 Practice

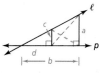

ASSIGNMENT GUIDE

Basic: 4–5, 6–20 even, 21, 22
Average: 4–26
Advanced: 4–28
Standardized Test Prep: 29–32
Mixed Review: 33–40

Reasoning exercises have blue headings.
Applications exercises have red headings.

EXERCISE 22: Use the Think About a Plan worksheet in the **Practice and Problem Solving Workbook** (also available in the Teaching Resources in print and online) to further support students' development in becoming independent learners.

HOMEWORK QUICK CHECK

To check students' understanding of key skills and concepts, go over Exercises 5, 8, 20, 21, and 22.

ANSWER The midpoints of ABC are $D(a, \sqrt{3}a)$, $E(3a, \sqrt{3}a)$, and $F(2a, 0)$. By the Distance Formula, $DE = 2a$, $EF = 2a$, and $DF = 2a$. Since the sides of DEF are all the same length, it is an equilateral triangle.

Answers

Lesson Check

1a.

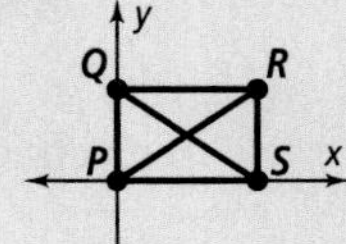

b. $(0, b)$, (a, b), and $(a, 0)$

c. Given: Rectangle $PQRS$
Prove: $\overline{PR} \cong \overline{SQ}$

d. Answers may vary. Sample: By the Distance Formula, $PR = \sqrt{(0-a)^2 + (0-b)^2} = \sqrt{a^2 + b^2}$ and $SQ = \sqrt{(0-a)^2 + (b-0)^2} = \sqrt{a^2 + b^2}$. So $\overline{PR} \cong \overline{SQ}$.

2. Answers may vary. Sample: Place the vertices on the x- and y-axes so that the axes are the diagonals of the rhombus.

3. Your classmate assumes $PQRO$ is an isosc. trapezoid.

Practice and Problem-Solving Exercises

4a. $\sqrt{(b+a)^2 + c^2}$

b. $\sqrt{(a+b)^2 + c^2}$

c. The Distance Formula shows that $\overline{EG}$ and $\overline{FH}$ are the same length.

5a. $M(-a, b)$, $N(a, b)$

b. $PN = \sqrt{9a^2 + b^2}$, $RM = \sqrt{9a^2 + b^2}$

c. The Distance Formula shows that $\overline{PN}$ and $\overline{RM}$ are the same length.

6. Yes; use Distance Formula.

7. Yes; use Slope Formula.

8. Yes; use Slope Formula and property of $\perp$ lines.

9. Yes; use Midpoint Formula.

10. Yes; show two points on $\overline{AB}$ equidistant from the sides of $\angle CAD$.

11. No; you need $\angle$ measures.

12. Yes; use Slope Formula and property of $\perp$ lines.

13. Yes; use Distance Formula.

14. Yes; answers may vary. Sample: Show two sides $\cong$.

15. Yes; answers may vary. Sample: Show four sides have the same length or show diagonals $\perp$.

16. Yes; show they have same midpt.

17. No; you need $\angle$ measures.

18. Yes; find intersection point of segments.

19–27. See back of book.

Answers

Practice and Problem-Solving Exercises (continued)

28a. $(a, 0)$

b. $D(-b, 0)$, $B(-b, a)$

c. By the Slope Formula, the slope of ℓ_1 is $\frac{b}{a}$ and the slope of ℓ_2 is $\frac{a}{-b}$. So the product of the slopes is $\left(\frac{b}{a}\right)\left(\frac{a}{-b}\right) = \frac{ab}{-ab} = -1$.

29. 50

30. 10

31. 19

32. 15

33. $(a, -b)$

34. Answers may vary. Sample: $\angle A \cong \angle C$, $\angle ADB \cong \angle CDB$, and $\overline{AD} \cong \overline{CD}$ (Given), so $\triangle ABD \cong \triangle CBD$ by ASA. Then $\overline{AB} \cong \overline{CB}$ because corresp. parts of ≅ ▵ are ≅.

35. Answers may vary. Sample: $\overline{HE} \cong \overline{FG}$, $\overline{EF} \cong \overline{GH}$, (Given) and $\overline{HF} \cong \overline{HF}$ (Refl. Prop. of ≅), so $\triangle HEF \cong \triangle FGH$ by SSS. Then $\angle 1 \cong \angle 2$ because corresp. parts of ≅ ▵ are ≅.

36. $\overline{KN} \cong \overline{ML}$ (Given), $\angle KNL \cong \angle MLN$ (All rt. ▵ are ≅.), and $\overline{NL} \cong \overline{NL}$ (Refl. Prop. of ≅). Then $\triangle KNL \cong \triangle MLN$ by SAS, and $\angle K \cong \angle M$ because corresp. parts of ≅ ▵ are ≅.

37. 12, −12

38. 8, −8

39. 5, −5

40. 16.6, −16.6

28. Prove: If two lines are perpendicular, the product of their slopes is −1.

Proof **a.** Two nonvertical lines, ℓ_1 and ℓ_2, intersect as shown at the right. Find the coordinates of C.

b. Choose coordinates for D and B. (*Hint:* Find the relationship between ∠1, ∠2, and ∠3. Then use congruent triangles.)

c. Complete the proof that the product of slopes is −1.

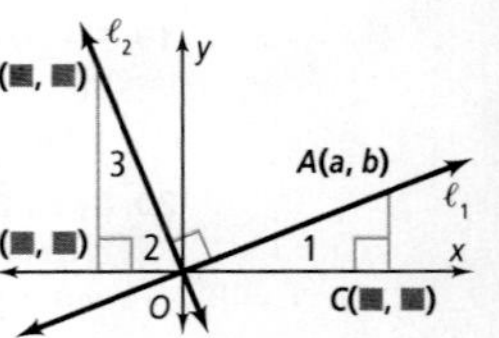

Standardized Test Prep

GRIDDED RESPONSE

SAT/ACT

29. The endpoint of a segment is (27, −3). The midpoint is (3, 4). What is the length of the segment?

30. In the diagram of △POR at the right, $PO = 16$ and $OR = 12$. What is OM?

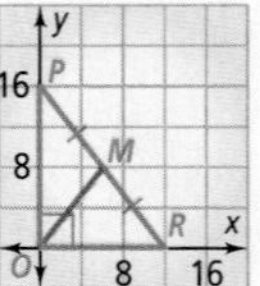

31. ▱FGHI has sides with lengths $FG = 2x + 5$, $GH = x + 7$, $HI = 3x - 2$, and $FI = 2x$. What is the length of the longer sides of ▱FGHI?

32. In △ABC, $m\angle A = 55$. If $m\angle C$ is twice $m\angle A$, what is $m\angle B$?

Mixed Review

33. A rectangle $ABCD$ is centered at the origin with $A(-a, b)$. Without using any new variables, what are the coordinates of point C?

See Lesson 6-8.

Explain how you can use SSS, SAS, ASA, or AAS with corresponding parts of congruent triangles to prove each statement true.

See Lessons 4-2, 4-3, and 4-4.

34. $\overline{AB} \cong \overline{CB}$

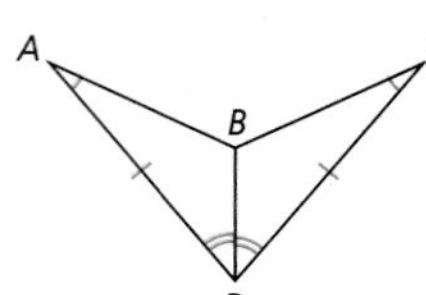

35. ∠1 ≅ ∠2

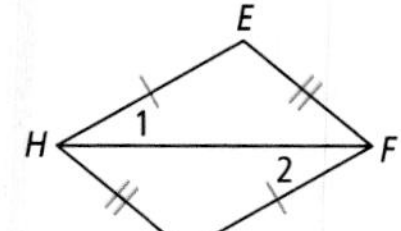

36. ∠K = ∠M

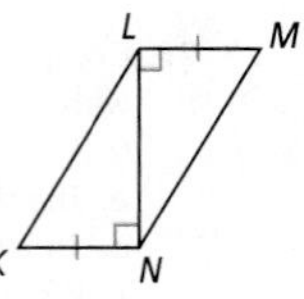

Get Ready! **To prepare for Lesson 7-1, do Exercises 37–40.**

Algebra Solve. Round to the nearest tenth if necessary.

See p. 827.

37. $x^2 = 144$

38. $r^2 - 3 = 61$

39. $y^2 + 10 = 35$

40. $7^2 + k^2 = 18^2$

6-9 Lesson Resources

Differentiated Remediation

Instructional Support

Geometry Companion

Students can use the **Geometry Companion** worktext (4 pages) . . .

- New Vocabulary
- Key Concepts
- Got It for each Problem
- Lesson Check

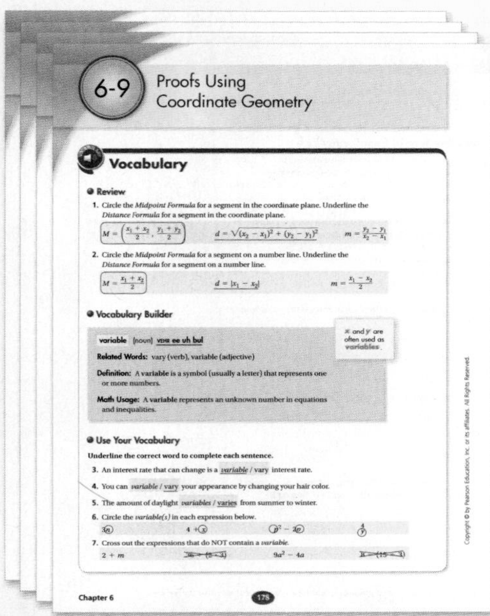

6-9 Proofs Using Coordinate Geometry

Vocabulary

Review

1. Circle the *Midpoint Formula* for a segment in the coordinate plane. Underline the *Distance Formula* for a segment in the coordinate plane.

$M = \left(\frac{x_1 + x_2}{2}, \frac{y_1 + y_2}{2}\right)$ $d = \sqrt{(x_2 - x_1)^2 + (y_2 - y_1)^2}$ $m = \frac{y_2 - y_1}{x_2 - x_1}$

2. Circle the *Midpoint Formula* for a segment on a number line. Underline the *Distance Formula* for a segment on a number line.

$M = \frac{x_1 + x_2}{2}$ $d = |x_1 - x_2|$ $m = \frac{x_1 - x_2}{2}$

Vocabulary Builder

variable (noun) VEHR ee uh bul

Related Words: vary (verb), variable (adjective)

Definition: A variable is a symbol (usually a letter) that represents one or more numbers.

Math Usage: A variable represents an unknown number in equations and inequalities.

x and *y* are often used as variables.

Use Your Vocabulary

Underline the correct word to complete each sentence.

3. An interest rate that can change is a *variable* / vary interest rate.
4. You can *variable* / vary your appearance by changing your hair color.
5. The amount of daylight *variables* / varies from summer to winter.
6. Circle the *variable(s)* in each expression below.

$3n$ $4 + x$ $p^2 - 2p$ $\frac{4}{y}$

7. Cross out the expressions that do NOT contain a *variable*.

$2 + m$ $9a^2 - 4a$

Copyright © by Pearson Education, Inc. or its affiliates. All Rights Reserved.

Chapter 6 178

ELL Support

Connect to Prior Knowledge Use the plans for the coordinate proofs created by students in the last lesson for practice writing coordinate proofs.

Focus on Communication Place students in heterogeneous groups. Have students write the theorems from each lesson on one side of an index card. Students discuss the theorems and then write a summary on the reverse side of the card. Encourage students to engage in discussion using questions. For example: What does this mean? How would you use that theorem? How are these two theorems related? Students can share the results of their discussions, particularly what they learned from each other. The cards can then be used for review.

5 Assess & Remediate

Lesson Quiz

1. Write a coordinate proof to show that the midpoints of the sides of an isos. rt. △ form another isos. rt. △.

Given: *ABC* is an isosceles right triangle with coordinates *A*(0, 0), *B*(0, 2*a*), *C*(2*a*, 0)

Prove: *LMN* is an isosceles right triangle.

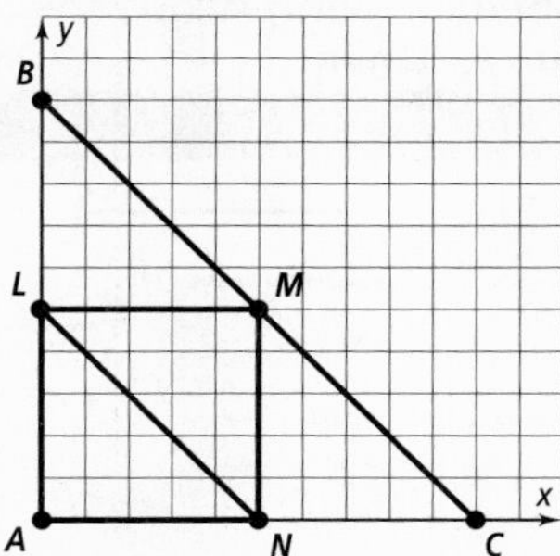

2. **Do you UNDERSTAND?** Why should you use variables as coordinates when writing a coordinate proof?

ANSWERS TO LESSON QUIZ

1. The midpoints of *ABC* are *L*(0, *a*), *M*(*a*, *a*), and *N*(*a*, 0). By the Distance Formula, $LM = a$, $MN = a$, and $LN = a\sqrt{2}$. So, △*LMN* is isosceles since two of its sides are congruent. Since $\overline{LM}$ is horizontal and $\overline{MN}$ is vertical, they are ⊥ and form a right angle. So, *LMN* is an isos. rt. △.
2. You want to show that the relationships you demonstrate are true for any values of the variables.

PRESCRIPTION FOR REMEDIATION

Use the student work on the Lesson Quiz to prescribe a differentiated review assignment.

Points	Differentiated Remediation
0	Intervention
1	On-level
2	Extension

PowerGeometry.com

5 Assess & Remediate

Assign the Lesson Quiz. Appropriate intervention, practice, or enrichment is automatically generated based on student performance.

Intervention

- **Reteaching** (2 pages) Provides reteaching and practice exercises for the key lesson concepts. Use with struggling students or absent students.
- **English Language Learner Support** Helps students develop and reinforce mathematical vocabulary and key concepts.

All-in-One Resources/Online

Reteaching

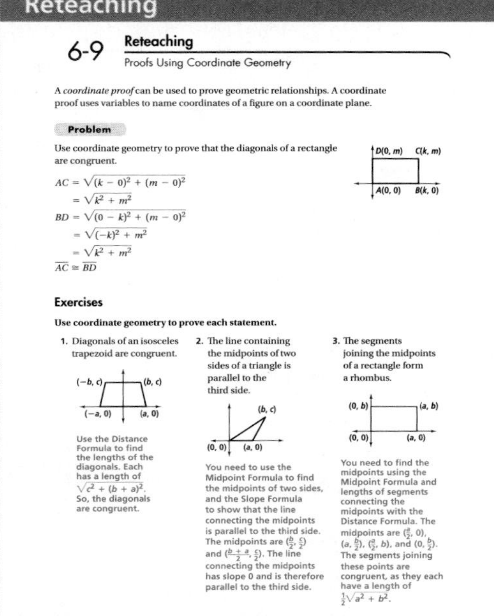

6-9 Reteaching

Proofs Using Coordinate Geometry

A *coordinate proof* can be used to prove geometric relationships. A coordinate proof uses variables to name coordinates of a figure on a coordinate plane.

Problem

Use coordinate geometry to prove that the diagonals of a rectangle are congruent.

D(0, m) C(k, m) A(0, 0) B(k, 0)

$AC = \sqrt{(k - 0)^2 + (m - 0)^2}$
$= \sqrt{k^2 + m^2}$
$BD = \sqrt{(0 - k)^2 + (m - 0)^2}$
$= \sqrt{(-k)^2 + m^2}$
$= \sqrt{k^2 + m^2}$
$\overline{AC} \cong \overline{BD}$

Exercises

Use coordinate geometry to prove each statement.

1. Diagonals of an isosceles trapezoid are congruent.

(−b, c) (b, c) (−a, 0) (a, 0)

Use the Distance Formula to find the lengths of the diagonals. Each has a length of $\sqrt{c^2 + (b + a)^2}$. So, the diagonals are congruent.

2. The line containing the midpoints of two sides of a triangle is parallel to the third side.

(b, c) (0, 0) (a, 0)

You need to use the Midpoint Formula to find the midpoints of two sides, and the Slope Formula to show that the line connecting the midpoints is parallel to the third side. The midpoints are $(\frac{b}{2}, \frac{c}{2})$ and $(\frac{b + a}{2}, \frac{c}{2})$. The line connecting the midpoints has slope 0 and is therefore parallel to the third side.

3. The segments joining the midpoints of a rectangle form a rhombus.

(0, b) (a, b) (0, 0) (a, 0)

You need to find the midpoints using the Midpoint Formula and lengths of segments connecting the midpoints with the Distance Formula. The midpoints are $(\frac{a}{2}, 0)$, $(a, \frac{b}{2})$, $(\frac{a}{2}, b)$, and $(0, \frac{b}{2})$. The segments joining these points are congruent, as they each have a length of $\frac{1}{2}\sqrt{a^2 + b^2}$.

All-in-One Resources/Online

English Language Learner Support

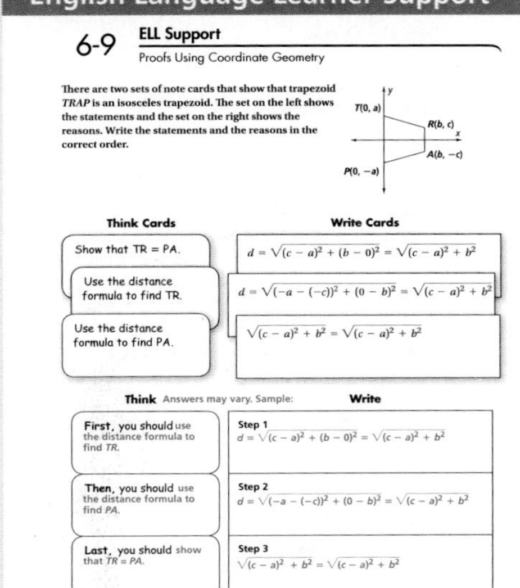

6-9 ELL Support

Proofs Using Coordinate Geometry

There are two sets of note cards that show that trapezoid *TRAP* is an isosceles trapezoid. The set on the left shows the statements and the set on the right shows the reasons. Write the statements and the reasons in the correct order.

T(0, a) R(b, c) A(b, −c) P(0, −a)

Think Cards	Write Cards
Show that TR = PA.	$d = \sqrt{(c - a)^2 + (b - 0)^2} = \sqrt{(c - a)^2 + b^2}$
Use the distance formula to find TR.	$d = \sqrt{(-a - (-c))^2 + (0 - b)^2} = \sqrt{(c - a)^2 + b^2}$
Use the distance formula to find PA.	$\sqrt{(c - a)^2 + b^2} = \sqrt{(c - a)^2 + b^2}$

Think (Answers may vary. Sample:)	Write
First, you should use the distance formula to find *TR*.	Step 1 $d = \sqrt{(c - a)^2 + (b - 0)^2} = \sqrt{(c - a)^2 + b^2}$
Then, you should use the distance formula to find *PA*.	Step 2 $d = \sqrt{(-a - (-c))^2 + (0 - b)^2} = \sqrt{(c - a)^2 + b^2}$
Last, you should show that *TR* = *PA*.	Step 3 $\sqrt{(c - a)^2 + b^2} = \sqrt{(c - a)^2 + b^2}$

Differentiated Remediation *continued*

On-Level

- **Practice** (2 pages) Provides extra practice for each lesson. For simpler practice exercises, use the Form K Practice pages found in the All-in-One Teaching Resources and online.
- **Think About a Plan** Helps students develop specific problem-solving skills and strategies by providing scaffolded guiding questions.
- **Standardized Test Prep** Focuses on all major exercises, all major question types, and helps students prepare for the high-stakes assessments.

Practice and Problem Solving Wkbk/ All-in-One Resources/Online

Practice page 1

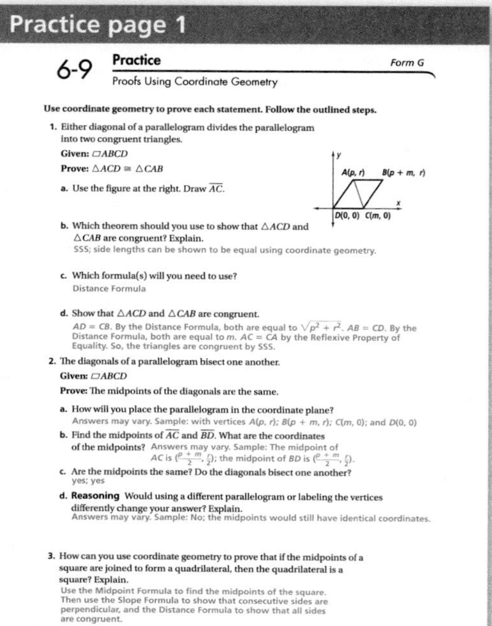

6-9 **Practice** *Form G*
Proofs Using Coordinate Geometry

Use coordinate geometry to prove each statement. Follow the outlined steps.

1. Either diagonal of a parallelogram divides the parallelogram into two congruent triangles.
   Given: ▱$ABCD$
   Prove: $\triangle ACD \cong \triangle CAB$
   a. Use the figure at the right. Draw $\overline{AC}$.
   b. Which theorem should you use to show that $\triangle ACD$ and $\triangle CAB$ are congruent? Explain.
   SSS; side lengths can be shown to be equal using coordinate geometry.
   c. Which formula(s) will you need to use?
   Distance Formula
   d. Show that $\triangle ACD$ and $\triangle CAB$ are congruent.
   $AD = CB$. By the Distance Formula, both are equal to $\sqrt{p^2 + r^2}$. $AB = CD$. By the Distance Formula, both are equal to m. $AC = CA$ by the Reflexive Property of Equality. So, the triangles are congruent by SSS.

2. The diagonals of a parallelogram bisect one another.
   Given: ▱$ABCD$
   Prove: The midpoints of the diagonals are the same.
   a. How will you place the parallelogram in the coordinate plane?
   Answers may vary. Sample: with vertices $A(p, r)$; $B(p + m, r)$; $C(m, 0)$; and $D(0, 0)$
   b. Find the midpoints of $\overline{AC}$ and $\overline{BD}$. What are the coordinates of the midpoints? Answers may vary. Sample: The midpoint of AC is $(\frac{p+m}{2}, \frac{r}{2})$; the midpoint of BD is $(\frac{p+m}{2}, \frac{r}{2})$.
   c. Are the midpoints the same? Do the diagonals bisect one another?
   yes; yes
   d. **Reasoning** Would using a different parallelogram or labeling the vertices differently change your answer? Explain.
   Answers may vary. Sample: No; the midpoints would still have identical coordinates.
3. How can you use coordinate geometry to prove that if the midpoints of a square are joined to form a quadrilateral, then the quadrilateral is a square? Explain.
   Use the Midpoint Formula to find the midpoints of the square. Then use the Slope Formula to show that consecutive sides are perpendicular, and the Distance Formula to show that all sides are congruent.

Practice and Problem Solving Wkbk/ All-in-One Resources/Online

Practice page 2

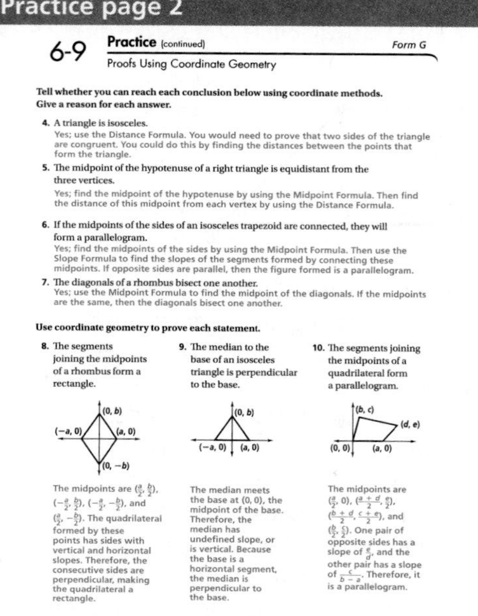

6-9 **Practice** (continued) *Form G*
Proofs Using Coordinate Geometry

Tell whether you can reach each conclusion below using coordinate methods. Give a reason for each answer.

4. A triangle is isosceles.
   Yes; use the Distance Formula. You would need to prove that two sides of the triangle are congruent. You could do this by finding the distances between the points that form the triangle.
5. The midpoint of the hypotenuse of a right triangle is equidistant from the three vertices.
   Yes; find the midpoint of the hypotenuse by using the Midpoint Formula. Then find the distance of this midpoint from each vertex by using the Distance Formula.
6. If the midpoints of the sides of an isosceles trapezoid are connected, they will form a parallelogram.
   Yes; find the midpoints of the sides by using the Midpoint Formula. Then use the Slope Formula to find the slopes of the segments formed by connecting these midpoints. If opposite sides are parallel, then the figure formed is a parallelogram.
7. The diagonals of a rhombus bisect one another.
   Yes; use the Midpoint Formula to find the midpoint of the diagonals. If the midpoints are the same, then the diagonals bisect one another.

Use coordinate geometry to prove each statement.

8. The segments joining the midpoints of a rhombus form a rectangle.
   The midpoints are $(\frac{a}{2}, \frac{b}{2})$, $(-\frac{a}{2}, \frac{b}{2})$, $(-\frac{a}{2}, -\frac{b}{2})$, and $(\frac{a}{2}, -\frac{b}{2})$. The quadrilateral formed by these points has sides with vertical and horizontal slopes. Therefore, the consecutive sides are perpendicular, making the quadrilateral a rectangle.
9. The median to the base of an isosceles triangle is perpendicular to the base.
   The median meets the base at (0, 0), the midpoint of the base. Therefore, the median has undefined slope, or is vertical. Because the base is a horizontal segment, the median is perpendicular to the base.
10. The segments joining the midpoints of a quadrilateral form a parallelogram.
   The midpoints are $(\frac{a}{2}, 0)$, $(\frac{a+d}{2}, \frac{e}{2})$, $(\frac{b+d}{2}, \frac{c+e}{2})$, and $(\frac{b}{2}, \frac{c}{2})$. One pair of opposite sides has a slope of $\frac{e}{d}$, and the other pair has a slope of $\frac{c}{b-a}$. Therefore, it is a parallelogram.

Extension

- **Enrichment** Provides students with interesting problems and activities that extend the concepts of the lesson.
- **Activities, Games, and Puzzles** Worksheets that can be used for concepts development, enrichment, and for fun!

All-in-One Resources/Online

Enrichment

6-9 **Enrichment**
Proofs Using Coordinate Geometry

Another Type of Coordinate Plane

Another way to position a point in a plane is to use *polar coordinates.* A polar coordinate consists of two values separated by a semicolon, the *polar distance* and the *polar angle.* For example, $A(4; 45°)$ represents a point with a distance of 4 units from the origin or pole and a 45° angle measure from the positive x-axis. This point is graphed to the right on a polar graph. It is customary to measure angles counterclockwise from the positive x-axis. However, if the given angle measure is negative, then the angle is measured clockwise from the positive x-axis. For example, $B(2; -120°)$ would be graphed as shown on the diagram at the right.

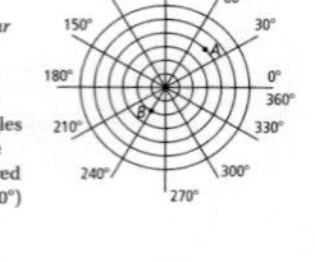

Graph and label the following points on the polar graph provided at the right.

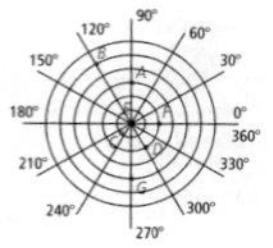

1. $A(3; 90°)$
2. $B(5; 120°)$
3. $C(1; 225°)$
4. $D(2; -60°)$
5. $E(0; 330°)$
6. $F(2; 360°)$
7. $G(4; -90°)$

Use the polar graph at the right, and provide the polar coordinate for the indicated point on the graph.

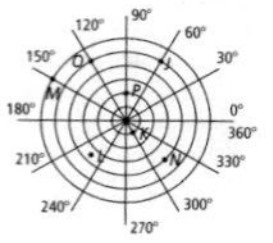

8. J (5; 60°)
9. K (1; 300°)
10. L (3.5; 225°)
11. M (6; 150°)
12. N (4; 315°)
13. O (5; 120°)
14. P (2; 90°)

Graph each figure on a polar graph and provide coordinates for its vertices.
Check students' drawings.

15. isosceles triangle Answers may vary. Sample: (2; 0°), (3; 120°), (3; 240°)
16. rectangle Answers may vary. Sample: (2; 30°), (2; 150°), (2; 210°), (2; 330°)
17. trapezoid Answers may vary. Sample: (2; 30°), (3; 120°), (3; 240°), (2; 330°)

Practice and Problem Solving Wkbk/ All-in-One Resources/Online

Think About a Plan

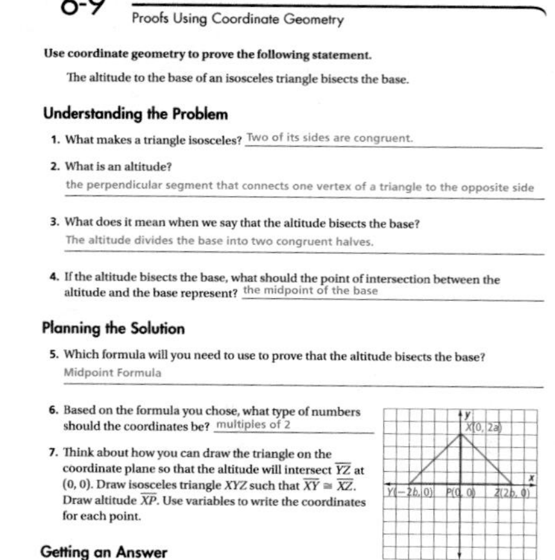

6-9 **Think About a Plan**
Proofs Using Coordinate Geometry

Use coordinate geometry to prove the following statement.

The altitude to the base of an isosceles triangle bisects the base.

Understanding the Problem

1. What makes a triangle isosceles? Two of its sides are congruent.
2. What is an altitude?
   the perpendicular segment that connects one vertex of a triangle to the opposite side
3. What does it mean when we say that the altitude bisects the base?
   The altitude divides the base into two congruent halves.
4. If the altitude bisects the base, what should the point of intersection between the altitude and the base represent? the midpoint of the base

Planning the Solution

5. Which formula will you need to use to prove that the altitude bisects the base?
   Midpoint Formula
6. Based on the formula you chose, what type of numbers should the coordinates be? multiples of 2
7. Think about how you can draw the triangle on the coordinate plane so that the altitude will intersect $\overline{YZ}$ at (0, 0). Draw isosceles triangle XYZ such that $\overline{XY} \cong \overline{XZ}$. Draw altitude $\overline{XP}$. Use variables to write the coordinates for each point.

Getting an Answer

8. Use the Midpoint Formula to find the midpoint of $\overline{YZ}$.
   $M = \left(\frac{? + ?}{2}, \frac{? + ?}{2}\right)$ $(\frac{-2b + 2b}{2}, \frac{0 + 0}{2}) = (0, 0)$
9. Does the altitude to the base of an isosceles triangle bisect the base? Explain.
   Yes; the coordinates of the midpoint of the base are the same as the coordinates of the intersection of the altitude and the base.

Practice and Problem Solving Wkbk/ All-in-One Resources/Online

Standardized Test Prep

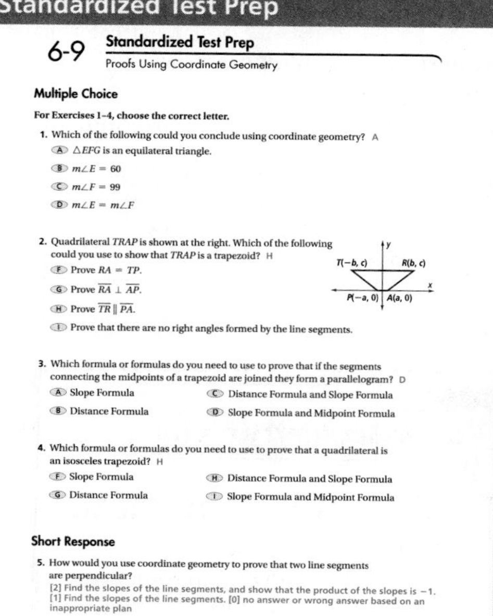

6-9 **Standardized Test Prep**
Proofs Using Coordinate Geometry

Multiple Choice

For Exercises 1–4, choose the correct letter.

1. Which of the following could you conclude using coordinate geometry? A
   A. $\triangle EFG$ is an equilateral triangle.
   B. $m\angle E = 60$
   C. $m\angle F = 99$
   D. $m\angle E = m\angle F$
2. Quadrilateral $TRAP$ is shown at the right. Which of the following could you use to show that $TRAP$ is a trapezoid? H
   F. Prove $RA = TP$.
   G. Prove $\overline{RA} \perp \overline{AP}$.
   H. Prove $\overline{TR} \parallel \overline{PA}$.
   I. Prove that there are no right angles formed by the line segments.

3. Which formula or formulas do you need to use to prove that if the segments connecting the midpoints of a trapezoid are joined they form a parallelogram? D
   A. Slope Formula
   B. Distance Formula
   C. Distance Formula and Slope Formula
   D. Slope Formula and Midpoint Formula
4. Which formula or formulas do you need to use to prove that a quadrilateral is an isosceles trapezoid? H
   F. Slope Formula
   G. Distance Formula
   H. Distance Formula and Slope Formula
   I. Slope Formula and Midpoint Formula

Short Response

5. How would you use coordinate geometry to prove that two line segments are perpendicular?
   [2] Find the slopes of the line segments, and show that the product of the slopes is −1. [1] Find the slopes of the line segments. [0] no answer or wrong answer based on an inappropriate plan

Online Teacher Resource Center

Activities, Games, and Puzzles

6-9 **Activity: Round-Robin Proofs**
Proofs Using Coordinate Geometry

For each proof, one member of your group should start by completing the first step. Then, he or she should pass the proof to another member of the group. The second member should check the first step and complete the second step before passing the proof to the third member, and so on until the proof is complete. Teammates may help each other, but you must do the writing on your turn.

a. Draw and label a diagram.
b. Write the Given and Prove statements.
c. State the formulas and what they should be used to show.
d. Apply the formulas and draw a valid conclusion.

Answers may vary. See samples below.

1. The diagonals of a rectangle are congruent.
   a. Diagram: R(0,b), E(a,b), T(0,0), C(a,0)
   b. Given: Rectangle $RECT$
   Prove: $\overline{RC} \cong \overline{ET}$
   c. Formulas and plan:
   Use the distance formula to show that $\overline{RC} \cong \overline{ET}$; $d = \sqrt{(x_2 - x_1)^2 + (y_1 - y_2)^2}$
   d. Work and conclusion:
   $RC = \sqrt{(a - 0)^2 + (0 - b)^2} = \sqrt{a^2 + b^2}$
   $TE = \sqrt{(a - 0)^2 + (b - 0)^2} = \sqrt{a^2 + b^2}$
   $\overline{RC} \cong \overline{ET}$
2. The diagonals of a square are perpendicular.
   a. Diagram: R(0,a), U(a,a), S(0,0), Q(a,0)
   b. Given: Square $SRUQ$
   Prove: $\overline{SU} \perp \overline{RQ}$
   c. Formulas and plan:
   Use the slope formula to show that the product of the slopes of $\overline{SU}$ and $\overline{RQ}$ is −1; $m = \frac{y_2 - y_1}{x_2 - x_1}$
   d. Work and conclusion:
   $m_{\overline{SU}} = \frac{a - 0}{a - 0} = 1$; $m_{\overline{RQ}} = \frac{0 - a}{a - 0} = -1$;
   $m_{\overline{SU}} \cdot m_{\overline{RQ}} = 1 \cdot (-1) = -1$ so $\overline{SU} \perp \overline{RQ}$
3. The diagonals of a parallelogram bisect each other.
   a. Diagram: L(2b − 2a,2c), R(2b,2c), P(0,0), A(2a,0)
   b. Given: Parallelogram $PLRA$
   Prove: $\overline{PR}$ bisects $\overline{AL}$ and $\overline{AL}$ bisects $\overline{PR}$.
   c. Formulas and plan:
   Use the midpoint formula to show that the midpoints of $\overline{PR}$ and $\overline{AL}$ have the same coordinates; $M = \left(\frac{x_1 + x_2}{2}, \frac{y_1 + y_2}{2}\right)$
   d. Work and conclusion:
   $M_{\overline{PR}} = \left(\frac{0 + 2b}{2}, \frac{0 + 2c}{2}\right) = (b, c)$; $M_{\overline{AL}} = \left(\frac{2a + (2b - 2a)}{2}, \frac{0 + 2c}{2}\right) = (b, c)$; The midpoint of $\overline{PR}$ and the midpoint of $\overline{AL}$ are the same point, so $\overline{PR}$ bisects $\overline{AL}$ and $\overline{AL}$ bisects $\overline{PR}$.

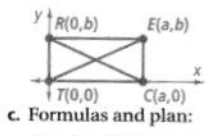

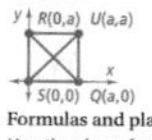

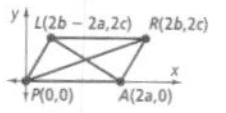

Pull It All Together

To solve these problems you will pull together many concepts and skills that you have learned about polygons.

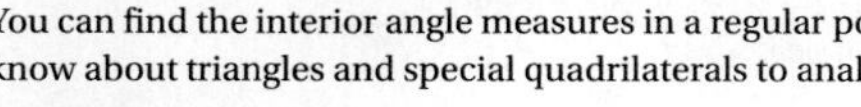

BIG idea Measurement and Reasoning and Proof

You can find the interior angle measures in a regular polygon and then use what you know about triangles and special quadrilaterals to analyze complex figures.

Task 1

ABCDEF is a regular hexagon. What is the most precise classification of quadrilateral *GBHE*? How do you know? What are the interior angle measures of *GBHE*?

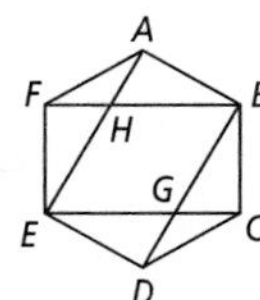

Task 2

JKLM is a parallelogram. If you extend each side by a distance *x*, what kind of quadrilateral is *PQRS*? How do you know?

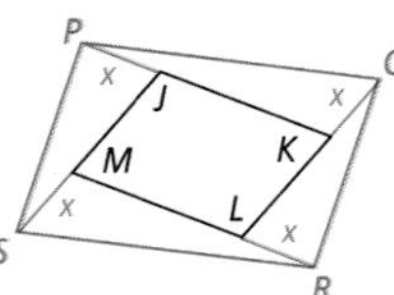

BIG idea Coordinate Geometry and Reasoning and Proof

You can use coordinates and certain relationships between pairs of corresponding parts to prove triangles congruent in the coordinate plane.

Task 3

What are two methods for proving the two triangles congruent? Use one of your methods along with coordinate geometry to prove that the two triangles are congruent.

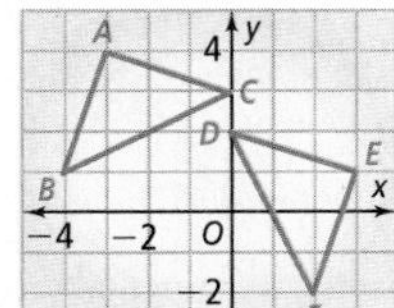

Performance Task

Pull It All Together

The concepts and skills required to solve these problems are from several lessons within this chapter and from the previous chapter. As students solve these problems, they will demonstrate their reasoning strategies and their growth as independent problem solvers.

The following questions are designed to:

- Help support students as they do the Tasks.
- Gauge the amount of support students need as they become independent problem solvers.

Task 1

- How can you prove sides of the quadrilateral congruent?
- How can you find the angle measures of the quadrilateral?

Task 2

- What sides of the inner quadrilateral are congruent?
- What is the length of each extended side?
- What triangles can you use to prove congruent sides?

Task 3

- What are the coordinates of each vertex?
- Which sides correspond to one another?
- Which formulas from coordinate geometry can you use to prove the triangles congruent?

Assess Performance

Pull It All Together

See p. 69 for a holistic scoring rubric to gauge a student's progress on Understanding the Problem, Planning a Solution, Getting an Answer, and Assessing Autonomy.

SOLUTION OUTLINES

1. *GBHE* is a rhombus. $m\angle G = m\angle H = 120$, and $m\angle HBG = m\angle GEH = 60$. Possible plan to explain how you know the classification of *GBHE*: Since *ABCDEF* is regular, all of its sides are ≅ and all of its ⦣ are ≅. So $\triangle EFA$, $\triangle BAF$, $\triangle BCD$, and $\triangle EDC$ are ≅ isosc. ⦣ by SAS and def. of isosc. △. $\overline{FB} \cong \overline{BD} \cong \overline{CE} \cong \overline{EA}$ and $\angle FAE \cong \angle AFB \cong \angle ECD \cong \angle BDC$ so $\triangle HFA \cong \triangle GCD$ by ASA. $\triangle HFA$ and $\triangle GCD$ are isosc. by the Converse of the Isosc. △ Thm. $\overline{HA} \cong \overline{HF} \cong \overline{GC} \cong \overline{GD}$ since the ⦣ are ≅ and isosc. By subtraction, you can show that $HB = BG = GE = EH$. Since opp. sides are ≅, *GBHE* is a ▱. Because all sides are ≅ and it is a ▱, *GBHE* is a rhombus.
2. *PQRS* is a parallelogram. Possible plan to explain how you know: Consider $\triangle PJS$ and $\triangle RLQ$. Each △ includes ⦣ that are suppl. to ≅ ⦣ of ▱*JKLM*, sides of length *x*, and sides of equal length + *x*. So $\triangle PJS \cong \triangle RLQ$ by SAS. So $\overline{PS} \cong \overline{RQ}$. Similarly, $\overline{PQ} \cong \overline{RS}$. Since opp. sides are ≅, *PQRS* is a ▱.
3. SSS or SAS; plan for proof by SAS: Using the Distance Formula, show that $AB = AC = DE = EF = \sqrt{10}$. Show that the product of the slopes of $\overline{AC}$ and $\overline{AB}$ and $\overline{ED}$ and $\overline{EF}$ equal -1, so that $m\angle CAB = m\angle FED = 90$, so the ⦣ are ≅.

Essential Questions 

BIG idea Measuring

ESSENTIAL QUESTION How can you find the sum of the measures of polygon angles?

ANSWER You can find the sum of the measures of any convex polygon using a formula based on the number of its sides.

BIG idea Reasoning and Proof

ESSENTIAL QUESTION How can you classify quadrilaterals?

ANSWER If you know certain information about the sides, angles, or diagonals of a quadrilateral, you can classify it.

BIG idea Coordinate Geometry

ESSENTIAL QUESTION How can you use coordinate geometry to prove general relationships?

ANSWER Coordinate proofs use variable coordinates to prove relationships in the coordinate plane.

6 Chapter Review

Connecting BIG ideas and Answering the Essential Questions

1 Measurement
You can find the sum of the interior angle measures of any polygon using a formula based on its number of sides.

Polygon Angle-Sum Theorems (Lesson 6-1)
Sum = $(n - 2)180$, where n is the number of sides

2 Reasoning and Proof
If you know certain information about the sides, angles, or diagonals of a quadrilateral, you can classify it.

Parallelograms (Lessons 6-2 and 6-3)

Trapezoids and Kites (Lesson 6-6)
Trapezoid
Kite

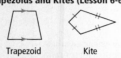

Special Parallelograms (Lessons 6-4 and 6-5)
Rhombus
Rectangle
Square

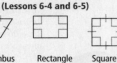

3 Coordinate Geometry
Coordinate proofs use variable coordinates to prove relationships in the coordinate plane.

Applying Coordinate Geometry (Lessons 6-7 and 6-8)
midpoint: $\left(\frac{x_1 + x_2}{2}, \frac{y_1 + y_2}{2}\right)$
distance: $\sqrt{(x_2 - x_1)^2 + (y_2 - y_1)^2}$
slope: $\frac{y_2 - y_1}{x_2 - x_1}$

Coordinate Proofs (Lesson 6-9)

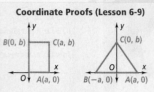

Chapter Vocabulary

- base, base angle, and leg of a trapezoid (p. 389)
- consecutive angles (p. 360)
- coordinate proof (p. 408)
- equiangular, equilateral polygon (p. 354)
- isosceles trapezoid (p. 389)
- kite (p. 392)
- midsegment of a trapezoid (p. 391)
- opposite angles (p. 359)
- opposite sides (p. 359)
- parallelogram (p. 359)
- rectangle (p. 375)
- regular polygon (p. 354)
- rhombus (p. 375)
- square (p. 375)
- trapezoid (p. 389)

Choose the vocabulary term that correctly completes the sentence.

1. A parallelogram with four congruent sides is a(n) __?__.
2. A polygon with all angles congruent is a(n) __?__.
3. Angles of a polygon that share a side are __?__.
4. A(n) __?__ is a quadrilateral with exactly one pair of parallel sides.

Summative Questions UbD

Use the following prompts as you review this chapter with your students. The prompts are designed to help you assess your students' understanding of the BIG Ideas they have studied.

- How can you form triangles inside other polygons? How does this relate to the formula for angle measures?
- What are the special types of parallelograms?
- What formulas can you use to help with coordinate proofs?

Answers

Chapter Review

1. rhombus
2. equiangular polygon
3. consecutive angles
4. trapezoid

6-1 The Polygon Angle-Sum Theorems

Quick Review

The sum of the measures of the interior angles of an n-gon is $(n - 2)180$. The measure of one interior angle of a regular n-gon is $\frac{(n-2)180}{n}$. The sum of the measures of the exterior angles of a polygon, one at each vertex, is 360.

Example

Find the measure of an interior angle of a regular 20-gon.

$$\text{Measure} = \frac{(n-2)180}{n}$$ Corollary to the Polygon Angle-Sum Theorem

$$= \frac{(20-2)180}{20}$$ Substitute.

$$= \frac{18 \cdot 180}{20}$$ Simplify.

$$= 162$$

The measure of an interior angle is 162.

Exercises

Find the measure of an interior angle and an exterior angle of each regular polygon.

5. hexagon **6.** 16-gon **7.** pentagon

8. What is the sum of the exterior angles for each polygon in Exercises 5–7?

Find the measure of the missing angle.

9.

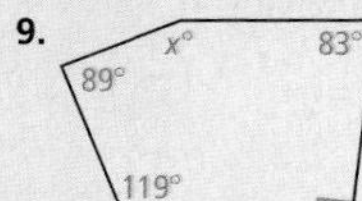

10.

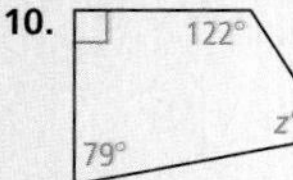

6-2 Properties of Parallelograms

Quick Review

Opposite sides and **opposite angles** of a **parallelogram** are congruent. **Consecutive angles** in a parallelogram are supplementary. The diagonals of a parallelogram bisect each other. If three (or more) parallel lines cut off congruent segments on one transversal, then they cut off congruent segments on every transversal.

Example

Find the measures of the numbered angles in the parallelogram.

Since consecutive angles are supplementary, $m\angle 1 = 180 - 56$, or 124. Since opposite angles are congruent, $m\angle 2 = 56$ and $m\angle 3 = 124$.

Exercises

Find the measures of the numbered angles for each parallelogram.

11.

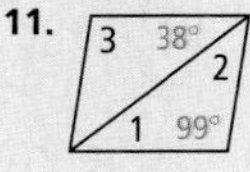

12.

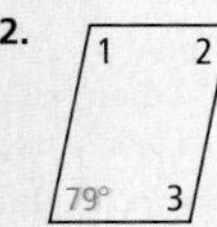

13.

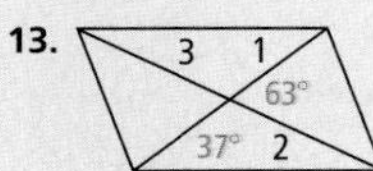

14.

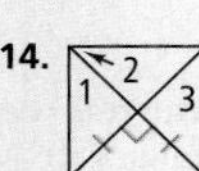

Find the values of x and y in $\square ABCD$.

15. $AB = 2y, BC = y + 3, CD = 5x - 1, DA = 2x + 4$

16. $AB = 2y + 1, BC = y + 1, CD = 7x - 3, DA = 3x$

5. 120, 60
6. 157.5, 22.5
7. 108, 72
8. 360, 360, 360
9. 159
10. 69
11. $m\angle 1 = 38, m\angle 2 = 43, m\angle 3 = 99$
12. $m\angle 1 = 101, m\angle 2 = 79, m\angle 3 = 101$
13. $m\angle 1 = 37, m\angle 2 = 26, m\angle 3 = 26$
14. $m\angle 1 = 45, m\angle 2 = 45, m\angle 3 = 45$
15. $x = 3, y = 7$
16. $x = 2, y = 5$

Answers

Chapter Review (continued)

17. no
18. yes
19. $x = 29, y = 28$
20. $x = 4, y = 5$
21. $m\angle 1 = 58, m\angle 2 = 32, m\angle 3 = 90$
22. $m\angle 1 = 124, m\angle 2 = 28, m\angle 3 = 62$
23. sometimes
24. always
25. sometimes
26. sometimes
27. sometimes
28. always

6-3 Proving That a Quadrilateral Is a Parallelogram

Quick Review

A quadrilateral is a parallelogram if any one of the following is true.

- Both pairs of opposite sides are parallel.
- Both pairs of opposite sides are congruent.
- Consecutive angles are supplementary.
- Both pairs of opposite angles are congruent.
- The diagonals bisect each other.
- One pair of opposite sides is both congruent and parallel.

Example

Must the quadrilateral be a parallelogram?

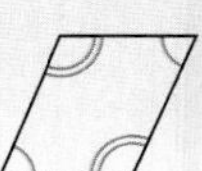

Yes, both pairs of opposite angles are congruent.

Exercises

Determine whether the quadrilateral must be a parallelogram.

17.

18.

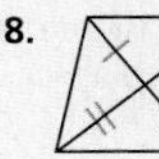

Algebra Find the values of the variables for which *ABCD* must be a parallelogram.

19.

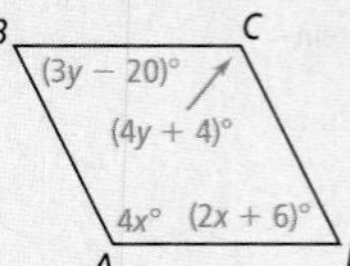

20.

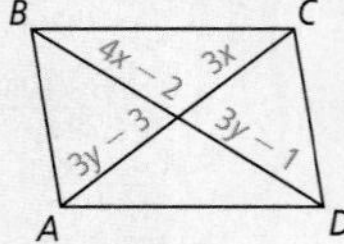

6-4 Properties of Rhombuses, Rectangles, and Squares

Quick Review

A **rhombus** is a parallelogram with four congruent sides.

A **rectangle** is a parallelogram with four right angles.

A **square** is a parallelogram with four congruent sides and four right angles.

The diagonals of a rhombus are perpendicular. Each diagonal bisects a pair of opposite angles.

The diagonals of a rectangle are congruent.

Example

What are the measures of the numbered angles in the rhombus?

$m\angle 1 = 60$	Each diagonal of a rhombus bisects a pair of opposite angles.
$m\angle 2 = 90$	The diagonals of a rhombus are $\perp$.
$60 + m\angle 2 + m\angle 3 = 180$	Triangle Angle-Sum Thm.
$60 + 90 + m\angle 3 = 180$	Substitute.
$m\angle 3 = 30$	Simplify.

Exercises

Find the measures of the numbered angles in each special parallelogram.

21.

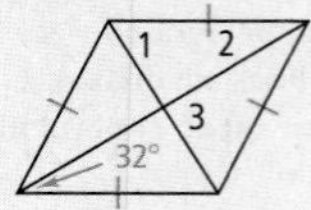

22.

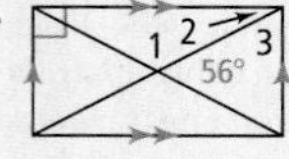

Determine whether each statement is *always, sometimes,* or *never* true.

23. A rhombus is a square.

24. A square is a rectangle.

25. A rhombus is a rectangle.

26. The diagonals of a parallelogram are perpendicular.

27. The diagonals of a parallelogram are congruent.

28. Opposite angles of a parallelogram are congruent.

6-5 Conditions for Rhombuses, Rectangles, and Squares

Quick Review

If one diagonal of a parallelogram bisects two angles of the parallelogram, then the parallelogram is a rhombus. If the diagonals of a parallelogram are perpendicular, then the parallelogram is a rhombus. If the diagonals of a parallelogram are congruent, then the parallelogram is a rectangle.

Example

Can you conclude that the parallelogram is a rhombus, rectangle, or square? Explain.

Yes, the diagonals are perpendicular, so the parallelogram is a rhombus.

Exercises

Can you conclude that the parallelogram is a rhombus, rectangle, or square? Explain.

29.

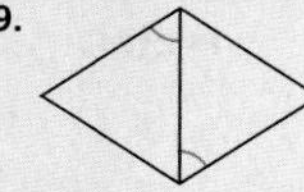

30.

For what value of x is the figure the given parallelogram? Justify your answer.

31. Rhombus

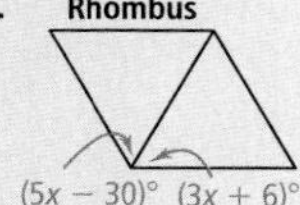

32. Rectangle

6-6 Trapezoids and Kites

Quick Review

The parallel sides of a **trapezoid** are its **bases** and the nonparallel sides are its **legs.** Two angles that share a base of a trapezoid are **base angles** of the trapezoid. The **midsegment of a trapezoid** joins the midpoints of its legs.

The base angles of an isosceles trapezoid are congruent. The diagonals of an isosceles trapezoid are congruent.

The diagonals of a kite are perpendicular.

Example

***ABCD* is an isosceles trapezoid. What is $m\angle C$?**

Since $\overline{BC} \parallel \overline{AD}$, $\angle C$ and $\angle D$ are same-side interior angles.

$m\angle C + m\angle D = 180$	Same-side interior angles are supplementary.
$m\angle C + 60 = 180$	Substitute.
$m\angle C = 120$	Subtract 60 from each side.

Exercises

Find the measures of the numbered angles in each isosceles trapezoid.

33.

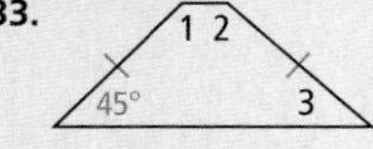

34.

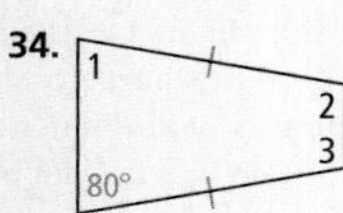

Find the measures of the numbered angles in each kite.

35.

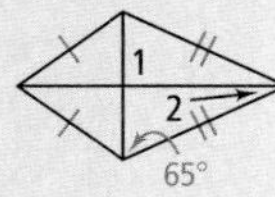

36.

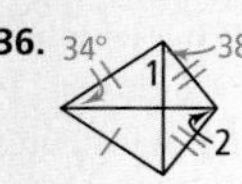

37. Algebra A trapezoid has base lengths of $(6x - 1)$ units and 3 units. Its midsegment has a length of $(5x - 3)$ units. What is the value of x?

29. No; two sides are ∥ in all ▱s.
30. Yes; the ▱ is a rhombus and a rectangle so it must be a square.
31. $x = 18$; a diagonal bisects a pair of ∠s in a rhombus.
32. $x = 4$; a rectangle has ≅ diagonals that bisect each other.
33. $m\angle 1 = 135$, $m\angle 2 = 135$, $m\angle 3 = 45$
34. $m\angle 1 = 80$, $m\angle 2 = 100$, $m\angle 3 = 100$
35. $m\angle 1 = 90$, $m\angle 2 = 25$
36. $m\angle 1 = 56$, $m\angle 2 = 52$
37. 2

Answers

Chapter Review (continued)

38. scalene
39. isosceles
40. parallelogram
41. kite
42. rhombus
43. isosc. trapezoid
44. $F(0, 2b)$, $L(a, 0)$, $P(0, -2b)$, $S(-a, 0)$
45. $(a - b, c)$
46. Answers may vary. Sample:

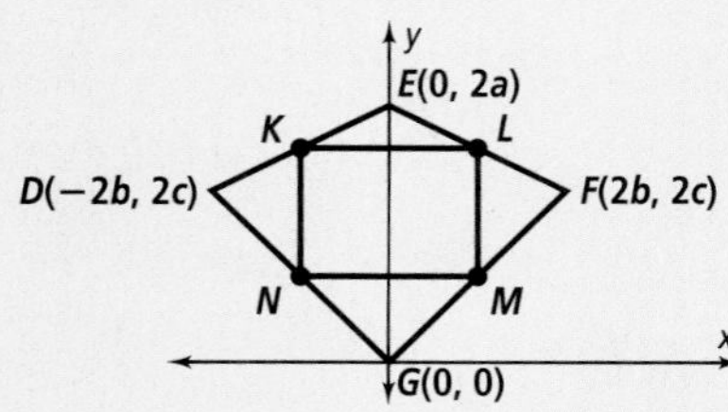

Given: Kite $DEFG$, K, L, M, N are midpoints of sides

Prove: $KLMN$ is a rectangle.

By the Midpoint Formula, coordinates of midpoints are $K(-b, a + c)$, $L(b, a + c)$, $M(b, c)$, and $N(-b, c)$. By the Slope Formula, slope of $\overline{KL}$ = slope of $\overline{NM} = 0$, and slope of $\overline{KN}$ and slope of $\overline{LM}$ are undefined. $\overline{KL} \parallel \overline{NM}$ and $\overline{KN} \parallel \overline{LM}$ so $KLMN$ is a ▱. $\overline{KL} \perp \overline{LM}$, $\overline{LM} \perp \overline{NM}$, $\overline{KN} \perp \overline{NM}$, and $\overline{KN} \perp \overline{KL}$ so $KLMN$ is a rectangle.

6-7 Polygons in the Coordinate Plane

Quick Review

To determine whether sides or diagonals are congruent, use the Distance Formula. To determine the coordinate of the midpoint of a side, or whether the diagonals bisect each other, use the Midpoint Formula. To determine whether opposite sides are parallel, or whether diagonals or sides are perpendicular, use the Slope Formula.

Example

$\triangle XYZ$ has vertices $X(1, 0)$, $Y(-2, -4)$, and $Z(4, -4)$. Is $\triangle XYZ$ *scalene, isosceles,* or *equilateral*?

To find the lengths of the legs, use the Distance Formula.

$$XY = \sqrt{(-2 - 1)^2 + (-4 - 0)^2} = \sqrt{9 + 16} = 5$$

$$YZ = \sqrt{(4 - (-2))^2 + (-4 - (-4))^2} = \sqrt{36 + 0} = 6$$

$$XZ = \sqrt{(4 - 1)^2 + (-4 - 0)^2} = \sqrt{9 + 16} = 5$$

Two side lengths are equal, so $\triangle XYZ$ is isosceles.

Exercises

Determine whether $\triangle ABC$ is *scalene, isosceles,* or *equilateral.*

38.

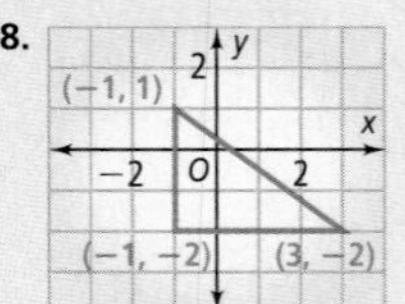

39.

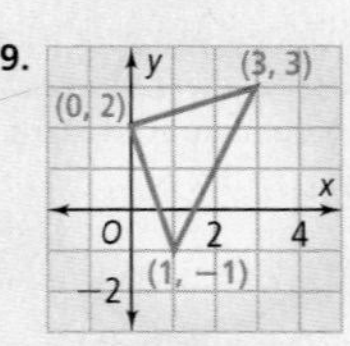

What is the most precise classification of the quadrilateral?

40. $G(2, 5)$, $R(5, 8)$, $A(-2, 12)$, $D(-5, 9)$

41. $F(-13, 7)$, $I(1, 12)$, $N(15, 7)$, $E(1, -5)$

42. $Q(4, 5)$, $U(12, 14)$, $A(20, 5)$, $D(12, -4)$

43. $W(-11, 4)$, $H(-9, 10)$, $A(2, 10)$, $T(4, 4)$

6-8 and 6-9 Coordinate Geometry and Coordinate Proofs

Quick Review

When placing a figure in the coordinate plane, it is usually helpful to place at least one side on an axis. Use variables when naming the coordinates of a figure in order to show that relationships are true for a general case.

Example

Rectangle $PQRS$ has length a and width $4b$. The x-axis bisects $\overline{PS}$ and $\overline{QR}$. What are the coordinates of the vertices?

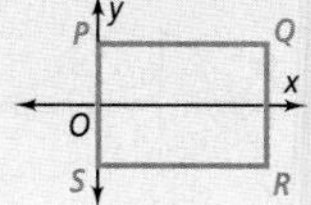

Since the width of $PQRS$ is $4b$ and the x-axis bisects $\overline{PS}$ and $\overline{QR}$, all the vertices are $2b$ units from the x-axis. $\overline{PS}$ is on the y-axis, so $P = (0, 2b)$ and $S = (0, -2b)$. The length of $PQRS$ is a, so $Q = (a, 2b)$ and $R = (a, -2b)$.

Exercises

44. In rhombus $FLPS$, the axes form the diagonals. If $SL = 2a$ and $FP = 4b$, what are the coordinates of the vertices?

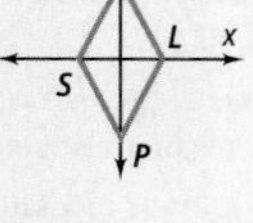

45. The figure at the right is a parallelogram. Give the coordinates of point P without using any new variables.

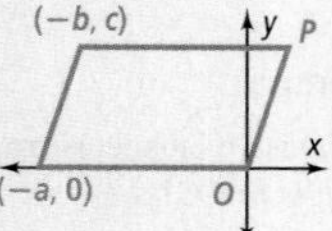

46. Use coordinate geometry to prove that the quadrilateral formed by connecting the midpoints of a kite is a rectangle.

Chapter Test

Do you know HOW?

1. What is the sum of the interior angle measures of a polygon with 15 sides?
2. What is the measure of an exterior angle of a 25-gon?

Graph each quadrilateral *ABCD*. Then determine the most precise name for it.

3. $A(1, 2)$, $B(11, 2)$, $C(7, 5)$, $D(4, 5)$
4. $A(3, -2)$, $B(5, 4)$, $C(3, 6)$, $D(1, 4)$
5. $A(1, -4)$, $B(1, 1)$, $C(-2, 2)$, $D(-2, -3)$

Algebra Find the values of the variables for each quadrilateral.

6. 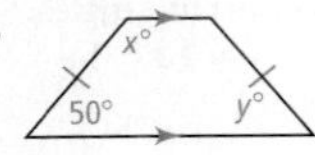
7. 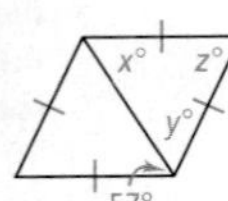
8. 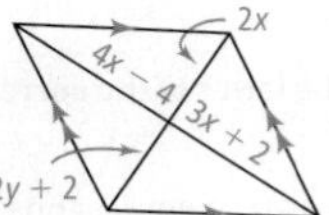
9. 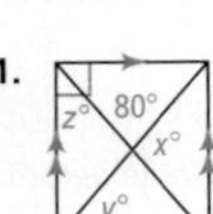
10.
11. 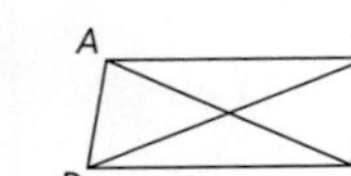

Does the information help you prove that *ABCD* is a parallelogram? Explain.

12. $\overline{AC}$ bisects $\overline{BD}$.
13. $\overline{AB} \cong \overline{DC}$, $\overline{AB} \parallel \overline{DC}$
14. $\overline{AB} \cong \overline{DC}$, $\overline{BC} \cong \overline{AD}$
15. $\angle DAB \cong \angle BCD$, $\angle ABC \cong \angle CDA$

16. **Algebra** Determine the values of the variables for which *ABCD* is a parallelogram.

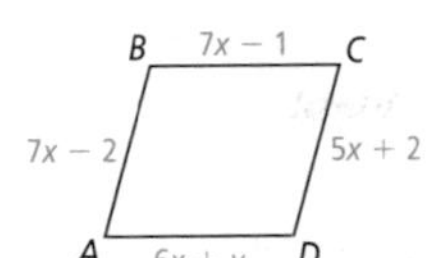

Give the coordinates for points *S* and *T* without using any new variables. Then find the midpoint and the slope of $\overline{ST}$.

17. rectangle

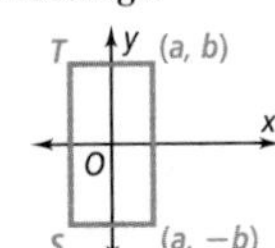

18. parallelogram

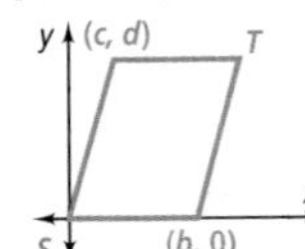

19. Prove that the diagonals of square *ABCD* are congruent.

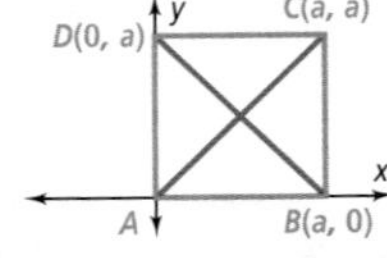

20. Sketch two noncongruent parallelograms *ABCD* and *EFGH* such that $\overline{AC} \cong \overline{BD} \cong \overline{EG} \cong \overline{FH}$.

Do you UNDERSTAND?

21. **Open-Ended** Write the coordinates of four points that determine each figure with the given conditions. One vertex is at the origin and one side is 3 units long.
    a. square
    b. parallelogram
    c. rectangle
    d. trapezoid
22. **Writing** Explain why a square cannot be a kite.
23. **Error Analysis** Your classmate says, "If the diagonals of a quadrilateral intersect to form four congruent triangles, then the quadrilateral is always a parallelogram." How would you correct this statement? Explain your answer.
24. **Reasoning** *PQRS* has vertices $P(0, 0)$, $Q(4, 2)$, and $S(4, -2)$. Its diagonals intersect at $H(4, 0)$. What are the possible coordinates of *R* for *PQRS* to be a kite? Explain.

Answers

Chapter Test

1. 2340
2. 14.4
3. 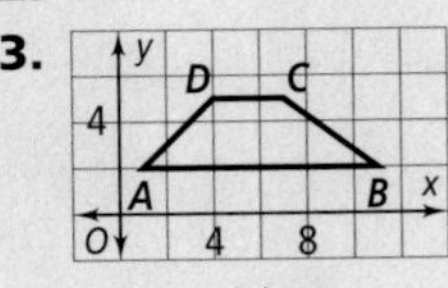
trapezoid
4. 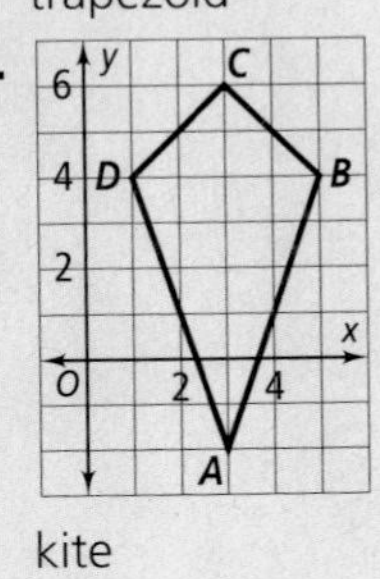
kite
5. 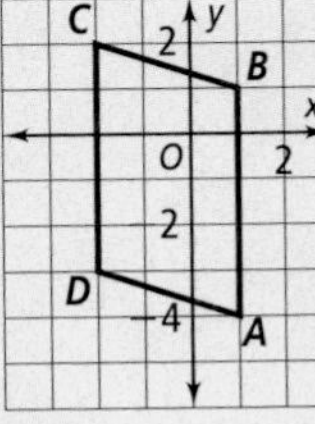
▱
6. $x = 130$, $y = 50$
7. $x = 57$, $y = 57$, $z = 66$
8. $x = 6$, $y = 5$
9. $x = 36$, $y = 108$, $z = 72$
10. $x = 90$, $y = 30$
11. $x = 100$, $y = 50$, $z = 40$
12. No; both diagonals must bisect each other.
13. Yes; if opp. sides are ≅ and ∥, then the quad. is a ▱.
14. Yes; if both pairs of opp. sides are ≅, then the quad. is a ▱.
15. Yes; if both pairs of opp. ∡ are ≅, then the quad. is a ▱.
16. $x = 2$, $y = 1$
17. $S(-a, -b)$, $T(-a, b)$; midpt. $(-a, 0)$; slope: undefined
18. $S(0, 0)$, $T(b + c, d)$; midpt. $\left(\frac{b+c}{2}, \frac{d}{2}\right)$; slope: $\frac{d}{b+c}$
19. Answers may vary. Sample:
Given: Square *ABCD*
Prove: $\overline{AC} \cong \overline{BD}$
By the Distance Formula, $AC = a\sqrt{2}$ and $BD = a\sqrt{2}$. $AC = BD$, so $\overline{AC} \cong \overline{BD}$.
20. Answers may vary. Sample:

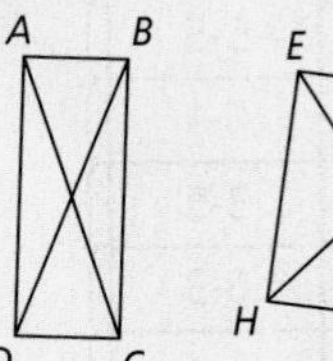
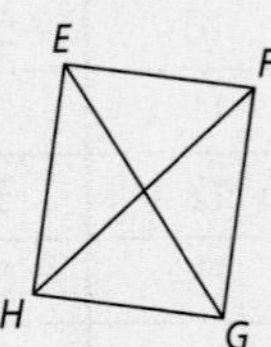

21. Answers may vary. Samples are given.
    a. (0, 0), (3, 0), (3, 3), (0, 3)
    b. (0, 0), (3, 0), (4, 2), (1, 2)
    c. (0, 0), (3, 0), (3, 5), (0, 5)
    d. (0, 0), (3, 0), (2, 2), (1, 2)
22. Answers may vary. Sample: The def. of kite states opp. sides are not ≅. The def. of square states all sides are ≅.
23. Answers may vary. Sample: Change "parallelogram" to "rhombus" because four sides must be ≅.
24. *R* is any point $(x, 0)$, where $x > 4$ and $x \neq 8$. The *x*-axis is the bisector of $\overline{QS}$ and so if *R* is not on the line, then $\overline{QR}$ and $\overline{SR}$ will not be ≅.

Item Number	Lesson
1	6-6
2	6-8
3	5-6
4	6-6
5	5-3
6	6-4
7	6-6
8	3-3
9	6-6
10	5-5
11	6-1
12	3-5
13	6-3
14	2-4
15	6-1
16	1-5
17	6-6
18	1-8
19	6-1
20	5-6
21	6-1
22	6-7
23	1-8

6 Cumulative Test Prep

TIPS FOR SUCCESS

Some questions on tests ask you to find an angle measure in a figure. Read the sample question at the right. Then follow the tips to answer it.

In rhombus $QRST$, what is $m\angle RST$?

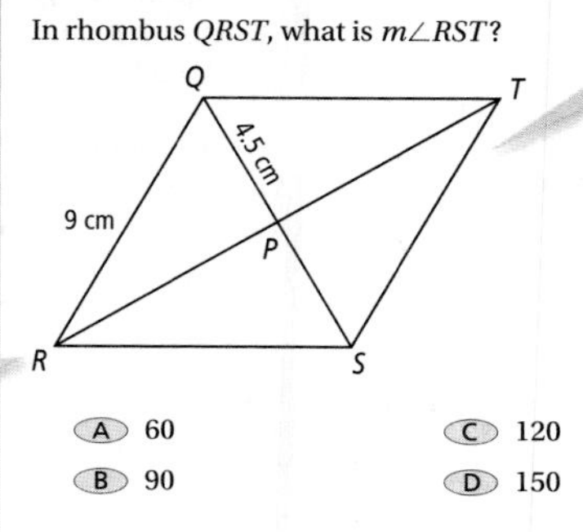

Ⓐ 60 Ⓑ 90 Ⓒ 120 Ⓓ 150

TIP 1
The diagonal $\overline{QS}$ forms $\triangle QRS$.

TIP 2
Use the properties of a rhombus to find RS and QS.

Think It Through
$RS = 9$ cm because a rhombus has four congruent sides. The diagonals of a rhombus bisect each other, so $QS = 2 \cdot 4.5 = 9$ cm. Since $QR = RS = QS$, $\triangle QRS$ is equilateral, and thus equiangular. So $m\angle RSQ = 60$. Since the diagonals of a rhombus also bisect the angles, $m\angle RST = 2 \cdot 60 = 120$. The correct answer is C.

Vocabulary Builder

As you solve test items, you must understand the meanings of mathematical terms. Choose the correct term to complete each sentence.

A. Two lines that intersect to form right angles are (parallel, perpendicular) lines.

B. A quadrilateral with two pairs of adjacent sides congruent and no opposite sides congruent is called a (rhombus, kite).

C. The (circumcenter, incenter) of a triangle is the point of concurrency of the perpendicular bisectors of the sides of the triangle.

D. Two angles are (complementary, supplementary) angles if the sum of their measures is 90.

E. In a plane, two lines that never intersect are (parallel, skew) lines.

Multiple Choice

Read each question. Then write the letter of the correct answer on your paper.

1. Which quadrilateral must have congruent diagonals?

Ⓐ kite
Ⓑ rectangle
Ⓒ parallelogram
Ⓓ rhombus

2. $STUV$ is a parallelogram. What are the coordinates of point U?

Ⓕ (x, y)
Ⓖ $(x + z, y)$
Ⓗ (y, z)
Ⓘ (z, y)

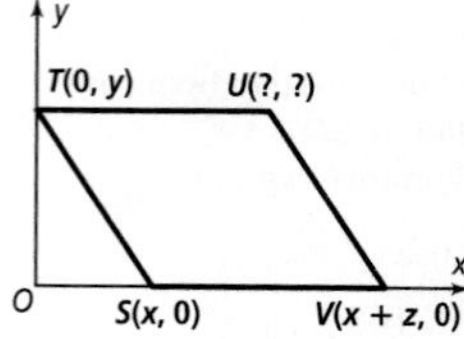

Answers

Cumulative Test Prep

A. perpendicular
B. kite
C. circumcenter
D. complementary
E. parallel
1. B
2. I

3. Which list could represent the lengths of the sides of a triangle?

A 7 cm, 10 cm, 25 cm
B 4 in., 6 in., 10 in.
C 1 ft, 2 ft, 4 ft
D 3 m, 5 m, 7 m

4. Which of the following quadrilaterals does NOT always have a pair of adjacent sides congruent?

F square
G kite
H rhombus
I rectangle

5. What is the circumcenter of $\triangle ABC$ with vertices $A(-7, 0)$, $B(-3, 8)$, and $C(-3, 0)$?

A $(-7, -3)$
B $(-5, 4)$
C $(-4, 3)$
D $(-3, 4)$

6. *ABCD* is a rhombus. To prove that the diagonals of a rhombus are perpendicular, which pair of angles below must you prove congruent by using corresponding parts of congruent triangles?

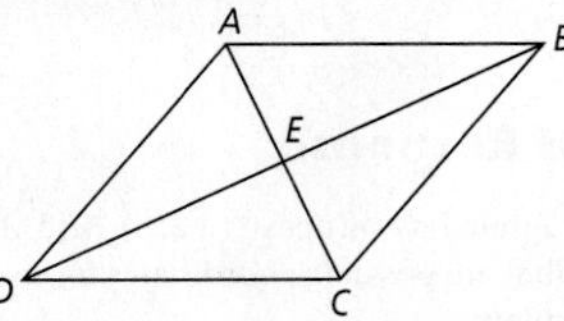

F $\angle AEB$ and $\angle DEC$
G $\angle AEB$ and $\angle AED$
H $\angle BEC$ and $\angle AED$
I $\angle DAB$ and $\angle ABC$

7. *FGHJ* is a quadrilateral. If at least one pair of opposite angles in quadrilateral *FGHJ* is congruent, which statement is false?

A Quadrilateral *FGHJ* is a trapezoid.
B Quadrilateral *FGHJ* is a rhombus.
C Quadrilateral *FGHJ* is a kite.
D Quadrilateral *FGHJ* is a parallelogram.

8. For which value of x are lines g and h parallel?

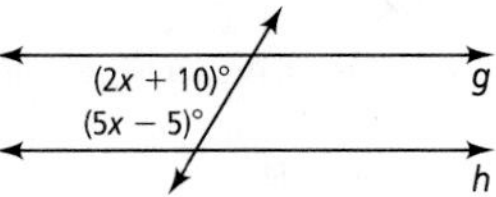

F 12
G 15
H 18
I 25

9. Which quadrilateral CANNOT contain four right angles?

A square
B rhombus
C trapezoid
D rectangle

10. In $\triangle GHJ$, $\overline{GH} \cong \overline{HJ}$. Using the indirect proof method, you attempt to prove that $\angle G$ and $\angle J$ are right angles. Which theorem will contradict this claim?

F Triangle Angle-Sum Theorem
G Side-Angle-Side Theorem
H Converse of the Isosceles Triangle Theorem
I Angle-Angle-Side Theorem

11. The measure of each interior angle in a regular polygon is 140. What type of polygon is it?

A hexagon
B decagon
C octagon
D nonagon

12. Which angles could an obtuse triangle have?

F two right angles
G two acute angles
H two obtuse angles
I two vertical angles

13. What values of x and y make the quadrilateral below a parallelogram?

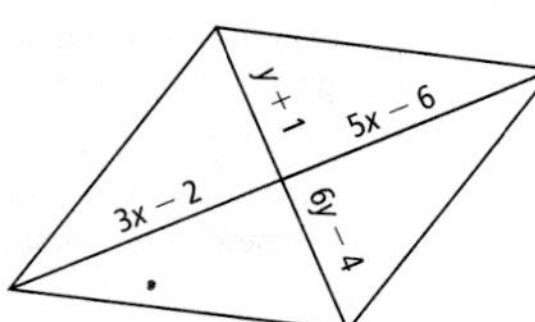

A $x = 2, y = 1$
B $x = 3, y = 5$
C $x = 1, y = 2$
D $x = 2, y = \frac{9}{7}$

3. D
4. I
5. B
6. G
7. A
8. I
9. C
10. F
11. D
12. G
13. A

Answers

Cumulative Test Prep (continued)

14. H

15. 52

16. 38

17. 68

18. 174

19. 108

20. [2] The lengths must satisfy the $\triangle$ Inequality Thm.:
$n + 1 + 2n > 5n - 4$ (so $3n + 1 > 5n - 4$, $5 > 2n$, $n < 2.5$)
$n + 1 + 5n - 4 > 2n$ (so $6n - 3 > 2n$, $4n > 3$, $n > 0.75$),
and $2n + 5n - 4 > n + 1$ (so $7n - 4 > n + 1$, $6n > 5$, $n > \frac{5}{6}$).
So $\frac{5}{6} < n < 2.5$.

[1] correct answer, without work shown

21. [2] The sum of the measures of the pentagon $\angle$ and the two hexagon $\angle$s is $108 + 120 + 120 = 348$. A circle has 360° so there is a gap of 12°.

[1] missing information OR computation error

22. [4] If L and N are opp. vertices, then the fourth vertex is $(-4, 2)$.
If L and M are opp. vertices, then the fourth vertex is $(0, 8)$.
If M and N are opp. vertices, then the fourth vertex is $(6, -2)$.

[3] correct method with one computational error

[2] correct method with more than one error, OR incorrect method solved correctly

[1] correct vertices, without explanation

23. [4] **a.** 4 times as large; old area is ℓw and new area is $(2\ell)(2w) = 4\ell w$.

b. More than twice as long; since the new yard has 4 times the area, he will take 4 times as long to mow it.

[3] correct answers with one error

[2] correct answer to one part, error on other

[1] correct answers, with no work shown

14. Which is the most valid conclusion based on the statements below?

If a triangle is equilateral, then it is isosceles. $\triangle ABC$ is not equilateral.

(F) $\triangle ABC$ is not isosceles.

(G) $\triangle ABC$ is isosceles.

(H) $\triangle ABC$ may or may not be isosceles.

(I) $\triangle ABC$ is equilateral.

GRIDDED RESPONSE

15. What is $m\angle 1$ in the figure below?

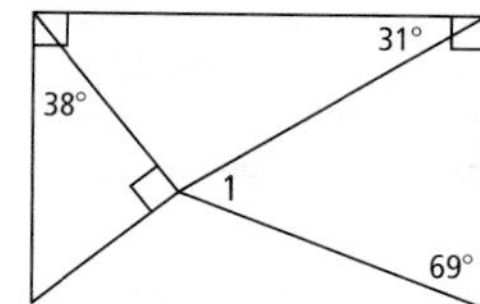

16. $\angle ABE$ and $\angle CBD$ are vertical angles and both are complementary with $\angle FGH$. If $m\angle ABE = (3x - 1)$, and $m\angle FGH = 4x$, what is $m\angle CBD$?

17. What is the value of x in the kite below?

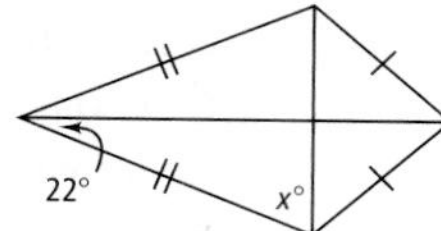

18. A 3-ft-wide walkway is placed around an animal exhibit at the zoo. The exhibit is rectangular in shape and has length 15 ft and width 8 ft. What is the area, in square feet, of the walkway around the exhibit?

19. The outer walls of the Pentagon in Arlington, Virginia, are formed by two regular pentagons, as shown below. What is the value of x?

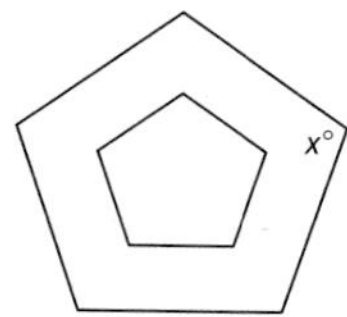

Short Response

20. What are the possible values for n to make ABC a valid triangle? Show your work.

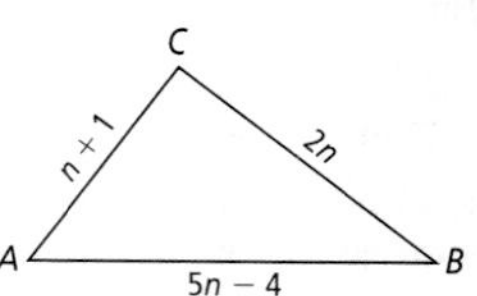

21. The pattern of a soccer ball contains regular hexagons and regular pentagons. The figure at the right shows what a section of the pattern would look like on a flat surface. Use the fact that there are 360° in a circle to explain why there are gaps between the hexagons.

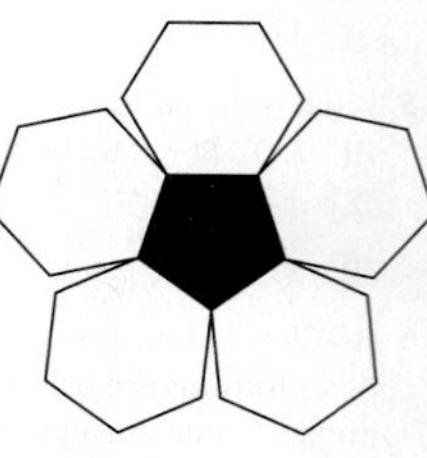

Extended Response

22. A parallelogram has vertices $L(-2, 5)$, $M(3, 3)$, and $N(1, 0)$. What are possible coordinates for its fourth vertex? Explain.

23. Jim is clearing out trees and planting grass to enlarge his backyard. He plans to double both the width and the length of his current rectangular backyard, as shown below.

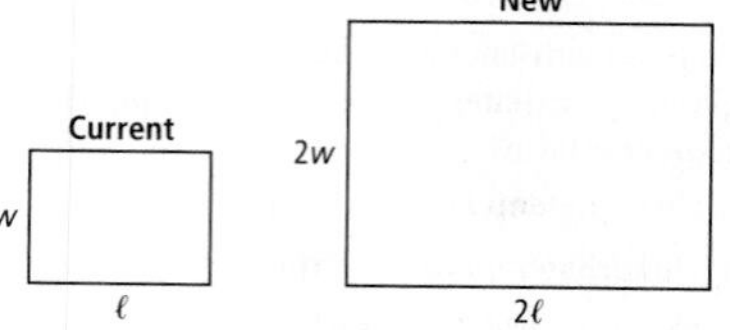

a. How will the area of Jim's new backyard compare to the area of his current backyard?

b. Will it take Jim twice as long to mow his new backyard than his old backyard? Explain. (Assume Jim mows at the same rate for both yards.)

Skills Handbook Contents

Skills Handbook

Using a Ruler and Protractor

Knowing how to use a ruler and protractor is crucial for success in geometry.

Example

Draw a triangle that has a 28° angle between sides of length 5.2 cm and 3.0 cm.

Step 1 Use a ruler to draw a segment 5.2 cm long.

0 1 2 3 4 5 6
centimeters

Step 2 Place the hole of a protractor at one endpoint of the segment. Make a small mark at the 28° position along the protractor.

The angle opens to the left, so read measures from the top scale.

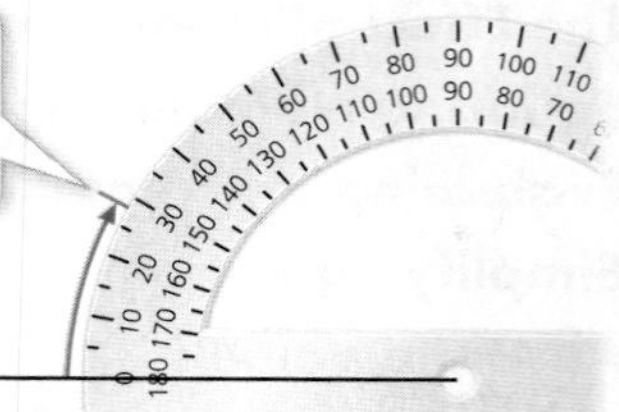

Step 3 Align the ruler along the small mark and the same endpoint. Place the zero point of the ruler at the endpoint. Draw a segment 3.0 cm long.

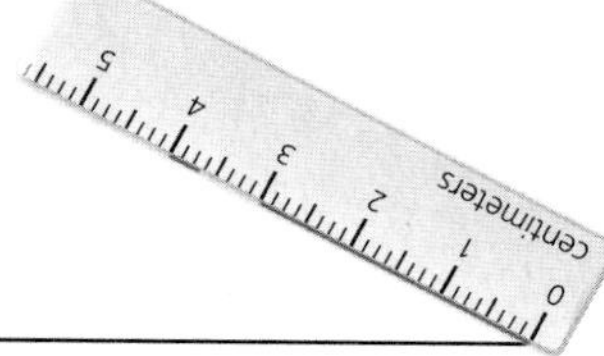

Step 4 Complete the triangle by connecting the endpoints of the first and second segments.

Exercises

1. Measure sides $\overline{AB}$ and $\overline{BC}$ of $\triangle ABC$ to the nearest millimeter.
2. Measure each angle of $\triangle ABC$ to the nearest degree.
3. Draw a triangle that has a side of length 2.4 cm between a 43° angle and a 102° angle.

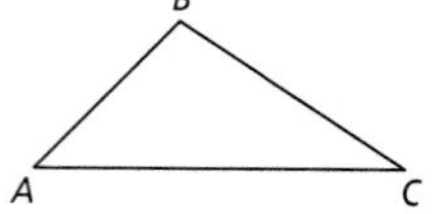

Answers

Using a Ruler and Protractor

1–2. Answers may vary slightly due to measuring method.

1. 20 mm; 25 mm
2. $m\angle A = 43$; $m\angle B = 103$; $m\angle C = 34$
3. 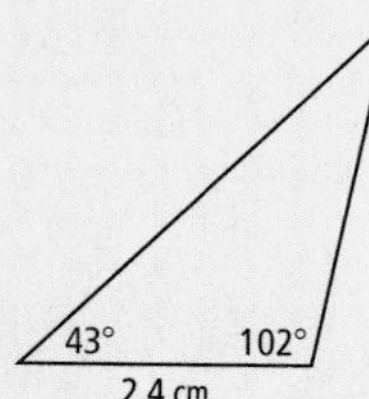

Classifying Triangles

You can classify a triangle by its angles and sides.

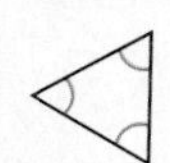
Equiangular
all angles congruent

Acute
all angles acute

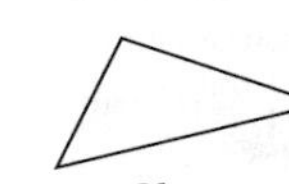
Right
one right angle

Obtuse
one obtuse angle

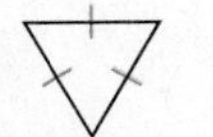
Equilateral
all sides congruent

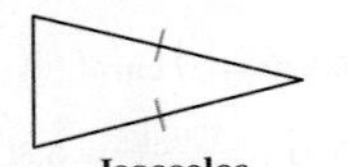
Isosceles
at least two sides congruent

Scalene
no sides congruent

Example

What type of triangle is shown below?

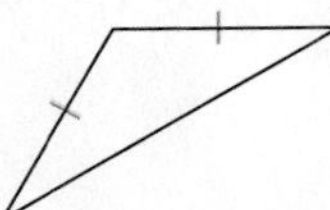

At least two sides are congruent, so the triangle is isosceles. One angle is obtuse, so the triangle is obtuse. The triangle is an obtuse isosceles triangle.

Exercises

Classify each triangle by its sides and angles.

1. 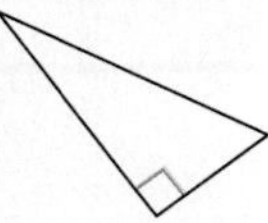 **2.** 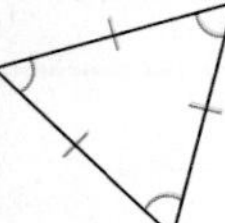 **3.** 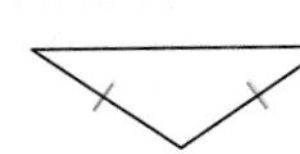

If possible, draw a triangle to fit each description. Mark the triangle to show known information. If you cannot draw the triangle, write *not possible* and explain why.

4. acute equilateral
5. right equilateral
6. obtuse scalene
7. acute isosceles
8. right isosceles
9. acute scalene

Classifying Triangles

1. right, scalene
2. acute equiangular, equilateral
3. obtuse, isosceles
4. 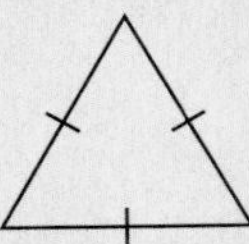
5. Not possible; a rt. △ will always have one longest side opposite the rt. ∠.
6. 
7. 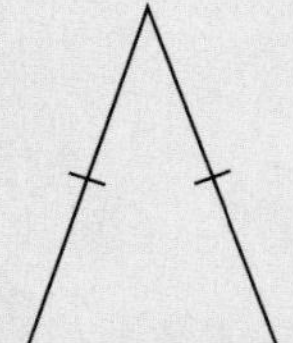
8.  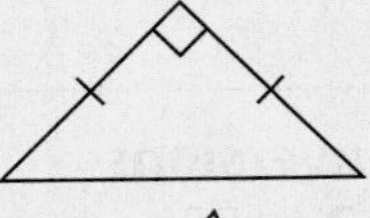
9. 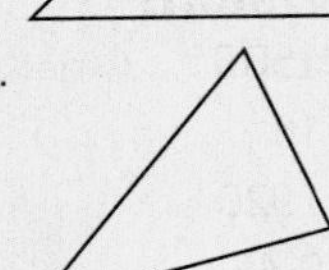

Skills Handbook

Measurement Conversions

To convert from one unit of measure to another, you multiply by a conversion factor in the form of a fraction. The numerator and denominator are in different units, but they represent the same amount. So you can think of this as multiplying by 1.

An example of a conversion factor is $\frac{1 \text{ ft}}{12 \text{ in.}}$. You can create other conversion factors using the table on page 837.

Example 1

Complete each statement.

a. **88 in. = ■ ft**

$88 \text{ in.} \cdot \frac{1 \text{ ft}}{12 \text{ in.}} = \frac{88}{12} \text{ ft} = 7\frac{1}{3} \text{ ft}$

b. **5.3 m = ■ cm**

$5.3 \text{ m} \cdot \frac{100 \text{ cm}}{1 \text{ m}} = 5.3(100) \text{ cm} = 530 \text{ cm}$

Area is always in square units, and volume is always in cubic units.

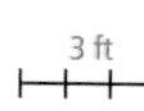

1 yd = 3 ft

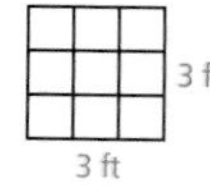

1 yd² = 9 ft²

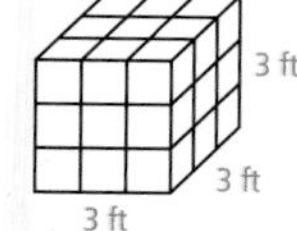

1 yd³ = 27 ft³

Example 2

Complete each statement.

a. **300 in.² = ■ ft²**

$1 \text{ ft} = 12 \text{ in., so } 1 \text{ ft}^2 = (12 \text{ in.})^2 = 144 \text{ in.}^2.$

$300 \text{ in.}^2 \cdot \frac{1 \text{ ft}^2}{144 \text{ in.}^2} = 2\frac{1}{12} \text{ ft}^2$

b. **200,000 cm³ = ■ m³**

$1 \text{ m} = 100 \text{ cm, so } 1 \text{ m}^3 = (100 \text{ cm})^3 = 1{,}000{,}000 \text{ cm}^3.$

$200{,}000 \text{ cm}^3 \cdot \frac{1 \text{ m}^3}{1{,}000{,}000 \text{ cm}^3} = 0.2 \text{ m}^3$

Exercises

Complete each statement.

1. 40 cm = ■ m
2. 1.5 kg = ■ g
3. 60 cm = ■ mm
4. 200 in. = ■ ft
5. 28 yd = ■ in.
6. 1.5 mi = ■ ft
7. 15 g = ■ mg
8. 430 mg = ■ g
9. 34 L = ■ mL
10. 1.2 m = ■ cm
11. 43 mm = ■ cm
12. 3600 s = ■ min
13. 14 gal = ■ qt
14. 4500 lb = ■ t
15. 234 min = ■ h
16. 3 ft^2 = ■ in.^2
17. 108 m^2 = ■ cm^2
18. 21 cm^2 = ■ mm^2
19. 1.4 yd^2 = ■ ft^2
20. 0.45 km^2 = ■ m^2
21. 1300 ft^2 = ■ yd^2
22. 1030 in.^2 = ■ ft^2
23. 20,000,000 ft^2 = ■ mi^2
24. 1000 cm^3 = ■ m^3

826

Answers

Measurement Conversions

1. 0.4
2. 1500
3. 600
4. $16\frac{2}{3}$
5. 1008
6. 7920
7. 15,000
8. 0.43
9. 34,000
10. 120
11. 4.3
12. 60
13. 56
14. $2\frac{1}{4}$
15. 3.9
16. 432
17. 1,080,000
18. 2100
19. 12.6
20. 450,000
21. $144\frac{4}{9}$
22. $7\frac{11}{72}$
23. $\frac{3125}{4356}$
24. 0.001

Measurement, Rounding Error, and Reasonableness

There is no such thing as an *exact* measurement. Measurements are always approximate. No matter how precise it is, a measurement actually represents a range of values.

Example 1

Chris's height, to the nearest inch, is 5 ft 8 in. What range of values does this measurement represent?

The height is given to the nearest inch, so the error is $\frac{1}{2}$ in. Chris's height, then, is between 5 ft $7\frac{1}{2}$ in. and 5 ft $8\frac{1}{2}$ in., or 5 ft 8 in. $\pm \frac{1}{2}$ in. Within this range are all the measures that, when rounded to the nearest inch, equal 5 ft 8 in.

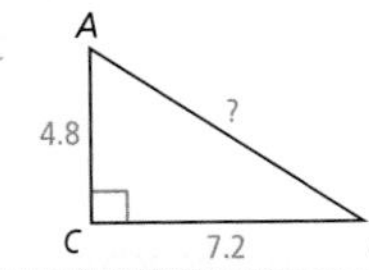

As you calculate with measurements, errors can accumulate.

Example 2

Jean drives 18 km to work each day. This distance is given to the nearest kilometer. What is the range of values for the round-trip distance?

The driving distance is between 17.5 and 18.5 km, or 18 $\pm$ 0.5 km. Double the lower limit, 17.5, and the upper limit, 18.5. Thus, the round trip can be anywhere between 35 and 37 km, or 36 $\pm$ 1 km. Notice that the error for the round trip is double the error for a single leg of the trip.

So that your answers will be reasonable, keep precision and error in mind as you calculate. For example, in finding AB, the length of the hypotenuse of $\triangle ABC$, it would be inappropriate to give the answer as 8.6533 if the sides are given to the nearest tenth. Round your answer to 8.7.

A, 4.8, ?, C, 7.2, B

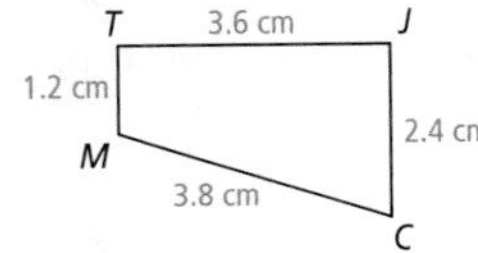

Exercises

Each measurement is followed by its unit of greatest precision. Find the range of values that each measurement represents.

1. 24 ft (ft)
2. 124 cm (cm)
3. 340 mL (mL)
4. $5\frac{1}{2}$ mi. $\left(\frac{1}{2}\text{ mi}\right)$
5. 73.2 mm (0.1 mm)
6. 34 yd^2 (yd^2)
7. The lengths of the sides of $TJCM$ are given to the nearest tenth of a centimeter. What is the range of values for the figure's perimeter?
8. To the nearest degree, two angles of a triangle are 49° and 73°. What is the range of values for the measure of the third angle?
9. The lengths of the legs of a right triangle are measured as 131 m and 162 m. You use a calculator to find the length of the hypotenuse. The calculator display reads 208.33867. What should your answer be?

T, 3.6 cm, J, 1.2 cm, 2.4 cm, M, 3.8 cm, C

Measurement, Rounding Error, and Reasonableness

1. $23\frac{1}{2}$ ft to $24\frac{1}{2}$ ft
2. $123\frac{1}{2}$ cm to $124\frac{1}{2}$ cm
3. $339\frac{1}{2}$ mL to $340\frac{1}{2}$ mL
4. $5\frac{1}{4}$ mi to $5\frac{3}{4}$ mi
5. 73.15 mm to 73.25 mm
6. $33\frac{1}{2}$ yd^2 to $34\frac{1}{2}$ yd^2
7. 10.8 cm to 11.2 cm
8. 57 to 59
9. 208 cm

Skills Handbook

The Effect of Measurement Errors on Calculations

Measurements are always approximate, and calculations with these measurements produce error. Percent error is a measure of accuracy of a measurement or calculation. It is the ratio of the greatest possible error to the measurement.

$$\text{percent error} = \frac{\text{greatest possible error}}{\text{measurement}}$$

Example

The dimensions of a box are measured as 18 in., 12 in., and 9 in. What is the percent error in calculating the box's volume?

The measurements are to the nearest inch, so the greatest possible error is 0.5 in.

Volume:

as measured	maximum value	minimum value
$V = \ell \cdot w \cdot h$	$V = \ell \cdot w \cdot h$	$V = \ell \cdot w \cdot h$
$= 18 \cdot 12 \cdot 9$	$= 18.5 \cdot 12.5 \cdot 9.5$	$= 17.5 \cdot 11.5 \cdot 8.5$
$= 1944 \text{ in.}^3$	$\approx 2196.9 \text{ in.}^3$	$\approx 1710.6 \text{ in.}^3$

Possible Error:

maximum value − measured	measured − minimum value
$2196.9 - 1944 = 252.9$	$1944 - 1710.6 = 233.4$

$$\text{percent error} = \frac{\text{greatest possible error}}{\text{measurement}}$$
$$= \frac{252.9}{1944}$$
$$\approx 0.1300926$$

The percent error is about 13%.

Exercises

Find the percent error in calculating the volume of each box given its dimensions. Round to the nearest percent.

1. 10 cm by 5 cm by 20 cm

2. 1.2 mm by 5.7 mm by 2.0 mm

3. 1.24 cm by 4.45 cm by 5.58 cm

4. $8\frac{1}{4}$ in. by $17\frac{1}{2}$ in. by 5 in.

Find the percent error in calculating the perimeter of each figure.

5.

6.

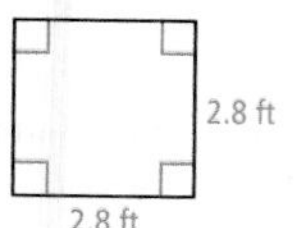

7.

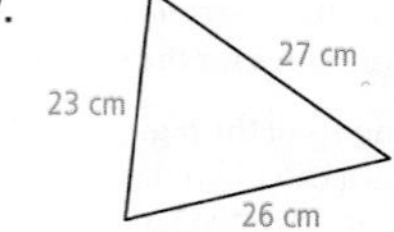

Answers

The Effect of Measurement Errors on Calculations

1. 18%

2. 8%

3. 1%

4. 5%

5. ≈ 7%

6. ≈ 2%

7. ≈ 2%

Squaring Numbers and Finding Square Roots

The square of a number is found by multiplying the number by itself. An exponent of 2 is used to indicate that a number is being squared.

Example 1

Simplify.

a. 5^2

$5^2 = 5 \cdot 5$

$= 25$

b. $(-3.5)^2$

$(-3.5)^2 = (-3.5) \cdot (-3.5)$

$= 12.25$

c. $\left(\frac{2}{7}\right)^2$

$\left(\frac{2}{7}\right)^2 = \frac{2}{7} \cdot \frac{2}{7}$

$= \frac{4}{49}$

The square root of a number is itself a number that, when squared, results in the original number. A radical symbol ($\sqrt{\ }$) is used to represent the positive square root of a number.

Example 2

Simplify. Round to the nearest tenth if necessary.

a. $\sqrt{36}$

$\sqrt{36} = 6$, since $6^2 = 36$.

b. $\sqrt{174}$

$\sqrt{174} \approx 13.2$, since $13.2^2 \approx 174$.

You can solve equations that include squared numbers.

Example 3

Algebra Solve.

a. $x^2 = 144$

$x = 12$ or -12

b. $a^2 + 3^2 = 5^2$

$a^2 + 9 = 25$

$a^2 = 16$

$a = 4$ or -4

Exercises

Simplify.

1. 11^2
2. $(-14)^2$
3. 5.1^2
4. $\left(\frac{8}{5}\right)^2$
5. -6^2
6. $\left(-\frac{3}{7}\right)^2$

Simplify. Round to the nearest tenth if necessary.

7. $\sqrt{100}$
8. $\sqrt{169}$
9. $\sqrt{74}$
10. $\sqrt{50}$
11. $\sqrt{\frac{4}{9}}$
12. $\sqrt{\frac{49}{81}}$

Algebra Solve. Round to the nearest tenth if necessary.

13. $x^2 = 49$
14. $a^2 = 9$
15. $y^2 + 7 = 8$
16. $5 + x^2 = 11$
17. $8^2 + b^2 = 10^2$
18. $5^2 + 4^2 = c^2$
19. $p^2 + 12^2 = 13^2$
20. $20^2 = 15^2 + a^2$

Squaring Numbers and Finding Square Roots

1. 121
2. 196
3. 26.01
4. $\frac{64}{25}$
5. -36
6. $\frac{9}{49}$
7. 10
8. 13
9. 8.6
10. 7.1
11. $\frac{2}{3}$
12. $\frac{7}{9}$
13. ± 7
14. ± 3
15. ± 1
16. ± 2.4
17. ± 6
18. ± 6.4
19. ± 5
20. ± 13.2

Skills Handbook

Evaluating and Simplifying Expressions

To evaluate an expression with variables, substitute a number for each variable. Then simplify the expression using the order of operations. Be especially careful with exponents and negative signs. For example, the expression $-x^2$ always yields a negative or zero value, and $(-x)^2$ is always positive or zero.

Order of Operations

1. Perform any operation(s) inside grouping symbols.
2. Simplify any term with exponents.
3. Multiply and divide in order from left to right.
4. Add and subtract in order from left to right.

Example 1

Algebra **Evaluate each expression for $r = 4$.**

a. $-r^2$

$-r^2 = -4^2 = -16$

b. $-3r^2$

$-3r^2 = -3(4^2) = -3(16) = -48$

c. $(r + 2)^2$

$(r + 2)^2 = (4 + 2)^2 = (6)^2 = 36$

To simplify an expression, you eliminate any parentheses and combine like terms.

Example 2

Algebra **Simplify each expression.**

a. $5r - 2r + 1$

Combine like terms.
$5r - 2r + 1 = 3r + 1$

b. $\pi(3r - 1)$

Use the Distributive Property.
$\pi(3r - 1) = 3\pi r - \pi$

c. $(r + \pi)(r - \pi)$

Multiply polynomials.
$(r + \pi)(r - \pi) = r^2 - \pi^2$

Exercises

Algebra **Evaluate each expression for $x = 5$ and $y = -3$.**

1. $-2x^2$ **2.** $-y + x$ **3.** $-xy$ **4.** $(x + 5y) \div x$

5. $x + 5y \div x$ **6.** $(-2y)^2$ **7.** $(2y)^2$ **8.** $(x - y)^2$

9. $\frac{x + 1}{y}$ **10.** $y - (x - y)$ **11.** $-y^x$ **12.** $\frac{2(1 - x)}{y - x}$

13. $x \cdot y - x$ **14.** $x - y \cdot x$ **15.** $\frac{y^3 - x}{x - y}$ **16.** $-y(x - 3)^2$

Algebra **Simplify.**

17. $6x - 4x + 8 - 5$ **18.** $2(\ell + w)$ **19.** $-(4x + 7)$ **20.** $y(4 - y)$

21. $-4x(x - 2)$ **22.** $3x - (5 + 2x)$ **23.** $2t^2 + 4t - 5t^2$ **24.** $(r - 1)^2$

25. $(1 - r)^2$ **26.** $(y + 1)(y - 3)$ **27.** $4h + 3h - 4 + 3$ **28.** $\pi r - (1 + \pi r)$

29. $(x + 4)(2x - 1)$ **30.** $2\pi h(1 - r)^2$ **31.** $3y^2 - (y^2 + 3y)$ **32.** $-(x + 4)^2$

830

Answers

Evaluating and Simplifying Expressions

1. -50 **2.** 8
3. 15 **4.** -2
5. 2 **6.** 36
7. 36 **8.** 64
9. -2 **10.** -11
11. 243 **12.** 1
13. -20 **14.** 20
15. -4 **16.** 12
17. $2x + 3$ **18.** $2\ell + 2w$
19. $-4x - 7$ **20.** $4y - y^2$
21. $-4x^2 + 8x$ **22.** $x - 5$
23. $-3t^2 + 4t$ **24.** $r^2 - 2r + 1$
25. $1 - 2r + r^2$ **26.** $y^2 - 2y - 3$
27. $7h - 1$ **28.** -1
29. $2x^2 + 7x - 4$
30. $2\pi hr^2 - 4\pi hr + 2\pi h$
31. $2y^2 - 3y$ **32.** $-x^2 - 8x - 16$

Simplifying Ratios

The ratio of the length of the shorter leg to the length of the longer leg for this right triangle is 4 to 6. This ratio can be written in three ways.

4 to 6 $\qquad \frac{4}{6} \qquad$ 4 : 6

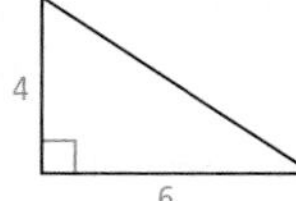

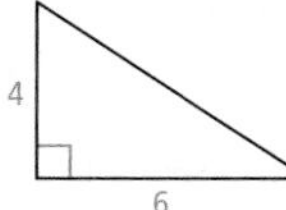

Example

Algebra **Simplify each ratio.**

a. **4 to 6**

$$4 \text{ to } 6 = \frac{4}{6}$$
$$= \frac{2 \cdot 2}{2 \cdot 3} \quad \text{Find and remove the common factor.}$$
$$= \frac{2}{3}$$

b. **$3ab : 27ab$**

$$3ab : 27ab = \frac{3ab}{27ab}$$
$$= \frac{3ab \cdot 1}{3ab \cdot 9}$$
$$= \frac{1}{9}$$

c. $\frac{4a + 4b}{a + b}$

$$\frac{4a + 4b}{a + b} = \frac{4(a + b)}{a + b}$$

Factor the numerator. The denominator cannot be factored. Remove the common factor ($a + b$).

$$= 4$$

Exercises

Algebra **Simplify each ratio.**

1. 25 to 15
2. 6 : 9
3. $\frac{36}{54}$
4. 0.8 to 2.4
5. $\frac{7}{14x}$
6. $\frac{12c}{14c}$
7. $22x^2$ to $35x$
8. $0.5ab : 8ab$
9. $\frac{4xy}{0.25x}$
10. $1\frac{1}{2}x$ to $5x$
11. $\frac{x^2 + x}{2x}$
12. $\frac{1}{4}r^2$ to $6r$
13. $0.72t : 7.2t^2$
14. $(2x - 6) : (6x - 4)$
15. $12xy : 8x$
16. $(9x - 9y)$ to $(x - y)$
17. $\frac{\pi r}{r^2 + \pi r}$
18. $\frac{8ab}{32xy}$

Express each ratio in simplest form.

19. shorter leg : longer leg
20. hypotenuse to shorter leg
21. $\frac{\text{shorter leg}}{\text{hypotenuse}}$
22. $\frac{\text{longer leg}}{\text{hypotenuse}}$
23. longer leg to shorter leg
24. hypotenuse : longer leg

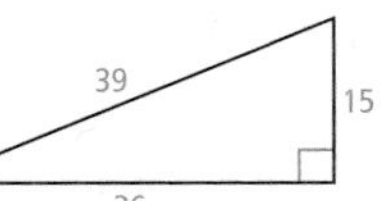

Skills Handbook

Simplifying Ratios

1. $\frac{5}{3}$ **2.** $\frac{2}{3}$
3. $\frac{2}{3}$ **4.** $\frac{1}{3}$
5. $\frac{1}{2x}$ **6.** $\frac{6}{7}$
7. $\frac{22x}{35}$ **8.** $\frac{1}{16}$
9. $16y$ **10.** $\frac{3}{10}$
11. $\frac{x + 1}{2}$ **12.** $\frac{r}{24}$
13. $\frac{1}{10t}$ **14.** $\frac{x - 3}{3x - 2}$
15. $\frac{3}{2}$ **16.** 9
17. $\frac{\pi}{r + \pi}$ **18.** $\frac{ab}{4xy}$
19. $\frac{5}{12}$ **20.** $\frac{13}{5}$
21. $\frac{5}{13}$ **22.** $\frac{12}{13}$
23. $\frac{12}{5}$ **24.** $\frac{13}{12}$

Skills Handbook

Skills Handbook

Absolute Value

Absolute value is used to represent the distance of a number from 0 on a number line. Since distance is always referred to as a nonnegative number, the absolute value of an expression is nonnegative.

On the number line at the right, both 4 and −4 are four units from zero. Therefore, $|4|$ and $|-4|$ are both equal to four.

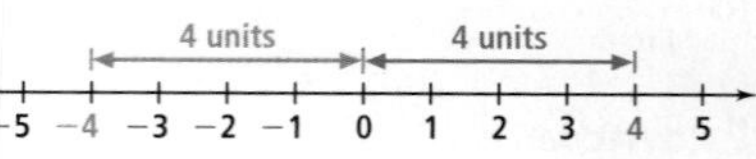

When working with more complicated expressions, always remember to simplify within absolute value symbols first.

Example 1

Simplify each expression.

a. $|4| + |-19|$

$|4| + |-19| = 4 + 19$
$= 23$

b. $|4 - 8|$

$|4 - 8| = |-4|$
$= 4$

c. $-3|-7 - 4|$

$-3|-7 - 4| = -3|-11|$
$= -3 \cdot 11$
$= -33$

To solve the absolute value equation $|x| = a$, find all the values x that are a units from 0 on a number line.

Example 2

Algebra Solve.

a. $|x| = 7$

$x = 7$ or -7

b. $|x| - 3 = 22$

$|x| - 3 = 22$
$|x| = 25$
$x = 25$ or -25

Exercises

Simplify each expression.

1. $|-8|$
2. $|11|$
3. $|-7| + |15|$
4. $|-12| - |-12|$
5. $|-5| - |10|$
6. $|-4| + |-2|$
7. $10 - |-20|$
8. $|-9| - 15$
9. $|4 - 17|$
10. $|-9 - 11|$
11. $2|-21 + 16|$
12. $-8|-9 + 4|$

Algebra Solve.

13. $|x| = 16$
14. $1 = |x|$
15. $|x| + 7 = 27$
16. $|x| - 9 = 15$

832

Answers

Absolute Value

1. 8
2. 11
3. 22
4. 0
5. −5
6. 6
7. −10
8. −6
9. 13
10. 20
11. 10
12. −40
13. −16 or 16
14. −1 or 1
15. −20 or 20
16. −24 or 24

The Coordinate Plane

Two number lines that intersect at right angles form a coordinate plane. The horizontal axis is the x-axis and the vertical axis is the y-axis. The axes intersect at the origin and divide the coordinate plane into four sections called quadrants.

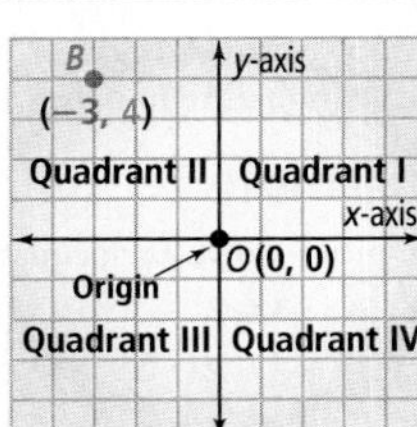

An ordered pair of numbers names the location of a point in the plane. These numbers are the coordinates of the point. Point B has coordinates $(-3, 4)$.

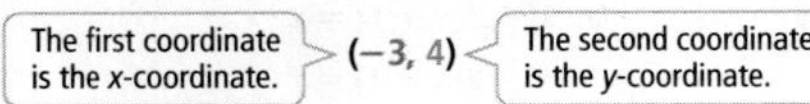

You use the x-coordinate to tell how far to move right (positive) or left (negative) from the origin. You then use the y-coordinate to tell how far to move up (positive) or down (negative) to reach the point (x, y).

Example 1

Graph each point in the coordinate plane. In which quadrant or on which axis would you find each point?

a. Graph point $A(-2, 3)$ in the coordinate plane.

To graph $A(-2, 3)$, move 2 units to the left of the origin. Then move 3 units up. Since the x-coordinate is negative and the y-coordinate is positive, point A is in Quadrant II.

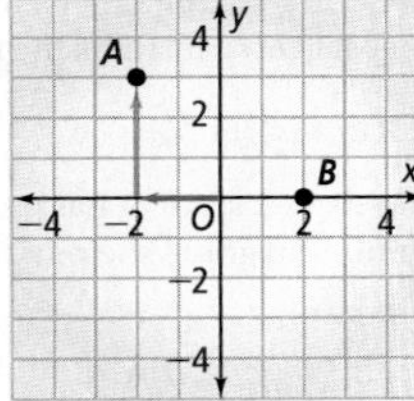

b. Graph point $B(2, 0)$ in the coordinate plane.

To graph $B(2, 0)$, move 2 units to the right of the origin. Since the y-coordinate is 0, point B is on the x-axis.

Exercises

Name the coordinates of each point in the coordinate plane at the right.

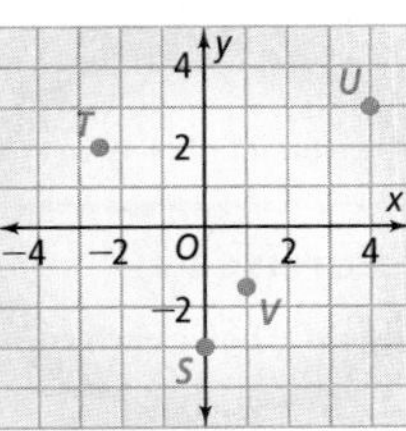

1. S **2.** T **3.** U **4.** V

Graph each ordered pair in the same coordinate plane.

5. $(0, -5)$ **6.** $(4, -1)$ **7.** $(-2, -2)$ **8.** $\left(-1\frac{1}{2}, 4\right)$

In which quadrant or on which axis would you find each point?

9. $(0, 10)$ **10.** $\left(1\frac{1}{2}, -3\right)$ **11.** $(-5, 0)$ **12.** $(-9, -2)$

The Coordinate Plane

1. $(0, -3)$

2. $\left(-2\frac{1}{2}, 2\right)$

3. $(4, 3)$

4. $\left(1, -1\frac{1}{2}\right)$

5–8.

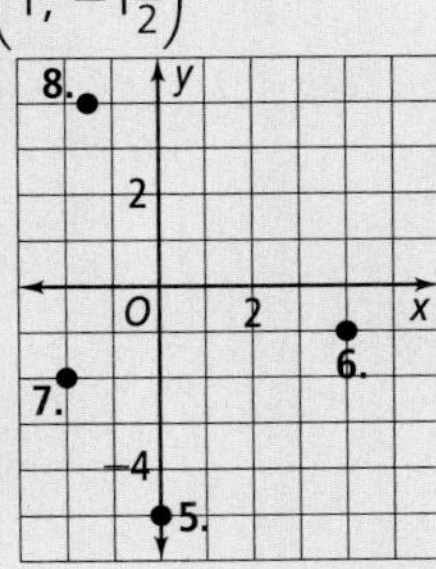

9. y-axis

10. IV

11. x-axis

12. III

Skills Handbook

Solving and Writing Linear Equations

To solve a linear equation, use the properties of equality and properties of real numbers to find the value of the variable that satisfies the equation.

Example 1

Algebra **Solve each equation.**

a. $5x - 3 = 2$

$5x - 3 = 2$

$5x = 5$ Add 3 to each side.

$x = 1$ Divide each side by 5.

b. $1 - 2(x + 1) = x$

$1 - 2(x + 1) = x$

$1 - 2x - 2 = x$ Use the Distributive Property.

$-1 - 2x = x$ Simplify the left side.

$-1 = 3x$ Add $2x$ to each side.

$-\frac{1}{3} = x$ Divide each side by 3.

You will sometimes need to translate word problems into equations. Look for words that suggest a relationship or some type of mathematical operation.

Example 2

Algebra **A student has grades of 80, 65, 78, and 92 on four tests. What is the minimum grade she must earn on her next test to ensure an average of 80?**

Relate average of 80, 65, 78, 92, and next test is 80 — Pull out the key words and numbers.

Define Let x = the grade on the next test. — Let a variable represent what you are looking for.

Write $\frac{80 + 65 + 78 + 92 + x}{5} = 80$ Write an equation.

$\frac{315 + x}{5} = 80$ Combine like terms.

$315 + x = 400$ Multiply each side by 5.

$x = 85$ Subtract 315 from each side.

The student must earn 85 on the next test for an average of 80.

Exercises

Algebra **Solve each equation.**

1. $3n + 2 = 17$
2. $5a - 2 = -12$
3. $2x + 4 = 10$
4. $3(n - 4) = 15$
5. $4 + 2y = 8y$
6. $-6z + 1 = 13 - 3z$
7. $6 - (3t + 4) = t$
8. $7 = -2(4n - 4.5)$
9. $(w + 5) - 5 = (2w + 5)$
10. $\frac{5}{7}p - 10 = 30$
11. $\frac{m}{-3} - 3 = 1$
12. $5k + 2(k + 1) = 23$

13. Twice a number subtracted from 35 is 9. What is the number?

14. The Johnsons pay \$9.95 a month plus \$.035 per min for local phone service. Last month, they paid \$12.75. How many minutes of local calls did they make?

Answers

Solving and Writing Linear Equations

1. 5 **2.** −2
3. 3 **4.** 9
5. $\frac{2}{3}$ **6.** −4
7. $\frac{1}{2}$ **8.** $\frac{1}{4}$
9. −5 **10.** 56
11. −12 **12.** 3
13. $35 - 2x = 9$; 13
14. $\$9.95 + \$.035m = \$12.75$; 80 min

Percents

A percent is a ratio in which a number is compared to 100. For example, the expression *60 percent* means "60 out of 100." The symbol % stands for "percent."

A percent can be written in decimal form by first writing it in ratio form, and then writing the ratio as a decimal. For example, 25% is equal to the ratio $\frac{25}{100}$ or $\frac{1}{4}$. As a decimal, $\frac{1}{4}$ is equal to 0.25. Note that 25% can also be written directly as a decimal by moving the decimal point two places to the left.

Example 1

Convert each percent to a decimal.

a. 42%
$42\% = 0.42$

b. 157%
$157\% = 1.57$

c. 12.4%
$12.4\% = 0.124$

d. 4%
$4\% = 0.04$

To calculate a percent of a number, write the percent as a decimal and multiply.

Example 2

Simplify. Where necessary, round to the nearest tenth.

a. 30% of 242

30% of $242 = 0.3 \cdot 242$
$= 72.6$

b. 7% of 38

7% of $38 = 0.07 \cdot 38$
$= 2.66 \approx 2.7$

For a percent problem, it is a good idea to check that your answer is reasonable by estimating it.

Example 3

Estimate 23% of 96.

$23\% \approx 25\%$ and $96 \approx 100$. So 25% $\left(\text{or } \frac{1}{4}\right)$ of $100 = 25$.
A reasonable estimate is 25.

Exercises

Convert each percent to a decimal.

1. 50% **2.** 27% **3.** 6% **4.** 84.6% **5.** 109% **6.** 2.5%

Simplify. Where necessary, round to the nearest tenth.

7. 21% of 40 **8.** 45% of 200 **9.** 6% of 120 **10.** 23.8% of 176

Estimate.

11. 12% of 70 **12.** 48% of 87 **13.** 73% of 64 **14.** 77% of 42

Skills Handbook

Percents

1. 0.5 **2.** 0.27
3. 0.06 **4.** 0.846
5. 1.09 **6.** 0.025
7. 8.4 **8.** 90
9. 7.2 **10.** 41.9
11–14. Answers may vary. Samples are given.
11. 7 **12.** 43
13. 45 **14.** 32

Skills Handbook

Probability

Probability is a measure of the likelihood of an event occurring. All probabilities range from 0 to 1, where 0 is the probability of an event that cannot happen and 1 is the probability of an event that is certain to happen. An event with probability 0.5, or 50%, has an equal chance of happening or not happening.

The formula $P(E) = \frac{\text{number of favorable outcomes}}{\text{number of possible outcomes}}$ is used to calculate the probability of event E.

Example 1

The numbers 2 through 21 are written on pieces of paper and placed in a hat. One piece of paper is drawn at random. Determine the probability of selecting a perfect square.

The total number of outcomes, 2, 3, 4, · · · , 21, for this event is 20.

There are 3 favorable outcomes: 4, 9, and 16.

$P(\text{selecting a perfect square}) = \frac{3}{20}$

Example 2

Determine the probability of getting exactly two heads when two coins are tossed.

The total number of outcomes, (H, H), (H, T), (T, H), (T, T), for this event is 4.

There is 1 favorable outcome, (H, H).

$P(\text{two heads}) = \frac{1}{4}$

Exercises

A jar contains 3 white balls, 7 red balls, and 4 green balls. A ball is selected at random from the jar. Determine each probability.

1. $P(\text{red})$
2. $P(\text{white})$
3. $P(\text{green})$
4. $P(\text{green or white})$
5. A red ball is removed from the jar. What is the probability that the next ball selected will be green?

You roll a 12-sided number cube. Determine each probability.

6. $P(2)$
7. $P(4 \text{ or } 5)$
8. $P(\text{even number})$
9. $P(\text{odd number})$
10. $P(\text{prime number})$
11. $P(\text{factor of } 8)$

A coin is flipped three times. Determine the probability of each outcome.

12. exactly two tails
13. two heads and one tail
14. no more than two tails
15. no more than one head
16. at least one tail
17. all tails or all heads

836

Answers

Probability

1. $\frac{1}{2}$
2. $\frac{3}{14}$
3. $\frac{2}{7}$
4. $\frac{1}{2}$
5. $\frac{4}{13}$
6. $\frac{1}{12}$
7. $\frac{1}{6}$
8. $\frac{1}{2}$
9. $\frac{1}{2}$
10. $\frac{5}{12}$
11. $\frac{1}{3}$
12. $\frac{3}{8}$
13. $\frac{3}{8}$
14. $\frac{7}{8}$
15. $\frac{1}{2}$
16. $\frac{7}{8}$
17. $\frac{1}{4}$

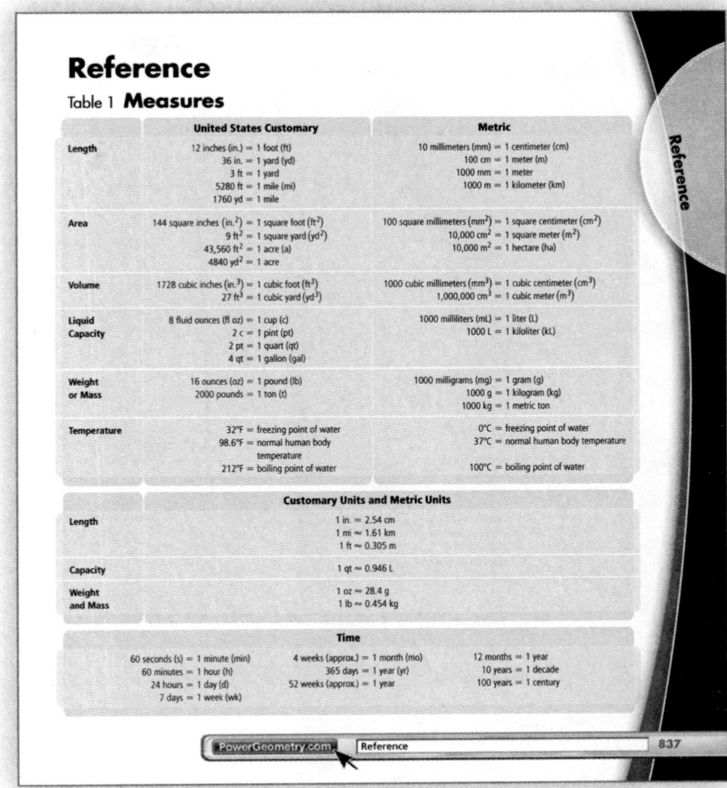

Reference

Table 1 Measures

	United States Customary	Metric
Length	12 inches (in.) = 1 foot (ft) 36 in. = 1 yard (yd) 3 ft = 1 yard 5280 ft = 1 mile (mi) 1760 yd = 1 mile	10 millimeters (mm) = 1 centimeter (cm) 100 cm = 1 meter (m) 1000 mm = 1 meter 1000 m = 1 kilometer (km)
Area	144 square inches ($in.^2$) = 1 square foot (ft^2) 9 ft^2 = 1 square yard (yd^2) 43,560 ft^2 = 1 acre (a) 4840 yd^2 = 1 acre	100 square millimeters (mm^2) = 1 square centimeter (cm^2) 10,000 cm^2 = 1 square meter (m^2) 10,000 m^2 = 1 hectare (ha)
Volume	1728 cubic inches ($in.^3$) = 1 cubic foot (ft^3) 27 ft^3 = 1 cubic yard (yd^3)	1000 cubic millimeters (mm^3) = 1 cubic centimeter (cm^3) 1,000,000 cm^3 = 1 cubic meter (m^3)
Liquid Capacity	8 fluid ounces (fl oz) = 1 cup (c) 2 c = 1 pint (pt) 2 pt = 1 quart (qt) 4 qt = 1 gallon (gal)	1000 milliliters (mL) = 1 liter (L) 1000 L = 1 kiloliter (kL)
Weight or Mass	16 ounces (oz) = 1 pound (lb) 2000 pounds = 1 ton (t)	1000 milligrams (mg) = 1 gram (g) 1000 g = 1 kilogram (kg) 1000 kg = 1 metric ton
Temperature	32°F = freezing point of water 98.6°F = normal human body temperature 212°F = boiling point of water	0°C = freezing point of water 37°C = normal human body temperature 100°C = boiling point of water

	Customary Units and Metric Units
Length	1 in. = 2.54 cm 1 mi ≈ 1.61 km 1 ft ≈ 0.305 m
Capacity	1 qt ≈ 0.946 L
Weight and Mass	1 oz ≈ 28.4 g 1 lb ≈ 0.454 kg

Time		
60 seconds (s) = 1 minute (min) 60 minutes = 1 hour (h) 24 hours = 1 day (d) 7 days = 1 week (wk)	4 weeks (approx.) = 1 month (mo) 365 days = 1 year (yr) 52 weeks (approx.) = 1 year	12 months = 1 year 10 years = 1 decade 100 years = 1 century

PowerGeometry.com Reference 837

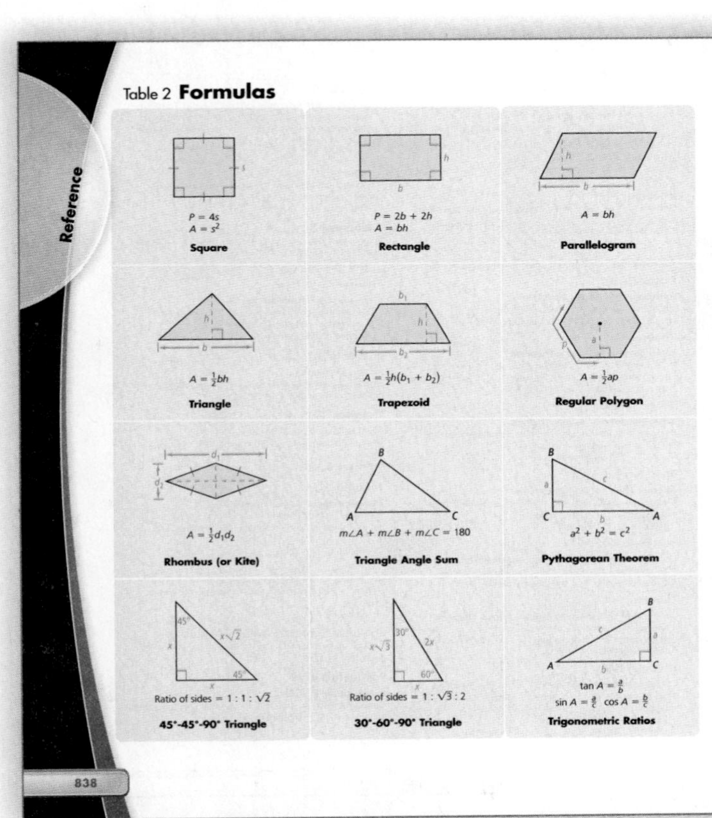

Table 2 Formulas

$P = 4s$, $A = s^2$ — **Square**

$P = 2b + 2h$, $A = bh$ — **Rectangle**

$A = bh$ — **Parallelogram**

$A = \frac{1}{2}bh$ — **Triangle**

$A = \frac{1}{2}h(b_1 + b_2)$ — **Trapezoid**

$A = \frac{1}{2}ap$ — **Regular Polygon**

$A = \frac{1}{2}d_1d_2$ — **Rhombus (or Kite)**

$m\angle A + m\angle B + m\angle C = 180$ — **Triangle Angle Sum**

$a^2 + b^2 = c^2$ — **Pythagorean Theorem**

Ratio of sides = $1 : 1 : \sqrt{2}$ — **45°-45°-90° Triangle**

Ratio of sides = $1 : \sqrt{3} : 2$ — **30°-60°-90° Triangle**

$\tan A = \frac{a}{b}$, $\sin A = \frac{a}{c}$, $\cos A = \frac{b}{c}$ — **Trigonometric Ratios**

838

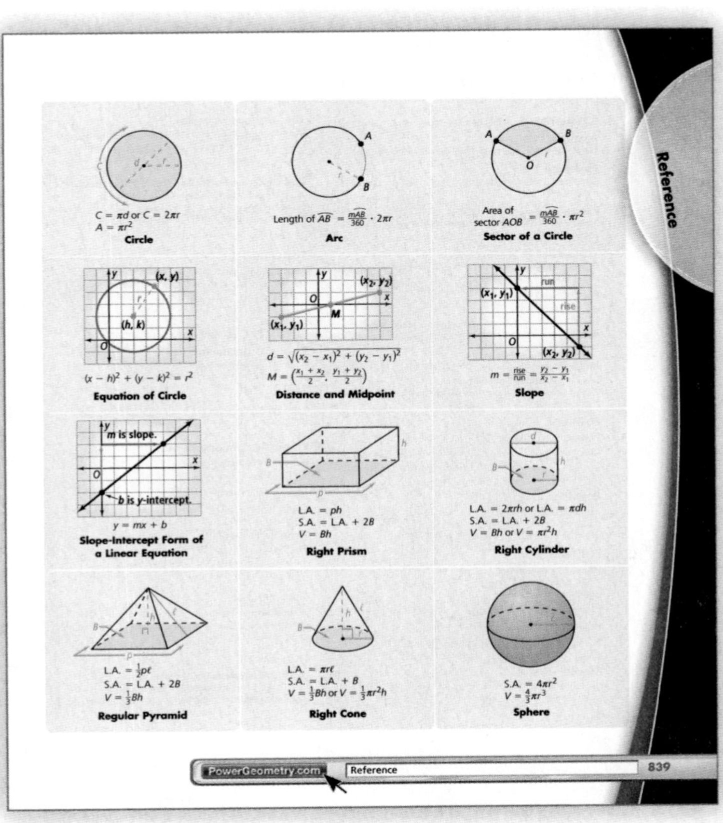

$C = \pi d$ or $C = 2\pi r$, $A = \pi r^2$ — **Circle**

Length of $\widehat{AB} = \frac{m\widehat{AB}}{360} \cdot 2\pi r$ — **Arc**

Area of sector $AOB = \frac{m\widehat{AB}}{360} \cdot \pi r^2$ — **Sector of a Circle**

$(x - h)^2 + (y - k)^2 = r^2$ — **Equation of Circle**

$d = \sqrt{(x_2 - x_1)^2 + (y_2 - y_1)^2}$, $M = \left(\frac{x_1 + x_2}{2}, \frac{y_1 + y_2}{2}\right)$ — **Distance and Midpoint**

$m = \frac{rise}{run} = \frac{y_2 - y_1}{x_2 - x_1}$ — **Slope**

$y = mx + b$ (m is slope. b is y-intercept.) — **Slope-Intercept Form of a Linear Equation**

L.A. $= ph$, S.A. $=$ L.A. $+ 2B$, $V = Bh$ — **Right Prism**

L.A. $= 2\pi rh$ or L.A. $= \pi dh$, S.A. $=$ L.A. $+ 2B$, $V = Bh$ or $V = \pi r^2h$ — **Right Cylinder**

L.A. $= \frac{1}{2}p\ell$, S.A. $=$ L.A. $+ 2B$, $V = \frac{1}{3}Bh$ — **Regular Pyramid**

L.A. $= \pi r\ell$, S.A. $=$ L.A. $+ B$, $V = \frac{1}{3}Bh$ or $V = \frac{1}{3}\pi r^2h$ — **Right Cone**

S.A. $= 4\pi r^2$, $V = \frac{4}{3}\pi r^3$ — **Sphere**

PowerGeometry.com Reference 839

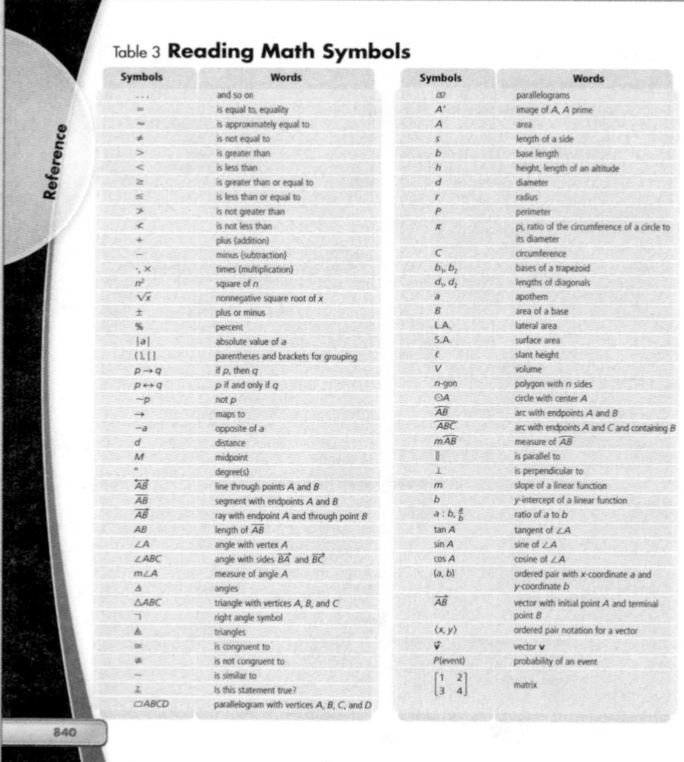

Table 3 **Reading Math Symbols**

Symbols	Words
$\ldots$	and so on
$=$	is equal to, equality
$\approx$	is approximately equal to
$\neq$	is not equal to
$>$	is greater than
$<$	is less than
$\geq$	is greater than or equal to
$\leq$	is less than or equal to
$\not>$	is not greater than
$\not<$	is not less than
$+$	plus (addition)
$-$	minus (subtraction)
$\cdot, \times$	times (multiplication)
n^2	square of n
$\sqrt{x}$	nonnegative square root of x
$\pm$	plus or minus
%	percent
$\lvert a \rvert$	absolute value of a
( ), [ ]	parentheses and brackets for grouping
$p \rightarrow q$	if p, then q
$p \leftrightarrow q$	p if and only if q
$\sim p$	not p
$\rightarrow$	maps to
$-a$	opposite of a
d	distance
M	midpoint
$^\circ$	degree(s)
$\overleftrightarrow{AB}$	line through points A and B
$\overline{AB}$	segment with endpoints A and B
$\overrightarrow{AB}$	ray with endpoint A and through point B
AB	length of $\overline{AB}$
$\angle A$	angle with vertex A
$\angle ABC$	angle with sides $\overrightarrow{BA}$ and $\overrightarrow{BC}$
$m\angle A$	measure of angle A
$\measuredangle$s	angles
$\triangle ABC$	triangle with vertices A, B, and C
⌝	right angle symbol
$\triangle$s	triangles
$\cong$	is congruent to
$\ncong$	is not congruent to
$\sim$	is similar to
$\stackrel{?}{=}$	Is this statement true?
$\square ABCD$	parallelogram with vertices A, B, C, and D
▱s	parallelograms
A'	image of A, A prime
A	area
s	length of a side
b	base length
h	height, length of an altitude
d	diameter
r	radius
P	perimeter
π	pi, ratio of the circumference of a circle to its diameter
C	circumference
b_1, b_2	bases of a trapezoid
d_1, d_2	lengths of diagonals
a	apothem
B	area of a base
L.A.	lateral area
S.A.	surface area
ℓ	slant height
V	volume
n-gon	polygon with n sides
$\odot A$	circle with center A
$\overset{\frown}{AB}$	arc with endpoints A and B
$\overset{\frown}{ABC}$	arc with endpoints A and C and containing B
$m\overset{\frown}{AB}$	measure of $\overset{\frown}{AB}$
$\parallel$	is parallel to
$\perp$	is perpendicular to
m	slope of a linear function
b	y-intercept of a linear function
$a : b, \frac{a}{b}$	ratio of a to b
$\tan A$	tangent of $\angle A$
$\sin A$	sine of $\angle A$
$\cos A$	cosine of $\angle A$
(a, b)	ordered pair with x-coordinate a and y-coordinate b
$\overrightarrow{AB}$	vector with initial point A and terminal point B
$\langle x, y \rangle$	ordered pair notation for a vector
$\vec{\mathbf{v}}$	vector $\mathbf{v}$
P(event)	probability of an event
$\begin{bmatrix} 1 & 2 \\ 3 & 4 \end{bmatrix}$	matrix

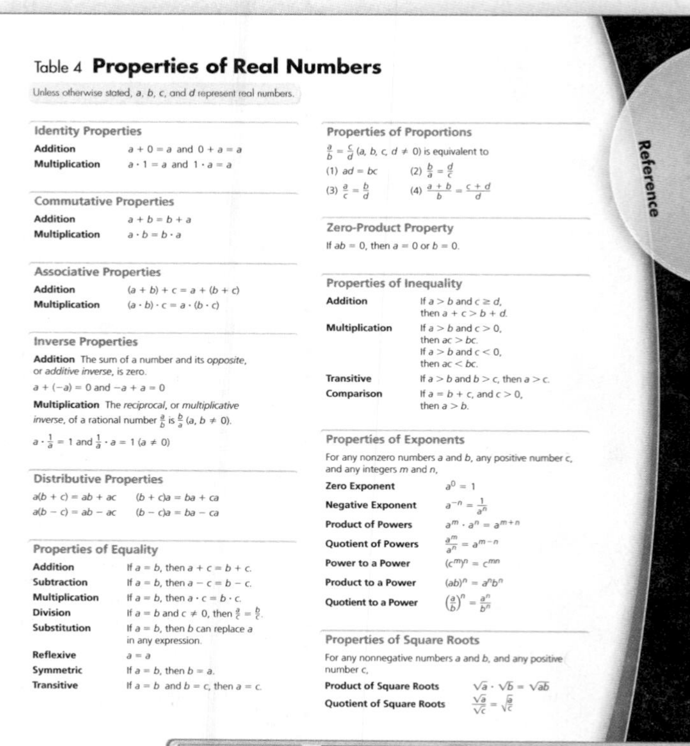

Table 4 **Properties of Real Numbers**

Unless otherwise stated, a, b, c, and d represent real numbers.

Identity Properties

Addition $a + 0 = a$ and $0 + a = a$

Multiplication $a \cdot 1 = a$ and $1 \cdot a = a$

Commutative Properties

Addition $a + b = b + a$

Multiplication $a \cdot b = b \cdot a$

Associative Properties

Addition $(a + b) + c = a + (b + c)$

Multiplication $(a \cdot b) \cdot c = a \cdot (b \cdot c)$

Inverse Properties

Addition The sum of a number and its *opposite*, or *additive inverse*, is zero.

$a + (-a) = 0$ and $-a + a = 0$

Multiplication The *reciprocal*, or *multiplicative inverse*, of a rational number $\frac{a}{b}$ is $\frac{b}{a}$ $(a, b \neq 0)$.

$a \cdot \frac{1}{a} = 1$ and $\frac{1}{a} \cdot a = 1$ $(a \neq 0)$

Distributive Properties

$a(b + c) = ab + ac$ $(b + c)a = ba + ca$

$a(b - c) = ab - ac$ $(b - c)a = ba - ca$

Properties of Equality

Addition If $a = b$, then $a + c = b + c$.

Subtraction If $a = b$, then $a - c = b - c$.

Multiplication If $a = b$, then $a \cdot c = b \cdot c$.

Division If $a = b$ and $c \neq 0$, then $\frac{a}{c} = \frac{b}{c}$.

Substitution If $a = b$, then b can replace a in any expression.

Reflexive $a = a$

Symmetric If $a = b$, then $b = a$.

Transitive If $a = b$ and $b = c$, then $a = c$.

Properties of Proportions

$\frac{a}{b} = \frac{c}{d}$ $(a, b, c, d \neq 0)$ is equivalent to

(1) $ad = bc$ (2) $\frac{b}{a} = \frac{d}{c}$

(3) $\frac{a}{c} = \frac{b}{d}$ (4) $\frac{a + b}{b} = \frac{c + d}{d}$

Zero-Product Property

If $ab = 0$, then $a = 0$ or $b = 0$.

Properties of Inequality

Addition If $a > b$ and $c \geq d$, then $a + c > b + d$.

Multiplication If $a > b$ and $c > 0$, then $ac > bc$. If $a > b$ and $c < 0$, then $ac < bc$.

Transitive If $a > b$ and $b > c$, then $a > c$.

Comparison If $a = b + c$, and $c > 0$, then $a > b$.

Properties of Exponents

For any nonzero numbers a and b, any positive number c, and any integers m and n,

Zero Exponent $a^0 = 1$

Negative Exponent $a^{-n} = \frac{1}{a^n}$

Product of Powers $a^m \cdot a^n = a^{m+n}$

Quotient of Powers $\frac{a^m}{a^n} = a^{m-n}$

Power to a Power $(c^m)^n = c^{mn}$

Product to a Power $(ab)^n = a^n b^n$

Quotient to a Power $\left(\frac{a}{b}\right)^n = \frac{a^n}{b^n}$

Properties of Square Roots

For any nonnegative numbers a and b, and any positive number c,

Product of Square Roots $\sqrt{a} \cdot \sqrt{b} = \sqrt{ab}$

Quotient of Square Roots $\frac{\sqrt{a}}{\sqrt{c}} = \sqrt{\frac{a}{c}}$

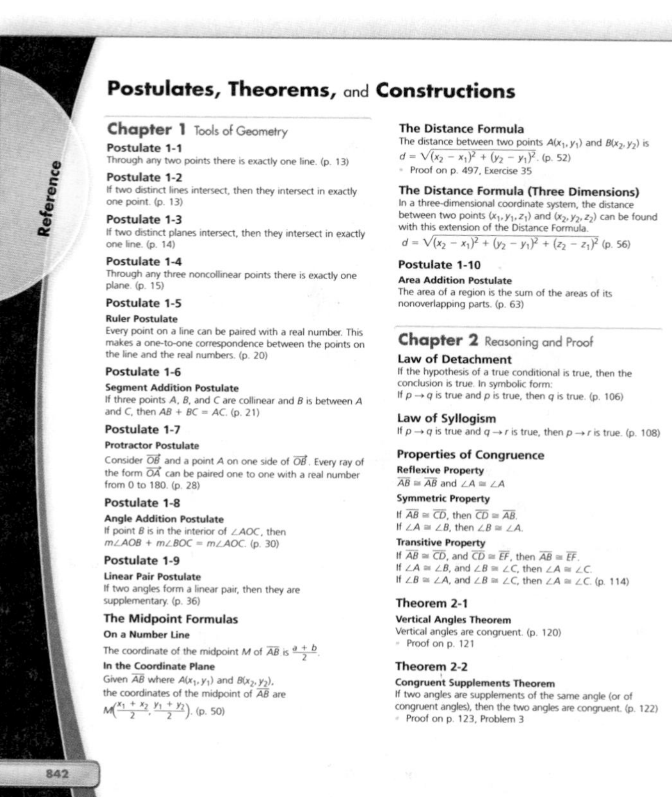

Postulates, Theorems, and Constructions

Chapter 1 Tools of Geometry

Postulate 1-1
Through any two points there is exactly one line. (p. 13)

Postulate 1-2
If two distinct lines intersect, then they intersect in exactly one point. (p. 13)

Postulate 1-3
If two distinct planes intersect, then they intersect in exactly one line. (p. 14)

Postulate 1-4
Through any three noncollinear points there is exactly one plane. (p. 15)

Postulate 1-5
Ruler Postulate
Every point on a line can be paired with a real number. This makes a one-to-one correspondence between the points on the line and the real numbers. (p. 20)

Postulate 1-6
Segment Addition Postulate
If three points A, B, and C are collinear and B is between A and C, then $AB + BC = AC$. (p. 21)

Postulate 1-7
Protractor Postulate
Consider $\overrightarrow{OB}$ and a point A on one side of $\overrightarrow{OB}$. Every ray of the form $\overrightarrow{OA}$ can be paired one to one with a real number from 0 to 180. (p. 28)

Postulate 1-8
Angle Addition Postulate
If point B is in the interior of $\angle AOC$, then $m\angle AOB + m\angle BOC = m\angle AOC$. (p. 30)

Postulate 1-9
Linear Pair Postulate
If two angles form a linear pair, then they are supplementary. (p. 36)

The Midpoint Formulas
On a Number Line
The coordinate of the midpoint M of $\overline{AB}$ is $\frac{a+b}{2}$.
In the Coordinate Plane
Given $\overline{AB}$ where $A(x_1, y_1)$ and $B(x_2, y_2)$, the coordinates of the midpoint of $\overline{AB}$ are $M\left(\frac{x_1 + x_2}{2}, \frac{y_1 + y_2}{2}\right)$. (p. 50)

The Distance Formula
The distance between two points $A(x_1, y_1)$ and $B(x_2, y_2)$ is $d = \sqrt{(x_2 - x_1)^2 + (y_2 - y_1)^2}$. (p. 52)
- Proof on p. 497, Exercise 35

The Distance Formula (Three Dimensions)
In a three-dimensional coordinate system, the distance between two points (x_1, y_1, z_1) and (x_2, y_2, z_2) can be found with this extension of the Distance Formula.
$d = \sqrt{(x_2 - x_1)^2 + (y_2 - y_1)^2 + (z_2 - z_1)^2}$ (p. 56)

Postulate 1-10
Area Addition Postulate
The area of a region is the sum of the areas of its nonoverlapping parts. (p. 63)

Chapter 2 Reasoning and Proof

Law of Detachment
If the hypothesis of a true conditional is true, then the conclusion is true. In symbolic form:
If $p \rightarrow q$ is true and p is true, then q is true. (p. 106)

Law of Syllogism
If $p \rightarrow q$ is true and $q \rightarrow r$ is true, then $p \rightarrow r$ is true. (p. 108)

Properties of Congruence
Reflexive Property
$\overline{AB} \cong \overline{AB}$ and $\angle A \cong \angle A$
Symmetric Property
If $\overline{AB} \cong \overline{CD}$, then $\overline{CD} \cong \overline{AB}$.
If $\angle A \cong \angle B$, then $\angle B \cong \angle A$.
Transitive Property
If $\overline{AB} \cong \overline{CD}$, and $\overline{CD} \cong \overline{EF}$, then $\overline{AB} \cong \overline{EF}$.
If $\angle A \cong \angle B$, and $\angle B \cong \angle C$, then $\angle A \cong \angle C$.
If $\angle B \cong \angle A$, and $\angle B \cong \angle C$, then $\angle A \cong \angle C$. (p. 114)

Theorem 2-1
Vertical Angles Theorem
Vertical angles are congruent. (p. 120)
- Proof on p. 121

Theorem 2-2
Congruent Supplements Theorem
If two angles are supplements of the same angle (or of congruent angles), then the two angles are congruent. (p. 122)
- Proof on p. 123, Problem 3

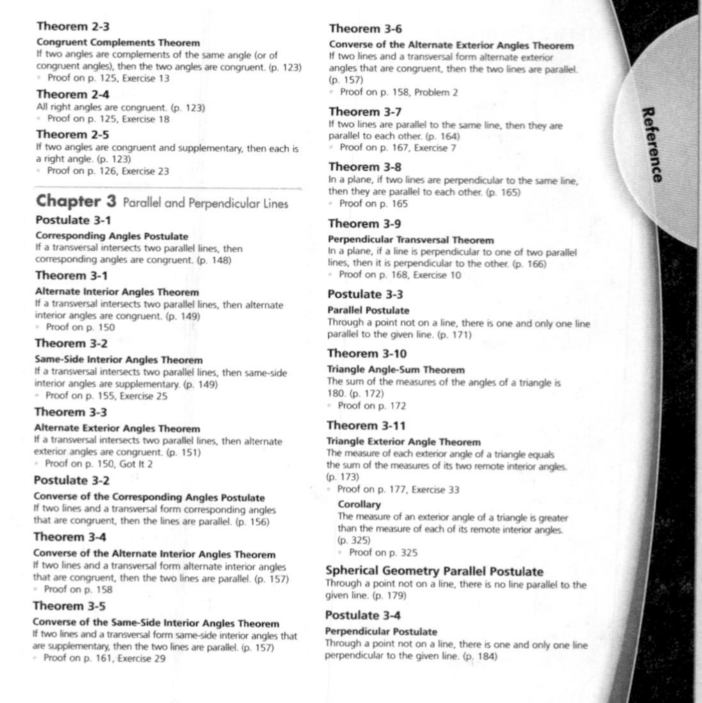

Theorem 2-3
Congruent Complements Theorem
If two angles are complements of the same angle (or of congruent angles), then the two angles are congruent. (p. 123)
- Proof on p. 125, Exercise 13

Theorem 2-4
All right angles are congruent. (p. 123)
- Proof on p. 125, Exercise 18

Theorem 2-5
If two angles are congruent and supplementary, then each is a right angle. (p. 123)
- Proof on p. 126, Exercise 23

Chapter 3 Parallel and Perpendicular Lines

Postulate 3-1
Corresponding Angles Postulate
If a transversal intersects two parallel lines, then corresponding angles are congruent. (p. 148)

Theorem 3-1
Alternate Interior Angles Theorem
If a transversal intersects two parallel lines, then alternate interior angles are congruent. (p. 149)
- Proof on p. 150

Theorem 3-2
Same-Side Interior Angles Theorem
If a transversal intersects two parallel lines, then same-side interior angles are supplementary. (p. 149)
- Proof on p. 155, Exercise 25

Theorem 3-3
Alternate Exterior Angles Theorem
If a transversal intersects two parallel lines, then alternate exterior angles are congruent. (p. 151)
- Proof on p. 150, Got It 2

Postulate 3-2
Converse of the Corresponding Angles Postulate
If two lines and a transversal form corresponding angles that are congruent, then the lines are parallel. (p. 156)

Theorem 3-4
Converse of the Alternate Interior Angles Theorem
If two lines and a transversal form alternate interior angles that are congruent, then the two lines are parallel. (p. 157)
- Proof on p. 158

Theorem 3-5
Converse of the Same-Side Interior Angles Theorem
If two lines and a transversal form same-side interior angles that are supplementary, then the two lines are parallel. (p. 157)
- Proof on p. 161, Exercise 29

Theorem 3-6
Converse of the Alternate Exterior Angles Theorem
If two lines and a transversal form alternate exterior angles that are congruent, then the two lines are parallel. (p. 157)
- Proof on p. 158, Problem 2

Theorem 3-7
If two lines are parallel to the same line, then they are parallel to each other. (p. 164)
- Proof on p. 167, Exercise 7

Theorem 3-8
In a plane, if two lines are perpendicular to the same line, then they are parallel to each other. (p. 165)
- Proof on p. 165

Theorem 3-9
Perpendicular Transversal Theorem
In a plane, if a line is perpendicular to one of two parallel lines, then it is perpendicular to the other. (p. 166)
- Proof on p. 168, Exercise 10

Postulate 3-3
Parallel Postulate
Through a point not on a line, there is one and only one line parallel to the given line. (p. 171)

Theorem 3-10
Triangle Angle-Sum Theorem
The sum of the measures of the angles of a triangle is 180. (p. 172)
- Proof on p. 172

Theorem 3-11
Triangle Exterior Angle Theorem
The measure of each exterior angle of a triangle equals the sum of the measures of its two remote interior angles. (p. 173)
- Proof on p. 177, Exercise 33

Corollary
The measure of an exterior angle of a triangle is greater than the measure of each of its remote interior angles. (p. 325)
- Proof on p. 325

Spherical Geometry Parallel Postulate
Through a point not on a line, there is no line parallel to the given line. (p. 179)

Postulate 3-4
Perpendicular Postulate
Through a point not on a line, there is one and only one line perpendicular to the given line. (p. 184)

Reference

Slopes of Parallel Lines
If two nonvertical lines are parallel, then their slopes are equal. If the slopes of two distinct nonvertical lines are equal, then the lines are parallel. Any two vertical lines or horizontal lines are parallel. (p. 197)
- Proofs on p. 457, Exercises 33, 34

Slopes of Perpendicular Lines
If two nonvertical lines are perpendicular, then the product of their slopes is −1. If the slopes of two lines have a product of −1, then the lines are perpendicular. Any horizontal line and vertical line are perpendicular. (p. 198)
- Proofs on p. 418, Exercise 28; p. 497, Exercise 51

Chapter 4 Congruent Triangles

Theorem 4-1
Third Angles Theorem
If the two angles of one triangle are congruent to two angles of another triangle, then the third angles are congruent. (p. 220)
- Proof on p. 220

Postulate 4-1
Side-Side-Side (SSS) Postulate
If the three sides of one triangle are congruent to the three sides of another triangle, then the two triangles are congruent. (p. 227)

Postulate 4-2
Side-Angle-Side (SAS) Postulate
If two sides and the included angle of one triangle are congruent to two sides and the included angle of another triangle, then the two triangles are congruent. (p. 228)

Postulate 4-3
Angle-Side-Angle (ASA) Postulate
If two angles and the included side of one triangle are congruent to two angles and the included side of another triangle, then the two triangles are congruent. (p. 234)

Theorem 4-2
Angle-Angle-Side (AAS) Theorem
If two angles and a nonincluded side of one triangle are congruent to two angles and the corresponding nonincluded side of another triangle, then the triangles are congruent. (p. 236)
- Proof on p. 236

Theorem 4-3
Isosceles Triangle Theorem
If two sides of a triangle are congruent, then the angles opposite those sides are congruent. (p. 250)
- Proofs on p. 251; p. 255, Exercise 22

Corollary
If a triangle is equilateral, then the triangle is equiangular. (p. 252)
- Proof on p. 255, Exercise 24

Theorem 4-4
Converse of the Isosceles Triangle Theorem
If two angles of a triangle are congruent, then the sides opposite the angles are congruent. (p. 251)
- Proof on p. 255, Exercise 23

Corollary
If a triangle is equiangular, then the triangle is equilateral. (p. 252)
- Proof on p. 255, Exercise 24

Theorem 4-5
If a line bisects the vertex angle of an isosceles triangle, then the line is also the perpendicular bisector of the base. (p. 252)
- Proof on p. 255, Exercise 26

Theorem 4-6
Hypotenuse-Leg (HL) Theorem
If the hypotenuse and a leg of one right triangle are congruent to the hypotenuse and a leg of another right triangle, then the triangles are congruent. (p. 259)
- Proof on p. 259

Chapter 5 Relationships Within Triangles

Theorem 5-1
Triangle Midsegment Theorem
If a segment joins the midpoints of two sides of a triangle, then the segment is parallel to the third side and is half as long. (p. 285)
- Proof on p. 415, Got It 2

Theorem 5-2
Perpendicular Bisector Theorem
If a point is on the perpendicular bisector of a segment, then it is equidistant from the endpoints of the segment. (p. 293)
- Proof on p. 298, Exercise 32

Theorem 5-3
Converse of the Perpendicular Bisector Theorem
If a point is equidistant from the endpoints of a segment, then it is on the perpendicular bisector of the segment. (p. 293)
- Proof on p. 298, Exercise 33

Theorem 5-4
Angle Bisector Theorem
If a point is on the bisector of an angle, then the point is equidistant from the sides of the angle. (p. 295)
- Proof on p. 298, Exercise 34

Theorem 5-5
Converse of the Angle Bisector Theorem
If a point in the interior of an angle is equidistant from the sides of the angle, then the point is on the angle bisector. (p. 295)
- Proof on p. 298, Exercise 35

Theorem 5-6
Concurrency of Perpendicular Bisectors Theorem
The perpendicular bisectors of the sides of a triangle are concurrent at a point equidistant from the vertices. (p. 301)
- Proof on p. 302

Theorem 5-7
Concurrency of Angle Bisectors Theorem
The bisectors of the angles of a triangle are concurrent at a point equidistant from the sides of the triangle. (p. 303)
- Proof on p. 306, Exercise 24

Theorem 5-8
Concurrency of Medians Theorem
The medians of a triangle are concurrent at a point that is two-thirds the distance from each vertex to the midpoint of the opposite side. (p. 309)
- Proof on p. 417, Exercise 25

Theorem 5-9
Concurrency of Altitudes Theorem
The lines that contain the altitudes of a triangle are concurrent. (p. 310)
- Proof on p. 417, Exercise 26

Comparison Property of Inequality
If $a = b + c$ and $c > 0$, then $a > b$. (p. 324)
- Proof on p. 324

Theorem 5-10
If two sides of a triangle are not congruent, then the larger angle lies opposite the longer side. (p. 325)
- Proof on p. 330, Exercise 40

Theorem 5-11
If two angles of a triangle are not congruent, then the longer side lies opposite the larger angle. (p. 326)
- Proof on p. 326

Theorem 5-12
Triangle Inequality Theorem
The sum of the lengths of any two sides of a triangle is greater than the length of the third side. (p. 327)
- Proof on p. 331, Exercise 45

Theorem 5-13
The Hinge Theorem (SAS Inequality Theorem)
If two sides of one triangle are congruent to two sides of another triangle and the included angles are not congruent, then the longer third side is opposite the larger included angle. (p. 332)
- Proof on p. 338, Exercise 25

Theorem 5-14
Converse of the Hinge Theorem (SSS Inequality)
If two sides of one triangle are congruent to two sides of another triangle and the third sides are not congruent, then the larger included angle is opposite the longer third side. (p. 334)
- Proof on p. 334

Chapter 6 Polygons and Quadrilaterals

Theorem 6-1
Polygon Angle-Sum Theorem
The sum of the measures of the angles of an n-gon is $(n - 2)180$. (p. 353)
- Proof on p. 357, Exercise 40

Corollary
The measure of each angle of a regular n-gon is $\frac{(n-2)180}{n}$. (p. 354)
- Proof on p. 358, Exercise 43

Theorem 6-2
Polygon Exterior Angle-Sum Theorem
The sum of the measures of the exterior angles of a polygon, one at each vertex, is 360. (p. 355)
- Proofs on p. 352 (using a computer); p. 357, Exercise 39

Theorem 6-3
If a quadrilateral is a parallelogram, then its opposite sides are congruent. (p. 359)
- Proof on p. 360

Theorem 6-4
If a quadrilateral is a parallelogram, then its consecutive angles are supplementary. (p. 360)
- Proof on p. 365, Exercise 32

Theorem 6-5
If a quadrilateral is a parallelogram, then its opposite angles are congruent. (p. 361)
- Proof on p. 361, Problem 2

Theorem 6-6
If a quadrilateral is a parallelogram, then its diagonals bisect each other. (p. 362)
- Proof on p. 364, Exercise 13

Theorem 6-7
If three (or more) parallel lines cut off congruent segments on one transversal, then they cut off congruent segments on every transversal. (p. 363)
- Proof on p. 366, Exercise 43

Theorem 6-8
If both pairs of opposite sides of a quadrilateral are congruent, then the quadrilateral is a parallelogram. (p. 367)
- Proof on p. 373, Exercise 20

Theorem 6-9
If an angle of a quadrilateral is supplementary to both of its consecutive angles, then the quadrilateral is a parallelogram. (p. 368)
- Proof on p. 373, Exercise 21

Theorem 6-10
If both pairs of opposite angles of a quadrilateral are congruent, then the quadrilateral is a parallelogram. (p. 368)
- Proof on p. 373, Exercise 18

Theorem 6-11
If the diagonals of a quadrilateral bisect each other, then the quadrilateral is a parallelogram. (p. 369)
- Proof on p. 369

Theorem 6-12
If one pair of opposite sides of a quadrilateral is both congruent and parallel, then the quadrilateral is a parallelogram. (p. 370)
- Proof on p. 373, Exercise 19

Theorem 6-13
If a parallelogram is a rhombus, then its diagonals are perpendicular. (p. 376)
- Proof on p. 377

Theorem 6-14
If a parallelogram is a rhombus, then each diagonal bisects a pair of opposite angles. (p. 376)
- Proof on p. 381, Exercise 45

Theorem 6-15
If a parallelogram is a rectangle, then its diagonals are congruent. (p. 378)
- Proof on p. 381, Exercise 41

Theorem 6-16
If the diagonals of a parallelogram are perpendicular, then the parallelogram is a rhombus. (p. 383)
- Proof on p. 383

Theorem 6-17
If one diagonal of a parallelogram bisects a pair of opposite angles, then the parallelogram is a rhombus. (p. 384)
- Proof on p. 387, Exercise 23

Theorem 6-18
If the diagonals of a parallelogram are congruent, then the parallelogram is a rectangle. (p. 384)
- Proof on p. 387, Exercise 24

Theorem 6-19
If a quadrilateral is an isosceles trapezoid, then each pair of base angles is congruent. (p. 389)
- Proof on p. 396, Exercise 45

Theorem 6-20
If a quadrilateral is an isosceles trapezoid, then its diagonals are congruent. (p. 391)
- Proof on p. 396, Exercise 54

Theorem 6-21
Trapezoid Midsegment Theorem
If a quadrilateral is a trapezoid, then
(1) the midsegment is parallel to the bases, and
(2) the length of the midsegment is half the sum of the lengths of the bases. (p. 391)
- Proofs on p. 409, Problem 3; p. 415, Problem 2

Theorem 6-22
If a quadrilateral is a kite, then its diagonals are perpendicular. (p. 392)
- Proof on p. 392

Chapter 7 Similarity

Postulate 7-1
Angle-Angle Similarity (AA ~) Postulate
If two angles of one triangle are congruent to two angles of another triangle, then the triangles are similar. (p. 450)

Theorem 7-1
Side-Angle-Side Similarity (SAS ~) Theorem
If an angle of one triangle is congruent to an angle of a second triangle, and the sides that include the two angles are proportional, then the triangles are similar. (p. 451)
- Proof on p. 457, Exercise 35

Theorem 7-2
Side-Side-Side Similarity (SSS ~) Theorem
If the corresponding sides of two triangles are proportional, then the triangles are similar. (p. 451)
- Proof on p. 458, Exercise 36

Theorem 7-3
The altitude to the hypotenuse of a right triangle divides the triangle into two triangles that are similar to the original triangle and to each other. (p. 460)
- Proof on p. 461

Corollary 1
The length of the altitude to the hypotenuse of a right triangle is the geometric mean of the lengths of the segments of the hypotenuse. (p. 462)
- Proof on p. 466, Exercise 42

Corollary 2
The altitude to the hypotenuse of a right triangle separates the hypotenuse so that the length of each leg of the triangle is the geometric mean of the length of the hypotenuse and the length of the segment of the hypotenuse adjacent to the leg. (p. 463)
- Proof on p. 466, Exercise 43

Theorem 7-4
Side-Splitter Theorem
If a line is parallel to one side of a triangle and intersects the other two sides, then it divides those sides proportionally. (p. 471)
- Proof on p. 472

Converse
If a line divides two sides of a triangle proportionally, then it is parallel to the third side.
- Proof on p. 476, Exercise 37

Corollary
If three parallel lines intersect two transversals, then the segments intercepted on the transversals are proportional. (p. 473)
- Proof on p. 477, Exercise 46

Theorem 7-5
Triangle-Angle-Bisector Theorem
If a ray bisects an angle of a triangle, then it divides the opposite side into two segments that are proportional to the other two sides of the triangle. (p. 473)
- Proof on p. 477, Exercise 47

Chapter 8 Right Triangles and Trigonometry

Theorem 8-1
Pythagorean Theorem
If a triangle is a right triangle, then the sum of the squares of the lengths of the legs is equal to the square of the length of the hypotenuse.
$a^2 + b^2 = c^2$ (p. 491)
- Proof on p. 497, Exercise 49

Theorem 8-2
Converse of the Pythagorean Theorem
If the sum of the squares of the lengths of two sides of a triangle is equal to the square of the length of the third side, then the triangle is a right triangle. (p. 493)
- Proof on p. 498, Exercise 52

Theorem 8-3
If the square of the length of the longest side of a triangle is greater than the sum of the squares of the lengths of the other two sides, then the triangle is obtuse. (p. 494)
- Proof on p. 498, Exercise 53

Theorem 8-4
If the square of the length of the longest side of a triangle is less than the sum of the squares of the lengths of the other two sides, then the triangle is acute. (p. 494)
- Proof on p. 498, Exercise 54

Theorem 8-5
45°-45°-90° Triangle Theorem
In a 45°-45°-90° triangle, both legs are congruent and the length of the hypotenuse is $\sqrt{2}$ times the length of a leg.
hypotenuse $= \sqrt{2} \cdot$ leg (p. 499)
- Proof on p. 499

Theorem 8-6
30°-60°-90° Triangle Theorem
In a 30°-60°-90° triangle, the length of the hypotenuse is twice the length of the shorter leg. The length of the longer leg is $\sqrt{3}$ times the length of the shorter leg.
hypotenuse $= 2 \cdot$ shorter leg
longer leg $= \sqrt{3} \cdot$ shorter leg (p. 501)
- Proof on p. 501

Law of Sines
$\frac{\sin A}{a} = \frac{\sin B}{b} = \frac{\sin C}{c}$ (p. 522)
- Proof on p. 523, Exercise 1

Law of Cosines
$a^2 = b^2 + c^2 - 2bc \cos A$
$b^2 = a^2 + c^2 - 2ac \cos B$
$c^2 = a^2 + b^2 - 2ab \cos C$ (p. 522)
- Proof on p. 523, Exercise 2

Chapter 9 Transformations

Theorem 9-1
A translation or rotation is a composition of two reflections. (p. 584)

Theorem 9-2
A composition of reflections across two parallel lines is a translation. A composition of reflections across two intersecting lines is a rotation. (p. 585)

Theorem 9-3
Fundamental Theorem of Isometries
In a plane, one of two congruent figures can be mapped onto the other by a composition of at most three reflections. (p. 586)

Theorem 9-4
Isometry Classification Theorem
There are only four isometries. They are translation, rotation, reflection, and glide reflection. (p. 587)

Chapter 10 Area

Theorem 10-1
Area of a Rectangle
The area of a rectangle is the product of its base and height.
$A = bh$ (p. 616)

Theorem 10-2
Area of a Parallelogram
The area of a parallelogram is the product of a base and the corresponding height.
$A = bh$ (p. 616)

Theorem 10-3
Area of a Triangle
The area of a triangle is half the product of a base and the corresponding height.
$A = \frac{1}{2}bh$ (p. 618)

Theorem 10-4
Area of a Trapezoid
The area of a trapezoid is half the product of the height and the sum of the bases.
$A = \frac{1}{2}h(b_1 + b_2)$ (p. 623)

Theorem 10-5
Area of a Rhombus or a Kite
The area of a rhombus or a kite is half the product of the lengths of its diagonals.
$A = \frac{1}{2}d_1d_2$ (p. 624)

Postulate 10-1

If two figures are congruent, then their areas are equal. (p. 630)

Theorem 10-6

Area of a Regular Polygon
The area of a regular polygon is half the product of the apothem and the perimeter.
$A = \frac{1}{2}ap$ (p. 630)
- Proof on p. 630

Theorem 10-7

Perimeters and Areas of Similar Figures
If the scale factor of two similar figures is $\frac{a}{b}$, then
(1) the ratio of their perimeters is $\frac{a}{b}$ and
(2) the ratio of their areas is $\frac{a^2}{b^2}$. (p. 635)

Theorem 10-8

Area of a Triangle Given SAS
The area of a triangle is half the product of the lengths of two sides and the sine of the included angle.
Area of $\triangle ABC = \frac{1}{2}bc(\sin A)$ (p. 645)
- Proof on p. 645

Postulate 10-2

Arc Addition Postulate
The measure of the arc formed by two adjacent arcs is the sum of the measures of the two arcs.
$m\widehat{ABC} = m\widehat{AB} + m\widehat{BC}$ (p. 650)

Theorem 10-9

Circumference of a Circle
The circumference of a circle is π times the diameter.
$C = \pi d$ or $C = 2\pi r$ (p. 651)

Theorem 10-10

Arc Length
The length of an arc of a circle is the product of the ratio $\frac{\text{measure of the arc}}{360}$ and the circumference of the circle.
length of $\widehat{AB} = \frac{m\widehat{AB}}{360} \cdot 2\pi r$ or
length of $\widehat{AB} = \frac{m\widehat{AB}}{360} \cdot \pi d$ (p. 653)

Theorem 10-11

Area of a Circle
The area of a circle is the product of π and the square of the radius.
$A = \pi r^2$ (p. 660)

Theorem 10-12

Area of a Sector of a Circle
The area of a sector of a circle is the product of the ratio $\frac{\text{measure of the arc}}{360}$ and the area of the circle.
Area of sector $AOB = \frac{m\widehat{AB}}{360} \cdot \pi r^2$ (p. 661)

Chapter 11 Surface Area and Volume

Theorem 11-1

Lateral and Surface Areas of a Prism
The lateral area of a right prism is the product of the perimeter of the base and the height of the prism.
L.A. $= ph$
The surface area of a right prism is the sum of the lateral area and the areas of the two bases.
S.A. $=$ L.A. $+ 2B$ (p. 700)

Theorem 11-2

Lateral and Surface Areas of a Cylinder
The lateral area of a right cylinder is the product of the circumference of the base and the height of the cylinder.
L.A. $= 2\pi rh$, or L.A. $= \pi dh$
The surface area of a right cylinder is the sum of the lateral area and areas of the two bases.
S.A. $=$ L.A. $+ 2B$, or S.A. $= 2\pi rh + 2\pi r^2$ (p. 702)

Theorem 11-3

Lateral and Surface Areas of a Pyramid
The lateral area of a regular pyramid is half the product of the perimeter p of the base and the slant height ℓ of the pyramid.
L.A. $= \frac{1}{2}p\ell$
The surface area of a regular pyramid is the sum of the lateral area and the area B of the base.
S.A. $=$ L.A. $+ B$ (p. 709)

Theorem 11-4

Lateral and Surface Areas of a Cone
The lateral area of a right cone is half the product of the circumference of the base and the slant height of the cone.
L.A. $= \frac{1}{2} \cdot 2\pi r\ell$, or L.A. $= \pi r\ell$
The surface area of a right cone is the sum of the lateral area and the area of the base.
S.A. $=$ L.A. $+ B$ (p. 711)

Theorem 11-5

Cavalieri's Principle
If two space figures have the same height and the same cross-sectional area at every level, then they have the same volume. (p. 718)

Theorem 11-6

Volume of a Prism
The volume of a prism is the product of the area of the base and the height of the prism.
$V = Bh$ (p. 718)

Theorem 11-7

Volume of a Cylinder
The volume of a cylinder is the product of the area of the base and the height of the cylinder.
$V = Bh$, or $V = \pi r^2 h$ (p. 719)

Theorem 11-8

Volume of a Pyramid
The volume of a pyramid is one third the product of the area of the base and the height of the pyramid.
$V = \frac{1}{3}Bh$ (p. 726)

Theorem 11-9

Volume of a Cone
The volume of a cone is one third the product of the area of the base and the height of the cone.
$V = \frac{1}{3}Bh$, or $V = \frac{1}{3}\pi r^2 h$ (p. 728)

Theorem 11-10

Surface Area of a Sphere
The surface area of a sphere is four times the product of π and the square of the radius of the sphere.
S.A. $= 4\pi r^2$ (p. 734)

Theorem 11-11

Volume of a Sphere
The volume of a sphere is four thirds the product of π and the cube of the radius of the sphere.
$V = \frac{4}{3}\pi r^3$ (p. 735)

Theorem 11-12

Areas and Volumes of Similar Solids
If the scale factor of two similar solids is $a : b$, then
- the ratio of their corresponding areas is $a^2 : b^2$, and
- the ratio of their volumes is $a^3 : b^3$. (p. 743)

Chapter 12 Circles

Theorem 12-1

If a line is tangent to a circle, then the line is perpendicular to the radius at the point of tangency. (p. 762)
- Proof on p. 763

Theorem 12-2

If a line in the plane of a circle is perpendicular to a radius at its endpoint on the circle, then the line is tangent to the circle. (p. 764)
- Proof on p. 769, Exercise 30

Theorem 12-3

If two segments are tangent to a circle from a point outside the circle, then the two segments are congruent. (p. 766)
- Proof on p. 768, Exercise 23

Theorem 12-4

Within a circle or in congruent circles, congruent central angles have congruent arcs. (p. 771)
- Proof on p. 777, Exercise 19

Converse
Within a circle or in congruent circles, congruent arcs have congruent central angles. (p. 771)
- Proof on p. 778, Exercise 35

Theorem 12-5

Within a circle or in congruent circles, congruent central angles have congruent chords. (p. 772)
- Proof on p. 777, Exercise 20

Converse
Within a circle or in congruent circles, congruent chords have congruent central angles. (p. 772)
- Proof on p. 778, Exercise 36

Theorem 12-6

Within a circle or in congruent circles, congruent chords have congruent arcs. (p. 772)
- Proof on p. 777, Exercise 21

Converse
Within a circle or in congruent circles, congruent arcs have congruent chords. (p. 772)
- Proof on p. 778, Exercise 37

Theorem 12-7

Within a circle or in congruent circles, chords equidistant from the center (or centers) are congruent. (p. 772)
- Proof on p. 773

Converse
Within a circle or in congruent circles, congruent chords are equidistant from the center (or centers). (p. 772)
- Proof on p. 778, Exercise 38

Theorem 12-8

In a circle, if a diameter is perpendicular to a chord, it bisects the chord and its arc. (p. 774)
- Proof on p. 777, Exercise 22

Theorem 12-9

In a circle, if a diameter bisects a chord (that is not a diameter), it is perpendicular to the chord. (p. 774)
- Proof on p. 774

Theorem 12-10

In a circle, the perpendicular bisector of a chord contains the center of the circle. (p. 774)
- Proof on p. 778, Exercise 33

Theorem 12-11

Inscribed Angle Theorem
The measure of an inscribed angle is half the measure of its intercepted arc. (p. 780)
- Proofs on p. 781; p. 785, Exercises 26, 27

Corollary 1
Two inscribed angles that intercept the same arc are congruent. (p. 782)
- Proof on p. 786, Exercise 31

Corollary 2
An angle inscribed in a semicircle is a right angle. (p. 782)
- Proof on p. 786, Exercise 32

Corollary 3
The opposite angles of a quadrilateral inscribed in a circle are supplementary. (p. 782)
- Proof on p. 786, Exercise 33

Theorem 12-12

The measure of an angle formed by a tangent and a chord is half the measure of the intercepted arc. (p. 783)
- Proof on p. 786, Exercise 34

Theorem 12-13

The measure of an angle formed by two lines that intersect inside a circle is half the sum of the measures of the intercepted arcs. (p. 790)
- Proof on p. 791

Theorem 12-14

The measure of an angle formed by two lines that intersect outside a circle is half the difference of the measures of the intercepted arcs. (p. 790)
- Proofs on p. 796, Exercises 35, 36

Theorem 12-15

For a given point and circle, the product of the lengths of the two segments from the point to the circle is constant along any line through the point and circle. (p. 793)
- Proofs on p. 793; p. 796, Exercises 37, 38

Theorem 12-16

An equation of a circle with center (h, k) and radius r is $(x - h)^2 + (y - k)^2 = r^2$. (p. 798)
- Proof on p. 799

Constructions

Construction 1

Congruent Segments
Construct a segment congruent to a given segment. (p. 43)

Construction 2

Congruent Angles
Construct an angle congruent to a given angle. (p. 44)

Construction 3

Perpendicular Bisector
Construct the perpendicular bisector of a segment. (p. 45)

Construction 4

Angle Bisector
Construct the bisector of an angle. (p. 45)

Construction 5

Parallel Through a Point Not on a Line
Construct the line parallel to a given line and through a given point that is not on the line. (p. 182)

Construction 6

Quadrilateral With Parallel Sides
Construct a quadrilateral with one pair of parallel sides of lengths a and b. (p. 183)

Construction 7

Perpendicular Through a Point on a Line
Construct the perpendicular to a given line at a given point on the line. (p. 184)

Construction 8

Perpendicular Through a Point Not on a Line
Construct the perpendicular to a given line through a given point not on the line. (p. 185)

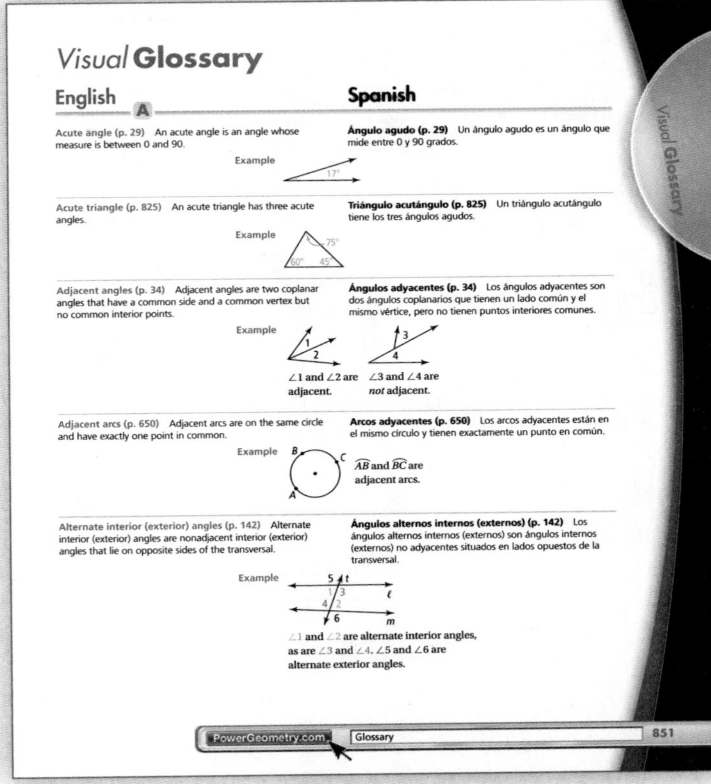

Visual Glossary

English / Spanish

A

Acute angle (p. 29) An acute angle is an angle whose measure is between 0 and 90.

Ángulo agudo (p. 29) Un ángulo agudo es un ángulo que mide entre 0 y 90 grados.

Example

Acute triangle (p. 825) An acute triangle has three acute angles.

Triángulo acutángulo (p. 825) Un triángulo acutángulo tiene los tres ángulos agudos.

Example

Adjacent angles (p. 34) Adjacent angles are two coplanar angles that have a common side and a common vertex but no common interior points.

Ángulos adyacentes (p. 34) Los ángulos adyacentes son dos ángulos coplanarios que tienen un lado común y el mismo vértice, pero no tienen puntos interiores comunes.

Example

$\angle 1$ and $\angle 2$ are adjacent. $\angle 3$ and $\angle 4$ are *not* adjacent.

Adjacent arcs (p. 650) Adjacent arcs are on the same circle and have exactly one point in common.

Arcos adyacentes (p. 650) Los arcos adyacentes están en el mismo círculo y tienen exactamente un punto en común.

Example

$\widehat{AB}$ and $\widehat{BC}$ are adjacent arcs.

Alternate interior (exterior) angles (p. 142) Alternate interior (exterior) angles are nonadjacent interior (exterior) angles that lie on opposite sides of the transversal.

Ángulos alternos internos (externos) (p. 142) Los ángulos alternos internos (externos) son ángulos internos (externos) no adyacentes situados en lados opuestos de la transversal.

Example

$\angle 1$ and $\angle 2$ are alternate interior angles, as are $\angle 3$ and $\angle 4$. $\angle 5$ and $\angle 6$ are alternate exterior angles.

PowerGeometry.com | Glossary 851

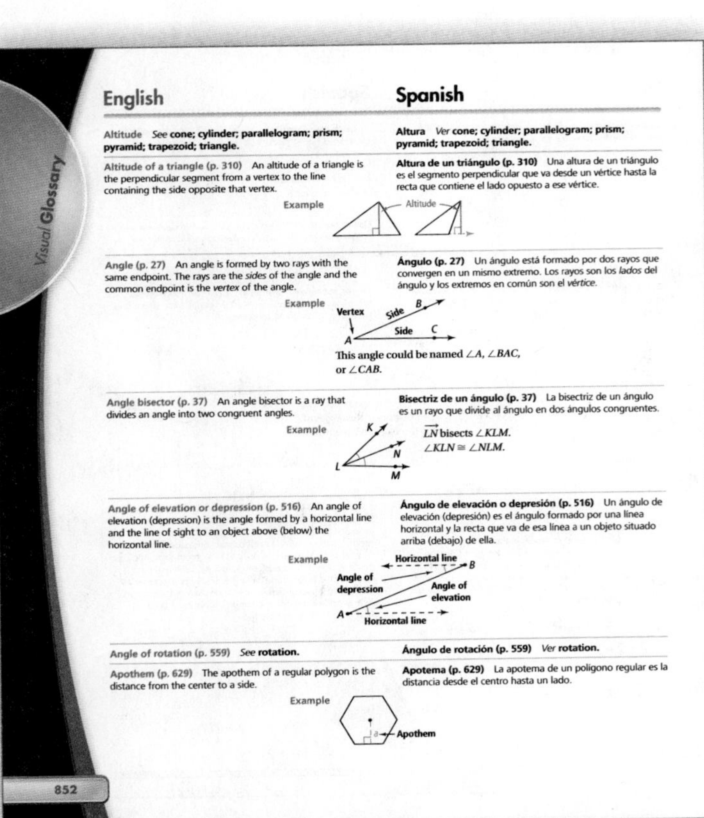

English / Spanish

Altitude *See* **cone; cylinder; parallelogram; prism; pyramid; trapezoid; triangle.**

Altura *Ver* **cone; cylinder; parallelogram; prism; pyramid; trapezoid; triangle.**

Altitude of a triangle (p. 310) An altitude of a triangle is the perpendicular segment from a vertex to the line containing the side opposite that vertex.

Altura de un triángulo (p. 310) Una altura de un triángulo es el segmento perpendicular que va desde un vértice hasta la recta que contiene el lado opuesto a ese vértice.

Example

Angle (p. 27) An angle is formed by two rays with the same endpoint. The rays are the *sides* of the angle and the common endpoint is the *vertex* of the angle.

Ángulo (p. 27) Un ángulo está formado por dos rayos que convergen en un mismo extremo. Los rayos son los *lados* del ángulo y los extremos en común son el *vértice*.

Example

This angle could be named $\angle A$, $\angle BAC$, or $\angle CAB$.

Angle bisector (p. 37) An angle bisector is a ray that divides an angle into two congruent angles.

Bisectriz de un ángulo (p. 37) La bisectriz de un ángulo es un rayo que divide al ángulo en dos ángulos congruentes.

Example

$\overrightarrow{LN}$ bisects $\angle KLM$. $\angle KLN \cong \angle NLM$.

Angle of elevation or depression (p. 516) An angle of elevation (depression) is the angle formed by a horizontal line and the line of sight to an object above (below) the horizontal line.

Ángulo de elevación o depresión (p. 516) Un ángulo de elevación (depresión) es el ángulo formado por una línea horizontal y la recta que va de esa línea a un objeto situado arriba (debajo) de ella.

Example

Angle of rotation (p. 559) *See* **rotation.**

Ángulo de rotación (p. 559) *Ver* **rotation.**

Apothem (p. 629) The apothem of a regular polygon is the distance from the center to a side.

Apotema (p. 629) La apotema de un polígono regular es la distancia desde el centro hasta un lado.

Example

852

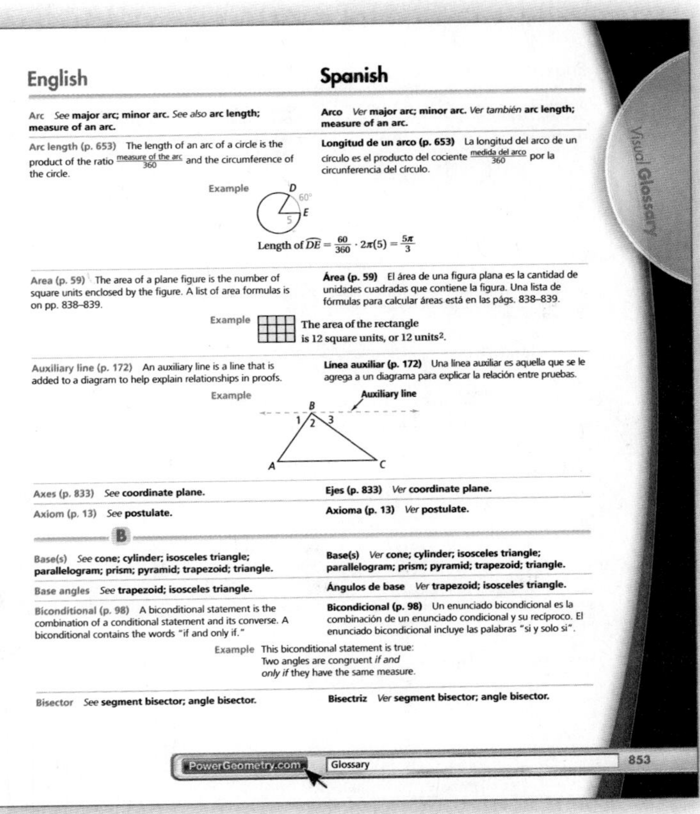

English / Spanish

Arc *See* **major arc; minor arc.** *See also* **arc length; measure of an arc.**

Arco *Ver* **major arc; minor arc.** *Ver también* **arc length; measure of an arc.**

Arc length (p. 653) The length of an arc of a circle is the product of the ratio $\frac{\text{measure of the arc}}{360}$ and the circumference of the circle.

Longitud de un arco (p. 653) La longitud del arco de un círculo es el producto del cociente $\frac{\text{medida del arco}}{360}$ por la circunferencia del círculo.

Example

Length of $\widehat{DE} = \frac{60}{360} \cdot 2\pi(5) = \frac{5\pi}{3}$

Area (p. 59) The area of a plane figure is the number of square units enclosed by the figure. A list of area formulas is on pp. 838–839.

Área (p. 59) El área de una figura plana es la cantidad de unidades cuadradas que contiene la figura. Una lista de fórmulas para calcular áreas está en las págs. 838–839.

Example The area of the rectangle is 12 square units, or 12 units^2.

Auxiliary line (p. 172) An auxiliary line is a line that is added to a diagram to help explain relationships in proofs.

Línea auxiliar (p. 172) Una línea auxiliar es aquella que se le agrega a un diagrama para explicar la relación entre pruebas.

Example

Axes (p. 833) *See* **coordinate plane.**

Ejes (p. 833) *Ver* **coordinate plane.**

Axiom (p. 13) *See* **postulate.**

Axioma (p. 13) *Ver* **postulate.**

B

Base(s) *See* **cone; cylinder; isosceles triangle; parallelogram; prism; pyramid; trapezoid; triangle.**

Base(s) *Ver* **cone; cylinder; isosceles triangle; parallelogram; prism; pyramid; trapezoid; triangle.**

Base angles *See* **trapezoid; isosceles triangle.**

Ángulos de base *Ver* **trapezoid; isosceles triangle.**

Biconditional (p. 98) A biconditional statement is the combination of a conditional statement and its converse. A biconditional contains the words "if and only if."

Bicondicional (p. 98) Un enunciado bicondicional es la combinación de un enunciado condicional y su recíproco. El enunciado bicondicional incluye las palabras "si y solo si".

Example This biconditional statement is true: Two angles are congruent *if and only if* they have the same measure.

Bisector *See* **segment bisector; angle bisector.**

Bisectriz *Ver* **segment bisector; angle bisector.**

PowerGeometry.com | Glossary 853

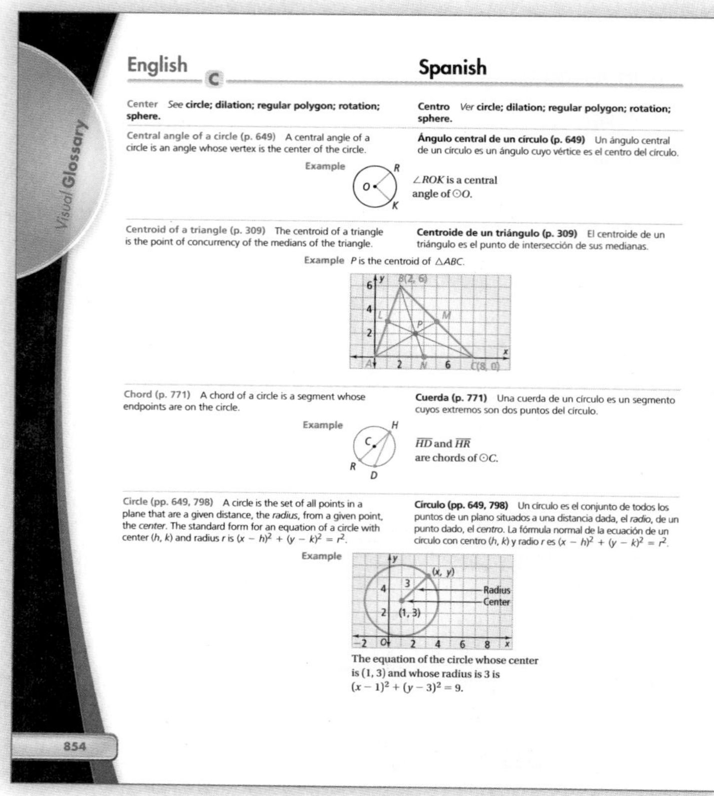

Visual Glossary

English C **Spanish**

Center *See* **circle; dilation; regular polygon; rotation; sphere.**

Centro *Ver* **circle; dilation; regular polygon; rotation; sphere.**

Central angle of a circle (p. 649) A central angle of a circle is an angle whose vertex is the center of the circle.

Ángulo central de un círculo (p. 649) Un ángulo central de un círculo es un ángulo cuyo vértice es el centro del círculo.

Example $\angle ROK$ is a central angle of $\odot O$.

Centroid of a triangle (p. 309) The centroid of a triangle is the point of concurrency of the medians of the triangle.

Centroide de un triángulo (p. 309) El centroide de un triángulo es el punto de intersección de sus medianas.

Example P is the centroid of $\triangle ABC$.

Chord (p. 771) A chord of a circle is a segment whose endpoints are on the circle.

Cuerda (p. 771) Una cuerda de un círculo es un segmento cuyos extremos son dos puntos del círculo.

Example $\overline{HD}$ and $\overline{HR}$ are chords of $\odot C$.

Circle (pp. 649, 798) A circle is the set of all points in a plane that are a given distance, the *radius*, from a given point, the *center*. The standard form for an equation of a circle with center (h, k) and radius r is $(x - h)^2 + (y - k)^2 = r^2$.

Círculo (pp. 649, 798) Un círculo es el conjunto de todos los puntos de un plano situados a una distancia dada, el *radio*, de un punto dado, el *centro*. La fórmula normal de la ecuación de un círculo con centro (h, k) y radio r es $(x - h)^2 + (y - k)^2 = r^2$.

Example The equation of the circle whose center is $(1, 3)$ and whose radius is 3 is $(x - 1)^2 + (y - 3)^2 = 9$.

854

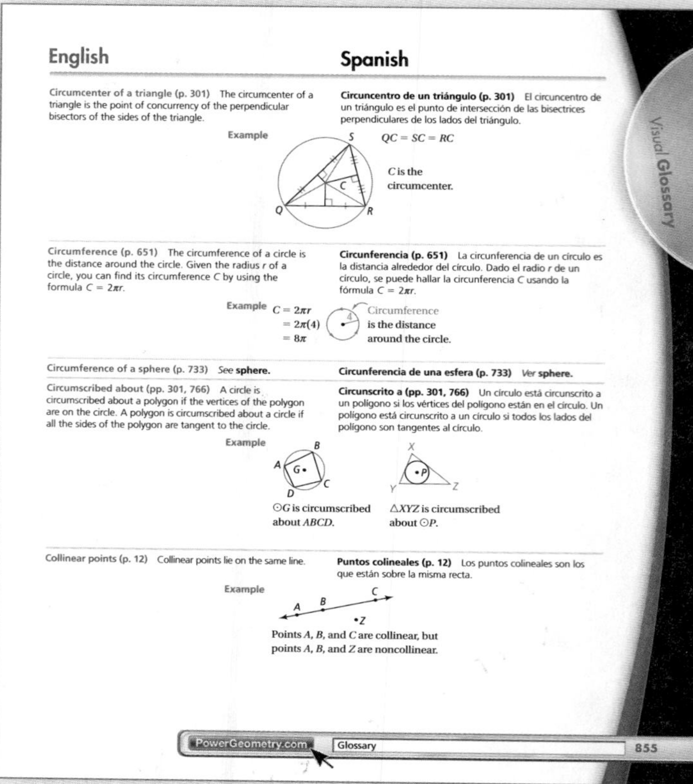

English **Spanish**

Circumcenter of a triangle (p. 301) The circumcenter of a triangle is the point of concurrency of the perpendicular bisectors of the sides of the triangle.

Circuncentro de un triángulo (p. 301) El circuncentro de un triángulo es el punto de intersección de las bisectrices perpendiculares de los lados del triángulo.

Example $QC = SC = RC$

C is the circumcenter.

Circumference (p. 651) The circumference of a circle is the distance around the circle. Given the radius r of a circle, you can find its circumference C by using the formula $C = 2\pi r$.

Circunferencia (p. 651) La circunferencia de un círculo es la distancia alrededor del círculo. Dado el radio r de un círculo, se puede hallar la circunferencia C usando la fórmula $C = 2\pi r$.

Example $C = 2\pi r = 2\pi(4) = 8\pi$

Circumference is the distance around the circle.

Circumference of a sphere (p. 733) *See* **sphere.**

Circunferencia de una esfera (p. 733) *Ver* **sphere.**

Circumscribed about (pp. 301, 766) A circle is circumscribed about a polygon if the vertices of the polygon are on the circle. A polygon is circumscribed about a circle if all the sides of the polygon are tangent to the circle.

Circunscrito a (pp. 301, 766) Un círculo está circunscrito a un polígono si los vértices del polígono están en el círculo. Un polígono está circunscrito a un círculo si todos los lados del polígono son tangentes al círculo.

Example $\odot G$ is circumscribed about $ABCD$. $\triangle XYZ$ is circumscribed about $\odot P$.

Collinear points (p. 12) Collinear points lie on the same line.

Puntos colineales (p. 12) Los puntos colineales son los que están sobre la misma recta.

Example Points A, B, and C are collinear, but points A, B, and Z are noncollinear.

PowerGeometry.com Glossary 855

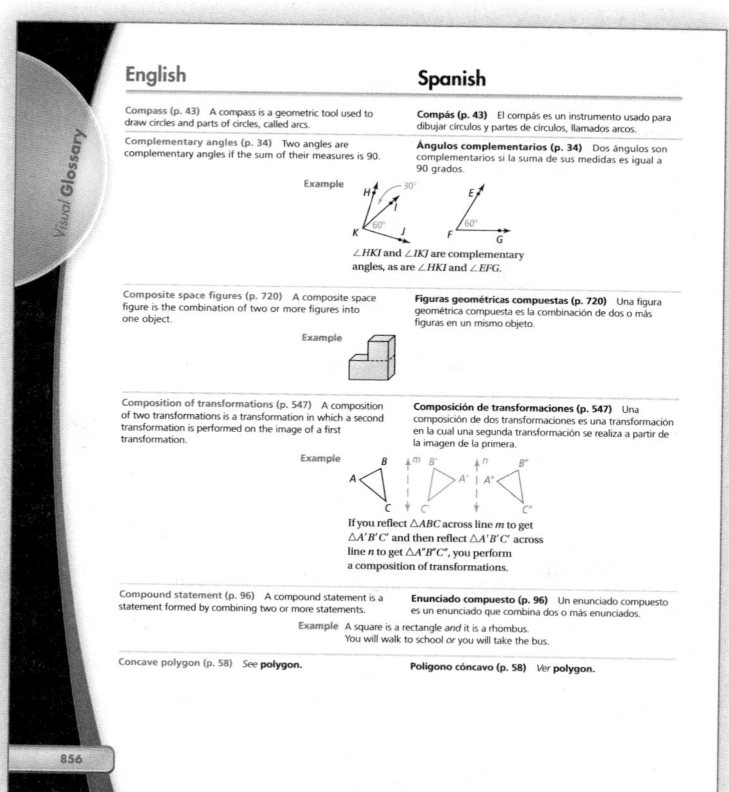

English **Spanish**

Compass (p. 43) A compass is a geometric tool used to draw circles and parts of circles, called arcs.

Compás (p. 43) El compás es un instrumento usado para dibujar círculos y partes de círculos, llamados arcos.

Complementary angles (p. 34) Two angles are complementary angles if the sum of their measures is 90.

Ángulos complementarios (p. 34) Dos ángulos son complementarios si la suma de sus medidas es igual a 90 grados.

Example $\angle HKI$ and $\angle IKJ$ are complementary angles, as are $\angle HKI$ and $\angle EFG$.

Composite space figures (p. 720) A composite space figure is the combination of two or more figures into one object.

Figuras geométricas compuestas (p. 720) Una figura geométrica compuesta es la combinación de dos o más figuras en un mismo objeto.

Example

Composition of transformations (p. 547) A composition of two transformations is a transformation in which a second transformation is performed on the image of a first transformation.

Composición de transformaciones (p. 547) Una composición de dos transformaciones es una transformación en la cual una segunda transformación se realiza a partir de la imagen de la primera.

Example If you reflect $\triangle ABC$ across line m to get $\triangle A'B'C'$ and then reflect $\triangle A'B'C'$ across line n to get $\triangle A''B''C''$, you perform a composition of transformations.

Compound statement (p. 96) A compound statement is a statement formed by combining two or more statements.

Enunciado compuesto (p. 96) Un enunciado compuesto es un enunciado que combina dos o más enunciados.

Example A square is a rectangle *and* it is a rhombus. You will walk to school *or* you will take the bus.

Concave polygon (p. 58) *See* **polygon.**

Polígono cóncavo (p. 58) *Ver* **polygon.**

856

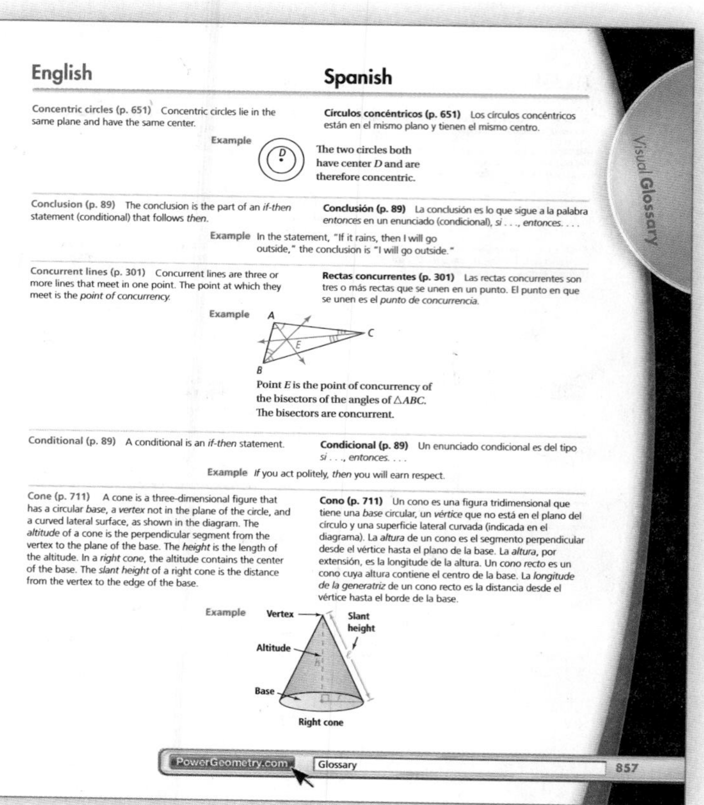

English **Spanish**

Concentric circles (p. 651) Concentric circles lie in the same plane and have the same center.

Círculos concéntricos (p. 651) Los círculos concéntricos están en el mismo plano y tienen el mismo centro.

Example The two circles both have center D and are therefore concentric.

Conclusion (p. 89) The conclusion is the part of an *if-then* statement (conditional) that follows *then*.

Conclusión (p. 89) La conclusión es lo que sigue a la palabra *entonces* en un enunciado (condicional), *si . . ., entonces. . . .*

Example In the statement, "If it rains, then I will go outside," the conclusion is "I will go outside."

Concurrent lines (p. 301) Concurrent lines are three or more lines that meet in one point. The point at which they meet is the *point of concurrency.*

Rectas concurrentes (p. 301) Las rectas concurrentes son tres o más rectas que se unen en un punto. El punto en que se unen es el *punto de concurrencia.*

Example Point E is the point of concurrency of the bisectors of the angles of $\triangle ABC$. The bisectors are concurrent.

Conditional (p. 89) A conditional is an *if-then* statement.

Condicional (p. 89) Un enunciado condicional es del tipo *si . . ., entonces. . . .*

Example *If* you act politely, *then* you will earn respect.

Cone (p. 711) A cone is a three-dimensional figure that has a circular *base*, a *vertex* not in the plane of the circle, and a curved lateral surface, as shown in the diagram. The *altitude* of a cone is the perpendicular segment from the vertex to the plane of the base. The *height* is the length of the altitude. In a *right cone*, the altitude contains the center of the base. The *slant height* of a right cone is the distance from the vertex to the edge of the base.

Cono (p. 711) Un cono es una figura tridimensional que tiene una *base* circular, un *vértice* que no está en el plano del círculo y una superficie lateral curvada (indicada en el diagrama). La *altura* de un cono es el segmento perpendicular desde el vértice hasta el plano de la base. La *altura*, por extensión, es la longitude de la altura. Un *cono recto* es un cono cuya altura contiene el centro de la base. La *longitude de la generatriz* de un cono recto es la distancia desde el vértice hasta el borde de la base.

Example Vertex, Slant height, Altitude, Base

Right cone

PowerGeometry.com Glossary 857

Visual Glossary

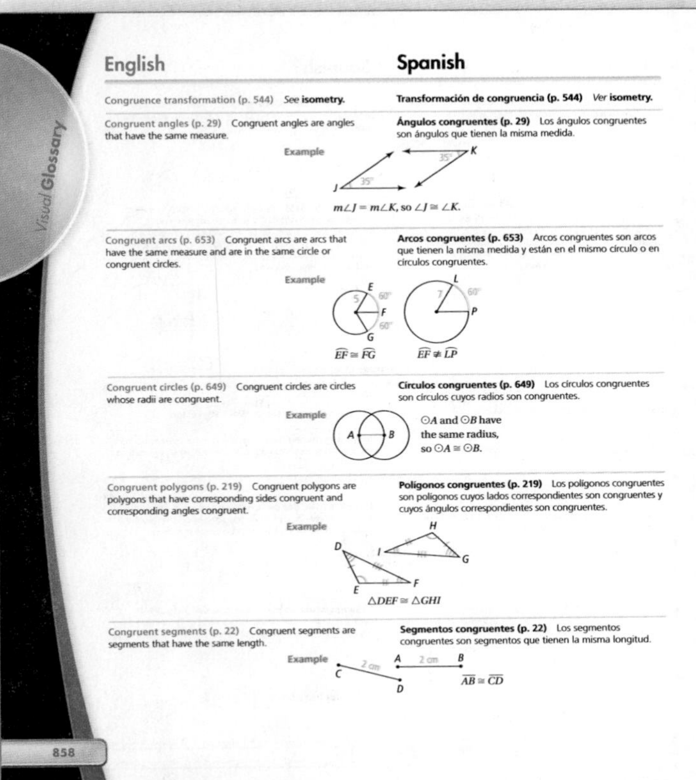

Visual Glossary

English | **Spanish**

Congruence transformation (p. 544) *See* **isometry.**

Transformación de congruencia (p. 544) *Ver* **isometry.**

Congruent angles (p. 29) Congruent angles are angles that have the same measure.

Ángulos congruentes (p. 29) Los ángulos congruentes son ángulos que tienen la misma medida.

Example

$m\angle J = m\angle K$, so $\angle J \cong \angle K$.

Congruent arcs (p. 653) Congruent arcs are arcs that have the same measure and are in the same circle or congruent circles.

Arcos congruentes (p. 653) Arcos congruentes son arcos que tienen la misma medida y están en el mismo círculo o en círculos congruentes.

Example

$\widehat{EF} \cong \widehat{FG}$ $\widehat{EF} \ncong \widehat{LP}$

Congruent circles (p. 649) Congruent circles are circles whose radii are congruent.

Círculos congruentes (p. 649) Los círculos congruentes son círculos cuyos radios son congruentes.

Example

$\odot A$ and $\odot B$ have the same radius, so $\odot A \cong \odot B$.

Congruent polygons (p. 219) Congruent polygons are polygons that have corresponding sides congruent and corresponding angles congruent.

Polígonos congruentes (p. 219) Los polígonos congruentes son polígonos cuyos lados correspondientes son congruentes y cuyos ángulos correspondientes son congruentes.

Example

$\triangle DEF \cong \triangle GHI$

Congruent segments (p. 22) Congruent segments are segments that have the same length.

Segmentos congruentes (p. 22) Los segmentos congruentes son segmentos que tienen la misma longitud.

Example

$\overline{AB} \cong \overline{CD}$

858

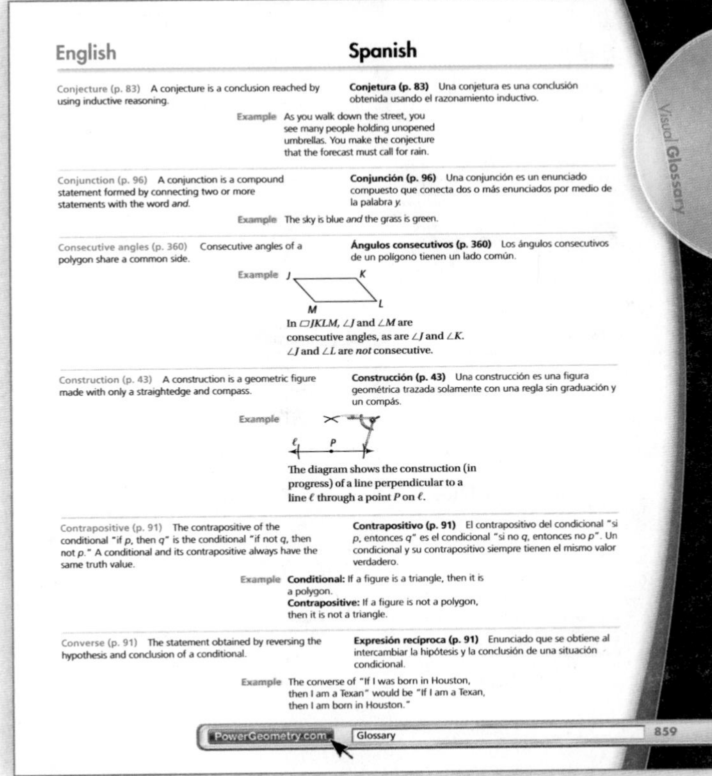

Visual Glossary

English | **Spanish**

Conjecture (p. 83) A conjecture is a conclusion reached by using inductive reasoning.

Conjetura (p. 83) Una conjetura es una conclusión obtenida usando el razonamiento inductivo.

Example As you walk down the street, you see many people holding unopened umbrellas. You make the conjecture that the forecast must call for rain.

Conjunction (p. 96) A conjunction is a compound statement formed by connecting two or more statements with the word *and*.

Conjunción (p. 96) Una conjunción es un enunciado compuesto que conecta dos o más enunciados por medio de la palabra *y*.

Example The sky is blue *and* the grass is green.

Consecutive angles (p. 360) Consecutive angles of a polygon share a common side.

Ángulos consecutivos (p. 360) Los ángulos consecutivos de un polígono tienen un lado común.

Example

In ▱$JKLM$, $\angle J$ and $\angle M$ are consecutive angles, as are $\angle J$ and $\angle K$. $\angle J$ and $\angle L$ are *not* consecutive.

Construction (p. 43) A construction is a geometric figure made with only a straightedge and compass.

Construcción (p. 43) Una construcción es una figura geométrica trazada solamente con una regla sin graduación y un compás.

Example

The diagram shows the construction (in progress) of a line perpendicular to a line ℓ through a point P on ℓ.

Contrapositive (p. 91) The contrapositive of the conditional "if *p*, then *q*" is the conditional "if not *q*, then not *p*." A conditional and its contrapositive always have the same truth value.

Contrapositivo (p. 91) El contrapositivo del condicional "si *p*, entonces *q*" es el condicional "si no *q*, entonces no *p*". Un condicional y su contrapositivo siempre tienen el mismo valor verdadero.

Example **Conditional:** If a figure is a triangle, then it is a polygon.
Contrapositive: If a figure is not a polygon, then it is not a triangle.

Converse (p. 91) The statement obtained by reversing the hypothesis and conclusion of a conditional.

Expresión recíproca (p. 91) Enunciado que se obtiene al intercambiar la hipótesis y la conclusión de una situación condicional.

Example The converse of "If I was born in Houston, then I am a Texan" would be "If I am a Texan, then I am born in Houston."

PowerGeometry.com Glossary 859

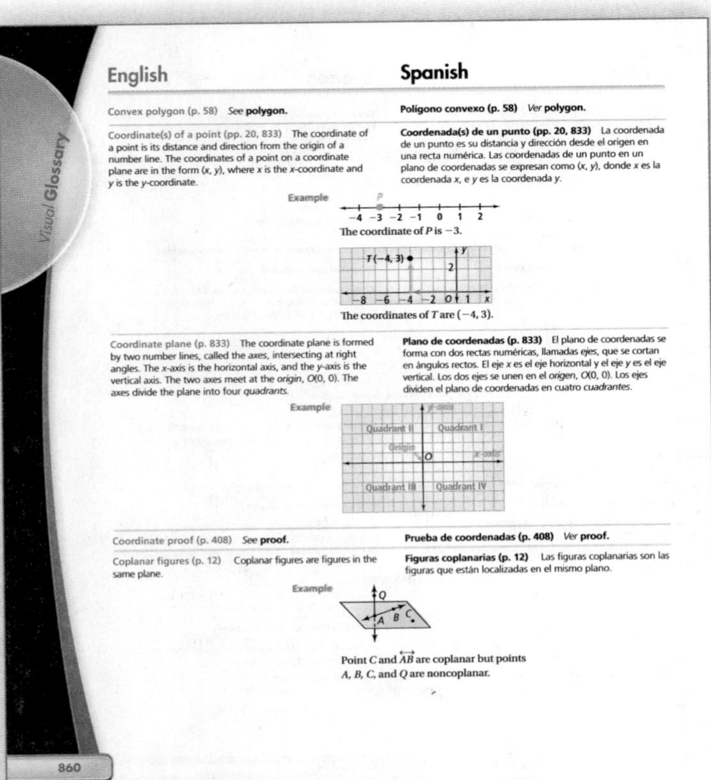

Visual Glossary

English | **Spanish**

Convex polygon (p. 58) *See* **polygon.**

Polígono convexo (p. 58) *Ver* **polygon.**

Coordinate(s) of a point (pp. 20, 833) The coordinate of a point is its distance and direction from the origin of a number line. The coordinates of a point on a coordinate plane are in the form (*x*, *y*), where *x* is the *x*-coordinate and *y* is the *y*-coordinate.

Coordenada(s) de un punto (pp. 20, 833) La coordenada de un punto es su distancia y dirección desde el origen en una recta numérica. Las coordenadas de un punto en un plano de coordenadas se expresan como (*x*, *y*), donde *x* es la coordenada *x*, e *y* es la coordenada *y*.

Example

The coordinate of P is -3.

The coordinates of T are $(-4, 3)$.

Coordinate plane (p. 833) The coordinate plane is formed by two number lines, called the *axes*, intersecting at right angles. The *x*-axis is the horizontal axis, and the *y*-axis is the vertical axis. The two axes meet at the *origin*, *O*(0, 0). The axes divide the plane into four *quadrants*.

Plano de coordenadas (p. 833) El plano de coordenadas se forma con dos rectas numéricas, llamadas *ejes*, que se cortan en ángulos rectos. El eje *x* es el eje horizontal y el eje *y* es el eje vertical. Los dos ejes se unen en el *origen*, *O*(0, 0). Los ejes dividen el plano de coordenadas en cuatro *cuadrantes*.

Example

Coordinate proof (p. 408) *See* **proof.**

Prueba de coordenadas (p. 408) *Ver* **proof.**

Coplanar figures (p. 12) Coplanar figures are figures in the same plane.

Figuras coplanarias (p. 12) Las figuras coplanarias son las figuras que están localizadas en el mismo plano.

Example

Point C and $\overleftrightarrow{AB}$ are coplanar but points A, B, C, and Q are noncoplanar.

860

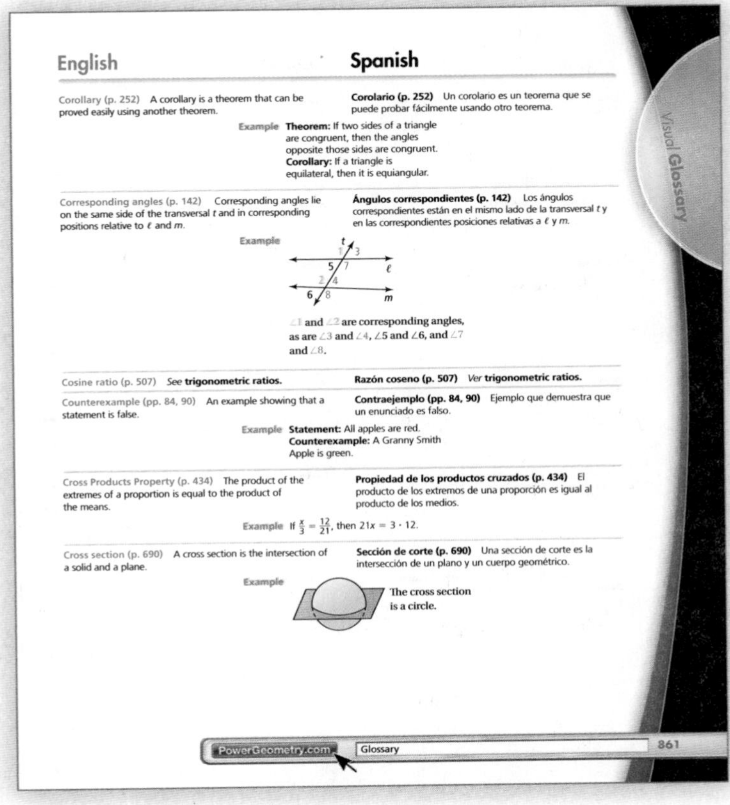

Visual Glossary

English | **Spanish**

Corollary (p. 252) A corollary is a theorem that can be proved easily using another theorem.

Corolario (p. 252) Un corolario es un teorema que se puede probar fácilmente usando otro teorema.

Example **Theorem:** If two sides of a triangle are congruent, then the angles opposite those sides are congruent.
Corollary: If a triangle is equilateral, then it is equiangular.

Corresponding angles (p. 142) Corresponding angles lie on the same side of the transversal *t* and in corresponding positions relative to *ℓ* and *m*.

Ángulos correspondientes (p. 142) Los ángulos correspondientes están en el mismo lado de la transversal *t* y en las correspondientes posiciones relativas a *ℓ* y *m*.

Example

$\angle 1$ and $\angle 2$ are corresponding angles, as are $\angle 3$ and $\angle 4$, $\angle 5$ and $\angle 6$, and $\angle 7$ and $\angle 8$.

Cosine ratio (p. 507) *See* **trigonometric ratios.**

Razón coseno (p. 507) *Ver* **trigonometric ratios.**

Counterexample (pp. 84, 90) An example showing that a statement is false.

Contraejemplo (pp. 84, 90) Ejemplo que demuestra que un enunciado es falso.

Example **Statement:** All apples are red.
Counterexample: A Granny Smith Apple is green.

Cross Products Property (p. 434) The product of the extremes of a proportion is equal to the product of the means.

Propiedad de los productos cruzados (p. 434) El producto de los extremos de una proporción es igual al producto de los medios.

Example If $\frac{x}{3} = \frac{12}{21}$, then $21x = 3 \cdot 12$.

Cross section (p. 690) A cross section is the intersection of a solid and a plane.

Sección de corte (p. 690) Una sección de corte es la intersección de un plano y un cuerpo geométrico.

Example

The cross section is a circle.

PowerGeometry.com Glossary 861

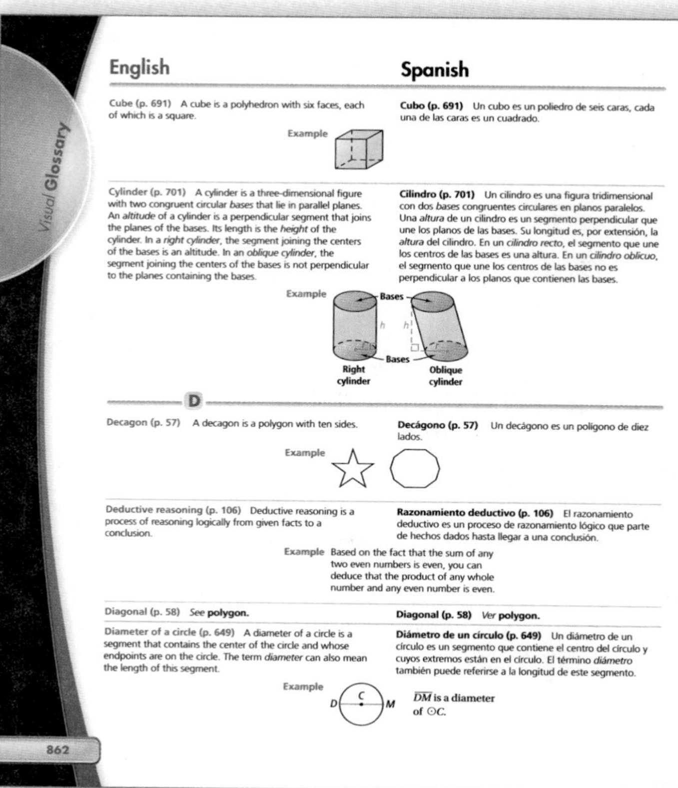

English | Spanish

Cube (p. 691) A cube is a polyhedron with six faces, each of which is a square.

Cubo (p. 691) Un cubo es un poliedro de seis caras, cada una de las caras es un cuadrado.

Example

Cylinder (p. 701) A cylinder is a three-dimensional figure with two congruent circular *bases* that lie in parallel planes. An *altitude* of a cylinder is a perpendicular segment that joins the planes of the bases. Its length is the *height* of the cylinder. In a *right cylinder*, the segment joining the centers of the bases is an altitude. In an *oblique cylinder*, the segment joining the centers of the bases is not perpendicular to the planes containing the bases.

Cilindro (p. 701) Un cilindro es una figura tridimensional con dos *bases* congruentes circulares en planos paralelos. Una *altura* de un cilindro es un segmento perpendicular que une los planos de las bases. Su longitud es, por extensión, la *altura* del cilindro. En un *cilindro recto*, el segmento que une los centros de las bases es una altura. En un *cilindro oblicuo*, el segmento que une los centros de las bases no es perpendicular a los planos que contienen las bases.

Example

D

Decagon (p. 57) A decagon is a polygon with ten sides.

Decágono (p. 57) Un decágono es un polígono de diez lados.

Example

Deductive reasoning (p. 106) Deductive reasoning is a process of reasoning logically from given facts to a conclusion.

Razonamiento deductivo (p. 106) El razonamiento deductivo es un proceso de razonamiento lógico que parte de hechos dados hasta llegar a una conclusión.

Example Based on the fact that the sum of any two even numbers is even, you can deduce that the product of any whole number and any even number is even.

Diagonal (p. 58) *See* **polygon.**

Diagonal (p. 58) *Ver* **polygon.**

Diameter of a circle (p. 649) A diameter of a circle is a segment that contains the center of the circle and whose endpoints are on the circle. The term *diameter* can also mean the length of this segment.

Diámetro de un círculo (p. 649) Un diámetro de un círculo es un segmento que contiene el centro del círculo y cuyos extremos están en el círculo. El término *diámetro* también puede referirse a la longitud de este segmento.

Example

$\overline{DM}$ is a diameter of $\odot C$.

862

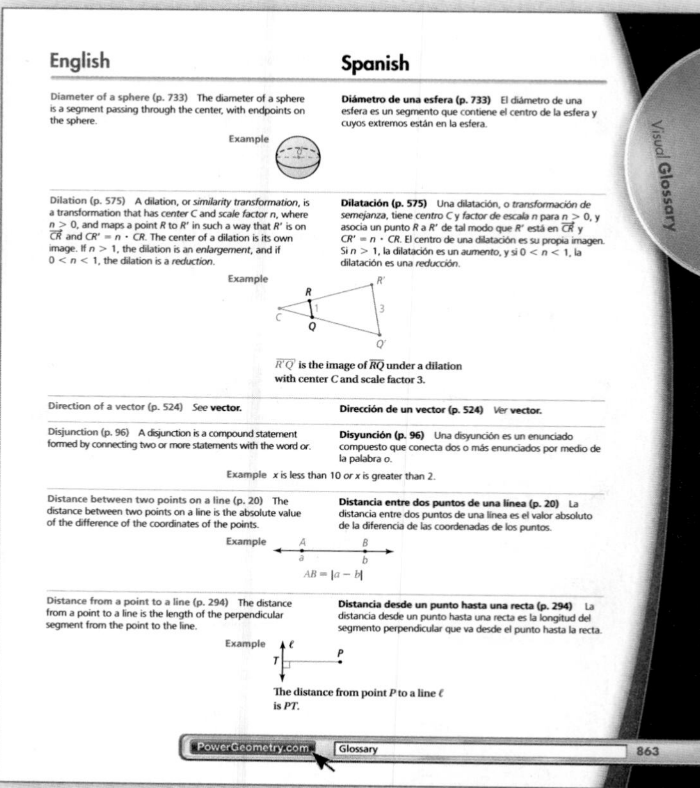

English | Spanish

Diameter of a sphere (p. 733) The diameter of a sphere is a segment passing through the center, with endpoints on the sphere.

Diámetro de una esfera (p. 733) El diámetro de una esfera es un segmento que contiene el centro de la esfera y cuyos extremos están en la esfera.

Example

Dilation (p. 575) A dilation, or *similarity transformation*, is a transformation that has *center C* and *scale factor n*, where $n > 0$, and maps a point R to R' in such a way that R' is on $\overrightarrow{CR}$ and $CR' = n \cdot CR$. The center of a dilation is its own image. If $n > 1$, the dilation is an *enlargement*, and if $0 < n < 1$, the dilation is a *reduction*.

Dilatación (p. 575) Una dilatación, o *transformación de semejanza*, tiene *centro C* y *factor de escala n* para $n > 0$, y asocia un punto R a R' de tal modo que R' está en $\overrightarrow{CR}$ y $CR' = n \cdot CR$. El centro de una dilatación es su propia imagen. Si $n > 1$, la dilatación es un *aumento*, y si $0 < n < 1$, la dilatación es una *reducción*.

Example

$\overline{R'Q'}$ is the image of $\overline{RQ}$ under a dilation with center C and scale factor 3.

Direction of a vector (p. 524) *See* **vector.**

Dirección de un vector (p. 524) *Ver* **vector.**

Disjunction (p. 96) A disjunction is a compound statement formed by connecting two or more statements with the word *or*.

Disyunción (p. 96) Una disyunción es un enunciado compuesto que conecta dos o más enunciados por medio de la palabra *o*.

Example x is less than 10 *or* x is greater than 2.

Distance between two points on a line (p. 20) The distance between two points on a line is the absolute value of the difference of the coordinates of the points.

Distancia entre dos puntos de una línea (p. 20) La distancia entre dos puntos de una línea es el valor absoluto de la diferencia de las coordenadas de los puntos.

Example

$AB = |a - b|$

Distance from a point to a line (p. 294) The distance from a point to a line is the length of the perpendicular segment from the point to the line.

Distancia desde un punto hasta una recta (p. 294) La distancia desde un punto hasta una recta es la longitud del segmento perpendicular que va desde el punto hasta la recta.

Example

The distance from point P to a line ℓ is PT.

PowerGeometry.com | Glossary 863

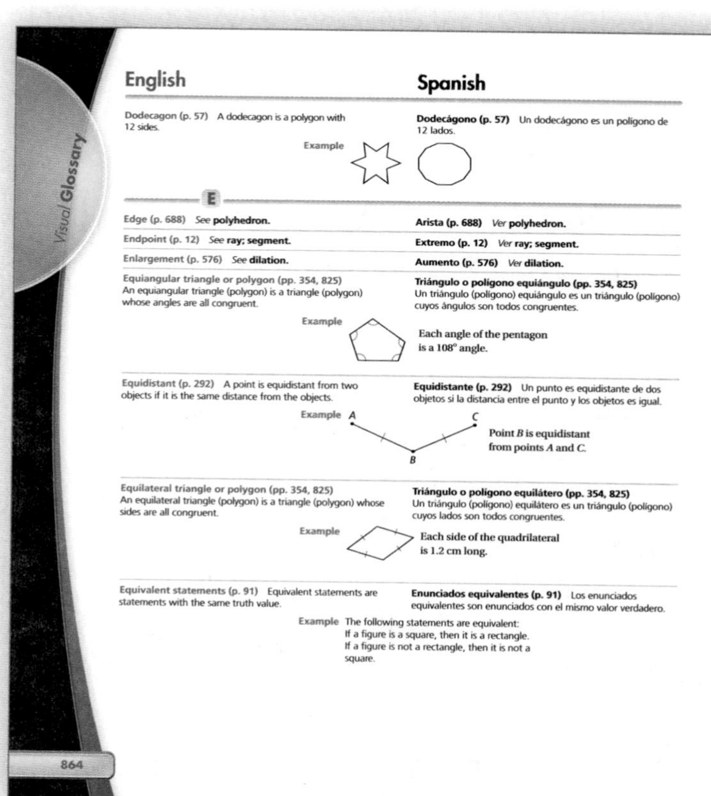

English | Spanish

Dodecagon (p. 57) A dodecagon is a polygon with 12 sides.

Dodecágono (p. 57) Un dodecágono es un polígono de 12 lados.

Example

E

Edge (p. 688) *See* **polyhedron.**

Arista (p. 688) *Ver* **polyhedron.**

Endpoint (p. 12) *See* **ray; segment.**

Extremo (p. 12) *Ver* **ray; segment.**

Enlargement (p. 576) *See* **dilation.**

Aumento (p. 576) *Ver* **dilation.**

Equiangular triangle or polygon (pp. 354, 825) An equiangular triangle (polygon) is a triangle (polygon) whose angles are all congruent.

Triángulo o polígono equiángulo (pp. 354, 825) Un triángulo (polígono) equiángulo es un triángulo (polígono) cuyos ángulos son todos congruentes.

Example

Each angle of the pentagon is a 108° angle.

Equidistant (p. 292) A point is equidistant from two objects if it is the same distance from the objects.

Equidistante (p. 292) Un punto es equidistante de dos objetos si la distancia entre el punto y los objetos es igual.

Example

Point B is equidistant from points A and C.

Equilateral triangle or polygon (pp. 354, 825) An equilateral triangle (polygon) is a triangle (polygon) whose sides are all congruent.

Triángulo o polígono equilátero (pp. 354, 825) Un triángulo (polígono) equilátero es un triángulo (polígono) cuyos lados son todos congruentes.

Example

Each side of the quadrilateral is 1.2 cm long.

Equivalent statements (p. 91) Equivalent statements are statements with the same truth value.

Enunciados equivalentes (p. 91) Los enunciados equivalentes son enunciados con el mismo valor verdadero.

Example The following statements are equivalent:
If a figure is a square, then it is a rectangle.
If a figure is not a rectangle, then it is not a square.

864

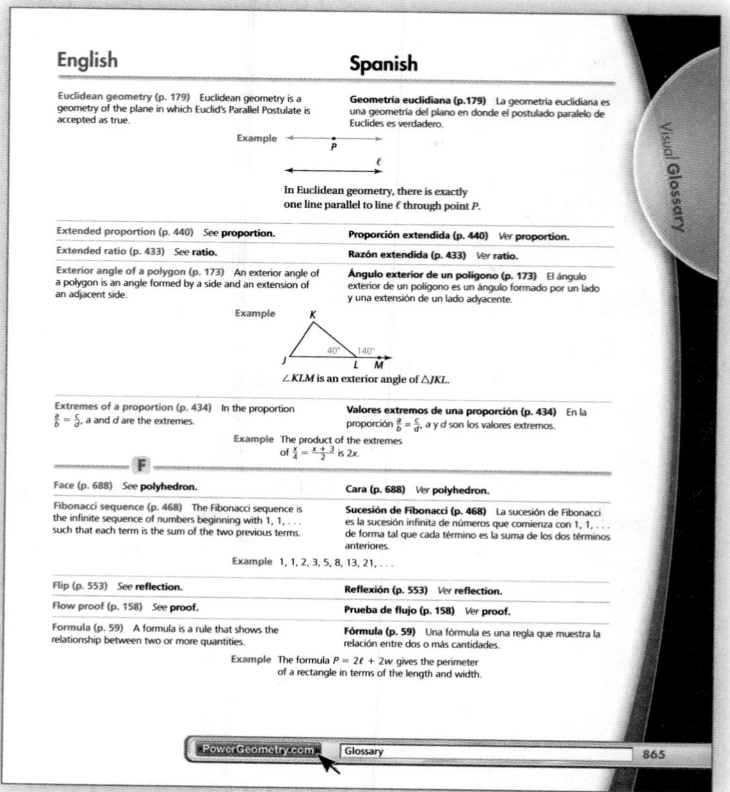

English | Spanish

Euclidean geometry (p. 179) Euclidean geometry is a geometry of the plane in which Euclid's Parallel Postulate is accepted as true.

Geometría euclidiana (p.179) La geometría euclidiana es una geometría del plano en donde el postulado paralelo de Euclides es verdadero.

Example

In Euclidean geometry, there is exactly one line parallel to line ℓ through point P.

Extended proportion (p. 440) *See* **proportion.**

Proporción extendida (p. 440) *Ver* **proportion.**

Extended ratio (p. 433) *See* **ratio.**

Razón extendida (p. 433) *Ver* **ratio.**

Exterior angle of a polygon (p. 173) An exterior angle of a polygon is an angle formed by a side and an extension of an adjacent side.

Ángulo exterior de un polígono (p. 173) El ángulo exterior de un polígono es un ángulo formado por un lado y una extensión de un lado adyacente.

Example

$\angle KLM$ is an exterior angle of $\triangle JKL$.

Extremes of a proportion (p. 434) In the proportion $\frac{a}{b} = \frac{c}{d}$, a and d are the extremes.

Valores extremos de una proporción (p. 434) En la proporción $\frac{a}{b} = \frac{c}{d}$, a y d son los valores extremos.

Example The product of the extremes of $\frac{x}{4} = \frac{x+3}{2}$ is $2x$.

F

Face (p. 688) *See* **polyhedron.**

Cara (p. 688) *Ver* **polyhedron.**

Fibonacci sequence (p. 468) The Fibonacci sequence is the infinite sequence of numbers beginning with 1, 1, . . . such that each term is the sum of the two previous terms.

Sucesión de Fibonacci (p. 468) La sucesión de Fibonacci es la sucesión infinita de números que comienza con 1, 1, . . . de forma tal que cada término es la suma de los dos términos anteriores.

Example 1, 1, 2, 3, 5, 8, 13, 21, . . .

Flip (p. 553) *See* **reflection.**

Reflexión (p. 553) *Ver* **reflection.**

Flow proof (p. 158) *See* **proof.**

Prueba de flujo (p. 158) *Ver* **proof.**

Formula (p. 59) A formula is a rule that shows the relationship between two or more quantities.

Fórmula (p. 59) Una fórmula es una regla que muestra la relación entre dos o más cantidades.

Example The formula $P = 2\ell + 2w$ gives the perimeter of a rectangle in terms of the length and width.

PowerGeometry.com | Glossary 865

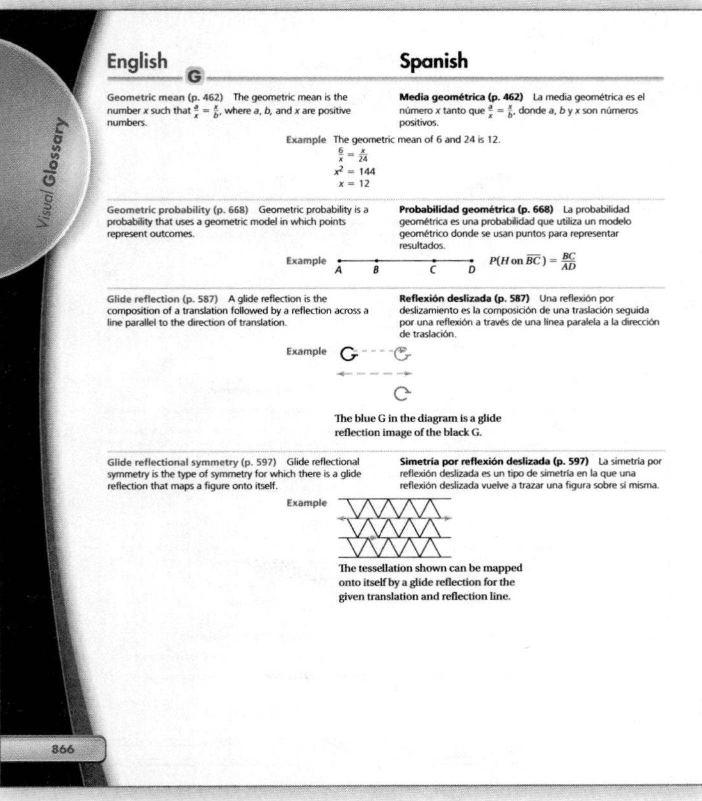

Visual Glossary

English — **Spanish**

G

Geometric mean (p. 462) The geometric mean is the number x such that $\frac{a}{x} = \frac{x}{b}$, where a, b, and x are positive numbers.

Media geométrica (p. 462) La media geométrica es el número x tanto que $\frac{a}{x} = \frac{x}{b}$, donde a, b y x son números positivos.

Example The geometric mean of 6 and 24 is 12.
$\frac{6}{x} = \frac{x}{24}$
$x^2 = 144$
$x = 12$

Geometric probability (p. 668) Geometric probability is a probability that uses a geometric model in which points represent outcomes.

Probabilidad geométrica (p. 668) La probabilidad geométrica es una probabilidad que utiliza un modelo geométrico donde se usan puntos para representar resultados.

Example A B C D $P(H \text{ on } \overline{BC}) = \frac{BC}{AD}$

Glide reflection (p. 587) A glide reflection is the composition of a translation followed by a reflection across a line parallel to the direction of translation.

Reflexión deslizada (p. 587) Una reflexión por deslizamiento es la composición de una traslación seguida por una reflexión a través de una línea paralela a la dirección de traslación.

Example The blue G in the diagram is a glide reflection image of the black G.

Glide reflectional symmetry (p. 597) Glide reflectional symmetry is the type of symmetry for which there is a glide reflection that maps a figure onto itself.

Simetría por reflexión deslizada (p. 597) La simetría por reflexión deslizada es un tipo de simetría en la que una reflexión deslizada vuelve a trazar una figura sobre sí misma.

Example The tessellation shown can be mapped onto itself by a glide reflection for the given translation and reflection line.

866

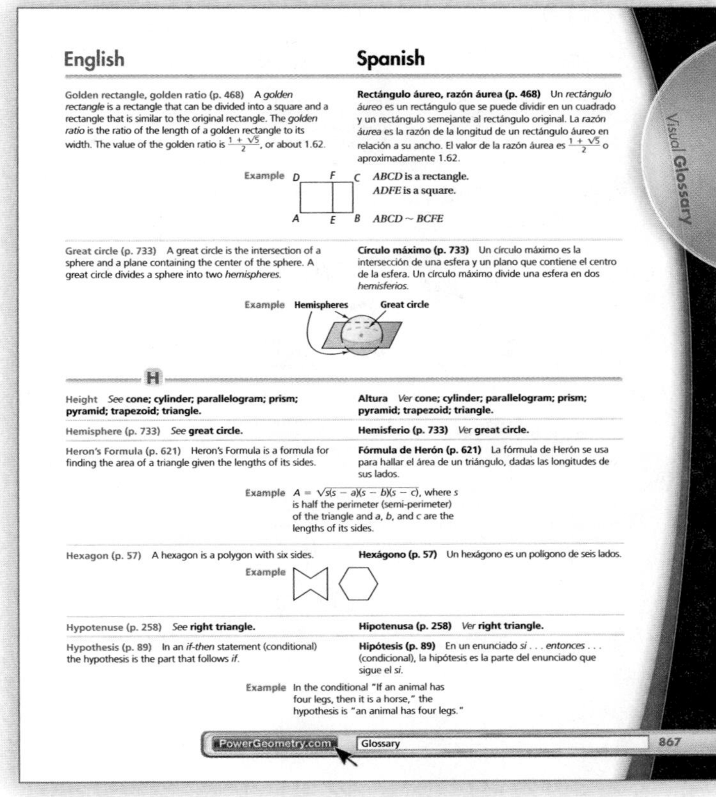

English — **Spanish**

Golden rectangle, golden ratio (p. 468) A *golden rectangle* is a rectangle that can be divided into a square and a rectangle that is similar to the original rectangle. The *golden ratio* is the ratio of the length of a golden rectangle to its width. The value of the golden ratio is $\frac{1 + \sqrt{5}}{2}$, or about 1.62.

Rectángulo áureo, razón áurea (p. 468) Un *rectángulo áureo* es un rectángulo que se puede dividir en un cuadrado y un rectángulo semejante al rectángulo original. La *razón áurea* es la razón de la longitud de un rectángulo áureo en relación a su ancho. El valor de la razón áurea es $\frac{1 + \sqrt{5}}{2}$ o aproximadamente 1.62.

Example D F C A E B
$ABCD$ is a rectangle.
$ADFE$ is a square.
$ABCD \sim BCFE$

Great circle (p. 733) A great circle is the intersection of a sphere and a plane containing the center of the sphere. A great circle divides a sphere into two *hemispheres*.

Círculo máximo (p. 733) Un círculo máximo es la intersección de una esfera y un plano que contiene el centro de la esfera. Un círculo máximo divide una esfera en dos *hemisferios*.

Example Hemispheres Great circle

H

Height *See* **cone; cylinder; parallelogram; prism; pyramid; trapezoid; triangle.**

Altura *Ver* **cone; cylinder; parallelogram; prism; pyramid; trapezoid; triangle.**

Hemisphere (p. 733) *See* **great circle.**

Hemisferio (p. 733) *Ver* **great circle.**

Heron's Formula (p. 621) Heron's Formula is a formula for finding the area of a triangle given the lengths of its sides.

Fórmula de Herón (p. 621) La fórmula de Herón se usa para hallar el área de un triángulo, dadas las longitudes de sus lados.

Example $A = \sqrt{s(s-a)(s-b)(s-c)}$, where s is half the perimeter (semi-perimeter) of the triangle and a, b, and c are the lengths of its sides.

Hexagon (p. 57) A hexagon is a polygon with six sides.

Hexágono (p. 57) Un hexágono es un polígono de seis lados.

Example

Hypotenuse (p. 258) *See* **right triangle.**

Hipotenusa (p. 258) *Ver* **right triangle.**

Hypothesis (p. 89) In an *if-then* statement (conditional) the hypothesis is the part that follows *if*.

Hipótesis (p. 89) En un enunciado *si . . . entonces . . .* (condicional), la hipótesis es la parte del enunciado que sigue el *si*.

Example In the conditional "If an animal has four legs, then it is a horse," the hypothesis is "an animal has four legs."

PowerGeometry.com Glossary 867

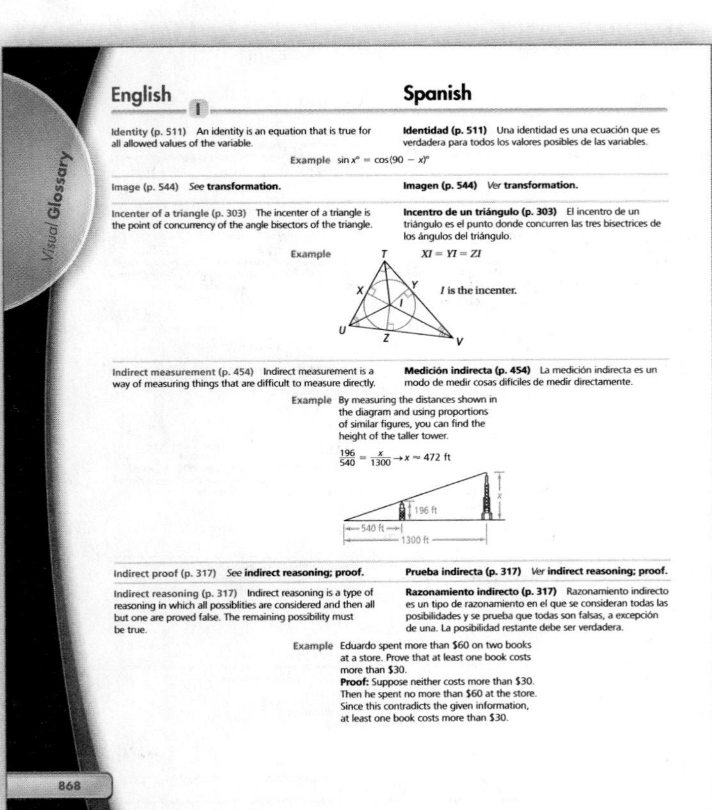

Visual Glossary

English — **Spanish**

I

Identity (p. 511) An identity is an equation that is true for all allowed values of the variable.

Identidad (p. 511) Una identidad es una ecuación que es verdadera para todos los valores posibles de las variables.

Example $\sin x° = \cos(90 - x)°$

Image (p. 544) *See* **transformation.**

Imagen (p. 544) *Ver* **transformation.**

Incenter of a triangle (p. 303) The incenter of a triangle is the point of concurrency of the angle bisectors of the triangle.

Incentro de un triángulo (p. 303) El incentro de un triángulo es el punto donde concurren las tres bisectrices de los ángulos del triángulo.

Example T X Y I U Z V
$XI = YI = ZI$
I is the incenter.

Indirect measurement (p. 454) Indirect measurement is a way of measuring things that are difficult to measure directly.

Medición indirecta (p. 454) La medición indirecta es un modo de medir cosas difíciles de medir directamente.

Example By measuring the distances shown in the diagram and using proportions of similar figures, you can find the height of the taller tower.

$\frac{196}{540} = \frac{x}{1300} \rightarrow x \approx 472$ ft

196 ft, x, 540 ft, 1300 ft

Indirect proof (p. 317) *See* **indirect reasoning; proof.**

Prueba indirecta (p. 317) *Ver* **indirect reasoning; proof.**

Indirect reasoning (p. 317) Indirect reasoning is a type of reasoning in which all possiblities are considered and then all but one are proved false. The remaining possibility must be true.

Razonamiento indirecto (p. 317) Razonamiento indirecto es un tipo de razonamiento en el que se consideran todas las posibilidades y se prueba que todas son falsas, a excepción de una. La posibilidad restante debe ser verdadera.

Example Eduardo spent more than \$60 on two books at a store. Prove that at least one book costs more than \$30.
Proof: Suppose neither costs more than \$30. Then he spent no more than \$60 at the store. Since this contradicts the given information, at least one book costs more than \$30.

868

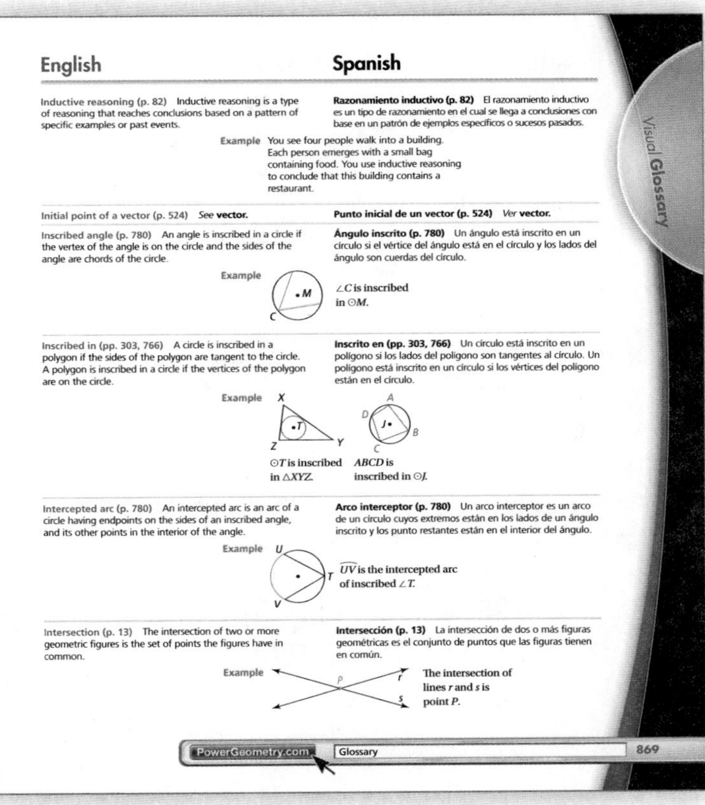

English — **Spanish**

Inductive reasoning (p. 82) Inductive reasoning is a type of reasoning that reaches conclusions based on a pattern of specific examples or past events.

Razonamiento inductivo (p. 82) El razonamiento inductivo es un tipo de razonamiento en el cual se llega a conclusiones con base en un patrón de ejemplos específicos o sucesos pasados.

Example You see four people walk into a building. Each person emerges with a small bag containing food. You use inductive reasoning to conclude that this building contains a restaurant.

Initial point of a vector (p. 524) *See* **vector.**

Punto inicial de un vector (p. 524) *Ver* **vector.**

Inscribed angle (p. 780) An angle is inscribed in a circle if the vertex of the angle is on the circle and the sides of the angle are chords of the circle.

Ángulo inscrito (p. 780) Un ángulo está inscrito en un círculo si el vértice del ángulo está en el círculo y los lados del ángulo son cuerdas del círculo.

Example $\angle C$ is inscribed in $\odot M$.

Inscribed in (pp. 303, 766) A circle is inscribed in a polygon if the sides of the polygon are tangent to the circle. A polygon is inscribed in a circle if the vertices of the polygon are on the circle.

Inscrito en (pp. 303, 766) Un círculo está inscrito en un polígono si los lados del polígono son tangentes al círculo. Un polígono está inscrito en un círculo si los vértices del polígono están en el círculo.

Example $\odot T$ is inscribed in $\triangle XYZ$. $ABCD$ is inscribed in $\odot J$.

Intercepted arc (p. 780) An intercepted arc is an arc of a circle having endpoints on the sides of an inscribed angle, and its other points in the interior of the angle.

Arco interceptor (p. 780) Un arco interceptor es un arco de un círculo cuyos extremos están en los lados de un ángulo inscrito y los punto restantes están en el interior del ángulo.

Example $\widehat{UV}$ is the intercepted arc of inscribed $\angle T$.

Intersection (p. 13) The intersection of two or more geometric figures is the set of points the figures have in common.

Intersección (p. 13) La intersección de dos o más figuras geométricas es el conjunto de puntos que las figuras tienen en común.

Example The intersection of lines r and s is point P.

PowerGeometry.com Glossary 869

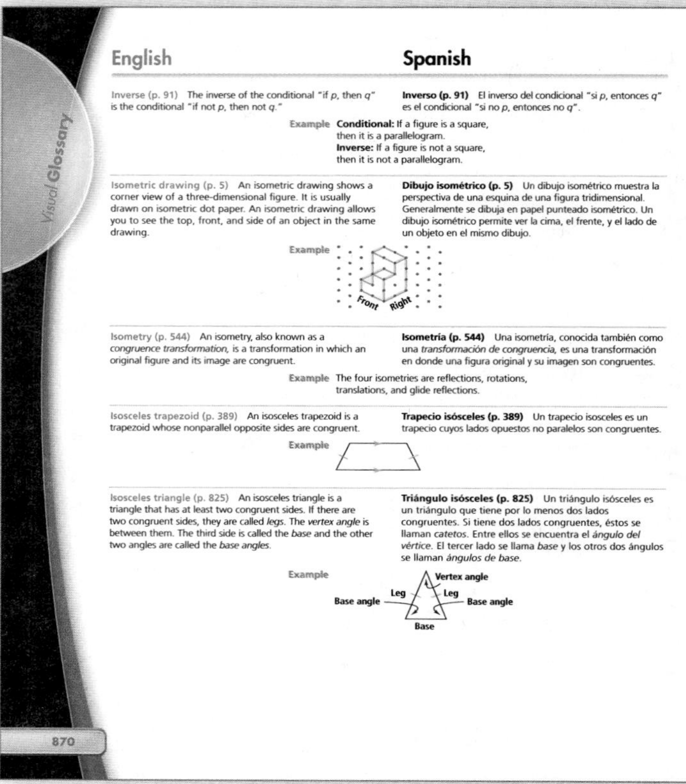

English | Spanish

Inverse (p. 91) The inverse of the conditional "if p, then q" is the conditional "if not p, then not q."

Inverso (p. 91) El inverso del condicional "si p, entonces q" es el condicional "si no p, entonces no q".

Example **Conditional:** If a figure is a square, then it is a parallelogram. **Inverse:** If a figure is not a square, then it is not a parallelogram.

Isometric drawing (p. 5) An isometric drawing shows a corner view of a three-dimensional figure. It is usually drawn on isometric dot paper. An isometric drawing allows you to see the top, front, and side of an object in the same drawing.

Dibujo isométrico (p. 5) Un dibujo isométrico muestra la perspectiva de una esquina de una figura tridimensional. Generalmente se dibuja en papel punteado isométrico. Un dibujo isométrico permite ver la cima, el frente, y el lado de un objeto en el mismo dibujo.

Example (Front, Right)

Isometry (p. 544) An isometry, also known as a *congruence transformation,* is a transformation in which an original figure and its image are congruent.

Isometría (p. 544) Una isometría, conocida también como una *transformación de congruencia,* es una transformación en donde una figura original y su imagen son congruentes.

Example The four isometries are reflections, rotations, translations, and glide reflections.

Isosceles trapezoid (p. 389) An isosceles trapezoid is a trapezoid whose nonparallel opposite sides are congruent.

Trapecio isósceles (p. 389) Un trapecio isosceles es un trapecio cuyos lados opuestos no paralelos son congruentes.

Example

Isosceles triangle (p. 825) An isosceles triangle is a triangle that has at least two congruent sides. If there are two congruent sides, they are called *legs*. The *vertex angle* is between them. The third side is called the *base* and the other two angles are called the *base angles*.

Triángulo isósceles (p. 825) Un triángulo isósceles es un triángulo que tiene por lo menos dos lados congruentes. Si tiene dos lados congruentes, éstos se llaman *catetos*. Entre ellos se encuentra el *ángulo del vértice*. El tercer lado se llama *base* y los otros dos ángulos se llaman *ángulos de base*.

Example (Vertex angle, Leg, Leg, Base angle, Base angle, Base)

870

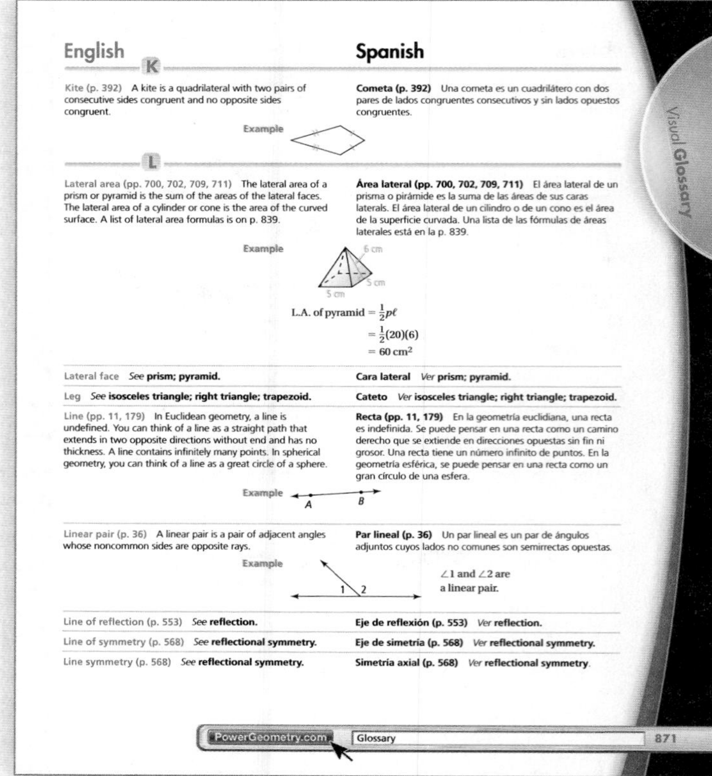

English | Spanish

K

Kite (p. 392) A kite is a quadrilateral with two pairs of consecutive sides congruent and no opposite sides congruent.

Cometa (p. 392) Una cometa es un cuadrilátero con dos pares de lados congruentes consecutivos y sin lados opuestos congruentes.

Example

L

Lateral area (pp. 700, 702, 709, 711) The lateral area of a prism or pyramid is the sum of the areas of the lateral faces. The lateral area of a cylinder or cone is the area of the curved surface. A list of lateral area formulas is on p. 839.

Área lateral (pp. 700, 702, 709, 711) El área lateral de un prisma o pirámide es la suma de las áreas de sus caras laterals. El área lateral de un cilindro o de un cono es el área de la superficie curvada. Una lista de las fórmulas de áreas laterales está en la p. 839.

Example (6 cm, 5 cm, 5 cm)

$$\text{L.A. of pyramid} = \frac{1}{2}p\ell = \frac{1}{2}(20)(6) = 60\ \text{cm}^2$$

Lateral face *See* **prism; pyramid.** | **Cara lateral** *Ver* **prism; pyramid.**

Leg *See* **isosceles triangle; right triangle; trapezoid.** | **Cateto** *Ver* **isosceles triangle; right triangle; trapezoid.**

Line (pp. 11, 179) In Euclidean geometry, a line is undefined. You can think of a line as a straight path that extends in two opposite directions without end and has no thickness. A line contains infinitely many points. In spherical geometry, you can think of a line as a great circle of a sphere.

Recta (pp. 11, 179) En la geometría euclidiana, una recta es indefinida. Se puede pensar en una recta como un camino derecho que se extiende en direcciones opuestas sin fin ni grosor. Una recta tiene un número infinito de puntos. En la geometría esférica, se puede pensar en una recta como un gran círculo de una esfera.

Example (A, B)

Linear pair (p. 36) A linear pair is a pair of adjacent angles whose noncommon sides are opposite rays.

Par lineal (p. 36) Un par lineal es un par de ángulos adjuntos cuyos lados no comunes son semirrectas opuestas.

Example $\angle 1$ and $\angle 2$ are a linear pair.

Line of reflection (p. 553) *See* **reflection.** | **Eje de reflexión (p. 553)** *Ver* **reflection.**

Line of symmetry (p. 568) *See* **reflectional symmetry.** | **Eje de simetría (p. 568)** *Ver* **reflectional symmetry.**

Line symmetry (p. 568) *See* **reflectional symmetry.** | **Simetría axial (p. 568)** *Ver* **reflectional symmetry**.

PowerGeometry.com | Glossary | 871

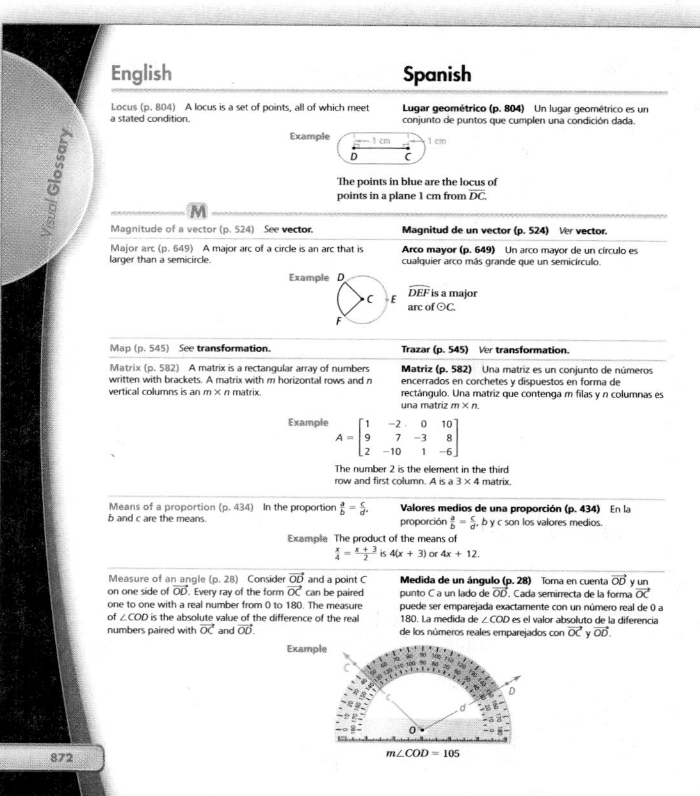

English | Spanish

Locus (p. 804) A locus is a set of points, all of which meet a stated condition.

Lugar geométrico (p. 804) Un lugar geométrico es un conjunto de puntos que cumplen una condición dada.

Example (1 cm, 1 cm, D, C)

The points in blue are the locus of points in a plane 1 cm from $\overline{DC}$.

M

Magnitude of a vector (p. 524) *See* **vector.** | **Magnitud de un vector (p. 524)** *Ver* **vector.**

Major arc (p. 649) A major arc of a circle is an arc that is larger than a semicircle.

Arco mayor (p. 649) Un arco mayor de un círculo es cualquier arco más grande que un semicírculo.

Example $\widehat{DEF}$ is a major arc of $\odot C$.

Map (p. 545) *See* **transformation.** | **Trazar (p. 545)** *Ver* **transformation.**

Matrix (p. 582) A matrix is a rectangular array of numbers written with brackets. A matrix with m horizontal rows and n vertical columns is an $m \times n$ matrix.

Matriz (p. 582) Una matriz es un conjunto de números encerrados en corchetes y dispuestos en forma de rectángulo. Una matriz que contenga m filas y n columnas es una matriz $m \times n$.

Example

$$A = \begin{bmatrix} 1 & -2 & 0 & 10 \\ 9 & 7 & -3 & 8 \\ 2 & -10 & 1 & -6 \end{bmatrix}$$

The number 2 is the element in the third row and first column. A is a 3×4 matrix.

Means of a proportion (p. 434) In the proportion $\frac{a}{b} = \frac{c}{d}$, b and c are the means.

Valores medios de una proporción (p. 434) En la proporción $\frac{a}{b} = \frac{c}{d}$, b y c son los valores medios.

Example The product of the means of $\frac{x}{4} = \frac{x+3}{2}$ is $4(x + 3)$ or $4x + 12$.

Measure of an angle (p. 28) Consider $\overrightarrow{OD}$ and a point C on one side of $\overrightarrow{OD}$. Every ray of the form $\overrightarrow{OC}$ can be paired one to one with a real number from 0 to 180. The measure of $\angle COD$ is the absolute value of the difference of the real numbers paired with $\overrightarrow{OC}$ and $\overrightarrow{OD}$.

Medida de un ángulo (p. 28) Toma en cuenta $\overrightarrow{OD}$ y un punto C a un lado de $\overrightarrow{OD}$. Cada semirrecta de la forma $\overrightarrow{OC}$ puede ser emparejada exactamente con un número real de 0 a 180. La medida de $\angle COD$ es el valor absoluto de la diferencia de los números reales emparejados con $\overrightarrow{OC}$ y $\overrightarrow{OD}$.

Example

$m\angle COD = 105$

872

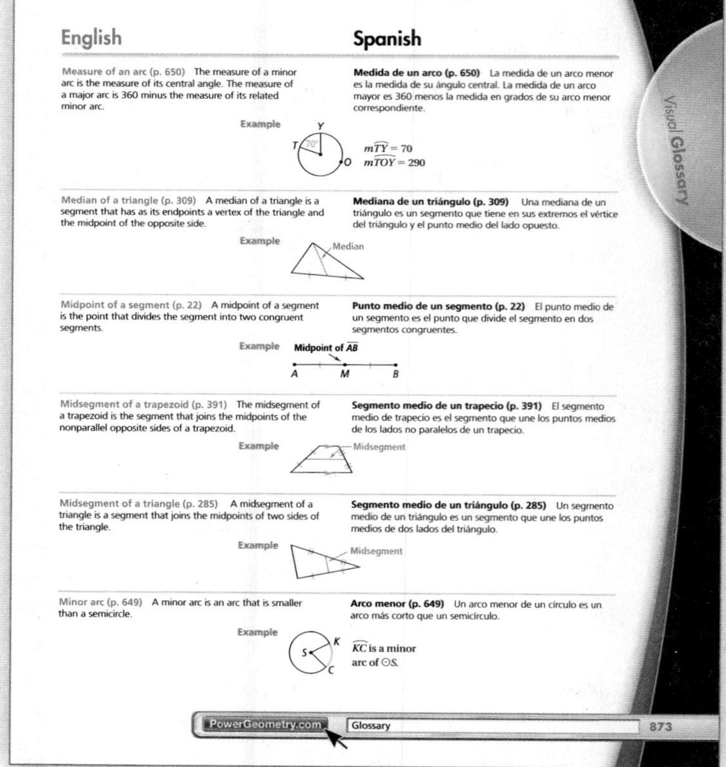

English | Spanish

Measure of an arc (p. 650) The measure of a minor arc is the measure of its central angle. The measure of a major arc is 360 minus the measure of its related minor arc.

Medida de un arco (p. 650) La medida de un arco menor es la medida de su ángulo central. La medida de un arco mayor es 360 menos la medida en grados de su arco menor correspondiente.

Example $m\widehat{TY} = 70$, $m\widehat{TOY} = 290$

Median of a triangle (p. 309) A median of a triangle is a segment that has as its endpoints a vertex of the triangle and the midpoint of the opposite side.

Mediana de un triángulo (p. 309) Una mediana de un triángulo es un segmento que tiene en sus extremos el vértice del triángulo y el punto medio del lado opuesto.

Example (Median)

Midpoint of a segment (p. 22) A midpoint of a segment is the point that divides the segment into two congruent segments.

Punto medio de un segmento (p. 22) El punto medio de un segmento es el punto que divide el segmento en dos segmentos congruentes.

Example Midpoint of $\overline{AB}$ (A, M, B)

Midsegment of a trapezoid (p. 391) The midsegment of a trapezoid is the segment that joins the midpoints of the nonparallel opposite sides of a trapezoid.

Segmento medio de un trapecio (p. 391) El segmento medio de trapecio es el segmento que une los puntos medios de los lados no paralelos de un trapecio.

Example (Midsegment)

Midsegment of a triangle (p. 285) A midsegment of a triangle is a segment that joins the midpoints of two sides of the triangle.

Segmento medio de un triángulo (p. 285) Un segmento medio de un triángulo es un segmento que une los puntos medios de dos lados del triángulo.

Example (Midsegment)

Minor arc (p. 649) A minor arc is an arc that is smaller than a semicircle.

Arco menor (p. 649) Un arco menor de un círculo es un arco más corto que un semicírculo.

Example $\widehat{KC}$ is a minor arc of $\odot S$.

PowerGeometry.com | Glossary | 873

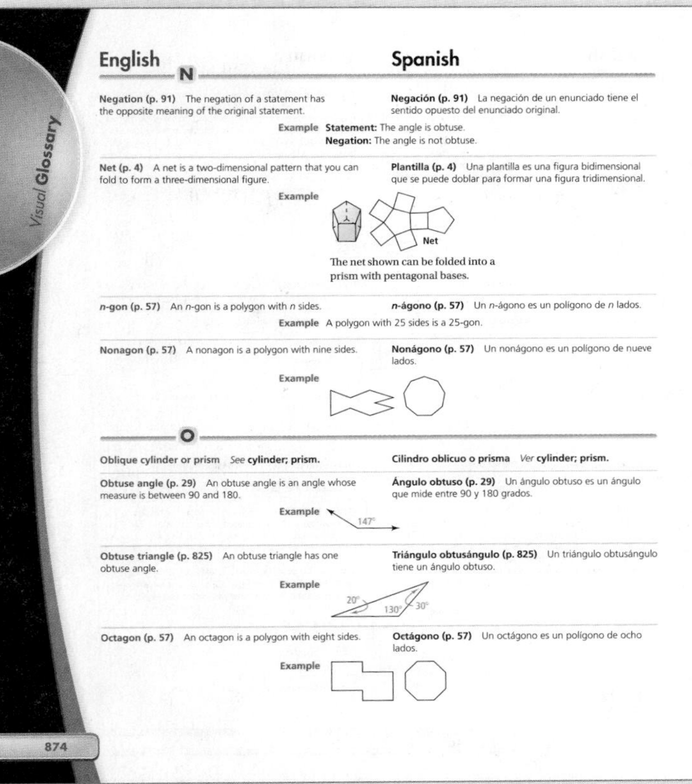

English | Spanish

N

Negation (p. 91) The negation of a statement has the opposite meaning of the original statement.

Negación (p. 91) La negación de un enunciado tiene el sentido opuesto del enunciado original.

Example **Statement:** The angle is obtuse.
Negation: The angle is not obtuse.

Net (p. 4) A net is a two-dimensional pattern that you can fold to form a three-dimensional figure.

Plantilla (p. 4) Una plantilla es una figura bidimensional que se puede doblar para formar una figura tridimensional.

Example

The net shown can be folded into a prism with pentagonal bases.

***n*-gon (p. 57)** An *n*-gon is a polygon with *n* sides.

***n*-ágono (p. 57)** Un *n*-ágono es un polígono de *n* lados.

Example A polygon with 25 sides is a 25-gon.

Nonagon (p. 57) A nonagon is a polygon with nine sides.

Nonágono (p. 57) Un nonágono es un polígono de nueve lados.

Example

O

Oblique cylinder or prism *See* **cylinder; prism.**

Cilindro oblicuo o prisma *Ver* **cylinder; prism.**

Obtuse angle (p. 29) An obtuse angle is an angle whose measure is between 90 and 180.

Ángulo obtuso (p. 29) Un ángulo obtuso es un ángulo que mide entre 90 y 180 grados.

Example

Obtuse triangle (p. 825) An obtuse triangle has one obtuse angle.

Triángulo obtusángulo (p. 825) Un triángulo obtusángulo tiene un ángulo obtuso.

Example

Octagon (p. 57) An octagon is a polygon with eight sides.

Octágono (p. 57) Un octágono es un polígono de ocho lados.

Example

874

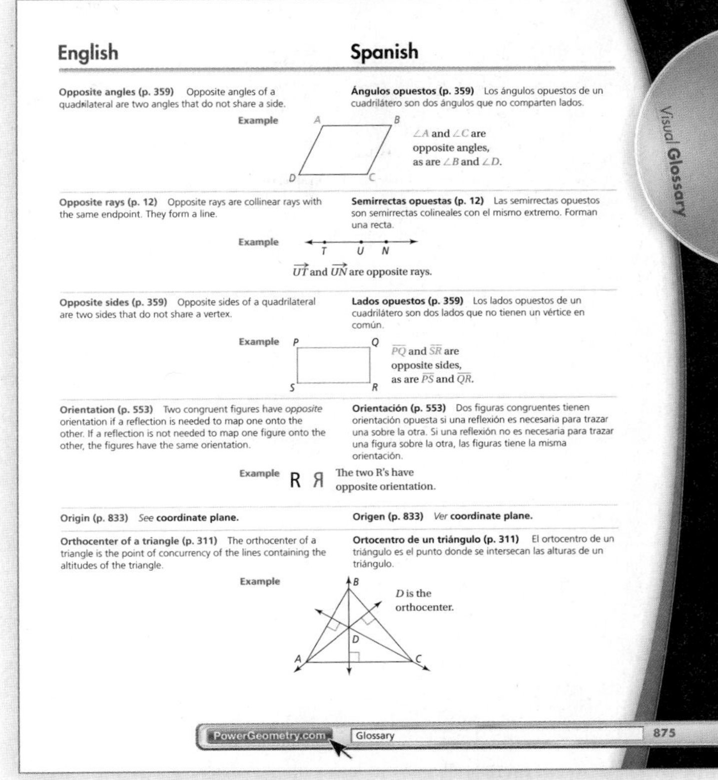

English | Spanish

Opposite angles (p. 359) Opposite angles of a quadrilateral are two angles that do not share a side.

Ángulos opuestos (p. 359) Los ángulos opuestos de un cuadrilátero son dos ángulos que no comparten lados.

Example

$\angle A$ and $\angle C$ are opposite angles, as are $\angle B$ and $\angle D$.

Opposite rays (p. 12) Opposite rays are collinear rays with the same endpoint. They form a line.

Semirrectas opuestas (p. 12) Las semirrectas opuestos son semirrectas colineales con el mismo extremo. Forman una recta.

Example

$\overrightarrow{UT}$ and $\overrightarrow{UN}$ are opposite rays.

Opposite sides (p. 359) Opposite sides of a quadrilateral are two sides that do not share a vertex.

Lados opuestos (p. 359) Los lados opuestos de un cuadrilátero son dos lados que no tienen un vértice en común.

Example

$\overline{PQ}$ and $\overline{SR}$ are opposite sides, as are $\overline{PS}$ and $\overline{QR}$.

Orientation (p. 553) Two congruent figures have *opposite* orientation if a reflection is needed to map one onto the other. If a reflection is not needed to map one figure onto the other, the figures have the same orientation.

Orientación (p. 553) Dos figuras congruentes tienen orientación opuesta si una reflexión es necesaria para trazar una sobre la otra. Si una reflexión no es necesaria para trazar una figura sobre la otra, las figuras tiene la misma orientación.

Example

The two R's have opposite orientation.

Origin (p. 833) *See* **coordinate plane.**

Origen (p. 833) *Ver* **coordinate plane.**

Orthocenter of a triangle (p. 311) The orthocenter of a triangle is the point of concurrency of the lines containing the altitudes of the triangle.

Ortocentro de un triángulo (p. 311) El ortocentro de un triángulo es el punto donde se intersecan las alturas de un triángulo.

Example

D is the orthocenter.

PowerGeometry.com | Glossary 875

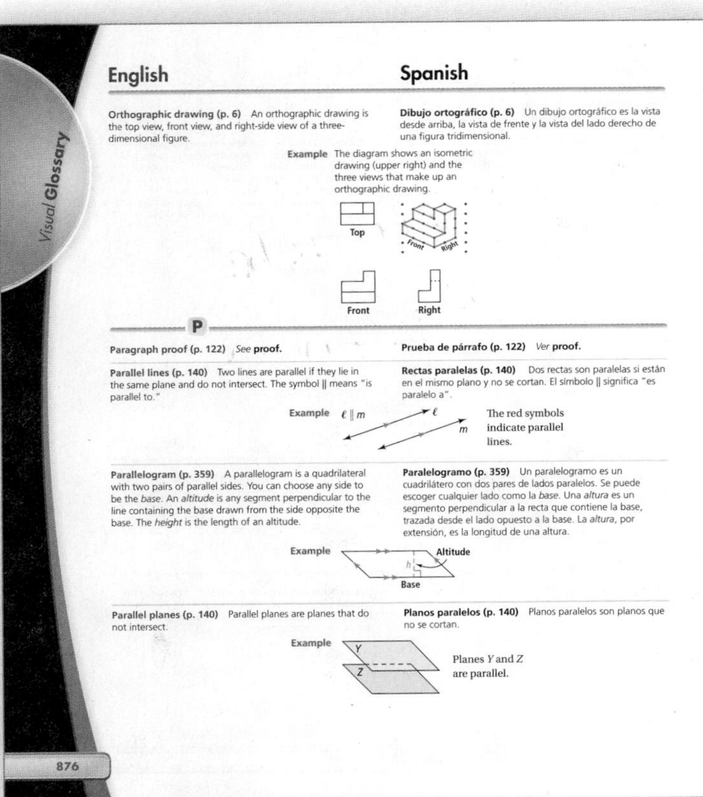

English | Spanish

Orthographic drawing (p. 6) An orthographic drawing is the top view, front view, and right-side view of a three-dimensional figure.

Dibujo ortográfico (p. 6) Un dibujo ortográfico es la vista desde arriba, la vista de frente y la vista del lado derecho de una figura tridimensional.

Example The diagram shows an isometric drawing (upper right) and the three views that make up an orthographic drawing.

P

Paragraph proof (p. 122) *See* **proof.**

Prueba de párrafo (p. 122) *Ver* **proof.**

Parallel lines (p. 140) Two lines are parallel if they lie in the same plane and do not intersect. The symbol ∥ means "is parallel to."

Rectas paralelas (p. 140) Dos rectas son paralelas si están en el mismo plano y no se cortan. El símbolo ∥ significa "es paralelo a".

Example $\ell \parallel m$

The red symbols indicate parallel lines.

Parallelogram (p. 359) A parallelogram is a quadrilateral with two pairs of parallel sides. You can choose any side to be the *base*. An *altitude* is any segment perpendicular to the line containing the base drawn from the side opposite the base. The *height* is the length of an altitude.

Paralelogramo (p. 359) Un paralelogramo es un cuadrilátero con dos pares de lados paralelos. Se puede escoger cualquier lado como la *base*. Una *altura* es un segmento perpendicular a la recta que contiene la base, trazada desde el lado opuesto a la base. La *altura*, por extensión, es la longitud de una altura.

Example

Parallel planes (p. 140) Parallel planes are planes that do not intersect.

Planos paralelos (p. 140) Planos paralelos son planos que no se cortan.

Example

Planes *Y* and *Z* are parallel.

876

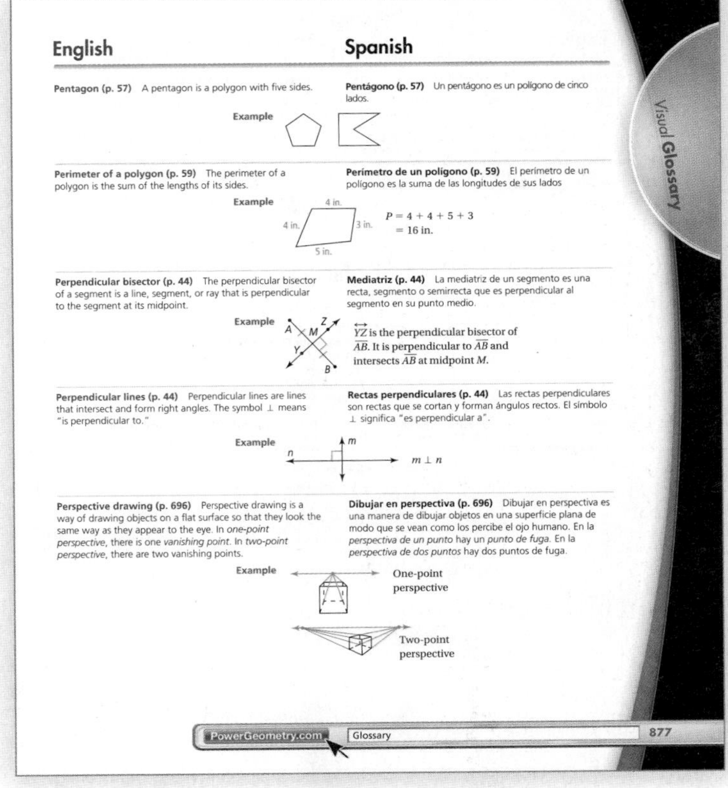

English | Spanish

Pentagon (p. 57) A pentagon is a polygon with five sides.

Pentágono (p. 57) Un pentágono es un polígono de cinco lados.

Example

Perimeter of a polygon (p. 59) The perimeter of a polygon is the sum of the lengths of its sides.

Perímetro de un polígono (p. 59) El perímetro de un polígono es la suma de las longitudes de sus lados

Example

$P = 4 + 4 + 5 + 3$
$= 16$ in.

Perpendicular bisector (p. 44) The perpendicular bisector of a segment is a line, segment, or ray that is perpendicular to the segment at its midpoint.

Mediatriz (p. 44) La mediatriz de un segmento es una recta, segmento o semirrecta que es perpendicular al segmento en su punto medio.

Example

$\overleftrightarrow{YZ}$ is the perpendicular bisector of $\overline{AB}$. It is perpendicular to $\overline{AB}$ and intersects $\overline{AB}$ at midpoint *M*.

Perpendicular lines (p. 44) Perpendicular lines are lines that intersect and form right angles. The symbol ⊥ means "is perpendicular to."

Rectas perpendiculares (p. 44) Las rectas perpendiculares son rectas que se cortan y forman ángulos rectos. El símbolo ⊥ significa "es perpendicular a".

Example

$m \perp n$

Perspective drawing (p. 696) Perspective drawing is a way of drawing objects on a flat surface so that they look the same way as they appear to the eye. In *one-point perspective*, there is one *vanishing point*. In *two-point perspective*, there are two vanishing points.

Dibujar en perspectiva (p. 696) Dibujar en perspectiva es una manera de dibujar objetos en una superficie plana de modo que se vean como los percibe el ojo humano. En la *perspectiva de un punto* hay un *punto de fuga*. En la *perspectiva de dos puntos* hay dos puntos de fuga.

Example
One-point perspective

Two-point perspective

PowerGeometry.com | Glossary 877

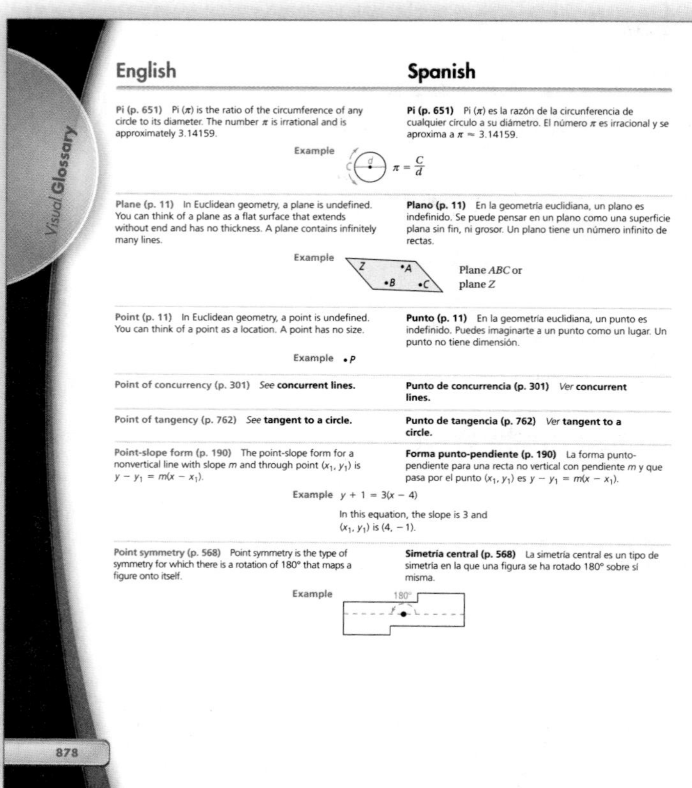

English / Spanish

Pi (p. 651) Pi (π) is the ratio of the circumference of any circle to its diameter. The number π is irrational and is approximately 3.14159.

Pi (p. 651) Pi (π) es la razón de la circunferencia de cualquier círculo a su diámetro. El número π es irracional y se aproxima a $\pi \approx 3.14159$.

Example $\pi = \frac{C}{d}$

Plane (p. 11) In Euclidean geometry, a plane is undefined. You can think of a plane as a flat surface that extends without end and has no thickness. A plane contains infinitely many lines.

Plano (p. 11) En la geometría euclidiana, un plano es indefinido. Se puede pensar en un plano como una superficie plana sin fin, ni grosor. Un plano tiene un número infinito de rectas.

Example Plane ABC or plane Z

Point (p. 11) In Euclidean geometry, a point is undefined. You can think of a point as a location. A point has no size.

Punto (p. 11) En la geometría euclidiana, un punto es indefinido. Puedes imaginarte a un punto como un lugar. Un punto no tiene dimensión.

Example • P

Point of concurrency (p. 301) *See* **concurrent lines.**

Punto de concurrencia (p. 301) *Ver* **concurrent lines.**

Point of tangency (p. 762) *See* **tangent to a circle.**

Punto de tangencia (p. 762) *Ver* **tangent to a circle.**

Point-slope form (p. 190) The point-slope form for a nonvertical line with slope m and through point (x_1, y_1) is $y - y_1 = m(x - x_1)$.

Forma punto-pendiente (p. 190) La forma punto-pendiente para una recta no vertical con pendiente m y que pasa por el punto (x_1, y_1) es $y - y_1 = m(x - x_1)$.

Example $y + 1 = 3(x - 4)$

In this equation, the slope is 3 and (x_1, y_1) is $(4, -1)$.

Point symmetry (p. 568) Point symmetry is the type of symmetry for which there is a rotation of 180° that maps a figure onto itself.

Simetría central (p. 568) La simetría central es un tipo de simetría en la que una figura se ha rotado 180° sobre sí misma.

Example 180°

878

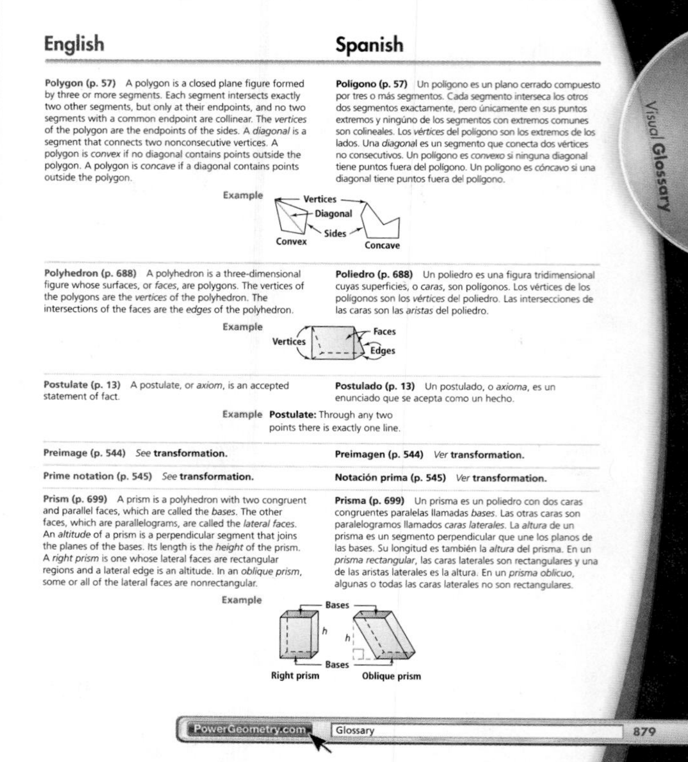

English / Spanish

Polygon (p. 57) A polygon is a closed plane figure formed by three or more segments. Each segment intersects exactly two other segments, but only at their endpoints, and no two segments with a common endpoint are collinear. The *vertices* of the polygon are the endpoints of the sides. A *diagonal* is a segment that connects two nonconsecutive vertices. A polygon is *convex* if no diagonal contains points outside the polygon. A polygon is *concave* if a diagonal contains points outside the polygon.

Polígono (p. 57) Un polígono es un plano cerrado compuesto por tres o más segmentos. Cada segmento interseca los otros dos segmentos exactamente, pero únicamente en sus puntos extremos y ningúno de los segmentos con extremos comunes son colineales. Los *vértices* del polígono son los extremos de los lados. Una *diagonal* es un segmento que conecta dos vértices no consecutivos. Un polígono es *convexo* si ninguna diagonal tiene puntos fuera del polígono. Un polígono es *cóncavo* si una diagonal tiene puntos fuera del polígono.

Example Vertices, Diagonal, Sides, Convex, Concave

Polyhedron (p. 688) A polyhedron is a three-dimensional figure whose surfaces, or *faces*, are polygons. The vertices of the polygons are the *vertices* of the polyhedron. The intersections of the faces are the *edges* of the polyhedron.

Poliedro (p. 688) Un poliedro es una figura tridimensional cuyas superficies, o *caras*, son polígonos. Los vértices de los polígonos son los *vértices* del poliedro. Las intersecciones de las caras son las *aristas* del poliedro.

Example Vertices, Faces, Edges

Postulate (p. 13) A postulate, or *axiom*, is an accepted statement of fact.

Postulado (p. 13) Un postulado, o *axioma*, es un enunciado que se acepta como un hecho.

Example **Postulate:** Through any two points there is exactly one line.

Preimage (p. 544) *See* **transformation.**

Preimagen (p. 544) *Ver* **transformation.**

Prime notation (p. 545) *See* **transformation.**

Notación prima (p. 545) *Ver* **transformation.**

Prism (p. 699) A prism is a polyhedron with two congruent and parallel faces, which are called the *bases*. The other faces, which are parallelograms, are called the *lateral faces*. An *altitude* of a prism is a perpendicular segment that joins the planes of the bases. Its length is the *height* of the prism. A *right prism* is one whose lateral faces are rectangular regions and a lateral edge is an altitude. In an *oblique prism*, some or all of the lateral faces are nonrectangular.

Prisma (p. 699) Un prisma es un poliedro con dos caras congruentes paralelas llamadas *bases*. Las otras caras son paralelogramos llamados *caras laterales*. La *altura* de un prisma es un segmento perpendicular que une los planos de las bases. Su longitud es también la *altura* del prisma. En un *prisma rectangular*, las caras laterales son rectangulares y una de las aristas laterales es la altura. En un *prisma oblicuo*, algunas o todas las caras laterales no son rectangulares.

Example Bases, h, Right prism, Oblique prism

PowerGeometry.com Glossary 879

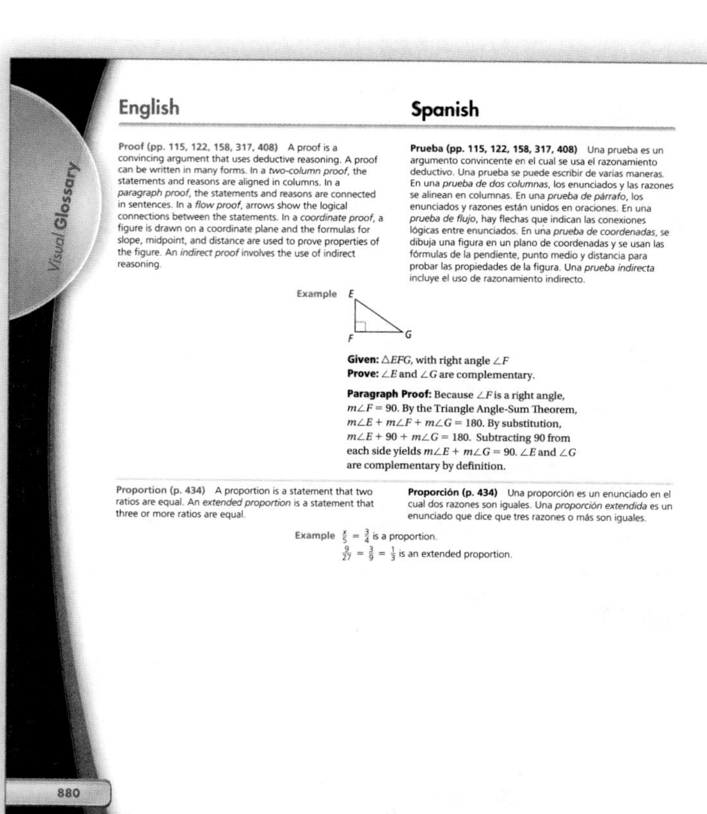

English / Spanish

Proof (pp. 115, 122, 158, 317, 408) A proof is a convincing argument that uses deductive reasoning. A proof can be written in many forms. In a *two-column proof*, the statements and reasons are aligned in columns. In a *paragraph proof*, the statements and reasons are connected in sentences. In a *flow proof*, arrows show the logical connections between the statements. In a *coordinate proof*, a figure is drawn on a coordinate plane and the formulas for slope, midpoint, and distance are used to prove properties of the figure. An *indirect proof* involves the use of indirect reasoning.

Prueba (pp. 115, 122, 158, 317, 408) Una prueba es un argumento convincente en el cual se usa el razonamiento deductivo. Una prueba se puede escribir de varias maneras. En una *prueba de dos columnas*, los enunciados y las razones se alinean en columnas. En una *prueba de párrafo*, los enunciados y razones están unidos en oraciones. En una *prueba de flujo*, hay flechas que indican las conexiones lógicas entre enunciados. En una *prueba de coordenadas*, se dibuja una figura en un plano de coordenadas y se usan las fórmulas de la pendiente, punto medio y distancia para probar las propiedades de la figura. Una *prueba indirecta* incluye el uso de razonamiento indirecto.

Example E, F, G

Given: $\triangle EFG$, with right angle $\angle F$

Prove: $\angle E$ and $\angle G$ are complementary.

Paragraph Proof: Because $\angle F$ is a right angle, $m\angle F = 90$. By the Triangle Angle-Sum Theorem, $m\angle E + m\angle F + m\angle G = 180$. By substitution, $m\angle E + 90 + m\angle G = 180$. Subtracting 90 from each side yields $m\angle E + m\angle G = 90$. $\angle E$ and $\angle G$ are complementary by definition.

Proportion (p. 434) A proportion is a statement that two ratios are equal. An *extended proportion* is a statement that three or more ratios are equal.

Proporción (p. 434) Una proporción es un enunciado en el cual dos razones son iguales. Una *proporción extendida* es un enunciado que dice que tres razones o más son iguales.

Example $\frac{x}{5} = \frac{3}{4}$ is a proportion.
$\frac{9}{27} = \frac{3}{9} = \frac{1}{3}$ is an extended proportion.

880

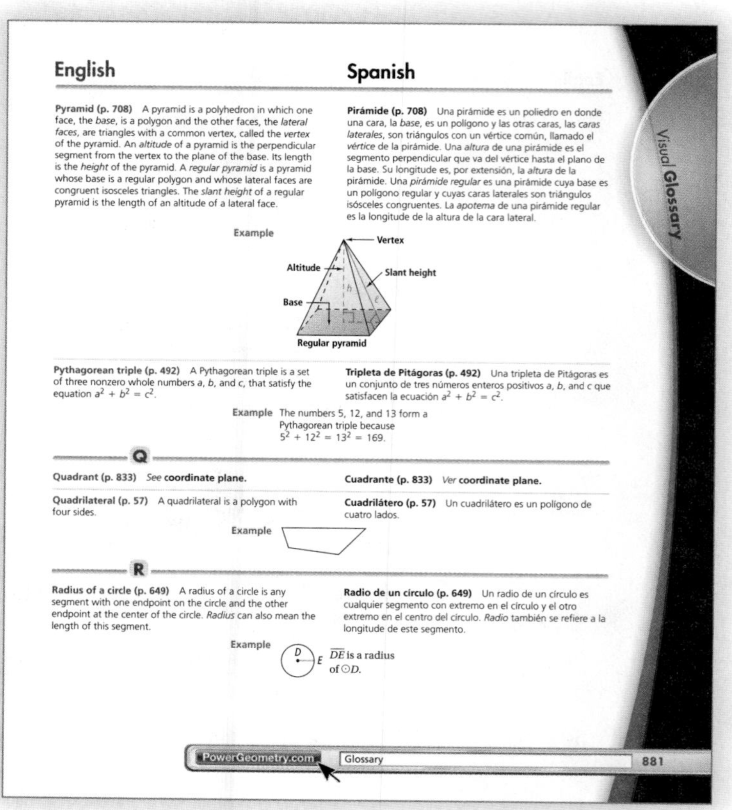

English / Spanish

Pyramid (p. 708) A pyramid is a polyhedron in which one face, the *base*, is a polygon and the other faces, the *lateral faces*, are triangles with a common vertex, called the *vertex* of the pyramid. An *altitude* of a pyramid is the perpendicular segment from the vertex to the plane of the base. Its length is the *height* of the pyramid. A *regular pyramid* is a pyramid whose base is a regular polygon and whose lateral faces are congruent isosceles triangles. The *slant height* of a regular pyramid is the length of an altitude of a lateral face.

Pirámide (p. 708) Una pirámide es un poliedro en donde una cara, la *base*, es un polígono y las otras caras, las *caras laterales*, son triángulos con un vértice común, llamado el *vértice* de la pirámide. Una *altura* de una pirámide es el segmento perpendicular que va del vértice hasta el plano de la base. Su longitude es, por extensión, la *altura* de la pirámide. Una *pirámide regular* es una pirámide cuya base es un polígono regular y cuyas caras laterales son triángulos isósceles congruentes. La *apotema* de una pirámide regular es la longitude de la altura de la cara lateral.

Example Vertex, Altitude, Slant height, Base, Regular pyramid

Pythagorean triple (p. 492) A Pythagorean triple is a set of three nonzero whole numbers a, b, and c, that satisfy the equation $a^2 + b^2 = c^2$.

Tripleta de Pitágoras (p. 492) Una tripleta de Pitágoras es un conjunto de tres números enteros positivos a, b, and c que satisfacen la ecuación $a^2 + b^2 = c^2$.

Example The numbers 5, 12, and 13 form a Pythagorean triple because $5^2 + 12^2 = 13^2 = 169$.

Q

Quadrant (p. 833) *See* **coordinate plane.**

Cuadrante (p. 833) *Ver* **coordinate plane.**

Quadrilateral (p. 57) A quadrilateral is a polygon with four sides.

Cuadrilátero (p. 57) Un cuadrilátero es un polígono de cuatro lados.

Example

R

Radius of a circle (p. 649) A radius of a circle is any segment with one endpoint on the circle and the other endpoint at the center of the circle. *Radius* can also mean the length of this segment.

Radio de un círculo (p. 649) Un radio de un círculo es cualquier segmento con extremo en el círculo y el otro extremo en el centro del círculo. *Radio* también se refiere a la longitude de este segmento.

Example $\overline{DE}$ is a radius of $\odot D$.

PowerGeometry.com Glossary 881

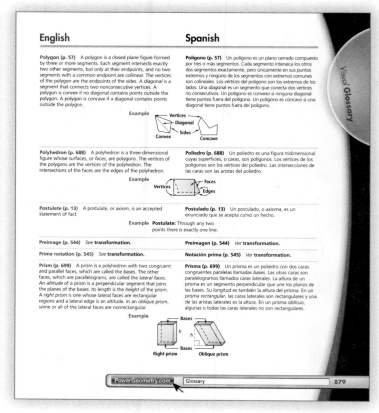

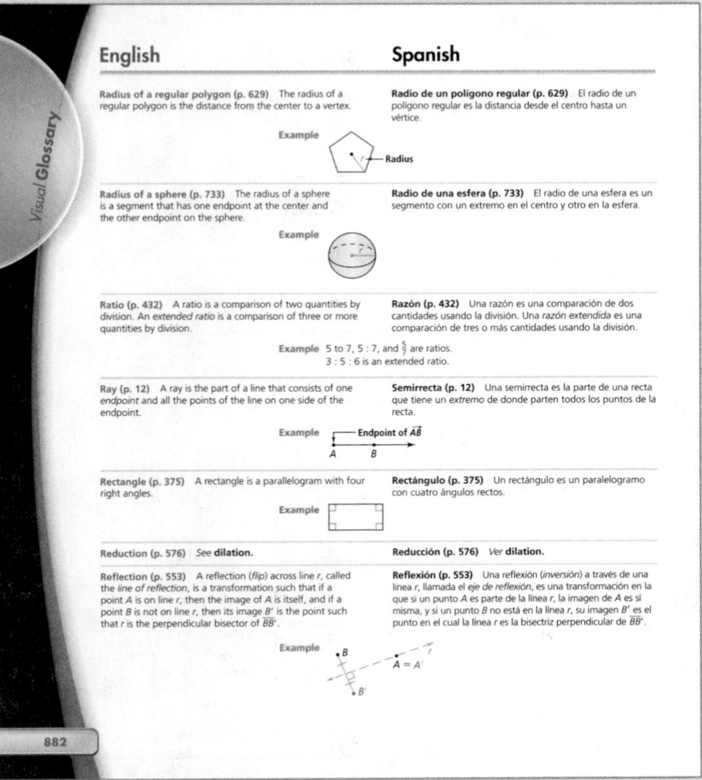

Visual Glossary

English | **Spanish**

Radius of a regular polygon (p. 629) The radius of a regular polygon is the distance from the center to a vertex.

Radio de un polígono regular (p. 629) El radio de un polígono regular es la distancia desde el centro hasta un vértice.

Example

Radius of a sphere (p. 733) The radius of a sphere is a segment that has one endpoint at the center and the other endpoint on the sphere.

Radio de una esfera (p. 733) El radio de una esfera es un segmento con un extremo en el centro y otro en la esfera.

Example

Ratio (p. 432) A ratio is a comparison of two quantities by division. An *extended ratio* is a comparison of three or more quantities by division.

Razón (p. 432) Una razón es una comparación de dos cantidades usando la división. Una *razón extendida* es una comparación de tres o más cantidades usando la división.

Example 5 to 7, 5 : 7, and $\frac{5}{7}$ are ratios.
3 : 5 : 6 is an extended ratio.

Ray (p. 12) A ray is the part of a line that consists of one *endpoint* and all the points of the line on one side of the endpoint.

Semirrecta (p. 12) Una semirrecta es la parte de una recta que tiene un *extremo* de donde parten todos los puntos de la recta.

Example

Rectangle (p. 375) A rectangle is a parallelogram with four right angles.

Rectángulo (p. 375) Un rectángulo es un paralelogramo con cuatro ángulos rectos.

Example

Reduction (p. 576) *See* **dilation.**

Reducción (p. 576) *Ver* **dilation.**

Reflection (p. 553) A reflection (*flip*) across line *r*, called the *line of reflection*, is a transformation such that if a point *A* is on line *r*, then the image of *A* is itself, and if a point *B* is not on line *r*, then its image *B′* is the point such that *r* is the perpendicular bisector of $\overline{BB'}$.

Reflexión (p. 553) Una reflexión (*inversión*) a través de una línea *r*, llamada el *eje de reflexión*, es una transformación en la que si un punto *A* es parte de la línea *r*, la imagen de *A* es sí misma, y si un punto *B* no está en la línea *r*, su imagen *B′* es el punto en el cual la línea *r* es la bisectriz perpendicular de $\overline{BB'}$.

Example

882

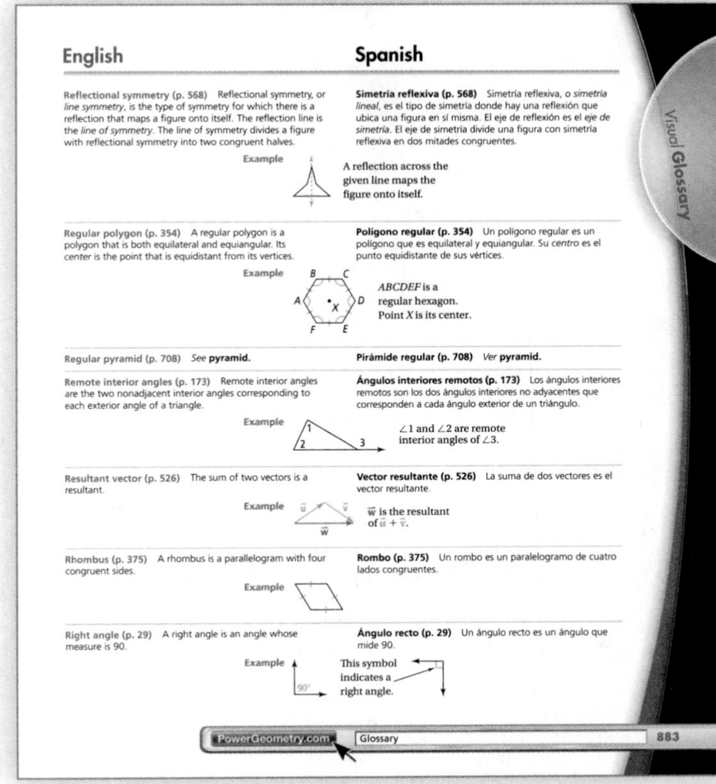

English | **Spanish**

Reflectional symmetry (p. 568) Reflectional symmetry, or *line symmetry*, is the type of symmetry for which there is a reflection that maps a figure onto itself. The reflection line is the *line of symmetry*. The line of symmetry divides a figure with reflectional symmetry into two congruent halves.

Simetría reflexiva (p. 568) Simetría reflexiva, o *simetría lineal*, es el tipo de simetría donde hay una reflexión que ubica una figura en sí misma. El eje de reflexión es el *eje de simetría*. El eje de simetría divide una figura con simetría reflexiva en dos mitades congruentes.

Example A reflection across the given line maps the figure onto itself.

Regular polygon (p. 354) A regular polygon is a polygon that is both equilateral and equiangular. Its *center* is the point that is equidistant from its vertices.

Polígono regular (p. 354) Un polígono regular es un polígono que es equilateral y equiangular. Su *centro* es el punto equidistante de sus vértices.

Example

ABCDEF is a regular hexagon. Point *X* is its center.

Regular pyramid (p. 708) *See* **pyramid.**

Pirámide regular (p. 708) *Ver* **pyramid.**

Remote interior angles (p. 173) Remote interior angles are the two nonadjacent interior angles corresponding to each exterior angle of a triangle.

Ángulos interiores remotos (p. 173) Los ángulos interiores remotos son los dos ángulos interiores no adyacentes que corresponden a cada ángulo exterior de un triángulo.

Example

∠1 and ∠2 are remote interior angles of ∠3.

Resultant vector (p. 526) The sum of two vectors is a resultant.

Vector resultante (p. 526) La suma de dos vectores es el vector resultante.

Example

$\vec{w}$ is the resultant of $\vec{u} + \vec{v}$.

Rhombus (p. 375) A rhombus is a parallelogram with four congruent sides.

Rombo (p. 375) Un rombo es un paralelogramo de cuatro lados congruentes.

Example

Right angle (p. 29) A right angle is an angle whose measure is 90.

Ángulo recto (p. 29) Un ángulo recto es un ángulo que mide 90.

Example

This symbol indicates a right angle.

PowerGeometry.com Glossary 883

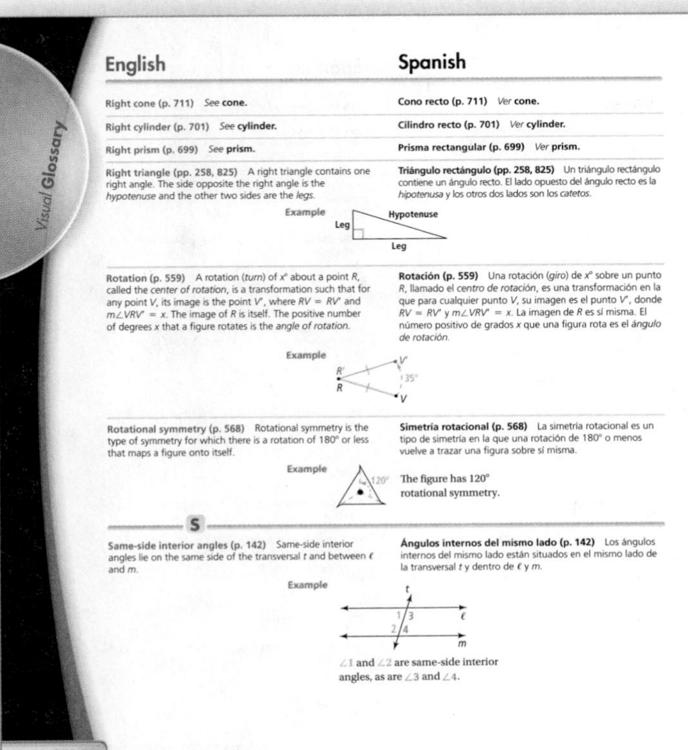

Visual Glossary

English | **Spanish**

Right cone (p. 711) *See* **cone.**

Cono recto (p. 711) *Ver* **cone.**

Right cylinder (p. 701) *See* **cylinder.**

Cilindro recto (p. 701) *Ver* **cylinder.**

Right prism (p. 699) *See* **prism.**

Prisma rectangular (p. 699) *Ver* **prism.**

Right triangle (pp. 258, 825) A right triangle contains one right angle. The side opposite the right angle is the *hypotenuse* and the other two sides are the *legs*.

Triángulo rectángulo (pp. 258, 825) Un triángulo rectángulo contiene un ángulo recto. El lado opuesto del ángulo recto es la *hipotenusa* y los otros dos lados son los *catetos*.

Example

Rotation (p. 559) A rotation (*turn*) of $x°$ about a point *R*, called the *center of rotation*, is a transformation such that for any point *V*, its image is the point *V′*, where $RV = RV'$ and $m\angle VRV' = x$. The image of *R* is itself. The positive number of degrees *x* that a figure rotates is the *angle of rotation*.

Rotación (p. 559) Una rotación (*giro*) de $x°$ sobre un punto *R*, llamado el *centro de rotación*, es una transformación en la que para cualquier punto *V*, su imagen es el punto *V′*, donde $RV = RV'$ y $m\angle VRV' = x$. La imagen de *R* es sí misma. El número positivo de grados *x* que una figura rota es el *ángulo de rotación*.

Example

Rotational symmetry (p. 568) Rotational symmetry is the type of symmetry for which there is a rotation of 180° or less that maps a figure onto itself.

Simetría rotacional (p. 568) La simetría rotacional es un tipo de simetría en la que una rotación de 180° o menos vuelve a trazar una figura sobre sí misma.

Example

The figure has 120° rotational symmetry.

S

Same-side interior angles (p. 142) Same-side interior angles lie on the same side of the transversal *t* and between *ℓ* and *m*.

Ángulos internos del mismo lado (p. 142) Los ángulos internos del mismo lado están situados en el mismo lado de la transversal *t* y dentro de *ℓ* y *m*.

Example

∠1 and ∠2 are same-side interior angles, as are ∠3 and ∠4.

884

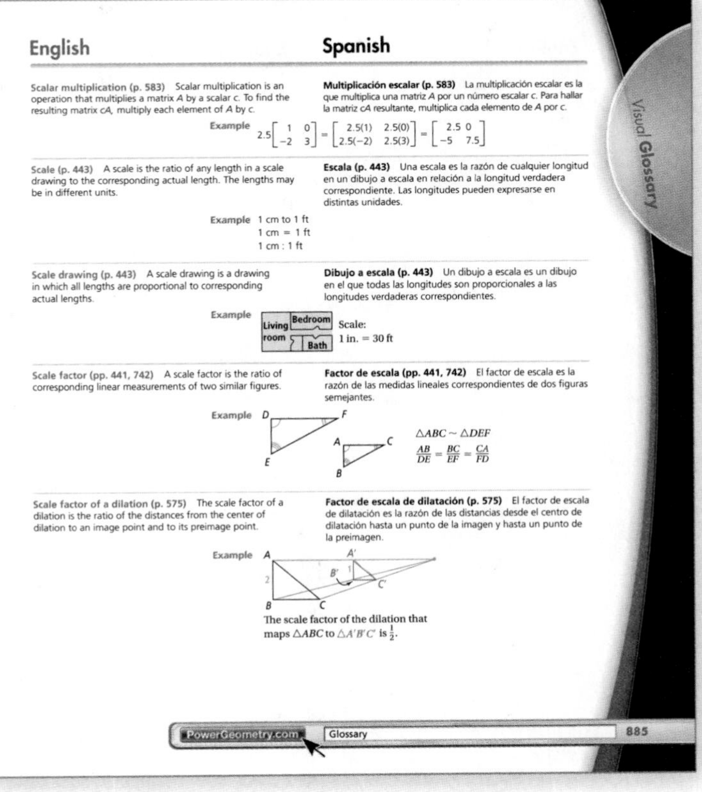

English | **Spanish**

Scalar multiplication (p. 583) Scalar multiplication is an operation that multiplies a matrix *A* by a scalar *c*. To find the resulting matrix *cA*, multiply each element of *A* by *c*.

Multiplicación escalar (p. 583) La multiplicación escalar es la que multiplica una matriz *A* por un número escalar *c*. Para hallar la matriz *cA* resultante, multiplica cada elemento de *A* por *c*.

Example $2.5\begin{bmatrix} 1 & 0 \\ -2 & 3 \end{bmatrix} = \begin{bmatrix} 2.5(1) & 2.5(0) \\ 2.5(-2) & 2.5(3) \end{bmatrix} = \begin{bmatrix} 2.5 & 0 \\ -5 & 7.5 \end{bmatrix}$

Scale (p. 443) A scale is the ratio of any length in a scale drawing to the corresponding actual length. The lengths may be in different units.

Escala (p. 443) Una escala es la razón de cualquier longitud en un dibujo a escala en relación a la longitud verdadera correspondiente. Las longitudes pueden expresarse en distintas unidades.

Example 1 cm to 1 ft
1 cm = 1 ft
1 cm : 1 ft

Scale drawing (p. 443) A scale drawing is a drawing in which all lengths are proportional to corresponding actual lengths.

Dibujo a escala (p. 443) Un dibujo a escala es un dibujo en el que todas las longitudes son proporcionales a las longitudes verdaderas correspondientes.

Example

Scale: 1 in. = 30 ft

Scale factor (pp. 441, 742) A scale factor is the ratio of corresponding linear measurements of two similar figures.

Factor de escala (pp. 441, 742) El factor de escala es la razón de las medidas lineales correspondientes de dos figuras semejantes.

Example

$\triangle ABC \sim \triangle DEF$

$\frac{AB}{DE} = \frac{BC}{EF} = \frac{CA}{FD}$

Scale factor of a dilation (p. 575) The scale factor of a dilation is the ratio of the distances from the center of dilation to an image point and to its preimage point.

Factor de escala de dilatación (p. 575) El factor de escala de dilatación es la razón de las distancias desde el centro de dilatación hasta un punto de la imagen y hasta un punto de la preimagen.

Example

The scale factor of the dilation that maps $\triangle ABC$ to $\triangle A'B'C'$ is $\frac{1}{2}$.

PowerGeometry.com Glossary 885

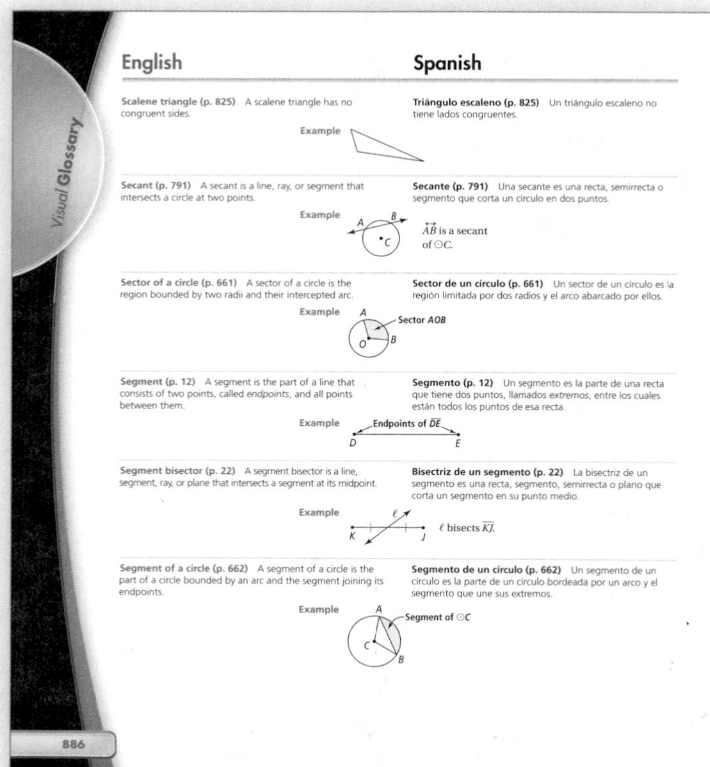

Visual Glossary

English | Spanish

Scalene triangle (p. 825) A scalene triangle has no congruent sides.

Triángulo escaleno (p. 825) Un triángulo escaleno no tiene lados congruentes.

Example

Secant (p. 791) A secant is a line, ray, or segment that intersects a circle at two points.

Secante (p. 791) Una secante es una recta, semirrecta o segmento que corta un círculo en dos puntos.

Example $\overleftrightarrow{AB}$ is a secant of $\odot C$.

Sector of a circle (p. 661) A sector of a circle is the region bounded by two radii and their intercepted arc.

Sector de un círculo (p. 661) Un sector de un círculo es la región limitada por dos radios y el arco abarcado por ellos.

Example Sector *AOB*

Segment (p. 12) A segment is the part of a line that consists of two points, called *endpoints*, and all points between them.

Segmento (p. 12) Un segmento es la parte de una recta que tiene dos puntos, llamados *extremos*, entre los cuales están todos los puntos de esa recta.

Example Endpoints of $\overline{DE}$

Segment bisector (p. 22) A segment bisector is a line, segment, ray, or plane that intersects a segment at its midpoint.

Bisectriz de un segmento (p. 22) La bisectriz de un segmento es una recta, segmento, semirrecta o plano que corta un segmento en su punto medio.

Example ℓ bisects $\overline{KJ}$.

Segment of a circle (p. 662) A segment of a circle is the part of a circle bounded by an arc and the segment joining its endpoints.

Segmento de un círculo (p. 662) Un segmento de un círculo es la parte de un círculo bordeada por un arco y el segmento que une sus extremos.

Example Segment of $\odot C$

886

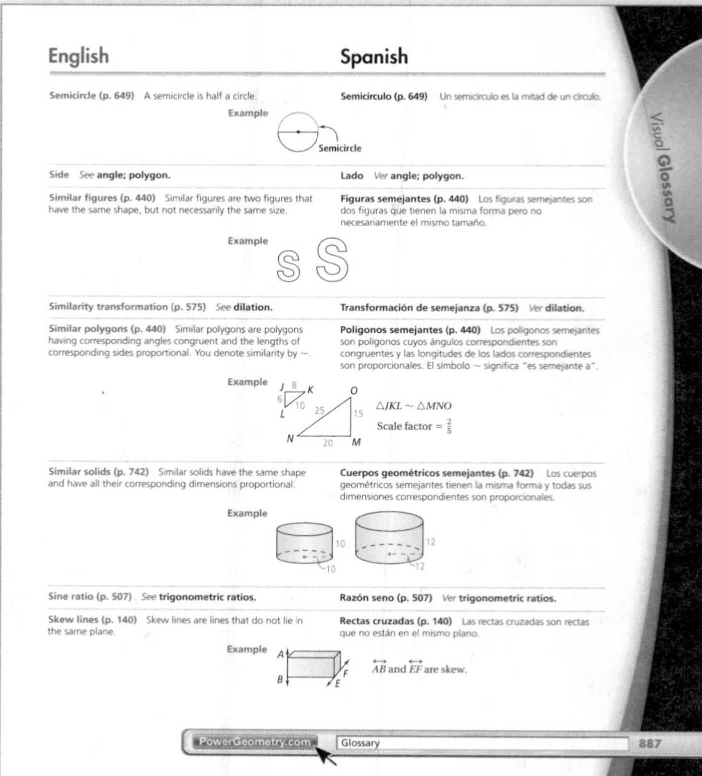

English | Spanish

Semicircle (p. 649) A semicircle is half a circle.

Semicírculo (p. 649) Un semicírculo es la mitad de un círculo.

Example Semicircle

Side *See* **angle; polygon.**

Lado *Ver* **angle; polygon.**

Similar figures (p. 440) Similar figures are two figures that have the same shape, but not necessarily the same size.

Figuras semejantes (p. 440) Los figuras semejantes son dos figuras que tienen la misma forma pero no necesariamente el mismo tamaño.

Example

Similarity transformation (p. 575) *See* **dilation.**

Transformación de semejanza (p. 575) *Ver* **dilation.**

Similar polygons (p. 440) Similar polygons are polygons having corresponding angles congruent and the lengths of corresponding sides proportional. You denote similarity by ~.

Polígonos semejantes (p. 440) Los polígonos semejantes son polígonos cuyos ángulos correspondientes son congruentes y las longitudes de los lados correspondientes son proporcionales. El símbolo ~ significa "es semejante a".

Example $\triangle JKL \sim \triangle MNO$

Scale factor $= \frac{2}{5}$

Similar solids (p. 742) Similar solids have the same shape and have all their corresponding dimensions proportional.

Cuerpos geométricos semejantes (p. 742) Los cuerpos geométricos semejantes tienen la misma forma y todas sus dimensiones correspondientes son proporcionales.

Example

Sine ratio (p. 507) *See* **trigonometric ratios.**

Razón seno (p. 507) *Ver* **trigonometric ratios.**

Skew lines (p. 140) Skew lines are lines that do not lie in the same plane.

Rectas cruzadas (p. 140) Las rectas cruzadas son rectas que no están en el mismo plano.

Example $\overleftrightarrow{AB}$ and $\overleftrightarrow{EF}$ are skew.

PowerGeometry.com Glossary 887

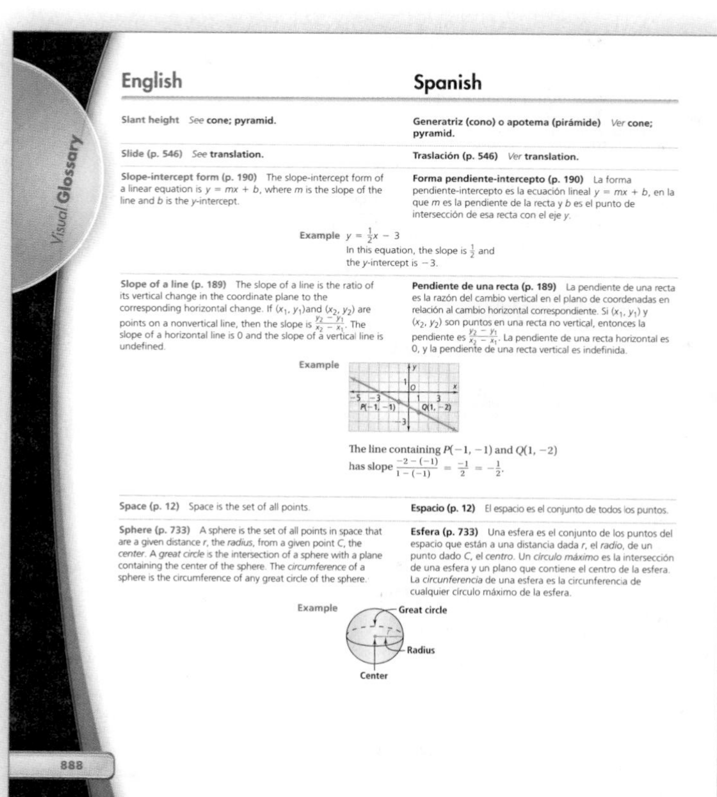

English | Spanish

Slant height *See* **cone; pyramid.**

Generatriz (cono) o apotema (pirámide) *Ver* **cone; pyramid.**

Slide (p. 546) *See* **translation.**

Traslación (p. 546) *Ver* **translation.**

Slope-intercept form (p. 190) The slope-intercept form of a linear equation is $y = mx + b$, where m is the slope of the line and b is the y-intercept.

Forma pendiente-intercepto (p. 190) La forma pendiente-intercepto es la ecuación lineal $y = mx + b$, en la que m es la pendiente de la recta y b es el punto de intersección de esa recta con el eje y.

Example $y = \frac{1}{2}x - 3$

In this equation, the slope is $\frac{1}{2}$ and the y-intercept is -3.

Slope of a line (p. 189) The slope of a line is the ratio of its vertical change in the coordinate plane to the corresponding horizontal change. If (x_1, y_1) and (x_2, y_2) are points on a nonvertical line, then the slope is $\frac{y_2 - y_1}{x_2 - x_1}$. The slope of a horizontal line is 0 and the slope of a vertical line is undefined.

Pendiente de una recta (p. 189) La pendiente de una recta es la razón del cambio vertical en el plano de coordenadas en relación al cambio horizontal correspondiente. Si (x_1, y_1) y (x_2, y_2) son puntos en una recta no vertical, entonces la pendiente es $\frac{y_2 - y_1}{x_2 - x_1}$. La pendiente de una recta horizontal es 0, y la pendiente de una recta vertical es indefinida.

Example

The line containing $P(-1, -1)$ and $Q(1, -2)$ has slope $\frac{-2-(-1)}{1-(-1)} = \frac{-1}{2} = -\frac{1}{2}$.

Space (p. 12) Space is the set of all points.

Espacio (p. 12) El espacio es el conjunto de todos los puntos.

Sphere (p. 733) A sphere is the set of all points in space that are a given distance r, the *radius*, from a given point C, the *center*. A *great circle* is the intersection of a sphere with a plane containing the center of the sphere. The *circumference* of a sphere is the circumference of any great circle of the sphere.

Esfera (p. 733) Una esfera es el conjunto de los puntos del espacio que están a una distancia dada r, el *radio*, de un punto dado C, el *centro*. Un *círculo máximo* es la intersección de una esfera y un plano que contiene el centro de la esfera. La *circunferencia* de una esfera es la circunferencia de cualquier círculo máximo de la esfera.

Example Great circle, Radius, Center

888

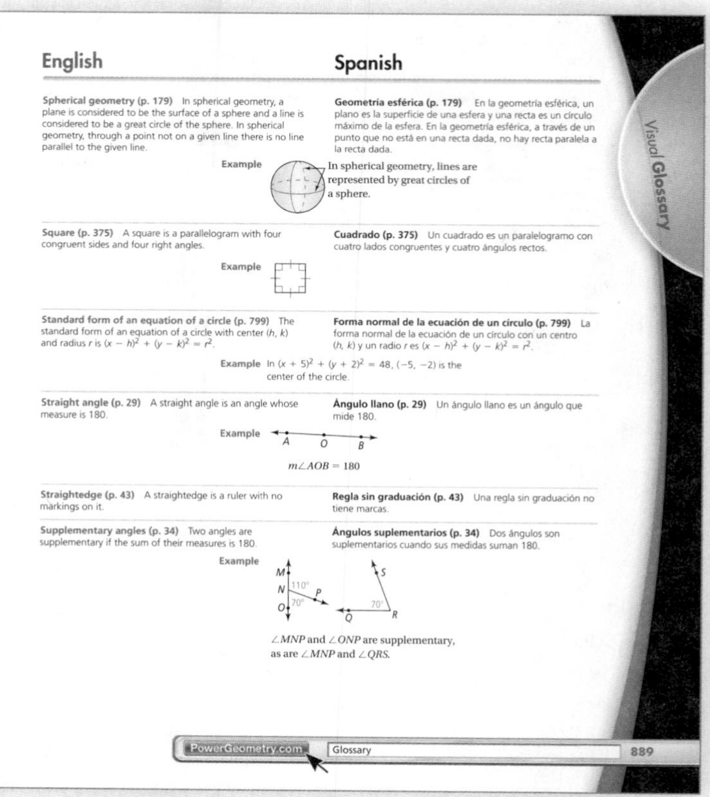

English | Spanish

Spherical geometry (p. 179) In spherical geometry, a plane is considered to be the surface of a sphere and a line is considered to be a great circle of the sphere. In spherical geometry, through a point not on a given line there is no line parallel to the given line.

Geometría esférica (p. 179) En la geometría esférica, un plano es la superficie de una esfera y una recta es un círculo máximo de la esfera. En la geometría esférica, a través de un punto que no está en una recta dada, no hay recta paralela a la recta dada.

Example In spherical geometry, lines are represented by great circles of a sphere.

Square (p. 375) A square is a parallelogram with four congruent sides and four right angles.

Cuadrado (p. 375) Un cuadrado es un paralelogramo con cuatro lados congruentes y cuatro ángulos rectos.

Example

Standard form of an equation of a circle (p. 799) The standard form of an equation of a circle with center (h, k) and radius r is $(x - h)^2 + (y - k)^2 = r^2$.

Forma normal de la ecuación de un círculo (p. 799) La forma normal de la ecuación de un círculo con un centro (h, k) y un radio r es $(x - h)^2 + (y - k)^2 = r^2$.

Example In $(x + 5)^2 + (y + 2)^2 = 48$, $(-5, -2)$ is the center of the circle.

Straight angle (p. 29) A straight angle is an angle whose measure is 180.

Ángulo llano (p. 29) Un ángulo llano es un ángulo que mide 180.

Example $m\angle AOB = 180$

Straightedge (p. 43) A straightedge is a ruler with no markings on it.

Regla sin graduación (p. 43) Una regla sin graduación no tiene marcas.

Supplementary angles (p. 34) Two angles are supplementary if the sum of their measures is 180.

Ángulos suplementarios (p. 34) Dos ángulos son suplementarios cuando sus medidas suman 180.

Example $\angle MNP$ and $\angle ONP$ are supplementary, as are $\angle MNP$ and $\angle QRS$.

PowerGeometry.com Glossary 889

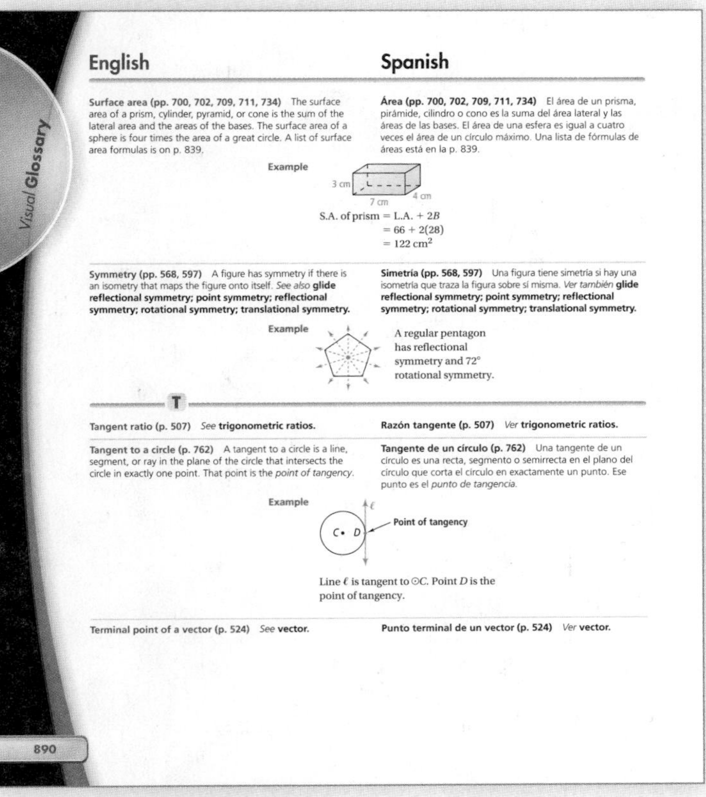

English / Spanish

Surface area (pp. 700, 702, 709, 711, 734) The surface area of a prism, cylinder, pyramid, or cone is the sum of the lateral area and the areas of the bases. The surface area of a sphere is four times the area of a great circle. A list of surface area formulas is on p. 839.

Área (pp. 700, 702, 709, 711, 734) El área de un prisma, pirámide, cilindro o cono es la suma del área lateral y las áreas de las bases. El área de una esfera es igual a cuatro veces el área de un círculo máximo. Una lista de fórmulas de áreas está en la p. 839.

Example

3 cm, 7 cm, 4 cm

$$\text{S.A. of prism} = \text{L.A.} + 2B = 66 + 2(28) = 122\ \text{cm}^2$$

Symmetry (pp. 568, 597) A figure has symmetry if there is an isometry that maps the figure onto itself. *See also* **glide reflectional symmetry; point symmetry; reflectional symmetry; rotational symmetry; translational symmetry.**

Simetría (pp. 568, 597) Una figura tiene simetría si hay una isometría que traza la figura sobre sí misma. *Ver también* **glide reflectional symmetry; point symmetry; reflectional symmetry; rotational symmetry; translational symmetry.**

Example A regular pentagon has reflectional symmetry and 72° rotational symmetry.

T

Tangent ratio (p. 507) *See* **trigonometric ratios.**

Razón tangente (p. 507) *Ver* **trigonometric ratios.**

Tangent to a circle (p. 762) A tangent to a circle is a line, segment, or ray in the plane of the circle that intersects the circle in exactly one point. That point is the *point of tangency*.

Tangente de un círculo (p. 762) Una tangente de un círculo es una recta, segmento o semirrecta en el plano del círculo que corta el círculo en exactamente un punto. Ese punto es el *punto de tangencia*.

Example

Point of tangency

Line ℓ is tangent to $\odot C$. Point D is the point of tangency.

Terminal point of a vector (p. 524) *See* **vector.**

Punto terminal de un vector (p. 524) *Ver* **vector.**

890

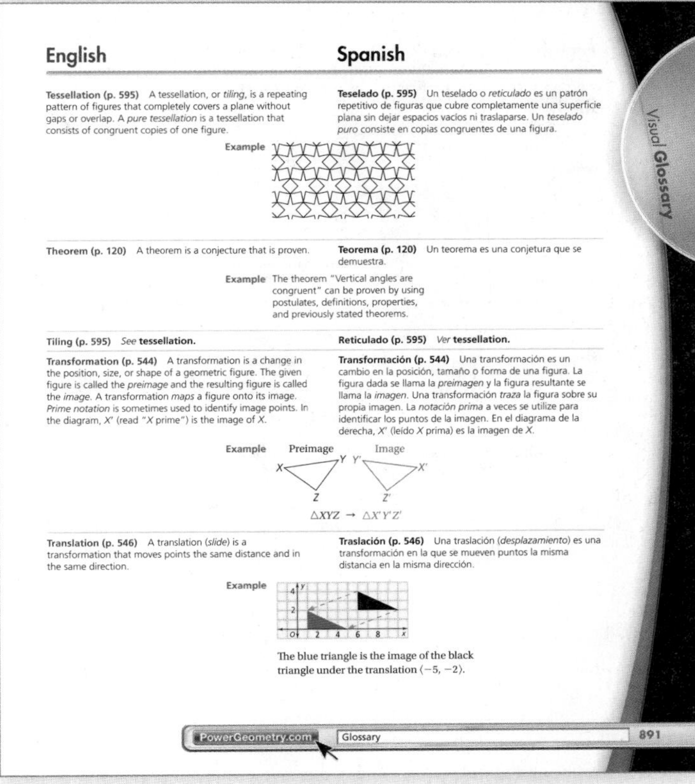

English / Spanish

Tessellation (p. 595) A tessellation, or *tiling*, is a repeating pattern of figures that completely covers a plane without gaps or overlap. A *pure tessellation* is a tessellation that consists of congruent copies of one figure.

Teselado (p. 595) Un teselado o *reticulado* es un patrón repetitivo de figuras que cubre completamente una superficie plana sin dejar espacios vacíos ni traslaparse. Un *teselado puro* consiste en copias congruentes de una figura.

Example

Theorem (p. 120) A theorem is a conjecture that is proven.

Teorema (p. 120) Un teorema es una conjetura que se demuestra.

Example The theorem "Vertical angles are congruent" can be proven by using postulates, definitions, properties, and previously stated theorems.

Tiling (p. 595) *See* **tessellation.**

Reticulado (p. 595) *Ver* **tessellation.**

Transformation (p. 544) A transformation is a change in the position, size, or shape of a geometric figure. The given figure is called the *preimage* and the resulting figure is called the *image*. A transformation *maps* a figure onto its image. *Prime notation* is sometimes used to identify image points. In the diagram, X' (read "X prime") is the image of X.

Transformación (p. 544) Una transformación es un cambio en la posición, tamaño o forma de una figura. La figura dada se llama la *preimagen* y la figura resultante se llama la *imagen*. Una transformación *traza* la figura sobre su propia imagen. La *notación prima* a veces se utilize para identificar los puntos de la imagen. En el diagrama de la derecha, X' (leído X prima) es la imagen de X.

Example Preimage, Image

$\triangle XYZ \rightarrow \triangle X'Y'Z'$

Translation (p. 546) A translation (*slide*) is a transformation that moves points the same distance and in the same direction.

Traslación (p. 546) Una traslación (*desplazamiento*) es una transformación en la que se mueven puntos la misma distancia en la misma dirección.

Example

The blue triangle is the image of the black triangle under the translation $\langle -5, -2 \rangle$.

PowerGeometry.com | Glossary 891

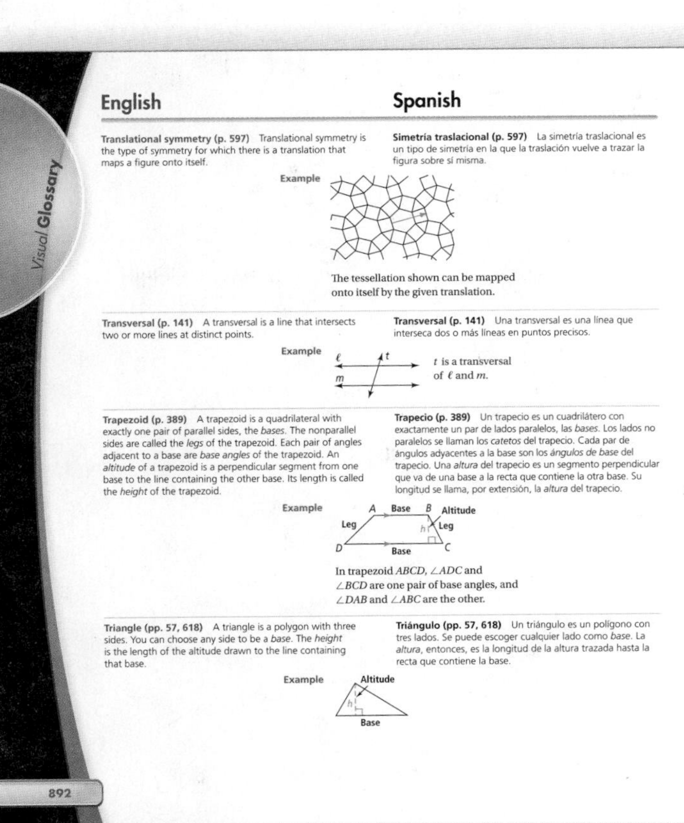

English / Spanish

Translational symmetry (p. 597) Translational symmetry is the type of symmetry for which there is a translation that maps a figure onto itself.

Simetría traslacional (p. 597) La simetría traslacional es un tipo de simetría en la que la traslación vuelve a trazar la figura sobre sí misma.

Example

The tessellation shown can be mapped onto itself by the given translation.

Transversal (p. 141) A transversal is a line that intersects two or more lines at distinct points.

Transversal (p. 141) Una transversal es una línea que interseca dos o más líneas en puntos precisos.

Example t is a transversal of ℓ and m.

Trapezoid (p. 389) A trapezoid is a quadrilateral with exactly one pair of parallel sides, the *bases*. The nonparallel sides are called the *legs* of the trapezoid. Each pair of angles adjacent to a base are *base angles* of the trapezoid. An *altitude* of a trapezoid is a perpendicular segment from one base to the line containing the other base. Its length is called the *height* of the trapezoid.

Trapecio (p. 389) Un trapecio es un cuadrilátero con exactamente un par de lados paralelos, las *bases*. Los lados no paralelos se llaman los *catetos* del trapecio. Cada par de ángulos adyacentes a la base son los *ángulos de base* del trapecio. Una *altura* del trapecio es un segmento perpendicular que va de una base a la recta que contiene la otra base. Su longitud se llama, por extensión, la *altura* del trapecio.

Example

In trapezoid $ABCD$, $\angle ADC$ and $\angle BCD$ are one pair of base angles, and $\angle DAB$ and $\angle ABC$ are the other.

Triangle (pp. 57, 618) A triangle is a polygon with three sides. You can choose any side to be a *base*. The *height* is the length of the altitude drawn to the line containing that base.

Triángulo (pp. 57, 618) Un triángulo es un polígono con tres lados. Se puede escoger cualquier lado como *base*. La *altura*, entonces, es la longitud de la altura trazada hasta la recta que contiene la base.

Example

892

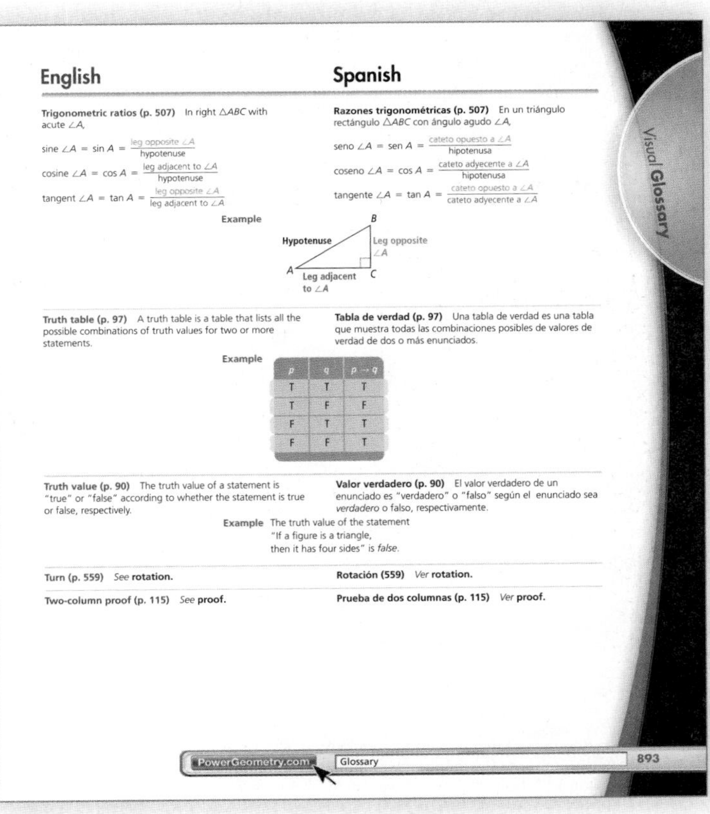

English / Spanish

Trigonometric ratios (p. 507) In right $\triangle ABC$ with acute $\angle A$,

$$\text{sine } \angle A = \sin A = \frac{\text{leg opposite } \angle A}{\text{hypotenuse}}$$

$$\text{cosine } \angle A = \cos A = \frac{\text{leg adjacent to } \angle A}{\text{hypotenuse}}$$

$$\text{tangent } \angle A = \tan A = \frac{\text{leg opposite } \angle A}{\text{leg adjacent to } \angle A}$$

Razones trigonométricas (p. 507) En un triángulo rectángulo $\triangle ABC$ con ángulo agudo $\angle A$,

$$\text{seno } \angle A = \text{sen } A = \frac{\text{cateto opuesto a } \angle A}{\text{hipotenusa}}$$

$$\text{coseno } \angle A = \cos A = \frac{\text{cateto adyecente a } \angle A}{\text{hipotenusa}}$$

$$\text{tangente } \angle A = \tan A = \frac{\text{cateto opuesto a } \angle A}{\text{cateto adyecente a } \angle A}$$

Example

Truth table (p. 97) A truth table is a table that lists all the possible combinations of truth values for two or more statements.

Tabla de verdad (p. 97) Una tabla de verdad es una tabla que muestra todas las combinaciones posibles de valores de verdad de dos o más enunciados.

Example

p	q	$p \rightarrow q$
T	T	T
T	F	F
F	T	T
F	F	T

Truth value (p. 90) The truth value of a statement is "true" or "false" according to whether the statement is true or false, respectively.

Valor verdadero (p. 90) El valor verdadero de un enunciado es "verdadero" o "falso" según el enunciado sea *verdadero* o falso, respectivamente.

Example The truth value of the statement "If a figure is a triangle, then it has four sides" is *false*.

Turn (p. 559) *See* **rotation.**

Rotación (559) *Ver* **rotation.**

Two-column proof (p. 115) *See* **proof.**

Prueba de dos columnas (p. 115) *Ver* **proof.**

PowerGeometry.com | Glossary 893

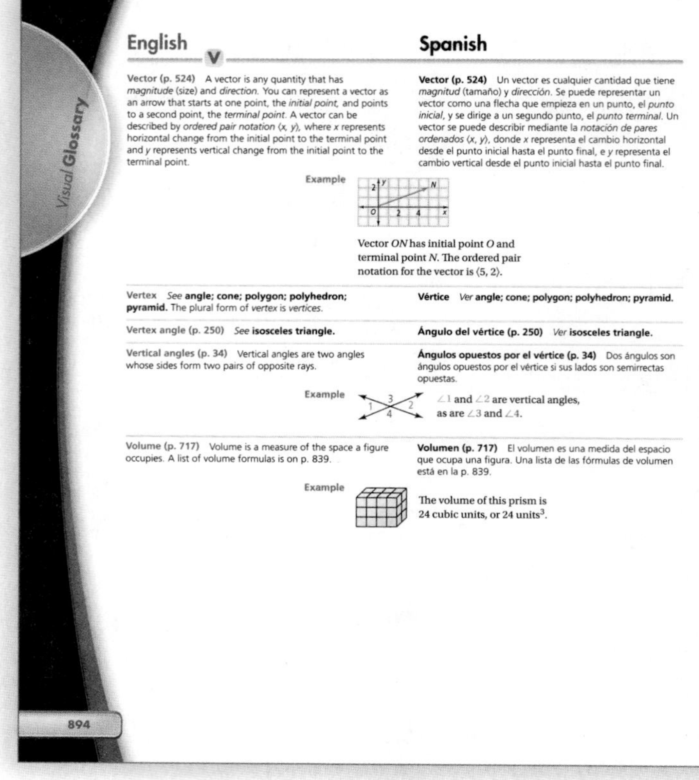

English — V — Spanish

Vector (p. 524) A vector is any quantity that has *magnitude* (size) and *direction*. You can represent a vector as an arrow that starts at one point, the *initial point*, and points to a second point, the *terminal point*. A vector can be described by *ordered pair notation* $\langle x, y \rangle$, where x represents horizontal change from the initial point to the terminal point and y represents vertical change from the initial point to the terminal point.

Vector (p. 524) Un vector es cualquier cantidad que tiene *magnitud* (tamaño) y *dirección*. Se puede representar un vector como una flecha que empieza en un punto, el *punto inicial*, y se dirige a un segundo punto, el *punto terminal*. Un vector se puede describir mediante la *notación de pares ordenados* $\langle x, y \rangle$, donde x representa el cambio horizontal desde el punto inicial hasta el punto final, e y representa el cambio vertical desde el punto inicial hasta el punto final.

Example

Vector ON has initial point O and terminal point N. The ordered pair notation for the vector is $\langle 5, 2 \rangle$.

Vertex *See* **angle; cone; polygon; polyhedron; pyramid.** The plural form of *vertex* is *vertices*.

Vértice *Ver* **angle; cone; polygon; polyhedron; pyramid.**

Vertex angle (p. 250) *See* **isosceles triangle.**

Ángulo del vértice (p. 250) *Ver* **isosceles triangle.**

Vertical angles (p. 34) Vertical angles are two angles whose sides form two pairs of opposite rays.

Ángulos opuestos por el vértice (p. 34) Dos ángulos son ángulos opuestos por el vértice si sus lados son semirrectas opuestas.

Example

$\angle 1$ and $\angle 2$ are vertical angles, as are $\angle 3$ and $\angle 4$.

Volume (p. 717) Volume is a measure of the space a figure occupies. A list of volume formulas is on p. 839.

Volumen (p. 717) El volumen es una medida del espacio que ocupa una figura. Una lista de las fórmulas de volumen está en la p. 839.

Example

The volume of this prism is 24 cubic units, or 24 units^3.

894

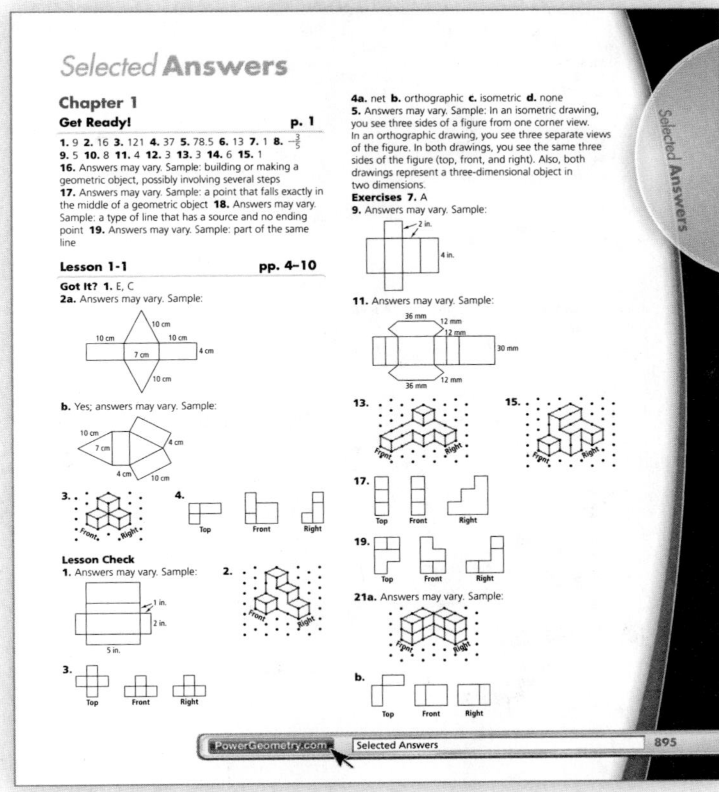

Selected Answers

Chapter 1

Get Ready! p. 1

1. 9 **2.** 16 **3.** 121 **4.** 37 **5.** 78.5 **6.** 13 **7.** 1 **8.** $-\frac{3}{5}$ **9.** 5 **10.** 8 **11.** 4 **12.** 3 **13.** 3 **14.** 6 **15.** 1 **16.** Answers may vary. Sample: building or making a geometric object, possibly involving several steps **17.** Answers may vary. Sample: a point that falls exactly in the middle of a geometric object **18.** Answers may vary. Sample: a type of line that has a source and no ending point **19.** Answers may vary. Sample: part of the same line

Lesson 1-1 pp. 4–10

Got It? 1. E, C
2a. Answers may vary. Sample:

b. Yes; answers may vary. Sample:

3. **4.**

Lesson Check
1. Answers may vary. Sample: **2.**

3.

4a. net **b.** orthographic **c.** isometric **d.** none
5. Answers may vary. Sample: In an isometric drawing, you see three sides of a figure from one corner view. In an orthographic drawing, you see three separate views of the figure. In both drawings, you see the same three sides of the figure (top, front, and right). Also, both drawings represent a three-dimensional object in two dimensions.
Exercises 7. A
9. Answers may vary. Sample:

11. Answers may vary. Sample:

13. **15.**

17.

19.

21a. Answers may vary. Sample:

b.

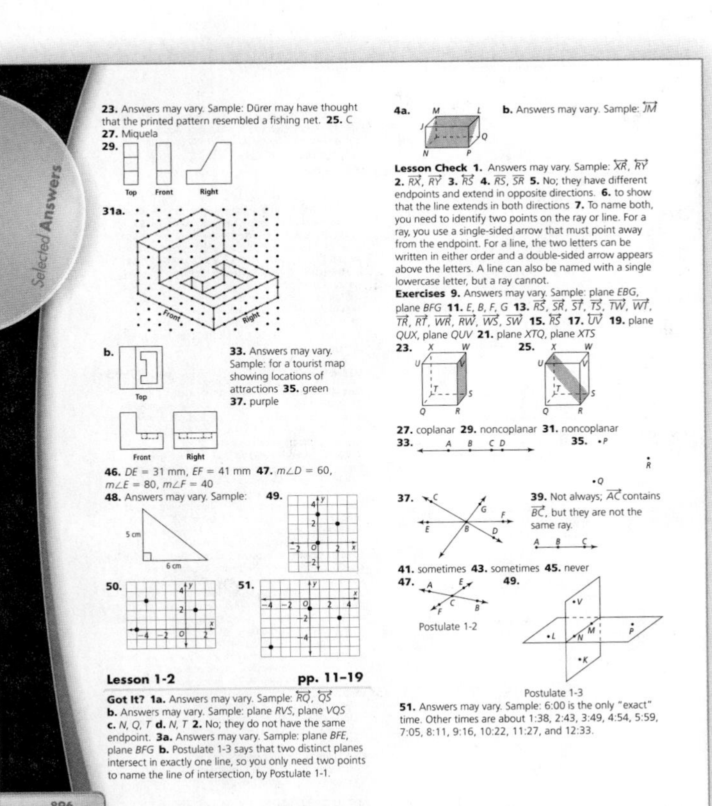

23. Answers may vary. Sample: Dürer may have thought that the printed pattern resembled a fishing net. **25.** C
27. Miquela
29.

31a.

b.

33. Answers may vary. Sample: for a tourist map showing locations of attractions **35.** green **37.** purple

46. $DE = 31$ mm, $EF = 41$ mm **47.** $m\angle D = 60$, $m\angle E = 80$, $m\angle F = 40$
48. Answers may vary. Sample: **49.**

50. **51.**

Lesson 1-2 pp. 11–19

Got It? 1a. Answers may vary. Sample: $\overleftrightarrow{RQ}$, $\overleftrightarrow{QS}$ **b.** Answers may vary. Sample: plane *RVS*, plane *VQS* **c.** *N, Q, T* **d.** *N, T* **2.** No; they do not have the same endpoint. **3a.** Answers may vary. Sample: plane *BFE*, plane *BFG* **b.** Postulate 1-3 says that two distinct planes intersect in exactly one line, so you only need two points to name the line of intersection, by Postulate 1-1.

4a.

b. Answers may vary. Sample: $\overleftrightarrow{JM}$

Lesson Check 1. Answers may vary. Sample: $\overleftrightarrow{XR}$, $\overleftrightarrow{RY}$ **2.** $\overrightarrow{RX}$, $\overrightarrow{RY}$ **3.** $\overleftrightarrow{RS}$ **4.** $\overline{RS}$, $\overline{SR}$ **5.** No; they have different endpoints and extend in opposite directions. **6.** to show that the line extends in both directions **7.** To name both, you need to identify two points on the ray or line. For a ray, you use a single-sided arrow that must point away from the endpoint. For a line, the two letters can be written in either order and a double-sided arrow appears above the letters. A line can also be named with a single lowercase letter, but a ray cannot.
Exercises 9. Answers may vary. Sample: plane *EBG*, plane *BFG* **11.** *E, B, F, G* **13.** $\overrightarrow{RS}$, $\overrightarrow{SR}$, $\overrightarrow{ST}$, $\overrightarrow{TS}$, $\overrightarrow{TW}$, $\overrightarrow{WT}$, $\overrightarrow{TR}$, $\overrightarrow{RT}$, $\overrightarrow{WR}$, $\overrightarrow{RW}$, $\overrightarrow{WS}$, $\overrightarrow{SW}$ **15.** $\overleftrightarrow{RS}$ **17.** $\overleftrightarrow{UV}$ **19.** plane *QUX*, plane *QUV* **21.** plane *XTQ*, plane *XTS*
23. **25.**

27. coplanar **29.** noncoplanar **31.** noncoplanar
33. **35.**

37.

39. Not always; $\overrightarrow{AC}$ contains $\overrightarrow{BC}$, but they are not the same ray.

41. sometimes **43.** sometimes **45.** never
47. **49.**

Postulate 1-2

Postulate 1-3

51. Answers may vary. Sample: 6:00 is the only "exact" time. Other times are about 1:38, 2:43, 3:49, 4:54, 5:59, 7:05, 8:11, 9:16, 10:22, 11:27, and 12:33.

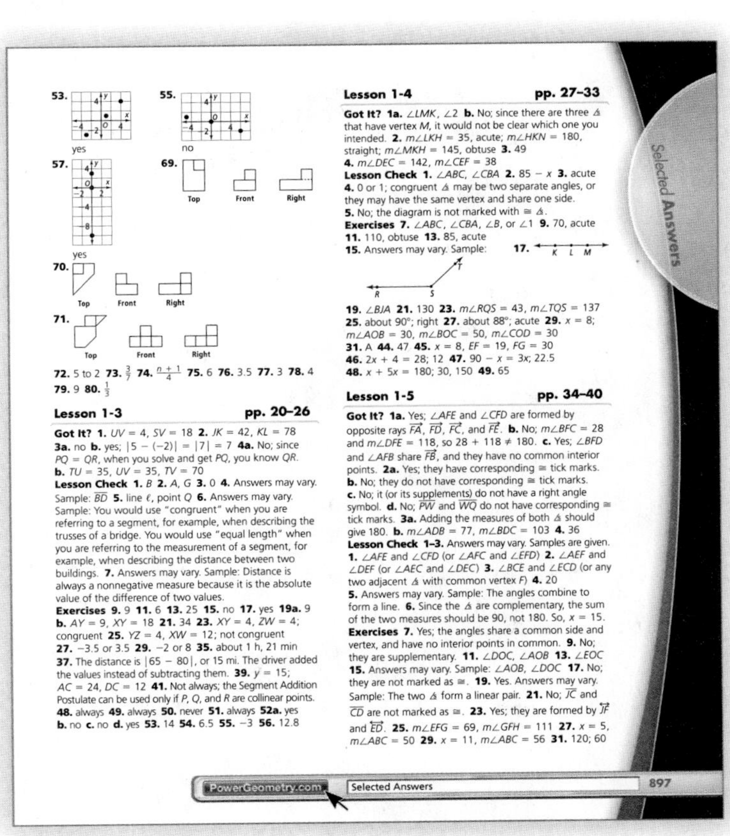

53. **55.**

yes no

57. **69.**

yes

70.

71.

72. 5 to 2 **73.** $\frac{3}{7}$ **74.** $\frac{n+1}{4}$ **75.** 6 **76.** 3.5 **77.** 3 **78.** 4 **79.** 9 **80.** $\frac{1}{3}$

Lesson 1-3 pp. 20–26

Got It? 1. $UV = 4$, $SV = 18$ **2.** $JK = 42$, $KL = 78$ **3a.** no **b.** yes; $|5 - (-2)| = |7| = 7$ **4a.** No; since $PQ = QR$, when you solve and get *PQ*, you know *QR*. **b.** $TU = 35$, $UV = 35$, $TV = 70$
Lesson Check 1. *B* **2.** *A, G* **3.** 0 **4.** Answers may vary. Sample: $\overline{BD}$ **5.** line ℓ, point *Q* **6.** Answers may vary. Sample: You would use "congruent" when you are referring to a segment, for example, when describing the trusses of a bridge. You would use "equal length" when you are referring to the measurement of a segment, for example, when describing the distance between two buildings. **7.** Answers may vary. Sample: Distance is always a nonnegative measure because it is the absolute value of the difference of two values.
Exercises 9. 9 **11.** 6 **13.** 25 **15.** no **17.** yes **19a.** 9 **b.** $AY = 9$, $XY = 18$ **21.** 34 **23.** $XY = 4$, $ZW = 4$; congruent **25.** $YZ = 4$, $XW = 12$; not congruent **27.** -3.5 or 3.5 **29.** -2 or 8 **35.** about 1 h, 21 min **37.** The distance is $|65 - 80|$, or 15 mi. The driver added the values instead of subtracting them. **39.** $y = 15$; $AC = 24$, $DC = 12$ **41.** Not always; the Segment Addition Postulate can be used only if *P, Q,* and *R* are collinear points. **48.** always **49.** always **50.** never **51.** always **52a.** yes **b.** no **c.** no **d.** yes **53.** 14 **54.** 6.5 **55.** -3 **56.** 12.8

Lesson 1-4 pp. 27–33

Got It? 1a. $\angle LMK$, $\angle 2$ **b.** No; since there are three ∠s that have vertex *M*, it would not be clear which one you intended. **2.** $m\angle LKH = 35$, acute; $m\angle HKN = 180$, straight; $m\angle MKH = 145$, obtuse **3.** 49
4. $m\angle DEC = 142$, $m\angle CEF = 38$
Lesson Check 1. $\angle ABC$, $\angle CBA$ **2.** $85 - x$ **3.** acute **4.** 0 or 1; congruent ∠s may be two separate angles, or they may have the same vertex and share one side. **5.** No; the diagram is not marked with ≅ ∠s.
Exercises 7. $\angle ABC$, $\angle CBA$, $\angle B$, or $\angle 1$ **9.** 70, acute **11.** 110, obtuse **13.** 85, acute
15. Answers may vary. Sample: **17.**

19. $\angle BJA$ **21.** 130 **23.** $m\angle RQS = 43$, $m\angle TQS = 137$ **25.** about 90°; right **27.** about 88°; acute **29.** $x = 8$; $m\angle AOB = 30$, $m\angle BOC = 50$, $m\angle COD = 30$ **31.** A **44.** 47 **45.** $x = 8$, $EF = 19$, $FG = 30$ **46.** $2x + 4 = 28$; 12 **47.** $90 - x = 3x$; 22.5 **48.** $x + 5x = 180$; 30, 150 **49.** 65

Lesson 1-5 pp. 34–40

Got It? 1a. Yes; $\angle AFE$ and $\angle CFD$ are formed by opposite rays $\overrightarrow{FA}$, $\overrightarrow{FD}$, $\overrightarrow{FC}$, and $\overrightarrow{FE}$. **b.** No; $m\angle BFC = 28$ and $m\angle DFE = 118$, so $28 + 118 \neq 180$. **c.** Yes; $\angle BFD$ and $\angle AFB$ share $\overrightarrow{FB}$, and they have no common interior points. **2a.** Yes; they have corresponding ≅ tick marks. **b.** No; they do not have corresponding ≅ tick marks. **c.** No; it (or its supplements) do not have a right angle symbol. **d.** No; $\overline{PW}$ and $\overline{WQ}$ do not have corresponding ≅ tick marks. **3a.** Adding the measures of both ∠s should give 180. **b.** $m\angle ADB = 77$, $m\angle BDC = 103$ **4.** 36
Lesson Check 1–3. Answers may vary. Samples are given. **1.** $\angle AFE$ and $\angle CFD$ (or $\angle AFC$ and $\angle EFD$) **2.** $\angle AEF$ and $\angle DEF$ (or $\angle AEC$ and $\angle DEC$) **3.** $\angle BCE$ and $\angle ECD$ (or any two adjacent ∠s with common vertex *F*) **4.** 20 **5.** Answers may vary. Sample: The angles combine to form a line. **6.** Since the ∠s are complementary, the sum of the two measures should be 90, not 180. So, $x = 15$.
Exercises 7. Yes; the angles share a common side and vertex, and have no interior points in common. **9.** No; they are supplementary. **11.** $\angle DOC$, $\angle AOB$ **13.** $\angle EOC$ **15.** Answers may vary. Sample: $\angle AOB$, $\angle DOC$ **17.** No; they are not marked as ≅. **19.** Yes. Answers may vary. Sample: The two ∠s form a linear pair. **21.** No; $\overline{JC}$ and $\overline{CD}$ are not marked as ≅. **23.** Yes; they are formed by $\overleftrightarrow{JF}$ and $\overleftrightarrow{ED}$. **25.** $m\angle EFG = 69$, $m\angle GFH = 111$ **27.** $x = 5$, $m\angle ABC = 50$ **29.** $x = 11$, $m\angle ABC = 56$ **31.** 120; 60

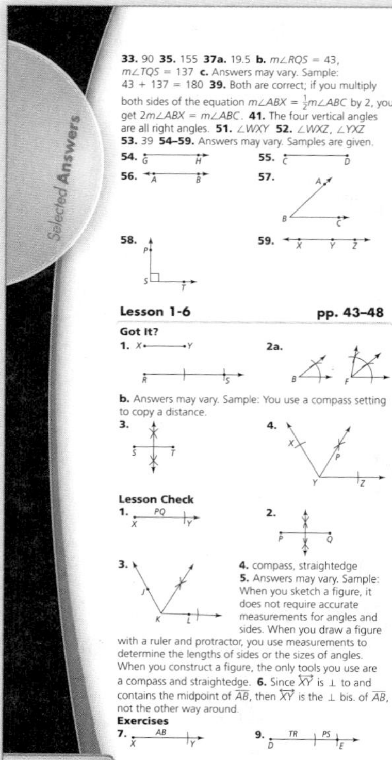

33. 90 **35.** 155 **37a.** 19.5 **b.** $m\angle RQS = 43$, $m\angle TQS = 137$ **c.** Answers may vary. Sample: $43 + 137 = 180$ **39.** Both are correct; if you multiply both sides of the equation $m\angle ABX = \frac{1}{2}m\angle ABC$ by 2, you get $2m\angle ABX = m\angle ABC$. **41.** The four vertical angles are all right angles. **51.** $\angle WXY$ **52.** $\angle WXZ$, $\angle YXZ$ **53.** 39 **54–59.** Answers may vary. Samples are given.

54. **55.** **56.** **57.** **58.** **59.**

Lesson 1-6 pp. 43–48

Got It?
1. **2a.**

b. Answers may vary. Sample: You use a compass setting to copy a distance.
3. **4.**

Lesson Check
1. **2.**
3. **4.** compass, straightedge **5.** Answers may vary. Sample: When you sketch a figure, it does not require accurate measurements for angles and sides. When you draw a figure with a ruler and protractor, you use measurements to determine the lengths of sides or the sizes of angles. When you construct a figure, the only tools you use are a compass and straightedge. **6.** Since $\overleftrightarrow{XY}$ is ⊥ to and contains the midpoint of $\overline{AB}$, then $\overleftrightarrow{XY}$ is the ⊥ bis. of $\overline{AB}$, not the other way around.

Exercises
7. **9.**

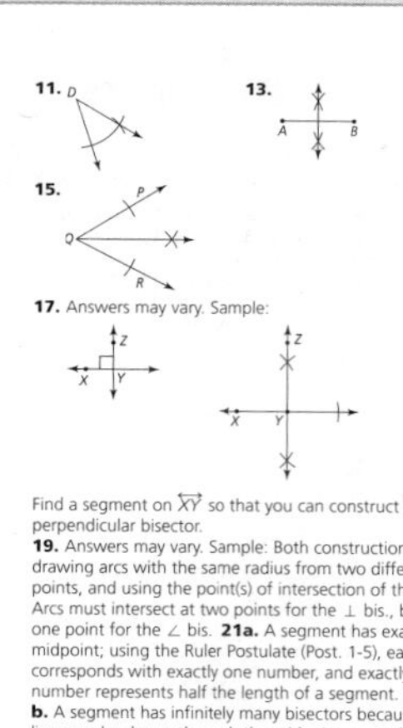

11. **13.** **15.**
17. Answers may vary. Sample:

Find a segment on $\overleftrightarrow{XY}$ so that you can construct $\overleftrightarrow{YZ}$ as its perpendicular bisector.
19. Answers may vary. Sample: Both constructions involve drawing arcs with the same radius from two different points, and using the point(s) of intersection of those arcs. Arcs must intersect at two points for the ⊥ bis., but only one point for the ∠ bis. **21a.** A segment has exactly one midpoint; using the Ruler Postulate (Post. 1-5), each point corresponds with exactly one number, and exactly one number represents half the length of a segment.
b. A segment has infinitely many bisectors because many lines can be drawn through the midpoint. **c.** In the plane with the segment, there is one ⊥ bis. because only one line in that plane can be drawn through the midpoint so that it forms a right angle with the given segment.
d. Consider the plane that is the ⊥ bis. of the segment. Any line in that plane that contains the midpoint of the segment is a ⊥ bis. of the segment, and there are infinitely many such lines.
23. **25a.** With P as center, draw an arc with radius slightly more than $\frac{1}{2}PQ$. Keeping that radius, draw an arc with Q as center. Those two arcs meet at 2 points; the line through those 2 points intersects $\overline{PQ}$ at its midpoint. **b.** Follow the steps in part (a) to find the midpoint C of $\overline{PQ}$. Then repeat the process for segments $\overline{PC}$ and $\overline{CQ}$.
27. possible

29. Not possible; the two 2-cm sides do not meet.
31a. **b.** The measure of each angle is 60°. **c.** Draw an angle congruent to one of the angles of the triangle from part (a) to get a 60° ∠. Then construct its angle bisector to get two 30° ∠s.
39. 116 **40.** yes; $m\angle TUV + m\angle VUW = 180$
41. 6 **42.** 10 **43.** 4 **44.** 3 **45.** 196 **46.** 10 **47.** −1

Lesson 1-7 pp. 50–56

Got It? **1a.** −4 **b.** (4, −2) **2.** (11, −13) **3a.** 15.8 **b.** Yes; the diff. of the coordinates are opposite, but their squares are the same. $VU = \sqrt{(-11)^2 + 8^2} = \sqrt{185} = 13.6$ **4.** $\sqrt{1325}$ m, or about 36.4 m
Lesson Check **1.** (0.5, 5.5), or $\left(\frac{1}{2}, \frac{11}{2}\right)$ **2.** (7, −8) **3.** $\sqrt{73}$, or about 8.5 units **4.** Answers may vary. Sample: For two different points, the expression $(x_2 - x_1)^2 + (y_2 - y_1)^2$ in the Distance Formula is always positive. So the positive square root of a positive number is positive. **5.** He did not keep the x-value and y-values together; so, $d = \sqrt{(1-3)^2 + (5-8)^2} = \sqrt{4+9} = \sqrt{13}$ units.
Exercises **7.** −1.5, or $-\frac{3}{2}$ **9.** −10 **11.** (3, 1) **13.** (6, 1) **15.** $\left(3\frac{7}{8}, -3\right)$ **17.** (5, −1) **19.** (12, −24) **21.** (5.5, −13.5) **23.** 18 **25.** 9 **27.** 10 **29.** 12.2 **31.** 8.2 **33.** 8.5 **35.** Everett, Charleston, Brookline, Fairfield, Davenport **37a.** 5.8 **b.** $\left(\frac{3}{2}, \frac{1}{2}\right)$, or (1.5, 0.5) **39a.** 5.4 **b.** $\left(-\frac{5}{2}, 3\right)$, or (−2.5, 3) **41a.** 2.8 **b.** (−4, −4) **43a.** 5.4 **b.** $\left(3, \frac{1}{2}\right)$, or (3, 0.5) **45.** 165 units; flying T to V then to U is shortest distance. **47a.** Answers may vary. Sample: Distance Formula (Find KP, then divide it by 2.) **b.** Answers may vary. Sample: Distance Formula (If M is the given midpoint, find KM and then multiply it by 2.) **49a.** 10.7 **b.** (3, −4)
51a.

The midpoints are the same, (5, 4).
b. Answers may vary. Sample: The diagonals bisect each other. **53.** 7 mi **55.** 3.2 mi **57a.** Answers may vary. Sample: (0, 2) and (4, 2); (2, 0) and (2, 4); (0, 4) and (4, 0); (0, 0) and (4, 4) **b.** Infinitely many; draw a circle with center (2, 2) and radius 4. Any diameter of that circle has length 8 and midpoint (2, 2).
65. **66.**
67. $\angle PQR$, $\angle RQP$ **68.** 150 **69.** $10\frac{5}{6}$ **70.** 504 **71.** 9 **72.** 10,560

Review p. 58

1. yes **3.** no; not a plane figure **5.** Sample: $FBWMX$; sides are $\overline{FB}$, $\overline{BW}$, $\overline{WM}$, $\overline{MX}$, $\overline{XF}$; angles are ∠F, ∠B, ∠W, ∠M, ∠X. **7.** Sample: $AGNHEPT$; sides are $\overline{AG}$, $\overline{GN}$, $\overline{NH}$, $\overline{HE}$, $\overline{EP}$, $\overline{PT}$, $\overline{TA}$; angles are ∠A, ∠G, ∠N, ∠H, ∠E, ∠P, ∠T. **9.** nonagon or enneagon, convex

Lesson 1-8 pp. 59–67

Got It? **1a.** 24 in. **b.** 32 in. **2a.** 48π m **b.** 75.4 m
3. 20 units **4.** 74 ft^2 **5a.** 49π ft^2 **b.** 153.9 ft^2 **c.** Answers may vary. Sample: $\frac{22}{7}$; it gives a result without fractions or decimals.
6a. **b.** 64 ft^2
Lesson Check **1.** 20 in.; 21 in.^{2} **2a.** 56.5 in.; 254.5 in.^{2} **b.** 22.9 m; 41.9 m^2 **3.** $(12 + 2\sqrt{2})$ units; 10 square units **4.** Answers may vary. Sample: To fence a garden you would find the perimeter; to determine the material needed to make a tablecloth you would find the area.
5. Answers may vary. Sample: Remind your friend that $2\pi r$ has only one variable, so it must compute the circumference. πr^2 has one variable squared, and square units indicate area.
6. The classmate seems to have forgotten to multiply r^2 by π. The correct answer is $A = \pi r^2 = \pi(30)^2 = 900\pi \approx 2827.4$ in.^{2}.

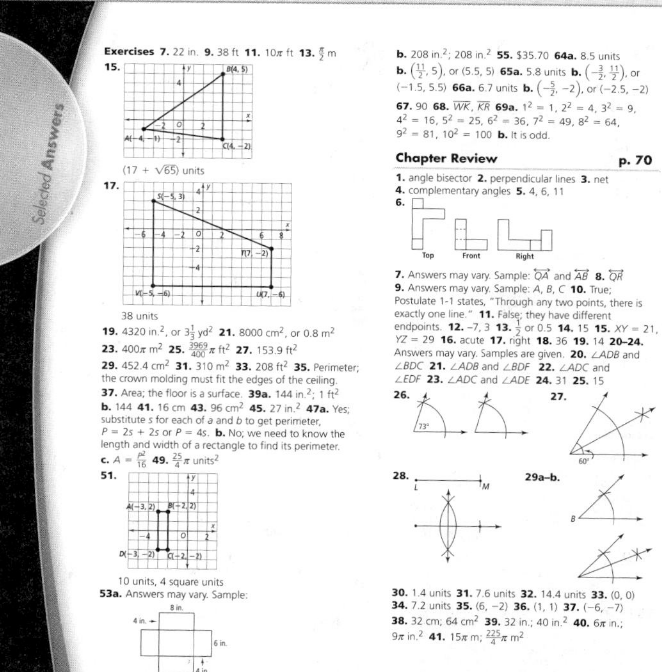

Exercises **7.** 22 in. **9.** 38 ft **11.** 10π ft **13.** $\frac{\pi}{2}$ m
15. $(17 + \sqrt{65})$ units
17. 38 units
19. 4320 in.^{2}, or $3\frac{1}{3}$ yd^2 **21.** 8000 cm^2, or 0.8 m^2 **23.** 400π m^2 **25.** $\frac{3969}{400}\pi$ ft^2 **27.** 153.9 ft^2 **29.** 452.4 cm^2 **31.** 310 m^2 **33.** 208 ft^2 **35.** Perimeter; the crown molding must fit the edges of the ceiling. **37.** Area; the floor is a surface. **39a.** 144 in.^{2}; 1 ft^2 **b.** 144 **41.** 16 cm **43.** 96 cm^2 **45.** 27 in.^{2} **47a.** Yes; substitute s for each of a and b to get perimeter, $P = 2s + 2s$ or $P = 4s$. **b.** No; we need to know the length and width of a rectangle to find its perimeter. **c.** $A = \frac{P^2}{16}$ **49.** $\frac{25}{4}\pi$ units^2
51. 10 units, 4 square units
53a. Answers may vary. Sample:

b. 208 in.^{2}; 208 in.^{2} **55.** \$35.70 **64a.** 8.5 units **b.** $\left(\frac{11}{2}, 5\right)$, or (5.5, 5) **65a.** 5.8 units **b.** $\left(-\frac{3}{2}, \frac{11}{2}\right)$, or (−1.5, 5.5) **66a.** 6.7 units **b.** $\left(-\frac{5}{2}, -2\right)$, or (−2.5, −2)
67. 90 **68.** $\overline{WK}$, $\overline{KR}$ **69a.** $1^2 = 1$, $2^2 = 4$, $3^2 = 9$, $4^2 = 16$, $5^2 = 25$, $6^2 = 36$, $7^2 = 49$, $8^2 = 64$, $9^2 = 81$, $10^2 = 100$ **b.** It is odd.

Chapter Review p. 70

1. angle bisector **2.** perpendicular lines **3.** net **4.** complementary angles **5.** 4, 6, 11
6. Top Front Right
7. Answers may vary. Sample: $\overleftrightarrow{QA}$ and $\overleftrightarrow{AB}$ **8.** $\overleftrightarrow{QR}$ **9.** Answers may vary. Sample: A, B, C **10.** True; Postulate 1-1 states, "Through any two points, there is exactly one line." **11.** False; they have different endpoints. **12.** −7, 3 **13.** $\frac{1}{2}$ or 0.5 **14.** 15 **15.** $XY = 21$, $YZ = 29$ **16.** acute **17.** right **18.** 36 **19.** 14 **20–24.** Answers may vary. Samples are given. **20.** ∠ADB and ∠BDC **21.** ∠ADB and ∠BDF **22.** ∠ADC and ∠EDF **23.** ∠ADC and ∠ADE **24.** 31 **25.** 15
26. **27.** **28.** **29a–b.**
30. 1.4 units **31.** 7.6 units **32.** 14.4 units **33.** (0, 0) **34.** 7.2 units **35.** (6, −2) **36.** (1, 1) **37.** (−6, −7) **38.** 32 cm; 64 cm^2 **39.** 32 in.; 40 in.^{2} **40.** 6π in.; 9π in.^{2} **41.** 15π m; $\frac{225}{4}\pi$ m^2

Chapter 2

Get Ready! p. 79

1. 50 **2.** −3 **3.** 25.5 **4.** 10.5 **5.** 15 **6.** 11 **7.** 7 **8.** 5 **9.** 6 **10.** 20 **11.** 18 **12.** ∠ACD, ∠DCA **13.** 3 **14.** $m\angle 1 = 48$, $m\angle 2 = 42$ **15.** ∠ADC and ∠CDB **16.** ∠1 and ∠2 **17.** ∠ADB or ∠BDA **18.** Answers may vary. Sample: Similar: They are both statements you start with. Different: In geometry you do not try to prove the hypothesis of a statement. **19.** Answers may vary. Sample: A conclusion in geometry answers questions raised by the hypothesis. **20.** Answers may vary. Sample: In geometry you use deductive reasoning to draw conclusions from other information.

Lesson 2-1 pp. 82–88

Got It? **1a.** 25, 20 **b.**
2. Every 3rd term is B, so the 21st term will be B. **3.** The sum of the first 30 odd numbers is 30^2, or 900. **4a.** Sales will be about 500 fewer than 8000, or 7500. **b.** No; sales may increase because students may want backpacks for school. **5a–c.** Answers may vary. Samples are given. **a.** A carnation can be red, and it is not a rose. **b.** When three points are collinear, the number of planes that can be drawn through them is infinite. **c.** When you multiply 5 (or any odd number) by 3, the product is not divisible by 6.
Lesson Check **1.** 31, 37 **2.**

G	P
B	R

B	G
R	P

3. Answers may vary. Sample: any nonsquare rectangle **4.** One meaning of *counter* is "against," so a counterexample is an example that goes against a statement. **5.** In the pattern 2, 4, . . . , the next term is 6 if the rule is "add 2"; the next term is 8 if the rule is "double the previous term"; and the next term is 7 if the rule is "add 2, then add 3, then add 4, . . ." Just giving the first 2 terms does not give enough information to describe the pattern.
Exercises **7.** Find the next square; 36, 49. **9.** Multiply the previous term by $\frac{1}{2}$; $\frac{1}{16}$, $\frac{1}{32}$. **11.** Subtract 3 from the previous number; 3, 0. **13.** the first letter of the months; J, J **15.** the Presidents of the U.S.; Madison, Monroe **17.** state postal abbreviations in alphabetical order; CO, CT **19.** **21.** blue **23.** blue
25–30. Answers may vary. Samples are given. **25.** The sum of the first 100 positive odd numbers is 100^2, or 10,000. **27.** The sum of two odd numbers is even. **29.** The product of two even numbers is even. **31.** 1 mi **33–37.** Answers may vary. Samples are given. **33.** two right angles **35.** −2 and −3 **37.** −2 and −3 **39.** Add 1 then add 3; add 1 then add 3; . . . ; 10, 13. **41.** Multiply by 3, add 1; multiply by 3, add 1; . . . ; 201, 202. **43.** Add $\frac{1}{2}$, add $\frac{1}{4}$, add $\frac{1}{8}$ . . . ; $\frac{31}{32}$, $\frac{63}{64}$. **45.** 123,454,321 **47.** **49.** 102 cm
51a. sì-shí-sān; liù-shí-qī; bā-shí-sì **b.** Yes; the second part of the number repeats each ten numbers. **53.** His conjecture is probably false because most people's growth slows by 18 until they stop growing sometime between 18 and 22 years. **62.** 16π in.^{2} **63.** 20 m **64.** 2 **65.** True; explanations may vary. Sample: If the two even numbers are $2a$ and $2b$, the sum is $2a + 2b = 2(a + b)$, which is the form of an even number. **66.** True; explanations may vary. Sample: if the three odd numbers are $2a + 1$, $2b + 1$, and $2c + 1$, the sum is $2(a + b + c) + 2 + 1 = 2(a + b + c + 1) + 1$, which is the form of an odd number.

Lesson 2-2 pp. 89–95

Got It? **1.** Hypothesis: An angle measures 130. Conclusion: The angle is obtuse. **2.** If an animal is a dolphin, then it is a mammal. **3a.** False; January has 28 days, plus 3 more. **b.** True; the sum of the measures of two angles that form a linear pair is 180.
4. Counterexamples may vary. Samples are given. Converse: If a vegetable contains beta carotene, then it is a carrot. Inverse: If a vegetable is not a carrot, then it does not contain beta carotene. Contrapositive: If a vegetable does not contain beta carotene, then it is not a carrot. The conditional and the contrapositive are true. The converse and inverse are false; counterexample: any vegetable, such as spinach, that contains beta carotene.
Lesson Check **1.** Hypothesis: Someone is a resident of Key West. Conclusion: The person lives in Florida. Conditional: If someone is a resident of Key West, then that person lives in Florida. **2.** Converse: If a figure has a perimeter of 10 cm, then it is a rectangle with sides 2 cm and 3 cm. Inverse: If a figure is not a rectangle with sides 2 cm and 3 cm, then it does not have a perimeter of 10 cm. Contrapositive: If a figure does not have a perimeter of 10 cm, then it is not a rectangle with sides 2 cm and 3 cm. The original conditional and the contrapositive are true. **3.** The hypothesis and conclusion were exchanged. The conditional should be "If it is Sunday, then you jog." **4.** Both are true because a conditional and its contrapositive have the same truth value, and a converse and an inverse have the same truth value.
Exercises **5.** Hypothesis: You are an American citizen. Conclusion: You have the right to vote. **7.** Hypothesis: You want to be healthy. Conclusion: You should eat

vegetables. **9.** If $3x - 7 = 14$, then $3x = 21$. **11.** If an object or example is a counterexample for a conjecture, then the object or example shows that the conjecture is false. **13.** If something is blue, then it has a color. **15.** If something is wheat, then it is a grain. **17.** false; Mexico **19.** true **21.** Conditional: If a person is a pianist, then that person is a musician. Converse: If a person is a musician, then that person is a pianist. Inverse: If a person is not a pianist, then that person is not a musician. Contrapositive: If a person is not a musician, then that person is not a pianist. The conditional and contrapositive are true. The converse and inverse are false; counterexample: a percussionist is a musician. **23.** Conditional: If a number is an odd natural number less than 8, then the number is prime. Converse: If a number is prime, then it is an odd natural number less than 8. Inverse: If a number is not an odd natural number less than 8, then the number is not prime. Contrapositive: If a number is not prime, then it is not an odd natural number less than 8. All four statements are false; counterexamples: 1 and 11. **25.** If a group is half the people, then that group should make up half the Congress. **27.** If an event has a probability of 1, then that event is certain to occur. **29.** Answers may vary. Sample: If an angle is acute, its measure is less than 90; if the measure of an angle is 85, then it is acute. **31.** Natalie is correct because a conditional statement and its contrapositive have the same truth value.

33. Juniors / Seniors / Captains

35. If $|x| = 6$, then $x = -6$; false, $x = 6$ is a counterexample.

37. If $x^3 < 0$, then $x < 0$; true. **39.** If you wear Snazzy sneakers, then you will look cool. **41.** If two figures are congruent, then they have equal areas. **51.** Answers may vary. Sample: 4 collinear points **52.** Answers may vary. Sample: 0.5 **53.** 36 in. **54.** 21 cm **55.** 4.5 yd or 162 in. **56.** 23.2 m or 2320 cm **57.** If tomorrow is October 1, then today is September 30; both the statement and the converse are true. **58.** If $\overline{AB}$ and $\overline{CD}$ are perpendicular, then $\overline{AB}$ is the perpendicular bisector of $\overline{CD}$; the statement is true and the converse is false.

Lesson 2-3 **pp. 98–104**

Got It? 1. Converse: If two angles are congruent, then the angles have equal measure; true. Biconditional: Two angles have equal measure if and only if the angles are congruent. **2.** If two numbers are reciprocals, then their product is 1. If the product of two numbers is 1, then the numbers are reciprocals. **3.** Yes, it is reversible; an angle is a straight angle if and only if its measure is 180. **4a.** No, it is not precise; a rectangle is also a figure with four right angles. **b.** Answers may vary. Sample: Obtuse angles have measures between 90 and 180.
Lesson Check 1. If points are collinear, then they lie on the same line. If points lie on the same line, then they are collinear. **2.** This month is June if and only if next month is July. **3.** Two angles are vertical angles if and only if their sides are opposite rays. **4.** The prefix *bi-* means "two." **5.** The word *gigantic* is not precise. **6.** The second statement is a better definition. A counterexample for the first statement is any two nonadjacent right angles.
Exercises 7. Converse: If two segments are congruent, then they have the same length; true. Biconditional: Two segments have the same length if and only if they are congruent. **9.** Converse: If a number is even, then it is divisible by 20; false. **11.** Converse: If it is Independence Day in the United States, then it is July 4; true. Biconditional: In the United States, it is July 4 if and only if it is Independence Day. **13.** If a line bisects a segment, then it intersects the segment only at its midpoint. If a line intersects a segment only at its midpoint, then the line bisects the segment. **15.** If you live in Washington, D.C., then you live in the capital of the United States. If you live in the capital of the United States, then you live in Washington, D.C. **17.** If an angle is a right angle, then it measures 90. If an angle measures 90, then it is a right angle. **19.** A line, segment, or ray is a perpendicular bisector of a segment if and only if it is perpendicular to the segment at its midpoint. **21.** A person is a Tarheel if and only if the person was born in North Carolina. **23.** not reversible **25.** No, it is not reversible; some endangered animals are not red wolves. **27.** No, it is not precise; straightedges and protractors are geometric tools. **29.** yes **31.** No; a straight angle has a measure greater than 90, but it is not an obtuse angle. **33.** That statement, as a biconditional, is "an angle is a right angle if and only if it is greater than an acute angle." Counterexamples to that statement are obtuse angles and straight angles. **35.** A point is in Quadrant III if and only if it has two negative coordinates. **37.** A number is a whole number if and only if it is a nonnegative integer. **39.** good definition **41.** good definition **43.** If $\angle A$ and $\angle B$ are a linear pair, then they are supplementary. **45.** If $\angle A$ and $\angle B$ are a linear pair, then they are adjacent, supplementary angles. **52.** If your grades suffer, then you do not get enough sleep. **53.** If you have a good voice, then you are in the school chorus. **54.** true **55.** 60, 50 **56.** 4, $\frac{4}{5}$ **57.** 4, −2

Lesson 2-4 **pp. 106–112**

Got It? 1a. Marla is not safe out in the open. **b.** No conclusion is possible. **2a.** If a whole number ends in 0, then it is divisible by 5; Law of Syllogism. **b.** No conclusion is possible. **3a.** The Nile is the longest river in

the world; Law of Syllogism and Law of Detachment. **b.** Yes; if you use the Law of Detachment first, then you must use it again to reach the same conclusion. The Law of Syllogism is not used.
Lesson Check 1. No conclusion is possible. **2.** Figure *ABC* is a triangle; Law of Detachment. **3.** If it is Saturday, then you wear sneakers; Law of Syllogism. **4.** The Law of Detachment cannot be applied because the hypothesis is not satisfied. **5.** Answers may vary. Sample: Deductive reasoning uses logic to reach conclusions, while inductive reasoning bases conclusions on unproved (but possibly true) conjectures.
Exercises 7. No conclusion is possible; the hypothesis has not been satisfied. **9.** No conclusion is possible; the hypothesis has not been satisfied. **11.** If an animal is a Florida panther, then it is endangered. **13.** If a line intersects a segment at its midpoint, then it divides the segment into two congruent segments. **15.** Alaska's Mount McKinley is the highest mountain in the U.S. **17.** If you are studying botany, then you are studying a science. (Law of Syllogism only) No conclusion can be made about Shanti. **19.** Must be true; by E and A, it is breakfast time; by D, Julio is drinking juice. **21.** May be true; by E and A, it is breakfast time. You don't know what Kira drinks at breakfast. **23.** May be true; by E, Maria is drinking juice. You don't know if she also drinks water. **25.** strange **27.** If a figure is a square, then it is a rectangle; *ABCD* is a rectangle. **29.** If a person is a high school student, then the person likes art; no conclusion is possible because the hypothesis is not satisfied. **35.** A type of reasoning is called inductive if and only if it is based on patterns that you observe. **36.** $\angle AOB$, $\angle BOA$ **37.** $\angle BOC$, $\angle COB$ **38.** $\overrightarrow{OB}$ **39.** acute

Lesson 2-5 **pp. 113–119**

Got It? 1. 75; $x = 2x - 75$ (Def. of an ∠ bis.); $x + 75 = 2x$ (Add. Prop. of Eq.); $75 = 2x - x$ (Subtr. Prop. of Eq.); $75 = x$ **2a.** Sym. Prop. of ≅ **b.** Distr. Prop. **c.** Mult. Prop. of Eq. **d.** Refl. Prop. of Eq. **3a.** Answers may vary. Sample: $\overline{AB} \cong \overline{CD}$ (Given); $AB = CD$ (≅ segments have = length.); $BC = BC$ (Refl. Prop. of Eq.); $AB + BC = BC + CD$ (Add. Prop. of =); $AB + BC = AC$, $BC + CD = BD$ (Seg. Add. Post.); $AC = BD$ (Trans. Prop. of Eq.); $\overline{AC} \cong \overline{BD}$ (Segments with = length are ≅.) **b.** Answers may vary. Sample: You need to establish equality in order to add the same quantity ($m\angle 2$) to each side of the equation in Statement 3.
Lesson Check 1. Trans. Prop. of Eq. **2.** Distr. Prop. **3.** Subtr. Prop of Eq. **4a.** Given **b.** Subtr. Prop. of Eq. **c.** Div. Prop. of Eq.
Exercises 5a. Mult. Prop. of Eq. **b.** Distr. Prop. **c.** Add. Prop. of Eq. **7a.** def. of suppl. $\angle$s **b.** Subst. Prop. **c.** Distr. Prop. **d.** Subtr. Prop. of Eq. **e.** Div. Prop. of Eq. **9.** Subtr. Prop. of Eq. **11.** Sym. Prop. of ≅ **13a.** Given **b.** A midpt. divides a seg. into two ≅ segments. **c.** Substitution **d.** $2x = 12$ **e.** Div. Prop. of Eq. **15.** $\angle K$ **17.** 3 **19.** $\angle XYZ \cong \angle WYT$ **21.** Since $\overline{LR}$ and $\overline{RL}$ are two ways to name the same segment and $\angle CBA$ and $\angle ABC$ are two ways to name the same ∠, then both statements are examples of saying that something is ≅ to itself. **23.** $KM = 35$ (Given); $KL + LM = KM$ (Seg. Add. Post.); $(2x - 5) + 2x = 35$ (Subst. Prop.); $4x - 5 = 35$ (Distr. Prop.); $4x = 40$ (Add. Prop. of Eq.); $x = 10$ (Div. Prop. of Eq.); $KL = 2x - 5$ (Given); $KL = 2(10) - 5$ (Subst. Prop.); $KL = 15$ (Simplify) **34.** Walt's science teacher is concerned. **35.** 80 **36.** 65 **37.** 125 **38.** 90 **39.** 50 **40.** 90 **41.** 35

Lesson 2-6 **pp. 120–127**

Got It? 1. 40 **2a.** $\angle 1 \cong \angle 2$ (Given); $\angle 1 \cong \angle 3$, $\angle 2 \cong \angle 4$ (Vert. $\angle$s are ≅); $\angle 1 \cong \angle 4$, $\angle 2 \cong \angle 3$ (Trans. Prop. of ≅); $\angle 1 \cong \angle 2 \cong \angle 3 \cong 4$ (Trans. Prop. of ≅) **b.** Answers may vary. Sample: $m\angle 1 + m\angle 2 = 180$ because they form a linear pair. So $m\angle 1 = 90$ and $m\angle 2 = 90$ because $\angle 1 \cong \angle 2$. Then, using the relationship that $m\angle 2 + m\angle 3 = 180$ and $m\angle 1 + m\angle 4 = 180$, you can show that $m\angle 3 = m\angle 4 = 90$ by the Subtr. Prop. of Eq. Then $\angle 1 \cong \angle 2 \cong \angle 3 \cong \angle 4$ because their measures are =. **3.** Answers may vary. Sample: $\angle 1$ and $\angle 3$ are vert. $\angle$s because it is given. $\angle 1$ and $\angle 2$ are suppl. and $\angle 2$ and $\angle 3$ are suppl. because $\angle$s that form a linear pair are suppl. So, $m\angle 1 + m\angle 2 = 180$ and $m\angle 2 + m\angle 3 = 180$ by the def. of suppl. $\angle$s. By the Trans. Prop. of Eq., $m\angle 1 + m\angle 2 = m\angle 2 + m\angle 3$. By the Subtr. Prop. of Eq., $m\angle 1 = m\angle 3$. So, $\angle 1 \cong \angle 3$ because $\angle$s with the same measure are ≅.
Lesson Check 1. $m\angle 1 = 90$, $m\angle 2 = 50$, $m\angle 3 = 40$ **2.** B **3.** $\angle B \cong \angle C$ because both are suppl. to $\angle A$ and if two $\angle$s are suppl. to the same ∠, then they are ≅. **4.** He used the Trans. Prop. of ≅, which does not apply here. $\angle 2$ and $\angle 3$ are ≅, not compl. If two $\angle$s are compl. to the same ∠, then they are ≅ to each other. **5.** Answers may vary. Sample: A postulate is a statement that is assumed to be true, while a theorem is a statement that is proved to be true.
Exercises 7. $x = 38$, $y = 104$ **9.** 60, 60 **11.** 120, 120 **13a.** 90 **b.** 90 **c.** $m\angle 3$ **d.** ≅ **15.** Answers may vary. Sample: scissors **17.** $x = 14$, $y = 15$; $3x + 8 = 50$, $5x - 20 = 50$, $5x + 4y = 130$ **19.** $x = 50$, $y = 50$ **21.** $\angle EIG \cong \angle FIH$ because all rt. $\angle$s are ≅; $\angle EIF \cong \angle HIG$ because each one is compl. to $\angle FIG$ and compl. of the same ∠ are ≅. **23a.** It is given. **b.** $m\angle V$ **c.** 180 **d.** Division **e.** right **25.** By Theorem 2-5: If two $\angle$s are ≅ and suppl., then each is a right ∠. **27.** $m\angle A = 30$, $m\angle B = 60$ **29.** $m\angle A = 90$, $m\angle B = 90$ **40.** Subtr. Prop. of Eq. **41.** Div. Prop. of Eq. **42.** Trans. Prop. of ≅

43. points *F*, *I*, *H*, *B* **44.** no **45.** yes **46.** line *r* (or $\overleftrightarrow{EG}$, $\overleftrightarrow{GH}$, $\overleftrightarrow{HC}$, and so on) **47.** any three of $\overleftrightarrow{FI}$ (or $\overleftrightarrow{IF}$), $\overleftrightarrow{FH}$, $\overleftrightarrow{FB}$, $\overleftrightarrow{IH}$, $\overleftrightarrow{IB}$, $\overleftrightarrow{HB}$ **48.** point *H*

Chapter Review **pp. 129–133**

1. conclusion **2.** deductive reasoning **3.** truth value **4.** converse **5.** biconditional **6.** theorem **7.** hypothesis **8.** Divide the previous term by 10; 1, $\frac{1}{10}$. **9.** Multiply the previous term by −1; 5, −5. **10.** Subtract 7 from the previous term; 6, −1. **11.** Multiply the previous term by 4; 1536, 6144. **12.** Answers may vary. Sample: $-1 \cdot 2 = -2$, and −2 is not greater than 2 **13.** Answers may vary. Sample: Portland, Maine **14.** If a person is a motorcyclist, then that person wears a helmet. **15.** If two nonparallel lines intersect, then they intersect in one point. **16.** If two $\angle$s form a linear pair, then the $\angle$s are supplementary. **17.** If today is one of a certain group of holidays, then school is closed. **18.** Converse: If the measure of an ∠ is greater than 90 and less than 180, then the ∠ is obtuse. Inverse: If an angle is not obtuse, then it is not true that its measure is greater than 90 and less than 180. Contrapositive: If it is not true that the measure of an ∠ is greater than 90 and less than 180, then the ∠ is not obtuse. All four statements are true. **19.** Converse: If a figure has four sides, then the figure is a square. Inverse: If a figure is not a square, then it does not have four sides. Contrapositive: If a figure does not have four sides, then it is not a square. The conditional and the contrapositive are true. The converse and inverse are false. **20.** Converse: If you play an instrument, then you play the tuba. Inverse: If you do not play the tuba, then you do not play an instrument. Contrapositive: If you do not play an instrument, then you do not play the tuba. The conditional and the contrapositive are true. The converse and inverse are false. **21.** Converse: If you are busy on Saturday night, then you baby-sit. Inverse: If you do not baby-sit, then you are not busy on Saturday night. Contrapositive: If you are not busy on Saturday night, then you do not baby-sit. The conditional and the contrapositive are true. The converse and inverse are false. **22.** No; it is not reversible; a magazine is a counterexample. **23.** yes **24.** No; it is not reversible; a line is a counterexample. **25.** A phrase is an oxymoron if and only if it contains contradictory terms. **26.** If two $\angle$s are complementary, then the sum of their measures is 90; if the sum of the measures of two $\angle$s is 90, then the $\angle$s are complementary. **27.** Colin will become a better player. **28.** $m\angle 1 + m\angle 2 = 180$ **29.** If two angles are vertical, then their measures are equal. **30.** If your father buys new gardening gloves, then he will plant tomatoes. **31a.** Given **b.** Seg. Add. Post. **c.** Subst. Prop. **d.** Distr. Prop. **e.** Subtr. Prop. of Eq. **f.** Div. Prop. of Eq. **32.** *BY* **33.** $p - 2q$ **34.** 18 **35.** 74 **36.** 74 **37.** 106 **38.** $\angle 1$ is compl. to $\angle 2$, $\angle 3$ is compl. to $\angle 4$, and $\angle 2 \cong \angle 4$ are all given. $m\angle 2 = m\angle 4$ by the def. of ≅. $\angle 1$ and $\angle 4$ are compl. by the Subst. Post. $\angle 1 \cong \angle 3$ by the ≅ Compl. Thm.

Chapter 3

Get Ready! **p. 137**

1. $\angle 1$ and $\angle 5$, $\angle 5$ and $\angle 2$ **2.** $\angle 3$ and $\angle 4$ **3.** $\angle 1$ and $\angle 2$ **4.** $\angle 1$ and $\angle 5$, $\angle 5$ and $\angle 2$ **5.** Div. Prop. of = **6.** Trans. Prop. of ≅ **7.** 4 **8.** 61 **9.** 15 **10.** 5 **11.** $2\sqrt{17}$ **12.** $\sqrt{17}$ **13.** Answers may vary. Sample: A figure divides a plane or space into three parts: the figure itself, the region inside the figure—called its interior—and the region outside the figure—called its exterior. **14.** Answers may vary. Sample: *Trans-* means "cross"; a transversal crosses other lines. **15.** Answers may vary. Sample: A flow proof shows the individual steps of the proof and how each step is related to the other steps.

Lesson 3-1 **pp. 140–146**

Got It? 1a. $\overline{EH}$, $\overline{BC}$, $\overline{FG}$ **b.** Sample: They are both in plane *FEDC*, so they are coplanar. **c.** plane *BCG* ∥ plane *ADH* **d.** any two of $\overline{AB}$, $\overline{BF}$, $\overline{EF}$, and $\overline{AE}$ **2.** any three of $\angle 1$ and $\angle 3$, $\angle 2$ and $\angle 4$, $\angle 8$ and $\angle 6$, $\angle 7$ and $\angle 5$ **3.** corresp. $\angle$s
Lesson Check 1–7. Answers may vary. Samples are given. **1.** $\overline{EF}$ and $\overline{HG}$ **2.** $\overline{EF}$ and $\overline{GC}$ **3.** plane *ABF* ∥ plane *DCG* **4.** $\angle 8$ and $\angle 6$ **5.** $\angle 3$ and $\angle 8$ **6.** $\angle 1$ and $\angle 3$ **7.** $\angle 1$ and $\angle 4$ **8.** Although lines that are not coplanar do not intersect, they are not parallel. **9.** Alt. int. $\angle$s are $\angle$s between two lines on opposite sides of a transversal. **10.** Carly; the lines are coplanar since they are both in plane *ABH*, so $\overline{AB} \parallel \overline{HG}$.
Exercises 11. plane *JCD* ∥ plane *ELH* **13.** $\overleftrightarrow{GB}$, $\overleftrightarrow{JE}$, $\overleftrightarrow{CL}$, $\overleftrightarrow{FA}$ **15.** $\overleftrightarrow{GB}$, $\overleftrightarrow{DH}$, $\overleftrightarrow{CL}$ **17.** $\angle 7$ and $\angle 6$ (lines *a* and *b* with transversal *d*), $\angle 2$ and $\angle 5$ (lines *b* and *c* with transversal *e*) **19.** $\angle 5$ and $\angle 6$ (lines *d* and *e* with transversal *b*); $\angle 2$ and $\angle 4$ (lines *b* and *e* with transversal *c*) **21.** $\angle 1$ and $\angle 2$ are corresp. $\angle$s; $\angle 3$ and $\angle 4$ are alt. int. $\angle$s; $\angle 5$ and $\angle 6$ are corresp. $\angle$s. **23.** $\angle 1$ and $\angle 2$ are corresp. $\angle$s; $\angle 3$ and $\angle 4$ are same-side int. $\angle$s; $\angle 5$ and $\angle 6$ are alt. int. $\angle$s. **25.** 2 pairs **27.** 2 pairs **29.** Skew; answers may vary. Sample: Since the paths are not coplanar, they are skew. **31.** False; $\overleftrightarrow{ED}$ and $\overleftrightarrow{HG}$ are skew. **33.** False; the planes intersect. **35.** False; both lines are in plane *ABC*. **37.** always **39.** always **41.** sometimes **43a.** Lines may be intersecting, parallel, or skew. **b.** Answers may vary. Sample: In a classroom, two adjacent edges of the floor are intersecting, two opposite edges of the floor are parallel, and one edge of the floor is skew to each of the

vertical edges of the opposite wall. **45a.** The lines of intersection are ∥. **b.** Sample: The lines of intersection of a wall with the ceiling and floor (or the lines of intersection of any of the 6 planes with two different, opposite faces) **53.** 121 **54.** 59 **55.** 29.5 **56.** 16, −32 **57.** corresp. $\angle$s **58.** alt. int. $\angle$s **59.** alt. ext. $\angle$s **60.** same-side int. $\angle$s

Lesson 3-2 **pp. 148–155**

Got It? 1a. Sample: $m\angle 7 = 55$, so $m\angle 5 = 55$ by the Vert. $\angle$s Thm. **b.** 125; sample: $m\angle 2 = 125$ by the Vert. $\angle$s Thm.; $m\angle 8 = 125$ by the Corresp. $\angle$s Post.; $m\angle 6 = 125$ by the Vert. $\angle$s Thm. **2.** (1) $a \parallel b$ (Given) (2) $\angle 1 \cong \angle 5$ (If lines are ∥, then corresp. $\angle$s are ≅.) (3) $\angle 5 \cong \angle 7$ (Vert. $\angle$s are ≅.) (4) $\angle 1 \cong \angle 7$ (Trans. Prop. of ≅) **3a.** 75; $m\angle 1 = m\angle 4$ by the Alt. Int. $\angle$s Thm. **b.** 75; $m\angle 2 = m\angle 4$ by the Corresp. $\angle$s Post. **c.** 105; $m\angle 5 = 105$ by the Corresp. $\angle$s Post. **d.** 105; Alt. Int. $\angle$s Thm. **e.** 105; Vert. $\angle$s. Thm. **f.** 105; $\angle 8 \cong \angle 6$ by the Corresp. $\angle$s Post. **4a.** $x = 64$, $y = 40$ **b.** Clockwise from the bottom left, the measures are 52, 128, 120, 60.
Lesson Check 1–2. Answer may vary. Samples are given. **1.** $\angle 4$ and $\angle 5$, $\angle 2$ and $\angle 6$, $\angle 3$ and $\angle 7$, $\angle 4$ and $\angle 8$ **2.** $\angle 2$ and $\angle 5$, $\angle 4$ and $\angle 7$ **3.** 70 **4.** 55 **5.** Alike: Two parallel lines are cut by a tra nsversal and the angles are congruent; different: The int. $\angle$s are between the two parallel lines, while the ext. $\angle$s are not between the two parallel lines. **6.** same-side ext. $\angle$s, because they are ext. $\angle$s on the same side of the transversal
Exercises 7. $\angle 1$ (vert. $\angle$s), $\angle 7$ (alt. int. $\angle$s), $\angle 4$ (corresp. $\angle$s) **9.** $\angle 3$ (alt. int. $\angle$s), $\angle 1$ (corresp. $\angle$s) **11.** (1) $a \parallel b$; $c \parallel d$ (Given) (2) $\angle 1 \cong \angle 4$ (Alt. int. $\angle$s are ≅.) (3) $\angle 4 \cong \angle 3$ (Corresp. $\angle$s are ≅.) (4) $\angle 1 \cong \angle 3$ (Trans. Prop. of ≅) **13.** $m\angle 1 = 120$ because corresp. $\angle$s are ≅; $m\angle 2 = 60$ because $\angle 2$ forms a linear pair with the given ∠. **15.** $x = 115$, $x - 50 = 65$ **17.** 20; $5x = 100$, $4x = 80$ **19.** $x = 135$, $y = 45$ **21.** 90; all the $\angle$s are ≅ because each pair form vert. $\angle$s, corresp. $\angle$s, or suppl. $\angle$s. **23a.** 117 **b.** same-side int. $\angle$s **25.** (1) $\ell \parallel m$ (Given) (2) $\angle 2 \cong \angle 6$ (Corresp. $\angle$s are ≅.) (3) $m\angle 2 + m\angle 3 = 180$ ($\angle$s that form a linear pair are suppl.) (4) $m\angle 2 = m\angle 6$ (Def. of ≅) (5) $m\angle 6 + m\angle 3 = 180$ (Substitution) (6) $\angle 6$ and $\angle 3$ are suppl. (If the sum of the measures of two $\angle$s is 180, then the $\angle$s are suppl.) **33.** never **34.** never **35.** never **36.** sometimes **37.** If a △ has a 90° angle, then it is a right △; true. **38.** If two $\angle$s are ≅, then they are vert. $\angle$s; false. **39.** If two $\angle$s are suppl., then they are same-side int. $\angle$s; false.

Lesson 3-3 **pp. 156–163**

Got It? 1. $\ell \parallel m$ by the Converse of the Corresp. $\angle$s Post. **2.** Answers may vary. Sample:

$\angle 1 \cong \angle 7$ (Given); $\angle 3 \cong \angle 1$ (Vertical $\angle$s are ≅.) → $\angle 3 \cong \angle 7$ (Transitive Prop. of ≅) → $\ell \parallel m$ (If corresp. $\angle$s are ≅, then the lines are ∥.) → $\angle 3 \cong \angle 5$ (If lines are ∥, then alt. int. $\angle$s are ≅.)

3. $\angle 2 \cong \angle 3$ (Vert. $\angle$s are ≅.), so $\angle 1 \cong \angle 3$ (Trans. Prop. of ≅). So $r \parallel s$ by the Converse of the Corresp. $\angle$s Post. **4.** 19
Lesson Check 1. Conv. of Corresp. $\angle$s Post. **2.** Conv. of Alt. Int. $\angle$s Thm. **3.** 115 **4.** If you want to prove that alt. int. $\angle$s are ≅, use the Alt. Int. $\angle$s Thm.; if you want to prove that two lines are parallel, use the Converse of the Alt. Int. $\angle$s Thm. **5.** Alike: Both give statements and reasons; different: The proofs use different formats. **6.** $\overleftrightarrow{DC}$ is the transversal, so the two same-side int. $\angle$s show that $\overleftrightarrow{AD}$ and $\overleftrightarrow{BC}$ are parallel.
Exercises 7. $\overleftrightarrow{BE} \parallel \overleftrightarrow{CG}$ by the Converse of the Corresp. $\angle$s Post. **9.** $\overleftrightarrow{CA} \parallel \overleftrightarrow{HR}$ by the Converse of the Corresp. $\angle$s Post. **11a.** Given **b.** $\angle 1$ and $\angle 2$ form a linear pair. **c.** $\angle$s that form a linear pair are suppl. **d.** $\angle 2 \cong \angle 3$ **e.** If corresp. $\angle$s are ≅, then lines are ∥. **13.** 30 **15.** 59 **17.** $a \parallel b$; if same-side int. $\angle$s are suppl., then the lines are ∥. **19.** $a \parallel b$; if same-side int. $\angle$s are suppl., then the lines are ∥. **21.** none **23.** $a \parallel b$ (Conv. of the Alt. Ext. $\angle$s Thm.) **25.** none **27.** 5 **29.** $m\angle 3 + m\angle 6 = 180$ (Given) and $m\angle 6 + m\angle 7 = 180$ ($\angle 6$ and $\angle 7$ form a linear pair). Then $\angle 3 \cong \angle 7$ ($\angle$s suppl. to the same ∠ are ≅.), and $\ell \parallel m$ (Converse of Corresp. $\angle$s Post.) **31.** $x = 10$; $m\angle 1 = m\angle 2 = 70$ **33.** $x = 2.5$; $m\angle 1 = m\angle 2 = 30$ **35.** Answers may vary. Sample: If $\angle 3 \cong \angle 5$, then $\ell \parallel n$ by the Converse of Corresp. $\angle$s Post. **37.** Answers may vary. Sample: If $\angle 5 \cong \angle 3$, then $j \parallel k$ by the Converse of the Corresp. $\angle$s Post. **39.** If alt. ext. $\angle$s are ≅, then the lines are ∥.

41. Answers may vary. Sample:

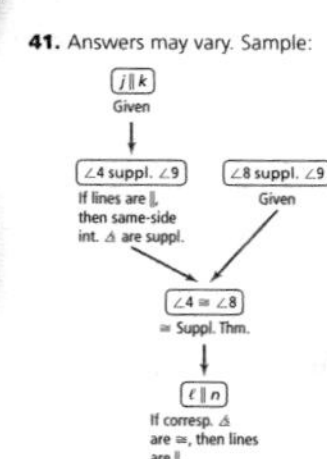

52. $m\angle 1 = 70$ ($\angle 1$ is suppl. to a $110°$ $\angle$.); $m\angle 2 = 110$ ($\angle 2$ is suppl. to $\angle 1$, which is a $70°$ angle.) **53.** $m\angle 1 = 66$ (Alt. int. ∠s are $\cong$.); $m\angle 2 = 86$ ($\angle 2$ is suppl. to a $94°$ angle.) **54.** always **55.** sometimes **56.** sometimes **57.** never

Lesson 3-4 pp. 164–169

Got It? 1. Yes; place the pieces with $60°$ ∠s opposite each other and place the pieces with $30°$ ∠s opposite each other. All four corners will be $90°$, so opposite sides will be $\parallel$. **2.** Yes; $a \parallel b$ because they are both $\perp$ to d, and in a plane, two lines $\perp$ to the same line are $\parallel$.
Lesson Check 1. They are $\perp$; using Main Street as a transversal, Avenue B $\perp$ Main Street by Thm. 3-9. **2.** $a \parallel b$; in a plane, if two lines are $\perp$ to the same line, then they are $\parallel$. **3.** Sample: Even if the 3 lines are not in the same plane, each line is parallel to the other 2 lines. **4.** Thm. 3-8 uses the Converse of the Corresp. ∠s Post.; the $\perp$ Trans. Thm. uses the Corresp. ∠s Post. **5.** The diagram should show that m and r are $\perp$.
Exercises 7a. corresp. ∠s **b.** $\angle 1$ **c.** $\angle 3$ **d.** Converse of Corresp. ∠s Post. **9.** Measure any three int. ∠s to be rt. ∠s and opp. walls will be $\parallel$ because two walls $\perp$ to the same wall are $\parallel$. **11.** The rungs are $\parallel$ to each other because they are all $\perp$ to the same side. **13.** The rungs are $\perp$ to both sides. The rungs are $\perp$ to one of two $\parallel$ sides, so they are $\perp$ to both sides. **15.** The rungs are $\parallel$ because they are all $\perp$ to one side. **17.** Sample: Using the diagram underneath Thm. 3-9, $\overleftrightarrow{EC}$ and $\overleftrightarrow{AB}$ are both $\perp$ to $\overleftrightarrow{AC}$, but $\overleftrightarrow{EC}$ and $\overleftrightarrow{AB}$ are skew, so they cannot be $\parallel$. **31.** 53 **32.** 46 **33.** right **34.** obtuse **35.** acute **36.** 60 **37.** 20 **38.** 40 **39.** 58

Lesson 3-5 pp. 171–178

Got It? 1. 29 **2.** 127, 127, 106 **3.** Yes; answers may vary. Sample: $m\angle ACB$ must $= 100$, so by the $\triangle$ $\angle$-Sum Thm., $m\angle A + 30 + 100 = 180$, and $m\angle A = 50$.
Lesson Check 1. 58 **2.** 45 **3.** 68 **4.** $130 - x$ **5.** $m\angle 1 = 130$ **6.** $m\angle 3 = 38$ **7.** Answers may vary. Sample: Consider the int. $\angle A$ of $\triangle ABC$. By the $\triangle$ $\angle$-Sum Thm., the sum of the measures of angles A, B, and C is $180°$. $\angle A$ is suppl. to its ext. $\angle$. So the sum of the measures of angles B and C is equal to the measure of the ext. $\angle$ of $\angle A$. **8.** A; all 3 ∠s are int. ∠s, so the solution should use the $\triangle$ $\angle$-Sum Thm.
Exercises 9. 30 **11.** 90 **13.** $x = y = 80$ **15a.** $\angle 5, \angle 6, \angle 8$ **b.** For $\angle 5$: $\angle 1$ and $\angle 3$; for $\angle 6$: $\angle 1$ and $\angle 2$; for $\angle 8$: $\angle 1$ and $\angle 2$ **c.** $\angle 6 \cong \angle 8$ **17.** 123 **19.** $m\angle 3 = 92$, $m\angle 4 = 88$ **21.** 114 **23.** 60, 80 **25.** 102, 65, 13 **27.** 60; answers may vary. Sample: $180 \div 3 = 60$, so each $\angle$ is 60. **29.** $x = 37$; $m\angle P = 65$, $m\angle Q = 78$, $m\angle R = 37$ **31.** $a = 67$, $b = 58$, $c = 125$, $d = 23$, $e = 90$ **33.** $\angle 1$ is an ext. $\angle$ of the $\triangle$. (Given); $\angle 1$ and $\angle 4$ are suppl. (∠s that form a straight $\angle$ are suppl.); $m\angle 1 + m\angle 4 = 180$ (Def. of suppl.); $m\angle 2 + m\angle 3 + m\angle 4 = 180$ ($\triangle$ $\angle$-Sum Thm.); $m\angle 1 + m\angle 4 = m\angle 2 + m\angle 3 + m\angle 4$ (Subst. Prop.); $m\angle 1 = m\angle 2 + m\angle 3$ (Subtr. Prop. of $=$) **35.** 40, 50 **47.** $a \parallel c$; if 2 same-side ext. ∠s are suppl., then the lines are $\parallel$. **48.** $a \parallel b$; if 2 lines are $\parallel$ to the same line, they are $\parallel$ to each other. **49.** 32 **50.** $m\angle 1 = m\angle 2 = 90$; sample: If the sum of two equal numbers is 180, then each number is 90.

51.

52. **53.**

Lesson 3-6 pp. 182–188

Got It? 1. $\angle 1$ and $\angle NHJ$ are corresp. ∠s for lines m and ℓ. Since $\angle 1 \cong \angle NHJ$, then $m \parallel \ell$.

2a. Answers may vary. Sample:

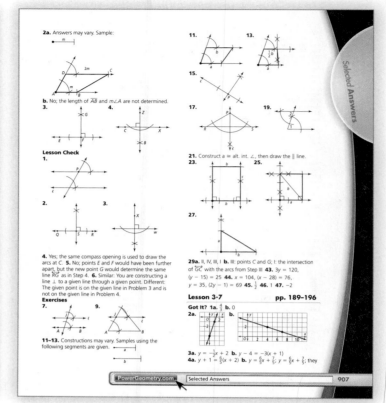

b. No; the length of $\overline{AB}$ and $m\angle A$ are not determined.

3. **4.**

Lesson Check

1.

2. **3.**

4. Yes; the same compass opening is used to draw the arcs at C. **5.** No; points E and F would have been further apart, but the new point G would determine the same line $\overleftrightarrow{RG}$ as in Step 4. **6.** Similar: You are constructing a line $\perp$ to a given line through a given point. Different: The given point is on the given line in Problem 3 and is not on the given line in Problem 4.

Exercises

7. **9.**

11–13. Constructions may vary. Samples using the following segments are given.

11. **13.**

15.

17. **19.**

21. Construct a $\cong$ alt. int. $\angle$, then draw the $\parallel$ line.

23. **25.**

27.

29a. II, IV, III, I **b.** III: points C and G; I: the intersection of $\overleftrightarrow{GC}$ with the arcs from Step III **43.** $3y = 120$, $(y - 15) = 25$ **44.** $x = 104$, $(x - 28) = 76$, $y = 35$, $(2y - 1) = 69$ **45.** $\frac{1}{2}$ **46.** 1 **47.** -2

Lesson 3-7 pp. 189–196

Got It? 1a. $\frac{4}{3}$ **b.** 0

2a. **b.**

3a. $y = -\frac{1}{2}x + 2$ **b.** $y - 4 = -3(x + 1)$
4a. $y + 1 = \frac{6}{5}(x + 2)$ **b.** $y = \frac{6}{5}x + \frac{7}{5}$; $y = \frac{6}{5}x + \frac{7}{5}$; they

represent the same line. **5a.** horizontal: $y = -3$; vertical: $x = 4$ **b.** No; the slope is undefined for a vertical line, so you cannot use the slope-intercept form because that requires a value for the slope.
Lesson Check 1. 5 **2.** -2 **3.** $y = 8x + 10$ **4.** $y - 3 = 4(x - 3)$ or $y - 7 = 4(x - 4)$ **5.** Answers may vary. Sample: The slope-intercept form $y = mx + b$ uses the slope m and the y-intercept b; the point-slope form $y - y_1 = m(x - x_1)$ uses a point (x_1, y_1) on the line and the slope m. **6.** The lines have the same y-int., but one line has a steep positive slope and the other has a less steep negative slope. **7.** Your classmate switched the x- and y-values in the formula for slope. The slope of the line is undefined.
Exercises 9. $-\frac{5}{6}$ **11.** $-\frac{3}{2}$ **13.** -8 **15.** undefined

17. **19.**

21. **23.**

25. $y = \frac{1}{2}x - 5$ **27.** $y + 1 = -3(x - 4)$
29. $y - 6 = -(x + 2)$ or $y - 3 = -(x - 1)$
31. $y - 2 = -\frac{1}{2}(x - 6)$ or $y - 4 = -\frac{1}{2}(x - 2)$
33. $y = \frac{1}{2}(x + 1)$ or $y + 1 = \frac{1}{2}(x + 3)$ **35.** horizontal: $y = -2$; vertical: $x = 3$ **37.** horizontal: $y = 4$; vertical: $x = 6$ **39.** **41.**

43. Yes; if the ramp is 24 in. high and 72 in. long, the slope will be $\frac{24}{72} = 0.\overline{3}$, which is less than the maximum slope of $\frac{4}{11} = 0.\overline{36}$. **45.** $y = -x + 2$ **47.** $y = -\frac{3}{2}x + 5$ **49.** $(6, -4)$ **51.** $(-1, 3)$

53. No; answers may vary. Sample: $\frac{1}{12} < \frac{3}{10}$ so the ramp would need to zigzag to comply with the law.

55a. Undefined; the y-axis is a vertical line, and the slope of a vertical line is undefined. **b.** $x = 0$ **57a.** $y = \frac{5}{2}x$ **b.** $y - 5 = -\frac{5}{2}(x - 2)$ or $y = -\frac{5}{2}x + 10$ **c.** The abs. value of the slopes is the same, but one slope is pos. and the other is neg. One y-int. is 0 and the other is 10.

69.

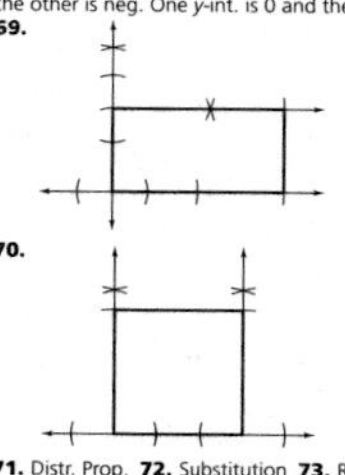

70.

71. Distr. Prop. **72.** Substitution **73.** Reflexive Prop. of $\cong$ **74.** Symmetric Prop. of $\cong$ **75.** $\frac{1}{2}$ **76.** $\frac{5}{2}$ **77.** -5

Lesson 3-8 pp. 197–204

Got It? 1. No; the slope of ℓ_3 is $\frac{6 - 2}{-13 - (-1)} = \frac{4}{-12} = -\frac{1}{3}$ And the slope of ℓ_4 is $\frac{6 - 7}{3 - 6} = \frac{-1}{-3} = \frac{1}{3}$. The slopes are not equal. **2.** $y - 3 = -(x + 5)$ **3.** No; the slope of ℓ_3 is $\frac{7 - (-1)}{2 - 3} = \frac{8}{-1} = -8$ and the slope of ℓ_4 is $\frac{6 - 7}{-2 - 8} = \frac{-1}{-10} = \frac{1}{10}$. Since the product of the slopes is not -1, the Lines are not $\perp$. **4.** $y - 7 = \frac{1}{3}(x + 3)$ **5.** $y - 40 = \frac{1}{3}(x - 90)$
Lesson Check 1. $\perp$; the slope of $\overleftrightarrow{AB}$ is 2 and the slope of $\overleftrightarrow{CD}$ is $-\frac{1}{2}$. Since $(2)\left(-\frac{1}{2}\right) = -1$, the lines are $\perp$. **2.** $\parallel$; the slope of $\overleftrightarrow{AB}$ is 6 and the slope of $\overleftrightarrow{CD}$ is 6. Since the slopes are equal, the lines are $\parallel$. **3.** Neither; the slope of $\overleftrightarrow{AB}$ is 0 and the slope of $\overleftrightarrow{CD}$ is 1. Since the slopes are not equal and their product is not -1, the lines are neither $\parallel$ nor $\perp$. **4.** Answers may vary. Sample: $y + 3 = \frac{1}{4}(x - 2)$ **5.** The second line should say "slope of parallel line = 3" because $\parallel$ lines have equal slopes. **6.** Sample: $\parallel$ line equations have equal slopes. $\perp$ line equations have slopes with product -1.

Exercises

7. Yes; the slope of ℓ_1 is $-\frac{1}{2}$ and the slope of ℓ_2 is $-\frac{1}{2}$, and two lines with the same slope are $\parallel$. **9.** No; the slope of ℓ_1 is $\frac{3}{2}$ and the slope of ℓ_2 is 2. Since the slopes are not equal the lines are not $\parallel$. **11.** $y = -2x + 3$

13. $y - 4 = \frac{1}{2}(x + 2)$ **15.** Yes; the slope of ℓ_1 is $-\frac{1}{2}$ and the slope of ℓ_2 is 2. Since the product of the slopes is -1, the lines are $\perp$. **17.** No; the slope of ℓ_1 is -1 and the slope of ℓ_2 is $\frac{4}{5}$. Since the product of the slopes is not -1, the lines are not $\perp$. **19.** $y - 6 = -\frac{3}{2}(x - 6)$ **21.** $y - 4 = \frac{1}{2}(x - 4)$ **23.** Yes; both slopes are -1 so the lines are $\parallel$. **25.** No; the slope of the first line is $-\frac{3}{4}$ and the slope of the second line is -3. Since the slopes are not equal, the lines are not $\parallel$. **27.** -4 **29.** No; if two equations represent lines with the same slope and the same y-intercept, the equations must represent the same line. **31.** slope of $\overline{AB}$ = slope of $\overline{CD} = -\frac{3}{4}$, $\overline{AB} \parallel \overline{CD}$; slope of $\overline{BC}$ = slope of $\overline{AD} = 1$, $\overline{BC} \parallel \overline{AD}$ **33.** slope of $\overline{AB}$ = slope of $\overline{CD} = 0$, $\overline{AB} \parallel \overline{CD}$; slope of $\overline{BC} = 3$, slope of $\overline{AD} = \frac{3}{2}$, $\overline{BC} \nparallel \overline{AD}$ **35.** A **37.** Yes; the equations represent a horizontal line and a vertical line, and every horizontal line is $\perp$ to every vertical line. **39.** Answers may vary. Sample: The three lines must have the same slope or undefined slope, so all three lines are $\parallel$.
41a. $y = -\frac{1}{2}x + 100$ **b.** $(100, 50)$ **c.** 112 yd
43. Slope of $\overline{AB}$ is $-\frac{1}{8}$; slope of $\overline{CD}$ is 8; the lines are $\perp$. **53.** $y = -\frac{1}{2}x + 3$ **54.** $y - 2 = \frac{5}{3}(x + 4)$ or $y - 7 = \frac{5}{3}(x + 1)$ **55.** $y + 2 = \frac{3}{4}(x - 3)$ or $y + 8 = \frac{3}{4}(x + 5)$ **56.** Reflexive Prop. of $\cong$ **57.** Mult. Prop. of Equality **58.** Distr. Prop. **59.** Symmetric Prop. of $\cong$ **60.** Yes; $\angle 1$ and $\angle 2$ are vert. ∠s, and vert. ∠s are $\cong$. **61.** Yes; $\angle 1$ and $\angle 2$ are both rt. ∠s, and all rt. ∠s are $\cong$. **62.** No; $m\angle 1 = 54$ (Given) and $m\angle 2 = 90 - 54 = 36$ (because $\angle 1$ and $\angle 2$ are compl.).

Chapter Review pp. 206–210

1. transversal **2.** ext. $\angle$ **3.** point-slope **4.** alt. int. ∠s **5.** skew lines **6.** slope-intercept **7.** $\angle 2$ and $\angle 7$, a and b, transversal d; $\angle 3$ and $\angle 6$, c and d, transversal e; $\angle 3$ and $\angle 8$; b and e; transversal c **8.** $\angle 5$ and $\angle 8$, lines a and b, transversal c; $\angle 2$ and $\angle 6$; a and e; transversal d **9.** $\angle 1$ and $\angle 4$, lines c and d, transversal b; $\angle 2$ and $\angle 4$, lines a and b, transversal d; $\angle 2$ and $\angle 5$, lines c and d, transversal a; $\angle 1$ and $\angle 5$, lines a and b, transversal c; $\angle 3$ and $\angle 4$; b and c; transversal e **10.** $\angle 1$ and $\angle 7$, lines c and d, transversal b **11.** corresp. ∠s **12.** alt. int. ∠s **13.** $m\angle 1 = 120$ because corresp. ∠s are $\cong$; $m\angle 2 = 120$ because $\angle 1$ and $\angle 2$ are vert. ∠s. **14.** $m\angle 1 = 75$ because same-side int. ∠s are suppl.; $m\angle 2 = 105$ because alt. int. ∠s are $\cong$. **15.** $x = 118$, $y = 37$ **16.** 20 **17.** 20 **18.** $n \parallel p$; if corresp. ∠s are $\cong$, then the lines are $\parallel$. **19.** none; $\angle 3$ and $\angle 6$ form a linear pair. **20.** $\ell \parallel m$; if same-side int. ∠s are suppl., then the lines are $\parallel$. **21.** $n \parallel p$; if alt. int. ∠s are $\cong$, then the lines are $\parallel$. **22.** $\parallel$ **23.** a **24.** 1st Street and 3rd Street are $\parallel$ because they are both $\perp$ to Morris Avenue. Since 1st Street and 5th street are both $\parallel$ to 3rd Street, 1st Street and 5th Street are $\parallel$ to each other. **25.** $x = 60$, $y = 60$ **26.** $x = 45$, $y = 45$ **27.** 30 **28.** 55 **29.** 3

30. **31.**

32. **33.**

34. -1 **35.** undefined
36. slope: 2; y-intercept: -1 **37.** slope: -2; point: $(-5, 3)$

38. $y = -\frac{1}{2}x + 12$ **39.** $y + 9 = 3(x - 1)$
40. $y - 2 = 4(x - 4)$ or $y + 2 = 4(x - 3)$
41. neither **42.** $\parallel$ **43.** $\perp$ **44.** $\parallel$
45. $y - 2 = 8(x + 6)$ **46.** $y + 3 = -6(x - 3)$

Chapter 4

Get Ready! p. 215

1. $AB = 4$, $BC = 3$, $AC = 5$ **2.** $AB = 8$, $BC = \sqrt{265}$, $AC = \sqrt{137}$ **3.** $AB = \sqrt{58}$, $BC = \sqrt{32}$, $AC = \sqrt{58}$ **4.** $\angle J \cong \angle L$ **5.** $m\angle M = m\angle N = 90$ **6.** $\angle B$ is a rt. $\angle$. **7.** $\angle AFB \cong \angle CFD$ **8.** $\angle B \cong \angle C$, $\angle A \cong \angle D$, $\angle AEB \cong \angle CED$ **9.** $\angle DAC \cong \angle BCA$, $\angle DCA \cong \angle BAC$, $\angle DAB \cong \angle BCD$, $\angle B \cong \angle D$ **10.** $m\angle A = 21$, $m\angle B = 71$, $m\angle C = 88$ **11-13.** Answers may vary. Sample: **11.** The base is the side that meets each of the two $\cong$ sides of the $\triangle$. **12.** The legs are the $\cong$ sides of an isosc. $\triangle$. **13.** Corresp. parts are the sides or ∠s that are in the same relative position in each figure.

Lesson 4-1 pp. 218–224

Got It? 1. $\overline{WY} \cong \overline{MK}$, $\overline{YS} \cong \overline{KV}$, $\overline{WS} \cong \overline{MV}$, $\angle W \cong \angle M$, $\angle Y \cong \angle K$, $\angle S \cong \angle V$ **2.** $m\angle V = 83$; $\angle W \cong \angle M$ and $\angle Y \cong \angle K$ because they are corresp. parts of $\cong$ $\triangle$s. By the Triangle Angle-Sum Theorem, $m\angle M + m\angle K + m\angle V = 180$. By substitution, $62 + 35 + m\angle V = 180$. So by subtraction, $m\angle V = 83$. **3.** Answers may vary. Sample: You know that $\overline{AD} \cong \overline{CD}$ (Given) and $\overline{BD} \cong \overline{BD}$ (Reflexive Prop. of $\cong$), but you have no other information about the sides and $\angle$s of the $\triangle$, so you cannot conclude that $\triangle ABD \cong \triangle CBD$. **4.** $\angle A \cong \angle D$ (Given), and $\angle ABE \cong \angle DBC$ because vertical $\angle$s are $\cong$. Also, $\angle AEB \cong \angle DCB$ (Third $\angle$s Theorem). The three pairs of sides are $\cong$ (Given), so $\triangle AEB \cong \triangle DCB$ by the def. of $\cong$ $\triangle$s.
Lesson Check 1a. $\overline{NY}$ **b.** $\angle X$ **2a.** $\overline{RO}$ **b.** $\angle T$ **3a.** $\angle A$ **b.** $\overline{KL}$ **c.** *CKLU* **4a.** $\angle M \cong \angle T$ **b.** 92 **5.** Answers may vary. Sample: finding the correct top for a food container **6.** No; the $\triangle$s could be the same shape but not necessarily the same size. **7.** He has not shown that corresp. $\angle$s are $\cong$.
Exercises 9. $\overline{EF} \cong \overline{HI}$, $\overline{FG} \cong \overline{IJ}$, $\overline{EG} \cong \overline{HJ}$, $\angle EFG \cong \angle HIJ$, $\angle FGE \cong \angle IJH$, $\angle FEG \cong \angle IHJ$ **11.** $\overline{CM}$ **13.** $\angle B$ **15.** $\angle J$ **17.** $\triangle CLM$ **19.** $\triangle MCL$ **21.** $\angle P \cong \angle S$, $\angle O \cong \angle I$, $\angle L \cong \angle D$, $\angle Y \cong \angle E$ **23.** 45 ft **25.** 52 **27.** 280 ft **29.** 128 **31.** No; there are not three pairs of $\cong$ corresp. sides. **33.** C **35.** $m\angle A = m\angle D = 20$ **37.** $BC = EF = 8$ **39.** 43 **41.** 5 **43.** Answers may vary. Sample: If $\triangle PQR \cong \triangle XYZ$, then $\overline{PQ} \cong \overline{XY}$, $\overline{QR} \cong \overline{YZ}$, $\overline{PR} \cong \overline{XZ}$, $\angle P \cong \angle X$, $\angle Q \cong \angle Y$, and $\angle R \cong \angle Z$. **45.** Two pairs of $\cong$ sides are given, and the third pair of sides are $\cong$ because $\overline{PQ}$ bisects $\overline{RT}$, so $\overline{TS} \cong \overline{RS}$. $\overline{PR} \parallel \overline{TQ}$, so $\angle P \cong \angle Q$ and $\angle R \cong \angle T$ because they are alt. int. $\angle$s; the third pair of $\angle$s are vertical $\angle$s, so they are $\cong$. Thus $\triangle PRS \cong \triangle QTS$ by the def. of $\cong$ $\triangle$s. **54.** $y = -\frac{2}{3}x + \frac{25}{3}$ **55.** $y = -\frac{1}{4}x + \frac{5}{4}$ **56.** 5 **57.** 18 **58.** 10 **59.** $\overline{AB} \cong \overline{DE}$, $\angle C \cong \angle F$ **60.** $\angle Q \cong \angle S$, $\angle QPR \cong \angle SRP$, $\angle QPR$ and $\angle SPR$ are adjacent, $\angle QRP$ and $\angle SRP$ are adjacent. **61.** $\angle M \cong \angle U$, $\overline{TO} \cong \overline{NV}$, $\overline{TV} \cong \overline{NO}$, $\angle MOT$ and $\angle MON$ are adjacent and suppl., $\angle UVT$ and $\angle UVN$ are adjacent and suppl.

Lesson 4-2 pp. 226–233

Got It? 1. Two pairs of sides are given as $\cong$, and $\overline{BD} \cong \overline{BD}$ by the Refl. Prop. of $\cong$. So $\triangle BCD \cong \triangle BFD$ by SSS. **2.** $\overline{LE} \cong \overline{BN}$ **3.** SSS; three pairs of corresp. sides are $\cong$.
Lesson Check 1a. $\angle PEN$ (or $\angle E$) **b.** $\angle NPE$ (or $\angle P$) **2a.** $\overline{HA}$ and $\overline{HT}$ **b.** $\overline{TH}$ and $\overline{TA}$ **3.** SAS **4.** SSS **5.** Answers may vary. Sample: Alike: Both use three pairs of $\cong$ parts to prove $\triangle$s $\cong$. Different: SSS uses three pairs of $\cong$ sides, while SAS uses two pairs of $\cong$ sides and their $\cong$ included $\angle$s. **6.** No; the $\cong$ $\angle$s are not included between the pairs of $\cong$ sides. **7.** No; the $\triangle$s have the same perimeter, but the three side lengths of one $\triangle$ are not necessarily = to the three side lengths of the other $\triangle$, so you cannot use SSS. There is no information about the $\angle$s of the $\triangle$s, so you cannot use SAS.
Exercises
9. *F* is the midpt. of $\overline{GI}$ (Given), so $\overline{IF} \cong \overline{GF}$ because a midpt. divides a segment into two $\cong$ segments. The other two pairs of sides are given as $\cong$, so $\triangle EFI \cong \triangle HFG$ by SSS. **11.** You need to know $\overline{LG} \cong \overline{MN}$; the diagram shows that $\overline{LT} \cong \overline{MQ}$ and $\angle L \cong \angle M$. $\angle L$ is included between $\overline{LG}$ and $\overline{LT}$, and $\angle M$ is included between $\overline{MN}$ and $\overline{MQ}$. **13.** Not enough information; the congruent vertical angles *TQP* and *RQS* are not included by the pairs of $\cong$ sides. **15.** If the 40° $\angle$ is *always* included between the two 5-in. sides, then all the $\triangle$s will be $\cong$ by SAS. If the 40° $\angle$ is *never* included between the two 5-in. sides, then the angles of the $\triangle$ will be 40°, 40°, and 100°, with the 100° angle included between the 5-in. sides, so all the $\triangle$s will be $\cong$ by SAS. But a $\triangle$ with the 40° angle included between the 5-in. sides will not be $\cong$ to a $\triangle$ with the 40° angle not included between the 5-in. sides. **17.** *X* is the midpt. of $\overline{AG}$ and $\overline{NR}$ (Given), so $\overline{AX} \cong \overline{GX}$ and $\overline{NX} \cong \overline{RX}$ by the def. of midpt. Also, $\angle AXN \cong \angle GXR$ because they are vertical $\angle$s, so $\triangle ANX \cong \triangle GRX$ by SAS. **19.** $AB = \sqrt{25 + 16} = \sqrt{41}$ and $DE = \sqrt{16 + 36} = \sqrt{52}$, so $\triangle ABC \ncong \triangle DEF$. **21.** Answers may vary. Sample: roof trusses for a house, sections of a ferris wheel, sawhorses used by a carpenter; explanations will vary.
23a. Answers may vary. Sample: **b.** Answers may vary. Sample:

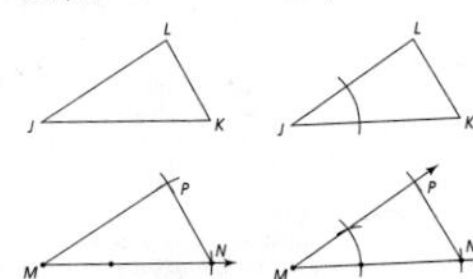

25. Not enough information; you need $\overline{DY} \cong \overline{TK}$ to show the $\triangle$s are $\cong$ by SSS, or you need $\angle H \cong \angle P$ to show the $\triangle$s are $\cong$ by SAS. **27.** Not necessarily; the $\cong$ $\angle$s are not included between the pairs of $\cong$ sides. **29.** $\overline{AE}$ and $\overline{BD}$ bisect each other (Given), so $\overline{AC} \cong \overline{EC}$ and $\overline{DC} \cong \overline{BC}$ (Def. of bisector). $\angle ACB \cong \angle ECD$ (Vert. $\angle$s are $\cong$.), so $\triangle ACB \cong \triangle ECD$ by SAS. **31.** Given the $\perp$ segments, $\angle B \cong \angle CMA$ because all rt. $\angle$s are $\cong$. *M* is the midpt. of $\overline{AB}$ (Given), so $\overline{AM} \cong \overline{MB}$ by the def. of midpt. Since $\overline{DB} \cong \overline{CM}$ (Given), then $\triangle AMC \cong \triangle MBD$ by SAS.
39. $\angle E$ **40.** $\overline{AB}$ **41.** $\overline{FG}$ **42.** $\angle C$ **43.** If $2x = 6$, then $x = 3$; both are true. **44.** If $x^2 = 9$, then $x = 3$; the statement is true and its converse is false. **45.** $\overline{JH}$ **46.** $\angle MNL$ (or $\angle N$)

Lesson 4-3 pp. 234–241

Got It? 1. $\triangle HGO \cong \triangle ACT$ because $\overline{HG} \cong \overline{AC}$ and the $\cong$ segments are included between two pairs of $\cong$ $\angle$s. **2.** $\angle B \cong \angle E$ because all rt. $\angle$s are $\cong$. $\overline{AB} \cong \overline{AE}$ and $\angle CAB \cong \angle DAE$ (Given), so $\triangle ABC \cong \triangle AED$ by ASA. **3a.** $\overline{RP}$ bisects $\angle SRQ$ (Given), so $\angle SRP \cong \angle QRP$ by the def. of $\angle$ bisector. $\angle S \cong \angle Q$ (Given) and $\overline{RP} \cong \overline{RP}$ (Refl. Prop. of $\cong$), so $\triangle SRP \cong \triangle QRP$ by AAS. **b.** After Step 3 in the proof, state that $\angle MRW \cong \angle KWR$ by the Third $\angle$s Theorem and write Step 4, so $\triangle WMR \cong \triangle RKW$ by ASA. **4.** Yes; $\overline{PR} \cong \overline{SR}$ and $\angle A \cong \angle I$ (Given). $\angle ARP \cong \angle IRS$ (Vert. $\angle$s are $\cong$.), so $\triangle PAR \cong \triangle SIR$ by AAS.
Lesson Check 1. $\overline{RS}$ **2.** $\angle N$, $\angle O$ **3.** ASA **4.** AAS **5.** Answers may vary. Sample: Alike: Both postulates use three pairs of $\cong$ corresp. parts. Different: To use the ASA Postulate, the sides must be included between the pairs of corresp. $\angle$s, while to use the SAS Postulate, the $\angle$s must be included between the pairs of corresp. sides. **6.** $\overline{LM}$ is not included between the pairs of $\cong$ corresp. $\angle$s. **7.** $\angle F \cong \angle G$; $\angle D \cong \angle H$
Exercises
9. $\triangle ABC \cong \triangle EDF$ **11.** $\overline{AC} \perp \overline{BD}$ (Given), so $\angle ACB \cong \angle ACD$ because $\perp$ lines form rt. $\angle$s, and all rt. $\angle$s are $\cong$. $\angle BAC \cong \angle DAC$ (Given) and $\overline{AC} \cong \overline{AC}$ (Refl. Prop. of $\cong$), so $\triangle ABC \cong \triangle ADC$ by ASA. **13a.** Vert. $\angle$s are $\cong$. **b.** Given **c.** $\overline{TQ} \cong \overline{RQ}$ **d.** AAS **15.** Given the $\perp$ segments, $\angle Q \cong \angle S$ because $\perp$ lines form rt. $\angle$s, and all rt. $\angle$s are $\cong$. It is given that *T* is the midpt. of $\overline{PR}$, so $\overline{PT} \cong \overline{RT}$ by the def. of midpt. $\angle PTQ \cong \angle RTS$ because vert. $\angle$s are $\cong$, so $\triangle PQT \cong \triangle RST$ by AAS. **17.** $\triangle UST \cong \triangle RTS$ by AAS. **19.** It is given that $\angle N \cong \angle P$ and $\overline{MO} \cong \overline{QO}$. Also, $\angle MON \cong \angle QOP$ because vert. $\angle$s are $\cong$. So $\triangle MON \cong \triangle QOP$ by AAS. **21.** Answers may vary. Sample: Yes; ASA guarantees a unique triangle with vertices at the oak tree, the maple tree, and the time capsule. **23.** No; the common side is included between the two $\cong$ $\angle$s in one $\triangle$, but it is not included between the $\cong$ $\angle$s in the other $\triangle$. **25.** $\overline{AE} \parallel \overline{BD}$ (Given), so $\angle A \cong \angle DBC$ (If $\parallel$ lines, corresp. $\angle$s are $\cong$.). Since $\angle E \cong \angle D$ and $\overline{AE} \cong \overline{BD}$ (Given), then $\triangle AEB \cong \triangle BDC$ by ASA.
27. Answers may vary. Sample:

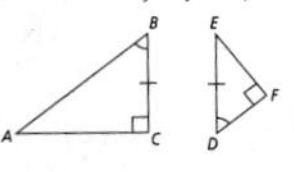

36. SSS; you are given two pairs of $\cong$ sides. Another pair of sides are $\cong$ by the Refl. Prop. of $\cong$. **37.** SAS; you are given two pairs of $\cong$ sides. The pair of included angles are congruent because they are vertical angles. **38.** $\angle T \cong \angle L$, $\angle I \cong \angle O$, $\angle C \cong \angle K$ **39.** $\overline{TI} \cong \overline{LO}$, $\overline{IC} \cong \overline{OK}$, $\overline{TC} \cong \overline{LK}$

Lesson 4-4 pp. 244–248

Got It? 1. $\overline{BA} \cong \overline{DA}$ and $\overline{CA} \cong \overline{ED}$ (Given). $\angle CAB \cong \angle EAD$ (Vert. $\angle$s are $\cong$.) So $\triangle ABC \cong \triangle ADE$ by SAS and $\angle C \cong \angle E$ because corresp. parts of $\cong$ $\triangle$s are $\cong$. **2a.** It is given that *M* is the midpt. of $\overline{BC}$, so $\overline{BM} \cong \overline{CM}$ by the def. of midpt. $\overline{AB} \cong \overline{AC}$ (Given) and $\overline{AM} \cong \overline{AM}$ (Refl. Prop. of $\cong$), so $\triangle AMB \cong \triangle AMC$ by SSS. Thus $\angle AMB \cong \angle AMC$ because corresp. parts of $\cong$ $\triangle$s are $\cong$. **b.** No; while $\overline{TR} \perp \overline{RS}$, if point *L* is not at sea level, then $\overline{TR}$ would not be $\perp$ to $\overline{RL}$.
Lesson Check 1. SAS; so $\overline{EA} \cong \overline{MA}$ because corresp. parts of $\cong$ $\triangle$s are $\cong$. **2.** SSS; so $\angle U \cong \angle E$ because corresp. parts of $\cong$ $\triangle$s are $\cong$. **3.** "Corresp. parts of $\cong$ $\triangle$s are $\cong$" is a short version of the def. of $\cong$ $\triangle$s. **4.** $\triangle KHL \cong \triangle NHM$ by AAS Thm.
Exercises 5. $\triangle KLJ \cong \triangle OMN$ by SAS; $\overline{KJ} \cong \overline{ON}$, $\angle K \cong \angle O$, $\angle J \cong \angle N$. **7.** $\overline{OM} \cong \overline{EB}$ and $\overline{ME} \cong \overline{RO}$ (Given). $\overline{OE} \cong \overline{OE}$ by the Refl. Prop. of $\cong$. $\triangle MOE \cong \triangle REO$ by SSS, so $\angle M \cong \angle R$ because corresp. parts of $\cong$ $\triangle$s are $\cong$. **9.** A pair of $\cong$ sides and a pair of $\cong$ $\angle$s are given. Since $\overline{PT} \cong \overline{PT}$ (Refl. Prop. of $\cong$), then $\triangle STP \cong \triangle OTP$ by SAS. $\angle S \cong \angle O$ because corresp. parts of $\cong$ $\triangle$s are $\cong$. **11.** $\overline{KL}$ bisects $\angle PKQ$, so $\angle PKL \cong \angle QKL$. $\overline{KL} \cong \overline{KL}$ by Refl. Prop. of $\cong$. $\triangle PKL \cong \triangle QKL$ by SAS, so $\angle P \cong \angle Q$ because corresp. parts of $\cong$ $\triangle$s are $\cong$. **13.** $\angle PLK \cong \angle QLK$ because $\perp$ lines form rt. $\angle$s, and all rt. $\angle$s are $\cong$. From the def. of $\angle$ bisector, $\angle PKL \cong \angle QKL$. So with $\overline{KL} \cong \overline{KL}$ by the Refl. Prop. of $\cong$, $\triangle PKL \cong \triangle QKL$ by ASA and $\angle P \cong \angle Q$ because corresp. parts of $\cong$ $\triangle$s are $\cong$. **15.** $\overline{BA} \cong \overline{BC}$ (Given) and $\overline{BD}$ bisects $\angle ABC$ (Given) $\angle ABD \cong \angle CBD$ (Def. of $\angle$ bisector). $\overline{BD} \cong \overline{BD}$ (Refl. Prop. of $\cong$), so $\triangle ABD \cong \triangle CBD$ by SAS. $\angle ADB \cong \angle CDB$ (Corresp. parts of $\cong$ $\triangle$s are $\cong$.) and $\angle ADB$ and $\angle CDB$ are suppl. so they must be rt. $\angle$s. By def. of $\perp$ lines, $\overline{BD} \perp \overline{AC}$. $\overline{AD} \cong \overline{CD}$ (Corresp. parts of $\cong$ $\triangle$s are $\cong$.), so $\overline{BD}$ bisects $\overline{AC}$ (Def. of seg. bisector). **17.** The construction makes $\overline{AC} \cong \overline{BE}$, $\overline{AD} \cong \overline{BF}$, and $\overline{CD} \cong \overline{EF}$. So $\triangle ACD \cong \triangle BEF$ by SSS. Thus $\angle A \cong \angle B$ because corresp. parts of $\cong$ $\triangle$s are $\cong$.

19. It is given that $\overline{JK} \parallel \overline{QP}$, so $\angle K \cong \angle Q$ and $\angle J \cong \angle P$ because they are alt. int. $\angle$s. With $\overline{JK} \cong \overline{PQ}$ (Given), $\triangle KJM \cong \triangle QPM$ by ASA and then $\overline{JM} \cong \overline{PM}$ because corresp. parts of $\cong$ $\triangle$s are $\cong$. Thus *M* is the midpt. of $\overline{JP}$ by def. of midpt. So $\overline{KQ}$, which contains point *M*, bisects $\overline{JP}$ by the def. of segment bisector. **27.** ASA **28.** AAS **29.** $\overline{AC}$ **30.** $\angle C$ **31.** $\angle A$ **32.** 105

Lesson 4-5 pp. 250–256

Got It? 1a. Yes; since $\overline{WV} \cong \overline{WS}$, $\angle WVS \cong \angle S$ by the Isosc. $\triangle$ Thm.; yes; since $\angle WVS \cong \angle S$, and $\angle R \cong \angle WVS$ (Given), $\angle R \cong \angle S$ (Trans. Prop. of $\cong$). Therefore, $\overline{TR} \cong \overline{TS}$ by the Converse of isosc. $\triangle$ Thm. **b.** No; there is not enough information about the sides or $\angle$s of $\triangle RUV$. **2.** 63 **3.** $m\angle A = 61$, $m\angle BCD = 119$
Lesson Check 1a. 70 **b.** 53 **2a.** 75 **b.** 48 **3.** 23, 134 **4a.** The $\angle$s opposite the $\cong$ sides are $\cong$. **b.** All three $\angle$s have measure 60, and all three sides are $\cong$. **5.** The $\cong$ $\angle$s should be opposite the $\cong$ sides.
Exercises 7. $\overline{UW}$; Converse of Isosc. $\triangle$ Thm. **9.** Answers may vary. Sample: $\angle VUY$; Isosc. $\triangle$ Thm. **11.** $x = 38$, $y = 4$ **13.** 108 **15.** 45 and 45; the sum of the measures of the acute $\angle$s must be 90, so the measure of each acute $\angle$ must be half of 90. **17.** 2.5 **19.** 35 **21.** 20, 80, 80 or 50, 50, 80 **23a.** $\overline{RS}$ **b.** $\overline{RS}$; Proof: $\overline{RS} \cong \overline{RS}$ (Refl. Prop. of $\cong$) and $\angle PRS \cong \angle QRS$ (def. of $\angle$ bisector). Also, $\angle P \cong \angle Q$ (Given). So $\triangle PRS \cong \triangle QRS$ by AAS. $\overline{PR} \cong \overline{QR}$ because corresp. parts of $\cong$ $\triangle$s are $\cong$. **25.** $\overline{AE} \cong \overline{DE}$ (Given), so $\angle A \cong \angle D$ by the Isosc. $\triangle$ Thm. Since $\overline{AB} \cong \overline{DC}$ (Given), then $\triangle ABE \cong \triangle DCE$ by SAS. **27a.** isosc. $\triangle$s **b.** 900 ft; 1100 ft **c.** The tower is the $\perp$ bisector of each base.
29.

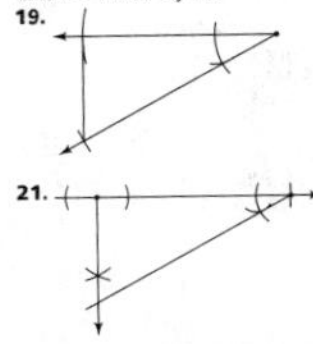

Draw $\overline{AB}$. Using *AB* as a radius, draw arcs with centers *A* and *B*. The intersection of these arcs is *C*. Since $\triangle ABC$ is equilateral, $\triangle ABC$ is equiangular by the Corollary to Theorem 4-3. **31.** $m = 36$, $n = 27$ **41.** $RC = GV$; there are three pairs of $\cong$ $\angle$s and one pair of $\cong$ sides, so $\triangle TRC \cong \triangle HGV$ by AAS or ASA, and $\overline{RC} \cong \overline{GV}$ because corresp. parts of $\cong$ $\triangle$s are $\cong$. **42.** The letters are the first letters of the days of the week; S, S. **43.** Yes; the $\triangle$s share a common side, so they are $\cong$ by SAS. **44.** Yes; the vertical $\angle$s are $\cong$, so the $\triangle$s are $\cong$ by SAS.

Algebra Review p. 257

1. $(-3, -7)$ **3.** no solution **5.** infinitely many solutions **7.** infinitely many solutions

Lesson 4-6 pp. 258–264

Got It? 1a. $\triangle PRS$ and $\triangle RPQ$ are rt. $\triangle$s with $\cong$ hypotenuses ($\overline{SP} \cong \overline{QR}$) and $\cong$ legs ($\overline{PR} \cong \overline{PR}$). So $\triangle PRS \cong \triangle RPQ$ by HL. **b.** Yes; the two $\triangle$s satisfy the three conditions of the HL Thm., so they are $\cong$. **2.** It is given that $\overline{AD}$ is the $\perp$ bisector of $\overline{CE}$, so $\triangle CBD$ and $\triangle EBA$ are rt. $\triangle$s and $\overline{CB} \cong \overline{EB}$ by the def. of $\perp$ bisector. Also, $\overline{CD} \cong \overline{EA}$ (Given), so $\triangle CBD \cong \triangle EBA$ by HL.
Lesson Check 1. yes; $\triangle BCA \cong \triangle EFD$ **2.** yes; $\triangle MPL \cong \triangle MNO$ **3.** no **4.** yes; $\triangle XVR \cong \triangle TVR$ **5.** 13 cm; the hypotenuse is the longest side of a rt. $\triangle$. **6.** Answers may vary. Sample: Alike: They both require information on two pairs of sides and one pair of $\angle$s. Different: For HL, the rt. $\angle$s are NOT included between the two pairs of $\cong$ sides, while for SAS the $\angle$s ARE included between the two pairs of $\cong$ sides. **7.** No; $\triangle LMJ$ and $\triangle JKL$ are rt. $\triangle$s with $\cong$ hypotenuses ($\overline{MJ} \cong \overline{KL}$) and $\cong$ legs ($\overline{LJ} \cong \overline{LJ}$), so $\triangle LMJ \cong \triangle JKL$ by HL.
Exercises 9a. $\triangle ABE$ and $\triangle DEB$ are rt. $\triangle$s. **b.** $\overline{BE} \cong \overline{EB}$ **c.** $\overline{AB} \cong \overline{DE}$ **d.** HL **11.** From the given information about $\perp$ segments, $\triangle PTM$ and $\triangle RMJ$ are rt. $\triangle$s. $\overline{PM} \cong \overline{RJ}$ (Given), and since *M* is the midpt. of $\overline{TJ}$, $\overline{TM} \cong \overline{JM}$. Thus $\triangle PTM \cong \triangle RMJ$ by HL. **13.** $x = -1$, $y = 3$ **15.** Yes; the two $\triangle$s are rt. $\triangle$s with $\cong$ hypotenuses and one pair of $\cong$ legs, so the two $\triangle$s are $\cong$ by HL. Then $\overline{RQ} \cong \overline{CB}$ because corresp. parts of $\cong$ $\triangle$s are $\cong$. **17.** Using the information about $\perp$ segments, $\triangle RST$ and $\triangle TUV$ are rt. $\triangle$s. $\overline{RS} \cong \overline{TU}$ (Given), and *T* is the midpt. of $\overline{RV}$ (Given), so $\overline{RT} \cong \overline{TV}$ (Def. of midpt.). Thus $\triangle RST \cong \triangle TUV$ by HL.
19.

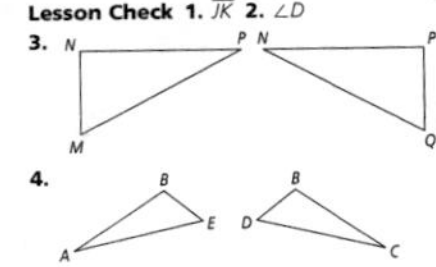

21.

23. From the given information about an isosc. $\triangle$, rt. $\angle$s, and midpt., you can conclude that $\overline{KG} \cong \overline{KE}$ (Def. of isosc. $\triangle$), $\triangle LKG$ and $\triangle DKE$ are rt. $\triangle$s (Def. of rt. $\triangle$), and $\overline{LK} \cong \overline{DK}$ (Def. of midpt.). So $\triangle LKG \cong \triangle DKE$ by HL, and $\overline{LG} \cong \overline{DE}$ because corresp. parts of $\cong$ $\triangle$s are $\cong$. **25.** No, the triangles are not $\cong$. Explanations may vary. Sample: $\overline{DF}$ is the hypotenuse of $\triangle DEF$, so it is the longest side of the triangle. Therefore, it is greater than 5 and greater than 13 because it is longer than either of the legs. So $\overline{DF}$ cannot be congruent to $\overline{AC}$, which is the hypotenuse of $\triangle ABC$ and has length 13. **32.** $\triangle STU$ is isosceles. $\overline{ST} \cong \overline{UT}$ because corresp. parts of $\cong$ $\triangle$s are $\cong$. **33.** $\triangle STU$ is equilateral. $\overline{ST} \cong \overline{US}$, $\overline{TU} \cong \overline{ST}$, and $\overline{US} \cong \overline{TU}$ because corresp. parts of $\cong$ $\triangle$s are $\cong$. **34.** Yes; $\triangle ABC \cong \triangle LMN$ by HL. **35.** No; $\triangle LMN$ and $\triangle HJK$ have one pair of $\cong$ sides and one pair of $\cong$ $\angle$s, but that is not enough to conclude that they are $\cong$. **36.** No; the hypotenuse of rt. $\triangle ABC$ is $\cong$ to a leg of rt. $\triangle RST$, so the $\triangle$s cannot be $\cong$.

Lesson 4-7 pp. 265–271

Got It? 1a. $\overline{AD}$ **b.** $\overline{AB}$ **2.** It is given that $\triangle ACD \cong \triangle BDC$, so $\angle ADC \cong \angle BCD$ because corresp. parts of $\cong$ $\triangle$s are $\cong$. Therefore, $\overline{CE} \cong \overline{DE}$ by the Converse of the Isosc. $\triangle$ Thm. **3.** $\triangle PSQ \cong \triangle RSQ$ by SAS because $\overline{PS} \cong \overline{RS}$ (Given), $\angle PSQ \cong \angle RSQ$ (Given), and $\overline{SQ} \cong \overline{SQ}$ (Refl. Prop. of $\cong$). So $\overline{PQ} \cong \overline{RQ}$ and $\angle PQT \cong \angle RQT$ (Corresp. parts of $\cong$ $\triangle$s are $\cong$.). Also, $\overline{QT} \cong \overline{QT}$ (Refl. Prop. of $\cong$), so $\triangle QPT \cong \triangle QRT$ by SAS. **4.** Using $\overline{AD} \cong \overline{AD}$ (Refl. Prop. of $\cong$) and the two given pairs of $\cong$ $\angle$s, $\triangle ACD \cong \triangle AED$ by AAS. Then $\overline{CD} \cong \overline{ED}$ (Corresp. parts of $\cong$ $\triangle$s are $\cong$.) and $\angle BDC \cong \angle FDE$ (Vert. $\angle$s are $\cong$.). Therefore, $\triangle BDC \cong \triangle FDE$ by ASA, and $\overline{BD} \cong \overline{FD}$ because corresp. parts of $\cong$ $\triangle$s are $\cong$.
Lesson Check 1. $\overline{JK}$ **2.** $\angle D$
3.
4.
5. No; there are several $\angle$s with vertex *J* and several $\angle$s with vertex *K*, and a different $\angle$ at each vertex is in each $\triangle$. **6.** Answers may vary. Sample: Based on the given statement that $\triangle PSY \cong \triangle SPL$, $\overline{PL} \cong \overline{SY}$, and $\angle L \cong \angle Y$ because corresp. parts of $\cong$ $\triangle$s are $\cong$. $\angle PRL \cong \angle SRY$ because vert. $\angle$s are $\cong$. So $\triangle PRL \cong \triangle SRY$ by AAS. **7.** Answers may vary. Sample: Prove $\triangle AEB \cong \triangle CED$ (by SAS) to get $\overline{AB} \cong \overline{CD}$ and $\angle BAE \cong \angle DCE$. Use those $\cong$ segments and $\cong$ angles, along with rt. $\angle$s *ADC* and *ABC*, to show $\triangle ACD \cong \triangle CAB$ by ASA.
Exercises 9. $\overline{DF}$
11.

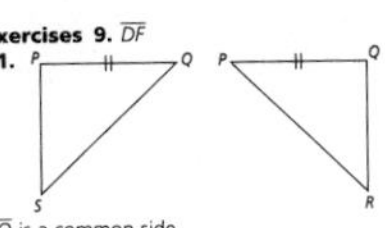

$\overline{PQ}$ is a common side.
13.
$\overline{KL}$ is a common side.
15. $\overline{RS} \cong \overline{UT}$ and $\overline{RT} \cong \overline{US}$ (Given), and $\overline{ST} \cong \overline{ST}$ (Refl. Prop. of $\cong$), so $\triangle RST \cong \triangle UTS$ by SSS. **17.** $\angle 1 \cong \angle 2$ and $\angle 3 \cong \angle 4$ (Given), and $\overline{QB} \cong \overline{QB}$ by the Refl. Prop. of $\cong$. So $\triangle QTB \cong \triangle QUB$ by ASA. Thus $\overline{QT} \cong \overline{QU}$ (Corresp. parts of $\cong$ $\triangle$s are $\cong$.). $\overline{QE} \cong \overline{QE}$ (Refl. Prop. of $\cong$), so $\triangle QET \cong \triangle QEU$ by SAS. **19.** Since $VT = VU + UT = UT + TS = US$, $\overline{VT} \cong \overline{US}$. Therefore, $\triangle QVT \cong \triangle PSU$ by SAS. **21.** It is given that $\overline{AC} \cong \overline{EC}$ and $\overline{CD} \cong \overline{CB}$, and $\angle C \cong \angle C$ by the Refl. Prop. of $\cong$. So $\triangle ACD \cong \triangle ECB$ by SAS, and $\angle A \cong \angle E$ because corresp. parts of $\cong$ $\triangle$s are $\cong$. **23.** Answers may vary. Sample:
25. $\overline{TE} \cong \overline{RI}$ and $\overline{TI} \cong \overline{RE}$ (Given) and $\overline{EI} \cong \overline{EI}$ (Refl. Prop. of $\cong$), so $\triangle TEI \cong \triangle RIE$ by SSS. Thus $\angle TIE \cong \angle REI$ because corresp. parts of $\cong$ $\triangle$s are $\cong$. Also, $\angle TDI \cong \angle ROE$ because $\angle TDI$ and $\angle ROE$ are rt. $\angle$s (Given) and all rt. $\angle$s are $\cong$. So $\triangle TDI \cong \triangle ROE$ by AAS and $\overline{TD} \cong \overline{RO}$ because corresp. parts of $\cong$ $\triangle$s are $\cong$.
33a. right **b.** right **c.** Reflexive **d.** HL
34.
35. (1, 2) **36.** (1.5, 5.5) **37.** (1, 1)

Chapter Review pp. 273–276

1. legs **2.** hypotenuse **3.** corollary **4.** congruent polygons **5.** $\overline{ML}$ **6.** $\angle U$ **7.** $\overline{ST}$ **8.** *ONMLK* **9.** 80 **10.** 3 **11.** 5 **12.** 35 **13.** 100 **14.** 145 **15.** $\angle D$ **16.** $\overline{MR}$ **17.** not enough information **18.** not enough information **19.** SAS **20.** AAS or ASA **21.** $\triangle TVY \cong \triangle YWX$ by AAS, so $\overline{TV} \cong \overline{YW}$ because corresp. parts of $\cong$ $\triangle$s are $\cong$.

22. $\triangle BEC \cong \triangle DEC$ by ASA, so $\overline{BE} \cong \overline{DE}$ because corresp. parts of $\cong$ ▲ are $\cong$. **23.** $\triangle BEC \cong \triangle DEC$ by SSS, so $\angle B \cong \angle D$ because corresp. parts of $\cong$ ▲ are $\cong$. **24.** If $\parallel$ lines, alt. int. ∠s are $\cong$, so $\angle LKM \cong \angle NMK$. Then $\triangle LKM \cong \triangle NMK$ by SAS, and $\overline{KN} \cong \overline{ML}$ because corresp. parts of $\cong$ ▲ are $\cong$. **25.** $x = 4$, $y = 65$ **26.** $x = 55$, $y = 62.5$ **27.** $x = 65$, $y = 90$ **28.** $x = 7$, $y = 60$ **29.** $\overline{LN} \perp \overline{KM}$ (Given), so $\triangle KLN$ and $\triangle MLN$ are rt. ▲. $\overline{KL} \cong \overline{ML}$ (Given) and $\overline{LN} \cong \overline{LN}$ (Refl. Prop. of $\cong$), so $\triangle KLN \cong \triangle MLN$ by HL. **30.** The given information on $\perp$ segments means $\triangle PSQ$and $\triangle RQS$ are rt. ▲. You know $\overline{PQ} \cong \overline{RS}$ (Given) and $\overline{QS} \cong \overline{QS}$ (Refl. Prop. of $\cong$). So $\triangle PSQ \cong \triangle RQS$ by HL. **31.** $\triangle AEC \cong \triangle ABD$ by SAS or ASA or AAS. **32.** $\triangle FIH \cong \triangle GHI$ by SAS. **33.** $\triangle TAR \cong \triangle TSP$ by ASA.

Chapter 5

Get Ready! p. 281

1. **2.**

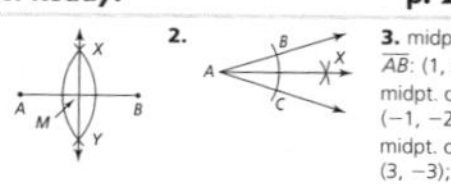

3. midpt. of $\overline{AB}$: (1, 2); midpt. of $\overline{BC}$: (−1, −2); midpt. of $\overline{AC}$: (3, −3); $AB = 2\sqrt{17}$; $BC = 2\sqrt{29}$; $AC = 4\sqrt{5}$ **4.** midpt. of $\overline{AB}$: (4, 2); midpt. of $\overline{BC}$: (4, 5); midpt. of $\overline{AC}$: (−1, 5); $AB = 10$; $BC = 2\sqrt{34}$; $AC = 6$ **5.** midpt. of $\overline{AB}$: (0, −3); midpt. of $\overline{BC}$: (1, 0); midpt. of $\overline{AC}$: (−1, 0); $AB = 4$; $BC = 2\sqrt{10}$; $AC = 2\sqrt{10}$ **6.** The team did not win. **7.** It is too late. **8.** $m\angle R \le 60$ **9.** −6 **10.** $-\frac{8}{3}$ **11.** undefined **12.** the length of a segment from a vertex to the opposite side **13.** the length of a $\perp$ segment from the point to the line **14.** a segment that connects the midpts. of 2 sides of the $\triangle$ **15.** The lines intersect at one point, or the lines have exactly one point in common.

Lesson 5-1 pp. 285–291

Got It? 1a. $\overline{AC} \parallel \overline{YZ}$, $\overline{CB} \parallel \overline{XY}$, $\overline{AB} \parallel \overline{XZ}$ **b.** 65; $\overline{UV}$ is a midsegment of $\triangle NOM$, so by the $\triangle$ Midseg. Thm., $\overline{UV} \parallel \overline{NM}$. Then $m\angle VUO = m\angle N = 65$ because corresp. ∠s of $\parallel$ lines are $\cong$. **2.** $DC = 6$; $AC = 12$; $EF = 6$; $AB = 15$ **3.** 1320 ft
Lesson Check 1. $\overline{NO}$ **2.** 23 **3.** 4 **4.** A midsegment is a segment whose endpoints are the midpts. of two sides of a triangle. **5.** The segments are $\parallel$. **6.** The student is assuming that L is the midpt. of $\overline{OT}$, which is not given.
Exercises 7. $\overline{UY} \parallel \overline{XV}$, $\overline{UW} \parallel \overline{TX}$, $\overline{YW} \parallel \overline{TV}$ **9.** $\overline{FE}$ **11.** $\overline{AB}$ **13.** $\overline{AC}$ **15.** 40 **17.** 160 **19.** 13 **21.** 6 **23.** 17 **25.** 156 m **27.** 114 ft 9 in.; because the red segments divide the legs into four $\cong$ parts, the white segment divides each leg into two $\cong$ parts. The white segment is a midsegment of the triangular face of the building, so its length is one half the length of the base. **29.** 40; $\overline{ST}$ is a midsegment of $\triangle PQR$, so by the $\triangle$ Midseg. Thm., $\overline{ST} \parallel \overline{PR}$. Then $m\angle QPR = m\angle QST$ because corresp. ∠s of $\parallel$ lines are $\cong$. **31.** 60 **33.** 100 **35.** 18.5 **37.** C **39.** 50 **41.** $x = 6$; $y = 6.5$ **43.** 24 **45.** Draw $\overrightarrow{CA}$. Find P on $\overrightarrow{CA}$ such that $CA = AP$. Draw $\overline{PD}$. Construct the $\perp$ bisector of $\overline{PD}$. Label the intersection point B. Draw $\overline{AB}$. This is a midsegment of $\triangle CPD$. According to the $\triangle$ Midsegment Thm., $\overline{AB} \parallel \overline{CD}$ and $AB = \frac{1}{2}CD$. **53.** $\triangle FBD \cong \triangle FCE$, $\triangle BAE \cong \triangle CAD$, $\triangle DAF \cong \triangle EAF$, $\triangle ABF \cong \triangle ACF$ **54.** Answers may vary. Sample: $\angle BFD \cong \angle CFE$ because they are vertical ∠s. $\angle 1 \cong \angle 2$ is given. By the $\angle$ Addition Post., it follows that $\angle BFA \cong \angle CFA$. $\overline{BF} \cong \overline{CF}$ is given, and $\overline{FA} \cong \overline{FA}$ by the Refl. Prop. Therefore, $\triangle BFA \cong \triangle CFA$ by SAS. $\overline{AB} \cong \overline{AC}$ because corresp. parts of $\cong$ ▲ are $\cong$. **55.** 6 **56.** 68 **57.**

Lesson 5-2 pp. 292–299

Got It? 1. 8 **2a.** Any point on the $\perp$ bis. of $\overline{PS}$ **b.** At the intersection point of ℓ and the perpendicular bisector of $\overline{PS}$; let X be the intersection point of ℓ and the perpendicular bisector of $\overline{PS}$. By the $\perp$ Bis. Thm., $XR = XS$ and $XS = XP$, so $XR = XS = XP$. Thus, X is equidistant from R, S, and P. **3.** 21
Lesson Check 1. $\overline{AC}$ is the $\perp$ bisector of $\overline{DB}$. **2.** 15 **3.** 18 **4.** Answers may vary. Sample:

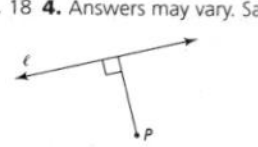

5. Draw the $\perp$ segments that join P to $\overrightarrow{OL}$ and $\overrightarrow{OX}$. Use a ruler to determine if $OL = OX$. If $OL = OX$, then P is on the bisector of $\angle LOX$.
Exercises 7. 3 **9.** Coleman School; it is on 6th Ave., which is (approximately) the $\perp$ bisector of 14th St. between 8th Ave. and Union Square. **11.** Draw $\overline{HS}$ and find its midpt., M. Through M, construct the line $\perp$ to $\overline{HS}$. Any point on this line will be equidistant from H and S. **13.** $\overrightarrow{HL}$ bisects $\angle KHF$; point L is equidistant from the sides of the $\angle$, so L is on the bisector of $\angle KHF$ by the Converse of the $\angle$ Bisector Thm. **15.** 54; 54 **17.** $y = 3$, $ST = 15$, $TU = 15$ **19.** 10 **21.** isosc.,

because $TW = ZW$ **23.** At the point on $\overline{XY}$ that lies on the bisector of $\angle GPL$; the goalie does not know to which side of her the player will aim his shot, so she should keep herself equidistant from the sides of $\angle GPL$. Points on the bisector of $\angle GPL$ are equidistant from $\overline{PG}$ and $\overline{PL}$. If she moves to a point on the $\perp$ bisector of $\overline{GL}$, she will be closer to $\overline{PL}$ than to $\overline{PG}$.
25a.

b. Answers may vary. Sample: They meet at a single point. **27.** A pt. is on the bisector of an $\angle$ if and only if it is equidistant from the sides of the $\angle$. **29.** No; A is not equidistant from the sides of $\angle TXR$. **31.** Yes; A is equidistant from the sides of $\angle TXR$. **33.** $\overline{PA} \cong \overline{PB}$ (Given) and $\angle AMP \cong \angle BMP$ because all rt. ∠s are $\cong$. Also, $\overline{PM} \cong \overline{PM}$ by the Refl. Prop. of $\cong$. So rt. $\triangle PMA \cong$ rt. $\triangle PAB$ by HL and $\overline{AM} \cong \overline{BM}$ because corresp. parts of $\cong$ ▲ are $\cong$. Therefore $\overleftrightarrow{PM}$ is the $\perp$ bisector of $\overline{AB}$, by the def. of $\perp$ bisector. **35.** In rt. $\triangle SPQ$ and rt. $\triangle SRQ$, $\overline{SP} \cong \overline{SR}$ (Given) and $\overline{QS} \cong \overline{QS}$ (Refl. Prop. of $\cong$), so $\triangle SPQ \cong \triangle SRQ$ by HL. Thus $\angle PQS \cong \angle RQS$ because corresp. parts of $\cong$ ▲ are $\cong$, and $\overrightarrow{QS}$ bisects $\angle PQR$ by the def. of $\angle$ bisector. **43.** 6 **44.** 120 **45.** $\frac{1}{3}$ **46.** undefined **47.** Answers may vary. Sample: It is a vertical line that contains the point (5, 0).

Lesson 5-3 pp. 301–307

Got It? 1. (6, 5) **2.** at the circumcenter of the $\triangle$ whose vertices are the three trees

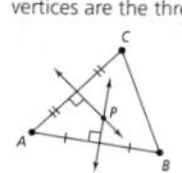

3a. 61 **b.** No; answers may vary. Sample: The distance from Q to $\overline{KL}$ is QN, the length of the shortest segment from Q to $\overline{KL}$. From part (a), $QN = 61$, so $QP > 61$.
Lesson Check 1. (3, 2.5) **2.** 6 **3.** obtuse $\triangle$ **4.** Since the three $\perp$ bisectors of a $\triangle$ are concurrent, the third $\perp$ bisector goes through the pt. of intersection of the other two $\perp$ bisectors. **5.** Answers may vary. Sample: The diagram does not show that $\overline{QC}$ bisects $\angle SQR$, so you cannot conclude that point C is equidistant from the sides of $\angle SQR$. **6.** Each one is a point of concurrency of bisectors of parts of a $\triangle$, each is equidistant from three parts of the $\triangle$, and each is the center of a ⊙ that contains three points of the $\triangle$. The circumcenter is equidistant from three points, while the incenter is equidistant from three segments. The $\triangle$ is inside the ⊙ centered at the circumcenter and outside the ⊙ centered at the incenter.
Exercises 7. (−2, −3) **9.** (1.5, 1) **11.** (−3, 1.5) **13.** (3.5, 3) **15.** C **17.** 2 **19.** Isosceles; $SR = ST$, so $\angle SRT \cong \angle STR$ (Isosc. $\triangle$ Thm.). Since P is the incenter of $\triangle RST$, $\overline{PR}$ and $\overline{PT}$ are $\angle$ bisectors. So $m\angle PRT = \frac{1}{2}m\angle SRT = \frac{1}{2}m\angle STR = m\angle PTR$. Thus $PR = PT$ by the Converse of the Isosc. $\triangle$ Thm. **21.** Same method as for Exercise 20.

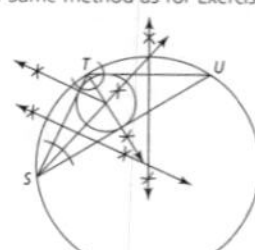

23. An interpretation of the passage is that the treasure is equidistant from three Norway pines. To find the treasure, Karl can find the circumcenter of the $\triangle$ whose vertices are the three pines. **25.** P; the markings in the diagram show that P is the incenter of the triangular station and C is the circumcenter. If you stand at P, you will be equidistant from the three sides along which the buses are parked. If you move away from P, you will move closer to some of the buses. **27.** true
29.

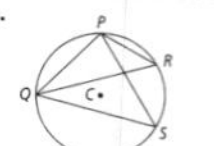

As the diagram shows, circle C is circumscribed about both $\triangle PQR$ and $\triangle PQS$, so points R and S do not have to coincide.
37. 4 **38.** 17 **39.** (3, 8) **40.** (5, 3.5)

Lesson 5-4 pp. 309–315

Got It? 1a. 13.5 **b.** 2 : 1; $ZA = \frac{2}{3}CZ$ and $AC = \frac{1}{3}CZ$, so $ZA : AC = \frac{2}{3} : \frac{1}{3} = 2 : 1$. **2a.** A median; it connects a vertex of $\triangle ABC$ and the midpt. of the opposite side. **b.** Neither; E is a midpt. of $\triangle ABC$, but G is not a vertex of $\triangle ABC$. **c.** An altitude; it extends from a vertex of $\triangle ABC$ and is $\perp$ to the opposite side. **3.** (1, 2)
Lesson Check 1. median **2.** 6 **3.** 7.5 **4.** $\overline{AB}$, $\overline{AC}$ **5.** $\overline{HJ}$ does not contain a vertex of $\triangle ABC$, so it is not an altitude of $\triangle ABC$. **6.** No; any pair of altitudes meet at the orthocenter of the $\triangle$. **7.** They are $\perp$; since A is the orthocenter of $\triangle ABC$, A lies on the altitude from B to $\overline{AC}$. B also lies on this altitude, so the altitude from B to $\overline{AC}$ must be $\overline{BA}$. Therefore, $\overline{BC} \perp \overline{AC}$.

Exercises 9. $ZY = 4.5$, $ZU = 13.5$ **11.** Median; it connects a vertex of $\triangle ABC$ and the midpt. of the opposite side. **13.** Altitude; it extends from a vertex of $\triangle ABC$ and is $\perp$ to the opposite side. **15.** (6, 4) **17.** H **19.** J **21.** 125
23.

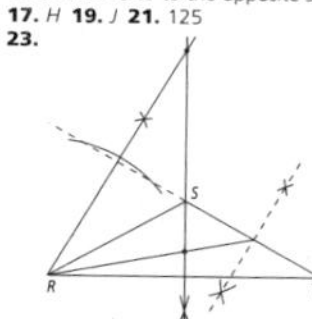

25. $\overline{BD}$ **27.** $\overline{OD}$ **29.** The folds should show the $\perp$ bisectors of the sides to identify the midpt. of each side, and also show the fold through each vertex and the midpt. of the opposite side. **31.** C **33.** Answers may vary. Sample: The $\angle$ bisector of the vertex $\angle$ forms two ▲ that are $\cong$ by SAS. Therefore the 2 segments formed on the base are $\cong$ (so the $\angle$ bisector contains a median), and the two ∠s formed by the $\angle$ bisector and the base are rt. ∠s (so the $\angle$ bisector contains an altitude). Thus the median and the altitude are the same. **43.** Both; the markings show directly that $\overline{XY}$ is a $\perp$ bisector. The two ▲ formed are congruent by SAS, so the two ∠s at top are $\cong$. Therefore, $\overline{XY}$ is also an $\angle$ bisector. **44.** Neither; $\overline{XY}$ connects vertex X and the midpt., Y, of side $\overline{PQ}$, so $\overline{XY}$ is a median. **45.** Two angles are not congruent. **46.** You are 16 years old. **47.** $m\angle A \ge 90$

Lesson 5-5 pp. 317–322

Got It? 1a. Assume temporarily that $\triangle BOX$ is acute. **b.** Assume temporarily that no pair of shoes you bought cost more than \$25. **2a.** II and III **b.** No; if $\triangle ABC$ is an isosc., nonequilateral $\triangle$, then Statement III is true but Statement II is not true. Therefore, Statements II and III are not equivalent. **3.** Assume temporarily that $y = 6$. Then $7(x + 6) = 70$; divide each side by 7 to get $x + 6 = 10$ and so $x = 4$. But this contradicts the given statement that $x \ne 4$. The temporary assumption that $y = 6$ led to a contradiction, so we can conclude that $y \ne 6$.
Lesson Check 1. Assume temporarily that at least one $\angle$ in quadrilateral $ABCD$ is not a rt. $\angle$. **2.** Lines a and b meet at P. **3.** The negation of "$\angle A$ is obtuse" is "$\angle A$ is an acute or a rt. $\angle$."
Exercises 5. Assume temporarily that $\angle J$ is a rt. $\angle$. **7.** Assume temporarily that no $\angle$ is obtuse. **9.** Assume temporarily that $m\angle 2 \le 90$. **11.** I and III **13.** I and II **15a.** rt. $\angle$ **b.** rt. ∠s **c.** 90 **d.** 180 **e.** 90 **f.** 90 **g.** 0 **h.** more than one rt. $\angle$ **i.** at most one rt. $\angle$ **17.** Assume temporarily $\ell \parallel p$. Then $\angle 1 \cong \angle 2$ because if lines are $\parallel$ then corresp. ∠s are $\cong$. But this contradicts the given statement that $\angle 1 \not\cong \angle 2$. Therefore the temporary assumption is false, and we can conclude that $\ell \nparallel p$. **19.** Assume temporarily that $\overline{XB} \not\cong \overline{XA}$. **21.** I and III **23.** Assume temporarily that at least one base $\angle$ is a rt. $\angle$. Then both base ∠s must be rt. ∠s, by the Isosc. $\triangle$ Thm. But this contradicts the fact that a $\triangle$ is formed, because in a plane two lines $\perp$ to the same line are $\parallel$. Therefore the temporary assumption is false that at least one base $\angle$ is a rt. $\angle$, and we can conclude that neither base $\angle$ is a rt. $\angle$. **25.** Assume temporarily that an obtuse $\triangle$ can contain a rt. $\angle$. Then the measure of the obtuse $\angle$ plus the measure of the rt. $\angle$ must be greater than $90 + 90 = 180$. This contradicts the $\triangle$ Angle-Sum Thm., so the temporary assumption that an obtuse $\triangle$ can contain a rt. $\angle$ is incorrect. We can conclude that an obtuse $\triangle$ cannot contain a rt. $\angle$. **27.** The culprit entered the room through a hole in the roof; all the other possibilities were ruled out. **35.** 24 cm **36.** 30 and 120 **37.** Law of Syllogism **38.** $\overline{AC}$, $\overline{BC}$, $\overline{AB}$ **39.** $\overline{CA}$, $\overline{BC}$, $\overline{BA}$

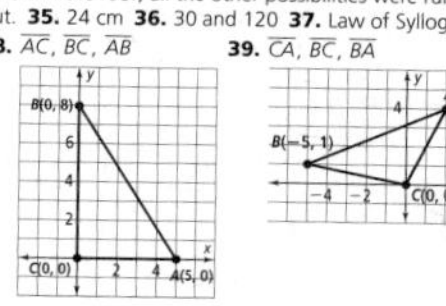

40. $\overline{AB}$, $\overline{AC} \cong \overline{BC}$

Algebra Review p. 323

1. $x \le -1$ **3.** $x > -10.5$ **5.** $a \le 90$ **7.** $z > 0.5$ **9.** $n \le -\frac{7}{2}$ **11.** $x > -5$ **13.** $x \le -1$ **15.** $x > -8$ **17.** $x \ge -362$

Lesson 5-6 pp. 324–331

Got It? 1. $\angle 5$ is an ext. $\angle$ of $\triangle ACD$, so by the Corollary to the $\triangle$ Ext. $\angle$ Thm., $m\angle 5 > m\angle C$. **2.** Holingsworth Rd. and MLK Blvd. **3.** $\overline{OX}$; $m\angle X = 180 - (130 + 24) = 26$, so $m\angle O > m\angle X > m\angle S$. By Theorem 5-11, $SX > OS > OX$. **4a.** No; $2 + 6 \ngtr 9$. **b.** Yes; the sum of the lengths of any two sides is greater than the length of the third side. **5.** 3 in. $< x <$ 11 in.
Lesson Check 1. $\overline{BC}$ **2.** $\angle C$ **3.** No; $5 + 4 \ngtr 10$. **4.** If the perimeter is 16 and the length of one side is 8, then the sum of the lengths of the other two sides is $16 - 8 = 8$. However, the $\triangle$ Inequality Thm. tells you that if the length of one side is 8, then the sum of the lengths of the other two sides is greater than 8. So the friend is incorrect. **5.** No; the adjacent interior $\angle$ would measure 92. Then, because a second $\angle$ of the $\triangle$ measures 90, the sum of the $\angle$ measures would exceed 180, which contradicts the $\triangle$ Angle-Sum Thm.
Exercises 7. This is true by the Corollary to the $\triangle$ Ext. $\angle$ Thm. **9.** $\angle M$, $\angle L$, $\angle K$ **11.** $\angle G$, $\angle H$, $\angle J$ **13.** $\angle E$, $\angle F$, $\angle D$ **15.** $\overline{MN}$, $\overline{NO}$, $\overline{MO}$ **17.** $\overline{TU}$, $\overline{UV}$, $\overline{TV}$ **19.** $\overline{EF}$, $\overline{DE}$, $\overline{DF}$ **21.** No; $2 + 3 \ngtr 6$. **23.** No; $8 + 10 \ngtr 19$. **25.** Yes; $2 + 9 > 10$, $9 + 10 > 2$, and $2 + 10 > 9$. **27.** 4 ft $< x <$ 20 ft **29.** 0 cm $< x <$ 12 cm **31.** 3 yd $< x <$ 11 yd **33.** Place the computer at the corner that forms a rt. $\angle$; place the bookshelf along the wall opposite the rt. $\angle$. In a rt. $\triangle$ the rt. $\angle$ is the largest $\angle$, and the longest side of a $\triangle$ is opposite the largest $\angle$. **35.** The dashed red line and the courtyard walkway determine three sides of a $\triangle$, so by the $\triangle$ Inequality Thm., the path that follows the dashed red line is longer than the courtyard walkway. **37.** $\overline{RS}$ **39.** $\overline{XY}$ **41.** Answers may vary. Sample: The sum of the $\angle$ measures of a $\triangle$ is 180, so $m\angle T + m\angle P + m\angle A = 180$. Since $m\angle T = 90$, $m\angle P + m\angle A = 90$ and so $m\angle T > m\angle A$ (Comparison Prop. of Inequality). Therefore $PA > PT$ by Thm. 5-11. **50.** Assume temporarily that the side is less than 2 ft long. **51.** Assume temporarily that no two ∠s of $\triangle PQR$ are $\cong$. **52.** SSS **53.** 40 **54.** 25 **55.** no

Lesson 5-7 pp. 332–339

Got It? 1a. $LN > OQ$ **b.** Assume temporarily that $m\angle P \ngtr m\angle A$. If $m\angle P = m\angle A$, then $\triangle ABC \cong \triangle PQR$ (SAS), but this contradicts the fact that $BC \ne QR$. If $m\angle P < m\angle A$, then by the Hinge Thm., $QR < BC$. This contradicts the fact that $QR > BC$. Therefore, $m\angle P > m\angle A$. **2.** The 40° opening; the lengths of the blades do not change as the scissors open. The included angle between the blades of the 40° opening is greater than the included angle of the 35° opening, so by the Hinge Thm., the distance between the blades is greater for the 40° opening. **3.** $-6 < x < 24$ **4.** From the given information, $LO = ON$ (def. of midpt.) and $m\angle MOL = 100$ (suppl. $\angle$ to $\angle MON$). Since $\overline{MO} \cong \overline{MO}$, and $m\angle MOL > m\angle MON$, the Hinge Thm. yields $LM > MN$.
Lesson Check 1. $FD > BC$ **2.** $m\angle UST > m\angle VST$ **3.** Answers may vary. Sample: As a door opens, and the angle between the door and doorway increases, the distance between the door jamb and the nonhinge vertical edge of the door increases. **4.** The two ∠s that are formed by $\cong$ sides are $\angle ABD$ and $\angle CDB$. Since the side opposite $\angle ABD$ is longer than the side opposite $\angle CDB$, the correct conclusion is $m\angle ABD > m\angle CDB$. **5.** Answers may vary. Sample: Both deal with a pair of ▲ that have two pairs of $\cong$ corresponding sides along with a relationship between the ∠s formed by those sides.
Exercises 7. $PR < RT$ **9.** no conclusion **11.** $6 < x < 38$ **13.** $3.5 < y < 17.5$ **15a.** Converse of Isosc. $\triangle$ Thm. **b.** Given **c.** Def. of midpt. **d.** $BC = CD$ **e.** Given **f.** Hinge Theorem **17.** $m\angle QTR > m\angle RTS$; $m\angle PTQ + m\angle QTR + m\angle RTS = 180$, so $m\angle PTQ + m\angle RTS = 88$. Thus $m\angle RTS < 88$ by the Comparison Prop. of Inequality, so $m\angle QTR > m\angle RTS$ by the Transitive Prop. of Inequality. **19a.** The two labeled ∠s are formed by $\cong$ corresp. sides of the two ▲, so the side opposite the 94° $\angle$ should be longer than the side opposite the 91° $\angle$, by the Hinge Thm. Thus the side labeled "13" must be longer than the side labeled "14." **b.** Answers may vary. Sample: Switch the angle labels 91° and 94°. **21.** A **23.** $\triangle ABE \cong \triangle CBD$ (Given) so $\triangle ABE$ and $\triangle CBD$ are isosc. with $AB = EB = DB = CB$. Since $m\angle EBD > m\angle ABE$ (Given), $ED > AE$ by the Hinge Thm. **31.** $\angle T$, $\angle F$, $\angle R$ **32.** $\angle M$, $\angle L$, $\angle K$ **33.** 4 cm $< x <$ 34 cm **34.** 5 ft $< x <$ 17 ft **35.** 0 in. $< x <$ 6 in. **36.** $\overline{GH}$ **37.** $\frac{3}{4}$ **38.** $-\frac{8}{3}$ **39.** 1

Chapter Review pp. 341–344

1. median **2.** distance from a point to a line **3.** incenter **4.** 15 **5.** 11 **6.** $L\left(\frac{5}{2}, -\frac{1}{2}\right)$; $M\left(\frac{7}{2}, \frac{1}{2}\right)$; slope of $\overline{AB} = 1$ and slope of $\overline{LM} = 1$, so $\overline{LM} \parallel \overline{AB}$; $AB = 2\sqrt{2}$ and $LM = \sqrt{2}$, so $LM = \frac{1}{2}AB$. **7.** Let point S be second base and point T be third base. Find the midpt. M of $\overline{ST}$ and then through M construct the line $\ell \perp$ to $\overline{ST}$. Points of the baseball field that are on line ℓ are equidistant from second and third base. **8.** 40 **9.** 40 **10.** 6 **11.** 11 **12.** 33 **13.** 33 **14.** (0, 0) **15.** (3, 2) **16.** (4, 4) **17.** (5, 1) **18.** 45 **19.** 40 **20.** 25 **21.** $\overline{AB}$ is an altitude; it is a segment from a vertex that is $\perp$ to the opposite side. **22.** $\overline{AB}$ is a median; it is a segment from a vertex to the midpt. of the opposite side. **23.** $QZ = 8$, $QM = 12$ **24.** (0, −1) **25.** (2, −3) **26.** Assume temporarily that neither of the two numbers is even. That means each number is odd, so the product of the two numbers must be odd. That contradicts the statement that the product of the two numbers is even. Thus the temporary assumption is false, and we can conclude that at least one of the numbers must be even. **27.** Assume temporarily that the third line intersects neither of the first two. Then it is ∥ to both of them. Since the first two lines are ∥ to the same line, they are ∥ to each other. This contradicts the given information. Therefore the temporary assumption is false, and the third line must intersect at least one of the two others. **28.** Assume temporarily that there is a △ with two obtuse ∠s. Then the sum of the measures of those two ∠s is greater than 180, which contradicts the △ Angle-Sum Thm. Therefore the temporary assumption is false, and a △ can have at most one obtuse ∠. **29.** Assume temporarily that an equilateral △ has an obtuse ∠. Since all the ∠s are ≅ in an equilateral △, then all three ∠s must be obtuse. But we showed in Ex. 28 that a △ can have at most one obtuse ∠. Therefore the temporary assumption is false, and an equilateral △ cannot have an obtuse ∠. **30.** Assume temporarily that each of the three integers is less than or equal to 3. Then the sum of the three integers must be less than or equal to 3 · 3, or 9. This contradicts the given statement that the sum of the three integers is greater than 9. Therefore the temporary assumption is false, and you can conclude that one of the integers must be greater than 3. **31.** $\overline{RS}$, $\overline{ST}$, $\overline{RT}$ **32.** No; $5 + 8 \ngtr 15$. **33.** Yes; $10 + 12 > 20$, $10 + 20 > 12$, and $12 + 20 > 10$. **34.** 1 ft $< x <$ 25 ft **35.** $<$ **36.** $>$ **37.** $<$

Chapter 6

Get Ready! p. 349

1. 30 **2.** 42 **3.** 22 **4.** yes **5.** no **6.** yes **7.** ∥ **8.** ⊥ **9.** neither **10.** ASA **11.** SAS **12.** AAS **13.** Answers may vary. Sample: polygon in which all the ∠s are ≅ **14.** Answers may vary. Sample: four-sided figure formed by joining two isosc. △s **15.** Answers may vary. Sample: Angles that follow one right after the other.

Lesson 6-1 pp. 353–358

Got It? 1a. 2700 **b.** Answers may vary. Sample: Divide 1980 by 180, and then add 2. **2.** 140 **3.** 102 **4.** 40
Lesson Check 1. 1620 **2.** 360 **3.** 144, 36 **4.** Yes; explanations may vary. Sample: rectangle that is not square **5.** ∠2 and ∠4; their measures are equal; answers may vary. Sample: Two ∠s suppl. to the same ∠ must be ≅. **6.** Answers may vary. Sample: ext. ∠ would measure 50, which is not a factor of 360.
Exercises 7. 900 **9.** 2160 **11.** 180,000 **13.** 150 **15.** 60, 120, 120, 60 **17.** 145 **19.** 10 **21.** 3.6 **23.** 8 **25.** 18 **27.** octagon; $m\angle 1 = 135$, $m\angle 2 = 45$ **29.** $y = 103$, $z = 70$ **31.** 36 **33.** 144; 10 **35.** 150; 12 **37.** 45, 45, 90 **39a.** $180n$ **b.** $(n - 2) \cdot 180$ **c.** $180n - [(n - 2) \cdot 180] = 360$ **d.** Polygon Ext. ∠ Sum Theorem **41.** octagon **49.** $\overline{CD}$; the longer side is opposite the larger ∠. **50.** Distr. Prop. **51.** Refl. Prop. of ≅ **52.** Sym. Prop. of ≅ **53.** ASA **54a.** ∠HGE **b.** ∠GHE **c.** ∠HEG **d.** $\overline{GH}$ **e.** $\overline{HE}$ **f.** $\overline{EG}$

Lesson 6-2 pp. 359–366

Got It? 1. 94
2. 1. ABCD is a ▱ and $\overline{AK} \cong \overline{MK}$. (Given)
2. ∠A ≅ ∠BCD (Opp. ∠s of a ▱ are ≅.)
3. ∠A ≅ ∠CMD (Isosc. △ Theorem)
4. ∠BCD ≅ ∠CMD (Transitive Prop. of ≅)

3a. $x = 4$, $y = 5$, $PR = 16$, $SQ = 10$ **b.** No; answers may vary. Sample: Solutions to a system of equations do not depend on the method used to solve it. **4.** 5
Lesson Check 1. 53 **2.** 127 **3.** 5 **4.** 7 **5.** $ED = 12$, $FD = 24$ **6.** Answers may vary. Sample: The ∠ opposite the given ∠ is congruent to it. The other two ∠s and the given ∠ are consecutive ∠s, so they are supplements of the given ∠. **7.** A quad. and a ▱ both have four sides, but if both pairs of opp. sides are ∥, then the figure is a ▱. **8.** It is not given that $\overleftrightarrow{PQ}$, $\overleftrightarrow{RS}$, and $\overleftrightarrow{TV}$ are ∥.
Exercises 9. 127 **11.** 100 **13a.** Def. of ▱ **b.** If lines are ∥, then alt. int. ∠s are ≅. **c.** Opp. sides of a ▱ are ≅. **d.** △ABE ≅ △CDE **e.** Corresp. parts of ≅ △s are ≅. **f.** $\overline{AC}$ and $\overline{BD}$ bisect each other at E. **15.** $x = 5$, $y = 7$ **17.** 3 **19.** 9 **21.** 2.25 **23.** 4.5 **25.** 20 **27.** $x = 12$, $y = 4$ **29.** 22, $AB = 23.6$, $BC = 18.5$, $CD = 23.6$, $AD = 18.5$ **31a.** 2.5 ft **b.** 129 **c.** Answers may vary. Sample: As $m\angle E$ increases, $m\angle D$ decreases. ∠E and ∠D are suppl.
33. Answers may vary. Sample:
1. ▱s LENS and NGTH (Given)
2. ∠L ≅ ∠ENS and ∠GNH ≅ ∠T. (Opp. ∠s of a ▱ are ≅.)
3. ∠ENS ≅ ∠GNH (Vert. ∠s are ≅.)
4. ∠L ≅ ∠T (Transitive Prop. of ≅)

35. Answers may vary. Sample:
1. ▱s LENS and NGTH (Given)
2. ∠E is suppl. to ∠ENS. (Consecutive ∠s in a ▱ are suppl.)
3. ∠GNH ≅ ∠ENS (Vert. ∠s are ≅.)
4. ∠GNH ≅ ∠T (Opp. ∠s of a ▱ are ≅.)
5. ∠ENS ≅ ∠T (Transitive Prop. of ≅)
6. ∠E is suppl. to ∠T. (Substitution Prop.)

37. 1. ▱s RSTW and XYTZ (Given)
2. $\overline{XY} \parallel \overline{TZ}$ and $\overline{TZ} \parallel \overline{RS}$. (Def. of ▱)
3. $\overline{XY} \parallel \overline{RS}$ (If two lines are ∥ to the same line, then they are ∥ to each other.)

39. $m\angle 1 = 71$, $m\angle 2 = 28$, $m\angle 3 = 81$

41. $AB = CD = 13$, $BC = AD = 33$ **49.** 1440 **50.** 2520 **51.** 4140 **52.** 6840 **53.** $\overline{AC} \perp \overline{DB}$ (or ∠ACD and ∠ACB are rt. ∠s) **54.** 42

Lesson 6-3 pp. 367–374

Got It? 1. $x = 10$, $y = 43$ **2a.** No; DEFG could be an isosc. trapezoid. (One pair of sides must be both ≅ and ∥.) **b.** yes
1. ∠ALN ≅ ∠DNL; ∠ANL ≅ ∠DLN (Given)
2. $\overline{AN} \parallel \overline{LD}$ and $\overline{AL} \parallel \overline{ND}$. (If alt. int. ∠s are ≅, then lines are ∥.)
3. LAND is a ▱. (Def. of ▱)

3. 6 ft; explanations may vary. Sample: The maximum height occurs when $\overline{QP}$ is vertical.
Lesson Check 1. 112 **2.** Yes; opp. ∠s are ≅. **3.** No; the diagonals may not bisect each other. **4.** because Thm. 6-3 and its converse are both true **5.** Thm. 6-11 and Thm. 6-6 are converses of each other. Use Thm. 6-11 if you need to show the figure is a ▱. Use Thm. 6-6 if it is given that the figure is a ▱. **6.** It is a ▱ only if the same pair of opp. sides are ≅ and ∥.
Exercises 7. 5 **9.** $x = 21$, $y = 39$ **11.** 5 **13.** Yes; both pairs of opp. sides are ≅. **15.** Yes; both pairs of opp. ∠s are ≅. **17.** A quad. is a ▱ if and only if its opp. sides are ≅; a quad. is a ▱ if and only if its consecutive ∠s are suppl.; a quad. is a ▱ if and only if its opp. ∠s are ≅; a quad. is a ▱ if and only if its diagonals bisect each other.
19. Answers may vary. Sample:
1. Draw $\overline{BD}$. (Construction)
2. ∠CBD ≅ ∠ADB (Alt. int. ∠s are ≅.)
3. $\overline{BC} \cong \overline{DA}$ (Given)
4. $\overline{BD} \cong \overline{BD}$ (Refl. Prop. of ≅)
5. △BCD ≅ △DAB (SAS)
6. ∠BDC ≅ ∠DBA (Corresp. parts of ≅ △s are ≅.)
7. $\overline{AB} \parallel \overline{CD}$ (If alt. int. ∠s are ≅, then lines are ∥.)
8. ABCD is a ▱. (Def. of ▱)

21. Answers may vary. Sample:
1. ∠A is suppl. to ∠B. (Given)
2. $\overline{BC} \parallel \overline{AD}$ (Converse of Corresp. ∠s Postulate)
3. ∠A is suppl. to ∠D. (Given)
4. $\overline{AB} \parallel \overline{DC}$ (Converse of Corresp. ∠s Postulate)
5. ABCD is a ▱. (Def. of ▱)

23. $x = 3$, $y = 11$
25. Answers may vary. Sample:
1. △TRS ≅ △RTW (Given)
2. $\overline{SR} \cong \overline{WT}$ and $\overline{ST} \cong \overline{WR}$. (Corresp. parts of ≅ △s are ≅.)
3. RSTW is a ▱. (If both pairs of opp. sides of a quad. are ≅, then the quad. is a ▱.)

32. $a = 8$, $h = 30$, $k = 120$ **33.** $m = 9.5$, $x = 15$ **34.** $c = 204$, $e = 13$, $f = 11$
35. 1. $\overline{AD} \cong \overline{BC}$, ∠DAB ≅ ∠CBA (Given)
2. $\overline{AB} \cong \overline{AB}$ (Refl. Prop. of ≅)
3. △ACB ≅ △BDA (SAS)
4. $\overline{AC} \cong \overline{BD}$ (Corresp. parts of ≅ △s are ≅.)

36. 7.47 **37.** 7.47 **38.** 7.47 **39.** 3.5 **40.** 13.2 **41.** 124 **42.** 56 **43.** 56 **44.** 28

Lesson 6-4 pp. 375–382

Got It? 1. Rhombus; opp. sides of a ▱ are ≅, so all sides of EFGH are ≅, and there are no rt. ∠s. **2.** $m\angle 1 = m\angle 2 = m\angle 3 = m\angle 4 = 38$ **3a.** 43 **b.** Isosc.; diagonals of a rectangle are ≅ and bisect each other.
Lesson Check 1. Square; it is a rectangle because of the rt. ∠, and a rhombus because it has 4 ≅ sides. **2.** Rhombus; it has 4 ≅ sides, and no rt. ∠s. **3.** $m\angle 1 = 40$, $m\angle 2 = 90$, $m\angle 3 = 50$ **4.** 4, 4 **5.** rectangle and square; rhombus and square **6.** The first step should be $2x + 8 + 9x - 6 = 90$.
Exercises 7. Rectangle; the ▱ has 4 rt. ∠s and does not have 4 ≅ sides. **9.** $m\angle 1 = m\angle 2 = m\angle 3 = m\angle 4 = 37$ **11.** $m\angle 1 = 118$, $m\angle 2 = m\angle 3 = 31$ **13.** $m\angle 1 = 32$, $m\angle 2 = 90$, $m\angle 3 = 58$, $m\angle 4 = 32$ **15.** $m\angle 1 = 55$, $m\angle 2 = 35$, $m\angle 3 = 55$, $m\angle 4 = 90$ **17.** $m\angle 1 = 90$, $m\angle 2 = 55$, $m\angle 3 = 90$ **19.** $x = 3$; $LN = MP = 7$ **21.** $x = 9$; $LN = MP = 67$ **23.** $x = 2.5$; $LN = MP = 12.5$ **25.** ▱ **27.** rectangle **29.** ▱, rhombus, rectangle, square **31.** ▱, rhombus, rectangle, square **33.** ▱, rhombus, rectangle, square **35.** rectangle, square **37.** rhombus, square **39.** $x = 5$, $y = 4$; all sides are 3. **41a.** Given **b.** Def. of rectangle **c.** Refl. Prop. of ≅ **d.** Def. of rectangle **e.** $\overline{AB} \cong \overline{DC}$ **f.** △ABC ≅ △DCB **g.** All rt. ∠s are ≅. **h.** Corresp. parts of ≅ △s are ≅. **43.** $x = 5$, $y = 32$, $z = 7.5$
45. Answers may vary. Sample:
1. ABCD is a rhombus. (Given)
2. $\overline{AB} \cong \overline{AD}$ and $\overline{CB} \cong \overline{CD}$. (Def. of rhombus)
3. $\overline{AC} \cong \overline{AC}$ (Refl. Prop. of ≅)
4. △ABC ≅ △ADC (SSS)
5. ∠3 ≅ ∠4 and ∠2 ≅ ∠1. (Corresp. parts of ≅ △s are ≅.)
6. $\overline{AC}$ bisects ∠BAD and ∠BCD. (Def. of ∠ bisector)

47. $m\angle H = m\angle J = 58$, $m\angle K = m\angle G = 122$, $HK = KJ = JG = GH = 6$ **49.** $AC = BD = 16$ **51.** $AC = BD = 1$ **59.** Yes; both pairs of opp. sides of the quad. are ≅. **60.** No; two opp. sides are ≅ and two opp. sides are ∥, but not the same pair of opp. sides. **61.** Yes; diagonals of the quad. bisect each other. **62.** 6 **63.** 16 **64.** 5 **65.** $\overline{RQ}$ **66.** $\overline{PR}$ **67.** $\overline{ST}$ **68.** Answers may vary. Sample: **69.** Answers may vary. Sample:

Lesson 6-5 pp. 383–388

Got It? 1a. The ▱ is not a rectangle or a square because ∠s are not rt. ∠s. It might be a rhombus. **b.** No; the fact that the diagonals bisect each other is true of all ▱s. **2.** 4 **3.** Yes; make diagonals ⊥. The result will be a rectangle and a rhombus, so it is square.
Lesson Check 1. Rectangle; diagonals are ≅. **2.** Rhombus; diagonals are ⊥. **3.** 2 **4.** 3 **5a.** rhombus, square **b.** rectangle, square **c.** rhombus, square **d.** rectangle, rhombus, square **e.** rhombus, square **6.** The only ▱s with ⊥ diagonals are rhombuses and squares. **7.** Rectangle; diagonals are ≅.
Exercises 9. Rhombus; diagonals are ⊥. **11.** 12 **13.** 10 **15.** Answers may vary. Sample: Measure the lengths of the frame's diagonals. If they are ≅, then the frame has the shape of a rectangle, and therefore a parallelogram; measure the two pairs of alt. int. ∠s formed by the turnbuckle (the transversal). If both pairs of ∠s are ≅, then both pairs of opposite sides of the frame are ∥. **17.** 11 **19.** 16
21. Rhombus; answers may vary. Sample:

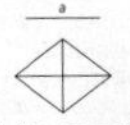

23. Answers may vary. Sample:
1. $\overline{AB}$ bisects ∠BAD and ∠BCD. (Given)
2. ∠1 ≅ ∠2 and ∠3 ≅ ∠4. (Def. of bisect)
3. $\overline{AC} \cong \overline{AC}$ (Refl. Prop. of ≅)
4. △ABC ≅ △ADC (ASA)
5. $\overline{AB} \cong \overline{AD}$ and $\overline{BC} \cong \overline{CD}$. (Corresp. parts of ≅ △s are ≅.)
6. $\overline{AB} \cong \overline{CD}$ and $\overline{BC} \cong \overline{AD}$. (Opp. sides of a ▱ are ≅.)
7. $\overline{AB} \cong \overline{AD} \cong \overline{BC} \cong \overline{CD}$ (Trans. Prop. of ≅)
8. ABCD is a rhombus. (Def. of rhombus)

25. Construct the midpt. of each diagonal. Copy the diagonals so the two midpts. coincide. Connect the endpoints of the diagonals. **27.** Construct the midpts. of each diagonal. Construct two ⊥ lines, and mark off diagonal lengths on the ⊥ lines. Connect the endpoints of the diagonals. **36.** $m\angle 1 = 128$, $m\angle 2 = 26$, $m\angle 3 = 26$ **37.** $m\angle 1 = 57$, $m\angle 2 = 57$, $m\angle 3 = 66$ **38.** $m\angle 1 = 90$, $m\angle 2 = 58$, $m\angle 3 = 90$ **39.** A ▱ is a rhombus if and only if its diagonals are ⊥. **40.** A ▱ is a rectangle if and only if its diagonals are ≅. **41.** $a = 5.6$, $b = 6.8$; 4.5, 4.5, 4.2, 4.2 **42.** 3; 18, 4.8, 18, 16.4 **43.** $m = 5$, $n = 15$; 15, 15, 21, 21

Lesson 6-6 pp. 389–397

Got It? 1a. $m\angle P = m\angle Q = 74$, $m\angle S = 106$ **b.** Yes; $\overline{DE} \parallel \overline{CF}$ so same-side int. ∠s are suppl. **2.** obtuse ∠ measure: 102; acute ∠ measure: 78 **3a.** 6; 23 **b.** 3; 1; A △ has 3 midsegments joining any pair of side midpts. A trapezoid has 1 midsegment joining the midpts. of the two legs. **4.** $m\angle 1 = 90$, $m\angle 2 = 54$, $m\angle 3 = 36$
Lesson Check 1. $m\angle 1 = 78$, $m\angle 2 = 90$, $m\angle 3 = 12$ **2.** $m\angle 1 = 94$, $m\angle 2 = 132$ **3.** 20 **4.** No; a kite's opp. sides are not ≅ or ∥. **5.** Answers may vary. Sample: Similar: diagonals are ⊥, consecutive sides ≅. Different: one diagonal of a kite bisects opp. ∠s but the other diagonal does not; all sides of a rhombus are ≅. **6.** Def. of trapezoid is a quad. with exactly one pair of ∥ sides. A ▱ has two pairs of ∥ sides, so a ▱ is not a trapezoid.
Exercises 7. $m\angle 1 = 77$, $m\angle 2 = 103$, $m\angle 3 = 103$ **9.** $m\angle 1 = 49$, $m\angle 2 = 131$, $m\angle 3 = 131$ **11.** $m\angle 1 = m\angle 2 = 115$, $m\angle 3 = 65$ **13.** 9 **15.** 9 **17.** $m\angle 1 = 90$, $m\angle 2 = 45$, $m\angle 3 = 45$ **19.** $m\angle 1 = 90$, $m\angle 2 = 26$, $m\angle 3 = 90$ **21.** $m\angle 1 = 90$, $m\angle 2 = 55$, $m\angle 3 = 90$, $m\angle 4 = 55$, $m\angle 5 = 35$ **23.** $m\angle 1 = 90$, $m\angle 2 = 90$, $m\angle 3 = 90$, $m\angle 4 = 90$, $m\angle 5 = 46$, $m\angle 6 = 34$, $m\angle 7 = 56$, $m\angle 8 = 44$, $m\angle 9 = 56$, $m\angle 10 = 44$
25. Answers may vary. Sample:

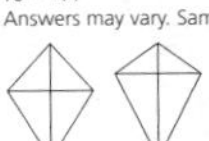

27. No; explanations may vary. Sample: Assume $\overline{KM}$ bisects both ∠s. Then ∠MKL ≅ ∠MKN ≅ ∠KML ≅ ∠KMN. Both pairs of sides of KLMN would be ∥, and KLMN would be a ▱. It is impossible for an isosc. trap. to also be a ▱, so $\overline{KM}$ cannot bis. ∠LMN and ∠LKN. **29.** 15 **31.** $AD = 4$, $EF = 9$, $BC = 14$ **33.** $HG = 2$, $CD = 5$, $EF = 8$ **35.** $x = 35$, $y = 30$ **37.** Isosc. trapezoid; $\overline{AB} \parallel \overline{DC}$ (If alt. int. ∠s are ≅, then lines are ∥) and $\overline{AD} \cong \overline{BC}$. (Corresp. parts of ≅ △s are ≅.) **39.** Yes; the ≅ ∠s can be obtuse. **41.** Yes; if two ≅ ∠s are rt. ∠s, they are suppl. The other two ∠s are also suppl. **43.** Yes; the ≅ ∠s each have measure 45.
45. Answers may vary. Sample:
1. Draw $\overline{AE} \parallel \overline{DC}$. (Construction)
2. AECD is a ▱. (Def. of ▱)
3. $\overline{AE} \cong \overline{DC}$ (Opp. sides of a ▱ are ≅.)
4. ∠1 ≅ ∠C (If ∥ lines, corresp. ∠s are ≅.)
5. ∠B ≅ ∠1 (Isosc. △ Thm.)
6. ∠B ≅ ∠C (Transitive Prop. of ≅)
7. ∠D and ∠C are suppl. (If ∥ lines, same-side int. ∠s are suppl.)
8. ∠BAD and ∠B are suppl. (If ∥ lines, same-side int. ∠s are suppl.)
9. ∠BAD ≅ ∠D (∠s suppl. to ≅ ∠s are ≅.)

47. Isosc. trapezoid; answers may vary. Sample:
49. Rectangle, square; answers may vary. Sample:
51. Kite, rhombus, square; answers may vary. Sample:
53. Answers may vary. Sample:
1. $\overline{AB} \cong \overline{DC}$ (Given)
2. ∠BAD ≅ ∠CDA (Base ∠s of an isosc. trapezoid are ≅.)
3. $\overline{AD} \cong \overline{AD}$ (Refl. Prop. of ≅)
4. △BAD ≅ △CDA (SAS)
5. $\overline{BD} \cong \overline{CA}$ (Corresp. parts of ≅ △s are ≅.)

55. Answers may vary. Sample:
1. Draw $\overline{TA}$ and $\overline{PR}$. (Construction)
2. $\overline{TR} \cong \overline{PA}$ (Given)
3. ∠TRA ≅ ∠PAR (Base ∠s of an isosc. trapezoid are ≅.)
4. $\overline{RA} \cong \overline{RA}$ (Refl. Prop. of ≅)
5. △TRA ≅ △PAR (SAS)
6. ∠RTA ≅ ∠APR (Corresp. parts of ≅ △s are ≅.)

57. True; a square is a ▱ with 4 rt. ∠s. **59.** False; a rhombus has 4 ≅ sides, and a kite does not. **61.** False; counterexample: kites and trapezoids are not ▱s. **71.** 61 **72.** 27 **73.** 12 **74.** 89 **75.** (1, 3); $\sqrt{200}$ or $10\sqrt{2}$ **76.** $-\frac{1}{4}$

Algebra Review p. 399

1. $5\sqrt{2}$ **3.** 8 **5.** $4\sqrt{3}$ **7.** $6\sqrt{2}$ **9.** 6 **11.** $7\sqrt{2}$ **13.** $2\sqrt{6}$ **15.** $\frac{3\sqrt{10}}{2}$

Lesson 6-7 pp. 400–405

Got It? 1. scalene **2a.** Yes; slope of $\overline{MN}$ = slope of $\overline{PQ} = -3$ and slope of $\overline{NP}$ = slope of $\overline{MQ} = \frac{1}{3}$, so opp. sides are ∥. The product of slopes is -1, so sides are ⊥. **b.** Yes; $MN = PQ = NP = MQ = \sqrt{10}$. **c.** Yes; slope of $\overline{AB} = \frac{3}{4}$ and slope of $\overline{BC} = -\frac{4}{3}$, so the product of their slopes is -1. Therefore, $\overline{AB} \perp \overline{BC}$ and ∠B is a rt. ∠. So △ABC is a rt. △ by def. of rt. △. **3.** rhombus (The length of each side is $\sqrt{13}$.)
Lesson Check 1. isosceles **2.** No; explanations may vary. Sample: The diagonal lengths ($\sqrt{29}$ and 5) are not equal. **3.** Find the coordinates and use the Distance Formula to compare lengths. **4.** Answers may vary. Sample: DEFG is not a ▱.
Exercises 5. Scalene; side lengths are 4, 5, and $\sqrt{17}$. **7.** Isosceles; side lengths are $2\sqrt{2}$, $\sqrt{34}$, and $\sqrt{34}$. **9.** Rhombus; explanations may vary. Sample: All four sides are ≅ (with length $\sqrt{5}$), and diagonals are not ≅ (with lengths 2 and 4). **11.** None; explanations may vary. Sample: Consecutive sides are not ≅ or ⊥. **13.** Rhombus; explanations may vary. Sample: All sides are ≅ and consecutive sides are not ⊥. **15.** rhombus
17. scalene; not rt. △
19. scalene; not a rt. △
21. isosc. trapezoid
23. kite
25. rhombus

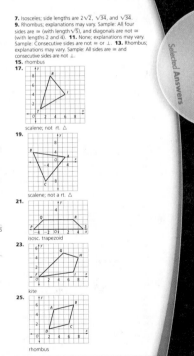

Selected Answers

27.

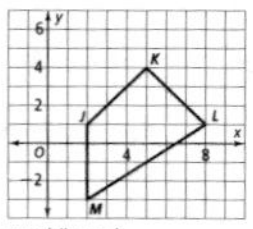

quadrilateral

29.

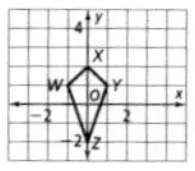

kite

31. Yes; $PR = SW = 4$, $PQ = ST = \sqrt{10}$, $QR = TW = 3\sqrt{2}$, so $\triangle PQR \cong \triangle STW$ by SSS. **33.** ▱; 24 units² **35.** slope of $\overline{DE} = 2$; slope of $\overline{AB} = 2$; $DE = \frac{1}{2}\sqrt{5}$; $AB = \sqrt{5}$. So $\overline{DE} \parallel \overline{AB}$ and $DE = \frac{1}{2}AB$. **37.** Answers may vary. Sample: Chairs are not at vertices of a ▱. Move right-most chair down by 1 grid unit. **49.** $m\angle 1 = 62$, $m\angle 2 = m\angle 3 = 118$, $x = 2.5$ **50.** (3, 2) **51.** (−3, −4) **52.** −1 **53.** 0 **54.** $\frac{b}{c + d - a}$

Lesson 6-8 pp. 406–412

Got It? 1a. $R(-b, 0)$, $E(-b, a)$, $C(b, a)$, $T(b, 0)$ **b.** $K(-b, 0)$, $I(0, a)$, $T(c, 0)$, $E(0, -a)$ **2a.** Answers may vary. Sample: x-coordinate of B is $2a$ more than x-coordinate of C. **b.** yes; $TR = AP = \sqrt{a^2 - 2ab + b^2 + c^2}$

3.

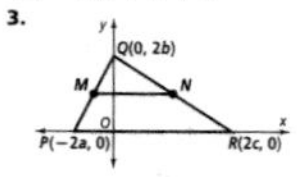

Given: $\triangle PQR$, midpoints M and N
Prove: $\overline{MN} \parallel \overline{PR}$ and $MN = \frac{1}{2}PR$

- First, use the Midpoint Formula to find the coordinates of M and N.
- Then, use the Slope Formula to determine whether the slopes of $\overline{MN}$ and $\overline{PR}$ are equal. If they are, then $\overline{MN} \parallel \overline{PR}$.
- Finally, use the Distance Formula to find and compare the lengths of $\overline{MN}$ and $\overline{PR}$.

Lesson Check 1. $K(2b, c)$, $M(2a, 0)$ **2.** The slope of $\overline{KM}$ is $\frac{c}{2b - 2a}$, and the slope of $\overline{OL}$ is $\frac{c}{2a + 2b}$. **3.** $\left(a + b, \frac{c}{2}\right)$ **4.** Answers may vary. Sample: Using variables allows the figure to represent all possibilities. **5.** rectangle **6.** Answers may vary. Sample: Classmate ignored the coefficient 2 in the coordinates. The endpoints are (b, c) and $(a + d, c)$.
Exercises 7. $O(0, 0)$, $S(0, h)$, $T(b, h)$, $W(b, 0)$ **9.** $S\left(-\frac{b}{2}, -\frac{b}{2}\right)$, $T\left(-\frac{b}{2}, \frac{b}{2}\right)$, $W\left(\frac{b}{2}, \frac{b}{2}\right)$, $Z\left(\frac{b}{2}, -\frac{b}{2}\right)$ **11.** $W(r, 0)$, $T(0, t)$, $S(-r, 0)$, $Z(0, -t)$ **13.** Yes, $ABCD$ is a rhombus. The slope of $\overline{AC} = -1$, and the slope of $\overline{BD} = 1$, so the diagonals are ⊥.
15. Answers may vary. Sample:

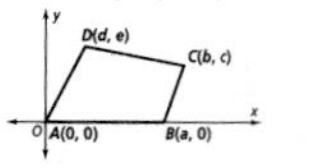

17. $P(c - a, b)$ **19.** $P(-b, 0)$
21a. Answers may vary. Sample:

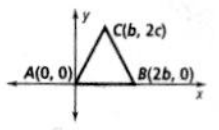

b. Answers may vary. Sample:

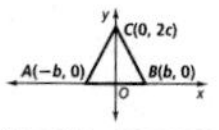

c. $\sqrt{b^2 + 4c^2}$, $\sqrt{b^2 + 4c^2}$ **d.** $\sqrt{b^2 + 4c^2}$, $\sqrt{b^2 + 4c^2}$ **e.** The results are the same. **23.** Answers may vary. Sample: Place vertices at $A(0, 0)$, $B(a, 0)$, $C(a + b, 0)$, and $D(b, c)$. Use the Distance Formula to find the lengths of opp. sides. **25.** Answers may vary. Sample: Place vertices at $A(0, 0)$, $B(0, a)$, $C(a, a)$, and $D(a, 0)$. Use the fact that a horizontal line is ⊥ to a vertical line. **27.** isosc. trapezoid **29.** square
31. Answers may vary. Sample:

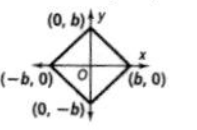

42. No; product of slopes is not −1, so there are no rt. ∠s. **43a.** If $x \neq 51$, then $2x \neq 102$. **b.** If $2x \neq 102$, then $x \neq 51$. **44a.** If $a \neq 5$, then $a^2 \neq 25$. **b.** If $a^2 \neq 25$, then $a \neq 5$. **45a.** If b not less than −4, then b is not negative. **b.** If b is not negative, then b is not less than −4. **46a.** If c is not greater than 0, then c is not positive. **b.** If c is not positive, then c is not greater than 0. **47a.** If the sum of the measures of the interior ∠s of a polygon is 360, then the polygon is a quadrilateral. **b.** If a polygon is a quadrilateral, then the sum of the measures

of the interior ∠s of the polygon is 360. **48.** $y = \frac{5}{4}x$ **49.** $y - q = \frac{a}{b}(x - p)$

Lesson 6-9 pp. 414–418

Got It? 1. The factor 2 avoids fractions.
2. Answers may vary. Sample:

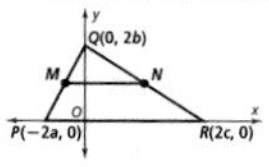

Given: $\triangle PQR$, midpoints M and N
Prove: $\overline{MN} \parallel \overline{PR}$, $MN = \frac{1}{2}PR$
By the Midpoint Formula, coordinates of the midpoints are $M(-a, b)$ and $N(c, b)$. By the Slope Formula, slope of $\overline{MN}$ = slope of $\overline{PR} = 0$, so $\overline{MN} \parallel \overline{PR}$. By the Distance Formula, $MN = \sqrt{(c + a)^2}$ and $PR = 2\sqrt{(c + a)^2}$, so $MN = \frac{1}{2}PR$.
Lesson Check
1a.

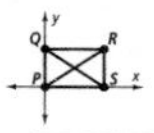

b. $(0, b)$, (a, b), and $(a, 0)$ **c.** Given: Rectangle $PQRS$ Prove: $\overline{PR} \cong \overline{SQ}$ **d.** Answers may vary. Sample: By the Distance Formula, $PR = \sqrt{(0 - a)^2 + (0 - b)^2} = \sqrt{a^2 + b^2}$ and $SQ = \sqrt{(0 - a)^2 + (b - 0)^2} = \sqrt{a^2 + b^2}$. So $\overline{PR} \cong \overline{SQ}$.
2. Answers may vary. Sample: Place the vertices on the x- and y-axes so that the axes are the diagonals of the rhombus. **3.** Your classmate assumes $PQRO$ is an isosc. trapezoid.
Exercises 5a. $M(-a, b)$, $N(a, b)$ **b.** $PN = \sqrt{9a^2 + b^2}$, $RM = \sqrt{9a^2 + b^2}$ **c.** The Distance Formula shows that $\overline{PN}$ and $\overline{RM}$ are the same length. **7.** Yes; use Slope Formula. **9.** Yes; use Midpoint Formula. **11.** No; you need ∠ measures. **13.** Yes; use Distance Formula. **15.** Yes; answers may vary. Sample: Show four sides have the same length or show diagonals ⊥. **17.** No; you need ∠ measures.
19. Answers may vary. Sample:

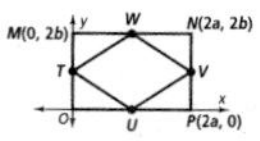

Given: $MNPO$ is a rectangle.
T, W, V, U are midpoints of its sides.
Prove: $TWVU$ is a rhombus.
By the Midpoint Formula, the coordinates of the midpoints are $T(0, b)$, $W(a, 2b)$, $V(2a, b)$, and $U(a, 0)$.
By the Slope Formula,

$$\text{slope of } \overline{TW} = \frac{2b - b}{a - 0} = \frac{b}{a}$$
$$\text{slope of } \overline{WV} = \frac{2b - b}{a - 2a} = -\frac{b}{a}$$
$$\text{slope of } \overline{VU} = \frac{b - 0}{2a - a} = \frac{b}{a}$$
$$\text{slope of } \overline{UT} = \frac{b - 0}{0 - a} = -\frac{b}{a}$$

So $\overline{TW} \parallel \overline{VU}$ and $\overline{WV} \parallel \overline{UT}$. Therefore, $TWVU$ is a ▱. By the Slope Formula, slope of $\overline{TV} = 0$, and slope of $\overline{WU}$ is undefined. $\overline{TV} \perp \overline{WU}$ because horiz. and vert. lines are ⊥. Since the diagonals of ▱$TWVU$ are ⊥, it must be a rhombus.
21. Answers may vary. Sample:

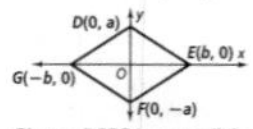

Given: $DEFG$ is a parallelogram.
Prove: $\overline{GE} \perp \overline{DF}$
By the Slope Formula, slope of $\overline{GE} = \frac{0 - 0}{b - (-b)} = 0$, and slope of $\overline{DF} = \frac{a - (-a)}{0 - 0}$, which is undefined. So $\overline{GE}$ must be horizontal and $\overline{DF}$ must be vertical. Therefore, $\overline{GE} \perp \overline{DF}$ because horiz. and vert. lines are ⊥.
23. Answers may vary. Sample:

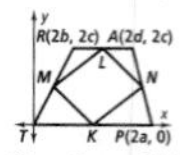

Given: Trapezoid $TRAP$, M, L, N, and K are midpoints of its sides
Prove: $MLNK$ is a ▱.
By the Midpoint Formula, the coordinates of the midpoints are $M(b, c)$, $L(b + d, 2c)$, $N(a + d, c)$, and $K(a, 0)$. By the Slope Formula, the slope of $\overline{ML} = \frac{c}{d}$, the slope of $\overline{LN} = \frac{c}{b - a}$, the slope of $\overline{NK} = \frac{c}{d}$, and the slope of $\overline{KM} = \frac{c}{b - a}$. Since slopes are =, $\overline{ML} \parallel \overline{NK}$ and $\overline{LN} \parallel \overline{KM}$. Therefore, $MLNK$ is a ▱ by def. of ▱.
25a. $L(3q, 3r)$, $M(3p + 3q, 3r)$, $N(3p, 0)$
b. equation of $\overleftrightarrow{AM}$: $y = \frac{r}{p + q}x$
equation of $\overleftrightarrow{BN}$: $y = \frac{2r}{2q - p}(x - 3p)$
equation of $\overleftrightarrow{CL}$: $y = \frac{r}{q - 2p}(x - 6p)$
c. $P(2p + 2q, 2r)$
d. The coordinates of P satisfy the equation for

$\overleftrightarrow{CL}$: $y = \frac{r}{q - 2p}(x - 6p)$.
$2r = \frac{r}{q - 2p}(2p + 2q - 6p)$
$2r = \frac{r}{q - 2p}(2q - 4p)$
$2r = 2r$
e. $AM = \sqrt{(3p + 3q - 0)^2 + (3r - 0)^2} = \sqrt{(3p + 3q)^2 + (3r)^2}$;
$\frac{2}{3}AM = \frac{2}{3}\sqrt{(3p + 3q)^2 + (3r)^2} = \sqrt{\frac{4}{9}\left[(3p + 3q)^2 + (3r)^2\right]} = \sqrt{\left[\frac{2}{3}(3p + 3q)^2\right] + \left[\frac{2}{3}(3r)^2\right]} = \sqrt{(2p + 2q)^2 + (2r)^2}$;
$AP = \sqrt{(2p + 2q - 0)^2 + (2r - 0)^2} = \sqrt{(2p + 2q)^2 + (2r)^2}$
So $AP = \frac{2}{3}AM$. You can find the other two distances similarly.
33. $(a, -b)$ **34.** Answers may vary. Sample: $\angle A \cong \angle C$, $\angle ADB \cong \angle CDB$, and $\overline{AD} \cong \overline{CD}$ (Given), so $\triangle ABD \cong \triangle CBD$ by ASA. Then $\overline{AB} \cong \overline{CB}$ because corresp. parts of ≅ ▵ are ≅. **35.** Answers may vary. Sample: $\overline{HE} \cong \overline{FG}$, $\overline{EF} \cong \overline{GH}$, (Given) and $\overline{HF} \cong \overline{HF}$ (Reflexive Prop. of ≅), so $\triangle HEF \cong \triangle FGH$ by SSS. Then $\angle 1 \cong \angle 2$ because corresp. parts of ≅ ▵ are ≅. **36.** $\overline{KN} \cong \overline{ML}$ (Given), $\angle KNL \cong \angle MLN$ (All rt. ∠s are ≅.), and $\overline{NL} \cong \overline{NL}$ (Reflexive Prop. of ≅). Then $\triangle KNL \cong \triangle MLN$ by SAS, and $\angle K \cong \angle M$ because corresp. parts of ≅ ▵ are ≅. **37.** 12, −12 **38.** 8, −8 **39.** 5, −5 **40.** 16.6, −16.6

Chapter Review pp. 420–424

1. rhombus **2.** equiangular polygon **3.** consecutive angles **4.** trapezoid **5.** 120, 60 **6.** 157.5, 22.5 **7.** 108, 72 **8.** 360, 360, 360 **9.** 159 **10.** 69 **11.** $m\angle 1 = 38$, $m\angle 2 = 43$, $m\angle 3 = 99$ **12.** $m\angle 1 = 101$, $m\angle 2 = 79$, $m\angle 3 = 101$ **13.** $m\angle 1 = 37$, $m\angle 2 = 26$, $m\angle 3 = 26$ **14.** $m\angle 1 = 45$, $m\angle 2 = 45$, $m\angle 3 = 45$ **15.** $x = 3$, $y = 7$ **16.** $x = 2$, $y = 5$ **17.** no **18.** yes **19.** $x = 29$, $y = 28$ **20.** $x = 4$, $y = 5$ **21.** $m\angle 1 = 58$, $m\angle 2 = 32$, $m\angle 3 = 90$ **22.** $m\angle 1 = 124$, $m\angle 2 = 28$, $m\angle 3 = 62$ **23.** sometimes **24.** always **25.** sometimes **26.** sometimes **27.** sometimes **28.** always **29.** No; two sides are ∥ in all ▱s. **30.** Yes; the ▱ is a rhombus and a rectangle so it must be a square. **31.** $x = 18$; a diagonal bisects a pair of ∠s in a rhombus. **32.** $x = 4$; a rectangle has ≅ diagonals that bisect each other. **33.** $m\angle 1 = 135$, $m\angle 2 = 135$, $m\angle 3 = 45$ **34.** $m\angle 1 = 80$, $m\angle 2 = 100$, $m\angle 3 = 100$ **35.** $m\angle 1 = 90$, $m\angle 2 = 25$ **36.** $m\angle 1 = 52$, $m\angle 2 = 52$ **37.** 2 **38.** scalene **39.** isosceles **40.** parallelogram **41.** kite **42.** rhombus **43.** isosc. trapezoid **44.** $F(0, 2b)$, $L(a, 0)$, $P(0, -2b)$, $S(-a, 0)$ **45.** $(a - b, c)$
46. Answers may vary. Sample:

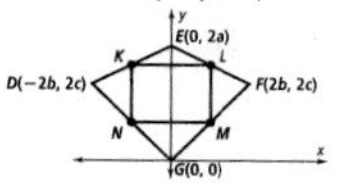

Given: Kite $DEFG$, K, L, M, N are midpoints of sides
Prove: $KLMN$ is a rectangle.
By the Midpoint Formula, coordinates of midpoints are $K(-b, a + c)$, $L(b, a + c)$, $M(b, c)$, and $N(-b, c)$. By the Slope Formula, slope of $\overline{KL}$ = slope of $\overline{NM} = 0$, and slope of $\overline{KN}$ and slope of $\overline{LM}$ are undefined. $\overline{KL} \parallel \overline{NM}$ and $\overline{KN} \parallel \overline{LM}$ so $KLMN$ is a ▱. $\overline{KL} \perp \overline{LM}$, $\overline{LM} \perp \overline{NM}$, $\overline{KN} \perp \overline{NM}$, and $\overline{KN} \perp \overline{KL}$ so $KLMN$ is a rectangle.

Chapter 7

Get Ready! p. 429

1. 70; if lines are ∥, same-side int. ∠s are suppl. **2.** 110; if lines are ∥, corresponding ∠s are ≅. **3.** 70; adjacent angles forming a straight ∠ are suppl.
4. 70; it is a vert. ∠ with ∠1; vert. ∠s are ≅. **5.** $\overline{DL}$ **6.** ∠A **7.** ∠DLH **8.** △APC **9.** $\triangle KNP \cong \triangle LNM$ by SAS. **10.** $\triangle BAC \cong \triangle BED$ by AAS. **11.** $\triangle UGH \cong \triangle UGB$ by SSS. **12.** 6, 6 **13.** 4.7, 9.4 **14.** Answers may vary. Sample: The relative sizes of the body parts in the drawing are the same as those of a real person. **15.** Answers may vary. Sample: They might be similar if they have the same shape. **16.** Answers may vary. Sample: Measure the number of inches on the map between the two cities, and multiply that number of inches by the number of miles represented by 1 in.

Lesson 7-1 pp. 432–438

Got It? 1. 3 : 4 **2.** 36, 144 **3.** 12 cm, 21 cm, 27 cm **4a.** 63 **b.** 0.25 **5a.** $\frac{7}{y}$; Prop. of Proportions (1) **b.** $\frac{x + 6}{6}$; Prop. of Proportions (3) **c.** The proportion is equivalent to $\frac{x - 6}{6} = \frac{y - 7}{7}$ by Prop. of Proportions (1). Then by Prop. of Proportions (3), $\frac{x - 6 + 6}{6} = \frac{x - 7 + 7}{7}$, which simplifies to $\frac{x}{6} = \frac{y}{7}$.

Lesson Check 1. 23 : 42 **2.** $5x$, $9x$ **3.** 12 **4a.** $\frac{a}{13} = \frac{7}{b}$ **b.** $\frac{a - 7}{7} = \frac{13 - b}{b}$ **c.** $\frac{7}{a} = \frac{b}{13}$ **5.** A ratio is a single comparison, while a proportion is a statement that two ratios are equal. **6.** Answers may vary. Sample: 3 in., 6 in., 7 in.; or 6 in., 12 in., 14 in. **7.** The second line should equate the product of the means and the product of the extremes: $7x = 12$. Then the third line would be $x = \frac{12}{7}$. **8.** $\frac{9}{6} = \frac{18}{12}$, $\frac{9}{18} = \frac{6}{12}$, $\frac{12}{6} = \frac{18}{9}$, or $\frac{12}{18} = \frac{6}{9}$
Exercises 9. $\frac{14}{5}$ or 14 : 5 **11.** $\frac{10}{17}$ or 10 : 17 **13.** won 110, lost 44 **15.** 24 cm, 28 cm, 36 cm **17.** 4 **19.** $\frac{36}{5}$ **21.** 32 **23.** 7 **25.** 6 **27.** $\frac{4}{3}$; Prop. of Proportions (1) **29.** $\frac{a}{3}$; Prop. of Proportions (2) **31.** $\frac{7}{4}$; Prop. of Proportions (3) **33.** 1 **35.** 4 **37.** length: 15 in.; width: 10 in. **39a.** 12 in. **b.** 1.5 in. **41.** 1.5 **43.** 0.2
45.

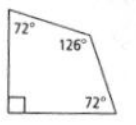

47. The product of the means is $26 \cdot 16 = 416$, and the product of the extremes is $10 \cdot 42 = 420$. Since $416 \neq 420$, it is not a valid proportion. **49.** $\frac{9}{4}$; divide each side by $4n$. **51.** $\frac{b}{2}$; Prop. of Proportions (3) **53.** $\frac{c}{d}$; Prop. of Proportions (2), then (3), then (2) **66.** Use the coordinates $A(0, 0)$, $B(a, 0)$, $C(a, a)$, and $D(0, a)$ for square $ABCD$. The slope of diagonal $\overline{AC}$ is $\frac{a}{a} = 1$ and the slope of diagonal $\overline{BD}$ is $\frac{a}{-a} = -1$. The slopes are negative reciprocals, so $\overline{AC} \perp \overline{BD}$. **67.** I and III **68.** II and III **69.** $\angle A \cong \angle H$, $\angle B \cong \angle I$, $\angle C \cong \angle J$, $\overline{AB} \cong \overline{HI}$, $\overline{BC} \cong \overline{IJ}$, $\overline{AC} \cong \overline{HJ}$

Algebra Review p. 439

1. −7, 2 **3.** −3, $-\frac{1}{2}$ **5.** $\frac{5 + \sqrt{3}}{2}$, $\frac{5 - \sqrt{3}}{2}$; 3.37, 1.63 **7.** −4, $\frac{5}{2}$ **9.** 0, 4 **11.** $\frac{-5 + \sqrt{55}}{6}$, $\frac{-5 - \sqrt{55}}{6}$; 0.40, −2.07

Lesson 7-2 pp. 440–447

Got It? 1a. $\angle D \cong \angle H$, $\angle E \cong \angle J$, $\angle F \cong \angle K$, $\angle G \cong \angle L$ **b.** $\frac{DE}{HJ} = \frac{EF}{JK} = \frac{FG}{KL} = \frac{GD}{LH}$ **2a.** not similar **b.** $ABCDE \sim SRVUT$ or $ABCDE \sim UVRST$; 2 : 1 **3.** $\frac{10}{3}$ **4.** 28.8 in. high by 48 in. wide **5a.** Using 0.8 cm as the height of the towers, then $\frac{1}{200} = \frac{0.8}{h}$ and $h = 160$ m. **b.** No; using a scale of 1 in. = 50 ft, the paper must be more than 12 in. long.
Lesson Check 1. ∠H **2.** JT **3.** yes; $DEGH \sim PLQR$; 3 : 2 **4.** 6 **5.** Answers may vary. Sample: The scale indicates how many units of length of the actual object are represented by each unit of length in the drawing.
6. A is incorrect. Sample explanation: In the diagram, ∠T corresp. to ∠P (or to ∠U), but in the similarity statement $TRUV \sim NPQV$, ∠T corresp. to ∠N. **7.** Every figure is ~ to itself, so similarity is reflexive. If figure 1 ~ figure 2 and figure 2 ~ figure 3, then figure 1 ~ figure 3, so similarity is transitive. If figure 1 ~ figure 2, then figure 2 ~ figure 1, so the similarity is symmetric. **8.** any three of the following: $\triangle ABS \sim \triangle PRS$, $\triangle ASB \sim \triangle PSR$, $\triangle SAB \sim \triangle SPR$, $\triangle SBA \sim \triangle SRP$, $\triangle BAS \sim \triangle RPS$, $\triangle BSA \sim \triangle RSP$
Exercises 9. $\angle R \cong \angle D$, $\angle S \cong \angle E$, $\angle T \cong \angle F$, $\angle V \cong \angle G$; $\frac{RS}{DE} = \frac{ST}{EF} = \frac{TV}{FG} = \frac{VR}{GD}$
11. $\angle K \cong \angle H$, $\angle L \cong \angle G$, $\angle M \cong \angle F$, $\angle N \cong \angle D$, $\angle P \cong \angle C$; $\frac{KL}{HG} = \frac{LM}{GF} = \frac{MN}{FD} = \frac{NP}{DC} = \frac{PK}{CH}$
13. $ABDC \sim FEDG$ (or $ABDC \sim FGDE$, $ABDC \sim DEFG$, $ABDC \sim DGFE$); scale factor is 2 : 3. **15.** Not similar; sample explanation: The ratio of the longer sides is $\frac{12}{9}$ or $\frac{4}{3}$, and the ratio of the shorter sides is $\frac{10}{8}$ or $\frac{5}{4}$. Since $\frac{4}{3} \neq \frac{5}{4}$, the corresp. sides are not proportional and the figures are not ~. **17.** Not similar; sample explanation: The ∠ measures are not the same. **19.** $x = 8$, $y = 9$, $z = 5.25$ **21.** 120 pixels wide by 90 pixels high **23.** 5 in. **25.** 3 : 5 **27.** 5 : 3 **29.** 25 **31a.** The slope of $\overline{AB}$, $\overline{CD}$, $\overline{AE}$, and $\overline{FG}$ is −2. The slope of $\overline{BC}$, $\overline{AD}$, $\overline{EF}$, and $\overline{AG}$ is $\frac{1}{2}$. For each pair of consecutive sides of $ABCD$, the slopes are negative reciprocals, so $ABCD$ has four rt. ∠s. Similarly, $AEFG$ has four rt. ∠s. The measure of ∠A, ∠ABC, ∠BCD, ∠CDA, ∠E, ∠F, and ∠G, is 90. **b.** By the Distance Formula, $AB = BC = CD = AD = \sqrt{5}$ and $AE = EF = FG = AG = 2\sqrt{5}$. **c.** All the angles of $AEFG$ and $ABCD$ are ≅. $\frac{AB}{AE} = \frac{BC}{EF} = \frac{CD}{FG} = \frac{AD}{AG} = \frac{\sqrt{5}}{2\sqrt{5}} = \frac{1}{2}$ The corresp. sides are proportional, so $AEFG \sim ABCD$. **33.** No; for polygons with more than 3 sides, you also need to know that corresp. ∠s are ≅ in order to state that the polygons are ~. **35.** 1 : 3 **37.** $x = 10$; 2 : 1 **43.** always **45.** sometimes **47.** 21 ft by 40 ft **55.** $7y$ **56.** $\frac{7}{9}$ **57.** $\frac{y + 9}{9}$ **58.** △BDC, △AEC, △FED **59.** $\overline{BD}$, $\overline{AF}$ **60.** 8 **61.** 69 **62.** SSS **63.** SAS **64.** ASA

Lesson 7-3 pp. 450–458

Got It? 1a. The measures of the two acute ∠s in each △ are 39 and 51, so the ▵ are ~ by the AA ~ Post. **b.** Each of the base ∠s in the △ at the left measures 68, while each of the base ∠s in the △ at the right measures $\frac{1}{2}(180 - 62) = 59$; the ▵ are not ~. **2a.** The ratio for each of the three pairs of corresp. sides is 3 : 4, so $\triangle ABC \sim \triangle EFG$ by SSS ~. **b.** ∠A is in each △ and $\frac{AL}{AC} = \frac{AW}{AE} = \frac{1}{2}$, so $\triangle ALW \sim \triangle ACE$ by SAS ~.
3a. $\overline{MP} \parallel \overline{AC}$ (given), so $\angle A \cong \angle P$ and $\angle C \cong \angle M$ because if two lines are ∥, then alt. int. ∠s are ≅. So $\triangle ABC \sim \triangle PBM$ by AA ~. **b.** No; the ≅ vertical angles are not included by the proportional sides, so it is not possible to prove that the triangles are similar. **4.** The triangles formed will not be similar unless both Darius and the cliff form right angles with the ground.

Lesson Check 1. Yes; $m\angle R = 180 - (35 + 45) = 100$, and $\angle AEZ \cong \angle REB$ (Vert. ∡ are ≅.), so $\triangle AEZ \sim \triangle REB$ by AA~. **2.** Yes; the ratios of corresp. sides are all 2 : 3, so $\triangle ABC \sim \triangle FED$ by SSS~. **3.** Yes; $\angle G \cong \angle E$ and $\frac{UG}{FE} = \frac{AG}{BE} = \frac{4}{5}$, so $\triangle GUA \sim \triangle EFB$ by SAS ~. **4.** Answers may vary. Sample: Measure your shadow and the flagpole's shadow. Use the proportion $\frac{\text{your shadow}}{\text{flagpole's shadow}} = \frac{\text{your height}}{\text{flagpole's height}}$
5. Method A is not correct because the ratio, $\frac{4}{8}$ does not use corresp. sides. **6a.** Answers may vary. Sample: Both use two pairs of corresp. sides and the ∡ included by those sides, but SAS~ uses pairs of equal ratios, while SAS ≅ uses pairs of ≅ sides. **b.** Both involve all three sides of a △, but corresp. sides are proportional for SSS ~ and ≅ for SSS ≅.
Exercises 7. $\triangle FGH \sim \triangle KJH$; AA~ **9.** $\triangle RST \sim \triangle PSQ$; SAS~ **11.** Not ~; $m\angle U = 180 - (25 + 35) = 120$, while $m\angle A = 110$. **13.** $\angle A \cong \angle A$ (Refl. Prop. of ≅) and $\angle ABC \cong \angle ACD$ (given), so $\triangle ABC \sim \triangle ACD$ by AA~. **15.** There are a pair of ≅ vert. ∡ and a pair of ≅ rt. ∡, so the ▲ are ~ by AA~; 180 ft **17.** about 169.2 m **19.** $\triangle LMN \sim \triangle SMT$ by AA~. **21a.** No; the ratios of the sides that form the vertex ∡ are =, but the vertex ∡ may not be ≅. **b.** Yes; sample explanation: An isosc. rt. △ has two ∡ 45°, so any two isosc. rt. ▲ are ~ by AA~. **23.** 180 ft **25.** 20 **27.** In $\triangle PQR$ and $\triangle STV$, $\angle Q \cong \angle T$ because ⊥ lines form rt. ∡, which are ≅. The sides that contain the ∡ are proportional (given). So $\triangle PQR \sim \triangle STV$ by SAS~, and $\angle KRV \cong \angle KVR$ because corresp. ∡ of ~ ▲ are ≅. Thus $\triangle VKR$ is isosc. by the Converse of Isosc. △ Thm. **29.** Yes; the two ∥ lines and the two sides determine two pairs of ≅ corr. ∡, so the two ▲ are ~ by AA~. **31.** 4 : 3; sample explanation: Since $\angle P \cong \angle S$ and $\angle PQM \cong \angle STR$, $\triangle PQM \sim \triangle STR$ by AA~. So the ratio $\frac{MQ}{RT} = \frac{PM}{SR}$ = the ratio of corresp. sides in $\triangle PMN$ and $\triangle SRW$ namely, 4 : 3. **41.** 2 : 3 **42.** 135 **43.** 12 **44.** $\frac{3}{2}$ **45.** 125; obtuse **46.** 88; acute **47.** 180; straight **48.** 110; obtuse **49.** 8, 18; x, 24; 6 **50.** m, 18; 12, 20; $\frac{40}{3}$ or $13\frac{1}{3}$ **51.** x + 2, 9; 15, x; 3 **52.** x + 4, 5; x − 3, 9; $\frac{47}{4}$ or 11.75

Lesson 7-4 pp. 460–467

Got It? 1a. $\triangle PRQ \sim \triangle SPQ \sim \triangle SRP$ **b.** $\frac{SR}{SP} = \frac{SP}{SQ}$, $\frac{SR}{SP} = \frac{PR}{QP}$ **2.** $6\sqrt{2}$ **3.** $x = 6, y = 2\sqrt{5}$ **4.** 12 in.
Lesson Check 1. 6 **2.** $\sqrt{48}$ or $4\sqrt{3}$ **3.** h **4.** g **5.** j, h or h, j **6.** d, d **7a.** $\overline{RT}$ **b.** $\overline{RP}, \overline{PT}$ **c.** $\overline{PT}$ **8.** The length 8 is the entire hypotenuse, so the segments of the hypotenuse have lengths 3 and 5. The correct proportion is $\frac{3}{x} = \frac{x}{5}$.
Exercises 9. Answers may vary. Sample: $\triangle KJL \sim \triangle NJK \sim \triangle NKL$ **11.** Answers may vary. Sample: $\triangle OMN \sim \triangle PMO \sim \triangle PON$ **13.** 12 **15.** $\sqrt{63}$ or $3\sqrt{7}$ **17.** 14 **19.** $x = 20, y = 10\sqrt{5}$
21. $x = 3\sqrt{7}, y = 12$ **23a.** 4 cm
b.

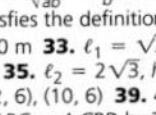

c. Answers may vary. Sample: Draw a 10-cm segment. Construct a ⊥ of length 4 cm that is 2 cm from one endpoint; connect to form a △. **25.** 2.5 **27.** 1 **29.** Yes; the proportion $\frac{a}{\sqrt{ab}} = \frac{\sqrt{ab}}{b}$ is true by the Cross Products Prop. and satisfies the definition of the geometric mean. **31.** 8.50 m **33.** $\ell_1 = \sqrt{2}, \ell_2 = \sqrt{2}, a = 1, s_2 = 1$ **35.** $\ell_2 = 2\sqrt{3}, h = 4, a = \sqrt{3}, s_1 = 1$ **37.** (−2, 6), (10, 6) **39.** 4 **41.** 5 **43.** $\triangle ABC \sim \triangle ACD$ and $\triangle ABC \sim \triangle CBD$ by Thm. 7-3. Then $\frac{AB}{AC} = \frac{AC}{AD}$ and $\frac{AB}{CB} = \frac{BC}{BD}$ because corresp. sides of ~ ▲ are proportional. **51.** $\angle R \cong \angle P$ (given) and $\angle RNM \cong \angle PNQ$ (Vert. ∡ are ≅.), so $\triangle NRM \sim \triangle NPQ$ by AA ~. **52.** $x = 5, y = 8$ **53.** $x = 3, y = 4$ **54.** 28 cm **55.** 9.8 in. **56.** $\frac{24}{7}$ mm or $3\frac{3}{7}$ mm

Lesson 7-5 pp. 471–478

Got It? 1a. 8 **b.** $RS = \frac{1}{2}XZ$ (Midsegment Thm.) **2.** 5.76 yd **3.** 14.4
Lesson Check 1. d **2.** c **3.** d **4.** 5 **5.** 15 **6.** Answers may vary. Sample: The corollary to the Side-Splitter Thm. takes the same three (or more) ∥ lines as in Thm. 6-7, but instead of cutting off ≅ segments it allows the segments to be proportional. **7.** Answers may vary. Sample: Alike: Both involve a △ and a seg. from one vertex to the opposite side of the △. Different: In Corollary 1 to Thm. 7-3, the △ is a rt. △ and the seg. is an alt., while in the △-∠-Bis. Thm. the △ does not have to be a rt. △ and the seg. is an ∠ bis. **8.** The Side-Splitter Thm. involves only the segments formed on the two sides intersected by the ∥ line. (To find x, you can use a proportion involving the two ~ ▲.)
Exercises 9. 7.5 **11.** 10 **13.** 8 mm **15.** 7.5 **17.** $3\frac{5}{13}$ **19.** 6 **21.** 35 **23.** Use the Side-Splitter Thm. to write the proportion $\frac{AB}{BD} = \frac{AC}{CE}$, then find the values of BD, AC, and CE to calculate the unknown length AB. **25.** KS by the △-∠-Bis. Thm. **27.** JP by the Side-Splitter Thm. **29.** KM by the △-∠-Bis. Thm. **31.** 575 ft **33.** 20 **35.** $\frac{2}{7}$ or 3 **37.** $\frac{XR}{RQ} = \frac{YS}{SQ}$ (Given); $\frac{XR + RQ}{RQ} = \frac{YS + SQ}{SQ}$ (Prop. of Proportions (3)); $XQ = XR + RQ$, $YQ = YS + SQ$ (Seg. Add. Post.); $\frac{XQ}{RQ} = \frac{YQ}{SQ}$ (Subst.); $\angle Q \cong \angle Q$ (Refl. Prop. of ≅); $\triangle XQY \sim \triangle RQS$ (SAS ~ Post.); $\angle 1 \cong \angle 2$ (Corresp. ∡ of ~ ▲ are ≅.); $\overline{RS} \parallel \overline{XY}$ (If corresp. ∡ are ≅, the lines are ∥.) **39.** no; $\frac{28}{12} \neq \frac{24}{10}$ **41.** 12.5 cm or 4.5 cm **43.** Isosc.; AC : BC is 1 : 1 by the △-∠-Bis. Thm. **45.** 5.2 **47.** By the Side-Splitter Thm., $\frac{CD}{DB} = \frac{CA}{AF}$. By the Corresp. ∡ Post., $\angle 3 \cong \angle 1$. Since $\overrightarrow{AD}$ bisects $\angle CAB$, $\angle 1 \cong \angle 2$. By the

Alt. Int. ∡ Thm., $\angle 2 \cong \angle 4$. So, $\angle 3 \cong \angle 4$ by the Trans. Prop. of ≅. By the Converse of the Isosc. △ Thm., $BA = AF$. Substituting BA for AF, $\frac{CD}{DB} = \frac{CA}{BA}$.
55. m **56.** m **57.** c **58.** h **59.** (3, −3) **60.** (0, 2) **61.** (1.5, 2.5) **62.** $(3\text{ m})^2 = 9\text{ m}^2$, $(4\text{ m})^2 = 16\text{ m}^2$, $(5\text{ m})^2 = 25\text{ m}^2$ **63.** $(5\text{ in.})^2 = 25\text{ in.}^2$, $(12\text{ in.})^2 = 144\text{ in.}^2$, $(13\text{ in.})^2 = 169\text{ in.}^2$
64. $(4\text{ m})^2 = 16\text{ m}^2$, $(4\sqrt{2}\text{ m})^2 = 32\text{ m}^2$

Chapter Review pp. 480–482

1. similar **2.** proportion **3.** scale factor **4.** means, extremes (in either order) **5.** 1 : 116 or $\frac{1}{116}$ **6.** 36 **7.** 6 **8.** $\frac{55}{4}$ or $13\frac{3}{4}$ **9.** 6 **10.** 7 **11.** JEHN ~ JKLP; 3 : 4 **12.** $\triangle PQR \sim \triangle XYZ$; 3 : 2 **13.** 120 ft **14.** 45 ft **15.** The ratios of each pair of corresp. sides is 2 : 1, so $\triangle AMY \sim \triangle ECD$ by SSS~. **16.** If lines are ∥, then corresp. ∡ are ≅, so $\triangle RPT \sim \triangle SGT$ by AA~. **17.** 12 **18.** $2\sqrt{15}$ **19.** $x = 6\sqrt{2}, y = 6\sqrt{6}$ **20.** $\sqrt{35}$ **21.** $x = 2\sqrt{21}; y = 4\sqrt{3}$ **22.** $x = 12, y = 4\sqrt{5}$ **23.** 7.5 **24.** 3.6 **25.** 22.5 **26.** 12 **27.** 17.5 **28.** 77

Chapter 8

Get Ready! p. 487

1. 4.648 **2.** 40.970 **3.** 6149.090 **4.** −5 **5.** AA ~ **6.** SSS ~ **7.** SAS ~ **8.** 12 **9.** 8 **10.** $2\sqrt{13}$ **11.** 9 **12.** Answers may vary. Sample: When something is "elevated" you look up to see it, so an ∠ of elevation is formed by a horizontal line and the line of sight. **13.** Answers may vary. Sample: The magnitude of a line segment is the length of the segment. **14.** Answers may vary. Sample: The prefix *tri-* means 3; triangles are associated with trigonometric ratios.

Lesson 8-1 pp. 491–498

Got It? 1a. 26 **b.** Yes; 10, 24, and 26 are whole numbers that satisfy $a^2 + b^2 = c^2$. **2.** $6\sqrt{3}$ **3.** 15.5 in. **4a.** No; $16^2 + 48^2 \neq 50^2$. **b.** No; $a^2 + b^2 = b^2 + a^2$ for any values of a and b. **5.** acute
Lesson Check 1. 37 **2.** $\sqrt{130}$ **3.** 4 **4.** $4\sqrt{3}$ **5.** The three numbers a, b, and c must be whole numbers that satisfy $a^2 + b^2 = c^2$. **6.** The longest side is 34, so the student should have tested $16^2 + 30^2 \stackrel{?}{=} 34^2$.
Exercises 7. 10 **9.** 34 **11.** 97 **13.** no; $4^2 + 5^2 \neq 6^2$ **15.** yes; $15^2 + 20^2 = 25^2$ **17.** $\sqrt{33}$ **19.** $\sqrt{105}$ **21.** $5\sqrt{3}$ **23.** 17 m **25.** no; $8^2 + 24^2 \neq 25^2$ **27.** acute **29.** acute **31.** right **33.** 4.2 in. **35a.** $|x_2 - x_1|$; $|y_2 - y_1|$ **b.** $PQ^2 = (x_2 - x_1)^2 + (y_2 - y_1)^2$ **c.** $PQ = \sqrt{(x_2 - x_1)^2 + (y_2 - y_1)^2}$ **37.** $8\sqrt{5}$ **39.** 29
41. 84 **43–48.** Answers may vary. Samples are given. **43a.** 6 **b.** 7 **45a.** 8 **b.** 11 **47a.** 8 **b.** 10 **49.** $\frac{q}{b} = \frac{b}{c}$ and $\frac{r}{a} = \frac{a}{c}$ because each leg is the geometric mean of the adj. hypotenuse segment and the hypotenuse. By the Cross Products Property, $b^2 = qc$ and $a^2 = rc$. Then $a^2 + b^2 = qc + rc = c(q + r)$. Substituting c for q + r gives $a^2 + b^2 = c^2$. **51a.** Horiz. lines have slope 0, and vert. lines have undef. slope. Neither could be mult. to get −1. **b.** Assume the lines do not intersect. Then they have the same slope m. Then $m \cdot m = m^2 = -1$, which is impossible. So the lines must intersect. **c.** Let ℓ, be $y = \frac{b}{a}x$ and ℓ_2 be $y = -\frac{a}{b}x$. Define C(a,b), A(0,0), and $B(a, -\frac{a^2}{b})$.

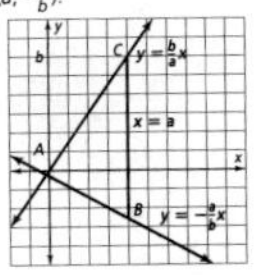

Using the Distance Formula, $AC = \sqrt{a^2 + b^2}$, $BA = \sqrt{a^2 + \frac{a^4}{b^2}}$, and $CB = b + \frac{a^2}{b}$. Then $AC^2 + BA^2 = CB^2$ and $m\angle A = 90$ by the Conv. of the Pythagorean Thm. So $\ell_1 \perp \ell_2$.
59. 4, 5 **60.** $\sqrt{3}$ **61.** $15\sqrt{2}$ **62.** $\frac{16\sqrt{3}}{3}$

Lesson 8-2 pp. 499–505

Got It? 1. $5\sqrt{6}$ **2a.** $5\sqrt{2}$ **b.** $\frac{\sqrt{2}}{\sqrt{2}} = 1$, so multiplying by $\frac{\sqrt{2}}{\sqrt{2}}$ is the same as multiplying by 1. **3.** 141 ft **4.** $\frac{10\sqrt{3}}{3}$ **5.** 15.6 mm
Lesson Check 1. $7\sqrt{2}$ **2.** 3 **3.** $4\sqrt{2}$ **4.** $6\sqrt{3}$ **5.** Rika; 5 should be opposite the 30° ∠ and $5\sqrt{3}$ should be opposite the 60° ∠. **6.** Answers may vary. Sample: The △ is isosc. The length of each leg is the same. Use the Pythagorean Thm. to find the hypotenuse; 6, $6\sqrt{2}$.
Exercises 7. $x = 8, y = 8\sqrt{2}$ **9.** $60\sqrt{2}$ **11.** $5\sqrt{2}$ **13.** 14.1 cm **15.** $x = 20, y = 20\sqrt{3}$ **17.** $x = 5, y = 5\sqrt{3}$ **19.** $x = 4, y = 2$ **21.** 50 ft **23.** $a = 7, b = 14, c = 7, d = 7\sqrt{3}$ **25.** $a = 10\sqrt{3}, b = 5\sqrt{3}, c = 15, d = 5$ **27.** $a = 3, b = 7$ **29.** 14.4 s **31.** Answers may vary. Sample: A ramp up to a door is 12 ft long. The ramp forms a 30° ∠ with the ground. How high off the ground is the door? 6 ft **38.** $\sqrt{11}$ in. **39.** $4\sqrt{21}$ cm **40.** $\frac{12}{7}$ **41.** $\frac{54}{11}$ **42.** $\frac{15}{2}$ **43.** $\frac{60}{7}$

Lesson 8-3 pp. 507–513

Got It? 1. $\frac{15}{17}$; $\frac{8}{17}$; $\frac{15}{8}$ **2a.** 13.8 **b.** 1.9 **c.** 3.8 **d.** 44 ft **3a.** 68 **b.** No; you can use any of the three trigonometric ratios as long as you identify the appropriate leg that is opp. or adj. to each acute ∠.
Lesson Check 1. $\frac{8}{10}$ or $\frac{4}{5}$ **2.** $\frac{6}{10}$ or $\frac{3}{5}$ **3.** $\frac{8}{6}$ or $\frac{4}{3}$ **4.** $\frac{6}{10}$ or $\frac{3}{5}$ **5.** $\frac{8}{10}$ or $\frac{4}{5}$ **6.** $\frac{6}{8}$ or $\frac{3}{4}$ **7.** 12.1 **8.** 57.5 **9.** The word is made up of the first letters of each ratio: $S = \frac{O}{H}$, $C = \frac{A}{H}$, and $T = \frac{O}{A}$. **10.** No; $\sin X = \frac{YZ}{YX}$, $\sin A = \frac{BC}{BA}$, and $\triangle XYZ \sim \triangle ABC$ by AA ~, so $\frac{YZ}{YX} = \frac{BC}{BA}$ because corresp. sides of ~ ▲ are proportional. Therefore, $\sin X = \sin A$.
Exercises 11. $\frac{7}{25}$; $\frac{24}{25}$; $\frac{7}{24}$ **13.** $\frac{\sqrt{3}}{2}$; $\frac{1}{2}$; $\sqrt{3}$ **15.** 8.3 **17.** 17.0 **19.** 21.4 **21.** 1085 ft **23.** 58 **25.** 59 **27.** 66 **29.** about 17 ft 8 in. **31.** $\cos X \cdot \tan X = \frac{\text{adjacent}}{\text{hypotenuse}} \cdot \frac{\text{opposite}}{\text{adjacent}} = \frac{\text{opposite}}{\text{hypotenuse}} = \sin X$ **33.** $w = 3, x \approx 41$ **35.** $w \approx 68.3, x \approx 151.6$ **37a.** They are equal; yes; sine and cosine of compl. ∡ are =. **b.** ∠B; ∠A **c.** Sample: The cosine is the complement's sine.
39a.

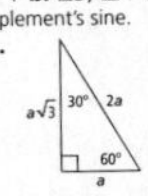

Using the ratio of sides $1 : \sqrt{3} : 2$ for a 30°-60°-90° △, $\tan 60° = \frac{\sqrt{3}}{1} = \sqrt{3}$.
b. Answers may vary. Sample: $\sin 60° = \sqrt{3} \cdot \cos 60°$ **41.** $\frac{15}{9}$ or $\frac{5}{3}$ **43.** $\frac{15}{9}$ or $\frac{5}{3}$ **45.** $\frac{12}{9}$ or $\frac{4}{3}$ **47a.** No; answers may vary. Sample: $\tan 45° + \tan 30° = 1 + \frac{\sqrt{3}}{3} \approx 1.6$, but $\tan 75° \approx 3.7$. **b.** No; assume $\tan A - \tan B = \tan(A - B)$; $\tan A = \tan B + \tan(A - B)$ by the Add. Prop. of =; let $A = B + C$, then $\tan(B + C) = \tan B + \tan C$ by the Subst. Prop.; part (a) proved this false; this contradicts the assumption, so $\tan A - \tan B \neq \tan(A - B)$. **57.** 4, $4\sqrt{3}$ **58.** $5\sqrt{2}$ units **59.** ∠7 **60.** ∠11 **61.** ∠6 **62.** 90

Lesson 8-4 pp. 516–521

Got It? 1a. ∠ of elevation from the person in the hot-air balloon to bird **b.** ∠ of depression from the person in the hot-air balloon to base of mountain **2.** about 631 ft **3.** about 6.2 km
Lesson Check 1. ∠ of elevation from C to A **2.** ∠ of depression from A to C **3.** ∠ of elevation from A to D **4.** ∠ of elevation from A to B **5.** ∠ of depression from B to A **6.** $\angle 1 \cong \angle 2$ (alt. int. ∡); $\angle 4 \cong \angle 5$ (alt. int. ∡) **7.** Answers may vary. Sample: An ∠ of elevation is formed by two rays with a common endpoint when one ray is horizontal and the other ray is above the horizontal ray. **8.** Answers may vary. Sample: The ∠ labeled in the sketch is the complement of the ∠ of depression.
Exercises 9. ∠ of elevation from sub to boat **11.** ∠ of elevation from boat to tree **13.** ∠ of elevation from Max to top of waterfall **15.** ∠ of depression from top of waterfall to Max **17.** 34.2 ft **19.** 986 m **21.** 0.6 km **23.** 64° **25.** 72, 72 **27.** 27, 27 **29a.** length of any guy wire = distance on the ground from the tower to the guy wire div. by the cosine of the ∠ formed by the guy wire and the ground **b.** height of attachment = distance on the ground from the tower to the guy wire times the tangent of the ∠ formed by the guy wire and the ground **31.** about 2.8 **33.** 3300 m **39.** 85.2 m **40.** 38.2 ft **41.** 45 **42.** $2\sqrt{17} \approx 8.2$ **43.** $\sqrt{229} \approx 15.1$ **44.** $2\sqrt{37} \approx 12.2$

Lesson 8-5 pp. 524–532

Got It? 1. ⟨−307.3, −54.2⟩ **2a.** 60° south of west **b.** Yes; it can also be described as 30° west of south. **3a.** about 257.5 mi at 17.2° north of east **b.** No; distance is always nonnegative. **4.** ⟨−2, 1⟩ **5.** about 13.2° north of west
Lesson Check
1.

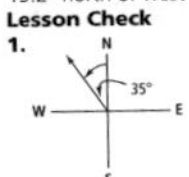

2.

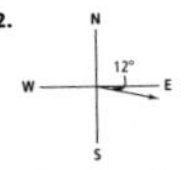

3. about 6.1 **4.** about 5.7 **5.** ⟨10, 5⟩ **6.** ⟨8, 6⟩ **7.** Answers may vary. Sample: Both have an endpoint. A ray extends indefinitely in a direction, while a vector has a terminal point and a magnitude. **8.** Yes; explanations may vary. Sample: if a vector has the direction 35° south of east, and you relate that vector to due south, you can see that the vector is 55° east of south. **9.** The magnitude of each vector is $\sqrt{149}$.
Exercises 11. ⟨−29.3, 41.8⟩ **13.** 15° south of west (or 75° west of south) **15.** 40° east of south (or 50° south of east)
17.

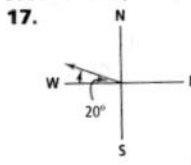

19.

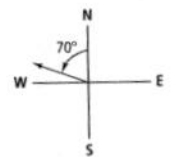

21.

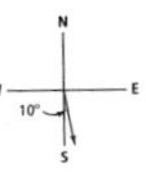

23. about 707 mi at 65° south of west **25.** about 4805 km at 12° north of west **27.** ⟨−1, 3⟩ **29.** ⟨−2, 3⟩
31. ⟨−6, 2⟩

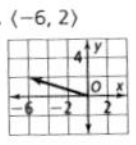

33. ⟨1, −1⟩

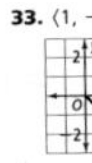

35. ⟨−2, −9⟩

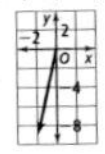

37. 304 mi/h at 9° east of south **39.** Answers may vary. Sample: Two vectors are parallel if and only if they have the same or opposite direction.
41. ⟨−3, −7⟩

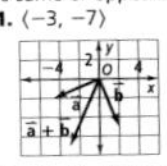

43. ⟨3, −3⟩

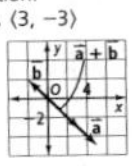

45a. ⟨5, 5⟩, ⟨5, 5⟩ **b.** ⟨10, 4⟩, ⟨10, 4⟩ **c.** Commutative Prop. and Associative Prop. **d.** Answers may vary. Sample: ⟨a, b⟩ + ⟨c, d⟩ = ⟨a + c, b + d⟩ and ⟨c, d⟩ + ⟨a, b⟩ = ⟨a + c, b + d⟩; (⟨a, b⟩ + ⟨c, d⟩) + ⟨e, f⟩ = ⟨a + c, b + d⟩ + ⟨e, f⟩ = ⟨a + c + e, b + d + f⟩ and ⟨a, b⟩ + (⟨c, d⟩ + ⟨e, f⟩) = ⟨a, b⟩ + ⟨c + e, d + f⟩ = ⟨a + c + e, b + d + f⟩

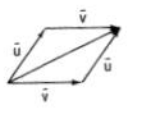

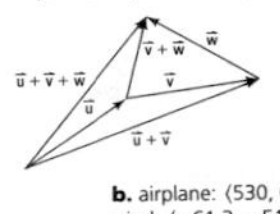

47a.

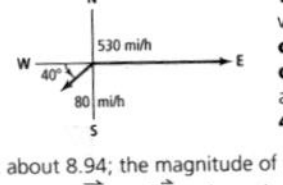

b. airplane: ⟨530, 0⟩, wind: ⟨−61.3, −51.4⟩ **c.** ⟨468.7, −51.4⟩ **d.** about 471.5 mi/h at 6.3° south of east **49a.** ⟨4, 8⟩ **b.** about 4.47; about 8.94; the magnitude of $2\vec{w}$ is two times the magnitude of $\vec{w}$. **c.** If $\vec{v} = \langle v_1, v_2 \rangle$ and k is a constant, then $k\vec{v} = \langle kv_1, kv_2 \rangle$. The magnitude of $k\vec{v} = k$ (magnitude of $\vec{v}$). **56.** 4492 ft **57.** Yes; explanations may vary. Sample: both pairs of opposite sides are parallel. **58.** $\overline{EF}$ **59.** $\overline{AC}$ **60.** $\overline{BC}$ **61.** ∠G **62.** ∠A **63.** ∠F

Chapter Review pp. 534–536

1. vector **2.** ∠ of elevation **3.** resultant **4.** Pythagorean triple **5.** $2\sqrt{113}$ **6.** 17 **7.** $12\sqrt{2}$ **8.** $9\sqrt{3}$ **9.** $x = 7, y = 7\sqrt{2}$ **10.** $5\sqrt{2}$ **11.** $x = 6\sqrt{3}, y = 12$ **12.** $x = 7, y = 7\sqrt{3}$ **13.** 70.7 ft **14.** $\frac{2\sqrt{19}}{20}$ or $\frac{\sqrt{19}}{10}$; $\frac{18}{20}$ or $\frac{9}{10}$; $\frac{2\sqrt{19}}{18}$ or $\frac{\sqrt{19}}{9}$ **15.** $\frac{16}{20}$ or $\frac{4}{5}$; $\frac{12}{20}$ or $\frac{3}{5}$; $\frac{16}{12}$ or $\frac{4}{3}$ **16.** 16.5 **17.** 33.1 **18.** 38.2 ft **19.** 206.2 km at 76.0° south of west (or 14.0° west of south) **20.** 503.1 mi/h at 26.6° north of west (or 63.4° west of north) **21.** ⟨1, 4⟩ **22.** 67.4° south of west (or 22.6° west of south)

Chapter 9

Get Ready! p. 541

1. △ADC **2.** △LJK **3.** △RTS **4.** △LHC **5.** 108 **6.** 135 **7.** 144 **8.** 160 **9.** always **10.** never **11.** sometimes **12.** always **13.** 50 ft **14.** 0.25 in. **15.** left hand; 4 ft **16.** the point at the center of the clock **17.** Answers may vary. Sample: When you dilate a geometric figure, you change its size. **18.** Answers may vary. Sample: A tiling is a repeating pattern of geometric shapes that completely fills a plane.

Lesson 9-1 pp. 544–551

Got It? 1a. Yes; the transformation is a flip. **b.** Yes; the transformation is a flip and a slide. **2a.** ∠U; P **b.** $\overline{NI}$ and $\overline{SU}$, $\overline{ID}$ and $\overline{UP}$, $\overline{DN}$ and $\overline{PS}$ **3a–b.** Graph:

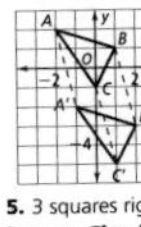

a. A′(−1, −2), B′(2, −3), C′(1, −5) **b.** $\overline{AA'} \cong \overline{BB'} \cong \overline{CC'}$ and $\overline{AA'} \parallel \overline{BB'} \parallel \overline{CC'}$; you can use the Distance Formula to show that the length of each segment is $\sqrt{17}$. The slope of each segment is −4. **4.** (x, y) → (x + 7, y − 1)
5. 3 squares right and 5 squares down
Lesson Check 1. P′; $\overline{T'J'}$
2.

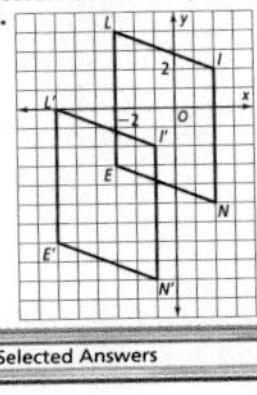

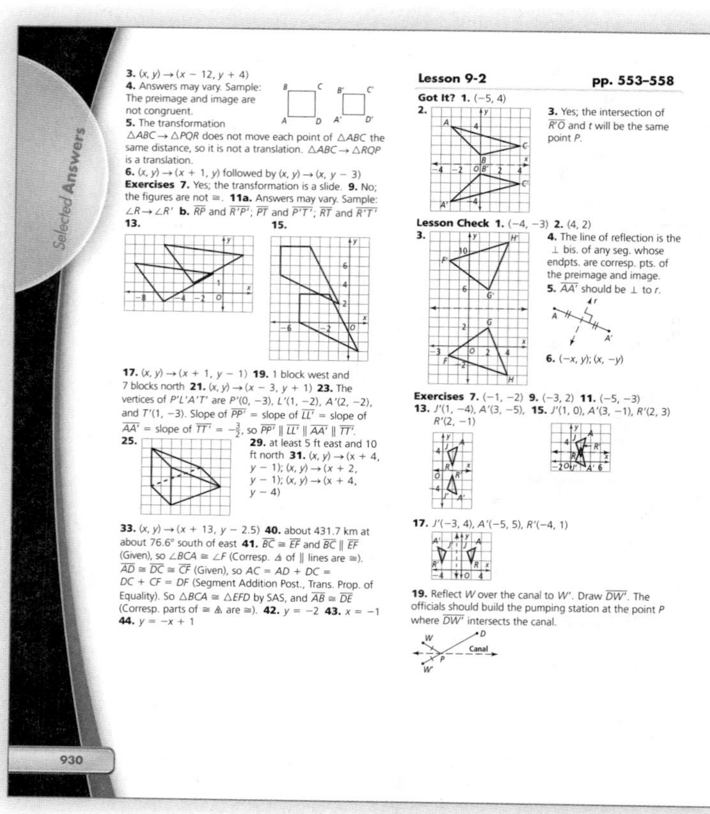

3. $(x, y) \rightarrow (x - 12, y + 4)$
4. Answers may vary. Sample: The preimage and image are not congruent.
5. The transformation $\triangle ABC \rightarrow \triangle PQR$ does not move each point of $\triangle ABC$ the same distance, so it is not a translation. $\triangle ABC \rightarrow \triangle RQP$ is a translation.
6. $(x, y) \rightarrow (x + 1, y)$ followed by $(x, y) \rightarrow (x, y - 3)$

Exercises **7.** Yes; the transformation is a slide. **9.** No; the figures are not ≅. **11a.** Answers may vary. Sample: $\angle R \rightarrow \angle R'$ **b.** $\overline{RP}$ and $\overline{R'P'}$; $\overline{PT}$ and $\overline{P'T'}$; $\overline{RT}$ and $\overline{R'T'}$

13. **15.**

17. $(x, y) \rightarrow (x + 1, y - 1)$ **19.** 1 block west and 7 blocks north **21.** $(x, y) \rightarrow (x - 3, y + 1)$ **23.** The vertices of $P'L'A'T'$ are $P'(0, -3)$, $L'(1, -2)$, $A'(2, -2)$, and $T'(1, -3)$. Slope of $\overline{PP'}$ = slope of $\overline{LL'}$ = slope of $\overline{AA'}$ = slope of $\overline{TT'} = -\frac{3}{2}$, so $\overline{PP'} \parallel \overline{LL'} \parallel \overline{AA'} \parallel \overline{TT'}$.

25. **29.** at least 5 ft east and 10 ft north **31.** $(x, y) \rightarrow (x + 4, y - 1)$; $(x, y) \rightarrow (x + 2, y - 1)$; $(x, y) \rightarrow (x + 4, y - 4)$

33. $(x, y) \rightarrow (x + 13, y - 2.5)$ **40.** about 431.7 km at about 76.6° south of east **41.** $\overline{BC} \cong \overline{EF}$ and $\overline{BC} \parallel \overline{EF}$ (Given), so $\angle BCA \cong \angle F$ (Corresp. ∡ of ∥ lines are ≅). $\overline{AD} \cong \overline{DC} \cong \overline{CF}$ (Given), so $AC = AD + DC = DC + CF = DF$ (Segment Addition Post., Trans. Prop. of Equality). So $\triangle BCA \cong \triangle EFD$ by SAS, and $\overline{AB} \cong \overline{DE}$ (Corresp. parts of ≅ ▲ are ≅). **42.** $y = -2$ **43.** $x = -1$ **44.** $y = -x + 1$

Lesson 9-2 pp. 553–558

Got It? **1.** $(-5, 4)$
2.
3. Yes; the intersection of $\overline{R'O}$ and t will be the same point P.

Lesson Check **1.** $(-4, -3)$ **2.** $(4, 2)$
3.
4. The line of reflection is the ⊥ bis. of any seg. whose endpts. are corresp. pts. of the preimage and image.
5. $\overline{AA'}$ should be ⊥ to r.
6. $(-x, y)$; $(x, -y)$

Exercises **7.** $(-1, -2)$ **9.** $(-3, 2)$ **11.** $(-5, -3)$
13. $J'(1, -4)$, $A'(3, -5)$, $R'(2, -1)$ **15.** $J'(1, 0)$, $A'(3, -1)$, $R'(2, 3)$
17. $J'(-3, 4)$, $A'(-5, 5)$, $R'(-4, 1)$
19. Reflect W over the canal to W'. Draw $\overline{DW'}$. The officials should build the pumping station at the point P where $\overline{DW'}$ intersects the canal.

930

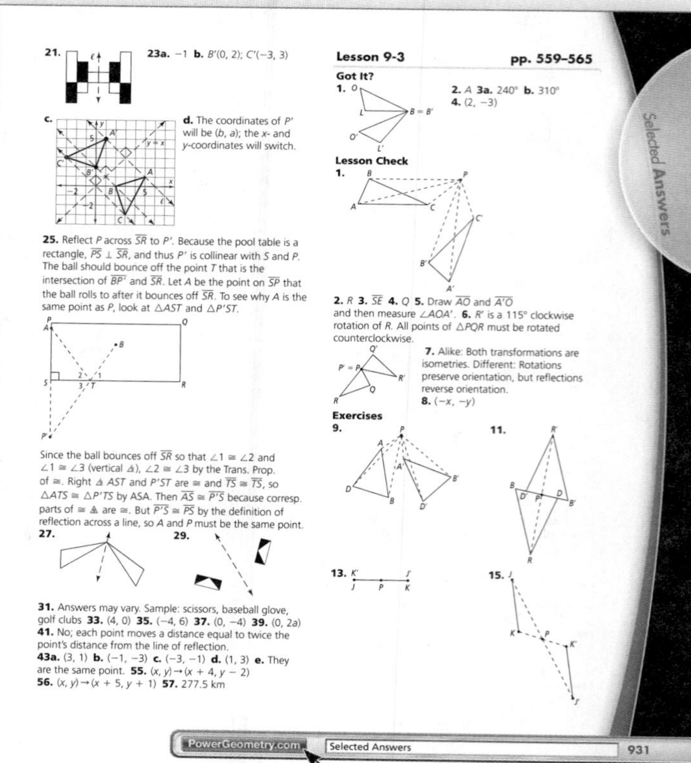

21. **23a.** -1 **b.** $B'(0, 2)$; $C'(-3, 3)$
c. **d.** The coordinates of P' will be (b, a); the x- and y-coordinates will switch.

25. Reflect P across $\overline{SR}$ to P'. Because the pool table is a rectangle, $\overline{PS} \perp \overline{SR}$, and thus P' is collinear with S and P. The ball should bounce off the point T that is the intersection of $\overline{BP'}$ and $\overline{SR}$. Let A be the point on $\overline{SP}$ that the ball rolls to after it bounces off $\overline{SR}$. To see why A is the same point as P, look at $\triangle AST$ and $\triangle P'ST$.

Since the ball bounces off $\overline{SR}$ so that $\angle 1 \cong \angle 2$ and $\angle 1 \cong \angle 3$ (vertical ∡), $\angle 2 \cong \angle 3$ by the Trans. Prop. of ≅. Right ∡ AST and $P'ST$ are ≅ and $\overline{TS} \cong \overline{TS}$, so $\triangle ATS \cong \triangle P'TS$ by ASA. Then $\overline{AS} \cong \overline{P'S}$ because corresp. parts of ≅ ▲ are ≅. But $\overline{P'S} \cong \overline{PS}$ by the definition of reflection across a line, so A and P must be the same point.

27. **29.**

31. Answers may vary. Sample: scissors, baseball glove, golf clubs **33.** $(4, 0)$ **35.** $(-4, 6)$ **37.** $(0, -4)$ **39.** $(0, 2a)$ **41.** No; each point moves a distance equal to twice the point's distance from the line of reflection.
43a. $(3, 1)$ **b.** $(-1, -3)$ **c.** $(-3, -1)$ **d.** $(1, 3)$ **e.** They are the same point. **55.** $(x, y) \rightarrow (x + 4, y - 2)$ **56.** $(x, y) \rightarrow (x + 5, y + 1)$ **57.** 277.5 km

Lesson 9-3 pp. 559–565

Got It?
1. **2.** A **3a.** 240° **b.** 310° **4.** $(2, -3)$

Lesson Check
1.
2. R **3.** $\overline{SE}$ **4.** Q **5.** Draw $\overline{AO}$ and $\overline{A'O}$ and then measure $\angle AOA'$. **6.** R' is a 115° clockwise rotation of R. All points of $\triangle PQR$ must be rotated counterclockwise.
7. Alike: Both transformations are isometries. Different: Rotations preserve orientation, but reflections reverse orientation.
8. $(-x, -y)$

Exercises
9. **11.** **13.** **15.**

PowerGeometry.com | Selected Answers 931

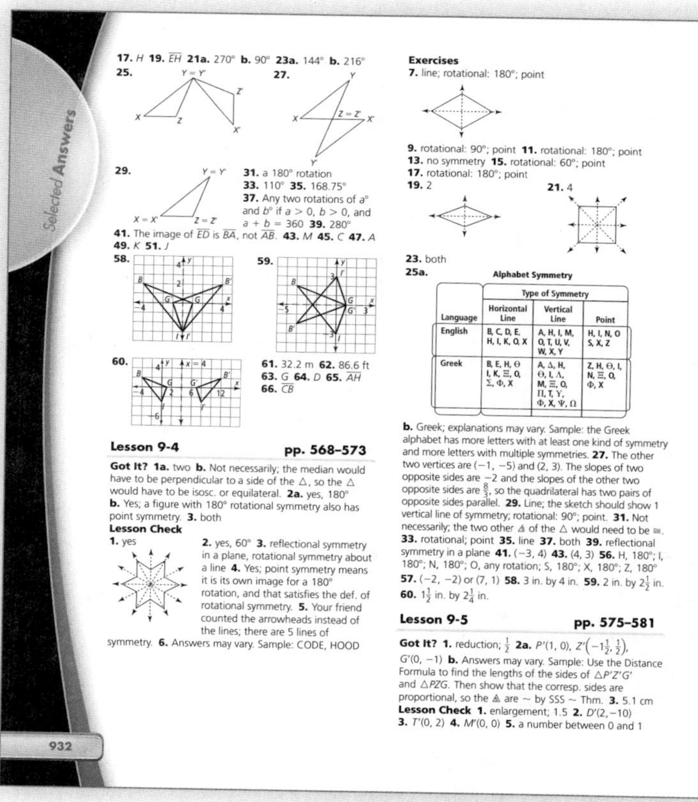

17. H **19.** $\overline{EH}$ **21a.** 270° **b.** 90° **23a.** 144° **b.** 216°
25. **27.**
29. **31.** a 180° rotation **33.** 110° **35.** 168.75° **37.** Any two rotations of $a°$ and $b°$ if $a > 0$, $b > 0$, and $a + b = 360$ **39.** 280°
41. The image of $\overline{ED}$ is $\overline{BA}$, not $\overline{AB}$. **43.** M **45.** C **47.** A **49.** K **51.** J
58. **59.**
60. **61.** 32.2 m **62.** 86.6 ft **63.** G **64.** D **65.** $\overline{AH}$ **66.** $\overline{CB}$

Lesson 9-4 pp. 568–573

Got It? **1a.** two **b.** Not necessarily; the median would have to be perpendicular to a side of the △, so the △ would have to be isosc. or equilateral. **2a.** yes, 180° **b.** Yes; a figure with 180° rotational symmetry also has point symmetry. **3.** both

Lesson Check
1. yes **2.** yes, 60° **3.** reflectional symmetry in a plane, rotational symmetry about a line **4.** Yes; point symmetry means it is its own image for a 180° rotation, and that satisfies the def. of rotational symmetry. **5.** Your friend counted the arrowheads instead of the lines; there are 5 lines of symmetry. **6.** Answers may vary. Sample: CODE, HOOD

Exercises
7. line; rotational: 180°; point
9. rotational: 90°; point **11.** rotational: 180°; point **13.** no symmetry **15.** rotational: 60°; point **17.** rotational: 180°; point
19. 2 **21.** 4
23. both
25a.

Alphabet Symmetry

Language	Type of Symmetry		
	Horizontal Line	Vertical Line	Point
English	B, C, D, E, H, I, K, O, X	A, H, I, M, O, T, U, V, W, X, Y	H, I, N, O S, X, Z
Greek	B, E, H, Θ I, K, Ξ, O, Σ, Φ, X	A, Δ, H, Θ, I, Λ, M, Ξ, O, Π, T, Υ, Φ, X, Ψ, Ω	Z, H, Θ, I, N, Ξ, O, Φ, X

b. Greek; explanations may vary. Sample: the Greek alphabet has more letters with at least one kind of symmetry and more letters with multiple symmetries. **27.** The other two vertices are $(-1, -5)$ and $(2, 3)$. The slopes of two opposite sides are -2 and the slopes of the other two opposite sides are $\frac{8}{3}$, so the quadrilateral has two pairs of opposite sides parallel. **29.** Line; the sketch should show 1 vertical line of symmetry; rotational: 90°; point. **31.** Not necessarily; the two other ∡ of the △ would need to be ≅. **33.** rotational; point **35.** line **37.** both **39.** reflectional symmetry in a plane **41.** $(-3, 4)$ **43.** $(4, 3)$ **56.** H, 180°; I, 180°; N, 180°; O, any rotation; S, 180°; X, 180°; Z, 180° **57.** $(-2, -2)$ or $(7, 1)$ **58.** 3 in. by 4 in. **59.** 2 in. by $2\frac{1}{2}$ in. **60.** $1\frac{1}{2}$ in. by $2\frac{1}{4}$ in.

Lesson 9-5 pp. 575–581

Got It? **1.** reduction; $\frac{1}{2}$ **2a.** $P'(1, 0)$, $Z'\left(-1\frac{1}{2}, \frac{1}{2}\right)$, $G'(0, -1)$ **b.** Answers may vary. Sample: Use the Distance Formula to find the lengths of the sides of $\triangle P'Z'G'$ and $\triangle PZG$. Then show that the corresp. sides are proportional, so the ▲ are ~ by SSS ~ Thm. **3.** 5.1 cm
Lesson Check **1.** enlargement; 1.5 **2.** $D'(2, -10)$ **3.** $T'(0, 2)$ **4.** $M'(0, 0)$ **5.** a number between 0 and 1

932

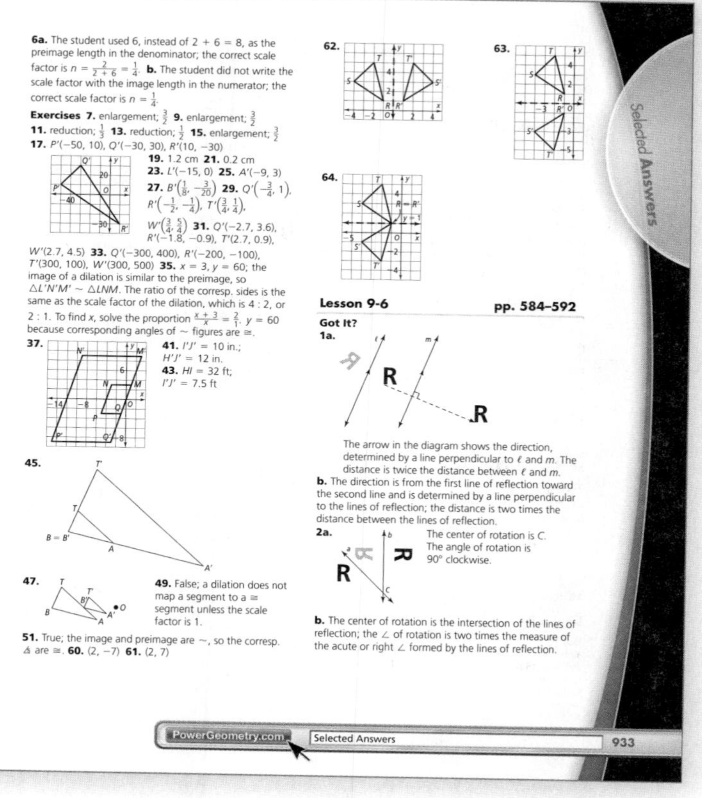

6a. The student used 6, instead of $2 + 6 = 8$, as the preimage length in the denominator; the correct scale factor is $n = \frac{2}{2 + 6} = \frac{1}{4}$. **b.** The student did not write the scale factor with the image length in the numerator; the correct scale factor is $n = \frac{1}{4}$.

Exercises **7.** enlargement; $\frac{3}{2}$ **9.** enlargement; $\frac{3}{2}$ **11.** reduction; $\frac{1}{3}$ **13.** reduction; $\frac{1}{2}$ **15.** enlargement; $\frac{3}{2}$ **17.** $P'(-50, 10)$, $Q'(-30, 30)$, $R'(10, -30)$
19. 1.2 cm **21.** 0.2 cm **23.** $L'(-15, 0)$ **25.** $A'(-9, 3)$ **27.** $B'\left(\frac{1}{8}, -\frac{3}{20}\right)$ **29.** $Q'\left(-\frac{3}{4}, 1\right)$, $R'\left(-\frac{1}{2}, -\frac{1}{4}\right)$, $T'\left(\frac{3}{4}, \frac{1}{4}\right)$, $W'\left(\frac{3}{4}, \frac{5}{4}\right)$ **31.** $Q'(-2.7, 3.6)$, $R'(-1.8, -0.9)$, $T'(2.7, 0.9)$, $W'(2.7, 4.5)$ **33.** $Q'(-300, 400)$, $R'(-200, -100)$, $T'(300, 100)$, $W'(300, 500)$ **35.** $x = 3$, $y = 60$; the image of a dilation is similar to the preimage, so $\triangle L'N'M' \sim \triangle LNM$. The ratio of the corresp. sides is the same as the scale factor of the dilation, which is 4 : 2, or 2 : 1. To find x, solve the proportion $\frac{x + 3}{x} = \frac{2}{1}$. $y = 60$ because corresponding angles of ~ figures are ≅.
37. **41.** $I'J' = 10$ in.; $H'J' = 12$ in. **43.** $HI = 32$ ft; $I'J' = 7.5$ ft
45.
47. **49.** False; a dilation does not map a segment to a ≅ segment unless the scale factor is 1.
51. True; the image and preimage are ~, so the corresp. ∡ are ≅. **60.** $(2, -7)$ **61.** $(2, 7)$

62. **63.** **64.**

Lesson 9-6 pp. 584–592

Got It?
1a. The arrow in the diagram shows the direction, determined by a line perpendicular to ℓ and m. The distance is twice the distance between ℓ and m.
b. The direction is from the first line of reflection toward the second line and is determined by a line perpendicular to the lines of reflection; the distance is two times the distance between the lines of reflection.
2a. The center of rotation is C. The angle of rotation is 90° clockwise.
b. The center of rotation is the intersection of the lines of reflection; the ∠ of rotation is two times the measure of the acute or right ∠ formed by the lines of reflection.

PowerGeometry.com | Selected Answers 933

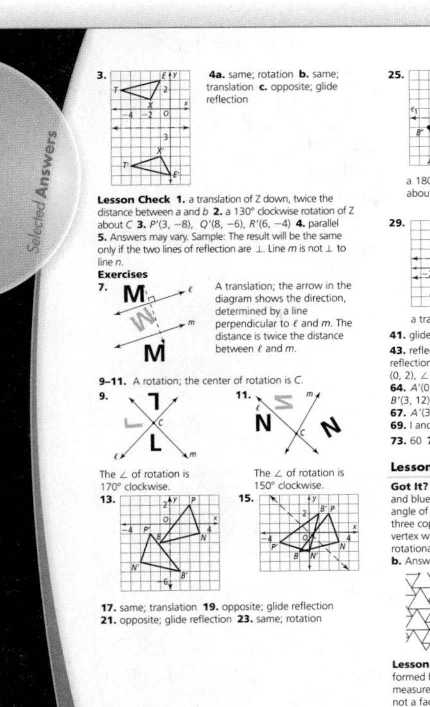

3. **4a.** same; rotation **b.** same; translation **c.** opposite; glide reflection

Lesson Check **1.** a translation of Z down, twice the distance between a and b **2.** a 130° clockwise rotation of Z about C **3.** $P'(3, -8)$, $Q'(8, -6)$, $R'(6, -4)$ **4.** parallel **5.** Answers may vary. Sample: The result will be the same only if the two lines of reflection are ⊥. Line m is not ⊥ to line n.

Exercises

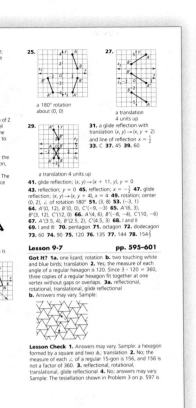

7. A translation; the arrow in the diagram shows the direction, determined by a line perpendicular to ℓ and m. The distance is twice the distance between ℓ and m.

9–11. A rotation; the center of rotation is C.

9. The ∠ of rotation is 170° clockwise. **11.** The ∠ of rotation is 150° clockwise.

13. **15.**

17. same; translation **19.** opposite; glide reflection **21.** opposite; glide reflection **23.** same; rotation

25. a 180° rotation about (0, 0) **27.** a translation 4 units up

29. a translation 4 units up **31.** a glide reflection with translation $(x, y) \rightarrow (x, y + 2)$ and line of reflection $x = \frac{1}{2}$ **33.** C **37.** 45 **39.** 60

41. glide reflection; $(x, y) \rightarrow (x + 11, y)$, $y = 0$ **43.** reflection; $y = 0$ **45.** reflection; $x = -\frac{1}{2}$ **47.** glide reflection; $(x, y) \rightarrow (x, y + 4)$, $x = 4$ **49.** rotation; center (0, 2), ∠ of rotation 180° **51.** (3, 8) **53.** (−3, 1) **64.** $A'(0, 12)$, $B'(0, 0)$, $C'(-9, -3)$ **65.** $A'(6, 3)$, $B'(3, 12)$, $C'(12, 0)$ **66.** $A'(4, 6)$, $B'(-8, -4)$, $C'(10, -6)$ **67.** $A'(3.5, 4)$, $B'(2.5, 2)$, $C'(4.5, 3)$ **68.** I and II **69.** I and III **70.** pentagon **71.** octagon **72.** dodecagon **73.** 60 **74.** 90 **75.** 120 **76.** 135 **77.** 144 **78.** $154\frac{2}{7}$

Lesson 9-7 pp. 595–601

Got It? 1a. one lizard; rotation **b.** two touching white and blue birds; translation **2.** Yes; the measure of each angle of a regular hexagon is 120. Since 3 · 120 = 360, three copies of a regular hexagon fit together at one vertex without gaps or overlaps. **3a.** reflectional, rotational, translational, glide reflectional **b.** Answers may vary. Sample:

Lesson Check **1.** Answers may vary. Sample: a hexagon formed by a square and two ▵; translation **2.** No; the measure of each ∠ of a regular 15-gon is 156, and 156 is not a factor of 360. **3.** reflectional, rotational, translational, glide reflectional **4.** No; answers may vary. Sample: The tessellation shown in Problem 3 on p. 597 is

934

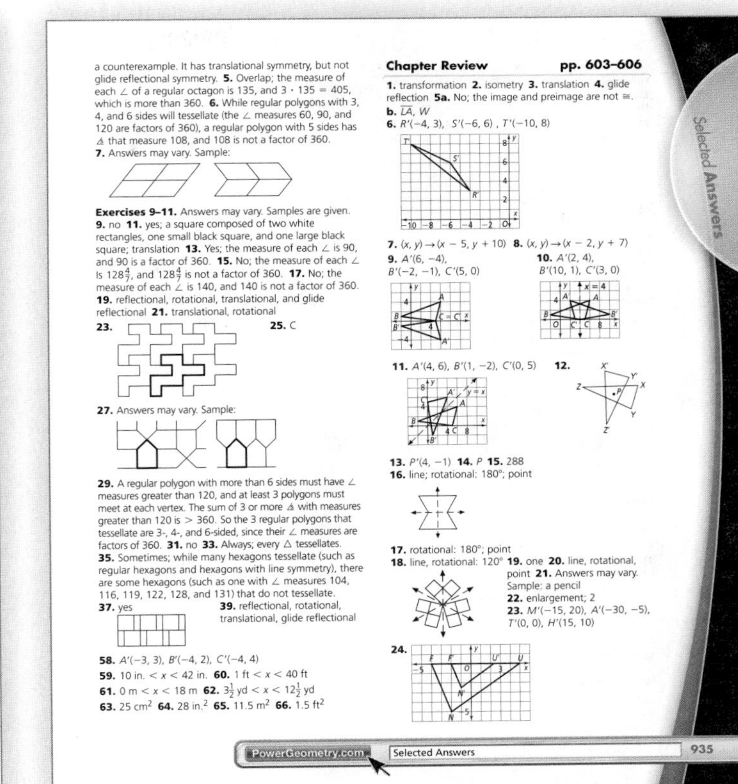

a counterexample. It has translational symmetry, but not glide reflectional symmetry. **5.** Overlap; the measure of each ∠ of a regular octagon is 135, and 3 · 135 = 405, which is more than 360. **6.** While regular polygons with 3, 4, and 6 sides will tessellate (the ∠ measures 60, 90, and 120 are factors of 360), a regular polygon with 5 sides has ▵ that measure 108, and 108 is not a factor of 360. **7.** Answers may vary. Sample:

Exercises 9–11. Answers may vary. Samples are given. **9.** no **11.** yes; a square composed of two white rectangles, one small black square, and one large black square; translation **13.** Yes; the measure of each ∠ is 90, and 90 is a factor of 360. **15.** No; the measure of each ∠ is $128\frac{4}{7}$, and $128\frac{4}{7}$ is not a factor of 360. **17.** No; the measure of each ∠ is 140, and 140 is not a factor of 360. **19.** reflectional, rotational, translational, and glide reflectional **21.** translational, rotational **23.** **25.** C

27. Answers may vary. Sample:

29. A regular polygon with more than 6 sides must have ∠ measures greater than 120, and at least 3 polygons must meet at each vertex. The sum of 3 or more ▵ with measures greater than 120 is > 360. So the 3 regular polygons that tessellate are 3-, 4-, and 6-sided, since their ∠ measures are factors of 360. **31.** no **33.** Always; every △ tessellates. **35.** Sometimes; while many hexagons tessellate (such as regular hexagons and hexagons with line symmetry), there are some hexagons (such as one with ∠ measures 104, 116, 119, 122, 128, and 131) that do not tessellate. **37.** yes **39.** reflectional, rotational, translational, glide reflectional

58. $A'(-3, 3)$, $B'(-4, 2)$, $C'(-4, 4)$ **59.** 10 in. < x < 42 in. **60.** 1 ft < x < 40 ft **61.** 0 m < x < 18 m **62.** $3\frac{1}{3}$ yd < x < $12\frac{1}{3}$ yd **63.** 25 cm² **64.** 28 in.² **65.** 11.5 m² **66.** 1.5 ft²

Chapter Review pp. 603–606

1. transformation **2.** isometry **3.** translation **4.** glide reflection **5a.** No; the image and preimage are not ≅. **b.** $\overline{LA}$, W **6.** $R'(-4, 3)$, $S'(-6, 6)$, $T'(-10, 8)$

7. $(x, y) \rightarrow (x - 5, y + 10)$ **8.** $(x, y) \rightarrow (x - 2, y + 7)$ **9.** $A'(6, -4)$, $B'(-2, -1)$, $C'(5, 0)$ **10.** $A'(2, 4)$, $B'(10, 1)$, $C'(3, 0)$

11. $A'(4, 6)$, $B'(1, -2)$, $C'(0, 5)$ **12.**

13. $P'(4, -1)$ **14.** P **15.** 288 **16.** line; rotational: 180°; point

17. rotational: 180°; point **18.** line, rotational: 120° **19.** one **20.** line, rotational, point **21.** Answers may vary. Sample: a pencil **22.** enlargement; 2 **23.** $M'(-15, 20)$, $A'(-30, -5)$, $T'(0, 0)$, $H'(15, 10)$

24.

PowerGeometry.com | Selected Answers 935

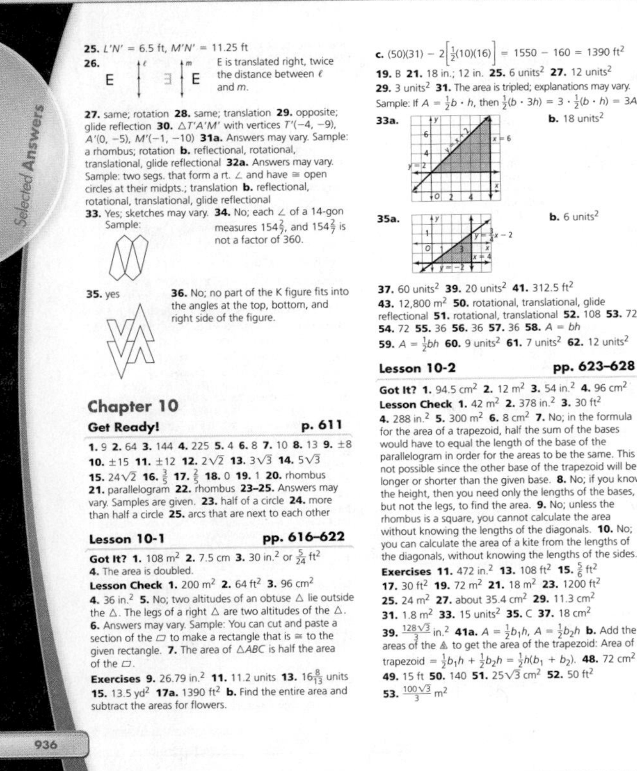

25. $L'N' = 6.5$ ft, $M'N' = 11.25$ ft **26.** E is translated right, twice the distance between ℓ and m.

27. same; translation **28.** same; translation **29.** opposite; glide reflection **30.** △T'A'M' with vertices $T'(-4, -9)$, $A'(0, -5)$, $M'(-1, -10)$ **31a.** Answers may vary. Sample: a rhombus; rotation **b.** reflectional, rotational, translational, glide reflectional **32a.** Answers may vary. Sample: two segs. that form a rt. ∠ and have ≅ open circles at their midpts.; translation **b.** reflectional, rotational, translational, glide reflectional **33.** Yes; sketches may vary. Sample: **34.** No; each ∠ of a 14-gon measures $154\frac{2}{7}$, and $154\frac{2}{7}$ is not a factor of 360.

35. yes **36.** No; no part of the K figure fits into the angles at the top, bottom, and right side of the figure.

Chapter 10

Get Ready! p. 611

1. 9 **2.** 64 **3.** 144 **4.** 225 **5.** 4 **6.** 8 **7.** 10 **8.** 13 **9.** ±8 **10.** ±15 **11.** ±12 **12.** $2\sqrt{2}$ **13.** $3\sqrt{3}$ **14.** $5\sqrt{3}$ **15.** $24\sqrt{2}$ **16.** $\frac{3}{5}$ **17.** $\frac{2}{5}$ **18.** 0 **19.** 1 **20.** rhombus **21.** parallelogram **22.** rhombus **23–25.** Answers may vary. Samples are given. **23.** half of a circle **24.** more than half a circle **25.** arcs that are next to each other

Lesson 10-1 pp. 616–622

Got It? 1. 108 m² **2.** 7.5 cm **3.** 30 in.² or $\frac{5}{24}$ ft² **4.** The area is doubled.

Lesson Check **1.** 200 m² **2.** 64 ft² **3.** 96 cm² **4.** 36 in.² **5.** No; two altitudes of an obtuse △ lie outside the △. The legs of a right △ are two altitudes of the △. **6.** Answers may vary. Sample: You can cut and paste a section of the ▱ to make a rectangle that is ≅ to the given rectangle. **7.** The area of △ABC is half the area of the ▱.

Exercises **9.** 26.79 in.² **11.** 11.2 units **13.** $16\frac{8}{11}$ units **15.** 13.5 yd² **17a.** 1390 ft² **b.** Find the entire area and subtract the areas for flowers.

c. $(50)(31) - 2\left[\frac{1}{2}(10)(16)\right] = 1550 - 160 = 1390$ ft² **19.** B **21.** 18 in.; 12 in. **25.** 6 units² **27.** 12 units² **29.** 3 units² **31.** The area is tripled; explanations may vary. Sample: If $A = \frac{1}{2}b \cdot h$, then $\frac{1}{2}(b \cdot 3h) = 3 \cdot \frac{1}{2}(b \cdot h) = 3A$.

33a. **b.** 18 units²

35a. **b.** 6 units²

37. 60 units² **39.** 20 units² **41.** 312.5 ft² **43.** 12,800 m² **50.** rotational, translational, glide reflectional **51.** rotational, translational **52.** 108 **53.** 72 **54.** 72 **55.** 36 **56.** 36 **57.** 36 **58.** $A = bh$ **59.** $A = \frac{1}{2}bh$ **60.** 9 units² **61.** 7 units² **62.** 12 units²

Lesson 10-2 pp. 623–628

Got It? 1. 94.5 cm² **2.** 12 m² **3.** 54 in.² **4.** 96 cm²

Lesson Check **1.** 42 m² **2.** 378 in.² **3.** 30 ft² **4.** 288 in.² **5.** 300 m² **6.** 8 cm² **7.** No; in the formula for the area of a trapezoid, half the sum of the bases would have to equal the length of the base of the parallelogram in order for the areas to be the same. This is not possible since the other base of the trapezoid will be longer or shorter than the given base. **8.** No; if you know the height, then you need only the lengths of the bases, but not the legs, to find the area. **9.** No; unless the rhombus is a square, you cannot calculate the area without knowing the lengths of the diagonals. **10.** No; you can calculate the area of a kite from the lengths of the diagonals, without knowing the lengths of the sides.

Exercises **11.** 472 in.² **13.** 108 ft² **15.** $\frac{5}{6}$ ft² **17.** 30 ft² **19.** 72 m² **21.** 18 m² **23.** 1200 ft² **25.** 24 m² **27.** about 35.4 cm² **29.** 11.3 cm² **31.** 1.8 m² **33.** 15 units² **35.** C **37.** 18 cm² **39.** $\frac{128\sqrt{3}}{3}$ in.² **41a.** $A = \frac{1}{2}b_1h$, $A = \frac{1}{2}b_2h$ **b.** Add the areas of the ▵ to get the area of the trapezoid: Area of trapezoid $= \frac{1}{2}b_1h + \frac{1}{2}b_2h = \frac{1}{2}h(b_1 + b_2)$. **48.** 72 cm² **49.** 15 ft **50.** 140 **51.** $25\sqrt{3}$ cm² **52.** 50 ft² **53.** $\frac{100\sqrt{3}}{3}$ m²

936

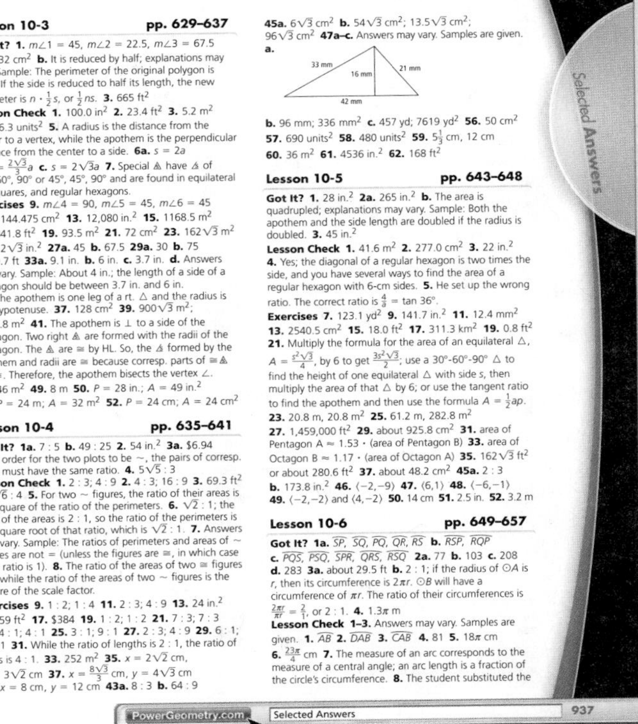

Lesson 10-3 pp. 629–637

Got It? 1. m∠1 = 45, m∠2 = 22.5, m∠3 = 67.5 **2a.** 232 cm² **b.** It is reduced by half; explanations may vary. Sample: The perimeter of the original polygon is n · s. If the side is reduced to half its length, the new perimeter is $n \cdot \frac{1}{2}s$, or $\frac{1}{2}ns$. **3.** 665 ft²

Lesson Check **1.** 100.0 in² **2.** 23.4 ft² **3.** 5.2 m² **4.** 166.3 units² **5.** A radius is the distance from the center to a vertex, while the apothem is the perpendicular distance from the center to a side. **6a.** $s = 2a$ **b.** $s = \frac{2\sqrt{3}}{3}a$ **c.** $s = 2\sqrt{3}a$ **7.** Special ▵ have ▵ of 30°, 60°, 90° or 45°, 45°, 90° and are found in equilateral ▵, squares, and regular hexagons.

Exercises **9.** m∠4 = 90, m∠5 = 45, m∠6 = 45 **11.** 2144.475 cm² **13.** 12,080 in.² **15.** 1168.5 m² **17.** 841.8 ft² **19.** 93.5 m² **21.** 72 cm² **23.** $162\sqrt{3}$ m² **25.** $12\sqrt{3}$ in.² **27a.** 45 **b.** 67.5 **29a.** 30 **b.** 75 **31.** 9.7 ft **33a.** 9.1 in. **b.** 6 in. **c.** 3.7 in. **d.** Answers may vary. Sample: About 4 in.; the length of a side of a pentagon should be between 3.7 in. and 6 in. **35.** The apothem is one leg of a rt. △ and the radius is the hypotenuse. **37.** 128 cm² **39.** $900\sqrt{3}$ m²; 1558.8 m² **41.** The apothem is ⊥ to a side of the pentagon. Two right ▵ are formed with the radii of the pentagon. The ▵ are ≅ by HL. So, the ▵ formed by the apothem and radii are ≅ because corresp. parts of ≅ ▵ are ≅. Therefore, the apothem bisects the vertex ∠. **48.** 46 m² **49.** 8 m **50.** P = 28 in.; A = 49 in.² **51.** P = 24 m; A = 32 m² **52.** P = 24 cm; A = 24 cm²

Lesson 10-4 pp. 635–641

Got It? 1a. 7 : 5 **b.** 49 : 25 **2.** 54 in.² **3a.** $6.94 **b.** In order for the two plots to be ∼, the pairs of corresp. sides must have the same ratio. **4.** $5\sqrt{5}$: 3

Lesson Check **1.** 2 : 3; 4 : 9 **2.** 4 : 3; 16 : 9 **3.** 69.3 ft² **4.** $\sqrt{6}$: 4 **5.** For two ∼ figures, the ratio of their areas is the square of the ratio of the perimeters. **6.** $\sqrt{2}$: 1; the ratio of the areas is 2 : 1, so the ratio of the perimeters is the square root of that ratio, which is $\sqrt{2}$: 1. **7.** Answers may vary. Sample: The ratios of perimeters and areas of ∼ figures are not = (unless the figures are ≅, in which case each ratio is 1). **8.** The ratio of the areas of two ≅ figures is 1, while the ratio of the areas of two ∼ figures is the square of the scale factor.

Exercises **9.** 1 : 2; 1 : 4 **11.** 2 : 3; 4 : 9 **13.** 24 in.² **15.** 59 ft² **17.** $384 **19.** 1 : 2; 1 : 2 **21.** 7 : 3; 7 : 3 **23.** 4 : 1; 4 : 1 **25.** 3 : 1; 9 : 1 **27.** 2 : 3; 4 : 9 **29.** 6 : 1; 36 : 1 **31.** While the ratio of lengths is 2 : 1, the ratio of areas is 4 : 1. **33.** 252 m² **35.** $x = 2\sqrt{2}$ cm, $y = 3\sqrt{2}$ cm **37.** $x = \frac{8\sqrt{3}}{3}$ cm, $y = 4\sqrt{3}$ cm **39.** x = 8 cm, y = 12 cm **43a.** 8 : 3 **b.** 64 : 9

45a. $6\sqrt{3}$ cm² **b.** $54\sqrt{3}$ cm²; $13.5\sqrt{3}$ cm²; $96\sqrt{3}$ cm² **47a–c.** Answers may vary. Samples are given. **a.**

b. 96 mm; 336 mm² **c.** 457 yd; 7619 yd² **56.** 50 cm² **57.** 690 units² **58.** 480 units² **59.** $5\frac{1}{3}$ cm, 12 cm **60.** 36 m² **61.** 4536 in.² **62.** 168 ft²

Lesson 10-5 pp. 643–648

Got It? 1. 28 in.² **2a.** 265 in.² **b.** The area is quadrupled; explanations may vary. Sample: Both the apothem and the side length are doubled if the radius is doubled. **3.** 45 in.²

Lesson Check **1.** 41.6 m² **2.** 277.0 cm² **3.** 22 in.² **4.** Yes; the diagonal of a regular hexagon is two times the side, and you have several ways to find the area of a regular hexagon with 6-cm sides. **5.** He set up the wrong ratio. The correct ratio is $\frac{4}{h}$ = tan 36°.

Exercises **7.** 123.1 yd² **9.** 141.7 in.² **11.** 12.4 mm² **13.** 2540.5 cm² **15.** 18.0 ft² **17.** 311.3 km² **19.** 0.8 ft² **21.** Multiply the formula for the area of an equilateral △, $A = \frac{s^2\sqrt{3}}{4}$, by 6 to get $\frac{3s^2\sqrt{3}}{2}$; use a 30°-60°-90° △ to find the height of one equilateral △ with side s, then multiply the area of that △ by 6; or use the tangent ratio to find the apothem and then use the formula $A = \frac{1}{2}ap$. **23.** 20.8 m, 20.8 m² **25.** 61.2 m, 282.8 m² **27.** 1,459,000 ft² **29.** about 925.8 cm² **31.** area of Pentagon A ≈ 1.53 · (area of Pentagon B) **33.** area of Octagon B ≈ 1.17 · (area of Octagon A) **35.** $162\sqrt{3}$ ft² or about 280.6 ft² **37.** about 48.2 cm² **45a.** 2 : 3 **b.** 173.8 in.² **46.** (−2, −9) **47.** (6,1) **48.** (−6, −1) **49.** (−2, −2) and (4, −2) **50.** 14 cm **51.** 2.5 in. **52.** 3.2 m

Lesson 10-6 pp. 649–657

Got It? 1a. $\overline{SP}$, $\overline{SQ}$, $\overline{PQ}$, $\overline{QR}$, $\overline{RS}$ **b.** $\widehat{RSP}$, $\widehat{RQP}$ **c.** $\widehat{PQS}$, $\widehat{PSQ}$, $\widehat{SPR}$, $\widehat{QRS}$, $\widehat{RSQ}$ **2a.** 77 **b.** 103 **c.** 208 **d.** 283 **3a.** about 29.5 ft **b.** 2 : 1; if the radius of ⊙A is r, then its circumference is 2πr. ⊙B will have a circumference of πr. The ratio of their circumferences is $\frac{2\pi r}{\pi r} = \frac{2}{1}$, or 2 : 1. **4.** 1.3π m

Lesson Check 1–3. Answers may vary. Samples are given. **1.** $\overline{AB}$ **2.** $\widehat{DAB}$ **3.** $\widehat{CAB}$ **4.** 81 **5.** 18π cm **6.** $\frac{23\pi}{4}$ cm **7.** The measure of an arc corresponds to the measure of a central angle; an arc length is a fraction of the circle's circumference. **8.** The student substituted the

PowerGeometry.com | Selected Answers 937

Selected Answers

diameter into the formula that requires the radius.
Exercises 9. $\widehat{BC}, \widehat{BD}, \widehat{CD}, \widehat{CE}, \widehat{DE}, \widehat{DF}, \widehat{EF}, \widehat{FB}$ **11.** $\widehat{BCE}, \widehat{BFE}, \widehat{CBF}, \widehat{CDF}$ **13.** 180 **15.** 270 **17.** 308 **19.** 90 **21.** 90 **23.** 270 **25.** 6π ft **27.** 14π in. **29.** 19 in. **31.** 8π ft **33.** 33π in. **35.** $\frac{5\pi}{4}$ m **37.** 70 **39.** 110 **41.** 235 **43.** about 183.3 ft **45.** Find the measure of the major arc, then use Thm. 10-10; or find the length of the minor arc using Thm. 10-10, then subtract that length from the circumference of the circle. **47.** 38 **49.** 31 m **51.** 3 : 4 **53.** 2.6π in. **55.** 7.9 units **64.** $m\angle 1 = 30$, $m\angle 2 = 15$, $m\angle 3 = 75$, $m\angle 4 = 30$ **65.** 18.6 mm **66.** Answers may vary slightly. Samples: 120 mm; 1116 mm^2 **67.** No; it could be an isosc. trapezoid. **68.** Yes; the diagonals bis. each other, so it is a ▱. **69.** Yes; one pair of sides is both ≅ and ∥, so it is a ▱. **70.** 17π in. or about 53.4 in. **71.** 3π cm or about 9.4 cm

Lesson 10-7 pp. 660–666

Got It? 1a. about 1385 ft^2 **b.** The area is $\frac{1}{4}$ the original area; explanations may vary. Sample: half the radius is $\frac{r}{2}$. So, if $A = \pi r^2$, then $\pi\left(\frac{r}{2}\right)^2 = \frac{1}{4}\pi r^2 = \frac{1}{4}A$.
2. 2π in.^{2} **3.** 4.6 m^2
Lesson Check 1. 64π in.^{2} **2.** $\frac{135}{8}\pi$ in.^{2}, or 16.875π in.^{2} **3.** $\left(\frac{4}{3}\pi - \sqrt{3}\right)$ m^2 **4.** A sector of a circle is a region bounded by an arc and the two radii to the endpoints of the arc. A segment is a part of a circle bounded by an arc and the seg. joining the arc's endpoints. **5.** No; the central ∠s corresponding to the arcs and the radii of the circles may be different. Circles with different radii do not have the same area. **6.** 6^2 was incorrectly evaluated as $6 \cdot 2$.
Exercises 7. 9π m^2 **9.** 0.7225π ft^2 **11.** about 282,743 ft^2 **13.** 40.5π yd^2 **15.** $\frac{169\pi}{6}$ m^2 **17.** 12π ft^2 **19.** $\frac{25\pi}{4}$ m^2 **21.** 24π in.^{2} **23.** 22.1 cm^2 **25.** 3.3 m^2 **27.** $(54\pi + 20.25\sqrt{3})$ cm^2 **29.** $(4 - \pi)$ ft^2 **31.** $(784 - 196\pi)$ in.^{2} **33.** 314 ft^2 **35.** 116 mm^2 **37.** 22.6 mm^2 **39.** 12 in. **41a.** Answers may vary. Sample: Subtract the minor arc segment from the area of the circle; or add the areas of the major sector and the △ that is part of the minor arc sector. **b.** $(25\pi - 50)$ units^2; $(75\pi + 50)$ units^2 **43.** 4.4 m^2 **55.** 10π cm **56.** 2π m **57.** 28π in. **58.** $11\frac{1}{4}$ in., $11\frac{1}{4}$ in., $11\frac{1}{4}$ in., $15\frac{1}{4}$ in. **59.** 4 : 9 **60.** $\frac{1}{6}$ **61.** $\frac{1}{3}$ **62.** $\frac{1}{2}$ **63.** $\frac{1}{2}$

Lesson 10-8 pp. 668–674

Got It? 1. $\frac{1}{2}$ or 50% **2.** $\frac{1}{5}$ or 20% **3.** $\frac{1}{2}$ or 50% **4a.** 0.04, or 4% **b.** The black zone; the area of the black zone is greater than the area of the red zone, so $P(\text{black zone}) > P(\text{red zone})$.
Lesson Check 1. $\frac{3}{7}$ **2.** $\frac{6}{7}$ **3.** $\frac{4}{7}$ **4.** $\frac{3}{7}$ **5.** about 0.09, or 9% **6.** $\frac{2}{3}$; explanations may vary. Sample: Since $\frac{SQ}{QT} = \frac{1}{2}$, you can let $SQ = x$ and $QT = 2x$, where x is not 0. Then $ST = 3x$ and the ratio $\frac{QT}{ST} = \frac{2x}{3x} = \frac{2}{3}$. **7.** The numerator should be (area of square − area of semicircles); the favorable region is the shaded region and its area is the area left when the areas of the semicircles are subtracted from the area of the square.
Exercises 9. $\frac{1}{10}$ **11.** $\frac{2}{5}$ **13.** $\frac{2}{5}$ **15.** $\frac{2}{5}$, or 40% **17.** $\frac{2}{9}$, or about 22% **19.** $\frac{5}{9}$, or about 56% **21.** $\frac{1}{49}$, or about 2% **23.** $\frac{24}{49}$, or about 49% **25.** $\frac{3}{10}$, or 30% **27.** $\frac{3}{20}$, or 15% **29.** $\frac{9}{19}$, or about 47% **31.** $\frac{1}{4}$; $m\widehat{AB} = 90$, so the length of $\widehat{AB} = \frac{90}{360} \cdot 2\pi r = \frac{1}{4} \cdot 2\pi r$. The ratio of the length of $\widehat{AB}$ to the circumference is $\frac{1}{4}$. **33.** $\frac{3}{5}$ **35.** $\frac{1}{10}$ **37.** $\frac{1}{40}$ **39.** $\frac{\pi}{20}$, or about 16% **41.** 36 s **43a.** about 8.7% **b.** about 19.6% **51.** 100π ft^2 **52.** 12π cm^2 **53.** rotational, reflectional **54.** reflectional **55.** reflectional

56. 57. 58. 59.

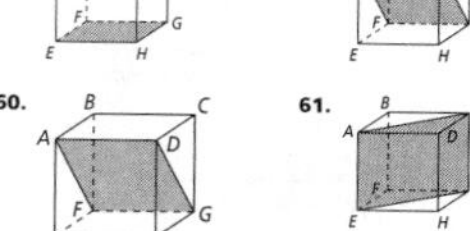

62. Sample:

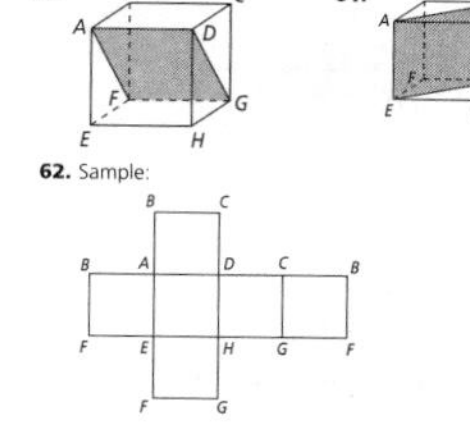

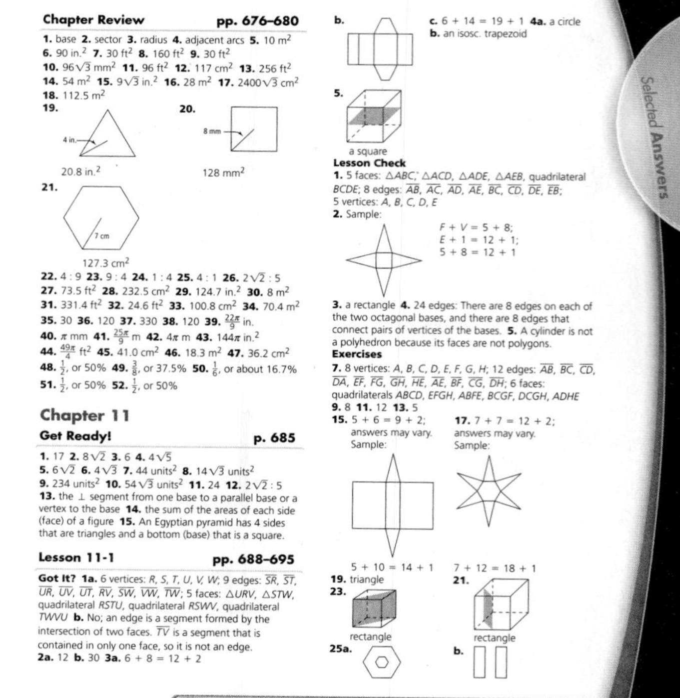

Chapter Review pp. 676–680

1. base **2.** sector **3.** radius **4.** adjacent arcs **5.** 10 m^2 **6.** 90 in.^{2} **7.** 30 ft^2 **8.** 160 ft^2 **9.** 30 ft^2 **10.** $96\sqrt{3}$ mm^2 **11.** 96 ft^2 **12.** 117 cm^2 **13.** 256 ft^2 **14.** 54 m^2 **15.** $9\sqrt{3}$ in.^{2} **16.** 28 m^2 **17.** $2400\sqrt{3}$ cm^2 **18.** 112.5 m^2

19. 4 in. — 20.8 in.^{2} **20.** 8 mm — 128 mm^2

21. 7 cm — 127.3 cm^2

22. 4 : 9 **23.** 9 : 4 **24.** 1 : 4 **25.** 4 : 1 **26.** $2\sqrt{2} : 5$ **27.** 73.5 ft^2 **28.** 232.5 cm^2 **29.** 124.7 in.^{2} **30.** 8 m^2 **31.** 331.4 ft^2 **32.** 24.6 ft^2 **33.** 100.8 cm^2 **34.** 70.4 m^2 **35.** 30 **36.** 120 **37.** 330 **38.** 120 **39.** $\frac{22\pi}{9}$ in. **40.** π mm **41.** $\frac{25\pi}{9}$ m **42.** 4π m **43.** 144π in.^{2} **44.** $\frac{49\pi}{4}$ ft^2 **45.** 41.0 cm^2 **46.** 18.3 m^2 **47.** 36.2 cm^2 **48.** $\frac{1}{2}$, or 50% **49.** $\frac{3}{8}$, or 37.5% **50.** $\frac{1}{6}$, or about 16.7% **51.** $\frac{1}{2}$, or 50% **52.** $\frac{1}{2}$, or 50%

Chapter 11

Get Ready! p. 685

1. 17 **2.** $8\sqrt{2}$ **3.** 6 **4.** $4\sqrt{5}$ **5.** $6\sqrt{2}$ **6.** $4\sqrt{3}$ **7.** 44 units^2 **8.** $14\sqrt{3}$ units^2 **9.** 234 units^2 **10.** $54\sqrt{3}$ units^2 **11.** 24 **12.** $2\sqrt{2} : 5$ **13.** the ⊥ segment from one base to a parallel base or a vertex to the base **14.** the sum of the areas of each side (face) of a figure **15.** An Egyptian pyramid has 4 sides that are triangles and a bottom (base) that is a square.

Lesson 11-1 pp. 688–695

Got It? 1a. 6 vertices: R, S, T, U, V, W; 9 edges: $\overline{SR}, \overline{ST}, \overline{UR}, \overline{UV}, \overline{UT}, \overline{RV}, \overline{SW}, \overline{VW}, \overline{TW}$; 5 faces: $\triangle URV$, $\triangle STW$, quadrilateral $RSTU$, quadrilateral $RSWV$, quadrilateral $TWVU$ **b.** No; an edge is a segment formed by the intersection of two faces. $\overline{TV}$ is a segment that is contained in only one face, so it is not an edge.
2a. 12 **b.** 30 **3a.** 6 + 8 = 12 + 2 **b.** **c.** 6 + 14 = 19 + 1 **4a.** a circle **b.** an isosc. trapezoid
5. a square
Lesson Check
1. 5 faces: $\triangle ABC$, $\triangle ACD$, $\triangle ADE$, $\triangle AEB$, quadrilateral $BCDE$; 8 edges: $\overline{AB}, \overline{AC}, \overline{AD}, \overline{AE}, \overline{BC}, \overline{CD}, \overline{DE}, \overline{EB}$; 5 vertices: A, B, C, D, E
2. Sample: $F + V = 5 + 8$; $E + 1 = 12 + 1$; $5 + 8 = 12 + 1$
3. a rectangle **4.** 24 edges: There are 8 edges on each of the two octagonal bases, and there are 8 edges that connect pairs of vertices of the bases. **5.** A cylinder is not a polyhedron because its faces are not polygons.
Exercises
7. 8 vertices: A, B, C, D, E, F, G, H; 12 edges: $\overline{AB}, \overline{BC}, \overline{CD}, \overline{DA}, \overline{EF}, \overline{FG}, \overline{GH}, \overline{HE}, \overline{AE}, \overline{BF}, \overline{CG}, \overline{DH}$; 6 faces: quadrilaterals $ABCD$, $EFGH$, $ABFE$, $BCGF$, $DCGH$, $ADHE$
9. 8 **11.** 12 **13.** 5
15. 5 + 6 = 9 + 2; answers may vary. Sample: 5 + 10 = 14 + 1 **17.** 7 + 7 = 12 + 2; answers may vary. Sample: 7 + 12 = 18 + 1
19. triangle **21.** rectangle **23.** rectangle
25a. **b.**

PowerGeometry.com | Selected Answers 939

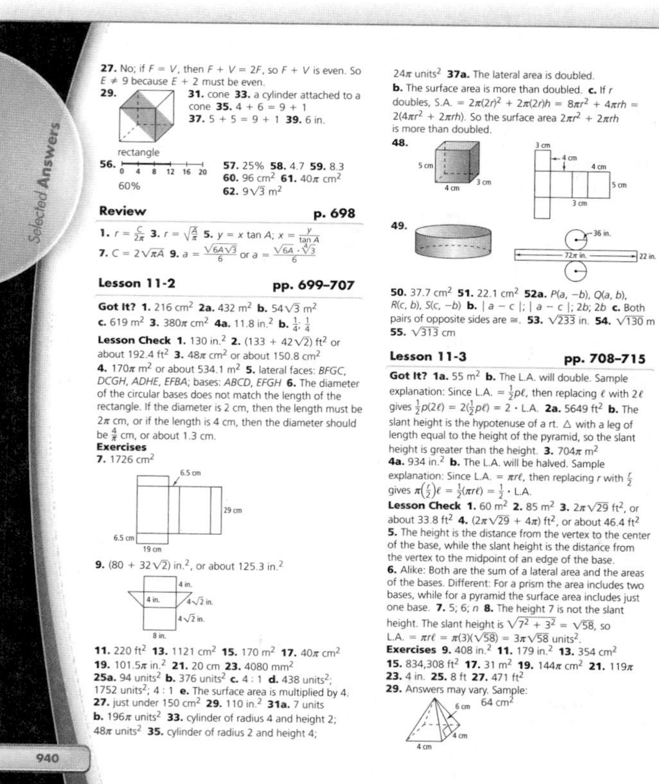

27. No; if $F = V$, then $F + V = 2F$, so $F + V$ is even. So $E \neq 9$ because $E + 2$ must be even.
29. rectangle **31.** cone **33.** a cylinder attached to a cone **35.** 4 + 6 = 9 + 1 **37.** 5 + 5 = 9 + 1 **39.** 6 in.
56. 0 4 8 12 16 20; 60% **57.** 25% **58.** 4.7 **59.** 8.3 **60.** 96 cm^2 **61.** 40π cm^2 **62.** $9\sqrt{3}$ m^2

Review p. 698

1. $r = \frac{C}{2\pi}$ **3.** $r = \sqrt{\frac{A}{\pi}}$ **5.** $y = x \tan A$; $x = \frac{y}{\tan A}$ **7.** $C = 2\sqrt{\pi A}$ **9.** $a = \frac{\sqrt{6A\sqrt{3}}}{6}$ or $a = \frac{\sqrt{6A} \cdot \sqrt[4]{3}}{6}$

Lesson 11-2 pp. 699–707

Got It? 1. 216 cm^2 **2a.** 432 m^2 **b.** $54\sqrt{3}$ m^2 **c.** 619 m^2 **3.** 380π cm^2 **4a.** 11.8 in.^{2} **b.** $\frac{1}{4}$; $\frac{1}{4}$
Lesson Check 1. 130 in.^{2} **2.** $(133 + 42\sqrt{2})$ ft^2 or about 192.4 ft^2 **3.** 48π cm^2 or about 150.8 cm^2 **4.** 170π m^2 or about 534.1 m^2 **5.** lateral faces: $BFGC$, $DCGH$, $ADHE$, $EFBA$; bases: $ABCD$, $EFGH$ **6.** The diameter of the circular bases does not match the length of the rectangle. If the diameter is 2 cm, then the length must be 2π cm, or if the length is 4 cm, then the diameter should be $\frac{4}{\pi}$ cm, or about 1.3 cm.
Exercises
7. 1726 cm^2 (6.5 cm, 29 cm, 6.5 cm, 19 cm)
9. $(80 + 32\sqrt{2})$ in.^{2}, or about 125.3 in.^{2} (4 in., 4 in., $4\sqrt{2}$ in., $4\sqrt{2}$ in., 8 in.)
11. 220 ft^2 **13.** 1121 cm^2 **15.** 170 m^2 **17.** 40π cm^2 **19.** 101.5π in.^{2} **21.** 20 cm **23.** 4080 mm^2 **25a.** 94 units^2 **b.** 376 units^2 **c.** 4 : 1 **d.** 438 units^2; 1752 units^2; 4 : 1 **e.** The surface area is multiplied by 4. **27.** just under 150 cm^2 **29.** 110 in.^{2} **31a.** 7 units **b.** 196π units^2 **33.** cylinder of radius 4 and height 2; 48π units^2 **35.** cylinder of radius 2 and height 4; 24π units^2 **37a.** The lateral area is doubled. **b.** The surface area is more than doubled. **c.** If r doubles, S.A. $= 2\pi(2r)^2 + 2\pi(2r)h = 8\pi r^2 + 4\pi rh = 2(4\pi r^2 + 2\pi rh)$. So the surface area $2\pi r^2 + 2\pi rh$ is more than doubled.
48. (5 cm, 4 cm, 3 cm; 3 cm, 4 cm, 4 cm, 5 cm, 3 cm)
49. (36 in., 72π in., 22 in.)
50. 37.7 cm^2 **51.** 22.1 cm^2 **52a.** $P(a, -b)$, $Q(a, b)$, $R(c, b)$, $S(c, -b)$ **b.** $|a - c|$; $|a - c|$; $2b$; $2b$ **c.** Both pairs of opposite sides are ≅. **53.** $\sqrt{233}$ in. **54.** $\sqrt{130}$ m **55.** $\sqrt{313}$ cm

Lesson 11-3 pp. 708–715

Got It? 1a. 55 m^2 **b.** The L.A. will double. Sample explanation: Since L.A. $= \frac{1}{2}p\ell$, then replacing ℓ with 2ℓ gives $\frac{1}{2}p(2\ell) = 2(\frac{1}{2}p\ell) = 2 \cdot$ L.A. **2a.** 5649 ft^2 **b.** The slant height is the hypotenuse of a rt. △ with a leg of length equal to the height of the pyramid, so the slant height is greater than the height. **3.** 704π m^2 **4a.** 934 in.^{2} **b.** The L.A. will be halved. Sample explanation: Since L.A. $= \pi r\ell$, then replacing r with $\frac{r}{2}$ gives $\pi\left(\frac{r}{2}\right)\ell = \frac{1}{2}(\pi r\ell) = \frac{1}{2} \cdot$ L.A.
Lesson Check 1. 60 m^2 **2.** 85 m^2 **3.** $2\pi\sqrt{29}$ ft^2, or about 33.8 ft^2 **4.** $(2\pi\sqrt{29} + 4\pi)$ ft^2, or about 46.4 ft^2 **5.** The height is the distance from the vertex to the center of the base, while the slant height is the distance from the vertex to the midpoint of an edge of the base. **6.** Alike: Both are the sum of a lateral area and the areas of the bases. Different: For a prism the area includes two bases, while for a pyramid the surface area includes just one base. **7.** 5; 6; n **8.** The height 7 is not the slant height. The slant height is $\sqrt{7^2 + 3^2} = \sqrt{58}$, so L.A. $= \pi r\ell = \pi(3)(\sqrt{58}) = 3\pi\sqrt{58}$ units^2.
Exercises 9. 408 in.^{2} **11.** 179 in.^{2} **13.** 354 cm^2 **15.** 834,308 ft^2 **17.** 31 m^2 **19.** 144π cm^2 **21.** 119π **23.** 4 in. **25.** 8 ft **27.** 471 ft^2
29. Answers may vary. Sample: 64 cm^2 (6 cm, 4 cm, 4 cm)

31. Cylinder; the L.A. of 2 cones is 30π in.^{2}, and the L.A. of the cylinder is 48π in.^{2}. **33a.** $\ell = \frac{\text{S.A.}}{\pi r} - r$ **b.** $r = \frac{-\pi\ell + \sqrt{\pi^2\ell^2 + 4\pi \cdot \text{S.A.}}}{2\pi}$ **35.** $s = 12$ m, L.A. $= 240$ m^2; S.A. $= 384$ m^2 **37.** cone with $r = 4$ and $h = 3$; 36π **49.** 76 ft^2 **50.** 127 in.^{2} **51.** 26 in. **52.** 4 cm^2 **53.** 176.7 in.^{2}

Lesson 11-4 pp. 717–724

Got It? 1a. 60 ft^3 **b.** No; explanations may vary. Sample: The volume is the product of the three dimensions, and multiplication is commutative. **2a.** 150 m^3 **b.** The volume is doubled. Using $V = B \cdot h$ and replacing h with $2h$ gives $B \cdot (2h) = 2 \cdot B \cdot h = 2 \cdot V$. **3a.** 3π m^3 **b.** The volume is $\frac{1}{4}$ the volume of the cylinder in part (a). Using $V = \pi r^2h$ and replacing r with $\frac{r}{2}$ gives $\pi\left(\frac{r}{2}\right)^2h = \frac{1}{4}\pi r^2h = \frac{1}{4} \cdot V$. **4.** 501 in.^{3}
Lesson Check 1. 54 ft^3 **2.** 339 in.^{3} **3.** Yes; it is a combination of a cylinder and a cone. **4.** Alike: Both are the product of the base area and the height. Different: For a prism the base is a polygon, while for a cylinder the base is a circle. **5.** The volumes are the same, 24 m^3, because multiplication is commutative.
Exercises 7. 80 in.^{3} **9.** 14 cm^3 **11.** 22.5 ft^3 **13.** 22.5 in.^{3} **15.** 40π cm^3; 125.7 cm^3 **17.** π yd^3; 3.1 yd^3 **19.** 144 cm^3 **21.** 1747 lb **23.** 40 cm **25.** 6 ft **27.** 96 ft^3 **29.** Volume is 27 times greater. Using $V = B \cdot h = \ell \cdot w \cdot h$ for a rectangular prism, $(3\ell) \cdot (3w) \cdot (3h) = 27 \cdot \ell \cdot w \cdot h = 27 \cdot V$. **31.** Answers may vary. Sample: If two plane figures have the same height and the same width at every level, then they have the same area. **33.** 80 units^3 **35.** bulk; cost of bags = \$1167.50, cost of bulk ≈ \$1164 **37.** 125.7 cm^3 **39.** cylinder with $r = 2$ and $h = 4$; 16π units^3 **41.** cylinder with $r = 2$ and $h = 4$; 16π units^3 **50.** 204.2 mm^2 **51.** 469.2 ft^2 **52.** 37 cm **53.** 240 ft

Lesson 11-5 pp. 726–732

Got It? 1. 32,100,000 ft^3 **2.** 960 m^3 **3a.** 77 ft^3 **b.** The volume of the original tepee is 8 times the volume of the child's tepee. **4a.** 144π m^3; 452 m^3 **b.** They are equal because both cones have the same base and same height.
Lesson Check 1. 96 in.^{3} **2.** 3.1 cm^3 **3.** Alike: Both formulas are $\frac{1}{3}$ the area of the base times height. Different: Because the bases are different figures, the base area will require different formulas. **4.** The areas of the bases are not equal; the area of the base of the pyramid is $13^2 = 169$ ft^2, but the area of the base of the cone is $\pi(6.5)^2 \approx 132.7$ ft^2.
Exercises 5. 200 cm^3 **7.** 50 m^3 **9.** 443.7 cm^3 **11.** 2048 m^3 **13.** 3714.5 mm^3 **15.** about 66.4 cm^3 **17.** $\frac{16}{3}\pi$ ft^3; 17 ft^3 **19.** 4π m^3; 13 m^3 **21.** Volume is halved; $V = \frac{1}{3}Bh$, so if h is replaced with $\frac{h}{2}$, then the volume is $\frac{1}{3}B\left(\frac{h}{2}\right) = \frac{1}{2}\left[\frac{1}{3}Bh\right]$. **23.** 123 in.^{3} **25.** 10,368 ft^3 **27a.** 79,000 m^3 **b.** $20\frac{2}{3}$ m, or about 20.7 m **29a.** 120π ft^3 **b.** 60π ft^3 **c.** 240π ft^3 **31.** 3 **33.** cone with $r = 4$ and $h = 3$; 16π **43.** 3600 cm^3 **44.** $JC > KN$ **45.** 7.1 in.^{2} **46.** 13 cm

Lesson 11-6 pp. 733–740

Got It? 1. 196π in.^{2}; 616 in.^{2} **2.** 100 in.^{2} **3a.** 113,097 in.^{3} **b.** The volume is $\left(\frac{1}{2}\right)^3 = \frac{1}{8}$ of the original volume. Using $V = \frac{4}{3}\pi r^3$, replacing r with $\frac{r}{2}$ gives $V = \frac{4}{3}\pi\left(\frac{r}{2}\right)^3 = \frac{1}{8}\left(\frac{4}{3}\pi r^3\right)$. **4.** 1258.9 ft^2
Lesson Check 1. 144π ft^2 **2.** 904.8 ft^3 **3.** 193 cm^2 **4.** 1 : 4 **5.** The surface area will quadruple, but the volume will be 8 times the original volume. $V = \frac{4}{3}\pi(2r)^3 = 8\left(\frac{4}{3}\pi r^3\right)$
Exercises 7. 400π in.^{2} **9.** $40{,}000\pi$ yd^2 **11.** 441π cm^2 **13.** 62 cm^2 **15.** 20 cm^2 **17.** $\frac{500}{3}\pi$ ft^3; 524 ft^3 **19.** $\frac{1125}{2}\pi$ in.^{3}; 1767 in.^{3} **21.** 2304π yd^3; 7238 yd^3 **23.** 451 in.^{2} **25.** 130 cm^2 **27.** Answers may vary. Sample: sphere with $r = 3$ in., cylinder with $r = 3$ in. and $h = 4$ in. **29.** 0.9 in. **31.** 1.7 lb **33.** An infinite number of planes pass through the center of a sphere, so there are an infinite number of great circles. **35.** 36π in.^{3} **37.** $\frac{500}{3}\pi$ mm^3 **39.** 288π cm^3 **41.** $\frac{1125}{2}\pi$ mi^3 **43a.** about 8.9 in.^{2} **b.** The answer is less than the actual surface area since the dimples on the golf ball add to the surface area. **45a.** on **b.** inside **c.** outside **47.** 38,792.4 ft^3 **49.** 22π cm^2; $\frac{46}{3}\pi$ cm^3 **51.** 22π cm^2; $\frac{14}{3}\pi$ cm^3 **53.** Answers may vary. Sample: You could lift the small ball because it weighs about 75 lb. The big ball would be much harder to lift since it weighs about 253 lb. **65.** 16 m^3 **66.** 19 in.^{3} **67.** 19,396 mm^3 **68.** 35; 55 **69.** 109, 71, 109, 71 **70.** yes; 3 : 1 **71.** yes; $3 : \sqrt{2}$ or $3\sqrt{2} : 2$

Lesson 11-7 pp. 742–749

Got It? 1. yes; 6 : 5 or $\frac{6}{5}$ **2a.** 2 : 3 **b.** No; the bases are similar but the heights may not be in the same ratio as the edges of the bases. **3.** 160 m^2 **4.** 4.05 lb
Lesson Check 1. Cone 1 and Cone 3 are similar; 2 : 3. **2.** about 155 in.^{2} **3.** Answers may vary. Sample: There are many relationships that must be true for the solids to be similar: all corresponding angles must be ≅; the corresponding faces must be similar and all corresponding edges and heights proportional. **4.** Your classmate found

PowerGeometry.com | Selected Answers 941

the scale factor of the smaller cube to the larger cube. The scale factor should be 8 : 7.
Exercises **5.** no **7.** yes; 2 : 3 **9.** yes; 2 : 3 **11.** 5 : 6 **13.** 3 : 4 **15.** 240 in.^{3} **17.** 24 ft^3 **19.** 112 m^2 **21.** 6000 toothpicks **23a.** It is 64 times the volume of the smaller prism. **b.** It is 64 times the weight of the smaller prism. **25.** No; explanations may vary. Sample: If the scale factor is $\frac{1}{10}$, then the weight of the smaller clock should be $\frac{1}{1000}$ the weight of the existing clock. **27.** about 1000 cm^3 **29.** No; the same increase to all the dimensions does not result in proportional ratios unless the original prism is a cube. **31a.** 3 : 1 **b.** 9 : 1 **33.** 864 in.^{3} **35.** 9 : 25; 27 : 125 **37.** 5 : 8; 25 : 64 **47.** about 1790 cm^2 and 1937 cm^2 **48.** 113.1 in.^{3} **49.** 8.2 m^3 **50.** 904.8 in.^{3} **51a.** $8\sqrt{3}$ mm, or about 13.9 mm **b.** $4\sqrt{21}$ mm, or about 18.3 mm **c.** $8\sqrt{7}$ mm, or about 21.2 mm **52.** 20 **53.** 15 **54.** 15

Chapter Review pp. 751–754

1. sphere **2.** pyramid **3.** cross section **4–5.** Answers may vary. Samples are given.

4. **5.**

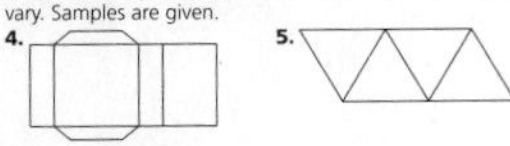

6. 8 **7.** 8 **8.** 5 **9.** a circle

10. **11.** 36 cm^2 **12.** 66π m^2 **13.** 208 in.^{2} **14.** 36π cm^2 **15.** 32.5π cm^2 **16.** 185.6 ft^2 **17.** 576 m^2 **18.** 50.3 in.^{2} **19.** 391.6 in.^{2}

20. $B = \frac{\text{S.A.} - \text{L.A.}}{2}$ **21.** 84 m^3 **22.** 24.5 ft^3 **23.** 410.5 yd^3 **24.** 13.9 m^3 **25.** S.A. = 314.2 in.^{2}; V = 523.6 in.^{3} **26.** S.A. = 153.9 cm^2; V = 179.6 cm^3 **27.** S.A. = 50.3 ft^2; V = 33.5 ft^3 **28.** S.A. = 8.0 ft^2; V = 2.1 ft^3 **29.** 904.78 cm^3 **30.** 314 m^2 **31.** 8.6 in.^{3}
32. Answers may vary. Sample:

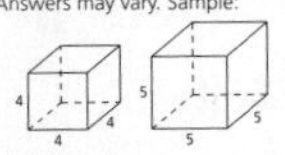

33. 27 : 64 **34.** 64 : 27 **35.** 324 pencils

Chapter 12

Get Ready! p. 759

1. 82 **2.** $6\frac{2}{3}$ **3.** 15 **4.** 25 **5.** $6\sqrt{2}$ **6.** 5 **7.** 6 **8.** 18 **9.** 24 **10.** 45 **11.** 60 **12.** $4\sqrt{2}$ **13.** 13 **14.** $\sqrt{10}$

15. 6 **16.** Answers may vary. Sample: A tangent touches a circle at one point. **17.** Answers may vary. Sample: An inscribed ∠ has its vertex on a circle and its sides are inside the circle. **18.** Answers may vary. Sample: An intercepted arc is the part of a circle that lies in the interior of an ∠.

Lesson 12-1 pp. 762–769

Got It? **1a.** 52 **b.** $x = 180 - c$ **2.** about 127 mi **3.** $5\frac{1}{3}$ **4.** no; $4^2 + 7^2 = 65 \neq 8^2$ **5.** 12 cm
Lesson Check **1.** 32 **2.** 6 units **3.** $\sqrt{63} \approx 7.9$ units **4.** Answers may vary. Sample: *Tangent ratio* refers to a ratio of the lengths of two sides of a rt. △, while *tangent to a circle* refers to a line or part of a line that is in the plane of a circle and touches the circle in exactly one point. **5.** If $\overline{DF}$ is tangent to ⊙E, then $\overline{DF} \perp \overline{EF}$. That would mean that △$DEF$ contains two rt. ∠s, which is impossible. So $\overline{DF}$ is not a tangent to ⊙E.
Exercises **7.** 47 **9.** 253.0 km **11.** 178.9 km **13.** 3.6 cm **15.** no; $5^2 + 15^2 \neq 16^2$ **17.** yes; $6^2 + 8^2 = 10^2$ **19.** 14.2 in. **21.** All 4 are ≅; the two tangents to each coin from A are ≅, so by the Transitive Prop. of ≅, all the tangents are ≅. **23.** 1. $\overline{BA}$ and $\overline{BC}$ are tangent to ⊙O at A and C. (Given) 2. $\overline{AB} \perp \overline{OA}$ and $\overline{BC} \perp \overline{OC}$ (If a line is tan. to a ⊙, it is ⊥ to the radius.) 3. △BAO and △BCO are rt. △s. (Def. of rt. △) 4. $\overline{AO} \cong \overline{OC}$ (Radii of a circle are ≅.) 5. $\overline{BO} \cong \overline{BO}$ (Refl. Prop. of ≅) 6. △BAO ≅ △BCO (HL) 7. $\overline{BA} \cong \overline{BC}$ (Corresp. parts of ≅ △s are ≅.) **25.** 1. ⊙A and ⊙B with common tangents $\overline{DF}$ and $\overline{CE}$ (Given) 2. $GD = GC$ and $GE = GF$ (Two tan. segments from a pt. to a ⊙ are ≅.) 3. $\frac{GD}{GC} = 1$, $\frac{GF}{GE} = 1$ (Div. Prop. of =) 4. $\frac{GD}{GC} = \frac{GF}{GE}$ (Trans. Prop. of =) 5. ∠DGC ≅ ∠EGF (Vert. ∠s are ≅.) 6. △GDC ~ △GFE (SAS ~ Thm.) **27.** 57.5
29. 4 units **36.** 3 : 4 or $\frac{3}{4}$ **37.** 9 : 16 or $\frac{9}{16}$ **38.** 27 : 64 or $\frac{27}{64}$ **39.** 29.1 **40.** 28.1 **41.** 68.2 **42.** $\frac{11\sqrt{2}}{2}$ **43.** 5 **44.** 28

Lesson 12-2 pp. 771–779

Got It? **1.** Since the circles are ≅, their radii are = and △s BOC and DPF are isosceles. So $\overline{OB} \cong \overline{OC} \cong \overline{PD} \cong \overline{DF}$. Since ∠$B$ ≅ ∠D and the △s are isosceles, ∠B ≅ ∠C ≅ ∠D ≅ ∠F. So △BOC ≅ △DPF by AAS. So ∠O ≅ ∠P.

Therefore, $\overline{BC} \cong \overline{DF}$ (either by corresp. parts of ≅ △s are ≅ or by within ≅ circles, ≅ central ∠s have ≅ chords) and $\widehat{BC} \cong \widehat{DF}$ (within ≅ circles, ≅ central ∠s have ≅ arcs). **2.** 16; ≅ chords are equidistant from the center **4.** $\overline{BA}$ is the hypotenuse of rt. △BAC, so the Pythagorean Theorem can be used.
Lesson Check **1.** 50; ∠COD ≅ ∠AOB (Vert. ∠s are ≅), so $\widehat{CD} \cong \widehat{AB}$ because ≅ central ∠s have ≅ arcs. Therefore, $m\widehat{CD} = m\widehat{AB}$. **2.** $\widehat{CA} \cong \widehat{BD}$ because in a circle ≅ chords have ≅ arcs. **3.** The distances are equal because in a circle ≅ chords are equidistant from the center. **4.** A radius is *not* a chord because one of its endpoints is not on the circle. A diameter *is* a chord because both of its endpoints are on the circle. **5.** Chords $\overline{SR}$ and $\overline{QP}$ are equidistant from the center, so their lengths must be equal.
Exercises **7.** Answers may vary. Sample: $\widehat{ET} \cong \widehat{GH} \cong \widehat{JN} \cong \widehat{ML}$; $\overline{ET} \cong \overline{GH} \cong \overline{JN} \cong \overline{ML}$; ∠$TFE$ ≅ ∠HFG; ∠JKN ≅ ∠MKL **9.** 8 **11.** The center is at the intersection of $\overline{GH}$ and $\overline{KM}$, because if a chord is the ⊥ bis. of another chord, then the first chord is a diameter; two diameters intersect at the center of a circle. **13.** 6 **15.** 20.8 **17.** 6 in. **19.** Since ∠AOB ≅ ∠COD, it follows that $m\angle AOB = m\angle COD$. Now $m\angle AOB = m\widehat{AB}$ and $m\angle COD = m\widehat{CD}$ (Definition of arc measure). So $m\widehat{AB} = m\widehat{CD}$ (Substitution). Therefore, $\widehat{AB} \cong \widehat{CD}$ (Definition of ≅ arcs). **21.** ⊙O with $\overline{AB} \cong \overline{CD}$ (Given); $\overline{AO} \cong \overline{BO} \cong \overline{CO} \cong \overline{DO}$ (All radii of a ⊙ are ≅); △AOB ≅ △COD (SSS); ∠AOB ≅ ∠COD (Corresp. parts of ≅ △s are ≅.); $\widehat{AB} \cong \widehat{CD}$ (≅ central ∠s have ≅ arcs.). **23.** 5 in. **25.** 10 ft **27.** 9.2 units **29.** The length of a chord or an arc is determined not only by the measure of the central ∠s, but also by the radius of the ⊙. **31.** 90 **33.** $\overline{XW} \cong \overline{XY}$ (All radii of a circle are ≅); X is on the ⊥ bis. of $\overline{WY}$ (Converse of ⊥ Bis. Thm.); ℓ is the ⊥ bis. of $\overline{WY}$ (Given); X is on ℓ (Subst. Prop.), so ℓ contains the center of ⊙X. **44.** 40 **45.** 5.5 **46.** 7.6 in. and 18.4 in. **47-49.** Answers may vary. Samples are given. **47.** $\widehat{STQ}$ **48.** $\widehat{ST}$ **49.** $\widehat{STR}$ **50.** 86 **51.** 180 **52.** 121

Lesson 12-3 pp. 780–787

Got It? **1a.** 90 **b.** $m\angle A = 95$, $m\angle B = 77$, $m\angle C = 85$, and $m\angle D = 103$ **c.** The sum of the measures of opposite ∠s is 180. **2.** $m\angle 1 = 90$, $m\angle 2 = 110$, $m\angle 3 = 90$, $m\angle 4 = 70$ **3a.** $x = 35$, $y = 55$ **b.** An inscribed ∠, and an ∠ formed by a tangent and chord, are both equal to half the measure of the intercepted arc. Since the ∠s intercept the same arc, their measures are = and they are ≅.
Lesson Check **1.** $\widehat{BD}$ **2.** ∠D **3.** ∠A and ∠C are suppl., and ∠B and ∠D are suppl. **4.** Sample answer: For inscribed ∠ABC, B is the vertex and A, B, and C are points on the circle. The intercepted arc of ∠ABC consists of points A, C, and all the points on the circle in the interior of ∠ABC. **5.** ∠A is not inscribed in a semicircle.
Exercises **7.** 180 **9.** $a = 54$, $b = 30$, $c = 96$ **11.** $a = 101$, $b = 67$, $c = 84$, $d = 80$ **13.** $a = 85$, $b = 47.5$, $c = 90$ **15.** $p = 90$, $q = 122$ **17.** $x = 65$, $y = 130$ **19.** Rectangle; opposite ∠s are ≅ (because figure is ▱) and suppl. (because opp. ∠s intercept arcs whose measures sum to 360). ≅ suppl. ∠s are rt. ∠s, so the inscribed ▱ must be a rectangle. **21a.** 40 **b.** 50 **c.** 40 **d.** 40 **e.** 65 **23.** $a = 26$, $b = 64$, $c = 42$ **25.** $a = 30$, $b = 60$, $c = 62$, $d = 124$, $e = 60$ **27.** ⊙S with inscribed ∠PQR (Given); $m\angle PQT = \frac{1}{2}m\widehat{PT}$ (Inscribed ∠ Thm., Case I); $m\angle RQT = \frac{1}{2}m\widehat{RT}$ (Inscribed ∠ Thm., Case I); $m\widehat{PR} = m\widehat{PT} - m\widehat{RT}$ (Arc Add. Post.); $m\angle PQR = m\angle PQT - m\angle RQT$ (∠ Add. Post.); $m\angle PQR = \frac{1}{2}m\widehat{PT} - \frac{1}{2}m\widehat{RT}$ (Subst. Prop.); $m\angle PQR = \frac{1}{2}m\widehat{PR}$ (Subst. Prop.) **29.** No; since opposite ∠s of a quadrilateral inscribed in a circle must be supplementary, the only rhombus that meets the criteria is a square. **31.** ⊙O, ∠A intercepts $\widehat{BC}$, and ∠D intercepts $\widehat{BC}$ (Given); $m\angle A = \frac{1}{2}m\widehat{BC}$ and $m\angle D = \frac{1}{2}m\widehat{BC}$ (Inscribed ∠ Thm.); $m\angle A = m\angle D$ (Subst. Prop.); ∠A ≅ ∠D (Def. of ≅ ∠s). **33.** Quadrilateral $ABCD$ inscribed in ⊙O (Given); $m\angle A = \frac{1}{2}m\widehat{BCD}$ and $m\angle C = \frac{1}{2}m\widehat{BAD}$ (Inscribed ∠ Thm.); $m\angle A + m\angle C = \frac{1}{2}m\widehat{BCD} + \frac{1}{2}m\widehat{BAD}$ (Add. Prop.); $m\widehat{BCD} + m\widehat{BAD} = 360$ (Arc measure of circle is 360); $\frac{1}{2}m\widehat{BCD} + \frac{1}{2}m\widehat{BAD} = 180$ (Mult. Prop.) $m\angle A + m\angle C = 180$ (Subst. Prop.); ∠A and ∠C are suppl. (Def. of suppl.); $m\angle B = \frac{1}{2}m\widehat{ADC}$ and $m\angle D = \frac{1}{2}m\widehat{ABC}$ (Inscribed ∠ Thm.); $m\angle B + m\angle D = \frac{1}{2}m\widehat{ADC} + \frac{1}{2}m\widehat{ABC}$ (Add. Prop.); $m\widehat{ADC} + m\widehat{ABC} = 360$ (Arc measure of circle is 360); $\frac{1}{2}m\widehat{ADC} + \frac{1}{2}m\widehat{ABC} = 180$ (Mult. Prop.) $m\angle B + m\angle D = 180$ (Subst. Prop.); ∠B and ∠D are suppl. (Def. of suppl. ∠s). **44.** 17.3 **45.** 34.6 **46.** 17.5 **47.** 5 : 2 or $\frac{5}{2}$ **48.** 57 **49.** 28.5 **50.** 2 **51.** 4

Lesson 12-4 pp. 790–797

Got It? **1a.** 250 **b.** 40 **c.** 40 **2a.** 160 **b.** The probe is closer; as an observer moves away from Earth, the viewing angle decreases and the measure of the arc of Earth that is viewed gets larger and approaches 180. **3a.** 13.8 **b.** 3.2
Lesson Check **1.** 5.4 **2.** 65 **3.** 11.2 **4.** 100, 260 **5.** A secant is a line that intersects a circle at two points; a tangent is a line that intersects a circle at one point. **6.** No; we can find the sum of the measures of the two arcs (in this situation, that sum is 230), but there is not enough information to find the measure of each arc.

7. The student forgot to multiply by the length of the entire secant seg.; the equation should be $(13.5)(6) = x^2$.
Exercises **9.** 50 **11.** 60 **13.** $x = 72$, $y = 36$ **15.** 15 **17.** 13.2 **19.** $x = 25.8$, $y \approx 12.4$ **21.** $360 - x$ **23.** $180 - y$ **25.** 16.7 **27.** 95, 104, 86, 75 **29.** $c = b - a$ **31.** ∠1 is a central ∠, so $m\angle 1 = x$; ∠2 is an inscribed ∠, so $m\angle 2 = \frac{1}{2}x$; ∠3 is formed by the secants, so $m\angle 3 = \frac{1}{2}(x - y)$. **33.** $x \approx 8.9$, $y = 2$ **35.** 1. ⊙ O with secants $\overline{CA}$ and $\overline{CE}$ (Given) 2. Draw $\overline{BE}$ (2 pts. determine a line.) 3. $m\angle BEC = \frac{1}{2}m\widehat{BD}$ and $m\angle ABE = \frac{1}{2}m\widehat{AE}$ (The measure of an inscribed ∠ is half the measure of its intercepted arc.) 4. $m\angle BEC + m\angle BCE = m\angle ABE$ (Ext. ∠ Thm.) 5. $\frac{1}{2}m\widehat{BD} + m\angle BCE = \frac{1}{2}m\widehat{AE}$ (Subst. Prop. of =) 6. $m\angle BCE = \frac{1}{2}m\widehat{AE} - \frac{1}{2}m\widehat{BD}$ (Subst. Prop. of =) 7. $m\angle BCE = \frac{1}{2}(m\widehat{AE} - m\widehat{BD})$ (Distr. Prop.) 8. ∠BCE ≅ ∠ACE (Refl. Prop. of ≅) 9. $m\angle ACE = \frac{1}{2}(m\widehat{AE} - m\widehat{BD})$ (Subst. Prop. of =)
37.
Given: A ⊙ with secant segments $\overline{XV}$ and $\overline{ZV}$
Prove: $XV \cdot WV = ZV \cdot YV$.
Proof: Draw $\overline{XY}$ and $\overline{ZW}$ (2 pts. determine a line); ∠XVY ≅ ∠ZVW (Refl. Prop. of ≅); ∠VXY ≅ ∠WZV (2 inscribed ∠s that intercept the same arc are ≅); △XVY ~ △ZVW (AA~); $\frac{XV}{ZV} = \frac{YV}{WV}$ (In similar figures, corresp. sides are proportional); $XV \cdot WV = ZV \cdot YV$ (Prop. of Proportion) **39a.** △ACD **b.** $\tan A = \frac{DC}{AC} = \frac{DC}{1} = DC$, length of tangent seg. **c.** secant $A = \frac{AD}{AC} = \frac{AD}{1} = AD$, length of secant seg. **48.** $a = 50$, $b = 55$, $c = 105$ **49.** $a = 55$, $b = 35$, $c = 30$ **50.** 30 **51.** 42 **52.** 57 **53.** 5.8 **54.** 12.8 **55.** 5.8

Lesson 12-5 pp. 798–803

Got It? **1a.** $(x - 3)^2 + (y - 5)^2 = 36$ **b.** $(x + 2)^2 + (y + 1)^2 = 2$ **2.** $(x - 4)^2 + (y - 3)^2 = 29$
3a. The center of the circle represents the cell tower's position. The radius represents the cell tower's transmission range.
b. center (2, 3); radius 10

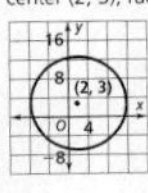

Lesson Check **1.** $x^2 + y^2 = 16$ **2.** $(x - 1)^2 + (y + 1)^2 = 5$ **3.** center (8, 0); radius 3 **4.** center (−2, 4); radius $\sqrt{7}$ **5.** its center and its radius; its center and its radius **6.** Using the two known points, use the Distance Formula to find the distance between them; that is the radius. Then use the center and the radius to write the standard equation for the circle. **7.** Sample explanation: The student should have rewritten the equation as $(x - 2)^2 + (y - (-3))^2 = 16$ to realize that the center is (2, −3).
Exercises **9.** $x^2 + (y - 3)^2 = 49$
11. $(x - 5)^2 + (y + 1)^2 = 144$
13. $(x + 9)^2 + (y + 4)^2 = 5$
15. $(x + 4)^2 + y^2 = 9$
17. $(x + 4)^2 + (y - 2)^2 = 16$
19. $(x + 2)^2 + (y - 6)^2 = 16$
21. $(x - 7)^2 + (y + 2)^2 = 52$
23. $(x - 6)^2 + (y - 5)^2 = 61$
25. center (−7, 5); radius 4 **27.** center (−4, 1); radius 5
29. position (5, 7); range 9 **31.** $x^2 + y^2 = 4$ **33.** $x^2 + (y - 3)^2 = 4$ **35.** $(x - 2)^2 + (y - 2)^2 = 16$ **37.** $(x - 4)^2 + (y - 3)^2 = 25$ **39.** $(x - 3)^2 + (y - 3)^2 = 8$ **41.** Yes; it is a circle with center (1, −2) and radius 3. **43.** No; the x term is not squared. **45.** $(x - 4)^2 + (y - 7)^2 = 36$
47. $(x - h)^2 + (y - k)^2 = r^2$
$(y - k)^2 = r^2 - (x - h)^2$
$y - k = \pm\sqrt{r^2 - (x - h)^2}$
$y = \pm\sqrt{r^2 - (x - h)^2} + k$
49. (4, −1), (−4, 1)
51. (2, 4) **53.** (3, 5)

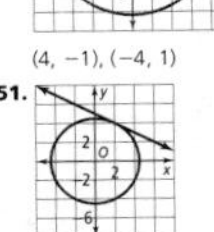

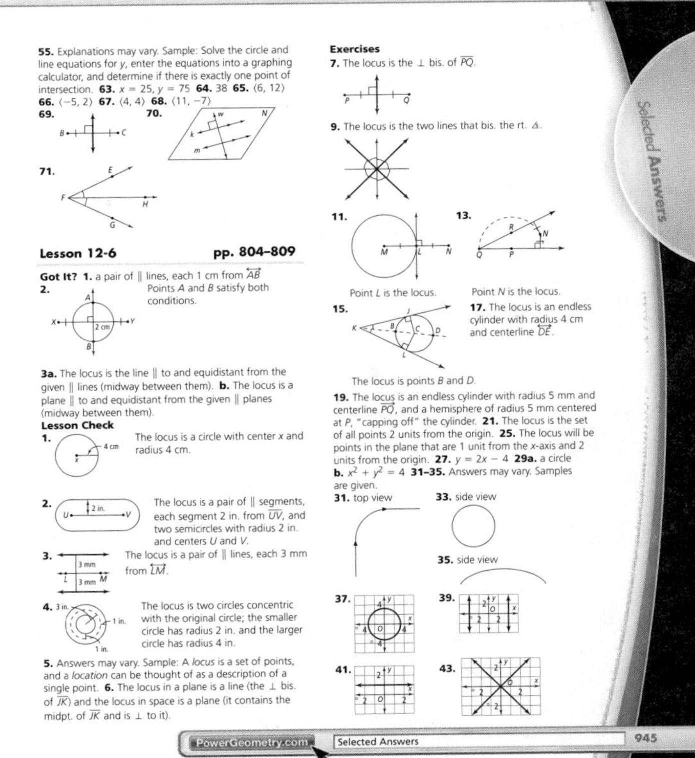

55. Explanations may vary. Sample: Solve the circle and line equations for y, enter the equations into a graphing calculator, and determine if there is exactly one point of intersection. **63.** $x = 25$, $y = 75$ **64.** 38 **65.** ⟨6, 12⟩ **66.** ⟨−5, 2⟩ **67.** ⟨4, 4⟩ **68.** ⟨11, −7⟩
69. **70.** **71.**

Lesson 12-6 pp. 804–809

Got It? **1.** a pair of ∥ lines, each 1 cm from $\overleftrightarrow{AB}$
2. Points A and B satisfy both conditions.
3a. The locus is the line ∥ to and equidistant from the given ∥ lines (midway between them). **b.** The locus is a plane ∥ to and equidistant from the given ∥ planes (midway between them).
Lesson Check
1. The locus is a circle with center x and radius 4 cm.
2. The locus is a pair of ∥ segments, each segment 2 in. from $\overline{UV}$, and two semicircles with radius 2 in. and centers U and V.
3. The locus is a pair of ∥ lines, each 3 mm from $\overleftrightarrow{LM}$.
4. The locus is two circles concentric with the original circle; the smaller circle has radius 2 in. and the larger circle has radius 4 in.
5. Answers may vary. Sample: A *locus* is a set of points, and a *location* can be thought of as a description of a single point. **6.** The locus in a plane is a line (the ⊥ bis. of $\overline{JK}$) and the locus in space is a plane (it contains the midpt. of $\overline{JK}$ and is ⊥ to it).

Exercises
7. The locus is the ⊥ bis. of $\overline{PQ}$.
9. The locus is the two lines that bis. the rt. ∠s.
11. Point L is the locus. **13.** Point N is the locus.
15. The locus is points B and D. **17.** The locus is an endless cylinder with radius 4 cm and centerline $\overleftrightarrow{DE}$.
19. The locus is an endless cylinder with radius 5 mm and centerline $\overrightarrow{PQ}$, and a hemisphere of radius 5 mm centered at P, "capping off" the cylinder. **21.** The locus is the set of all points 2 units from the origin. **25.** The locus will be points in the plane that are 1 unit from the x-axis and 2 units from the origin. **27.** $y = 2x - 4$ **29a.** a circle **b.** $x^2 + y^2 = 4$ **31–35.** Answers may vary. Samples are given.
31. top view **33.** side view **35.** side view
37. **39.** **41.** **43.**

45a. Sample: **b.** The locus is the ⊥ bis. of the base except for the midpt. of the base. **c.** Sample explanation: The vertex of the isosc. △ must be equidistant from the endpoints of the base, and all the points (in a plane) that are equidistant from two points lie on the ⊥ bis. of the segment whose endpoints are the two given points.
47. The locus is a circle of radius 11 cm, concentric with the original. **58.** $(x - 6)^2 + (y + 10)^2 = 25$
59. $(x - 1)^2 + (y - 7)^2 = 36$
60. $(x + 8)^2 + (y + 1)^2 = 13$ **61.** 510 in.^{2}
62. 175.9 ft^2 **63.** 4π units^2 **64.** $\frac{64\pi}{5}$ units^2
65. 10π units^2

Chapter Review pp. 811–814

1. secant of **2.** chord **3.** tangents to **4.** inscribed ∠ **5.** locus **6.** 20 units **7.** $\sqrt{3}$ **8.** 120 **9.** 90 **10.** 2 : 1 or $\frac{2}{1}$ **11.** $\overline{AB}$ is a diameter of the circle. **12.** 4.5 **13.** $\frac{\sqrt{181}}{2} \approx 6.7$ **14.** $a = 80, b = 40, c = 40, d = 100$ **15.** $a = 40, b = 140, c = 90$ **16.** $a = 118, b = 49, c = 144, d = 98$ **17.** $a = 90, b = 90, c = 70, d = 65$ **18.** 37 **19.** $a = 95, b = 85$ **20.** 6.5 **21.** 4 **22.** $x^2 + (y + 2)^2 = 9$ **23.** $(x - 3)^2 + (y - 2)^2 = 4$ **24.** $(x + 3)^2 + (y + 4)^2 = 25$ **25.** $(x - 1)^2 + (y - 4)^2 = 9$ **26.** center (7, −5); radius 6 **27.** The locus is the ray that bisects the ∠. **28.** The locus is a circle, concentric with the given circle, with radius 7 cm.
29. The locus is two lines, one on each side of the given line and ∥ to it, each at a distance of 8 in. from the given line. **30.** The locus consists of a cylinder with radius 6 in. that has $\overline{AB}$ as its centerline, along with two hemispheres with centers A and B, each with radius 6 in.

Skills Handbook

p. 824 **1.** Answer may vary slightly due to measuring method. Sample: 20 mm; 25 mm

3.

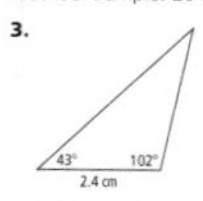

p. 825 **1.** right, scalene **3.** obtuse, isosceles **5.** Not possible; a rt. △ will always have one longest side opposite the rt. ∠.

7.

9.

p. 826 **1.** 0.4 **3.** 600 **5.** 1008 **7.** 15,000 **9.** 34,000 **11.** 4.3 **13.** 56 **15.** 3.9 **17.** 1,080,000 **19.** 12.6 **21.** $144\frac{4}{9}$ **23.** $\frac{3125}{4356}$

p. 827 **1.** $23\frac{1}{2}$ ft to $24\frac{1}{2}$ ft **3.** $339\frac{1}{2}$ mL to $340\frac{1}{2}$ mL **5.** 73.15 mm to 73.25 mm **7.** 10.8 cm to 11.2 cm **9.** 208 cm

p. 828 **1.** 18% **3.** 1% **5.** ≈ 9% **7.** ≈ 2%

p. 829 **1.** 121 **3.** 26.01 **5.** −36 **7.** 10 **9.** 8.6 **11.** $\frac{2}{3}$ **13.** ±7 **15.** ±1 **17.** ±6 **19.** ±5

p. 830 **1.** −50 **3.** 15 **5.** 2 **7.** 36 **9.** −2 **11.** 243 **13.** −20 **15.** −4 **17.** $2x + 3$ **19.** $-4x - 7$ **21.** $-4x^2 + 8x$ **23.** $-3t^2 + 4t$ **25.** $1 - 2r + r^2$ **27.** $7h - 1$ **29.** $2x^2 + 7x - 4$ **31.** $2y^2 - 3y$

p. 831 **1.** $\frac{5}{3}$ **3.** $\frac{2}{3}$ **5.** $\frac{1}{2x}$ **7.** $\frac{22x}{35}$ **9.** $16y$ **11.** $\frac{x + 1}{2}$ **13.** $\frac{1}{10t}$ **15.** $\frac{3y}{2}$ **17.** $\frac{\pi}{r + \pi}$ **19.** $\frac{5}{12}$ **21.** $\frac{5}{13}$ **23.** $\frac{12}{5}$

p. 832 **1.** 8 **3.** 22 **5.** −5 **7.** −10 **9.** 13 **11.** 10 **13.** −16 or 16 **15.** −20 or 20

p. 833 **1.** (0, −3) **3.** (4, 3)

5–8. **9.** y-axis **11.** x-axis

p. 834 **1.** 5 **3.** 3 **5.** $\frac{2}{3}$ **7.** $\frac{1}{2}$ **9.** −5 **11.** −12 **13.** $35 - 2x = 9$; 13

p. 835 **1.** 0.5 **3.** 0.06 **5.** 1.09 **7.** 8.4 **9.** 7.2 **11–14.** Answers may vary. Samples are given. **11.** 7 **13.** 45

p. 836 **1.** $\frac{1}{2}$ **3.** $\frac{2}{7}$ **5.** $\frac{4}{13}$ **7.** $\frac{1}{6}$ **9.** $\frac{1}{2}$ **11.** $\frac{1}{3}$ **13.** $\frac{3}{8}$ **15.** $\frac{1}{2}$ **17.** $\frac{1}{4}$

Additional Answers

Chapter 1

Lesson 1-1

Got It? **page 5**

2a. Answers may vary. Sample:

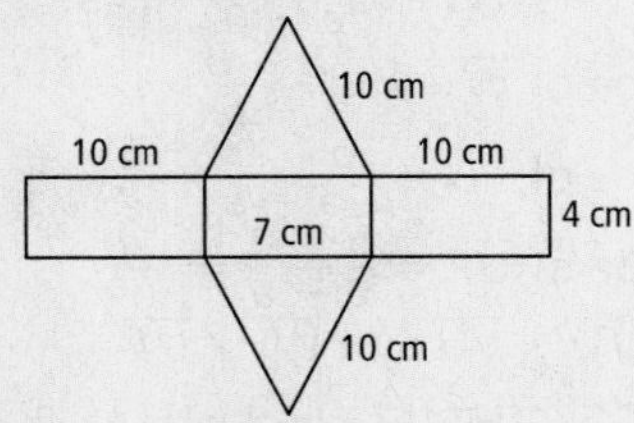

b. Yes; answers may vary. Sample:

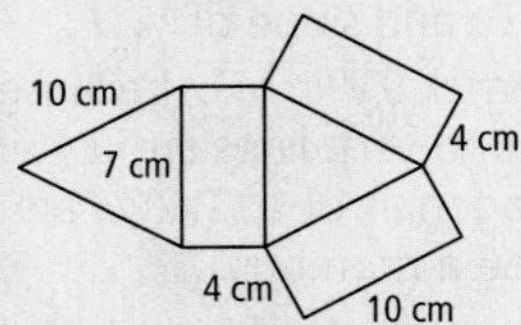

Lesson 1-6

Practice and Problem-Solving Exercises **page 48**

35.

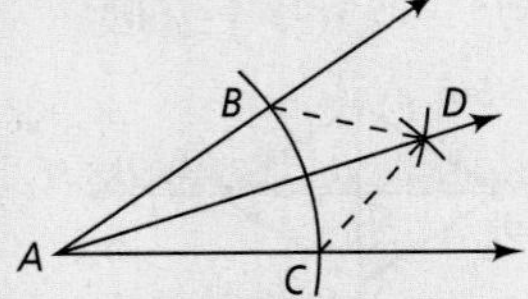

In the angle bisector construction, $\overline{AB} \cong \overline{AC}$, $\overline{BD} \cong \overline{CD}$, and $\overline{AD} \cong \overline{AD}$. Using the statement that two triangles are ≅ if three pairs of sides are ≅, then $\triangle ABD \cong \triangle ACD$. Since the ⚠ are ≅, each ∠ of one △ is ≅ to an ∠ of the other △. So, $\angle BAD \cong \angle CAD$ and $\overrightarrow{AD}$ is the ∠ bisector of $\angle BAC$.

36. D

37. I

38. [2] $x^2 - 2 = x$
$x^2 - x - 2 = 0$
$(x - 2)(x + 1) = 0$
$x - 2 = 0$ or $x + 1 = 0$
$x = 2$ or $x = -1$ (not possible)
$x = 2$

[1] incomplete steps OR both values for x OR incorrect factoring of equation OR incorrect equation

39. 116

40. yes; $m\angle TUV + m\angle VUW = 180$

41. 6 **42.** 10

43. 4 **44.** 3

45. 196 **46.** 10

47. −1

Chapter 3

Lesson 3-6

Practice and Problem-Solving Exercises **page 186**

7.

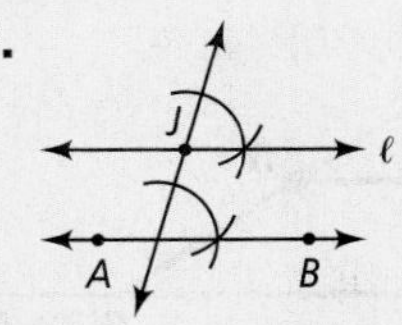

8.

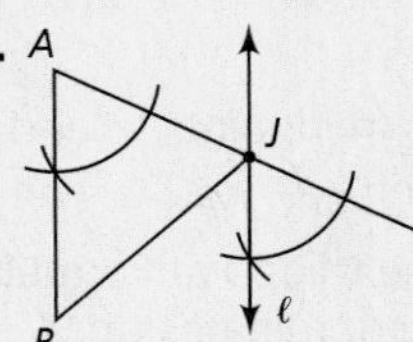

9.

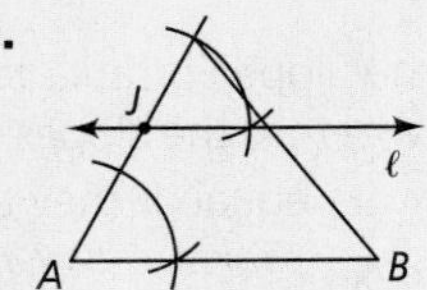

10.

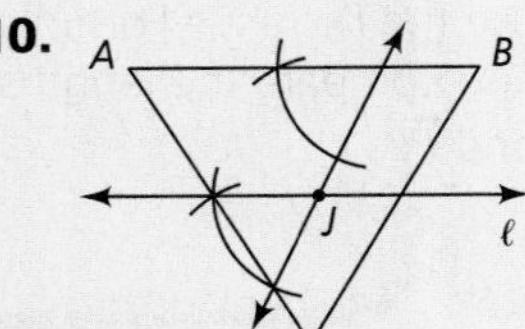

11–13. Constructions may vary. Samples using the following segments are given.

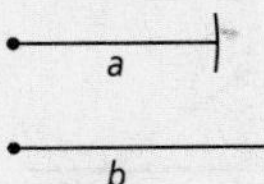

11.

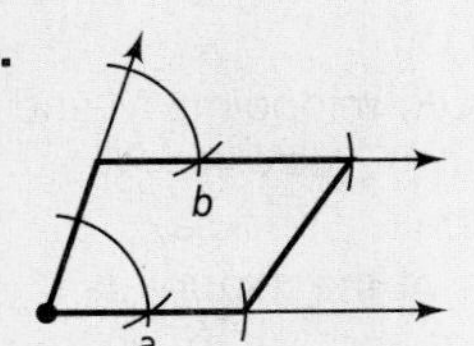

12.

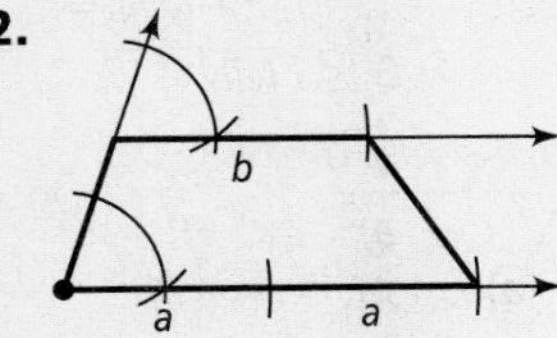

13.

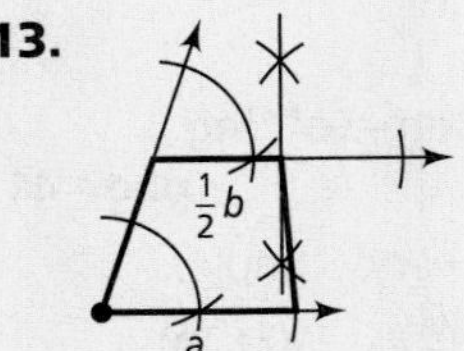

14.

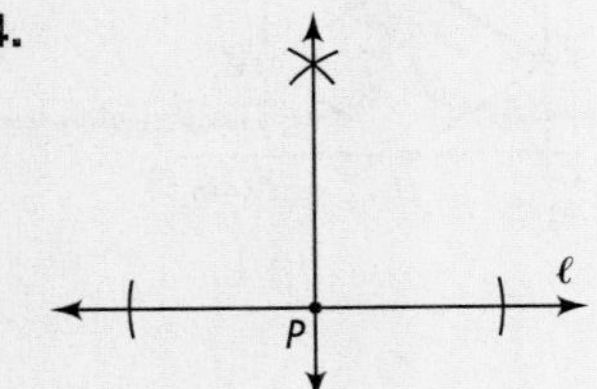

15.

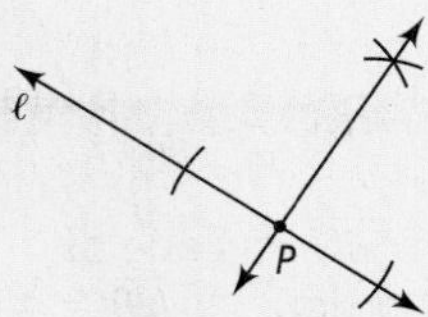

16.

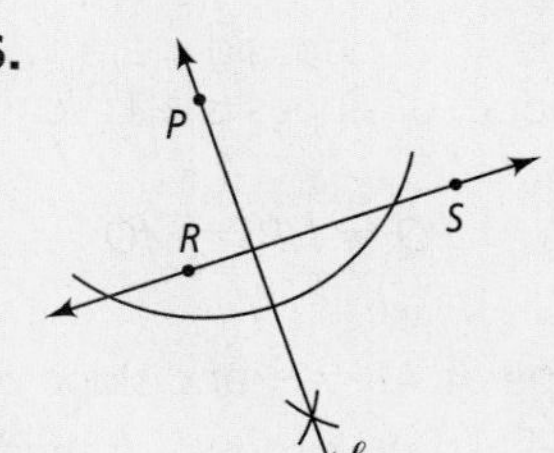

17.

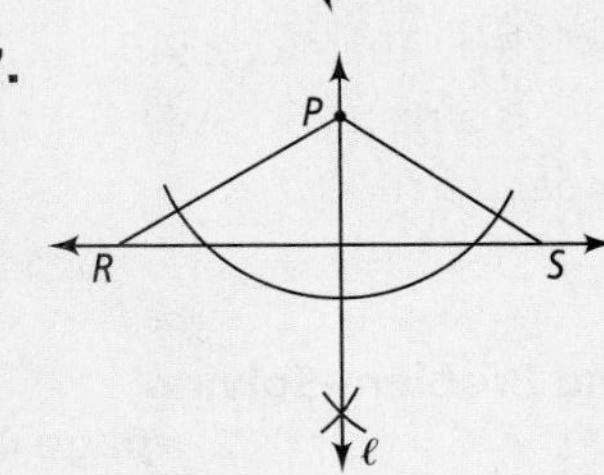

18.

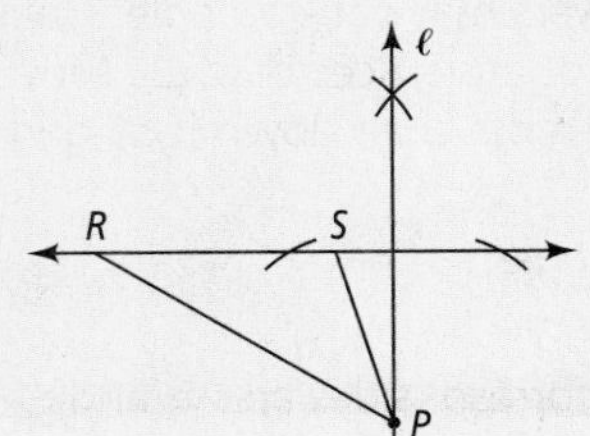

19.

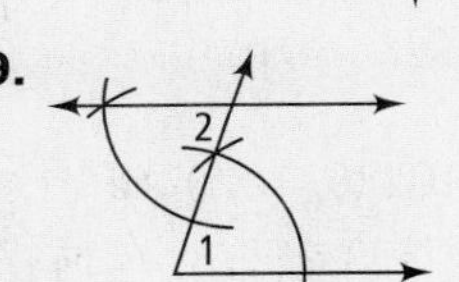

20.

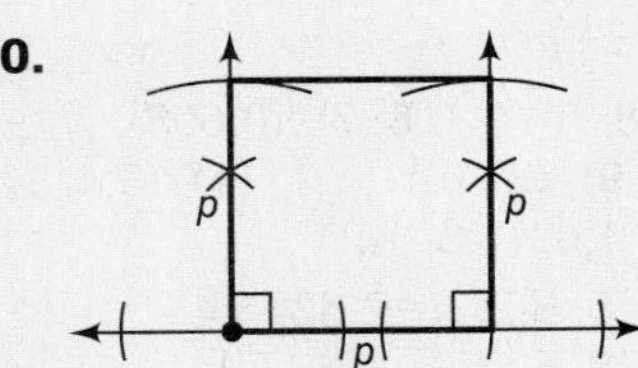

Chapter 4

Lesson 4-7

Got It? **page 267**

4. Using $\overline{AD} \cong \overline{AD}$ (Refl. Prop. of ≅) and the two given pairs of ≅ ⚠, $\triangle ACD \cong \triangle AED$ by AAS. Then $\overline{CD} \cong \overline{ED}$ (Corresp. parts of ≅ ⚠ are ≅.) and $\angle BDC \cong \angle FDE$ (Vert. ⚠ are ≅.). Therefore, $\triangle BDC \cong \triangle FDE$ by ASA, and $\overline{BD} \cong \overline{FD}$ because corresp. parts of ≅ ⚠ are ≅.

Chapter 6

Lesson 6-7

Got It? **page 401**

1. scalene

2a. Yes; slope of $\overline{MN}$ = slope of $\overline{PQ} = -3$ and slope of $\overline{NP}$ = slope of $\overline{MQ} = \frac{1}{3}$, so opp. sides are ∥. The product of slopes is −1, so sides are ⊥.

b. Yes; $MN = PQ = NP = MQ = \sqrt{10}$.

c. Yes; slope of $\overline{AB} = \frac{3}{4}$ and slope of $\overline{BC} = -\frac{4}{3}$, so the product of their slopes is −1. Therefore, $\overline{AB} \perp \overline{BC}$ and ∠B is a rt. ∠. So △ABC is a rt. △ by def. of rt. △.

Lesson 6-7

Practice and Problem-Solving Exercises **page 405**

37. Answers may vary. Sample: Chairs are not at vertices of a ▱. Move right-most chair down by 1 grid unit.

38a. rectangle

b. rectangle

c. Yes; corresp. sides are ≅ and corresp. ∠s are ≅ (rt. ∠s), so *ABCD* ≅ *EFGH*.

39. G(−4, 1), H(1, 3)

40. (0, 7.5), (3, 10), (6, 12.5)

41. $\left(-1, 6\frac{2}{3}\right), \left(1, 8\frac{1}{3}\right), (3, 10), \left(5, 11\frac{2}{3}\right), \left(7, 13\frac{1}{3}\right)$

42. (−1.8, 6), (−0.6, 7), (0.6, 8), (1.8, 9), (3, 10), (4.2, 11), (5.4, 12), (6.6, 13), (7.8, 14)

43. (−2.76, 5.2), (−2.52, 5.4), (−2.28, 5.6), . . . , (8.52, 14.6), (8.76, 14.8)

44. $\left(-3 + a\left(\frac{12}{n}\right), 5 + a\left(\frac{10}{n}\right)\right)$ for $a = 1, 2, 3, \ldots, n - 1$

45. D

46. G

47. A

48. [2] No; the slope of $\overline{AC}$ is 0, the slope of $\overline{AB}$ is $-\frac{3}{2}$, and the slope of $\overline{BC}$ is 1. No slopes have product of −1, so the sides are not ⊥.

[1] correct answer with no explanation

49. $m\angle 1 = 62$, $m\angle 2 = m\angle 3 = 118$, $x = 2.5$

50. (3, 2)

51. (−3, −4)

52. −1

53. 0

54. $\frac{b}{c + d - a}$

Lesson 6-8

Got It? **page 409**

3.

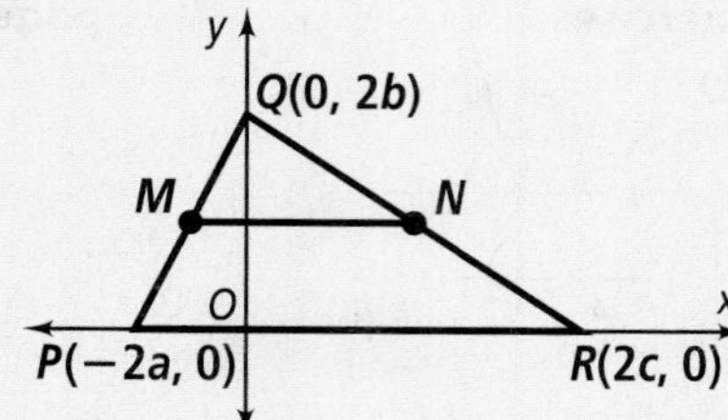

Given: △PQR, midpoints M and N

Prove: $\overline{MN} \parallel \overline{PR}$ and $MN = \frac{1}{2}PR$

- First, use the Midpoint Formula to find the coordinates of M and N.
- Then, use the Slope Formula to determine whether the slopes of $\overline{MN}$ and $\overline{PR}$ are equal. If they are, then $\overline{MN} \parallel \overline{PR}$.
- Finally, use the Distance Formula to find and compare the lengths of $\overline{MN}$ and $\overline{PR}$.

Lesson 6-9

Got It? **page 415**

2. Answers may vary. Sample:

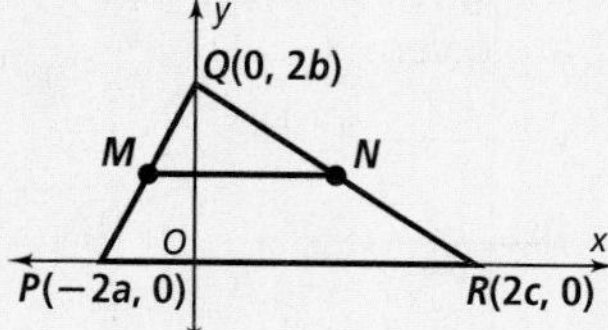

Given: △PQR, midpoints M and N
Prove: $\overline{MN} \parallel \overline{PR}$, $MN = \frac{1}{2}PR$
By the Midpoint Formula, coordinates of the midpoints are M(−a, b) and N(c, b). By the Slope Formula, slope of $\overline{MN}$ = slope of $\overline{PR} = 0$, so $\overline{MN} \parallel \overline{PR}$.

By the Distance Formula, $MN = \sqrt{(c + a)^2}$ and $PR = 2\sqrt{(c + a)^2}$, so $MN = \frac{1}{2}PR$.

Lesson 6-9

Practice and Problem-Solving Exercises **page 417**

19. Answers may vary. Sample:

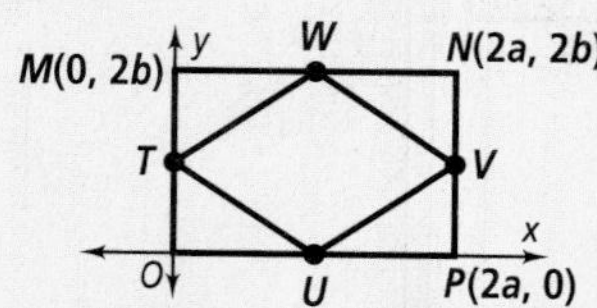

Given: *MNPO* is a rectangle. *T, W, V, U* are midpoints of its sides.

Prove: *TWVU* is a rhombus.

By the Midpoint Formula, the coordinates of the midpoints are T(0, b), W(a, 2b), V(2a, b), and U(a, 0). By the Slope Formula,

slope of $\overline{TW} = \frac{2b - b}{a - 0} = \frac{b}{a}$

slope of $\overline{WV} = \frac{2b - b}{a - 2a} = -\frac{b}{a}$

slope of $\overline{VU} = \frac{b - 0}{2a - a} = \frac{b}{a}$

slope of $\overline{UT} = \frac{b - 0}{0 - a} = -\frac{b}{a}$

So $\overline{TW} \parallel \overline{VU}$ and $\overline{WV} \parallel \overline{UT}$. Therefore, *TWVU* is a ▱.

By the Slope Formula, slope of $\overline{TV} = 0$, and slope of $\overline{WU}$ is undefined. $\overline{TV} \perp \overline{WU}$ because horiz. and vert. lines are ⊥. Since the diagonals of ▱*TWVU* are ⊥, it must be a rhombus.

20. Answers may vary. Sample: Lines are ⊥ when product of their slopes is −1; it is difficult to find the product without using coordinate methods.

21. Answers may vary. Sample:

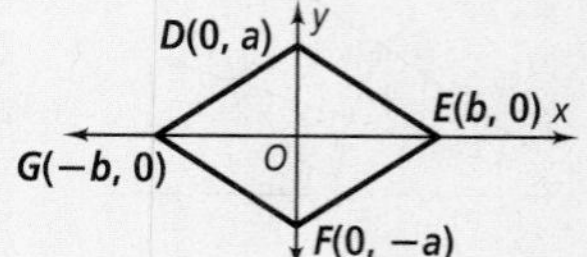

Given: *DEFG* is a rhombus.
Prove: $\overline{GE} \perp \overline{DF}$
By the Slope Formula, slope of $\overline{GE} = \frac{0 - 0}{b - (-b)} = 0$, and slope of $\overline{DF} = \frac{a - (-a)}{0 - 0}$, which is undefined. So $\overline{GE}$ must be horizontal and $\overline{DF}$ must be vertical. Therefore, $\overline{GE} \perp \overline{DF}$ because horiz. and vert. lines are ⊥.

22. Answers may vary. Sample:

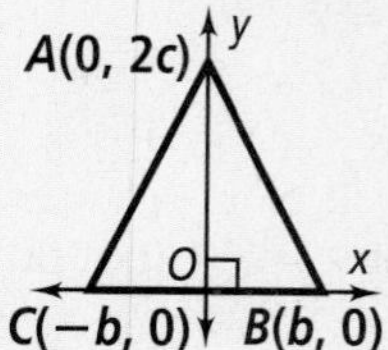

Given: Isosc. △ABC with base $\overline{BC}$ and altitude $\overline{AO}$
Prove: $\overline{AO}$ bisects $\overline{BC}$.
By the Distance Formula, $CO = \sqrt{[0 - (-b)]^2 + (0 - 0)^2} = b$ and $BO = \sqrt{(b - 0)^2 + (0 - 0)^2} = b$. Since $CO = BO$, $\overline{CO} \cong \overline{BO}$, so $\overline{AO}$ bisects $\overline{BC}$ by def. of seg. bisect.

23. Answers may vary. Sample:

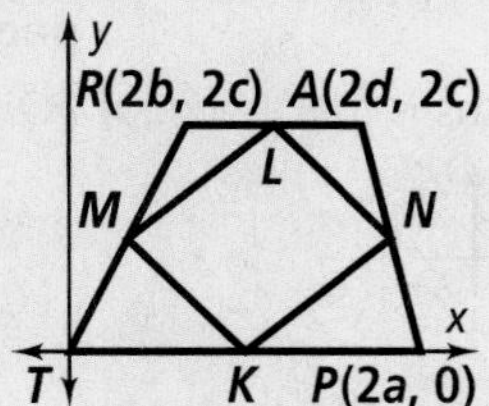

Given: Trapezoid *TRAP*, *M*, *L*, *N*, and *K* are midpoints of its sides
Prove: *MLNK* is a ▱.
By the Midpoint Formula, the coordinates of the midpoints are $M(b, c)$, $L(b + d, 2c)$, $N(a + d, c)$, and $K(a, 0)$. By the Slope Formula, the slope of $\overline{ML} = \frac{c}{d}$, the slope of $\overline{LN} = \frac{c}{b - a}$, the slope of $\overline{NK} = \frac{c}{d}$, and the slope of $\overline{KM} = \frac{c}{b - a}$. Since slopes are =, $\overline{ML} \parallel \overline{NK}$ and $\overline{LN} \parallel \overline{KM}$. Therefore, *MLNK* is a ▱ by def. of ▱.

24. Answers may vary. Sample:

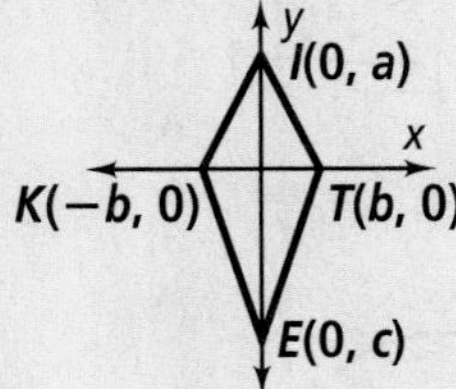

Given: Kite *KITE*
Prove: $\triangle KIE \cong \triangle TIE$
By the Distance Formula, $KI = IT = \sqrt{a^2 + b^2}$ and $KE = TE = \sqrt{b^2 + c^2}$, and $IE = \sqrt{(a - c)^2}$. $\overline{IE} \cong \overline{IE}$ by the Refl. Prop. of ≅. So $\triangle KIE \cong \triangle TIE$ by SSS.

25a. $L(3q, 3r)$, $M(3p + 3q, 3r)$, $N(3p, 0)$

b. equation of $\overleftrightarrow{AM}$: $y = \frac{r}{p + q}x$
equation of $\overleftrightarrow{BN}$:
$y = \frac{2r}{2q - p}(x - 3p)$ equation of $\overleftrightarrow{CL}$: $y = \frac{r}{q - 2p}(x - 6p)$

c. $P(2p + 2q, 2r)$

d. The coordinates of *P* satisfy the equation for $\overleftrightarrow{CL}$:

$$y = \frac{r}{q - 2p}(x - 6p).$$
$$2r = \frac{r}{q - 2p}(2p + 2q - 6p)$$
$$2r = \frac{r}{q - 2p}(2q - 4p)$$
$$2r = 2r$$

e.

$$AM = \sqrt{(3p + 3q - 0)^2 + (3r - 0)^2} = \sqrt{(3p + 3q)^2 + (3r)^2};$$
$$\frac{2}{3}AM = \frac{2}{3}\sqrt{(3p + 3q)^2 + (3r)^2} =$$
$$\sqrt{\frac{4}{9}\left[(3p + 3q)^2 + (3r)^2\right]} =$$
$$\sqrt{\left[\frac{4}{9}(3p + 3q)^2\right] + \left[\frac{4}{9}(3r)^2\right]} =$$
$$\sqrt{\left[\frac{4}{9}(9p^2 + 18pq + 9q^2)\right] + \left[\frac{4}{9}(9r^2)\right]} =$$
$$\sqrt{(4p^2 + 8pq + 4q^2) + (4r^2)} =$$
$$\sqrt{(2p + 2q)^2 + (2r)^2};$$
$$AP = \sqrt{(2p + 2q - 0)^2 + (2r - 0)^2} =$$
$$\sqrt{(2p + 2q)^2 + (2r)^2}$$

So $AP = \frac{2}{3}AM$. You can find the other two distances similarly.

26a. $\frac{b}{c}$

b. The point-slope formula for point $(a, 0)$ and $m = \frac{b}{c}$ is $y - 0 = \frac{b}{c}(x - a)$ or $y = \frac{b}{c}(x - a)$.

c. $x = 0$

d. The ordered pair $\left(0, \frac{-ab}{c}\right)$ satisfies the equation of line *q*, $x = 0$. When $x = 0$, $y = \frac{b}{c}(x - a)$ $= \frac{b}{c}(0 - a) = \frac{-ab}{c}$. So *p* and *q* intersect at $\left(0, -\frac{ab}{c}\right)$.

e. $\frac{a}{c}$

f. The point-slope formula for point $(b, 0)$ and $m = \frac{a}{c}$ is $y - 0 = \frac{a}{c}(x - b)$ or $y = \frac{a}{c}(x - b)$.

g. The ordered pair $\left(0, \frac{-ab}{c}\right)$ satisfies the equation of line *q*, $x = 0$. When $x = 0$, $y = \frac{a}{c}(x - b) = \frac{a}{c}(0 - b) = \frac{-ab}{c}$. So *q* and *r* intersect at $\left(0, -\frac{ab}{c}\right)$.

h. $\left(0, \frac{-ab}{c}\right)$

27a. Answers may vary. Sample: The area of a △ with base *b* and height *c* is $\frac{1}{2}bc$. The area of a △ with base *d* and height *a* is $\frac{1}{2}ad$. In both cases, the remaining area of the triangle has base $(b - d)$ and height *a*. Therefore $\frac{1}{2}ad = \frac{1}{2}bc$ by the Transitive Prop. of Eq. So $ad = bc$.

b. Slope of $\ell = \frac{a}{b}$ or $\frac{c}{d}$. So $\frac{a}{b} = \frac{c}{d}$ and $ad = bc$.

Chapter 9

Lesson 9-2

Lesson Check page 555

1. (−4, −3)

2. (4, 2)

3.

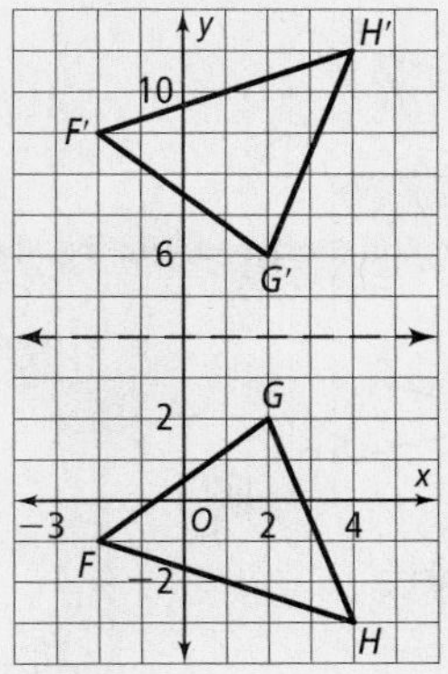

4. The line of reflection is the ⊥ bis. of any seg. whose endpts. are corresp. pts. of the preimage and image.

5. $\overline{AA'}$ should be ⊥ to *r*.

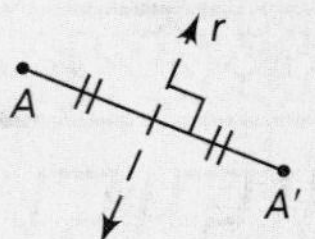

6. $(-x, y)$; $(x, -y)$

Lesson 9-6

Got It? page 585

1a.

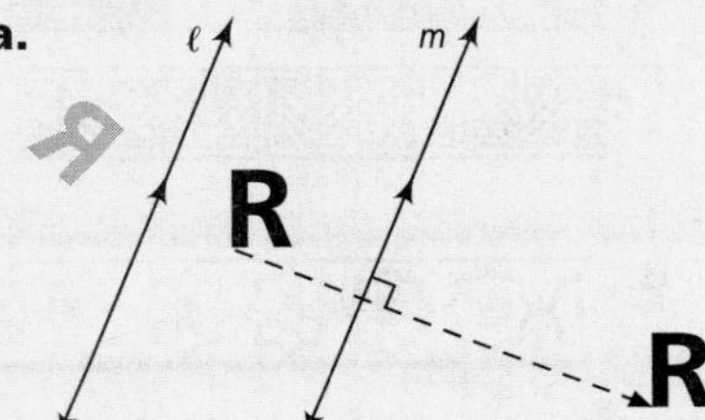

The arrow in the diagram shows the direction, determined by a line perpendicular to ℓ and *m*. The distance is twice the distance between ℓ and *m*.

b. The direction is from the first line of reflection toward the second line and is determined by a line perpendicular to the lines of reflection; the distance is two times the distance between the lines of reflection.

Got It? page 587

2a.

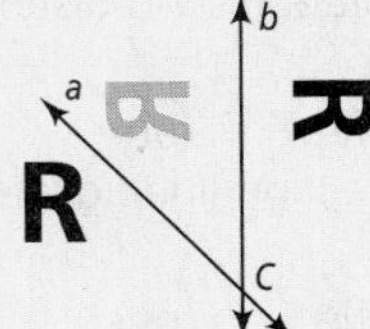

The center of rotation is *C*. The angle of rotation is 90° clockwise.

b. The center of rotation is the intersection of the lines of reflection; the ∠ of rotation is two times the measure of the acute or right ∠ formed by the lines of reflection.

3.

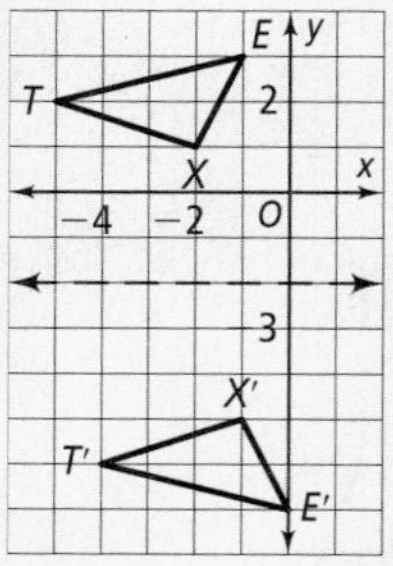

Concept Byte

Exercises page 593

3. Patterns with rotational symmetry have an infinite number of centers of rotation. The diagrams show the centers of rotation in one portion of the repeating pattern.

B. 

C.

D. 

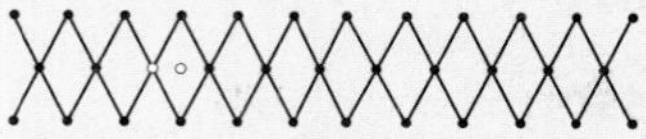

E. 

F. 

4.

B. 

D. 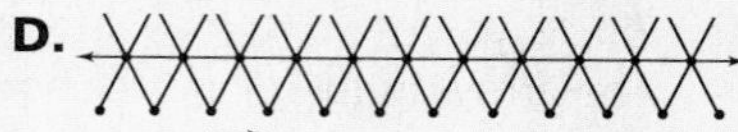

E. 

F. 

5. translation, reflection (two distinct vertical reflection lines)

6. translation, reflection (two distinct vertical reflection lines), rotation (two distinct centers), glide reflection

7. translation, rotation (two distinct centers)

8. translation; reflection (one horizontal reflection line), glide reflection

9. translation; reflection (one horizontal reflection line), glide reflection

10. translation; reflection (two distinct vertical reflection lines), rotation (two distinct centers), glide reflection

Chapter 11

Lesson 11-1

Got It? page 689

1a. 6 vertices: R, S, T, U, V, W;
9 edges: $\overline{SR}, \overline{ST}, \overline{UR}, \overline{UV}, \overline{UT}, \overline{RV}, \overline{SW}, \overline{VW}, \overline{TW}$;
5 faces: $\triangle URV$, $\triangle STW$, quadrilateral $RSTU$, quadrilateral $RSWV$, quadrilateral $TWVU$

b. No; an edge is a segment formed by the intersection of two faces. $\overline{TV}$ is a segment that is contained in only one face, so it is not an edge.

2a. 12

b. 30

Chapter 12

Lesson 12-6

Lesson Check page 806

1. 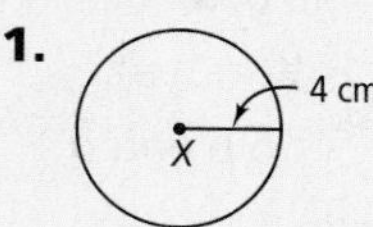

The locus is a circle with center X and radius 4 cm.

2. 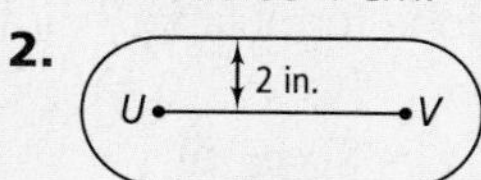

The locus is a pair of $\parallel$ segments, each segment 2 in. from $\overline{UV}$, and two semicircles with radius 2 in. and centers U and V.

3. 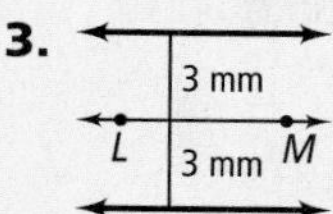

The locus is a pair of $\parallel$ lines, each 3 mm from $\overleftrightarrow{LM}$.

4. 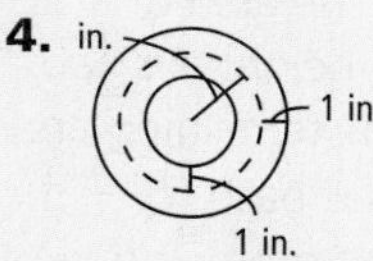

The locus is two circles concentric with the original circle; the smaller circle has radius 2 in. and the larger circle has radius 4 in.

5. Answers may vary. Sample: A *locus* is a set of points, and a *location* can be thought of as a description of a single point.

6. Alike: Both contain the midpt. of $\overline{JK}$ and are $\perp$ to $\overline{JK}$. Differences: The locus in a plane is a line and the locus in space is a plane.

Practice and Problem-Solving Exercises page 806

7. The locus is the $\perp$ bis. of $\overline{PQ}$.

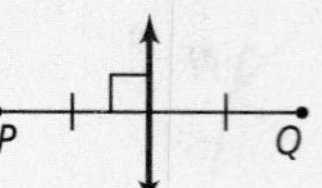

8. The locus is the ray that bis. $\angle ABC$.

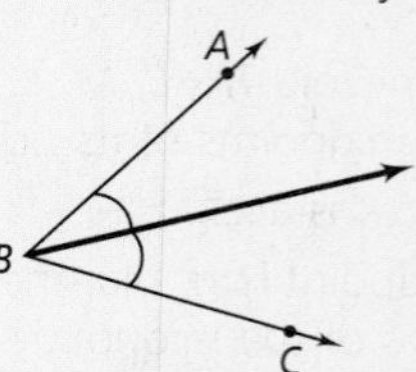

9. The locus is the two lines that bis. the rt. $\angle$s.

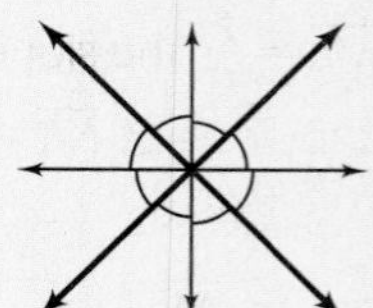

10. The locus is a circle, concentric with the given circle, with radius 1 cm.

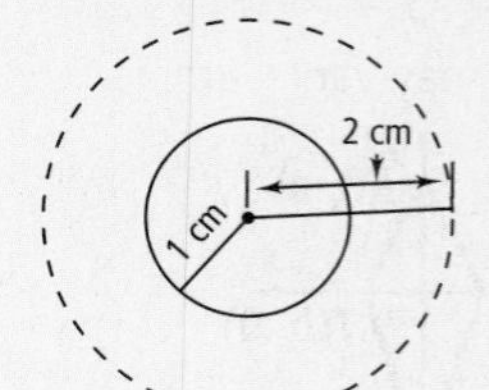

11.

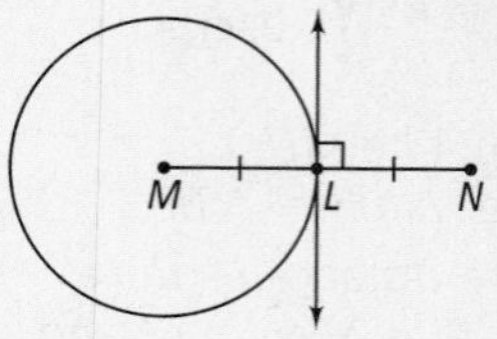

The locus is point L.

12. 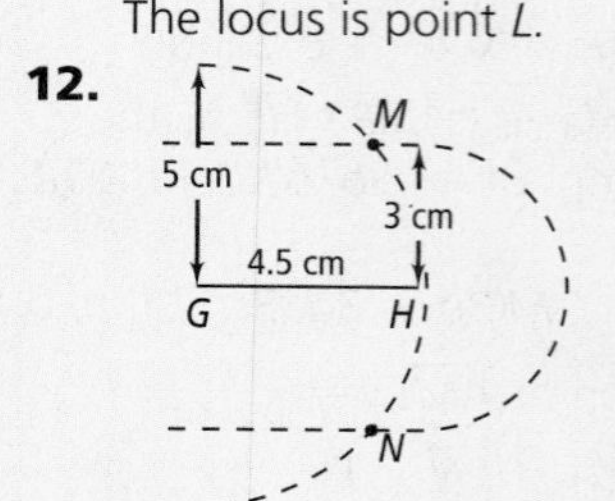

The locus is points M and N.

13. 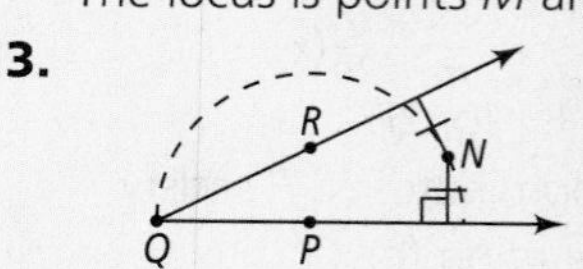

The locus is point N.

14. 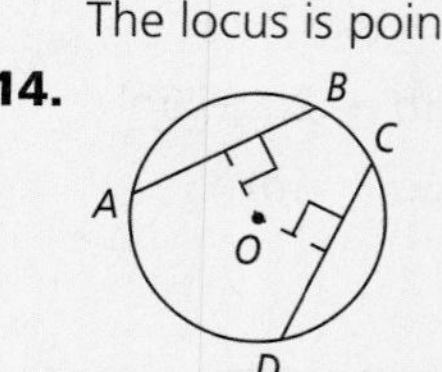

The locus is the center O.

15. 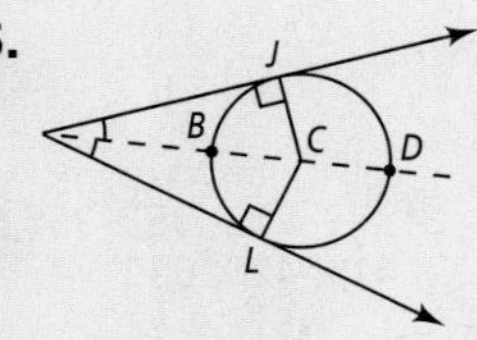

The locus is points B and D.

16. The locus is a sphere with center F and radius 3 cm.

17. The locus is an endless cylinder with radius 4 cm and centerline $\overleftrightarrow{DE}$.

18. The locus is two planes, each $\parallel$ to plane M, and each 1 in. from M.

19. The locus is an endless cylinder with radius 5 mm and centerline $\overrightarrow{PQ}$, and a hemisphere of radius 5 mm centered at P, "capping off" the cylinder.

20. The locus is the set of all points in the interior of $\angle A$ and equidistant from the sides of $\angle A$.

21. The locus is the set of all points 2 units from the origin.

22. The locus is the set of all points equidistant from two $\parallel$ planes M and N.

23. Check students' work.

24. Yes; if the collinear pts. are A, B, and C, then the locus of pts. equidist. from A and B is a plane M, $\perp$ to $\overline{AB}$ at its midpt. Similarly, pts. equidist. from B and C are on plane N, $\perp$ at the midpt. of $\overline{BC}$. But $M \parallel N$.

25. The locus is the set of points in the plane that are 1 unit from the x-axis and 2 units from the origin.

26. $y = x$

27. $y = 2x - 4$

28. $y = -x + 3$

29a. a circle

b. $x^2 + y^2 = 4$

Index

A

Index

B

C

D

Index

F

G

H

I

K

L

P

Q

R

S

T

Acknowledgments

Staff Credits

The people who made up the High School Mathematics team—representing composition services, core design digital and multimedia production services, digital product development, editorial, editorial services, manufacturing, marketing, and production management—are listed below.

Dan Anderson, Scott Andrews, Christopher Anton, Carolyn Artin, Michael Avidon, Margaret Banker, Charlie Bink, Niki Birbilis, Suzanne Biron, Beth Blumberg, Kyla Brown, Rebekah Brown, Judith Buice, Sylvia Bullock, Stacie Cartwright, Carolyn Chappo, Christia Clarke, Tom Columbus, Andrew Coppola, AnnMarie Coyne, Bob Craton, Nicholas Cronin, Patrick Culleton, Damaris Curran, Steven Cushing, Sheila DeFazio, Cathie Dillender, Emily Dumas, Patty Fagan, Frederick Fellows, Jorgensen Fernandez, Mandy Figueroa, Suzanne Finn, Sara Freund, Matt Frueh, Jon Fuhrer, Andy Gaus, Mark Geyer, Mircea Goia, Andrew Gorlin, Shelby Gragg, Ellen Granter, Gerard Grasso, Lisa Gustafson, Toni Haluga, Greg Ham, Marc Hamilton, Chris Handorf, Angie Hanks, Scott Harris, Cynthia Harvey, Phil Hazur, Thane Heninger, Aun Holland, Amanda House, Chuck Jann, Linda Johnson, Blair Jones, Marian Jones, Tim Jones, Gillian Kahn, Brian Keegan, Jonathan Kier, Jennifer King, Tamara King, Elizabeth Krieble, Meytal Kotik, Brian Kubota, Roshni Kutty, Mary Landry, Christopher Langley, Christine Lee, Sara Levendusky, Lisa Lin, Wendy Marberry, Dominique Mariano, Clay Martin, Rich McMahon, Eve Melnechuk, Cynthia Metallides, Hope Morley, Christine Nevola, Michael O'Donnell, Michael Oster, Ameer Padshah, Jeffrey Paulhus, Jonathan Penyack, Valerie Perkins, Brian Reardon, Wendy Rock, Marcy Rose, Carol Roy, Irene Rubin, Hugh Rutledge, Vicky Shen, Jewel Simmons, Ted Smykal, Emily Soltanoff, William Speiser, Jayne Stevenson, Richard Sullivan, Dan Tanguay, Dennis Tarwood, Susan Tauer, Tiffany Taylor-Sullivan, Catherine Terwilliger, Maria Torti, Mark Tricca, Leonid Tunik, Ilana Van Veen, Lauren Van Wart, John Vaughan, Laura Vivenzio, Samuel Voigt, Kathy Warfel, Don Weide, Laura Wheel, Eric Whitfield, Sequoia Wild, Joseph Will, Kristin Winters, Allison Wyss, Dina Zolotusky

Additional Credits: Michele Cardin, Robert Carlson, Kate Dalton-Hoffman, Dana Guterman, Narae Maybeth, Carolyn McGuire, Manjula Nair, Rachel Terino, Steve Thomas

Illustration

Stephen Durke: 4, 5, 8, 9, 11, 18, 20, 25, 27, 32, 43, 50, 53, 54, 59, 60, 61, 66, 67, 69, 140, 148, 156, 161, 164, 168, 171, 174, 179, 182,189, 195, 197, 203, 218, 219, 222, 226, 228, 232, 234, 235, 240, 244, 245, 248, 250, 255, 265, 270, 284, 289, 291, 293, 295, 296, 300, 302, 304, 305, 308, 313, 316, 322, 324, 328, 330, 331, 332, 334, 338, 466, 504, 511, 515, 516, 519, 520, 521, 547, 620, 641, 655, 656, 657, 665, 809, 810; **Jennifer Fairman:** 593; **Jeff Grunwald represented by Wilkinson Studios, Inc.:** 82, 83, 89, 94, 98, 106, 109, 111, 113, 120, 125, 128, 200, 357, 359, 371, 375, 383, 385, 389, 400, 404, 406, 417, 437, 440, 443, 446, 450, 454, 456, 464, 465, 466, 471, 473, 475, 476, 479, 499, 516, 524, 528, 531, 533, 639.; **Phil Guzy:** 34, 320, 330, 491, 496, 507, 513, 544, 548, 553, 557, 559, 568, 584, 594, 595, 600, 616, 623, 643, 649, 652, 655, 672, 673, 688, 697, 699, 703, 705, 706, 708, 717, 720, 726, 728, 733, 735, 739, 742, 748, 758, 762, 770, 771, 780, 790, 792, 798; **XNR Productions:** 526, 555, 556, 623, 804, 808.

Technical Illustration

Datagrafix, Inc.

Photography

All photographs not listed are the property of Pearson Education.

Back Cover: Bon Appetit/Almay

Chapter 1: Page 3, Julian Smith/Corbis; **15,** Kelly Redinger/ Design Pics Inc./Alamy; **30,** Pete Saloutos/zefa/Corbis; **32,** Stuart Melvin/ Alamy; **39,** Richard Menga/Fundamental Photographs; **62,** Charles O. Cecil/Alamy.

Chapter 2: Page 81, Hoge Noorden/epa/Corbis; **126,** IPS Co., Ltd./ Beateworks/Corbis; **103,** www.Lifeprint.com.

Chapter 3: Page 139, Laurent Gillieron/epa/Corbis; **144,** Kevin Fleming/ Corbis; **154,** photo courtesy of Frank Adelstein, Ithaca, NY; **143,** Peter Cade/Iconica/Getty Images; **176,** Bill Brooks/Alamy; **159,** Robert Slade/ Manor Photography/Alamy; **162,** Robert Llewellyn/Corbis.

Chapter 4: Page 217, Robin Utrecht/Staff/AFP/Getty Images; **227,** Stan Honda/Staff/AFP/Getty Images; **246,** Viktor Kitaykin/iStockphoto; **253,** John Wells/Photo Researchers, Inc; **263,** Image Source Black/ Jupiterimages; **258,** Tony Freeman/PhotoEdit; **260,** Paul Jones/Iconica/ Getty Images; **260,** Llado, M./Plainpicture Photography/Veer; **266,** Photo by Pearson Education, created by JC Nolan, folded by Sara Adams.

Chapter 5: Page 281, Floto + Warner/Arcaid/Alamy; **286,** Momatiuk - Eastcott/Corbis; **288,** Joseph Sohm/Visions of America, LLC/Alamy; **331,** Gunter Marx Photography/Corbis.

Chapter 6: Page 351, White Star/Friedrichsmeier/B. Nasner/ imagebroker/Alamy; **354 l,** Dr. Dennis Kunkel/Visuals Unlimited/Getty Images; **354 r,** Anthony Bannister/Gallo Images/Corbis; **356 l,** Inger Hogstrom/DanitaDelimont.com; **356 c,** Laurie Strachan/Alamy; **356 r,** BestShot/iStockphoto; **360,** Eric Hood/iStockphoto; **365,** Esa Hiltula/Alamy; **367,** Victor Fraile/Reuters; **376,** Kirsty McLaren/Alamy; **379 l,** Claro Cortes IV/Reuters/Landov; **379 r,** Michael Jenner/Alamy; **387,** Rodney Raschke; **395,** Colin Underhill/Alamy.

Chapter 7: Page 431, Michel Setboun/Corbis; **432,** Chuck Eckert/Alamy; **443,** Ron Watts/Corbis; **466,** James L. Amos/Corbis; **469 l,** Mark A. Johnson/Corbis; **469 c,** Corey Hochachka/Design Pics/Fotosearch; **469 r,** Photodisc/Fotosearch; **475,** Victor R. Boswell Jr./Contributor/ National Geographic/Getty Images.

Chapter 8: Page 489, Tim Woodcock/Alamy; **493,** Petra Wegner/Alamy; **502,** Hemera Technologies/Jupiterimages; **508,** Steve Vidler/ImageState; **517,** Dave Reede/All Canada Photos/Alamy; **524,** Jeff Foott/Discovery Channel Images/Getty Images.

Chapter 9: Page 543, I G Kinoshita/amana images/Getty Images; **544,** RubberBall/Alamy; **557,** North Wind Picture Archives/Alamy; **564,** Alan Copson/City Pictures/Alamy; **561 all,** Ron Kimball/kimballstock; **563 l,** Catalog No. 29.0/349 Courtesy of the Division of Anthropology, American Museum of Natural History; **563 c,** Jerry Jacka/Jacka Photography; **563 r,** Humberto Olarte Cupas/Alamy; **570 l,** Image Source/Jupiterimages; **570 c,** iStockphoto; **570 r,** Andy Crawford/Dorling Kindersley; **571 l,** Vladimir Wrangel/Alamy; **571 r,** Peter Blackwell/ naturepl.com; **572 tl,** Owaki - Kulla/Corbis; **572 tr,** D. Hurst/Alamy; **572 c,** Chevrolet and Saturn logos courtesy of The General Motors Corporation; **572 bl,** Honda logo courtesy of Honda Motors Inc.; **572 br,** Mitsubishi logo courtesy of Mitsubishi Motors North America, Inc.; **575,** Martin William Allen/Alamy; **577 l,** Keith Leighton/Alamy; **577 r,** Reven T.C. Wurman/Alamy; Keith Leighton/Alamy; **591 l,** Elisa Locci/Alamy; **591 c,** age fotostock/SuperStock; **591 r,** Alfred Pasieka/ Photo Researchers, Inc; **595,** M.C. Escher's "Symmetry E69" © 2009 The M.C. Escher Company-Holland. All rights reserved. www.mcescher.com; **596 l,** M.C. Escher's "Symmetry E56" © 2009 The M.C. Escher Company-Holland. All rights reserved. www.mcescher.com; **596 r,** M.C. Escher's "Symmetry E18" © 2009 The M.C. Escher Company-Holland. All rights reserved. www.mcescher.com; **598 t both,** mediacolor's/Alamy; **598 bl,** Petr Svarc/Alamy; **598 br,** Paul Panayiotou/Alamy; **602,** Douglas Kirkland/Corbis.

Chapter 10: Page 613, Jim West/Alamy; **618,** Bob Gates/Alamy; **627,** artpartner-images.com/Alamy; **625,** Joe Sohm/Visions of America, LLC/Alamy; **633,** Dennis Marsico/Corbis; **644,** Alan Schein Photography/ Corbis; **661,** Matthias Tunger/Photonica/Getty Images; **668,** Clive Streeter/Dorling Kindersley; **670,** amana images inc./Alamy.

Chapter 11: Page 685, Associated Press; **693,** Sports Bokeh/Alamy; **705,** Ron Chapple Stock/Alamy; **710,** Adam Eastland/Alamy; **727,** age fotostock/SuperStock; **728,** John E Marriott/Alamy; **733,** D. Hurst/Alamy; **737 l,** Andrew Paterson/Alamy; **737 c,** Stockbyte/Getty Images; **737 r,** Image Source/Getty Images; **738,** Stephen Sweet/Alamy; **744,** Jupiterimages/BananaStock/Alamy; **745,** Andre Jenny/Alamy.

Chapter 12: 761, NASA and STScl; **764 t,** T. Pohling/Alamy; **764 b,** NASA Marshall Space Flight Center Collection; **768,** Clive Streeter/Dorling Kindersley; **775,** Cris Bouroncle/Staff/AFP/Getty Images; **785,** Vario Images GmbH & Co.KG/Alamy; **792,** NASA Marshall Space Flight Center Collection; **794,** Melvyn Longhurst/Alamy; **795,** dpa/Corbis; **807,** matthiasengelien.com/Alamy.